DEVONSH
PREPARATO

69, Fitzjohn's Avenue, Ha

A co-educational Prep and Pre-Prep fo
3 - 13 with its own **OAK TREE NUR**
For children from 2½ - 3½

OPEN MORNINGS

Wednesday, 15th October 2008
Thursday, 16th October 2008
Thursday, 15th January 2009

For more information contact the Admissions' Secretary:
enquiries@devonshirehouseprepschool.co.uk

020 7435 1916

HAWKESDOWN HOUSE SCHOOL

An IAPS school for boys aged 3 to 8,
in Kensington, W8

SY2009/SYB5/e

For further details please contact the Admissions' Secretary.

Hawkesdown House School,
27, Edge Street, Kensington,
London W8 7PN.
Telephone: 020 7727 9090.
Facsimile: 020 7727 9988.
Email: admin@hawkesdown.co.uk

INDEPENDENT SCHOOLS YEARBOOK

2008–2009

Boys' Schools, Girls' Schools,
Co-educational Schools
and Preparatory Schools

Details of Schools whose Heads are members of one of the Constituent Associations of the Independent Schools Council (ISC):

Headmasters' and Headmistresses' Conference (HMC)

Girls' Schools Association (GSA)

Society of Headmasters and Headmistresses of Independent Schools (SHMIS)

IAPS (Independent Association of Prep Schools)

Independent Schools Association (ISA)

EDITED BY
JUDY MOTT

A & C BLACK • LONDON

36 Soho Square
London W1D 3QY

Tel: 020 7758 0200
e-mail: isyb@acblack.com
website: www.isyb.co.uk

A CIP catalogue record for this book is available from the British Library.

ISBN: 978-1-4081-0403-3

Typeset by AMA DataSet Limited Preston PR5 6QE
Printed in the UK by CPI William Clowes Beccles NR34 7TL

This book is produced using paper that is made from wood grown in managed, sustainable forests. It is natural, renewable and recyclable. The logging and manufacturing processes conform to the environmental regulations of the country of origin.

INDEPENDENT SCHOOLS YEARBOOK 2008–09

CONTENTS

. . ./continued

INDEPENDENT SCHOOLS COUNCIL (ISC)

ISC is the representative body for the UK independent schools sector, on behalf of its eight Associations and its 1,280 member schools, which educate more than 500,000 children.

The Constituent Associations of ISC are:

Association of Governing Bodies of Independent Schools (AGBIS)
Council of British International Schools (COBIS)
Girls' Schools Association (GSA)
Headmasters' and Headmistresses' Conference (HMC)
IAPS (Independent Association of Prep Schools)
Independent Schools Association (ISA)
Independent Schools' Bursars Association (ISBA)
Society of Headmasters and Headmistresses of Independent Schools (SHMIS)

Chairman
Dame Judith Mayhew Jonas

Acting Chief Executive
Matthew Burgess

Communications Director
Andy Cook

Director, Induction & Recruitment
Judith Fenn

The Independent Schools Council exists to promote choice, diversity and excellence in education; the development of talent at all levels of ability; and the widening of opportunity for children from all backgrounds to achieve their potential. ISC carries out research; gives advice to schools and parents; responds to Government consultations; and works to ensure that independent education is fairly and accurately represented to Government and to the media.

The professionally independent inspection service, ISI (Independent Schools Inspectorate), inspects (under statute) ISC schools in England.

Independent Schools Council
St Vincent House
30 Orange Street
London WC2H 7HH

Tel: 020 7766 7070
Fax: 020 7766 7071
e-mail: office@isc.co.uk

website: www.isc.co.uk

HEADMASTERS' AND HEADMISTRESSES' CONFERENCE

The HMC dates from 1869, when the celebrated Edward Thring of Uppingham asked thirty-seven of his fellow headmasters to meet at his house to consider the formation of a 'School Society and Annual Conference'. Twelve headmasters accepted the invitation. From that date there have been annual meetings. Thring's intention was to provide an opportunity for discussion at regular intervals, both on practical issues in the life of a school and on general principles in education. He believed that his guests would discharge their practical business the more effectively at a residential meeting where they could also enjoy being in the company of like-minded men. Annual Meetings of the HMC still combine formal debate on current educational questions with the second element of conversational exchanges in an agreeable environment. These gatherings, which up to 1939 were usually at individual schools, then took place at a University. Nowadays they are held in major hotels and Conference centres in the Autumn term. In addition to these annual conferences attended by all members, there are local meetings each term arranged by the ten branches or Divisions into which the country is divided.

Present full membership of the HMC is a total of two hundred and fifty one, which now includes headmasters and headmistresses of boys', girls' and co-educational schools. In considering applications for election to membership, the Committee has regard to the degree of independence enjoyed by the Head and his/her school. Eligibility also depends on the academic standards obtaining in the school, as reflected by the proportion of pupils in the Sixth Form pursuing a course of study beyond the General Certificate of Secondary Education and by the school's A Level results.

The Constitution provides that the full membership shall consist only of heads of independent schools. At the same time, it is held to be a strength to the Conference to include heads of schools of other status. There is provision therefore for the election of a small number of heads of Maintained schools (Additional Membership).

In addition the HMC has a number of International members, who are heads of noteworthy schools in the Commonwealth and other countries around the world. There is also a small number of Honorary Associates who have been elected to life membership on retirement.

The HMC is closely associated with the other independent sector associations that also belong to the Independent Schools Council (ISC), and with the Association of School and College Leaders (ASCL), which represents the Heads of secondary maintained schools and colleges.

The HMC Committee – 2008/09

Chairman	Tim Hastie-Smith	Dean Close School
Vice-Chairman	Dr Bernard Trafford	RGS Newcastle
Chairman Elect	Andrew Grant	St Albans School
Hon Treasurer	Barry Martin	Hampton School
Chairman – East Division	Howard Blackett	The Royal Hospital School
Secretary – East Division	Chris King	Leicester Grammar School
Chairman – Irish Division	Jay Piggott	Campbell College
Chairman – London	David Levin	City of London School
Secretary – London	Richard Russell	Colfe's School
Chairman – North East	David Humphreys	Woodhouse Grove School
Secretary – North East	Richard Smyth	St Peter's School
Chairman – North West	Philip Capes	St Bees School
Secretary – North West	Paul Dixon	Cheadle Hulme School
Chairman – Scottish	John Broadfoot	Kelvinside Academy
Secretary – Scottish	Andrew Hunter	Merchiston Castle School
Chairman – South Central	Anne Coutts	Headington School
Secretary – South Central	Nick England	Ryde School
Chairman – South East	Gino Carminati	Worth School
Secretary – South East	Nick Haddock	St John's School
Chairman – South West	Simon Eliot	Sherborne School
Secretary – South West	Ian Davenport	Blundell's School
Chairman – West	Ed Halse	Warwick School
Secretary – West	Margie Burnet-Ward	Wycliffe College
Co-opted Members		
Chairman of Education and Academic Policy	Chris Ray	Manchester Grammar School
Chairman of Professional Development	Kenneth Durham	University College School
Chairman of Universities Sub-Committee	Tim Hands	Magdalen College School
Inspection Steering Group	Stephen Cole	Woodbridge School
	Charlie Bush	Oundle School

Secretary: G H Lucas, BA, MEd, PGCE (Tel: 01858 469059)
Membership Secretary: R V Peel, BSc, PGCE, FRSA (Tel: 01858 465260)

Headmasters' and Headmistresses' Conference
12 The Point, Rockingham Road, Market Harborough, Leicestershire LE16 7QU
Tel: 01858 465260 • Facsimile: 01858 465759
e-mail: hmc@hmc.org.uk • website: www.hmc.org.uk

GIRLS' SCHOOLS ASSOCIATION

The Girls' Schools Association (GSA) is the professional association of the Heads of leading independent secondary schools for girls in the UK, educating over 110,000 girls. Schools in the Association offer a choice of day, boarding, weekly and flexi-boarding education; and range in type from large urban schools of 1,000 pupils to small rural schools of around 200. Many schools have junior and pre-prep departments, and can offer a complete education from four to eighteen. A significant proportion of schools also have religious affiliations. All the senior schools in the Girls' Day School Trust (GDST) are in membership of GSA.

GSA schools are widely recognised for their exceptional record of examination achievements. Education is, however, not only about success in exams. Girls' schools offer wider development opportunities, and are special for a number of reasons. They provide an environment in which girls can learn to grow in confidence and ability. In a girls' school, the needs and aspirations of girls are the main focus, and the staff are specialists in the teaching of girls. Girls hold all the senior positions in the school, and are encouraged by positive role models in the schools' teaching staff and management. Expectations are high. In GSA schools, girls do not just have equal opportunities, they have *every* opportunity. Members of GSA share a commitment to the values and benefits of single-sex schools for girls, and a belief that all girls, regardless of educational setting, deserve the opportunity to realise their potential, to be active and equal, confident and competent leaders, participants and contributors.

The Girls' Schools Association plays a vital role in advising and lobbying educational policy makers on issues relating to girls' schools and the education of girls. As the specialist organisation for the education of girls, the Association is regularly consulted by the Department for Children, Schools and Families (DCSF), the Office for Standards in Education, the Qualifications and Curriculum Authority and other bodies. However, GSA is not only a 'single-issue' organisation, and is a powerful and well respected voice within the educational establishment. The GSA is one of the constituent bodies of the Independent Schools Council. The ISC operates, on behalf of GSA, a strict accreditation scheme for schools wishing to join the Association. Once in membership, schools are required to undergo a regular cycle of inspections to ensure that these rigorous standards are being maintained. Schools must also belong to the Association of Governing Bodies of Independent Schools, and Heads must be in membership of the Association of School and College Leaders (ASCL).

A programme of professional development for members ensures that the Heads of all GSA schools are highly trained, and are fully up-to-date with all aspects of their profession. Courses are also regularly held for staff and opportunities are available for subject teachers to meet together on curriculum issues.

The Association's Secretariat is accommodated in Leicester in premises shared with the Association of School and College Leaders (ASCL).

Council and Committees of the Girls' Schools Association 2008

Officers

President:	Vicky Tuck	The Cheltenham Ladies' College
Vice-President:	Pat Langham	Wakefield Girls' High School
President Elect:	Jill Berry	Dame Alice Harpur School
Treasurer:	Sue Marks	Tormead School

Committee Chairmen

Boarding:	Jan Scarrow	Badminton School
Education & Academic Policy:	Kathy Mills	Alderley Edge School for Girls
Education Research:	Ruth Weeks	Edgbaston High School
Inspections:	Janet Pickering	Withington Girls' School
Membership:	Pam Maynard	Lodge School
Professional Development:	Christine Lee-Jones	Manchester High School for Girls
Universities:	Cynthia Hall	School of St Helen & St Katharine

Regional Representatives

East:	Tricia Kelleher	Perse School for Girls
London:	Kerstin Lewis	Abbot's Hill School
Midland:	Biddie O'Connor	Loughborough High School
North East:	Denise Davidson	Gateways School
North West:	Kathy Mills	Alderley Edge School for Girls
South Central:	Alice Phillips	St Catherine's School Bramley
South East:	Rosemary Martin	Combe Bank School
South West & Wales:	Daphne West	The Maynard School
Scotland:	Gillian Stobo	Craigholme School

Secretariat

Executive Director:	Sheila Cooper
Membership & Communications Director:	Jane Carroll
Administrator:	Sue Massey
PA to Executive Director:	Jeven Sharma
Administrative Assistant:	Kate Curran

Girls' Schools Association
130 Regent Road, Leicester LE1 7PG
Tel: 0116 254 1619 • Fax: 0116 255 3792
e-mail: office@gsa.uk.com • website: www.gsa.uk.com

SOCIETY OF HEADMASTERS AND HEADMISTRESSES OF INDEPENDENT SCHOOLS

website: www.shmis.org.uk

The Society is an Association of Headmasters and Headmistresses of some 100 well-established independent schools. It was founded in 1961 at a time when the need arose from the vitality and growth of the independent sector in the 1950s and the wish of a group of Heads to share ideas and experience.

The Society continues to provide a forum for the exchange of ideas and consideration of the particular needs of the smaller independent school. These are frequently different from the problems and approach of the larger schools. All members value their independence, breath in education and the pursuit of excellence, particularly in relation to academic standards.

The Society's policy is to maintain high standards in member schools, to ensure their genuine independence, to foster an association of schools which contributes to the whole independent sector by its distinctive character and flexibility, to provide an opportunity for the sharing of ideas and common concerns, to promote links with the wider sphere of higher education, to strengthen relations with the maintained sector and with local communities.

Within the membership there is a wide variety of educational experience. Some schools are young, some have evolved from older foundations, some have behind them a long tradition of pioneer and specialist education, the great majority are now co-educational but we also have boys' and girls' schools. Many of the member schools have a strong boarding element but some have become day schools. Some have specific religious foundations and some are non-denominational. All offer a stimulating Sixth Form experience and at the same time give a sound and balanced education to pupils of widely varying abilities and interests.

The Society is one of the constituent bodies of the Independent Schools Council. Every Full Member school has been accredited by ISC and is subject to a Review Visit by the Independent Schools Inspectorate every six years to ensure that standards are monitored and good practice and sound academic results are maintained. The Society is also represented on many other educational bodies.

All members are in membership of the Association of School and College Leaders (ASCL) and Full Member schools belong to AGBIS or otherwise satisfy the Society on their Governance.

There is also a category of Additional Membership to which are elected Heads whose schools do not fulfil all the criteria for Full Membership but whose personal contribution to the Society is judged to be invaluable. They are recorded separately at the end of the entries.

The Society meets together each term: in London; at a member school; and for a three-day residential conference at a hotel or conference centre.

Officers 2008–2009

Chairman 2008 & Vice-Chairman 2009: Ian Power, Lord Wandsworth College
Vice-Chairman 2008: Dr Peter C Bodkin, Tettenhall College
Chairman Designate 2009: Nicholas Dorey, Bethany School
Hon Treasurer: Isobel Nixon, Chetwynde School

SHMIS Committee 2008–2009

Dr Peter C Bodkin, Tettenhall College
Philip Cottam, Halliford School
Nicholas Dorey, Bethany School
Gerry Holden, Rendcomb College
Tim Kirkup, Scarborough College
Toby Mullins, Seaford College
Isobel Nixon, Chetwynde School
Joe A Peake, St George's College
Ian G Power, Lord Wandsworth College
Andy Waters, Grenville College

Secretariat

General Secretary: Dr D J Richardson

Society of Headmasters and Headmistresses of Independent Schools
12 The Point, Rockingham Road, Market Harborough, Leicestershire LE16 7QU
Tel: 01858 433760 • Fax: 01858 461413 • e-mail: gensec@shmis.org.uk

Members who are also members of the Headmasters' and Headmistresses' Conference:

Dr Peter C Bodkin, Tettenhall College
Keith J Budge, Bedales School
Philip J S Cantwell, The King's School, Tynemouth
Martin G Cooke, Clayesmore School
Gregg Davies, Shiplake College
David M Dunn, Yarm School
John H Dunston, Leighton Park School
Dr Nicholas J England, Ryde School with Upper Chine
Gerry Holden, Rendcomb College
Susan Freestone, The King's School, Ely
Patrick Lee-Browne, Rydal Penrhos
David W Jarrett, Reed's School
Dr John R Jennings, Royal Russell School
Michael Windsor, Reading Blue Coat School
Toby Mullins, Seaford College
David Buxton, St Columba's College
Joe A Peake, St George's College
Ian G Power, Lord Wandsworth College
Nicholas Hammond, Wisbech Grammar School
Peter J Simpson, Ackworth School
Darryl Wideman, Silcoates School
Douglas R Walker, Kirkham Grammar School

Members who are also members of the Girls' Schools Association:

Sue Bradley (Stover School)
Sarah H Evans (King Edward VI High School for Girls)
Rachael Hodgson (Howell's School, Denbigh)
Thomas Packer (Teesside High School)
Lesley Watson (Moira House Girls' School)

Associate Members

J C Baggaley (formerly Headmaster, Silcoates School)
R D Balaam (formerly Headmaster, Royal Russell School)
M Barratt (formerly Headmaster, Rannoch School)
D J Beeby (formerly Headmaster, Clayesmore School)
N Bevan (formerly Headmaster, Shiplake College)
D I Brooks (formerly Headmaster, Churcher's College)
I Brown (formerly Headmaster, Rougemont School)
D Bryson (formerly Headmaster, St Andrew's School)
P Bujak (formerly Headmaster, Stover School)
Dr M C V Cane (formerly Headmaster, Grenville College)
D G Crawford (formerly Headmaster, Colston's School)
J Cummings (formerly Headmaster, Duke of York's Royal Military School)
M Downward (formerly Headmaster, West Buckland School)
D J Farrant (formerly Headmaster, Abbotsholme School)
D M Green (formerly Headmaster, Warminster School)
Carole Hawkins (formerly Head, Royal School, Hampstead)
Revd P C Hunting (formerly Headmaster, St George's College)
M A B Kirk (formerly Headmaster, Royal Hospital School)
Jane Laing (formerly Head, Friends' School)
E Mitchell (formerly Headmaster, Abbey Gate College)
H Moxon (formerly Headmaster, Stanbridge Earls School)
I Mullins (Licenced Victuallers' School)
N O'Sullivan (formerly Headmaster, St Columba's College)
The Hon Martin Penney (formerly Headmaster, Bearwood College)
C Reid (formerly Headmaster, St Christopher School)
C Robinson (formerly Headmaster, Hipperholme Grammar School)
Rosemary Simmons (formerly Head, La Retraite Swan)
T Slack (formerly Headmaster, Bedales School)
J Tolputt (formerly Headmaster, The Purcell School)
N Ward (formerly Headmaster, Royal Hospital School)
Col G H Wilson (formerly Headmaster, Duke of York's Royal Military School)
G S Wilson (formerly Headmaster, Bedstone College)
Anne Wood (formerly Head, Lincoln Minster School)
S Wormleighton (formerly Headmaster, Grenville College)

IAPS (INDEPENDENT ASSOCIATION OF PREP SCHOOLS)

Schools
IAPS schools include boys', girls' and co-educational; boarding, day and mixed; urban, suburban and rural schools. The size varies from over 800 to under 100 pupils, with the majority between 150 and 400. Most schools are charitable trusts, some are limited companies and a few are proprietary. There are also junior schools attached to senior schools, choir schools, schools with a particular religious affiliation, and schools that offer some specialist provision. The average pupil/ teacher ratio throughout the Association is 1 to 10.05.

Curriculum
The targets of the National Curriculum are regarded as a basic foundation, which is greatly extended by the wider programmes of study typically available in IAPS prep schools. Specialist subject teaching is widely available from Year 3 onwards. More than thirty sports and games are played competitively and recreationally to very high standards.

Membership
At present there are over 580 member schools in the United Kingdom with a total of 150,000 pupils. In addition the Heads of some 30 schools overseas are in membership.

Qualification for membership
In order to be elected to membership a Head must be suitably qualified, and schools must be accredited. Accreditation is accorded only after a satisfactory inspection.

Services
IAPS offers a wide variety of services in support of its members and of the schools of which they are the Heads. A comprehensive and up-to-date programme of continuing professional development is provided for Heads and staff, helping to maintain excellent teacher quality and high standards of school management. Further information about these services is obtainable from IAPS Headquarters.

History
IAPS was founded in 1892 and incorporated in 1923. Until 1980 membership was confined to Heads of boys' and co-educational schools. In 1981 IAPS amalgamated with the Association of Headmistresses of Preparatory Schools, which had been founded in 1929 and which at that time had 120 schools in membership. The combined Association took the name IAPS. In 1991 IAPS moved from Kensington to Leamington Spa. The development and expansion of the Association's current professional services date from that time.

Organization
IAPS is divided into twelve Districts which cover the whole of the United Kingdom. It is controlled by an elected Council which has 20 members and meets three times a year. The Chairman is elected by Council. The Chief Executive and officials work from the IAPS Headquarters. Their names and addresses are given below.

The Council and Officers for 2008–2009

President: H Davies Jones

Chairman: Mrs D E Watkins

Chairman-Elect: J Tranmer

Immediate Past Chairman: M W Spinney

Vice-Chairman: Miss E M Craig

Members of Council:
Mr J A Brett, Mrs L E G Cavanagh, K S Crombie, M Dunning, A I Falconer, M A Gunn, Mrs A Hedley, C S Heinrich, W C R Ibbetson-Price, M A Ives, Mrs M A Jackson, Mrs P S Kirk, A J P Nott, C G J Oldershaw, Mrs S C Piper, H S Thackrah, P D Westcombe, N R Yelland

Officials:
Chief Executive: D Hanson
Director of Education: Mrs B Ingram
Treasurer: D E Leafe
Schools Administration Adviser: Mrs H A Kingham
Courses and Conferences Manager: Mrs L N Curzon
Association Administrator: Mrs C M McCrudden
Membership Officer: Dr J M Wharfe

IAPS
11 Waterloo Place, Leamington Spa CV32 5LA
Tel: 01926 887833 • Fax: 01926 888014
email: iaps@iaps.org.uk • website: www.iaps.org.uk

INDEPENDENT SCHOOLS ASSOCIATION

The Independent Schools Association, which celebrated its centenary in 1979, is one of the oldest of the various organisations of independent schools. It differs from most of the others in that it is not confined to any one type of school, but includes Senior, Preparatory, Junior, Nursery, Co-educational, Single-sex, Boarding, and Day schools. The only criterion is that the school should be good of its kind.

The Association began as the Association of Principals of Private Schools, and was the first attempt to encourage high standards in private schools and to foster friendliness and cooperation among Heads who had previously worked in isolation. In 1895 it was incorporated as The Private Schools Association. In 1927 the word 'private' was replaced by 'independent', since by then many of the schools were no longer 'private' in the sense of being owned by private individuals. At present, although a number of the smaller schools are still privately owned, most are controlled by Boards of Governors constituted as Educational Trusts or Companies.

Membership is limited to Heads of schools which charge fees and are not under the control of the DCSF or a Local Education Authority. Heads of such schools are eligible provided the Executive Council is satisfied as to their suitability and the efficiency of the school. In addition the school must fulfil the Accreditation requirements of the Independent Schools Council.

The Association exists:

- To promote friendship and fellowship among Members nationally and through Area meetings
- To provide opportunities for pupils in ISA schools to take part in Area and National competitions in Sport and the Arts
- To provide information and advice from the ISA office and from Area Coordinators which will help and support individual Members
- To arrange Conferences and Professional Development Courses which will foster excellence in education
- To influence educational debate and promote independence and choice and to work actively with other associations as appropriate

Membership is vested in the individual Head, and not in the school as a corporate body. A Head appointed to succeed an existing member will normally be accepted provisionally for two or three terms while arrangments are made for a visit by representatives of the Association to confirm membership. As well as pursuing the professional and educational aims set out above, the Association has an extensive programme of social, cultural, and sporting activities. The Annual Conference enables members to exchange views, hear distinguished speakers, and enjoy various social occasions both formal and informal. There is one other shorter conference in the Autumn and a full range of professional development courses arranged throughout the year. The seven Areas into which the Association is divided organise their own programmes of meetings. The Association currently represents some 300 schools with a roll of 70,000 pupils.

The Council and Officers for 2008–2009

President: B J Maybee, JP, MA

Vice-Presidents:
C J Ashby, BSc, PGCE
Mrs M Grant, CertEd
Mrs M J Milner-Williams, CertEd
P F Smith, BA, CertEd
Mrs A D Stranack, BA, CertEd

Honorary Officers (*2008*):
Mrs D Odysseas-Bailey, BA, PGCE (*Chairman*)
J Gibson, BA, CertEd (*Vice-Chairman*)
Mrs J M Mumby, BA (*Vice-Chairman*)

Honorary Officers (*2009*):
J Gibson, BA, PGCE (*Chairman*)
G R Gorton BA, PGCE (*Vice-Chairman*)
Mrs D Odysseas-Bailey, BA, PGCE (*Vice-Chairman*)

Elective Councillors:
Mrs C A Baker, BEd, MA
R H Brierly, BEd
A Hampton, BA, LTCL, MEd, NPQH
M W Malley, BEd
P Moss, CertEd
Mrs J Nicol, MA, CertEd, CertPDE
M K Savjani, BSc
D G Vanstone, MA, PGCE
R M Walden, MA, CertEd, MEd, FCollP
J T Wilding, BSc
J R Wood, MA, PGCE
Miss S J Woodward, BA, FRSA

Area Coordinators:
A G Bray, CertEd (*London West*)
Mrs A Culley, CertEd (*London South*)
R A Fowke, BEd (*South West*)
G R Gorton, BA, PGCE (*London North*)
M J Hewett, BA, FCollP (*East Anglia*)
D Williams, BA, MA (*North*)
D R Wood, BEd, FLS, CBiol, MIBiol, MRI (*Midlands*)

Advisers

Consultant Accountants and Auditors: Messrs Russell, New and Co, The Courtyard, Shoreham Road, Upper Beeding, Steyning, West Sussex BN44 3TN. Tel: 01903 816699.

Insurance Advisers: HSBC Insurance Brokers Ltd (Education Division), 9-17 Perrymount Road, Haywards Heath, West Sussex RH16 3DU. Tel: 01444 458144.

Solicitors: Messrs Pothecary Witham Weld, 70 St George's Square, London SW1V 3RD. Tel: 020 7821 8211.

Officials

General Secretary: Jane Le Poidevin, BEd, NPQH
Membership Secretary: Ruth Howe
Professional Development Officer: Maggie Turner, BA
Treasurer: Michael Phizacklea, FCA
Office Secretary: Liz Dean
Office Assistant: Catherine Turtle

Independent Schools Association
1 Boys' British School, East Street, Saffron Walden, Essex CB10 1LS
Tel: 01799 523619 • e-mail: isa@isaschools.org.uk • website: www.isaschools.org.uk

COBIS

COUNCIL OF BRITISH INTERNATIONAL SCHOOLS

COBIS is a Membership Association of high-quality British international schools worldwide, with member schools and affiliates in more than 25 countries. COBIS members undergo an inspection by the Independent Schools Inspectorate (ISI) to gain accreditation.

COBIS provides:

- Quality assurance in member schools.
- Representation with the British Government, educational bodies, and the corporate sector.
- A network of support through contacts, consultancies, information and marketing.
- A forum for discussion through conferences, seminars, and continuing professional development.
- Access to information about developments and trends in UK education.

COBIS holds an Annual Conference in London in May for Heads, Governors, and members of school Senior Leadership Teams. COBIS also runs inset conferences for teachers at different international venues based in its member schools. COBIS aims to support its members and represent their interests in Britain and overseas in order to advance the interests of British schools outside the UK.

COBIS was founded in 1981 as COBISEC (Council of British Independent Schools in the European Communities) and is a Charitable Association registered in The Hague. The Association is managed by an elected Executive Committee which includes both Heads and Governors. In 2000 the Association became affiliated to the Independent Schools Council (ISC) in the UK, and adopted the ISI inspection scheme as the route to full accreditation for its members. In 2008 COBIS became a constituent member association of the ISC. The work of COBIS is supported by a UK Secretariat based at Oxford Brookes University.

COBIS Executive 2008/2009

Honorary President

Sir Dick Pantlin CBE

Honorary Vice Presidents

Lord Sharman OBE

Dr Arthur Hearnden OBE DPhil

Michael Cooper OBE

Sir Mervyn Brown KCMG OBE

The Rt Hon The Lord Macgregor OBE

Sybil Melchers MBE

Jean Scott

Executive Committee

Jennifer Bray MBE (*Inspections Officer*)

Nigel Collins, British School in the Netherlands

Jane Crowley, British International Primary School of Stockholm

Roger Fry CBE (*Chairman*)

David Johnson, King's College, Madrid

Jeremy Long, Prague British School

Simon O'Grady, The British International School, Cairo

John Price, Jerudong International School, Brunei

Mike Roberts OBE, British School of Amsterdam (*Treasurer*)

Trevor Rowell, Governor, British School of Paris

David Smith, St Julian's School, Portugal (*Secretary*)

Secretariat

General Secretary: Dr Fiona Rogers

Council of British International Schools

Oxford Brookes University, Harcourt Hill Campus, Oxford, OX2 9AT

Tel: 01865 488 564 • Fax: 01865 488 666

e-mail: general.secretary@cobis.org.uk • website: www.cobis.org.uk

AGBIS

ASSOCIATION OF GOVERNING BODIES OF INDEPENDENT SCHOOLS

REGISTERED CHARITY NO. 1108756

The Object of the Association is to advance education in independent schools and, in furtherance of that object, but not otherwise, the Association shall have power:

(a) to discuss matters concerning the policy and administration of such schools and to encourage cooperation between their Governing Bodies;
(b) to consider the relationship of such schools to the general educational interests of the community;
(c) to consider and give guidance on matters of general or individual concern to the Governing Bodies of such schools;
(d) to promote good governance in such schools;
and
(e) to express the views of the Governing Bodies of such schools on any of the foregoing matters and to take such action as may be appropriate in their interests.

Full Membership
The Governing Body of any independent school in the United Kingdom, which is a registered or exempt charity, may apply for full membership of the Association, subject to conditions determined by the Executive Committee. Admission to full membership of AGBIS will be conditional upon the educational and other standards of the school and admission of the Head to membership of The Headmasters' and Headmistresses' Conference, The Girls' Schools Association, The Society of Headmasters and Headmistresses of Independent Schools, The Independent Association of Prep Schools or The Independent Schools Association within one year. COBIS Schools and others from outside the United Kingdom should have similar characteristics to those expected of UK applicants.

Associate Membership
Any Independent School in the United Kingdom which is not a charity but whose head is a member of one of the above listed Heads' Associations or is expected to become a member within one year, may apply for Associate Membership of the Association. Such schools must show evidence of the existence of the arrangements for governance which may be in the form of an advisory board or similar.

Any independent school within the United Kingdom which meets the requirements as above, apart from membership of an ISC Heads' Association, and is in membership of either SCIS or WISC, and schools outside the United Kingdom in membership of COBIS, BISW or similar organisations and which are inspected by ISI, at the discretion of the AGBIS Executive Committee, may also apply for Associate Membership.

Executive Committee

Chairman: Sam Alder (King William's College, IOM)
Joint Deputy Chairmen: Miss June Taylor (Godolphin and Latymer School); Richard Green (Prior's Field School)
Honorary Treasurer: Charles Paull (Kimbolton School)

Michael Button (Taunton School)
Marco Chiappelli (St Margaret's School, Edinburgh)
Revd Dr Martin Dudley (City of London School for Girls)
Anthony Eady (Sir William Perkins's School)
Tony Evans (Sevenoaks School)
Michael Fowle (Rugby School)
Richard Haynes (Pocklington School)
Baroness Morris of Bolton (co-opted, Bolton Schools)
Mrs Jane Richardson (Shrewsbury High School)
Mrs Joy Richardson (Uppingham School)
Harry Salmon (Benenden School)
Thomas Wheare (Exeter School, Port Regis School & Dragon School)
Jerry Wooding OBE (Arnold School)

General Secretary: M S (Shane) Rutter-Jerome

Association of Governing Bodies of Independent Schools
***Address*: Renshaw Barns, Upper Woodford, Salisbury, Wiltshire SP4 6FA**
Tel: 01722 782900 • e-mail: gensec@agbis.org.uk • website: www.agbis.org.uk

INDEPENDENT SCHOOLS' BURSARS ASSOCIATION

Membership
Full membership of the Association is open to Schools who are members of one of the constituent associations in membership of the Independent Schools Council. Bursars or other officials of other independent schools may apply for Associate Membership provided that the school is recognised as an educational charity.

The Work of the Association
The Association exists in order to advance education and it achieves this through supporting and advancing financial and operational performance in Independent Schools. It assists members in their work by the sharing of best practice and information on matters of common interest and undertakes joint negotiation with Government Departments and other bodies where this is considered advisable. Close contact is maintained with the Association of Governing Bodies of Independent Schools, the Headmasters' and Headmistresses' Conference, the Society of Headmasters and Headmistresses of Independent Schools, the Girls' Schools Association, the Independent Association of Prep Schools and the Independent Schools Association through a Joint Council on which sit representatives of each body.

A full professional development programme is run that includes events such as an annual conference and new bursars' course. In addition to the Bursar's Review, the in-house journal, bulletins are circulated at intervals to all members containing notices about decisions of the Executive Committee, information received by the Secretary, and other matters of day to day interest, as well as contributions from members and digests of information collected by means of questionnaires. There is also an Annual Report. The Association has a very comprehensive and active website.

Schools Represented
The first meeting of the Association was held in London in 1932, and was attended by representatives of 47 Schools. There are now over 900 Schools in membership.

Management
The Executive Committee consists of the Chairman of the Association, Mr N Marten, the Bursar of The John Lyon School and the bursars of eleven other leading independent schools.

The Independent Schools' Bursars Association is a Registered Charity, number 1121757, and a Company Limited by Guarantee, registered in England and Wales, number 6410037.

General Secretary: Mr Jonathan Cook

***Registered Office*: Unit 11-12, Manor Farm, Cliddesden, Basingstoke, Hampshire RG25 2JB**
Tel: 01256 330369 • e-mail: office@theisba.org.uk • website: www.theisba.org.uk

BOARDING SCHOOLS' ASSOCIATION

The BSA is the UK Association promoting and serving boarding education.

Full school membership of the Association is only open to schools accredited by one of the school member associations of the Independent Schools Council or the State Boarding Schools' Association.

The BSA enjoys Associate Membership of the Independent Schools Council.

The Department for Children, Schools and Families supports the BSA in its Professional Development and Publication Programmes.

Aims
The BSA's aims are:

- To promote the qualities of boarding life provided by all types of boarding schools in membership of the Association
- To encourage the highest standards of welfare for boarding pupils in its member schools
- To provide information to parents and young people considering boarding education about boarding and boarding schools which are in membership of the BSA
- To organise a professional development programme for all staff and governors of boarding schools
- To produce appropriate publications on boarding issues and good practice in boarding
- To conduct and authorise appropriate research
- To work with other bodies concerned with boarding education
- To develop links with boarding associations and boarding schools worldwide
- To maintain a regular dialogue with appropriate Government Ministers and their departments, Members of Parliament, and Local Government Officers

Membership
Membership is open to all schools with boarders which are accredited to the Independent Schools Council (ISC), to schools in membership of the Scottish Council of Independent Schools (SCIS), and also to state maintained boarding schools (which may then also become members of the State Boarding Schools' Association – SBSA). Membership may also be offered to boarding schools overseas at the discretion of the Executive Committee. Current membership comprises over 500 schools (fully boarding, weekly/flexi boarding, or day schools with boarding provision; co-educational or single-sex; preparatory or secondary).

Associate Membership is available to individuals, schools and other bodies at the discretion of the Executive Committee. They will be entitled to receive all Association mailings. Associate membership is open to former heads of member schools and anyone else interested in supporting the cause of boarding.

Support for Schools

The Professional Development Programme

In partnership with Roehampton University and the Department for Children, Schools and Families (DCSF), the BSA has established a Professional Development Programme for all staff working in boarding schools. These BSA courses lead to university validated Certificates of Professional Practice in Boarding Education. There is a programme of Day Courses on a range of topics including Child Protection, Anti-Bullying strategies, the role of Gap Assistants, Boarding Legislation and Good Practice, Boarding Governance. There are also individual courses tailored to the particular needs of a school or group of schools.

BSA training is available to all staff who work in boarding schools and to the Governors of boarding schools.

BSA Training Programmes are also used by schools and boarding associations throughout the world.

Residential Conferences

Four conferences are held annually for:

Heads of Boarding Schools and representatives of their member associations
Deputy Heads
Housemasters and Housemistresses
Matrons and Medical Staff

The latter two conferences incorporate part of the BSA/Roehampton University Professional Development Programme.

Publications

These include:

- ***Good Practice in Boarding Schools – A Resource Handbook for all those working in boarding***
  Edited by Tim Holgate
- ***Duty of Care***
  By Dr Tim Hawkes (amended by Tim Holgate)
- ***World Class***
  By Christopher Greenfield and Philip Hardaker
- ***Running a School Boarding House – A legal Guide for Housemasters and Housemistresses***
  By Robert Boyd
- ***Parenting the Boarder***
  By Libby Purves
- ***Being a Boarder***
  By Rose Heiney
- ***Choosing a Boarding School – A guide for Parents***
  By Tim Holgate
- ***Boarding School*** – the BSA magazine published twice a year
- ***The BSA Bulletin*** – published every two months
- ***Boarding Briefing Papers*** – are published at regular intervals on matters concerning boarding legislation and good practice

BSA publications are supported by the DCSF which also approves:

Parents' Guide to Maintained Boarding Schools

National Boarding Standards

The Association liaises with the Department of Health, Ofsted, and the Independent Schools Inspectorate on the inspection of boarding schools under the National Minimum Standards for Boarding schools.

Liaison with National Bodies

The Association meets regularly with the Department for Children, Schools and Families to discuss issues concerned with boarding.

It also liaises with Local Government, ISI (Independent Schools Inspectorate), Ofsted (Office for Standards in Education), CEAS (Children's Education Advisory Service) and all the national educational organisations.

Organisation

At the Annual General Meeting, held at the Heads' Annual Conference, Officers of the Association are elected together with the Executive Committee, on which are representatives of all the constituent Associations of the Independent Schools Council (ISC). Co-opted members include representatives from National Bodies involved in boarding education. The Honorary Treasurer is usually a Bursar from a member school.

National Director
Hilary Moriarty, e-mail: bsa@boarding.org.uk

Director of Training
Alex Thomson, e-mail: training@boarding.org.uk

The Boarding Schools' Association
Grosvenor Gardens House, 35-37 Grosvenor Gardens, London SW1W 0BS
Tel: 020 7798 1580 • Fax: 020 7798 1581 • website: www.boarding.org.uk

INDEPENDENT SCHOOLS INSPECTORATE

AND THE ISI CONSULTANCY DIVISION

The Independent Schools Inspectorate (ISI) is the body approved by the Secretary of State to inspect schools in England in membership of the ISC. Inspection is conducted in accordance with the Education Act 2002, amended by Schedule 8 of the Education Act 2005 and under the professional scrutiny of Her Majesty's Inspectors (HMI) in the Office for Standards in Education, Children's Services and Skills (Ofsted) who monitor ISI's work on behalf of the Department for Children, Schools and Families (DCSF). ISI inspects schools according to a schedule agreed with the DCSF, currently every six years, although early years settings are inspected every three years. ISI also inspects schools in membership of the ISC Associations overseas, using a modified framework that takes account of the schools' international setting. Inspection reports are published to parents and made available, with other related material, on the ISI website, www.isi.net.

ISI inspections are led by professional Reporting Inspectors, who are mainly either former HMI or Ofsted Registered Inspectors or are former head teachers who have qualified as Reporting Inspectors. The remainder of the inspection team is drawn from serving headteachers or other senior staff from ISC schools, trained by ISI. This incorporation of peer review gives the teams the vital combination of professional rigour with an immediate understanding of the diverse character of the schools and a grasp of current educational developments.

ISI also, through its consultancy division, offers a range of seminars, INSET and consultancy services to schools in the UK and overseas on matters related to inspection and school improvement.

Chief Inspector/CEO: Christine Ryan
Head of Communications: Durell Barnes
Head of Administration: Lisa Brooks
Business Development Manager: Rowenna Bailey

***ISI Office*: CAP House, 9–12 Long Lane, London EC1A 9HA**
Tel: 020 7600 0100 • Fax: 020 7776 8849
e-mail: info@isi.net • website: www.isi.net

BOARD OF MANAGEMENT FOR METHODIST INDEPENDENT SCHOOLS

Methodist Church House, 25 Marylebone Road, London NW1 5JP
Tel: 020 7935 3723 • website: www.methodisteducation.co.uk

Chairman: Baroness Richardson of Calow
Secretary: Mr Graham Russell, MA

Schools for Boys and Girls
Culford School, Bury St Edmunds, Suffolk IP28 6TX. Tel: 01284 728615.
Edgehill College, Bideford, North Devon EX39 3LY. Tel: 01237 471701.
Kent College, Canterbury, Kent CT2 9DT. Tel: 01227 763231.
Queen's College, Taunton, Somerset TA1 4QS. Tel: 01823 272559.
Shebbear College, Shebbear, North Devon EX21 5HJ. Tel: 01409 281228.
Truro School, Truro, Cornwall TR1 1TH. Tel: 01872 272763.
Woodhouse Grove School, Apperley Bridge, West Yorks BD10 0NR. Tel: 0113 2502477.

Schools for Girls
Farringtons School, Chislehurst, Kent BR7 6LR. Tel: 020 8467 0256.
Kent College Pembury, Tunbridge Wells, Kent TN2 4AX. Tel: 01892 822006.

OTHER METHODIST INDEPENDENT SCHOOLS

Schools for Boys and Girls
Ashville College, Harrogate, North Yorks HG2 9JP. Tel: 01423 566358.
Kingswood School, Bath, Somerset BA1 5RG. Tel: 01225 734200.
The Leys School, Cambridge CB2 2AD. Tel: 01223 508900.
Rydal Penrhos School, Colwyn Bay, North Wales LL29 7BT. Tel: 01492 530155.
Wesley College, Dublin. Tel: 00 353 1 2987066.
Methodist College, Belfast. Tel: 028 9020 5202.

Schools for Girls
Queenswood School, Hatfield, Herts AL9 6NS. Tel: 01707 602500.

A School prospectus, together with particulars of fees, and other information may be obtained from the Headmaster or Headmistress.

In cases of need applications may be made to a Central Bursary Fund for financial help to enable Methodist children to attend these schools. This fund is available to day pupils as well as boarding pupils. Details are available from the Board of Management.

Information regarding other sources of assistance with fees may be obtained from The Independent Schools Council, St Vincent House, 30 Orange Street, London WC2H 7HH. Tel: 020 7766 7070.

CATHOLIC INDEPENDENT SCHOOLS' CONFERENCE

www.CatholicIndependentSchools.org

Objects

The CISC exists to:

- promote the work of 140 Catholic Independent Schools throughout the UK;
- give support and advice to member schools;
- organise an annual Conference, Study Days and Workshops;
- liaise with Dioceses, the Catholic Education Service and ISC;
- provide a help line for those seeking a Catholic Independent School for their children.

Schools

There are 140 schools currently in membership of the CISC. The majority of members are also in membership of one or more of the seven independent schools' associations that constitute the Independent Schools Council. Schools in membership include day and boarding schools, single-sex and co-educational, senior and junior schools and special schools.

Membership

There are two categories of Members: **Full Members** and **Associate Members**.

Full Members

Full Members may be invited by the Committee to take up membership. He/She will be the Head or Principal of a school which satisfies the following seven conditions:

(a) The school shall be recognised by the local Catholic bishop as being Catholic.
(b) The school shall have been recognised as a charitable foundation by the Charity Commissioners.
(c) The school shall be independent.
(d) The school shall be in the United Kingdom.
(e) The school will have been subjected to a nationally accredited inspection and found to be in good standing.
(f) The expectation is that the head of the school will be a practising Catholic. Where governors appoint a head who is not a Catholic CISC will expect governors to provide training and support for the head to enable the head to lead a Catholic school, and will assist them in so doing.
(g) Full members only attend the AGM.

Associate Members

Associate Members may be invited by the Chairman to take up membership, but do not attend the AGM.
The following are eligible for associate membership:

(a) Heads of proprietary-owned schools, which meet the conditions of Full Membership apart from not being recognised by the Charity Commissioners as a charitable foundation.
(b) Retired full Members.
(c) Catholics, and other Christians, who are in sympathy with the aims of CISC.
(d) Heads of Foundation or Voluntary-Aided Schools, which meet the conditions of Full Membership, apart from not being recognised by the Charity Commissioners as a charitable foundation.
(e) Heads of Catholic Independent Schools outside the United Kingdom.

Officers for 2008–2009

Chairman: Mr Adrian Aylward, MA – Leweston School
Vice-President: Dr Giles Mercer, MA, DPhil, KSG – Prior Park College
Vice-Chairman: Mr Charles Foulds, BA – Grace Dieu Manor School

Committee:
Mrs Mary Breen, MSc – St Mary's School Ascot
Mr Joe Peake, MA – St George's College
Mrs Bridget Williams, MA – Notre Dame Senior School
Mr Chris Cleugh, MSc – St Benedict's School
Miss Bridgeen Banks, MA – St Pius X Preparatory School
Mr John Shinkwin, MA – Princethorpe College
Mrs Jayne Triffitt, MA – Woldingham School.

General Secretary: Mr Philip Sweeney, BA

***Address*: 10 Shrewsbury Road, Prenton, Merseyside CH43 1UX**
Tel: 0151 652 4326 • Fax: 0151 652 5351 • e-mail: p-sweeney@btconnect.com

INDEPENDENT SCHOOLS EXAMINATIONS BOARD
COMMON ENTRANCE EXAMINATIONS

Chairman: M S Spurr, MA, DPhil

General Secretary: Mrs J Williams, BA, PGCE
Independent Schools Examinations Board, Jordan House, Christchurch Road, New Milton, Hampshire BH25 6QJ
Telephone 01425 621111; Fax: 01425 620044; e-mail: enquiries@iseb.co.uk; website: www.iseb.co.uk

The Common Entrance Examinations are used for transfer to senior schools at the ages of 11+ and 13+. The syllabuses are devised and regularly monitored by the Independent Schools Examinations Board which comprises members of the Headmasters' and Headmistresses' Conference, the Girls' Schools Association and the Independent Association of Prep Schools.

The papers are set by examiners appointed by the Board, but the answers are marked by the senior school for which a candidate is entered. A list of schools using the examination is given below. Common Entrance is not a public examination as, for example, GCSE, and candidates may normally be entered only if they have been offered a place at a senior school, subject to their passing the examination.

Candidates normally take the examination in their own junior or preparatory schools, either in the UK or overseas.

Dates
The 11+ examination is held in mid-January.
The 13+ examination commences either on the last Monday in January or on the first Monday in June.

Entries
In cases where candidates are at schools in membership of the Independent Association of Prep Schools, it is usual for heads of these schools to make arrangements for entering candidates for the appropriate examination after consultation with parents and senior school heads. In the case of candidates at schools which do not normally enter candidates, it is the responsibility of parents to arrange for candidates to be entered for the appropriate examination in accordance with the requirements of senior schools.

Conduct of the Examination
Regulations for the conduct of the examination are laid down by the Independent Schools Examinations Board.

Fees
The Independent Schools Examinations Board decides the fees to be charged for each candidate. Schools are notified annually in the spring term of fees payable for the following three terms. Parents seeking information about current fees should look on the ISEB website or contact the ISEB office.

Correspondence
Correspondence about academic matters relating to the Common Entrance examinations and requests for further information about the administration of the examinations should be addressed (as above) to the General Secretary, ISEB.

SENIOR SCHOOLS USING THE COMMON ENTRANCE EXAMINATIONS TO INDEPENDENT SCHOOLS

MEMBERS OF THE HEADMASTERS' AND HEADMISTRESSES' CONFERENCE

Abingdon School
Aldenham School
Ampleforth College
Ardingly College
Ashville College
Barnard Castle School
Bedales School
Bedford School
Bedford Modern School
Berkhamsted Collegiate School
Bishop's Stortford College
Bloxham School
Blundell's School
Bootham School
Bradfield College
Brentwood School
Brighton College
Bromsgrove School
Bryanston School
Canford School
Caterham School
Charterhouse
Cheltenham College
Chigwell School
Christ College
Churcher's College
City of London School
City of London Freemen's School
Clayesmore School
Clifton College
Colfe's School
Cranleigh School
Culford School
Dauntsey's School
Dean Close School
Denstone College
Downside School
Dulwich College
Durham School
Eastbourne College
Ellesmere College
Eltham College
Emanuel School
Epsom College
Eton College
Felsted School
Fettes College
Forest School
Framlingham College
Frensham Heights
Giggleswick School
Glenalmond College
Gresham's School
Haberdashers' Aske's School
Haileybury
Hampton School
Harrow School
Headington School
Hereford Cathedral School
Highgate School
Hurstpierpoint College
Ipswich School
Kelly College
Kent College
Kimbolton School
King Edward's School, Witley
King's College, Taunton
King's College School, Wimbledon
King's School, Bruton

King's School, Canterbury
King's School, Ely
King's School, Gloucester
King's School, Rochester
Kingston Grammar School
Kingswood School
Lancing College
Latymer Upper School
Leighton Park School
The Leys School
Lord Wandsworth College
Loretto School
Loughborough Grammar School
Magdalen College School
Malvern College
Marlborough College
Merchant Taylors' School
Merchiston Castle School
Millfield School
Mill Hill School
Monkton Combe School
Monmouth School
Norwich School
Oakham School
Oratory School
Oundle School
Pangbourne College
Plymouth College
Pocklington School
Portsmouth Grammar School
Prior Park College
Queen's College
Radley College
Ratcliffe College
Reading Blue Coat School
Reed's School
Reigate Grammar School
Rendcomb College
Repton School
Royal Grammar School, Guildford
Royal Hospital School
Royal Russell School
Rugby School
Ryde School with Upper Chine
St Albans School
St Benedict's School
St Columba's College, Dublin
St Columba's College, St Albans
St Edmund's College
St Edmund's School
St Edward's School
St George's College
St John's School
St Paul's School
St Peter's School
Seaford College
Sedbergh School
Sevenoaks School
Sherborne School
Shiplake College
Shrewsbury School
Stamford School
Stonyhurst College
Stowe School
Strathallan School
Sutton Valence School
Taunton School
Tonbridge School
Trent College
Trinity School
Truro School
University College School
Uppingham School
Victoria College
Wellingborough School
Wellington College
Wellington School
Wells Cathedral School
Westminster School
Whitgift School
Woodbridge School
Worksop College
Worth School
Wrekin College
Wycliffe College

MEMBERS OF THE GIRLS' SCHOOLS ASSOCIATION

Badminton School
Benenden School
Bruton School for Girls
Casterton School
The Cheltenham Ladies' College
Downe House
Godolphin School
Haberdashers' Monmouth School
Heathfield St Mary's
Kent College Pembury
Leweston School
Malvern St James
More House School, London
Moreton Hall School
Princess Helena College
Queen Anne's School
Queen Margaret's School
Queenswood School
Roedean School
Rye St Antony School
St George's School, Ascot
St Leonard's-Mayfield School
St Mary's School, Calne
St Mary's School, Shaftesbury
St Swithun's School
Sherborne School for Girls
Stonar School
Tudor Hall School
Westonbirt
Woldingham School
Wycombe Abbey School

THE FOLLOWING SCHOOLS USE THE COMMON ENTRANCE FOR SOME CANDIDATES

MEMBERS OF THE SOCIETY OF HEADMASTERS AND HEADMISTRESSES OF INDEPENDENT SCHOOLS

Battle Abbey School
Bearwood College
Bedstone College
Bethany School
Box Hill School
Claremont Fan Court School
Cokethorpe School
d'Overbroeck's College
Ewell Castle School
Halliford School
Kingham Hill School
Langley School
Licensed Victuallers' School
Lincoln Minster School
Milton Abbey School
Portland Place School
Scarborough College
St Bede's School
St James Independent School
St Joseph's College

MEMBERS OF THE INDEPENDENT SCHOOLS ASSOCIATION

Chilton Cantelo School
Claires Court School
Heathfield School, Wolverley
Lewes Old Grammar School
Newlands Manor School
Queen Ethelburga's College
Sackville School
Sherfield School

OTHER SCHOOLS

Academic International School, Africa
Ballard School
Gordonstoun School
Hampton Court House School
Harrodian School
Hillcrest Secondary School, Nairobi
Peponi Secondary School, Nairobi
St Andrew's School, Kenya
St Leonards School

THE GIRLS' DAY SCHOOL TRUST (GDST)

100 Rochester Row London SW1P 1JP
Tel: 020 7393 6666 • Fax: 020 7393 6789
e-mail: info@wes.gdst.net • website: www.gdst.net

What difference do GDST schools make to our students?

Young people at GDST schools enjoy taking on mental and physical challenges both in the classroom and beyond it. They learn to be adaptable and adventurous, to get a taste of leadership and teamwork, and to balance risks against rewards.

They learn that independence, ambition, hard work and self-discipline are important, but that the ties of family, friendship and community need their time and care too if they are to become fulfilled and balanced individuals.

They learn to value their own and each other's strengths and talents – creative, practical, enterprising and constructive – while aiming always to develop themselves and enhance their own skills.

They learn to be energetic, thoughtful, fluent, enterprising and self-sufficient – the knowledge and skills they need to succeed in a global economy and be leading citizens of a global society, whatever path in life they choose.

Above all, they leave GDST schools with the academic achievements that allow them access to their first choice of schools, universities and jobs.

Key facts about the GDST

- The Girls' Day School Trust (GDST) is one of the largest, longest established and successful groups of independent schools in the UK, with 29 schools, over 20,000 students and 4,000 staff.
- Our students outperform their state sector and independent school peers at GCSE and A Level, and the most popular A Level subjects are biology, chemistry, English, and maths. 98% of our A Level students go on to higher education, the majority to their first-choice university, and 16% study medicine and allied subjects.
- Students cultivate a wide range of life skills, through programmes such as student exchange, peer mentoring, leadership training, and the GDST's unique 'CareerStart' initiative.
- Nearly 45,000 former students in 75 countries are in our Minerva Network, with members who are national and international leaders in every professional field – ambassadors for the GDST and support for our present students.
- We provide a rich and distinctive curriculum from the nursery to the Sixth Form, supporting choice and diversity for girls and, increasingly, boys. We continue to invest, grow and diversify, introducing co-education at certain levels in some of our schools and developing a group of preparatory schools, some of which are mixed, and two mixed Sixth Form Colleges.
- Our schools are broadly selective. All GDST schools are non-denominational day schools, and The Royal High School, Bath also takes boarders.
- We have a first-class in-service staff training programme tailored to our requirements
- E-learning extends and enriches our curriculum, promoting independent learning outside as well as in school.

Our exceptional network

At the GDST our commitment to education is at the heart of our charitable status. Our duty is, and will continue to be, to our current and future pupils, not unaccountable shareholders. All our income is reinvested in our schools for the benefit of the students. This commitment, along with our size, long history and sound operational management, provides the parents of our students with invaluable peace of mind.

Within our framework, each school retains the independence and flexibility to respond both to local needs and changes on the national and global stage. Cooperative programmes and collaborations flourish both in the individual schools and at GDST level and we are keen to extend our range of partnerships, including working with the UK government on its Academy programme.

We recognise that to successfully prepare our students for life in a rapidly changing global society we must continue to grow and evolve. Our innovative vision includes overseas ventures in Asia, and other international outreach plans.

Our mission for the 21st century is to ensure that the GDST remains at the forefront of education, extending excellence and innovation in dynamic educational settings.

GDST all-through schools

Blackheath High School
Brighton & Hove High School
Bromley High School
Central Newcastle High School
Croydon High School
Heathfield School
Howell's School, Llandaff
Ipswich High School
Northampton High School
Norwich High School for Girls
Notting Hill & Ealing High School
Nottingham Girls' High School
Oxford High School
Portsmouth High School
Putney High School
Royal High School
Sheffield High School
Shrewsbury High School
South Hampstead High School
Streatham & Clapham High School
Sutton High School
Sydenham High School
Wimbledon High School

GDST prep schools

Great Houghton Preparatory School
The Hamlets Prep School
Hilden Grange Preparatory School
Kensington Prep School

GDST Academies

The Belvedere Academy
Birkenhead High School (from September 2009)

Information on the schools can be found in the Yearbook or on the GDST website: www.gdst.net
The Girls' Day School Trust is a Registered Charity, number 306983.

CHOIR SCHOOLS' ASSOCIATION

www.choirschools.org.uk

Patron: The Duchess of Kent

Committee:

Chairman: Mr Jonathan Milton, Westminster Abbey Choir School

Treasurer: Mr R Bacon, St Edmund's Junior School, Canterbury

Mrs E Cairncross, Wells Cathedral School
The Revd G Everitt, Ampleforth College
Mr I Hawksby, The Chorister School, Durham
Mrs C Moreland, Chetham's School, Manchester
Mr H Munro, Bristol Cathedral School
Mr R Overend, King's Preparatory School, Rochester
Mr N Robinson, King's College School, Cambridge
Mr J Waszek, St Edward's College, Liverpool

Administrator: Mrs Susan Rees, Wolvesey, College Street, Winchester, Hampshire SP23 9ND
Tel: 01962 890530, Fax: 01962 869978, e-mail: admin@choirschools.org.uk
Director of Development: Mr R White, e-mail: riwhite@talk21.com
Information Officer: Jane Capon, Tel: 01359 221333, e-mail: info@choirschools.org.uk

CSA Full and Associate Members

Blackburn Cathedral
Bristol Cathedral School
King's College School, Cambridge
St John's College School, Cambridge
St Edmund's School, Canterbury
St John's College, Cardiff
Carlisle Cathedral
St Cedd's School, Chelmsford
The Prebendal School, Chichester
The Chorister School, Durham
St Mary's Music School, Edinburgh
The King's School Junior School, Ely
Exeter Cathedral School
The King's School, Gloucester
St James' School, Grimsby
Lanesborough School, Guildford
Chapel Royal, Hampton Court
Hereford Cathedral School
Leeds Cathedral (RC)
Leicester Cathedral
Lichfield Cathedral School
Lincoln Minster School
Runnymede St Edward's School, Liverpool
St Edward's College, Liverpool
The Cathedral School, Llandaff
City of London School
The London Oratory School
St Paul's Cathedral School, London
Westminster Abbey Choir School, London
Westminster Cathedral Choir School, London
Chetham's School of Music, Manchester
St Nicholas Cathedral, Newcastle-upon-Tyne
Norwich School
Christ Church Cathedral School, Oxford
Magdalen College School, Oxford
New College School, Oxford
The King's School, Peterborough
The Portsmouth Grammar School
Reigate St Mary's Choir School
The Cathedral Choir School, Ripon
King's Preparatory School, Rochester
Salisbury Cathedral School
Sheffield Cathedral
The Minster School, Southwell
Polwhele House School, Truro
Queen Elizabeth Grammar Junior School, Wakefield
Warwick School
Wells Cathedral School
The Pilgrims' School, Winchester
St George's School, Windsor
St Peter's Church, Wolverhampton
The King's School, Worcester
The Minster School, York
Ampleforth College, York

Overseas Members:

St Andrew's Cathedral School, Sydney, Australia
St Patrick's Cathedral Choir School, Dublin
The Cathedral Grammar School, Christchurch, New Zealand
National Cathedral School, Washington DC, USA
St Thomas Choir School, New York, USA

The 46 schools in the UK are all attached to cathedrals, churches or college chapels and educate over 24,000 pupils, including 1,300 choristers. Westminster Abbey Choir School is the only school to educate choristers and probationers only. The Association's associate membership includes cathedrals and churches without choir schools.

Choir schools offer a very special opportunity for children who enjoy singing. They receive a first-class academic and all-round education combined with excellent music training. The experience and self-discipline choristers acquire remain with them for life. There is a wide range of schools: some cater for children aged 7–13, others are junior schools with senior schools to 18; most are Church of England but the Roman Catholic, Scottish and Welsh churches are all represented.

Most CSA members are fee-paying schools and nine out of ten choristers qualify for financial help with fees. Some chorister places are completely free and most parents can expect to pay less than half fees. Deans and Chapters provide generous fee assistance while Government support comes in the shape of the Choir Schools' Scholarship Scheme. Under the umbrella of the Music and Dance Scheme, funds are available to help those who cannot afford even the reduced school fees. The Government funding, along with other monies in its Chorister Fund, is administered by the CSA. Each application is means-tested and an award made once a child has secured a place at a choir school.

Each CSA member school has its own admissions procedure for choristers. However, every child will be assessed both musically and academically. A growing number of children are given informal voice tests which enable the organist or director of music to judge whether they have the potential to become choristers. Some are offered places immediately, but most will be urged to enter the more formal voice trial organised by the school. In some cases a family may be advised not to proceed. Alternatively, the child's voice may be more suitable for one of the other choir schools.

A number of special ingredients help make a good chorister: potential, a keen musical ear and an eagerness to sing. A clutch of music examination certificates is not vital – alertness and enthusiasm are! At the same time, school staff must be satisfied that a new recruit can cope with school work and the many other activities on offer as well as the demanding choir workload.

To find out more about choir schools please visit the CSA website: **www.choirschools.org.uk**
CSA members can be contacted or you can write, e-mail or telephone
for further information about choir schools and the Chorister Fund to:

Jane Capon, Information Officer, Windrush, Church Road, Market Weston, Diss, Norfolk IP22 2NX
Telephone: 01359 221333; e-mail: info@choirschools.org.uk

The Association publishes a newsletter *Singing Out* and *Choir Schools Today*, an annual round-up of news and information.

UNITED CHURCH SCHOOLS TRUST

23 Chapel Street, Titchmarsh, Northamptonshire NN14 3DA
Tel: 01832 735105 • Fax: 01832 734760
e-mail: admin@church-schools.com • website: www.ucst.org.uk

United Church Schools Trust Schools

Arnold School (HMC, IAPS, day)
Ashford School (SHMIS, IAPS, boarding and day)
Bramcote Lorne School (IAPS, boarding and day)
Brigg Preparatory School (IAPS, day)
Caterham School (HMC, IAPS, boarding and day)**
Guildford High School (HMC, IAPS, day)
Hampshire Collegiate School (SHMIS, boarding and day)
Hull Collegiate School (SHMIS, ISA, day)
Lincoln Minster School (SHMIS, IAPS, boarding and day)
Sunderland High School (SHMIS, day)
Surbiton High School (HMC, GSA, IAPS, day)

(Particulars of the schools will be found in the Yearbook under the above titles).

**LGB Local Governing Body*
***Associate School*

The Trust's objective is to bring out 'the best in everyone', enabling each pupil to become a balanced, happy and articulate person with the intellectual freedom to be creative, confidence to initiate, flexibility to respond to challenge, change and adversity, compassion to serve others, spirit to enjoy life, integrity to be trustworthy and motivation to have a lifelong love of learning.

The United Church Schools Trust was founded as an educational charity in 1883 with the principal objective of creating schools that would offer pupils a good academic education based on Christian principles with particular reference to the Church of England. The Trust is non-denominational: it welcomes pupils and staff from all faiths and none to its schools.

The Trust has developed the concept of a group of individually strong schools each capable of offering a broad and challenging education. To achieve this it has invested in the provision of excellent buildings and facilities at each school in the belief that growth helps to enhance the academic and extra-curricular opportunities available to pupils in both the primary and secondary stages of education. The success of this policy is reflected in the growth in pupil numbers from 3,200 in 1990 to almost 7,500 in 2008.

This ideal of strong schools embraces not just academic learning to high standards, but also the development of skills that will be essential throughout life both at work and socially. Teamwork, leadership, an enthusiastic response to challenge and an active concern for others are all attributes which are valued at the United Church Schools Trust. These skills, increasingly identified by employers as the key to future success, are developed throughout each young person's time in school from the earliest years through to the Sixth Form.

Academic scholarships, exhibitions and bursaries are awarded at all schools. In addition Church Schools Foundation Assisted Places are available at each school. The tuition fees vary according to age and school, from £4,023 to £13,377 a year (day) and £13,950 to £24,336 (boarding).

The United Church Schools Trust is a Registered Charity, number 1016538. It is an educational charity with a leading reputation for its management of schools across both the independent and state sectors.

***Head Office*: Woodard Schools, High Street, Abbots Bromley, Rugeley, Staffordshire WS15 3BW**
Tel: 01283 840120 • Fax: 01283 840893 • e-mail: jillshorthose@woodard.co.uk
website: www.woodard.co.uk

Owned Schools

Abbots Bromley School for Girls
Ardingly College
Ardingly College Prep School
Bloxham School, Banbury
The Cathedral School, Llandaff
Denstone College, Uttoxeter
Ellesmere College
Grenville College, Bideford
Hurstpierpoint College
Hurstpierpoint College Preparatory School
King's College, Taunton
King's Hall, Taunton
The King's School, Tynemouth
Lancing College
Lancing College Prep School at Mowden
Peterborough High School
Prestfelde School, Shrewsbury
Queen Mary's School, Thirsk
Ranby House School, Retford
Smallwood Manor Preparatory School, Uttoxeter
St James' School, Grimsby
St Margaret's School, Exeter
Worksop College

Information on all of the schools can be found on the website www.woodard.co.uk

Woodard Schools form the largest group of Anglican schools in England and Wales. In addition to the above list of owned schools a further 19 schools, in the independent and maintained sectors both in the United Kingdom and abroad, choose to be affiliated. The schools are not exclusive and take pupils of all faiths and of none. In total over 25,000 pupils are taught in schools owned by, or affiliated to, Woodard Schools.

This unique partnership of schools, independent and state, boarding and day, junior and senior, co-educational and single-sex, is united by a determination to provide a first-class holistic education within a distinctive Christian ethos. The schools were founded by Nathaniel Woodard in the nineteenth century and aim to prepare children from a wide variety of backgrounds for responsibility, leadership and service in today's world.

We seek to provide flexible, stimulating, demanding and appropriate schemes of academic study together with a rich variety of sporting, artistic and recreational opportunities. We encourage personal success, self-confidence and self-respect whilst also stressing the importance of responsible citizenship, high moral values and a commitment to use one's gifts in the service of others.

With the geographical spread and diversity of schools included in the group we are able to offer parents a wide range of educational options for their children. Woodard owned schools operate bursary and scholarship schemes including all classes of concession. Fees vary from school to school and are set locally.

The Woodard Corporation is a Registered Charity (No. 1096270) and Company (No. 4659710). The objects of the charity are to promote and extend education in accordance with the doctrines and principles of the Church of England/Church in Wales by directly or indirectly carrying on schools.

MONTESSORI SCHOOLS ASSOCIATION

18 Balderton Street, London W1K 6TG
Tel: 020 7493 8300 • Fax: 020 7493 9936
e-mail: centre@montessori.org.uk

website: www.montessori.org.uk/msa

The Montessori Schools Association (MSA) was founded to support and represent all Montessori schools across the United Kingdom. Supported by the Montessori St Nicholas Charity (founded in 1963), the MSA works through 9 national regions each with its own Regional Chairman.

The aims of the Association are:
- to create an all-encompassing, open-minded environment to foster communication and unity within the Montessori movement throughout the United Kingdom;
- to provide support and guidance as a charity to our members irrespective of size, premises or situation;
- through mutual support and guidance to foster higher standards and promote awareness of Montessori teaching.

The central offices in London work to support schools, make representations to government on behalf of the Montessori movement and conduct research programmes into the effectiveness of Montessori teaching. Providing information on Montessori philosophy to the general public is also a central objective of both the charity and the MSA. From 2008 the MSA is introducing a national accreditation scheme for Montessori schools.

The Montessori Schools Association currently has over 2,500 members and schools ranging in size from 15 to 400+ pupils covering the 0–11 age range.

Trustees of the Montessori Charity

The Montessori Schools Association

Officers

COUNCIL FOR INDEPENDENT EDUCATION (CIFE)

President:
Baroness Perry of Southwark (Pro-Chancellor of the University of Surrey)

Vice Presidents:
Professor Kelvin Fidler (Vice Chancellor of the University of Northumbria at Newcastle)
Sir Michael Heron (Chairman of the Council for Industry and Higher Education, CIHE)
Hugh Monro, MA

Chairman:
Fiona Pocock, MA, PGCE (Principal of Oxford Tutorial College)

Vice-Chairman:
Neil Roskilly, BA Hons, PGCE, NPQH, FRSA, FRGS
(Principal of Cambridge Centre for Sixth-form Studies)

Independent sixth-form colleges are extremely well-placed to offer what is needed to students preparing for university and beyond. The best such colleges are members of CIFE, the Council for Independent Education, an organisation which is in its 34th year, which guarantees high standards, and which has its results independently audited and published by the British Accreditation Council. There are 14 CIFE colleges, geographically spread across the country, each one offering something individual but all subject to the same high standards of accreditation.

So, for example, there are some colleges that specialise in students wishing to retake in order to improve exam grades, some serving a cosmopolitan mix of students, some offering GCSE and pre-GCSE programmes as well as A Levels, some which are residential, or homestay, or day, or a mix of all three. Several colleges offer foundation programmes and are twinned with universities. In short, CIFE colleges aim to offer a wide range of educational environments where students can succeed.

Teaching in CIFE colleges really helps and supports students since teaching groups are small and teachers highly experienced and able. The 'tutorial' system derives directly from Oxbridge where it continues to be world famous. A student in a small group receives a greater degree of individual attention. Regular testing ensures that she/he maintains good progress, and the emphasis on study skills provides essential support for the AS/A2 subjects.

It is not surprising that a student gains confidence and self-belief within such an environment. Colleges engender a strong work ethic in their student communities. Many of the minor rules and regulations essential for schools are not necessary at CIFE colleges. Good manners and an enthusiastic attitude are every bit as important, but uniform, strict times for eating or homework, assemblies or games participation are not part of the picture. It can be seen from the large numbers of students going on to higher education from CIFE colleges that universities regard our students highly.

Increasing numbers of young people are deciding to move school at the age of 16, not because they are unhappy with their school, but because they see the need for a change at this stage. It may be that they wish to study a subject which their school does not offer, such as Accounting, Law, Psychology or Photography. Maybe they are looking for a more adult environment or one where they can focus on their academic subjects to the exclusion of other things. However, it would be misleading to suggest that CIFE colleges are lacking in extra-curricular activities of all sorts, sporting, social and creative. All colleges recognise the need for enrichment. The difference is that activities are at the choice of the student.

As with schools, choosing a college calls for careful research. CIFE colleges adhere to a strict code of conduct governing the provision and standards of teaching, safety and pastoral care. Colleges undergo regular inspection and their examination results are independently audited. While each college has its own individual character, all share the desire to provide each individual student with a superb preparation for higher education.

Members of CIFE
Ashbourne Independent Sixth Form College
Bales College
Bath Academy
Bosworth Independent College
Brooke House College
Cambridge Centre for Sixth-form Studies
Chelsea Independent College
Collingham
Duff Miller Sixth Form College
Exeter Tutorial College
Harrogate Tutorial College
Lansdowne College
Mander Portman Woodward, London
Oxford Tutorial College

Further information can be obtained from:

CIFE
Tel: 020 8767 8666
e-mail: enquiries@cife.org.uk • www.cife.org.uk

ISCO

ISCO is the independent schools careers service from The Inspiring Futures Foundation

www.isco.org.uk • www.inspiringfutures.org.uk

Contacts

Who to ask for information and help

Advice on ISCO services:
Contact your Regional Director (see below) or the Information Helpline on 01276 687515

Further information on The Inspiring Futures Foundation:
Chief Executive: Andrew Airey (e-mail: a.airey@inspiringfutures.org.uk)

Purpose and Aims

The Inspiring Futures Foundation is a not-for-profit, careers guidance organisation. It exists to help young people make decisions and develop skills which maximize their potential, enhance their employment opportunities and allow them to make a fulfilling contribution to the world in which they live.

In order to do this, Inspiring Futures works with like-minded people and organisations to provide expert careers guidance, innovative learning resources and personal skills training to young people from all backgrounds, particularly those entering higher education.

Each of these services is based around the ongoing needs of the young person and is delivered through a unique, integrated approach, which is practical, progressive and provides a foundation for lifelong learning.

The ISCO careers service for independent and international schools provides schools with a range of careers and higher education related services to complement and reinforce school programmes with impartial and professional expertise. Services include the Futurewise personalised careers guidance programme, Expanding Horizons courses and training events for students and a range of professional services to support schools' careers staff.

ISCO Regional Directors

by area of operation

Scotland:	Joan Smith (Tel: 0131 441 9950, e-mail: joan.smith@isco.org.uk)
West Midlands:	Sarah Frend (Tel: 0121 705 5692, e-mail: sarah.frend@isco.org.uk) (also ISCO Training Manager)
North East:	Gillian Binns (Tel: 01937 843569, e-mail: gillian.binns@isco.org.uk)
North West:	Chris Marley (Tel: 0161 904 8676, e-mail: chris.marley@isco.org.uk)
Manchester & Liverpool:	Rod Morley (Tel: 0161 428 1013, e-mail: rod.morley@isco.org.uk)
Oxford:	Helen Burns (Tel 01993 774325, e-mail: helen.burns@isco.org.uk)
Berkshire:	Amanda Spurrier (Tel: 01635 863911 e-mail: amanda.spurrier@isco.org.uk)
East:	John Watson (Tel: 01572 823073, e-mail: john.watson@isco.org.uk)
North London:	Steve Cane (Tel: 020 8447 3955, e-mail: steve.cane@isco.org.uk)
Essex/Suffolk:	Linda Levett (Tel: 01621 783828, e-mail: linda.levett@isco.org.uk)
Sussex and Kent:	Helen Davison (Tel: 01342 317537, e-mail: helen.davison@isco.org.uk)
South London:	Carey Irwin (Tel: 020 8544 9749, e-mail: carey.irwin@isco.org.uk)
Surrey & Hampshire:	Alison France (Tel: 01420 564081, e-mail: alison.france@isco.org.uk)
London & Surrey:	Helen Rogers (Tel: 01932 566224, e-mail: helen.rogers@isco.org.uk)
South West/Bristol:	Jonathan Hardwick (Tel: 01453 827761, e-mail: jonathan.hardwick@isco.org.uk)
Dorset:	John MacArthur (Tel: 01252 661957, e-mail: john.macarthur@isco.org.uk)
Europe:	Julia Watson (Tel: 01572 823073, e-mail: julia.watson@isco.org.uk)
Middle East:	Simon Clarke (Tel: 020 8946 4414, e-mail: simon.clarke@isco.org.uk)
Asia:	John Broadbent (e-mail: john.broadbent@isco.org.uk)

ASSOCIATION FOR MARKETING AND DEVELOPMENT IN INDEPENDENT SCHOOLS (AMDIS)

FOUNDED 1993

website: www.amdis.co.uk

Objectives:
- To promote and develop good marketing practice in independent education
- To help increase the effectiveness of the marketing representatives of Member Schools
- To encourage personal development within the schools' marketing profession

Achieved through:
- Termly seminars on a variety of marketing-led subjects (a list of recent seminar topics may be obtained from the General Secretary) held at locations throughout the country
- Annual residential conference
- Regional networking lunches
- Training – Diploma in Schools' Marketing & Certificate in Admissions Management
- Newsletters with articles from Member Schools and invited contributors
- Help Line
- Website
- On-line News bulletins throughout the year
- Speakers provided for conferences, inset days and similar

Membership:
- School Membership, renewable annually by subscription
- Associate membership considered on application
- Corporate membership considered on application

The Association is directed by a Chairman, Vice Chairman and Treasurer together with an Executive Committee of 12 members. The Chairman, Vice Chairman and Treasurer together with members of the Executive Committee are selected (or re-elected) by prior nomination, annually at the AMDIS AGM.

***General Secretary*: Tory Gillingham, 2 St Michael's Street, Malton, North Yorkshire YO17 7LJ**
Tel: 07000 623347 • e-mail: enquiries@amdis.co.uk

ASSOCIATION OF REPRESENTATIVES OF OLD PUPILS' SOCIETIES (AROPS)

Founded in 1971

website: www.arops.org.uk

Founder and Past President: Mike Comer (Old Johnian)
Immediate Past President: Roy Elliott (Old Caterhamian)
President: Margaret Carter-Pegg (Old Crohamian)
Vice-Presidents: John Kidd (Old Portmuthian), Guy Cliff (Old Silcoatian), Roger Moulton (Old Pauline)

Committee
Chairman: Bill Gillen (Old Arnoldian)
Secretary: Melanie Whitfield (Hampshire Collegiate FP)
Treasurer: Tim Neale (Old Radleian)
Registrar: Maggy Douglas (St Albans High School OGA)
and 10 committee members

Aim: To provide a forum for the exchange of views and experiences between representatives of old pupils' societies.

Membership: Open to representatives of any old pupils' society.

Meetings:
Each May AROPS holds a whole day Conference. Venues vary from year to year and are chosen with regard to geographical location and differing type of school – day, boarding, co-educational or single sex.

Each Conference is divided into four sessions which aim to cover a wide range of topics that will be of assistance and interest to society representatives. Recent topics have been data protection, attracting younger members, society/school relations, subscriptions and charitable status. During the day there are ample opportunities for representatives to meet and talk with each other. The day always finishes with the conference dinner.

The AGM is held on a weekday evening in October at a school in the London area and is followed by a buffet supper.

The AROPS Committee meets five times a year to deal with the running of the Association, prepare for the Conference and AGM and to respond to correspondence from old pupils' societies. It also arranges surveys providing information on matters of current interest such as registers and life membership subscriptions.

AROPS works with the Independent Schools Council (ISC) and its constituent members whose officers are invited to attend AROPS conferences.

AROPS is a non-political body, but its interests are opposed to any threat to independent education. Changes in national policy are carefully considered on behalf of member societies.

Subscription: £18 per year. Societies interested in membership should write to: The Chairman, AROPS, c/o The Independent Schools Council, St Vincent House, 30 Orange Street, London WC2H 7HH or email chairman@arops.org.uk.

MEDICAL OFFICERS OF SCHOOLS ASSOCIATION

FOUNDED 1884

website: www.mosa.org.uk

Objects

Mutual assistance of members in promoting school health, and the holding of meetings for consideration of all subjects connected with the special work of medical officers of schools.

Membership

Medical officers of schools and medical and dental practitioners especially concerned with the health of the schoolchild are eligible for membership, and members of the teaching profession for associate membership. The membership currently stands at 400.

The work of the Association

The Council meets three times a year and is chaired by the current President, Dr Miriam Edelsten, MO to New Hall School, Chelmsford. The Hon Secretary sends out three newsletters a year and is available for advice to members and non-members. Clinical meetings are arranged each year together with an annual summer visit to a school. Research projects are carried out individually and collectively. The Association strongly recommends that all independent schools appoint medical officers to carry out preventative medicine duties which are undertaken in maintained schools by the School Health Service.

Publications

The 18th edition of the Handbook of School Health, published in May of 1998, deals in detail with the administrative, ethical, public health and clinical aspects of the school medical officer's work and is widely accepted as the definitive guide to current practice. A Proceedings and Report are published annually. The Association also publishes appropriate guidelines for its clinical Medical Officers and these are updated regularly.

For further information about the Association and other related business enquiries should in the first instance be directed to:

The Hon Secretary: Dr Neil D Arnott
Amherst Medical Practice, 21 St Botolph's Road, Sevenoaks, Kent TN13 3AQ.
Tel: 01732 459255 • Fax: 01732 450751

For administrative information and background please contact:
The Executive Secretary: Mrs Louise Fortune
email: execsec@mosa.org.uk

ENGLISH-SPEAKING UNION OF THE COMMONWEALTH

Secondary School Exchange Scholarships to the United States and Canada

Chairman: The Rt Hon The Lord Hunt of Wirral, MBE, PC

Executive Secretary: Katherine Plummer, Education Programmes Manager

A number of North American Independent Schools generously offer free places for a year or six months to UK students with the intention of furthering understanding between Britain and North America. These scholarships give young people the opportunity of living and studying with their counterparts in the USA and Canada. The scholarship comprises free board and tuition worth approximately $35,000; travel and incidental expenses are met by the scholar.

In addition each year UK boarding schools offer free board and tuition to senior students from North America.

British applicants should apply in their final A-level year. Candidates applying for the full year will be selected on the basis of predicted A-level grades and those applying for six months after their results are known. Selection for the scholarship is through application form and an interview.

For further information please contact the English-Speaking Union.

The English-Speaking Union, Dartmouth House, 37 Charles Street, London W1J 5ED
Tel: 020 7529 1550 • Fax: 020 7495 6108 • e-mail: education@esu.org • website: www.esu.org

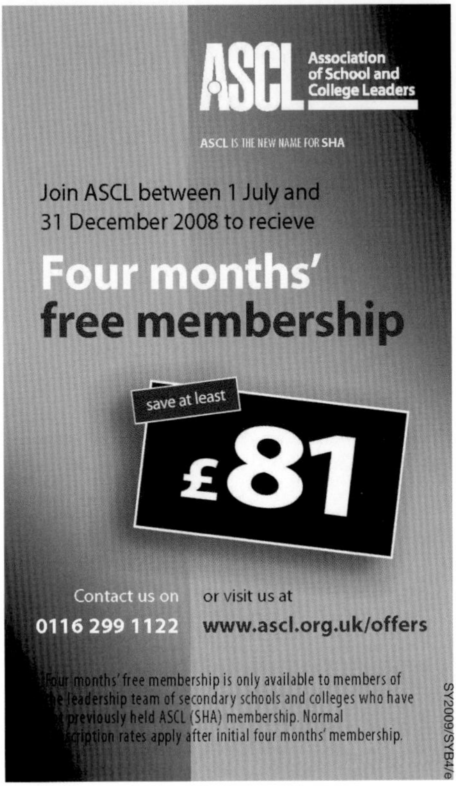
ASCL
Association of School and College Leaders
ASCL IS THE NEW NAME FOR SHA
Join ASCL between 1 July and 31 December 2008 to recieve
Four months' free membership
save at least
£81
Contact us on
0116 299 1122
or visit us at
www.ascl.org.uk/offers
our months' free membership is only available to members of
e leadership team of secondary schools and colleges who have
previously held ASCL (SHA) membership. Normal
cription rates apply after initial four months' membership.
SY2009/SYB4/e

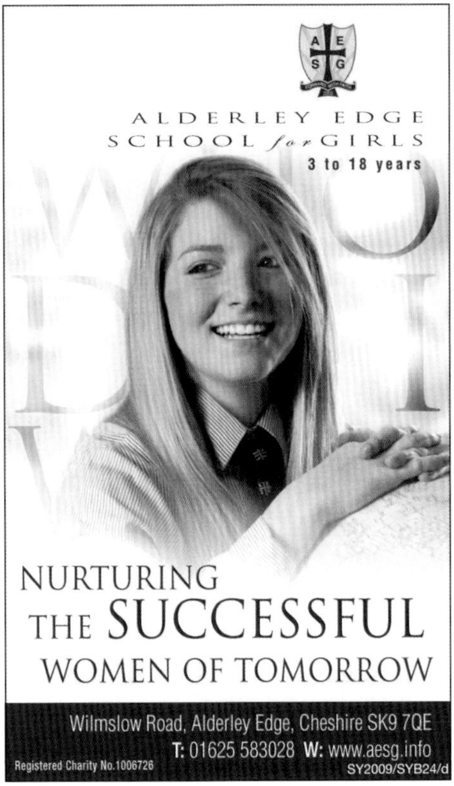
A E S G
ALDERLEY EDGE SCHOOL for GIRLS
3 to 18 years
NURTURING THE SUCCESSFUL WOMEN OF TOMORROW
Wilmslow Road, Alderley Edge, Cheshire SK9 7QE
T: 01625 583028 W: www.aesg.info
Registered Charity No.1006726
SY2009/SYB24/d

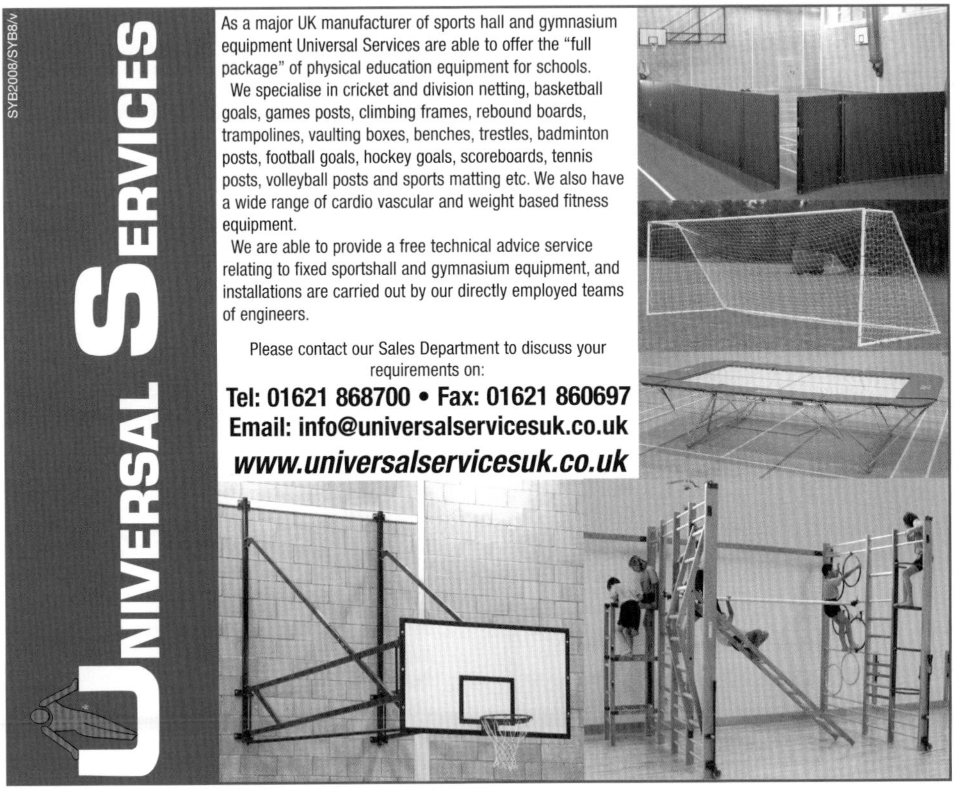
SYB2008/SYB8/v
UNIVERSAL SERVICES
As a major UK manufacturer of sports hall and gymnasium equipment Universal Services are able to offer the "full package" of physical education equipment for schools.
We specialise in cricket and division netting, basketball goals, games posts, climbing frames, rebound boards, trampolines, vaulting boxes, benches, trestles, badminton posts, football goals, hockey goals, scoreboards, tennis posts, volleyball posts and sports matting etc. We also have a wide range of cardio vascular and weight based fitness equipment.
We are able to provide a free technical advice service relating to fixed sportshall and gymnasium equipment, and installations are carried out by our directly employed teams of engineers.
Please contact our Sales Department to discuss your requirements on:
Tel: 01621 868700 • Fax: 01621 860697
Email: info@universalservicesuk.co.uk
www.universalservicesuk.co.uk

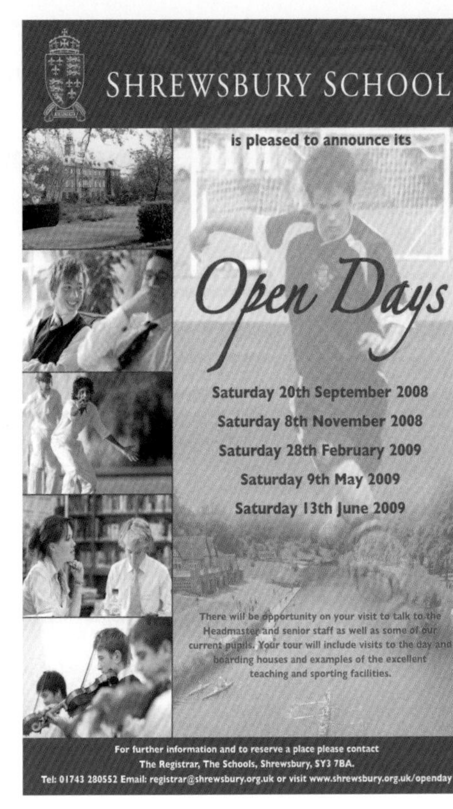

SHREWSBURY SCHOOL
is pleased to announce its
Open Days
Saturday 20th September 2008
Saturday 8th November 2008
Saturday 28th February 2009
Saturday 9th May 2009
Saturday 13th June 2009
There will be opportunity on your visit to talk to the Headmaster and senior staff as well as some of our current pupils. Your tour will include visits to the day and boarding houses and examples of the excellent teaching and sporting facilities.
For further information and to reserve a place please contact
The Registrar, The Schools, Shrewsbury, SY3 7BA.
Tel: 01743 280552 Email: registrar@shrewsbury.org.uk or visit www.shrewsbury.org.uk/openday

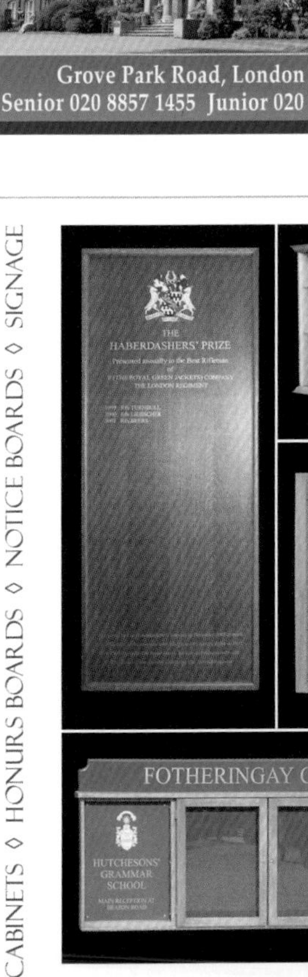

THE HABERDASHERS' PRIZE

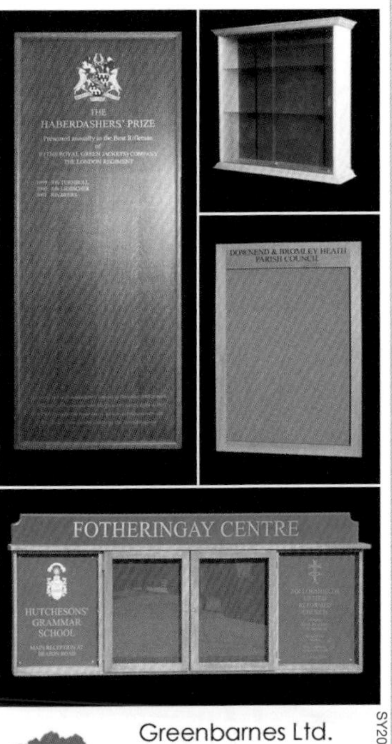

FOTHERINGAY CENTRE
HUTCHESONS' GRAMMAR SCHOOL

PART I

Schools whose Heads are members of the Headmasters' and Headmistresses' Conference

ALPHABETICAL LIST OF SCHOOLS

UK & Ireland

* co-educational schools

GEOGRAPHICAL LIST OF HMC SCHOOLS
UK & Ireland

Symbols used in Staff Listings

* Head of Department	§ Part Time or Visiting
† Housemaster/Housemistress	¶ Old Pupil

Individual School Entries UK & Ireland

Abingdon School

Park Road Abingdon Oxfordshire OX14 1DE
Tel: 01235 521563 School
01235 849041 Registry
01235 849022 Bursar
Fax: 01235 849077 Headmaster
01235 849079 School
01235 849085 Registry
e-mail: hm.sec@abingdon.org.uk
admissions@abingdon.org.uk
bursars.sec@abingdon.org.uk
website: www.abingdon.org.uk

The foundation of the School appears to date from the twelfth century; the first clear documentary reference occurs in 1256. After the dissolution of Abingdon Abbey, the School was re-endowed in 1563 by John Roysse, of the Mercers' Company in London. It was rebuilt in 1870 on its present site, and many further buildings have been added with the most recent £8m sports development newly completed. Abingdon Preparatory School, formerly known as Josca's, is situated close by at Frilford (*see entry in IAPS section*). The total establishment numbers about 1,100 boys.

Stewards:
N E Guiver
Mr and Mrs Q M E Hoodless
Mrs T Hendley
Mr and Mrs D Whibley

Governing Body:
C R Dick, MA, CEng (*Chairman*)
Professor R W Ainsworth, MA, DPhil, FRAeS (*Vice-Chairman*)
D P Lillycrop, LLB, FCMI (*Vice-Chairman*)

The Mayor of Abingdon
The Master of Christ's Hospital, Abingdon
Professor K M Burk, BA, MA, DPhil, FRHistS, AIWS
Miss J E Cranston
Dr O R Darbishire, MA, MSc, PhD
E Ferguson
J R Gabitass, MA
Mrs M T Hawley, BA
Dr E H T Lumsden
M W Matthews
G R Morris, FCA
C J W Owen, MA
Mrs H Ronaldson
C C Scott
A Saunders-Davies, MRICS, MBA
Sir Michael Wakeford, OBE, MA, LLB
Dr P R Williams, CBE, DL, PhD, BSc, DLC, FInstP, DSc

Clerk to the Governors: T J Pegram, MA

***Headmaster*: M Turner**, MA

Second Master: D J Dawswell, BSc
Deputy Head, Academic: G May, BA
Deputy Head, Pastoral: A D Watkins, BEd, MPhil, MEd
Chaplain: Revd H L Kirk, BD, MA
Upper Master: D J Wicks, MA
Middle Master: P D B Gooding, MA
Master of Scholars: Dr C J Burnand, MA, DPhil
Master i/c the Other Half: S A Evans, BA

Housemasters:

Boarders:
School House: D G Aitken, BA
Crescent House: J D J Williams, BA
Phelps' House: W T Phelps, BA

Dayboys:
D A Boyd, BA
A C Christodoulou, MSc, BEng
D J T Franklin, MA
N J O'Doherty, BSc
Dr J E J Older, BSc, PhD
M R Webb, BSc

Lower School:
A M Broadbent, BEd
A J Jenkins, BA

Assistant Masters:
S Balderson, BA, MSc
J S Barker, BA (*to Dec 2008*)
D J Bickerton, MSc
S E Bliss, BSc
Dr M Bowen-Jones, DPhil
Miss C D Briggs, MBioChem
J P G Brooks, BSc
G B Callan, BSc
R Castle, BSc
O Cobbe, BA
A C D Crook, BA, MPhil
Mrs C Cross, CertEd
E S Davies, BA
Ms F A Donovan, BA
A J P English, BA, MLitt
D Evans, BA
I C Fishpool, BSc, FRGS
Mrs J E Fishpool, MA
C Fletcher-Campbell, MA
M W Forth, MChem
D J W Freyhan, MA
Ms J Gardner, BSc, MA
Dr M R Gibbs, BSc, PhD
S J Grills, MSc
Dr T C Gunn, BA, PhD
A S Hall, BA
D Haworth, BSc, LRAM
Miss P E Henderson, BA
Miss V E Hicks, BA
D M Hughes, BA
A T Hundermark, BSc
Dr R K Jeffreys, BSc, PhD
Mrs J P Jennings, MA
M I Litchfield, BSc
A J Loughe, MA, MSc
I A Macdonald, BA
Miss L Man, BSc
Miss J R Matthews, BA, MPhil
Dr C J May, BA, PhD
D R McGill, BA
R S K Mearns, MA, MLitt, LLB
I Middleton, MA
G R Moody, MA
H C G Morgan, MMath
J P Nairne, BFA
Mrs E O'Doherty, MA
Mrs S A Payne, MA
Mrs V D Penrose, BSc
D J Pope, MA
H F C Price, BA
N A F Pritchard, MA
N M Revill, BA
Miss C Shephard, MA
D C Shirazi, MA
Mrs E M-T Slatford, MA
Dr D P Smith, MEng, PhD
R Southwell-Sander, BA
M A Stinton, MA, ARCM, LRAM
N P Stokes, BSc
A P Swarbrick, BA, MPhil
J H Taylor, BA
S R Whalley, MA, MSt
Dr J S Wiejak, PhD
Mrs S Wigmore, BEd
P Willerton, MA
Dr A P Willis, BSc, PhD
Dr P J Wilmore, BSc, PhD
J H Winters, MA

Librarian: Mrs G J Cooper, BSc

Part-time:
Mrs J Bentley, BSc
Mrs V A Clark, BSc
J D E Drummond-Hay, BEd
A J Glass, BA
Mrs J P Jelley, BA, DipAppSocSci
A J Mansfield, BSc
Mrs M Pringle, MMus, FTCL, LRAM
Mrs A K Quick, BA
Dr S J Ridd, MA, PhD
Mrs A M Soper, BA, MLitt
Mrs A M Streatfield, BEd
Mrs V M Walker, BA, FRSA

Bursar: J M C Webster, BSc, ACA
Estates Bursar: D J M Carson
Registrar: Mrs J H Jørgensen, MA
Medical Officer: Dr M F Khan, MBChB, FRCS, DRCOG, DFFP

In the Senior School there are about 800 boys aged 11–18, of whom approximately 130 are boarders.

Boarding is organised in three houses: School House (Mr D G Aitken), Phelps' House (Mr W T Phelps) and Crescent House (Mr J D J Williams). The School values its boarding element very highly and has recently completed a major programme of reconstruction and reorganisation, involving the conversion of existing accommodation and the development of new facilities. Weekly boarding features highly as part of a policy aimed at asserting a distinctive regional identity for the School.

Pastoral Care. The Lower School has a self-contained system of pastoral care, led by two housemasters. All boys join a senior house on entering the Middle School. Within the house system there are distinct tutoring arrangements for Middle School and Upper School boys, which are coordinated by the Middle Master and Upper Master respectively. Special emphasis is placed on the value of parental involvement and also on the provision of careers guidance at appropriate points in a boy's development. Great importance is attached to pastoral care and the School's teaching philosophy is based on a tutorial approach.

Land and Buildings. The School is surrounded by 35 acres of its own grounds, yet is within a few hundred yards of the historic centre of Abingdon, which lies 6 miles down the Thames from Oxford. A further 30 acres of playing fields are located at the Preparatory School, three miles from Abingdon.

The last quarter-century has seen a considerable expansion in the School's stock of buildings. A major development in the 1990s was Mercers' Court, which celebrated the School's historical link with the Mercers' Company of London. In 2003 a £3m Arts Centre was opened providing purpose-designed facilities for music, art and drama.

Sports facilities have been greatly enhanced by a new £8m sports centre with a superb 8-lane swimming pool, fitness suites, classroom space, squash courts, a climbing wall, and a martial arts and fencing studio. This follows the opening in 2003 of a beautiful timber-framed boathouse situated on the River Thames a short distance from the School.

Courses of Study. The School is essentially academic in character and intention and levels of both expectation and achievement are high. Subjects taught include English, History, French, German, Spanish, Mandarin Chinese, Latin, Greek, Ancient History, Economics, Business Studies, Geography, Mathematics, Physics, Chemistry, Biology, Art, Religious Studies, Music and Theatre Studies. Over the last few years there has been increasing collaboration with the School of St Helen and St Katharine with joint tuition particularly in Theatre Studies, Greek, Government and Politics and History of Art. The School is well equipped with computing facilities and audio-visual teaching aids.

All boys spend three years in the Middle School (13 to 16 year olds), in which many different subject combinations are possible, and there is no specialisation before the Sixth Form, although some pupils take early GCSEs in Mathematics, French and Latin. In the Sixth Form many boys combine courses in arts and sciences; four subjects are normally taken at AS in the Lower Sixth, followed by three or four at A2 in the Upper Sixth. Classroom teaching at all levels is supplemented by a programme of specialist lectures and outside visits. In general terms, the curriculum aims to combine academic discipline and excellence with the fullest encouragement of a wide range of interests and pursuits.

Games and Activities. The School enjoys some 80 acres of playing fields and has its own sports hall, swimming pool, fitness suites, squash and tennis courts and a boathouse on the River Thames. The major sports are rowing, rugby, cricket, hockey, tennis, athletics and cross-country. Special success has been achieved recently in rowing, fencing, badminton and shooting. Other sports include sailing, golf and fives.

Importance is attached to the development of a sense of social responsibility, through voluntary membership of Community Service and the Duke of Edinburgh's Award Schemes. There is a contingent of the Combined Cadet Force based on voluntary recruitment.

There are numerous societies catering for all kinds of interests and enthusiasms. Music is particularly strong, with over half the boys taking instrumental or vocal lessons in the School. In addition to the Chapel Choir, Choral Society and three orchestras, there are excellent opportunities for ensemble playing, including jazz.

Religion. The School is Anglican by tradition, but boys of other denominations are welcome, and normally attend by year group the short non-denominational service with which the working day begins.

Health. The School has its own doctor and there is a well-equipped health centre in the school grounds. In cases of emergency boys are admitted to one of the local hospitals.

Admission. The normal ages of entry to the Senior School are 11, 13 and 16; there are occasionally vacancies at other ages. About half of each year's intake enter the School at age 11 and most of the rest at age 13. Registration at age 9 or 10 is recommended. Abingdon Preparatory School has its own entrance arrangements (*see entry in IAPS section*).

Details of the entrance examination procedures for 11 and 13 year old candidates are available from the Registry. Entry to the Sixth Form at 16 generally depends on promising GCSE grades and written tests where it is appropriate, as well as on interviews and a report from the previous school.

Term of Entry. September is the usual date of entry and is preferred by the School. Boys may be accepted in any of the three terms, if vacancies occur in their age group.

Fees per term (2008-2009). The tuition fee, for dayboys, is £4,250. This includes the cost of lunches and textbooks.

For boarders, the total fee (including tuition and all extras except for instrumental music lessons and some disbursements directly incurred by individual boys) is £7,520 (weekly) and £8,320 (full).

Scholarships and Bursaries. (*see Scholarship Entries section*). The School offers a number of means-tested Scholarships and bursaries at ages 11, 13 and 16; full details are published in the spring of each year and are available, on application, from the Registry.

Honours. Numerous places are won each year at Oxford and Cambridge and on other highly selective university courses.

Old Abingdonian Club. Administrator: c/o Abingdon School.

Charitable status. Abingdon School Limited is a Registered Charity, number 1071298. It exists to provide educational opportunities which are open to talented boys without regard to their families' economic standing. Its curriculum is designed to promote intellectual rigour, personal versatility and social responsibility.

Ackworth School

Ackworth Pontefract West Yorkshire WF7 7LT
Tel: 01977 611401
Fax: 01977 616225
e-mail: admissions@ackworthschool.com
website: www.ackworthschool.com

This co-educational boarding and day school was founded in 1779 and occupies a large rural estate which surrounds the gracious Georgian buildings and spacious gardens and playing fields which form the School Campus. It is one of the seven Quaker Schools in England.

Governing Body:
Members appointed by The Religious Society of Friends

Clerk: Chris Moore

Secretary and Bursar: John Lebeter, ICSA

Full time Teaching Staff:

***Head*: Peter J Simpson**, MA, MA

Deputy Head: Lorna Anthony, BSc, PGCE

Deputy Head (*Curriculum*): Jeffrey D Swales, MA Oxon, PGCE

Director of Marketing: Marion Mitchell, BA, PGCE

Head of Sixth Form: Andrew Ward, BSc London, PGCE

Heads of Subject Departments:
Mark Birch, MA Cantab, PGCE (*English*)
Rebecca Durham, BA, PGCE (*Drama*)
Lucinda Hamill, MA, BEd, BA (*Mathematics*)
Andrew Ward, BSc, PGCE (*Biology*)
Taras Anthony, MA (*Chemistry*)
Francis Hickenbottom, BSc, PGCE (*Physics*)
Helen Smith, MA, MA (*German*)
Elizabeth Rayner, BA Hons, PGCE (*French*)
Derek Wilkinson, BEd (*Design & Technology*)
David Palmer, BSc, PGCE (*Information Technology*)
Sarah Rose, BA (*Art*)
Rhiannon Davies, MA (*Music*)
Thomas Plant, BA, PGCE (*History*)
Stephen Minihan, BA, PGCE (*Geography*)
Marion Mitchell, BA, PGCE (*Business Studies*)
Martin Gosney, CertEd (*Physical Education*)
Julie Hoar, BEd (*Physical Education*)

Heads of Boarding Houses:
Boys: Christopher Bailey, BSc
Girls: Claire Cougan, BSc, PGCE

Coram House (Junior School):
Head: Mary Wilson, BA Hons, PGCE

§Librarian: Erin Nephin, BA, MSc

Nursing Sister: Pamela Evans, SRN
Medical Officer: Gwenan Davenport, MBChB, MRCGP

There are 574 girls and boys aged from 4 to 18 years, 467 of whom are day pupils. Some of the pupils are from Quaker homes, but the School has long been open to boys and girls unconnected with the Society of Friends, and these pupils are now in the majority. The pattern of school life is based on the Quaker belief that religion and life are one: that spiritual conviction directly affects the way in which people behave toward each other and determines their attitude to life in general. However, while the life of the School is based on the Quakers' interpretation of Christianity, the approach is broad-based and open-minded, for the life of the community is enriched by contributions made by those of other denominations and faiths. Although all pupils attend school assemblies and Meetings for Worship, arrangements can generally be made for pupils to worship in their own churches and boys and girls can be prepared for confirmation.

Houses. Boys and girls live separately in two houses, with resident house staff and matrons responsible for their welfare.

Curriculum. Pupils follow courses leading to GCSE and Advanced level examinations. A wide range of subjects can be taken. The main foreign languages taught are French, German and Spanish. There is a strong Music department and group instrumental tuition is part of the First Year (Year 7) course; Design and Technology and Art are also very well provided for, and all of these subjects are integral parts of the core curriculum. The School also has a strong sporting tradition with many successful teams, thanks to excellent coaching and first-rate facilities. The large academic Sixth Form, which offers all of the traditional subjects as well as more recent additions like Sport and PE and Drama, prepares students extremely well for university entry and for life beyond School.

The most recent addition to our provision is our flourishing International Centre. Here, intensive English coaching is offered to students of Sixth Form age who wish to go on to follow Advanced Level courses.

Leisure Time. The many clubs and societies on offer cater for all ages and all tastes. The facilities for crafts, art and music are freely available outside the teaching day, and pupils participate in a huge range of team and individual sports. There is a very full programme of weekend activities and visits.

Buildings. A policy of expansion and upgrading has been maintained over the years and within the last decade wide-ranging improvements have been made to the School's facilities. Study accommodation for Sixth Formers has been enlarged and modernised and the science laboratories have been re-equipped. The modern Music Centre and Fothergill Theatre provide spacious facilities for individual and ensemble music making, together with an excellent venue for concerts and School productions. The Design and Technology Centre houses a thriving department and numerous creative after-school clubs, and the spacious, well-appointed study, reference and careers library caters for all age groups. The superb, modern Sports Centre and fully resourced Information Technology Centre are in constant use. The most recent changes have been to boarding accommodation – the girls have specially designed, purpose-built furniture, while the boys' rooms have been re-designed to include en-suite facilities.

Scholarships and Bursaries. (*see Scholarship Entries section*). A number of awards are made each year to selected boys and girls entering the School who show high academic ability or exceptional talent in Music or Art. Bursaries are available to members of the Society of Friends and others according to need. Travel Scholarships are available to members of the Sixth Form.

Admission. Interested parents will be sent a prospectus upon application to the Head and visits can always be arranged promptly. There are also two Open Mornings during the year, at which parents and families are welcome to tour the School and to talk to staff and pupils. Pupils for entry at age 7 and above take the School's entrance test, while entry at age 4 is based on interview. The majority of children enter the Senior School at the age of 11, but there is also a sizeable entrance at 12, 13, 14 and 16+. Entry is always possible at other ages if places are available, and there is a direct entry into the Sixth Form for pupils who are able to take the full two-year A level course.

Coram House (Junior School). Coram House caters for day boys and girls aged 4 to 11, the majority of whom move on into the Senior School. In September 2002 a nursery opened catering for pupils aged 2 to 4 years.

Pre-prep classes are housed in new, spacious, purpose-built accommodation. From Reception onwards, emphasis is placed on a thorough understanding of the basic skills in reading, literacy, numeracy and science. In addition, a wide-ranging curriculum is provided to encourage creativity and physical ability through Art, Craft, Technology, Drama, Music and Sport.

In the Preparatory Department pupils work to a more structured timetable and are gradually introduced to specialist subject teaching. Staffing in Coram House is generous, so a thorough grounding can be given in the core subjects of English, Mathematics and Science. A broad curriculum is provided which includes French, Art and Crafts, Technology, Drama, Music and Sport – the children thus receive a rounded education and are able to develop their individual talents.

Before-school care from 8.00 am and after-school care until 5.30 pm are both available, at no extra charge.

Fees per term (2008-2009). Coram House: £2,253–£2,317 (day); Senior School: £5,939 (boarding), £3,628 (day); International Centre: £8,214 (boarding). The day pupil fees include lunch (and other meals if required).

The Ackworth Old Scholars' Association. This is a flourishing Association with a membership of over two thousand. Annual gatherings are held at Ackworth at Easter and there are Guild Meetings held in the regions at other times in the year. The General Secretary is Keith Daniel, 8 Derwent Court, Silsden, Keighley, West Yorkshire.

Charitable status. Ackworth is a Registered Charity, number 529280. It was established for the purpose of providing independent education.

Aldenham School

Elstree Herts WD6 3AJ
Tel: 01923 858122
Fax: 01923 854410
e-mail: enquiries@aldenham.com
website: www.aldenham.com

The School was founded in 1597 by Richard Platt, 'Cytyzen and Brewer of London.' The Founder originally endowed his Foundation with 'All those three Pastures of Ground lying nighe the Churche of St Pancrasse in the County of Mid'x. besides London . . . together with all and singular Woods, Underwoods, Hedgrowes, Trees and Ponds, Waters and Fishings in or upon the same P'emysses'.

Motto: '*In God is all our Trust.*'

Governing Body:
Chairman: J S Lewis, DL, FCIS
Field Marshal The Lord Vincent, GBE, KCB, DSO (OA)
P J Easby (OA)
Dr R C Nolan
B Watkins
B Woodrow, OBE, DL, MA, FCIPD (OA)
S J B Redman
J R Baugh (OA)
Mrs S Campion, MA
Revd Canon Dr M Sansom
H M Saunders
H D Page Croft
P Carr
J H Jones
D T Tidmarsh, BSc
C J Hayfield
Mrs L Thornton

***Headmaster*: J C Fowler**, MA

Deputy Head: Mrs D MacGinty, BEd
Senior Master: N D Pulman, MA
Director of Studies: D S Watts, MA, CChem, MRSC
Head of Sixth Form & Careers: R P Collins, BA, MSc

Heads of Department:
Art: Ms R Razzak, BA
Biology: Dr P J Reid
Business Studies: P S Green, BA
Classics: Miss A Addinall, MA
Chemistry: S P Williams, MA, BSc
Design Technology: Miss S E Nicholl, BSc
Drama: Ms J Bannister, BA
English: C R Jenkins, MA
Games and Physical Education: A P Stephenson, BA
Geography: (*to be appointed*)
Girls' Games: Mrs T A Layton, BEd
History: W P N Pietrek, BA
Academic ICT: D J Michael, BSc
Learning Support: Miss V Berry, MA
Mathematics: D A Chorley, BSc
Modern Languages: J P Stait, BA
Director of Music: J R Wyatt, GRSM, LRAM, ARCO
Physics: R A C Pomeroy, BSc
Sciences: S P Williams, MA, BSc
Theology: C D Bembridge, BTheol

Head of Prep School: K J Whiskerd, BA
Deputy Head of Prep School & Head of Foundation Stage: Mrs C J Watts, CertEd

Houses and Housemasters:

Boarding Houses:
McGill's: P M Dunstan, BA
Beevor's: S W Mainwaring, BEd
Kennedy's: W P N Pietrek, BA
Paull's: A O Dean, BA

Day Houses:
Paull's: A O Dean, BA
Leeman's: C S Irish, BSc
Riding's: A P Stephenson, BA
Martineau's: Mrs L Gall, BEd
Deputy: P S Turner, PhD, BSc

Chaplain: Revd D M Bond, BA
Librarian: M Cook, MA, MCLIP
Bursar: A W C Fraser, FCIS

Number in School. 675, of which there are 124 boarders, 3 dayboarders and 548 day pupils. (There are 125 girls in the School including the Preparatory School.)

Aldenham is situated in its own beautiful grounds of more than 110 acres in the Hertfordshire green belt, with excellent access to London (First Capital Connect/Jubilee Line) and within the M25, close to the M1. Aldenham's particular reputation as a close knit, small and supportive community with a strong boarding ethos makes it the very best environment for a high-quality all-round education encouraging children to enterprise. The achievement of every child's academic potential remains central but the building of confidence comes too from sports, music and drama, and by living and working together within the disciplined and vigorous community that is Aldenham today.

Admission. The first step towards gaining a place is to visit the School. A fully illustrated prospectus is available on request from the Admissions Secretary and prospective parents are encouraged to visit the School with their sons and daughters, either individually or at one of the school's 2 open days in June and October.

At 11, entry is by tests and interview, at 13 by interview and reference, and at 16 by interview and GCSE results. Every effort is made to meet parents' wishes as regards which House is chosen for their son. All girls enter Paull's House at 13.

Registration fee £50; Deposit £1,000.

Fees per term (2008-2009). Boarders £5,812–£8,117; Day Pupils £3,881–£5,584. These fees include most compulsory extras.

Scholarships and other awards. (*see Scholarship Entries section*). Scholarships, Exhibitions and Bursaries are available at each point of entry.

Curriculum. From 11 to 16 the timetable closely reflects the National Curriculum. Boys and girls are prepared for GCSEs across a range of subjects including Maths, English, French, Science and a number of other Arts and language options. Care is taken that all pupils include Art, Music, Technology and Computing in their programme and there is a progressive course of Theology throughout the School with GCSE taken in Year 11. The aim is to ensure that subject choices affecting AS/A2 levels are made as late as possible and the ISCO programme of tests and interviews are used as a basis for career planning and AS/A2 level choice in Year 11.

Those in the Lower Sixth Form normally take 4 AS levels from a range of 25 subjects, which narrows to three choices at A2 in the Upper Sixth year. In combination with the extensive extra-curricular programme, work experience and UCAS advice, the curriculum in the Sixth Form continues to give pupils their best opportunities for university entry. The majority go on to degree courses at universities. There are regular successes at Oxford and Cambridge. All those in the Sixth Form attend an Introduction to Industry Conference, and Aldenham runs a European-wide Work Experience Scheme.

Games and Other Activities. Great value is placed on the participation of every pupil in Games and Activities. A programme integrated into the working week offers enormous variety across all ages. The School has a fine record in traditional team games. Soccer, Hockey, Cricket and Athletics are the major sports for boys, whilst girls benefit from a breadth of in and out of school activities including Hockey, Tennis, Badminton, Dance, Squash, Netball, Trampolining, Aerobics and Sailing. In addition there is a full programme of House and School competitions in Squash, Eton Fives, Basketball, Tennis, Sailing, Fencing, Badminton, Table Tennis, Shooting, Swimming, and Cross-country. Volleyball, Horse Riding, Climbing, Judo and Golf are also available. The Sports Hall provides excellent facilities for expert and novice alike and incorporates a full size indoor hockey pitch, dance studio, martial arts room, gymnasium and a rifle range. Time is set apart for activities and societies; these include CCF, Adventure activities, the Duke of Edinburgh's Award Scheme, Community Service, Electronics, Chess, Computing, Motor Club, Photography and Model Railway. The Debating and Philosophy societies meet regularly throughout the year

Music and Drama. Music flourishes in the School. More than one third of the School have individual instrumental tuition. There is a Chapel Choir, School Orchestra and wind and brass groups. A spring concert is performed annually, taking place in the Barbican concert hall to celebrate the School's Quatercentenary, and in The Colloseum, Watford and St Albans Arena. A number of boys and girls learn to play on the fine, modern, 3-manual pipe organ in the Chapel. A music school with practice and performance facilities was opened in September 2000.

A new school theatre opened in 2007 encourages a high calibre of Drama students. In addition to an annual School Play there are Senior and Junior House Play competitions and boys and girls have the opportunity to produce and design as well as to perform in the various productions. The School's proximity to London makes possible frequent visits to theatres and concerts. Theatre Studies is offered as a full A Level subject.

Organisation. Whilst the framework of the School is contemporary, it takes as its basis the long established 'House' system. Each House creates an extended family and provides the formal and social focus of the School. There are four boarding and three day Houses together with a distinct yet fully integrated Junior House for 11–13 year olds. Each has a Housemaster or Housemistress and a team of tutors so every pupil has a personal tutor. In the Boarding Houses the Housemaster, his family, Matron and tutors live at the centre of the community ensuring the well-being of each child.

Boarding. Aldenham's unique array of day and boarding options enables it to provide the educational benefits of a boarding school to Day and Day Boarding pupils and to offer real flexibility with its arrangements for boarders, the vast majority of whom live within 20 miles of the School. Boys and girls may board from entry at 11+.

Religion. Aldenham is a Church of England foundation and seeks to maintain a strong Christian ethos to which those of other faiths are warmly welcomed.

Old Aldenhamian Society. There is a thriving Old Aldenhamian Society. Further details from the Secretary at the School.

Charitable status. The Aldenham School Company is a Registered Charity, number 298140. It exists to provide high quality education and pastoral care to enable children to achieve their full potential in later life.

Alleyn's School

Townley Road Dulwich London SE22 8SU
Tel: 020 8557 1500
Headmaster: 020 8557 1493
Bursar: 020 8557 1450
Fax: 020 8557 1462
e-mail: enquiries@alleyns.org.uk
website: www.alleyns.org.uk

The School is part of the foundation known as 'Alleyn's College of God's Gift' which was founded in 1619 by Edward Alleyn, the Elizabethan actor.

Motto: '*God's Gift*'

The Governing Body:

Chairman: R J R Cousins, BSc Eng, FICE
M Fosten, BA
T Franey, FIMI
P George, FCA
T R Hands, BA, AKC, DPhil
C Holloway, MA
Miss A M Horne, LLB
Prof A K Kakkar, BSc, PhD, FRCS
Prof M Meredith Smith, PhD, DSc, FLS
J I K Murray, MA, FCA
J F Pretlove
Sir Keith Whitson

***Headmaster*: Dr Colin Diggory**, BSc, MA, EdD, CMath, FIMA, FRSA

Senior Deputy Head: A R Faccinello, MA

Deputy Head: J G Lilly, BA

Assistant Heads:
A W A Skinnard, MA (*Head of Upper School; Religious Studies*)
D C A Morton, BA (*Head of Middle School; Geography*)
S E Smith, BA (*Headmaster of Lower School; Classics*)
Miss M Hunnaball, BSc, MA Ed (*Director of Studies; Physics*)
Miss S P Chandler, BSc (*Assistant Head Co-Curricular, PE*)

Bursar: S R Born, BA

Registrar: Mrs L Aldwinckle

Teaching Staff:
* *Head of Department*
† *Head of House*
§ *Part-time*

Ms A K S Ackerman, MA (**Religious Studies*)
D S Adkins, MA, MMus (*Music*)
R J Alldrick, BA (*†Brown's House, Field Centre Coordinator*)
B D Allen, BA (*Design Technology*)
Mrs S E Arthur, BSc (*§Chemistry*)
P J Barlow, MA, AdvCertCouns (**Classics*)
P Berman, BA (*Games, General Studies*)
Miss A Blythe, BA (*Geography*)
Miss A L Boltsa, BA (*Art*)
Mrs S Briffa, MA (*§Art*)
A M Bruni, BSc, BEd (*Mathematics*)
The Revd Canon A Buckley, MA (*History, Chaplain*)
M Bush, BA (*History*)
P M Cochrane, BSc (*†Roper's House, Chemistry*)
Miss C Coles, BSc (*PE*)

Miss W L Collins, BSc (*Chair of Science, *Chemistry*)
Ms S B Connolly, BA (*†Cribb's House, Music*)
Mrs R Conway, BA (*Religious Studies*)
Miss C V Copeland, MA (*Assistant Head Upper School, Classics*)
R Cross, MA (*History*)
Revd S C Dalwood, BA (*Examinations Officer, Mathematics*)
Mrs E-JC Doherty, BA (*Classics*)
Miss J Doley (*Music*)
Ms S M Dury, MA (**Psychology, History*)
Mr S Dutta, MA (*Classics*)
Mrs H F Eagle, BSc (*Design Technology*)
K Ellen, BSc (*OC CCF, IT, Geography*)
G English, BA (*PE*)
C M Fish, BA (*Music*)
P L Friedlander, DipAD (*Art*)
Ms L Gardner, GRSM, LRAM (*Music, School Counsellor*)
R L Geldeard, MA (*†Spurgeon's House, Classics, *Philosophy*)
Miss M Georgiou, BSc (*Physics, Chemistry*)
Miss K A Goff, BA (*Modern Languages*)
Miss S Gore, BA (*Religious Studies*)
A E W Grant, BA, PGCE (*History*)
Mrs K M Green, BSc (*Mathematics*)
N J W Green, BEd (*PE*)
M F Grogan, BA (*English, Acting Head of Media Studies*)
Mrs P Hall, BA (*Spanish*)
R G Halladay, BA (*Deputy Head Middle School, English*)
D J Harley, BSc (*Deputy Head Upper School, *History, Politics*)
P Harper, BA (*Modern Languages*)
D O A Hawes, PhD, MA (*History*)
Mrs M L Heaton-Caffin, CertEd (*§PE*)
Miss J Hewitson, BSc (*Geography*)
J Hodgkinson, MA (**General Studies, English*)
Miss K S Hopley, MSc (*Chemistry*)
G L Jenkins, MA (*English*)
Mrs M A Joel, BA (*Deputy Head Middle School, Modern Languages*)
E M D Jones, MA, BEd (**Geography*)
S P Kelly, PhD, BA (**German*)
Mrs S Kent, MA (*History*)
A T Kermode, MA (**Director of Music*)
N R Kinnear, MA (*Mathematics*)
Miss G V Kirby, BA (*English*)
Miss S Lamy, BSc (*Biology*)
Miss S A Lane, MA, CertEd (*Deputy Head Upper School, PE*)
Mrs H E Lawrence, BA (*English, Learning Support*)
Miss A M Legg, MA (*†Tyson's House, English*)
P M MacDonagh, BSc (**Information Technology*)
P A Mackie, MA (**Modern Languages*)
A Macmillan, BA (**Design Technology*)
E D Mann, BA (*Mathematics*)
Mrs S Mathieson, CertEd, (**Food Technology*)
M McCaffrey, BA (**French*)
S Milne, MA (*Economics & Business Studies*)
E K Mitchell, MA, DPhil (*Mathematics*)
Miss E M Nicoll, BA (*Modern Languages*)
Mrs E O'Donnell, BA, Grad Dip Lib SC (*Librarian*)
R N Ody, BEd (**Boys' PE*)
Miss R L Ottey, BSc (**Physics*)
Miss K J Owens, BEd (*Deputy Head Lower School, Head of PSHE, Design Technology*)
Mrs A E Parker, BA (*English*)
R D W Payne, BSc (*Information Technology*)
Ms V Penglase, BA (*Drama, Theatre Studies*)
C Perez, BSc (*Biology*)
Miss M Pokorny, BSc (*Deputy Head PSHE, Psychology, Biology*)
Miss A Poole, BSc (**Mathematics*)
N Price, MA (*Art*)
G Reid, MA (*†Brading's House, Religious Studies*)
A W J Robertson, BSc, MBA (**Economics & Business Studies*)
Dr A Roy, PhD, MA, MPhil (*Music*)
P J Ryder, BEng (*Mathematics*)
Miss A Schüller, MA (*Modern Languages*)
J G Shelton, BEd, RSA Dip IT (*Information Technology*)
P R Sherlock, CertEd (*†Tulley's House, PE*)
Miss J M Sixsmith, BA (*Modern Languages*)
J R Skidmore, BSc (*Chemistry*)
Miss K Slack, BA (*English*)
Mrs B Slater, BEd (*Physics*)
Mrs E Smith, BSc (*Biology*)
P A Smith, BMus, LRAM, ARCM (*Head of Instrumental Studies*)
R G Stevens, BSc, MA (*§Economics & Business Studies*)
A D Stocker, BA (**Drama, Theatre Studies*)
V A Strain, BA (*Modern Languages*)
Mrs R Sulkin, MA (**Learning Support*)
R J D Sutton, MA (**Art, Photography*)
Ms C H Symes, BSc (*Academic Assistant to Senior Deputy Head, Information Technology*)
Mrs J M Tait, BA (**Food Technology*)
Miss G Taylor, MA (**English*)
P Thomas, BA (*§Mathematics*)
C W Tibbits, BSc, PhD (*Biology*)
G J Tonkin, BA (**Theatre Studies*)
D Tuohey, BSc (*Physics*)
Miss J C Verdon, MA (*Biology*)
Miss M J Walker, BA (*Director of PE and Sport*)
W R Walker, BA (*Mathematics*)
Mrs C L Wells, BSc (*Mathematics*)
Miss H Williamson, BA, PG Dip Fine Art (*Art*)
A Živanić, BA (*Biology, Chemistry*)

The School. Alleyn's is a co-educational day school for pupils aged 11 to 18 years, some 960 strong, of whom approximately 280 are in the Sixth Form. The Headmaster is a member of the Headmasters' and Headmistresses' Conference.

It is, with Dulwich College, the lineal descendant of the School for 12 poor scholars endowed by Edward Alleyn, the Elizabethan actor manager, under a Royal Charter of 1619.

It was a Direct Grant school from 1958 until the abolition of this status in 1975; the Governors then opted for Independence and at the same time opened the entry to girl pupils. The school is now fully co-educational, with 479 boys and 480 girls.

Alleyn's Junior School, for ages 4 to 10 years, which opened in September 1992, is also on the site. (*See entry in IAPS section.*)

Entrance. A registration fee of £50 is charged for all applications.

(1) Admission to the School is by competitive examination open to both boys and girls at age 11, the normal age for transfer from primary to secondary school; entrance is decided on the basis of the examination held in January for entry the following September. A report is requested from the Head of the applicant's school and, if they reach a satisfactory standard in the examination, boys and girls are invited for interview. Fee-paying pupils enter by this means, and scholarships are given on the results of the entrance examination and interview. Means-tested bursaries are available for acdemically able children whose parents could not afford full fees. The examination consists of a Reasoning paper, an English paper and a Mathematics paper. Candidates should be entered at the School before the end of November, for admission the following September.

A similar procedure operates for entry at 16+.

(2) There is a smaller entry by examination open to both boys and girls at age 13. The procedure is similar to that for the

11 year old entry, with the addition of papers in Languages and Science and the omission of Reasoning papers.

(3) Opportunities for entry at other ages occur from time to time. Subject to the agreement of their Headteachers, overseas candidates may take the entrance paper at their own schools by arrangement.

(4) At age 4, 7 and 9 Junior School places are awarded on the basis of an assessment held in January for entry the following September.

Fees per term (2008-2009). £4,332 (£12,996 per annum).

Scholarships and Bursaries. (*see Scholarship Entries section*).

Curriculum. All students follow a broad and balanced curriculum in the first three years, including English, Mathematics, French, Latin and/or additional foreign languages (German or Spanish), Biology, Chemistry, Physics, Geography, History, Religious Studies, Art, ICT, Music and Design Technology. In Years 10–11, pupils take nine or ten GCSE subjects which will include English, English Literature, Mathematics, Sciences. In addition they choose four option subjects. In Year 12, four main subjects are followed to AS Level and most pupils also take General Studies at A Level. In Year 13, three or four A Levels are taken. In addition to those subjects listed above, Business Studies, Classical Civilisation, Computing, Economics, Classical Greek, Italian, Media Studies, Philosophy, Politics, Psychology, Physical Education and Theatre Studies are also available.

On the results obtained pupils are admitted to universities, medical and dental schools, and Art Colleges. Some 95% plus enter higher education each year. Selected pupils are prepared and entered for Colleges at Oxford and Cambridge, where a good record of places is maintained each year.

Organisation. The Lower School (Year 7 and Year 8) has its own separate building and its own Head. Pupils in the Upper and Middle Schools have a Head of Upper School and a Head of Middle School, and belong to one of eight Houses. Each Head of House is responsible, not only for organised games, but also for the welfare of each of their pupils during their time in the school. This care is supplemented by a system of form tutors for supervision of academic progress and the giving of appropriate advice. Parents are invited to Open Evenings during the year, at which pupils' work and progress are discussed with the teaching staff. The Headmaster and all members of the teaching staff are available for private meetings by appointment.

Games. The School stands in its own grounds of 26 acres and offers a wide variety of sports and games including Soccer, Hockey, Cricket, Swimming, Athletics, Netball, Cross-Country Running, Rugby Fives, Water Polo, Gymnastics, Badminton, Fencing, Golf, Basketball, Tennis, Rounders, Trampolining, Aerobics, Fitness and Weight Training, Squash and Horse Riding.

Religious Education. The Foundation belongs to the Church of England. Religious Education of a non-denominational nature is given throughout the school, and pupils also attend regular worship in Assembly and once each term in the Foundation Chapel or in St Barnabas Church. The School Chaplain holds voluntary Holy Communion Services during term-time. Pupils may be excused from religious education if parents request.

Buildings. The main school building dates from 1887. The school has a fully-equipped sports hall, with cardio-vascular room, an indoor swimming pool, a technology centre, a music school, two digital language laboratories, an all-weather playing surface, a new pavilion, computer rooms, a library/resource centre and from September 2008 a 400-seat performing arts centre. The various buildings are linked together by fibre optic cabling so that some 500+ computers are linked together on the school's network. The School has its own Field Centre near Buxton.

The **Library** is available to all pupils for private study and was opened in 2002 following the building of a major extension and refurbishment of the old Library.

Music, Drama and Art feature very strongly in the life of the school. There are 5 major concerts each year; the school runs 3 orchestras, 3 bands, 3 choirs and has over 30 Chamber groups, chosen by ability rather than age. 4 or 5 dramatic productions are staged each year. All pupils are taught to work in different media (Painting, Drawing, Sculpture and Ceramics).

There are many clubs and societies in the school; these include, in addition to Drama groups, Debating, Photography, Chess, Bridge, Politics, Science and the Christian Union.

The Combined Cadet Force has long been one of the most flourishing in the country, containing Army, Navy and RAF sections, and providing opportunities for such other activities as canoeing, rock climbing, sailing and flying. Pupils are encouraged to join at age 14 and serve for a minimum of 2 years. Pupils who do not join the CCF are expected to join either the Duke of Edinburgh's Award scheme or to give time to the community in the Community Service Group.

Career Guidance is given by specialised staff with the time and facilities for this important work. In Year 11 systematic aptitude testing is followed up by talks by parents themselves who give their time to talk about their own careers and who give help with offers of work experience to pupils.

University lecturers come in to help pupils to develop their skills on Upper School "Interview Day" and experts from leading firms offer their advice on "Interface Day".

A School Council, with members of all ages from Year 9 to Year 13, consults the Headmaster on many school matters.

Relations with Parents. Close touch is maintained with parents throughout the pupil's school career. The Alleyn's Association deals with all matters of interest to parents and its Social Sub-Committee raises considerable funds for the benefit of the school's Pupil Support Fund.

The Edward Alleyn Club. Past pupils are automatically members of the Edward Alleyn Club. This enables them to keep in touch with the school and their contemporaries, and also to take part in sporting activities if they wish. The Club is open to both boys and girls. Communications should be sent to the Alumni Officer, Mrs Susie Schofield, c/o Alleyn's School (alumni@alleyns.org.uk).

Charitable status. Alleyn's College of God's Gift is a Registered Charity, number 1057971. Its purpose is to provide Independent Education for boys and girls from age 4 to 18.

Ampleforth College

York YO62 4ER
Tel: 01439 766000
Fax: 01439 788330
e-mail: admin@ampleforth.org.uk
website: www.ampleforthcollege.york.sch.uk

Ampleforth Abbey was founded in 1607 at Dieulouard in Lorraine by English Benedictine monks who had strong links with the mediaeval Benedictines of Westminster Abbey. After the French Revolution the monastic community was resettled at Ampleforth in 1802 and the present School was started there soon after.

The Community is dedicated, first to prayer, and then to religious and charitable works. Ampleforth College and St Martin's Ampleforth are the works of St Laurence Educational Trust. The other works of the Community include parishes in Yorkshire, Lancashire and Cumbria, St Benet's Hall in Oxford and pastoral involvement both at Ampleforth and elsewhere.

Motto: '*Dieu le Ward*'.

Governance:

The Abbot of Ampleforth is elected by the Community for eight years at a time and presides over the Community and its works.

The Abbot is Chairman of the Ampleforth Abbey Trustees, which is the legal institute that owns and governs its foundation. St Laurence Education Trust is a separate limited company formed by the Abbey Trust. This also has charitable status and is responsible for both Ampleforth College and St Martin's Ampleforth.

The governance of these works is the responsibility of the Abbot who, with structured advice, appoints the officials, monastic and lay, who are in charge of their administration.

Governing Body:

The Abbot of Ampleforth is the Chairman of Governors acting with the Council and Chapter of Ampleforth Abbey. He is assisted by a lay Advisory Body.

***Headmaster*: Rev C G Everitt**, OSB, MA, DPhil

Deputy Head: Mr J R Browne, BA
Director of Studies: Mr I F Lovat, BSc, MInstP
Director of Professional Development: Mrs R M A Fletcher, MA
Director of Admissions: Mr N J Leiper, BSc
Head of Sixth Form: Mr W F Lofthouse, MA
Guestmaster: Rev H Lewis-Vivas, OSB, MA

Academic Departments:

Christian Theology:
*Mr M B Fogg, BA
†Rev W Peterburs, OSB, BA, PhD
Rev C G Everitt, OSB, MA, DPhil
Rev A McCabe, OSB, MA
Mr A D Kendry, BA
Mrs A M McNeill, BA
Mr J M Mishra, BA
†Mrs G M O McGovern, MA
Mr C E McDonough, BA
Miss E A Abbott, BA

Christian Living:
Ms A Le Gall, MA
Mrs M B Carter, BSc

Classics:
*Miss E R Ellis, MA
Mr W F Lofthouse, MA
Mr J Layden, BA
Miss J Sutcliffe, BA

History:
*Mr P T Connor, MA
†Mr H C Codrington, BEd
†Rev C Boulton, OSB, BA
Mr G D Thurman, BEd
Dr E J Fern, MA, PhD
Miss B Fuller, BA
Mr R C Day, BA

English:
*Mr A C Carter, MA
Mrs R M A Fletcher, MA (*Head of Professional Development*)
Mr D R Lloyd, MA (*Special Needs*)
Miss H K R Thomson, MA
Miss E A Chadwick, BA
Dr D Moses, MA, DPhil
Miss H R Brown, BA
Mr T A Barfield, MA

Modern Languages:
*Mr S R Owen, MA
Mr J P Ridge, MA
Mr K J Dunne, BA
Mr M J McPartlan, BA
*Miss S M Mulligan, BA (*EAL*)
Mr M Torrens-Burton, BA (*EAL*)
Rev A McCabe, OSB, MA
Mrs B E Abbott, BA
Mrs F Garcia-Ortega, BA
Mrs C M T Olley, BA
Rev J Callaghan, MA

Geography:
*Mrs C R M Dent, BSc
†Mr P M Brennan, BSc, FRMetSoc
Miss C Willey, BSc, MSc
†Mr A P Smerdon, BSc

Modern Studies:
*Mr M F Harris, BSc
Mr M A Dent, BSc
Miss J M C Simmonds, BSc
Mrs J Stannard, BA

Mathematics:
*Mr C G H Belsom, BA, MPhil, CMath, FIMA
Mrs P J Melling, BSc, BA
Dr R Warren, BSc, PhD (*Head of Middle School*)
†Mr D Willis, BEd, MEd
Mr C G O'Donovan, BSc
Dr J M Weston, BSc, DPhil
Dr J W Large, BSc, PhD

Physics:
*Mr J O Devitt, MPhys
Mr I F Lovat, BSc, MInstP
Mr A B Garnish, BSc (*Careers Master*)
Mr O Peck, BSc (*Physics and Biology*)

Chemistry:
*Mr A S Thorpe, BSc, CChem, MRSC (*Head of Science and Technology*)
Dr D L Allen, MA, DPhil, CChem, MRSC (*Chemistry and Physics*)
Mr S J Howard, BSc
Miss E R Bradley, BA

Biology:
Mr A J Hurst, BSc
Rev O McBride, OSB, BSc
Miss J O'Brien, BSc

Music:
*Mr I D Little, MA, MusB, FRCO, ARCM, LRAM
Mr W J Dore, MA, FRCO
Mrs K E Morgan, MusB
Mr D de Cogan, DipRCM, ARCM
Mr P J McBeth, MusB
Mr S Lloyd, MA, GMus (*Conductor of the College Orchestra*)

Design and Technology:
*Mr B W Gillespie, BEd
†Mr B J Anglim, BEng
†Mrs V Anglim, BEng

ICT:
*Mr M A Barras, BSc
Mrs L Canning, BSc

Art:
*Mr S G Bird, BA, ATC, DipAD
Mr T J W Walsh, MA
Mrs M A Young, BA
Miss L E Bolton, BA

Theatre Director:
Miss J Sutcliffe, BA

PE and Games:
*Mr G D Thurman, BEd (*Games Master*)
Mr G J Muckalt, BA (*Head of PE*)

Mr J G Liley, BSc (*Director of Rugby; Mathematics*)
Miss J N Horn, BA (*Head of Girls' Games*)
Mr J J Owen, BEd

Houses and Housemasters/Housemistresses:
St Aidan's (*girls*): Mrs E V Fogg, MA
St Bede's (*girls*): Mr B and Mrs V Anglim, BEng
St Margaret's (*girls*): Mrs G M O McGovern, MA
St Cuthbert's: Mr D Willis, MEd
St Dunstan's: Rev O McBride, OSB, BSc
St Edward's and St Wilfrid's: Mr A P Smerdon, BSc
St Hugh's: Mr H C Codrington, BEd
St John's: Rev W Peterburs, OSB, BA, PhD
St Oswald's: Rev C Boulton, OSB, BA
St Thomas's: Mr P M J Brennan, BSc, FRMetSoc

Counsellor: Mr J G J Allisstone, BA

Procurator: Mr P N Bryan, BA, ACA
Deputy Procurator: Mr M S McFetrich, FCIPD

Medical Officers:
Dr Kaye Mechie, MBChB
Dr G Black, MBChB, MRCGP, DRCOG

Headmaster's Secretary: Mrs L M Featherstone

Number in School. There are 613 students, of whom 515 are Boarders, including 166 girls, 57 are Day Boys and 41 are Day Girls.

Our aims are:

- to share with parents in the spiritual, moral and intellectual formation of their children, in a Christian community with which their families may be joined in friendship and prayer for the rest of their lives.
- to educate the young in the tradition and sacramental life of the Church and to encourage each towards a joyful, free and self-disciplined life of faith and virtue.
- to work for excellence in all our endeavours, academic, sporting and cultural. We ask students to give of their best. We ask much of the gifted and we encourage the weak. Each is taught to appreciate the value of learning and the pursuit of the truth.
- to help Ampleforth boys and girls grow up mature and honourable, inspired by high ideals and capable of leadership, so that they may serve others generously, be strong in friendship, and loving and loyal towards their families.

Organisation. St Martin's Ampleforth, an independent preparatory school at Gilling Castle, educates boys and girls from 3 to 13 years old. (*For further details, see entry in IAPS section.*)

The upper school has 7 houses for boys aged 13 to 18, one house for girls aged 16 to 18 and two houses for girls aged 13 to 18. Houses are kept small and are home to no more than 60 boarders, 45 in the case of the sixth form girls' house and there are some day students in each.

Each house has its own separate accommodation and all students eat their meals in their own house refectory and are joined at lunch by their Housemaster/Housemistress and other teaching staff.

The work and games of the whole school are centrally organised. At least five tutors are allocated to each house to supervise students' work and provide the appropriate guidance at each stage in their school career. The Careers Master provides information and assistance and can arrange expert advice for pupils, parents and tutors. Much of the non-teaching life of the school is organised around the houses. These activities help to create a strong house loyalty.

There has been over £25m invested in the school in the last 10 years. Future projects include an equestrian centre, an observatory and major extensions to the Sports Centre. A new Sixth Form Centre was opened in September 2006, furnished with Mouseman tables, chairs and bar.

Curriculum. The first year (year 9) provides a broad basis from which to make informed GCSE choices. In the second and third years a core of English, Mathematics, Science and Christian Theology is studied to GCSE together with a balanced selection from a wide range of subjects. In the first year of the sixth form (year 12) up to 5 subjects may be studied to AS level. One of those subjects may be AS level Christian Theology but, if not, students follow a Christian Theology short course. Normally three subjects will be taken on to A level in the second year (year 13). A comprehensive health education programme is provided in all years.

Games and Activities. There are opportunities to play a wide variety of representative sports at all levels with excellent indoor and outdoor facilities. Many activities and games take place during the week and weekends, including drama, debating, outdoor pursuits, creative arts and a wide variety of sports. These sports range from lacrosse to rugby. The school has its own outstanding 9-hole golf course and has recently completed a new all-weather hockey surface and new tennis courts. In addition, the college has its own all-weather athletics track.

Music, which is a strong academic subject, plays a major part in the extra-curricular life of the school. The Schola Cantorum, our liturgical choir, sing for Mass in the Abbey and perform sacred music in Britain and abroad. They have been responsible for the production of several commercial CDs in recent years. The Schola Puellarum, our girls choir, sings afternoon prayer on Fridays and has undertaken tours to Dublin (2006) and Bordeaux (2007). They have also recently released their own CD.

Further enquiries may be made directly to the Games Master on 01439 766729 or the Director of Music on 01439 766730.

Admission. Applications may be made through the Admissions Office. Registration Fee: £75.

Fees per term (2008-2009). Boarders: £8,575; Day Boys/Girls: £5,245.

The fees are inclusive, the only normal extras being for individual tuition in Music: £27.75 per lesson, £25.75 for a second instrument; TEAL £730 per term; extra English £44.50 per class.

Entrance Scholarships. (*see Scholarship Entries section*). Academic, Music and All-Rounder scholarships are awarded at 13+ and for entry to the Sixth Form.

Charitable status. St Laurence Educational Trust is a Registered Charity, number 1063808. Its aim is to advance Roman Catholic religion.

Ardingly College
A Woodard School

Haywards Heath West Sussex RH17 6SQ
Tel: 01444 893000
Fax: 01444 893001
e-mail: head@ardingly.com
website: www.ardingly.com

Ardingly is a co-educational School in the Woodard Family founded to teach the Christian Faith.

Our aim is to enable all boys and girls to develop their love of learning, academic potential and individual talents, in a caring community which fosters sensitivity, confidence, a sense of service and enthusiasm for life

Motto: '*Beati Mundo Corde*'.

School Council:

Chairman: R Alston, Esq, CMG

The Rt Revd Lindsay Urwin, OGS, MA (*Provost*)
Mrs C Bennet

***Headmaster*: Peter Green**, MA

Deputy Headmaster: Richard Bool, BA

Chaplain: The Revd I Colson, BSc, BTh

Head of the Prep School: Chris Calvey, BEd

Bursar: T Waitson

Medical Officer: Dr B Lambert

History and development of the College. Ardingly College, the third of Nathaniel Woodard's schools was founded in Shoreham in 1858 and moved to its present beautiful site in Mid Sussex, about halfway between Gatwick and Brighton in 1870. The College now consists of a Pre-Prep Day School and a boarding and day Prep School, for boys and girls between the ages of 2½ and 13, and of a boarding and day Senior School for boys and girls aged between 13 and 18.

In the Prep School, which has been co-educational since 1986, there are 239 pupils, of whom 149 are boys and 90 are girls, and 11 are boarders. There are 77 boys and girls in the Pre-Prep.

In the Senior School, which started to become fully co-educational in 1982, there are 474 pupils of whom 201are in the Sixth Form. There are 293 boys and 181 girls, and 230 are boarders.

For further details about the Ardingly Prep School and the Ardingly Pre-Preparatory School (The Farmhouse) see entries in the IAPS section.

Academic. Ardingly has an extremely good academic record in both arts and science subjects achieved by boys and girls who come from a wide spectrum of ability. The A level and IB percentage pass rate has been 100% for the past 3 years. Every year about four to six Ardinians gain entry to Oxford or Cambridge and overall more than 95% of the Upper Sixth go on to Higher Education. At GCSE the A B C pass rate is usually about 98% and most candidates take 8 subjects or more.

Curriculum. *First year*: A broad course in which all pupils do virtually everything: second Modern Language (German or Spanish), Classical Studies; Expressive Arts, Design Technology and Information Technology for all.

GCSE (2nd and 3rd years): All take English and English Literature, Maths, Sciences, at least one Modern Language, and the usual wide range of options.

Sixth Form Curriculum: Standard choices in a highly flexible 5 block system at AS/A2. In Sept 2001, Ardingly also introduced the International Baccalaureate alongside A Levels.

All Lower Sixth pupils receive a refresher course in Information Technology.

Pastoral. There are 7 Middle School Houses, four for boys and three for girls which contain everyone from the first year to the Lower Sixth. In the Upper Sixth all boys and girls transfer to a separate, integrated co-educational House, "Woodard" (opened in 1988), in which they are able to concentrate more fully on their studies and can be given greater responsibility for themselves and be better prepared for life at University or in the outside world. Each House has its own Housemaster or Housemistress, Assistant and House Tutors. In addition every boy and girl will have a Tutor (chosen after the first year by the pupil) who has responsibility for the work, progress, choices and many other aspects of the pupil's life. Tutorials are regular, one to one and usually weekly. Tutors work closely with careers staff which includes a professional adviser who comes in one day a week.

In the second year pupils study and discuss life topics in small mixed groups as part of a specially designed course called 'Learning for Living' and within the Religious Studies course in other years, and General course in the Lower Sixth.

There is an efficient compact Medical Centre in the centre of the school with a residential Sister in charge. The School Doctor takes three surgeries a week in the School and is always on call.

Two new Boys' Boarding Houses were opened in September 2003.

Since September 2005 School on Saturdays has been discontinued.

Expressive Arts. *Music*: Choir, Chamber Choir, Choral Society, Jazz Singers, Orchestras, Concert Band, Jazz Band, Chamber Music. Instrumental lessons taken by about half the boys and girls.

Art: Painting, drawing, printing, ceramics, sculpture, fashion & textiles, photography, etching.

Design Technology: Real design problems solved in a variety of materials and forms.

Drama: Many productions in the course of the year for all ages. Large flexible theatre and a small workshop theatre.

All four of these expressive arts are studied in modular form in the first year, are options for GCSE and A Level and offer scholarships for talented candidates, at both 13+ and for the Sixth Form.

Sport. Boys play Football, Hockey, Cricket, Tennis; Girls play Hockey, Netball, Tennis, Rounders. (Football and cricket are also available for girls).

Also (for both boys and girls) there is Squash, Cross Country, Swimming, Shooting, Golf, Volleyball, Horseriding, Clay Pigeon Shooting, Basketball, Badminton (new Sports Hall opened in 1999), Judo, Multigym, Croquet, Sailing, etc.

The indoor pool is open to both Prep and Senior Schools and pupils who cannot swim are taught to do so.

Activities. Combined Cadet Force (Army based), Outward Bound (compulsory modular programme in first year), Duke of Edinburgh's Award, Cooking, Sewing, Stage work, Modern dance, Photography, Computers, etc.

International Students Programme. Ardingly offers places to children from Europe and the rest of the world for periods of a term or more. (In the Sixth Form the minimum stay is 1 year.)

After Ardingly. A Level and IB candidates are encouraged to consider taking a 'Gap' year between school and university, particularly in Third World placements with Schools Partnership Worldwide, Operation Raleigh or GAP.

Admissions. Admission to the Senior School normally takes place at 13+ or directly into the Sixth Form at 16+. Admission is also possible at 14+ but is not advisable at the beginning of the years in which GCSE or A Levels are taken unless there are very special reasons.

At 13+ entry is either by Common Entrance or the School's own test papers (for those not attending Preparatory Schools) in English and Maths, together with IQ test, report and interview. The selection of candidates for direct entry to the Sixth Form takes place at the end of November in the year prior to entry. All candidates are interviewed and take and English paper and the school's standard Verbal Reasoning test. A report from their Head is also required. Places will then be offered subject to the candidate gaining a minimum of 4 grade Bs and 2 grade Cs or above at GCSE. Modifications of these procedures and of the timing for individuals at any stage are almost always possible.

The Prep School has entry at 7+ and 11+, or at any other time between the ages of 7 and 11. Transfer into the Senior School is by Common Entrance.

Scholarships. A number of Scholarships are offered for annual competition at 13+ and 16+. They include Academic, Art, DT, Drama, Music and Sports Awards. Ashdown Awards for all-rounders are offered for those entering at 13+. The Prep School offers Academic, Art, Music and Sports Awards at 11+ with Academic Awards at 7+. Some Prep School awards are tenable in the Senior School and others are for the Prep School years only. Along with other HMC schools, the maximum value of a scholarship is 40% of the basic fees per annum but all may be supplemented by a means-tested bursary if need can be shown.

A limited number of bursaries (value up to 40% of basic fees per annum) are available for the children of the Clergy.

Up to ten Music awards may be made each year to those who show that they will have an active contribution to make to the musical life of the School, not only as soloists on their own particular instruments, but in ensemble work, orchestras, choirs and productions, etc. Six of these awards may be to the value of 40% of fees pa, two being reserved for orchestral string players and two for choristers in attendance at schools which are in membership of the Choir Schools Association. All awards include free music tuition. Any combination of instrument(s) and/or voice may be offered and, although it is hoped that candidates will offer a good standard of playing/singing, beginners who show really good potential and enthusiasm may be considered.

Two Choral Scholarships may be offered for boys entering the Sixth Form. These may be worth 33% of fees and carry free singing/instrumental tuition for two instruments.

Two entrance scholarships in Art may be awarded annually. Both awards may be worth up to 40% of fees per annum. Both 13+ and Sixth Form entrants are eligible. Candidates will be interviewed by the Director of Art and will be expected to bring a portfolio of their work with them. They will also be expected to do a practical test. Art may be taken in its widest sense and any form of two or three-dimensional work which shows candidates' interests and ability is acceptable.

Please address all enquiries about admissions, scholarships and bursaries to either School to the Registrar (Tel: 01444 893000; fax: 01444 893001; e-mail: registrar@ardingly.com).

Term of Entry. Main 13+ and Sixth Form intake in September. Intake at other ages and other times on an individual basis.

Registration. The School Prospectus may be obtained from the Registrar, and is sent whenever an enquiry about a vacancy is received. Registration (where a non-returnable fee of £60 is charged) can be made at any age subject to the availability of places. No separate registration is required for children transferring from the Prep to the Senior School.

Fees per term (2008-2009). Senior School: £8,000–£8,200 (boarders), £6,000–£6,150 (day pupils). Casual boarding: £45 per night. Prep School: £5,150 (boarders), £3,150–£4,000 (day pupils). Pre-Prep: £1,300–£2,200.

Fees are inclusive. There is a surcharge of £180 per term for those entering at the Sixth Form stage.

Further Particulars. For further information, application should be made to the Registrar. A personal visit to the School is an easy matter from London: frequent fast trains run from Victoria to Haywards Heath – and a taxi can always be found outside the railway station.

Charitable status. Ardingly College Limited is a Registered Charity, number 1076456. It exists to provide high quality education for boys and girls aged 2½ to 18.

Arnold School (UCST)

Blackpool

Lytham Road Blackpool Lancashire FY4 1JG

Tel: 01253 346391 Senior & Junior School
Fax: 01253 336250 Senior School
01253 336251 Junior School
e-mail: principal@arnoldschool.com
admissions@arnoldschool.com
juniorheadmaster@arnoldschool.com
website: www.arnoldschool.com

The foundation dates from 1896 when Frank Truswell Pennington opened a school with 8 pupils in his rooms in Bright Street, South Shore, Blackpool. In 1903 he moved the school to the present site in Lytham Road and called it Arnold House after a school which had previously occupied the building.

In 1937 the School was reconstituted, since when it has been administered by a Governing Council of 15 members, the majority of whom are Old Arnoldians. In 1938 the School – now called Arnold School – was placed on the Direct Grant list where it continued to flourish before reverting to independent status in 1976. Arnold has been fully co-educational since September 1980 and is now a 4-form entry day school for 750 boys and girls (11–18 years) with a Junior School for 350 boys and girls (2–11 years).

The Governors are committed to an on-going capital development programme. The campus includes a Sports Complex, Performing Arts Studio, Languages Centre, Music Centre, Design and Technology Centre, ICT suites, a large extension to the Junior School and an all-weather playing surface.

Motto: '*Honor Virtutis Praemium*'.

Governing Council:
Chairman: J M Wooding, OBE, BSc, CEng, FRAeS
Vice Chairman: ¶J C Armfield, OBE, DL
Deputy Chairman: ¶M S Brennand

D Aird LLB
A E D Baines, BA, RIBA
W B Beaumont, OBE
M C Brook, BA, FCA
Mrs S C Carr, OBE
Mrs G M Connolly, BSc, MA
S Dawkins, BA, MA
A F Grime, BEng, BMA, CEng, MICE, FCIWEM
Mrs A Jack, CertEd
P Maguire, ACA
¶P M Owen, ACIB
Mrs R Pigott, OBE, LLB
¶J R Taylor, LLB

Bursar and Clerk to the Council: Commander P McCarthy, RN

¶ *Old Arnoldian*
* *Head of Department*
† *Head of House*

Tutorial Staff:

***Principal*: B M Hughes**, BSc, MRSC, NPQH

Vice-Principal: J Keefe, BA
Director of Studies: C W Jenkinson, MA
Director of Marketing and Admissions: C F D White, BEd
Senior Teacher (*Higher Education, Careers & Administration*): Mrs M A Thornton, BSc
Head of Sixth Form: A J McKeown, BSc
Head of the Middle School: P E Hayden, BA
Head of the Lower School: J A Nicholls, CertEd

Heads of House:
School: R Bedford, BSc Econ
Howarth: P R Oliver, GCLCM
Pennington: P McMahon, BA, MSc
Liston: Mrs M M Ingham, BEd

Archivist: K S Shenton
Marketing and Admissions Secretary: Miss L V Rogers

Biology:
*S Downey, BSc
Miss N Strino, BSc
A J Treharne, BSc, PhD, CBiol, MIBiol (*Examinations Officer*)
A J McKeown, BSc
Miss J J Harvey, BSc

Business Studies:
†*R Bedford, BSc Econ
G R McIntyre, BA

Chemistry:
*J Young, BSc, DPhil (*Head of Science*)
Mrs M Thornton, BSc
M B Kirkham, BSc, CChem, MRSC
P J Collinson, BSc

Classics:
*I J Morton, MA

Design Centre:
*M J Salmon, BSc
E R Lawson, BEng, CEng, MIMechE
Mrs H R Caunce, BA
Miss C Norris, BA

Drama and Theatre Studies:
*C G Snell, BA

Economics:
*Mrs S Donald BSc
J Keefe, BA

English:
J L Bridges, BA
D E Smyth, BEd, MA, MA Lit
P E Hayden, BA
Mrs D Mayhew, BA
Ms M Johnson, BA
S Alsop, BA

Geography/Geology:
*K H Lee, BSc
J B Ashcroft, BA
I R Winterflood, BSc

History:
*J R Davey, BA
Mrs J A Nicholls, CertEd
R E Golding, BA History, BA Theology
G R McIntyre, BA

ICT:
*D Culpan, BSc

Library:
Mrs J E Darkins, BSc

Mathematics:
*†P McMahon, BA, MSc
A J G Bell, BA
Mrs D Nield, BSc
Mrs P J Taylor, BSc
D R Bruce, BSc
H Banks, BSc
L Sobey, BSc

Modern Languages:
Mrs D J Pailing, BA
Mrs D A Jenkinson, BA
Miss E Alabart-Lorenzo
P Draper, BA, MEd
Mrs F Burnett, BA
Miss S L Lunn, BA

Music:
*J Ross, BMus
Miss G Church, BMus

Physics:
*Miss R Matheson, BSc
K W Ward, BSc, BA
K D Bleakley, BSc

Physical Education:
*R L Jones, BEd
M L Evans, BSc
†Mrs M M Ingham, BEd
Miss G Raby, TCert
Ms K E Preston, RAD, BTDA
†P R Oliver, GCLCM, DPLM
Mrs M Whorlton-Jones, BEd
Mrs J M Malin, BEd
Miss A DeMiranda, BEd
G Smith

Psychology:
Mrs C Davis, BSc

Religious Education:
*M A Harding, BEd
Mrs J A Nicholls, CertEd
R E Golding, BA History, BA Theology
Miss A Jordan, BRelsci, BA, MA

Instrumental Staff:
Miss P Holt, BA
T Reaney
M Skyrme
Mrs M Johnstone
Mrs K Dangerfield
Mr A Harrison
Mrs R Whatton

Careers and Higher Education:
*Mrs M A Thornton, BSc
P E Hayden, BA
L Sobey, BSc
Miss G Raby, TCert

Combined Cadet Force:
CO: Lt Col J B Ashcroft
SSI: WO1 T F Beck, MISM

Royal Navy Section:
OC: Lt Commander E R Lawson, RNR
Sub Lt S Howard
Sub Lt T Brown

Army Section:
OC: Capt A Treharne
2nd Lt W Chadwick

Royal Airforce Section:
OC: Sqn Ldr P R Oliver
Flt Lt J R Davey

Junior School (including Infants and Kindergarten)

Head of Junior School: P Hopkinson, BA, PGCE
Deputy Headmaster: J Storey, CertEd
Head of Foundation Stage: Miss J Allen, BA Ed Hons
Head of Key Stage 1: Mrs D Smith, BEd
Head of Key Stage 2: Mrs S Knight, BA
Mrs A Briggs, BSc, QTS
Mrs L Buck, BSc
Mrs L Cole, BEd
A Coyne, BEd (*ICT)
Miss A Duxbury
R A Fielder, BEd
Mrs L Fielder, BEd
Mrs E Foster, BEd
Mrs M Hecht, CertEd, DipSpLD
A Hodgkinson, BSc, PGCE
Mrs S Taylor, CertEd
Mrs G Ward, BEd Hons
Mrs J Woodhead, CertEd
Kindergarten Manager: Mrs K Hartley, NNEB
Kindergarten Supervisor: Miss N Metcalfe, BTec, NDip
Senior Nursery Nurse: Mrs T Dagger, NNEB, ULCI Child Development
Senior Nursery Nurse: Miss R Hutchinson, NVQ3
Senior Nursery Nurse: Mrs S McGivern, NVQ3
Mrs J Laing, PPADip
Mrs S Rigby, BTecCert
Miss L Robinson, NVQ3
Miss L Gray, NVQ3
Miss RWatson, NVQ2
Miss S Rowson, NVQ3

Site and Buildings. The School lies on the south side of Blackpool, half a mile from the sea. The facilities include the normal classrooms and specialist rooms, modern well-equipped laboratories, 3 ICT Suites, a modern Music facility, a Sixth Form Centre and the Memorial Hall. Recent additions include a Sports Complex, Performing Arts Studio and Languages Centre, Design and Technology Centre, The Lawrence House Music Centre and an all-weather pitch which is adjacent to our playing fields. The School also possesses an Outdoor Pursuits Centre at Glenridding in Cumbria.

The Junior School (2–11 years) is situated on the same site as the Senior School and is therefore able to benefit from its facilities.

Curriculum. The School aims to give its boys and girls a broad education in general, and in particular to prepare them for public examinations and for entry to Universities (including Oxford and Cambridge) and other places of Further Education. The curriculum is broadly based up to GCSE level and includes Design/Technology, Computing, Drama, Latin, German and Spanish. The Advanced Level specialisations include Economics, Business Studies, Theatre Studies and Psychology in addition to the more traditional options. There are about 160 students in Sixth Form, the vast majority of whom proceed to degree courses.

A period of work experience is arranged for all Year 11 pupils immediately after the GCSE examinations. The School has excellent links with Industry. Careers education is provided from the Year 9 onwards.

Clubs and Activities. There is a very wide range of co-curricular activities: Art, Brass Band, Basketball, Chess, Choir, Dance, Drama, Debating, Fencing, Greek, Orchestra, Photography, Orienteering, Community Service, Outdoor Pursuits and the Duke of Edinburgh's Award Scheme.

Games. Organised games and Physical Education periods play an important part in School life and every pupil is expected to participate unless excused on medical grounds. Playing fields of 13 acres adjoin the School for Rugby Football and Hockey in the Winter terms and for Cricket, Tennis and Athletics in the Summer. Other Sports include Golf, Squash,

Basketball, Badminton, Swimming, Netball and Fencing. There are dance classes in both ballet and modern dancing for the girls.

Combined Cadet Force. Membership is open to all pupils from Year 9, and pupils may join the RAF, Naval or the Army Section. The Contingent has a successful record and emphasis is placed upon Adventure Training. The Naval Section has an excellent base on Windermere and there is a fleet of various dinghies and other craft.

Junior School. Since September 1970 girls have been admitted as well as boys. All Junior School pupils occupy buildings that have been built since 1970. Admission is at 2+, 4+ or 7+. Entry at other ages depends upon vacancies occurring. Pupils transfer to the Senior School at 11 years conditional upon maintaining suitable progress in Key Stage Two. The Junior School has its own separate buildings (including an ICT Centre) and a distinct corporate life, though it is situated alongside the Senior School whose facilities it also uses. The games played are Association Football, Rugby, Hockey, Netball and Cricket. Athletics and Swimming sports are held annually. Music is encouraged and there is a flourishing Choir. There is a full range of co-curricular activities, including Games, Chess, Dancing, Gardening, Gymnastics, Horse-Riding, ICT, Orchestra, Science, Speech & Drama, Yoga and Choir. Recent developments have included the expansion of the Kindergarten and the addition of new changing rooms, Common Room, classrooms, Art and Science Room and Resource Room. All classrooms are networked to a centrally managed ICT facility.

(*For further details see entry in IAPS section.*)

Admission. Prospectus and Admissions forms can be obtained from the Marketing and Admissions Secretary.

All entries to the Senior School are made through the Principal. Pupils are admitted to the Senior School on the basis of the School's examinations in English, Mathematics and Non-Verbal Reasoning. The main intake to the Senior School is at 11 years at the beginning of the Autumn term, though entry at other times is possible depending on availability of places.

For entry at Sixth Form level respectable GCSE grades in at least five subjects are normally expected in addition to a satisfactory report from a pupil's current Head.

Entry into the Junior School (2–11 years) is at the age of 2, 4 and 7. Enquiries should be made to the Marketing and Admissions Secretary.

Fees per term (2008-2009). Senior School Tuition £2,778; Junior School and Infants Tuition £2,126, including books and stationery. Kindergarten fees are payable by the half-day session (£20). Extras are minimal. Lunch is provided at cost.

Entrance Scholarships. (*see Scholarship Entries section*). Several scholarships (including those for Music, Art & Design, and Sport) are available for entry at 11+. Music, Sport, Art, Design & Technology, and Drama scholarships are available in the Sixth Form.

Registration. Pupils may be registered at any time although this should be as early as possible if entry is requested at ages other than 2, 4, 7 or 11 years. Candidates will be called for examination in the year of entry although those who live at a distance may have the papers sent to their schools.

Charitable status. The United Church Schools Trust (to which Arnold School belongs) is a Registered Charity, number 1016538. Its aims and objectives are to provide pupils with a sound education based on and inspired by Christian principles.

Ashville College

Green Lane Harrogate North Yorkshire HG2 9JP
Tel: 01423 566358
Fax: 01423 505142
e-mail: ashville@ashville.co.uk
website: www.ashville.co.uk

Ashville was founded in 1877 by the United Methodist Free Church, but has been strengthened by taking under its wing at different times two older non-conformist schools: Elmfield College, founded by the Primitive Methodists in 1864, which amalgamated with Ashville in 1932; and New College, which began in 1850 with strong Baptist connections and merged with Ashville in 1930.

Motto: '*Esse quam videri*'

Visitor: The President of the Methodist Conference

Governing Body:
Chairman: Mr R Manby
Deputy Chairman: Mrs A Willey, BA

***Headmaster*: Mr A A P Fleck**, BSc, MA Nottingham

Deputy Heads:
Mr A T Johnson, BA Dunelm (*Head of Classics*)
Mrs E Fisher, BSc Strathclyde

Chaplain: Revd Marty Presdee, BA Wales

Director of Studies: Mr T M Cundy, MA Cantab, MSc Leeds

Year Heads:
Year 7: Mrs M Burrell, BA Hull
Year 8: Miss J Ellis, BA Brighton
Year 9: Mr D Grainger, BSc Edinburgh
Year 10: Ms E Ekstein, BA Leeds, MA Leeds
Year 11: Mrs N Mellor, BSc York, MA Leeds ATCL
Head of Sixth Form: Revd G S Warren, BA Dunelm, MA Leeds (*Head of Religious Studies*)
Assistant Head of Sixth Form: Mrs K Rutter, BEd Leeds

Senior Housemaster: Mr P N Hampson, BEd Exon

Heads of Departments:
Science: Mr M Finch, BSc Surrey
Physics: Mr C Davies, BSc Sussex
Chemistry: Mr D J Normanshire, BSc Bangor
Biology: Mr P D Forster, BSc Salford
Classics: Mr A T Johnson, BA Dunelm
Modern Languages: Mr I W Kendrick, MA Leeds, BA
French: Mrs J M Wilcocks, MA Leicester, BA London
German: Mr I A Popley, BSc Aston
Drama: Mrs J Normanshire, BA Wales
Music:
Director of Music: Mr J Dunford, GTC Hons, LTCL, ARCO, ALCM, AMusTCL
Head of Instrumental Studies: Mr R Simpson, BA Salford
English: Mr K A Bolton, MA Cantab, Cert SLS
Mathematics: Dr J Dekanski, BSc, PhD Leeds
Art: Mr J Mullin, MA Edinburgh Dip AD
CDT: Mr C Pearce, BEd Leeds
Geography: Mrs J Williams, BA Wales
History: Mr A J Barker, MA St Andrews
Sport:
Girls' Games: Mrs M J Petts, CertEd, ICSP Assoc
Boys' Games: Mr I Gould, BA Leeds
PE Academic: Mr J Goldthorpe, BSc Loughborough
Home Economics: Mrs P Cousen, CertEd
EFL: Mr P Gilmore, MA York, BSc
Economics/Business Studies: Mr N P Cornforth, BSc Wales
AVCE: Mrs C Guy, BA John Moores
Religious Studies: Revd G S Warren, BA Dunelm, MA Leeds
ICT: Mr D Taylor, BSc Sheffield MSc Manchester
Learning Support: Mrs M G Levey, BA Leeds, BDA Di

Junior School:
Head: Mr C J Britt-Compton, CertEd Worcester
Deputy Head: Mr J Thompson, BEd Dunelm
Head of Junior School Music: Miss H J Dexter, BMus London, LGSM

Pre-Prep:
Head: Miss L Savage, BA Leeds

Deputy Head: Mrs C Berrie, BEd Hull

Bursar: Mrs E Sanderson, BA, MA, ACA

Registrar & Headmaster's PA: Mrs C Butcher

Medical Officer: Mrs J Tullet

Although a Methodist foundation a large proportion of its pupils come from non-Methodist homes, and the school welcomes pupils from overseas. Until 1976 Ashville was a Direct Grant school. When the Government decided to bring Direct Grant to an end, it was unanimously resolved that Ashville should revert to fully Independent status. In 1982 the school became co-educational.

Numbers. Ashville is a co-educational boarding and day school. There are over 500 boys and girls in the Senior School, 160 in the Junior School (aged 7–11), and approximately 100 in the Pre-Prep.

Site and Buildings. The Ashville estate consists of 60 acres of land on the south side of Harrogate.

The original house has been considerably extended to provide all the administrative accommodation and also houses the library and several of the arts faculties.

A programme of continuous building and improvement has taken place over the last 20 years. A successful appeal in 1989 provided a new Music and Drama Centre. In 1994 a magnificent Sixth Form Centre was opened, and at the same time, the Design Technology workshop was extended, a pottery was created for the Art Department and an additional Biology Laboratory was built. A Pre-Prep was opened in 1995, and moved into its own purpose-built accommodation in September 2000. Twenty acres of land were purchased for hockey and rugby pitches in 1997. An Activities Hall has been built following an appeal to coincide with the 125th anniversary of the school in 2003.

Curriculum. The Pre-Prep and Junior Schools aim to give a firm grounding in National Curriculum core and foundation subjects. French is introduced at 7+. All pupils are prepared for the General Certificate of Secondary Education at 16, and the Advanced Level GCE examinations two years later. From the age of 11 pupils spend five years on the GCSE course, which includes the study of English Language and Literature, History, Geography, Music, Art, Religious Education, French, German, Spanish, Latin, Mathematics, Physics, Chemistry, Biology, Design Technology, Home Economics, Business Studies, and Physical Education. At Advanced Level Economics, ICT, History of Art, English Language and Physical Education are also available. Guidance is given by the Careers Staff in the choice of Sixth Form studies and decisions are made after consultation with parents. Most pupils who complete the Advanced Level course go on to study at university or other institution of higher education. In addition to their specialist subjects all pupils continue their general education and most offer General Studies as a subject at GCE A level.

Physical Education. Physical Education is a part of the curriculum for all pupils, and there are games afternoons for all during the week.

The main school games are Rugby and Cricket for the boys, Netball and Rounders for the girls but there are school fixtures also in Hockey, Cross-Country, Swimming, Athletics, Lawn Tennis, Squash and Badminton.

Careers. Careers guidance is regarded as a very important part of the service provided by the school. Ashville is in membership of the Independent Schools Careers Organisation, and parents are encouraged to share with the careers staff the responsibility for giving appropriate guidance at the Fifth and Sixth Form stage. Pupils are helped in their choice of university and degree course, and arrangements are made for them to visit universities and go on careers courses.

Religious Life. All pupils attend Morning Prayers every weekday, and there is a school service for boarders on Sunday evening. Confirmation classes are held in the Spring Term each year, and boys and girls are prepared for Joint Confirmation in the Church of England and the Methodist Church. The School Chaplain is always glad to meet parents by appointment.

Leisure Activities. There are school societies which cater for a wide range of interests, and pupils are guided in the use of their free time in the early years. The school has no cadet corps, but boys and girls are enabled to take part in the Duke of Edinburgh's Award scheme. Drama has a strong following and the school play is a highlight of the year's programme.

Music is well provided for, and pupils are encouraged to take up the study of piano, organ or an orchestral instrument. The School Choir has acquired a high reputation by its contributions at the Harrogate and Wharfedale Festivals.

Admission. The school is prepared to admit pupils at any convenient time. Entry to the Junior School is by means of an interview and test papers in English and Arithmetic.

Candidates for entry at the age of 11 are required to take the Ashville Entrance Examination in the January preceding the September of entry. The examination consists of papers in English, Mathematics and Reasoning.

Candidates at Preparatory Schools seeking entry at the age of 13 are required to sit a similar examination.

Candidates for entry at other ages and into the Sixth Form are considered on the evidence of a headmaster's report and interview.

Registration forms and prospectus are obtainable from the Registrar. There is a registration fee of £25.

Fees per term (2008-2009). Tuition: Senior School £3,415–£3,445, Junior School £2,435–£2,940, Pre-Prep £2,015. Boarding (in addition to tuition fees): Full £1,950–£3,315, Weekly £1,755–£2,715.

Sibling Allowance: For a family with three or more children at Ashville, full tuition fees apply for the two youngest children, but tuition fees for all other children are reduced by 10%.

Scholarships and Bursaries. Discretionary Awards: Scholarships are awarded at the discretion of the Headmaster for excellence in academic performance or other disciplines, for example music. Scholarships are awarded to pupils for specific stages of their education at Ashville.

Financial Assistance: Bursaries are available at the discretion of the school and are means tested.

Forces Boarding Bursary: If a parent is serving in the armed forces and their children are boarding at Ashville, the bursary is 20% of tuition and boarding fees for junior school pupils and 10% for senior pupils.

Charitable status. Ashville College is a Registered Charity, number 529577, administered by Ashville College Trustee Ltd, company number 4552232. It aims to provide a boarding and day education for boys and girls.

Bablake School

Coundon Road Coventry CV1 4AU
Tel: 024 7627 1200
Fax: 024 7627 1290
e-mail: info@bablake.coventry.sch.uk
website: www.bablake.com

Bablake School was originally part of the College of the same name founded by Queen Isabella in 1344. After the dissolution of the monasteries it was refounded in 1560 by the city; it is chiefly associated with the name of Thomas Wheatley, whose indentures of 1563 put its finances on a firm foundation.

The Governing Body is Coventry School Foundation, on which are represented Sir Thomas White's Charity, the Coventry Church Charities, Coventry General Charities, Oxford and Warwick Universities and the University of Coventry. There are also several co-opted governors.

Chairman of Governors: Mr B Connor

***Headmaster*: Mr J W Watson**, MA

Deputy Heads:
Mr C R Seeley, BA, MPhil
Mrs G F Thomas, BA

Assistant staff:
Mrs L B Alexander, BSc
Dr P B M Archer, BSc, PhD
Mr L Atwal, BSc
Mrs K Baker, BA
*Mrs K Barnacle, BSc
Miss N D Beasley, BSc
Mrs H M Billings, BA
Miss R M Blattner, BSc
Mrs D R Booth, BSc
Mr J M Bunce, MA
Mr P F Burden, MA
*Mr R L Burdett, BSc
Mr J G Burns, MA (*Head of Sixth Form*)
Miss L R T Cheffings, BA
Mr A D Chowne, BSc
*Mr P Cleaver, MA
Mrs C B Davey, BSc
Mrs G C Dolphin, MBA, BSc, ACIB
Mr R J Dougall, MA
Mr J M Drury, BSc
*Mr M Duerdin, BSc
Mr S P Enstone, BSc
*Mr D L Faulkner, BSc
Mrs M C Field, L-ès-L
Mrs L J Fletcher, LLB
Mrs L French, BSc
*Mrs C Friebe, CertEd (*Learning Support*)
Mr J M Grantham, BA
*Mr A M Hall, BSc
Miss C E Hall, BSc
Mrs S V Harris, BA (*Director of Marketing & Admissions*)
Mrs A S Heath, BEd, CertEd
Mrs S E Hill, BA
Mr J C Hobday, BSc
Mr T Hyde, BSc (*Head of Lower School*)
Miss C A Rees, BA
Mrs L J Jackson, BA
*Mr S W Jackson, BSc
Mrs A J Jones, BSc (*Head of Shells; First Year*)
Miss A Jones, BA
*Dr P J Knight, BSc, PhD, MPhil
Mrs P J Marchant, CertEd
*Mr M J Masters, BSc
*Mr A J McConaghy, BA (*Director of Studies*)
*Mr C Mellers, CertEd
Mr S Memon, BSc
*Mr D Menashe, BA
Mrs C Mills, CertEd
Mr C W Mohamed, BSc
*Miss L J Neale, BA
Mrs M O'Neill, BA
Mr G L Park, BA
Mr D J Parkins, CertEd
Mr J R H Pease, BA
Mr A Phillips, BSc
Mr D F Prescott, BA (*Director of Drama*)
Mrs M R Prowse, BSc
Mrs A J Reed
Mr D M Rhodes, BSc
Mrs C L Scott, CertEd
Mr P Shelley, BA
Miss J L Simmons, MSCI
*Ms H Skilton, BA
Mrs J Smith, BA
Mr R A Smith, BSc
*Mrs S M Smith
*Mrs E D Surgey, CertEd
*Mr B J Sutton, MusB, GRSM, ARMCM
Miss S Symonds, BSc
Mrs P A G Tatum, LRAM (*Head of Middle School*)
*Mrs D A Thomas, BEd
*Mrs G A Timothy, BA
*Mr S C R Timothy, BSc, MSc
Mrs A J Tumber, BA
*Mr K J Tyas, BEd
*Mr C R West, BEd
Mr C Wiles, BA
Mr B G Wilson, BEd
Mrs B Wood, BA
Mr M G A Woodward, BA (*Head of Careers*)
Mrs L A Yates, BA, MPhil
Miss R F Young, BSc

Junior School
Headmaster: Mr N A Price, BA

Assistant staff:
Mr A Bogyor, CertEd, NCollP (*Deputy Head*)
Miss G Davies, BA
Mrs K Francis, BEd
Mrs T Horton, BEd
Miss K Love, BSc
Mrs M Mason, BEd
Mr S Norman, BEd
Mrs K Price, BA
Mrs A Reed, CertEd
Miss S Tatum, BA

Headmaster's Personal Assistant: Mrs R Mohomed

Number in School. There are about 900 Day Pupils (including 450 girls) and 180 in the Junior School.

Buildings. In the Home Field of 11 acres stand the main buildings which have been considerably extended to include a Sports Hall, squash courts, heated indoor swimming pool and a purpose-built Modern Languages block. A purpose-built English, Music and Drama block was completed in July 2000. In 1993 Bablake Junior School was opened on the Home Field site for pupils aged 7–11. The school has its own nationally recognised weather station. At Hollyfast Road there are 27 acres of playing fields, a large pavilion and two all-weather hockey pitches. The school has a study centre in Fougères in the Normandy region of France and each pupil spends one week there during Year 8.

Curriculum. The Junior School is for children aged 7 to 11. There is a broad and balanced curriculum which encourages excellence and individual achievement. (*For further details, see Bablake Junior School entry in IAPS section.*)

Pupils take and must pass the Governors' Examination for entry to the Main School at either Bablake or King Henry VIII. The Main School provides courses leading to the GCSE examinations and GCE A Levels. Subjects available include: English, History, Geography, German, Spanish, Religious Studies, Latin, Classical Civilisation, French, Physics, Chemistry, Biology, Psychology, Music, Art, Mathematics, Home Economics, Design and Technology, Information Technology and Textiles. Design Technology and Home Economics courses are followed by both boys and girls. The separate sciences are taught up to GCSE. All pupils take a short GCSE course in ICT.

Pupils study 10 subjects at GCSE, the majority progressing into the Sixth Form where 4 subjects and sometimes 5 are taken at AS Level. At A2 Level all students take a minimum of three subjects. Most of the subjects named are available up to AS Level and A2 Level. In addition several new subjects are available, including Business Studies, Economics, Electronics, Geosciences, Psychology, Sports Studies and Theatre Studies. There is a wide range of General Studies options including Art, Computing, Design and Music. All pupils follow a structured programme of PE and Games.

Games and Activities. Rugby, Hockey, Netball, Basketball, Cross-Country Running, Athletics, Rounders, Tennis, Cricket, Soccer, Squash and Swimming. The school has an extensive artificial turf games area, used mainly for hockey, but providing in the summer an additional 24 tennis courts. A wide range of extra-curricular activities is offered, ranging from Music to Water Polo. There are approximately 50 societies and clubs. All pupils are involved in the charity work of the school and there is a large Community Service programme for the Senior pupils in the Fifth and Sixth Forms.

Scholarships. The Governors award annually a number (not fixed) of Entrance bursaries each year. These are dependent on academic ability and on parental means. Academic, Art and Music scholarships are also available.

Academic, Sports and Music scholarships are available in the Sixth Form.

Fees per term (2008-2009). Senior School £2,793; Junior School £2,115.

Admission. Entry is via the School's own Entrance Examination held annually in January for entrance the following September. The normal age of entry is 11 but there are smaller intakes at 12 and 13. Entry to the Sixth Form is based on gaining 5 GCSE passes at level B and an interview with the Headmaster and Head of Sixth Form. Enquiries about admissions should be addressed to the Admissions Officer, Mrs L Baines.

Charitable status. Coventry School Foundation is a Registered Charity, number 528961. It exists to provide quality education for boys and girls.

Bancroft's School

Woodford Green Essex IG8 0RF
Tel: 020 8505 4821
Fax: 020 8559 0032
e-mail: head@bancrofts.essex.sch.uk
website: www.bancrofts.essex.sch.uk

By the Will of Francis Bancroft (1727) all his personal estate was bequeathed on trust to the Worshipful Company of Drapers of the City of London to build and endow almshouses for 24 old men, with a chapel and schoolroom for 100 poor boys and 2 dwelling-houses for masters. The Foundation was originally situated at Mile End, but by a scheme established by the Charity Commissioners in 1884 the almshouses were abolished and the School transferred to Woodford Green, Essex. In 1976 the School reverted to independence, and became a fully co-educational day school, with a Preparatory School being added in 1990.

Motto: '*Unto God only be honour and glory*'

Trustees: The Worshipful Company of Drapers

Visitor: The Master of the Drapers' Company

Governors:

Appointed by the Drapers' Company:
S P Foakes, TD, DL, FCIB
Major General A W Lyons, CBE (*Chairman*)
Mrs C G Bonnor-Moris
G E Clutton

Appointed by the London Borough of Redbridge:
R I Barden
M Stark

Appointed by the Essex CC:

Co-optative:
Mrs R Abbott
R J Priestley, BA
R Wallace
M Jones
Mrs A Papathomas
Dr A Philp
Dr P Southern, MA, PhD

***Head*: Mrs M E Ireland**, BSc, DipEd, CBiol,MIBiol

Deputy Head: J G Bromfield, BA

Assistant Heads:
M Dixon, BSc
Mrs A H Taylor, BA

Headmaster, Preparatory School: C M Curl, MA, BEd

Assistant Staff:
† *Housemaster/mistress*

†T R C Jones, MA
C H Pearson, BA
†G E Watkins, BSc
N R Poore, BSc, MPhil
R F Tatam, MA
N Gleeson, MA
C J Bates, PhD
A P Macleod, BEd
A H J Krzyz, MSc
C N Taylor, BA
L M Gibbon, MA MPhil
Miss P Telford, BEd
J K Lever, Essex CCC & England
Mrs A M Scurfield, BSc
Mrs S P Thompson, BSc
S P Woolley, BSc
Mrs C Tootell,
†Mrs P R Tindall, BA
†Miss J K Robbins, BA
Ms H M Andrews, BSc
Mrs R Philip, BEd
Mrs C Lavender, BA
Mrs P Morley, Cert Ed
N A Jaques, BA
Mrs C A Rampton, BA
Mrs E Weaver, ABSM, FTCL
†T P Ward, BA, MA
R M Bluff, MA, FRCO
Mrs R Porter, BA
Mrs J Colman, CertEd
G F Welstead, BA
†R C de Renzy Channer, BA
J C Pollard, BEd
Miss H J Prescott-Morrin, BSc
S Burton, BA
Miss J M Green, BA
S A Hunn, BA, DPhil
N Goalby, MEng
I Moore, MA, MTh
Mrs N Doctors, BA
†Miss C G Edwards, BA
Mrs E F de Renzy Channer, BA
†Miss A M H Wainwright, BA
Mrs V Talbot, BA
P A Caira, BSc
Miss G R Abrams, MSc
Mrs S Bhangal, BEd
A J Smethurst, BA
C A F Butler, BSc
P Davies, BSc
K P Gallagher, BA
Mrs A Hunter, MA
Mrs J M Hitching, BA
D Bailey, BA
D J Argyle, BEd
Mrs A Watkins
J J P Layburn, MA
N E Lee, BSc
M Flaherty, MA
Mrs M Baker, BA
R M Hitching, BA
J Prole, BSc
P J Fellows, MBiomedSc
Mrs O Firek, BSc
Mrs E Tynan, MEng
Miss V Beattie, BA
Mrs L Coyne, BA
G Ismail, BSc, PhD
Miss I Ward, BA, MA
Mrs A Patel, BSc
S Oakes, PhD
M Piper, BA
Mrs M Parsons, JP, BSc
Miss D Mardell, BA
J Wunderle, MA
R Maclean, BSc
Mrs K Yelverton, BA
Mrs S Jones, BA
Mrs K Rogers, BA
M Dixon, BSc
Miss H Gartland, BA
S Hawkins, BA
Mrs M Wright, BA
Miss S James, BSc
Mrs S O'Sullivan, BA, MA
L Brennand, BA
Mrs K Dixon
G Biston, BA Ed
M Capuano, BEd
Miss N Rees, BA
Miss G Turner, BA

Bursar: M W Jackson

Matron: Mrs L A Summers, SRN, OHNC

Bancroft's School is a co-educational day school of about 1,000 pupils. It stands in its own grounds with about five acres of playing fields and it has a further 16 acres of playing fields near Woodford Station. Its buildings have successfully combined the spacious style of the original architecture with the constant additions demanded by developing needs. These include a Swimming Pool, a Creative Arts Centre, improved Science facilities and Music resources. In 2006 a new building housing kitchens, teaching space and a new Sixth Form Centre were opened, and a new Sports centre and Performing Arts Studio were opened in 2007.

Meals are taken in a well-equipped central dining room, and there is a good variety of menu with self-service on the cafeteria principle.

Pupils are grouped in four Houses – North, East, West and School. Each of the Houses has its own Housemaster or Housemistress and a tutorial system.

The School offers a wide range of subjects at GCSE and A Level and has a strong record of academic success. Virtually all Bancroftians go on to university, with about 15 each year to Oxford or Cambridge.

The major sports for girls are Hockey, Netball, Tennis and Athletics. Rugby Football, Hockey and Cricket are the main games for boys. Swimming, Squash, and Basketball are also provided. The Physical Education programme includes gymnastics, trampolining, dance and badminton.

The School has a Contingent of the CCF, a Sea Scout Group, a Branch of the Duke of Edinburgh's Award Scheme, and a Social Service Group, each of which caters both for girls and boys. The School has enjoyed considerable success in the Engineering Education Scheme. The programme of concerts and plays through the school year offers opportunities for pupils of all age groups.

Preparatory School. The School opened in September 1990 occupying purpose built accommodation on a separate site within the school grounds. There are 8 classrooms, a hall, a library and specialist rooms for Art, computing, and languages. Extensive use is made of the sports, music and drama facilities of the main School. There are 11 specialist teachers and some sharing of staff with the main School.

(*For further details, see Preparatory School entry in IAPS section.*)

Admission. 65 places are available each year for boys and girls wishing to enter the Preparatory Department at 7+; entry tests take place in the January. Transfer to the Senior School is automatic. At 11+ there are another 60 places available for children entering Bancroft's who take an examination in mid-January. A few places are available for candidates at 13+; for candidates of other ages individual arrangements are made. Applications must be made before 1 January in the year of entry. There is a direct entry for boys and girls into the Sixth Form.

Scholarships. (*see Scholarship Entries section*). Each year up to 15 Scholarships, worth up to 50% of the full fees, are awarded to candidates at 11+. Two will generally be awarded as music scholarships. Five Scholarships, including Music awards, worth up to 50% of the full fees, are available each year to external candidates entering the Sixth Form; a further three awards are available to internal candidates.

Five Francis Bancroft Scholarships are available at age 11, which are means tested and can cover the full fees.

Fees per term (2008-2009). Senior School £3,850, Prep School £2,920. Fees include lunch and books.

Old Bancroftians' Association. Hon Secretary: Mrs A S Campbell, 46 Mayfair Gardens, Woodford Green, Essex IG8 9AB.

There is a strong Old Bancroftians' Association. The OBA also helps to organise work experience for members of the school.

Charitable status. Bancroft's School is a Registered Charity, number 1068532. It exists to provide an academic education to able children.

Bangor Grammar School

13 College Avenue Bangor Co Down BT20 5HJ
Northern Ireland

Tel: 028 9147 3734 (School)
028 9146 5085 (Sports Pavilion)
Fax: 028 9127 3245
e-mail: info@bgs.bangor.ni.sch.uk
website: www.bangorgrammarschool.org.uk

Bangor Endowed School was founded in 1856 as a result of a bequest by the Rt Hon Robert Ward. The School is now known as Bangor Grammar School.

Motto: '*Justitiae Tenax*'.

Governors:
The Governing Body is composed of 10 representative Governors elected by Subscribers, 4 Governors nominated by the Department of Education, 2 Parent Governors and 2 Teacher Governors.

Chairman: J Gillvray, OBE, BSc, CEng, FICE, FIHT

D G Gray, BSc Econ, LGSM, FCA (*Hon Secretary*)
W R T Dowdall
Mrs P Baird
I G Henderson, OBE, MSc Econ
Mrs D Hutchieson, MA
J Adrain, BSocSc Econ, FCA (*Hon Treasurer*)
P Blair, MD, FRCS
W McCoubrey, LLB (*Hon Asst Treasurer*)
B McKee, LLB
S J Robinson, BSc, PGCE
S Smith, BAgri (*Immediate Past Chairman*)
G Stoops
D B Thompson, BSc Econ, FCA, MIMC
S J Wolfenden, BA, PGCE

Bursar and Clerk to the Governors:
(*to be appointed*)

***Headmaster*: S D Connolly**, MA

Pastoral Vice-Principal: Mrs E P Huddleson, MSSc, BEd

Academic Vice-Principal: D Cairnduff, BA, MEd

Senior Teachers:
C C J Harte, BA
A J Mackie, BA
D Macpherson, BA
C M McDonald, MSc, PQH NI

Assistant Staff:
* *Head of Department*

Mrs P H Bates, BA
S A Beggs, BSc (**Geography*)
Mrs M C Sheeran, BA
A Cardwell, BSc, BAgr
Miss A Chapman, BA
B S M Christy, BSc
Mrs M Cree, BA
W A Cree, BA, MEd (**German*)
J W Culbert, BSc
D P Cunningham, MA
C Donaghy, BEng
Miss C S Evans, BEd
Mrs M Faulkner, BSc, PhD
Mrs S Forbes, BSc
D Gallagher, BA
Mrs M E Garland, BA, MSc (**Computing*)
F Gilmour, BSc
A Gray, BA
G Greer, BEd, MA, Adv CertEd (**English*)
P K Hancock, BLS
N Hawthorne, BEd
Mrs L Henry, BA (**RE*)
D S Holley, BA
D G Kennedy, BSc (**PE*)
A I J McCrea, BA
C M McDonald, MSc
Miss C L Mills, BSc, PhD
D J Napier, CertEd
M S Nesbitt, BD
N Nowatarski, BSc, HRes (**Biology*)
Mrs J K Payne, BSc, ATD (**Drama*)
Mrs K Quinn, BSc (**Mathematics*)
J Rea, BA, LTCL (**Music*)
D Robinson, BSc Econ, MBA, MEd (**Business Studies*)
S Robinson, BSc
MrsM-C Allsopp, BA
P Scullion, BA
Mrs R Shaw, BA
N J Shields, BA
S Sinclair, MA
B Smith, BSc, PhD (**Chemistry*)
Mrs C N Steele, BA (**Art*)
S W Stevenson, BA, PhD
W R Stevenson, BA, ATCL
J T Titterington, BEng (**Design Technology*)
J S Todd, BSc
C H M Turner, BEd
S Waddell, BA
A R Walker, BEng, MSc
Mrs I S Weir, BA (**French*)
J B Wilson, BA (**Politics*)
S Wolfenden, BA (**History*)

Headmaster's PA: Mrs S Cordner, BA

Preparatory Department:
J L Ekin, BA (*Head of Connor House*)
Mrs S Williams, BA, CertEd (*Deputy Head*)

Mrs M Baker, BEd
Mrs B Brittain, BA
Mrs J Alexander, BEd
Mrs A Ormsby
Miss C E Patterson, BEd
Mrs A Ruding, BSc
Mrs J Matthews, BA, MSc
Miss H West, BEd

Pre-Prep:
Mrs M Nelson
Mrs P Connolly (*Assistant*)

Secretary: Mrs D Young

There are 2 departments in the School: the Preparatory, with 130 boys and girls, and the Senior with 900 boys.

The Preparatory Department. Connor House is a self-contained unit with its own building adjoining the main campus. A full range of subjects is taught, including French. Sport is well catered for and mini-rugby, hockey, football and cricket are played against other schools.

There is a Pre-Prep in operation each morning in term-time for boys and girls of 3 and 4 years of age.

School Buildings. In the last decade there has been major development of new buildings and equipment. A new, full-sized Sports Hall and a new, three-storey Design Centre have been built. In addition, a new Sixth Form Centre, Library and Music Suite have been provided and 2 new fully-fitted Computer Laboratories were opened in December 1998. Six new classrooms have been added. A new Chemistry and Technology wing has been opened affording the most up-to-date facilities in both subjects. The oldest building in the school was refurbished in summer of 2005.

Admission and Curriculum. Boys are admitted to the Senior School after the age of 11 as a result of their performance in the Department of Education transfer procedure. All boys follow a common curriculum for the first three years. The choice of subjects for the Fourth and Fifth Forms is kept as wide as possible to enable boys to keep their future options open right up to the GCSE examinations. The School's policy is to encourage boys to undertake a wide range of studies. There is a very strong Music Department and high standards of choral and instrumental work are set and achieved.

A Sixth Form of 200 plus makes possible a wide range of subjects from which boys normally take four AS level and three or four A2 subjects.

Activities. School games include rugby football, cricket, sailing, tennis, squash, badminton, golf, hockey, swimming, athletics, basketball and cross-country running. There are numerous societies and clubs. Both drama and music flourish. There are two major play productions in the year with further smaller-scale productions in the Summer Term. Numerous opportunities are afforded for instrumental and choral performance throughout the year, both inside and outside school. Adventure training is catered for by a flourishing contingent of the Combined Cadet Force (with Army and Naval Sections) and the Duke of Edinburgh's Award Scheme. Boys are encouraged to gain an experience of social work through the active Community Service Group. Frequent continental visits are arranged and an expedition under the auspices of World Challenge takes place every other year.

The School has very high standards in sport. The rugby 1st XV dominated the Ulster Schools Rugby Cup in the Eighties, with seven appearances in the final, including four victories. Other teams have been successful in the Ulster Schools Golf Championship, the major Ulster Hockey cups, the Ulster and Irish Squash and Tennis Championships and in the major Ulster Cricket cups and the Ulster Badminton Championships. Recent foreign tours have included Zimbabwe and Canada (Rugby) and Australia (Cricket).

Careers. Extensive and continuous help is available to boys in connection with careers. There are five careers staff under the leadership of the Head of Careers. Careers courses, lectures, visits, interviews, work experience, work shadowing and a Challenge of Industry Conference are part of the regular careers structure for boys in Form III and above.

Honours. Boys from the School enter all the major universities in the British Isles. Places have been won regularly at Oxford, Cambridge and other universities.

Bangor Grammarians Association. *Hon Sec*: David Humphreys, 10 Alexandra Road, Donaghadee, BT21 0QD.

Barnard Castle School

Barnard Castle Co Durham DL12 8UN
Tel: 01833 690222
Fax: 01833 638985
e-mail: secretary@barneyschool.org.uk
website: www.barnardcastleschool.org.uk

The St John's Hospital in Barnard Castle was founded in the 13th century by John Baliol, whose widow founded the Oxford College. By a Scheme of the Charity Commissioners, bequests under the will of Benjamin Flounders of Yarm were combined with the funds of the St John's Hospital and public subscriptions to build and endow the present foundation in 1883. Originally known as the North Eastern County School, the name was changed to Barnard Castle School in 1924.

Motto: '*Parvis imbutus tentabis grandia tutus*'.

The school is ex Direct Grant.

The Governing Body:
Chairman: M McCallum
Vice-Chairmen:
D N Williams
Miss C Elgey, JP

J C Macfarlane, CBE
Cllr J R Hinchcliffe
D F Starr
Dr W J B Cherry
C Dennis
Mrs S Peat
Dr J E Delaney
Dr N Thorpe
M H Crosby
Mrs R Dent
Cllr Mrs M Hamilton
D C Osborne
A Fielder
Col N C T Millen
G G Ratcliffe, MBE

Clerk to the Governors: M White

***Headmaster*: D H Ewart**, BA, MA, DMS (*Geography*)

Deputy Head: O K Marlow, MA (*English*)
Senior Mistress: Mrs B Ellison, BA (*Modern Languages*)
Chaplain and Director of Studies: The Revd S J Ridley, MA

Assistant Staff:
* *Head of Department*
† *Housemaster/mistress*

†G Bishop, BA (**Economics & Business Studies*)
C P Johnson, BA (**Modern Languages*)
S Kean, BSc (*Mathematics*)
P McHarry, BSc (**Physics*)
Mrs E G Niven, MA (*EFL*)
*D C S Everall, BEd (*PE & Mathematics*)
*R M Anderson, MSc (*Information Technology*)
A M Waddington, BA (**English*)
Mrs S R Cuthbertson, BA, ATC (**Art*)
R Child, BSc, PhD (*Biology*)
M N R Fuller, BEd (**Biology, Careers*)
†J D N Gedye, BA (*Classics*)
M H Nicholson, BSc, BA (**Mathematics*)
Miss F Cover, BEd (*PE & Geography*)
Mrs C Shovlin, BA, ALA (*Librarian*)
Mrs A Armstrong, BEd (*PE*)
†D W Dalton, MA, BA (**Geography*)
M Donnelly, ALCM (*Music*)
D S Gorman, BA (**History & Politics*)
B C Usher, BSc (*Mathematics*)
†Mrs A Gorman, BA (*English*)
C H Alderson, BSc (*Geography & History*)
Mrs I V Ewart, BEd, DipSpLD, AMBDA (**Learning Support*)
†M P Ince, BA (*History & Politics*)
†M T Pepper, BA (*PE*)
N Toyne, BSc (*Mathematics*)
†A M Beaty, BSc (**Technology*)
Miss T C Broadbent, BA (*PE*)
Mrs A J Campbell, BA (*History & Politics*)
A J Allman, BA (**Religious Studies*)
I M Butterfield, BSc, PhD (*Chemistry*)
A Jacobs, BA (*Modern Languages, *Spanish*)
Miss K Welsh, BA (*Art*)
A M Mawhinney, MA, ARCO (*CHM*), ARCM, LTCL (**Director of Music*)
M L West, BSc (*Chemistry*)

Miss E E Thomas, BA (*English*)
J Bird, BSc (*Geography*)
Miss J Brown, BSc, MSc (**ICT*)
M S Atherton, MA, LTCL (*Music*)
Miss L Cragg, BA (*Modern Languages*)
L D Monument, BSc (*PE*)
J L Harrison, BA (*Religious Studies & Classics*)
Miss L Shorthouse, BEd (*PE*)
Mrs S F Whysall, MA (*Modern Languages*)
P Everitt, BEng (*Physics*)
P Oakley, BSc, MSc (*Technology*)
Mrs L C Rhodes, BA (*Religious Studies*)
Dr J Robson, BSc, PhD (**Chemistry*)
E G Shawcross, BSc (*Biology*)
Miss E Baldwin, BA (*English*)
S A Dawson, MPhys (*Physics*)
D Goldberg, MA (*Mathematics*)
A Maude, BSc (*Mathematics*)
Mrs M Abela, BA, LLCM (*TD*) (*Music*)
C R Butler, MSc (*Physics & Chemistry*)
N J Connor, BA (*Business Studies & ICT*)
Miss D L McDonald, BA (*English*)

Combined Cadet Force:
Com Officer: Major S Kean
M G Lewis, WO1, SSI

Preparatory School

Headmaster: E J Haslam, ACP, DipEd

Second Master: N I Seddon, BEd
Director of Studies: Miss C E Lane, MA, CertEd

A Dougherty, BEd, MEd, FRGS
Mrs S M Seddon, BEd
Mrs J C A Tulip, BEd
Mrs H Brown, BEd
Mrs L Rowlandson, BA
Mrs F M Killeen, BA
Mrs K L Eastwood, BA
Miss E Bennington, BA
Mrs R Robertson, BA
Mr S T Ayres, BA
Miss L E Bland, BA, MA

Bursar: A J White, BA, DMS

Medical Officer: Dr M Welsh

Medical Centre:
Mrs B Preece, RGN, BSc
Mrs L Thorman, RGN

Headmaster's Secretary: Mrs J A Hazell

Barnard Castle is a day and boarding school for boys and girls between the ages of 4 and 18.

Organisation and Numbers. There are 550 pupils aged 11–18 in the Senior School, of whom 188 are boarders. The Preparatory School comprises a Pre-Prep Department of 52 pupils between the ages of 4 and 7, and 150 pupils between the ages of 7 and 11, of whom 30 are boarders. (*See also Preparatory School entry in IAPS section.*) The Senior and Preparatory Schools are located on adjacent sites and operate separately on a day-to-day basis whilst enjoying the mutual benefits of being able to share a number of resources and facilities. Girls were first admitted in 1981 and the School has been fully co-educational since 1993.

Location. The School is situated in its own extensive grounds on the outskirts of an historic market town in an area of outstanding natural beauty. The area is well served by Durham Tees Valley and Newcastle airports and by Darlington railway station. The School also operates its own bus service for pupils from a wide area.

Curriculum. This is designed to provide a broad, balanced and flexible programme, avoiding undue specialisation at too early a stage. In the Prep School emphasis is given to literacy and numeracy skills, as well as Science, History, Geography, French (from age 8), Religious Education, Technology, Art, Music, Information Technology, Physical Education (including swimming) and Games. These subjects are developed further in the Senior School, with the addition of Latin or Classical Civilisation, Personal, Social and Health Education, and three separate sciences. German or Spanish is added at age 14, whilst Business Studies increases the list of GCSE options at age 15. There are some twenty A or AS Level subjects which give a wide choice in the Sixth Form. Almost all Sixth Form leavers go on to University or College courses. A Learning Support Department provides specialist help for those who need it in both the Preparatory and Senior Schools, and tuition is offered in English as a Second Language.

Religious Education. The School is a Christian foundation and the Chapel stands at the heart of the School in more than just a geographical sense. The School Chaplain, who plays an important role in the pastoral structure of the School as well as being responsible for Religious Studies and Chapel worship, is an ordained member of the Church of England, but the School is a multi-denominational one which welcomes and supports pupils of all faiths and none. Pupils attend weekday morning assemblies in Chapel, and there is a Sunday service for boarders.

Boarding and Day Houses. There are eight single-sex Houses within the Senior School – three boarding and five day – each small enough for pupils to know each other well, but large enough to allow a mixture of interests, backgrounds and abilities, as well as opportunities for leadership. Housemasters and Housemistresses, each supported by a team of Tutors and Assistants, are responsible for the welfare and progress of each pupil in their charge.

Junior Boarders (boys and girls aged 7–11) and Senior Girl Boarders live in their own modern Houses in the School grounds, alongside their Houseparents, Boarding Tutors and Matrons. The two Senior Boys' Boarding Houses have recently undergone a major programme of restructuring and refurbishment, and offer comfortable accommodation within the main building of the School. The resident Housemasters are supported by resident boarding tutors and matrons, and by the School Sister in the School's Medical Centre. The School Doctor visits daily.

Cultural and other activities. The School has a flourishing music department in which the Chapel Choir, Orchestras, Wind and Jazz Bands and smaller ensembles perform regularly.

Drama is also prominent, with a regular programme of productions taking place throughout the year. There is a strong tradition of after-school activities, which enables both day and boarding pupils to take part in a wide range of clubs and societies.

Games. Rugby, Hockey, Netball, Cricket, Athletics, Squash, Cross-Country Running, Tennis and Swimming are the main sports, and other options such as soccer, badminton, basketball and golf are available. The School has extensive playing fields, a modern Sports Hall, squash and tennis courts, and a heated indoor swimming pool. A full-size, floodlit "astroturf-style" pitch is available for all to use. Regular inter-school matches are arranged at all levels.

Outdoor Activities. There is a strong emphasis on providing instruction, opportunity and challenge in a wide range of outdoor activities. Much of this takes place under the auspices of a flourishing Cadet Force (Army and RAF sections) or the Duke of Edinburgh's Gold and Silver Award Schemes.

Careers. The School works closely with the Durham County Careers Service. There is a well-equipped Careers Room, and a team of careers staff work together with the Higher Education Coordinator to provide pupils at all stages of the School with expert advice and help in decision-making and application procedures.

Admission. Pupils are admitted at all stages either via the School's own Entrance Assessments or via the Common Entrance Examination. There is also direct entry into the Sixth Form subject to satisfactory performance at GCSE level. Details of the application procedure are obtainable from the Headmaster's Secretary.

Scholarships and assisted places. (*see Scholarship Entries section*). The School makes Entrance Awards on entry to the Senior School (including at Sixth Form level). In addition to academic awards, these may include awards for musical, artistic and sporting ability and potential. The School is also able to offer a small number of its own means-tested assisted places for able children whose parents would not otherwise be able to send them. Details are available from the Headmaster's Secretary.

Fees per term (2008-2009). Senior: £5,758 (Boarders), £3,332 (Day). Prep: £4,331 (Boarders), £2,327 (Day). Pre-Prep: £1,492. Fees are inclusive and subject to annual review.

Charitable status. Barnard Castle School is a Registered Charity, number 527383, whose aim is the education of boys and girls.

Batley Grammar School

Carlinghow Hill Batley West Yorkshire WF17 0AD
Tel: 01924 474980 (Head's Office)
01924 470020 (Finance Office)
Fax: 01924 471960
01924 420513 (Finance Office)
e-mail: info@batleygrammar.co.uk
website: www.batleygrammar.co.uk

Batley Grammar School was founded in 1612 by the Reverend William Lee "... to make such as be capable fit for the University". For some years the school was Voluntary Aided, but since 1978 it has been fully independent and is now represented on both the Headmasters' Conference and the Association of Governing Bodies of Independent Schools. There are 380 pupils in the school. Girls have been entering the Sixth Form since 1988, and in September 1996 the school welcomed its first co-educational intake at 11+. The Junior Department (3–11 years) opened in September 2000.

Motto: '*Forte non Ignave.*'

Governors:

Chairman: Mrs J E Gummer, MBE, JP, DL, LLB
Vice-Chairman: J Holroyd, JP, FRICS

Mrs M Bates, DL
Dr J L Bembridge, MB ChB
D Brereton
Mrs S J Brook, JP
Professor J A Double, BTech, PhD, DSc
Revd A P Johnson, BA
Dr B Knowles, BSc, PhD
A L Palfreeman, JP, BSc
R M Pearson, MA
J S W Sheard, DMS, DipM, GInstM, FIMgt
E Suleman, ACA
P D Taylor, JP, FCA, CTA
Dr Y Zia, MBBS, JCPT

Teaching Staff:

***Head*: Mrs B P Tullie**, BSc

Deputy Head: P Smith, BA

*D N Scriven, MA
*A Turnbull, BSc
*G Bellamy, MA, DipRE
*J C Sanderson, BEd
G Dawson, BA
*J L O'Dwyer, BA
*H P Bowden, MA
B G Woodley, MA
¶J E Hargreaves, BA
*J A Hartley, BA
*Mrs J E Wilson, BA
*S Haigh, BEd
Mrs N Rollinson, BEd
*H J Lorriman, FTCL, LTCL
*R S Bocking, BSc, MSc
T Hussain, BA
*¶D I Blamires, BA
J P R Arnold, BA, DPhil
N Foster, BA
*R Danes, BSc
E A Marshall, BSc
S J Lowther, BSc
*M D Bownass, BSc
Miss F N Thomas BA
Mrs K L Holmes, BA

Priestley House Junior School

Head: Mrs H Hawkes, BEd

Deputy Head: Mrs S R Stamp, BEd

Mrs K Barker, BSc
Ms F N Steinitz, BA, LLCM
Mrs H Tyson, BEd
Mrs M J Drummond, BA
Mrs J E Elsworth, BA
Miss H Thoroughgood, BA
Miss S N Wilson, BA

Facilities. The school has occupied its present site since 1878 with considerable expansion taking place during this period.

In 1980, shortly after Independence, the Science Block was built with six spacious and well-equipped laboratories and ancillary rooms.

In 1989 the new Sports Hall was finished, and extensions made to changing facilities, and in 1999 a Sports Studies laboratory was added.

In 1991 the Priestley Language Centre was added with 30 audio booths and satellite television. The Priestley Design and Technology Centre is fully equipped to teach GCSE and A Level.

The Information Technology department has two dedicated work centres. In 2006 the department was refitted.

From September 2000 the school had a new Careers Room, equipped with computer and CD-ROM facilities. A regular link has been opened with the local careers advisory service. A new resource centre and library was added in September 2000, In 2008 a new Sixth Form Centre and classroom block will open. A rolling programme of Science Laboratory refurbishment was begun in 2002.

During 1999 the former Headmaster's House was converted into a Junior Department which opened in September 2000. The age range is now 3–11, since two new classrooms were built in September 2002 to allow for expansion of Priestley House down to the age of 3 years.

Admissions. All candidates for admission must be registered and registration forms can be obtained from the Head's Secretary's Office. Entry is considered at all ages from 3–14 and in the Sixth Form. Entrance examinations for 7+, 11+, 12+ and 13+ take place in January for admission the following September. Admission is offered to the Sixth Form on the results of GCSE examinations and interview. A number of free Assisted Places are available at 11+ and for the Sixth Form.

Awards. The Governors award a number of Bursaries each year, mainly at 11+.

Fees per term (2008-2009). Excluding lunches: Senior School £2,769, Priestley House £1,935.

Curriculum. Normally entry to the senior school is at the age of eleven and in the first three years pupils are given a broadly-based curriculum. Almost all academic subjects are studied with the three sciences being covered separately as well as Information Technology and Design Technology.

At the end of the third year the pupils, in consultation with parents and staff, choose from a number of option blocks. All pupils follow a core curriculum supported by other options so that at the end of year eleven each sits a full range of nine or ten GCSE examinations.

In the Sixth Form the individual requirements of each student are catered for as much as possible with the vast majority taking four AS Levels, followed by three A2. Many students also take General Studies A Level.

Physical Education and Games. Physical Education is regarded as an essential part of the school curriculum. All pupils are expected to spend some time on general aspects of the subject each week, whilst each year group is allocated a separate session for Games within the timetable. In the Winter these games are Association Football, Hockey, Netball, Basketball and Cross Country, whilst in the Summer Term, Cricket, Athletics, Tennis and Rounders are the main alternatives.

The Sports Centre consists of a large multi-function sports hall with additional circuit-training and table tennis area linked to a weight-training area, changing rooms and showers. The four soccer/hockey pitches, two cricket squares, a hard-surface area with tennis and netball courts, and the athletics track are adjacent to the school.

The school is divided into four Houses; Akroyd, Benstead, Lee and Talbot. Inter-House competitions are organised in a variety of sports. In addition the school has regular fixtures in Association Football, Cricket, Athletics, Cross Country, Hockey and Netball in all relevant age-groups.

Clubs and Activities. The school has a very full range of societies, clubs and extra curricular activities, ranging from Drama to Textiles and from Skiing to Climbing. These encourage the pupils to develop their own interests and skills, widen horizons and experiences, and give service to the community. Parties of all ages regularly go to European countries and exchanges with French and German schools are arranged.

Each year the School Community Service Group gives generous support to local charities. The school has an Interact Club affiliated to the Rotary Club of Batley.

The CCF comprises Army and RAF Sections and is run on a purely voluntary basis. Recruits are admitted towards the end of the third year of the school. In addition to the specialist and adventure training in the programme Cadets may also prepare for the Duke of Edinburgh's Silver and Gold Awards.

Music plays an important part in the life of the school. The full-time members of the Music Department are assisted by six visiting instrumental teachers and other members of the school staff. The school has a Choir, a Concert Band, a Brass Ensemble and Recorder Groups. Bands regularly compete in regional competitions: in 1991 the Brass Band was the first school band ever invited to play at Wembley Stadium.

Leaving Scholarships and Exhibitions. Non-recurring grants are awarded by the Trustees each year to sixth formers proceeding to higher education/training. Most leavers go on to Further Education and 80-90% each year go to university.

Junior School Curriculum. The Curriculum in Priestley House is very close to the National Curriculum. Work in English, Mathematics and Science is aimed toward SATs tests. There are also lessons in History, Geography, DT, Music, PE, Computing, RE and Art. Languages are taught in Year 6.

Old Batelians Association. *Membership Secretary*: D I Blamires, Batley Grammar School.

Charitable status. The Batley Grammar School Foundation is a Registered Charity, number 529335. Its aims and objectives are to provide a first class education for pupils above the age of 3.

Bedales School

Petersfield Hampshire GU32 2DG
Tel: 01730 300100
Registrar: 01730 711733
Assistant Registrar: 01730 711569
Fax: 01730 300500
e-mail: admissions@bedales.org.uk
website: www.bedales.org.uk

Governors:
D Alexander, QC, BA, LLM
M N E Batstone, BA, MBA
Mrs F Bayliss, Froebel CertEd, FRSA
Dr B Ellis, BSc, PhD, MBA, MB BS, MRCGP, FRCP
Mrs S Ford, BA, PGCE
Mrs R Hollingsworth, BA, DipSocAdmin
Professor B Johnson, FRS, FRSE, FRSC, FAcadEuropa
T Parker, MA, MSc
A Redpath (*Chairman*)
N Vetch, ARICS
E Williams, MA, DipArch, RIBA

Clerk to the Governors and Bursar: M R Taylor

***Headmaster*: K J Budge**, MA University College, Oxford

Deputy Head: L Winkley, MA, CertEd

Assistant Head: J A Scullion, BA, MA

Secretary to the Headmaster: Mrs S Emson

Assistant Staff:
* *Head of Department*
† *Housemaster/Housemistress*

K J Adlam, BSc, PGCE (*Geography, Physical Education*)
Mrs V E Alderson-Smart, BSc, PGCE (*Biology*)
†Mrs J Alldridge, AISTD, ALAM (*Dance*)
G T H Banks, BA, PGCE (**English*)
J Barker, BLib, ARCM (*Bedales Arts Coordinator*)
C Bott, BA, PGCE (*History*)
Mrs R E Carpenter-Jones, BA, PGCE (*Spanish*)
Miss S Cartwright, BSc, PGCE (*Physical Education*)
A Cheese, BA (*Art*)
†Mrs S Chubb, CertEd (*PSE*)
P W Coates, BEd (**Outdoor Work, Mathematics*)
Ms K Connolly, BA, PGCE (*Art*)
†A Cooper, BSc, MSc, PGCE (*Information Technology*)
Ms S Couper, BSc, MA Ed, PGCE, CertAdvEdStudies (**Mathematics*)
R Crisswell, BA, PGCE (*English*)
†G D Dale, HDE SA (*Physics*)
Ms C Dewar, BA (*Art*)
T J F Drot-Troha, MA, PGCE (*French, Philosophy*)
S Farrow BA DPhil (*Director of Teaching & Learning*)
S Gardner, BA (*Drama*)
N E Gleed, MA, PGCE (**Director of Music*)
Ms V Godet, DipU, PGCE (**French*)
Ms J C Greenwood, MA (*Theatre Technical Manager*)
T A Hardy, BSc, MA, PGCE (**Physics*)
Ms L Harrison, MSc, PGCE (*Chemistry*)
G J Hatton, BA, CertEd (**Art*)
Mrs G Harris (**Learning Support*)
†Miss R L Hobson, BSc, PGCE (*Information Technology*)
Mrs M-E Houghton, BA, PGCE (*English*)
Mrs E Housden, LAMDA (*Speech & Drama*)
Mrs H Howarth, BA, ATC (*Design & Textiles*)
Ms V Hunter, LRAM, LTCL (*Speech & Drama*)
Mrs K Ireland, BSc, MSc, PGCE, DipSpLD (*Learning Support*)
Mrs J Jarman (*Registrar*)
R N Jayatissa, BSc, MBA, PGDE (*Physics*)
P Jones, BSc (*Business Studies*)
S Kingsley-Pallant, BA (*English*)
Mrs J Kirby, BSc, MSc (*Librarian*)
W Lithgow, Prof Cert Music RAM, PGCE (*Assistant Director of Music*)
Mrs S Mabe, BA, PGCE, DipSpLD (*Learning Support*)
A McNaughton, BSc, PGCE (*Design*)
Ms A Mason, BA, PGCE (*French, Spanish*)
Ms K McCathie, BSC (**Information Technology*)
A McConville, MA, PGCE (**Philosophy and Religious Studies*)

Ms D Morris, BA, MA (*Librarian*)
F McMorrow, BEd (**Physical Education*)
N Meigh, BA, PGCE (*History*)
Mrs J R Murphy, BEd (**Drama*)
Ms R Nash, CDE (*Dance*)
M C Newman, BSc, PGCE (*Chemistry*)
R Nice, PGCE (*Design*)
Ms S Oakley, BA, PGCE (*Art*)
†Ms S Oliver, BA, ATD, DipArtPsy (*Textiles*)
Mrs C Osborne, BSc, PGCE (*Biology*)
Mrs R Parkyn, MA, MPhil, PGCE (*German, Philosophy*)
†P C Parsons, BA, CertEd (*History*)
C W Prowse, BSc, MA, PhD (**Geography*)
Ms H Retter, BEd (*Physical Education*)
K A C Rowe, ARCM, LRAM (*Music*)
J A Scullion, BA, MA (**Economics & Business Studies*)
J K Selby, BA, PGCE (**History*)
†N Shannon, BA, PGCE (*French*)
B Shaw, BSc (**Design*)
R A Sinclair, BA, PGCE (*Biology*)
Mrs A M Skinner, BSc, MA, PGCE (*Psychology*)
G J Skinner, BA, PhD, DipEd, MIBiol (**Biology, *Science*)
J P Spencer, MA, PGCE (**Classics*)
Mrs J D Sueref, BA, PGCE (*Geography*)
Ms P Tribe, BEd (*Mathematics*)
M Truss, MPhys, PhD (*Mathematics*)
Mrs D Wallsgrove, BA, MA, PGCE (*English*)
Mrs J L Webster, BEd (*Mathematics; Head of Sixth Form*)

Dunhurst (*Junior School*)

Head: Mrs P A Watkins, BA
Deputy Head: J Beatty, BA
Director of Studies: D Kettle, BEd, DipEC
Senior Master and Boarding Housemaster: A Simmons, BA, CertEd
Head of Groups: Mrs K Olphert, BEd

A Alexander, BEd, CertEd (**Humanities*)
Mrs M Alexander, CertEd, DipC (*Group 2*)
Mrs L Banks, BEd (*Art*)
Mrs F Box, BEd, DipDysInst, AMBDA (**Learning Support*)
Mrs M Budge, BEd, DipSpLD (*Learning Support*)
Ms S Carnell, BA, PGCE (*French*)
Ms S Chubb, CertEd (*PSHE*)
Ms M Clark, BA, PGCE (*Group 2*)
Ms S Coates, BEd (*LAMDA Speech & Drama*)
M Collins, BEd (*Mathematics, Physical Education*)
Ms K Connolly, BA, PGCE (*IT Coordinator*)
D Ellis (*Physical Education*)
Ms G Graham, BEd, CertSpLD (*Learning Support*)
Miss R Hearnshaw, BA (**Physical Education*)
Mrs E Hewitt, BA (**Art and Design*)
Ms W Houston, BA, PGCE (**Modern Languages*)
Mrs C Innes, BA, ALCM (*Music*)
Ms J de Jongh (*LAMDA Speech & Drama*)
S Kingsley-Pallant, BA (**Drama and Performance*)
N Maddocks (*Physical Education, Outdoor Work*)
Mrs K McCathie, BSc (*Information Technology*)
Ms K Misson-Uttley, BA, PGCE (**Director of Music*)
Ms R Nash, CDE (*Dance*)
R Nice, PGCE (*Design Technology*)
Mrs C Osborne, BSc, PGCE (*PSHE*)
Ms D Payne (*Group 1*)
Ms L Perry (*Textiles*)
Ms E Pickett (*Latin and Greek*)
A Suart, BSc, PGCE (**Science*)
Ms P Tribe, BEd (*Mathematics*)
Ms J Walker, MA (**Humanities, Librarian*)
R Walsh (*Group 3*)
Ms M Watney, BSc, PGCE (*Group 2*)
Mrs P Weston, BSc (*Science, Girls' Housemistress*)
Ms P Wilson, BA (*Learning Support, Mathematics*)

Dunannie (*Pre-Prep School*)

Headmistress: Miss K Potter, BEd, RSADipEd
Deputy Head: D Stunt, BEd

Mrs L Banks, BEd (*Sculpture*)
Mrs J A Brown, BEd (*Reception*)
Ms C Canter, CertEd, CertSpLD (*Learning Support, English*)
Mrs C Claasen, BA, MA (*Year 3*)
Mrs A de Courcy, BEd (*Year 1*)
Ms N Curry, BA, PGCE (*Reception*)
Mrs C Innes, BA, ALCM (*Music*)
Ms K Misson-Uttley, BA, PGCE (**Director of Music*)
R Nice, PGCE (*Design Technology*)
Mrs S Rose, BA, QTS (*Dance and Drama*)
Mrs J Uttley, C&G (*Year 3, Art*)
Mrs F Willans, BEd (*Physical Education*)

School Physicians:
Dr A J H Holden, MB BS, DRCOG, DFFP
Dr F Jacklin, MB BS, DRCOG, DFFP, DipPaeds NZ, MRCGP, DA

Number in School. 450 in Senior School. Equal numbers of boys and girls. 70% boarders.

Bedales stands in an estate of 120 acres in the heart of the Hampshire countryside, overlooking the South Downs. Although only one hour from London by train, this is one of the most beautiful corners of rural England. Founded in 1893, Bedales is one of the oldest co-educational boarding schools. The community is a stimulating and happy one, in which tolerance and supportive relationships thrive at all levels.

The school has strong traditions in both the Humanities and the Sciences, in Art, Design, Drama and Music. The school estate supports an environmental project and a thriving 'Outdoor Work' programme, including the management of livestock and a variety of traditional crafts.

The school is known for its liberal values, the individualism and creativity of its students, and a sense that the students are generally at ease with who they are. The atmosphere is relaxed (first-name terms for staff and students; no uniform), but it is underpinned by a firm structure of values, some rules, guidance and support.

Admission. Entry to the School is from 3+ (see Dunannie), 8+, 9+, 10+, 11+ (see Dunhurst), 13+ and 16+ (Bedales). Once in the school, pupils are assessed before proceeding to the next stage.

Entry Tests. Entry for newcomers at 10+, 11+ and 13+ takes the form of residential tests in the January preceding the September entry. Entry at 16+ is by a series of interviews spread over a single day. Write in the first instance to the Registrar.

Senior School (13 to 18). Up to 96 in each year. A new curriculum in Blocks 4 and 5 (Years 10 and 11) was introduced in September 2006. In order to promote more stimulating, varied and wide-ranging work in these years, and to reduce prescriptive external assessment, students will typically take three externally moderated Bedales Assessed Courses (BACs) alongside seven GCSE subjects. BACs are designed to give a strong basis for A level study.

All current GCSE/BACs subjects (except Outdoor Work) are also offered in the Sixth Form at AS and A2 level, together with Classical Civilisation, Dance (AS), Economics, Further Mathematics, Psychology and Theatre Studies. A programme of personal and social education runs in Years 9 and 10, and a general course covering a wide range of topical and personal issues is taught in the Sixth Form. Students are attached to a tutor in groups of mixed ages, and meet their tutor on a regular basis.

Year 9 students spend a week at the Outward Bound Centre at Ullswater, Geography and Biology departments run sixth form field courses, and there are special interest trips such as a History visit to Russia. IT facilities are well funded, each student having an email address and monitored access to the Internet. Students have access to desktop computers throughout the day, and those with their own laptops have wireless access to the school network across the campus. There are excellent recreational facilities including extensive playing fields, gymnasium, sports hall with multi-gym, indoor heated swimming pool and a floodlit astroturf pitch. The Outdoor Work project is centred on two eighteenth-century barns reconstructed in the school grounds by students. The Bedales Gallery and Olivier Theatre run public programmes of art, drama, dance and music, and distinguished speakers visit the school to give assemblies or as part of the 'Civics' programme. Evening assemblies ('Jaw') and other talks often have a religious or moral theme, but there is no chapel; the school is non-denominational.

There are no prefects, but students take responsibility for a wide variety of aspects of school life by running activities for younger students, taking part in committees and putting forward individual initiatives. A School Council of elected representatives provides a forum for discussion including all levels of the school. Until the final year, students sleep in small mixed-age dormitories; in the final year they move to a co-educational house with exceptional facilities. This arrangement fosters very good relationships across the age range.

Dunhurst (8 to 13). (*See entry in IAPS section*).

Dunannie (3 to 8). Entrance at 3+ is by date of registration, after this acceptances are made following informal assessments should vacancies arise. 95 pupils. Dunannie has five classes including a nursery. It is in purpose-built buildings and shares facilities, extensive grounds and specialist teachers with the other two schools. Dunannie offers a lively, stimulating educational environment where there is emphasis on the individual development of the child. A thorough grounding is given within a broad, balanced curriculum.

Scholarships and Bursaries. (*see Scholarship Entries section*). Music scholarships are available at Dunhurst (10+ and older; exceptionally, 8+) and at Bedales (13+ and 16+). Other scholarships are available at 13+ and 16+.

Scholarships (except Music) attract an automatic award of £750, which can be increased through means testing.

Means-tested bursaries are also available to those of proven need.

For full details of scholarships, please apply to the Registrar.

Fees per term (2008-2009). Senior: Boarders £8,888, Day £6,992. Dunhurst: Boarders £6,109, Day £4,782. Dunannie: £1,189–£2,507.

Charitable status. Bedales School is a Registered Charity, number 307332. Its aims and objectives are to educate children as broadly as possible in a creative and caring environment.

Bedford Modern School

Manton Lane Bedford Bedfordshire MK41 7NT
Tel: 01234 332500
Fax: 01234 332550
e-mail: info@bedmod.co.uk
website: www.bedmod.co.uk

Bedford Modern School is one of the Harpur Trust Schools of Bedford, sharing equally in the educational endowment bequeathed for the establishment of a school in Bedford by Sir William Harpur in 1566. Bedford Modern School was a Direct Grant Grammar School which became independent in 1976. It became co-educational in September 2003.

Chairman of the School Committee: I McEwen, BPhil, MA, DPhil

***Headmaster*: S Smith**, MA

Second Master: C R Barcock, BA

Deputy Head (*Pastoral*): G M Lavery, BA, BMus

Deputy Head (*Academic*): M R Price, BA

Head of Sixth Form: (*to be appointed*)

Director of Sport: P L Jerram, BSc

Head of the Junior School: N R Yelland, BEd

Coordinator Co-Curricular Activities: R M Chadwick, DLC, BA, BISC

* *Head of Department*

Faculty of Art & Technology:
Head of Faculty: G O Jones, BEd

Art:
P Edwards, BA, MA
J McGregor, BA
*S Milton, BA
J Neil, BA

Design & Technology:
I C Grainger
G O Jones, BEd
P Kennington
A Rock, BSc
*J P White, BEd

ICT:
*S Harris, MA, MSc, CITP
D A Jenkins, BSc, MSc, DipEdTech
P J Smith, BSc

Faculty of Science:
Head of Faculty: N R Else, BEd, MA

Biology:
*R J Brand, BSc, MA
D Greenfield, BSc
S Sanctuary, BSc
B H Stratton, BSc
R Sumal, BSc, MSc

Chemistry:
D J Brooks, BSc, PhD
N Cordell, BEd
N R Else, BEd, MA
J P Fitton, BSc
*G R Hobbs, BSc, PhD

Physics:
S Bartlett, MPhys
W D Hallett, BA, MA
S S Harvey, BSc
T P Mullan, BSc
T E Rex, BEd
*R J Turner, BSc, MA

Psychology:
H J Kelly, BSc

Faculty of English:
Head of Faculty: S D Bywater, BA
C R Barcock, BA
J P Barnes, BA, PhD
S D Bywater, BA, MA
J Chumbley, BA
M D Hetherington, MA
A E Martin, BA
J Sanders, BA
E P Sheldon, BA
J Ware, BA

Film Studies:
J P Sanders, BA

Faculty of PE & Games:
Director of Sport: P L Jerram, BSc
*P Bignell, BEd
N J Chinneck, BEd
H L Gilbert, BA, MA
A G Higgens, BSc
S D W Orton, BEd, DipML
A D Tapper, BSc, MSt
N T Whitwham, BA

Faculty of Mathematics:
Head of Faculty: N D Shackleton, BSc
P J Birch, BSc
S A Brocklehurst, BA
L D'Arcy, BSc
A T Grounds, BA
I R Hay, BSc
N Hussain, BSc
D M King, BSc
S J Jacobs, BSc
P J Russell, BSc, MSc

Faculty of Humanities:
Head of Faculty: D J Kendall, BA, MA

Geography:
R M Chadwick, DLC, BA, BISC
B W Day, BSc
D Mistrano, BA
*N C Robinson, BSc, MA
I R D White, BA, MA

History:
C Webb, BA
S Boa, BA, PhD
*S E Wright, MA

RE:
D Kendall, BA, MA
C A Macro, MA
A J Rowley, BA, MA, PhD
*J Searle, BA

Classics:
M Baker, BA
*J Newton, MA
C W H Rees-Bidder, BA, MEd

Drama:
*H Rees-Bidder, BEd
J Riddington-Smith, MA

Speech & Drama:
*M A Burgess
R E Cassell, BA

Economics & Business Studies:
*A Pollard, MA
J R Ryan, BA
R Smith, BA

Government & Politics:
*S Baker, BSc

Modern Languages:
G Amoros, L-ès-L
M J Cooper, BEd
C De Vido, BA
M Harrington, BA, MEd
L Hendry, BA
R J Killen, BA
L Sedeño, BA
*G A Watkins, BA

Music:
G M Lavery, BA, BMus
*J Mower, GRSM, ARCO, ARCM, DipRAM
H D Shoukry, MA

Music Technology:
H D Shoukry, MA

Philosophy:
A J Rowley, BA, MA, PhD

Careers:
P Russell, BSc, MSc

SpLD (Academic Support):
*J Clarke, BEd, Adv Dip SEN, Dip SpLD
L Hendry, BA

Houses:
Bell House: A G Higgens
Farrar House: A T Grounds
Mobbs House: D J Brooks
Oatley House: P Edwards
Rose House: B Day
Tilden House: R J Killen

Junior School

Head: N R Yelland, BEd

Deputy Head: J C Rex, BA
Director of Studies: A M Noakes, BA
Head of Junior School Sports Development: T Bucktin, BSc, PGCE
H Avery, BEd
J Barlow, BEd
C Barrow, BEd
G M Colling, CertEd
H Farrow, BA, MA, LRAM
M Fox, BA
K Johnson, BA
J Leydon, BEd
S J Nicholls, BA
P Pacyna, BA
N S Reed, BA, MA
J Thomas, BA, CertEd, DipMus

Bursar: A T Smyth
Examinations Officer: P J Birch, BSc
School Librarian: M S Brown, BSc, ALA
SSI: Captain B Simpson, MInstLM
Senior School Nurse: M Jones, RGN

Number of Pupils. There are 221 pupils in the Junior School (aged 7–11) and 955 pupils in the Senior School (aged 11–18).

(*See also Bedford Modern Junior School entry in IAPS section.*)

Facilities. The School occupies an attractive forty-acre wooded site to the north of Bedford. The main buildings date from 1974 and there have been substantial additions since that time, most notably a new Assembly Hall, Performance Arena and classrooms to the Junior School (2002); a Sixth Form Study Centre and Refectory (The Rutherford Building – 2006) and new Library Resource Centre (2007). There are extensive facilities for Science, Technology and Information Technology. There have been recent extensions to the Music School and Performing Arts Centre. Each Year Group has its own Common Room as a pastoral centre.

The playing fields are all on the School site with extensive facilities for Rugby, Football, Cricket and Athletics. There is also a large swimming pool, a fitness suite, gym and sports hall. Recent additions include two large all-weather training areas and netball courts. The School shares a large and well-stocked Boathouse with the other Harpur Trust Schools on the River Ouse.

Admissions. Pupils are admitted between the ages of 7 and 16. The School conducts its own Entrance Assessments which are held in January.

Registration fee is £75.

Fees per term (2008-2009). Tuition: Junior School £2,468, Senior School £3,469.

Assistance with Fees. (*see Scholarship Entries section*). The School offers The Modern Awards which are available to students joining the School from Year 7 (11+) upwards. All Awards are means-tested and are also dependent on a student's academic success in the Entrance Assessments. Further details may be obtained from the School.

Curriculum. The Junior School (ages 7–10) curriculum covers Mathematics, English, Science, Technology, French, RE, PE, History and Geography. Pupils benefit both from a purpose-built Practical Skills Centre (Art, Computing, Technology, Science), and from the Senior School Music, PE and Games facilities.

In the Senior School, the curriculum includes all the core subjects, as well as Technology, IT, RE, PE, Music, Art and Drama. All students learn French and German at 11+, and at 12+ Latin is introduced. At 13+ Spanish becomes available. Students opt for ten GCSE subjects. For the Sixth Form, students select from a wide range of 29 subjects. In addition to all the traditional options, the choice of subjects also includes ICT, Government and Politics, Economics, Business Studies, Religious Studies, Philosophy, Systems & Control, Classical Civilisation, Theatre Studies, PE, Psychology, Film Studies and Music Technology. All subjects can be taken both to A2 and AS Level.

ICT Facilities. The School boasts a superb range of ICT facilities offering both staff and students an individual network account and e-mail address so that they are able to enjoy over 400 networked PCs across the School in addition to high speed broadband internet access, wireless classroom laptop sets, networked printing, and an extensive subject software library including a range of training courseware material.

A number of interactive whiteboards and presentation equipment are also available. The School's website can be viewed at www.bedmod.co.uk.

Religious and Moral Education. The School is multi-faith and multicultural, and religious and moral education is given throughout. The students learn about all major world religions and it is hoped that they can learn to be tolerant whilst accepting the place for firmly held beliefs. Personal and Social Education is a fundamental and well-established part of the timetable.

Individual Care. Every student has a personal tutor, who supervises and takes an interest in his or her academic progress, co-curricular activities and sporting interests. Tutors meet with their tutees on a daily basis and there is at least one longer pastoral session each week. Each Year Group has its own common room for use at break and lunchtimes and other non-taught times with a study area and recreational facilities.

We believe that common sense and courtesy lie at the heart of pastoral care. We stress self-discipline and high standards of personal conduct. The tutorial system and the academic organisation are discrete, working in parallel to complement each other. Teaching class sizes are a maximum of twenty-four and often many fewer. We aim to provide a relaxed but purposeful environment; a culture in which all feel at ease and are ambitious to achieve their best.

Drama. There are several productions each year, as well as a House Drama Festival and several smaller events. There are also separate Drama and Dance Studios. Speech and Drama is offered throughout the School, leading to LAMDA examinations. Ballet, tap and modern dance lessons follow the ISTD syllabus.

Music. Students can learn all the orchestral and band instruments as well as piano, keyboard, guitar/electric guitar and singing. The School has a large variety of choirs, orchestra, bands and ensembles. Students can follow courses for GCSE and A Level music as well as A Level Music Technology. Music accommodation includes an ICT suite with 10 new Apple computers.

Activities. There are many school societies and clubs catering for a variety of tastes and interests. The voluntary Combined Cadet Force is 180 strong with Army, Navy, RAF and Marine sections. Students may learn flying, sailing and paragliding. Community Service and the Duke of Edinburgh's Award Scheme are very popular.

Sport. Games and Physical Education are taught to all students below the Sixth Form. The Sixth Form have activity afternoons which include a number of team and individual sporting activities. Our main team sports are Hockey, Rugby, Football, Cricket and Rowing for boys and Hockey, Netball and Rowing for girls.

There are many other sports and activities to choose from including: aerobics, athletics, badminton, basketball, cycling, equestrian, fencing, fives, golf, rounders, sevens, shooting, snow sports, squash, synchronised swimming, swimming, table tennis, tennis, water polo and weights and fitness.

Higher Education. There were over 100 entrants to degree courses in 2007.

Old Bedford Modernians' Club. Secretary: R H Wildman, Esq, Bedford Modern School, Manton Lane, Bedford MK41 7NT.

Charitable status. The Bedford Charity (The Harpur Trust) is a Registered Charity, number 204817. It includes in its aims the provision of high quality education for boys and girls.

Bedford School

De Parys Avenue Bedford MK40 2TU
Tel: 01234 362200
Fax: 01234 362283
e-mail: registrar@bedfordschool.org.uk
website: www.bedfordschool.org.uk

A boarding and day school for boys aged 7–18 years, where fundamental traditions combine with innovative educational thinking. Established in 1552, the School has a national reputation for academic excellence with additional strengths in music, drama, art and sport. Situated on an estate of 40 acres in the heart of Bedford, the School is a lively community of day boys, weekly and full boarders. A distinctive feature is the way in which day houses are twinned with boarding houses enabling boys to mix freely in and out of the classroom.

Our highly qualified teaching staff are selected on their ability to communicate and inspire. The Bedford curriculum provides a varied choice of subjects that will stir the potential in each pupil and challenge his individual strengths. Academic excellence is our primary objective and success is demonstrated by a long history of impressive examination results at GCSE, A Level, and in the International Baccalaureate Diploma.

The pursuit of excellence extends beyond the classroom and the School offers an impressive range of extra-curricular activities. The new £3 million Music School is one of the largest in the country and has a full programme of concerts and performances throughout the year. The Recreation Centre incorporates a 250 seat theatre, large sports hall, squash courts and a 25-metre indoor swimming pool. Other recent developments include an observatory and planetarium, twin astroturf pitches and a £1.8 million library.

School Governors:

Chairman: H H Judge Simon Brown, QC
Deputy Chairman: Mrs S Peck
Chairman of the Harpur Trust: Dr M A H Cook, BSc

Governors:
D Palfreyman, MA, MBA, LLB
F D G Cattley
Cllr Mrs M Foster
D Doran, MSc, BSc
Mrs S Clark, MPhil, BSc

Co-opted Governors:
A L C Bell, MA
Air Chief Marshal Sir Clive Loader, KCB, OBE, FRACS, RAF
A A Mahon, MBA, BA
The Hon Dr J R Morris, MBChB, PGDL, Dipl MC RCS (Ed), FP Cert
Mrs C Lewis, MBA, BA
Prof S Mayson

***Head Master*: J S Moule**, MA Lady Margaret Hall, Oxford

Vice Master: C Baker, BSc Manchester, CChem, FRSC

Deputy Head (Academic): I Latif, BSc Kings College, London

Undermaster: I B Armstrong, BSc Sunderland, MSc Leeds
Director of International Baccalaureate: C Marsh, MA St John's College, Cambridge, MLitt Oxford
Registrar: R T Williams, BSc Dundee, DipEd
Senior Boarding Housemaster: R J Midgley, BA Ed
Senior Day Housemaster: Mrs F G McEwan-Cox, BA, RSA DipTEFL
Bursar and Clerk to the Governors: Col J M W Stenhouse, OBE, MVO, MBA
Director, Communications & Enterprises: Ms D Hunnie, BA, CIM
Foundation Director: A K Bannard-Smith, BSc, MBA

Assistant staff:
* *Head of Department*

Academic Support (EFL & SpLD):
*Mrs F G McEwan-Cox, BA, RSA DipTEFL

Art:
*R H Campbell, BA
M Croker, BA
S Chance, BA

Biology:
*M A Beale, BSc, MEd
L J Guise, BA
M J Gunn, BSc, MIBiol, CBiol
R J Midgley, BA Ed
W M Simper, BSc
Ms F Bell, BSc
C Palmer, BSc, BEd
Miss C Evans, BA
M J Mallalieu, BSc

Chemistry:
*I A Sheldon, MChem
C Baker, BSc, CChem, MRSC
A J Crowe, BSc, PhD
C W Duckworth, BSc
W G Suthers, BSc, MSc, PhD
B Johnson, MA, MSc, PhD

Classics:
*P J Arnold, MA, DPhil
R H Palmer, MA, PhD
M R Vogel, MA
Miss M E Ambler, MA

Computing:
*P E Davis, BSc
R A Eadie, MA (*Computer Manager*)

Design Technology:
*I B Armstrong, BSc, MSc
M Huddlestone, BA
L Holt, BA

Economics & Business Studies:
*C J Bury, BA
M H Cassell, BSc
Mrs C M Medley, BA
R E Heale, BSc

English:
*D G Ashton, BA
D M Cundall, BA, MA
A W Grimshaw, BA
Mrs L Di Niro, BA, MPhil
E N F Swanwick, BA, BEd
R H Palmer, MA, PhD

Geography:
*R J Walker, BA
M D Hopgood, MA
A Edwards, BSc
C Stearn, DPhil
W Montgomery, BSc

History:
*Ms E Parcell, BA
J N W Fleming, MA
J J Farrell, MA
M W Graham, BA

Library:
*Mrs L Harrison, BSc

Mathematics:
*Mrs J C Beale, BSc, MA
B J Burgess, BSc Ed
N J Cox, MA
A Eames-Jones, BSc, PhD, CEng, CPhys
Mrs S Staincliffe, BSc
J B Watson, MA
B C Woolley, BA, MA
P Sherwin, MEd
W Macro, BSc
Mrs R Down, BSc
S G Dale, BA

Modern Languages:
*F J G Inglis, BA, MLitt (**German*)
Ms C Geneve, MA (**French*)
A J R Huxford, MA (**Spanish*)
C L Marsh, MA, MLitt
J E J O'Neill, BA, MIL
J C Osman, BA
D C Gillett, BA
Miss J C Law, BA
Ms E Calleja-Rubio, BA
Mrs L Caldicott, BA
Mrs A Chen, MBA

Music:
*A W Morris, MA, BMus, MEd, GRSM, FTCL, ARAM, ARCO CHM, LRAM, ARCM
G V Bennett, GGSM
J A Rouse, MA, FRCO
M C Green, GRSM, LRAM, ARCM, DipRAM
R Heyes, MA, BMus, GRSM, LRAM, ARCO
M Hughes, GRSM, ARCM
A Charlton, BA, PhD
T J Watts, MA, MMus (*Composer in Residence*)

Physical Education:
*G M K Fletcher, BEd, DipPhysEd
B J Burgess, BSc Ed
R J Midgley, BA Ed

Physics:
*M A R Crisp, MEng
P N Brough, BSc
D J Waugh, BSc
R T Williams, BSc, DipEd
Dr E Palmer, MSc, PhD
J E P Honeysett, BA, MSci
S James, MPhys

Religious Education:
*A D Finch, MA
The Revd Fr D Lawrence-March, BA (*Chaplain*)
G S Woolner, MA

Theatre Studies:
*Mrs S Swidenbank, MA Ed

Houses and Housemasters:

Boarding Houses:
Sandersons: R J Midgley
Burnaby: R E Heale
Pemberley: Dr P J Arnold
Redburn: J J Farrell
Phillpotts: A W Grimshaw
Talbots: M H Cassell

Day Houses:
Ashburnham: B J Burgess
Bromham: Miss R K Down
Crescent: Miss J C Law
Paulo Pontine: E N F Swanwick
St Cuthberts: M D Hopgood
St Peter's: Mrs F G McEwan-Cox

Chaplain: The Revd Fr D L Lawrence-March, BA

Medical Officer: Dr D Fenske

Number in School. There are some 663 boys in the Upper School of whom some 242 are boarders and 421 day boys.

The Curriculum. Boys enter the Preparatory School from 7 and the Upper School at 13 years of age. The Preparatory School has its own Headmaster and specialist staff. (*See also Bedford Preparatory School entry in IAPS section.*)

A coordinated curriculum takes boys through the two Schools. The emphasis is on breadth of experience: as few doors as possible are closed at option stages. Boys are prepared for GCSE and for the new broader portfolio of AS and A Levels, and for Key Skills and General Studies. Since September 2003, boys have had the option to study the International Baccalaureate Diploma in the Sixth Form. Notably strong are Languages, Mathematics and the Sciences, and there has been heavy investment in Technology and Information Technology.

Boys are encouraged to make good use of non-teaching time. There are extensive departmental and central library facilities, and strong emphasis is placed upon Music, Art, Drama and IT. Clubs and Societies abound for both boarders and day boys. Concerts, plays, lectures and film performances are given in the Great Hall, the Recital Hall, the Erskine May Hall and the Theatre.

Classes. In the Preparatory School pupils are taught in forms until age 11, and are setted for most subjects. For all post-GCSE work, a generous block system is used which enables boys to study a variety of subjects at AS and A Level, combining, if desired, Arts and Science subjects. In addition a range of subsidiary teaching is provided including Citizenship.

Information Technology. A timetabled IT course is run for pupils in the 13+ age-group. During the remaining GCSE years IT is regarded as a cross-curricular subject, not appearing in the timetable but promoted within the teaching of other subjects. AS and A Level Computing and a number of non-examination Sixth Form courses are offered. Resources, using an extensive School network of some 200 computers, include five IT laboratories and computing facilities in almost all subject areas. The computers include PCs and Network computers, all of which can run the latest Microsoft packages. Activities include word-processing, art and graphics, desktop publishing, music composition, the Internet and E-mail.

Careers and Higher Education. The School is a member of the Independent Schools Careers Organisation. There is a team of Careers Staff who maintain close contact with the Services and professional bodies, and commercial and industrial undertakings. There are regular contacts with local industry and Institutes of Technology and Higher Education. Annual Careers Conventions are held in Bedford.

Annually almost all of the Upper Sixth enters Higher Education, with between 10 and 15 boys entering Oxford and Cambridge Universities every year.

Games. A great variety of sporting activities is offered, and senior boys in particular have a wide choice. The major sports are Cricket, Rugby Football, Rowing, Hockey; and there is ample opportunity also for Athletics, Swimming, Tennis, Association Football, Rugby Fives, Squash, Badminton, Fencing, Basketball, etc. In addition, there are regular PE classes. The Recreation Centre facilities include a large sports hall, squash courts and heated indoor swimming pool.

Services and Activities. The School offers a diverse programme of extra curricular activities every evening between 4.15 and 6 pm, many of which involve girls from other Harpur Trust schools. Boys are expected to participate fully in this programme during their time at the School. Activities include the CCF (Combined Cadet Force), Duke of Edinburgh's Award Scheme, Community Service, fund-raising groups, and more than 50 other clubs and societies from Astronomy to Young Enterprise.

Music. As well as the two Senior Symphony Orchestras, a Chamber Orchestra, a Concert Band and a large Choral Society, there are a Chapel Choir trained in the English Cathedral tradition, two Junior Orchestras, a Dance Band, Jazz Band, a large number of chamber music groups, and a Music Club. The new £3 million Music School was completed in Autumn 2005.

Drama. A range of formal and informal dramatic productions is performed annually by all age groups. The well-equipped School Theatre provides a venue for visiting touring companies, performing for the benefit of pupils and the general public. House Plays are also produced on a regular basis.

Association with The Harpur Trust Girls' Schools. A large variety of co-educational activities is organised in association with the girls at our sister schools. In particular, the School has a "memorandum of understanding" with Bedford High School (*see entry in GSA section*) which details all aspects of the extensive cooperation between the two schools. These include academic cooperation in minority subjects, joint seminars in major subjects, and involvement in concerts, debates, conferences and a wide range of more informal social events.

Pastoral Supervision. We have a highly developed Pastoral system. Upper School pupils are under the supervision of a Tutor within small Tutor Groups; these "family" groups are organised on a vertical structure in terms of age.

Boarders and Day Boys. In the Upper School a careful balance of Boarders and Day Boys is maintained. The organisation and tradition of the School is such as to promote mixing and to avoid any discrimination between the two groups. They are combined in work, games and all other School activities, and are equally eligible for positions of responsibility whether in House or School. There are six Senior Boarding Houses, each containing up to 51 boys; and one Junior boarding House of up to 35. There is also a Sixth Form boarding house.

Visits and Exchanges. Well-established language-exchanges occur annually between Bedford and schools in France, Spain and Germany. There are also plentiful opportunities for educational travel including outward-bound and adventure camps and expeditions, annual skiing holidays, cultural visits to a range of countries, and inter-continental sports tours.

Admission to the Upper School. Applications should be made to the Registrar. The Registration fee is £50. Applicants for the Upper School from Preparatory Schools are expected to take an Entrance Examination. All applicants must furnish evidence of good character from their previous school. Applicants from Maintained Schools are examined in English, Mathematics, Science and French. They also sit a Verbal Reasoning test.

Scholarships and Bursaries. (*see Scholarship Entries section*). Designed to open up new opportunities and bring out the best in every boy, Bedford's radical new Access Award & Scholarship Scheme is changing the face of independent education. Bedford now offers some £1 million per year of funding in recognition of academic, music or sporting potential to provide a wealth of opportunities for boys irrespective of background.

Awards are available for boys entering the School at 11,13 or 16 years.

For more information and an informal chat, please call our freephone helpline 0800 432 0084 or visit our website www.bedfordschool.org.uk.

Fees per term (2008-2009). Day Boys £4,789; Full Boarders £7,536; Weekly Boarders £7,287.

Fees are payable to The Clerk, Harpur Trust Office, Pilgrim Centre, Brickhill Drive, Bedford MK41 7PZ.

Old Bedfordians Club. *Director*: Mrs B Roberts, 2 Burnaby Road, Bedford MK40 2TT. Tel: 01234 362262.

Charitable status. The Bedford Charity (The Harpur Trust) is a Registered Charity, number 204817. It exists for the relief of poverty and the promotion of education in the Borough of Bedfordshire.

Belfast Royal Academy

Belfast Co Antrim BT14 6JL Northern Ireland
Tel: 028 9074 0423
Fax: 028 9075 0607
e-mail: enquiries@bfsra.belfast.ni.sch.uk
website: www.belfastroyalacademy.com

Board of Governors:
Mrs A Clements, BA (*Warden*)
J W Martin, FRICS (*Senior Vice Warden*)
Mrs J Weir, BSc, CMath, MIMA (*Honorary Secretary*)
W J Andrews, MD, FRCP Lond, FRCPI, FRCP Ed, DCH, JP
T M A Baldwin, BSc, MIBiol, CBiol
N W Beggs, Esq
Miss K M Bill, MBChB, FFARCSI
E W Bleakley, TCert, BA, MSc, BPGCUT
R Connolly, BSc
Mrs B Dass, BA, PhD
Ms C Dillon, BA
Mrs D Fitzsimons, MA Econ, MSc TP, FRICS, MRTPI, MIPI
Ms W E Graham, MA
J A Hill, FREng, FIAE, BSc, Hon DSc, CEng, FICE, FIStructE, FIEI, FIHT
K Knox, MSc
B W McCormack, BSc Econ, FCA
S B Orr, LLB
S R Potts, MB, BCh, BAO, FRCSI
Mrs L R Ryles, BA, FHEA
Mrs C Scoffield, CertEd, DipEd
P Sefton, LLB
G Simon, FRICS
D Walsh, BSc, MBA, CEng, MIME
S Warke, ACII, MSFA
M J Watt, Esq
A J Wilkinson, FCA
W T Wilson, BEd, LTCL
W S F Young, MA

***Headmaster*: W S F Young**, MA

Deputy Head: Mrs Y A Hollinger, BSc

Vice-Principals:
J M G Dickson, MA
L H Campbell, BSc, PhD

Senior Mistresses:
Mrs B Lomas, BA, MEd, PhD
Ms C N Scully, BSc, PhD, ALCM

Senior Masters:
A R Creighton, BEd
D R S Rankin, BA

Senior House Master: T M A Baldwin, BSc, MIBiol, CBiol

Deputy Senior Masters:
R D C Evans, BA
R J Jamison, BSc

Heads of Departments:
Mrs R McWhirter, DipAD, ATD (*Art*)
Mrs E McMorran, BSc (*Biology*)
Mrs G McQuiston, BEd (*Business Studies*)
Ms J R Adams, BEd (*Careers*)
B T McMurray, BSc, PhD (*Chemistry*)
J D L Reilly, MBE, BA (*Classics*)
Ms W E Graham, MA (*English*)
C A Stewart, BSc (*Geography*)
M McCoy, MA (*History*)
P Cupples, BSc (*ICT*)
G J N Brown, BA, PhD (*Mathematics*)
Miss S B Park, BA (*Modern Languages*)
Ms M McMullan, MA, MusB, LTCL, ALCM (*Music*)
W I McGonigle, BEd (*Physical Education and Boys' Games*)
Miss S Stewart, DipPE (*Physical Education and Girls' Games*)
R Budden, MSc (*Physics*)
A R Creighton, BEd (*Religious Studies*)
Mrs B Lomas, BA, MEd, PhD (*Social Science*)
N E Moore, BSc (*Technology*)

Senior Subject Teachers:
R D Evans, BA (*Drama and Theatre Studies*)
J M Patterson, BSc Econ, MSSc, DCG (*Economics*)
D R S Nash, BSc, MEd, DASE (*European Studies*)
Miss R McCay, MA (*German*)
Mrs R F Morrison, BA (*Home Economics*)
W G F Blair, MBE, BSc, PhD, CPhys, MInstP (*Physics*)
Mrs C Leyden, BA (*Spanish*)
Miss M P McCullough, BA (*Special Needs*)

Form Masters:
J Buchan, BEM, MA
J Carolan, MA
M C W Harte, BA
N Irwin, BEd
R K Lunn, BEd
M J Neill, MSc
M T Wilson, BSc

Form Mistresses:
Miss G C Black, BEd
Mrs M Gray, BSc
Mrs S R Letson, BSc
Mrs K McIntyre, BSc
Mrs R F Morrison, BA
Mrs A M Reynolds, BSc
Mrs J Robb, BSc

Assistant Staff:
Mrs N J Allen, BA
I P B Bamford, BA, PhD, MEd, DASE
A A W Bell, BSc, BAgrSc, PhD, AIEA
Mrs K Black, BA
Ms C Burns, BSc, PhD, MRSC
Mrs I A Cameron, BA
R Carroll, BEd
Miss V Carson, MA, ALCM
Mrs J A Connolly, BA
Mrs L Cowan, MSc
Mrs C E Currie, BA
P Dorman, BTh
Mrs F A Gilmore, BSc
S W Graham, MA
Mrs M L Gray, BA, MEd, DASE
Mrs V Heaslip, BEd
Miss C E Henry, BMus
Mrs N Henry, BSc
T Hughes, MSc
Mrs P Kerr, BA, ATD
Miss J Lindores, BSc
Mrs I Lyttle, MSc
Miss C Marcus, BSc
P J Martin, BEd
Mrs G McCadden, DipAD, ATD
Mrs P E McCamley, BA
C R McCarey, BSc
J A McCombe, BA, PhD
Mrs H Miller, BA
R A Moore, CertEd, PGCTE
D Morrison, MSc
S Murphy, BEd
Mrs D M Nicholl, BA
Mrs L I Nicholl, BSc
Mrs N S Nicholl, BA
Mrs R O'Donnell, BA, DipAD, ATD
P Porter, BA, BD Comm
Mrs S S Roberts, BA
W J W Spence, BEd, MA
Mrs A P Terek, BSc
Mrs M E M Thompson, BA
Miss R C Wallace, BA
Miss J L Warburton, BA
Miss K Wilson, BA
Mrs M N Wilson, BA

Classroom Assistants:
Miss B Burtenshaw, BA
Miss E Montgomery, BA
Mrs A Harte, MA

Careers Advisers:
Ms J R Adams, BEd
Ms D Keenan, MSc
Mrs C Leyden, BA
Mrs G McQuiston, BEd
Mrs S Millar, BEng
A K Moles, BSc
J M Patterson, BSc Econ, MSSc, DCG
Mrs H Tate, BA

Preparatory Department:

Principal: Mrs V M McCaig, BEd, DASE
Deputy Principal: W T Wilson, BEd, LTCL

Assistant Staff:
P J Ingram, BEd, MSc
S Johnston, BSc
Mrs P Lennon, BEd
Mrs B Marshall, CertEd
Mrs S Sherrard, CertEd
Mrs E N E Wilson, BEd
Mrs R Wilson, BA, BEd, LTCL

Classroom Assistants:
Mrs E L Philpott
Mrs R Turk, CertEd

Pre-Prep & Daycare Staff:
Mrs J Bradley
Mrs M Faulkner
Mrs J Kerr
Mrs E Moorhead
Mrs C Sempey

Administration:
Bursar: Miss E Hull, BSc, DipAcc, FCA
Assistant Bursar: D W Ritchie, BSc Econ
Headmaster's Secretary: Mrs P McClintock
General Office Manager: Ms P Ferguson
Office Administrator: Mrs L D Oliver
Receptionist/Telephonist: Mrs C A Clyde
Bursar's Secretary: Miss G Boyd, BA
Librarian: Ms T McGrattan, BA
ICT Manager: J R Cleland, BSc
Matron: Miss P McKenna, BSc
Alumni Officer: E G A McCamley, MA
Estates Manager: W J Thompson
Supervisor of Grounds: T D Robinson
Swimming Pool Manager: Mrs E Alexander, BA

Belfast Royal Academy, founded in 1785, is the oldest school in the city. It moved to its present site, on the Cliftonville Road in North Belfast, in 1880, and the Gothic building erected at that time has been extensively modernised and refurbished. The fourteen Science Laboratories were opened in 1971, a 25-metre indoor heated Swimming Pool was completed in 1974, a new building for Art and Craft came into full use in 1982, and a Sports Hall was opened to mark the Bi-Centenary year. In 1989 a new Sixth Form Centre and Careers Suite were opened and a purpose-built four-room Technology Suite was completed in September 1991. An additional classroom block for English and Drama was opened in September 1994, and a new building to house the Mathematics department came into use in 1998. Since 2001 four new ICT Suites have been provided, and there is extensive provision throughout the school for teaching and learning through information technology.

The Academy is a co-educational day grammar school and there is also a preparatory and kindergarten department. The grammar school has some 1,400 boys and girls, between the ages of 11 and 19. The kindergarten and preparatory department, known as Ben Madigan, has some 150 children, aged from 3 to 11; it is situated at 690 Antrim Road.

The curriculum has a strong academic bias and former pupils of the school are among the members of almost every university in the United Kingdom.

The work of the junior and middle Forms is directed mainly towards the GCSE examinations of the Northern Ireland Council for the Curriculum Examinations and Assessment, the Assessment and Qualifications Alliance or OCR, with a minimum of specialisation, all the usual subjects being provided and careful attention being given to the requirements of the universities and the professions. Religious studies are taught on a non-denominational basis.

There are more than 380 pupils in the Sixth Forms, where GCE Advanced Level courses are available in English, English Literature, Drama and Theatre Studies, French, German, Spanish, Latin, Mathematics (incorporating Mechanics and/or Statistics), Further Mathematics, Physics, Chemistry, Biology, Geography, History, Classical Civilisation, Economics, Politics, Art, Music, Home Economics, Business Studies, ICT, Physical Education, Religious Studies, Sociology and Technology. Some Sixth Formers take an additional Certificate of Competence in Information Technology, or a qualification in keyboard skills. Pupils are prepared for entry to Oxford or Cambridge in all the main subjects.

Much attention is given to careers guidance by the Careers Masters, the Careers Mistresses, other senior members of Staff, and the Form Masters and Form Mistresses.

The normal school day is from 8.40 am to 3.30 pm. There is no Saturday school but matches are played in the major sports on Saturdays. The school year runs from the beginning of September to the end of June, with holidays of about a fortnight at Christmas and at Easter.

There are some sixty different activities in the extra-curricular programme.

The principal games are, for boys, rugby, cricket, hockey, cross-country running, swimming and athletics; for girls, hockey, tennis, swimming, cross-country running and athletics. Show-jumping, life-saving and skiing are also available.

There is an orchestra, senior and junior choirs, a wind band, a Jazz band, several string ensembles and an Irish traditional group. Individual tuition in orchestral instruments is also provided. School organisations include Societies for Music, Drama, Chess, Bridge, Photography and Debating, an Air Training Corps, an Amateur Radio Club, Community Service and Christian Union groups and the Duke of Edinburgh's Award Scheme.

Parents pay a capital fee of £130 each year and a voluntary contingency charge of £19.50 per month.

In Ben Madigan, the annual fee is £2,790 for Years 1 to 3 and £2955 for Years 4 to 7.

BRA Old Boys' Association. Hon Secretary: Mr M Cooper, 2 The Glade, Station Road, Greenisland, BT38 8GL.

BRA Old Girls' Association. Hon Secretary: Mrs C Scoffield, 15 Glenshane Park, Newtownabbey, BT37 0QN.

Berkhamsted Collegiate School

Castle Street Berkhamsted Hertfordshire HP4 2BB
Tel: 01442 358000
Fax: 01442 358040
e-mail: info@bcschool.org
website: www.berkhamstedcollegiateschool.org.uk

In 1541 John Incent, Dean of St Paul's, was granted a Licence by Henry VIII to found a school in Berkhamsted, Incent's home town. Until the end of the 19th Century Berkhamsted School served as a grammar school for a small number of boys from the town but over the last century it has developed into a school of significance. In 1888 the foundation was extended by the establishment of Berkhamsted School for Girls. In 1996, these two schools formalised their partnership to become Berkhamsted Collegiate School, offering the highest quality education to pupils from ages 3 to 19.

There are 300 pupils in the flourishing co-educational Sixth Form; between the ages of eleven and sixteen 450 boys on Castle Campus and 300 girls on Kings Campus are taught in single-sex groups; and 450 pupils from ages three to eleven attend the Preparatory School.

The Principal is a member of both HMC and GSA.

Patron: Her Majesty The Queen.

The Governors:
¶Mr P J Williamson (*Chairman*)
¶Mrs A F Moore-Gwyn (*Vice-Chairman*)

Mr J J Apthorp
Mr A J Bright, QC
Dr Y A Burne
Mr C J Butcher, QC, Fellow of All Souls, Oxford
Mrs C Green
Mr R G Groom
Mr J N P B Horden, Fellow of All Souls, Oxford
¶Mr M P Horton
Mrs J Laws
Mr A H Noel
Mr B Parker, Fellow of St John's College, Cambridge
Mr W R Winfield
¶Miss S E Wolstenholme, OBE

Clerk to the Governors & Business Director: Mr P Maynard, RD, FCIS

***Principal*: M S Steed**, MA Cantab, MA Nottingham

Deputy Principal: Dr H Brooke, BSc, PhD
Deputy Head i/c Sixth Form: Mr G J Hartley, MA, MSc
Deputy Head (*Boys 11–16*): Mr C Nicholls, CertEd
Deputy Head (*Girls 11–16*): Mrs A J R Clancy, BEd
Assistant Deputy (*Boys 11–16*): Mr J M P Walker, BA, MA
Assistant Deputy (*Girls 11–16*): Mrs K M Woodrow, BSc
Director of Studies: Mr W R C Gunary, BSc
Chaplain: Revd S Golding, BA

Teaching staff:
Miss S Afsar, BA, LLM
*Mr C Allam, BEd, BSc
Mr P R Alley, BSc
Mr D H Anderson, BSc, MSc, BA Ed
Mr G W H Anker, BA
Dr J W R Baird, BA, PhD
Mrs E A Baker, BA
Miss N A Barker, BA
Mr M E Batchelder, CertEd, DipEd, MA
*Mrs K R Best, BA, CPhys, MInstP
†Miss R M Bradley, BA
Mrs L C Briand, BA, DipTESOL
Miss J E Brodie, BA
Mr G R Burchnall, BEd
*Ms H-C Burt, BTh
Mr N J Cale, BA
*Mr F Charnock, CertEd
Mrs S A E Clay, Dip CSSD, CertEd, MA
*Mr R W D Coupe, BA, MA
*Mr P C Cowie, MA
Miss E Cugley
Mr S J Dight, BA, DipEd
Mr E A H Dingwall, BA
Mr P E Dobson, BSc, CChem, MRSC
*Mrs A M Doggett, BSc
Mr S P Dolan, BSc
Mrs S M Dolan, BSc
Mrs A Dunmall, BSc, DipSpLD
†Mr C H Eaton, BSc
Mr A J R Esland, MA, MMus
Mrs B Evans, MA
†Mr B P Evers, BA
Mrs I M Feord, BA
Mrs S C Foster, BSc
Mrs L J Francis, BA
Mr V Fung, BSc
Miss D D Furtado, BEd
*Mr R A Fysh, BSc, MEd
Mr R B Garner, BA
Ms F M Garratt, BSc
Miss E L Gent, BA, MA, ATC
Mr D J Gibson, BSc
Miss N L Gold, BA
Mrs M S Goodwin, BA, MA
†Mr T A Grant, MA
§Mrs H A A Green, BSc
*Mr S R Hargreaves, BEd
Dr A J Harker, BA, MA, PhD
*Ms C M E Harrison, MA, BA
*Mr P J Harvey, BA
Dr P Hatfield-Iacoponi, BA, PhD
Mrs A Hatton, BA
*Mr P J Hopkins, BA, BMus, FRCO, ARCM
Miss J J Hughes, BSc
†Dr S P S Hundal, BSc, PhD
†Mrs S J James, BEd
*Mr D Jeffers, BSc
Ms S P Jennings, BSc
Miss H C Johnson, BA
Mr E Keane, BSc
Mrs P Kent, CertEd
†Miss S B Kirton, BA, MA
Mr A Lansdell, DipEd
*Mr T D Lines, BA, MA, MEd
Mr P R Luckraft, BA
*Mr R I Mackay, BA Ed
Mr B R Mahoney, BEd
Mrs M Manrique, MA
Mr R H Mardo, BSc
Mr R D Matthews, BSc
†Mr H R Maxted, BA
†Miss R McColl, BA, MPhil
Mr R J McIlwaine, CertEd, BA
Mr R P Messik, BA
§Mrs R E Miles, BSc
*Ms C J Moss, BA
†Mr R K Mowbray, MA
Mrs A Mulcahy, DipEd, MIL
†Mr R F Newport, BA
Mrs S Nicholls
†Mr P H Northcroft, BA
Miss J Osborn
Mrs V A Ostle, BA, CertEd
†Mr D R Pain, BA, BComm
†Mr M S Pett, BA
§Mrs J F Phillips, BA, MA
*Mrs A M Pike, CertEd, RSADipSLD
Dr S A Redman, BSc, PhD
Mr S J E Rees, BA
†Mr D G Richardson, BSc
†Mrs E A Richardson, BA
*Mr P T Riddick, MA, MSc
†Mr S C Robinson, BSc
†Mrs C G Ryder, BSc
*Mr C H Savill, BA
Mr B P Shepherd, BSc
†Mrs S M Shipton, DEUG Licence
Mr D W Short, BA

Mr D H Simpson, CertEd, AdvDipDT
Mrs K Sobczyk, BSc
Mr M Sparrow, BA
*Mr I R Stewart, BA, MA
Mr P D Swaffield, BA, MA, BATh
Mrs G S Swart, BA
†Mr R Thompson, BA
Mr M J Thum, MA
Mrs K E Tomlin, BA, MA
Mrs L Van Der Merwe, BEd
Mr A van Straten, BA
†Mrs K Warde, BSc, DipSpLD
†Mr W A Webb, BA, BEd, MEd
Mr S A Whyte, BSc, MSc
Mrs J M Wild, GLCM, ALCM, LLCM TD
†Mr D J Wiles, BSc, MA
§Mrs A S Winslett, BA

Additional Staff:

Music:
There are 30 visiting music staff offering instrumental teaching in: acoustic guitar, bagpipes, bassoon, cello, clarinet, double bass, electric guitar, euphonium, flute, French horn, harpsichord, jazz piano, oboe, organ, percussion (including kit drumming), piano, recorder, saxophone, trombone, trumpet, tuba, viola and violin.

Lacrosse Coach & Development Officer: Mrs L Richardson
Sports Centre Manager: Mr H Adler
Librarian: Miss R Guy, BA, MA
Medical Officer: Dr N Ormiston, MB BS, MRCP, DRCOG

Principal's PA: Mrs N M Golder (Tel: 01442 358002; Fax: 01442 358003)
Deputy Principal's PA: Mrs L Hornsey (Tel: 01442 358109; Fax: 01442 358003)
Deputy Head's PA (Senior Boys): Mrs J Carruthers (Tel: 01442 358031; Fax: 01442 358032)
Deputy Head's PA (Senior Girls): Miss I Flude (Tel: 01442 358161; Fax 01442 358162)
Deputy Head's PA (Sixth Form): Mrs P M Webb (Tel: 01442 358052; Fax 01442 358053)

Aims. The School seeks to enable pupils to achieve their full potential. In addition to the development of the intellect, social, sporting and cultural activities play an important part within the framework of a disciplined and creative community based on Christian values. It is important that pupils come to value both the individual and the Community through School life. The School seeks to encourage spiritual and moral values and a sense of responsibility as an essential part of the pursuit of excellence.

Location. The School stands in the heart of Berkhamsted, an historic and thriving town only thirty miles from London. It enjoys excellent communications to London, the airports, to the Midlands and the communities of Buckinghamshire, Bedfordshire and Hertfordshire.

Facilities. The original site has at its heart a magnificent Tudor Hall used as a Schoolroom for over 300 years. Other buildings are from late Victorian to modern periods and of architectural interest (especially the Chapel modelled on the Church of St Maria dei Miracoli in Venice). There are new Science laboratories, Library and Learning Resources Centres, Information Technology suites, Sixth Form centres, Careers libraries, Dining hall, Medical centre, House rooms, Deans' Hall (an Assembly Hall and Theatre) and Centenary Hall (a modern 500-seat Hall also used for concerts and theatre productions). Recreational and sports facilities include extensive playing fields, Fives courts, Squash courts, Tennis courts, Gymnasium, Drama studio, Music school and Art studios. A new Sports Hall and 25m indoor swimming pool were opened in 2004 and a state-of-the-art Design Centre in 2008.

Organisation.

The **Berkhamsted Collegiate Preparatory School** is housed in separate buildings nearby, including a nursery. The school is fully co-educational from Y1 to Y6.

For further information, please see entry in IAPS section.

At age 11, boys and girls transfer into **single-sex senior schools** on adjacent sites, where they are taught separately up to GCSE. Pupils are supported by a coordinated pastoral system and many extra-curricular activities take place across the campuses.

At age 16, pupils join the **fully co-educational Sixth Form**, which offers an extensive range of A Level subject choices with highly experienced staff and impressive teaching facilities. Clubs, societies, sports, work experience and community service all complement a stimulating programme of activities, which provide students with valuable opportunities for responsibility and enhance their university applications.

Curriculum. The curriculum includes: English, English Literature, Mathematics, Biology, Chemistry, Physics, History, Geography, Religious Studies, French/German/Spanish, Latin/Classics, Music, Art, Design and Technology. Up to eleven subjects may be taken for GCSE. In the Sixth Form, AS/A2 courses are offered in around 27 subjects, complemented by AS General Studies. Pupils are prepared for university entrance, including Oxbridge. All pupils are taught computer skills and have access to Information Technology centres. Careers guidance and personal tutoring are offered throughout.

Day and Boarding. Pupils may be full boarders, weekly/flexible boarders or day pupils. The two Boarding houses, accommodating boys and girls separately, are well equipped and within a few minutes walk of the main campus. There are up to 100 boarding places. Day pupils come from both Berkhamsted and the surrounding area of Hertfordshire, Buckinghamshire and Bedfordshire.

Pastoral Care and Discipline. The main social and pastoral unit is the House; the Head of House and House Tutors provide continuity of support and advice and monitor each individual pupil's progress.

The aim is to encourage self-discipline so that pupils work with a sense of responsibility and trust. Pupils are expected to be considerate, courteous, honest and industrious. Any breach of good manners or of common sense is a breach of the School Rules as is any action which may lower the School's good name. Bullying is regarded as a most serious offence. Alcohol, proscribed drugs and smoking are banned. Every member of the School is expected to take a pride in his or her appearance and to wear smart school uniform.

There is a Medical Centre with qualified staff. The School Medical Officer has special responsibility for boarders. A qualified Counsellor is available to all pupils for confidential counselling. The school also has a full-time Chaplain.

Sport and Leisure Activities. A number of different sports are pursued including Athletics, Badminton, Cricket, Cross-Country, Eton Fives, Fencing, Golf, Hockey, Judo, Lacrosse, Netball, Rowing, Rugby, Shooting, Soccer, Squash, Swimming and Tennis. Team games are encouraged and pupils selected for regional and national squads.

There is a flourishing Duke of Edinburgh's Award scheme at all levels. The CCF, community service, work experience and 'Young Enterprise' are offered, along with clubs for gymnastics, drama, computing and technology. Regular school theatre productions, orchestral and choral concerts achieve high standards of performance.

Careers. A team of advisors, internal and external, is directed by the Head of Careers. Heads of House oversee pupils' applications for higher education, together with parents and Careers advisors. The great majority of leavers proceeds to university and higher education.

Entry. Entry to the Preparatory School from the age of 3 onwards and entry to the Senior School from 11. The School's Entrance Assessments and an interview are required. Sixth Form entry normally requires at least 6 A*–C grades at GCSE with A or B grades in the four subjects chosen for A Level.

Scholarships and Bursaries. (*see Scholarship Entries section*). Details of the range of awards (eg academic, music, art, sport) can be obtained from the School.

Fees per term (from April 2008). Day Pupils: Nursery £2,190; Preparatory £2,585–£3,453; Senior £4,207–£4,947. Boarding Pupils: £7,076–£7,816.

Old Berkhamstedians. President: Mrs Natasha Charlton, 1 Warwick Close, Aston Clinton, Bucks HP22 5JF. Tel: 01296 631371.

Charitable status. Berkhamsted Collegiate School is a Registered Charity, number 311056. It is a leading Charitable School in the field of Junior and Secondary Education.

Birkdale School

Oakholme Road Sheffield S10 3DH
Tel: 0114 266 8408
Fax: 0114 267 1947
e-mail: headmaster@birkdaleschool.org.uk
admissions@birkdaleschool.org.uk
enquiries@birkdaleschool.org.uk
website: www.birkdaleschool.org.uk

Birkdale School is a day school for 790 pupils, boys from 4 to 18 with a co-educational Sixth Form. The 4–11 Preparatory School is on a separate campus nearby. (*For further details see IAPS section.*) The Sixth Form was launched in 1988 and now has around 180 pupils, 95% of whom in recent years have entered university. The Governing Body is in membership of the Association of Governing Bodies of Independent Schools.

Motto: '*Res non verba*'

Chairman of Governors: Revd S A P Hunter, JP, MA

The Rt Revd C Ashton, MA
D F Booker, BA, FCA
M H Crosby, MA
Dr J R Goepel, MBChB, FRCPath
Revd M Porter, BA, BTh, MA
Mrs A M Rees, MA, BEd, FRSA
Dr R Richardson
Mrs M C Townsend, BSc, BDS, MA
J A Viner, MA, MBA, DipM, MCIM
Mrs K M Walker

Bursar and Clerk to the Governors: D H Taylor, BSc

***Head Master*: R J Court**, MA Clare College, Cambridge

Deputy Head: A S Gloag, BA

Director of Studies: E Stevens, BSc

Senior Tutors:
K D Brook, BSc
S H Kenyon, MA
Mrs A M Oliver, BA
Mrs H A Parsons, MA
Mrs V Stolz, BEd

Assistant Staff:
G T AbouZeid, BSc, PhD
*J D Allen, BSc
A J Alsop, BSc
S Bacsich, MA
M J Beardsley, BA
Miss E Bottaro, MA
*Mrs S J Burt, BA
T Clark, BSc
Mrs H Clark, BSc
*M S Clarke, MA
C J Cook, BSc
*R J Cottom, BEd
*D Craddock, BEng
*Mrs M A Daly, BA
N Deans, BA
*S R Gordon, MA
Dr J Greenhalgh, MA, PhD
Mrs R J Greenslade, MA
S Haslam, BSc, PhD
*R D Heaton, BEd
*Mrs K M Higham, BA, MEd
J C Hudson, MA
*A M Jordan, BMus
D J Julian, BA
*P Lancaster, BEd
*Mrs M Linford, MEd
Miss K McKay, BA
Miss S D Miles, BA
Mrs L J Mitchell
*Dr P D Myatt, BSc, DPhil
*W M Newton, BSc, PhD
J R Nolan, BEng
H Parker, BSc
*T J Pearson, BA
Mrs P Pickford, BA
Dr S Pitfield, PhD, BMus
M A Potter, BEd
*Mrs M B Reynolds, BEd, Cert SocEd Studies, PGCert Dyslexia/Literacy
S T Reynolds, BSc
*M Roach, BSc
C F Rodgers, BSc
*M H Rose, MA
*Mrs K Rose, MA
*Mrs F Rusling, BA
Mrs S L Ryan, BA
A M Sanderson, MA
Mrs J A Savage, BA
Miss R M Sever, MA
*Mrs H V Sherborne, MA
P C Snell, BSc
Mrs F M Stevens, BA
*S B Stoddard, BA
Mrs H Thaw, BA
J J Turner, MEd
Mrs J M White, BSc
A J Woodley, BEd

Librarian: Mrs J McQuillin

Preparatory School
Acting Head of Prep School: J R Leighton, BEd
Head of Prep School (*from January 2009*): C J Burch, BA, PGCE

Director of Studies: A J Oakey, MSc Ed, BA
Senior Mistress: Mrs J Witte, MA, BEd
Deputy Head: J R Leighton, BEd

Assistant Staff:
Mrs E J Arcari, BA
Mrs F Bailey, BA, PGCE
Mrs E A Barratt, BA
Miss J V Black, MSc, BEd
Mrs C Brewster, BA, DipSEN, PGDip Dyslexia
Mrs C A Carter-Shepherd, BA
N Dymock, BSc
Mrs C Edge
Mrs H E Fletcher, BMus
Mrs C Grover, BA
Mrs N Hall, CertEd
D P Jones, GGSM
Mrs M Jones, BEd
F G Kirkham, TD, BEd
Miss R M Kitt, BEd
J M Lockwood, MPhil, BA
J Marsh, BSc
Mrs K J Massey, MA
Mrs F G Noble, DipAD, BEd
Mrs H J Oakey, BEd
Mrs C Simpson, CertEd, DipSEN, DipSpLD Dys
Mrs J E Taylor, CertEd
Mrs G Vallance, CertEd, CertDys
Mrs F L M Walton, MA
Mrs P Watkin, BA
Mrs M S Whitt, BA

Visiting Music Staff:
Miss L Beavers (*Clarinet/Saxophone*)
J Beatty, PPRNCM, PgDip (*Trombone*)
G Bish, BMus (*Guitar*)
T Canneli (*Percussion*)
J Draper (*Cello*)
Ms J Dungworth (*Oboe*)
T James (*French Horn*)
J A Kirwan (*Guitar*)
Mrs V Leppard, BMus, LRAM (*Flute/Piano*)
Miss C L Osborne, BMus, MMus, LRAM (*Singing*)
M Redfearn, BMus, LTCL (*Trumpet*)
D Sanderson, BEd, LRAM, ARCM, TL (*Piano*)
Dr M Slater (*Piano/Music Theory*)
Mrs S Slater, BA (*Flute*)
A Thompson, BMus, CertPG Perf Studies (*Trumpet*)
Mrs E Tipple, ARCM, BMus (*Violin/Viola*)
Mrs J Wright, ARMSC, GRSM (*Violin*)

Head Master's Secretary: Ms S van der Merwe, BSc

Registrar: Mrs C M Brown, BA

Set in a pleasant residential area near the University 1.5 miles from the city centre, and 5 miles from the Peak District National Park, the school has expanded in recent years to provide for Sheffield and South Yorkshire the only independent secondary school for boys, with a co-educational Sixth Form. Birkdale Preparatory School for 300 boys is on a separate campus half a mile from the Senior School. School coaches bring pupils from Worksop, Chesterfield, North Derbyshire, Rotherham and Barnsley.

Birkdale is a Christian school, reflecting its foundation in the evangelical tradition. There is nothing exclusive about this: entrance is open to all, and there is no denominational emphasis. We seek to develop the full potential of each individual: body, mind and spirit. Within a framework of high academic standards, pastoral care is given a high priority, balanced by an emphasis on sport and outdoor pursuits, music and drama with a range of extra-curricular activities available.

At 18, over 95% of pupils go on to university, with a good proportion each year gaining places at Oxford and Cambridge.

Admission. The main ages of admission are at 4, 7, 11 and 16, although it is possible to admit pupils at other ages if a place is available. Entrance examinations for candidates at 11 are held annually towards the end of January. Entrance to the co-educational Sixth Form is subject to interview and a satisfactory performance in GCSE examinations. In the first instance, enquiries should be addressed to the Registrar.

Academic Curriculum. Over 20 subjects are offered at AS and A level. A full range of academic subjects are offered to GCSE. All pupils study English Language and Literature, Mathematics, Double Award Science, at least one Modern Foreign Language (French, German, Spanish) and at least one of the Humanities subjects (Classical Studies, Geography, History, RE). Optional subjects include Art, DT: Electronic Products, DT: Resistant Materials, PE, Latin, Drama and Music. The wider curriculum includes ICT, Religious Education, Health Education, Careers and Economic Awareness. Latin, German and Spanish are compulsory subjects in the Lower School (11–13) in addition to the usual range of National Curriculum subjects.

Games and Outdoor Pursuits. The major games are Rugby, Soccer, Cricket and Athletics, with Cross Country, Hockey, Netball, Tennis, Squash, Basketball, Volleyball, Swimming and Golf also available. A £2 million sports pavilion was opened in 2006 at the playing fields which are a short bus ride away from the school. All members of the school play games weekly. Additional team practices take place on Saturdays or at other times, and there is a full fixture list in the major sports. The school enjoys regular use of the university swimming pool nearby. Additionally, we use two local international venues, Ponds Forge and the English Institute of Sport for basketball, netball, dance and athletics. Birkdale's Sports Hall is at the centre of the Senior School campus.

Outdoor Pursuits play an important part in the overall leadership training programme. All members of the school participate in regular training sessions leading in each age group to a major expedition. This programme culminates in the 4th Form camp held annually in Snowdonia: this includes a trek involving all participants in leadership training. Virtually all members of the Third Form take the Bronze Award of the Duke of Edinburgh's Award Scheme, and an increasing number progress to Silver and Gold awards.

Music and the Arts. Music, Art and Drama flourish both within and outside the formal curriculum. A full annual programme of dramatic and musical productions is arranged. Over 120 pupils receive weekly instrumental music lessons at school, and a wide range of orchestras and choirs provide opportunities for pupils to experience group musical activities at an appropriate level.

Extra-Curricular Activities. There is a broad range of clubs and societies which meet at lunchtime and outside the formal school day, providing opportunities for members of the school to explore and excel in activities such as Chess, Debating, Design and Drama, as well as in the usual activities such as sport, outdoor pursuits, art and music.

Careers. The school is a member of the Independent Schools' Careers Organisation, and there is a well equipped Careers Centre in the Grayson Building. A biennial Careers Convention is held in the school and regular visits are made by services liaison officers and others to give advice and help to individual members of the school under the guidance of the school's careers staff.

All members of the Lower Sixth participate in a Work Experience scheme for a week, placed in a work environment in line with their possible choice of career.

The school runs Young Enterprise companies each year which introduce Sixth Formers to the world of business and management, and awards are often won in local competition.

Information and Communications Technology. In addition to the main ICT Centre, the computer network extends throughout the Campuses of both the Senior and Preparatory schools. Each member of the school is able to access the system in every part of the school. ICT is incorporated in a variety of ways into teaching across the curriculum. All pupils have supervised access to the Internet.

Learning Support Unit. Both the Senior and Preparatory school have their own Learning Support Centres. Pupils with dyslexic difficulties are given expert help within the school context and in full consultation with subject staff and are encouraged to achieve their full potential in public examinations.

Fees per term (2008-2009). Senior School £3,248, Preparatory School £2,682, Pre-Preparatory Department £2,267, including lunches, books and stationery.

Scholarships. (*see Scholarship Entries section*). The following Scholarships are available: Academic Scholarships at 11 and 16; Music Scholarships at 11 and 16.

Most scholarships are worth up to 25% of fees, with Bursaries available up to 100% of fees in cases of need.

Charitable status. Birkdale School is a Registered Charity, number 1018973, and a Company Limited by Guarantee, registered in England, number 2792166. It exists to develop the full potential of its members within a Christian community.

Birkenhead School

58 Beresford Road Oxton Birkenhead Merseyside CH43 2JD
Tel: 0151 652 4014
Fax: 0151 651 3091
e-mail: enquire@birkenheadschool.co.uk
website: www.birkenheadschool.co.uk

Birkenhead School was opened in 1860, with the object of providing a public-school education, both Classical and Modern.

Motto: *'Beati mundo corde'*

Visitor: The Rt Revd The Lord Bishop of Chester, DD

President: The Rt Hon Lord Nicholls of Birkenhead, MA Cantab, LLB, Hon LLD Liverpool

Vice-Presidents:	*Emeritus Vice-Presidents*:
S J Haggett	W T C Rankin
D I Mackay	K J Speakman-Brown
J A Gwilliam	H W McCready
A G Hurton	G De Ritter
Lord Wade of Chorlton	D A Fletcher
A Whittam Smith	
A B L Thomson	

Governors:
Chairman: Dr A G Mathie, MB, BSc, FRCGP
I G Boumphrey
A J Cross, LLB
Mrs L Dodd, BA, FSI
C C Johnson, FRICS, FSVA
G E Jones, MA
Dr J K Moore, FRCA, MBA
M B Owen, BA
W D C Rushworth, BA
A Sutton, MA, FCA
A F Watson, FCA

***Headmaster*: D J Clark**, MA Exeter College, Oxford

Deputy Headmaster: D R Edmunds, BSc

Deputy Head (*Academic*): R A Barlow, BSc

Assistant Head: M Roden, BA

Assistant Head: C D McKie, MA (*Head of History*)

Bursar and Clerk to the Governors: C F Button, BSc, CDir

Assistant Teachers:
W I H Allister, MA
P G Armstrong, BSc (*Head of Year 8*)
A J Blain, BEd (*Head of Art*)
K M Britton, MA, MSc
R J Brookes MA (*Head of Modern Languages*)
S Burns, MSc
S W Clark
A S Davies, MA (*Head of ICT*)
G J Ellis, BEd (*Director of Music*)
J L Fox, MA
S M Gill, MA (*Head of Geography*)
Mrs M T Gonzalez BA (*Head of Classics*)
Ms E A Grey, BA (*Head of Religious Education*)
M J Hayward, BSc (*Head of Science*)
D A Hendry, BEd (*Head of Year 11*)
T M Higginbottom, BEng
D W Highcock, BSc (*Head of Physics*)
Ms M L Holgate, BA (*Head of French*)
S W Hope, BSc (*Head of Mathematics*)
G Hopkins, MA (*Head of Sixth Form*)
W A Hughes, MA, PhD (*Head of Biology, Head of Year 9*)
P Lindberg, BSc (*Head of Chemistry, Assistant Head of Sixth Form*)
R E Lytollis, BSc (*Head of Physical Education*)
Mrs A McGoldrick, BA (*Head of English*)
J McGrath, MA (*Head of Careers*)
Miss S E McIlwaine, BEd (*Head of Instrumental Music*)
J G Melville, MSc
J H C Moore, BA
S J Parry, BA (*Head of Year 10*)
C Rimmer, BA
D K Rule, BA (*Head of Economics*)
A Rymer, BSc
A J Sheldon, BSc
C L Smale, MA
Ms L Smeaton, BA (*Head of Year 7*)
Miss J M Smith, BA
Miss L D Swift, BSc
M L Warrilow, BSc
Ms E Wilday, BA
R G Wiltshire, BSc (*Head of Design Technology*)

Houses and Housemasters:
Beresford House: C L Smale
Shrewsbury House: A W Rymer
Bidston House: K M Britton
Kingsmead House: J G Melville

Chaplain: Revd Canon Ian Davenport
Librarian: Mrs E Reeve, BA
SSI: Captain Alan Joseph, BEM
Careers Liaison Officer: P Currall
Nurse: Mrs J Pizer, RGN, RSCN
Commercial Manager: B Donelan

Preparatory School

Headmistress: Mrs J A Skelly, BEd
Deputy Head: M H Anderton, MSc

Assistant Staff:

Mrs V Belchier, TCert	Mrs L J Dale-Jones, BEd
Miss A C Bentley, BA	N J Frowe, BA
N J Corran, BEng	Mr R A Halpin, BSc
Miss S J Harris, BA	Ms P Relph, BA
Mrs D M Hodgkinson, TCert	Mrs S Sharman, TCert
Mrs S J Hurst, BA (*Head of KS1*)	Mrs I Smith, TCert
	M G Stockdale, BA
Dr S M Jarvis, BSc, PhD	Miss E Talbot, BSc
Mrs P J McDonald, TCert	Miss A C Wells, BA
Mrs S G Mills, BEd	Miss C E Winn, BSc
Mrs S Porter, TCert	Mrs C E Winn, BEd

The School consists of a Nursery, a Pre-Prep, a Preparatory School and a Senior School including a Sixth Form. Previously an all-boys School, the Sixth Form became co-educational in September 2000 and the remainder of the School became co-educational in 2008. Heads of Year and Head of Sixth Form have direct responsibility for the pastoral welfare of pupils in their section of the School and each oversees and coordinates the work of a team of Form Tutors. Pupils in Years 7 and 8 are mostly taught in their own building, *Overdale*.

Pupils come from all areas of Wirral, North Cheshire and North Wales. Public transport is good and there is an extensive network of School buses.

The School buildings are grouped around a spacious campus in the residential area of Oxton, and a development programme in recent years has added very considerably to the School's already extensive facilities. The Preparatory School occupies the whole of the Shrewsbury Road site, a purpose-built Infant Department was completed in 1992 and a new Pre-Prep was opened in October 2004. Developments in the Senior School include a new Science Block, a Sports Hall, and most recently a new Music Department, a new IT Suite within the Modern Languages building and a substantial extension to facilities for Technology and Electronics. Separate recreational facilities for Sixth Form and Years 7–11 have also been developed. An indoor climbing wall was opened in 2001 and major building work is planned for 2008–2009.

Curriculum. All pupils follow a common curriculum in Years 7 and 8 with a choice of two languages from French, Latin, German or Spanish in Year 8. The wide spectrum of subjects means that pupils are then ideally placed to make GCSE option choices at the end of Year 9. As well as the compulsory subjects – Mathematics, English, and three Sciences – pupils choose four more subjects from Art, French, Design Technology, Geography, German, Greek, Spanish, Religious Studies, History, Latin and Music. Almost all combinations are possible, but attention is given to ensuring at this stage that pupils choose appropriate subjects which will not restrict their future career choices. The School has remained committed to the teaching of Biology, Chemistry and Physics as separate subjects, but also offers Dual Award Science for some pupils. An "Enhancement" option in Year 10 includes non-examined drama, the European Computer Driving Licence, the Sports Leaders certificate, and a Thinking Skills course. A programme of Personal Social and Health Education is provided for all pupils from Year 7 to Year 11, drawing on external agencies, as well as the School's own expertise. Compulsory Games and PE lessons not only support our highly successful sports teams but are also based on a philosophy of "Games for all" with students of all abilities encouraged to enjoy physical activity by specialist games teachers.

The vast majority of pupils move into an academic Sixth Form environment where their AS and A Level preparation is geared towards post-18 university openings. Lower Sixth pupils can choose four AS Levels from Ancient History, Art, Biology, Chemistry, Design and Technology, Economics, Electronics, English Language, English Literature, French, Further Mathematics, Geography, German, Greek, History, ICT, Latin, Mathematics, Music, Physical Education, Physics, Religious Studies, Spanish and Theatre Studies. AS Critical Thinking and AS General Studies are offered as additional options within the "Beyond the Curriculum" programme, which also includes the European Computer Driving Licence, Young Enterprise, Sculpture and our innovative outreach programme

"Science in the Community". Upper Sixth students continue with three or four A Levels. An important part of the curriculum for all Sixth Form pupils is the Friday Lecture given by guest speakers from a wide range of backgrounds. The Careers Department provides talks and individual preparation for university applications; for most pupils the careers staff will have been involved in their decision-making from as early as Year 9. Advice on direct employment is also offered, although in practice over 95% of leavers move into Higher Education.

School Chapel. The School has its own Chapel and close links with St Saviour's, the local parish church and its Chaplains. There is an outstanding Chapel Choir which sings at daily services and at the regular Sunday Evensong. Each summer the Chapel Choir performs in cathedrals and churches both in Britain and abroad.

Parents' Association. There is an active Parents' Association which provides opportunities for parents to meet informally and organises social events, as well as being involved on a day-to-day basis in the life of the School and in the funding of special projects.

Societies. Involvement in extra-curricular activities is strongly encouraged and there is a wide range of clubs from which to choose, including scientific, cultural and recreational. There is a strong tradition of drama, with regular productions, and an annual House Drama competition. The School has an Orchestra, a Concert Band and Brass Ensemble. The School has a fine reputation for choral music and for a number of years the Choral Society, consisting of pupils, parents and friends of the School, has performed a major choral work annually at the Philharmonic Hall in Liverpool.

Games. Competitive sports are rugby, hockey, netball and lacrosse during the winter terms and cricket, athletics, tennis, rounders and golf during the summer. There are representative teams at all levels and the playing fields cover about 40 acres on three different sites. At McAllester Field a floodlit astroturf surface for hockey and tennis is shared with Oxton Cricket Club. A large sports complex, including a squash court and climbing wall, provides a focus for the School's comprehensive 'Sport for All' programme.

CCF and Outdoor Pursuits. The School has Army, Navy and RAF sections. From Year 9 onwards pupils may join one of these sections. The School runs its own Duke of Edinburgh's Award Scheme. Outdoor Pursuits also form part of the regular games programme. Climbing is available as part of the PE curriculum. The School also has a Community Service programme.

Admission is by progression from Birkenhead Preparatory School or by the School's own Entrance and Scholarship Examination held on a Saturday at the end of January for pupils over ten but not over twelve on 1st September. Entrance at thirteen is through the Common Entrance Examination or our own Supplementary Examination. Sixth Form entrants are also welcome and this selection is based on GCSE grades and interview. Prospective parents are always welcome to visit the School and the Headmaster is happy to meet parents and assist with queries over dates, methods of entry, SEN and learning support.

Fees per term (2008-2009). Senior School £2,785–£2,909; Preparatory School £2,049–£2,235. The Birkenhead School Foundation Trust was established in 1998 to provide Bursaries and Funded Places. Scholarships are also available. Particulars may be obtained from the Headmaster.

The Old Birkonian Society. Hon Secretary: Ian W Bakewell, Richmond Villa, 1 Middlewood Road, Aughton L39 6RG.

Charitable status. Birkenhead School is a Registered Charity, number 1093419. Our charitable status means the School not only accepts fee paying pupils but can offer places to able children from less advantaged backgrounds.

Bishop's Stortford College

Maze Green Road Bishop's Stortford Herts CM23 2PJ
Tel: 01279 838575
Fax: 01279 836570
e-mail: admissions@bsc.biblio.net
website: www.bishops-stortford-college.herts.sch.uk

Bishop's Stortford College is a friendly, co-educational, day and boarding community providing high academic standards, good discipline and an excellent all-round education. We aim to equip our pupils with the vital qualifications, skills, adaptability and, above all, confidence to thrive as adults in a rapidly changing world. A flourishing Junior School and a Pre-Prep Department, sharing many facilities with the Senior School, give all the advantages of educational continuity whilst retaining their own distinctive characters.

When founded in 1868, it was intended that the College should provide "a liberal and religious education" acceptable to non-conformist families in the Eastern Counties. In practice, Bishop's Stortford College welcomes boys and girls of all denominations and faiths, and, while the majority of present pupils' homes are in the Home Counties and East Anglia, a substantial number of parents work and live overseas.

Motto: '*Soli Deo Gloria*'.

Governing Council:
J R Tee, MA (*Chairman*)
P J Hargrave, BSc, PhD (*Vice-Chairman*)
C Havers, MA
Mrs S Jellis
Sir Stephen Lander
L Lindop, ACMA
R B Norden, FRICS
Mrs I Pearman, MA, MRICS
Dr J Swainsbury
M Farmer
G Brant, MA
A A Trigg
A M Nicholls, MA, PhD

***Headmaster*: J G Trotman**, MA (St Edmund Hall, Oxford)

Assistant staff:
* *Head of Department*
† *Housemaster/mistress*

Mrs K Adkins, CertEd
N P Alexander, MSc (**Mathematics*)
Dr G Allcock, BSc, PhD (*Careers Manager*)
S Bacon, BSc (**ICT*)
Mrs H G Bailey, BA (**German*)
A H Baker, BSc (**Physics*)
C S Bannister, MA (**Chemistry*)
P Bashford
J N Birchall, MA (**Business Studies/Economics*)
T G S Borton, BA (*Head of Sixth Form*)
Mrs S J Bousfield, BA
Mrs M Brace, BA
G R Brooks, BA (*Joint Deputy Head*)
Mrs S Brown, BA
A M Bruce, BA (*Director of College Music*)
C Bruce, BA
C de Bruyn
Mrs P Bull, BA
Ms N Byart, BSc
Ms E Chaplin, BA
Mrs L G Dickinson, BA
M Drury, BSc
Mrs S Ellison, BA (**English*)
B Fearnley, BA
Miss C Flynn, BA
Mrs F M Freckelton, MSc
Mrs M E P Garrett, ALA (*Librarian*)
Ms M Götze
Ms E Greenwood, BA
P M Griffin, BSc (*†School House*)
Mrs K Griffiths (*Marketing Coordinator*)
Miss M K Harvey
T A Herbert, MA (*Examinations*)
Mrs P Hinge, BSc
R M Honey, MA (**Art, †Robert Pearce House*)

T G Hudson, MA (*Modern Languages*)
K Irvine, BA
Mrs K King, BA
J Kirton, BSc
R D Kisby, BA, DPE (**PE*)
Mrs W E Livingstone-Chambers
Mrs G Lynch, MA (**Latin, †Collett House*)
Mrs E Mackenzie-Lambert, BSc (*†Sutton House*)
Miss V Marriott, BA
Mrs J Marshall, BSc
Revd M D Marshall, BSc (*Chaplain*)
Mrs P Mullender, MA (*Senior Mistress, †Benson House*)
Ms C I Munck, BA
Mrs C E Murphy, BA
R Norman, BA (*Director of Drama*)
I Nunez, BMus, PGDip, MM GSMD
P W O'Connor, PhD (**Geography*)
Ms E Oakley, MSc
Mrs J Oldfield, BSc
J Parker
Mrs A Picton, BA
N J Prowse, BSc
Mrs A Self, BA
Mrs H Sheehan, BA
Mrs A N Sloman, CertEd (**Girls' Games, †Young House*)
T Stuart, MA (**History*)
M A Tomkys, BA (**Media, †Hayward House*)
J H Trant, BA (**Design & Technology*)
J F Wareham, BA
G Westell, BA
Mrs E A Wheeler, BSc
C H Williams, BSc (*Director of Studies*)
Mrs F H M Williams, BA (*Librarian; ESL*)
Mrs J Williams, BSc
J Williams, PhD (**Science*)
Mrs S J Wilson, BA (*†Alliott House*)
Mrs J Windley
Mrs P Wonfor, BA, BSc
C J Woodhouse, BSc (*Joint Deputy Head*)
Mrs T Wright, MA

Learning Support:
Mrs R J Gearing, CertEd, DipSpLD
Mrs K M F Hunt, CertEd, DipSpLD

Junior School
Head of Junior School: J A Greathead, BEd

S Bailey, CertEd (**Geography*)
A R J Barnard
Mrs R Borthwick, BA
M Brett, BA
Mrs K Brooks, BA
Miss B Callow, BEd
R J Clough, BA
N B Courtman, BA (**Mathematics*)
M A Crossley, BEd (*Joint Deputy Head*)
N R Eddom, BEd
D Edwards, BA (*Joint Deputy Head*)
C W Fisher, BA (**French*)
Mrs V J Foulkes-Arnold, BEd (*Senior Mistress*)
Mrs T Handford, BSc (**Science*)
A Hanrahan, MA
Mrs N P Hatchett, BEd
†A J Hathaway, Bed
†Mrs A Hathaway
W A Heap, PhD
D A Herd, BSc
J J Herd, BSc
M Ingham, BSc
E C Jones, LLB
G Millard, BA
C I Murchie, BA
Mrs S Murchie, BA
Miss E J Neville, BA (**Art*)
Mrs J North, BA
Miss K Perkins, BA
Mrs R A Pike, BA (*Librarian*)
M J Self, BSocSc
Mrs W Sharman, MSc
Mrs L Shepherd, BEd
Miss A Shields, BA
G Sloman, BA
J Spackman, BSc
G Sutcliffe, BA
Miss K Taylor, BA

Pre-Preparatory Department:
Head: Mrs A M Cullum, BA

Miss E Barfoot
Mrs B J Birley, CertEd
Mrs P Field
Mrs A D Foy, RSA, SPLD, CLANSA
Mrs P Hopkinson, BA
Mrs C Martin, MA
Mrs S Pearson-Philips, BEd
Mrs J Perkins, MEd
Mrs R Pradhan
Mrs J Prowse, BA
Mrs S J Shepherd
Miss L Smith, BSc

Bursar: I J McCulloch

Senior School Admissions Officer: Mrs M-L Gough
Junior School Admissions Officer: Mrs F Brett

There are 497 boys and girls in the Senior School (boarders and day), 425 boys and girls in the Junior School and 118 in the Pre-Prep Department.

Location. Bishop's Stortford is almost mid-way between London and Cambridge and is quickly reached from Liverpool Street or via the M25 and M11 motorways. Stansted Airport is a ten minute drive. The College is situated on the edge of the town adjacent to open countryside. The gardens and grounds cover over 100 acres.

Facilities. In addition to the various classroom blocks, there are modern Science Laboratories, a Language Laboratory and three Computer Centres; there are well-equipped centres for Art, Design and Technology and Music/Drama and a purpose-built Centre for Physics, Technology and Information Technology. The main school Library and state-of-the-art Swimming Pool are notable features. The Houses offer a comfortable, family-like environment with computer access and library facilities on hand.

At the centre of the School stands the Memorial Hall, used daily for Assembly, which was erected in 1921 as a memorial to Old Boys who served and fell in the 1914–18 war.

Academic Organisation. The Curriculum is designed to give as broad a course of study as possible up to the inevitable specialisation at A and AS Level and Oxbridge entry.

In addition to the three Sciences, French, English, Maths, Geography and History, all new pupils joining the Fourth Form (Year 9) take Design and Technology, ICT, Art and Music as well as one period each of RE and PE/Swimming. Most also begin German and a significant number continue with Latin.

In the Lower and Upper Fifth Forms (Years 10 and 11), the 'core' subjects, taken by all, are English, English Literature, Maths and the three Sciences. Four other subjects, one of which must be a modern foreign language, are chosen from History, Geography, Design and Technology, Latin, French, German, Art, Music, Drama and Religious Studies. Pupils also have one period each of RE, PE/Swimming and ICT. GCSE Spanish can also be taken as an additional subject outside the normal timetable.

At all stages, progress is carefully monitored by Housemasters, Housemistresses and Tutors, and in Staff Meetings.

The Sixth Form. Pupils will choose between three and five subjects at AS level in the Lower Sixth, before specialising in three or four in the Upper Sixth at A2 level. Some may take an extra AS level in the Upper Sixth, while others will take one of a variety of extension subjects such as Japanese or Spanish. Sixth Formers will select from the following subjects: Art, Biology, Business Studies, Chemistry, Classical Civilisation, Design and Technology, Economics, English Literature, French, Geography, German, History, Maths, Further Maths, Latin, Media Studies, Music, Music Technology, Physical Education, Physics, Politics, Psychology, Theatre Studies

An extensive PHSE programme operates throughout the school and there is a weekly Upper Sixth Form lecture.

Each Department organises visits and invites guest speakers to meetings of Societies, which are held in lunch hours or evenings. These, together with small group teaching, seminars and excellent resources, help to encourage students to develop their self-reliance, their analytical skills and their spirit of academic enquiry to equip them for Higher Education and beyond.

The progress of Sixth Formers is constantly assessed by House Masters/Mistresses and Academic Tutors, and in Staff Meetings under the overall supervision of the Head of Sixth Form. Parents are closely involved and regular Parents' Meetings are held.

Throughout the Senior School, grades for Effort and Attainment are given twice termly, and full written reports are sent home twice a year for each year group.

Careers. A purpose built Careers Centre is open daily and managed by specialist staff. The College has close ties with ISCO, local commerce and industry and the Hertfordshire Careers Service. Links with local business are strong and there is an extensive programme of Work Shadowing/Experience organised for pupils in the Upper Fifth and Lower Sixth Forms.

Worship. The Religious Instruction and Sunday Worship are inter-denominational. Pupils are prepared for membership of their own Churches and a Confirmation Service is held each year.

Activities. Whether as Boarders or Day Pupils, our young people are involved in an environment of wholehearted participation. A diverse range of extra-curricular activities alongside high academic standards provides the opportunity for every child to discover areas of interest and success that might otherwise lie untapped.

In addition to the meetings of Clubs and Societies, Wednesday and Friday sessions are set aside within the timetable for Activities, including those related to The Duke of Edinburgh's Award. We thus encourage pupils to pursue their own interests and introduce them to others, so that they will wish to carry these on into their spare time and beyond the confines of the School. Projects which promote a willingness to serve others are an important aspect of the breadth of activity offered.

Music and Drama. An interest in and appreciation of all kinds of music is encouraged throughout the school. In their 1st and 2nd Forms (Years 3 & 4), all pupils in the Junior School are taught an instrument in class and those who show promise are encouraged to continue individually in the Senior School.

There is an Orchestra, Wind Band, Dance Band and numerous other ensembles, a Choral Society, a Chapel Choir and a Chamber Choir. Pupils are also encouraged to make music in small groups from the earliest stages. There is a fully equipped Recording Studio. The Music Staff includes 27 visiting teachers of singing and all the main instruments, together with the Director of Music, 2 Assistant Directors and a Musician in Residence. The House Music Competition is a major event in the school year, involving all pupils. Pupils have regular opportunities to perform in public at Pupils' Concerts and in School Assemblies. Overseas tours also provide excellent performing experience.

Drama is an area of strength with significant developments in recent years to the theatre facilities, curriculum and performing opportunities. There are numerous opportunities for all pupils to participate. AS and A level Theatre Studies are offered, as is GCSE Drama.

Sport. The College has an excellent reputation in all areas of sporting achievement. Physical Education is taught in the Fourth and Fifth Forms and facilities include a Sports Hall, an impressive indoor swimming pool, two floodlit all-weather surface hockey pitches, hard tennis courts and 100 acres of playing fields.

Health. The Medical Centre is staffed by a resident Sister and her SEN Assistant. Regular Surgeries are held by the School's Medical Officer.

Varied and wholesome meals are provided in the College central Dining Hall, with plenty of choice. All day pupils take lunch at School and the cost is included in the fees.

Junior School. The organisation of the Junior School (for pupils up to age 13+) is largely separate from that of the Senior School, but the curricula of the two Schools are carefully integrated. Pupils are able to share Senior School resources in Sport, Design and Technology, Music and Drama.

(*For further details see entry in IAPS section.*)

Admission. The main ages of admission are 4, 7, 11, 13 and 16, but entry at intermediate stages is possible. Entry to the Senior School at 13+ is based on school reference, interview and entry test results. Sixth Form Entry Interviews and Examinations are held in the November before year of entry.

Scholarships. (*see Scholarship Entries section*). Academic, Art and Music Scholarships are awarded at three levels: (1) Sixth Form; (2) 13+ for Senior School Entry; (3) 10+ or 11+ for pupils entering the Junior School. All awards may be supplemented by Bursaries according to need.

Fees per term (2008-2009). Senior School: Full Boarders £6,281; Weekly Boarders £6,218; Day £4,517.

Junior School: Full Boarders £4,376–£4,761; Weekly Boarders £4,332–£4,713; Day £3,221–£3,613; Pre-Prep £2,112.

Fees are inclusive except for individual music tuition.

Charitable status. The Incorporated Bishop's Stortford College Association is a Registered Charity, number 311057. Its aims and objectives are to provide high quality Independent Boarding and Day education for boys and girls from age 4 to 18.

Bloxham School

A Woodard School

Bloxham Banbury Oxon OX15 4PE

Tel: 01295 720222
01295 724341 Headmaster
Fax: 01295 721714 Bursar
01295 721897 Registrar
01295 722962 Headmaster
e-mail: registrar@bloxhamschool.com
website: www.bloxhamschool.com

The School was founded in 1860 by the Revd P R Egerton. Since 1896 it has been a member of the Woodard Corporation.

Motto: '*Justorum Semita Lux Splendens.*'

The School Council of Governors:

Provost: The Rt Revd Lindsay Urwin

Chairman: B Hurst, Esq, BSc, CEng, FIEE

Members:

P J P Barwell, MBE
M R Deeley, Esq
D J B Long, Esq, BA
C P Jackson, Esq
R E Towner, Esq, MA
W J Wright, Esq, AMI MechE
N J E Bankes, Esq
Mrs M S Brounger, LLB
Mrs R A H Needham
Mrs F M Turner
Mrs P J Woodhouse, BMus Hons
M S Hedges, Esq, MA, FCA, FRSA

***Headmaster*: M E Allbrook**, MA

Deputy Head: Mrs E C Jeffrey, BA

Director of Studies: D A Cooper, BSc, BEd, MSc, MCollP

Chaplain: The Revd M G Price, MA, MPhil

Head of Sixth Form: C D Stewart, BA

Head of Lower School: G A Stindt, BSc

Teaching Staff:
* *Head of Department*

T I Hatton, BA (*Director of Sixth Form Studies; *History*)
C Newbould, BSc
S J Batten, MA (*Head of Scholars*)
T M Skevington, BEd (**Design & Technology*)
G P Cruden, BA
J L Ekers, MSc
C N Boyns, BSc
M Pye, DipFA (*Director of Art*)
C V Atkinson, BA (**Drama*)
J P Horton, CertEd (*Director of Sport*)
A G Whiffin, MA (**English*)
A C Benn, MA
N StJ D Pigott, BA (**Geography*)
J F Berry, BSc (**Mathematics*)
H J Alexander, MA (*Head of Dyslexia Course*)

D F McLellan, BA (**Modern Languages*)
Mrs J H White, BEd
M J M Moir, BSc
Mrs B M Whitehead, BA
N E Evans, BSc
D R Best, BA
R J Thompson, BSc (**Business Studies*)
Mrs A L Cooper, BA, BAdmin
Miss A Hickling, BA
D N Perrin, MA
M D Bull, BA
Ms M P Chaparro-Rincon, BA
Dr C E Evans, PhD, MSc
P Schonken, BCom (**ICT*)
A Goldsmith, BA
Miss G T Barbour, BA
Mrs C M McCaffrey, MA
Dr S Heaney, BA
Miss N Park, BSc
R W F Hastings, BA
R Longman, MEd, MA, FRSA, ARCO Dip CHD (**Director of Music*)
M Noone, MA (**Biology*)
D Jordan, BA
Miss E Hicks, BA

There are a number of visiting Instrumental teachers.

Houses and Housemasters/mistresses:

Boys' Houses:
Crake: D R Best
Egerton: R J Thompson
Seymour: C N Boyns
Wilson: T M Skevington

Girls' Houses:
Raymond: Mrs J H White
Wilberforce: Mrs A L Cooper

Lower School Weekly Boarders:
Park Close: Mr & Mrs A N Irvine

Headmaster's PA: Mrs H M Hill

Registrar: Mrs S H McClellan

Medical Officer: S A Haynes, MBBS, MRCGP, DFFP

State Registered Nurses:
Miss S Ashton, RGN
Mrs L A Deeley, RGN

Bursar: N A Halfpenny, BSc, MSc, MBIM

Director of Marketing & PR: A N Irvine, CertEd, MCIPR

Organisation. There are approximately 230 boarders and 190 day boarders. There are 4 senior houses for Boys and 2 for Girls. Day boarders are full members of their boarding houses and are allocated house rooms, studies, etc according to seniority in the same way as full boarders. They have all meals except breakfast at the School and may stay for homework.

Lower School, for day or weekly boarding pupils aged 11–13, is an integral part of the School and has its own boarding house.

School Buildings and Grounds. The School is situated in a delightful conservation village on the edge of the Cotswolds and yet just 3 miles from Banbury and 4 miles from the M40 (J11). It is within easy reach of both Heathrow and Birmingham International airports.

The attractive local Hornton stone enriches the School and the village. The last decade has been one of major investment and the school's facilities are now comparable with even the largest of schools. The Raymond Technology Centre (opened in 1997) continues to offer first class facilities and, as a further indication of Bloxham's intent to remain at the cutting edge of the use of technology in education, the school has invested in campus-wide wireless networking. Pupils are now given a laptop computer as they enter Year 10 which they may keep after their A levels.

The boarding houses provide excellent accommodation for all with all Sixth Formers enjoying individual studies. Lower School weekly boarders are housed in Park Close which offers superb, homely facilities and space for the youngest pupils to enjoy. The school has also recently constructed a second artificial grass hockey pitch and upgraded the Sports Centre lighting to complement the new indoor cricket school and opened two glass-backed squash courts.

An exciting new library building opened in March 2006. Music, art and the performing arts have also benefited from new additions to the Bloxham campus facilities throughout 2006/7.

The Sixth Form benefit from their own social centres which they manage themselves.

Admissions. We admit around 35 pupils each year at 11 (day pupils or weekly boarding pupils) by entrance examination set by the school.

At 13 (boarding and day). Those from prep schools are required to pass the Common Entrance Examination, while candidates from state schools are given an alternative examination specially designed to suit the National Curriculum.

At 16 (boarding and day). Those who wish to start a two year A level course are admitted to the Sixth Form on the basis of interview, school report and GCSE results.

There is a Dyslexia Course which takes up to six pupils each year, at age thirteen, with full scale IQs of 120+.

Applications should be made to the Headmaster.

Scholarships and Exhibitions. (*see Scholarship Entries section*). Scholarships and Exhibitions are awarded at 11+, 13+ and for entry to the Sixth Form. Academic awards are made on the basis of a competitive examination. Awards for Art, Design Technology, Music (with free instrumental tuition) and Sport (not at 11+) are also made.

All the above awards may be up to 50% of fees according to merit.

Chapel Centenary Awards of up to 10% of the fees per year may be awarded to good candidates of less than Exhibition standard on the basis of ability in the above areas, or of all-round merit and promise.

Sir Lawrence Robson Scholarships and Exhibitions are awarded each year to Sixth Form entrants. The value of these will be up to 50% of fees.

Age limits for candidates on 1st September: 11+ under 12, 13+ under 14, Sixth Form under 17.

Further details may be obtained from the Registrar.

Bursaries. Generous support is available to children of Armed Forces parents, Clergy and Teachers.

The Roger Raymond Trust Fund sponsors the boarding education of outstanding pupils who would not otherwise be able to attend the school.

Details may be obtained from the Headmaster.

Fees per term (2008-2009). Boarders £8,305; Day Boarders £6,420, both inclusive and covering all meals (lunch, tea and supper) taken at School by day pupils. Lower School: Weekly Boarders £5,760; Day £4,420 (inclusive of lunch and tea).

Information on the payment of fees by Insurance Schemes, and a School Fees Remission Scheme in case of absence, are obtainable from the Bursar.

Optional Extras. Private tuition in a particular subject, £39, £22, £17 and £14, according to the number of pupils in a group. Instrumental Music from £225 per term.

Curriculum. For the first three years pupils have a broad based curriculum which leads to nine or ten GCSEs. No choices need to be made in the Third Form and the full range of subjects is studied. In the Fourth and Fifth forms all pupils continue to study for GCSEs in English Language, English Literature, Mathematics, French, Physics, Chemistry, Biology,

Religious Studies (short course), and in addition choose three other subjects from a range of options including History, Geography, Spanish, German, Art, Music, Design Realisation, Electronics and Business Studies. In the Sixth Form A level Courses are available in Art, Biology, Business Studies, Chemistry, Design Technology, Economics, English, French, Further Mathematics, Geography, German, History, Mathematics, Music, Physics, Politics, Spanish, Theatre Studies, Physical Education and Psychology. A wide choice of combination is again offered. All pupils follow a comprehensive General Studies programme throughout the Sixth Form and the majority take General Studies A Level. Boys and girls are prepared for entrance to Oxford and Cambridge.

Tutorial System. In addition to the Housemaster or Housemistress, pupils have a House Tutor. Every Tutor looks after about 12 pupils and is thus able to give close personal attention to the development of each, both in and out of School. At regular intervals of three weeks the tutor reviews each pupil's Form Assessment which gives details of standard and approach to work in all subjects as well as information on extra mural activities.

Music. There is a wide range of instrumental and choral opportunities ranging from the School Orchestra and Concert Band to chamber ensembles and close harmony groups.

Games and Outdoor Activities. Boys and girls play the traditional major sports, rugby, athletics, hockey, cricket and netball according to season and in addition there are good facilities for badminton, basketball, squash, fives, sailing, shooting, swimming, canoeing, cross-country, fencing and tennis. Boys and Girls are strongly encouraged to develop their own particular talents. In the Third Form and below, pupils are expected to participate in major sports, but they have an increasing range of choices as they progress up the school. Boys and girls are also given the opportunity of participating in a flourishing Community Service Organisation.

CCF. All those in the Third Form enter the "Forty", where they undertake Duke of Edinburgh's Award Scheme type training. In their second year many join the CCF, to which there are various challenging alternatives. Adventure Training Camps are held annually at Easter as well as the usual CCF Summer Camps.

Societies. There is a large number of societies, academic and practical. All pupils are expected to participate in some of these activities according to their interest.

Old Bloxhamist Society. *Resident Secretary*: R L Stein.

Charitable status. Bloxham School Limited is a Registered Charity, number 1076484. Its aim is to provide high quality academic education in a Christian environment.

Blundell's School

Tiverton Devon EX16 4DN
Tel: 01884 252543
Fax: 01884 243232
e-mail: info@blundells.org
website: www.blundells.org

The School, with its attendant connection to Balliol and Sidney Sussex Colleges, was built and endowed in 1604 at the sole charge of the estate of Mr Peter Blundell, Clothier, of Tiverton, by his executor the Lord Chief Justice, Sir John Popham. In 1882 the School was moved to its present site on the outskirts of Tiverton.

Governors:
E D Fursdon, DL, MA Oxon, FRICS (*Chairman*)
N Arnold
R R A Breare, MA
M I R Bull, LLB
C M Clapp, FCA
Dr B K Cuthbert, DPhil
Dr K C Hannabuss, MA, DPhil (*Representative of Balliol College, Oxford*)
Mrs E V Heeley, BA
P M Johnson, MA
P J Lough, MA
Mrs S J Maunder
Mrs A C Mayes, MBC, BSc
J C Murrin, MA
The Revd Canon M J Rylands, BA
Ms L J Smith, BA
His Hon Judge W E M Taylor
B W Wills-Pope, MBE, FInstD
Sir Christopher Ondaatje, OC, CBE (*Governor Emeritus*)

Clerk to the Governors and Bursar: D Chambers, FCA

***Head Master*: I R Davenport**, BA Durham

Second Master: R W Thane, BA, FRGS

Senior Leadership Team:
Director of Studies: Miss E Jardine-Young, MA
Senior Master: P F Rivett, MA
Senior Mistress: *Mrs N J Klinkenberg, BSc
Head of Junior Department (*School House*): *J R W Postle, BA
Head of Boarding: *A J R Berrow, MA
Head of Science: Mrs G M L Batting, BEng

Chaplain: The Revd T C Hunt, MTh, BD, ARICS

Assistant Masters:
A J Deighton-Gibson, BSc
T D Dyke, MA
A H Barlow, MPhil, MA, FRSA
J G Pilbeam, BEd
S J Goodwin, BA
*N J Ridgway, BSc
J S Shrimpton, BA
*Mrs H M Barlow, BEd
*P H Gordon, BA, BEd
J W Brigden, BEd
Mrs D Brigden, BEd
M P Dyer, MSc
Mrs S J Rumble, BA
J T Balsdon, PhD, BSc
H G Thomas, BSc
Mrs A J Frankpitt, BSc
Miss D J Hosking, BEd
Mrs A M Menheneott, BEd
Miss I G Scott, BA
Mrs K J Wright, BA
Mrs R J Crease, BEd
C L L Gabbitass, BEd
R D J Matthew, BA
Miss S A Norman, BSc (*Careers*)
Mrs G J Charlesworth, BA
A J Coull, BA
*L Menheneott, BEd, MBA
Miss F A Baddeley, MA
C M Hamilton, BA
C G Hedley-Dent, CertEd
Miss R E Symonds, MA
S J Dawson, BA
Miss C C G Rebuffet, MA
Mrs J E A'Lee, BSc
Miss S L Burnett, BA
P I Chapman, BSc
P A Treseder, BSc
Mrs B A Nuttall-Owen, BSc
J M Trew, BA
B Wheatley, MA
Miss P J Black, CertEd
A J Guy, BSc
Miss H L Youngs, BTec
I R Chick, BA
Mrs R C Milne, BA
Mrs B C McElligott, BA
D Rhodes, BSc
Ms D M Drew, BTec
R J Turner, BA
Mrs L J Chick, BA
Mrs A D Cross, BA
Mrs C E West, BEng
Mrs T R Griffiths, BA
B M Marsden, BA
G A Bucknell, BSc
Miss A T Marks, BSc
M J Hawkins, BA
Miss A-J Murphy, BA
L Wynell-Mayow, BA
D J D Smart, BSc
Miss K Wilson, BSc
R J Holman, BA
Miss L R M Mimmack, BA
T R Wilks, BSc

Director of Foundation: P Armstrong, BSc

Head Master's Secretary: Mrs J A Gale

Registrars:
P J Klinkenberg, BEd
Mrs E Thane, BSc

Medical Officer: Dr F O'Kelly, MBE, MB BS, MRCGP, DA (UK), DCH, DRCOG

Admission. Entry is at 11 or 13 for most pupils. This is via the Blundell's Entrance Test or the Common Entrance Examination. Most join the School in September, though a January entry is welcome.

Numbers. There are 573 pupils of whom 227 are girls. 146 board or weekly/flexi board. There are three boys' Houses and two girls' Houses for Years 9–12 and a separate Upper Sixth House which was opened in 2004. The Junior Department (Years 7 and 8) shares facilities but is taught and housed separately.

Fees per term (2008-2009). Full Boarding £5,455–£8,085; Day £3,250–£5,215. Weekly and Flexi boarding are also available. A basic tuition fee is charged for those living within ten miles of Blundell's (over the age of 13).

Scholarships. (*see Scholarship Entries section*). Blundell's offers a wide range of generous fee remissions at the age of 13, primarily for academic merit. Each March awards are made of up to 50% of the chosen designation fee (ie boarding, weekly, flexi, day) on the basis of set examinations. Music, Art and All-Round awards are also examined at the School in March. Sporting aptitude is also taken into account and may be acknowledged with its own award. A generous Services Package is in place for sons and daughters of serving officers and diplomats. There are also four Foundation Awards for candidates from the Ancient Borough of Tiverton or those who reside in Devon. These can be awarded at the age of 11. Full details of all scholarships and bursaries are available from the Registrars.

School Work. There are four forms at age 11 and five at age 13. During the first three years most pupils will study Art, Biology, Chemistry, Design and Technology, Divinity, Drama, English, French, Geography, Health Education, History, Information Technology, Mathematics, Music (Class), Personal and Social Development, Physical Education and Physics. Latin, Greek, German and Spanish are also available.

During the GCSE years the range of subjects remains broad. Extensive advice is provided by the School to assist both GCSE and A Level choices and an Academic Fair is staged in the Spring Term. Parents are encouraged to enter their children for the Independent Schools' Careers Organisation Morrisby tests.

Sixth Form options enable a wide combination of subjects to be taken. Four of the following are taken to AS Level and three to A Level: Art, Biology, Business Studies, Chemistry, Classical Civilisations, Design Technology, Drama, Economics, English, Film Studies, French, Geography, German, History (Modern), ICT (AS only), Latin, Mathematics and Further Mathematics, Music, Music Technology, Photography, Physical Education, Physics, Psychology, Religious Studies (Ethics) and Spanish.

Mark Orders, Tutorial System and Reports. Good communication is a central concept. Frequent Mark Orders and Staff Meetings are held to monitor each pupil's work. The Blundell's "curriculum vitae" enables pupils to record their achievements and self-assessment is conducted once a term. All pupils have academic tutors. Parents receive termly formal written feedback in addition to receiving Mark Order summaries every few weeks. There are regular parents' meetings and information forums.

Music and Drama. Blundell's music is excellent. Based on our own music school there are several choirs, an orchestra and varying musical ensembles. These range from a jazz band through a chamber choir to brass, woodwind and string groups. The Department has a good electronic section and in addition to School concerts there are visits from professional musicians. The Choir undertakes a European tour at Christmas; recent destinations have included Prague, Paris, Oslo, and Venice.

Similarly, Drama plays a key role in the School. There are three major School Plays each year, as well as House plays. The magnificent, purpose-built Ondaatje Hall offers the combined facilities of a theatre, a concert hall and an art studio. Frequent visits are made by theatre companies and Blundell's is a cultural core for Mid-Devon.

Games and Physical Training. Boys play rugby football in the Autumn Term whilst girls play hockey. Lent Term sports include cross-country, squash, rugby fives, hockey, soccer, fencing, basketball, netball and rugby sevens. In the Summer Term cricket, tennis, swimming, athletics and sailing take place. Golf, clay pigeon shooting, canoeing and miniature range shooting are also available. The Sports Hall gives further scope to the range of sport, as does the all-weather floodlit pitch.

Computing and Technology. All Blundellians have access to the school IT network and will develop a range of skills during their time at school to support their studies.

Recent New Facilities. There have been extensive developments at Blundell's over the past two decades which include upgrading the Science Departments, provision of advanced technological and careers arrangements as part of the resources included in the redesigned Library, a new Modern Languages block, an Upper Sixth pre-university year House and an ongoing refurbishment of all boarding houses. With the relocation of St Aubyn's School (now called Blundell's Preparatory School) onto the Blundell's site, the whole campus provides education from the age of 3 to 18 years. The Blundell's Foundation has been set up to advance plans for the future and a major development plan was started to coincide with 2004, the school's quatercentenary. Two imaginative projects, a music school and an academic centre, opened in September 2007and there are more exciting plans on the horizon.

Community Service. The School is involved in a wide variety of activities, both local and national.

Adventure Training. Blundell's is well placed to make full use of Dartmoor and Exmoor, the coast and rivers of the area, for academic fieldwork or adventure training. For many years the School has entered teams for the Ten Tors Expedition on Dartmoor and canoes the Devizes–Westminster race.

CCF. Everyone in Years 9 and 10 serves for a year in the CCF. Thereafter it is manned by a body of volunteers who provide the NCO Instructors. There are links with the 18 Cadet Training Team, Derriford, and the Rifle Volunteers.

Boarding. Blundell's is built around the ethos of boarding and all pupils (full boarding, weekly, flexi-boarding and day) are accommodated in one of seven houses on the campus. A full range of weekend activities is offered including a Leadership Programme, Ten Tors, sport and a range of local trips and activities.

Religion. The School maintains a Christian tradition, while welcoming members of other faiths. All pupils are expected to attend weekday morning Chapel and boarders go to the School Service on Sundays. The Chaplain prepares boys and girls who offer themselves for Confirmation, which takes place annually in the Spring Term.

Accessibility. Blundell's is close to the M5, and is served by Tiverton Parkway Station, two hours from Paddington, London. Airports at Bristol and Exeter are close at hand.

Prospectus. Fuller details of School life are given in the prospectus, available from the Registrars. Prospective parents are invited to visit the School, when they will meet the Head Master, and a Housemaster or Housemistress and have a full tour of the School with a current pupil. The Blundell's website (www.blundells.org) is regularly updated throughout the academic year and as well as giving details of the school and academic departments, lists the main sporting, musical and dramatic events of each term and some match results.

Preparatory School. Blundell's Preparatory School for children aged 2½ to 11 years is on its own extensive site at Blundell's. For further information apply to the Headmaster, Mr N A Folland. (*See also entry in IAPS section*).

Charitable status. Blundell's School is a Registered Charity, number 1081249. It exists to provide education for children.

Bolton School Boys' Division

Chorley New Road Bolton BL1 4PA
Tel: 01204 840201
Fax: 01204 849477
e-mail: seniorboys@boltonschool.org
website: www.boltonschool.org/seniorboys

Bolton School Boys' Division seeks to realise the potential of each pupil. We provide challenge, encourage initiative, promote teamwork and develop leadership capabilities. It is our aim that students leave the School as self-confident young people equipped with the knowledge, skills and attributes that will allow them to lead happy and fulfilled lives and to make a difference for good in the wider community.

We do this through offering a rich and stimulating educational experience which encompasses academic, extra-curricular and social activities. We provide a supportive and industrious learning environment for pupils selected on academic potential, irrespective of means and background.

Motto: *'Mutare vel timere sperno'*.

Governors:
Chairman: M T Griffiths, BA, FCA
D H V Brookes
R J Byrom, JP, BA Arch, MPhil, RIBA, FSVA, FCIArb
Professor C L Cooper, CBE
C Cowling, BSc, FIA, CMath, FIMA
E Fairweather, FCIB, CeMAP, CeRGI
Mrs S E Fisher, MSc, MBChB, BDS, PDSRCS, FRCS
The Hon Mrs M J Heber-Percy
Mrs L Henthorn, ACMI
N Hirst, MA, CEng, FIChemE
Mrs L A Hopkinson, BEd
Mrs M Kenyon, DL, MA
B H Leigh-Bramwell, MA
Mrs W P Morris, OBE
A D Oldershaw
Mrs G E Sidebottom
Mrs S R Tonge, JP, DipHarb
Mrs F Windsor, BSc, MA, FCMA, FCIS, FRSA, MIBA, CBM

Clerk & Treasurer: S P Marsden, BA, MCMI

***Headmaster*: P J Britton**, MEd

Deputy Headmaster: R D Wardle, BA
Director of Studies: J L Taylor, BA
Senior Master: D J Jones, BSc

Teaching Staff:
* *Head of Department*

Art:
*M Frayne, BA
Mrs M A Ryder, BA
Miss L Turner, BA
Mrs P Wilson, BA, ATD

Biology:
*Dr F H Mullins, BSc, PhD
G Bonfante, BSc
Dr J C Catterall, BSc, PhD
M Hobbiss, BA
Dr N Morgan, BSc, DPhil
Dr S Wastie, BSc, PhD

Business Studies:
*Mrs C M Edge, BSc
D W Kettle, BA

Chemistry:
*Dr M Yates, BSc, PhD
Dr S P Cooper, BSc, MSc, PhD
Mrs J F Knibbs, BSc
Mrs E M Greenhalgh, BSc
Dr D Rogers BSc, DPhil
H H Schenk, BSc
Dr D G Watson, BSc, PhD

Classics
* Dr J E Reeson, MA, PhD
A E Jackson, BA
Mrs E D Watts, BA

Economics:
*A J Raitt, BA

English:
*R J Griffiths, MA
M A Bannister, BSc
N Cropper, BA
Dr S W Holland, BA, PhD
M Shewan, BEd, MA
Mrs C Spencer-Jones, MA

French:
*A C Robson, BA
Mrs H M Baker, BA
A I McNeil, MA
M H J Prentki, BA

Geography:
*A C R Compton, BA
K T Hunter, BA
P D Jackson, BSc
J A Rutter, BSc
Miss H Tunstall, MSc
R D Wardle, BSc

German:
*R A Freem, BA
K Brace, BA
R A Catterall, MA
K M Hiepko, MA

History:
* J W Rich, BA
B J Armstrong, MA
Miss S V Burgess, MA
C C Joseph, MA

ICT:
*P J Humphrey, BSc

Mathematics:
*D N Palmer, BSc
Dr R Booth, BSc, PhD
T Cairns, BSc
R M Harrison, BSc
N C Holmes, BSc, CIMA
C Hunter, BSc
Miss A Schroder
Mrs D Stevens, BSc
D L Stevens, BSc
J L Taylor, BSc

Music:
*S J Martin, BA
J Bleasdale, BA, LLCM
R Eastham, ABSM
Mrs A J Hampson, BMus

Physics:
*Dr J M Thatcher, BSc, PhD
A Altimeemy, BSc, PhD
E J Dawber, BSc
D J Jones BSc
Miss L Rollins, BSc
D S Thompson, BSc

Religious Studies:
Mrs C E Fox, BA

Russian:
*P G Davidson, BA
C A J Pownall, BA
Mrs V Tymchyshyn, BA

Physical Education:
*T P Pledger, BA
K Branagan, UEFA A Grade
P Fernside, BA
H Howard, BA
M Johnson, BSc
G Lövgreen, BA
G N McMillan

Technology:
*C J Walker, BA
P A Brownrigg, BSc
G J Butchart, BEd
C Coffey, BA

Instrumental Music Staff:
Miss F J Berry, BMus, LRSM, LTCL, LLCM (*Clarinet, Saxophone*)
Mrs T A Coglan, ARCM
G Curtain, BMus, MA (*Brass*)
I C Dawkins, Kneller Hall (*Clarinet & Saxophone*)
I K Forgrieve, GMus, RNCM, PPRNCM (*Percussion*)
P Fowles, BA, LLCM, AMus TCL, BIHE (*Guitar*)
J Gjylaci, BMus, RNCM (*Guitar*)
Mrs C Hall-Smith, GBRSM, PGRNCM
A Lockett (*Brass*)
M J Pain, MA, FRCO, LRAM, ARCM, CertEd (*Pianoforte & Organ*)
Mrs J Pearse, LTCL, LRAM, LGSM, AMusTCL
G F Watton (*Percussion*)
Mrs M F Webb, LRAM, GRSM (*Violin & Viola*)
Mrs C Whitmore, BA, LRSM (*Voice/Singing*)
M Wildgust, GMus, ARCM, LTCL (*Brass*)

Junior School:
Head of Junior School: S Whittaker, BEd
Deputy Head: S C Rashleigh, BA

Mrs T Clarke, DipEd
Mrs H De Maine
T Dickinson, BEd
M Duxbury
Mrs R Eynon
A B Harrison, DipEd
Mrs A L Hough, BSc, DPS
C D Hough, BSc
Mrs P J Lockett, BEd
Mrs S J Ives, BA
Mrs H J Willis, BMus

Headmaster's Personal Assistant: Ms M M Leather

Headmaster's Secretaries:
Mrs M P Jones
Mrs S Yates

The School, founded ante 1516, was rebuilt and endowed by Robert Lever in 1641. It was re-endowed in 1913 by Sir W H Lever, Bart (later Viscount Leverhulme).

Situated in imposing sandstone buildings on a thirty-two acre site, Bolton School Boys' Division at present contains almost 1,100 boys, all day pupils. Of these, 200 are members of the Junior School which is housed in an adjacent separate building close to the main site providing education for boys aged 7–11. In the Senior School of 900 boys, 250 are in the Sixth Form.

Curriculum. The GCSE programme comprises a core curriculum of English Language, English Literature, Mathematics, Biology, Chemistry, Physics and Sport. In addition, pupils select a further 4 options chosen from Art, Drama, French, Geography, German, History, Latin, Greek, Music, RE, Russian and Technology. One of these choices must be a foreign language. At A Level 28 different subjects are currently on offer. Boys study four subjects to AS Level, with the majority reducing to three A2 Levels in Year 13. In addition all boys have the option of taking General Studies to A2 Level. While many boys elect to take standard combinations of either Arts or Science subjects in the Sixth Form, a high degree of flexibility ensures that any desired combination of subjects can be offered. Throughout both years of the Sixth Form, there is an additional and extensive programme of academic work which supports the GCE Advanced curriculum.

Facilities and Organisation. The Boys' and Girls' Divisions of Bolton School are housed in separate buildings on the same site and, though the organisation of the two Divisions provides basically single-sex schools, there are many opportunities for boys and girls to meet and to cooperate in the life of the school community. In some subjects co-educational arrangements are in operation. The buildings of the Boys' Division include the Great Hall, two libraries, gymnasium, sports hall, swimming pool, laboratories, art rooms, sixth form common room and ICT learning centre, design technology centre, performing arts centre, classrooms and dining hall. The Junior School building contains eight form rooms and specialist rooms for ICT, art & design and science & technology together with a gymnasium, library and its own dining accommodation. Use of the sports hall, the adjacent 25-metre swimming pool and the arts centre is shared by all sections of the school.

Games and PE. The extensive playing fields which adjoin the School contain thirteen pitches. Principal games are football and cricket. Rugby, tennis, hockey, swimming, water polo, badminton, athletics, golf and orienteering are also all played at representative school level. Games and physical education feature in the timetable of all boys. The School is divided into four Houses for the purpose of internal competitions.

Art, Drama, Design, Music. In addition to timetabled sessions in each discipline there are many opportunities for extra-curricular activities in all these pursuits. Facilities in the art department include a pottery room with kiln; within the very active musical life of the School there are choral groups, orchestras and ensembles catering for all ages and abilities. In addition arrangements can be made for individual lessons on all orchestral instruments, piano, organ and in singing. Drama is an important part of the work of the English department and boys are encouraged to develop their talents in the drama studio and arts centre. The annual major school play, musical or opera is produced in cooperation with the Girls' Division. Design and technology features strongly in the curriculum in both Junior and Senior Schools with considerable success each year in the A level technology courses, many boys gaining industrial sponsorships as a result. In addition, a wide variety of extra-curricular opportunities exists in both the design technology base and the computer rooms. All boys are encouraged to take part in the extensive lunchtime programme when over 120 clubs, societies and practices are offered to different groups.

Outdoor Pursuits. All junior school pupils and all students up to and including Year 12 in the senior school undertake an annual period of outdoor education within curriculum time. In addition, camps, trips, exchanges and expeditions go to 63 destinations over two years, 17 of them abroad. The School has its own 60-bed Outdoor Pursuits Centre, Patterdale Hall in Cumbria, used by parties of boys regularly for curriculum, weekend, holiday and fieldwork expeditions. There is a large and active Scout Group with its own modern headquarters on school premises.

Religion. The School is non-denominational; all boys have periods devoted to religious education. In assemblies the basic approach is Christian although a great variety of readings and methods of presentation are adopted. Religious education is taught in a broad undogmatic style which encourages free discussion on many issues.

Careers and Higher Education. Careers education and guidance, and life-long learning are key elements of the curriculum. In Year 8 pupils take part in a Work Sampling Day. Careers Education is part of the Year 9 curriculum including a project marked by the Headmaster. As an aid to Sixth Form choices, the Morrisby Test with follow-up interviews and extensive feedback is undertaken in Years 10 and 11. All pupils take part in Work Experience placements at the end of Year 11 and throughout the Sixth Form.

In Year 12, all pupils attend a 3 day residential business training course at Patterdale Hall and take part in an e-business competition. Mock interviews are conducted on Interview Skills Evenings. Year 13 pupils are guided through UCAS procedures and careers advice is always available from two full-time Careers Assistants in the Careers Library. The Head of Careers oversees all these events and can be consulted by all parents and pupils.

Transport. The School provides an extensive coach service which offers secure and easy access for pupils from a wide surrounding catchment area. Currently twenty-two routes are being operated by either the School's own fleet of coaches or by contract hire arrangements.

Admission. An entrance examination is held in January annually for boys over 7 and under 8 on August 31st of the year of admission and also for those over 8 and under 9 on the same date. Fifty places are available at 7+ and a few additional places thereafter. Admission to the first year of the Senior School (120 places) is by entrance examination held annually on the third Thursday in January. Boys who are over 10 and under 12 on August 31st of the year of entry are eligible. Entry to the Sixth Form is available to boys who have taken GCSE examinations elsewhere on the basis of interview and agreed levels of performance in these public examinations. Boys are also admitted at other ages when vacancies occur; in these cases admission is gained through satisfactory interview and test performances. There is a co-educational pre-preparatory section of the Girls' Division (Beech House) where admission is from the age of 4 and for which enquiries should be made to infants@boltonschool.org. There is also a nursery providing facilities for children from 3 months to 4 years old.

Fees per term (2008-2009). Senior School £2,930; Junior School £2,198. Fees include lunch which is attended by all boys.

Fee Assistance. Foundation Grants are available to provide assistance with fees.

Prospectus and Open Day. The School holds an annual Open Morning for the benefit of prospective candidates and their parents. This is normally in early October. Individual tours can be arranged on working days. Further information concerning all aspects of the School is contained in the School Prospectus, copies of which may be obtained by writing to the Headmaster at the School, or telephoning the Headmaster's Secretary. More detail can be found on the School website: www.boltonschool.org/seniorboys. Enquiries concerning admission are welcome at any time of the School year.

Charitable status. The Bolton School is a Registered Charity, number 1110703. Its aims and objectives are to maintain in or near the County Borough of Bolton a public secondary school for boys and girls as a day school. Under the terms of the Charity it is administered as two separate Divisions providing for boys and girls under a separate Headmaster and Headmistress.

Bootham School

York YO30 7BU
Tel: 01904 623261 (School)
01904 623636 (Headmaster)
Fax: 01904 652106
e-mail: enquiries@boothamschool.com
website: www.boothamschool.com

Bootham offers Full and Weekly Boarding and Day Education to both boys and girls from 11–18, together with day education from the age of 3 at Bootham Junior School. There are now over 450 pupils in the Senior School, nearly one-third of whom are boarders. There are approximately 130 day pupils in the Junior School.

The School was founded in 1823 by Quakers, but pupils of all denominations or none are welcomed. All pupils attend Meetings for Worship and arrangements are made for pupils to be prepared for confirmation or membership of their own churches.

***Headmaster*: Jonathan Taylor**, MA Oxon

Deputy Headmaster: Graham J Ralph, BA, MA

Head of Junior School: Sue Ratcliffe, BEd, MEd

Director of Studies: Jennifer Royle, MA

Head of Schoolrooms: Colin Raper, CertEd

Head of Boarding, Head of Sixth Form: Michael Shaw, BSc (*†Evelyn House*)

Bursar: Chris Ignatowicz, MA, FCA

Assistant Staff:
* *Head of Department*
† *Housemaster/mistress*

Sarah Allen, BD, BEd (**Religious Education*)
Peter Anderson, BSc, MSc (**Biology*)
Rachel Antill, BA (*Art*)
Mathew D Aston, BEd (*Mathematics, †Fox House*)
Joan Atwell, BA (*Drama*)
Jennifer L Bailey, BA (**English*)
Richard M Barnes, BA, MA (**Art*)
Andrew Bell, BA (*Physical Education, English*)
Margaret Bland, BSc (*Mathematics*)
Elizabeth Brown, BSc, PhD (*Geography*)
Paul K Burton, BTech, MInstP, CPhys (**Physics*)
Richard N Burton, BA (*Music*)
Carol L Campbell, BA (*French, †Rowntree House*)
Judith Campbell, BEd (*Religious Studies, Music*)
Ben Coxon, BA (*Physical Education*)
Debbie Dawson, BSc (*Biology, Chemistry*)
Christopher Dobson, BSc (*Chemistry*)
Joanna Dowson, CertEd (*Physical Education*)
Margaret Drake, BA, CELTA (*EAL*)
Fiona Dunlop, BA, MA, PhD (*English*)
Harriet Ennis, BSc (**Psychology, Biology*)
Paul Feehan, BA (*Director of Music, †Penn House*)
Tim Fulford, BSc (*Design Technology*)
Susanne Gair, MA (**Learning Support*)
Elizabeth Gallagher-Coates, BA (*English, Psychology*)
Emma Glover, BA (*English*)
Robert E Graham, BEd (**Physical Education, Geography*)
Suzanne Hall, BA, PhD (*English*)
Margaret Hillier, BA, BEd (**Theatre Studies*)
Elisabeth Hooley, BA (**Physical Education, Mathematics*)
Freya Horsley, BA, MA (*Art*)
Robert Hudson, BA (*History*)
Paul Irvine, BA (*Spanish, French*)
Leslie Jackson, BA, MSc (*Art*)
Vicky Jackson, BA (*Art*)
William R Lewis, MA (**Mathematics*)
Clare Little, BMus (*Music*)
Elizabeth McCulloch, MA (*History*)
Eamonn Molloy, BEd (**Design & Technology*)
Catherine Morin (*French Language Assistant*)
Russell Newlands, MSc, BEng (*Physics*)
Sarah O'Keeffe, BSc (*Economics & Business Studies*)
Christina Oliver, BA, MA (*German*)
Robin L Peach, MA (**Classics*)
Peter Rankin, BEng (**Information Technology*)
Mark Robinson, BA, MA (**Chemistry*)
Sarah Robinson, BA (*Classics*)
Catherine Rowell BSc, PhD (*Biology*)
Sarah Shiels, MA (*History*)
Ruth Sillar, MA (*Religious Education*)
Richard Taylor, BA, MA (**Modern Foreign Languages*)
Robert Tribe, BSc (**Geography*)
Paula Turner, BA, PhD (*Classics*)
Angela Umpleby, BEd (*Physical Education*)
Anne Whittle, BSc (*Mathematics*)

Development Director: Jane Peake, BA

Registrar: Jenny Daly

Librarian: Marion Chalmers, BA

Archivist: Bridget Morris, BA, PhD

Curriculum. In Years 7–9 all pupils pursue a course of study which includes English (including Drama), History, Religious and General Studies, Careers, Geography, Latin, French, German, Spanish, Mathematics, the three separate Sciences, Music, Art and Craft, Physical Education, Design & Technology and Computer Studies.

In Years 10 and 11 pupils follow a curriculum leading to 10 or 11 subjects at GCSE.

The College Classes (Sixth Forms) are preparatory to university entrance. The majority of pupils remain at school until the age of 18 and each year there is a strong Oxbridge entry. A wide choice of subjects is offered. It is usual to study 4 or 5 examination subjects and to study subjects of wider interest.

The following subjects may be taken, in many combinations, to the AS & A2 and University Entrance levels: Mathematics, Further Mathematics, Physics, Chemistry, Psychology, Biology, English, French, German, Spanish, Modern History, Classical Studies, Geography, Economics, Business Studies, Music, Art, Design Technology, Information Techology, Religious Education, Drama and Theatre Studies, and Sports Studies. To counter-balance the effects of specialisation, pupils in the College classes are required to follow courses in Religious, Physical and General Education. In General Studies pupils follow a course in a wide range of topics such as English Literature, Political History, Music Appreciation and International Affairs, given by members of the staff and, from time to time, by specialists who visit the School for this purpose. Particular emphasis is placed on the study of personal relations and the structures of communities.

Site and Buildings. The School is situated close to York Minster. From the road it appears as an impressive line of Georgian houses but behind this is the spacious main school campus. There is a steady programme of development, and the buildings now include 7 well-equipped Laboratories, a Music School, 2 ITC Suites, 2 Workshops, an Astronomical Observatory, an up-to-date Physical Education Department with Sports

Hall, Indoor Swimming Pool and Squash Courts, and a modern Assembly Hall, which received a national RIBA award. There are many facilities for leisure time pursuits which are an important feature of the lives of pupils at the School. The buildings are complemented by formal gardens and a beautiful Cricket Field, overlooked by the Minster. Another large Playing Field is situated nearby, in Clifton, which also houses Bootham Junior School in a new purpose-built complex.

Pastoral Care. As a Quaker School, Bootham places great emphasis on caring relationships within a friendly community. There are four boarding houses, under the special care of House staff. Each House has its own recreational facilities. Throughout the School, both boarding and day pupils are supervised and guided by form tutors. In College, pupils have Personal Tutors who are responsible for both academic and pastoral matters, and guidance towards Higher Education.

Admission. Pupils from Preparatory Schools usually enter Bootham at the age of 13. Pupils from LEA Schools are admitted at 11, 12 or 13. For all pupils an entrance examination is held annually in the Spring Term. In special circumstances late entrants can be considered.

Applications for entry to Year 10 can be considered if places are available.

Bootham admits several entrants to the Sixth Form each year to study Advanced level courses. There is always strong demand for Sixth Form places and offers are made based on predicted GCSE grades and place availability. Sixth Form Entry Scholarships can be awarded to suitable applicants.

Leisure Time Activities. The School has long been recognised as a pioneer in the right use of leisure. The Natural History Society, founded in 1832, claims to be the oldest society of its kind with an unbroken history in this country. Other clubs and societies include Debates, Drama, Bridge, Chess, Cookery and Jazz. There are around 80 activities offered each week. Pupils follow the Duke of Edinburgh's Award scheme and are involved in Community Services.

Music. The Director of Music and his assistant are supported by 21 visiting teachers. Tuition is arranged in a wide variety of instruments and a strong tradition of music in the School is maintained. A recent leaver was named 'Young Composer of the Year' and there is a strong record of success in gaining Music College and University scholarships.

Games. Association Football, Hockey, Tennis, Fencing, Cricket, Swimming, Athletics, Netball, Badminton, Squash, Rounders. There is no cadet force.

Fees per term (2008-2009). Boarding: £4,600–£7,250. Day: £4,210–£4,530.

Fees for instrumental music lessons are extra. Enquiries for up to date information are welcome.

Scholarships. (*see Scholarship Entries section*). Up to four John Bright Memorial Boarding Scholarships of up to 50% of full fees are awarded at 11+ and 13+. Other Major and Minor Scholarships of up to 50% of full fees are also awarded to both boarding and day pupils at 11+, 13+ and 16+. Several Music Scholarships are available.

All scholarships are means tested beyond the first 5%.

Bootham Old Scholars' Association. There is an annual Reunion in York during the second weekend in May. The Bootham Old Scholars Association has branches in all parts of the country and Eire. The Secretary may be contacted through the School.

Charitable status. Bootham School is a Registered Charity, number 513645.

Bradfield College

Bradfield Reading Berkshire RG7 6AU
Tel: General Enquiries: 0118 964 4500
Headmaster: 0118 964 4510
Bursar: 0118 964 4530
Fax: 0118 964 4511
e-mail: headmaster@bradfieldcollege.org.uk
website: www.bradfieldcollege.org.uk

Bradfield College was founded in 1850 by Thomas Stevens, Rector and Lord of the Manor of Bradfield. There are approximately 700 girls and boys in the twelve boarding houses. The College is fully co-educational: at 13+ entry girls and boys enter Faulkner's, a purpose-built co-educational house for the first year at Bradfield. About sixty girls and boys join the large and vibrant Sixth Form through 16+ entry.

We define our ethos by the outcome of our pupils as they leave Bradfield. We aim to inspire our pupils to become caring, contributing and confident members of the new global community. We build on our pupils' strengths. Bradfield excellence is defined as a combination of the personal development of the individual, providing an excellent academic education and preparing its pupils for real life by emphasis on extra-curricular pursuits and service in the wider community. The College is a co-educational boarding school dedicated to the provision of the highest possible care for all its pupils.

Motto: '*Benedictus es, O Domine: Doce me Statuta Tua*'. Blessed are you, our Lord; teach me your laws (from Psalm 119).

Visitor: The Right Revd The Lord Bishop of Oxford

Council:
Sir Colin Lucas (*Warden*)
The Lord Iliffe
T N Clark
The Lady Ryder
P G F Lowndes
M H Young
J M Layton
Mrs M Riall
Mrs J Slot
M A Jones
Dr M Donald
A H Scott
D Shilton
P Saunders
The Lady Waller

Clerk of the Council: T M Sills

***Headmaster*: P J M Roberts**, MA

Second Master: S P Williams, MA, MLitt

Deputy Heads:
K J Collins, MA
Mrs A M C Acton, BA

Bursar: T W Llewellyn, BA, FCA
Director of Development: Mrs E L Masters, MA
Acting Director of Development: J Wyatt
Headmaster's PA: Mrs J Smith, BA
Admissions Secretary: Mrs N Williams
Chaplain: Revd R G Hilliard, MA, Dip Theol

Houses and Housemasters:
A – Loyd: J C Harding, MA
C – Army: A S Golding, BA
D – House on the Hill: S A Long, BEd
E – Field House: J P A Ball, MA
F – Hillside: C A Carlier, BA
G – House on the Hill: A R MacEwen, MA
H – The Close: G W S Masters, BA
I – Palmer House (*Girls*): Mrs A H Marshall, CertEd
J – Armstrong House (*Girls*): Mrs B A Eldridge, BA, MBA
K – Stevens House (*Girls*): Dr S C Beeson, BSc
L – Faulkner's (*Year 9*): Mr R J Wall, BA & Mrs F J C Wall, BA
M – Stanley House: Miss S R Duff, MA

Assistant Staff:
* *Head of Department*

Art:
*I P Dugdale, RAS Dip
Miss A Cowan, BA
Miss E Fedouloff, BA
Miss H R Jervis, BA (*Textiles*)
Mrs R M Swainston, MA

Biology:
*F R Dethridge, BSc (*Head of Science*)
Miss W Bangay, BSc, BA
Mrs E H Barnes, BSc
Miss D A Entwistle, BSc
Miss C Pegg, BSc
A J Smith, BSc, MA

Business Studies:
*Miss L C Marshall, BEd
A N Coventry, BA
Mrs B A Eldridge, BA, MBA
M R Rippon, BA

Chemistry:
*S T Lunt, MA
S C Allen, BA, MSci
Miss M Norden, BSc
T J Ronan, BSc, MSc

Classics:
*P C Armstrong, BA
Miss R L Cann, MA

Design & Technology:
*D L Lait, BSc
M K Goodwin, MA
P A Mahon, BA Ed

Economics:
*T H Chaloner, MA

English:
*Mrs E V Earnshaw, BA
Mrs E K Dunlop, MA, MPhil
K J Collins, MA
A S Golding, BA
J C Harding, MA
Mrs V L Hartwell, BA
Mrs S M Lyon, BA
Mrs E M McGill, BA
Miss H M Spencer, BA

EAL:
*Mrs H E Bebbington, BA, MA
Mrs L de Albuquerque, RSA, CELTA
Mrs D Bevan, TESOL Cert
Mrs J Kingston, BA
G Rush, CertTEFL

Film Studies:
*Miss A L Hatch, BA

Geography:
*R Keeley, MA
Miss S R Duff, MA
M Hill, BA
T J Kidson, BSc
R J Wall, BA

History:
*R J Veal, MA
Miss Y Baldwin, BA
C J Barnes, BA
C C Ellison, BEd
Miss F D Martin, BA
Miss T Roy, BA

History of Art:
*T E Goad, BA
Mrs B H Bond, BA

ICT:
*J A Nalty, BA
Mrs M Lawlor, BSc
R M Smith, BSc
Dr L S Vat, BSc

Mathematics:
*T Krueger, MEng
C A Baker, BSc
Dr S C Beeson, BSc
C B Burgess, MA, MEng
Dr D J Doole, BSc
A M Maynard, BEd
N J Taylor, BSc
S N Whalley, BSc

Modern Languages:
*M M Etherington, BA (*French & German*)
Mrs A M C Acton, BA (*German*)
Mrs M E Ashcroft, BA (*Spanish & EAL*)
C A Carlier, BA (*French & German*)
Miss E Cervera, BA (*Spanish*)
Miss A Davis, BA, MSt (*French*)
Mrs C Jones, BA (*French*)
Miss J Lynam, MA (*Italian & French*)
Mrs A Nalty, BA (*French*)
Mrs M L Poacher, BA (*Spanish*)
Mrs F J C Wall, BA (*French*)

Music:
*Ms A Wright, BA, FTCL
Mrs R Frost, MA
T O Anderson (*Music Technology*)
Miss V S Beattie, BA

PE:
*D J Clark, BA
Miss K J Larch, BA
S A Long, BEd
D J Mitchell, BSc
Mrs S K M Ronan, CertEd

Physics:
*M A T Harrison, BSc, CPhys, MInstP
Dr S J Bastow, BSc
Mrs R B Clamp, MSci, AMInstP
J van Es, BSc

Politics:
*A R MacEwen, MA
C Ashurst, BA

Psychology:
*Mrs J Mckoy, BSc

Religious Studies:
*J P A Ball, MA
Mrs P M Donnelly, BA
Revd R G Hilliard, MA, DipTheol
G W S Masters, BA
S P Williams, MA, MLitt

Support and Study Skills:
*Mrs C Whittingham, BSc, MA, SENCO PGC, DipSpLD
Mrs P C Brims, MA, MPhil
Mrs P Cole, BA, DipSpLD
Dr L C Hutchins, BSc
H McCartney, BSc
Mrs C Prior, BA, DipSpLD
Mrs I Smith, BEd
Mrs A Tibbs, CertEd, DipSpLD

Theatre Studies:
A Kilburn, BA, MPhil
Mrs J Crossley, BA

Librarian: Mrs J E Dyson, BA, MCLIP
Head of Careers: Mrs H L Allen, BSc

Visiting Staff:
M Allen, PPRNCM Llb (*Percussion*)
B Arthey (*Guitar*)
K Bartlett, GGSM (*Percussion*)
A Chamberlain, BMus (*Brass*)
N Charlton, LTCL (*Cello*)
Ms E Elliott (*Harp*)
M Frith, GGSM (*Clarinet, Flute & Saxophone*)
H Hetherington, BA Mus (*Singing*)
C Hobkirk, BA, ARCO (*Singing*)
Mrs C Hultmark, BA (*Violin*)
L Ingram (*Bagpipes*)
P Johnson (*Squash*)
D Lane (*Tennis*)
S Lasky, BA, MA (*Jazz*)
Mrs A Law GRSM, ARCM, Dip Rott (*Oboe*)
Miss M S Legg (*Dance*)
A Mosharrafa (*Electric Guitar*)
H Nelson, ARAM, LTCL (*Flute*)
T Osborne, LRAM, ARAM, CertEd, BACS (*Double Bass & Bass Guitar*)
Miss T Rowlinson, LRAM (*Bassoon*)
J Shaw (*Games*)
M J Stacey, BMus, LRAM (*Organist*)
Ms L Taylor (*Tennis*)
J M Thompson (*Fencing*)
Ms A White, BMus, MMus (*Piano*)
J Wood (*Cricket Coach*)

Location. Bradfield College occupies the village of Bradfield, 8 miles west of Reading and 9 miles east of Newbury. It is 2 miles from Junction 12 of the M4 (the Theale access point). There are good road and rail communications with Reading, Oxford, London and Heathrow.

Organisation. There are 700 pupils in the College, of whom about 120 are day pupils. 40 girls are admitted to the Sixth Form each year and 40 girls into Year 9. Girls and boys spend their first year in a state-of-the-art boarding house (Faulkner's) which includes its own facilities and dining hall. The College is divided into 11 houses (7 senior Boys Houses, 3 senior Girls Houses and 1 Sixth Form Girls House), each with its own sleeping, studying and recreational facilities. Day pupils are full members of boarding houses. The Housemaster/mistress is assisted by House Tutors and a Matron. Meals are served in the central Dining Hall and Faulkner's Hall.

Admission. The College is fully co-educational, with boy and girl boarders admitted from 13+, but there is also a significant entry of girls and boys at Sixth Form level.

They qualify by taking either the Common Entrance Examination, the Common Academic or Bradfield Scholarship Examination, or the Bradfield College Assessment; pupils are interviewed by the Headmaster and school reports are required. Admission to the Sixth Form is by GCSE profile, interview, internal tests and satisfactory school reports.

A school prospectus and details of the entry procedure may be obtained from the Admissions Secretary.

Fees per term (2008-2009). Boarders £8,700; Day pupils £6,960.

A fee of £25 is payable on registration. 20 months before the date of entry a Guaranteed Place fee of £1,000, which is later credited against the final account, is payable.

Entrance Scholarships. (*see Scholarship Entries section*). Academic Scholarships (up to 50%) and Exhibitions for All-Rounders (up to 30%) are awarded annually after competitive examinations in the Lent term. Music Scholarships up to 50% of the full fees are offered annually, and Drama, Sports, Art and Design Awards up to 20%. All awards are augmentable according to financial need. Full details may be obtained from the Headmaster's PA.

Academic Organisation. Pupils enter the College in September and will follow a three-year course to GCSE examinations, and then a two-year course to A Level.

In the first three years all the normal school subjects are taught in a core curriculum, but there is also opportunity to emphasise the linguistic or the aesthetic or the practical elements through a system of options.

In the Sixth Form GCE AS and A2 Level courses are offered in all subjects studied for GCSE with the addition of Economics, Politics, Philosophy and Ethics, History of Art, Theatre Studies, Photography, Psychology, Physical Education, Film Studies, Business Studies, Computing, Textiles and Critical Thinking.

Academic Staff. There are 99 members of the Academic Staff, who cover all the main subjects. These are almost entirely graduates recruited from British universities, although there are also native speakers of German, French and Spanish in the Modern Languages department.

Careers. The Careers Department provides a wide range of advice and guidance to all year groups, particularly at key decision points. The College is a full member of ISCO and through them, all pupils in Year 11 (and new pupils in Year 12) undertake the Morrisby psychometric tests, follow-up interviews and receive a detailed personal profile to help them plan for the future. In Year 12 and 13, pupils have opportunities to find out about various professions, industries and the Services through talks, visits and conventions and courses. Specialist advice is available on University entrance and Gap Years.

Games. The main games for boys are football in the Michaelmas term, hockey in the Lent term and cricket and tennis in the Summer term. The main games for girls are hockey in the Michaelmas term, netball in the Lent term and tennis and rounders in the Summer term. Girls also have the chance to play competitive lacrosse, football and cricket. In addition teams represent the College at squash, fives, cross-country, fencing, athletics, golf, sailing, swimming, shooting, badminton, basketball, clay pigeon shooting and polo. There are also opportunities to take part in dance classes and aerobics.

There are 2 all-weather artificial grass pitches used for hockey, football and tennis, a 3-court indoor Tennis Centre, 6 other hard tennis courts, 5 netball courts, 4 fives courts, 4 squash courts and a very large and modern Sports Complex, including an indoor swimming pool. The College grounds extend to nearly 250 acres and include fine playing fields, a nine-hole golf course and fly fishing on the river Pang.

Recreation, Drama and Music. Every encouragement is given to pupils to develop their interests and talents in a wide variety of creative activities. There is a modern and well-equipped studio for art and sculpture, an Information Technology Centre, a purpose-built and very extensive Design and Technology Centre and a Music School with a Concert Hall and practice rooms. The Greek Theatre is the venue of a classical Greek Play produced every three years, and of Shakespearean plays or musicals in the intervening years. There are also facilities for indoor productions. In addition, there are about 30 Societies covering a wide range of other interests.

Religion. Chapel services are those of the Church of England, and Religious Education is part of the core curriculum in Year 9. Confirmation Services are held each year for Anglicans in the College Chapel and for Catholics in the local parish.

Combined Cadet Force. The College maintains a contingent of the Combined Cadet Force which all pupils have the opportunity of joining. There is a full range of alternative activities, including Community Service and The Duke of Edinburgh's Award. All pupils take part in a programme of Adventure Training.

Old Bradfieldian Society. The College values its links with its former pupils and a series of social and sporting occasions is held each year to enable friendships to be maintained and renewed. Address: Old Bradfieldian Society, Bradfield College, Reading, Berkshire RG7 6AU.

Charitable status. Bradfield College is a Registered Charity, number 309089.

Bradford Grammar School

Keighley Road Bradford West Yorkshire BD9 4JP
Tel: 01274 542492; Headmaster: 01274 553701
Fax: 01274 548129
e-mail: hmsec@bradfordgrammar.com
website: www.bradfordgrammar.com

Bradford Grammar School is known to have existed in 1548 and received a title of Incorporation as 'The Free Grammar School of King Charles II at Bradford', in 1662. It was reorganised in 1871, and the Scheme was revised in 1909, and again in 1973, amended by Order of the Charity Commission in 1974, 1980, 1994, 2004 and 2005.

Motto: '*Hoc Age*'

Corporate Trustee: Bradford Grammar School Trustee Limited.

Governors:
Chairman: A H Jerome, MA
Vice-Chairman: Professor C Mellors, BA, MA, PhD

J E Barker, DL, MA
The Vicar of Bradford
W Bowser, ACIB
Professor A W Boylston, BA, MD, FRCPath
Mrs A C Craig, DL, DCR
I Crawford, FCA
Mrs C Hamilton-Stewart
His Honour Judge J A Lewis
Ms N S Mirza, BA
Lady L Morrison, LLB
T H Ratcliffe, MBE, LLB
J G Ridings, FCA
P T Smith, FRICS
C M Wontner-Smith, BA, FCA

Governor Emeritus:
P J M Bell, JP, FCIS, CText, FTI, FRSA
Mrs J D Fenton, MCSP, SRP

Bursar and Clerk to the Governors: R G Hancock, MA, FCIS, Chartered FCIPD, MCMI

***Head Master*: S R Davidson**, DL, BSc

Deputy Head: M J Sharpe, BSc, PhD

Assistant Heads:
R I Page, BA, MSc
N R Smith, BSc, MEd
J D Boardman, BSc
D S Conroy, BSc

Department Staff:
* *Head of Department*
§ *Part-time*

Art:
*R I Walker, BA
Ms J Barraclough, BA
§Mrs L A Hepworth-Wood, BA
Mrs S E Horsfield, BA
H R Thornton, BA

Biology:
*Mrs P M A Dunn, BSc
M J S Ashmore, BSc
Mrs M Bibby, BSc
Mrs D J Chalashika, BSc
S R Hoath, BSc

Business Studies:
*§Mrs D M Hicks, BSc
§Ms A C Dews, BSc

Chemistry:
*G C Fisher, BSc, MA
§Mrs G M Heywood, BSc
Mrs N S Nicholas, BSc
A B R Macnab, BSc
Mrs D J Mouat, BSc, PhD

Classics:
*Mrs M J Chapman, BA (*Asst Head Lower School*)
T C Bateson, MA
Ms J McNamara, BA, MA, PhD
§R A West, MA

Design and Technology:
*M D McKay, BA
D Leake, BEd
S G Taylor, BSc (*Asst Head Middle School*)
§N J Walker, BEd

Economics:
*R D Schofield, BA
Miss E Anthony, BSc

English and Drama:
*A P Johnson, BA
§K A Archer, BA
Miss S J Ball, BA
Mrs S Brear, BA
Mrs P Buckham-Bonnett, BA, MA
Miss G D'Arcy, BA, MA
S D Rees, BA
Miss L A Smith, BA
Miss S M Waring, BA

Geography:
*M D Raw, BA, MPhil
Miss L A M Cole, BSc (*Asst Head Careers*)
Miss F R Hughes, BA
A G Smith, BSc (**Geology*)

History:
*N A Hooper, MA, FRHistS
J D Devlin, BA, DPhil
J Reed-Purvis, BA, MA (*Head of Sixth Form*)
Mrs K E Wilde, BA (*Head of Lower School*)
§Mrs H Baines, BA

Information Technology:
*D S Conroy, BSc
C R Bright, BSc
Mrs S E Palmer, BEd
§Mrs C Harvey, BA, MA
Mrs C M Conroy, BSc

Mathematics:
*D W Fishwick, BSc, PhD
§A B Baines, BSc
Mrs E C Boyes-Watson, BA
A Crabtree, BSc
Ms S Harris, MMath, PhD
P Merckx, BSc (*Head of First Year*)
M A Thompson, BSc (*Head Middle School*)
§Miss B J Pickering, BSc
P Watson, BSc, PhD

Modern Languages:
*G P Woods, MA
§Mrs S K Bevan
R J Carter, BA
Miss B Fahy, BA (**Spanish*)
§S B Davis, MA, LTCL, MIL (**Russian*)
§Mrs E J Kingsley, BA
Miss C Ory, BA, MA
Ms K Murach, MA
R A Salter, MA
Mrs S Woodhead, BA
Mrs A P Simmonds, BA
Miss V Martí-Fernández, BA
Mrs E Tomlinson, BA (**French*)

Music:
*N A Mann, ALCM
C J Brook, BA
§D G Roberts, LRAM, LGSM

Physics and Electronics:
*P Shepherd, BEng, PhD
T W Carman, BSc, PhD, ARCS, CPhys, MInstP
§J R Charlton, BSc
P Ratcliffe, BSc
R W Morley, BSc, MA

PE and Games:
*C W Lines, BA
§S Darnbrough (*Rowing Coach*)
A J Galley, BEd
Mrs M E Harling, BSc, MA
C E Linfield, BA
Miss C A Stansfield, BA (*Asst Head Sixth Form*)
§B Townsend (*Swimming Coach*)
M A Wilde, BA

Politics:
*M P J Simpson, MA, DipSp (**Careers*)
Miss A Slater, BA

Psychology:
*A G Hartley, BA, MBA
Ms C J White, BSc

Religious Studies:
*K Ravenscroft, BA, MEd
R E Skelton, BA

The Clock House:
Head: G Lee-Gallon, BTech
Deputy Head: N H Gabriel, BA, DipArch

L W Hanson, BEd, MA
Mrs A C Hood, BEd
Miss K L Howes, BSc, MSc
Mrs L Morris, BEd
D Reddish, BEng
Mrs P Reddish, BSc
P Smales, BEd, BA
G P Smith, BEd
N E Sykes, GLCM, ARCM
§C Thorpe (*Sports Coach*)

Visiting Music Staff:
Ms A Brown, BMus (*woodwind*)
Mrs J Bryan, GMus, CT ABRSM, LRSM (*woodwind*)
A Cook, GLCM (*guitar*)
M Gaborak, GCLCM, LTCL (*guitar*)
J Griffett, ARCM (*singing*)
Ms J Harrison, GRNCM (*singing*)
Mrs P Jordan, ARCM (*piano*)
Mrs E Kenwood-Herriott, LTCL (*double reed instruments*)
M McGuffie, BA (*clarinet*)
G Rafnsson, PGRNCM (*drum kit*)
D Roberts, LRAM, LGSM (*brass*)
A J Sherlock, BA, ALCM (*piano, Instrumental Studies Coordinator*)
B Stevens, BA (*percussion*)
Miss A Verity, MA (*lower strings*)
Ms C Walker, LTCL (*upper strings*)

Bradford Grammar School aims to provide a stimulating and supportive environment in which bright boys and girls can work together to achieve their individual potential. There are currently 779 boys and 334 girls aged 6–18.

Situation and Buildings. The school stands in fine buildings and extensive grounds about one mile from the centre of Bradford. There are excellent road and rail links with Wharfedale, Airedale, Leeds City Centre, Calderdale and Huddersfield. The Junior School occupies Clock House, a seventeenth century Manor House within the school grounds, where it enjoys its own assembly hall, IT and DT facilities and teaching accommodation. Facilities available to both Senior and Junior Schools include the Hockney Theatre, the Library and Information Technology Centre, the school debating chamber, the Design and Technology Centre, Sports Hall, Sixth Form Centre, Music School and Swimming Pool. The Price Hall is the centrepiece of the main school building and provides a magnificent setting for assemblies, concerts and other major events.

Clock House Curriculum. All pupils study English, Mathematics, Geography, History, Science, Music, Art, IT, Design and Technology, Physical Education, Games, and Religious Studies – French and German (Year 6 only).

(*For further details about the Junior School, see entry in IAPS section.*)

Senior School Curriculum. In the First and Second Year all pupils study English, Mathematics, French, German, Latin, Biology, Physics, Chemistry, Geography, History, Art, Music, Design and Technology, Information Technology, Religious Studies, Physical Education and Games.

In the Third Year, pupils follow a common core of English, Mathematics, Geography, History, Physics, Chemistry, Biology, Religious Studies, Physical Education and Games, a choice of French, German or Spanish and two subjects from German, Russian, Latin, Greek, Art, Music, Design and Technology, and Spanish.

In the Fourth and Fifth Year, all pupils take English, Mathematics, Biology, Chemistry, Physics, PE and Games, a core modern foreign language, choosing between French, German and Spanish, and three subjects from: Geography, History, German, Russian, Latin, Spanish, Greek, Art, Music, Design and Technology, Information Technology, and Religious Studies. Pupils are entered for ten GCSEs. Pupils who have not chosen it as an option have one period per fortnight of ICT.

Sixth Form Curriculum. Pupils choose four Advanced Subsidiary Level subjects from Art, Biology, Business Studies, Chemistry, Classical Civilisation, French, German, Greek, Design and Technology, Economics, Electronics, English Language, English Literature, English Language & Literature, Geography, Geology, History, Information Technology, Latin, Mathematics and Further Mathematics, Music, Music Technology, Psychology, Physical Education, Physics, Politics, Russian, Religious Studies, Spanish and Theatre Studies. There is also a General Studies programme, which includes Japanese. There is the opportunity for senior pupils to sample Mandarin. In the Upper Sixth Form pupils take three or four A Level subjects. The school has a strong record of success at public examinations and university admissions; over the last nine years 133 pupils have gained places at Oxford or Cambridge. A comprehensive Career Service operates throughout the school.

Extra-Curricular Activities. There is a thriving culture of extra-curricular activities. Music and Drama are an important part of school life; Debating flourishes and there are active CCF units and Community Service groups. Most academic subjects have societies run by pupils, and religious interests are represented in the Christian Fellowship, Islamic Society and Inter Faith Forum. A wide variety of sporting activities is offered, including Athletics, Badminton, Basketball, Climbing, Cricket, Cross-Country Running, Hockey, Netball, Rounders, Rowing, Rugby, Sailing, Squash, Swimming, Table Tennis, Tennis, Water Polo and The Duke of Edinburgh's Award. Senior pupils also take part in the biennial World Challenge Expedition.

Pastoral Care. The Assistant Head (Pastoral) with his team of Year Heads and Form Teachers work closely with pupils and parents to ensure that support is available in school and at home. An extensive Peer Support scheme and a growing system of Year Group Councils are just two ways in which pupils are encouraged to take responsibility for each other and themselves in school.

Admission. Boys and girls can join the school at the ages of 6, 7, 8, 9, 10 in the Junior School or 11, 12, 13 in the Senior School. Pupils are admitted into the Sixth Form on the basis of interview and GCSE results. Candidates for entry at 6+, 7+ and 8+ are invited to spend an informal day in Clock House. Admission for all other ages is by examination in Mathematics and English in January each year.

Bursaries. Bursaries are available each year on a means-tested basis for entrants at 11+, 13+ and 16+ to support the education of the successful candidates throughout their time at the school. Family circumstances will be reviewed annually and the value of any bursary adjusted accordingly.

Fees per annum (2008-2009). Senior School £9,527; Junior School £7,424.

Old Bradfordians' Association. President: Mr J Hammond, c/o Bradford Grammar School.

The Parents' Association (previously BGS Society). Chairman: Mrs J Rosborough, c/o Bradford Grammar School.

Charitable status. The Free Grammar School of King Charles II at Bradford is a Registered Charity, number 529113. It exists to provide education for children.

Brentwood School

Ingrave Road Brentwood Essex CM15 8AS
Tel: 01277 243243
Fax: 01277 243299
e-mail: headmaster@brentwood.essex.sch.uk
website: www.brentwoodschool.co.uk

Brentwood School was founded in 1557 and received its charter as the Grammar School of Antony Browne, Serjeant at Law, on 5th July, 1558. The Founder became Chief Justice of Common Pleas shortly before the death of Queen Mary, and was knighted a few months before his death in 1567. The Foundation Stone over the door of Old Big School was laid on 10th April, 1568, by Edmund Huddleston and his wife Dorothy, who was the step-daughter of the Founder. The Elizabethan silver seal of the School Corporation is still in the possession of the Governors. In 1622 Statutes were drawn up for the School by Sir Antony Browne, kinsman of the Founder, George Monteigne, Bishop of London, and John Donne, Dean of St Paul's.

Motto: '*Virtue, Learning and Manners*'.

Governors:
C J Finch, FRICS (*Chairman*)
Sir Michael Snyder, DSc, FCA (*Vice-Chairman*)
K C Brown, FSI, ASIP
H E Flight, MA, MBA
Professor Emeritus Sir Roderick Floud, MA, DPhil, FBA, FCGI
Lord Hanningfield of Chelmsford
A M Lightowler, LLB, NP
The Venerable D Lowman, BD, AKC
Lady McAllister, BSc
J M May, MA, LLB
Mrs E Mimpriss
J H M Norris, CBE, DL
R W Owers
R E Ramsey, LLB, FRSA
Dr T J Stone, MA, PhD
R J Wilson, MA

Bursar and Clerk to the Governors: I F Bruton, BA Hons, MIoD

***Headmaster*: D I Davies**, MA, FRSA

Second Master: D M Taylor, GRSM, LRAM, MTC

Deputy Head: N J Carr, MA, MA (EconEd), ACEM, FRSA

Deputy Head (*Pastoral*): S D Weale, MA

Heads of Year:
Sixth Form: Mrs K Beston, MA
Sixth Form Deputy Head (*Curriculum*): J D Williams, BSc
Sixth Form Deputy Head (*Pastoral*): Mrs L E Bengston, BSc
Fifth Year: R Pritchard, BA
Fourth Year: Miss C A Holding, BA
Third Year: L P Bishun, MSc, MIS
Second Year: Mrs M E Belsham, BSc
First Year: J R Brown, BA

Houses & Housemasters/mistresses:
East: J MCann, BEng
Hough: P Rees, BA & Mrs C Rees
Mill Hill: J Shipway, BSc & Mrs J Shipway
North: N S Crosby, BA
South: C M Long, BA
Weald: Mrs M Parsons, BA
West: Dr G J Fisher, MA, PhD

Heads of Department:
Art: Mrs M Parsons, BA
Biology: A G Taylor, BSc Hons
Business Studies: Miss M Sorohan, BA, MA
Chemistry: J P Seaman, BSc Hons, MSc, CChem, MRSC
Classics: J Alderson, BA
Computing & ICT: J J McCann, BEng Hons
Director of Design Centre: G M Kiff, BA
Drama: L Jones, MA
Economics: P M Rees, BA
English: D S R Dunn, MA
English as an Additional Language: Mrs L J K Bowley, BA, PG Dip TEFL

Director of Extra-Curricular Activities: J L Killilea, BEd, AIST, MA
Food Technology: Mrs B Daly, BEd Hons
French: Dr E Rowlands, BA, PhD
Girls' Games: Miss J Saunders, BEd
Geography: N S Crosby, BA
German: I Walton, MA
History: Miss R Fairfull, MA
Director of IB: T Woffenden, MA
Learning Development: Mrs S Heyn, BA
Director of Life Skills: Mrs V Thorpe, BA
Mathematics: A J Drake, MA
Modern Languages: Dr R M Storey, BA, PhD
Director of Music: D J H Pickthall, MA, FRCO
Academic Music: Mrs H Khoo, GRSM
Sport: J Kayne, BSc Hons
Physics: R Hawley, BEng
Politics: M V Willis, BA
Psychology: Mrs A R Bailey, BSc
Religious Studies: B Clements, BA, MPhil
Science: Dr M Garstin, BSc, PhD
Spanish: Miss C Walker, BA Hons
Technology: A R Eckton, BSc Hons
University Entrance & Careers: Dr K J Cooper, BSc, PhD, MInstP, CPhys

Assistant Staff:
Mrs L J Acton, BA
Mrs H Barker, BA
Miss R Begum, BA
Mrs C A Bear, BSc
Miss R Bishop, BA
Miss N J Bixby, MA
Mrs K Bowes, BSc
Miss K Bryce, BA
Miss J P Byrne, BSc
Miss R Campbell, BA
Ms K Carmichael, BA
W Castleman (*Rugby Coach*)
Miss N Charogianni, BA, MA
R T Chapman, CertEd
M Clark, BA
P F Clark, BA
P Cleaves, BA
Mrs J J Coppin, BSc, MSc
Miss K L Crane, BA
Mrs B Daly, BEd
Mrs L G M Dearmer-Decup, BA
Mrs V Denman, BA
Miss A Denniss, BA
Mrs P Ebden, BSc, MSc
Ms C Edgar, BEd
Miss K Ellerbeck
Miss H English, BSc
R Flook, BSc
M Golland, BA
S L Gonsalves, BA
Mrs C Gordon-Johnson, BA
C A Graves, BSc
K Gray, BSc
Mrs R Hamborg, BSc
B R Hardie (*Cricket Professional*)
Mrs S Hardy, BSc, MIFST
Mrs C Harvey, BA, PhD
Mrs S Hawkings, BA
Miss C Haworth, CertEd
Mrs N C Heelam, BSc
Miss E Holland, MA
Mrs L A Hurlock, BA
L C Jenkins, MSc, FRAS
R Jenkins, BA
Mrs W L Juniper, BEd
Miss J Khush, MSc
Mrs S Knightbridge, BSc
Ms S Knowles, BEd
Miss S Lake, BSc
Miss A Leath, BA
Ms R Lees, BA
Miss C Lewis, MSc
G J Little, MA
Mrs E Lusty, BA, MA
Miss S F Mackie, BA
Mrs H Marquet, BA, MA
R Mazorodze, BSc, MSc
D McAuliffe, BA, MA
M McGowan, BSc
M Monro, BA
Ms J Moore, BA
Miss M Nash, BA
A Newby, BSc
A Pask, BSc
Miss I Penalver-Escamez, BA
G Pye, BSc
D Reith, BSc
Mrs S J Roast, BEd
S R Rumsey, BA
Mrs J Ryalls, BSc
Miss V Rutter BSc
D R Sach, BSc
I M Sanderson, BSc
Mrs P Sanderson, BSc
D E G Saunders, BA
H Shepherd, BA
P Slater, MA
J J Stevens, MA
A S Taker, BA
R Thornton, BEC Higher National Cert
Mrs M D Taylor, BA
Miss H Tully, BSc
Ms K Wallis, BA
Mrs S J Wells, BSc
Miss M E Wennell, BA
I Wignall, BA
J D Williams
Mrs F Wood, BSc
Mrs S Wood
Ms B Wray, BA
D Wright, BSc
T G Wright, MA

Admissions Registrar: Mrs M Henning

Headmaster's PA: Mrs P Scott

Chaplain: The Revd David Gilchrist, MA

School Medical Officer: Dr Nasif

Brentwood School is a co-educational school with a total of 1,497 pupils including 143 in the Pre-Preparatory School and 239 in the Preparatory School. The Pre-Preparatory School and Preparatory School are fully co-educational as is the Sixth Form but boys and girls are taught separately between the ages of 11 and 16. Boarding is available for boys and girls from 11.

Buildings and Grounds. The School occupies a 70 acre site on high ground at the northern end of the town some 20 miles north-east of London. Old Big School, the original school room, is still in regular use thus maintaining a direct link with the school's founder. Over recent years a major building programme has seen extensions to the Science and Modern Languages buildings and Dining Hall; refurbishment of the Preparatory School, Boarding Houses and Sixth Form accommodation; the building of the magnificent Brentwood School Sports Centre; a Performing Arts Centre, an all-weather pitch, an Art and Design Centre and an indoor heated swimming pool which was opened in September 2002. The School has recently been granted planning permission for a new Sixth Form Centre and Assembly Hall. The Sixth Form Centre will provide an exemplary educational environment for the International Baccalaureate programme, an assembly space for up to 400 students and staff, a performance venue for an audience of 300 and include 16 additional classrooms.

Organisation. The school is one community within which, for good educational reasons, girls and boys are taught separately from age 11 to 16. They are encouraged to participate together in all extra-curricular activities. The Senior School is divided into Year Groups. Each Year Group has a Head of Year and Deputy who oversee it. The vast majority of pupils join the school at 11 after successfully completing our Entrance Examination. A broad curriculum is followed through the first three years and this continues through careful choice of GCSE subjects to the end of the Fifth year. Entry to the Sixth Form is conditional upon success in the GCSE examinations. In the Sixth Form students take either four of the 27 AS level subjects or follow the International Baccalaureate Diploma programme. Most go on to University. Pass rates at Advanced Level reach 100% and many pupils gain places at Oxford and Cambridge each year.

Religion. The School is an Anglican Foundation. There is a resident Chaplain and all pupils attend Chapel fortnightly. Regular Communion Services are held. Members of other faiths are welcomed and their views respected.

Boarding. There are two Boarding Houses, both of which have been thoroughly modernised. The boys reside in Hough House which can accommodate up to 48 students; the girls reside in Mill Hill House where 27 can be accommodated. The public rooms are spacious and both Houses generously staffed. Full and weekly boarding are available. A qualified Matron runs an efficient Sanatorium.

Pastoral Care. Brentwood School takes very seriously its pastoral responsibilities and provides two supportive systems. Responsibility for pastoral care is vested in the Form Tutors under the guidance of the Heads of Year and the Deputy Head, Pastoral. This system is complemented by a strong House system with Housemasters/Mistresses and House Tutors. Partnership with parents is regarded as essential and they are encouraged to join in activities and to visit regularly.

Music, Drama and Art. Music plays an important part in the life of the School, as do drama and art. There are 4 orchestras and several ensembles and jazz groups. The Big Band is internationally acclaimed. There are at least three dramatic productions each year, together with regular Art Exhibitions.

Careers. There is an excellent University Entrance and Careers Department where students receive advice and can obtain information about courses and/or careers. Aptitude Tests; Work Experience; visits to colleges, universities and places of work; visiting speakers are all part of the provision. A careers convention is held in March each year.

CCF and CSU. All pupils either join the Combined Cadet Force or, through the Community Service Unit, engage in a wide-ranging series of activities which bring them into contact with the Community. The Duke of Edinburgh's Award Scheme runs alongside these activities.

School Societies. There are many flourishing societies covering a wide range of interests, catering for all ages.

Sports Facilities. The playing fields are part of the School complex and provide ample space for soccer, cricket, hockey, rugby and tennis. There is a cinder athletic track. The Brentwood School Sports Centre includes an indoor soccer/hockey pitch, six badminton courts, indoor cricket nets, basketball courts and a fencing salle, as well as squash courts and a fitness suite. There is a heated indoor swimming pool and an all-weather pitch. Provision is made for golf, sailing and table tennis.

Preparatory and Pre-Preparatory Schools. *See entry in IAPS section for details.*

Entry. Entrance Examinations for both boys and girls aged 11 are held at the School in January each year. Entries are also accepted at 13 plus, following the Common Entrance Examination, vacancies permitting. Transfers at other ages are also possible. Sixth Form entry is through GCSE success, and interview.

Scholarships and Bursaries. (*see Scholarship Entries section*). The school offers scholarships at 11+ and for entry to the Sixth Form for Music, Drama, Art, Sport and Choral in addition to Academic scholarships. Means-tested bursaries are also available.

Fees per term (2008-2009). Day £4,271; Boarding £7,535.

Old Brentwood's Society. There is a flourishing Society. The Secretary is Ian West, Quarry House, London Road, Newport, Saffron Walden, Essex CB11 3PN.

Charitable status. Brentwood School (part of Sir Antony Browne's School Trust, Brentwood) is a Registered Charity, number 310864. It is a Charitable Trust for the purpose of educating children.

Brighton College

Eastern Road Brighton BN2 0AL

Tel: 01273 704200
Head Master: 01273 704339
Bursar: 01273 704247
Junior School: 01273 704210
Fax: 01273 704204
e-mail: registrar@brightoncollege.net
website: www.brightoncollege.net

The first of the Sussex public schools, Brighton College was founded in 1845 with the object of providing a 'thoroughly liberal and practical education for the sons of the local gentry in conformity with the principles of the Established Church'. With its Victorian Gothic buildings, the front quad, largely unchanged since then, has the appearance of a Cambridge court in the heart of the Kemp Town, whilst to the North of the main range many modern buildings have been added in recent years.

The college first admitted girls into the Sixth Form in 1973 and became fully educational in 1988. There are now some 700 pupils in the college, of whom 27% are boarders and 40% girls. Pupils are divided into 11 houses.

Motto: TO Δ 'EY NIKAT Ω (*Let the right prevail*)

Patron and Visitor: The Right Revd The Lord Bishop of Chichester, DD

Council
President: Lord Renton of Mount Harry

Vice-Presidents:
S J Cockburn, BA
The Rt Hon Sir John Chilcot
I W Dodd
Mrs J Lovegrove, MA
P D C Points, MA
L C W Rea, MA Finset Pet
R J Seabrook, QC
Dr A F Seldon
Lady H Trafford, DSc, SRN
Dr J Wade, JP, MB, BChir
I J White, FRICS

Chairman: Prof Lord R Skidelsky, FBA

Vice-Chairman: I J White, FRICS

Governors:
N Abraham
Mrs C R Ash
M D L Chowen
Mrs J Deslandes, BA
Ms L A P Hayman, MA
R F Jones, DipMS, IPFA
Mrs T Mawer
G R Miller, FCIB
D A Nelson-Smith, MA
A Pettitt, MA
A J Symonds, MICOS, FRICS
Mrs L Ward,
R J S Weir, BA, FCA, MCT

***Headmaster*: R J Cairns**, MA, FRSA

Second Master: S G R Smith, BA, FRSA
Senior Deputy: Mrs L A Kenway, BSc
Academic Deputy: Mrs J A Riley, BA
Director of Studies: J Carr-Hill, MSc

Head of Sixth Form: M J Beard, MA
Head of Middle School: J R Weeks, BA
Head of Lower School: Mrs L Hamblett, MA (*Head of Religion and Philosophy*)

Director of Co-Curriculum: R A Nicholson, BEd (*Director of Sport*)
Director of Boarding: K A Grocott, MA
Director of Dyslexia Centre: D C Ollosson, BA
Bursar: D M Davies, BA
Director of Admissions: Mrs M A E Brightwell
Medical Officer: Dr Sue Lipscombe, MBChB, MRCP, FPCert

Academic Staff:
Ms T Acheson, BA
N Buoy, BSc (*Director of Rugby*)
N Carter, LTCL
S Chenery, MA (*Director of Music*)
Ms M Clarke, BA (*Director of Dance*)
Miss E T M J Cody, BA (*Housemistress, Chichester House*)
B Collie, BSc
Mrs S S D Collins, BA (*Head of Modern Languages*)
R Cowan, MA (*Head of Chemistry*)
Mrs F M Cremona, BA (*External Exams Officer*)
D A Crichton, BA (*Head of History; Housemaster, Ryle House*)
N L Dawson, BSc
Revd R Easton, BA, MTheol (*Chaplain*)

M J Edmunds, CertTEFL (*Head of EAL*)
A M Frost, MA (*Head of Biology*)
B Fryer, BSc (*Head of Academic PE*)
M Godfrey, BA (*Housemaster, School House*)
O Harris, BA
G Hart, BSc (*Housemaster, Aldrich House*)
S Hawkes, BA (*Head of DT; Housemaster, Durnford House*)
Ms V Hulme, BSc
Ms M Jerez Rios
J Jones, BA, MA
Mrs H C Jordan, BA
D Kerr, BA (*Director of Drama*)
D A P King, MA (*Head of Science*)
B L Lambe, BSc (*Head of Information Technology*)
Ms J Langhorne, BEd (*Head of Girls' Games*)
R Law, MA, MPhil
Ms M-L Lin, BA (*Head of Mandarin Chinese*)
M V Lewis, BSc
C Mayanobe, MA (*Librarian, Head of Careers*)
A Merrett, BSc
Mrs R Miller, BA (*Head of Classics*)
G Mitchell, BA (*Coordinator of Spanish*)
C Morrissey, BA (*Head of Psychology*)
Mrs M A Murphy, BA (*Housemistress, Fenwick House*)
N Murray, BA
R A Nicholson, BA (*Director of Sport*)
Mrs A Parish, BA (*Housemistress, Williams Parish*)
Ms L Prahin, L-ès-L
J C Prideaux, MA, MRSC (*Director of Curriculum*)
S Radojcic, BSc (*Proctor*)
P A Radley, BSc (*Head of Mathematics*)
M Reeve, BSc
D Roberts, BA, LSDC
R Ruz, MSc (*Director of IT*)
Ms R M Shiffner, BA
P J Smales, BEng
J Spencer, MA (*Head of Geography*)
Mrs J Thomas, MA
Mrs G Tissier, BSc (*Head of Physics; Admissions Tutor*)
E F Twohig, MA, NDipAD (*Director of Art*)
Miss B C Walsh, BA (*SENCO*)
Miss E Whipple, AGSM, CRD (*Housemistress, Williams Connor*)
J A St J Withers, BEd (*Housemaster, Hampden House*)
Mrs S A Woodmansey, BA (*Head of Business Studies*)

There are twenty Part-time Academic Staff and thirty Visiting Music Staff.

Buildings. The College is situated in the fashionable Kemp Town district of Brighton. The original north range and Headmaster's House was designed by Gilbert Scott in 1847. The Chapel was added in 1858 and extended in 1923 as a memorial to the Old Brightonians who gave their lives in the First World War. The south and west range of boarding houses was completed to a design by Sir Thomas Jackson (an Old Brightonian) in 1886. The Great Hall (1913), Swimming Pool, Armoury, covered Miniature Range and Squash Courts are all early twentieth century additions. New Workshops for Technical Studies and two day boy Houses were added in September 1959. A Classroom Block was completed in 1972, and the Sports Hall in 1973. The Lester Building, for IT and Mathematics was built in 1986, and girls' day accommodation in 1990. The Hordern Room, a small theatre and concert hall was opened by Sir Michael Hordern, an Old Boy, in January 1995 as part of the College's 150th Anniversary Celebrations.

An extensive programme of development is currently taking place. A new 3 storey Performing Arts Centre, incorporating a Dance Studio, Café de Paris and Music practice classrooms, opened in Summer 2000; a new Music and Drama School was acquired in 2003; at the same time a major refurbishment and upgrade of the Library also took place together with the creation of The Rose Lecture Theatre, which also serves as a cinema. In March 2008 the Alexander Centre for the Visual Arts and a new language laboratory were opened.

Admission. Pupils are admitted to the Fourth Form between the ages of 13 and 14 via the Common Entrance examination, the Scholarship Examination, or by special Assessment and interview, and into the Sixth Form for a two-year A2 course, between the ages of 16 and 17, subject to a minimum of 12 points at GCSE (based on three points for an A* grade, two points for an A grade and one point for a B grade) and ideally an A grade in each subject to be studied at A Level. In both cases pupils must also produce evidence of good character and conduct from their previous school. The college will admit boys and girls of 11 from September 2009. The College Prospectus and registration form can be obtained from the Director of Admissions.

Entry for new Fourth form and Sixth form pupils is at the beginning of the Michaelmas term.

Houses. Hampden, Leconfield, Aldrich, Durnford, Ryle, Chichester and Williams Connor and Williams Parish are Day Houses, each with their own premises. School House, Abraham and Fenwick are Boarding Houses, which are currently going an extensive programme of refurbishment. From September there will be 190 boarders in the school, 27% of the school roll. Weekly boarding is increasingly popular. Pupils may go home on Friday afternoon and return either on Sunday evening or on Monday morning.

Dyslexia Centre. The specialist Dyslexia Centre enables children who are assessed as Dyslexic, but with high intelligence, to take a suitably adjusted GCSE course within the normal College curriculum with the opportunity to proceed to A Levels in the Sixth Form.

Health. There is a Central Health Centre with a qualified Matron, and the Medical Officers visit regularly.

Catering. There is self-service dining room, managed by a qualified Catering Manager.

Holidays. The usual School holidays are about 3 weeks each at Christmas and Easter, and 8 weeks in the Summer. There is a half-term holiday of 1 week in all three terms.

Religion. A short morning service is held in Chapel on 3 days a week: Friday's service aims to embrace all faiths. There are services for all pupils on some Sundays to which parents and visitors are welcome. Candidates are prepared by the Chaplain for Confirmation.

Curriculum. The School is divided into 5 Forms – Fourth, Lower Fifth, Upper Fifth, Lower Sixth and Upper Sixth. (This will become 7 forms from 2009.) In the Sixth Form some 28 subjects are available at AS or A2 Level, the latest additions being Psychology, Photography and Dance. For GCSE, pupils select their 9 subjects at the end of the Fourth Form. 95% of pupils proceed to university. Preparation for the UCAS process begins in the second term of the Lower Sixth, and pupils are guided towards appropriate choices by the Head of Sixth Form in conjunction with the individual pupil's tutor.

Sport. The College enjoys a strong record of excellence at most sports. The main playing-field (the Home Ground) is part of the College campus and there is another ground a mile away at East Brighton Park. All pupils take part in the College's extensive games programme. The main sports for boys are rugby and cricket and for girls, netball, hockey and cricket. In addition, a host of other options are available including Soccer, Squash, Tennis, Golf, Fencing, Biathlon, Aerobics, Yoga, Athletics and Cross-Country. There is also a flourishing Sailing Club. The College has its own indoor swimming pool.

Service. All pupils from the Lower Fifth onwards are expected to participate in a service activity on one afternoon a week. This may involve entering one of the 3 sections of the CCF, or joining the Duke of Edinburgh's Award Scheme. In addition, pupils may participate in charity work or, in the Sixth Form, Community Service.

Music. One in three pupils learns at least one musical instrument. There is a strong musical tradition and pupils reach a very high level of performance. The Choir, Chamber Orchestra, Symphony Orchestra, Concert Band and Swing Band perform regularly both inside and outside the College. There are several Chamber groups, and the Choral Society and Orchestra usually perform major works at the annual Brighton Festival.

Drama. The College has a strong tradition of excellence in drama. There are opportunities for anyone to be involved and the College stages plays ranging from Tudor Interludes through Shakespeare, Restoration comedy and twentieth century classics. In addition to the regular calendar of a musical, Sixth Form studio production, Sixth Form play, Fourth Form play, Lower School play and House Drama festival, there are also many productions mounted entirely by pupils. There is also a junior Drama Club.

Activities. Creative activities are encouraged both in and out of school time, and the College has its own Art School and Gallery where exhibitions by leading Artists are regularly staged. Dance is an increasingly popular activity.

Careers. Ms Cecile Mayanobe heads a team of tutors who advise pupils on careers. The College is a member of the Independent Schools Careers Organisation.

Entrance Scholarships. (*see Scholarship Entries section*).

Fees per term (2008-2009). Full Boarders £8,540; Weekly Boarders £7,502; Day Pupils £5,330–£5,510. The Registration Fee is £75.

Old Brightonians' Association. The Old Brightonians' Association has annual Dinners and a number of flourishing sports clubs.

Preparatory School. The College has its own fully co-educational Junior School with a pre-preparatory department. (*For details see entry in IAPS section.*)

Brighton College Family Society. The society organises talks, outings and other social events and is open to all parents, Old Brightonians and friends of the College.

Charitable status. Brighton College is a Registered Charity, number 307061. It exists for the purpose of educating boys and girls.

Bristol Grammar School

University Road Bristol BS8 1SR
Tel: 0117 973 6006
Fax: 0117 946 7485
e-mail: headmaster@bgs.bristol.sch.uk
website: www.bristolgrammarschool.co.uk

'The Grammar School in Bristowe' existed under a lay master in 1532 in which year, under a charter of Henry VIII, it was endowed with the estates of St Bartholomew's Hospital by the merchant and geographer Robert Thorne and others. The trust was placed in the care of the Corporation of Bristol and then the Trustees of the Bristol Municipal Charities. In September 2004 the School incorporated as a company limited by guarantee with registered charitable status and is now governed under Memorandum and Articles of Association approved by the Charity Commission in 2004.

Co-educational since 1980, today BGS provides a wide-ranging and challenging education for boys and girls aged between 11 and 18.

Motto: '*Ex Spinis Uvas.*'

Governors:
L Perrin (*Chairman*)
A J Atkins BSc Hons, BArch Hons, RIBA, ARB
Mrs K Case, CertEd
R A R Cockitt, BSc
Mrs A Conway-Hughes, BSc Hons, MSc
N Dawes, BSc Hons
K Dawson, MA
B R England, DL, ACIB
N Fitzpatrick, BA, FIA, AIIMR, FRSA
D K Golledge, FCA
C J Haworth, BSc Hons, FRICS
S A Lipfriend, BA Hons
Mrs C J Monk, JP, BEd (*Vice-Chairman*)
Mrs A Nosowska, CertEd, BEd Hons, FRSA
Mrs M Potter, BA
N Reeve, FCA
P J Rilett, MBA, FCA
Professor K G Robbins, MA, DPhil, DLitt, FRHistS, FRSE
Dr C J Slater, MA, DPhil
J Symons, BSc Hons, MRICS

***Headmaster*: R I MacKinnon**, BSc

Deputy Heads:
Ms L Carleton, BA
P R Huckle, BA, MEd
P R Roberts, BSc, MSc

* *Head of Department*

Art:
*J Lever, MA
Mrs S Cooper, BA
Ms J Estdale, BA, MA
Miss B D Glanville, BA
Mrs H S Handcock
P Z Jakobek, BEd (*Head of House*)

Biology:
*R G W Morris, BSc, CBiol, MIBiol
Mrs R Cullen, BSc
Mrs N A Diamond, BSc
N S Fuller, BSc, MSc, CBiol, MIBiol
J S Harford, BSc (*Director of Sixth Form*)
J B Slowey, BSc
Ms K Surry, MA

Careers:
*Mrs M L Guy, CertEd

Chemistry:
*Dr J D Knox, BSc, PhD
Miss A Conboy, BSc
Mrs C C M Phillips, BSc
D J Stone, BSc
Dr J Stone, BSc, PhD

Classics:
*Mrs J Nesbitt, BA
C S Dammers, BA (*Head of Year 11*)
S R Holman, MA (*Senior Head of House*)
A J Keen, BA (*Head of House*)
Mrs V M Kendall, BA

Design & Technology:
*P M Whitehouse, BSc
Ms L-J Godfrey, BA
M Hilliard, BSc (*Head of SPD*)
A Martin, BA
P Thomas, BA

Drama:
*G L Martin, BA, MA (*Head of Year 7*)

Economics/Business Studies:
*G Butterworth, BA
A J Catchpole, BSc (*Head of House*)
Mrs D E S Dutton, MA
Ms J Thompson, MBA

English:
*D L Briggs, BA
R P Clare, MA
Mrs C V Maddock, BA, MEd
D S Mair, BA
D M Selwyn, BA, MMus

Mrs A Selvey, BA, MA
Mrs J Whitehead, BA
Ms E Yemenakis, BA

Geography:
*Mrs R Atkins, BSc
R A D Cox, BSc
Dr A J Dimberline, BSc, PhD (*Head of Leadership Development*)
Mrs J L Foster, BSc (*Director of Activities*)
P R Huckle, BA, MEd

History:
*Dr R A Massey, BA, PhD (*Director of Scholars*)
Ms S Bassett, BA
T J Dougall, MA
O R T Edwards, BA (*Head of House*)
Miss A Humphrey
Mrs S M Kaye, BA, MA
Mrs E M Thorne, BA

Information Technology/Computing:
*G S Clark, BSc
Mrs S Davies-Walters, BEd
R S Jones, BSc

Learning Support:
*Mrs E M Thorne, BA
Mrs J Benn

Mathematics:
*Miss S M Poole, BSc
A K Barker, BSc (*Head of Year 10*)
Dr R J Baxter, BSc, PhD
O L Chambers, BSc (*Head of Year 8*)
Mrs E Deaves, BSc
G R Iwi, MSc
Mrs K H Jones, BSc
W McCormack, BSc, BA
Miss A L Nicholsby, BSc
P R Roberts, BSc, MSc
Miss J Wall, BSc

Modern Languages:
*Dr M G Ransome, BA, PhD
Mrs R Allen, BA
Ms L Carleton, BA
Miss E Corrigan, BA (*Head of French*)
G D Fellows, BA
Miss S M Hancock, MA
Miss C M Hölzer, MA (*Head of German*)
Miss C L Jenkins, BA
Mrs A C Macro, BA (*Head of Spanish*)
Mrs D M G Swain, BA
Miss L E Williamson, BA

Music:
*R T Osmond, MA
Miss V Elcock, BA
Mrs N Pocock, BMus
Ms B M Stacey, GBSM, ABSSM, LRAM

PE/Games:
*R M Sellers, BSc
K R Blackburn, BSc
P Z Jakobek, BEd (*Head of House*)
Mrs R E John, BA
Miss F A Ripley, BSc (*Head of PE*)
Miss V L Ryan, BEd
B Scott, BEd (*Head of House*)
Miss K Trump, BEd

Physics:
*Dr D R Homer, MSc, PhD (*Chair of Science*)
P Clarke, MA
E J Knoop, BSc
Dr C A Rosser, BSc, PhD
Miss L Glenn, BEng

Psychology:
*Mrs L Dilley, BSc
Mrs K E Alexander, BSc, BA

Religious Studies:
*C P Wadey, MA
A Gunawardana, BA (*Head of House*)
Mrs J B Lewis, CertEd
R M Smith, BA (*Head of Year 9*)

Head Librarian: Ms D Brooks
Clerk to the Governors and Bursar: D F M Collyer
Director of Development and Marketing: Mrs A Pavier

Admissions Office:
Miss C Lee
Mrs N Steven
Mrs A Sawkins

PA to Headmaster: Miss C Vincent

Bristol Grammar School is a day school with c 1,050 pupils aged between 11 and 18. Students learn in an atmosphere that motivates them to enjoy their education and as a result BGS has a deserved reputation as one of the leading academic schools in the South West. The School is friendly and lively environment and students are encouraged to make the most of the wide ranging opportunities available to them. Students joining at age 11 have their own base in a purpose built block where many of their lessons take place. This helps ease the transition to senior school, as well as providing an important opportunity for the year group to bond socially. This continues up the School with each year group allocated form rooms, based in separate, self-contained buildings, although teaching is spread throughout the School's specialist facilities.

Close to the city centre and adjacent to the University, Bristol Grammar School is well placed to take advantage of the city's many amenities. It is also committed to a continuing programme of investment to ensure its own facilities continue to offer the best possible opportunities to its students.

The Houses. The School is divided into six houses, each organised by a head of house, with the assistance of house tutors. Older students become leaders within their House, whilst social, theatrical, musical and other opportunities allow those from all year groups to work together and become friends. As well as providing continuity of pastoral care and enhancing school/family links, the Houses operate as families within the school community, encouraging a real sense of belonging amongst pupils.

Curriculum. The school takes note of the National Curriculum but, in keeping with its academic ethos, a far wider range of subjects and opportunities is offered. Setting is used in some subjects, but there is no streaming. In the first two years all pupils follow a curriculum which includes English, Mathematics, Science, French, Spanish, History, Geography, Technology, IT, Latin, Religious Studies, Art, Music and Physical Education. Further up the School other subjects become available such as Russian, German, Greek and Business Studies and at the end of Year 11 all pupils take 10 GCSEs drawn from the core subjects of English, Mathematics, Science and a Modern Foreign Language, together with a selection of other subjects, chosen from a carefully balanced range of options. The Sixth Form provides a flexible range of A Level options chosen from English, Mathematics, the Sciences, Technology, Modern Languages, Classics, History, Geography, Economics, Business Studies, Computing, IT, Psychology, Theatre Studies, Sports Studies, Art and Music. In addition, all pupils follow enrichment courses and attend a richly diverse programme of weekly lectures by visiting speakers. Students from the Sixth Form proceed to a wide range of faculties at universities in the UK, and increasingly abroad. In 2007 11 students gained places at Oxbridge, with the majority of students securing places at their first-choice universities.

There are frequent opportunities for parents to consult form tutors, heads of houses and year heads and, in addition, regular meetings are held at which parents meet the teaching staff. All parents join the Friends of Bristol Grammar School, an association whose aim is to promote the well-being of the School.

The School also has two teachers to help students with SEN and a full-time careers advisor.

Games. The games options, which vary with different age groups, include Rugby, Hockey, Football, Cross-Country, Cricket, Athletics, Swimming, Golf, Tennis, Rounders and Netball. Facilities for Orienteering, Aerobics, Dance, Judo, Fencing, Badminton and Squash are available. There are extensive playing fields at Failand, which include an all-weather Hockey/Tennis area and an astroturf hockey pitch. Below the Sixth Form, all pupils, unless excused for medical reasons, participate in School games; the full range of sports is available to the Sixth Form on a voluntary basis.

Activities and Societies. All pupils take part in a wide-ranging programme of extra-curricular activities one afternoon a week and there are many voluntary clubs and societies at lunchtimes and after school. There are flourishing choirs and orchestras; tuition can be arranged in a large number of instruments. Drama productions are regularly staged by different age levels of the School and by the Houses. Ski trips are offered each year. Regular excursions are made abroad, as well as exchange visits, both on an individual and on a school basis. Pupils may join the Duke of Edinburgh's Award Scheme in Year 10 and there is an active Community Service Unit. Overseas expeditions take place every two years and have visited Bolivia, the Himalayas, Mongolia and Ecuador.

Admission. Entry to the School is normally in September at age 11+ following a satisfactory performance in the entrance examination held in the previous spring and a creditable school report. An additional 20–25 places become available each year at ages 13+ and 16+. Pupils may be accepted into the school during any term subject to the availability of places.

Applications should be made to the Admissions Office at the School. Prospective entrants and their families are always welcome to visit the School. Please see the website for information about Open Days and Visiting Days.

Bursaries. The School's Assisted Places Scheme is able to offer substantial financial assistance towards the fees of able pupils whose parents have limited means. The scheme is kept under regular review by the Governors who constantly seek to extend it. The School became a member of the Ogden Bursary Scheme in 2000.

Scholarships. (*see Scholarship Entries section*).

Fees per term (2008-2009). Upper School £3,280; Lower School £2,173. Fees include the cost of most textbooks and stationery.

Bristol Grammar School Lower School. The Lower School admits pupils aged 7–11 and is housed in its own buildings on the same site as the Upper School. (*For further details see entry in IAPS section.*)

Old Bristolians Society. Close contact is maintained with former pupils through the Old Bristolians Society whose honorary secretary can be contacted at the School.

Charitable status. Bristol Grammar School is a Registered Charity, number 1104425. It has existed since 1532 to provide an education for Bristol children.

Bromsgrove School

Worcester Road Bromsgrove Worcestershire B61 7DU
Tel: 01527 579679
Fax: 01527 576177
e-mail: admissions@bromsgrove-school.co.uk
website: www.bromsgrove-school.co.uk

The date of the School's Foundation is unknown but it was re-organised by Edward VI in 1553 and was granted a Royal Charter 6 years later. It was refounded in 1693 by Sir Thomas Cookes, Bt, at the same time as Worcester College, Oxford (formerly Gloucester Hall). The link between School and College has been maintained ever since.

Motto: '*Deo Regi Vicino.*'

Patron: A Denham-Cookes

President: G R John, CBE

A Vice-President: Mr J M Baron, TD, MA
A Vice-President: Prof Sir Michael Drury, OBE, FRCP, FRCGP, FRACGP
A Vice-President: J A Hall, FCA
A Vice-President: N J Birch, MIMechE
A Vice-President: Prof K B Haley, BSc, PhD, FIMA, CMath, FIEE, CEng

Governing Body:
T M Horton, BA (*Chairman*)
V S Anthony, BSc, Hon DEd, Hon FCP, FRSA
R D Brookes, FRICS
Miss F Horden
R Lane, MA
Air Commodore S P J Lilley, MA (RAF)
Miss J Longmuir
R G Noake, FCA, FCCA (*Vice-Chairman*)
Prof J G Perry, BEng, MEng, PhD, FICE, MAPM
T D Pile, BA
Dr A Silk, PhD
G Strong
S Towe
Mrs S Willmott
Mrs L Wyatt, ACIMA

Company Secretary: J Sommerville

***Headmaster*: C J Edwards**, MA Oxon

Financial Controller: Ms J Castle, BCom, FCA, ATII
Deputy Headmaster: P St J Bowen, BA, PGCE
Assistant Head (*Academic*): P S Ruben, BSc, MPhil, MBA
Assistant Head (*Admissions*): Miss R M Scannell, BA, PGCE
Assistant Head (*Pastoral*): Mrs C P M Maund, BSc, PGCE
School Medical Officer: Dr B Bywater, MBChB, DRCOG, FRCGP
Foundation Director: Group Captain J P Rogers

Staff:
* *Head of Department*
† *Houseparent*

B J Allen, BSc (**Technology; Examination Secretary*)
D Langlands, BSc, CertEd
Mrs E A Langlands, BSc, CertEd
A W Burton, MA Cantab, PGCE (*Timetable Coordinator*)
W K Hamflett BSc PGCE (*Senior Head of Department; Director of Planning*)
M D Bowen-Jones, BSc, MEd, PGCE (*Senior Master*)
Mrs A M Bowen-Jones, CertEd, BPhil (*Ed*) (*i/c Activities*)
S J Kingston, BEd
Mrs A Grunsell, BA, CertEd
Mrs P T Kenward, BA, PGCE
J Stateczny, BA, PGCE (**Politics*)
Mrs C E Turner, BA, PGCE
S Challoner, BSc, PGCE (*Director of Staffing; *Business Studies*)
C A Dowling MA Cantab, PGCE (**Chemistry; Academic Database Coordinator*)
Dr D A Wilson, BSc, PhD, PGCE (**Science*)
Dr A S Woollhead, BSc, PhD, PGCE (**Biology; Assessment Manager*)
†Dr M R Werrett, GRSC, PhD, PGCE
†M A Stone, BEng, ACGI, PGCE

Mrs H S Barnett, BSc, PGCE
R E W Stephens, BA, PGCE, MMus, ARCO, ARCM (*OC CCF*)
Mrs J A Holden, MA Oxon, PGCE
†J Wingfield, BA, PGCE
P S T Mullan, BA, PGCE (*Director of Sport and Extra-Curricular*)
Mrs K Linehan, BA, MA, PGCE (**English, President of Common Room*)
Miss S Dick, BSc, PGCE (*Head of Upper Fourth Form*)
†Dr A R Johns, BSc, PhD, PGCE
†Mrs K E Mackay, BA, PGCE
R A C Barr, BA, MA, PGCE (**Sixth Form Careers and UCAS*)
Mrs A Clee, BA, ALA (**ICT*)
Ms S J Cronin, BA, DMS, PGCE (*Coordinator of Vocational Education*)
Mrs F K Bateman, BSc, PGCE (*Head of Lower Sixth Form; *Sixth Form Enrichment Curriculum*)
Mrs C Bentham, BEd (*Coordinator, International Students; *EAL*)
Mrs S Wood, BEd, CertEd
J W B Brogden, BA, PGCE (**Media Studies*)
†Mrs S E Ascough, BSc, PGCE
†P Greetham, BA, QTS (**Boys' PE and Games; Master i/c Cricket*)
Miss K E Tansley, BA, MA, PGCE
†D G Wilkins, BA, SCITT
M A C Beet, MA Cantab, PGCE (**Modern Languages; i/c Oxbridge*)
†Mrs N R Wingfield, BEd
†D N Perry, BA, PGCE
F A Quinn, CertEd, DipPhysEd, SSI
M R Webb, BSc (*ICT Development Manager*)
Miss F E Diver, BA, PGCE (*Head of Lower Fourth Form, *Geography*)
†S D Coates, BSc, PGCE
Miss E M O'Brien, BA, MA, PGCE (*Head of Sixth Form – Pupil Progress*)
Miss Z L Leech, BA (**PSHE, Careers Adviser*)
D C Howard, MA, BEd, CertEd
M D Ravenscroft, MA
N C J Riley, BSc, PGCE (**Mathematics*)
Mrs E L E Buckingham, BA (**Girls PE & Games*)
Miss S A Franks, BSc, PGCE
Mrs M M Haycock, BA, PGCE (**Spanish*)
Mrs A L Bentall, BA, PGCE
†Mrs C AJohnson, BA, PGCE
Miss T L Cringle, BA, PGCE
G J Johnson, BSc, PGCE
R O Knight, MA Oxon, ARCO (*Assistant Director of Music*)
A D Langlands, BSc, PGCE (*Master i/c Hockey*)
O A Matthews, BEng, PGCE (**Design and Technology*)
B D White, BA, PGCE (*Head of Fifth Form*)
Mrs S LTaylor, BA, PGCE (**Textiles*)
Mrs N W Howard, BEd
Dr M Thompson, BSc, PhD, MInstP, PGCE (**Physics*)
R Watkins, BA, PGCE (**French*)
Mrs T James, BA, PGCE (**Drama*)
Revd P Hedworth, BEd, BA (*Chaplain, *Religious Studies*)
Miss C Ellis-Owen, BA, PGCE (**History*)
J Abrahams, BSc, PGCE (*Master i/c Rugby*)
Miss E Rein, BSc, PGCE (*i/c DofE*)
Mrs J L Spearing, BA, PGCE (**Critical Thinking*)
Dr M K Ruben, BA, PhD, PGCE
Miss M Wyatt, BA, PGCE
Miss C H Knight, BA (**General Studies*)
Miss L E McCutcheon, BA
Miss S J McWilliams, BA, PGCE
Miss S Morgans, BA, PGCE, DipND (**Art*)
Miss L Ferguson, BA, PGCE
Miss I Peric, BEd
Dr J Ogston, BSc, PhD, PGCE
Mrs M Deighan, BA, Adv Cert SpLD, PGCE (**Learning Support*)
Mrs J L Boonak, BA, PGCE
Miss C D Goddard, BA, PGCE
Mr J R Kingston, BMus, DipMusCh, PGCE, FRSA, (**Music*)
Mr A C Merrick, BSc, PGCE
H Bell, MA, PGCE
G Bowmer, BA, PGCE
M Crooks, BEng
Miss S J Jones, BA (*Maternity cover*)
A McClure, BA, PGCE (**Classics*)
P J Merrell, BA, PGCE, MPhil
Miss S Nelson, BSc, PGCE
Miss L Sutters, BA, PGCE
Miss J Zafar, BA, PGCE

Houses and Houseparents:
Boarding:
Elmshurst (*Boys*): D N Perry
Housman Hall (*Sixth Form*): J & Mrs N Wingfield
Mary Windsor (*Girls*): Mrs C A Johnson
Oakley (*Girls*): (Mrs S E Ascough) Miss T L Cringle (*Maternity cover*)
School (*Boys*): M A Stone
Wendron Gordon (*Boys*): Dr A R Johns

Day:
Hazeldene (*Girls*): Dr M R Werrett
Lupton (*Boys*): P Greetham
Lyttelton (*Boys*): S D Coates
Thomas Cookes (*Girls*): Mrs K E Mackay
Walters (*Boys*): D G Wilkins

Music Staff:
J R Kingston, BMus, DipMusCh, FRSA, PGCE (*Director of Music*)
Mrs C R Bayliss, MA, PGCE, LLCM (**Music, Preparatory School*)
R O Knight, MA Oxon, ARCO (*Assistant Director of Music*)
Miss K Miller, BA Cantab, PGCE
D J Wilkinson, BMus, PGCE
Miss M A Coulson, BA (*Music School Secretary*)

Visiting Music Staff:
Mrs J Ayres, ABSM (*Oboe*)
P Badley (*Voice*)
N Barry, GGSM, LTCL (*Piano*)
Miss H Bool, GBSM, ABSM, BTechNat (*Percussion*)
M Broadhead, LTCL, DipTCL, (*Cello*)
R Bull (*Guitar*)
W Coleman, BA, LTCL (*Singing*)
Mrs E Dempster, BA, LLCM, ALCM (*Piano*)
J Dunlop, BA, GBSM, ABSM (*Flute*)
A Gittens, BTec, HND (*Electric Guitar*)
D Harper (*Double Bass*)
Mrs J A Hattersley, CTABRSM, LRSM (*Brass*)
Mrs J Hiles, GBSM, ABSM (*Flute*)
Mrs V A Lee, BMus (*Percussion*)
T Martin (*Saxophone*)
A Osborne, BMus, PGDip, PPRNCM (*Singing*)
D Scally, MA, BMus, LTCL, DipCSM (*Piano*)
Ms F Swadling, BA, ABSM, GBSM, (*Viola, Violin, Piano*)
A D C Thayer, BMus, PGDip, MA (*Piano*)
D J G Whitehouse, ABSM (*Bassoon*)

Preparatory School

Headmaster: R Evans, BEd, AdvDipEdMan

Deputy Head: Mrs M Purdy, BSc, PGCE
Assistant Head (*Academic*): W R Caldwell, BA, MA, MEd, PGCE (**Modern Languages & Library*)
Assistant Head (*Pastoral*): S J P Loone, MEd, BA, BTheol, PGCE (**Religious Education*)

Mrs J Agnew, BA, PGCE
Mrs R Al-Nakeb, BEd (**Staff Appraisal and Professional Development*)
Miss R Anthony, BA, PGCE
Mrs L Billington, BSc, PGCE (*Maternity leave*)
Miss N C Barton, CertEd, CertSpLD
Mrs P Barton, CertEd
Mrs C R Bayliss, MA, PGCE, LLCM (**Music*)
Mrs G Butler, BEd
Mrs S M Bourne, BSc, PGCE (**Girls' Boarding, *Science*)
Mrs M L Caldwell, CertEd (*SENCO, *Learning Support & PSCHE*)
Miss S Cartwright, BSc, PGCE
G Clark, BEd (*Head of Year 7*)
L Falconer, BA, PGCE (**German, *Gifted and Talented*)
†C F Harris, DipPE, CertEd
M Hill, BA, CertEd (**Mathematics*)
Ms S Cadwallader, BA, PGCE (*Head of Year 6*)
G Jones, BA, PGCE (** Boys' PE*)
Mrs RWhiting , BA, PGCE
Mrs C M Leather, BSc, PGCE (**Junior Department*)
Mrs F Mack, MA, PGCE
J Marks, BEd (**Drama*)
Miss R McRandal, BA, PGCE (**Spanish*)
Miss K Miller, BA, PGCE
†Mrs E Mullan, BEd (*Head of Year 8*)
†Mrs H Newton, CertEd
†R J Newton, BEd (*Senior Teacher, *Boys' Boarding*)
Mrs J Ormerod, MEd, CertEd
C Pickering, BEd, DipCompEd, AdvCertEd, CertEd (**ICT*)
Mrs A Purver, BA, PGCE (**History*)
Ms A Read, BTec, BA, PGCE
Miss R Rhodes, BA, PGCE
Mrs R Sumner, BA, MLitt, MPhil Ed
P Sutherland, HD Ed (**Design & Technology*)
Ms Amina Urwin, BA
R Widdop, BA, DipSpPsy (**Geography*)
Miss K Winterbottom, BEd
Miss V Ziar, BA, PGCE, BIAD (**Art*)

Boarding Houses and Houseparents:
Cobham (*Boys*): Mr R & Mrs H Newton
Honeysuckle (*Junior boys and girls*): Mrs E Mullan
Page (*Girls*): Mr C & Mrs M Harris

Location. This co-educational boarding and day school is situated some 13 miles north of the Cathedral City of Worcester and an equal distance south of Birmingham. Birmingham International Airport and Station are a 20-minute drive by motorway. The M5, M6, M42 and M40 motorways provide easy access to the School.

The School stands in 100 acres of grounds on the south side and within walking distance of the market town of Bromsgrove.

Facilities. The school's £22 million building and development programme since 1994 has included all-weather, floodlit sports facilities, a state of the art Library and Resources Centre, extensions to the Maths and Modern Languages facilities, an award winning Art, Design and Technology Building and a new Humanities building. Boarding facilities have been enhanced by a 20-room Girls Sixth Form extension with single en-suite rooms and the opening of Housman Hall, the school's first mixed Sixth Form House.

Boarding. Nearly half of Bromsgrove Senior School's pupil body is made up of boarders accommodated between six houses, one of which is in the town. Loyalty to House and the traditions attendant upon it are significant factors of life at Bromsgrove. The boarding environment is happy, stable, disciplined and nurturing. House competition, day and boarding, from sport to drama, music to debating is keen.

The stability and continuity that enable boarders to thrive are provided by resident houseparents (all academic members of staff) and their families, assistant houseparents, house mothers and a team of house-based tutors. All meals are taken centrally in the School except in the case of the evening meal at Housman Hall, the Sixth Form-only House sited in the town.

A huge upgrading of boarding facilities is currently underway with one House now totally en suite and others set to follow.

Numbers. There are 800 pupils in the Senior School, of whom 430 are boys. The adjacent Preparatory School has a further 470 pupils aged 7 to 13. (*See also Preparatory School entry in IAPS section.*)

Curriculum. In the Preparatory School and throughout the first year in the Senior School a broadly based curriculum is followed. In addition to the usual academic subjects time is given to Art, Music, ICT, Drama, Design Technology and to a full programme of Physical Education. Languages on offer include French, German, Spanish and Latin.

As pupils move up the School other options become available and some narrowing of the curriculum is inevitable. 10 subjects is the norm at GCSE. 16 points is the minimum qualification for entry to the Sixth Form (A*=4, A=3, B=2, C=1). In the Lower Sixth Form most pupils study 4 AS level subjects. Subjects are as follows: Art, Biology, Business Studies, Chemistry, Classical Civilisation, Design Technology, Drama & Theatre Studies, Economics, English, French, Geography, German, History, ICT, Latin, Mathematics and Further Mathematics, Media Studies, Music, Physical Education, Physics, Politics and Government, Religious Studies, Spanish, Textiles. The School also offers an Applied A Level in Business and a BTEC course in Sports Performance and Excellence. About 90% stay on to do AS Levels. All students in the Sixth Form do a skills-based course, with a focus on ICT and communication skills. About 99% of A Level leavers go on to degree courses at Universities.

Music. Music flourishes as important and integral parts of the School's activities both within and outside the formal curriculum. There is plenty of scope for involvement in the School Ensembles, Chamber Groups, Jazz Bands, Chapel Choirs and Choral Society. The timetable is sufficiently flexible to allow special arrangements to be made for outstanding musicians. Visits to Bath Abbey to sing Evensong and Mozart's Requiem and Clarinet Concerto are two main features of 2008. A new chapel organ will be installed in February.

Careers. The school employs a fully qualified, full-time careers advisor and a comprehensive careers counselling programme is pursued for pupils of all ages.

Reports and Consultation. Pupils receive grades and tutor comments twice a term and there are regular reports and parents' evenings. Supervision is shared by Houseparents and House Tutors, whom parents may meet informally by appointment. There are regular parent-teacher evenings. Parents may arrange appointments to meet members of the Careers Department.

Extra-Curricular Activities. A wide range of sports and activities is offered, giving opportunities to participate at a competitive level in Rugby, Hockey, Netball, Athletics, Basketball, Clay Pigeon shooting, Cricket, Cross-Country, Debating, Fencing, Golf, Horse Riding, Rounders, Shakespeare Festival, Soccer , Squash, Swimming, Tennis and Young Enterprise.

The new Saturday timetable, in conjunction with the weekday programme, allows the activities' programme more flexibility to offer both recreational and academic choices. Pupils may select from a diverse range of recreational activities including Academic extension lessons, Accounting AS, Development Studies AS, Electronics AS, Aerobics, Art, GCSE, AS and A2 revision sessions, Badminton, Biology Olympiad, Board games including Chinese Chess and Mahjong, Ceramics, Corps of drums, Cultural Studies, Design Technology, Drama, Economics, Engineering, Textiles (with fashion), Film making, ICT, Italian, Jewellery making, Military skills, Outdoor pursuits (including climbing, high ropes, kayaking, orienteering, raft building, sailing), Oxbridge, Photography, Table tennis, Trampolining, Website design, Weight training and World Language club. There are opportunities to gain qualifications in Modern dance, Life saving, First Aid, Food hygiene, RADA and Taekwondo.

In addition to the activities programme, Year 9 pupils participate in Bromsgrove Badge; comprising a selection of activities that help to prepare them for the Bronze Duke of Edinburgh's Award and culminating in a four-day camp at the end of the year. There is a thriving Combined Cadet Force (Army and RAF); whist approximately 300 pupils are currently involved in the Duke of Edinburgh's Award Scheme. The School's Community Service programme caters for large numbers of pupils and provides a wide range of activities; some of the more popular options involve working in local schools, visiting residential homes and running a Fair Trade café. Others options include an Amnesty International group, compiling Aqua boxes, working in local charity shops, helping in animal sanctuaries and supporting conservation projects.

Religion. There is either a daily service in the School Chapel or an Assembly which all pupils are required to attend. The services and religious teaching are in accordance with the forms and principles of the Church of England. Boys and girls have the opportunity of being prepared for adult membership of the Anglican Communion. Pupils of other denominations and faiths are welcome as members of the School.

Admission. Entrance at 13 is by Common Entrance and/or English, Mathematics and Verbal Reasoning Tests. Boys and Girls may be admitted to the Preparatory School at any age from 7 to 12 inclusive. Entrance Tests take place in late January. Places are also available in the Sixth Form to boys and girls who have had their GCSE education elsewhere.

Although pupils are normally accepted into the School only at the start of the Michaelmas Term of the year in which they have reached their eleventh, thirteenth or sixteenth birthdays, the Headmaster considers sympathetically applications for admission at other ages and at other times of the academic year.

Entrance Scholarships. (*see Scholarship Entries section*). Awards are made on the results of open examinations held at the school in January: a significant number of scholarships and bursaries for pupils of academic, artistic, musical, sporting and all-round ability are awarded at 11+, 13+ and 16+.

Fees per term (2008-2009). Senior School (age 13+): £7,740 boarding, £8,475 international boarders, £3,950 day. Preparatory School (age 7–13): £5,600–£6,935 full boarding, £3,815–£4,675 weekly boarding, £2,815–£3,675 day.

Charitable status. Bromsgrove School is a Registered Charity, number 1098740. It exists to provide education for boys and girls.

Bryanston School

Blandford Dorset DT11 0PX
Tel: 01258 452411
Fax: 01258 484661
e-mail: head@bryanston.co.uk
website: www.bryanston.co.uk

Founded in 1928, Bryanston School aims above all to develop the all-round talents of individual pupils. A broad, flexible academic and extra-curricular programme together with an extensive network of adult support encourages pupils to maximise their particular abilities as well as to adapt positively to the demands of the society of which they are part. Creativity, individuality and opportunity are the school's key notes, but a loving community is the school's most important quality. Happy children growing up in a secure environment, aware of beliefs and values and confident of their own worth, will be well balanced 18 year olds. That is what we seek to produce.

Motto: '*Et Nova et Vetera*'.

Governors:
Chairman: R H Cox, BA
S F Bowes
Ms S A Buxton, MA, ACA
J A T Conran, DCL, DLIT
The Rt Revd S D Conway, MA
M Davies, MA, BA
Mrs S Foulser, BA
G E T Granter, MA
J R Greenhill, MA
Mrs B Hollond, MA, RSA
B M Irvani, MA, FCA
P Kosminsky, MA, FRSA, FRTS
M A S Laurence
Mrs V M McDonaugh, MA
R A Pegna, MA
Dr H M Pharaoh, MBBS, DRCOG
Dr M L Reynolds
A R Poulton, BA
Professor J F Smyth, MD, FRCP, FRSE
P G E Walker, FRICS
M A Wingate-Saul, MA

Bursar and Clerk to the Governors: P G Speakman, BA

***Head*: Ms S J Thomas**, BA

* *Head of Department*

Second Master: P J Hardy, JP, MA, PGCE (*Economics and Business*)
Director of Studies: P Simpson, MA (*History*)
Senior Mistress: Mrs E M Barkham, BA, MSc, PGCE (*Biology*)

Staff:
* *Head of Department*
† *Housemaster/Housemistress*

C S Poole, BSc, CertEd, AFIMA (**Mathematics*)
B G Stebbings, BA, CertEd (*Senior Teacher; Geography; Geology*)
F J Bristow, CertEd (*Technology*)
G Q Craddock, BSc, CertEd (*Mathematics*)
M J Adams, PhD, MA (*Biology*)
A M Taylor, BA, MSc (*Biology*)
Mrs T J Doble, BSc, PGCE (*Mathematics*)
P A L Rioch, BMus, BA (*Deputy Director of Music*)
S R L Long, CertEd (**PE; Sports Studies*)
D C Bourne, MA, PGCE, FRGS (*Geography; Senior Tutor*)
D Boyle, BA, CertEd (**German*)
Mrs S Stacpoole, BA (**History of Art*)
G S Elliot, BA, PGCE (*Chemistry*)
M N Pyrgos, BSc, PGCE (*Economics and Business*)
Mrs F K Pyrgos, BSc, PGCE (**Careers*)
†I R Haslam, CertEd (*Design and Technology*)
J N G Fisher, BEd, PGCE (*English*)
J L Jones, MA, PGCE (*Modern Languages*)
†Mrs E M Long, CertEd (*PSE*)
†D Fowler-Watt, MA (*Classics*)
Mrs J Ladd-Gibbon, MA (*Design*)
Mrs M F Barlow, BA (*Economics and Business*)
Mrs R A Simpson, BA (*English*)
Mrs J E Little, MA(Ed) (*Information Technology*)
†A J Marriott, BA, PGCE (*History*)
Mrs J S Le Hardy, BA, PGCE (**Spanish*)
Mrs G C Kohn, BA, PGCE (*Modern Languages*)
S J Richardson, BEd, MA, FRMetS, NPQH (*Geography; Academic Registrar*)
M T Kearney, MA, PhD (**Science; Physics*)
Ms P Quarrell, BA, PGCE (**History*)
†Mrs J A Price, BA, PGCE (*Music*)
Mrs J G S Strange, BA, PGCE (*History*)
M J Owens, MA, PGCE (**Art*)
Mrs S M Haslam, CertEd (*Art*)

†S J Turrill, BSc, PGCE (*Chemistry*)
Mrs K A Grugeon, BSc, PGCE, CChem (**Chemistry*)
N J Davies, BEd (*Design Technology*)
L C Johnson, BA, LTP (**French*)
Miss J F Quan, MA (*Director of Drama*)
Mrs D M Wellesley, MA (*Modern Languages*)
C T Holland, BA (**Classics*)
†P S Bachra, MA (*Economics and Business*)
S H Jones, BSc, PGCE (*Biology*)
Mrs A J Gilbert, BA, PGCE (*Modern Languages*)
†Mrs L C Kearney, BEd (*Geography*)
Mrs H E Dean, BA, PGCE (*Art*)
†Ms L Boothman, BA, PGCE (*English*)
†Mrs C L Miller, BEd (*Mathematics*)
R J Collcott, MEng, MSc (*Mathematics and Physics*)
A J Barnes, BA, CertEd (*Director of Technology*)
Dr H L Fearnley, BA, PhD (*Classics*)
D J Melbourne, BSc, PGCE (*Mathematics*)
†S M Vincent, BA, PGCE (*History*)
G M Scott, BA, ARCO, LTCL, PGCE (**Keyboard*)
Mrs O E Tory, BSc (*Biology*)
Miss C L Bentinck, BA (*English*)
J B Casely, BA, MPhil (*History of Art*)
A Day, BSc, PGCE (**Information Technology*)
L C E Blanco Gomez, BA (*Spanish*)
N M Kelly, BA, PGCE (**English*)
†W J Lockett, BA, PGCE (*Classics*)
J J A Beales, BA, PGCE (**Economics*)
G C Burton, BSc, PGCE (**Design and Technology*)
Mrs C S Scott, BMus, PGCE, FTCL, ARCM, LTCL (**Strings*)
G R Harwood, BSc, MSc (*Biology*)
Miss C M Dawson, LLB, PGCE (*English*)
J E J Sidders, MA, PGCE (**Physics*)
T J Scott, BA, PGCE (*Modern Languages*)
N Welford, BSc, PGCE (*Biology*)
Miss K J Witchell, BA, PGCE (*Drama, English*)
Miss N Morley, BSC, PGCE (*Physics*)
Miss C A Çava, MPhys (*Physics*)
Mrs C Gordon, BA, PGCE, AKC (**Spanish*)
D M Emerson, BMus, PGCE (*Director of Music*)
T W Sellers, BA, PGCE, AKC (*History*)
S Davies, MA (*English*)
A K Tarafder, BSc (*Mathematics*)
D J Webb, BA (**Academic Music*)
Miss C L Baxter, PGCE, BSc (*Chemistry*)
B J Lawes, BSc (*PE, Cricket*)
N C Davies, BSc PGCE (*Chemistry*)
P C A Croft, BA, PGCE (*Religious Studies, Geography*)
Mrs S L Worrall, BEd (*Mathematics*)
Miss M J Lowes, BA (*Biology*)
Miss R Eales, BSc, PGCE (*IT, Economics*)
Revd A M J Haviland, BEd, DipCMM (*Chaplain*)
M S Deketelaere, BA, MSc, DIC (**Geography*)
Miss A J Granville, BSc (*Chemistry*)
Miss C R Evans, BA (*Fine Art*)

Admissions Registrar: Mrs S J Birkill
Head's PA: Mrs F J Howard

Situation. Occupying a magnificent Norman Shaw mansion, the School is located in beautiful Dorset countryside near the market town of Blandford. There are 400 acres of grounds, which include a stretch of river used for rowing and canoeing, playing fields, woodland and parkland.

Numbers. There are approximately 375 boys and 275 girls in the School.

Admission. Boys and girls are normally admitted between 13 and 14 years of age on the results of Common Entrance or the School's own entrance exam. Sixth Form entrants are admitted after interview, conditional upon securing at least 40 points at GCSE.

Scholarships. (*see Scholarship Entries section*).

Organisation. The School is organised on a House basis with 5 senior boys' houses, 5 girls' houses, and 2 junior boys' houses. All pupils have a tutor throughout their time in the School. No tutor has more than 15 pupils. Feeding and medical care are organised centrally. All Sixth Form pupils in their final year have individual study-bedrooms. Lower Sixth Formers usually share study-bedrooms.

Religion. Religious instruction is widely based and is carried on throughout the School. There are two assemblies each week for the whole school. Pupils attend either assemblies or services on most Sundays during the term. Holy Communion is celebrated every Sunday and on some week days. A Chaplain is responsible for pastoral work and preparation for Confirmation.

School Work. The School aims at leading pupils, over a period of 5 years, from the comparative dependence on class teaching in which they join the school, to a state in which they are capable of working on their own, for a University degree or professional qualification, or in business. In addition to traditional class teaching, there is, therefore, increasing time given to private work as a pupil moves up the School. This is in the form of assignments to be completed within a week or a fortnight. Teachers are available to give individual help when required, and Tutors supervise pupils' work and activities in general.

Every pupil is encouraged to explore a range of opportunities. All pupils follow the same broad curriculum in Group D (the first year), if at all possible. This curriculum includes Latin, modern languages, three separate sciences, creative arts, technology and music. GCSE is taken after 3 years when a pupil is in Group B. There is a highly flexible choice of subjects at this level and subjects are setted independently. In the Sixth Form (Group A) pupils are expected to study up to five subjects at AS Level in the first year and to continue with three or four subjects to Advanced (A2) Level in the second year. 24 subjects are offered at AS Level and 22 at A2 Level and there are few restrictions on combinations. All Lower Sixth Formers follow a compulsory Personal and Social Education course and the Humanities programme provides supplementary courses to develop key skills and thinking techniques.

Music. Music plays a very important part in the life of the School. There are 2 Orchestras, a Concert Band, a Dance Band, a String Chamber Orchestra, five Choirs, a Choral Society and many informal ensembles: numerous professional and amateur concerts take place throughout the year. Lessons are given in all orchestral instruments and in piano, organ, guitar and singing. Class music is a compulsory part of the curriculum for all First Year pupils, who also receive introductory free tuition on an orchestral instrument. Well over half the pupils have regular instrumental lessons.

Drama. A well-equipped, modern theatre provides the venue for the many school productions which take place during the year and for touring professional companies. In addition to acting, pupils are involved in Stage Management, Stage Lighting and Sound, and front-of-house work. There is also a large Greek Theatre in the grounds.

Sport and Leisure. A wide variety of sports is on offer at the school, including Athletics, Archery, Badminton, Canoeing, Climbing, Cricket, Cross-Country, Fencing, Fives, Hockey, Lacrosse, Netball, Riding, Rowing, Rugby, Sailing, Shooting, Squash, Swimming and Tennis. Extensive playing fields between the School and the River Stour provide 46 tennis courts, 2 astroturf pitches, 9 netball courts, an athletics track and grass pitches for all major sports, an all-weather riding manège and cross-country course. A Sports Complex provides an indoor heated 25m Swimming Pool, Gymnasium, large Sports Hall, Squash courts and Fitness Centre. Sailing takes place at Poole Harbour where the School has 6 dinghies at its own base. In addition to sport, a number of clubs and societies, catering for a wide range of interests, meet in the evenings and at weekends.

Additional Activities. To encourage a sense of responsibility towards the community, a growing self-reliance and a practical training in the positive use of leisure, all pupils take part in all or some of the following:
(1) Community and Social Service.
(2) Extra-curricular activities chosen from a wide range of options.
(3) The Duke of Edinburgh's Award Scheme.
(4) Adventure Training.

Dress. There is no school uniform but there is a dress code.

Careers. There is a well-resourced Careers Room and the school maintains close links with ISCO. A full time member of staff runs a careers programme which covers the pupils' five years in the school. All pupils undertake Work Experience after their GCSEs and specific advice is given to help with A Level and University degree choices. In the Sixth Form, a mock interview course and the teaching of presentation skills ensure that pupils are well-prepared for the future.

Further Education. The vast majority of pupils in the Sixth Form gain admission to Universities or other academies of further education.

Fees per term (2008-2009). Boarders £8,995, Day Pupils £7,196.

Charitable status. Bryanston School Incorporated is a Registered Charity, number 306210. It is a charitable trust for the purpose of educating children.

Bury Grammar School Boys

Tenterden Street Bury Lancs BL9 0HN
Tel: 0161 797 2700
Fax: 0161 763 4655
e-mail: info@bgsboys.co.uk
website: www.bgsboys.co.uk

The School, formerly housed in the precincts of the Parish Church of St Mary the Virgin, was first endowed by Henry Bury in 1634, but there is evidence that it existed before that date. It was re-endowed in 1726 by the Revd Roger Kay and moved to its current site in 1966. The school is a selective grammar school which aims to provide a first-class academic and extra-curricular education; to nurture the whole person in a safe, stimulating, challenging and friendly community in which each individual is encouraged to fulfil his potential; and to prepare each boy for an adulthood of fulfilling work, creative leisure and responsible citizenship.

Motto: '*Sanctas clavis fores aperit.*'

Governing Body:
Chairman of Governors: The Revd Dr J C Findon (*St Mary the Virgin, Bury*)
Mrs S T Henry, Deputy Chairman (*Hulme Trust*)
W R Ullathorne, Deputy Treasurer (*Hulme Trust*)
B Allan (*University of Salford*)
Mrs P M Baumber (*co-opted*)
R D Calrow (*Estate Governors of Bury Grammar Schools*)
F Chaudhry (*Bury Metropolitan Borough Council*)
Mrs A M Davies (*co-opted*)
L A Goldberg (*Victoria University of Manchester*)
Mrs P Lomas (*Hulme Trust*)
A C Murray (*co-opted*)
Mrs B Peachment (*co-opted*)
J A Rigby (*Estate Governors of Bury Grammar Schools*)
J H Spencer (*Estate Governors of Bury Grammar Schools*)
Councillor R E Walker (*Bury Metropolitan Borough Council*)
Miss J Hartley (*co-opted*)
Mrs D L Hampson (*Victoria University of Manchester*)
A Marshall (*co-opted*)
Mrs J Pickering (*co-opted*)

Bursar and Clerk to the Governors: D A Harrison, BSc, FCA

***Headmaster*: The Revd S C Harvey**, MA

Second Master: D E Armsbey, BA (*History*)
Deputy Head (Academic): R N Marshall, MSc (*Head of Chemistry, Head of Science*)
Senior Master: D A Wilson, BA (*French*)

Assistant Staff:
M Ahmad, BSc (*Physics*)
B Alldred, BSc (*Mathematics*)
M Aston, BSc (*PE & Games*)
G R Barker, MA (*History*)
D S Benger, MA (*Music*)
D A Bishop, BSc (*Head of Geology*)
M R Boyd, BA (*Head of French*)
Mrs R L Bradley, BA (*Classics*)
Miss H M Brien, MA (*Head of English*)
Mrs C A Brooks, BSc (*Geography*)
T A Burns, BA (*Head of Art*)
Mrs H Campion, BA (*Economics & Business Studies*)
D P Cassidy, BSc (*Chemistry*)
A S Cawtherley, BA (*Head of Geography*)
Mrs S G Cawtherley, BA (*Religious Studies, SENCO*)
A P Christian, BA (*History & Politics*)
Mrs C Cooke, BA (*English*)
M J Cooke, BEd (*CDT & Electronics*)
K M Cryer, BA (*French*)
P F Curry, BSc (*Physics*)
C A R Davidson, BSc (*Head of Physics*)
A E Dennis, BSc (*Mathematics*)
W Elf, BSc, MA (*Mathematics*)
G D Feely, MA (*Classics*)
D A Ferguson, BA (*Computing*)
G A Ferguson, BSc (*Head of Biology, Head of Sixth Form*)
Mrs A C Gill, BSc (*Biology*)
D J Gordon, MA (*English*)
Miss K A Gore, BA (*Art*)
D Hailwood, BEd (*Head of CDT & Electronics*)
G Halpin, BEd (*Art*)
L M Hilton, BSc (*Head of PE & Games*)
Mrs J Hone, BA (*Head of Classics*)
M J Hone, MA (*Head of History & Politics*)
C N J Hyde, GRNCM (*Head of Music*)
Miss S J Kitchen, BA (*French & German*)
P Koziura, BEd (*PE & Games*)
D R Lee, BA (*Head of German*)
P Meakin, BSc (*Head of Computing*)
D T Newbury, BSc (*Geography*)
T J Nicholson, BA (*Head of Mathematics*)
N Parkinson, BA (*Head of Economics & Business Studies*)
A A Phillips, BA (*Chemistry*)
M D Richmond, BSc (*Mathematics*)
L W Robinson, BA (*English*)
Mrs H C Shan, MChem (*Chemistry*)
M J Sherlock, BSc (*Mathematics*)
A L Stacey, BEd (*Head of Religious Studies*)
Mrs T J Taylor, MA (*Geography*)
Mrs E A Tollitt, BA (*English*)
A D Watts, BSc (*Biology*)

Junior School:
D J Crouch, CertEd (*Head of Junior School*)
Mrs S A Faulkner, BA (*Deputy Head*)
Mrs C A Atkinson-Howard, BSc
Mrs T H Coward
Mrs J M Harrison, BEd
Mrs F M L Hartwell, BSc
P G Newton, MA
N G Robson, BA
B J Shakespeare, BA
S H Sheikh, BA
Miss C L Wheeler, BA

Headmaster's PA: Mrs A Cloke

Numbers of Boys. 750, aged 7 to 18.

Admission, Scholarships and Bursaries. Admission is by examination and interview. Most boys join the school at either 7 or 11, although, subject to places being available, admission is possible at other ages. One Kay Scholarship and a number of means-tested bursaries, based on academic performance and financial need, are awarded each year.

Fees per term (2008-2009). Senior School £2,566; Junior School £1,905.

Facilities and Development. This ancient grammar school, proud of its historic links with the town of Bury and the surrounding area, possesses a full range of modern facilities. These facilities enable the school to offer a broad and rich academic curriculum and extra-curricular programme. Since 1993 the Junior School has occupied its own site opposite the Senior School. Junior School pupils are able to take advantage of the additional specialist facilities and resources in the Senior School. A new Learning Resource Centre, consisting of a Library, extensive ICT provision and private study facilities, was opened in 2002, and a new Art Centre in 2004.

An Appeal was launched early in 2006 to raise funds for a new co-ed Kindergarten (being built on the Girls' School site, opposite the Boys' School); for a new Sixth Form Centre, to provide study and recreational facilities for both boys and girls; and for bursaries to extend the school's ability to welcome able boys whose parents cannot afford the fees.

Pastoral Care. Each boy has a Form Tutor who has primary responsibility for his pastoral care and for oversight of his academic progress and his extra-curricular programme. Form Tutors are led by Heads of Year. There is also a strong House system for a wide range of sporting, musical and cultural inter-house competitions.

Curriculum. The Junior School offers a balanced and enriched curriculum in a friendly, disciplined and caring environment in which the boys' all-round development is of paramount importance.

In the Senior School, First Form boys study English, Mathematics, French, Biology, Chemistry, Physics, Geography, History, Religious Studies, Music, Information Technology, Art and CDT. All Second Form boys are taught German and either Latin or Classical Civilisation. At GCSE, all boys study English, Mathematics, Science (with the choice of either coordinated science or separate sciences) and at least one Modern Foreign Language, and choose from a wide range of option subjects. Most boys offer ten subjects at GCSE.

In the Sixth Form, students study four subjects to AS Level and have the option of reducing to three subjects at A2 Level. A Level subjects are chosen from: Biology, Chemistry, Physics, Electronics, Mathematics, Further Mathematics, History, Politics, Economics, Business Studies, Geography, Geology, English Literature, French, German, Latin, Greek, Classical Civilisation, Religious Studies, Music, PE, Art and Computing. All Sixth Form students take AS General Studies, with the option of A2 General Studies in the Seventh Form.

Art. The new Art facility in the Senior School consists of two main studios and a separate sixth form studio. There is also a designated sculpture and pottery studio. In the first three years, all boys study Art and Pottery. Art is a popular choice at GCSE, AS and A2.

Music. Music is an important part of school life. As an academic subject it is offered at GCSE, AS and A2. At least three major musical events take place each year. Visiting peripatetic teachers teach over 180 pupils and also assist in running the wide range of extra-curricular music, including choir, orchestra, concert band, dance orchestra and several chamber groups.

Physical Education and Games. Boys participate in Games throughout the school and in Physical Education until the end of the Fourth Form. In addition, boys in the Junior School and in the First Form of the Senior School are taught swimming in the school's own pool. Indoor facilities include a sports hall, and outdoors there are extensive playing fields, a floodlit all-weather area and tennis courts. The major sports in the autumn and spring terms are Football and Rugby. In the summer term the major sport is Cricket. Other sports which are played at inter-school level are Athletics, Basketball, Cross-Country, Golf, Hockey, Swimming and Tennis.

Outdoor Education. In the Senior School, the Outdoor Activities programme includes a residential course for all First Form boys at the National Water Sports Centre at Plas Menai in Wales. A residential course at an outward-bound centre in the Lake District is offered to boys at the end of the Third Form. Boys in the Fifth, Sixth and Seventh Forms can choose Outdoor Activities as part of their Games programme. This includes a variety of activities and trips, including climbing, kayaking, dry-slope skiing and cycling.

CCF. Boys may join the CCF in the Third Form, and the school contingent is a strong one. The CCF helps the boys develop qualities such as self-discipline, resourcefulness and perseverance, a sense of responsibility and skills of man-management and leadership.

Careers. The Careers Department aims to provide all boys with access to the information and advice they need to make informed and sensible decisions about their futures. In addition to a very good Careers Library, guidance is provided by individual interviews. There are regular Careers Conventions. All boys complete a period of work experience after their AS examinations in the Sixth Form

Religion. The school has a Christian foundation but is proud of its tradition of being an open and inclusive community which welcomes boys and staff from different religious faiths as well as those who belong to no faith community.

Bury Grammar School Old Boys' Association. Secretary: Martin Entwistle, 8 Greenmount Drive, Greenmount, Bury, BL8 4HA. Tel: 01204 882502.

Charitable status. Bury Grammar Schools Charity is a Registered Charity, number 526622. The aim of the charity is to promote educational opportunities for boys and girls living in or near Bury.

Campbell College

Belmont Road Belfast Co Antrim BT4 2ND
Northern Ireland

Tel: 028 9076 3076
Fax: 028 9076 1894
e-mail: hmoffice@campbellcollege.co.uk
website: www.campbellcollege.co.uk

Campbell College, which was opened in 1894, was founded and endowed in accordance with the will of Henry James Campbell, Esq (Linen Merchant) of Craigavad, Co Down.

Motto: '*Ne Obliviscaris*'.

Governors:
J I Taggart, ARICS (*Chairman*)
M A D Moreland, LLB, FCA (*Vice-Chairman*)
P D Black, FCA
A J Boyd, BSc Econ, FCA
M G Chalkley (*Staff Governor*)
Mrs F Chamberlain, BA
M E J Graham, BSc, MSc, FCIOB
G F Hamilton, BA
Mrs S Hodgins (*Parent Governor*)
Mrs G Hool, BA
T M Horner, QC
M C Nesbitt, MA Cantab, DBA
M D M Rea, OBE, BSc, DipEd
W B W Turtle, LLB
J F Young, MA

***Headmaster*: J A Piggot**, MA

Vice-Principals:
M C Carville, BSc, PGCE
A R Cluff, BSc, PGCE
D Johnston, BA, PGCE

Senior Teachers:
W J McKee, BSc, DipEd
H J McKinney, BSc, CertEd
C G Oswald, BSc, PGCE, AdvCertEd, MEd

Assistant Teachers:
† *Housemaster*

†P J Mitchell, BSc, CertEd
†S D Quigg, BSc
D Catherwood, BMus, PGCE
†C G A Farr, BA, DASE, AdvCertEd, MEd, CertPD
†R J S Taylor, BSc, PGCE
D W D McDowell, BSc, PGCE
†D M McKee, BA, PGCE, DipModLit
Ms B M Coughlin, BEd, PGCertComp
Mrs S Boyce, BA, PGCE
Mrs K E Sheppard, MSc, BSc, PGCE
Mrs G E Wilson, BMus, MTD
†D Styles, BA, PGCE, Dip IndStudies
Mrs K P Crooks, BA, ATD
†S J Johnston, BSc, PGCE
B F Robinson, BA, PGCE, MSc
A W Templeton, BSc, PGCE
Mrs S L Coetzee, BMus, PCGE, PGCE Careers
N R Ashfield, BSc, PGCE
† S P Collier, BA, PGCE
†Mrs R M McNaught, MA, PGCE
G Fry, BA, PGCE
D Walker, BEd
Miss E A Woodhouse, BA, PGCE
Mrs E L P Hogg, MA, PGCE
Mrs K-A Roberts, BA, PGCE
†C McIvor, MA, PGCE
W A Dickey, MEng, PGCE
Mrs C Caldwell, BA, MA, PGCE, PG Dip FrLit
†B Meban, BSc, PGCE
†J McCurdy, BD, MA, PGCE
†M P Cousins, BSc, PGCE
Miss L Shaw, BA, PGCE
Miss D H Shields, MA, MSc, PGCE
M G Chalkley, BA, PGCE, MEd, PQH
†N McGarry, BA, PGCE
Mrs M Debbadi, BA, PGCE, MSc
†Dr J A Hamill, BSc, PGCE, PhD
†R D Hall, BSc, PGCE
Mrs E McIlvenny, BA, PGCE
Dr S S Reid, BA, MA, PGCE, Cert PD, PhD
A J Millen, MSci, PGCE
† Mrs K Magreehan, BA, PGCE
Miss L F Sparkes, BEd
Mrs F Gethin, BA, PGCE, CertPD Careers, LM
Mrs C E Woods, MA, BA, PGCE, PGH
Mrs F A Mottashaw, BA, PGCE
† H H Robinson, BSc, PGCE
Miss L Anderson, BA, QTS
Miss J Mount, BA, PGCE
Miss C A M Brown, BSc, PGCE
P D A Campbell, BEd
T R Thompson, BSc, PGCE
A McCrea, BEng, PGCE
Mrs W Pearson, BEd
†J H Rea, BSc, PGCE
Miss K McCarter, BSc, PGCE
Mrs V Reading, BA, PGCE
J Bell, BSc, PGCE
F N Mukula, BSc, MTh, PGCE

Visiting Music Teachers:
Mrs M Fenn (*Woodwind*)
Ms G McCutcheon (*Saxophone and Clarinet*)
Mrs J Leslie (*French Horn and Trumpet*)
M Wilson (*Trombone*)
Mrs H Neale (*Upper strings and Piano*)
Mrs H Marsden (*Violin*)
Mrs K Lowry (*Lower strings*)
M McGuffin (*Piano*)
Mrs L Molyneaux (*Guitar*)

Bursar: J M Monteith, FCA
Headmaster's Secretary: Mrs Y J Mallon
Medical Officer: Dr J M Bell, MB, BCh, DRCOG, MRCGP
Matron: Mrs E M Hoey, SRN

Junior School:
Head: Mrs H Rowan, BA, PGCE
Mrs E M Gwynne, BEd
A P Jemphrey, BEd, DASE
Miss P Paton, BEd Hons
Mrs V A Vance, BEd
Mrs E Boyd, MA
Miss S Neill, BSc, PGCE
Mrs F Mottram, BA, ATD
J Anderson, BEd Hons
Mrs H M Jennings, BEd Hons, Dip PD (*SENCO*)
Miss L M Rutherford, BEd Hons

At Campbell College we aim to promote all personalities, all talents and interests and to inculcate a culture of mutual trust. Academic and vocational study is vitally important to this school and we expect our students to reach for high grades, but Campbell's view of education celebrates the creative, physical and spiritual as well as the intellectual. Above all, we want our students to leave this school with an assured set of values; we want them to believe that they can make a difference in society; we want boys to leave this school with things that are going to matter to them for the rest of their lives.

Pastoral Care. Campbell places a high priority on the pastoral care of each boy in our community. We contend that boys flourish when they are known individually and feel valued within a supportive, encouraging ethos.

At Campbell we view pastoral care as a whole school responsibility recognising that all staff have a duty of care for ensuring the well-being of every boy. High expectations, hard work and mutual respect are accordingly the recurring themes of our school life.

Boarding has always been central to the life of the College. Boarding requires a boy to take responsibility for his own life and to get on with a community of other people. It also provides him with a secure base and a focus of loyalty in a large school, as well as an opportunity for exercising responsibility and leadership in a community. School House is presided over by the Head of Boarding, Mr Bert Robinson, recently appointed from Haileybury School. Mr Robinson is responsible for the academic, pastoral and social welfare of his boys and for dealings with their parents.

The Head of Boarding is assisted by three House Mothers, who look after the health of the boys and the domestic affairs of the House. Every boy is assigned to a House Tutor in School House whom he sees regularly, and has access to a range of medical, pastoral and counselling services. The House Tutor is the first point of contact for a boy.

As a boarding and day school, Campbell College is committed to providing a broadly-based education designed to enable all boys to discover their strengths, and to make the most out of their talents within Campbell and beyond. It is our belief that the experience of living in a boarding community engenders respect for individuality and the difference of others. In School House we seek to foster self-confidence, enthusiasm, perseverance, tolerance and integrity. Above all, however, we want all boarders to be happy during their time at Campbell.

Boarding at Campbell offers excellent value for money compared to other UK boarding schools; the accommodation facilities are of a very high standard. Middle School House boys (Years 8–10) board in dormitory style rooms and in a combination of 2, 4 or 5 boys per room; Senior School House boys have a study of their own.

School House has full use of all the College's facilities, including squash courts, tennis courts, two sports halls, an indoor swimming pool, two all weather surfaces, the College library and ICT suite. School House also has designated kitchen areas and well-equipped TV, DVD and Games rooms.

Academic. At Campbell, we cherish the life of the mind, whatever a student's academic profile. Indeed, when we see a student, we do not see a grade, or a label: we see an individual, with potential, and it is our duty to add value by helping a student achieve academic success and appreciate the joy of becoming a lifelong learner. Prepare to be challenged, stretched and tested at Campbell.

Key Stage 3. Upon entry boys are banded into 6 classes and all take English, Mathematics, Science, French, History, Geography, Drama, Religious Studies, Art, Music, Design and Technology, Information Communication Technology, Physical Education, Home Economics and Learning for Life and Work.

In Year 9 most boys take up German or Spanish whilst a minority receives additional support in Literacy and Numeracy.

In Year 10 Science is studied as the three separate disciplines of Biology, Chemistry and Physics. During Year 10, pupils select their courses of study for GCSE. Parents and pupils are encouraged to consult with subject teachers and Housemasters before any final decision is made.

GCSE (Key Stage 4). In Years 11 and 12 a varied programme of GCSE subjects is offered within the requirements of the Northern Ireland Curriculum. The subjects currently offered include English Language, English Literature, Journalism, Mathematics, Additional Mathematics, Science (offered as either Double Award Science or the three separate Sciences), Art & Design, History, Geography, Business Studies, French, German, Spanish, Religious Studies, Physical Education, Technology and Design, Drama, ICT and Music. Religious Studies and French are both offered as a Short Course GCSE as well as full GCSE courses. There is also some provision for pupils to vary the number of subjects they study at GCSE.

Sixth Form. Pupils in Year 13 (Lower Sixth) take three or four AS subjects chosen from a wide range, including Applied Business, Leisure Studies, Theatre Studies, Further Mathematics and Political Studies as well as the previously mentioned subjects. Pupils in Year 13 have the opportunity to select an Enrichment Programme from the range on offer.

In Year 14 (Upper Sixth) all of the above subjects may be taken to A2 Level. There is ample opportunity for discussion between parents, teachers, Housemasters and Careers Advisors before the final programme is decided.

The Careers Department advises pupils throughout their time at the College with guidance available within a taught programme and by individual interviews. Pupils also benefit from mock interviews, computer research, links with local industry and work experience.

Total Curriculum. At Campbell College we believe in a Total Curriculum. For us, education, like life itself, is about much more than the academic; students need to leave school with a range of knowledge and skills. Our duty is to identify the individual's strengths and then help foster their passion for those activities, be they in the classroom, the CCF, the drama studio, the music workshop, the sports field, the swimming pool.

We want every student at Campbell to find things to value, so that we can prepare him, both for the examinations he will sit within the College, and for the possibilities of the life beyond. That is why Campbell continues to invest so impressively in its campus and staff, to offer our students the broadest range of opportunities possible.

Drama. Every student takes Drama in Years 8 and 9 and those with aptitude and interest may take the subject through to A Level. The once tired Lecture Theatre has been transformed into an impressive Drama Studio providing a bright and modern learning environment: its virtues number a generous stage, tiered seating and a fully-kitted sound and lighting box. As a result, drama has prospered with lunchtime performances and a lunchtime theatre club where the boys script, direct and perform their own productions.

Music. Musical opportunities are readily available in the form of a Choir, the Junior, Senior and Full Orchestra, the Jazz Band, and the Pipe Band. Individual performances and ensemble playing take place at Family Services throughout the year and as part of the Easter Concert.

The Charity Committee. This is a group of staff and students (Years 11–14) who make a worthwhile contribution to the wider community. Two cherished events include, The Christmas Fair, which incorporates stalls from many international charities and raises a significant amount of money for the Committee's chosen projects; and the annual Daffodil Tea in March, which is popular with senior citizens. In addition, further events are organised with those who have care of children in need of special help.

Combined Cadet Force (CCF). All students in Year 10 join the Pioneers, which is led by the CCF staff. They will learn basic skills in First Aid, map and compass work and adventure training. From Year 11, students may join the Army, Navy or Air Force sections of the CCF where they are offered an exciting range of adventure training. They can explore a wide variety of rich opportunities and attend Field Days as well as Easter and Summer Camps. They may test themselves in competition, or join the bugles, pipes and drums of the Contingent's Pipe Band: a band that carries a valued history and tradition.

Members of the CCF, who have completed their training, may also choose to take a BTEC First Diploma in Public Services. This award is equivalent to 4 GCSEs and is recognised by employers and Universities as a worthwhile vocational qualification.

Duke of Edinburgh's Award. Boys have the opportunity to participate in the Award Scheme with Bronze, Silver and Gold Awards available throughout the year. At present, a maximum of 50 places for Middle School boys are available on the Bronze course. As this is a very popular activity, places are gained on a first-come, first-served basis.

Sport. We pride ourselves on offering an excellent selection of sporting opportunities and we are fortunate to accommodate most of them on-site. All students are encouraged to participate in some form of sport, whether it is in Inter-House Competitions or against other schools, and Campbell students are regularly selected to play representative sport at provincial and international level. Whatever the level of participation or ability, we strongly believe that sport is integral to the development of each individual.

Sports and Activities offered by the College are: Archery, Athletics, Badminton, Basketball, Chess, Cricket, Cross-Country, Fencing (there is an additional charge for this), Golf, Hockey, Rugby, Sailing, Soccer, Squash, Swimming, Tennis, Volleyball, Shooting.

Holidays. There are three annual holidays: two weeks at Christmas and Easter, and eight in the summer. In the Christmas and Easter terms there is a half-term break of one week, during which parents of boarders are required to make provision for their sons to be away from school.

Admissions. Campbell College welcomes students at all entry levels. Dayboys can begin in Kindergarten and stay through to Sixth Form; boarders may start at Year 8.The school structure is designed to offer our students easy transitions as they grow and mature; they begin in Junior School, then move at age 11 to Middle School, before progressing to Senior

School to prepare for their public examinations (GCSE, AS and A2 Level).

There are approximately 890 students in the College, of whom 73 are boarders. The admission number following the Transfer Procedure has been set at 140 by the Department of Education (NI) and we also welcome admissions at all year groups, in particular at 16+ for A Level study.

Fees per annum (2008-2009). Tuition Fee: £1,990. Boarding (available from age 11): £7,900. Junior School: £2,900–£3,150. Students from non-EC countries will pay a tuition fee of £5,800.

Campbell College is a Voluntary B Grammar School and as such is allowed to charge fees to all students attending the College. Fees for the academic year commencing in September are set in the previous Summer Term by the Board of Governors and are charged equally in September and January. Prompt payment is expected and many methods of payment, including direct debit (over 10 months), may be used. Boarding fees are also charged twice yearly.

Discounts are available to those having three or more children at day school (two or more in boarding), members of the clergy or those in the armed forces. The Governors will consider assistance to those families who suffer severe financial hardship.

Scholarships and Bursaries. *Years 8 & 9*: Boys who achieve an A grade in the Transfer Test will have their fees reduced in Years 8 and 9 by £1,000 and boys who achieve a grade B in the Transfer Test will have their fees reduced by £500.

Year 10: Up to 30 students may qualify for an Academic Bursary of £500 for Year 10. Qualification will be based on internal examinations.

In addition for exceptional music students, Scholarships for lesser amounts, are awarded for Years 10, 11 and 12.

Years 11 & 12: Up to 30 students may qualify for an Academic Bursary of £500 for Years 11 and 12. Qualification will be based on 3 special papers and results from other subjects. Pupils must apply to be considered for this Bursary.

Years 13 & 14: Bursaries of £500 will be awarded to Sixth Form students as follows:

Academic: Top 5 pupils based on GCSE results (award for Years 13 and 14).

Music: Achievement of Grade 7 of the Associated Board of the Royal School of Music.

Vocational & Arts: Awarded to those who show exceptional talent in their field.

Sports: To those achieving representative honours or achieving an exceptional level of performance at provincial level.

University: Grants of up to £1,000 per annum (for a maximum of 4 years) will be made to boys who achieve Oxbridge entry.

The decisions of the Board of Governors are final and all awards are in the gift of the Board of Governors.

Prospectus. Further information is included in our prospectus which can be obtained from the College Office or you may download a copy from the College website.

Old Campbellian Society. Register, 1894–2000, Sixth Edition, 2000. (There is also a link from College website.)

Charitable status. Campbell College is registered with the Inland Revenue as a charity, number XN45154/1. It exists to provide education for boys.

Canford School

Wimborne Dorset BH21 3AD
Tel: 01202 841254
Fax: 01202 881009
e-mail: admissions@canford.com
website: www.canford.com

Canford School was founded in 1923.

Motto: '*Nisi Dominus Frustra.*'

Governors:
Chairman: R G A Baxter, MA

Mrs F Costa, ARCM
A J L Cottam, BSc, FCA
B Coupe, BA, DipArch, RIBA
R W Daubeney, BA
Rear Admiral J M de Halpert, CBE
Mrs H A Fender, BA
D R Levin, BEcon, MA, FRSA
J D McGibbon, FCA
G F Page, CBE, MA, FRAeS
B W Richards
A F Simmons
A H Smith, BSc, FCA
Mrs V Stewart
Dr K J Torlot, MB BS, FRCAnaes
Mrs E T Watson, BA
Professor J M A Whitehouse, MA, MD, FRCP, FRCP Ed, FRCR

Secretary to the Governing Body: N A E Coulson, MA, MBA

***Headmaster*: J D Lever**, MA, PGCE

Deputy Head: R J Knott, MA, ARCM
Deputy Head (*Pastoral*): Dr H K Laver, BSc, PhD
Director of Studies: Dr S K Wilkinson, MSc, DPhil
Registrar: M A Owen, BA, PGCE
Bursar: D S B Phipps, BA

Assistant Staff:
* *Head of Department*
† *Housemaster/mistress*

English, History, Classics, Politics, Drama, Information Technology:
*Dr L J D Kennedy, BA, PhD (*English*)
*A C Fearnley, BA, MLitt, (*Politics*)
*S J Hattersley, DipEd Drama, LAMDA (*Drama*)
*C M S Rathbone, MA, PGCE (*History*)
*C A Wilson, BA, PGCE (*Classics*)
Miss C Barrett, BA, MA
Mrs S Ellis, BA, PGCE
K D R Hay, BA, Cert Ed
Mrs P J Knott, MA, PGCE
Mrs K M Orpwood, BA, MA
M A Owen, BA, PGCE
Dr C E Phillips, MA, PhD
†R M B Salmon, BA, PGCE
C Thomas, BA, PGCE
S Vandvik, MA
M H Walters, BA, MPhil
Ms K M Watts, BA, PGCE
Mrs M A Wilson, BA, PGCE

Geography and Economics:
*R S Raumann, MA, PGCE (*Geography*)
*J G Lyons, MA (*Economics*)
*Mrs C E Kilpatrick, BSc (*Business Studies*)
†R T Jones, BA, PGCE
D V Collison, BEd
†N H Jones, BA, PGCE
J R Orme, MA, PGCE
M J Pringle, BA
P D A Rossiter, MA, PGCE
†Mrs J Smith, BA, PGCE

Mathematics and Science:
R J Knott, MA, ARCM (*Mathematics*)
*C L Fenwick, BSc, PGCE (*Physics*)
*Dr D Neill, BSc, PhD, PGCE (*Chemistry*)
*A F U Powell, MA (*Biology*)

E Adie, BSc, PGCE
D J Allen, BSc, MSc, PGCE
†H Bishop, BSc, ACMA
Miss S E Boyns, BA
Mrs C D Byng, BA/Ed
Miss H L Chartres, BSc, PGCE
†L M Corbould, BSc, PGCE
†D P Culley, MA
D A Dodwell, MA, PGCE
S D Excell, BSc, PGCE
M D Harms, BSc, PhD
R H J Hooker, BSc
C H Jeffery, BA, MEng
D King, BA
D E Kirk, BEng, CertEd
Miss C E Lamb, BA, PGCE
A J Naden, BSC, BEng
G R Shaw, MChem, PGCE
T J Street, BSc, PGCE
Mrs E C Thornburrow, BSc, PGCE
A J Tyndall, MChem
Dr S K Wilkinson, MSc, DPhil

Modern Languages:
*Ms A P A Savage, BA, PGCE (*Modern Languages*)
*R J Wallis, BA, MSc (*Spanish*)
*R A Wilson BA, MA, PGCE (*German*)
W J Ainsworth, MA, DipEd
Miss C E Bloor, BA, PGCE
†Mrs M Marns, Maîtrise d'Anglais, PGCE
G F Mavor, BA, PGCE
A-S Neame, BA, MBA

Music:
*C C Sparkhall, MA, ARCO, PGCE (*Director of Music*)
Miss R F Partington, MusB (*Head of Woodwind*)
Miss F M McKinley, BA, LMusA (*Head of Strings*)
†Mrs E J F Hattersley, BA
D A Warwick, MA, FRCO, ARCM

Art and Design:
*D F Lloyd BA, PGCE (*Art*)
*N Watkins, BEd (*Design Technology*)
P A Effick, BEd, BSc
Ms J Jones, BA, PGCE
J V Martin, BEng, MSc, PGCE
D H Wright, MA, PGCE

Religious Studies:
*The Revd C Jervis, BEd, Cert Theol
The Revd K K Sugden, BSc, BA, PGCE (*Chaplain*)

Physical Education:
†M S Burley, BSocSci, MA (*Director of Sport*)
†N R Baugniet, BA
Miss F Ermgassen, BSc, PGCE

Careers and Higher Education: D A Dodwell, MA, PGCE
Examinations Officer: R H Peart, BEd
Information Officer: F T Ahern, MA, PGCE

Houses & Housemasters/mistresses:

Boarding Houses (Boys):
Court: R M B Salmon
Franklin: H Bishop
Monteacute: R Jones
School: L M Corbould

Boarding Houses (Girls):
Beaufort: Mrs J Smith
de Lacy: Mrs M Marns
Marriotts: Mrs E J F Hattersley

Mixed Day Houses:
Lancaster: D P Culley
Salisbury: N H Jones

Wimborne: N R Baugniet

Medical Officers:
P J N Dickens, MA, MB BS, DCH, DRCOG, MRCGP
B L Lear, MB BS, MRCGP
H Sankson, MB, MRCGP
R Skule, MB BS, MRCP, MRCGP

Since September 1995 the School has been co-educational. There are 370 boys and 244 girls; 416 boarders and 198 day pupils.

The School stands in an enclosed Park of 300 acres. It is 2 miles from Wimborne Minster. The Park contains many beautiful trees and is rich in bird life. The River Stour, which forms the northern boundary, is convenient for rowing, canoeing and fishing.

Buildings. The oldest part of the main building is the fine Hall known as John of Gaunt's Kitchen, which is all that remains of the medieval Canford Manor. To this was added the present house, designed by Blore in 1825 and remodelled by Sir Charles Barry in 1846. Since the foundation of the School in 1923 there have been many additions.

Houses. There are 4 boarding houses for boys, 3 boarding houses for girls and 3 mixed day houses.

The Curriculum. There is considerable breadth in the Lower School. In their Shell year pupils study the core subjects of English, and Mathematics. In addition they study Physics, Chemistry and Biology, French, German or Spanish, Latin or Classical Civilisation or Extra English, Music, Art and Design Technology, History and Geography, Drama, PE and General Studies. In the Fourth Form Economics is added to these non-core subjects, from which pupils are asked to choose seven to study for GCSE. At least two Sciences must be taken to GCSE, and PE and Classical Civilisation are not available at GCSE. The short course RS syllabus is followed.

A Level subjects offered are English, Latin, History, Religious Studies, Politics, Geography, Economics, Business Studies, French, German, Spanish, Mathematics, Physics, Chemistry, Biology, Music, Art, Design Technology, Theatre Studies, Computing, Classical Civilisation and Sports Studies. Combinations of subjects are as flexible as possible. All pupils follow a General Studies course, which includes Personal and Social Education.

Higher Education. 95% of pupils proceed to Higher Education, popular destinations recently being Bristol, Cambridge, Cardiff, Exeter, London, Nottingham and Oxford. About fifteen places are gained at Oxford and Cambridge annually.

Tutorial System. In addition to their Housemaster/mistress and House Tutor the pupils in the Sixth Form each have an Academic Tutor who is responsible with the Housemaster/mistress for academic progress, University entry, and careers guidance. There are monthly academic assessments throughout the school which are monitored by the tutorial staff and emailed to parents.

Religion. Chapel services are held in the Norman church of Canford Magna which stands in the school grounds, and also in the Music School and the Theatre. Arrangements can be made for those of different faiths and denominations to worship independently.

Music. Music is a compulsory subject for pupils in Year 9, and an option for GCSE and A Level. 400 individual music lessons are taken each week and more than half of pupils learn an instrument. Larger ensembles include senior orchestra, string orchestra, 2 concert bands, jazz band, Chapel Choir, Chamber Choir, Junior Choir and Choral Society while there is also a wide range of chamber ensembles. The Music School has 2 large rehearsal rooms, practice rooms and a computer suite. Regular concerts, both formal and informal, are given in the 200-seat Concert Hall as well as in prestigious outside venues.

Drama. In their first year, pupils have the opportunity to study drama as part of the curriculum and beyond that Drama and Theatre Studies are offered at GCSE and A Level. The 300-seat Layard Theatre is home to the Drama Department and provides an exciting venue for a wide range of school productions as well as hosting work from professional companies.

Art and Design Technology. Art and Design Technology are compulsory for all pupils in their first year during which they are introduced to drawing, painting, printing, sculpture, metalwork, woodwork, plastics and CAD/CAM. They may also pursue these interests in their daily activities time and at weekends. Pupils may take GCSE and A Level.

ICT. In their Shell year all pupils follow the BTEC course (Level 2). Thereafter the well-equipped Information Technology Centre provides cross-curricular induction courses to all, aiming to establish IT as a natural tool for learning and life, and enabling pupils to apply it to a range of academic and other work, from preps to projects, personal correspondence to school publications. Each department has a teacher assigned to the development of IT within its subject curriculum. There is open access to the centre for all pupils and staff throughout the day and in addition all houses are equipped with computers as is the library.

Games. All the pupils play games. The principal games are: in the Winter Term rugby for boys and hockey for girls; in the Spring Term hockey and rowing for boys, and netball and rowing for girls; in the Summer Term cricket for boys, and rowing, tennis and athletics for girls and boys. The school also has representative teams in cross-country, sailing, swimming, golf, squash and royal tennis. There are other sports available. The school facilities include: a well-equipped sports centre incorporating double-sized sports hall, dance studio, fitness suite and physiotherapy room; two astroturf pitches used for hockey and tennis; two hard court areas suitable for tennis and netball; four squash courts; a royal tennis court; a nine-hole golf course and a new indoor 25m, 6-lane pool to be constructed in time for September 2009. The school employs professional cricket, squash, royal tennis, rowing, hockey, rugby and netball coaches.

Societies, Hobbies and Activities. Various societies meet on a regular basis including Debating, Literary, Science and Art. Space is reserved for Hobbies and Activities.

Community Service. About 120 pupils work in the local community each week, teaching in schools, helping the elderly, the disabled, and visiting patients in hospices and respite care centres. They also help to give lessons in swimming and science and look after disadvantaged children. Each year parties of Canfordians help in orphanages in Southern India, Kenya and Argentina.

Combined Cadet Force. Army, Navy and Marines sections make up a 240 strong cadet force staffed by 12 officers. About 90% of pupils join in their second year on a voluntary basis and remain in the CCF for two years. A number stay on until the end of their sixth form as NCOs. There are numerous opportunities for training exercises in the UK and abroad, including Norway and France.

Careers. The careers programme at Canford accelerates in the Fifth Form. The whole year group has the opportunity to undergo testing for career directions and A Level choices. The Lower Sixth year starts the advice procedure for higher education applications with talks, lectures (Brian Heap) and one to one consultations. The Upper Sixth year completes these processes. A well appointed careers room is always available and parental participation at all stages of the programme is supported by regular visits by the ISCO Regional Secretary.

Medical. The newly built Health Centre is staffed 24 hours a day by two qualified nurses. A Medical Officer visits the Health Centre daily during the week.

Admission. Boys and girls may be registered at any time. Application should be made to the Admissions Office. The examination normally used for entry is the Common Entrance Examination, but the School uses its own entry tests for those who are not at preparatory schools. Pupils are usually admitted between their 13th and 14th birthdays or by a competitive examination at 16+.

Scholarships. (*see Scholarship Entries section*). It is Canford's policy to encourage excellence and to enable pupils to come to the school who, without the assistance of a scholarship, would not be able to do so. In accordance with the agreement of the majority of HMC schools, Canford limits the value of any one scholarship to 50% of fees. All Canford's scholarships are indexed as a percentage of the fees so that their relative value remains constant throughout the scholar's school career.

Scholarships at 13+. Scholarship examinations are held in February and March for the following awards: Academic, Music and Sport scholarships worth from 10% to 50% of the fees; Art, Drama and Design Technology scholarships worth from 10% to 20% of the fees; an academic Royal Naval scholarship worth 20% of the fees to the son/daughter of a serving Naval Officer. Candidates must be in Year 8 at the time of the examination. All scholarships are tenable with effect from the September of the year in which they are awarded. Candidates may enter for any combination of scholarships.

Entrance Scholarships at 16+. Entrants to the school at Sixth Form level may apply for any combination of the following scholarships: Academic, Music, Assyrian. The examinations are held in the November prior to entry. Assyrian awards are offered for an extra-curricular contribution of excellent quality to school life and are worth from 10% to 40% of the fees; Academic and Music scholarships are worth from 10% to 50% of the fees.

Bursaries. Means-tested bursaries are available from the School where the financial need of the parents has been established.

Further details about any awards can be obtained from the Registrar.

Fees per term (2008-2009). Boarders £8,560; Day £6,675.

Composition Fee. At any time in advance a composition fee at special rates may be paid to cover the cost of a pupil's education for his/her career at the School. Details are in the Prospectus which may be obtained from the Registrar.

Insurance. There is a fees insurance scheme also covering medical and operation expenses, at the option of the parents.

The Old Canfordian Society. Enquiries to The Old Canfordian Society, Canford School.

Charitable status. Canford School Limited is a Registered Charity, number 306315. It exists to provide education for children.

Caterham School

Harestone Valley Road Caterham Surrey CR3 6YA
Tel: 01883 343028
Fax: 01883 347795
e-mail: enquiries@caterhamschool.co.uk
admissions@caterhamschool.co.uk
website: www.caterhamschool.co.uk

Motto: *Veritas Sine Timore.*

Founded in 1811 in London as a school for the education of the sons of Congregational Ministers, the School is now open to boys and girls irrespective of denomination or creed.

In 1995 the School became an associate member of the United Church Schools Trust and benefits from the strength provided by this partnership.

Board of Governors:
Chairman: W R Broadhead
Vice-Chairman: M C Newlan, FInstD, MBIFM
J Bloomer, BSc, ARCS, FCA, CIMgt
A Chapman, MRICS
D P Charlesworth, MBIM, MIIM

J Joiner, BA Hons
Mrs N Perricone, BSc Hons, DipLaw
Revd N P Uden, BA
Mrs S Whittle

Bursar and Clerk to the Governors: J C L King, MBE

The School Staff:

***Headmaster*: J P Thomas**, BSc Hons, MBA, FRSA

Deputy Head: Mrs L E Redding, BSc Hons
Deputy Head (*Curriculum*): T J Murphy, MA Oxon
Senior Teacher & Head of Boarding: J P Seymour, BSc Hons
Director of Learning and Teaching: K Wells, MA Cantab
Assistant Head (*External Relations*): D Clark, BA, MPhil Cantab

Assistant Staff:

Art and Design:
*Mrs M Kyle, MA, MEd (*Head of Art & Design*)
M Sherrington, BA (*Head of Underwood, Head of Photography*)
Miss A Church, MA (*Head of Textiles*)
N Evans, MA
Miss C D Pateman, BA Hons
B Wilkinson, BA Hons (*Head of 3D Design, Head of Lewisham*)

Biology:
*D Quinton, MA Oxon (*Head of Science*)
S F Hayes, BSc (*Senior Housemaster, Head of Harestone*)
A P Taylor, BSc Hons
Miss H Whiteford, BSc Hons (*Assistant Head of Third Year*)
Miss A Munro, BSc Hons
S Marlow, BSc Hons

Chemistry:
*D Keyworth, MSc
Dr J Burnside, PhD, MChem Hons
Dr H Thomson, PhD, MSci
Mrs E Rivers, BSc (*Head of Fourth Year*)

Classics:
*K Waite, MA Oxon
Mrs S Carpenter, BA Oxon

Drama & Theatre Studies:
*Miss L McMullin, BA Hons

Economics and Business Studies:
*A Fahey, BA (*Assistant Head of Sixth Form*)
C James, BSc Hons, MBA
C Smith, BSc BEd
Mrs C Wallace, BA Hons, ACIB (*Head of Lower Sixth*)

English:
*G C Killingworth, MA Cantab, MA Oxon
Miss A Cox, BA
Miss A O'Donnell, MA Hons (*Head of Third Year*)
Miss A Symss, BA Hons (*Joint Second in Department*)
A Van-Niekerk, BA (*Head of Junior Boys Boarding*)
M Broughton, BA Hons (*Head of Fifth Year*)
Miss L Thomas, BA Hons (*Joint Second in Department*)
Mrs A L T Yankova, BA Hons

Geography:
*S Terrel, BA, MPhil
Mrs L Redding, BSc Hons (*Deputy Head*)
A Van-Niekerk, BA (*Head of Junior Boys Boarding*)
Mrs R Wallace, MA (*Assistant Head of Fifth Year*)

History:
*R Salem, MA Oxon (*Pupil Data Coordinator*)
M Lesser, MA, MBA (*Director of Sixth Form*)
N Mills, BA Hons (*Assistant Head of Fourth Year*)
Mrs S Carter-Esdale, BA Hons

Information Technology:
*P R Hoad, BA (*Director of ICT Development*)
M G Bailey, BA Hons, BEd (*Head of Sixth Form ICT*)

Mathematics:
*W Jaundrill, MA Cantab, MSc
J M Wallace, BA Hons, MBA (*Head of Townsend, Head of Upper Sixth*)
Miss N Dawrant, MA Oxon
Mrs R Stowell, MA (*Examinations Officer*)
J Ogilvie, BSc (*Head of Ridgefield*)
D R Todd, MA Oxon
Mrs J Dodd, MA Oxon (*Second in Department*)
S Lander, MA Oxon, MSc
C Ware, BSc Hons

Modern Languages:
*S Bird, MA (*Head of Modern Foreign Languages, Head of German*)
Mrs J Laverick, BEd Hons Cantab
*Mrs Z Roberts, BA Hons (*Head of Spanish*)
Mrs C M Clifton, BA Hons
Miss A Green, BA Hons
*Mrs N McVitty, DEUG, Licence d'Anglais (*Head of French*)
K Wells, MA Cantab (*Director of Learning & Teaching*)
Mrs S Carpenter, BA Oxon
Miss L P Glenn, LLB

Music:
*S Thompson, GRSM Hons, LRAM, ARAM (*Director of Music*)
Mrs H Richards, BMus Hons (*Assistant Director of Music, Head of Second Year*)
Miss R Miller, BMus Hons, PGDip, PGCert

Physical Education:
*P H D Lavery, CertEd (*Director of Sport*)
*Miss A P Collins, BEd Hons (*Head of Examination PE*)
R Smith, CertEd
*Mrs N Lomas, BA Hons (*Head of Girls' Games*)
A Patterson, MA (*Head of Hockey, Head of Aldercombe*)
Miss H Sandiford, BSc Hons (*Acting Head of Girls' Games*)

Psychology:
*Mrs A Davis, BSc Hons
Miss A P Collins, BEd Hons (*Head of Examination PE*)
Revd Dr R Mearkle, BA, MDiv, DMin

Physics:
*K G Simpson, BSc, BA
J P Armitage, BSc
L Dannatt, MEng
J Miller, BSc, MA

Politics:
*D Clark, BA, MPhil Cantab (*Assistant Head – External Relations*)
T J Murphy, MA Oxon (*Deputy Head – Curriculum*)

Religious Education:
*Revd Dr R Mearkle, BA, MDiv, DMin
Miss H Trehane, BA (*Examinations Officer*)
J Whyatt, BA, MA
Miss H Whiteford, BSc Hons (*Assistant Head of Third Year*)

Special Needs:
*Mrs L Tapley, BA, DipSpLD, AMBDA (*Head of Lower School, Head of First Year*)

EAL:
*C Berkley, BA Hons
J P Seymour, BSc Hons (*Senior Teacher, Head of Boarding*)

Careers:
Mrs C Brown

Registrar: Mrs P Mattinson

Preparatory School

Head Teacher: H W G Tuckett, MA
Deputy Head Teacher: Mrs V Gocher, BA Hons, PGCE
(*For further information see IAPS section*)

Number in School. In the Senior School there are 785 pupils, of whom 160 are boarders. In the Preparatory School there are 278 pupils.

Aims. The School admits both boarders and day pupils of all denominations. Strong links remain, however, with the United Reformed Church which is represented on the Board of Governors. From a pupil's earliest years in the School, the aim is to provide a broad education based on Christian principles and practice. Pupils learn the disciplines of work in an environment which is both friendly and firm, and they are able to develop character and talents whether they be academic, artistic or sporting.

Situation. The School's 80 acre site is situated in a beautiful wooded valley. This rural setting belies its good accessibility: Caterham Station is one mile away and the frequent trains to London take 45 minutes. Gatwick and Heathrow airports are in easy reach.

Every pupil is allocated to a House-based Tutor Group. The Tutor monitors academic progress and provides a regular point of pastoral contact for pupils and parents. In this way every pupil is known well and encouraged to develop their talents to the full. There are separate boarding houses for boys and girls. Common rooms, dormitories (for younger pupils) and study bedrooms are comfortably furnished, many with en-suite facilities.

In recent years there has been a substantial building and development programme. The boarding accommodation has been refurbished. There is a new sports centre, a new theatre/assembly hall, a language laboratory and very extensive investment has been made in ICT. The thirteen science labs and refectory were completed in 2006. A new Sixth Form Centre and Health Centre has just been opened.

The Preparatory School. This consists of 2 large houses in the school grounds. Mottrams contains the Pre-Prep department and the kitchen and dining rooms and a house for the Head Teacher of the Preparatory School. Shirley Goss contains classrooms, assembly hall, a library, an IT room, separate art and craft rooms, and changing accommodation for the Prep department. (*For further information see IAPS section.*)

Continuity of education is provided as boys and girls move from the Preparatory School to the Senior School at the age of eleven.

Admission. Details concerning the admission of pupils to the Pre-Preparatory and Preparatory School are published separately (*see entry in IAPS section*).

Admission to the Senior School is through an entrance examination at 11+ and 13+ and is conditional upon good GCSE grades at 16. For further details please contact the Registrar, Mrs P Mattinson, Tel: 01883 335058.

Term of Entry. Pupils are normally accepted for entry in September each year, but vacancies may be filled at other times.

Scholarships and Bursaries. (*see Scholarship Entries section*). Academic scholarships are awarded at 11+, 13+ and 16+ and also scholarships for excellence in Art, Music and Sport. In addition to these, pupils joining the school at 13+ may apply for All-Rounder scholarships, and pupils entering the Sixth Form may apply for Science scholarships.

Bursaries for the sons and daughters of URC Clergy, Old Caterhamians and Forces Personnel are available. There are also a number of Caterham Assisted Places for those joining the School at the age of 11.

Fees per term (2008-2009). Boarding £7,606–£8,018; Day £4,106–£4,298. Lunch for Day Pupils: £170.

Curriculum. Preparatory School: A wide range of subjects is provided following National Curriculum guidelines. (*For further details see entry in IAPS section.*)

Senior School: National Curriculum core subjects are taken by all pupils with a wide range of options in the GCSE years, including Art & 3D Design, Music, Business Studies/Economics, Latin, German, Spanish, ICT, Sports Studies, Drama, Religious Studies, History and Geography. Pupils may take a varied combination of subjects in the Sixth Form selecting from English, Mathematics and Further Mathematics, French, Spanish, German, Geography, History, Latin, Greek, Photography, Politics, Psychology, PE, ICT, Textiles, Drama and Theatre Studies, Religious Studies, Art & Design, 3D Design, Biological Sciences, Chemistry, Physics, Music, Economics and Business Studies.

Music, Drama and Creative Arts. Music is an important feature of the life of the School. Individual lessons are given on the piano, in string, brass and wind instruments, and the organ. The Choral Society performs at least one major choral work each year. Each term there is a School concert and a programme of recitals is arranged. Drama is also well-supported. Each year there is a major production which involves a large number of pupils both on and off stage. The Art Department encourages pupils to pursue their interests in creative work, such as ceramics, modelling, and graphic design. Robotics, Information Technology and desk-top publishing, textiles and photography courses are also provided.

Societies and Hobbies. All pupils are encouraged to pursue a hobby or constructive outside interest, and there are a large number of active School Societies, including: CCF, Choir, Chess, Christian Fellowship, Community Service, Computer Club, Orchestra, Debating, Duke of Edinburgh's Award, Technology, Moncrieff-Jones (Sixth Form Science), Music, Circus, Young Enterprise.

Games. Most of the playing fields adjoin the School including an 'all weather' synthetic grass pitch for Lacrosse, Hockey and Tennis. Overall there are 18 different sporting activities, but in each term at least one major game is played. For boys it is Rugby in the Autumn Term, Hockey in the Spring Term and Cricket in the Summer. Other options include Tennis, Football and Golf. The girls play Lacrosse, Netball, Rounders and Tennis. Pupils can also participate in Athletics, Fencing, Equestrian, Swimming, Badminton, Basketball, Cross-Country, Squash, Tae Kwon Do and, in the Summer Term, Sailing, Windsurfing and Canoeing.

Health. There is a well equipped Health Centre with SRN Sister. The School Doctor attends regularly.

Careers. The Careers staff are available to give advice. The School has membership of the Independent Schools Careers Organisation and parents are encouraged to enter their sons or daughters for the ISCO Aptitude Test in the Sixth Form year. The School arranges Careers and Higher Education Forums and the Headmaster and Careers staff are available to discuss careers with parents.

Old Caterhamians' and Parents' Associations. The School has flourishing Old Caterhamians' and Parents' Associations. Information about these may be obtained from the School.

Charitable status. Caterham School is a Registered Charity, number 1109508. Its aim is to develop the academic and personal potential of each pupil in a Christian context.

Charterhouse

Godalming Surrey GU7 2DX

Tel:	Admissions: 01483 291501
	Headmaster: 01483 291600
	Bursary and Enquiries: 01483 291500
Fax:	Admissions: 01483 291507
	Headmaster: 01483 291647

e-mail: admissions@charterhouse.org.uk
website: www.charterhouse.org.uk

Charterhouse was founded in 1611 as part of Thomas Sutton's dual foundation in London, and was moved to its present beautiful setting in Surrey in 1872. The original Medieval, Tudor and Jacobean buildings still survive behind St Bartholomew's Hospital, providing a meeting place for the Governing Body and for gatherings of Old Carthusians.

The School offers outstanding facilities on its 200 acre estate near Godalming. The boarding accommodation is divided into 11 houses. There are over 700 pupils including 100 girls in the Sixth Form. The School prides itself on the excellence of its all-round education, based on a long tradition of distinguished teaching and academic success.

Motto: '*Deo Dante Dedi*'.

Governing Body:
Chairman: J L Walker-Haworth, MA

The Archbishop of Canterbury
M J Collins, MA, DPhil
G A Reid, PhD
Professor G A Parker, BSc, PhD, EurIng, CEng, FIMechE, Mem ASME
The Hon. Mrs Sealy, MA
Lady Toulson, CBE, LlB
P J Drew
P G T Lewis, MA
Mrs C M Oulton, MA
G P Bristowe, MA, JP
Professor K R Willison, BSc, PhD
W S M Robinson, BA
R A Henley, FCA
P M R Norris, MA
N J Kempner, BSc

Clerk to the Governing Body and Bursar: D A E Williams, BA, FCA

***Headmaster*: The Revd J S Witheridge**, MA, FRSA

Deputy Headmaster: A J Bennett, BEd, MA, PhD

Assistant Headmaster (*Academic*): A J Turner, BA, LLM

Assistant Headmaster (*Pastoral*): N T Cooper, BA, MBA

Head of Girls: Mrs M H Swift, BDS

Assistant Staff:
Miss P Aguado, BA
Mrs S C Allen, MA
S P M Allen, MA
P G Allison
M G Armstrong, BA, MA (*Master of the Under School*)
Miss J C Attia, MA
Mrs A B Bailey, MA (*Head of Higher Education*)
M J Bailey, MA
S G Barker, BSc
Miss L F Batty, BSc
M J Begby, BA
M Bicknell
M L J Blatchly, MA, FRCO
R A Bogdan, MA
S M Bramwell, BA
Miss J K Bratten, BA, MLitt, PhD
S F C Brennan, BA
K D Brown
R A Brown, MPhys, PhD
O W Choroba, PhD
Mrs C F Clive, DipTEFL
M J Crosby
R A Crowsley
C J Ellis, BSc, PhD, MIBiol
M K Elston, BSc
O P Elton, BA
Mrs J L Faux, BSc
S P Fielder
Miss E J Fox, BA
J D Freeman, BA (*Director of Drama*)
J P Freeman, MA
P Funcasta, BA, MSc
H D Gammell, MA
N S Georgiakakis, MSc
G H M Gergaud, L-ès-L
M R Gillespie, BA
Miss Z Green, MA (*Writer-in-Residence*)
N Hadfield, MA
E Hadley, BA
T G Hager, BA
C R G Hall, MA
I J M Hamilton
The Revd S J Harker, MA
Miss E E Hawser, BA (*Artist-in-Residence*)
R W T Haynes, MA
J S Hazeldine, BA
S T Hearn, MSc, MInstP
I A Hoffmann de Visme, MSc
Mrs E H H Holloway, BSc, PhD
E J How, BA
A G Johnson, MSc
D R H Johnson, BSc, DPhil
A Johnston, MA, PhD
A J Jolliffe, BA
J H Kazi, MA
J J Knight, BA
D N Lancefield, CPhys, MInstP, MIEE, MIEEE
W J Lane, MA
P J Langman, BSc, PhD
B K Larrigan, BSc, MBA, CEng, MBCS
R V Lewis
M F D Lloyd, MA, DITE
The Revd R G Lloyd, MA (*Senior Chaplain*)
R C D Millard, MA, MPhil
N C Mills, MA, FRGS
A P Mogford, BA
P Monkman, MA (*Director of Art*)
Mrs E P Nelson, BSc, MSc
Mrs F C Noble, BEd
R P Noble, MA (*Director of Sport*)
S J Northwood, BA, MPhil, PhD
C J Oakes-Monger, BSc
Mrs M D B Olive, ACL (*Librarian*)
The Revd C J B O'Neill, MA, PhD, DCH, CertTheol, ALAM, LGSM
Mrs M H Orson, BA
J N Parsons, BA, LRAM, ARCM
N S Pelling, MA
Miss H E Pinkney, BA
P A Price, MA
Miss J Puri, BA
E J Reid, MMath
A N Reston, BA, MSL
T E Reynolds, MA, MSc
J M Richardson, BA
S A Rowse, BA, MA, DipSpLD
Miss E Ryder, BSc, PhD
R D Sarre, BSc, DPhil
Miss L Saxby, BTech, MA
J H B Schmitt, BA
J Sergison-Main, MSM
M N Shepherd, MA, FRCO, ARCM (*Director of Music*)
S J Shuttleworth, MA (*Master of the Scholars*)
J M Silvester, BSc
R W Smeeton, ARCM, LRPS, MLC
P R Stapleton BSc
B P Thurston, MA, MSt, DPhil
J C Troy, BSc
J Tully, BEng, FICS, FRGS
Miss H van Dyck, BA
Mrs R Wing, Dip SpLD
F Wiseman, MA, CertTEFL
D G Wright, LTCL
E H Zillekens, BA, DPhil (*Senior Librarian and Archivist*)

Senior Chaplain: The Revd R G Lloyd, MA

Admissions Registrar: H D Gammell, MA
Admissions Secretary: Mrs S Stevens

Estate Bursar: T A C Blackburn, FRICS
Accountant: P G Hay

Medical Officer: Dr A Borthwick, MA, MB, BChir

Counsellors:
The Revd C J B O'Neill
Mrs V Gordon-Graham, MA

Cricket Professionals: M Bicknell, R V Lewis
Rackets Professional: M J Crosby

Houses and Housemasters
Saunderites: S P M Allen and Mrs S C Allen
Verites: N Hadfield
Gownboys: M L J Blatchly
Girdlestoneites: B P Thurston
Lockites: A Johnston
Weekites: P R Stapleton
Hodgsonites: D G Wright
Daviesites: B K Larrigan
Bodeites: J S Hazeldine
Pageites: C J Ellis
Robinites: S T Hearn

Admission. Parents wishing to enter their sons for the School should contact the Registrar, Charterhouse, Godalming, Surrey GU7 2DX at least 3 years before they are due to come to the school. Boys normally join the School in September when they are between thirteen and fourteen years of age. At some time between the boy's 10th and 11th birthday a report from his current Headmaster will be sought concerning his suitability for Charterhouse. Parents can then be offered a guaranteed school place (subject to success in the Common Entrance Examination).

Parents wishing their sons or daughters to enter Charterhouse after GCSE to study A levels in the Sixth Form should contact the Registrar at the beginning of the summer term in the year before the September entry.

At least one term's notice is required before the removal of a pupil from the School.

Date of admission. Boys and girls are accepted for September entry only.

Fees per term (2008-2009). Inclusive fees: £9,160 for Boarders, £7,572 for Day pupils. The Governing Body reserves the right to alter the School Fee at its discretion.

Scholarships, Bursaries and Exhibitions. (*see Scholarship Entries section*). *For entry at 13+*: 10 Foundation Scholarships, 5 Exhibitions, a Benn Scholarship for Classics, a number of major Music Scholarships and 2 Art Scholarships are offered annually. In addition 5 Peter Attenborough Awards are given annually to candidates who demonstrate all-round distinction. The Park House Award is made annually to an exceptional sportsman. The Blackstone Award, for the sons of lawyers, is made two years before the winner joins the School.

For entry into the Sixth Form: 4 Sir Robert Birley Academic Scholarships, 7 Academic Exhibitions, 3 Music Scholarships and 2 Art Scholarships are offered.

All Awards (except Exhibitions) may be increased to the value of the full school fee in cases of proven financial need.

Music. A tradition of musical excellence at Charterhouse is maintained and enhanced with 6 full-time staff and 30 visiting staff. 400 music lessons a week are taught, and orchestral and choral standards are enviable.

Art. The Studio offers excellent facilities to study painting, print-making, ceramics, sculpture, photography and film-making. GCSE, AS and A2 Level are offered. Life-drawing and the study of art history and architecture complement the practical work.

Design. The John Derry Technology Centre provides facilities for the teaching of GCSE, AS and A level Design and Technology. The Centre offers boys and girls the opportunity to work in a wide range of materials.

Drama. The School has its own modern Theatre which is used extensively by pupils in term time, as well as by the public in school holidays.

Golf. A 9-hole golf course was given to the school in July 1988 by the Old Carthusian Golfing Society.

Sports Centre. A £3.8 million Sports Centre was opened by The Queen in February 1997. It includes a 25m x 6 lane Swimming Pool, a multi-purpose Sports Hall, Fitness Suite, an Activities Room and an internal Climbing Tower.

Athletics Track. An all-weather Athletics Track was opened during the autumn of 1996.

Old Carthusian Club. All enquiries should be made to Mrs M F Mardall, The Recorder, Charterhouse, Godalming, Surrey GU7 2DX.

Prospective parents and their children are warmly invited to visit Charterhouse where they normally meet the Headmaster or Registrar, other staff and members of the School.

Charitable status. Charterhouse School is a Registered Charity, number 312054. Its aims and objectives are the provision of education through the medium of a secondary boarding school for boys, and girls in the Sixth Form.

Cheadle Hulme School

Claremont Road Cheadle Hulme Cheadle Cheshire SK8 6EF
Tel: 0161 488 3330
Fax: 0161 488 3344
e-mail: headmaster@chschool.co.uk
website: www.cheadlehulmeschool.co.uk

Originally founded in 1885 as the Manchester Warehousemen & Clerks' School for Necessitous Children, today Cheadle Hulme School is one of the country's leading independent co-educational day schools offering both excellent academic teaching and outstanding extra-curricular opportunities.

Set in 83 acres of Cheshire countryside, the School nurtures motivated, happy pupils who take every opportunity to develop their talents, gaining the personal skills and confidence to shape their own futures in a rapidly changing world.

Motto: '*In loco parentis*'

President of the Foundation: Professor H C A Hankins, CBE, BSc(Tech), PhD, DSc, DEng, DUniv, FIEE, FEng

Governing Body:
P R Johnson (*Chairman*)

J M Anderson	C Oglesby
Mrs A Bradley	Dr D N Riley
Dr S Butler	D C Shipley
P J Driver	P Sidwell
Mrs M Kenyon	R Simon
L Morris	Mrs J M Squire

Bursar and Clerk to the Governors: Mrs A Bolton, MA, MBA

***Headmaster*: P V Dixon**, MA, MIBiol, CBiol

Second Master: L H Carr, BSc

Deputy Heads:
A Nolan, BSc
Mrs G Wallwork, BA

Assistant Masters and Mistresses:
Mrs P Aspinwall, BEd (*Head of Junior School*)
N Axon, BA, MA
Miss R Baker, BA
D J Ball, BSc (*Head of Physics*)
Miss V Ball, MSCI
Mrs L J Barfoot, BA
D Barnett, MSc
Mrs J Barton, BSc
Mrs K Booth, BSc
Miss R Y Breese, BA
Miss P Brogan, BA
P D Bullock, MA (*Deputy Head of Careers*)
S Burnage, BEd (*Head of Boys' PE*)
Dr A Carlin, MSc
Mrs E Carter, MA
Ms R A Chakrabarti, BEd
I Chippendale, BA (*Head of Chemistry*)
Ms L Cleary, BA
Mrs S Cocksedge, MA (*Deputy Director of Music*)
Miss C M Curtis, BSc
Mrs R Dalton-Wood, BSc, MSc (*Head of Food & Nutrition*)
Mrs S K Davies, BEd
R S Davis, BA (*Head of Middle School*)
P Dewhurst, BA (*Director of Music*)
Mrs J Drennan, BMus, MEd
Mrs V Ellison, BEd
Mrs M P Evans, BSc
Mrs S Evans, BMus
Mrs R Fisher, BA Ed

Mrs A Foster, BA, MEd
K Foster, BEd
Mrs L Fowler, BEd
Miss R Fox, BA
Miss S Gale, BSc (*Head Girls PE*)
Mrs A Gardener, BA
Miss R E Garrett, CertEd
Mrs K M Gilbertson, BSc (*Head of Psychology*)
Mrs H Giles, BA
Miss C Greenwood, BSc
M Hackney, BA (*Head of Lower Sixth*)
Mrs C Haffner, BA
Ms C Harms, BA (*Head of Drama/Theatre Studies*)
Mrs K M Haspell, Dip Theatre Arts
Mrs L Hayes, BA (*Coordinator of IT*)
Mrs V J Heath, BEd
Mrs L Hodges, BSc
Mrs L Holgate, BA QTS
Miss D A Hodgkinson, BEd
S Horsman, MA (*Head of Geography*)
Mrs A Hoverstadt, MSc (*Head of Careers*)
S Howells, BA
N J Hurst, BA (*Head of Classics*)
D A Jackson, BSc
Miss S John, BA
Mrs A M Johnson, BA (*Head of Year 11*)
Dr J E Johnstone, MPhys, PhD
Miss H Kelly, BSc
Ms R Lago Costa, BA
Miss J A Lederer, BA
Mrs R Leonard, BSc
Mrs H C Lewis, BA (*Deputy Head of Junior School*)
Mrs F Lucas, BA (*Head of French*)
J S MacGregor, MA
Mrs D Masters, Licence d'Anglais (*Head of Year 8*)
Mrs S M Matthews, BSc (*Learning Support Coordinator*)
C McAllister, BA (*Head of RE*)
Mrs N Meredith, BA (*Head of German*)
F Morris, BA
Mrs G M Mutch, BA
Mrs B A Myers, BA
S Pagan, MA (*Head of History & Politics*)
Ms M Pakay, BA
S Parkin, BA
K Pearson, BSc
G C Peat, BSc (*Head of Biology*)
Mrs S E Petrie, BA (*Head of Lower School*)
Mrs H Phillips, BEd
Miss S Plimmer, BA
Miss K J Purchase, BSc
Mrs B Rawling, BSc
L Richardson, BA (*Head of Economics & Business Studies*)
Mrs L Roberts, BA
Miss E P Roskell, BSc
Mrs K Sargent, BA
Mrs J D Shand, MA
Mrs S Sharples, BSc
Miss N Shea, BA, PGDip Teaching
P Shipston, MA (*Head of General Studies*)
M P Sparrow, BSocSc
Mrs J Stafford, BSc
Mrs E J Sweeting, BSc
Mrs J Sym, Bed
P Tann, BA (*Head of Upper School*)
Miss L Tarnowski, BSc Hons, MSc, PGCE
Mrs S Taylor, CertEd
S D Taylor, BSc
D Thomson, BA
S Treadway, BEd
Mrs K M Turner, BA (*Head of Upper Sixth & Deputy Head of Sixth Form*)
P Upton, BEd
Mrs A J Vernon, Bed
Mrs K Vlastos, BA Hons, PGCE
Mrs L Ward, CertEd (*KS1 Coordinator*)
Miss M J Webster, BA
P G J Welch, BSc
N O Westbrook, BA (*Head of English & Library*)
Mrs B J Williams, BSc (*Head of Year 9*)
J K A Wilson, MPhil (*Head of Spanish*)
J C Winter, BA (*Head of Sixth Form*)
Miss A Womersley, MEng, BMS, PGCE
A Wrathall, BSc
Miss K Wright, BA
Dr P Wright, BA, MA, PhD, PGCE
K Yearsley, BA (*Head of Art*)

Visiting Staff:
French Assistant
German Assistant
Spanish Assistant
Specialist Music Teachers

Number in School. 1,334 (717 boys, 617 girls) of whom 281 are in the Junior School and 252 in the Sixth Form.

Location. The School which is about 10 miles south of Manchester, 3 miles from the Airport and 10 miles from the Derbyshire Hills consists of the original and many new buildings in its own 80 acres of open land.

Admission. Pupils are admitted as a result of assessment at age 4, and examination at age 7, 8, 9 and 11; to the Sixth Form for A Level work; or at other ages when chance vacancies occur.

The entrance test, which is competitive because many more children apply than places exist, is designed to determine that the child can profit from the type of education provided.

Organisation and Curriculum. For pastoral care and administrative purposes the School is divided into Sixth Form; Upper (Years 10 & 11); Middle (Years 8 & 9); Lower (Year 7); Juniors and Infants. The curriculum is kept as broad as possible to the end of Year 11 and no vital choice has to be made between Arts and Sciences until this point. In the Sixth Form pupils choose their AS and A2 Levels from a wide range of subjects. Special provision is made for those who wish to enter Oxford or Cambridge. Extensions classes are available in all subjects.

On leaving virtually all pupils progress to University.

Clubs and Societies. There are many extra-curricular activities. These include a variety of music groups such as Concert Band, Big Band, Rock School, Wind and Guitar ensembles, Sinfonia and choirs, and there are annual dramatic and musical productions. Among the societies and clubs catering for those interested are Art, Bridge, Brain Aerobics, Multimedia ICT, Geography, Chess, Italian, Minimus Latin club, a wide range of Sports clubs, Debating, Philosophical Society, Amnesty International, Model United Nations, Young Enterprise, Think Tank, 'Diggers' History, Student Industrial Society, Volunteer and Community Groups and many others. Large numbers of pupils undertake the school's own 'Cheadle Hulme Challenge' which introduces them to a variety of new skills and expeditions to develop organisational and leadership abilities. Newly introduced 'Student Leader schemes' in over 50 extra-curricular clubs, give older pupils the opportunity to gain experience and skills working with and coaching younger pupils.

Games and Physical Activities. There is a full range of the usual field and team games, and, additionally, in Year 11 and Sixth Form, Yoga, Badminton, Volleyball and Basketball. Swimming is for all in the School's heated indoor pool.

Fees per term (2008-2009). (*see Scholarship Entries section*). Subject to termly review: Junior School £2,139–£2,230; Senior School £2,876.

The Foundation Scheme ensures that any current pupil who suffers the loss through death or disability of the major earner in his or her family can remain in the school.

Charitable status. Cheadle Hulme School is a Registered Charity, number 1077017.

Cheltenham College

Bath Road Cheltenham Gloucestershire GL53 7LD
Tel: College: 01242 265600
Admissions: 01242 265662
Fax: College: 01242 265630
Headmaster: 01242 265685
Bursar: 01242 265687
e-mail: admissions@cheltcoll.gloucs.sch.uk
website: www.cheltcoll.gloucs.sch.uk/cc

Cheltenham College is a fully co-educational boarding and day school. The first of the great Victorian schools, Cheltenham College was founded in 1841.

Motto: '*Labor Omnia Vincit.*'

Visitor: The Rt Revd The Lord Bishop of Gloucester

The Council:
President: The Revd J C Horan
Deputy President: Colonel J C A Smith

Dr L La Velle, BEd, MSc, PhD
Dr R Acheson PhD
Mrs J Blackburn
P Brettell
Mrs P K Cadbury, BA, FCA
A J L Glover, MA
Dr D P Hanson, MA, PhD
Mrs B Hodson-Cottingham, OBE
Mrs V Isaac, MA
Miss N MacManaway, MA, MPhil, BA
E L Rowlands, MA, Dip Ed
Dr B J Saunders
D C Shortt
C M Smyth, LLB
W J Straker-Nesbit
Canon Dr H Tomlinson, BA, PhD
G Ware
Dr J C Wilson, MA, PhD, FRSA

Secretary to Council: J Champion

***Headmaster*: J S Richardson**, MA Cantab

Bursar: J Champion
Deputy Head: A Peterken
Director of Teaching & Learning: Dr C A J Runacres, MA, PhD
Development Director: Ms B Vick
Chaplain: Revd Dr R de la Bat Smit, MA, PhD, FRSA
Senior Teacher: Mrs H L Lawrence, BSc
Senior Master: Revd N Lowton, MA, FRSA
Senior Housemaster: M W Stovold, CertEd
Senior Tutor: A J Gasson, MA
Curriculum Director: P R Summers, MA
Director of Sport: S P Johnson, BSc, MA
Director of Activities: D Faulkner, BSc

Assistant Masters and Mistresses:
Miss M Abbott, DipAD, DipTEFLA
T R C Adams, MA
Miss H T Allen, BA
S Bateman, BSc
W Bates
Ms M Bradshaw, BA
T Brewis, BA
M C Brunt, BEd
S F Bullock, BA
G S Busbridge, BA, MMus, FRCO CHM, ADCM, LRAM, ARCM
Miss J A Camargo-Duque, BA
Miss R K Cannon, BSc
T Carpenter, BSc
K T Carson, BA, MPhil
G Case, BSc
Miss J Casely, MA
Mrs A Chapman, MA
Dr P D Chipman, BSc, PhD
S G Clark, MBE
M K Coley, BSc
S E Conner, BSc
K A Cook, BA, PRA
J Coull, BA
A V Cutts, BEd
G J Cutts, BA
Miss B M Davies, BA
M Debenham, MSc, BSc
Miss J Doidge-Harrison, BA, MA
A M Durston, BSc
A Endicott, BA
Dr B E Enright, BSc, PhD
D Faulkner, BSc
A M M Ffinch, MA, ARCM
Miss L C Gallagher, BSc
A J Gasson, MA
Mrs C Goodman, BSc
Mrs C E Harrison, BSc
D J Harvey, BSc
Mrs S E Hillier-Richardson, BSc, MA
G Hughes-Games, BSc
Ms D Innes, BA
A Isaachsen, BEd
Ms G L Jardim, BA, MTh
S P Johnson, BSc, MA
J L Jones, MSc
Dr M D Jones, MA, PhD
Miss Z La Valette-Cooper, BA
B J Lambert, BSc
P Lelliott, BA
F J Llewellyn, BA
A J McNaught, GRSM, LRAM, ARCM
Mrs H Merigot, BA
Miss S L Millyard, BA
R Moore, BA
J Morton, BEng
S J C Morton, MSc
N Nelson, BA
Mrs C Park, BA
Miss K Parker, BSc
Mrs I T M Pemberton, BA
J Pepperman, MA
Mrs S Ramsay, HDE, FDE
C L Reid, MA
C Rouan, BSc
M W Simpson, BA
G L Smith, BA
M W Stovold, CertEd
P R Summers, MA
Mrs M E Swingler, MA
Mrs E C Taylor, BA
M Todd, BComm, DipAcc
Mrs R M Vazquez-Gonzalez, BA
M H Ward, CertEd
P Weir, BA
Mrs C Widdows, BA
J B Wild, MA
R D A Woodberry, MA, MLitt
C C Wright, MA
Miss L Zhao, BA

Houses and Housemasters/mistresses:

Boarding Boys:
Boyne House: S F Bullock
Christowe: A M Durston
Hazelwell: S Conner
Leconfield: K A Cook
Newick House: M W Stovold

Day Boys:
Southwood: B J Lambert

Boarding Girls:
Ashmead: Mrs A V Cutts
Chandos: Mrs S Ramsay

Day Girls:
Queen's: Mrs S Chipman
Westal: Mrs S Jackson

Location. Fine buildings and first-class playing fields provide a magnificent setting near the centre of Regency Cheltenham. Situated in the heart of the beautiful Cotswolds with excellent road and rail connections with London and the major airports, the College offers all the advantages of life in a thriving town community, whilst maintaining a separate campus life.

Numbers. Boys: 329 boarders; 62 day boys. Girls: 143 boarders; 69 day girls.

Admission. Entry at 13: Candidates are invited to complete a questionnaire about themselves and attend a pre-assessment in Spring Year 7. This comprises a standardised test in Maths and English, a VRQ, time spent with the House staff and a full report from the preparatory school. Guaranteed places will be offered wherever possible subject to, but with the expectation of, passing Common Entrance.

Able pupils may also be admitted at age 14 into the Fourth Form

A number of able pupils enter directly into the Sixth Form following scholarship and entry tests in November or March, good GCSE predictions and a testimonial from previous school.

Prospectuses and application forms may be obtained from the Director of Admissions, who will always be glad to welcome parents who wish to see the College. There is a registration fee of £75, and a final acceptance fee of £750 (for pupils aged 13–16) or £1,000 (for Sixth Form entrants) which is deducted from the final term's account.

Scholarships. (*see Scholarship Entries section*). Awards are available for entry at 13+ and for those joining the College at Sixth Form level. In addition to academic scholarships and exhibitions, awards are also made for Music, Art, Sport, Design Technology, and to candidates who display all-round ability.

Fees per term (2008-2009). Boarders £9,175; Day pupils £6,875. Sixth Form: Boarders £9,275, Day pupils £6,975.

Chapel. There is a ten-minute service in the Chapel each weekday morning and a main service each Sunday. There is a Confirmation service every year.

Recent Developments. The girls are in four houses: two boarding, one day and one new house providing a mix of day accommodation 13–18 with Sixth Form boarding. The College has also just completed a major programme of refurbishment for all six boys' houses. The resulting accommodation is outstanding for both boys and girls. The College now enters a new phase of development with exciting plans for teaching, studying and social facilities.

Curriculum. On entry at 13, pupils follow a broad course for one year, before embarking upon GCSE in the Fourth Form. The core of the curriculum at GCSE comprises: English, Mathematics, all three Sciences (examined as GCSE Dual Science Award), and French. All then choose four options from: Art, Design Technology (Resistant Materials, Textiles, Systems and Controls), Drama, German, Geography, Greek, History, Latin, Music, PE, Spanish and Religious Studies. In the Sixth Form, twenty-five AS and full A Level subjects are offered. Boys and girls and given extensive preparation for entrance to Oxford, Cambridge and other universities. Over 95% of leavers go on to university.

Cultural Activities. The Arts are central to the life of the College. At least six plays are staged each year, in Big Classical – the main theatre – in the Jack Ralphs Studio Theatre, or in other locations around the College. Art is housed in Thirlestaine House, a beautifully elegant early nineteenth century mansion, with a Gallery which houses an exhibition of current Art and which also serves as an excellent chamber music concert hall. The Chapel Choir, the orchestras and smaller musical ensembles perform in the Town Hall, Pump Rooms, as well as in the Chapel and other venues. The College Orchestra, Choir and Choral Society offer many opportunities to players and listeners. Music plays a vital part in the life of the College. Boys and girls are encouraged to attend concerts, plays, films and lectures in Cheltenham, London, Oxford, Stratford, Bristol and elsewhere and the College is a principal sponsor of Cheltenham's Jazz, Science, Literature and Music Festivals.

Games. The main boys' games are rugby, hockey, cricket and rowing. The main girls' games are hockey, netball, tennis and rowing. In addition to the two astroturf pitches, the Sports Hall and swimming pool, there are excellent facilities for other sports, which include rackets, squash, tennis, badminton, basketball, polo, sailing, climbing and shooting.

Service. There is a strong Community Service scheme which serves the town, and an Industrial Link scheme enables all College Sixth-formers to experience the world of work. The College's Humanitarian Aid Project raises funds for building and refurbishment work in a number of orphanages and schools and the members of the group regularly visit Romania and Kenya to provide practical assistance. Wherever possible, all College facilities are made available to the town, especially the festivals, and other schools. The CCF is compulsory in the Fourth year, except in cases of religious or conscientious objection, after which the pupils may choose the community service scheme or other service activities.

University entry and Careers. There is a full-time teacher in charge of Careers, and another responsible for University and Higher Education advice. In addition, every Sixth-former has a tutor who is charged with ensuring that he or she is fully aware of the opportunities and challenges available.

Cheltonian Society. The Secretary, Tel: 01242 265664.

Cheltenham College Junior School. *For details see entry in IAPS section.*

Charitable status. Cheltenham College Charity Trust is a Registered Charity, number 311720. As a charity it is established for the purpose of providing an efficient course of education for boys and girls.

Chetham's School of Music

Long Millgate Manchester M3 1SB
Tel: 0161 834 9644
Fax: 0161 839 3609
e-mail: chets@chethams.com
website: www.chethams.com

Chetham's is a co-educational school for boarding and day pupils aged eight to eighteen. The School teaches a broad curriculum set within a framework of music. At the centre of every child's course is a 'musical core' of experiences rooted in a determination to educate the whole person. Originally founded in 1653, through the Will of Humphrey Chetham, as a Bluecoat orphanage, the School was re-constituted in 1969 as a specialist music school.

Governors:
Dame A V Burslem, DBE (*Chairman*)
R Bailey
Prof J Beer
Prof E Gregson, BMus, GRSM, LRAM, FRAM
R Haylock
G D Henderson
C G Kenyon, MA
Mrs J Pickering
Mrs R Pike, JP
P Ramsbottom, MusB, FCA
The Very Revd Rogers Govender, Dean of Manchester Cathedral

Staff:

***Head*: Mrs Claire Hickman**, MA

Director of Music: S Threlfall, GRNCM Hons

Deputy Head, Pastoral: Ms C Rhind, BA

Deputy Head, Curriculum: C Newman, BA, MSc

Music:

Consultants:
Adam Gorb (*Composition*)
Christopher Rowland (*Chamber Music*)

Visiting Professors:
Steven Doane (*Cello*)
Lorand Fenyves (*Violin*)
Paul Galbraith (*Guitar*)
Brian Hawkins (*Viola*)
Ifor James (*Horn*)
Lewis Kaplan (*Violin*)

Peter Lloyd (*Flute*)
John Miller (*Trumpet*)
Gustavo Nunez (*Bassoon*)
Ronan O'Hora (*Piano*)
Eric Sammut (*Percussion*)
Patrick Sheridan (*Tuba*)
David Strange (*Cello*)
Evelyn Tubb (*Soprano*)
Michael Vaiman (*Violin*)
Zvi Zeitlin (*Violin*)

Full-time Tutorial Staff:
Miss S M Bettaney
Ms B Blewett, MA, ARCM
S Bottomley, GRNCM
M Bussey, MA (*Head of Academic & Choral Music*)
D Chatterton, MusB, GRNCM (*Head of Brass & Percussion*)
Ms S Fraser
Miss B Gough (*Head of Woodwind*)
N Jones, ARCM (*Head of Strings*)
S King, BA, MA, MPhil
P G Lawson, GRSM, ARMCM
D Mason, BA
M McLachlan, BA, MA, LRAM (*Head of Keyboard*)
N Oliver, GRSM, LRAM, PGRNCM
Mrs C Perkins, GRNCM
J Pike, MA, LRAM (*Head of Composition & Electronic Music*)
J M Ritchie, ARMCM, GRSM
C Stokes (*Head of Organ*)

Music Department Coordinator: I Mayer
Concert Administrator: D Curtis, BSc

Visiting instrumental tutors in association with the Royal Northern College of Music, the Hallé and BBC Philharmonic Orchestras.

Academic Music:
S King, BA, MA, MPhil, PhD
M Bussey, MA
D Mason, BA
A Dean, MA, FRCO
Mrs K Misson-Uttley, BA
S Jacobs, MusB Hons
P Sanderson, BA

Languages:
Miss S Davidson, MA
P Chillingworth, BA
Mrs C Law, MA, PhD
Mrs M Potts, BA

English:
Miss G Simpson, MA
I Little, BA
J Runswick-Cole, BA

Drama & Theatre Studies:
Miss K Brindle, BA

Special Needs/Compensatory Education:
Mrs B L Owen, BEd, RSA, DipSLD
Miss C Lynch, BA
Miss R McIntyre, BA

Sciences:
P Przybyla, BSc
Mrs A Dack, BSc
Mrs K Armstrong, BSc
J Thomson, MSc

Mathematics & Computer Studies:
Mrs P Janson, MA
Mrs F Holker, BSc
C Bramall, BA

Humanities:
A Kyle, BA
C Newman, MA
Mrs P Rigby, BA

Art:
Miss A Boothroyd, BA

Recreation:
Ms I Staszko, BEd, MA
Ms A Willems

PSE & RE:
Miss H Woods, BA
Revd Canon P Denby

Primary:
D Harris, BA

Librarian: Mrs R Jones, MA

Careers:
P G Lawson, GRSM, ARMCM (*Music Colleges*)
C Newman, MA (*Universities*)

Houses:
Mr & Mrs J Runswick-Cole (*Boys' House*)
Miss C Dickinson (*Girls' House*)
Dr & Mrs D Armstrong (*Victoria House*)

Bursar: Mrs S C Newman, BSc Hons, FCA
School Doctor: Dr J Tankel
Nurse: Mrs K Scott, RGN
Head's PA: Mrs L Haslam

The School numbers 292 pupils, of whom 158 are girls. There are 220 boarders. Admission is solely by musical audition, and any orchestral instrument, keyboard, guitar, voice or composition, may be studied. Each pupil studies two instruments, or voice and one instrument, as well as following academic courses which lead to GCSE and A Levels and to university entrance and music college. The School stands on the site of Manchester's original 12th century Manor House adjacent to the Cathedral, and is housed partly in the fine 15th century College Building, around which are grouped Palatine Building (1846), Millgate Building (1870, formerly The Manchester Grammar School), the 'Chapel' (1878) and the classroom and laboratory block (1954). A new boarding house has recently been built and academic classrooms have been completely renovated.

Music. Instrumental tuition is guided and monitored by the advisers in each specialism, who visit regularly to survey pupils' work, conduct internal examinations and give Master Classes. Internationally renowned musicians hold residences at the School for string, wind, brass, percussion and keyboard players. The Director of Music has responsibility for the full-time Music Staff and also for about 90 visiting tutors. All pupils receive three sessions of individual instrumental tuition each week. Practice is rigorously set and supervised. Music is normally studied at A Level.

Boarding. There are two boarding houses for girls and boys aged 13 to 18 and one for Juniors aged 8 to 13. Each House is run by Houseparents in residence, with resident assistants. All members of staff act as Tutors and are involved with pastoral care. In addition, when necessary, pupils have open access to the School Counsellors.

Recreation. Serious attention is paid to recreation, PE and games and the pupils' physical well-being. On-site facilities include an indoor swimming pool, gym, multi-gym and a squash court.

Applications, Visits. The Prospectus and application forms are sent on request. Preliminary assessment auditions are held throughout the year, with final auditions in the Christmas and Spring terms. Parents and prospective pupils are welcome to visit the School, by arrangement with the Head's Secretary.

Fees, Grants. (*see Scholarship Entries section*). All entrants from the United Kingdom are eligible for grants from Central Government. Parental contribution to cost is calculated according to circumstances under the DCSF Scheme.

Choristers. The School is a member of the Choir Schools' Association and Choristerships at Manchester Cathedral for day boys and girls are available under a separate scheme. Choristers' Fee: £8,346 pa (subject to Cathedral Bursaries).

Charitable status. Chetham's School of Music is a Registered Charity, number 526702. It exists to educate exceptionally gifted young musicians.

Chigwell School

Chigwell Essex IG7 6QF
Tel: 020 8501 5700 (School Secretary)
020 8501 5702 (School Registrar)
Fax: 020 8500 6232
e-mail: hm@chigwell-school.org
website: www.chigwell-school.org

The School was founded in 1629 by Samuel Harsnett, Archbishop of York, "to supply a liberal and practical education, and to afford instruction in the Christian religion, according to the doctrine and principles of the Church of England".

Motto: '*Aut viam inveniam aut faciam*', '*Find a Way or Make a Way*'.

Governing Body:
Chairman: C P de Boer, Esq
Mrs P B Aliker, BA, MBA, ACMA
J Cullis, Esq, MBE, BA, MSc
Sir Richard Dales, KCVO, CMG, MA
R Howard, Esq, MA
Mrs F Jamieson, LLB, DipM
Mrs E Laing, MP
D Morriss, Esq, BSc, CEng, FIEE, FBCS
J P Parry, Esq, PhD
The Venerable P F Taylor, MA, BD, LCD
Dr G Thurairajah, MBBS
R H Youndale, Esq, MA

Clerk to the Governors: Group Captain G M Maloney, FCMI, RAF

Bursar: D N Morrison, MA, PGCE

***Headmaster*: M E Punt**, MA, MSc

Deputy Head: D J Gower, BSc

Head of the Junior School: Mrs J Gwinn, BSc

Assistant Staff:
Miss V Barnes, BEd
Miss E Barrs, BA
Ms S Bell, BA
M L Bradley, BA, MMus, MLitt
Dr P F Burd, PhD, BSc
Miss K S Callaghan, BSc
Miss C A Carbonaro, BA
Mrs A Carroll, MA (*Senior Mistress*)
S M Chaudhary, MA
Dr P G Clayton, BSc
P I Cocks, BSc
T Coker, BA (*Director of Music*)
Revd Dr C P Collingwood, PhD, BMus (*Chaplain*)
S Coppell, BA
Miss B Corti
Ms E Creber, BSc
Mrs S T Davies, MA
W P Eardley, BSc
K Farrant, BEd
Mrs E M P Feeney
P R Fletcher, MA, DipTEFL
Mrs J Gray, BA
D Harryman, BSc
D J L Harston, MA
D W Hartland, MA
Dr E M Haynes, PhD
Miss A Hurribunce, DipEd
G S Inch, BA
Mrs N A Jermyn, BA
Mrs N J Jones, BA
Mrs L Joughin
Miss A Koppel, MA
Miss A Lapwood, BMus (*Director of Music*)
C K Lawrence, BA
Miss F M Leach, BMus
A Long, MSc
R A F Lonsdale, MA
C J Lord, MA
H J Lukesch, 1st & 2nd STEX
P W Marchant, BA (*Senior Master*)
Dr T Martin
Miss L McCormack, MA
Ms N McGrath, BA
A McKenzie, MA
C J Mills, BA
Miss J Mitchell, BEd
J P Morris, BSc
D N Morrison, MA
D J Morse, BA
R Ogle, BA
Ms J Osborne, BEd
R C Parry, BA
D Patel, BSc
Mrs P Pewsey, BSEd, TEFL
J S Porter, BA
Mrs A C Rae, BPrimEd
Mrs E R Rea, MA
Mrs H Russell
N M Saunders, BSc
R Sliwa, CertEd, DipSEA
R S Spicer, BA
J M Stedman, BA
R Steel, BA
Mrs R S Strong, AM, AB cum laude
A Stubbs, BA
Ms M C Teichman, BA
N Tester, BSc
Mrs C E Tilbrook, BEd, DipSEA
Miss N Weeks, BSc
Mrs S E Welsford, BEd
S C Wilson, MEd, BSc
D Yuravlivker, MSc, BA

Medical Officer: Dr F M Tranmer, MB BS, MRCS, MRCGP

Grounds. Chigwell School stands in a superb green belt location in 70 acres of playing fields and woodlands, midway between Epping and Hainault Forests and enjoys excellent communications. It is easily accessible from London (by Central Line Undergound network). Both the M25 and M11 motorways are close by, while Heathrow, Gatwick, Stansted and Luton Airports are all reachable from the School within the hour.

The School and the Buildings. The School was founded in 1629 and William Penn, founder of Pennsylvania, is the most famous Old Chigwellian. Currently there are just over 740 pupils, including over 50 Full and Weekly Boarders. The School became co-educational in September 1997.

The original building is still in use and houses the Senior School Swallow Library. There has been a considerable amount of building in the past 10 years and all the older buildings have been modernised while retaining their character. New buildings include the Junior School Classroom and Office Extension, the Junior School Library, the Sports Hall, the Art, Design and Technology Centre, the Information Technology and Economics Centres, the Browning Building for Maths and Modern Languages, the expanded and refurbished Science School, the Roding Lane Humanities Centre, the new Music School Extension and a state-of-the-art Drama Centre.

Organisation. The School is divided into the Senior and Junior Schools but is administered as a single unit with a common teaching staff.

The Head of the Junior School is responsible for all pupils between the ages of 7 and 13. The Junior School is on the same site as the Senior School and all facilities and grounds are used by Junior pupils. Assembly, Games and Lunch are all arranged separately from the Senior School. (*For further details, see Junior School entry in IAPS section.*)

In the Senior School, all the day pupils and boarders are divided into four Day Houses: Penn's (Mr J P Morris) Swallow's (Mrs A Carroll), Caswalls' (Mr G S Inch), Lambourne (Mr D J L Harston). Each House has a large House room, a small kitchen, a quiet room, studies for Senior pupils and a Housemaster's or Housemistress' study.

Curriculum. Pupils follow a broad based course leading to GCSE. Maths, English, Science and one modern language form the common core of subjects. Science is taken either as three separate subjects, (Physics, Biology, Chemistry) or as Coordinated Science. In addition, a wide range of options is taken at GCSE including Art and Design, Graphic Design, Design Technology, Electronics, French, German, Spanish,

Latin, Greek, Geography, History, Religious Studies, Drama and Music.

Sixth Form. The Head of the Sixth Form is Mr Andy Long. Almost all boys and girls take 5 AS Level subjects in the first year including General Studies and 3 A2 Level subjects in the second year. Subjects taken include, Latin, Greek, Classical Civilisation, French, German, English, Economics, History, Geography, Maths, Further Maths, Physics, Chemistry, Biology, Music, Art, Design and Technology, Religious Studies and Theatre Studies. Many of these subjects are available at AS Level.

Games and Activities. Cricket, Association Football, Rugby, Netball, Hockey (Boys and Girls), Athletics, Cross-Country Running, Swimming, Squash, Tennis, Golf, Basketball and Badminton. There are numerous School Societies and a large Venture Scout Troop. Many pupils join the Duke of Edinburgh's Award Scheme. There is a swimming pool, two Sports Halls and extensive playing fields on site, including 18 sports pitches.

Art & Design, Ceramics, and D & T. Art is taught throughout the School and there is excellent provision for Ceramics and D & T which form part of the curriculum for all pupils between the ages of 10 and 14.

Music. There are 2 Orchestras, Wind and Jazz Bands, 4 Choirs (Boys and Girls Choir, Chapel Choir, and a Chamber Choir) and a Choral Society. Pupils may learn any instrument (including the Organ). Several Concerts are given each year in addition to pupils' Concerts and Concerts given by visiting performers.

Boarding. Boy Boarders are accommodated in Grange Court, a fine Georgian mansion, led by Mr D N Morrison, the Senior Boarding House Master. Boys in the Sixth Form are provided with individual study bedrooms.

Sandon Lodge, set in the middle of the beautiful School Grounds, accommodates Sixth Form Girl Boarders under the care of Mrs A M Lord.

Hainault House, under the supervision of Mrs S McKenzie, lies adjacent to the Junior School and offers accommodation for girls.

Fees per term (2008-2009). Weekly boarding £5,831–£6,189; Full boarding £6,537; Day pupils £2,797–£4,301 plus Lunch/Tea charge £228 (day pupils only).

The fees are inclusive of all extra charges except some books and Instrumental Music. Fees vary depending upon age.

Entrance Scholarships and Bursaries. (*see Scholarship Entries section*). Sixth Form entrance interviews are held throughout the year, principally in November and January and there are generous Academic, Art, Drama and Music Scholarships available. Music Scholarships are also offered from age 11. A competitive examination for Academic Scholarships is held each year during the Lent Term for pupils aged 11+ and 16+. Further details may be obtained from the Headmaster.

Chigwell Bursaries may be available for able pupils who could not otherwise afford the opportunity to attend Chigwell.

Term of Entry. Pupils normally enter the School in September of each year, but exceptions may be made according to individual circumstances.

The Old Chigwellians' Association. c/o Development Office, Chigwell School, Essex.

Charitable status. Chigwell School is a Registered Charity, number 1115098. It exists to provide a rounded education of the highest quality for its pupils.

Christ College
Brecon

Brecon Powys LD3 8AG
Tel: 01874 615440 (Head)
01874 615440 (Bursar)
Fax: 01874 615475
e-mail: enquiries@christcollegebrecon.com
website: www.christcollegebrecon.com

Founded by Henry VIII, 1541. Reconstituted by Act of Parliament, 1853.

Motto: '*Possunt quia posse videntur*.'

Visitor: Her Majesty The Queen

Governing Body:
The Revd Professor D P Davies, MA, BD (*Chairman*)
The Rt Revd The Lord Bishop of Swansea and Brecon
The Venerable The Archdeacon of Brecon
W R M Chadwick
D G Clarke, DL
Prof R B Davies
His Honour T Michael Evans, QC
Dr A Gilbey
M Gittins
Mrs S A E Gwyer Roberts, BA, MEd, NPQH, FRSA
R J Harbottle, BA
Mrs J James
Sir Roger Jones, OBE, BPharm, MSc
Sir Andrew Large
The Hon Mrs E S J Legge-Bourke, LVO, Lord Lieutenant of Powys
R Morris
A L Price, CBE, QC, MA
H L P Richards
Mrs J M E Williams

Registrar: T J P Davenport, LLB

***Head*: Mrs Emma Taylor**, MA Oxon

Deputy Head: S A Spencer, BA (*English*)

Director of Studies: J D Bush, MA (*English*)

Assistant Staff:
S A Adams, MPhys (*Mathematics*)
*Mrs R E Allen, BA (*History*)
C Andras, BA (*Welsh/Modern Languages*)
*The Revd S A Baker, BEd (*Chaplain*)
*N C Blackburn, BSc (*Mathematics*)
Mrs K Buckley, BA (*English*)
*P Chandler, BA (*Classics*)
*Miss C L Collins, BA (*Modern Languages*)
J T Cooper, BA, ARCO (*Director of Choral Music*)
†A Copp, BSc (*Economics*)
P K Edgley, ARPS (*Photography*)
Mrs U Feldner, BA (*Art*)
Mrs A V Frazer, BEd (*Drama*)
D R Grant, BSc (*Chemistry*)
Miss J A Green, BA (*Modern Languages*)
Mrs C Halpin, BA (*Mathematics and Numeracy Support*)
†G Halpin, BSc (*Geography*)
*Mrs A Hefford, BA (*Art*)
*G Hope, BEng, MSc (*Physics & Science*)
*Mrs J Hope, MA (*English*)
†Mrs N C John, BSc (*PSHE*)
Miss S E Jones, BSc (*Biology*)
*Mrs F Kilpatrick, BA, RSA DipSpLD, AMBDA (*Learning Support*)
I J Owen, BSc (*Mathematics*)
D Phelps, MA, PhD (*History*)
*R G Rogers, BA (*Design & Technology*)
Mrs J Shannon, BEc (*Geography*)
†P Shannon, BSc (*Mathematics*)
*†M P Sims, BSc (*Biology*)
*R C Slaney, BA (*EAL*)
*P W Smith, BSc, PhD, MRSC, CChem (*Chemistry*)
C Thomas (*Physics*)
*N E Thomas, BSc (*Geography*)

T J Trumper, BEd (*PE*)
*C J Webber, BEd (*PE*)
†Mrs L Webber, CertEd, DipPsych, MEd Psych (*PE*)
*R West, MSc (*Director of Music*)
*G M Wolstenholme, BA (*Business Studies and Careers*)

Visiting Music Staff:
G Bradley, LWCMD, ARCM
A S Davies, GWCMD
J C Herbert
M W Jones, BMus, ARCO
Miss E Priday, LRAM, ARAM
N Ramirez Celis, BA, MA, ADWCMD
I Russell
Ms A Shingler, BA, ABSM, LRAM
Mrs D Taylor
Dr C E Slater, MA, PhD
Mrs C E Walker, MA Oxon, ARCM

Medical Officer: Dr M B J Heneghan, BSc, MB, BCh, MRCP, DRCOG

Bursar: K C Dempsey
Admissions Registrar: Mrs M L Stephens
SSI: W J Dowling, MBE
OBA Secretary: J D Payne, MA
Foundation & Marketing Director: S Maggs, BA, GCGI, PMICS

Christ College, Brecon lies in a setting of outstanding natural beauty at the foot of the Brecon Beacons on the edge of the small market town of Brecon, two minutes walk away on the opposite side of the river. The River Usk flows alongside the playing fields providing good canoeing and fishing while the nearby Llangorse Lake is available for sailing and windsurfing.

The school was founded by King Henry VIII in 1541 when he dissolved the Dominican Friary of St Nicholas. The 13th Century Chapel and Dining Hall are at the centre of school life and the school's mix of important, historic buildings and modern architecture represents the continuity of education at the school. In the last ten years a Library has been built, the music school extended, all the boarding houses refurbished, an Astroturf built as well as Fitness Suite, the Art School re-located and expanded while a Sixth Form Centre renovated and extensive landscaping of the school campus. Most pupils in the last two years of school enjoy single study-bedrooms.

Organisation. Christ College was a boys' only school until 1987 when girls were admitted to the Sixth Form. In 1995 the school became fully co-educational. There are 310 pupils in the school of whom 180 are boys and 130 girls. Approximately 70% of pupils board and there are three senior boys' houses (School House, Orchard House and St David's House), two senior girls' houses, Donaldson's House and de Winton House (recently extended) and a junior house (Alway House) for 11–13 year old boys and girls. The school eats centrally in a Dining Hall dating from the 13th century but served by modern kitchens.

Chapel. Chapel services are conducted in accordance with the liturgy of the Anglican church, but entrance to Christ College is open to boys and girls of all faiths. The ownership of Chapel by the boys and girls, demonstrated through their participation in services and their singing, is a feature of the school. Pupils are prepared for Confirmation by the School's Chaplain who lives on site.

Curriculum. Up to the Fifth Form pupils follow a balanced curriculum leading to GCSE at which most pupils take 10 subjects. Options are chosen at the end of form 3 (Year 9).Current subjects taught include English Language, English Literature, Mathematics, French, Spanish, Physics, Chemistry, Biology, History, Geography, Latin, Religious Studies, Art, Music, Design & Technology, Business Studies, Physical Education, Photography, Drama, PSE, Information Technology and Welsh. Greek is sometimes available as an extra subject outside the timetable.

In the Sixth Form a similar range of subjects is taken at AS and A2 Level plus opportunities to take Economics, Further Mathematics and Philosophy. All pupils have timetabled tutorial periods and in the Sixth Form periods are set aside for Careers advice.

Class sizes rarely exceed 20 up to GCSE and average fewer than 10 at A Level.

Games. The main school games are Rugby Football, Cricket, Hockey, Soccer, Netball, Cross-Country and Athletics. Tennis, Badminton, Squash, Volleyball, Basketball, Golf, Fishing, Swimming, Shooting, Mountain Biking, Canoeing, Fencing, Indoor Cricket, Climbing, Triathlon and Aerobics are also available. The playing fields are extensive and lie adjacent to the school. Christ College has entered into a corporate partnership with Cradoc Golf Club, two miles outside of Brecon, to encourage pupils of all ages and experience in the fundamentals of the game of golf. The opportunity to play at Cradoc Golf Club and receive professional instruction is also extended to all parents of pupils attending Christ College.

Thursday Afternoons. On Thursday afternoons the CCF Contingent meets. There is a choice between Royal Navy, Army and Royal Air Force sections and the CCF has its own Headquarters, Armoury and covered 30m Range in the school grounds. Pupils take their proficiency certificate after two years and may then choose to continue as Instructors, undergo training for the Duke of Edinburgh's Award Scheme or leave the CCF and may become involved in community service.

Music. The Chapel Choir is large and enjoys a good reputation with radio and television broadcasts as well as overseas tours to its credit. As befits a school in Wales singing on all school occasions is committed, energetic and frequently with natural harmony. The school has a Jazz Band, a junior orchestra and its pupils play a prominent role in the South Powys Youth Orchestra. There are many other opportunities to play in ensemble groups throughout the school. Individual instrumental and singing lessons are delivered by visiting musicians.

Activities. In addition to sporting pastimes a wide range of activities are available to pupils including Sixth Form Film Society, Advanced Chemistry, Archery, Art, Ballet/Dance, Badminton, Basketball, Brass Group, Canoeing, Chamber Choir, Chess, Choir, Climbing, Community Service, Disability Sport, Drama, Fencing, Fitness, Golf, Indoor Cricket, Jazz Band, Mandarin Chinese, Modern Language Film Society, Music Practice, Music Theory, Percussion Group, Shooting, Stage Management, String Group, String Quartet, Technology, Wado Kai Karate and Young Enterprise. The Duke of Edinburgh's Award Scheme has been popular for many years and the majority of pupils gain at least a Bronze award.

Overseas Travel is frequent and extensive. In recent years tours or expeditions have taken place to Beijing, Canada, Japan, Nepal, New York, Shanghai, Tibet and Barbados as well as a number of European destinations.

Careers. Three members of staff also serve in the Careers department which also enlists the help of the Independent Schools Careers Organisation as well as the local Careers organisations. Former pupils return annually for Careers evenings and in this the Old Breconian Association is very helpful.

Entrance. Pupils are admitted at the age of 11 and 13 following the school's own entrance papers in English and Mathematics plus an IQ test, school report and interview. These tests are usually held in February. The majority of 11 year old entrants come from State Primary Schools, those at 13 from Preparatory schools when, instead of the Common Entrance examination, pupils face the same entrance procedures as at 11. Boys and girls enter the Sixth Form on the basis of GCSE grade estimates, an IQ test and an interview.

Term of Entry. Pupils are accepted in the Michaelmas, Lent and Summer terms.

Scholarships. (*see Scholarship Entries section*). The maximum value of scholarships is half fees. Scholarships are available for entry aged 11, 13 and 16. At 11 the scholarships are awarded for Academic, Music and Sporting prowess. At 13 additionally for all-rounders, Art and Science. At Sixth Form on the same basis as at 13.

Bursaries are available at all ages and are subject to a means-test. Fees remissions are available for sons and daughters of Clergy, children of Service Personnel and for the sons and daughters of those currently in the teaching profession.

Fees per term (2008-2009). Years 7 and 8: Day £3,870; Boarders £5,330. Years 9–13: Day £4,405; Boarders £6,810.

Charitable status. Christ College, Brecon is a Registered Charity, number 525744. Its aims and objectives are to provide a fully rounded education for boys and girls between the ages of 11 and 18.

Christ's Hospital

Horsham West Sussex RH13 7LS
Tel: 01403 211293
Fax: 01403 211580
e-mail: enquiries@christs-hospital.org.uk
website: www.christs-hospital.org.uk

***Head Master*: John Franklin**, BA, MEd

Deputy Heads:
B Vessey, BA, MA
Mrs J Thomson, BA

Chaplain: (*to be appointed*)

Assistant Staff:
P A Andersen, BA
J Anderson, BA
Dr P Attwell, PhD
Miss J Azancot, BA
*R S Baker, BEd
(*Mrs R Brading, BA, MA, PhD*)
†Mrs E A Callaghan
T J Callaghan, BMus, LRAM
J B Callas, BSc
R M Castro, BSc
†G N Chandler, BA
Miss M Ciechanowicz, BA
A Cowley, BA
†Mrs J Davey
*S Davey, BSc, MA
*P Deller, BA
Mrs V Durkan, BA
S T Eason, BA, MIL
Miss C Farquharson-Roberts, BA
*Mrs M A Fleming, BA
*†N M Fleming, BA, DipArch, LRPS
J Forster, FRCH
Miss S Gamba, BA
M J Gladding, BSc
D Griffiths, BSc
B C W Grindlay, MA
Mrs E J Grindlay, MA
E Hansen, BA
P J P Heagerty, MA
*J Herbert, BA, PhD
H P Holdsworth, BA, CertEd
P D Holland, BA
V R Holme, BEd
†I B Howard, MA
Mrs C E Jacques, BSc
M R Jennings, BA, PhD
Dr E Keane, PhD
†D M L Kirby, BA
*K S Leadbeater, HDD
Miss F Mackenzie, MA
*P S Maddren, BSc, PhD
*S Mason, BSc
A Mayhew, BSc
*J Mayhew, BA, MA
K McArtney, BA
†Mrs D McCulloch, MSc
F McKenna, BTech
Miss H Morrell, BSc
†S J O'Boyle, BSc, ARCS
*M J Overend, MA
†A R B Phillips, BA
M J Potter, MBE, BEd
J Pybus, BA
†*Mrs E A Robinson, BA
Miss V Rowcroft, MA
Mrs H Rowland-Jones
*M Russell, BSc
A Saha, MA, BA
D P Saunders, BA
Miss C Shephard, BA
*Miss J M Simmonds, BSc
*A L Smith, BSc
S Sookhun, BSc, PhD
†Mrs D J Stamp, BEd
*I N Stannard, BA
*R W Stuart, MA, PhD
S Taylor
†Miss L E A Thornton, MA
S M Titchener
I H Torkington, MA
A Turner
J Turner, BSc
†S W Walsh, MA
T W Whittingham, BA, LTCL (*Bandmaster*)
†A M Williams, BSc
*Mrs J A Williams, BSc
C W W Wilson, BA
Mrs H Wilson, BSc
Miss S L Wilson, BA
†A R Wines, MA, PhD
Mrs L Wyld, MA
Mrs A J Yates, BSc
†W J M Yates, BSc

Clerk: P Tuckwell

Bursar: M R H Lower

Admissions Registrar: Mrs G Udeshi

Head Master's Assistant: Mrs C Clark

CHRIST'S HOSPITAL was founded in the City of London by King Edward VI in 1552. In 1902 the boys moved to Horsham, where they were joined by the girls from their Hertford school in 1985.

Christ's Hospital is now a fully co-educational 11–18 boarding school for up to 850 pupils set in over 1000 acres of magnificent Sussex countryside. Its very substantial Foundation allows it to maintain the charitable purposes of its Founder so that currently almost all pupils are subsidised in some degree; 14% are educated free of charge. Parental contributions are means-tested annually and range between nil and £19,752 (only 3%). Substantial reductions are available for siblings.

The normal age of entry is at 11 (into Year 7). Candidates for admission sit an initial assessment in November and, if successful, are invited for a residential assessment in the January before the academic year of entry, taking a number of tests and experiencing the atmosphere of a full boarding school. All candidates have to show they can respond positively to the academic challenges of a school which in due course will expect them successfully to take 11 GCSEs, followed by 4 AS Levels and 3 A2s. About 40% of entrants each year who have gained 'Presentations' are automatically offered places if they qualify academically. The remaining places are awarded competitively but, in the allocation of all places, the need of the candidate for an assisted place at a boarding school is an important factor. There is also a limited number of places, usually about 25, in the Lower Sixth, subject to assessment. Details on admissions and the presentation system can be obtained from the Admissions Office.

Christ's Hospital has remarkable facilities for all aspects of its life. Two new Boarding Houses have been completed for occupation by Grecians (Year 13) and all the other sixteen Houses, for boys or girls between 11 and 17, are being refurbished. These facilities join an already well-provided school, with an exceptional theatre, an extensive sports centre with swimming pool, gym, sports hall, squash and fives courts, and an astroturf. The original 1902 buildings include a noble chapel and imposing Dining Hall and Big School, each of which can accommodate the entire school and staff.

The school has a distinguished academic record, numbering four former heads of Oxford colleges among its former pupils. Other Old Blues include Samuel Taylor Coleridge, Charles Lamb, Edmund Blunden, Constant Lambert, Barnes Wallis, Sir Colin Davis, Charles Hazlewood and Bernard Levin. Notable aspects of the school's life include its music, art, sport, drama and community action.

The academic programme is compatible with the National Curriculum but not constrained by it. Emphasis is placed on encouraging each pupil to become a confident and independent learner, assisted by an extensive ICT network and an excellent library. The normal day is a busy blend of lessons, activities, games, meals, rehearsals, tutorials, private study and social time. Pupils become responsible in the allocation and use of their time. In addition to the support of House staff, the two Chaplains and an active peer-support group, each pupil in Year 9 and above has an individual tutor to assist with academic advice, learning and life skills. The Chapel provides a blend of corporate and voluntary services during the week which form an important aspect of the life of the school community. An energetic programme of hobbies and adventurous activities, including Scouts, Duke of Edinburgh's Award and Cadet Force, which gives pupils extensive opportunities for involvement in holidays too, is seen as an integral part of the educational provision of the School. Pupils receive extensive career guidance and nearly all leavers go on to university.

The Boarding House is a major focal point for pupils, who have generous personal space appropriate for study, as well as many social and recreational areas. The youngest are in groups of four in House and the top years have individual study-bedrooms. Each House has a resident Housemaster or Housemistress, a tutor and a matron. The Health Centre is served by three qualified nurses and the school doctors visit daily. Every third weekend pupils are encouraged to visit parents or friends, but arrangements are made to look after those who choose to stay in School.

Charitable status. Christ's Hospital Foundation is a Registered Charity, number 306975. It aims to provide outstanding education and care for children from all walks of life. Parents contribute according to their means.

Churcher's College

Petersfield Hampshire GU31 4AS
Tel: 01730 263033
Fax: 01730 231437
e-mail: enquiries@churcherscollege.com
website: www.churcherscollege.com

The College was founded in 1722 by a local philanthropist, Richard Churcher, who provided an endowment for boys to be taught English, Mathematics and Navigation in preparation for apprenticeships with the East India Company. The school relocated to more spacious grounds and accommodation in 1881. The College roll is 980 pupils. The Sixth Form totals 160 and the Junior Department (ages 4 to 11 years) totals 228.

The school is fully co-educational.

Motto: *'Credita Cœlo'* – Entrusted to Heaven

Governing Body:
M J Gallagher, DipArch Hons, RIBA, MIOD, FIMgmt (*Chairman*)
F W Parvin, ACIB (*Vice-Chairman*)
Mrs J Bloomer, LLB
Mrs D Cornish, BA, MLitt
P Dacam, BA
Mrs C Herraman-Stowers
M Leigh, BA, FCA
Mrs S M Lowson, RSCN, RGN, DMS, MSc
R May
A P Phillips, BDS
C J Saunders, MA
Ms A J Spirit, BA

***Headmaster*: S H L Williams**, BSc, MA

Deputy Heads:
P W Sutton, MA, PGCE
J A Hewitt, MBA, BA

Head of Sixth Form: Mrs V A Godeseth, MA, PGCE

Director of Studies: R J Lynn, BA, PGCE

Senior Teacher (*Staff*): Mrs S M J Dixon, BSc, PGCE
Senior Teacher (*Pastoral*): Mrs J E Jamouneau, BEd

Creative & Performing Arts Faculty:
Director of Music: B D Gudgeon, MA, BA
Head of Art: A Saralis, BA, AT Cert
Head of Drama: Miss K Chapman, BA, PGCE
Head of Physical Education: K F Donovan, CertEd
Director of Adventurous Activities: M A Eaton, BEd
Mrs S E Bates Little, BA, PGCE
D R Cox, BA
Mrs V E Dewing, BA
Mrs C Eaton, CertEd (*Head of Girls' Physical Education*)
Miss L Howe, BSc
Mrs D L Knight, BSc (*Head of Sports Studies*)

English Faculty:
Head of Faculty: Dr D P Cave, BA, PhD
Mrs L Blackman, BEd, RSADip
Mrs S Herrington, BA
J A Hillier, BA
Miss L E Jenkinson, BA
Ms C Reynolds, BEd
Mrs S M Weiss, BA, DipSocAdmin

Humanities Faculty:
Head of Faculty: Mrs J R Grill, BA MA, DMS (*Head of Religion & Philosophy*)
Head of Classics: J Hegan, BA
Head of Economics & Business Studies: P Ratinckx, BA
Head of Geography: D J Nighy, BSc
Head of History: J E Paget-Tomlinson, BA
W Baker, BA
Mrs S M J Dixon, BSc (*Senior Teacher, Staff*)
J A Hewitt, MBA, BA (*Deputy Head*)
Mrs D J Link, BA
Miss J A Parkinson, BA
Mrs D Pont, BA, DMS
K J Scott, BA

Mathematics Faculty:
Head of Faculty: Mrs T L Greenaway, BSc (*Head of Mathematics*)
Mrs M Buckle, BSc
Mrs B A Erith, BSc
Mrs H B G Groves, BA
Miss A Ladbury, MA
R J Lynn, BA (*Director of Studies*)

Modern Languages Faculty:
Head of Faculty: Mrs R P Smith, BA (*Head of French*)
Head of German: I M Crossman, BA (*Deputy Head of Sixth Form*)
Spanish Co-ordinator: Miss B J d'Inverno, BA
Mrs L E Gibson, MA
Miss I Brunet, MA
Mrs V A Godeseth, MA, PGCE (*Head of Sixth Form*)
Miss S Kean, BA
Mrs K A Shaw, BA
P W Sutton, MA (*Deputy Head*)

Science Faculty:
Head of Faculty: Mrs J B Millard, BSc, ARCS (*Head of Biology*)
Head of Chemistry: D J Dunster, BA
Head of Physics: M C Kelly, BSc
Dr T J K Dilks, BSc, BA Ed, DPhil, CBiol, MIBiol
R M Hoe, BSc
Mrs J E Jamouneau, BEd (*Senior Teacher, Pastoral*)
Dr R K Jeffreys, BSc, PhD
A F Robertson, MSc
Mrs F J Sefton-Smith, BSc
J G Yugin-Power, BSc

Technology Faculty:
Head of Faculty: M Parrish, BSc, DipArch (*Head of Design & Technology*)
Head of ICT: Mrs V J Farrar, HNC, BA
M J B Adams, BEd
Mrs C Lines, BA

Junior School
Head of Junior School: Mrs S M Rivett, CertEd, Dip Drama

Deputy Head: Mrs P Yugin-Power, BSc, MA Ed, QTS (*Class 6Y Teacher*)
Senior Mistress: Mrs J Ross, CertEd (*Class 4R Teacher*)
Head of Infant Department: Miss K M Humphreys, BEd (*Class 2 Teacher*)
Middle School Coordinator: Mrs S J Moore, ARCM, GRSM, PGHCE (*Class 4M Teacher*)
Upper School Coordinator: A R Greenaway, BEd, MA Ed (*Class 5G Teacher*)

Miss H Parry, BA, PGCE (*Class R Teacher*)
C Taylor, BSc (*Class 1 Teacher*)
Miss P Kirby, BEd (*Class 3K Teacher*)
Mrs N J Munro, CertEd (*Class 3M Teacher*)
Mrs A J Evans, BEd, DMus (*Class 5E Teacher*)
G Melrose, BA, PGCE (*Class 6M Teacher*)
Mrs S Bint, GMus RNCM, PGCE (*Music Teacher*)
Mrs R Cameron, CertEd, DipSpLD (*Learning Support*)

Librarians:
Mrs L M Robbins, BSc, MIEH
Dr R C Dunn, BSc, PhD

Bursar: D T Robbins, BSc, FCCA

Admission. The normal ages of admission to the Senior School are 11+ and 16+, and 4+ and 7+ in the Junior School after Churcher's assessment in the Spring Term. However, if vacancies exist, pupils are considered for admission at other ages.

A prospectus and application form, with details of fees, are available from the Headmaster.

The Sixth Form. Students are prepared for GCE A and AS Levels.

A wide combination of choices is offered from English, History, Geography, Economics, French, German, Spanish, Latin, Art & Design, Music, Drama, Philosophy & Ethics, Business Studies, Mathematics, Further Mathematics, Physics, Chemistry, Biology, Classical Civilisation, Design & Technology, Sport and Physical Education and ICT. All students take a course to prepare them for AS Level General Studies.

There is a fully-equipped Sixth Form Centre, for both study and recreation, a floor of the Library dedicated to Sixth Form private study, an excellent Careers Library and full-time Careers Officer and specialist Sixth Form teaching rooms and ICT facilities.

Years 1–5. From the 11+ entry all pupils follow a common academic programme comprising Mathematics, English, French, Physics, Chemistry, Biology, Latin, Classical Civilisation, Geography, Religion and Philosophy, Music, Art, Design & Technology, ICT, Drama and PE. In Year 2 an additional Modern European language (German or Spanish) is added to the programme. All pupils follow a broad curriculum and are not asked to specialise until they reach GCSE. All pupils follow GCSE courses in Mathematics, English, Science, a Modern Language, a Humanity and at least 2 additional optional subjects.

Pupils are tested and examined regularly with formal assessment procedures each half term and each end of term.

Facilities. Churcher's academic facilities include impressive purpose-built teaching accommodation, ICT suites, drama studios, art and design studios, design technology workshops, music centre and science block. Sports facilities include a swimming pool, sports halls and on-site tennis courts, netball courts, rugby pitches, all weather hockey pitches and cricket squares. Churcher's has the facilities and resources to support an extensive range of extra-curricular activities. The Sixth Form enjoys extensive recreational and teaching facilities. The Junior School is situated on its own spacious 10 acre site in Liphook, close to Petersfield.

Games and other Activities. The major sports played are Rugby, Hockey, Netball, Cricket and Rounders. There are also facilities for Badminton, Basketball, Volleyball, Tennis, Athletics, Aerobics and Cross-country, to name but a few. The School has a strong CCF unit with Army, Air Force and Naval Sections, and a flourishing Duke of Edinburgh's Award programme. Other activities include Mountain Biking, Canoeing, Gliding, Climbing, Adventurous Training, Young Enterprise Companies, Dance, Karate, Fencing, Football, Sailing, Horse-riding, Bridge, Chess, Debating, Drama and Photography.

Music and dance are both very strong in the school with School and House plays produced regularly and a wide range of out-of-school activities. The school also has an orchestra, wind band and choir and many more ensembles.

Careers. The College has a full-time Careers Adviser on the staff and regular visits are made by other professional Career Advisers. Talks are given to pupils in the Third Form and above, and individual interviews are arranged.

A **Parents' Association** was formed in 1967 and meetings are held each term.

Fees per term (2008-2009). Senior School £3,450; Junior School £2,195–£2,340. Fees include charges for examination fees and text books, but exclude lunches and individual music lessons.

Charitable status. Churcher's College, Petersfield, Hampshire is a Registered Charity, number 307320. Its aims and objectives are to provide a school for boys and girls between the ages of 4 and 18 in the Parish of Petersfield.

City of London Freemen's School

Ashtead Park Surrey KT21 1ET
Tel: 01372 277933
Fax: 01372 276165
e-mail: headmaster@clfs.surrey.sch.uk
website: www.clfs.surrey.sch.uk

The City of London Freemen's School was founded at Brixton by Warren Stormes Hale in 1854. It is one of 3 schools governed and maintained by the City of London Corporation. It removed to Ashtead Park in 1926.

Motto: '*Domine dirige nos*'

The Board of Governors:

Chairman: R A Eve, Deputy
Deputy Chairman: J A Bennett

Aldermen:
David Mauleverer
Jeffrey Evans

Common Councilmen:
J W Brewster, OBE
R A H Chadwick
B N Harris
M Henderson-Begg
Mrs W Mead
D J L Mobsby, MBE, Deputy
Mrs J Owen, MBE, Deputy
J L Simons
P J Willoughby, JP, Deputy
J H Spanner
W H Dove

Co-opted:
F M Bramwell
R J Fox
Mrs V Littlechild
Sir Clive Martin

Clerk to the Governors: Gemma Goulding

***Headmaster*: P MacDonald**, MA Oxon

Deputy Head: Mrs V E Buckman, BSc

Head of Junior School: I D Thorpe, BA Ed, MA Ed
Head of Upper School: Mrs E E Guest, BA
Head of Sixth Form: M G Hearne, MA

Assistant Staff:
* *Head of Department/Subject*

Art & Design:
*T J Rees, BA
Mrs R Houseman, BA

Business Studies & Economics:
*Mrs P A Brooks, MBA
Mrs R Sullivan, BA

Classics:
*A Chadwick, BA
M G Hearne, MA
Miss R Gregory, BA

Computing & Information Technology:
*R Crooks, BSc
Miss H L Crow, BSc, MEd

Design Technology:
*A D Kew, BEng
M J Collier, BEd (**Electronics & Technology*)
Mrs M A Smith, BEd (**Food Technology*)
D F Treloar, BEd
Mrs H Stratford, CertEd

Drama:
*P M Tong MA
Ms S M Chamberlain-Webber, BA

English:
*I Bentley, MA
Mrs J E Bathard-Smith, BA, MA
C E Bloomer, BA
Mrs E E Guest, BA
M G Hearne, MA
Mrs A M Sloper, BA
Mrs A R Trehearn, BA
Miss R Gregory, BA

Geography:
*J N Williams, BA
Miss C H Hinton, BSc
Mrs P J Stumbles, BSc
Mrs H M Williams, BA (**General Studies*)

History:
*A J Wright, BA, MA
Mrs R E Joss, BA
Mrs K S Edwards, BA
B J Lewis, BA

Mathematics:
*Mrs R M Hobbs, BSc, MEd
E Bramhall, BSc
Mrs M A Cast, BSc
Miss A K Gillespie, BSc
Mrs C A Inns, BA
Mrs E C Newhouse, MA
R G Retzlaff, BSc, BEd, MPhil

Modern Languages:
*Mrs S E Hankin, BA (**German*)
Ms L K Burningham, BA
Miss J T Desouches, MT
Mrs L A Headon, BA
Mrs C J Leighton, BA
Mrs C A Salisbury, BA (**Spanish*)
Miss L R Vickers, MA (**French*)
Mrs B C Wheatley, BA
Mrs M Willis-Jones, LFL

Music & Music Techology:
*P M Dodds, BA (*Director of Music*)
Miss N Z Krawec, BMus
M J Bird, GNSM, MTC

Physical Education:
*W T Deighton, BEd (**Boys Games*)
Ms K Ridley, BA (**Girls Games*)
Miss S L Bone, BEd
J S Gibson, BA (**Junior PE*)
Miss N C Higgins, BSc
J G Moore, BA (**A Level Sports Studies*)
Mrs L J Shaill, BEd

Politics & Sociology:
*K D Bloor, BA MA, MPhil

Psychology:
*Miss J C Vinall, BSc, MSc

Religious Education:
*Revd D F Rutherford, BA
Miss R Gregory, BA
A N Illingworth, BA

Science:
*J D Hallam, BSc (**Physics*)
Mrs V E Buckman, BSc
Miss V I Chong, BSc
Mrs R M Fox, BSc
Mrs S E Fraser, BEd
Mrs J S Hawkes, BSc
Mrs H M Irwin, BEd
I G Knowles, BSc (**Biology*)
P A Longden, MA
Mrs S J Mitchell, BSc, MSc (**Chemistry*)
Mrs S Meek, BSc
M A Newcome, BSc, MA Ed
R E Pratt, MA
Mrs K S Standish, BSc

Junior School:
Miss N S Chambers, BA
Mrs J E Cooper, BEd
Mrs N C David, BEd
S P Davies, BA
Miss R S Filby, BA
Mrs S Gillespie, BA
V E Ielpi, BPrimEd
Mrs L J Jowitt, MA (*Assistant Head Junior School*)
R A Metcalf, BA
Ms F I Moncur, BEd
Miss C A Page, BEd
Mrs M Restall, BA
Mrs E C Smith, LLB
Mrs V C Symonds, BSc
M P Valkenburg, HDE
Mrs L I Winter, BA
Mrs P G Whiteley, BSc

Senior Careers Advisor: B J Hall, MSc, HNC, DipCG, DMS, CMS

Learning Support Manager: A Illingworth, BA

Chaplain: Revd D F Rutherford, BA

Visiting Instrumental Staff:
Miss V Barnes, MMus, BA
Miss S Bixley, ARAM
Ms N Berg, BA, MA, ARCM
Miss R Chappell, AGSM
Miss G Cook, LRAM, GRSM
G Gottlieb, BA, MMus
C Hurn, BA, MusEd, LGSM
Miss K Keay, BMus
J O'Carroll, BMus
Miss E Pappalardo, BMus, MMus
N Perona-Wright, LRAM, LTCL, LLCM TD
Ms H Pritchard, BA, LTCL
G Russell, Hon FLCM, GRSM, LRAM, ARCM
P Smith
J Wallace
D Ward, AGSM

Music Department Administrator: Mrs L Loughlin, BA

Cricket Professional: N M Stewart
Cricket Consultant: M J Stewart

Swimming Coach: R Garfield

Bursar: Mrs Y Dunne, BA, ACA

Administrative Staff:
Assistant Bursar (Finance): Mrs A Wills
Assistant Bursar (Administration & Human Resources): Mrs A J Atkins, BCom, MCIPD
Marketing and Admissions Manager: B Crossan, BA
Catering and Domestic Services General Manager: S Thorne
Housemistress, Girls' Boarding House: Mrs L J Retzlaff
Housemaster, Boys' Boarding House: B J Lewis, BA
Assistant Housemistress (Girls): Miss S Bone, BEd
Assistant Housemaster (Boys): C E Bloomer, BA
House Parent (Boys): Mrs P Lewis
Headmaster's Secretary: Mrs D Emerson
Deputy Head's Secretaries: Mrs A Stephenson, BSc; Mrs S M Davis
Junior School Secretaries: Mrs G Anklesaria, Mrs S McCarthy
Senior School Secretaries: Mrs M J Bloor
Admissions Secretaries: Miss H Choudhry; Mrs H Langner, BEd
Bursar's Secretary: Mrs S Broughton
Assistant Bursars' Secretary: Mrs K Hills
Marketing Coordinator: Mrs J Guillem
Reprographics Officer: N Fairhurst
Reprographics Assistant: S Butcher
Finance Secretaries: Mrs A Thomas, Mrs G Bilsland
School Doctor: Dr G Carver MB, BCh
School Sisters: Mrs A Eversfield, SRN; Mrs C Quick, RSCN, RNMH
Senior Librarian: Mrs S Dawes, BLib, MCLIP
Assistant Librarians: Mrs L J Retzlaff, Mrs J Morris

The School numbers 860 – approximately equal numbers of boys and girls – including up to 20 girl and 25 boy boarders. There are 491 pupils over the age of 13, including a Sixth Form of approximately 207. The School stands in 57 acres of playing fields and parkland between Epsom and Leatherhead with easy access to Heathrow and Gatwick via the M25. Buildings include a central Georgian Mansion containing the Girls' Boarding House, Dining Hall and Music Department. Other facilities include a modern Assembly Hall and heated 6 lane swimming pool, a floodlit all-weather pitch and a Sports Hall complex completed in 1995. The School Medical Centre is attached to the Boys' Boarding House. The recent multi-million pound building programme includes the new Sixth Form Centre (opened 1997), a new Art and Design Centre (September 1998) and a new Science and Technology Centre (January 1999). New teaching facilities for all subject Departments were completed with the opening of the Haywood Centre in September 2000. This provides classrooms, a new Library/Resource Centre and multimedia facilities, as well as two Senior Computer Laboratories and the Careers Department. A new Studio Theatre was opened in October 2001, providing an auditorium for all productions, recitals, concerts and lecture facilities. An adventure playground for Junior School pupils was completed in 2003. In the same year, the swimming pool was refurbished and the all-weather pitch was replaced, bringing both up to modern national representative standards.

Junior School. Since September 1988 the Junior School, ages 7–13, has been accommodated in a new complex in Ashtead Park. (*See separate IAPS entry.*) This provides 18 classrooms with 3 classes of 20 pupils in each year group and therefore up to 360 pupils in total. The Junior School is fully integrated within the framework and policies of the whole school and other facilities include specialist rooms for Art and Design, Science, Music and an integrated Technology Centre as well as a large Assembly Hall and Library.

See also Junior School entry in IAPS section.

Organisation and Entry. The School is divided into 2 sections but is administered as a single unit. The Junior Department has its own specially trained staff and its own self-contained building, but otherwise all staff teach throughout the School.

Junior entry is by the School's own competitive examination at 7+ (normally in late January).

Senior School entry is by passing the Common Entrance examination, normally at the age of 13+, or by the School's own 13+ examination. Screening tests for Senior School entry have been introduced for Year 6 and Year 7 pupils as demand for places exceeds the available spaces at 13+. Junior School pupils may expect to transfer satisfactorily to the Senior School at 13+ without sitting a special examination.

Sixth Form entry is by obtaining good GCSE grades with a minimum of 50 points from nine subjects, 55 points from 10 subjects with at least 8 passes at GCSE (grade C or better) including English and Mathematics. Grade B must be obtained in any subject to be studied at AS or A Level, with grade A needed in French and Mathematics and strongly preferred in Physics. At least four grade B passes must be obtained at GCSE in appropriate subjects if new subjects are being studied at AS level. (A*=8, A=7, B=6, C=5)

Foundation entry is open to orphan children of Freemen at any age from 7+ to 16+, subject to satisfactory academic potential.

(Except for Foundationers, it is not necessary for applicants to be children of Freemen of the City.)

Curriculum. The first four years (7+ to 10+ in Years 3 to 6) are largely taught by class teachers up to Key Stage 2 following the broad outlines of the National Curriculum. Up to the age of about 14 all pupils have substantially the same curriculum which comprises English, French/German/Spanish, Mathematics, Physics, Chemistry, Biology, History, Geography, Religious Education, Design Technology, Information Technology, Food Technology, Art and Music. Thereafter, apart from a common core of English, French or German or Spanish, Mathematics and the 3 separate Sciences, selection is made, depending on choice and ability, for the course to GCSE from 15 other subjects including Spanish, German, French, Computer Studies, Drama, Electronics, Latin, Sociology and Design Technology so that the average pupil will offer 10 subjects. The principles of the National Curriculum are followed at all levels. Personal, Social and Health Education is included in the curriculum at all levels.

Sixth Form courses may include the following main AS and A Level subjects: Mathematics, Further Mathematics, Physics, Chemistry, Biology, Electronics, English, History, Geography, Politics, Classical Civilisation, French, German, Spanish, Business Studies, Computing, Drama, Art, Music, Physical Education, Food Technology, Design Technology, Music Technology, Information Technology, Economics, Psychology and Philosophy and Theology. All pupils are required to include some Physical Education and General Studies.

The School has an excellent academic record. Recent GCSE pass rates have exceeded 99%, as have the A level pass rates, and nearly all leavers go on to degree courses at universities or other higher education institutes.

Equipment and methods include modern aids and techniques. Computer Studies is well equipped and established, with specialist rooms in each of the Junior and Senior Schools, as well as substantial departmental IT resources as appropriate.

Each pupil is allocated to a House comprising a cross-section of boys and girls, both day and boarding, throughout the School. House teams compete in all forms of sport as well as Music and Drama.

Games. *For Boys*: Principally Rugby, Cricket, Athletics and Swimming. Badminton, Basketball, Hockey, Squash, Tennis are also available.

For Girls: Principally Hockey, Tennis, Athletics and Swimming. Badminton, Netball and Squash are also available.

There is a very wide choice of extra-curricular activities throughout the School. The Duke of Edinburgh's Award Scheme is a very popular option in the Senior School.

Fees per term (2008-2009). Tuition: £4,560 (Senior School); £3,395–£3,576 (Junior School). Boarding: £2,697 (in addition to tuition fees). Instrumental Music lessons: £192.

Scholarships and Exhibitions. (*see Scholarship Entries section*). Scholarships and Exhibitions valued at up to one half of tuition fees are awarded at the main entry points. These awards are open to both internal and external applicants.

City of London School

Queen Victoria Street London EC4V 3AL
Tel: 020 7489 0291
Fax: 020 7329 6887
e-mail: headmaster@clsb.org.uk
website: www.clsb.org.uk

The City of London School occupies a unique Thameside location in the heart of the capital and has 905 day boys between the ages of 10 and 18 from all social and ethnic groups and from all parts of the capital. It traces its origin to bequests left for the education of poor boys in 1442 by John Carpenter, Town Clerk of the City. The Corporation of London was authorised by Act of Parliament in 1834 to use this and other endowments to establish and maintain a School for boys. This opened in 1837 in Milk Street, Cheapside, and moved to the Victoria Embankment in 1883. In 1986 the School moved again, to excellent purpose-built premises provided by the Corporation on a fine riverside site in the City, to which a new Design Technology building was added in 1990. The school lies on the riverside with St Paul's Cathedral to the north and the Globe Theatre and Bankside Tate Gallery of Modern Art across the Thames to the south. The School's Board of Governors is a committee of the Court of Common Council, the Corporation of London's governing body and four independent members.

Chairman of Governors: W Dove, MBE, JP

***Headmaster*: D R Levin**, BSc, MA, FRSA

Second Master: G S Griffin, BA
Assistant Headmaster: C B Fillingham, MA
Director of Admissions: D R Heminway, BD
Director of Staff Development: J B Cook, BSc
Director of Studies: Miss N H Murphy, BA

Head of Sixth Form: G J Dowler, MA, JP
Deputy Head of Sixth Form (*Administrative*): Miss Z Connolly
Deputy Head of Sixth Form (*Pastoral*): N P McMillan, BEd
Head of Fifth Year: S S Fernandes, BSc, MA
Deputy Head of Fifth Year: O J Davies
Head of Fourth Year: B L Jones, BA
Deputy Head of Fourth Year: BA G W Dawson, BSc
Head of Third Year: G P L Farrelly
Deputy Head of Third Year: R D Sykes
Head of Second Year: J M Norman
Deputy Head of Second Year: K E Wratten
Head of First Form and OG: Miss V W Hornick
Deputy Head of First Form and OG: C A Hudson

* *Head of Department*

Classics:
*T R A Reader, MA
B L Jones, BA
W Ellis-Rees, MA
Miss C L Rose, BA
Miss Z Connolly, MA
J Pile, BA

Design & Visual Arts:
*R Pomeroy, BA
G P L Farrelly, BA

Drama:
M Biltcliffe, BA (*Director of Drama*)
Mrs S Dobson, BA

Economics:
*L M Redit, BSc
A Wingrove, BSc
N P McMillan, BEd

English:
*G Phillipson, MA
J B Keates, MA, FRSL
R S Blanch, MA
S McConnell, BA, BMus
T M J Wingate, BA, MEd
J M Norman, MA
J T Williams, BA

Geography:
*M D Close, BA
D C Pike, BSc
O J Davies, BSc
P S Marshall, MA

History and Politics:
*A J V McBroom, BA
G S Griffin, BA
Miss N H Murphy, BA
Miss F N Bennett, BA
Miss V W Hornick, BA
A J Bracken, BA
P N Brooke, BA
Ms K Saunt, BA
D Flower, BA

Information Technology:
*Mrs S L Ralph, BA
Mrs A M MacDonagh, BSc

Mathematics:
*D R Eade, BA
J F Allman, MA
R P Hubbard, BSc
T E Duley, MA, MSc
D J Chamberlain, BSc, MSc
Miss C A Hudson, BSc
S S Fernandes, BSc, MA
S A Caldecott, BSc, MSc
J A Ratnasabapathy, MA
Miss C S Samuels, MA

Modern Languages:
*R Edmundson, BA
R J Reardon, BA, MPhil
A T Laidlaw, MA (*French*)
P A Allwright, MA
G J Dowler, MA
Mrs A J Heaf, BA, MA
Miss V Vincent, MA
Mrs V Smith, BA
Miss A L King, BA
R D Sykes, BA

Music:
*P Harrison, GLCM, MA
J Fitzgerald, BA
Miss J Jones, BA

Physical Education:
C J Smith, CertEd, BEd (*Director of on-site Sport*)
N F Cornwell, BEd (*Director of off-site Sport*)
M Kerr, BSc, MSc
B Silcock, BPE

Religious Education:
*J Silvester, BA
D R Heminway, BD
Miss A C Dixon, BA
Miss K E Wratten, BA

Science:
H R S Jones, BSc (**Physics*, **Science*)
N O Mackinnon, BSc, PhD (**Biology*)
Mrs P C McCarthy, BSc (**Chemistry*)
R F Davey, BSc, MSc
J Easingwood, CertEd, BA
J B Cook, BSc
C H Branch, BSc, MSc
C Pearce, BA, PhD (**Careers*)
N J Baglin, BSc (*Deputy Head of Careers*)
K Khand, BSc, PhD
R Mackrell, BSc
G W Dawson, BSc

Dr S Tracey, BA, PhD
Miss A Eastman, BSc
E Whitcombe, BSc
B Costley-White, BSc
K L Rogers, MChem

There are Visiting Music Teachers for Bassoon, Cello, Double Bass, French Horn, Flute, Guitar, Jazz, Oboe, Organ, Percussion, Piano, Saxophone, Singing, Trombone, Trumpet, Tuba, Viola, Violin.

Learning Support:
Miss A Ross-Scott, BSc, Hornsby DipSpLD
D W Dyke, BA

Library:
*D A Rose, BA, Dip Lib, ALA
Ms J Grantham, MA

Finance Manager: P Everett
Headmaster's Secretary: Mrs J Williams
Admissions Secretary: Mrs J Brown

Admissions. Pupils are admitted aged 10, 11, 13 and 16 (as on 1st September of year of entry), on the results of the School's own entrance examination held once a year in January. Those admitted into the Sixth Form are selected by interview only in February. Application forms for admission may be obtained from the Admissions Secretary at the School.

Fees per term (2008-2009). £4,089.

Entrance Scholarships. (*see Scholarship Entries section*). At least 30 Scholarships, Music Scholarships with a value of up to half of the school fee, and a number of minor awards, are awarded annually to candidates at all ages of entry. Candidates for entry to the School may also apply for Choristerships at the Temple Church or the Chapel Royal, St. James's (the choristers of both choirs are pupils at the School): choristers receive Choral Bursaries whose value is two-thirds of the school fee. Potential choristers may also take auditions and academic tests at the age of 8 or 9: successful applicants will be offered an unconditional place in the school for the year after their 10th birthday.

Sponsored Awards. The School offers a number of Sponsored Awards, up to full fees, to assist those parents of academically very bright boys, who otherwise could not contemplate private education. These awards are available only at 11+ and 16+.

Curriculum. All boys follow the same broad curriculum up to and including the Third Form. The First Form curriculum includes an introduction to the use of computers: and in the Third Form boys spend some eight afternoons throughout the year on educational visits to institutions and places of interest in and around the City. Latin and French are started by all in the First Form and two choices from Greek, Classical Civilisations and drama. German and Spanish may be added as options in the Third Forms. Fourth and Fifth Form boys take a core of English, Mathematics, three Sciences (the core subjects are all IGCSEs), and at least one Modern Foreign Language (which can include Russian) and choose three other subjects from a wide range of subjects available for study to GCSE. In the Sixth Form boys take a combination of A2 or AS level subjects together with the ECDL. The majority of the Senior Sixth finish with four A Levels and usually over fifty per cent get four grade As. Virtually all boys leaving the Sixth Form proceed to their first choice of Russell Group University or Medical School.

Games. The School's playing fields, at Grove Park in South London, offer excellent facilities for football, cricket, athletics, and tennis. Sporting facilities on the School site include a sports hall, a gymnasium with conditioning room, three squash courts, a fencing salle, and a 25-metre swimming pool. Particular success has been achieved in football, water polo, fencing, table tennis, basketball and badminton.

School Societies. There is a large number of School Societies, catering for a very wide range of interests. Every encouragement is given to benefit from the School's central position by participation in the cultural and educational life of London and of the City in particular. The School has a strong musical tradition; tuition is available in any instrument, and membership of the School choirs and orchestras is encouraged. Choristers of the Temple Church and of the Chapel Royal are educated at the School as bursaried scholars provided that they satisfy the entrance requirements. There is much interest in Drama, and the staff includes a full-time Director of Drama: the School has a fully-equipped Theatre and also a Drama Studio. There is a large CCF Contingent which boys may join from the age of 13 until 18, with Army, Naval and RAF Sections. There is also a successful community service programme.

There is a flourishing **The Old Boys' Society** known as the John Carpenter Club. Letters to the Secretary can be addressed to the School.

Council of Governors:
Dr R Willis, MA, BM, BCh (*Chairman*)
J Andrews, LLB
C Campbell
P Dallyn, FRICS, FAAV
Mrs D Geary
D M Green, MA Cantab (*Vice-Chairman, Education*)
P Killick
Mrs A Levey
Mrs G Mander
R Morgan
R H C Phillips, BA Hons, CertEd, LGSM
Brigadier J Rucker
Mrs R Stiven
Rt Revd Tim Thornton, MA

***Headmaster*: M G Cooke**, BEd, FCollP

Deputy Head: J R Carpenter, BA

Assistant Head: Mrs F M Bailey, BA, PGCE

Director of Teaching & Learning: A R West, BA, MA, PGCE

Head of Sixth Form & Senior Master: R A Chew, MA

Bursar: D Little, BA

Assistant Staff:
Mrs A J A Balasingam, CertEd, OCRCertSpLD
Miss O H Blain, BSc, PGCE
B Brackstone, BA, OCRCertSpLD
S Berryman, BMus, MMus, DipABRSM
S K Byrne, BA
Mrs H N Christmas, BA
Miss T S Cook, BA
Mrs E A Cooke, BEd, AdvDipECSN
Mrs D M Denning, BA, PGCE
R J Denning, BA
Revd A J H Edwards, BA, BTh
Mrs H M Farley, BEd, RSASpLD
M S Fraser, BA
H J Gibbons, BSc, PGCE
P D Hall-Palmer, BA, PGCE
A Hanson-Stewart, BSc, PGCE
Miss J E Hayes, BEd
D A Humphreys, BSc Tech
Mrs R M Hunter, CertEd, BA, RSACertSpLD
A Jancis, BSc, PGCE
Dr A P G Jancis, BA, PhD, MIBiol, PGCE
P K Jones, BA, PGCE
J J Kimber, BA, MA
Mrs J M Martin, Dip SteinerEd, RSADipSpLD
Mrs M May, BA, PGCE
C R Middle, BA
Mrs S-J Newland, BSc, PGCE
Miss K E O'Rourke, BA, PGCE
Mrs F Pattenden, BA, CertTEFL
A H Peters, DipAD, CertEd,
Mrs V Peevor, CertEd, OCRDipSpLD
A G Pienaar, MSc, HDE
D K Pigot, BMus, ARCM, LTCL, CertEd
P J Randall, BA, PGCE
J Reach, BEng, PGCE
Miss S-J Rhead, BSc, PGCE
Mrs A M Rigby, BA, PGCE
D I Rimmer, MA
E R Robeson, MA, PGCE
Mrs K Ross, BA, PGCE
S A Smith, BSc, PGCE
H P Stevenson, BA, PGCE
Miss C L Storey, BA, PGCE
Mrs S E Tew, CertEd, BA, OCRCertSpLD
Dr F M Thomason, BSc, PhD, OCNCertSpLD, PGCE
Mrs C Thompson , BA, PGCE

Clayesmore School

Iwerne Minster Blandford Forum Dorset DT11 8LL
Tel: 01747 812122
Fax: 01747 813187
e-mail: hmsec@clayesmore.com
website: www.clayesmore.com

Developing the unique gifts of every girl and boy

P M Warren, BSc
T P A Weaver, CertEd, AMBDA, OCRCertSpLD
A K P Young, BSc, PGCE

Administrative Staff:
Headmaster's Secretary & Registrar: Mrs M B McCafferty
Bursar's Secretary & Assistant Registrar: Mrs H de Bie
School Secretaries: Mrs R Rutherford, Mrs H Horley

House Matrons:
Mrs J Lilley (*Wolverton*)
Mrs W Everest (*Gate*)
Mrs A Goates (*King's*)
Mrs J Dalton (*Manor*)
Mrs J Williams (*Devine*)

Medical Officer: Dr P L Kreeger, MB, BS, DRCOG
Nurses: Mrs D Snooks, RGN, RSCN; Mrs J Morrism RGN, RSCN, HV
Assistant: Mrs H Sanger

Director of Sport & Enterprise: Mr C Humpage, BH, PGCE
Assistant Director of Sport & Enterprise: Mr R S Miller, BSc, PGCE
School Staff Instructor: Mr C Evans
Buildings & Estate Manager: Mr J Handley
Catering Manager: Mr N D'Allen, MCHIMA
School Shop Manager: Mrs T Higgins
Head Groundsman: Mr R Norris, BSc, DipEnv
Librarian Assistant: Mrs J-A Murphy

Clayesmore Prep School

Headmaster: R D H Geffen, BEd

Deputy Head: Mrs E L Reach, BEd
Director of Teaching & Learning: Mrs S J Moulton, BA Hons, PGCE
Head of Pre-Prep & Nursery: Mrs J E Bolger, CertEd

Assistant Staff:
Mrs B Barnes, CertEd, RSADipSpLD, AMBDA
Mrs R Beal, BA Hons, PGCE, AMBDA
C Birchill, CertEd
Dr S Bragg, BA, PhD
D J Browse, BA
Mrs R Byrne, BA Hons, PGCE
Mrs C Caiger, BA, PGCE, PGDip
Mrs S M Chinnock, BA, PGCE
Mrs J E Coplan, BMus, MA, PGCE
D A Harrison, BSc
Mrs S Hart, CertEd
R Leighton, BEd Hons
Mrs P-A Middle, BA, PGCE
N Moore, BEd
Mrs M M Oakley, CertEd
Mrs S Panton, BSc, MA, PGCE
Mrs E F Pogson, BEd
Mrs M Pond, BSc, MA, RSADipSpLD, AMBDA, AdvDipEd
Mrs P Price, CertEd
Mrs C Ritchie, BA
Mrs I Rose, BA, PGCE
Miss N Rowse, BEd, RSACertSpLD
J Smith, BMus Hons, PGCE
Mrs J Warburton, CertEd, RSACertSpLD
Mr G Weaver, BA
Mrs C J Weeks, CertEd, RSACertSpLD
C Whytehead, BEd
R Wilson, BA
Mrs S L Wilson, BEd
S Wilson

Pre-Prep and Nursery School:
Miss G Ankers, BA Hons, PGCE
Mrs A Cowley
Mrs J Findon
Miss N Hitt
Mrs H Martin
Mrs A Williams

Administrative & Pastoral:
Headmaster's Secretary & Registrar: Mrs L Greig
Assistant Registrar: Mrs S Morris
School Secretary: Mrs M Pitcher
Assistant School Secretary: Mrs H Young

Sister in charge: Mrs H Proctor, SEN
Deputy Sisters: Mrs S Millard, RGN; Mrs R Flute, RGN
Matrons: Mrs S Edgar; Mrs H Galley

Librarian: Mrs H Bignold, BLib, MA, MCLIP

Clayesmore is a flourishing co-educational school with Senior (13–18) and Preparatory ($2^1/_2$–13) departments on one beautiful 62-acre site. There are 412 pupils in the Senior School, nearly two-thirds of whom are boarders, and another 237 at the Prep School where 72 board. There is also a Nursery School.

The school was founded in 1896 (the Prep in 1929) and the two schools came together in 1975 when the Prep School joined the Senior School at Iwerne Minster, in its own, new, purpose-built accommodation. Clayesmore is very much one organisation yet with two schools, each with its own Headmaster, staff and separate teaching areas.

Buildings and Grounds. Facilities have been radically improved in recent years and generally are excellent. The main building functions very much as the school's headquarters. The upper floors are used entirely as a girls' boarding house – Wolverton – whilst on the ground floor may be found a fine library complete with up to the minute computer facilities for private study and research, as well as reception rooms which are used for a myriad of purposes throughout term time.

In 2002, the magnificent prize-winning Jubilee Building came into use. Three storeys high, this is a major academic building which provides eight science laboratories, two computer suites (networked to the library) and a lecture theatre as well as the new, highly acclaimed Learning Support Centre. The construction of the Jubilee Building has, in turn, allowed the school to improve the boys' boarding accommodation in Gate House which has been very beneficial.

A second important new building opened in September 2004. Named The Spinney Centre, after a former distinguished Chairman of Council, this comprises superb, state-of-the-art classrooms for Careers, Geography, History and Business Studies. The Design and Technology Department has also been extended.

There is a superb Sports Centre complete with gymnasia, 25-metre indoor pool, squash courts, modern fitness suite, four badminton courts and indoor cricket nets. To mark the Senior School's centenary in 1996, this was complemented with a full-sized, floodlit all-weather hockey pitch which also provides 12 tennis courts for summer use.

There is an excellent Music School and Art School, as well as the Chapel, built in 1956 as a memorial to the 81 Old Clayesmorians who gave their lives in the two World Wars. The parkland grounds are quite outstanding, with excellent playing fields, a lake, and wonderful views towards historic Hambledon Hill with its Saxon fort.

Houses and Pastoral Care. In the Senior School, there are five houses (three for boys and two for girls) each with resident, married House Staff, and resident Tutor. It is an important element of our pastoral care that boarding pupils and day pupils are together – there are no day houses. All pupils have a Tutor to oversee academic progress and help with the important decisions at various points in a pupil's school career. Clayesmore is a school with a striking family atmosphere and the School's comparatively small size enables the Headmaster and the staff to get to know the girls and boys well. Great attention is paid to the pastoral care of the pupils, not only through the House and Tutor system, but through the full extra-curricular programme as well.

Entry arrangements. Entrance to Clayesmore School is at 13 with entrants from preparatory schools taking the usual Common Entrance examination. For those entering from maintained schools, there are tests in English, Mathematics and Science. Girls and boys may join Clayesmore earlier by becoming members of Clayesmore Preparatory School and it is quite normal for new pupils to arrive aged 11 and undertake Years 7 and 8 at the Prep School. Each year, between 10 and 20 young people join us as Sixth Formers, and the total number in the Sixth Form is roughly 120.

Scholarships. Means-tested scholarships are available in the usual way and information on these is available from the School.

Academic work. Academically, pupils follow the usual pattern. Year 9 serves as a useful foundation year prior to GCSE courses getting underway in Years 10 and 11. Sixth Form students pursue four AS levels in the Lower Sixth, taking three of these on to A2 in the Upper Sixth. The trend at Clayesmore at present is for year groups of 90 or so pupils in Years 9–11 divided roughly into five groups of 18–20 pupils. There is setting in core subjects and French, Spanish and German are all offered through to A level. There is much emphasis in the Sixth Form on preparing students for the world beyond Clayesmore both at university and in careers generally, and the Head of Sixth Form coordinates a highly structured and most effective group of Sixth Form tutors.

It is very much at the centre of Clayesmore's philosophy that we pay close attention to the needs of the individual boy or girl both academically and in other spheres of life. For many years, the School has had a strong reputation for helping pupils with dyslexia.

Clayesmore Preparatory School. Clayesmore is fairly unusual in having its Prep and Senior Schools together and this is an added strength for many parents, particularly of boarders, who are keen to keep their children together in one place. The opportunity for a seamless transition at 13 is one that pupils and parents value highly. The Prep School has its own main building containing many of the classrooms including a colourful, well-stocked library and an excellent Information Technology suite, as well as all the boarding and pastoral facilities. It has its own laboratories, Design Technology and Art studios, and shares use of the Music School, Sports Centre, Dining Hall and Chapel. In September 2007 the Pre-Prep and Nursery moved into new accommodation with its own dedicated play area and they have their own teaching and support staff. In 2008 a brand new state-of-the-art building will be opened. This will comprise five classrooms which will accommodate Years 3 and 4 and two new science laboratories. Pupils in Years 3 and 4 have a form teacher, but enjoy specialist teachers and classrooms for music, French, art and ICT. Entrance to the Preparatory School may take place into any year group assuming a place is available, and is dependent upon interview with the Headmaster and a report from the present school.

See also Clayesmore Preparatory School entry in IAPS section.

The wider life at Clayesmore. Sport is very much a strength at Clayesmore. Rugby, Hockey, Cricket, Athletics, Netball, Swimming and Cross-Country, are the major sports in the Senior School, and badminton, squash, sailing and orienteering are also very popular and successful subsidiary sports.

Pupils in Years 10 and 11 benefit from membership of the School's Combined Cadet Force with many enthusiasts continuing as NCOs into the Sixth Form. There is a strong link between the CCF and the Duke of Edinburgh's Award Scheme which is in operation at the School. In the Sixth Form, those who are not involved in CCF have opportunities to take part in Community Service. There is a comprehensive and wide-ranging activities programme which operates throughout the week.

There is a high standard of music-making and drama throughout Clayesmore. Every encouragement is given to pupils of all ages to learn instruments, participate in group activities and sing in the choirs. There are all sorts of ensembles and new ones are formed to suit different pupil interests when necessary. The Theatre is a really practical, intimate space, and is used with great imagination not only for the various termly productions but also for the GCSE and A level Theatre Studies. Recently, some A level performances were filmed by an exam board as exemplar material representing top grade work for other schools to see.

Fees per term (2007-2008). Senior School: £7,910 (boarding), £5,788 (day). Preparatory School: £5,248–£5,751 (boarding), £2,100–£4,271 (day).

Charitable status. Clayesmore School Limited is a Registered Charity, number 306214. It exists for educational purposes.

Clifton College

Bristol BS8 3JH
Tel: 0117 3157 000
Preparatory School Headmaster: 0117 3157 502
Fax: 0117 3157 101
e-mail: admissions@clifton-college.avon.sch.uk
website: www.cliftoncollegeuk.com

Clifton College was founded in 1862, and is a Corporation by Royal Charter granted 16 March 1877.

Motto: '*Spiritus intus alit.*'

Council:
President: Professor J P Barron, MA, DPhil, FSA

Chairman: A R Thornhill, BA, QC

Joint Vice-Chairmen:
D N Tarsh, OBE, BA
P L Howell-Richardson, BA

Treasurer: C W Smith, FCA

N J B Cooper, MA, LLB
B J Hanson, CBE, FRICS
S R Lang, BSc, PhD
Mrs C Lear, BA
Mrs D A Moore, BA
A W Morgan, MA, MBA
R M Morgan, MA
C Pople, ACA, ATII
T S Ross, MA
P L M Sherwood, MA, MBA
A Streatfeild-James, MA
R S Trafford, MA
B Worthington, MA

Secretary and Bursar: Mrs L K J Hanson, BSc, ACA

***Head Master*: M J Moore**, MA

Deputy Head (*Pastoral*): J P Middleton, MA
Deputy Head (*Academic*): A Spencer, BA
Senior Master: S J M Reece, MA
Senior Mistress: Miss A C Tebay, BSc
Chaplain: Revd K Taplin
Director of Admissions: P C Hallworth, MA, MEd
Director of External Relations: Mrs F J W Hallworth, MA

Heads of Department:
A J Wilkie, BA (*Art*)
H Besterman, BA Hons Cantab (*Biology*)
J Bobby, BA (*Boys' Games*)
T M Greene, BA, DPhil (*Chemistry & Science*)
W Huntington, MA (*Classics*)
M R Barnacle, BA (*Design & Technology*)
R Morris, BA (*Director of Drama*)

A Ballance, BSc (*Economics & Business Studies*)
Miss S A Clarke, MA (*English*)
Mrs H J Mann, MA, MSc (*Geography*)
O G Lewis, MA (*German*)
Mrs L A Catchpole, BA (*Girls' Games*)
P G Lidington, BA (*History*)
D Dean, MA, PhD (*Information Technology*)
Mrs E Noble, BA (*Mandarin*)
G E Simmons, BSc (*Mathematics*)
L Siddons, MA (*Modern Languages*)
J Hills, BA (*Director of Music*)
A Reeves, BSc (*Physics*)
Mrs N D Bright, BA (*PSHE*)
Miss V Bateson, MA (*Psychology*)
D Janke, BA (*Religious Studies*)
B Trivic, BA (*French*)
Miss M Harris, BA (*Spanish*)
P Askew, BEd (*Director of Sport*)

Houses and Housemasters/mistresses:

Boys Boarding:
School House: J H Hughes, MA
Moberly's: A J O'Sullivan, BA
Wiseman's: W J Huntington, MA
Watson's: J P Noad, BEng

Girls Boarding:
Oakeley's: Mrs K A Jeffery, BSc
Worcester: Mrs A D Musgrove, MA
Hallward's: Mrs K Pickles, BA

Boys Day:
North Town: D M Rodgers
South Town: J S Tait, BA
East Town: J H Thomson-Glover, BA

Girls Day:
West Town: Mrs L A Catchpole, BA Ed

Clifton College was founded in 1862, and incorporated by Royal Charter in 1877. It is situated in the City of Bristol, on the edge of Clifton Down and not far from open country. The School is well placed to take advantage of the many cultural and educational activities of the City, and to gain much else of value from its civic and industrial life. There are friendly links with the University and with other schools of various types.

Admission. Boy and girl boarders and day pupils are normally admitted in September between the ages of 13 and 14, and most are required to pass the Common Entrance examination, which can be taken at their Preparatory Schools. Credentials of good character and conduct are required. Registration Forms can be obtained from the Director of Admissions, 32 College Road, Clifton, Bristol BS8 3JH.

Houses. It is usual for a pupil to be entered for a particular House, but where parents have no preference or where no vacancy exists in the House chosen, the Head Master will make the necessary arrangements.

Day Pupils and Day-Boarders. Day Boys are divided into Houses: North Town, South Town and East Town. Day Girls enter West Town or Hallward's. The Town Houses have the same status as Boarding Houses and Day Pupils are encouraged to take a full part in the various activities of the School. A small number of Day-Boarder places are available for boys and girls.

Catering is managed by our own experienced caterers and boarders take all meals in the School Dining Hall. Day pupils and day-boarders are required to have their midday meal at School, and arrangements are made for their tea and supper at the School when necessary.

Fees per term (2008-2009). Boarders £8,510–£8,590, Day Boarders £7,375–£7,720, Day Pupils £5,740–£5,795.

Scholarships. (*see Scholarship Entries section*). All awards are limited to 25% of the fees on merit, but they may be augmented by means-tested bursaries. Candidates must be under 14 years of age on the 1st of September. Boys and girls under 14 already in the School may compete. The following Entrance Scholarships and Exhibitions are offered each year:

(a) Up to 20 Academic awards. (b) Awards for Music with free instrumental tuition. (c) Awards for Art. (d) A Birdwood Scholarship for sons or daughters of serving members of HM Forces. (e) Sports Scholarships for entry at 13+. (f) At least 6 scholarships a year for entrants at Sixth Form level (Academic, Music and Sport).

Award winners are assured of places in the School. The Head Master distributes them to Houses, if possible in accordance with parents' wishes.

Academic structure. Boys and girls enter the School in the Third Form, following a general course for their first year. Most GCSEs are taken at the end of the Fifth Form.

Thereafter boys and girls enter Block I (Sixth Forms) and take an advanced course consisting of 4 subjects at AS level, then 3 at A level, including a Key Skills course in ICT. A great many combinations of subjects are possible. Boys and girls are prepared for entrance to Oxford and Cambridge.

Service. All pupils are given a course in outdoor pursuits and other skills in the Third form. In the Fourth form they are given more advanced training, which may include involvement in the Duke of Edinburgh's Award Scheme, and at the end of the year they decide whether to join the Army, Navy or Air Force sections of the CCF or to take part in Community Service. There is regular use of a property owned by the school in the Brecon Beacons for all these activities.

Societies. Voluntary membership of Scientific, Historical, Literary, Dramatic, Geographical, Debating and many other Societies is encouraged.

Music and Art. The Musical activities of the School are wide and varied, and are designed for musicians of all standards. They include the Chapel Choir, Choral Society and Chamber Choir, a full orchestra, 2 string orchestras, 2 wind bands, a jazz band, as well as numerous chamber music activities. Visiting concert artists regularly run masterclasses, and there are wide opportunities for performance. Teaching is available on virtually all instruments and in all styles. Instrumental and vocal competitions are held at House level and individually annually. The well-equipped and recently refurbished Music Schools include practice facilities, computers, an extensive sheet music library and a large record/compact disc library.

Drawing, Painting, Sculpture, Pottery, Textiles and various Crafts are taught under the supervision of the Director of Art in the Art School. There is an annual House Art Competition and various exhibitions throughout the year.

Theatre. Drama plays an important part in the life of the School. The Redgrave Theatre is used for School Plays, the House Drama Festival, and for other Plays that may be put on (eg by individual houses, the staff or the Modern Language Society). Each House produces a play each year. It is also used for teaching purposes, and in addition for Concerts, Lectures and Meetings.

Information and Communication Technology. A new ICT Centre at the heart of the school houses the most advanced Internet Facility of any school in the west.

Physical Education. Physical Education is part of the regular School curriculum and games are played at least twice per week by all age groups.

In the Michaelmas Term, boys play Rugby Football and girls play Hockey. There is a multi-sport option for seniors who are not in team squads. In the Lent Term, Hockey and Soccer are the main options for the boys whilst the girls mostly play Netball. Rowing, Running, Squash, Swimming, Shooting, Tetrathlon and Fives are among the alternative options for senior boys and girls. In the Summer Term, Cricket is the main sport for the boys and Tennis for the girls, with Tennis, Athletics, Rowing, Swimming and Shooting as alternatives for seniors. The Clifton College playing fields in Abbots Leigh include three floodlit all-weather hockey and football pitches, six floodlit tennis courts, and a Real Tennis court. An indoor facility for tennis and netball is one of the best in the region.

Careers. Careers advice is the shared responsibility of the Head Master, Housemasters, Housemistresses, Heads of Departments and Careers Staff. The School is a subscribing member of the Independent Schools Careers Organisation and of the Careers Research and Advisory Centre at Cambridge. The proximity of the City of Bristol enables the Careers Department and other members of the staff to keep in close touch with Universities, business firms and professional bodies about all matters affecting boys' and girls' careers.

Clifton College Preparatory School. *Headmaster*: J Milne, BA, MBA

The Preparatory School has separate buildings (including its own Science laboratories, Arts Centre, ICT Centre and Music School) and is kept distinct from the Upper School. The two Schools nevertheless work closely together and share some of the facilities, including the Chapel, Theatre, Sports complex, all-weather playing surfaces and swimming pool. Most boys and girls proceed from the Preparatory School to the Upper School. Pupils are also prepared for schools other than Clifton. There is a Pre-Prep (Butcombe) for day pupils aged between 3 and 8. Older pupils are divided into ten houses, some boarding, some day and some mixed. Boys and girls are accepted at all ages and Scholarships are available at ages 7 and 11.

For further details see entries for Clifton College Preparatory School and Butcombe in IAPS section.

Old Cliftonian Society. *Secretary*: C M E Colquhoun, The Garden Room, 3 Worcester Road, Clifton, Bristol BS8 3JL (Tel: 0117 3157 156).

Charitable status. Clifton College is a Registered Charity, number 311735. It is a charitable trust providing boarding and day education for boys and girls aged 3–18.

Clongowes Wood College

Clane Co Kildare Ireland
Tel: 00 353 45 868202
Fax: 00 353 45 861042
e-mail: reception@clongowes.net
website: www.clongowes.com

Motto: '*Aeterna non Caduca*'

Clongowes Wood College was founded in 1814 in a rebuilt Pale castle – Castle Brown in North Kildare, about 25 miles from Dublin. A boarding school for boys from 12–18, the school has developed steadily ever since and now has 447 pupils on the rolls, all of whom are boarders.

Trustee of the School: Fr John Dardis, SJ, Provincial of the Society of Jesus in Ireland

Chairman of the Board of Management: Mr John Tierney

***Headmaster*: Fr Leonard Moloney**, SJ, BA, HDip, MDiv, MPhil (Ecum)

Assistant Headmaster: Mr Martin Nugent, MA, HDipEd, HDip in Educational Management

Deputy Assistant Headmaster: Mr Frank Kelly, BComm, HDip

The College is situated on 150 acres of land, mostly comprising sports fields and a 9-hole golf course. It is surrounded by about 300 acres of farmland. Clongowes is listed as an historic building.

Admission. Application for admission should be made to the Headmaster. There is a registration fee of €50. An assessment day is held in early October prior to the year of entry and entry is determined by a variety of factors including family association, geographical spread including Northern Ireland and abroad, date of registration, and an understanding of the values that animate the College. Normal entry is at the age of 12; entry in later years is possible in exceptional circumstances if a place becomes available.

Curriculum. A wide choice of subjects is available throughout the school and pupils are prepared for the Irish Junior Certificate and the Irish Leaving Certificate. This latter is the qualifying examination for entry to Irish Universities and other third-level institutions. It is acceptable for entry to almost all Universities in the United Kingdom, provided the requisite grades are obtained. All pupils take a Transition Year programme following the Junior Certificate. This programme is recommended by the Department of Education in Ireland. Work experience modules, social outreach programmes, exchanges with other countries and opportunities to explore different areas of study are all included in this programme.

Religious Teaching. Clongowes is a Jesuit school in the Roman Catholic tradition and there are regular formal and informal liturgies. Boys are given a good grounding in Catholic theology and are encouraged to participate in retreats, prayer groups and pilgrimages (Taize, Lourdes). Social Outreach is part of the curriculum in Transition Year and is encouraged throughout the school. A small number of boys of other faiths are pupils in the school.

Sport. All boys play rugby in their first year in school. They then have the choice to continue in that game or to play other games. Rugby pitches, a golf course, tennis courts, soccer pitches, squash courts, a cross-country track, an athletics and cricket oval, a gymnasium and a swimming pool provide plenty of opportunity for a variety of activities. Athletics, Gaelic football and cricket are popular activities in the third term. Clongowes has a strong rugby tradition and has won the Leinster Championship twice in the last decade.

Other activities. Following the Jesuit tradition, the school has a fine reputation for debating and has won competitions in three different languages (English, Irish, French) in the last decade. A large school orchestra and school choir gives a formal concert at Christmas and another before the summer holidays. Drama productions take place at every level within the school. A large-scale summer project for charity has been undertaken each year. A residential holiday project for children with disabilities takes place in the school each summer and is animated by teachers and pupils. The College has recently created link programmes with schools in Hungary and Romania.

Pastoral Care. The school is organised horizontally into Lines. Two 'prefects', or housemasters look after each year within a Line, composed of two years, with a Line Prefect in charge of the Line itself. In addition, an Academic Year Head oversees the academic work of each of the 70 pupils within each year. A Spiritual Father or Chaplain is attached to each line. There is a strong and positive relationship with parents and a good community spirit throughout the school. The school seeks to foster competence, conscience and compassionate commitment in each of the boys in its care.

Fees per annum (2008-2009). €16,500. Parents are also asked to support the continuing development of the College through various fund-raising activities.

Clongowes Union. This association of past pupils of the school can be contacted through: The Secretary, The Clongowes Union, Clongowes Wood College, Clane, Co Kildare. e-mail: development@clongowes.net.

Coleraine Academical Institution

Castlerock Road Coleraine Co Londonderry BT51 3LA Northern Ireland
Tel: 028 7034 4331
Fax: 028 7035 2632

e-mail: enquiries@coleraineai.coleraine.ni.sch.uk

Coleraine Academical Institution was opened on 1 May 1860, the foundation stone having been laid on the 4th June, 1857. The School owes its origin to the enterprise and generosity of a group of Coleraine merchants and gentry. It has been generously endowed by The Honourable The Irish Society and the Worshipful Company of Clothworkers of London.

Governing Body:

Chairman: J S Smyth

E Boyd	D McClarty
J Brown	R McDermott
J S Brown	R McKeag
Mrs S Cameron	G M Montgomery
P Campbell	F J Mullan
F Farrell	S Murdock
S H Graham	Mrs A Rowe
Mrs S Griffith	J C Stevenson
J D Hill	A Taggart
D A Irwin	D H Torrens
W A Linnegan	P J M Tweedie

***Headmaster*: Dr D R J Carruthers**, BSc, PhD, PGCE, PQH (NI)

Deputy Headmasters:
S L Turtle, BA, DipEd
M W McNay, BA, DipEd

Senior Masters:
*P W J Allen, BSc, PGCE
*W G McCluskey, BSc, DipEd

Assistant Teachers:

*J W Martin, BA, DipEd	*D Stewart, BSc, PGCE
J S Patterson, BSc Econ, PGCE	R McGregor, BSc, PGCE
	*G J Spence, BA, PGCE
*D A Harkness, BSc, DipEd	M Palmer, BSc, PGCE
*A Lee, BSc, FGS	S T Patterson, BSc, PGCE
*J Brown, BA, CertEd	*Mrs S Cameron, BMus, MTD
P Blayney, BSc, CEd	
J V Boyd, BA, DipEd	K A Peden, BA, PGCE
*S Graham, BEd	Miss G Watters, BA, PGCE
*W S A Mitchell, BSc, DipEd	S Gault, BEng, PGCE
	Dr G Hull, BSc, PhD, PGCE
N Cully, BSc, DPhil	Miss L Magee, BA, PGCE
R I Crown, BSc, PGCE	Miss P A McIntyre, BEd
*M Reavey, BEd	S Miller, BA, PGCE
R Kane, BSc, PGCE	*Miss P Murphy, BA, PGCE
J McCully, BA, PGCE	Miss S Pinkerton, MA, PGCE
*M Irwin, BEd	
G Knox, BA, PGCE	*Mrs K Taggart, BA, DipEd
Miss L Montgomery, BA, PGCE	Mrs A Weir, BSc, PGCE
	Miss V Calvin, BA, PGCE
R Beggs, BA, PGCE	Miss E Liddle, BA, PGCE
Mrs T Reid, BSc, PGCE	Miss L Coyle, BSc, PGCE

Bursar and Secretary to Governors: G Knight

Number of Pupils. Approximately 650 boys now attend.

Age of Entry. No boy under the age of 11 years is admitted, unless there are special circumstances.

Estate. The School stands on the outskirts of the Borough of Coleraine and commands a wide view over a beautiful landscape with the lower reaches of the River Bann in the middle distance and seventy acres of Playing Fields reaching from the School by terraces down to the river side. These comprise 10 rugby pitches, with 5 cricket wickets, 4 hard tennis courts, basketball facilities and a hard surfaced athletics complex.

Beside the river is a boathouse fitted with an indoor rowing tank for coaching purposes. This boathouse is the headquarters of a thriving Boat Club for rowing, canoeing and sailing on the Bann estuary. There is also a large Sports Hall.

Teaching Accommodation. The school has a fine suite of the most up-to-date classrooms. The Science Block contains 9 recently refurbished laboratories, with stores and preparation rooms for instruction in Physics, Chemistry and Biology up to A level and Open Scholarship standards. A modern, open-plan Technology Centre provides classrooms and fully equipped workshops. Recent refurbishment of the Old Boarding School provides eight new classrooms all equipped with interactive boards and digital projectors. This block also accommodates a purpose-built Drama Suite and a School Museum.

Library. In 2001, the School Library was substantially refurbished to provide a wide range of modern resources and an efficient service. Computers are an integral part of the information service provided by the Library, whether it is accessing the catalogue through ALICE, the computerised library system, or searching the Internet. A teacher-in-charge manages the Library and a School Librarian is employed during the day to help customers. All classes in Years 8, 9 and 10 have a Library period once a fortnight, and there is access at break and lunchtime.

Sixth Form Centre. A new Sixth Form Centre was opened in February 2003, for the use of boys in the Upper Sixth. It includes a comfortably equipped recreation area and a spacious study area.

Assembly Halls. A large Assembly Hall capable of seating the whole School is supplemented by an auditorium designed to accommodate 300. Underneath this auditorium is a suite of music class and practice rooms.

Physical Education. There is a large Sports Hall where basketball, volleyball, badminton and weight lifting are co-curricular activities. In a 25 metre heated pool, swimming coaching is part of the curriculum. This pool is also used for supervised casual swimming in the afternoons and is the headquarters of the life saving, personal survival and sub-aqua clubs, as well as being used for teaching canoe techniques and water safety precautions.

Education. The School aims at providing a full and thorough instruction in all branches of a liberal education. Boys in the lower school (Years 8–10) are given the foundations of a general education in a wide range of subjects. In the upper school a moderate amount of specialisation is allowed so that boys may give more time to 'Career Subjects'. The choice of subjects is a wide one, and normally a minimum of 8 is chosen for GCSE to be taken in Year 12. Special arrangements are made in the Sixth Form to enable boys to study subjects of their choice to A and Scholarship levels, and they are encouraged to compete for University Scholarships and Exhibitions. The Sixth Form timetable allows for a number of periods per week for General Studies, with additional allocations for private study.

Careers. A section of the Library is fitted out as a Careers Department, which is supervised by careers teachers from whom parents and boys can obtain information and advice about possible careers.

Games. Rugby, football, cricket, rowing, tennis, badminton, golf, cross-country running, athletics, swimming, canoeing and sailing are the chief sports and games for which excellent facilities are available.

Societies and Clubs. These include: Bridge, Junior and Senior Drama, Junior and Senior Debating, Junior and Senior Badminton, Junior and Senior Chess, Musical, Swimming, Canoeing, Sailing, Angling, Circuit Training and Weight Lifting, Table Tennis, Junior and Senior Scripture Unions, Choir, Orchestra and Charity Group.

Scholarships. No Entrance Scholarships are offered but a number of bursaries and prizes are annually awarded within the School.

Fees. Boys pay £130 per annum, provided their parents are EC Nationals and resident in Northern Ireland.

Charitable status. Coleraine Academical Institution is a Registered Charity, number XN45693.

Colfe's School

Horn Park Lane London SE12 8AW
Tel: 020 8852 2283
Fax: 020 8297 1216
e-mail: head@colfes.com
website: www.colfes.com

Colfe's is one of the oldest schools in London. The parish priest of Lewisham taught the local children from the time of Richard Walker's Charity, founded in 1494, until the dissolution of the monasteries by Henry VIII. Revd John Glyn re-established the school in 1568 and it was granted a Charter by Queen Elizabeth in 1574. Abraham Colfe, Vicar of Lewisham, became a Governor in 1613 and the School was re-founded bearing his name in 1652. Colfe declared that the aim of the School was to provide an education for "pupils of good wit and capacity and apt to learn", reflecting the School's emphasis on sound learning and academic achievement since the earliest times. Colfe's original vision was to educate the children of "the hundred of Blackheath" and although today our pupils travel to the School from all parts of London, a strong sense of local community remains, with most of the pupils coming from the four boroughs which surround the school. One of Abraham Colfe's wisest moves was to invite the Leathersellers' Company, one of the oldest of the city Livery Companies, to be the Trustee of his will. Links between the School and the company are strong.

Mottos: '*Soli Deo honor et gloria*' (Leathersellers) '*Ad Astra per Aspera*' (Colfe)

Visitor: HRH Prince Michael of Kent

Board of Governors:
I A Russell, MBE (*Chairman*)
M Biscoe, FRIBA, FRICS (*Vice-Chairman*)
Miss S Cheng, LLB
D R Curtis, MA
A Collinson (*Master of the Leathersellers' Company*)
A H Dobbin, MA Cantab
Canon D Garlick (*Vicar of Lewisham*)
Professor R J Hooley
Professor H J Mardon
Mrs J D Pickering, BSc
S W Polito, MA, LLB
N R Pullman, JP
Dr M Spurr, MA, OBE
A B Strong
A C L Thornton, QC

***Headmaster*: R F Russell**, MA Cantab

Senior Deputy Head: M L Taylor, BA
Academic Deputy Head: Mrs C I Butler, MA Oxon
Pastoral Deputy Head: Mrs S B O'Leary, BSc
Head of Sixth Form: Miss S L Ward, BSc

Senior School:
Miss F Adnan, BA
*J W F Arnold, MA, BA Cantab
R Ashley, BSc
Miss H Ball, BSc
Mr A Bateson, BA
*Ms S Beetlestone, BA
*A J Brooker, DLC, MIDPE
*G D Bruce, BA
Mrs J Burton, BA
Mrs A C Chapman, BA
*Major C J Cherry, BSc (*CO CCF*)
*Revd A C Collier, MA Cantab, DipTheol Oxon
N P Crowe, BEd, MA
*P C Cummins, BSc
Miss S Davies, BA
Miss C Dhein, BA
R H Dickson, BEd
Miss M Downs, BA
*S Drury, BA, MA
Mr C Dunsmore, BA
*Mrs B Durkin, BSc
Miss O Edwards, BSc
J Fishwick, BSc
C Foxall, BA
S R Gent, BSc
*Mrs J C German, BA
P R Gibbs, BA
*Miss R A Hargrave, BEd
A Harper, BMus, LTCL
Mrs M Hayward, LRAM, Prof Cert RAM
Miss E Heath, BSc, MA
*D G Jackson, BA
Mrs E Karavidas, BA, MA
*J G King, BSc, MA
Miss L E Lechmere, BA
Ms R Le Roux, BSc, MSc, MPhil
Dr J Lea PhD, BSc
Mrs S Lee, BA
*Mrs A McAuliffe, BA
Mrs F McAuliffe, BSc
N W E Miller, BSc
*C R Morriss, BSc
Ms L A Murphy, BEd
*A C Newell, BSc (*Examinations Officer*)
*Mrs L Oakes, BA, Licence Sorbonne
R Otley, BA
*A Pearson, BSc
Ms J S Price, BA, MSc
Mr C Quinton, BA
C E Rowe, BEd
*A Seddon, BA, MIL
Miss J Simmonite, BA
*C P Smith, BSc, CPhys, MInstP
*D S Smith, BEd, MA
J Smith, BA
*O A Snell, BSc, MSc
Miss M Soumah, BA
Mrs N Rayes, BEd
Mrs C A Stokes, BEd
Miss E Taylor, BA,BSc
Mrs J C Toms, BSc
R P Thompson, PhD, MMus, LGSM,
Mrs K Toynton, BA
*Mrs P K Turrent, OCR DipSpLD
Mrs J Vander Gucht, BA
*S P Varley, BA, MA
U Vijapura, BSc
Mr A Walker, BA
Mr W Walker, BA
M S West, BSc, MRSC, CChem
Dr E White, BSc, PhD
J A Worley, BSc
*Ms E Yates, BA
S R Zivanovic, BA

Preparatory School

Head of Preparatory School: J Gallagher, BA, MBA

Deputy Head: Miss D Lempriere, BA, PGCE
Director of Studies: M Heil, BEd
Head of Pre-Prep and Nursery: Mrs S N Redman, BEd

Mr S Biffen, BA, PGCE
Miss J Browne, BSc, PGCE
P Donoghue, BEd
Mrs L A Douglas, BA, PGCE, Dip SpLD
Mrs J Dunmore, BA, PGCE
Mrs S Gorgun, DipEd
Mrs E Higgs, BA, PGCE
Miss A D Manning, BA
Mrs E Otley, CertEd, DipSpLD
Miss K Martin, BSc, PGCE
C Stringfellow, CertEd
Mrs C Vaughan, BEd
Mrs Z Ward, BA, PGCE
Mrs S J Watts, BEd, LTCL, Dip Perf Stds Opera
Mrs V Welch, BA, DipEd

Pre-Preparatory and Nursery Staff:
Mrs A Bradley, NNEB
Mrs E R Frost, BA
Ms S J Grover, NNEB
Mrs S T Gurr, BEd
Mrs R J M Hall, BA, PGCE
Miss C Harknett, BTech (*Early Years*)
Mrs S Smith, NNEB
Miss L McNally, NNEB, NVQ2
Mrs M Moody, BEd, NNEB
Mrs L Mountford-Day, NVQ3
Mrs E Otley, TCert, DipSpLD
Mrs C Russell, NNEB, Cert EYp
Ms G Scala, NVQ3
Ms D L Wheater, BEd
Miss N J Williams, BA, PGCE
Mrs S Williams, BSc, PGCE

Bursar: S White, Cdr RN (Ret)
Registration Secretary: Mrs R Dyer
Librarian/Careers: Mrs J A Cardnell, BA, DipLib, ALA
School Counsellor: Mrs K Kashif, BEd, MA

Admissions. There are 700 pupils in the Senior School, including 200 in the Sixth Form. The Preparatory School, incorporating the Nursery and Pre-Preparatory departments, caters for a further 300 pupils. All sectors of the school are fully co-educational. The main points of entry to the Preparatory School are 3+ and 4+ (Nursery and Pre-Prep) and 7+. The majority of the Prep School pupils transfer to the Senior School at 11. Approximately 65 pupils from a range of local state primary and Prep schools enter the Senior School directly at 11 and there are a limited number of places available to pupils wishing to join in the Sixth Form at Year 12.

Buildings. All the teaching accommodation is modern and purpose built. Specialist on-site facilities include the Leisure Centre, comprising sports hall, swimming pool, and fitness suite. The Leathersellers' Sports Ground, located less than a mile from the main school campus, provides extensive playing fields and related facilities. A new centre for the Visual and Performing Arts was built in 2003 and an extensive all-weather pitch was completed in 2006. The Preparatory School, including Nursery and Pre-Preparatory departments, is housed in a separate modern building on the main school site.

Curriculum. The curriculum follows the spirit of the National Curriculum in both Preparatory and Senior Schools. Fast track pupils are entered for the separate Sciences at GCSE and follow the IGCSE Maths course. The AS course in Critical Thinking is also followed by a number of GCSE pupils. A wide range of subjects is available at A Level, 22 in total, including Drama, Government and Politics, Media Studies, Physical Education and Psychology.

Physical Education and Games. Physical Education and Games are compulsory for all pupils up to and including Year 11. Full use is made of the wide range of facilities available on-site, including a fully-equipped Sports Centre, swimming pool and all-weather surface.

The main sports for boys are rugby, football and cricket. Girls play hockey, netball, tennis and athletics. Other sports available include badminton, basketball, cross-country running, squash and swimming.

Music and Drama. Music and Drama thrive alongside each other in the purpose-built Performing Arts Centre. The music department is home to a wide range of performance groups ranging from beginners to advanced ensembles in both classical and contemporary genres. There are regular performance opportunities given throughout the year, some held in the purpose-built recital hall and others in external venues. A team of 20 visiting instrumental teachers provide further opportunities for pupils to enjoy making music. Drama is a popular subject at both GCSE and A level, with large numbers of pupils also involved outside the classroom. Many of the recent productions have been musicals, one of which, Grease, was taken on tour to South Africa in the autumn of 2005.

Careers. The Careers and Higher Education Department is staffed on a full-time basis. Regular events include University Information Evenings and Careers Fairs.

Fees per term (2008-2009). Senior School £3,927 (excluding lunch); Preparatory School £3,189 (excluding lunch); Pre-Preparatory £3,006 (including lunch); Nursery £2,745 (including lunch).

Scholarships and Bursaries. Academic Scholarships are awarded mainly on the basis of outstanding performance in the Entrance Examinations. The exams are designed to identify and reward academic potential, as well as achievement.

Means-tested bursaries are also available at 11+. Bursaries may, in exceptional circumstances, cover the total cost of tuition fees. Application forms are available from the Registrar.

A limited number of Music and Sports awards are also available at 11+. In the case of Music scholars, free instrumental tuition may accompany the award. Details of Music and Sports awards can be obtained from the Registrar.

A number of scholarships, bursaries and other awards are also available to candidates entering the school at 16+. Details can be obtained from the Registrar.

Preparatory School. The Preparatory School building, with splendid facilities, was opened by HRH Prince Michael of Kent in 1988. Specialist rooms of the Senior School are also used. While the curricular emphasis is on high standards in basic Mathematics and English, a wide range of other subjects is taught, including Science and French. There is also a range of activities similar to those enjoyed by the Senior School and all pupils are expected to participate. All pupils proceed to the Senior School if they achieve the qualifying standard. It is expected that virtually all pupils from the Prep school will proceed to the Senior school at 11.

(*For further details see entry in IAPS section.*)

Nursery and Pre-Prep. A co-educational nursery and pre-preparatory school for pupils aged 3 to 7 is housed in modern accommodation adjacent to the Prep School.

Old Colfeians' Association. Enquiries to the Hon Secretary, Eltham Road, London SE12 8UE. Tel: 020 8852 1181.

Charitable status. Colfe's School is a Registered Charity, number 1109650. It exists to provide education for boys and girls.

Colston's School

Stapleton Bristol BS16 1BJ
Tel: 0117 965 5207
Fax: 0117 958 5652
e-mail: enquiries@colstons.bristol.sch.uk
website: www.colstons.bristol.sch.uk

Colston's School, which is approaching its 300th anniversary in 2010, is a co-educational day school for pupils aged 3 to 18 with boarding for pupils in Year 10 and above. It is located on a spacious 32-acre site at Stapleton village in north Bristol, with the Lower and Upper Schools sharing the extensive facilities. The Estates Governors of the school are The Society of Merchant Venturers, Merchants' Hall, Bristol BS8 3NH.

Motto: '*Go, and do thou likewise.*'

Governors:
D J Marsh (*Chairman*)

Mrs A Bernays
C A Booy, OBE
M Broad
R Cotton
Mrs K Curling
S Davies
J Hunt
T Kenny
Mrs K Morgan, OBE
P J Mitchell
R Morris
Mrs P Morris
M C Pitman
G J Swarbrick
T Taylor
R Thornton

***Headmaster*: P T Fraser**, MA

Deputy Headmaster: A J Martinovic, BA

Director of Studies: M J Graham, MSc, MEd, CMath, MIMA

Staff:
Mrs E Arrand, BA Hons
T Arrand, BA
N Aspden, BSc
C Banning, BSc Hons
B Berry, BA
D J Betterton, BA
E Bicknell, BA
Mrs G Bicknell, MA
G G Boyce, BA
Mrs J Brighton, BSc
Miss J Burke, BA
Mrs R Carby, BMus
Mrs A J Chisnall, BA
Mrs D S Currie, BA
Mrs G Dann, BA, DipCG, IPD
Miss C Davies, BA Hons
Dr K Dawson, BA, PhD
Miss O De Zarate, BA
Miss D Drake
N J Drew, BA
M W Eyles, BSc
J A Fitzpatrick, BA
Miss C Flay, BA Hons
R P Gash, BSc
Miss K Goddard, BSc Hons
H Griffiths, MSc, MEd
J Gwilliam, BA Hons
Mrs C L Hambley, BA
Mrs A M Hart, BSc
Mrs R Johnson, BA
P A Jones, BSc
D Kaye, BA Hons
R D Mardle, BSc
Dr A D E Martin, BSc, PhD
D L Mason, BSc
L Masters, BSci
Miss S Melia, BA Hons
Mrs J L Poppy, BA
J Prichard, BA Hons

S Pritchard, MA
Mrs A Rounding
J Shooter, MA
P Temple, BSc
P T Thornley, BEd
Dr J A Tovey, PhD
Mrs J Urquhart, BA
Miss S Victor, BEd
Mrs C Wall, BSc
D Wall, BEd
C R Warren, CertEd
Miss L J Wight, BEd
T Williams
Ms C J Wyatt, BA
N C Y Yaxley, BEd
Miss E K Young, BEd

Lower School

Head of Lower School: Mrs C Aspden, MA

Deputy Head: M Weavers, BEd

Junior Department:
W J Barber, BSc
Miss H Blackley, BSc
Mrs R Carby, BMus
Miss F C Gillett, BA
Miss V Hawkings, BSc
T George
K Watts, BEd
Mrs P M Webley, BA
Mrs N Whitaker, BA

Pre-Prep:
Head of Pre-Prep: Mrs R Wyles, CertEd
Mrs K Blomfield, BA
Miss J Dixon, BA
Miss S Evans, BEd
Mrs S Lake, CertEd
Mrs R Rowe, BEd
Mrs P Shannak, BA

Assistants:
Mrs J Lloyd, NNEB
Mrs R Nowak, NVQ
Mrs C Tremlin, NVQ

Nursery:
Mrs C F Bastin, NNEB
Mrs W Gardiner, NNEB
Mrs K Glynne-Jones, BSc, PGCE
Mrs J Hosegood, NVQIII

Librarian: Mrs J Ghosh, BA, MCILIP
Headmaster's PA: Mrs D Sollis
Lower School Head's Secretary: Mrs C Pullin
Director of Finance: Mrs N Prosser
Accounts Manager: Mrs S Ogden
Facilities Manager: A Meakin
Catering Manager: Miss J Prichard
Officer Commanding CCF: Major T Scarll, BEM
SSI CCF: WO2 S Sinar
School Administrator: Mrs D Thomas
Matron: Mrs N Webb
Receptionist: Mrs E Hughes

Organisation. There are approximately 830 pupils at Colston's, one third of whom are girls. The Lower School, catering for the 3–11 age range, is adjacent to the main site which accommodates the Upper School (11–18 years). Pastoral care is exercised through a house system and Sixth Form of some 160 boys and girls.

For details of the Lower School, see entry in IAPS section.

Admission. Pupils are admitted at 11+ through the school's own examination or at 13+ through the Common Entrance Examination or the school's own examination. Admission direct into the Sixth Form is also quite normal. Awards and bursaries are available including music, art, drama and sports scholarships.

Work. The curriculum is broadly based, avoiding premature specialisation, and is in line with the provisions of the National Curriculum. German, Spanish, Religious Knowledge, Drama, Art, Music, Technology, Design Technology and ICT are optional subjects. There is a wide choice of A Level subjects in the Sixth Form.

Chapel. Colston's is a Church of England Foundation, and use is made of neighbouring Stapleton Parish Church for morning assembles. Boys and girls of other denominations are also welcomed.

Games and Activities. Colston's has over 30 acres of playing fields adjoining the school. A continuous programme of improvement has recently provided a floodlit Astroturf pitch and newly-refurbished floodlit tennis and netball courts. Pupils have use of a sports hall, squash courts, fitness suite and heated outdoor swimming pool. Principal boys' games are rugby, hockey and cricket. Principal girls' games are tennis, hockey, netball and rounders. In addition all pupils can take part in athletics, cross country, swimming, squash, badminton and basketball. The Colston's Combined Cadet Force has grown to record levels with over 240 cadets, and a new purpose-built headquarters building has recently opened. A range of adventure activities are provided through CCF including flying, gliding, sailing, canoeing and camping. The school also encourages pupils to undertake social and community service in Bristol.

Music and Drama. With a new concert hall and a superbly equipped theatre, music and drama play a very important part in the life of the school. There is a large element of devised work in drama, with all pupils having the opportunity to act and produce as well as helping with staging and lighting. Regular theatre visits are arranged. About half of all pupils learn musical instruments, and there is an orchestra, swing band and a variety of choirs.

Careers. There is ample opportunity for boys and girls to obtain professional advice on the choice of a career. Colston's is a member of the Independent Schools Careers Organisation whose services are available. The Head of Careers arranges a full week's work experience for all Year 10 pupils, and also arranges visits to Careers Conventions organised by employers and universities.

Fees per term (from January 2008). Full boarders £6,200; day pupils £3,090 (excluding lunches).

Modernisation. An extensive building programme has been carried out in recent years including a new concert hall and CCF headquarters. A full refurbishment of the library was completed in summer 2007, and the laboratories and Sixth Form facilities will be refurbished over the next two years.

Situation. Colston's is located in Stapleton village which is within the city of Bristol, and enjoys the advantage of having all its playing fields and facilities on site. The school makes full use of Bristol's extensive cultural and sporting opportunities, particularly with theatre and concert visits. Road and rail communications are excellent, particularly because the school is less than a mile from Junction 2 of the M32. London Heathrow can be reached in one-and-a-half hours by road or rail.

The school is large enough to sustain a wide range of activities at a high level and yet small enough for each boy or girl to contribute actively and be known as individuals. Every effort is made to provide for and develop each individual's abilities in academic, cultural and other extra-curricular activities.

Charitable status. Colston's School is a Registered Charity, number 1079552. Its aims and objectives are the provision of education.

Cranleigh School

Cranleigh Surrey GU6 8QQ
Tel: 01483 273666; 01483 276377 (Head)
Fax: 01483 267398; 01483 273696 (Head)
e-mail: enquiry@cranleigh.org
website: www.cranleigh.org

Cranleigh School was founded in 1865.

Motto: '*Ex cultu robur*'

Visitor: The Rt Revd The Lord Bishop of Winchester

Governing Body:
Chairman: J A V Townsend, MA
Deputy Chairman: D G Westcott, BA, BCL, QC

Dr R Chesser, MA, MB, BChir, MRCP
R L Johnson, BSc, MRAeS
A J Lajtha, MA, FCIB
B G Law, BA Hons PG, HDE
M J Meyer
Dr S Mockford, BSc, PhD, CEng, MIEE, FRSA
Mrs L A Muirhead, BA
D H Powell, MDes RCA, FCSD, FRSA
A C Ramsay, AADipl, RIBA
R A Robinson, FCA, MBA
Dr T J Seller, BSc, PhD
Mrs E Stanton, BSc, ACA
Dr J Stevenson, MA, DPhil
Major General C G C Vyvyan, MA, MSc, CB, CBE
J G M Wates, BA, MBA
O A R Weiss, MA
Mrs M J Williamson
Dr J C Wilson, MA, PhD

Bursar and Clerk to the Governors: P T Roberts, MBE

***Head*: Guy Waller**, MA, MSc, PGCE, FRSA (Worcester and Wolfson Colleges, Oxford)

Deputy Head: A J Griffiths, BSc, MSc, DIC, CGeol, FGS, QTS
Assistant Deputy Head: T I McConnell-Wood, BSc
Director of Studies: I M Allison, MA, PGCE
Head of School Administration: Ms A J Russell-Price

Members of Common Room:

† *Housemaster/mistress*

Mrs M C Allison, BEd (*†West*)
R M Allon-Smith, MA, PGCE
S J Artus, BA, PGCE
T H J Barnett, MA, DipAD
S J Batchelor
W N Bennett, DipEd
S D Bird, BA (*†East*)
Mrs D E Bloomfield, CertEd (*†South*)
C H D Boddington, BA, PGCE (*†Cubitt*)
D R Boggitt, BEng, PGCE
B W Browne, BSc, PGCE
E M Burnett, BSc, PGCE
Mrs V J Burnett, BA, PGCE
Mrs J A Childs, BA, RSA DipSpLD, AMBDA
R A Clarke, BA, BPhil, QTS
M J L Commander, BEng
Mrs A P L Cooke, BA
S T Cooke, BA
J L Copp, BA
D J Cresswell, BA
P J Crosfield, BA
Mrs E G M Dellière, BA
Mrs H Dixon, BA, CertEd
A J Ellison, BSc
T R Fearn, BSc, PGCE
A P Forsdike, MA
D J Futcher, BSc
Miss S L Greenwood, BA Ed
F T Hardee, BA
Mrs V A Harrison, BA
J G Haynes, BEd (*†North*)
Miss E L Herbert, BA
Mrs O B Hodgkinson, BA, PGCE
S R Hodgkinson, BA, MPhil, PhD
R A C Humes, BA
Dr C M Jackson, BSc, PhD
R G H J Jackson, BA, MEd
R C E K Kefford, BSc, PGCE
P J Kemp, MA
Dr S L Kemp, BSc, PhD, PGCE
R Lailey, MA
Miss S C Langdon, Dip RAM, ARAM
P Leggitt, MA
A A G Logan, BA, PGCE
P J Longshaw, MA
P R Maitland, MA, PGCE
J C E Mann, BSc, PhD, CBiol, MIBiol, QTS
Mrs M Maunder, BEd
Mrs S E McLaughlin, BEd
P A McNiven, DipAD, QTS (*Director of Art*)
A J Meryon, BMus
Miss S D Morgan, BSc
R A Morris, BA
T P Moschard, MA, FRCO, DipCHD
Miss O D Mullins, BA, PGCE
Mrs C Neill, BA, PGCE
G J N Neill, BA, PGCE
Miss C E Nicholls, MA, PGCE
Ms R P F Nicholson, BA, PGCE
S M Owen
The Revd P V Parker, BSc, BA, PGCE, FRGS (*Chaplain*)
M C Pashley, BMus (*Director of Music*)
Miss S M Peers, BSc, MSc, PGCE
Mrs J A Pimm, BEd
J S Ross, MA, PGCE
Dr A P Saxel, BSc, PhD (*Senior Teacher*)
R J Saxel, BA, DipRam, LRAM
W J Sheppard, BA
J A Smart, BA, PGCE
Mrs L R I Smart, BS, PGCE
A J Smith, MA, QTS (*Master of the Scholars*)
C N Staley, BA, PGCE (*†Loveday*)
Mrs N R Sutton, BA
J F G Thompson, MA PGCE (*Senior Teacher*)
B R Tyrrell, MChem, DPhil
M P Whitehead, BSc, PGCE (*Director of IT*)
Miss A Willis, BSc, PGCE
C A Wilson, BSc, PGCE
F J Wilson, BSc, PGCE
R A Wilson, LTCL
J M Witcombe, BSc, PGCE
Mrs U C Yardley, BA, PGCE
S A H Young, BSc, MSc, PhD, PGCE

Medical Officer: Dr G Tyrrell, MB BS, DObstRCOG

Preparatory School
(*see entry in IAPS section*)

Head: M T Wilson, BSc University of Keele
Deputy Head (*Academic*): R C Gainher, BSc
Deputy Head (*Pastoral*): Mrs S D Gravill, BA, PGCE

Members of Common Room:
J D R Adcock, BA, PGCE
A J Artman, BA
E T Batchelor, BSc
Mrs J Brown, HND
Mrs J F Derbyshire, BA, PGCE
B M Dixon, BA, CertEd
J Forster, BSc, PGCE
Mrs R Frett, MA, PGCE (*Chaplain*)
M J Halstead, BSc, PGCE
C D Henderson, BA, PGCE
D Hitchen, GRSM, ARMCM
M S F Howard, BA, CertEd
Mrs A Jolly, BSc, PGCE
Mrs H Kitson, CertEd
D S Manning, EDE
Mrs J J Marriott, BA, PGCE
Mrs H McNiven, BA
Mrs P R Meadows, BEd
P J B Millburn-Fryer, BEd
Miss F Nutley, BEd
Miss R Quinn, BEd
Mrs E Reed, BSc, PGCE
Mrs J C Robertson, PhD, MMus, BA
Mrs D S Storey, DipEd
Mr P B Storey, DipEd
T M Stroud, BSc
Mrs T Thistlethwaite, BEd, CertEd
Miss L Thompson, BA
Dr M Ward, PhD
Miss G Whiteley, BSc, PGCE

Head's PA: Mrs F M J Bundock (Tel: 01483 542051)
School Administrator: Mrs P Adams (Tel: 01483 542058)

Cranleigh School's principal aim is to provide an environment in which pupils can flourish, enabling them to capitalise on the diverse range of opportunities offered by the School and to achieve to the best of their ability within a framework of shared values and standards. The School's two hundred-acre site, situated eight miles from Guildford on the Surrey-West Sussex border, lies on the outskirts of Cranleigh Village and within 45 minutes of London. The School is fully co-educational, with some 200 girls and 400 boys between the ages of 13 and 18, including a Sixth Form of about 240. It is a predominantly boarding community, attracting boarders from both the local area and further afield; it also, however, welcomes day pupils, who are fully integrated into the Cranleigh community, playing their part in the activities of their respective Houses and benefiting from the advantages thereby offered.

Each House (separate for boys and girls) has a resident Housemaster or Housemistress, a resident Deputy, a Warden, two Matrons and a team of six Lower School Tutors; Sixth Formers can choose their own Tutor from the whole of Common Room. There is also a strong and active partnership between parents and the School.

Cranleighans are encouraged to relish challenge, to feel they are known as individuals, and to become talented and wise adults with an inherent ability to adapt to a fast-changing world. Aligned with this, the School boasts an impressive record in academic achievement. Almost all pupils achieve 3 A2 Levels plus at least one additional AS Level, and in recent years more than 98% have gone on to university – 90% to their first-choice university.

Academic Patterns. Our aim is to act within the spirit of the National Curriculum, but to offer more, taking full advantage of our independence and the extra time available to a boarding school. We therefore retain a very broad curriculum in the Fourth Form, and have an options system in the Lower and Upper Fifth Forms which enables a pupil to take between nine and eleven GCSE subjects before moving on to AS Levels in the Sixth Form. We offer the opportunity to do Triple Award Science, and a broadly-based Technology course, as well as giving good linguists the chance to take two foreign languages (with Latin if they wish). In the Sixth Form pupils have a wide choice from about twenty AS Level subjects.

Work on languages with an emphasis on commercial and colloquial fluency is encouraged for non-specialist linguists, and much use is made of the Language Laboratory. Exchanges take place with pupils in schools in France, Spain and Germany.

We have comprehensive facilities for Science with an emphasis on experimental work. Technology is catered for by the Electronics, Woodwork (we have our own Designer-in-Residence) and Engineering Workshops, which also provide extra-curricular hobby and recreational facilities. Information Technology is incorporated into the teaching of all other subjects, with each academic department having its own IT policy, coordinated by the Director of IT. There are seven teaching rooms with networked PCs and every House and academic department has PCs available for use, all linked to the School's network and the Internet.

All members of the Lower Sixth Form study a course in Critical Thinking and attend a series of regular lectures to help broaden their education.

Creative and Performing Arts. Cranleigh has maintained an enviable reputation for Music over many years, and the Merriman Music School offers pupils some of the finest facilities available. We send Choral Scholars to Oxford, Cambridge and major Music Departments and Colleges elsewhere; boys and girls of all ages successfully take part in national competitions and well over a third of the School learns a musical instrument. Keyboard players have access to a fine Grant Degens and Bradbeer tracker-action organ and to two Steinway concert grand pianos.

Cranleigh also boasts a strong Drama tradition. Large-scale productions take place in the Devonport Hall, to which is linked a studio theatre, the Vivian Cox Theatre. The School's proximity to London allows for regular attendance at professional theatre, music and opera productions.

The Art Department is staffed by practising artists, and the Art School offers a comprehensive range of disciplines in drawing and painting, sculpture, textiles, printmaking and ceramics; the studios are open every day and the Sixth Form has its own painting studio. Frequent use is made of the Art School Library and visits to galleries are organised as appropriate. The academic year culminates in the Upper Sixth Exhibition.

Sport. Cranleigh provides an extremely diverse range of sporting activities for all pupils.

The School possesses an impressive array of sports facilities, including three full-size Astroturf pitches (one of which is floodlit), a 9-hole golf course, riding stables with floodlit sand-school, 4 squash courts, 6 fives courts, 24 tennis courts, 8 netball courts and both indoor and outdoor swimming pools. The impressive Sports Hall complex (the Trevor Abbott Sports Centre) provides a popular venue for netball, tennis, badminton and basketball, along with an indoor cricket school, and also includes a separate dance studio and fully equipped fitness suite. High standards are set for the numerous competitive teams, with an extensive programme of fixtures at all levels and for all ages. "Sport for All" is a key philosophy at the School, supported by an experienced and talented team of coaches.

In the Michaelmas Term the majority sports are hockey for girls, and rugby for boys; in the Lent Term the majority sports are netball for girls, and hockey for boys. During the winter terms, pupils can also compete in lacrosse, cross-country, golf, water polo, soccer, fives, rugby-sevens, basketball, riding and squash, plus aerobics, badminton and canoeing for the Sixth Form. All pupils in the Fourth and Lower Fifth Forms take part in the majority sport, whilst an element of choice is gradually introduced for the older pupils. All pupils in the School take part in sport, even in the Sixth Form.

In the Summer Term, the main team sport for boys is cricket, whilst some boys compete in tennis, swimming, athletics and golf. For girls the main sport is tennis, with competitive swimming, athletics, rounders and cricket popular additional offerings.

Service Activities. There are opportunities for pupils to take part in a range of 'service' activities. Boys and girls may join the CCF, which has its own fire brigade section, or get involved with community service, ecology, first aid training or life saving. All these are designed to focus pupils' thoughts on life beyond the School. Cranleighans help elderly people in their homes and also have links with local schools for children with learning difficulties and with a home for adults with similar problems. Many Houses and the Fund-Raising Group raise money for various charities.

Religion. The striking, neo-Gothic Chapel was built as a central point of the School, and Cranleigh maintains its concern to present the Christian way of life.

Ongoing Developments. A new Languages and Science building is due for completion in October 2008, and a timber-pole Workshop Studio, designed using sustainable principles, is due to be completed in 2009.

Planning for our Pupils' Future. Cranleigh takes the future of its pupils very seriously. It maintains good contacts with the professions, industry and commerce, through links developed as part of the careers advice structure. All pupils are regularly assessed during their time at the School, and this process includes a period of Work Experience at the end of the Upper Fifth year. On a personal level, the Old Cranleighan Society enables current and past boys and girls to maintain lasting links with one another.

Admission and Registration. Parents wishing to enquire about places at the School or to request a copy of the detailed Prospectus should contact the Head of School Administration on 01483 276377, or visit the website on www.cranleigh.org. If you wish to visit the School, the Head would be delighted to welcome you: please telephone to make an appointment. Pupils between the ages of 13 and 14 are admitted in September, via the Common Entrance or the Scholarship examinations. There may be vacancies at other levels and there is a small intake at Sixth Form level. The entrance procedure at Sixth Form level includes a series of interviews and a written test for candidates for academic awards.

Awards. (*see Scholarship Entries section*). The Master of the Scholars has a specific responsibility for all Scholars. They are members of their Houses and attend normal lessons, but also have an additional programme throughout their time at the School that covers a wide variety of academic, cultural, social and commercial areas beyond the syllabus and which encourages independent thinking and research. At age thirteen, Academic, Music and Art Awards are available, along with Eric Abbott awards for candidates of good academic ability with at least one other clearly established area of excellence. Music awards include free musical tuition. In certain circumstances, additional consideration may be given to sons or daughters of public servants, members of the armed forces and the clergy of the Church of England. At Sixth Form level, Academic, Music, Art and Eric Abbott Awards are offered. All Awards are fees-linked and may be augmented in cases of proven financial need. Awards can be made to boys and girls already at the School if their progress merits it. Full details of awards can be obtained by telephoning 01483 276377. In addition, enquiries are welcomed with regards to Foundation Awards. Contact the Foundation Office on 01483 542118.

Fees per term (2008-2009). Boarders £8,680, Day Pupils £7,075.

It is the policy of the School to keep extras down to an absolute minimum, and limited to such charges as individual music tuition. Text books are supplied until the Sixth Form, at which point pupils are encouraged to buy their own so that they may take them on to university. A scheme is available for the payment of fees in advance.

Preparatory School. The School has its own Preparatory School and boys and girls are normally admitted at seven or eight, but also at other ages. For further information apply to the Head of the Preparatory School (*see entry in IAPS section*).

Charitable status. Cranleigh School is a Registered Charity, number 1070856. It exists to provide education for children aged 13–18 and the Preparatory School for those aged 7–13.

Culford School

Bury St Edmunds Suffolk IP28 6TX
Tel: 01284 728615
Fax: 01284 728631
e-mail: culfordschool@culford.co.uk
website: www.culford.co.uk

Founded in 1881 in Bury St Edmunds, Culford School moved to its present site in 1935. The School is under the overall control of the Board of Management for Methodist Residential Schools, but is administered by a Board of Governors, to whom local control is devolved.

Motto: '*Viriliter Agite Estote Fortes*'

Visitor: The President of the Methodist Conference

Governors:
Chairman: Professor R Swanston, DSc, FRICS, FIMgt

Air Cdre S Abbott, CBE, MPhil, BA
I H Angus
R J B Beaney, FRICS, FAAV
R J Black
Mrs R Black
Mrs M G Browning, MBE, MA
The Rt Hon Viscount Chelsea
M J Freeman, FRICS
C J Hilder
Mrs S E Kohl
G Russell, MCS
S R K Taylor, MA
The Revd G Thompson

***Headmaster*: J F Johnson-Munday**, MA, MBA

Deputy Head: Mrs B McCrea, MA

Director of Studies: Dr J Guntrip, BSc, PhD

Director of Sport: D V Watkin, BEd

Chaplain: The Revd Simon Battersby, BTh

Members of the Common Room:
* *Head of Department*
† *Housemaster/mistress*

Mrs R Ainscough, BSc
Mrs C Alfaro, BA
Mrs S L Antonietti, BSc
Mr S Arbuthnot, MSc
*M Barber, MA
D Bolton, DipMus
D Bosworth, BSc, PhD
A R Butler, BSc, PhD
J M Byrne, MA, PhD
†Mrs C Byrne, MA
R A Colenso, BA
Mrs J Cope, BA, Cert SpLD
*Mrs D A Copping, CertEd, Cert SpLD
R N Cox, BA
*A R Deane, BA
R J Davie, BA, BSc, MEd
*I C Devlin, BEd
†G E Draper, BA
*A Edgar, BEng
*A P Fisk, MSc
J Guntrip, BSc, PhD
*E Hall, BA
C Henderson, BSc
L Hoggar, BA
N Hopton, MA
*Dr A Hubbard, BSc, PhD
*Mrs B A Hunt, BA
*P M Jones, MA
Mrs K Kemp, BEd
Ms J Loco, BA
Mrs E Long
A H Marsh, CertEd
Mrs L Martin, MA, MCLIP
Mrs B McCrea, MA
C McCrea, MEd
Ms J Merris, BSc
Revd Dr AG Palmer, MTh, PhD
Mrs A Parsons, BSc
†Mrs B Recknell, MA
*J D Recknell, MA, FRCO
*Mrs A Reith, BA
*D Reith, MA
†G Reynolds, BEng
Mrs C Reynolds
Mrs L Robinson
†M Schofield, BEd
R P Shepperson, BSc
B Thomas
*N J Tully, BSc
*T Walsh, MPhil
D Watkin, BEd
*I Webber, BSc, CPhys
D S Weyers, MMus
D M Williams, BSc

Bursar: Lt Col M B Woolley

Medical Officer: R Soper, MRCS, LRCP

Headmaster's PA: Mrs C A Gordon

Registrar: Mrs K Tompkinson

Preparatory School
(*see entry in IAPS section*)

Headmaster: T J Collins, BA

Deputy Head: Miss J Hatton, BEd

Director of Studies: Mrs B Murray, DipSpLD

Mrs C Alston, BA
Mrs M Billitt, BEd
Mrs T Black
Mrs H Carrington, BA
D Dagnall, MA
Mrs R J Drury, BA
T Gregory, BA
P Harrison, BEng
Mrs E Holland, BSc
Mrs D Hollins, BA
Ms E Moran, BA
Mrs B Murray, DipSpLD
†Mrs J Pineo, BA
R Pineo, BSc
Mrs L M Scott, BSc
Mrs V Wallis-Miller, CertEd
*T Walsh, MPhil
D S Weyers, MMus
Mrs S Whitcombe
Mrs H Whiter, BA

Pre-Preparatory School:

Headmistress: Mrs S Preston, BA

Mrs J Gaskell, NNEB
Mrs E Grey, DPP
Mrs S Guntrip, BSc
Miss C Hamilton, BEd
Miss K Harrison, BEd
Mrs A McEwen-Smith, DPP
Mrs A Morrell, BEd
Mrs R Ratcliffe, BEd
Miss N Rodwell, BTEC
Miss K Trow, BTEC
Ms S Varley, BA
Miss S Widger, MSc
Mrs J Woolley

Culford School is a fully co-educational boarding and day school of about 650 pupils aged 3–18 years. The Senior, Prep and Pre-Prep schools are all situated in a beautiful 480-acre landscaped park, four miles north of Bury St Edmunds, close to the university town of Cambridge and within easy reach of Stansted Airport.

The Senior School, for 13 to 18 year olds, has 350 pupils of whom nearly half are boarders. There is a comprehensive programme of weekend activities on offer throughout each term.

Culford believes education should be challenging, enriching and fun. There is a clear commitment to excellence in all areas of school life, and hard work in the classroom is complemented by full sporting and extra curricular programmes. Integrity and respect for the individual are encouraged along with a sense of responsibility towards the wider community.

Pupils are given every opportunity to learn to take responsibility both for themselves and others. Well-founded House and tutorial systems ensure that the pastoral care is close and effective and this is made possible by a pupil/staff ratio of approximately 10:1. The School respects its Christian heritage as part of a Methodist foundation and is deliberately inclusive, welcoming pupils of all faiths and of none.

The Buildings and School Facilities. The main building is Culford Hall, an 18th century mansion formerly the seat of Marquis Cornwallis and Earl Cadogan. This building, with a blend of Robert Adam and Louis XVI interior design, has glorious views across Culford Park and houses the main reception, the Headmaster's study, the main Library and the Workman Library, and the Music School, as well as additional classrooms and the bursarial offices. A superb purpose-built Studio Theatre was constructed within the Hall in 2006.

Set in close proximity to Culford Hall and the Boarding Houses are the Hastings and Skinner Buildings, which are the main teaching blocks. Next to them lie the Bristol-Myers and William R Miller Science Centre, opened in 2001. The School also has excellent Art, Design and Technology facilities in the Pringle Centre.

A new Sports Centre, comprising a 25-metre pool, Squash Courts, Fitness Centre, Dance Studio, Sports Hall and changing facilities, was completed in 2002 and a climbing wall was installed in 2006. A championship standard four-court indoor Tennis Centre will open in 2008.

A £2.5m refurbishment of the day and boarding houses began in February 2004. There are five Houses; two for day pupils and the three for boarders. Boarders in their first year share study bedrooms moving into single rooms in the Upper Sixth. There is access throughout each House to the School's intranet and resource rooms for day pupils are similarly equipped. Cadogan House provides accommodation for boys and girls aged 8 to 13 years boarding at Culford Prep School.

In 1985 Culford Pre-Prep School opened in Fieldgate House. A combination of new and entirely refurbished buildings, it provides teaching for 80 boys and girls from Reception through to age seven in a delightful setting within the grounds. This School was extended in 1994 and in 2003 a multi-purpose assembly hall, the Weston Hall, was added. A purpose-designed Nursery opened in a separate building in 2008.

A fully-equipped Medical Centre, supervised by a resident SRN, includes provision for residential care when necessary. The School also has a Tuck Shop and Uniform Shop.

Games. The School is set in a 480-acre park of great beauty landscaped by Humphry Repton, and there are ample facilities for physical recreation. The Sports Centre and astroturf pitches were completed in 2002. The 1st XI Cricket pitch has been described as one of the most beautifully sited in the country. A championship standard four-court indoor Tennis Centre will open in 2008. The main games are Rugby, Hockey and Cricket for the boys, Hockey, Netball, Tennis and Rounders for the girls. However, many options are available to pupils including Athletics, Climbing, Swimming, Canoeing, Squash, Sailing, Sub-Aqua, Basketball, Golf and Riding. Pupils may also fish in our well-stocked lake or learn to clay pigeon shoot on the school's estate.

Curriculum. The aim of the School is to provide a broad and balanced education making the best of a pupil's academic potential. Core subjects at GCSE are English Language and Literature, Mathematics, Science and a foreign language. Pupils choose additional subjects from a range of options. Their choice is guided by their House Tutor who, with the Housemaster or Housemistress, has responsibility for their academic and social progress. Information and Communication Technology is an integral part of the curriculum. The Sixth Form offers a wide choice of subjects. Pupils usually study four subjects at AS level, followed by three at A2. The Head of Scholars runs an enhancement programme that is compulsory for all Scholars and Exhibitioners, and open to all other interested pupils. Several pupils each year gain admission to Oxford and Cambridge.

Religion. The School is a Methodist foundation but children of all backgrounds are welcomed. All pupils attend Christian assemblies and all boarders attend a service on Sunday. Pupils are prepared for confirmation into both the Anglican and Methodist Churches in accordance with their parents' wishes.

Music. Music plays an important part in the life of the School which has strong links with the Cathedral in Bury St Edmunds. There are many choirs, orchestras and chamber ensembles. Regular concerts are held in order to give pupils of all ages opportunities to perform in public. Individual music tuition is offered in voice, piano, organ and all orchestral instruments. Pupils are also encouraged to form their own bands and perform to the school at its annual music festival.

School Activities. There is an extensive range of clubs and societies from academic and creative through to sporting and outdoor pursuits. Many pupils participate in the Duke of Edinburgh's Award Scheme or choose to join the CCF. Drama is very strong, including House plays as well as major productions: these include regular musicals and plays for different sections of the school. The School arranges a varied programme of lectures and recitals of general interest. Pupils are encouraged to take part in Community Service Activities, which cover a wide range of services to the School and the local community. In addition, there are sponsored activities and events in support of local and national charities.

Members of staff regularly take pupils on visits and expeditions. Recent expeditions include China, Morocco and Venice, skiing in France, Switzerland and the USA, and sports tours in the United Kingdom, Asia, Europe and Australia.

Entry. The majority of pupils join in September at age 7+ and 11+ (Culford Preparatory School) and at 13+ and 16+ (Culford Senior School). Entrance examinations are held in the January and February of the year of entry or pupils may enter having passed Common Entrance in June. Entry to the Sixth Form is on the basis of GCSE performance or its equivalent for overseas candidates.

Entry to Culford Pre-Preparatory School is by informal assessment just prior to enrolment.

Applications are welcome from individuals throughout the year, subject to places being available.

Visits. If you wish to visit Culford, the Headmaster will be delighted to welcome you. Please contact the Admissions Office to arrange an appointment on 01284 729308 or to ask for a copy of the school prospectus. Alternatively visit www.culford.co.uk for more information.

Scholarships and Exhibitions. (*see Scholarship Entries section*). The School holds its own scholarship examinations between November (Sixth Form Scholarships) and January/February for entry in the following September.

Fees per term (2008-2009). Day £2,300–£4,840, Boarding £5,460–£7,600.

Old Culfordians' Association. Chairman of OCA, c/o Culford School.

Charitable status. Culford School is a Registered Charity, number 310486. It exists to provide education for boys and girls.

Dame Allan's Boys' School

Fenham Newcastle-upon-Tyne NE4 9YJ
Tel: 0191 275 0608 (School); 0191 274 5910 (Bursar)
Fax: 0191 275 1502 (School); 0191 275 1501 (Bursar)
e-mail: enquiries@dameallans.co.uk
website: www.dameallans.co.uk

The School was founded in 1705 by Dame Eleanor Allan and in 1935 was moved to Fenham on a site of 13 acres.

Governors:
Chairman: Mr E Ward
Vice-Chairman: Mr B W Adcock

Mrs K Bruce
Mrs G Coffey
Miss M Foster, BA, FRGS
Mrs O Grant, OBE
Dr J A Hellen, MA, PhD
Prof P D Manning
Mrs M E Slater, MBE, JP
Mrs J Slesenger
Mr A M Stanley
Mr D Tait Walker
Mr T St A Warde-Aldam
Miss J Weatherall
Revd N Wilson
Mr G I Wanless

Ex officio:
The Lord Mayor of Newcastle upon Tyne
The Dean of Newcastle upon Tyne
The Vicar of the Parish of St John

Clerk to the Governors and Bursar: J Fleck, ACMA

***Principal*: J R Hind**, MA Downing College, Cambridge, MEd Newcastle, PhD Durham

Vice-Principal: W J Lomas, BA, MA Newcastle
Assistant Head: S N Hamilton, BA, MA Durham
Head of Sixth Form: D C Henry, BSc Heriot-Watt, FIMLS
Assistant Head of Sixth Form: J C Downie, BSc Lancaster, MA Newcastle, CBiol, MIBiol
Chaplain: Revd Canon J M Dotchin

J A Benn, BA Newcastle
D R Bisset, BSc East Anglia
H R Borland, MA Aberdeen
J Carrick, BA Durham
A C Chuter, BA Warwick
A H Davison, BDS, BA Newcastle MA, DCCI OU
J L Devine, BA Liverpool
J Etherington, BSc Manchester
M J Ford, BSc, MEd Newcastle
L J Friel, BA Hull
J P Gardner, MA Girton College, Cambridge
R Gates, MA New Hall, Cambridge
N J Glover, BA Durham
F Gold, BA Oxford
P Healey, BSc Newcastle
W P Hudson, BSc Loughborough
T Kingston, BA Leeds
K S Lewis, BA Goldsmiths College, London, ATD Leicester, CDT Trent
E Marsh, BSc Hull
B Nixon, BSc Northumbria
D F O'Connor, BSc Durham
R Oliver BA Manchester
L Phillips, MA University College, Oxford, BSc Middlesex
J P E Procter, BA York
C Pulford, BA Leeds
E Renshaw, BSc Nottingham
G Sharp, BSc Durham
P Surrage, BSc Durham
D W Tallent, BMus Kansas
P Thompson, BA Northumbria
C N Tuck, BSc, PhD Aston
S Watt, BA Newcastle
B J Whitehouse, BA Liverpool
P Wildsmith, BSc Birmingham, CBiol, MIBiol, MBES
K Wilkinson, BA Sheffield
G J M Witney, BSc London
T J Wood, BA Newcastle
S E Wright, BA Northumbria

Junior Department:
Head: A J Edge, MA St Andrews

A Brown, BSc Northumbria
L P Cruickshank, BA Newcastle
D M Farren, BA Warwick
M Hallowell, BA Newcastle
K Carruthers, BSc Loughborough
K Ellis, BA Liverpool

There are approximately 500 boys in the School, which has a three-form entry at 11+. With the Girls' School, which is in the same building, it shares a mixed Sixth Form and a mixed Junior Department (8+ to 10+).

The Main School follows the normal range of subjects, leading to examination at GCSE. German is introduced in Year 8 and Spanish is offered in Year 9.

Most boys stay on into the Sixth Form and from there normally go on to Higher Education.

Buildings. In recent years, developments have included additional classrooms, a new Library, Computer Resource Centre, Technology Centre, ICT network, a new Sixth Form Centre, and a Drama and Dance Studio.

School Societies. The current list includes: outdoor pursuits (including Duke of Edinburgh's Award scheme and orienteering), choirs, orchestra, drama, computing, art, chess, Christian Fellowship, Amnesty International, history, science, electronics, mathematics, dance, public speaking, and debating.

Pastoral. Each boy is placed in the care of a Form Teacher who oversees his progress and development. In the Sixth Form he has a Tutor who is responsible for both academic and pastoral care.

Careers. There is a structured programme, beginning in Year 9, with a significant contribution from Connexions.

Sixth Form. In 1989 the Sixth Form was merged with that of our sister School, giving both Schools the rare constitution of single-sex education (11–16) with a co-educational Sixth Form. The Head of Sixth Form is Mr D C Henry who will welcome enquiries concerning admission.

Games. The principal games are Rugby Football and Cricket. The School playing field adjoins the premises. Cross-Country, Swimming and Athletics are also available. Hockey and Tennis are introduced as options from Year 9 and older boys may also participate in a range of other sporting activities.

Admission. Governors' Entrance Scholarships are awarded on the results of the Entrance Examinations held annually in the Spring Term at all ages from 8+ to 13+. A limited number of Bursaries are available to pupils aged 11+ and over on entry.

Fees per term (2008-2009). Senior School £2,894; Junior Department £2,277.

Dame Allan's Old Allanians Association. Joint President: Mr D Stewart, 49 Lanesborough Court, Gosforth, Newcastle, NE3 3BZ.

Charitable status. Dame Allan's Schools is a Registered Charity, number 1084965. It exists to provide education for children.

Dauntsey's School

West Lavington Devizes Wiltshire SN10 4HE
Tel: 01380 814500
Fax: 01380 814501
e-mail: information@dauntseys.wilts.sch.uk
website: www.dauntseys.wilts.sch.uk

Founded in 1542 by Alderman William Dauntesey of the Mercers' Company. New School buildings erected in 1895 and extended regularly from 1919 to the present.

Governors:
Chairman: R Handover, Esq
Vice-Chairman: Lady J Benson, OBE, JP, DL

Prof L M Harwood, MA, BSc, MSc, PhD, CChem, FRSC
D C Watney, Esq
Mrs D J Main
Mrs M Clough
M J H Liversidge, Esq, BA, FSA, FRSA
Major R P Matters
J A Rendell, Esq, BSc, FCA
A S Macpherson, Esq, BA, ACA, JP
The Hon Mrs H W Palmer
G D Sutton, Esq
J D Hedges, Esq
Mrs S Courth
Brigadier M S Rutter-Jerome
R M Bernard, Esq
Mrs P L P Floyer-Acland, MA, JP
A Silcock, Esq

Clerk to the Governors: P M A Nokes, Esq, MA, MPhil

***Head Master*: Stewart Roberts**, MA

Deputy Head: Mrs J F E Upton, BSc

Second Master: M C B McFarland, BA

Director of Studies: M A C Neve, BSc

Head of Lower School: Mrs S J Corke, BSc

Staff:
Dr T J Price, MA
A J Hatcher, BSc
W J Corke, BSc, CBiol, MIBiol
M K Dolan, MA
S J Hardman, BEd
T S L Gardiner, BA
G R Parry, BSc
Mrs C V Wakefield, BA
Mrs S Woods, BSc, CBiol, MIBiol
Miss E S Conidaris, HDipEd PE
Mrs N-J Wingham, MA, RCA
Mrs K M Phipps, BA
Mrs L Lloyd-Jukes, BA
Mrs E C Gardiner, BA
P K Wheatley, MA
T R Marris
N Yates, BSc, MSc
Miss J E Dalton, BA
Miss S Cooke, BA
J P Plews, BA
Mrs E A Edmonson-Smith, CertEd, DipRSA, AMBDA
A J Palmer, BSc, AIEA
T J Price, MA, DPhil
Miss L Scrace, BA PE, HDE
J F O'Hanlon, BSc
Mrs C Coupe, BEd
R A Allfree-Reid, BA
A J Lewis, BSc
A Pickford, BA
Mrs A Abbatt, BA
J J Hutchinson, BSc
M Olsen, BA
M R Dyson, BEd
Mrs E Scott, BSc
N J Spears, BA
Mrs C Hunter, BA
R M Jackson, BA
P J Wingham, MA
Mrs A Jackson, BA
A J F Brown, BA
Miss S Gifford, MA, BD
T Parker, MA, MSc
Mrs A C Dencher, MA
Miss L K Hill, BA
R V Lewis, BSc, PhD
D H Messenger, BA
Mrs M S Messenger, BSc
P J Thomas, BSc
Miss S Wells, MA, PhD
Mrs E O'Hanlon, BA
J Spencer, BA
Mrs S Shearn, BA
Mrs G Ward, BA
S Cloete
M D Collison, BSc
Miss E J Barwell, BA
L Björk, MA, MTh
Mrs A James, BSc
S Norton, MMath
Miss E J Wilson, BMus
Mrs E Crozier, BA
D Vernon-Jones, MA
Miss C Camacho, BA
Mrs K Morris, Ma
Miss M Ryan, BA
Miss J Gay
D Kenworthy, BA
Miss A Shuttleworth, BSc
T Bowley, BSc
P Clear, MA
D Blewitt, BSc
Mrs D Hills, BA
Mrs T Wilks, BA
Mrs S Aikman, BA

Music:
C B Thompson, GMus (*Director of Music*)
C Totney, BA (*Assistant Director of Music*)
Mrs D Thompson, GMus (*Coordinator of Instrumental Music*)
C W Sims (*Head of Music Technology*)
Miss E J Wilson (*Teacher of Music*)
Mrs G Alford, BA (*Oboe*)
Mrs L A Hatcher, (*Flute*)
P Skelton, BA, LRAM (*Piano*)
Miss R Jardine, BA, MTC, ALCM (*Brass*)
Mrs M J Payne, BA, LRAM, LTCL (*Piano*)
A D Stockley, LGSM (*Percussion*)
T C Richards, ARCM (*Violin and Viola*)
S Cippola, ERNCM, PPRNCM (*Clarinet and Saxophone*)
D R Kniveton, BA, LTCL (*Flute*)
Miss J A Britton, LWCMD, LTCL (*Clarinet and Saxophone*)
Miss P Price-Jones (*Singing*)
S Nicholls (*Electric Guitar*)
D J Arcoleo (*Guitar*)
A S Roberts (*Piano*)
Mrs W Sims (*Piano*)
M J Lomas (*Brass*)
P Henley (*Singing*)
Mrs J Morton (*Singing*)
Mrs C Notley (*Piano*)

Houses and Housemasters/Housemistresses:

Upper School:
Evans: Mr & Mrs N Yates
Farmer: Mr J F O'Hanlon
Fitzmaurice: Mr & Mrs R A Reid
Hemens: Mr P J Thomas
Jeanne: Mrs A L Jackson
King-Reynolds: Mrs E Crozier
Lambert: Mrs K M Phipps
Mercers: Mr & Mrs S J Hardman

Lower School:
Manor: Mr & Mrs D Messenger
Forbes: Mr J P Plews
Rendell: Mr M Olsen
Scott: Mrs G S Ward

Chaplain: Revd D R Johnson, MA, BSc

Bursar: Air Cdr S Lilley RAF Ret'd

Assistant Bursar: P W Hagelthorn, Esq

Registrar: Mrs J H Sagers, BA

Head Master's Secretary: Mrs D Caiger

Medical Officers:
B J Jones, MA, FRCS, DRCDG
C C Cowen, MA, FRCS, DRCDG

Sanatorium Sister: Sister S Crawford

Number. 750 Pupils aged between 11–18 years: 400 boys, 350 girls, approximately 40% board.

Residence. On entering the School at 11 or 13 pupils are in the Lower School where they stay until they reach the end of Year 9. They then move into the Senior School Houses. Half the Houses are for boarders and the other half for day pupils.

Situation. The School is set in an estate, of over 100 acres in the Vale of Pewsey in Wiltshire. The Manor House, a mansion with its own woodland and playing fields, is the Junior boarding house for pupils in Years 7–9.

Recent Developments. Generous benefactions by the Mercers' Company and the Farmer Trustand the generosity of parents and Old Dauntseians, have made possible the following additions: Memorial Hall which includes the Chapel; Music School; new Biology Laboratories. A Senior Girls' Boarding House opened in 1977 and was extended in 1988.. The Awdry

Sports Hall was built in 1980 and next to it a 25-metre Indoor Heated Swimming Pool opened in 1985. The Design and Technology Centre opened in 1987. A new Senior Boys' Boarding House in September 1991and another Senior Boys' Boarding House was extended in 1993 to accommodate additional demand for boarding places. An all-weather floodlit playing surface was completed during 1992. In 1995 there were major extensions to the Music and Dining facilities, and in 1996 a second senior girls' boarding house was opened. During 1999 a 5-Studio Art Centre opened, and in the summer of 2000 a new Library and Study Centre (including IT stations) opened. 2003 saw a new Biology Department and Physics and Chemistry laboratories. A new Senior Girls boarding house was added during 2004 and 2005 and since then an additional £5 million has been spent on boarding facilities.

Curriculum. The School is modern in its outlook and affords wide facilities. Briefly the curriculum (i) provides a good general education which includes Religious Education, English, History, Geography, Economics and Business Studies, French, German, Latin, Spanish, Greek, Russian, Pure and Applied Mathematics, Physics, Chemistry, Biology, Information Technology, Music, Art, Craft, Design, Technology; (ii) prepares for the General Certificate of Secondary Education, Advanced Subsidiary and Advanced Levels and University Entrance.

Games. The major sports are Rugby Football, Hockey, Cricket and Netball. Other games played include Tennis, Squash, Athletics, Swimming, Soccer, Water Polo, Fencing and Badminton. Special attention is given to Physical Education.

Societies and other Activities. Over 80 clubs and societies – from Mountaineering to Mandarin, Fashion Design to Fencing and Sub-Aqua to Symphony Orchestra. The Sailing Club provides ocean sailing and racing in the famous yacht 'Jolie Brise' (class winner of 2006 Tall Ships' Race and the 'Round the Island' race in 2004, 2005 and 2007).

All pupils in Year 9 are members of 'Moonrakers', an outward-bound programme culminating in a week's residential camp.

Fees per term (2008-2009). Boarders £7,950; Day Pupils £4,715. There are no compulsory extras.

Admission. Boys and girls are admitted at 11 on the result of a competitive examination; at 13 on the results of Scholarship and Common Entrance examinations; to Year 12 dependent upon academic record and reports.

Scholarships. (*see Scholarship Entries section*). Scholarships open to boys and girls are awarded on examinations held each year. Awards for Music and Art are available.

Full particulars from the Registrar.

Charitable status. Dauntsey's School is a Registered Charity, number 1115638. It is dedicated to the education of boys and girls.

Dean Close School

Shelburne Road Cheltenham Gloucestershire GL51 6HE
Tel: 01242 258000
Fax: 01242 258003
e-mail: headmaster@deanclose.org.uk
website: www.deanclose.org.uk

The School was opened in 1886, in memory of Francis Close, DD, Rector of Cheltenham 1826–56 and later Dean of Carlisle. Sitting on a beautifully landscaped 50-acre site in the Regency town of Cheltenham, the School is an attractive mixture of old, traditional buildings and modern, hi-tech structures. Co-educational since 1967, Dean Close is a Christian school which believes that education is as much about building character and relationships as it is about gaining knowledge. An independent Preparatory School was established in 1949.

Motto: '*Verbum Dei Lucerna.*'

Visitor: The Rt Revd Michael Perham, The Lord Bishop of Gloucester

President: The Baroness Cox of Queensbury

Council of Members:
[1]Sir John Adye, KCMG, MA
The Revd Canon N J W Barker, MA, BTh
G W Barnes, Esq
N Bewes, Esq
Captain A R Bird, BA
Professor P Broadfoot, CBE, DSc, AcSS
[1]A J Bruckland, BA
[1]¶C J Buckett, Esq, FCA
Mrs N Cansdale, BA, MA
[1]J M Carter, Esq
[1]M J Cartwright, BA, FCA (*Treasurer*)
Mrs G A M Cocks, BA, DipEd
The Revd R M Coombs, BSc, MA
[1]C R Evans, Esq, MA
¶Professor R J W Evans, MA, PhD, FBA
N Goodwin, Esq
[1]Mrs D Greenwood
Mrs L S M Hardy, OBE, JP
The Earl of Harrowly, MA, FRICS
S M Hill, Esq, MA
H Hodgkins, Esq, ACIB
[1]The Very Revd J D Irvine, MA
E A W Jones, Esq
[1]Mrs C M Lainé, BA, JP
¶C P Lynam, Esq, MA
[1]¶I W Marsh, Esq, BSc
[1]Sir John McColl, KCB, CBE, DSO
[1]Mrs P G Napier (*Chairman of Board of Trustees*)
Sir David Pepper, KCMG, MA, DPhil
C R H Rank, Esq
B F Ribeiro, Esq, CBE, FRCS, FRCSEd
The Rt Revd P St G Vaughan
[1]The Revd Canon T P Watson
[1]The Rt Revd J S Went, MA
¶The Revd P C Youde, LLB

[1] *Member of Board of Trustees*

The Trustees are elected by the Members of Council and oversee the overall governance of the School. They carry a substantial burden of financial and legal responsibility on an entirely voluntary basis and the School is greatly indebted to them.

***Headmaster*: The Revd T M Hastie-Smith**, MA Magdalene College Cambridge, CertTheol

Second Master: R F Taylor, MA, CertEd
Deputy Head (*Academic*): A R Marchand, MA, PGCE
Senior Mistress: Mrs J Davies, MA, PGCE
Director of Studies: D R Evans, MA

Housemasters & Housemistresses:
Brook Court: J Slade (*2004*)
Dale: J P Watson (*2004*)
Fawley: Mrs V E Burroughs (*1997*)
Field: P S Montgomery (*2005*)
Gate: D B W Marsh (*2006*)
Mead: Mrs P Watson (*2001*)
Shelburne: Mrs J D Kent (*2001*)
Tower: B W Williams-Jones (*2008*)

Assistant Staff:
* *Head of Department*

Miss S F Villiers, BA, PGCE
L S Allington, BA (**Drama*)
Mrs H L Porter, BA, LRAM, PGCE (*Director of Music*)

Mrs V E Burroughs, CertEd
D J R Pellereau, MA, PGCE (**Physics*)
Mrs J D Kent, GDLM
C J Leigh, BSc, DipTheol, CertEd FE (**Computing*)
P S Montgomery, MA, PGCE
Mrs F M Harris, MA, PGCE
Mrs C Allen, BMus, ALCM, LGSM, PGCE
Miss A E Ash, BDes, PGCE
P J P Anstis, MA, MEd, PhD, PGCE (*Examination Coordinator, *Chemistry*)
J M Allen, MA, PGCE (**Classics*)
D M Fullerton, MA (**Careers*)
Miss I M Carames-Castelo, BA, PGCE
J P Watson, BA, CertEd
Mrs P S Watson
Mrs M Cormack, MEd, Cert TEFLA
A J George, MA, PGCE (**Mathematics, Deputy Director of Studies*)
Dr S Thomas, BEd, MPhil, PhD (**Learning Support*)
Mrs L Chandler-Corris, BSc, FAETC, TEFL
C R Haslam, MA, PGCE (*Senior Tutor*)
J Slade, MA
S G Hamill, BA (**English*)
P J J Garner, MA, PGCE
Miss R J Donaldson, BSc, PGCE (**Academic PE*)
I T Dunbar, BA, PGCE
Miss L A Burton, BA (**Religious Studies*)
A J Davies, FISTC
Mrs H M Swan, BEd
Mrs B J Edkins, CertEd
Mrs C J Evans, BA, PGCE (*Director of Art*)
A R Needs, BSc, PGCE, AMRSC
R M Bishop, BMus (**Strings*)
Miss R M O Vines, BA, FVCM, LALAM, ALAM (**Speech & Drama*)
Mrs V Barbour, BSc, PGCE
D D Evans, BSc (**Design Technology*)
P Davies, MA, PGCE (**History*)
A R Swarbrick, BSc, PGCE
M D Tottman, MA, MBA (**Economics & Business Studies*)
G Tredgett
Miss K E Miller, BA
B W Nicholas, MA, ARCO (*Director of Choral Music*)
A A Groom, BA, PGCE
B P Price, BSc, PGCE
Mrs R S Rushton, BA, PGCE
The Revd E L Talbot, MA (*Chaplain*)
Miss A E Tebb, BA, PGCE
B W Williams-Jones, MA, PGCE
Miss J Underhill, MA, BA, PGCE, Cert TESOL
D B W Marsh, MEng, PGCE
R Gwilliam, BA, PGCE (*Director of Sport*)
A G A Milne, BA, PGCE
C J Hooper, BA, PGCE (**Modern Languages*)
Miss C Osolin, BA, PGCE
M J Clarkson, MA, PGCE
M D Jacobson
Mrs L Lawrence, BA
D J M Soward, MA, FRSA, LRAM, ARCM
Mrs D Stanley, BA
Miss K S Roberts, BSc
Miss J McFarlane, BA, PGCE
Miss G Hildick-Smith
J E Talbot, MA, PGCE (**Geography*)
J C Niblett, MA, PGCE (**Physics*)
P M Davies, BSc, PGCE (**Science*)
Miss A Y Webb, MA, PGCE
Dr M Bradley
Mr P J C Hicks
Miss T L Williams
Mr I V McGowan
Miss S T Webb

Medical Officers (both Schools):
I D Ramsay, MBChB, DObst, RCOG
C C Burgess, MBChB

SSI, CCF: WO2 B Lloyd

Preparatory School
(*see entry in IAPS section*)

Headmaster: The Revd Leonard Browne, MA
Deputy Head: A Brown, BEd
Director of Studies: Mrs L Sorrell, BA

Pre-Preparatory School
(*see entry in IAPS section*)

Headmistress: Mrs S E Bennett, CertEd
Deputy Head: Miss A E Naylor, BA
Key Stage 1 Coordinator: Mrs M L Badham, CertEd

Bursar: J M Lancashire, MA, ACA
Deputy Bursar (*Finance*) Mrs K A Walton, BA, ACA
Deputy Bursar (*Estates*) P L Bray

Admissions Tutor: Mrs M McClaran, MA
Registrar (*DCS*): Mrs S F H Smith, BSc, Mrs A E Taylor
Head of Marketing (*DCS*): Mrs T C Colbert-Smith, BA, MCIM
Admissions Tutor/Marketing (*DCPS*): Mrs R Chaplin, BSc

Headmaster's PA (*DCS*): Mrs J Harrington
Headmaster's PA (*DCPS*): Mrs R Koumi, BSc

Admission and Withdrawal. Admissions to the Senior School at 13 is through Common Entrance or English, Maths and Verbal Reasoning papers, as appropriate. Sixth Form: examination and interview, 4 Bs and 2 Cs minimum at GCSE. Prospectus and application forms are available from the Registrar who is also happy to arrange a visit at a time to suit. There is a non-returnable fee of £100 and a returnable deposit of £750 payable one year before entry. One term's notice is required before a pupil is withdrawn from the School.

Inclusive Fees per term (2008-2009). Boarders £8,720, Day Boarders £6,620, Day Pupils £6,160. The Governors normally set the fees in September and do not vary them during the year.

Term of Entry. We prefer to accept pupils in September but will make exceptions at any time of year, even in the middle of a term, if a good reason exists.

Scholarships. (*see Scholarship Entries section*). The School offers scholarships, exhibitions and bursaries at age 13 and for entry into the Sixth Form. The six areas of talent which are recognised are academic, music, sport, drama, art and design technology. An all-rounder award is also available at 13. The size of all awards is the subject of negotiation and a descriptive leaflet is available.

Number and Organisation. There are 492 in the Senior School (13–18). The Sixth Form comprises approximately 40% of the School. There are eight Houses (three for boarding boys, two for day boys, two for girl boarders and one for day girls). Housemasters take immediate responsibility for pupils' work, careers, applications for Universities and further education. A tutorial system ensures that all pupils have an adult who takes a particular interest in them, both academically and pastorally. There is a Careers Department. The Prep School (2½–13) has approximately 374 pupils of whom 162 are girls. There are scholarships available for entry into the Prep School.

Work. Pupils do not have to choose between science and arts until after GCSE and even then the choice of subjects for A Level is wide enough to allow a mixed course if desired. In the lower part of the School pupils are setted rather than streamed. Included in the Lower School timetable are design technology, physical education, ceramics, cooking, computer studies and art, as well as a normal academic curriculum. Modern Languages are taught with the aid of audio-active equipment. The language centre, high technology seminar room, music school, art school, modern laboratories, computer, electronics, photographic and creative workshops combine excellent teaching and leisure facilities which are available both in timetabled and extra-curricular time. Much of the accommodation has been built in the last twenty years and is modern and purpose-built. A professional 550-seat theatre houses an ambitious programme of productions. There is also an open-air theatre. As well as several orchestras, wind band, many ensembles and the Chapel Choir, the School has a Choral Society which performs a major work at least once a year. Tuition in any number of musical instruments is available as an extra. Free tuition is provided for music award holders and high-grade musicians. The theatre also affords first-class concert facilities.

Religious Education. The teaching and Chapel Services are in accordance with the Church of England and the School's strong Evangelical tradition is maintained. The Chaplain prepares members of the School for Confirmation each year. Most services are in the School Chapel. There is a fine pipe organ. There is a thriving Christian Union and each House has a Bible Study.

Games. The School has a 25m indoor swimming pool and a new £3m sports hall, both used all the year round. There are two astroturf pitches and a large number of tennis courts. Hockey, rugby, cricket, basketball, netball, rounders, badminton, athletics, tennis, squash and cross-country are the main sports.

Health. The School has three qualified Sisters with Assistants and visiting Doctors. There is a surgery and a sanatorium.

Outside Activities. A very active Combined Cadet Force with RN, RAF and Army sections trains every Wednesday afternoon and, for some, Silver and Gold Duke of Edinburgh's Awards can be pursued. A large Community Action group gets involved with projects on a local, national and international level.

Denstone College
A Woodard School

Uttoxeter Staffs ST14 5HN
Tel: 01889 590484
Fax: 01889 591295
e-mail: admissions@denstonecollege.org
website: www.denstonecollege.org

Denstone College is a Woodard School.

Achievement, Confidence and Happiness are central to the College philosophy, in which girls and boys are always encouraged to aim high and so reach their full potential. Founded in 1868, the College is rich in tradition and history, but combines this with a forward thinking approach to education.

The College offers a rounded education, where proper emphasis is placed on academic achievement and high standards are the top priority. A wide range of other opportunities, however, ensures that every individual finds and develops his or her own special talents. Denstonians emerge with a degree of self-esteem and confidence, possible only as a result of so much opportunity and challenge. They have the qualifications, skills and personality to make their mark in today's competitive world.

Motto: '*Lignum Crucis Arbor Scientiae.*'

Visitor: The Bishop of Lichfield

School Council:
E S Roper (*Custos*)
The Revd Canon B D Clover MA, LTCL (*Senior Provost*)
R J Bokros
A D Coley
Mrs P Gee
Mrs S R Gouldstone
His Honour Judge R T N Orme, LLB
A D Roper
Sqn Ldr S P H Smith
Miss E M Mullenger, BA, CertEd
J S F Cash, BSc, MRICS
Dr R Meredith, MBChB, MRCGP
Revd J D Makepeace, MA
J B Vinecombe
G Gregory, MA, BA Hons Econ
Mrs B C Hyde, BA Hons, Dip MS, MBA

***Headmaster*: D M Derbyshire**, BA, MSc

Second Masters:
B J Gillions, BEd
J Hartley, BA (*Registrar*)

Chaplain: The Revd J J Wilson, BSc, BTh

Masters and Mistresses:
J S Jilbert, BA, FRGS
N M Green, BTech
A N James, BA (*†Shrewsbury*)
D A Barker, BSc
Miss J R Morris, GMus (*†Meynell*)
T P S O'Brien, DA
R C Menneer, BSc, CNAA
M P Raisbeck, BA, CNAA (*†Selwyn*)
Mrs S A Leak, BEd
S J Phennah, BEd
Mrs K Hood, BSc
Miss J H Plewes, BA (*†Woodard*)
A J Wray, BA
M J Bennett, BSc (*Head of Middle School*)
Mrs R L Smith, BSc
J M Tomlinson, BSc (*†Heywood*)
Mrs V A Derbyshire, BA
Mrs P Jilbert, BA
Mrs P A Provan
A C Bonell, BEd
R Ayton, BA
D T Önac, BSc
M S Skipper, BMus
J S Peel, BSc
Miss F L Toomey
C J Sassi, MA
Mrs S Parsons, BA, MA
M J Porter, BA (*†Philips*)
N J Hill, BSc
P D Brice, BA
Mrs M J Oakes, BA
J P Tuxford, BA
Miss A M Donnelly, BA
B J R Duerden, BSc
G A J Mason, BEd
S Nandi, BSc
Mrs K Rylance, BSc
L J Cottrell, BSc
Miss R C Dubsky, BA
R M Journeaux, BA
Miss E Walpole, BSc
Dr J H Cocker, BSC, PhD
S R Francis, BSc
Miss M Bodnarova
Miss M P Falces
C J Lush
Mrs M Moore
M R M Norris (*Head of Senior School*)
Dr R Norris
Mrs M Silvey
Mrs J A Teather (*†Moss Moor*)

Visiting Music Staff:
Mrs A O'Brien, DRSAMD, PGDip RSAMD, ARCM (*Piano, Singing, Recorder*)
D Gore (*Guitar*)
R Banks, FTCL, ARAM, ARCM, LGSM (*Brass*)
B Griffiths (*Percussion*)
Mrs S Bloor, GRSM, LRAM (*Piano*)
Mrs S Stewart, GRNCM (*Violin*)
Miss A Chadwick, GBSM, ABSM (*Flute*)
R Shaw, BA, GRSM, PGDip, ARCM, ABSM (*Saxophone, Clarinet*)
S J Ryde, ARCM, ARCO
Ms S Harrop, GBSM, PGDip
Ms C M Thomson, LRAM, GRSM, PGCE, CDRS
Ms H Puutio, LMOC Finland

Chapel Organist: G Walker, MA, ARCO, FRSA

Finance Bursar and Clerk to the School Council: D M Martin, ACIB

Operations Bursar: J S Peel, BSc

Headmaster's Secretary: Mrs T F Wedgwood, BA

Admissions Secretary: Mrs V J Carman

Preparatory School: Smallwood Manor

Headmaster: Mr C Cann

(*For further details about the Prep School, see entry in IAPS section.*)

Location. Denstone College is situated on the Staffordshire/Derbyshire border, 6 miles north of Uttoxeter in 100 acres of grounds. The site is located in magnificent countryside, but is well served by road, rail and air.

Organisation. The College is divided into the following units: Junior School (ages 11–14, Years 7, 8 and 9), Middle School (ages 14–16, Years 10 and 11), and Senior School (ages 17–18, Sixth Form which typically numbers around 130 pupils).

All girls and boys are in one of the six houses, each numbering about 85 members, with a total roll of 528. Weekly boarding is a popular option. Just over a quarter of our pupils board, and one third are girls, who have separate boarding accommodation.

Smallwood Manor, also a Woodard School, is 9 miles away. Age range 3–11.

Buildings. The main building contains classrooms, day and boarding areas, studies, Dining Hall, Chapel, Theatre and resident staff accommodation. A great deal of school life is thus centred in this main block, which also includes IT facilities, library, and a language laboratory.

The Sports Hall, laboratories, other classrooms, indoor heated swimming pool, Art Centre, Design and Technology Centre, Music School and other buildings, such as the Medical Centre and School Shop, are elsewhere in the grounds.

Recent and Future Developments. Over £3 million has been spent on improving our buildings and on building new facilities in recent years.

Most recent developments include a second Astroturf (December 2006), £750,000 invested in the kitchens and dining area, and the updating of boarding facilities, including the development of a Sixth Form girls' boarding house. Further expenditure, particularly on a new classroom block, is planned over the next three years.

Curriculum. In the Junior School (ages 11 to 14, Years 7, 8 & 9) all follow roughly the same spread of subjects: English, Drama, French, Spanish, Mathematics, Physics, Chemistry, Biology, History, Geography, Art, Music, DT, Religious Studies, Information Technology, and PE.

Girls and boys enter the Middle School at the beginning of Year 10. Subjects are studied in option blocks. Mathematics, English Language and Literature, a Modern Language, RS and Science are core subjects, and three others are chosen from those listed above, along with Business and Economics GCSE.

Girls and boys then specialise in AS and A2 Levels, chosen in an option system appropriate to the current discussions regarding Sixth Form Curriculum nationally. Four AS Levels will normally be taken in the Lower Sixth. Subjects offered are Mathematics, Further Maths, Critical Thinking, Physics, Chemistry, Biology, English Language, English Literature, French, Spanish, History, Geography, Economics, Psychology, Politics, Art, Theatre Studies, PE, and DT. There will also be a minority who will study, in varying numbers from year to year, Music and Religious Studies. An extremely flexible timetable is possible and we aim to offer most combinations of subjects.

The majority of pupils take A Levels, with the aim of going on to University. Each year, some girls and boys are prepared for Oxford or Cambridge entrance. Over 50% of the 2007 Upper Sixth were accepted into one of the Russell Group Universities.

The School is well-equipped with computer rooms, laboratories, and a 200-seat Theatre. Each department remains up-to-date with subject development and members of staff regularly attend courses and conferences.

Class sizes are small. Up to Year 11, 20 is an average class size, and in the Sixth Form sets vary from 6 to 14.

In addition to having a Head of School and Head of House each pupil has a Tutor with whom he or she meets regularly to discuss work and progress, and both half termly and end of term grades and reports are issued.

Pupils in both Junior and Middle School have a number of staff supervised Homework sessions incorporated into the school day. Boarding members of Fifth Form, Lower Sixth and Upper Sixth have shared or single studies.

Out of Class Activities. The aim is to provide as wide a variety of opportunities for pupils of differing aptitudes and inclinations as possible.

Games: The College has 2 full-size all-weather hockey pitches, one of which is floodlit and provides 9 tennis courts. A nine-hole handicap-standard golf course has been laid out to the west of the College. There is an indoor heated swimming pool, and the Sports Hall accommodates indoor sports as well as a fitness room.

The main sports in the Michaelmas Term are rugby for the boys and hockey for the girls, with opportunities for other games. In the Lent Term these change to hockey and football for the boys and netball for the girls, along with swimming, cross country and others. In the summer there is a degree of choice between cricket, athletics, swimming, golf, and tennis and rounders for girls.

In the course of the year there is opportunity for boys and girls to take part in a wide variety of sports, in which they can represent both their House and the School.

CCF and Pioneers: There is also a Combined Cadet Force with Army and Royal Air Force sections, a climbing group and The Duke of Edinburgh's Award Scheme. Over the last decade about 25% of sixth formers have gained the Gold Award.

The Arts: There are set times each week when priority is given to non-sporting clubs and activities, giving pupils opportunities in a wide range of experiences. Music plays a central role in College life. There is a School Orchestra, Swing Band, and Jazz Ensemble.The Chapel choir sings at the main service each Friday. In addition, there are also other specialist choirs and small instrumental groups. Music is included in the curriculum of Years 7-9 and in addition tuition in most instruments from both resident and visiting staff is available. A number of musical events takes place annually.

Traditionally there is a major play or musical at the end of the Michaelmas term. The College has a proud record of 104 Shakespearean productions. The 2007 School Play was "The Visit", in addition to which were the Junior School Play ("Four Canterbury Tales" in 2007), the Junior Drama Festival and performances from GCSE Drama and A Level Theatre Studies students.

The DT Department is fully equipped with Art and Pottery centres. These facilities are housed in the Centenary Building and allow pupils to fulfil abilities in design, woodwork, metalwork, painting, drawing, ceramics, and printing.

Entrance. Pupils wishing to join Year 7 (age 11+) or Year 9 (age 13+) sit examinations at the College in January. Pupils wishing to join Year 9 (age 13+) from Independent Preparatory Schools sit the Common Entrance examination in June. There is also entry in the Sixth Form, an increasingly popular option for girls and boys after their GCSEs.

Occasionally pupils enter at other ages and times. They need to show that they have attained the necessary academic standard either by public examination results or by sitting papers set by the College.

The Registration Fee is £50 and the Joining Fee is £100.

Scholarships. (*see Scholarship Entries section*). Scholarships and Exhibitions are offered annually, of varying value up to 40%. They are competed for in three main age groups:

First, some are awarded to the best candidates in the January and February examinations referred to above; second, to candidates from Preparatory Schools (and internal College candidates) who are under 14 on 1 June of the year in which the examination is taken; and third for Sixth Form entry.

In all Scholarships, in addition to academic excellence, all-round ability and out-of-school activities and interests are taken into account.

Scholarships are offered annually for Music (instrumental and choral), Art, DT, Drama, Sport, Golf and 'All Round' ability.

A number of bursaries may be awarded to those in genuine financial need. Special consideration is given to the children of Clergy, Old Denstonians and Service Children.

Fees per term (2008-2009). Boarding: £5,735 Junior School, £6,287 Middle/Senior School (including all items of board and education other than music lessons and extra tuition).

Day: £2,988 Junior School, £3,610 Middle/Senior School.

The Old Denstonian Club. *Secretary*: Mr M S Smith, Denstone College, Uttoxeter, Staffs. Regional Clubs based in London, Manchester and at the College.

Charitable status. Denstone College is a Registered Charity, number 1102588. It exists to provide Christian education for children.

Dollar Academy

Dollar Clackmannanshire FK14 7DU
Tel: 01259 742511
Fax: 01259 742867
e-mail: rector@dollaracademy.org.uk
website: www.dollaracademy.org.uk

The Academy, founded in 1818 and the oldest co-educational boarding and day school in Britain, is situated in forty acres of its own grounds on the southern slopes of the Ochil Hills, 30 miles from Edinburgh, 38 from Glasgow, 40 from St Andrews and 10 miles east of Stirling. The Academy is renowned for its academic reputation, for its inclusive international outlook, and for its range of co-curricular activities. In recent years, all the boarding houses have been extensively refurbished, and the quality of the facilities throughout the school campus is of the highest order. The A-listed Playfair Building of 1821 is surrounded by a number of impressive modern buildings named after distinguished Scots.

Motto: '*Juventutis veho fortunas*'

Governors:
Chairman: J B Cameron, CBE, FRAgS, AIAgE

Vice-Chairmen:
Professor J McEwen, MBChB, FRCP, FFPH, FFOM, FDSRCS, FMEdSci
Professor R E Morris, MA, DPhil

Members:
M W Balfour, BCom, CA
A T Black
K M Brown, MA
Mrs D A Burt, MCSP
Cllr A D Campbell, CA
A I Campbell
D M Clark, MA, LLB, WS
Dr G B Curry, BA Mod, PhD, DIC
Revd S Fletcher, BA, MA, MDiv
R P S Harris, BCom, DipCom, CA
Mrs G Hepburn
Dr M A Hogg, LLB, LLM, PhD, NP, FRSA
E T I King, LVO, MBA
J McAslan, RIBA, FRSA, ARIAS
C J Milne
Dr H W Sutherland, MBChB, FRCOG
A P M Walls, CA
A G Webb, BCom

Bursar and Clerk to Governors: J StJ Wilkes, MA
Assistant Bursar: Mrs J Johnson, MA, ACA
Bursar's PA: Mrs M Campbell, BA

***Rector*: J S Robertson**, MA

Deputy Rector: G P Daniel, MA (Eng Lit/Lang), MA (Med Lit)

Assistant Rectors:
Mrs K Robertson, MA (*also Head of Prep & Junior School*)
J M Hendry, BSc, PhD, CPhys, MInstP
Mrs L H Hutchison, BA

Director of Studies: S P Johnson, MA
Director of Sport: J Foster, DipPE

* *Head of Department*
† *Houseparent*
‡ *Head of Year*

Prep & Junior School:
Mrs J G Adamson, BA, AUPE (*Assistant Head, Prep School*)
Mrs A W Alexander, DipCE
Miss L L Beattie, BEd
Mrs A N Briggs, BA, DipCE, AUPE
Mrs V Currie, DipCE
Mrs E M M Dow, DipCE
Miss R E Foster, MA
Ms O Gannon, BA
Miss F M Goudie, BEd (*Assistant Head, Junior School*)
Mrs M E Hamilton, BA, DipCE
Miss S Horne, BEd
Mrs L Hudson, BA
Ms M Jedrzejewska, MA, BEd
Mrs N M Letford, BEd
†Mrs G A McFadyean, BA
A Mills, BEd
Mrs J W Moffat, BEd
Mrs J Montgomery, BA, CertFPS
Mrs A M Morrison, BA
Miss L S Pollock, BEd, AVCM

Mrs K Bunyan (*Prep Assistant*)
Mrs P Ramsay (*Prep Assistant*)

Senior School:

Art:
*A K MacLean, DA
Mrs C L Kelly, BA
Ms A Lindsay, BA
Mrs T L Livingstone, BA
Mrs C MacLean, DA
Ms E Scott, MA

Biology:
*A N Morton, BSc
‡C K Ainge, BSc
Mrs P Ferguson, BA
J B Fraser, BSc
Mrs F McDonald, BSc
Dr L A Payne, BSc, PhD

Biotechnology:
*Mrs M A Smith, BSc

Business Education:
*W W McFarlane, BA
Mrs H M Duncan, BA
Miss N J Griffith, BA
M C Moore, BSc
Mrs A L Robinson, MA
Ms T Spencer, BA
Mrs M A Waddell, DipCom

Chemistry:
*Dr W Beveridge, BSc, PhD, CChem, MRSC
‡N F Blezard, BSc, MRSC
Dr R Johnson, BSc, PhD
‡D J Lumsden, BSc
Dr S Scheuerl, BSc, PhD, MRSC
‡C Smith, BSc

Classics:
*D H Hall, MA, MPhil
*Mrs C B Mason, MA
Dr E Macleod, MA, PhD

Computing:
*R W Marchant, BSc
Ms R McGuinness, MSc

English:
*Mrs C Murray, MA, MPhil
Mrs K G du Vivier, MA
Ms E M Langley, MA
Mrs H K Moore, BA, MLitt
Mrs J Nozedar, MA
F O'Connor, BA, DEA
*P G Russell, BA (*Head of Drama*)
Mrs M E Tetley, BA, MSc
Ms H Walker, MA

Geography:
*Ms N L Cowan, MA
Mrs F M McBride, MA
Mrs S A Scott, BSc

History & Modern Studies:
*Miss M D Sharp, MA
N G McEwan, MA

*†N J McFadyean, MA, MPhil (*Head of World Studies*)
Mrs I Morrison, MA
Miss G McCord, MA
R W Welsh, MA

Home Economics:
Mrs A E Kean, DipDomSci
Mrs C Maciver, DipHomeEc

Mathematics:
*S P Johnson, MA
†Dr J T Brooks, BSc, PhD
Miss S Cannon, BSc
Mrs C M Childs, BSc
R W Durran, BA
Mrs L A Jeffrey, BA
I Mackenzie, BSc
Mrs M Pennie, BSc
Mrs F G Stewart, BSc

Modern Languages:
*D Delaney, MA
†J A Allan, MA
†Mrs S Brooks, MA
Mrs A R Bryce, BA
Dr J M Fotheringham, BA, PhD
Ms J C Popelka, MA
Mr S K Young, BA
Mrs J Young, MA

Assistants:
Monsieur R Lemothe (*French*)
Herr G Straßburger (*German*)
Señorita B Gallego (*Spanish*)

Music:
*J McGonigle, DipMus, RSAMD
D M Christie, BA, LLCM, ALCM
Mrs K Fitzpatrick, MSc, BMus
Mrs M Leggatt, MusB, DipMTh, LGSM, LLCM
Ms S A Herbert, BMus

Physical Education:
*S R Newton, BSc
‡Mrs E A Borrowman, DipPE
J G A Frost, BEd, MSc
Mrs C C Galloway, BEd
M I Hose, BEd
Mrs V A Smith, BA
Mrs G M Robb, BEd

Physics:
*J T A Fulton, BSc
Dr S Fulton, BSc, PhD
‡A N Johns, BSc, CPhys, MInstP
*Dr D A Keys, BA, PhD (*Head of Applied Science & Engineering*)

Support for Learning:
Mrs S Birrell, BA, MSc
Mrs A Gibson, DipCE

Technology:
*R Farthing, BSc
S W Cochrane, BEdTech
Mrs P Webster, BEdTech

Head of Communications (*Publications etc*): (*to be appointed*)
Head of Communications (*Website etc*): Ms H Walker, MA, PGDip
Counsellor: Mrs L A Jeffrey, BA
Librarian: (*to be appointed*)
Rector's PA: Mrs W M Pearson
School Office Manager: Mrs E C Gallagher
Assistant Network Manager: J L Tracey
IT Support Assistant: A J Kenny
Janitor: W Anderson
Groundsman: R W Meldrum
Piping Instructors: C Stewart & D Methven
Pool Manager / Swimming Instructor: R W Kidd, FIOS, MSTA, TEAQ

Houseparents:
Argyll: Dr & Mrs J T Brooks
Heyworth: Mr & Mrs J A Allan
McNabb/Tait: Mr & Mrs N J McFadyean

Organisation. The Academy is divided into the Senior School (ages 12–18, 851 pupils); the Junior School (ages 10–12, 180 pupils) and the Prep School (ages 5–9, 211 pupils). It is fully co-educational throughout.

Academic. Pupils in the first two stages follow a course of study based upon the Scottish 5–14 Curriculum. In the Senior School, pupils are prepared for the Scottish Certificate of Education at Standard Grade or Intermediate 2 (generally in 7 or 8 subjects) and Higher Grades (usually in 5 subjects); and then afterwards for a range of Advanced Highers, further Highers or wider interest modules. The timetable is created around the needs of the pupils rather than requiring them to slot into pre-arranged subject blocks. Three Modern Languages are offered from age 10, besides co-curricular Japanese and Russian, and the separate sciences are available from 13.

Beyond Dollar. Senior staff offer advice on Careers and Higher Education to current and former pupils. In addition, all pupils are offered the services of a professional careers adviser, and both Kudos and Centigrade programmes are used. The Academy has a flourishing Work Experience programme for seniors locally, and in France, Germany and Spain.

International links. Contact with other countries has increased notably in recent years. For example, Biology trips are organised in Malaysia; the Art department visits Paris, Berlin and London; the Modern Languages department runs exchange programmes and trips to France, Germany, Spain and Japan, while sporting links are firmly established elsewhere in Europe, in Japan, Ireland, Australia and South Africa. The Pipe Band has recently toured in the Far East and mainland Europe. The boarding community includes boys and girls from every continent.

Games and Activities. The extensive playing fields are immediately adjacent to the school, as are the Games Hall, 25 metre indoor heated swimming pool and the rifle range. A new Sports Centre opened in August 2005.

Teams represent the school in rugby, hockey, cricket, tennis, athletics, swimming, skiing, shooting, curling, fencing, football, golf, badminton and basketball.

The Duke of Edinburgh's Award Scheme is widely supported at all three award levels. The Combined Cadet Force has equal numbers of boys and girls in a Royal Signals troop, an Infantry section, a REME section, an RAF section, an RN section and two Pipe Bands.

Dollar follows the principle of allowing pupils to opt into co-curricular activities as well as games, and an extraordinarily wide variety of clubs is on offer, from surfing and clay-pigeon shooting to knitting and t'ai chi.

The Arts. Music is taught as part of the curriculum, and tuition is offered as an extra in most orchestral instruments, besides bagpipes, guitar, drums and clarsach. There are six choirs, four orchestras and two Jazz bands. Junior and Senior Musical productions are performed annually. Drama productions and clubs are found throughout the age range; a new Studio Theatre opened in August 2005. Art Clubs take place outwith the timetabled lessons in the new Maguire Art department, and exhibitions are held throughout the year. Dance – whether it be Scottish Country, Latin American, Flamenco or Egyptian Belly Dancing – is taught at all levels. Debating and Public Speaking are popular and competitive activities at Dollar.

Boarding. Boarding pupils are accepted from the age of nine. There is one Boys' and two Girls' Houses. Weekly or flexible boarding arrangements can be made to suit pupils' and parents' needs.

Fees per term (2008-2009). Tuition: £2,265 (Prep), £2,604 (Junior), £3,030 (Senior). Boarding fee: £3,885 (full), £3,513 (weekly).

Admission. This is by interview and/or test with the Head of the Prep and Junior School for ages 5–14; and by interview and current school report for ages 14–18. The biggest single intakes are at age 5, and at 10 and 11 to the Junior School; there are intakes in other years as vacancies occur.

Charitable status. The Governors of Dollar Academy Trust is a Registered Charity; it exists to provide education for boys and girls.

Dulwich College

London SE21 7LD
Tel: 020 8693 3601
Fax: 020 8693 6319
e-mail: info@dulwich.org.uk
website: www.dulwich.org.uk

Dulwich College was founded by Edward Alleyn, the famous Elizabethan actor-manager. On 21 June 1619, a licence was granted for his 'College of God's Gift' at Dulwich, a foundation consisting of a Master, a Warden, 4 Fellows, 12 poor scholars and 12 alms people. In 1857 Alleyn's College was reconstituted by a special Act of Parliament. The upper part of the Foundation was henceforth known as Dulwich College, and in 1870 moved to its present site.

Motto: '*Detur gloria soli Deo*'.

The Governing Body:

Chairman: Lord George, GBE, PC

V P Bazalgette, MA
Dr F Benjamin, OBE, Hon DLitt Exeter
M L Coombs
W A Foster, MA, PhD
R D V Knight, OBE, MA
Mrs J F R Quint, LLB, AKC
P C D Southern, PhD
N A Tatman, FSI
S A Taylor, FRICS
S M Till, CBE
Lord Turnbull, KCB, CVO
G N C Ward, CBE, FCA, FEI
Mrs C Waugh, BSc, RHV

Clerk to the Governors: Ms K Jones, LLB

***Master of the College*: G G Able**, MA, MA, FRSA

Deputy Masters:
S R Northcote-Green, BA (*Pastoral*)
A J S Kennedy, BA (*Academic*)
R I Mainard, BA, MA Theol, MA Ed (*External*)

Director of Operations: S R Girling, MA
Director of Finance: N Prout, BA, ACA
Head of Learning Assessment: J P Devlin, BA, PhD
Head of Upper School: C S B Pyke, MA
Head of Middle School: T J Cook, BA
Head of Lower School: J L H Scarisbrick, BSc
Head of Junior School: Mrs P A Horsman, CertEd
Head of DUCKS (*Kindergarten and Infants School*): Mrs H M Friell, DipEd
Registrar: Mrs S Betts
Archivist: Mrs C Lucy, BA, MCLIP
School Administration Manager: N P Young, BSc

Assistant Masters:
* *Head of Department*
† *Housemasters*

Miss J Akrill, BA
Mrs F M Angel, BA
A Avshu, BSc, PhD (*†Blew House*)
T Barratt, ARAM, GRSM, LRAM, ARCM, LMusTCL, ATCL
A A Barrett-Greene, MA
R R S Baylis, MA, MA (**French*)
S A A Bennie, BA (*†Ivyholme*)
A J Binns, BA
N D Black, BA (**History*)
Miss O C Boyd, BA
Mrs A M Bradnock, BA, ALA, DipNZLS, MIInfSci (**Information Services*)
Mrs J Briggs, BA
Miss J N A Brind, BEd
I R T Brinton, MA
R E Broughton, BA
N C Brown, BEd
M Burdekin, BA
P Callender, CertEd
J Carnelley, BMus, MMus, ARCO
Mrs A Cartwright, BA, MA
J D Cartwright, MA (**Computer Science*)
W E S Casson, BSc
Mrs I Chetwood, BSc
S N Clark, BA
Mrs L Clarke, BA, DipSpLD
P J Claydon, MA
Mrs R M R Collier, BA
D J Cooper, BSc (*†Orchard House*)
N T Croally, MA, PhD (**Classics*)
Ms D Cronin, BA, DipRSA
Mrs S C J Crossley, BA, MTh
P J Cue, BSc, PhD (**Biology*)
M K Davidson, BA
Mrs A E Dawson, ALA
Mrs M J Doherty, BA
Ms B Downing, BA, MSc
T Edge, BA (**Politics*)
N G Ellis, BA
M J Emson, BSc
Miss H N Etherington, BA
K G Eyre, MA
J H Fox, BA (**Religious Studies*)
J E Fry, BSc
N K M Fyfe, BA
M J Gabriel, BSc, PHD
Mrs S Gardener, BA
M R Geach, BSc
T W Goodrich, BA
M Grantham-Hill, BSc
Mrs S Griffiths, BA
N A J Harper, MA, FRCO, ADCM, ARCM
E W G Hatton, BA
R A Henderson, BSc
P S Holton, BA
S D Howard, BA
S G Hoyle, BA, PhD
D Hutchins, BA
Miss M A Jarman, MA
Mrs G M Jenkins, BA (**Art*)
K R Jepson, BA
Miss H T Johnson, BSc
Mrs C M Johnstone, MA
P V Jolly, BA, DipRSA (**Director of Drama*)
R O Jones, MA, MSc, PhD
Ms C J Juyol, BA
W L S Keat, MA (**General and Liberal Studies*)
R D Kemp, BEng
D Kent, BA (*PE*)
J Kinch, BA, BPhil, DPhil (**Critical Thinking*)
A J G King, BA
J King
J R King, BEd (**Director of Sport*)
Mrs U Kite, BA, MA, CertEd
B R H Kulatunge, BSc
A P Lacheze-Beer, BSc, MPhil, BA
Mrs B Lake, GRSM, LTCL
Miss L Larkum, BMus, MMus, DipRCM, ASCM
Ms Y M G Le Troadec, MA
T Llewellyn, MA (**Geography*)
S Lock, BSc
J Lord, BSc, AFIMA
D Ludford Thomas, BA, FRSM
Ms J A K Mackay, BEd
Miss M Q Maclean, BA
N Mair, BA (**Modern Languages*)
Miss C Malloch, BA (**Physics*)
C A Malston, BA
Miss H C Mann, BA
I R Martin, BEd, BA
Miss C E Matthewson, BA
H Maxfield, BSc
K J Maycock, MA

R G Mayo, MA, MusB, FRCO (**Music*)
Ms L McRobert, BSc, MSc, PhD
Mrs A E R Meachen, BSc
S B Medland, BA
S C J Middleton, BEd
Miss K J Millburn, MA (**Chemistry*)
R J Mills, MA
M Nash, MA (**Spanish*)
G R Nicholls, MSc, HTC (**Design & Technology*)
J M O'Neill, BSc, MSc, PhD
C J Ottewill, BA, MPhil (**Mathematics*)
R Oubridge, BEd
Mrs A J Owen, CertEd
R G Pavey, MA
B Pelly, BA
Mrs T J Price, BSc, MSc
S A Purchase, BSc, MSc, PhD
T Quilter, BA
Miss L V A Rand, MChem
E J Read, BA (**German*)
E J Rees, BA Ed
Miss S A Roberts, BSc, DMS
Ms M K Russell, MA
G E Rutter, BA, CertEd, HTC
Ms M J Schramm, BA, BA (**Debating*)
I Senior, BA, MA, MSc, CBiol, MIBiol
Mrs H Shao, MA
Mrs R G Shawe-Taylor, BA, MA
Ms E Sioufi, MA
D R Smith, BA
R Smith, BMus, Dip GSMID, ARCM
Mrs F Southern, BA
C G Spikesman, BEd, BA, DipMus
D J Stanley, BSc
K A Stinson, CertEd
A C Storey, BA, MSc, PhD (**Director of ICT*)
P J Storey, BA
R F Sutton, BA (**English*)
S Talwar, BSc, PhD
S Tanna, BA
A Tate, BA
Miss J J Thomas, BSc
A J Threadgould, BSc (**Economics and Business Studies*)
C Trussell, BA, MA
S A H Wakely, MA
M J Weatheritt, BSc
R Weaver, BA, MA, FSA Scot (*Keeper of the Fellows' Library*)
S T Whittaker, BA, MSc
Ms N Wiedemann, BA
H I L Williams, BSc (**Science Administrator*)
P H Williams, BSc
Miss S Wood, BSc
Revd S E Young, BD, AKC, PhD (*Chaplain*)
C Zekraoui, BA, MPhil

Visiting Music Staff:
K C Abbott, Dip Perf RCM (*Horn*)
L Annesley, BA, MPhil (*Clarinet*)
Ms N J Baigent, BA (*Clarinet/Sax*)
R R Ball, BMus (*Percussion*)
J P Barber, GLCM, LTCL TD, ALCM (*Piano*)
Ms C Barnes, GRNCM DipNCOs (*Violin*)
E Barry, DipMus LTCL (*Violin*)
D Bates, BMus, PGDip RAM, LRAM (*Singing*)
Mrs E Bates, BA, MSTAT
Ms J Beament, LRAM, GRSM (*Piano*)
P Beer (*Trombone/Euphonium*)
Miss M E Bruce-Mitford, LRAM, ARCM (*Cello*)
N Clarke, BA, ARCO
J D Clarkson, MA Cantab (*Singing*)
D Ellis (*Percussion*)
Mrs C Emery, Hon RCM, GTCL, LTCL, PGCE (*Double Bass*)
R C Faulkner, BEd (*Guitar*)
S Foley, LTCL (*Guitar*)
Mrs J Friend, ARCM (*Cello*)
Mrs J A Gillard, LRAM, ARAM (*Violin*)
B Graham, FTCL, LTCL, ARCM (*Big Band/Sax*)
Ms S Grint, GRSM, ARCM, LRAM (*Oboe*)
Mrs H Gritton, LRAM, CTABRSM (*Piano*)
Mrs S Hadzic, MMus (*Piano*)
H Hambleton, ARAM (*Clarinet*)
A Hendrie, DRSAM, ARMCM (*Trumpet*)
D-M Landowski, BMus (*Percussion*)
C McCann, BMus (*Percussion*)
N McLaren, ARCM, FTCL (*Flute*)
J J McVinnie, BA, FRCO (*Organ*)
Ms G Morgan, BA, ARCM (*Voice*)
E J Morris, BMus (*Percussion*)
Mrs M Porter, GRSM, LRAM, ARCM (*Piano*)
R Smith, BMus, Dip GSMID, ARCM (*Trumpet*)
P Tebb, BA (*Singing*)
Ms J Treggor, BMus (*Flute*)
J Turville, MA, PGCE (*Jazz Piano*)
M D Venner, BA (*Singing*)
P Worley, BA, MA (*Guitar*)
Mrs H McPhail

DUCKS (Dulwich College Kindergarten and Infants School)

T Davy, BA
Mrs C Delacroix, CertEd
Mrs A Dipré, BA, PGCE
Mrs S Donaldson, NNEB (*Head of Kindergarten*)
Mrs S Evans, CertEd
Miss J Harvey, BA, BSc
Miss L Z Humm, BA
Mme S Igharben, Lic (*Paris*)
Ms K Hall, BEd
Miss G Jamieson, BA
Mrs K Ma, BEd
Mrs C Medland, BA, CertAdvStudies
Miss S Obed, BA, PGCE
Mrs M Williams, CertEd

Medical Centre Charge Nurse: Mrs P Heaton, RGN, RM, RSN, BSc Hons Specialist Community Practitioner, Dip Counselling
College Counsellor: Ms J De Heger, BEd, Dip Art Therapy
Medical Officer: R A Leonard, MBE, MA, MB, BChir, MRCGP, DRCOG
Master's PA: Mrs R Weavers

Organisation. The College is divided into 5 sections but is administered as a single unit.

DUCKS provides a childcare facility for children aged three months to three years in its Kindergarten and an Infants School education for children aged 3 to 7 years. DUCKS is co-educational. There is no automatic transfer to the Junior School.

In both the Junior School (Y3–Y6) and the Lower School (Y7 and Y8) all forms at the same level follow a common curriculum.

Between the ages of 13 and 16 boys are in the Middle School (Y9–Y11) following a broadly based, balanced programme leading to ten subjects at GCSE.

Boys in the Upper School, consisting of the Remove and the Sixth Form, study at Advanced Level and in a limited number of subjects a Pre-U course is followed. In the Remove, they select four subjects from a wide range. All boys will take the two core components of the Cambridge Pre-University Diploma; these are Global Perspectives and the Independent Reseach Project which together lead to a qualification. In addition, boys take a course in General Studies or Critical Thinking which is examined, along with their four chosen subjects. In the Sixth Form, boys continue with three or four of their chosen subjects, as appropriate and they are prepared for university entrance. Oxford and Cambridge feature prominently among the many places gained, while increasing numbers also succeed in their application for university places in the United States.

Entry. Boys are admitted to the College as day boys, boarders or weekly boarders. The school year runs from 1 September and ages for entry are calculated at that date. Places are available at age 7, 11, 13 and 16. Casual vacancies occur from time to time at ages 8, 9, 10 and 12. At age 7 places are awarded on the basis of interview, report and practical assessment during the Lent Term. At age 11 places are awarded on the results of the Combined Entrance and Scholarship Examination held in the Lent Term. Candidates take papers in English and Mathematics and also a Verbal Reasoning test. At age 13 boys may take the College's own Entrance Examinations held in the Lent Term. Entrance is by examination and interview. At 16+ places are offered on the results from subject specific tests, interview and GCSE grades. Application should generally be in the year before desired date of entry.

Term of Entry. Boys normally enter the College at the beginning of the Michaelmas term. Only in exceptional circumstances are they accepted at other times of the year.

Boarding Houses. There are three Boarding Houses, Blew House (Dr A Avshu), Ivyholme (Mr S A A Bennie) and Orchard House (Mr D J Cooper). Full and weekly boarding is available.

Fees and Expenses per term (2008-2009). The consolidated Day fee of £4,392 covers tuition, use of class, text and library books, school stationery, scientific materials and games. It does not cover fees for external examinations.

Boarding fees (in addition to Tuition fees): £4,452 Full Boarders; £4,106 Weekly Boarders.

Scholarships and Bursaries. (*see Scholarship Entries section*). A significant number of academic scholarships are awarded each year up to one-third of the tuition fee. Scholarships can be enhanced by Bursaries in cases of financial need. There are also scholarships for music, art and sports. The College has a substantial Bursary Fund from which means-tested awards are made annually.

Scholarships and bursaries are available for competition for all new boys entering the College at the ages of 7, 11 and 13 years on 1 September in the year of entry.

Each year the Master awards some scholarships to boys already in the College upon entering Year 7 at age 11 and Year 9 at age 13.

The Alleyn Club for former pupils is the overall organisation for sporting clubs, dinners, and other gatherings of old boys, both at home and abroad. Reunions are held regularly at the College.

Charitable status. Alleyn's College of God's Gift; Dulwich College is a Registered Charity, number 312755. It exists for the education of children.

The High School of Dundee

Euclid Crescent Dundee Tayside DD1 1HU
Tel: 01382 202921
Fax: 01382 229822
e-mail: enquiries@dundeehigh.dundeecity.sch.uk
website: www.highschoolofdundee.co.uk

The present School traces its origins directly back to a 13th century foundation by the Abbot and Monks of Lindores. It received a Royal Charter in 1859. Various Acts of Parliament in the 19th Century were finally consolidated in an Order in Council constituting the High School of Dundee Scheme 1965, which was revised in 1987.

Motto: '*Prestante Domino*'.

Board of Directors:
The Board comprises, Chairman, 2 ex officiis Directors, viz, The Lord Dean of Guild and The Parish Minister of Dundee. The Guildry of Dundee, the Nine Trades of Dundee, the Old Boys' Club and the Old Girls' Club and the Parents' Association each elect one Director. Six Directors are elected by The Patrons' Association and 6 co-opted by the Board.

School Staff:

***Rector*: Dr J D Halliday**, BA Hons, PhD

Deputy Rector & Head of Senior School: P J Tinson, MA Aberdeen

Head of Junior School: Mrs G McLaren, MA, CEY

Bursar: C M Sharp, FCCA

Deputy Heads:
Mrs A F McDonald, MA, DipEd
C J G Allison, MA, DipEd
Mrs K J I McIntosh, DipCE
R W Illsley, MA
Mrs J Rose, BEd

Director of ICT: J Christie, BEng Hons

Junior School

Mrs P L Hourd, BSc (*Junior/Senior Transition Coordinator*)

Mrs L J Mooney, DipCE
Mrs L Docherty, DipCE
Mrs E D Cargill, DipCE
Mrs M A Mordente, BEd
Miss M Cardno, MA, PGCE
Mrs G M Wood, DipCE
Mrs L Smith, BEd
Mrs M A Ross, MA, PGCE
Miss C E Hulbert, MA, PGCE
Mrs A Davie, BEd
Mrs P J Halliwell, BEd
Mrs S Tonner, BEd
Mrs I Goddard, BEd
Mrs C Powrie, BSc
Miss F S Ramsay, BEd
Miss G Alexander, BEd
Mrs L Coupar, BEd

Senior School
* *Head of Department*

English:
*Mrs J Phillips, MA
T F W Durrheim MA
Mrs D M Wilson, MA
Mrs D Keogh, MA
M Stewart, MA, MPhil
Miss M Jones, MA
Ms L Dunn, MA

Drama and Media Studies:
*Mrs L M Drummond, Dip Drama
I R Cowieson, BA

Modern Studies:
*G J Rennet, MA
G Fyall, BA

History:
*I E R Wilson, MA
Mrs L A Hudson, MA
G Fyall, BA
Miss K McKie, MA

Geography:
*Mrs V A Vannet, MA, DipEd
C R McAdam, MA
Mrs S B Williams, MA
P J Tinson, MA
D Foulds, BSc

Religious Studies:
*D J Goodey, BA, MA
Ms B D Quigley, MTheol

Economics:
*Miss A L Laing, DipCom, DipEd
Mrs R M Crighton, DipCom

Classics:
*J Meehan, MA
S A A McKellar, MA

Modern Languages:
*N A MacKinnon, MA
Mrs I M McGrath, MA
Mrs F Cram, MA
Mrs G A Mackenzie, BA
C J G Allison, MA, DipEd
Miss L McCulloch, MA
D A Summerville, BA
Mrs S Godley, BA
Mr J Brown, BA

Mathematics:
*G A Mordente, BSc
A G Blackburn, BSc
Mrs M A Oliver, BSc
D J C Elgin, BSc, MSc
R C Middleton, BSc
Miss D MacDonald, BSc
Mrs L A Craig, BSc

Chemistry:
*D A Brett, BSc
N P Forrest, BSc
Mrs C A Sinclair, BSc
Mrs G Spinks, BSc
Mrs L Boath, BSc

Biology:
*Dr E Duncanson, BSc, PhD

Mrs L A Woodley, BSc
Dr M W Fotheringham, BA, PhD
G M S Rodger, BSc

Physics:
*Mrs S H Fletcher, BSc, MSc
T Guild, BSc
Dr G MacKay, BSc, MSc, PhD
Miss L E Boath, BSc

Technology:
*C Rose, BA
D Preston, MA, BEd

Computer Studies:
*D Smith, BSc
C P Stuart, BSc
Miss T Grant, BSc

Art and Craft:
*G R Mackenzie, DipGrDes
Mrs M Angus, BA
Miss A Douglas, BDes
Miss J Campbell, MDes

Music:
*Mrs J F Melville, DipMusEd
Mrs S J Magill, BMus
D G Love, DipMusEd, DRSAMD
Mrs M Scott-Brown, LTCL
Mrs G Robertson, DipMus, ALCM
S Armstrong, DRSAM
Mrs S Sneddon, LTCL, ALCM
Miss A Evans, BA, LTCL
J McAuley, BA
Ms S Morgan, BA

Learning Skills:
*Mrs P A Maxwell, BEd

Mrs D Burt, MA
Mrs C E Kirkpatrick, BEd, MEd

Physical Education:
*B Beckett, BEd
G W Spowart, BEd
Mrs J A Hutchison, DipPE
Mrs P Spowart, BEd
P N Gallagher, BEd
Mrs P Stott (*Coach*)
W Nicol (*SSI/Instructor in Outdoor Activities*)
E Jack, BEd
Mrs E Rudman, BA
Mrs L Christie, BA

Home Economics:
*Mrs G A Madden, DipHome Econ
Miss L J Smith, MA

Guidance:

Principal Teachers:
Mrs L Hudson, MA
C R McAdam, MA
G W Spowart, BEd
Mrs P Spowart, BEd

Assistant Principal Teachers:
Mrs F Cram, MA
Mrs J Hutchison, DipPE
C Stuart, BSc
Mrs S Williams, MA

Careers Coordinators:
Miss L Smith, MA
G M S Rodger, BSc

Co-Curricular Activities:
*G J Rennet, MA
G Ross, BA (*Outdoor Education Instructor*)

Admission. The School comprises two sections:

The Junior School – 364 pupils (Primary 1 to Primary 7). The Senior School – 682 pupils (Form 1 to Form 6).

The normal stages of entry are Primary 1 and Form 1. Entry to Primary 1 (age 4½ to 5½ years) is by interview held in January and to Form 1 (age 11 to 12 years) by an Entrance Examination held in January. Entrance is usually available at all other stages subject to satisfactory performance in an entrance test and interview.

Bursaries. A limited number of bursaries are provided to pupils entering Form 1.

Fees per term (2008-2009). Junior School (Classes L1 to L5) £2,143; Junior School (Classes L6 and L7) £2,450; Senior School £3,047.

Buildings. The 5 main school buildings are in the centre of the city and form an architectural feature of the area. Two excellent playing fields – Dalnacraig and Mayfield – are situated some 1½ miles to the east of the school. The Mayfield Sports Centre, comprising state-of-the-art games hall, dance studio, gymnasium and fitness suite, is adjacent to the playing fields.

Curriculum. The Junior School follows the primary curriculum set down in the 5–14 Programme. Subject specialists are employed in Physical Education, Art, Home Economics, Music, French, Information Technology.

In the Senior School, after two years of a general curriculum, some specialisation takes place with pupils prepared for the Scottish Qualifications Authority Examinations at Standard Grade, Intermediate 2, Higher and Advanced Higher which lead directly to university entrance.

Co-Curricular Activities. A wide range of activities is offered. There is a flourishing contingent of the Combined Cadet Force including a pipe band. Drama, Public Speaking and Debating, Chess and The Duke of Edinburgh's Award Scheme are examples of the wide variety of activities available.

Music plays an important part in the life of the school. Special tuition is provided in a wide variety of instruments.

Charitable status. The Corporation of the High School of Dundee is a Registered Charity, number SC011522. The school is a charity to provide quality education for boys and girls.

Durham School

Durham City DH1 4SZ
Tel: 0191 386 4783
Fax: 0191 383 1025
e-mail: d.woodlands@durhamschool.co.uk
website: www.durhamschool.co.uk

Durham School is one of the oldest in England. It probably has a continuous history from Saxon times and has always been closely associated with the Diocese of Durham. As the Bishop's School it was re-organised and endowed by Cardinal Langley in 1414 and was re-founded in 1541 by Henry VIII as a Lay Foundation under the control of the Dean and Chapter of Durham. In 1995 it left the Cathedral Foundation to become a separate body. The school is now fully co-educational 3–18, incorporating Bow, Durham School (3–11).

Governing Body:
Mr A MacConachie, OBE, DL (*Chairman*)
Mr F Nicholson (*Deputy Chairman*)
Mr A B Anderson
Mr P S Bell
Canon S A Cherry
Miss G Kerr
Mr R A Langdon
Mr D Welsh
Mrs H G Weston

Development Director and Clerk to the Governors: G Simpson, ACA, BSc

***Acting Headmaster to April 2009*: D R Best**, BA
Headmaster from April 2009: E M George, BA, MBA Ed

* *Head of Department*
† *Housemaster/mistress*

Deputy Headmaster: D R Best, BA (**History*)
Director of Development & Services: G Simpson, ACA, BSc
Deputy Head (*Curriculum*): D W Goodhew, BA, PGCE
Deputy Head (*Pastoral*): Mrs F M Parker, BEd
Director of Marketing: R Thomas, MA
Chaplain: Mrs A de Lange, BA, MA
Admissions Secretary: Mrs D C Woodlands

Assistant Staff:
D B Aitken, BSc
M P Alderson, BA, MA (*†School House, *Modern Languages*)
M C T Baldwin, BA (**Art and DT*)
M F Burke, BSc (**Biology*)
Miss F E Burnie, BSc
Dr J M Burns, BA, PhD (*†Pimlico House*)
M J Bushnell, BSc (*†Poole House, *Economics*)
I J Campbell, BEng (*Junior† Caffinites House*)
M J Clayton, BA

J Curry, MA, BSc (**Physics*)
T A Davies, BA (*Director of Lower School Studies, *Classics*)
H S Dias, BA
Mrs K E Dougall, BA (**Girls' Games*)
R J Duff, BEd (*Assistant Housemaster, Poole House*)
Mrs C Eccleston, BA
C S Fordyce, BSc (*Assistant Housemaster, Caffinites House*)
P C Gerrard, BEd (*Director of Sixth Form Studies, *PE*)
R Gibbon, BSc
G Hallam, BSc (*†Caffinites House*)
Mrs E L P Hewitt, MA
R N Hewitt, BEd
Miss L J Hinde, MA
Miss V Holmes, BA (*Junior† Pimlico House*)
J G James, BSc
K S Jones, BSc (*†School House, *Chemistry*)
Mrs S Kerridge, BSc, BA
S J M Kime, BA (**English*)
Miss J M Linthwaite, BA, MPhil, MEd
B M Mason, BEd (**Games, Assistant Housemaster, School House*)
R A Muttitt, BMus, ARCO, FRSA (*Director of Middle School Studies, *Music*)
Miss L M Nicholson, BA (*Junior† MacLeod House*)
Mrs M F Proud, MA (**Religious Studies*)
J C Renshaw, BA (**Geography*)
Ms E J Ross, BA (**Learning Support*)
O Stacey, BA
M O Stephens, BA
Mrs N J Thompson, BA (*†MacLeod House*)
S Thompson, BA
A R Wallace, BSc
M D Ward, BEd (**ICT*)
Mrs K L Wilkinson, BA
J Williamson, BA (*Rowing Coach*)
P R Wilson, BA, MA (*Junior† School House, *Mathematics*)
M Younger, BA (*Junior† Poole House*)

Location. The School is magnificently situated above the steep banks of the River Wear, overlooked by the west towers of Durham Cathedral on the opposite bank, and has occupied its present site since 1844. The School is physically compact – all the buildings are within 2 minutes' walk of each other; the playing fields and the river are adjacent. The School still has connections with Durham Cathedral and all pupils attend Chapel on a regular basis and the cathedral once a term.

Aims. While pursuing the highest academic standards, the School has an intellectual range which includes both prospective Oxford or Cambridge entrants and pupils who will succeed at A level only with the careful teaching and support the School provides. The School's main objective is to bring out the best in every pupil. Everyone is expected to contribute fully to the life of the School and thus to develop all their talents to the full. The School provides the care, the teaching and the facilities to do this in happy and attractive surroundings.

Size. Numbers are relatively small, around 450, with an excellent staffing ratio. Our Preparatory School (age 3–11) currently caters for around 150 day pupils, boys and girls. (*For further details, see Bow, Durham School entry in IAPS section.*)

The House System. The House system is one of the great strengths of the School, enabling pastoral care of the highest order. There are 5 Houses: three for boys (School House, Poole House and Caffinites House) and two for girls (Pimlico House and MacLeod House). Junior House staff look after the interests of Years 7 and 8 and in the boys' Houses Assistant Housemasters are in charge of Years 10 and 11. Although most pupils are day pupils, the School still offers full, weekly or part-time boarding and has some 80 boarders (girls and boys). Day pupils enjoy all the benefits of a "boarding style" education during the day (including breakfast and supper, included in the fee), the same leisure facilities as the boarders and space for private study.

Admission. Entry at age 11 is by way of the Durham School 11+ Entrance Examination. Pupils joining at age 13 will have sat either the King's Scholarship Examination or the School's own 13+ Entrance Examination. It is also possible to join in the Sixth Form. Such admission is by interview, testimonial and GCSE results, although there are also generous academic and non-academic awards. All Entrance and Scholarship examinations and interviews take place in late January/early February (see scholarships below). A prospectus with full details can be obtained on application to the Admissions Secretary.

Academic. Academic courses are followed to GCSE, AS and A2 Levels. A broad programme is pursued during the years up to GCSE and there is a wide choice and flexible programme for the Sixth Form, which numbers about 120. There is a fully developed Careers Advisory Service.

Extra-Curricular Activities. A wide variety of musical, dramatic, sporting and other activities is available and new facilities have recently been provided for all of these, including an all-weather sports pitch. Sports on offer include rugby, hockey, rowing, cricket, netball, rounders, squash, swimming, athletics, cross-country, tennis and water polo. Various types of Adventure Training are pursued through the CCF and pupils can take part in World Challenge expeditions and the Duke of Edinburgh's Award scheme.

Scholarships and Bursaries. (*see Scholarship Entries section*). Generous academic and non-academic awards are available at 11, 13 and 16 (up to a maximum of 50% of fees). Bursaries are available at all ages in cases of financial need and these can be held alongside academic and non-academic awards. Additionally, each year the School awards up to three Foundation Bursaries at 11+. There are generous concessions for brothers and sisters, children of clergy and the Armed Forces.

Fees per term (2008-2009). Years 7–8: £5,545 (full boarding), £4,878 (weekly boarding), £3,333 (day).Years 9–13: £6,663 (full boarding), £5,996 (weekly boarding), £4,666 (day).

Extras are kept to a minimum.

Bow, Durham School (formerly Bow School) is Durham School's Preparatory School and caters for girls and boys from 3–11. It is situated in its own beautiful grounds half a mile away from the Senior School and makes use of some of the Senior School facilities. (*For further details, see Bow, Durham School entry in IAPS section.*)

Charitable status. Durham School is a Registered Charity, number 1023407. It exists to provide a high quality education for boys and girls.

Eastbourne College

Old Wish Road Eastbourne East Sussex BN21 4JX
Tel: Headmaster: 01323 452320
Bursar: 01323 452300
Fax: Headmaster: 01323 452327
Bursar: 01323 452307
e-mail: reception@eastbourne-college.co.uk
website: www.eastbourne-college.co.uk

Founded 1867; Incorporated 1911.

Governing Body:
President: His Grace The Duke of Devonshire, CBE

Vice-Presidents:
The Bishop of London
The Earl of Burlington

Council:
¶Dr T Alfillé, MA, PhD
Ms A H Anderson (*Treasurer*)
Mrs J E Atkinson
¶M T Barford, MA, FCA
¶P A J Broadley, MA, FCA, FRSA (*Vice-Chairman*)
H Davies Jones, MA
¶Admiral Sir Ian Forbes, KCB, CBE (*Chairman*)
¶Mrs V J Henley, BA
¶A O Mackay, FRICS
¶Sir Charles Masefield, MA, CEng, FRAeS, FIMechE
Dr R A McNeilly, MB BS, DCH, MRCOG
¶Gen Sir David Richards, KCB, CBE, DSO
T S Richardson, FRICS
¶E G S Roose
¶Dr D L Smith, MA, PhD, PGCE, FRHistS
¶D Winn, OBE, MInstM
¶S J D Yorke, MA

In attendance:
J Crawshaw
S P Davies, MA
C H D Everett, CBE, MA
J R G Griffith, BA
D A Stewart

Clerk to the Council: Ms C Meade, MA

Senior Management Team:

***Headmaster*: S P Davies**, MA

Deputy Head: M M Turnbull, BA, MA
Bursar: Ms C Meade, MA
Assistant Head (*Co-curricular*): C S Bostock, MA, MSc
Assistant Head (*Curriculum*): J M Gilbert, BSc, MRSC
Assistant Head (*Teaching and Learning*): D J Ruskin, BA
Registrar: L Chu, BA
Marketing and Communications: Mrs J S B Lowden, BA

In attendance:
Assistant Head and Housemistress School House: Mrs K F MacGregor, MA, MSc
Senior Hsm: J R Wooldridge, MA
By invitation:
Development Director: D A Stewart

* *Head of Department*

Art:
*Ms S J Collins, BA
Mrs J L A Harriott, BA
Miss K M Hobden, MA
§¶Ms J Lathbury, DipFA

Classics:
*S J Beal, BA
M J Banes, BA
H B Jourdain, BA
¶Miss J H Meakin, BA
¶I P Sands, MA

Design and Technology:
*M B Wilders, BSc, DipArch
N J Clark, BA
Ms Z B Cosgrove, BA, MA (**Textiles*)
G L McDonald, BEd
W L Trinder, BEd
§Mrs A Young, MA

Drama:
*T W Marriott, BA
§Miss C N Huckle, BA
†Mrs A F Marriott, BA, MA Ed
†Mrs L A Salway, BA, MA

Economics & Business Studies:
*C I Bainbridge, BA
¶C M B Roberts, BA
L F Rees, BA
†J P S Toy, MA, MSc

English:
*Ms T C Stevens, BSc, MA
J R Heal, BA, CELTA
P J A Honeyford, BA, MA, MA, NPQH (*Deputy HoD*)
Mrs L J Jourdain, BA
P H Lowden, MA
†N J Russell, MA

English as an Additional Language:
§Miss K Briedenhann, BSecEd, CELTA

Geography:
*Miss H-J Boyes, BSc
H E Freeman, BA
G J L Kene, BSc
A T Lamb, BA, FRGS
M M Turnbull, BA, MA

History:
*J C Miller, BA
†R H Bunce, MA
Revd C K Macdonald, BA (*Chaplain*)
B J Sadler, BA

History of Art:
*¶D N West, BA

Information and Communication Technology:
*I R Shakespeare, BSc
Miss M A Smith, BSc

Learning Resources:
*P D Martin, BA, MA
§Mrs S E East, BA, MCLIP
§Mrs A K Penfold
§Mrs P J Keeley

Learning Support:
*M L Saul, BEd
§J M Tibbles, BEd, RSADip
§Mrs G L Williams, BA, RSADipTEFL

Life and Learning Skills:
*¶A S Wood, BSc

Mathematics:
*†J R Wooldridge, MA
§C H Allison, BA
Miss L C Ashdown, BA (*Deputy HoD*)
¶S E Beal, BA
†Mrs K F MacGregor, BA, MSc
¶S F G Mattingly, BSc
N G Pendry, BSc, BA
†J C Stevens, BEng

Modern Languages:
*Mrs G A Webb, BA
§Miss M Bordessoules, BA
Miss V E Burford, MA
L Chu, BA
§Mrs Q Liang, BA, MA, MIL
§Miss P Novillo Navarro, BA
§Ms H Rünger-Field, BA
D J Ruskin, BA
Miss J L Sassen, BA, MA
Miss M J Sheridan, BA
J Thornley, BA
Mrs M C Tripp, BA, CMIL, DipTrans IoL (*Deputy HoD*)
P A Westgate, BA, MA

Music:
*G L Jones, BA
P Barton Hodges, BMus
D R S Force, BA
S W Parry, BMus

Physical Education:
*S H K Maddock, BA, MTeach
†Mrs G E Taylor-Hall, BA
¶Mrs C F B V Roberts, BSc
Miss J M Barrett, BA

Religious Studies:
*Revd D Peat, BA, MA

Biology:
*D J Beer, BSc
Miss C S Arnold, BSc
C S Bostock, BA, MSc
†C C Corfield, BSc

Chemistry:
*Miss A R Whitehead, BSc
§Mrs R M Crum, MChem
J M Gilbert, BSc, MRSC
§Revd N H Green, MA, CertTh
D C Miller, BSc
Ms J D Thornhill, MA

Physics:
*D J Hodkinson, BSc (*also *Science*)
Dr A Ball, BSc, PhD
J M Hall, BSc, CPhys, MInstP
§G L Jones, MA, PhD
D J Talbot, MPhys

Visiting Music Staff:
Mrs Ansy Boothroyd, MA, ARCM (*Singing*)
Ms M Brazier, ALCM (*Piano*)
Miss S Carter, GMus (*Flute*)
Miss R Dines, ARAM, MMus, BMus, LRAM, ARCM (*Piano*)
J Eady, BMus, PGDipMus, MMus, LRAM, LTCL, FARCO, AKC (*Cello, Organ*)
P Edwards, MMus, GRSM (**Woodwind*)
Mrs R Elias, BMus, LRAM (*Oboe*)
M Elliott, MA (**Vocal Studies*)
Miss C Emery (*Double Bass*)
D Fuller, BMus, LGSMD (*Horn*)
K Goddard (*Guitar and Bass Guitar*)
C Greenwood, BA (*Jazz Piano*)
S Hollamby, ARCM, DipRCM (*French Horn, Trumpet, Trombone*)
H Jones, AGSM, PGDip GSMD (*Bassoon, Percussion*)
Mrs J Lakin, GRSM, ARCM, LRAM (*Piano*)
T Lees (*Guitar*)
Mrs J Mansergh, FTCL, LTCL, ARCO (**Keyboard*)
Mrs R Parry, BMus, PGDipPerf (*Violin*)

Mrs R Walker, LTCL, FTCL
Ms L Wigmore, GRSM, ARCM (*Violin*)

Situation. The College is situated 400 metres from the sea in the prime residential part of the town of Eastbourne, adjacent to the national Tennis Centre at Devonshire Park, the Congress Theatre and the Cultural Centre. There is easy access to a wide range of cultural opportunities. The train to Gatwick Airport and London Victoria is under ten minutes walking distance; it is 1½ hours travel to London. The College links closely with the local community assisting people through its extensive S@S (Service at School) and PIPS (Pupils in Primary Schools) programmes, as well as providing opportunities for local musicians through its support of the town's orchestra and choral society. There are a number of successful partnership schemes with local schools in the maintained sector.

Organisation and Pastoral Care. The College is a medium-sized boarding and day community where the ethos is of full boarding education. The College is co-educational with a ratio of girls to boys of 40:60. In 2007–2008 there were 625 pupils, of whom half were boarders. There are five boarding houses, three of which are for boys (Gonville, Pennell and Wargrave) and two are for girls (Nugent and School). There are five day houses, three of which are for boys (Craig, Powell and Reeves) and two are for girls (Blackwater and Watt). Day and boarding houses have similar facilities and are run on similar lines with resident house staff and full tutorial teams. All day pupils take supper at school and do prep in houses before returning home, some on school buses. There is great commitment from staff and pupils in all areas and there is strong system of pastoral care.

Curriculum. Pupils study the full range of subjects in their first year which includes the opportunity to study both Latin and Classical Greek along with a second modern language. For GCSE, pupils study biology, chemistry, English, French, mathematics and physics, as well as four other subjects from a choice of 14. At AS level, most pupils select four subjects from a choice of 23. Critical Thinking and Life & Learning skills are available in addition. At A2 level most pupils study three subjects and all follow an extensive General Studies programme. ICT is central to the teaching and learning experience and the College is networked with its own Intranet.

Sport. A wide variety of sports is offered: major sports are cricket, hockey and rugby for boys; and hockey, netball and tennis for girls. Athletics, cross-country running, fencing, fives, football, golf, rowing, sailing, squash, swimming and tennis are also offered. All games pitches are within a short walking distance. Two Astroturf hockey pitches form 24 tennis courts in the summer. The school has its own 25-metre indoor swimming pool and a sports hall. Most major sports enjoy international tours at regular intervals.

Religion. The College is a Church of England foundation and the Chapel is at the heart of the school. All pupils experience regular Christian worship and religious education is compulsory in the first three years. There is a strong choral tradition and the Chapel or Chamber Choir leads the worship every Sunday in term time.

Development Plan. All boarding and day houses have been rebuilt or refurbished recently. A sizeable new extension to Nugent House now accommodates rising girl boarding numbers. An award-winning Science Centre was built in 2002; a new Design & Technology Centre and an ICT Centre were opened in 2003; and a new Music Centre is planned. The modern Cavendish Learning Resources Centre (1998) has an extensive fiction and reference stock and is in the centre of the school buildings. A new digital language laboratory opened in 2005. Future plans include enlargement to the dining hall and a classroom block.

Activities. A wide variety of activities are undertaken as part of the junior school programme and numerous and diverse clubs and societies flourish throughout the school. All pupils are encouraged to do something well and standards in art, drama, dance and music are all high. The school has three theatres: Big School Theatre, the Le Brocq Studio and the Dell Theatre for outdoor productions. The CCF, Duke of Edinburgh's Award Scheme and S@S (Service at School) all offer opportunity for leadership and initiative testing. Regular College expeditions have recently visited Bolivia, Borneo, Kyrgyzstan, Mongolia, Peru and India whilst other outdoor activities thrive on the Sussex "Sunshine Coast".

Admission. Boys and girls are generally admitted between the ages of 13 and 14 years in Year 9 or for the Sixth Form in Year 12 after GCSE examinations. A prospectus and application form may be obtained from the Admissions Secretary. The website contains more information and parents and prospective pupils who wish to visit the school are welcomed. Early registration for a place is recommended, preferably a year in advance; a small fee is charged and places are confirmed with a guaranteed place fee within a year of entry. (£550 of the guaranteed place fee is held as a deposit against extras and returned on the final account.) All pupils start in September, although exceptional cases are occasionally considered at other times.

Scholarships and Bursaries. (*see Scholarship Entries section*). Academic, Art, Drama, Design & Technology, Music and Sports Scholarships are offered up to 50% at 13 to candidates of sufficient merit. Applicants must be under 14 on 1 September in the year they are due to enter the College. Academic Scholarships (including Art and the Scoresby Science Scholarships) and Music Scholarships are offered to pupils who join the school in Year 12 after GCSEs.

Fees per term (2008-2009). Boarding £8,210, Day £5,435 including meals and almost all extras.

Preparatory School. The College has close links with St Andrew's School, Eastbourne following the merger in 1977 with Ascham, the College Preparatory School. St Andrew's is an Independent Preparatory School preparing boys and girls for a variety of schools but with a significant number of pupils coming on to the College.

The **Old Eastbournian Association** celebrated its century in 1995. Strong links are maintained with former pupils and a careers' directory links alumni and offers assistance to current pupils. The OEA runs a convention every year to support the careers and higher education programme.

The **Collegial Society** meets regularly and comprises friends and parents of former pupils as well as College employees.

The **Eastbourne College Society** is the friend-raising arm of the College.

There is a thriving **Foundation Office** to direct fund-raising for bursaries and new developments.

The **Devonshire Society** (legacy club) meets annually.

Charitable status. Eastbourne College Incorporated is a Registered Charity, number 307071. It exists for the purpose of educating children.

The Edinburgh Academy

42 Henderson Row Edinburgh EH3 5BL
Tel: 0131 556 4603
Fax: 0131 624 4990
e-mail: enquiries@edinburghacademy.org.uk
website: www.edinburghacademy.org.uk

Lord Cockburn, Leonard Horner and John Russell, WS, were chiefly responsible for the foundation of The Edinburgh Academy, which was incorporated by Royal Charter 5th Geo. IV. Sir Walter Scott, one of the original Directors, presided at the opening ceremony in 1824. The Academy is an independent School governed by a Court of Directors.

Court of Directors:

Chairman: Mr S A Mackintosh

Extraordinary Directors:
Lord Cameron of Lochbroom
Professor J P Percy
Mr J H W Fairweather
Mr J B Leggat
Mr M W Gregson (*PPC Chairman*)
Mr A F Zegleman (*Chairman FGPC*)

Elected Directors:
Mr R G Adams
Mrs J L Allan
Mr P I Bell
Mr A D Burnett
Mr A M Duncan
Dr A E Gebbie
Mr J D Hood
Mrs F Houston Wood
Mr G N Hunt
Ms M McNeill
Mr D H Scott (*Chairman Enterprises*)
Mr F S D Spratt (*Academical Club Representative; Chairman Property Committee*)
Mr A M R Tod (*FGPC; Chairman EA Foundation*)
Miss S J M Whitley
Mr J D B Workman

Co-opted Members:
The Rector
The Headteacher of Junior School

Secretary to Court and Bursar:
Mr A W Blackett, OBE

FGPC = Finance & General Purposes Committee
PPC = Planning & Policy Committee

***Rector*: M G Longmore**, MA Edinburgh, FRSA

Deputy Rector: D M Standley, MA Oxon, CPhys, MInstP

Senior School Staff:
* *Head of Department*

Classics:
*A K Tart, MA Cantab;
J J C Fenton, MA Cantab (*Director of Administration*)

English:
*J R Meadows, BA Dunelm
G M Trotter, MTheol St Andrews (*2nds/3rds Year Head*)
S A Mair, MA Edinburgh
Miss K Roy, BA Cantab
Mrs C M Armour, MA Glasgow

Drama:
*G M Trotter
Miss K Roy, BA Cantab

Geography:
*M Bryce, BSc Stirling (*4ths/5ths Year Head*)
J D Hudson, BSc Belfast (*Geits Year Head, Head of RE and PSD*)
Miss D J Carr, BSc Aberdeen, PhD Edinburgh
Mrs T L E Robinson, MA Dundee

History and Politics:
*G H Harris, MA Cantab
J E Miller, MA Oxon
C M Turley, BA Dunelm

Mathematics:
*D F Buckley, BA Oxon, AIA
M A L Shipley, BSc Heriot-Watt
C A Brookman, BSc Edinburgh, PhD Edinburgh, GRSC, MInstP
Mrs R L Strudwick, BSc Edinburgh
Miss F M Campbell

Modern Languages:
*D M Bonnyman, MA, BPhil St Andrews, MIL (*Head of German*)
Mrs S G S Heintze, MA, MPhil Glasgow, MIL
Mrs Y D Harley, LL Paris Sorbonne
Mrs E Stark, MA St Andrews
Mrs T J Irving, MA Heriot-Watt

Biology:
*A W MacPherson, BSc Edinburgh, MSc Birmingham, PhD Reading
Miss G Arbuthnott, BSc St Andrews
D M Lowe, BSc Edinburgh

Chemistry:
*Mrs J R Coutts, BSc Dunelm, DPhil Oxon
T Blackmore, BSc, PhD Bristol, MRSC
K D Mitchell BSc Heriot-Watt, PhD Heriot-Watt

Physics:
*N Armstrong, MA Oxon, CPhys, MInstP
R T Wightman, BSc Edinburgh, PhD OU (*Director of 6th Form*)
K S Gilroy, BSc Manchester, PhD Cantab
J A Smith, BSc Heriot-Watt, PhD UMIST

Computer Studies:
C I M Hamilton, MA, MLitt Edinburgh

Art:
*D L Prossser, BA
Mrs P E Prosser, BA London
C R Murray, BA Edinburgh College of Art
Ms E Mackinlay, BA London

Design & Technology:
*Miss S M Hennessy, BA Cardiff, MA Manchester Metropolitan
B N Brown, BSc Loughborough

Business Studies:
*W J Turkington, BA Heriot-Watt

Music:
*P N Coad, MA, PhD Cantab, FRCO (*Director*)
P E Backhouse, BMus Edinburgh, ARCM, FRCO
L Morrison, DRSAM
Mrs M A Fergusson, DRSAM

Physical Education:
*M J de G Allingham, MSc
E K G Saunders, BA Leeds Metropolitan
Miss L McWilliam, BEd Edinburgh
R W Sayles, BSc Napier

Support for Learning:
*Mrs B Bellis, MA St Andrews
Mrs M J Robinson, MA Glasgow
Mrs S F Gray, BA Bristol

Religious Education:
H Jarrold, M Theol St Andrews

Careers:
R T Wightman
S A Mair
Mrs Y D Harley
(and Year Heads)

Librarian: Mrs E Mackay

CO, CCF: Sqn Ldr S G S Heintze, RAF
CCF Staff Instructor: Captain E B Burnett, Hldrs

Junior School Staff
Headteacher: Mrs C S Bashford, BA Edinburgh
Deputy Head: B Dean, BEd Hons

Assistant Heads:
Mrs L A Becher, DCE Dundee, INSC (*Head of Early Years*)
Mrs E Denholm, DipEd Moray House (*Head of Nursery*)
Mrs B Robertson, BEd Dundee, DPSE Moray House (*Head of Upper Primary*)

Mrs E F Black, BEd Stirling, PGD, DipCE Moray House
Miss M P Murray, DCE Call Park
Miss A Thomson, BSc Napier, PGCE Paisley
Mrs C Petrie, BEd, HDNS Northern College
Mrs K L McLean, BEd Northern College
Mrs E B Mackie, CertEd Lancaster
Mrs C Chan, BEd Jord
Mrs S Walker, DCE Call Park
Mrs S E M Clark, LLB Glasgow, DipLP, PGCE
P Bertolotto, BEd Hons CREDL, PGCE
Mrs G A Wood, CELTA, MA Hons Glasgow, PGCE
S MacDonald, BA Napier, PGCE
C McCloghry, BA Moray House, HNC Telford, PGCE
R Tyrell, BSc
M Enos, MA Edinburgh, BA Strathclyde, PGCE (**PE & Games*)
Mrs E Russell, BEd Hons (*Music*)
R Zbikowski, MA (*Science*)
Mrs C Bingham, BEd Hons 1st
Miss J Purves Hume, BEd Hons
Mrs A Kelly, LLB2.1
Mrs V Lewis, MA Hons, PGCE
Miss S Black, BEd Primary Aus
Miss N Kelly, MA, PGCE
M Willis, BA, PGDE
Mrs E Dunlop, DCE Aberdeen College of Ed

Support for Learning:
Mrs M Marlborough, BSc, MEd Edinburgh
Mrs E Watt, CertEd Moray House, PGCE, CertSpLD

Nursery:
Mrs P Howden Thomson BEd Hons 1st
Mrs A Addison, NNEB
Mrs K Thomson, NNEB
Mrs K Jones, NNEB
Mrs T A Sutherland, NNEB
Mrs F Ho, HNC
Mrs S Stewart, NNEB
Miss J Evans, NNEB
Mrs D Galbraith, NNEB
Miss E Hill, NNEB
Mrs S Semple, NNEB
Miss A Hill, NNEB
Mrs G Scott, NNEB

The Edinburgh Academy will be fully co-educational by August 2008 with girls starting in all year groups. At present The Edinburgh Academy consists of a Senior School, containing about 440 boys and 60 girls (ages 10½ to 18), a Junior School containing about 275 boys and 50 girls (ages 4½ to 10½), and a Nursery Department of 90 pupils.

Site and Buildings. The Senior School occupies a site in Henderson Row, less than a mile from Princes Street and at the northern limits of the Georgian 'New Town', of which it was designed to be a part. The buildings there include a School Hall, Library, a Music School built in 1990, Dining Hall, Gymnasium, Miniature Rifle Range, Fives Courts, and the new James Clerk Maxwell Science Centre which was completed in November 2006. In the Spring of 1977 an adjacent school in its own grounds was acquired thereby doubling the area of the existing site and allowing for a programme of immediate development aimed at major improvements to the general facilities of the Senior School. The Playing Fields are about half a mile from the main buildings – Raeburn Place (8½ acres) (shared with the Old Boys), New Field in Inverleith Place (20 acres), and a further 5 acres, also at Inverleith, with a Running Track. There are Squash Rackets courts and all-weather Tennis Courts at Inverleith. A small all-weather pitch will be open for use at Inverleith in August 2008 and two full-sized all-weather pitches are planned to follow at New Field. The Academy possesses its own Field Centre in the Highlands (Glen Doll, Angus). A new Sports Hall was built in 1997. A new purpose-built nursery and after-school facility will be opened in August 2008.

Forms. (Senior School only). Seventh and Sixth Classes: by tutor groups studying either GCE A Levels or Highers. Fifths: 3 Classes in sets for subjects. Fourths: 3 Classes in sets for subjects. Thirds: 3 Classes in sets for subjects. Seconds: 3 Classes in sets for subjects. Firsts: 3 Classes. No teaching group consists of more than 24 pupils, and many are substantially smaller. In the Junior School maximum class sizes are 20 (P1–P3) and 22 (P4–P6)

Scheme of Work. In the Junior classes of the Upper School all pupils do English, History, Geography, Latin, French, Mathematics, Science, Art and DT, Electronics, Computing, Drama and Music. Either German or Spanish is started in the Seconds, Business Studies, Design Technology, Electronics, Drama, PE, RE, Art and Music may be studied as full subjects in the Fourths. GCSE is taken in the Fifths. In the Sixths the majority of pupils take SCE Highers (whereby many achieve Scottish university entrance qualifications) and others do first year work in preparation for GCE A Level. A wide choice of subjects is possible. GCE A Levels are taken in the Sevenths in Classics, History, English, Modern Languages, Mathematics, Physics, Chemistry, Biology, Geography, Business Studies, Economics, Art, Music, and pupils are prepared for University entrance. Places at Oxford and Cambridge have been regularly won in all departments. In 2007 84% of our pupils went on to study degree courses.

Divinity. An assembly for Prayers is held at 8.50 am each morning, and is attended by the whole school. In every class one period a week is devoted to Religious Education. School Services for the whole School are held on several occasions during each term.

Physical Education and Games. All pupils take Physical Education and Games (which are regarded as an integral part of the curriculum) unless they are specially exempted on medical grounds. Rugby Football is played in the Autumn Term and during half of the Spring Term as are Hockey and Association Football. Cross-Country Running and other games occupy the first part of this Term. Hockey is the main sport for girls. In the Summer Term boys and girls choose from Cricket, Athletics, Hockey, Sailing, Shooting, Swimming and Tennis according to their year groups. Golf, Rugby Fives, Squash Rackets and Badminton are also played, and instruction in Fencing and Judo is available.

Combined Cadet Force. All pupils over 14½ join the CCF unless specially exempted and they may enter directly into either the RN, Army or RAF Sections. All members of the CCF are required to attend at least the Annual Camp in their first year and in one other year of their choice. After three and a half terms of service pupils are free to leave the CCF. The Academy has a Pipe Band. Piping and Drumming classes are held for pupils in the Junior classes of the Upper School as well as for members of the CCF.

Duke of Edinburgh's Award and Outdoor Activities. Considerable importance is attached to outdoor education. Apart from The Duke of Edinburgh's Award Scheme there are residential trips for both 1st and 3rd year pupils. The Academy's Field Centre in Glen Doll, Angus, is ideally situated as a centre for Hill-Walking, Climbing, Skiing, Fishing, and for Geographical and Biological Field Studies.

Music, Drama, Art. A purpose-built Music School was opened in 1992. In addition to the full-time Music Staff, there are a number of visiting teachers for various instruments. Musical appreciation and Singing form part of the curriculum of the Junior Classes. Throughout the rest of the Senior School there are regular periods of Music Appreciation. Pupils are encouraged to learn a Musical Instrument and over 300 do. There is a Choral Society, a Choir, and a special Chamber Choir, a School Orchestra, Junior Orchestra, and a Wind Band. Inter-Division Music Competitions, both Choral and Instrumental, are held annually. Also important are the Pipe Band and the Dance Band and Jazz Band.

There are several Senior and Junior Dramatic productions each year, including a major Play, Opera or Musical, and there are Drama Competitions involving all pupils in the Fourth classes and for Divisions (Houses) A major Choral work is performed each year, and a number of informal Saturday evening Concerts are given through the year. A new performing arts area is being created out of the north wing of the original 1824 building.

Art and DT are included in the curriculum from the Junior Classes and there are regular lessons in Art Appreciation throughout the School. Pupils are regularly prepared for GCSE and A Level or for SCE Higher in Music, Art, DT and Drama.

Other Activities. There are Arts, Debating, History, Modern Languages, Photographic, Jazz, Mountaineering, Politics, Computer and Electronic, Scientific and Mathematical Societies; Scripture Union and Video Club, Bridge, Chess, and Classes for the further study of Art and for Scottish Country Dancing. All pupils have an opportunity each week to devote some time to some creative art or craft, Music, Painting, Pottery, etc. for which good facilities are available.

Junior School. The Senior Department of the Junior School (ages $6\frac{1}{2}$ to $10\frac{1}{2}$) is in a building opened in 1960, close to New Field. The Early Years Department (ages $4\frac{1}{2}$ to $6\frac{1}{2}$) is in Denham Green House, built in 1987 on the same site. The work of the Junior School is arranged so as to ensure a smooth transition to the Senior School. All pupils in the Junior School have Physical Education. Rugby and Association Football, Hockey, Athletics and Cricket all have their place. For Music, there are 2 full-time teachers and a number of visiting teachers for various instruments. Musical Appreciation and singing form part of the curriculum and every encouragement is given to pupils to learn a Musical Instrument and to take part in the wide range of Musical Activities offered by various Choirs and Instrumental Groups.

(*See also Junior School entry in IAPS section.*)

Residence. No pupil may attend the Academy who does not live under the charge of his parents or legal guardian. Exemptions from this rule are rarely made by the Directors, and only in very exceptional cases.

Fees per term (from April 2008). Junior School P1–P6 £1,950–£2,440, Lunch £156–£159.50. Senior School: £2,700 (Geits), £3,360 (2nds–7ths). Lunch: £184.40.

When 3 or more brothers or sisters are in attendance at the School at the same time, a reduction of one-third of the tuition fees is made for each brother or sister after the first two.

Scholarships and Bursaries. (*see Scholarship Entries section*). A number of external Scholarships are offered each year at all ages from age 11. The Examination takes place in mid February. Further details are available from the Rector's PA. Means-tested Bursaries are available to both new and existing pupils in cases of need which may arise.

Admission. The majority of new pupils are admitted at the beginning of the Autumn Term in late August, though they can be accepted at any time. Places can always be found at P5 ($8\frac{1}{2}$–$9\frac{1}{2}$), and there are places each year at Sixth Form level in the Upper School, and also in the First and Third classes ($10\frac{1}{2}$–$12\frac{1}{2}$), where special provision is made for pupils who have previously done no languages; and there are often casual vacancies at other levels.

All candidates for admission to the Academy must first be assessed by the School. For admission in August, candidates for the Junior Department of the Junior School are assessed in January; those for the Senior Department, and for the Upper School in February. Pupils should be registered as candidates for entry as early as possible. Application forms are obtainable from the Rector's PA. There is a registration fee of £20.

Academical Club. There is a strong Academical Club, whose headquarters are at Raeburn Place, Edinburgh 4 (Tel: 0131 332 1070). *Secretary*: Mr Alan Fyfe, The Edinburgh Academy, 42 Henderson Row, Edinburgh EH3 5BL (Tel: 0131 556 4603).

Charitable status. The Edinburgh Academy is a Registered Charity, number SC016999. It exists to provide good quality education.

Elizabeth College

The Grange St Peter Port Guernsey Channel Islands GY1 2PY
Tel: 01481 726544
Fax: 01481 714176
e-mail: secretary@elizabethcollege.guernsey.net
website: www.elizcoll.org

Elizabeth College was founded in 1563 by Queen Elizabeth I in order to provide education for boys seeking ordination in the Church of England. It is one of the original members of the Headmasters' Conference and has Direct Grant status. It provides a broad education while maintaining the Christian aspirations of its Foundress. There are approximately 700 boys in the College, of whom about 200 are in the Lower School. Girls are accepted into the Sixth Form.

Motto: '*Semper Eadem*'.

Visitor: The Bishop of Winchester

Directors:
The Very Revd Canon Paul Mellor, Dean of Guernsey (*Chairman*)
Mr D Grut
Mr L S Trott
Mr P M A Palmer
Mr J L Burton
Mr K M Hudson
Professor R Conder
Mr S Le Maitre
Mrs M Wheatley

***Principal*: N D Argent**, BA, PhD

Vice-Principal: S G D Morris, BSc
Director of Studies: A R Cross, MA
Head of Sixth Form: R J W James, BA

Members of Teaching Staff:
Mrs E M Adams, DipAD
B W Allen, CertEd
B E H Aplin, BSc
Miss K Brent, BEng, BSc
Mrs M Campbell, BA, MA
B Clarke, BA
C R W Cottam, MA, CTABRSM
G S Cousens, BA
R Davis, BA
T R De Putron, BSc
Mrs M C Dudley, BA
T Edge, BA, MA
Miss J Flood, BA, MA
M Garnett, BA
A Good, BSc
Mrs M Gordon, MA
A Hale, BSc
Mrs T L Halton, BSc
M N Heaume, BSc
M P Higgins, BSc
J J Hills, BA
J R Hooker, BA
S J Huxtable, BA
D R L Inderwick, BA, MA
A M Jewell, BEd, MEd
M E Kinder, BEd
Miss K Labbé, Licence (Lit)
R G Le Sauvage, BSc
Mrs P E Maher, BA, ARCM
D F Raines, BSc, DPhil
Miss E Ryder, BSc Hons, PhD
Mrs C L Saunal, BA
T C Slann, DipNEBSS
M A G Stephens, BA
Mrs A Thibeault, BA, MA
C D van Vlymen, BSc, PhD
M Wesley, BSc
G Wilce, BSc, MSc

Chaplain: The Revd R G Harnish, BSc, DPhil, MA
Director of Music: P C Harris, GRSM, ARCM

Games and Physical Education: D Wray, BEd

Head of the Junior School: Mrs S Battey, CertEd
Deputy Head: C Veron, BEd
Mrs M Boyle, BSc
Mrs C Crittell, BA
Miss K Henry, BA
Mrs M Kinder, CertEd
Mrs D M McLaughlin, BSc
Mrs A Pollard, BA
Mrs K Robinson, BEd
Miss D Wenman, BA

Head of Pre-Prep: Mrs J Veron, BEd
Mrs C Bowden, BEd
Miss E Carré, BA
Mrs S Dorey, BEd
Miss C Kimber, BSc
Miss K Parrott, BSc
L Purdue, BSc

Bursar and Clerk to the Directors: J M Willis, MCMI

Buildings and Grounds. The Upper School (for pupils over 11 years) is situated in imposing buildings dating from 1829 which stand on a hill overlooking the town and harbour of St Peter Port. The classrooms and laboratories, all of which are equipped with appropriate modern teaching aids, the Hall, Sports Hall and Swimming Pool are accommodated on this site. Recent improvements have included a new Sixth Form Centre, improved Design and Technology and ICT facilities. There are two large games fields, one of which includes an artificial pitch for hockey, soccer and tennis. Elizabeth College Junior School comprises Beechwood, a prep school, and Acorn House, a pre-prep and nursery school. Beechwood has its own site some ten minutes' walk from Elizabeth College. It takes boys and girls from 7 to 11 years old. Acorn House accepts boys and girls from 4 to 7 years old and also has a pre-school facility for younger children.

Academic Curriculum. In their first three years in the Upper School boys follow a broad curriculum which is common to all – covering arts, sciences, creative and practical subjects. Information Technology is timetabled in all three years to develop the skills needed for the demands of GCSE and A Level courses. Opportunity is also afforded to boys to sample both Latin and a second Modern Foreign Language in addition to French. PSHE, RE, PE, Games and Drama are timetabled throughout. In Years 10 and 11 the aim is to produce a high level of achievement and choice at GCSE by offering flexibility wherever possible. Three separate sciences will, therefore, be taken by some, but the majority do Core and Additional Science. At least one modern language must be taken, although two are available as an option. English Literature is studied within the English teaching groups, but is not compulsory for all. Other GCSE options combine the traditional with the contemporary. Art, Business Studies, Classics, Drama, Graphics, History, Information Technology, Latin, Music, PE and RS are currently offered. Alongside the GCSE courses PSHE and RE continue to be taught. The Sixth Form is run in partnership with The Ladies' College, with interchange of pupils between schools and shared teaching of many groups. The Sixth Form offers a very broad array of choices. Students are able to study varying combinations of AS and A2 Levels up to a maximum of four A2 Levels and one AS Level. Tutorial periods enable vocational, careers and pastoral guidance to be available.

Music. There are two orchestras, a brass band, a wind band and a number of chamber music groups. The College choir makes regular visits to the French mainland to sing in Cathedrals and at concerts. Instruction is available in all the usual orchestral instruments in addition to the piano and organ. The Junior School has its own choir, orchestra and recorder group. Each summer holiday the College hosts a week-long orchestral course when tuition is provided by eminent professionals to over one hundred and fifty boys and girls.

Games. The sports fields cover some 20 acres. The Junior School has its own small playing field, and also has access to the facilities of the Upper School. The major College games are Association Football, Hockey and Cricket. Athletics, Badminton, Basketball, Cross-country Running, Fencing, Golf, Rugby Football, Sailing, Shooting, Squash, Swimming, Tennis and Volleyball also flourish. Physical Education forms a regular part of the curriculum for all boys up to the end of Year 11. Some seniors specialise in Outdoor Pursuits (principally canoeing and climbing) as their "sport". This is under the guidance of a fully qualified expert. Despite the size of the Island, plentiful opposition is available. The College competes against other Island schools, has a traditional rivalry with Victoria College in Jersey, makes regular tours to the mainland and hosts return visits from UK schools.

Combined Cadet Force. The Contingent includes all three arms: Royal Navy, Army and Royal Air Force sections. Parties go annually on Summer Camp and Adventurous Training. The College Shooting VIII forms a part of the Combined Cadet Force and has a long and distinguished record at Bisley. The CCF is the only weapon-carrying force in the Island and, therefore, has an important role in providing guards of honour on many ceremonial occasions.

Duke of Edinburgh's Award. Boys are encouraged to participate in this scheme at all three levels. The expedition work necessarily takes place on the mainland during the Easter and Summer holidays.

Community Service Unit. This Unit draws boys from Year 10 and above. It serves those in need and those who are handicapped throughout the Island community.

Scouts. There is an active Scout Group, whose headquarters are situated on the College Field. At the Junior School there is a Cub Scout Group.

Clubs and Societies. The College stresses the importance of extra-curricular activity. Among currently active clubs are those which foster Bridge, Canoeing, Chess, Debating, Drama, Fencing, Life Saving, Model Railways, Music, Sailing, Science, Shooting, Table Tennis, Tai-Chi, War Gaming and Windsurfing.

Pastoral Care. In the Upper School each year has a Head of Year assisted by four Tutors. Acorn and Beechwood each have a Headmistress. All these staff provide pastoral care and academic guidance for their own sections of the College. They are supported by a full-time Chaplain who conducts services in all three schools as well as preparing boys for Confirmation.

Parental Involvement. Parents are strongly encouraged to take an active part in their son's education. There are regular assessments and reports to which they are invited to respond, either immediately or at annual parents' evenings. Those responsible for pastoral matters are also available on the telephone during out of school hours for discussion about problems or progress.

Admission. The principal ages for admission into the school are 4, 7, 11, 13 and 16, but there are usually vacancies for entry at other ages. Entry is by means of tests and/or interview which are adapted to the age of the applicant. There is a £110 non-refundable registration fee. Applications for entry should be addressed to the Principal.

Scholarships to the College. (*see Scholarship Entries section*). The Gibson Fleming Fund provides Scholarships for current pupils. The award value depends to some extent upon the needs of the applicant's parents. The Trustees review their Scholars each year and take account of general personal qualities as well as academic performance. Entries should be made by the end of the Lent Term.

Choral and Instrumental Scholarships are also available to current pupils. Details of these may be obtained from the Principal.

Scholarships to the Universities. The College Exhibitions, Scholarships and Prizes include the Queen's Exhibition, the Lord de Sausmarez Exhibition; the Mainguy Scholarship; the Mansell Exhibition and the Mignot Fund. The Gibson Fleming Trust can also provide awards to its Scholars for their future education.

Travel. There are several flights each day from Southampton (half an hour), Gatwick (about three quarters of an hour) and Stansted (about one hour). There are also regular flights to the West Country and to Midlands and northern airports. There are frequent sailings to and from Portsmouth, Poole and Weymouth, which offer vehicle transportation.

Old Boys. The Honorary Secretary of the Old Elizabethan Association is Gresham Barber who may be contacted via www.oea.org.gg.

Fees per term (2008-2009). Acorn (Pre-Prep and Nursery): £2,078; Beechwood (Prep): £2,311; Upper School (11–18): £2,311.

Ellesmere College
A Woodard School

Ellesmere Shropshire SY12 9AB
Tel: 01691 622321
Fax: 01691 623286
e-mail: hmsecretary@ellesmere.com
website: www.ellesmere.com

Ellesmere College is one of the Schools of the Society of SS Mary and John of Lichfield, part of the Woodard Corporation, and was opened on 8 September 1884.

Motto: '*Pro Patria Dimicans.*'

Founder: The Revd Nathaniel Woodard, DCL, then Dean of Manchester

Visitor: The Rt Revd The Lord Bishop of Lichfield

College Council:
The Provost
Mrs D H Griffith (*Custos*)
J K Jones, OBE, BA
G R Wigginton
Mrs F M Christie, MRPhS
The Right Revd Dr A G C Smith, MA, Bishop of Shrewsbury
Wing Commander J O Jewiss
R Savage
Mrs C S Newbold, BA
J A Mathias, FCA
J S Hopkins
A L Morris
C Clutton
Professor S Eisenstein, MB BCh, PhD, FRCS

***Headmaster*: B J Wignall**, BA, MA, MCMI, FRSA

Deputy Head (*Pastoral*): M D T Sampson, BSc

Deputy Head (*Academic*): Mrs S V Pritt-Roberts, BEd, MEd, NPQH

Head of Sixth Form: P A Wood, MA

Head of Middle School: Mrs S Owen, BEd

Head of Lower School: W J Hutchings, BEd

Director of Activities: Mrs D Joynson-Brooke, BEd

Chaplain: The Revd David Slim

Director of Finance: N Haworth

Director of Operations: K Brockless

Teachers:
*T C Howitt-Dring, CertEd
*S F W Purcell, BA
P A Goodwin, BEd
†G Hutchinson, MA
†M P Clewlow, BSc
Mrs J E Purcell, BA
F S Williams, CertEd
P J Hayes, MA
Mrs H Scarisbrick, BA
*Mrs R A McCarthy, BA, MA, DipBDA, AMBDA
Mrs J Hibbott, BA
Mrs S Hooper, BA
Mrs A M Hendrikson, BA, AMBDA
Mrs S E Morgan, BEd
Mrs D Joynson-Brooke, BEd
C R Davies, BA
*H B Orr, BD
*Dr M T Gareh, BSc, MSc, PhD, MRSC
T F Bongers, BCom
*J H Cowley, BSc
D J Morgan, BSc
Mrs J Evans, BEd, MA, AMBDA
Mrs M Amako, BA
Mrs J R Nicolson, MA
*Dr R Chatterjee, MSc, BSc, PhD
Mrs Z J Fisher, BA
Mrs K L Jenkins, BSc
Miss B Jones, BA
*Mrs L A Paton, BA
Mrs E Lewis, BEd
†C Cawcutt, DipEd
*M Coats, BSc
R J Macintosh, BSc
*S B Mullock, BA
Mrs E J John, BA
*I L Williams, BEd
Mrs J Cowan, CertEd, AMBDA
D W Crawford, BA
†Mrs P M Fox, BA
Mrs V M Howle, BEd
Mrs E Phillips, BSc
Mrs S Philips, MA
R J Purnell, BSc
Mrs J M Davies, BA
Ms C Allen, BA
Miss H L Goss, BSc
*R C Paul, BA
Dr J K Ripley, BSc, PhD
*Dr I G Tomkins, MA, DPhil
Mrs M Ollier, BA
R P Boswell, BA
Ms S M Abbots, MA
I L Roberts, BA
Miss S Ryan, BA
P E Swainson, BSc
R J Townsend, BEd
G Owen, BEd
Mrs V Hart, MA
Ms G Ansell, CertEd
J Baggaley, BA
Ms E Baker, BSc
Mrs A Darrant, BSc
D Hawkins, BSc
Mrs J Hibbott, BA
Mrs N Hoy, LTA Club Coach
Mrs M Hutchings, MA
Ms H Napal
K Paul, BSc
Miss A Pugh, BSc
Mrs L Stewart-Harris, MSc
Ms M Thomas, MA
Mrs C Walker
Mrs D Walker-Smith, BA
Ms C Westwood, BA
Ms E Baker, BSc

School Medical Officer: Dr E A M Greville, MBChB

Sanatorium Sisters:
Mrs J Slim, RGN
Mrs M Moore, RGN
Mrs M Haynes, SEN

The College Building. The main school building contains three boys' Boarding and Day Houses, as well as a mixed 10–12 junior Boarding and Day House, bachelor and married accommodation for Housemasters and Housemistresses and/or Assistant Housemasters and Housemistresses, the Chapel and the Dining Hall. St Luke's Boarding House with 26 double en-suite bedrooms for Sixth Form boys in their final year completes the main quadrangle. A 13–16 girls' Boarding and Day house has its own wing in the main building and was opened in response to demand in 1996. The girls' Sixth Form Boarding and Day House which accommodates 50 girls in a combination of shared and single study bedrooms and dayrooms was completed in 1986. A Gymnasium, Big School (Assembly Hall) which houses the Schulze Organ, and three subject Departments are also located in the main building. September 2004 saw the opening of the College's new Sports Hall, which adds to facilities that include two other gymnasia and squash courts.

Additional wings contain the Learning Support Department, Library and Sixth Form Centre. Other subjects are taught in their own Departmental blocks close to the main building, and include Science laboratories, a Modern Languages Department with a Language Laboratory, an Art School, a Design & Technology Centre, and a Business Studies department with its own computer suite. A purpose-built Lower School for Years 3–8 was opened in 1999.

The House System. The Lower School (ages 7–13) has a competitive system based on 3 Houses. The Senior School has a competitive system based on 4 Houses all of which are co-educational and combine boarding and day pupils. Separate from the competitive Houses is the residential House system for living arrangements. There are 2 Girls' Houses, catering for age 13–16 and Sixth Form respectively; there are 3 Boys' Houses: two for age 13–16 and two Sixth Form Houses; there is also a Mixed House catering for ages 10–12.

School Work. Until GCSE all boys and girls are guided in their academic work by a Tutor, whom they see at least once a week to report progress. In the Sixth Form each pupil has an academic supervisor who is a teacher in the pupil's primary A Level or International Baccalaureate Diploma subject. The IB Diploma was introduced in September 2006.

In the first year in the Senior School a full range of fourteen subjects is studied, including Art, Design and Technology, Computing and Technical Drawing. This curriculum is designed to give all pupils a comprehensive introduction before reducing to a basic eight subjects for GCSE. At GCSE all pupils take English, Mathematics, and either Dual Award Science or the three Sciences studied separately. Other subjects depend on individual aptitude and choice.

In the Sixth Form over 20 different academic subjects are available for study to A Level or IB Diploma to prepare for University Entrance or entry to the Services and the Professions.

Music. The College has a very strong musical tradition. It possesses two of the finest organs in the country, including the internationally renowned St Mary Tyne Dock Schulze Organ. The Chapel Choir has a wide repertoire of Church Music. There is a Big Band, a Choral Society, a Jazz Group and other ensembles, all of which give regular concerts. There are House Music Competitions every year.

An annual programme of Celebrity Concerts brings distinguished musicians to the College.

The Music School is part of the College Arts Centre which provides first-class facilities, including 8 Practice Rooms, a Recording Studio, Teaching Rooms and a Studio Theatre designed for small concerts and seating 220 people.

The department has 2 full-time and 16 part-time teachers.

Arts Centre. This purpose-built complex was opened in 1976 for Drama, Dance, Film, Music and Art Exhibitions. A programme is organised in which international artists in all these fields visit the Centre, which shares its facilities with the local community.

Careers. At all levels pupils are encouraged to seek advice from the College careers masters and mistresses as well as representatives from the Independent Schools Careers Organisation. The ISCO aptitude tests are available for all pupils in their GCSE level year. A Careers' Convention is held each year for pupils in Year 11.

School Societies. There are a large number of flourishing societies which range from debating and play reading to bridge and chess, from architecture and electronics to philately and photography.

Games and Physical Education. All members of the School are required to participate in a regular programme of games, though particular inclinations and aptitudes are taken fully into consideration. Facilities include a sports hall, a floodlit multi-sports area, a fitness centre, squash courts, a heated indoor swimming pool, indoor and outdoor shooting range, a gymnasium, 6 floodlit all-weather tennis courts, a golf course, rugby pitches, hockey pitches, cricket squares, and an athletics track. Ellesmere has a long tradition of sporting excellence, particularly in rugby and tennis.

Ellesmere is superbly placed for outdoor pursuits. Easily accessible lakes, rivers and hills provide opportunities to develop talents and interests.

Sailing takes place on Whitemere. The School owns six boats and pupils are allowed to bring their own craft. Canoeing takes place on the Ellesmere canal and on local rivers such as the Dee and the Severn.

All pupils are expected to join one of the following: Outdoor Training Unit; CCF; Social Service. These activities occur on one full afternoon a week, but, in order to extend their activities, twice a year 3 days are set aside when all members of the School participate in 48-hour expeditions. In the Lent Term a single day is devoted to expeditions.

Admission. Boys and girls are admitted at all points of entry into the school. Entrance examinations are held in February for Lower School entry. Scholarships for Prep School candidates are held in May, while others take the Common Entrance Examination in June.

Scholarships and Exhibitions. (*see Scholarship Entries section*). A wide range of Scholarships and Exhibitions recognising a range of talents is available. Bursaries are awarded to the sons of Clergy, and Foundation Awards to sons of parents who could not normally afford this type of education. All details may be obtained from the Headmaster. In cases of need these awards may be further supplemented.

Fees per term (2008-2009). Boarders £6,260–£7,384, Weekly Boarders £5,827–£5,990, Day £3,255–£4,636, Years 4 and 5 £2,829. Fees are inclusive of general School charges.

Music lessons are given at a charge of £219 for ten lessons and individual tuition for dyslexic pupils also incurs an extra cost. A scheme of insurance is in force under which the School Fees may be insured for a small termly premium for any number of years and which enables a pupil to remain at Ellesmere to complete his/her education free of all board and tuition fees, if a parent dies before the pupil's School career is ended. There is also a School Fees Remission Scheme for insurance of fees in cases of absence through illness and of surgical and medical expenses. Arrangement can be made for a single advance payment of fees.

'Old Boys and Girls'. Former pupils of the school normally become members of the Old Ellesmerian Club, which in turn enables them to take part in a number of societies and activities. For further information contact: John Harvey, Old Ellesmerian Club Secretary, Ellesmere College, Ellesmere, Shropshire, SY12 9AB.

Charitable status. Ellesmere College is a Registered Charity, number 1103049. It exists to provide education for children.

Eltham College

Grove Park Road London SE9 4QF
Tel: 020 8857 1455
Fax: 020 8857 1913
e-mail: mail@eltham-college.org.uk
website: www.eltham-college.org.uk

Governors:
The Governing Body consists of a maximum of 11 elected Trust Governors, 1 Governor nominated by the Baptist Missionary Society, 1 by the Council for World Mission, 1 by the United Reformed Church, 2 parent nominated and 1 teacher nominated Governors, 1 Governor nominated by each of the London Boroughs of Bexley and Bromley.

Chairman of the Board: D A Robins, Esq, BSc

***Headmaster*: P J Henderson**, BA, FRSA

Deputy Head: E R Cavendish, BA

Bursar: D Cooper, ACCA

Development Director: S J McGrahan, MSc

Academic Staff:
P D Agate, BA (*Sculpture and Ceramics*)
J Backhouse, BA (*Head of Mathematics*)
K L Barron, MA (*Senior Master; English*)
A D Beattie, MA (*Geography*)
D Boudon (*French*)
Dr Helen Bowes, MSc, PhD (*Chemistry/Biology*)
Ms E Brass, BA, MA (*Head of Art*)
V Broncz, BSc (*Mathematics*)
P G Cheshire, MA (*German and French*)
Mrs H Clough, BSc (*Biology*)
S Coquelin, M-ès-L (*Director of Assessment; French*)
D K Cotterill, BSc (*Head of Marketing; Head of Geography*)
N M Culshaw, BSc (*Chemistry*)
Mrs S M Donaldson, BA (*Physics*)
Revd R J Draycott, MA, MTh (*Chaplain and Head of RS*)
Ms S Dunne, BA (*Spanish and French*)
Mrs S B Fearn, BA, ALA (*Librarian*)
A Fermor-Dunman, BSc, MA (*Geography; Physical Education*)
J P Floyd, MA (*Head of Politics; History*)
Ms M Franklin, MA (*Artist-in-Residence*)
D R Grinstead, BA (*Head of History*)
Mrs C A Head-Rapson, BSc (*Mathematics; Head of Girls and Community Service*)
A C Hillary, BEd (*Design and Technology*)
J F Hind, BSc (*Mathematics*)
Mrs C M Hobbs, BSc (*Head of Biology*)
Miss A Hobot, BSc (*Economics, Business Studies and PSE Coordinator*)
T A Hotham, BA (*Head of Classics*)
P A Howls, BA (*Deputy Head of Sixth Form; French, German, Russian*)
T J Johnson, MA (*Director of Music*)
N A Levy, GGSM, Cert Mgmt (*Music*)
Miss R Lewis, BSc (*Geography*)
M M MacKenzie, BSc (*Head of Physics*)
P J Mander, BA (*History; Politics*)
P C McCartney, BSc, MSc (*Head of Chemistry and Geology; Exams Officer*)
T C Mitchell, BA (*English; Drama*)
Dr G S Morgan, MA, PhD (*Chemistry*)
Dr J Munn, MA, PhD (*Mathematics*)
Mrs L Oldfield, BA (*Music*)
B Pollard, MA (*Head of Modern Languages, German and French*)
M Pollard (*Head of English*)
J P Pringle, BSc (*Head of IT and Computing; Physics*)
K G Roberts, TEng, DipEd (*Head of Design and Technology*)
A Ross, BSc (*Biology*)
K Shipton, MA (*English*)
Mrs L Smith, HNC (*IT/Computing*)
Mrs C M J Taylor, BA (*Latin & RS*)
A Thomas, BEd (*Head of Physical Education*)
E Thorogood, BSc (*Physical Education*)
J D Walker, BSc (*Head of Economics and Business Studies*)
L Watts, BSc (*Head of Sixth Form and Careers*)
O Weatherly, BA (*History*)
P Wren, TEng (*Design and Technology*)
J A C Yarnold, BA (*Head of Drama*)
P Zdarzil, LLM (*Director of Information Technology Services*)

Part-time:
Ms B Alvarez (*Spanish*)
Mrs E M Galloway, MA (*Physics*)
Mrs C D Green, DipEd (*English*)
Mr P Hoby (*English*)
Mrs A C E Richards, BA (*Art and Design*)
Mrs A Senior, L-ès-L (*French*)
Miss I Sadler (*Spanish*)
Mrs I Faunders (*French*)
Mrs C Shipp, BA, MA, CertSpLD, DipSpLD, AMBDA (*Learning Support*)
M Stickings (*German*)
Ms S Wood, BSc (*Mathematics*)

Junior School:

Master of the Junior School: K L John, BSc

Mr K Cowley, BA
Joanna Donegan, BA
Miss L Evelyn-Rahr, BA Ed
Ms J Galpin, BSc
Mrs A Hallett, BEd
R Johnston, BHSc
Mrs L Jones, BEd
M O'Dwyer, BEd
J Poole, BA
K L Schaper, MA (*Deputy Master*)
W Schaper, BEd
Mrs L Wrafter, CertEd

Part-time:
Mrs N Chamberlain, BA
Ms M McCullough (*Mandarin*)

Eltham College was a Direct Grant School which reverted to independent status in 1976. It was founded in 1842 as the School for the Sons of Missionaries. In 1912 the School moved from Blackheath to its present site, and thereafter began to admit boarders and day boys in increasing numbers. The School has always contained a nucleus of boys who have come as scholars in accordance with the foundation scheme, but the majority of pupils now come from a wider range of backgrounds.

Eltham College is now a day school only and the aim of the School is to provide a balanced and stimulating education based on Christian principles and practice. The buildings are surrounded by 42 acres of playing fields. There are about 550 boys and 65 girls in the Senior School, and there is a Junior School of some 205 boys attached.

Main School Buildings. The main part of the School is built round a large country mansion, now extended and adapted to include a Library and Sixth Form Reading Room, Dining Hall, Art and Sculpture Studios, and other teaching areas. An extensive teaching block, including newly-equipped laboratories devoted to Science, Computing, Technology and Mathematics was extended in 1998. A fine Performing Arts Centre, for curricular drama, plays and concerts, has been in use since 1987. There is also a magnificent Sports Centre opened in 1996, with an indoor Swimming Pool, Sports Hall, Fitness Suite and Dance Studio. The School Chapel stands as a separate building. Within the Old Quad, there are classrooms for Modern Languages and a Language Laboratory (re-equipped in 2004); the new Music School was created in the old Boarding House in 2005 with extensive teaching and practice facilities.

Curriculum. In the Lower and Middle School the curriculum is broad based. In the Middle School boys normally take 10 subjects, always including a range of both Arts and Science studies, for the GCSE examination, before entering the Sixth Form, in which they specialise in courses leading to the AS and A Level. Subjects available include Art, Biology, Business Studies, Chemistry, Computer Science, Design and Technology, Drama, Economics, English, French, Geography, Geology, German, History, Latin, Mathematics (Pure, Applied and Statistics), Music, Politics, Physics, Religious Studies and Spanish. 95% of pupils enter Higher Education, with some 15% being accepted to Oxford and Cambridge.

A proportion of the Sixth Form timetable is given to Community Service, Liberal Studies and Games.

Physical Education forms part of every pupil's timetable, and all are expected to take part in games. In the Autumn term Rugby Football is the major sport, whilst in the Spring term it is Hockey. Other sports offered are Association Football, Cross-Country, Badminton, Basketball and Netball; and in the Summer term Cricket, Athletics, and Tennis. Swimming and Water Polo is available all year round and there are opportunities for Table Tennis, Weight training and Aerobics. There are facilities for private music lessons; and in addition to a wide range of School Societies there are many hobby activities. It is the School's policy to arrange frequent expeditions abroad and adventure courses in the UK. There are links with schools in France, Germany, Russia, Estonia, Italy, Argentina, Nepal, Australia and South Africa, and foreign exchanges are actively encouraged.

Forms in the Lower and Middle School are composed of about 25 boys. There is some streaming in languages and science, and setting in Mathematics.

The Careers Master and other staff undertake to provide detailed and regular advice and information on Higher Education, GAP years and choice of career at the appropriate stages.

The role of parents in partnership with the School is regarded as extremely valuable, and there is a very strong and active Parent/Teacher Association.

Admission. Boys are admitted by entrance examination to the Main School at the age of 11 and a few places may be available at 13 and other ages. Sixth Form places are available by examination for both boys and girls.

Scholarships. (*see Scholarship Entries section*). Up to 20 scholarships may be awarded on performance in the entrance examination at age 11, also Music and Sports scholarships. Those seeking entrance at age 13 may, by the same token, apply for an Academic or a Music scholarship. At age 16, a number of Sixth Form Academic scholarships (usually 15) and Music, Sports, Art and Drama scholarships, are offered annually to qualified boys or girls. Details on application.

Term of Entry. The School normally accepts pupils only for the beginning of the academic year in September but, if gaps in particular year groups occur, it is willing to interview and test at any point in the year with a view to immediate or subsequent entry.

Junior School. The Grange, a large house on the School estate has been converted and extended to accommodate about 200 day boys in classes of not more than 25. A major refurbishment and extension was completed in November 2004 providing 8 new form rooms, Assembly Hall, Science Room, Music Room, and Art, Design and Technology Room. There is ample provision for Cricket, Rugby, Association Football, Hockey, Swimming, Athletics, Basketball, Tennis, Fencing and Judo. The teaching is in the charge of an experienced master responsible to the Headmaster. Admission is at the age of 7, though a small number of candidates are admitted at 8, and Junior School boys almost always qualify for admission to the Senior School at 11.

The School thus provides an opportunity for 11 years' uninterrupted education in healthy surroundings.

Applications should be made to the Junior School Secretary.

Fees per term (2008-2009). Senior School £3,875; Junior School £3,340.

Honours. 130 pupils have gained entry to Oxford and Cambridge during the last ten years.

Charitable status. Eltham College is a Registered Charity, number 1058438. It exists to provide education for boys.

Emanuel School

Battersea Rise London SW11 1HS
Tel: 020 8870 4171
Fax: 020 8877 1424
e-mail: enquiries@emanuel.org.uk
website: www.emanuel.org.uk

The School was founded in Westminster by Lady Anne Dacre in 1594, and moved to its present site on the north side of Wandsworth Common in 1883 as one of the three schools of the United Westminster Schools Foundation.

Motto: *Pour bien désirer*

Governing Body:

Chairman: F R Abbott, Esq, BA

B F W Baughan, Esq
Mrs S Chambers
Ms M A D'Mello, BSc, MSc
The Hon Jamie Douglas-Home
H Hughes, Esq, FCA
P M Kennerley, Esq, RD, FRICS
Ms C McGuinness, MA
Mrs M M Parsons, MA
Dr D Ricks, University of London
The Venerable Stephen Roberts
C Scott, Esq
T Smith, Esq
J Wates, Esq
Dr P Zutshi

Clerk and Receiver: R W Blackwell, MA

***Headmaster*: M D Hanley-Browne**, MA

Deputy Headmaster: J A Hardy, MA
Director of Studies: W M Rogers, BSc
Head of the Lower School: S J Gregory, MA, ARCO
Senior Tutor & Head of Middle School: J F W Benn, BA
Senior Tutor of Girls: Mrs S M Williams-Ryan, L-ès-L, MA (**Modern Languages, *French*)
Head of Sixth Form: R R Marriott, MA
Chaplain: Revd P M Hunt, MA, MTh

Teaching staff:
* *Head of Department*

S P Andrews, BA
A Ball, BA (**DT*)
R Berlie, MA (**History*)
Mrs J E Bettesworth, Dip AD, ATC
E Braun, BEng
Miss L K Brown, MA
Ms H Burnett, BA
Miss L Butler, BSc
G Cassidy, BA
Ms L C Cleveland, BA, MTh (**Religious Studies*)
Ms R Collins, BA
Dr M Dancy, BSc, PhD
†J M Driver, BD, AKC
S Fairlamb, BEd
N Fazaluddin, BSc (**Mathematics*)
†Miss L Fitzgibbon, BSc
Miss G Fornari, BA
A P Friell, BEd
S J Halliwell, BA
Miss J Halsey, BSc
D C Hand, BA
Mr M Healy, BSc
Miss J O Henderson, BA
J Holmes, BMus, MA, FRCO, ARCM (**Music*)
Mrs S Holmes, MA, ARCO
H Jackson, BA (**German*)
Miss M Jimenez, BA
A F S Keddie, MA, ACIB
Miss A Kennedy
R Khuman, BSc
P King, BEd
C O Labinjo, BSc
Dr B W Last, BA, MPhil, PhD (**Drama*)
Mrs J Lawton, BSc

†J P Layng, BSc, MNCA
V Le Gac, BA
Mrs R A Lewis, MA
Mrs F Lindsey-Clark, BA
Miss O Lopez, BA
Miss S E MacMillan, BA (**Art*)
Mrs C M Maher, BSc (**Chemistry*)
Miss H Malik, BSc
Ms G Marmion, BSc
Ms P S Marmion, TCert
†P McMahon, MA
Mrs J Morrison-Bartlett, BSc (**Science, *Physics*)
N M Mullen, MA (**Classics*)
Miss R Musson, BA
Dr A Noori, PhD
†W J Purkis, BSc (**Geography*)
K Ragkousis, BSc
Dr B A Reynolds, PhD (**Biology*)
Miss O Roncero-Refoyo, BA
R Skinner, BSc
M Sowden, BSc
M Swift, BA
C Thomas, BSc
R Tong, BA (**Business Studies*)
Mrs G Wright, BSc
Miss M Yan, BA
A Zaratiegui, MA (**Spanish*)

Visiting Music Teachers:
Mr F Baird, Dip TCL, ARCM (*Percussion*)
Mr F Crowther, BMus London (*Jazz Piano*)
Mr M Crowther, Dip GGSM (*Brass*)
Mrs P Crowther, Dip AGSM (*Brass*)
Ms J Hayter, BMus RAM, LRAM, PG Dip RCM (*Bassoon/Piano*)
Mr A Kendall, MA (*Singing*)
Ms K Lauder, BMus RNCM, PPRNCM (*French Horn/Piano*)
Ms E Marshall, BMus (*Flute/Piano*)
Ms R Philips, MMus GSMD, BMus RCM (*Oboe/Piano*)
Ms A Piatigorsky, BMus (*Piano*)
Mr R Schunter (*Guitar*)
Ms L Selwood, MMus (*Cello*)
Ms P Sharda (*Guitar*)
Ms N Shephard, PG Dip RAM (*Clarinet/Saxophone*)
Ms H Twoney, BMus, LTCL, PGCE (*Violin*)
Mr J Webb (*Drums*)

Librarian: T Jones, BA
Director of Finance and Administration: D Taylor, BA
Development Director: Ms S Fisher, BA
Headmaster's Secretary: Mrs J Wood
Admissions Secretary: Ms D Shuttleworth

Emanuel is a fully co-educational day school. We have approximately 700 pupils, with 160 in the Sixth Form.

Admission. Each September about 20 pupils are admitted at age ten, 90 pupils at age eleven and about 15 at age thirteen.

Entry at age ten and eleven is by competitive examination, held at the school each year in January. Applications to sit these examinations should be made before 1st December of the preceding year.

Entry at age thirteen is by an Emanuel examination in January, with occasional places by sitting the Common Entrance Examination in June.

Entry to the Sixth Form is by interview and tests. Unconditional or conditional offers may be made.

Full details from the Admissions Secretary.

Fees per term (2008-2009). £4,410 covering tuition, stationery, books and lunch. Extras charged are for individual instrumental tuition and some external visits and trips.

Site and Buildings. Emanuel was founded in 1594. In 1883 it moved from Westminster to the present site in Wandsworth. The original building is the core of the school, with most of its classrooms and a fine dining hall and chapel. The first addition made was the new building of 1896, which now houses our concert hall and music rooms, and the science laboratories. These have been completely refurbished in the last few years to a very high standard.

Over the last century many further additions have been made, including a large sixth form centre. The school's playing fields adjoin the school buildings together with a full size swimming pool. Our facilities include fives courts and a sports hall. The school has a boathouse on the Thames by Barnes Bridge.

Scholarships, Exhibitions and Bursaries. (*see Scholarship Entries section*).

Organisation. There is one form for pupils who join at age ten. Pupils joining at age eleven are streamed by ability in five forms, and primary responsibility for their care rests with the form teacher and the head of year, under the overall supervision of the head of the lower school, who deals with the Hill year 6, and years 7 and 8. As all pupils move from year 9 into year 10 there is a re grouping along the lines of the subjects chosen for GCSE examinations. In the sixth form a tutor system operates.

Pupils are placed in houses when they join the school, and they stay in these houses throughout their school career. Although originally intended as a means of fostering competition in games, these houses have developed over many years a strong community spirit, often involving former pupils.

For fuller details please ask for the school prospectus.

Times. The normal school day runs from 8.30 am to 3.45 pm, but many activities extend into the late afternoon after school. Many school activities, especially games, also take place on Saturday mornings.

Curriculum. Pupils are prepared for the GCSE. There is a wide range of options; most pupils take nine subjects.

Thereafter, in the sixth form, there is a further range of options from which pupils choose four AS level subjects leading to examination at the end of the lower sixth. They can then choose to continue with all four or to take 3 through to A level. The vast majority of sixth form leavers go on to university, art college, or other forms of higher education.

Religious Education. The chaplain and his assistant work in the school, whose general religious tenor is that of the Church of England. A daily service is held in the school chapel. Pupils in the Hill, years 7, 8 and 9 receive one or two periods per week of religious education, which continues into years 10, 11 and sixth forms as a GCSE or A level option.

The Arts. Emanuel has a long-standing tradition of excellence in these areas and all pupils are encouraged to participate in one or more of these activities. The school has a chapel choir and a chamber choir, an orchestra and ensemble groups, and a major musical production is presented each year.

There is a specialist suite of art rooms with facilities for all kinds of creative activity. A great deal of high quality work is displayed around the school and several pupils a year go on to foundation courses at art college.

Drama is taught throughout the school and there is a major school production every year, usually in the autumn term, and smaller scale events during the year.

We have an annual arts festival in July with an art exhibition, summer serenade, performances by pupils and visitors, and a series of talks by visiting speakers.

Games and Activities. At present cricket, rowing, rugby and athletics are the main school games for the boys. For the girls the main activities are netball, tennis, athletics, rowing and swimming. Many other activities become available as a pupil moves up the school. Each pupil will have one games afternoon each week, and other opportunities for physical education and swimming. The school has its own playing fields, sports hall, swimming pool, fives courts, and boathouse on the Thames.

The Duke of Edinburgh's Award scheme is offered at all levels to pupils from year 9 upwards. Community service is arranged for senior pupils and can involve hospital visiting, voluntary work in local primary schools or charity shops, or our local hospice. More formal work experience is offered as part of an extensive careers and further education advice programme from year 9 upwards.

Careers. Careers and further education advice is readily available from an experienced team. There is an annual careers convention for the senior school when many representatives from the professions and commerce visit the school to talk about career options.

Old Emanuel Association. *Membership Secretary*: Mr R Udall, 43 Howard Road, Coulsdon, Surrey CR5 2EB.

Charitable status. Emanuel School (administered by the United Westminster Schools' Foundation) is a Registered Charity, number 309267. Its aims and objectives are for "the bringing up of children in virtue and good and laudable arts".

Epsom College

Epsom Surrey KT17 4JQ

Tel: 01372 821004 (Headmaster)
01372 821234 (Admissions Registrar)
01372 821130 (Bursar)
Fax: 01372 821237
e-mail: admissions@epsomcollege.org.uk
website: www.epsomcollege.org.uk

Epsom College was founded in 1855 evolving from The Royal Medical Benevolent College that began in 1853 when Dr John Propert raised funds to build a foundation to help widows and orphans of the medical profession. It lies about 15 miles south of London, yet close to open and attractive countryside. The College occupies 80 acres of its own land within the beautiful Epsom Downs and all the buildings and playing fields are within the grounds.

In the last twenty years the boarding and day houses have been modernised and extended and many new buildings have been erected, including an award-winning Library, a state-of-the-art classroom block for Humanities, a studio for Theatre Studies, and a new girls' boarding and day house. The Science laboratories have been redeveloped and further modernisation is planned, there is a fine Department of Design Technology, and a newly refurbished dining room. Games facilities have also been greatly extended, including the construction of an indoor Sports Centre with a swimming pool, two large sports halls, 6 squash courts, a gymnasium, a fitness room, martial arts facilities, and a climbing wall. There are also two astroturf hockey pitches, one floodlit, and new netball courts which provide further tennis courts. Over ten million pounds have been spent in recent years on the development of the College, and further extensions to houses and a Performing Arts Centre are planned.

Motto: '*Deo non Fortuna*'.

Patron: Her Majesty The Queen

President: Professor The Lord McColl, CBE, MS, FRCS, FACS

Visitor: The Right Reverend The Lord Bishop of Guildford

Governing Body:
Chairman: G B Pincus, MIPA
Vice-Chairman: Dr A J Vallance-Owen, MBChB, FRCS Edin, MBA
Treasurer: P G Hakim, FCA

Mrs H M Allely, FCA
G E Andrews, FCA
Dr J Bolton, FRCPsych
Dr H H Bowen-Perkins, LMSSA, MRCS Eng, LRCP Lond, MB BS
K Budge, MA
A F Fernandes
J A Hay
Mrs K Lindberg, BA, MBA
D Maunder, MA
Surgeon Vice-Admiral A L Revell, CB, CStJ, MBChB, FRCA Hon MD
Sir Richard Thompson, KCVO, DM, FRCP
Dr A J Wells, MB BS, DRCOG, MRCGP

Bursar & Clerk to the Governing Body: Mrs S E Teasdale, BSc, ACA

The Royal Medical Foundation Administrator & Secretary to Council: Mrs F Anderson, BSc

***Headmaster*: S R Borthwick**, BSc, CPhys, FRSA

Deputy Head: J R L Hartley, BSc
Deputy Head (Academic): Mrs A M Drew, BA, MBA
Deputy Head (Staff): R Gill, MA
Director of Admissions and Communications: P E D Green, BSc, MA, CBiol, MIBiol

Director of Extra-Curricular Activities: E A Huxter, MA, PhD, FRGS
Director of Information Technology: C J Davies, BSc, CEng, MBCS, CMath, MIMA
Assistant Deputy Head: M C Oliver, BSc
Head of Transition: P J Williams, BSc

Housemasters/mistresses:
Carr (boys' boarding and day): M Day, BEd
Crawfurd (girls' boarding and day): Mrs H E Keevil, BA (*Senior Housemistress*)
Fayrer (boys' boarding): S J Head, BSc
Forest (boys' boarding): A J Bustard, BA
Granville (boys' boarding): M A L Tod, MA, PhD, FSA Scot
Holman (boys' boarding): C I Holiday, BEd ACP (*Senior Housemaster*)
Propert (boys' day): A Wolstenholme, BEd
Raven (girls' day): Mrs J N Vernon-Harcourt, BSc
Robinson (boys' day): M C Conway, MA
Rosebery (girls' day): Mrs N Wilson, BSc
White House (girls' Sixth Form boarding & day): Mrs C C Winmill, MA
Wilson (girls' boarding): Miss K R Adams, BA

Senior Chaplain: Revd Fr P Thompson, BA
Lay Chaplain: Mrs H H Hynd, BA, MA, FRSA

Teaching Staff:
* *Head of Department*

Art:
*G Poupart, DA
*Mrs K H P Lenham, BA
Mrs I Friedler, BA
I D Newman, BA

Biology:
*M D Hobbs, BSc
P E D Green, BSc, MA, CBiol, MIBiol
Mrs G N Jerritt, MA
Mrs V Patel, BSc, PhD
Mrs J N Vernon-Harcourt, BSc
S A Wade, BSc, PhD
Mrs P S Woolmer, BSc

Classics:
*K Siviter, MA, MBA

Chemistry:
*Mrs T M Muller, MA
L Matthews, BSc
Mrs M Odendaal, MPhil
N S A Payne, BSc
Mrs S E Williams, MA

Design & Technology:
*Miss A M R Wickham, MA
M Day, BEd
P M Shephard, CertEd

Economics & Business Studies:
*Miss N C Morrow, MA
P J Gillespie, BA
S J Head, BSc
Mrs E G Irvine, MA, PGDip Tourism
D N Rice, BSc, DLC
R C G Young, BSc

English:
*Ms A J Brookfield, MA
Miss K D Cloonan, BA
Mrs A M Drew, BA, MBA
Miss C E Huxter, MA
I M C McClure, MA, PhD

R Worrall, BA, MA
R M Wycherley, BA
M Zacharias, BA

Geography:
*P J Irvine, MA
C J Baverstock, BSc
E A Huxter, MA, MSc, PhD, FRGS
R I Whiteley, MA

History, Government & Politics:
*A G Scadding, BA
Miss K R Adams, BA
A J Bustard, BA
Miss K H Butler, BA
D J R Campbell, BA
M C Conway, MA
T S Cooper, MA
M A L Tod, MA, PhD, FSA Scot

Information Technology:
*T C V Thomas, BSc
C J Davies, BSc, CEng, CITP, MBCS, CMath, MIMA
R A Johnstone, BTheol
I M Winmill, BSc

Learning Support:
*Mrs R Doyle, BEd, BPhil, RSA Dip TEFL, Adv Dip SpEd
Mrs M-A Barnett, BA
Mrs G H Borthwick, BA, Cert Tesol
Mrs A Davies, CertEd, CTEFLA
Mrs B C Day, BA,CTEFLA
Mrs J A Luke, BSc, RSA Dip SpLD

Mathematics:
*A J Wilson, BSc, MSc
S Hibbitt, BA
G D Kennedy, BEng
M C Oliver, BSc
Mrs K E Sinnett, BA

J F Stephens, BSc
A P Thompson, BSc
P J Williams, BSc

Modern Languages:
*R Ellison, MA
Miss C L Creevey, BA
R Gill, MA
Mrs C Guyon, TCert
Mrs R J B Harrop, BA
M P Hynd, MA
Mrs M Jones, TCert
Mrs H E Keevil, BA
Mrs D Reisinger, BA
Mrs C C Winmill, MA
Mrs S Yvon-Case, LLCE

Music:
*G A Lodge, MA, BMus, LTCL
M Hampshire, BA, FRSA
C I Holiday, BEd, ACP

Physical Education:
*Mrs F C Drinkall, BSc
Mrs S L Church-Jones, BA
Mrs C M Rice, CertEd
Mrs N Wilson, BSc
A Wolstenholme, BEd

Physics:
*A W Hughes, BEng, PhD
R D B Burgess, BSc, ACMA
S R Borthwick, BSc, CPhys, FRSA
Miss N C Crossland, MPhys
J M Drinkall, BSc
J R L Hartley, BSc
D R Poore, BSc

Theatre Studies:
*Miss K Chandley, BA
P A Henson, BA

Theology and Philosophy:
*Mrs H H Hynd, BA, MA, FRSA
B G MacDowel, MTheol
Revd Fr P Thompson, BA

Visiting Instrumental Tutors for bassoon, cello, clarinet, drum kit, flute, French horn, guitar, harpsicord, oboe, organ, percussion, piano, recorder, saxophone, singing, trumpet, violin.

Librarian: Mrs S Perry, BA, MA
Development Director: R Love
Medical Officer: Dr T Richardson, MBBS, MRCGP
Headmaster's PA: Mrs C Beesley
Admissions Registrar: Mrs C Kent

Numbers and Houses. From September 1996 the College became fully co-educational. There are 720 students in the School, 403 boarders, weekly boarders or day boarders and 321 day students, divided among 7 boarding houses and 5 day houses There are 324 in the Sixth Form. The boy/girl ratio is nearly 2:1.

There are 5 separate houses for girls: two boarding houses, Crawfurd and Wilson; two day houses, Raven and Rosebery; and a Sixth Form house, White, for both boarding and day girls.

The boys' boarding houses are: Fayrer, Forest, Granville, Holman, with some boarding in Carr. All boarding Sixth and Fifth Formers and Upper Fourth Formers have study-bedrooms in the modernised Houses. In the Autumn Term full boarders have 2 weekend exeats from Friday pm to Monday am in addition to a 2-week half-term holiday. In the Lent and Summer Terms boarders have 'boarders' leave' on up to two weekends, giving them extra time at home. Weekly boarders may go home each weekend.

The day boy Houses are: Carr, Propert and Robinson and. Day boys and girls are full members of the School community and have lunch and tea in College. All members of the School, boarders and day, eat centrally in the Dining Room which makes for efficiency and strengthens the sense of community.

Pupils who are ill are looked after in the School Medical Centre which has 8 beds with a qualified sister always on duty. One of the two (one male, one female) School Doctors visits daily except Sundays.

Academic Work. Below the Sixth Form the course is broad and involves little specialisation. All pupils take English, French, Mathematics, Physics, Chemistry, Biology and Religious Studies while substantial numbers do Drama, Latin, Spanish, German, Geography, History, Art, Music, Information Technology and Design Technology. The normal programme is to enter the Middle Fourth at the age of thirteen and take the main block of GCSEs at the end of Year 11. Almost everyone then enters the large Sixth Form of over 300 pupils. A wide range of 22 AS and A2 Level subjects is offered, including the Sciences, French, German and Spanish as Modern Languages, Theatre Studies, Business Studies, Politics and Government, Economics, Classical Civilisation, Religious Studies (Philosophy and Theology), and Physical Education. In the Lower Sixth, pupils can opt to follow a course in Critical Thinking and some are able to join the Young Enterprise scheme. There are excellent facilities for work in one's own study, in the main Library or one of the specialist Libraries. The school is fully networked, including all Houses, and has over 500 computers, as well as digital projectors and electronic whiteboards used across the curriculum. There are four fully equipped Information Technology rooms, and all pupils are introduced to Information Technology in their first year.

Higher Education. Almost all students go on to university, with the occasional student choosing to follow another path, such as Art Foundation. Over the past two years pupils have applied to undertake a very wide range of courses, from the more traditional, such as Medicine, Dentistry, Architecture, Law, Veterinary Science and English to Media Studies, Hispanic Studies, Politics and Marine Geography, to some more unusual choices, such as Childhood and Youth Studies, International Fashion Marketing, Optometry and Chemistry with Management and South Asian Studies.

Careers. There is a well-stocked Careers Room attached to the Library, and much care is taken to assess a pupil's potential and aptitude and to provide proper guidance on careers. All pupils belong to the ISCO Scheme and all Fifth Form pupils take careers aptitude tests. A Careers Convention is organised each year for the Lower Sixth.

The **Religious Teaching** and the Chapel Services follow the doctrines of the Church of England, but there are always pupils of other denominations and faiths. There are two Resident Chaplains who work together with a visiting Rabbi and a Hindu priest to ensure a multi-faith approach. Muslim pupils attend prayers at the College.

Games and other Activities. Games contribute much to the general physical development of boys and girls at Epsom and the College has a strong tradition of high standards in many sports. The very large number of teams means that almost all pupils are able to represent the School each year. A wide range of sports is available: Rugby, Hockey, Netball, Cricket, Tennis, Athletics and Swimming, Squash (6 courts), Rifle Shooting (with a .22 range), Soccer, Cross-Country, Fencing, Golf, Badminton, Rounders, Basketball, Judo and Sailing. The Indoor Sports Centre, housing two sports halls, a fencing salle and climbing wall, was opened in 1989 by the Patron of Epsom College, Her Majesty the Queen. In January 2007 a new extensive fitness suite was completed. The Target

Rifle Team has been National Champions at Bisley winning the Ashburton Shield 11 times in 18 years between 1990 and 2007.

The CCF has Naval, Army and RAF Sections and pupils over the age of 14 are expected to join for 2 years when much time is spent on camping and expeditions. Older boys and girls may join instead the Duke of Edinburgh's Award Scheme, while others are involved with Social Service work in Epsom.

The College ensures that all pupils take advantage of a wide range of activities from Jazz Dance to Journalism.

Music, Art and Drama. There are three full-time Music teachers and a large staff of visiting music teachers. Over one-third of the pupils learn musical instruments and virtually any instrument can be taught, and many take singing lessons. There are four Choirs, a School Orchestra and seven major instrumental ensembles, including Big Band, Clarinet, Saxophone and Classical Guitar. Visits are arranged each term to concerts in London and elsewhere. The Music School has a Concert Hall and 18 practice rooms. Recent productions have included 'Dido and Aeneas', 'The Marriage of Figaro' and 'West Side Story'.

Art, which includes pottery, printing and sculpture as well as painting and drawing, is housed in a spacious building with 3 studios, a Library, an Exhibition Room and an Exhibition Hall. There are three full-time Art teachers and one part-time, and Art is studied up to GCSE and A Level.

There are several major productions each year, from classical theatre to the modern musical, produced by a range of staff and pupils. These give boys and girls an opportunity to develop their talents and interests in Drama. In 2004 staff and pupils wrote their own show which was performed at the Royal Albert Hall, with over 1,000 performers, to mark the 150th Anniversary of the College.

Admission. Almost all pupils enter Epsom College in September. Most pupils come at the age of 13 after reaching a satisfactory standard in the Common Entrance or Scholarship Examination or the Epsom College January Entry Test examination set specially for those who are not prepared for Common Entrance. An examination for those who may be deemed borderline may be sat in advance of Common Entrance. Since many girls, and some boys, expect to transfer schools at 11 rather than 13, we offer the opportunity for children to sit an 11+ examination in Year 6. If the required standard is achieved, a pupil will be offered a place for entry at 13+, conditional upon maintaining the same standards at the present school and to a test being taken in the year of entry for setting purposes. Some enter the school later than this and there is always a direct entry into the Sixth Form, both for girls and boys.

A boy or girl may be registered at any age by sending in the registration form and fee. All enquiries should be sent to the Admissions Registrar from whom a prospectus may be obtained.

Fees per term (2008-2009). Boarders £8,965; Weekly Boarders £8,180; Day Boarders £7,500; Day Pupils £6,124.

The fees are inclusive and cover the normal cost of a pupil's education. The main extras are for examination fees, private tuition and a pupil's personal expenses. Fees for day pupils include lunch and tea.

There is a College Store for the provision of uniform, clothing and other requirements.

Entrance Scholarships and Bursaries. (*see Scholarship Entries section*). In recent years over 40 Awards have been made, usually at 13+ and 16+. Awards are rarely above 20% of the annual fees. Some scholarships and means-tested bursaries are available especially for those from disadvantaged backgrounds who specifically wish to pursue a career in medicine. Candidates must be under 14 on 1st September of the year of entry or entering the Sixth Form.

Foundation Scholarships and Bursaries, up to full fees, are awarded to sons and daughters of doctors in cases of need.

Full details of all Scholarships and Awards are available from the Admissions Registrar.

Old Epsomians. There is a flourishing Old Epsomian Club with strong cricket, shooting, golf and Business sections. There are regular dinners at the College where the OE Secretary is also based.

Charitable status. Epsom College is a Registered Charity, number 312046. It exists for the advancement of education.

Eton College

Windsor Berkshire SL4 6DW
Tel: 01753 671249 (Admissions)
01753 671231 (Head Master)
01753 671213 (Bursar)
Fax: 01753 671248
e-mail: admissions@etoncollege.org.uk
website: www.etoncollege.com

The King's College of our Lady of Eton beside Windsor was founded by Henry VI in 1440. The College Foundation comprises a Provost, 11 Fellows, Head Master, Deputy Head Pastoral (Lower Master), Deputy Head Curriculum, Bursar, Chaplain and 70 Scholars. There are some 1,200 Oppidans, or boys not on the Foundation.

Motto: '*Floreat Etona*'.

Visitor: The Rt Revd The Lord Bishop of Lincoln

Provost and Fellows (Governing Body):
Sir Eric Anderson, KT, MA, BLitt, HonDLitt, FRSE (*Provost*)
Dr Andrew Gailey, CVO, MA, PhD (*Vice-Provost*)
Professor Ross Harrison, MA, PhD
Sir Dominic Cadbury, MA, MBA
David Verey, CBE, MA
Michael Proudfoot, MA
Professor Christopher Dobson, MA, DPhil, FRS
Sir Michael Peat, KCVO, FCA
Sir Michael Burton, MA
The Lord Waldegrave of North Hill, PC
The Marchioness of Douro

Honorary Fellows:
John Butterwick, TD
Sir David Money-Coutts, KCVO, MA
The Hon Mrs Lee Annenberg
Nicholas Kessler

Steward of the Courts: The Rt Hon the Lord Carrington, KG, GCMG, CH, MC, PC

Conduct: The Revd Canon K H Wilkinson, MA

Precentor and Director of Music: R Allwood, BA, Hon FRSCM, Hon ARAM

Bursar and Clerk to the Provost and Fellows: A G Wynn, LVO, MA

Director of Finance: H F Richardson, MA, FCA

Assistant Bursars:
I C Mellor, ARICS, DipProjMan
J G James, MBE, BA
R J Schooley, BSc, FCIPD, ACIS
A Harris, BSc, FRICS

Director of Development: W O'Hearn, AB, JD
College Librarian & Keeper of College Collections: Mrs R Bond, MA
Keeper of Special Collections: M C Meredith, MA
College Archivist: Mrs P Hatfield, MA, DAA

***Head Master*: A R M Little**, MA

Deputy Head, Pastoral (*Lower Master*): R M Stephenson, BSc, PhD

Deputy Head, Curriculum: Revd J C Puddefoot, MA, BD

Tutor for Admissions: W H Rees, MA

School Office Manager: R A Hutton

School Doctor: J J C Holliday, MB BS, MRCS, LRCP, MRCGP, DCH, DRCOG, DFFP

Assistant Masters:
* *Head of Department/Subject*
† *House Master*

Art:
I Burke, MA *
A Forsyth, BA
E J V Parker, MA
D Reid, BA

Classics:
M J Atkinson, MA, DPhil
A J Chirnside, MA
I Harris, MA †
T E W Hawkins, MA *
M T Holdcroft, BA
S A Lambert, BA
J D Macartney, BA
A J Maynard, MA
R D Oliphant-Callum, MA †
J R B Scragg, BA
R E C Shorrock, BA, MPhil, PhD
C J Smart, BA
P B Smith, MA, MSt †

Computing:
D M L Maxwell, MA *

Design:
N W Alston, BA
S E Hearsey, BSc
K R N Ross, BSc *
S G P Tilley, BA

Divinity:
Revd M R Bean, BTh, MA (*Chaplain*)
Revd R E R Demery, BTh, MA (*Chaplain*)
Revd N G Heap, BA, DPhil (*Roman Catholic Chaplain*)
Revd P A Hess, BA, MTh (*Chaplain*)
Revd C M Jones, MA †
E J N Russell, PhD
R Stewart, BA
M L Wilcockson, MA *
Revd Canon K H Wilkinson, MA (*Conduct*)

Economics:
T Allen, MA
D J Fox, BA
G T Galletly, MA
D M Gregg, BSSc †
R G G Pratt, MA †
L J Purshouse, PhD
G B Riley, MA *
P R Thackeray, BA

English:
M J L Bashaarat, MA †
P Broad, MA †
C J Davis, MA †
S H S Dormandy, MA (*Head of Theatre Studies*)
J E Francis, BA *
A C D Graham-Campbell, MA
M A Grenier, BA †
M Liviero, Dott Ling, PhD
R J Martin, BA †
S M McPherson, BComm, MA
C W Milne, BA, MPhil
J D Newton, BA
J M Noakes, MA †
J M O'Brien, MA
H-E Osborne, MA (*Director of Drama*)
N R F Welsh, MA

Geography:
D E Anderson, BA, DPhil
T F X Eddis, BA *
A B Henshilwood, MA
A S Jennings, BA
P I Macleod, BEd, BA
M G H Mowbray, MA
M A Town, MA

History:
V S J Clark, BA
B Cole, MA, DPhil
D Eltis, MA, DPhil
J L Grant, MA, DPhil †
S L Green, MA
J D Harrison, MA (*History of Art*)
S C Henderson, MA *
B J C Horan BA
N A E Jeffery, BA
G D Mann, MA
T E J Nolan, MA †
H S J Proctor, MA
A S Robinson, MA, MLitt †
P E P Walsh, BA

Mathematics:
N Adams, BSc
K J Baker, MSc
J P Barker, BSc
S J Dean, MA
N J Fowkes, BSc
R J Gazet, MA*
D A Griffiths, MA
L J Henderson, BA
B J Holdsworth, MA
N A Leamon BA
P J McKee, MA †
W F Moore, BSc †
J Moston, BSc, PhD
Revd J C Puddefoot, MA, BD
M J Salter, MA
M Strutt, BSc
J E Thorne, BSc
S P Vivian, MA, MSc, CStat
A Warnes, BSc, PhD †
C M B Williams, MA, MSc
P G Williams, MA

Modern Languages:
T E Beard, BA, PhD
R A A Coward, MA †
G J D Evans, MA
R A Fletcher, BA, MPhil
J M Gibbons, BA, MPhil, DPhil
J L Gonzalez-Medina, MA, DPhil *
A D Halksworth, MA, MLitt
D C Henderson, BA
J R King, MA
M-L Lin, BA (*Chinese*)
K S K Pierce, MA (*German*)
M J Polglase, MA †
A Powles, BA (*French*)
P V Reznikov, BA (*Russian*)
N J Roberts, MA †
N C W Sellers, MA †
H A Shirwani, BA (*Arabic*)
P A Simpson, MA
D M Stanford-Harris, MA (*Japanese*)
J W F Stanforth, MA

Music:
R Allwood, BA *
N D Goetzee, LRAM
D W Goode, MSc, MPhil
M A O'Donovan, BA, MMus
I M Wallace, BA

Jewish Tutor: J M Paull, MA, DIPM, MCIM

Muslim Tutor: Imam M Hussain, BTh

Hindu Tutor: J Lakhani, MSc

Roman Catholic Chaplain: Revd N G Heap, BA, DPhil

The King's Scholars (Collegers) normally number 70 and are boarded in College, each in his own room, under the care of the Master-in-College. About 14 Scholarships are awarded each year. Candidates need be registered only a few weeks before the examination. For information apply to *The College Examination Secretary, Admissions Office, Eton College Windsor SL4 6DB*. (*See also Scholarship Section entries.*)

The Scholarship Examination is held at Eton in May. Candidates must be under 14 (and over 12) on 1st September. Boys normally enter College between the ages of 12.9 and 13.11. All candidates take English, Mathematics A, General I (general questions requiring thought rather than knowledge) and Science. They must also offer three or more of the following French (written, aural and oral), Latin, Greek, Mathematics B General II (Literature, the Arts, moral and religious issues etc), and a paper combining History, Geography and Divinity.

Scholarships are to the value of 10% of the full fee, and all of them will be supplemented up to the value of full fees (subject to means-testing).

A Scholarship is normally tenable for five years.

Term of Entry. With just occasional exceptions, all boys enter in September.

J B Wortley

Physical Education:
P I Macleod, BEd, BA
P K Manley, BEd, MSc
W E Norton, BA *
G J Pierce, BEd

Science:

Biology:
A Z Bridges, MA
R Fisher, BSc
K Frearson, MA (*Science*)
G D Fussey, BSc
P M Gillam, MA
N P T Leathers, BSc
J H Owen, BSc, PhD
R M Stephenson, BSc, PhD
P S T Wright, MA

Chemistry:
F W S Benfield, DPhil
A K Copsey, BSc
R N Edmonds, BA, PhD
P K Manley, BEd, MSc
A M Miles, BSc *
R Montgomerie BA
G R Pooley, BSc, PhD †
A J Saunders, MChem, DPhil
J A Steadman, MA, PhD

Physics:
J D Dangerfield, MSc *
M N Fielker, BSc †
R P D Foster, MA †
I R Gray, BSc, PhD
P R Harrison, MA, DPhil
L C MacMaster, BEng, PhD
Dr P D A Mann, MSc, PhD
S P Martin, BSc

Fees per term (2008-2009). £9,360. Entrance Fee £1,500 (£1,050 refunded when the boy leaves the school with all fees settled).

Oppidans. There are about 1,230 Oppidans (non-Collegers) housed in 24 Boarding Houses, each under the care of a House Master, and every boy has his own room. A boy must normally be aged between 12.11 and 14.01 on 1st September of the year of admission, and must pass the Common Entrance unless granted exemption on his performance in the Scholarship Examination.

Parents wishing to send their sons to Eton as Oppidans should apply to *The Tutor for Admissions, Eton College, Windsor SL4 6DB* for a copy of the Prospectus, which gives full details of the registration procedure. Information is also available on the website at www.etoncollege.com. Boys may be registered at any time between birth and the age of ten and a half and take a preliminary assessment at eleven.

Music Scholarships. Up to eight scholarships can be awarded annually, each to the value of 10% of the full fee, and all of them supplemented up to the value of full fees (subject to means-testing). All awards carry remission of instrumental lesson fees up to 135 minutes tuition per week. In addition there are up to six Music Exhibitions, carrying remission of instrumental lesson fees up to 135 minutes tuition per week. One also carries a place in the school, the other five being open only to boys who already have Conditional Places following the assessment at 11. Two Honorary Exhibitions may also be awarded, carrying no financial remission. Special consideration will be given to cathedral choristers who would still be able to sing treble in the College Chapel Choir. Further particulars and entry forms may be obtained from *The Tutor for Admissions, Eton College, Windsor SL4 6DB*.

Bursaries. A number of Bursaries are available for boys who would be unable to receive education at Eton without financial assistance. All bursaries are awarded according to need, normally up to a maximum of half the School fee but in certain cases up to 100%. The sons of OE clergymen, university and school teachers and other professional parents are generally considered particularly sympathetically. Further details are available on the website at www.etoncollege.com.

Junior Scholarships and Junior Music Scholarship. Up to 4 Junior Scholarships and 1 Junior Music Scholarship may be awarded each year to candidates over 10 and under 11 on 1 September of the year of the examination who are attending state schools. An examination is held at Eton in January each year. Candidates need be registered only a few weeks before the examination. For information apply to *The School Office Manager, Eton College, Windsor SL4 6DW*.

A Junior Scholarship / Junior Music Scholarship is tenable for 2 or 3 years at a Preparatory School (St George's, Windsor Castle in the case of Junior Music Scholarship) as a day-boy or a boarder, and, depending on the parental means, will cover the whole or part of the fees and other educational expenses at the Preparatory School and subsequently at Eton.

Sixth Form Scholarships. Up to 8 Sixth Form Scholarships are offered each year to enable boys to have two years of Sixth Form education at Eton. Each year in February, selected candidates are invited to attend interviews in those subjects which they intend to offer at A Level. All those attending the interviews will sit a written General Paper and an aptitude test. Candidates must register on, or before, a date specified in mid-December. The scholarships will cover the whole or part of the fees, and other educational expenses depending on the Scholar's financial need. An Open Afternoon is held in November for anyone interested in coming to visit the school. For information apply to *The School Office Manager, Eton College, Windsor SL4 6DW*.

Charitable status. Eton College is an exempt Charity, tax reclaim reference number X6839, by Charter of Henry VI confirmed by Acts of Parliament.

Exeter School

Victoria Park Road Exeter Devon EX2 4NS
Tel: 01392 273679 (Headmaster/Registrar)
01392 258712 (Bursar/Office)
Fax: 01392 498144
e-mail: admissions@exeterschool.org.uk
website: www.exeterschool.org.uk

Founded in 1633, Exeter School occupies a 25 acre site, located within a mile of the city centre, having moved from its original location in the High Street in 1880. Some of its well designed buildings date from that time but many new buildings have been added over the past twenty years and the school now enjoys first rate facilities on a very attractive open site. The school is fully co-educational and offers education to boys and girls from 7 to 18. It has its own Junior School of around 180 pupils, nearly all of whom transfer to the Senior School at the age of 11. The Senior School has around 660 pupils, including a Sixth Form of 200.

Exeter School is a well run school with high all-round standards and very good academic results. It prides itself on strong cultural, sporting and extra curricular achievement. Its music is outstanding and there is a strong tradition of performance drawn from all age groups in the School. It offers a very wide range of sports and maintains consistently high standards especially in hockey, rugby and cricket. It is well placed for outdoor pursuits (eg Duke of Edinburgh's Award Scheme and Ten Tors on Dartmoor) and has its own very large voluntary CCF unit. The School is closely involved with the life of the City of Exeter and its university and it has a substantial commitment to support the local community.

Motto: ΧΡΥΣΟΣ ΑΡΕΤΗΣ ΟΥΚ ΑΝΤΑΞΙΟΣ

Patrons:
The Lord Lieutenant of the County of Devon
The Right Reverend the Lord Bishop of Exeter
The Right Worshipful the Lord Mayor of Exeter

Governors:
Appointed by the Devon County Council:
Mrs C Channon, MA, ARIC

Appointed by the Exeter City Council:
J F Landers, ACII

Appointed by the Governors of St John's Hospital:
¶A C W King (*Vice-Chairman*)
Mrs M Giles, LLB

Representatives of the Universities of Exeter, Cambridge and Oxford:
Exeter: Professor W E Yates, MA, PhD, FBA (*Vice-Chairman*)
Cambridge: ¶Dr T Lewens, MA, MPhil, PhD
Oxford: Dr M C Grossel, MA, PhD

Co-opted Governors:
M G Golby, ChM. FRCS
¶T E Hawkins
¶D A Evennett, BDS LDS RCS
A K Dawson, MA (*Vice-Chairman*)
J D Gaisford, BSc, ACA
Mrs B Meeke, LLB (*Chairman*)
T D Wheare, MA, FRSA
¶A P Burbanks, BA

***Headmaster*: R Griffin**, MA

Deputy Headmaster: P M Šljivić, MA
Director of Administration: J W Davidson, MA, MSc
Director of Studies: M J Hughes, MA

Assistant Staff:
* *Head of Department*
† *Housemaster/mistress*
§ *Part-time or Visiting*
¶ *Former pupil*

Art & Design:
*J F Mason, BA
§Miss M E Doyle, BA, BSc
§R Frampton, MA

Biology:
*P J C Boddington BSc (*Director of Science*)
D Wybrow, BSc
†M S W Rodgers, BEd
¶R H S Donne, MA
M K Chitnavis, BSc, CChem, MRSC
Dr K L Page, MA,PhD

Careers Adviser:
§D F Moss-Gibbons, BSc (*Outdoor Pursuits Administrator*)

Chemistry:
*J R Ricketts, BSc
†S J Harris, MA
M K Chitnavis BSc, CChem, MRSC
A J Armstrong, MChem

Classical Subjects:
*N P L Keyes, MA
§S Kennedy, MA
§Mrs F Boorer, BA

Computing & Information Systems:
*Mrs R Cull, BSc, MIITT, CMath, MIMA
§R M Fryer, MA
N F Howard, BA

Design Technology:
*I R Lowles, BA
†N W Moon, BSc

Drama:
*Mrs S H Chrupek, BA
§A J Chrupek

Electronics:
*§P Scott, BSc
Dr A W Houghton, MA, MSc, PhD

English:
*D K Morton, MA
§G P Strugnell, BA, MLitt
Miss H Nathanson, BA
§Mrs J C Tarleton, BA
Miss L D Jakes, BA
Mrs J H Daybell, MA

Geography:
*Mrs H M Sail, BA
J W Davidson, MA, MSc (*Director of Administration*)
*L P Hunt, BA (*Head of Critical Thinking*)
§Mrs U M Cloke, BA (*Head of Girls*)
P M Šljivić, MA (*Deputy Headmaster*)

History:
*G N Trelawny, BEd, MA
J D Poustie, BEd
§Mrs S L Bartholomew, BA
¶Miss S Bell, BA

Languages:
*†R C Dawson, MA
†M C Wilcock, BEd
Mrs J M Fenner, BA
§Ms P J Knight, BSc (*German*)
Mrs A M Francis, MA (*French*)
§Mrs S C Wilson, BA

Mathematics:
*A J Reynolds, BSc
Dr A P Tyrer, MA, DPhil
†G R Willson, BSc
D Beckwith, BA, MSc
†Dr P M Smallwood, BSc, PhD
W J Daws, BA
M J Hughes, MA (*Director of Studies*)
Dr G J D Chapman, PhD, BSc, MSc (*CCF Contingent Commander*)

Music:
*Dr S D Foxall, BMus, PhD, LGSM (*Director of Music*)
§R J Sutton, BA, ARCM, LRAM
§Mrs E Williams, BA
§A Gillett, ARCM
§D Bowen, BEd
§P Painter, DipMusEd
§Mrs R Mitchell, LTCL, BA, Dip Mus
§Mrs F McLean, BA, Cert RAM
§B Moore, MA

Physical Education and Games:
*A C F Mason, BA (*Director of Sport*)
†M S W Rodgers, BEd
§Ms C L Gimber, BA
§Mrs A Marsh, BEd
J W Fawkes, BSc
§F L Smith (*CCF SSI*)

Physics:
*G S Bone, BSc
T J Clark, BSc
§P Scott, BSc
M K Chitnavis BSc, CChem, MRSC
Dr A W Houghton, MA, MSc, PhD
Dr J L Wilson, MPhys

Religious Studies:
*†M H R Porter, BA
†Miss J M K Pegg, BA (*PSE Coordinator*)
§J A Allan, BA (*Chaplain*)
§Mrs A Marsh, BEd

Social Studies:
*R G Walker, BA (**Economics*)
*R J Baker, BA (**Politics*)
§I H Chapman, BSc

Learning Support:
Mrs A Southcott, BEd

Junior School

Headmistress: Mrs A J Turner, MA

Assistant Head: J S Wood, BA

Assistant Staff:
R Bland, BEd
Mrs R A S Garnham, CertEd
Mrs P L Butler, BA
¶G E L Ashman, BA
Mrs P A Goldsworthy, BA, LTCL
R J Pidwell, BA
Mrs R Forbes, MA
§Mrs R M Parkin, CertEd
Ms V K Randerson, CertEd
D Cageao, BA

School Doctor: Dr A Morris, BM, BS, DRCOG, MRCGP

Bursar, Clerk to the Governors and Company Secretary: Brig G D Williams, BA

Registrar: Mrs W M Drake

Headmaster's PA: Mrs A C Goswell

Buildings, Grounds and General Facilities. The Senior School block includes a large multi-purpose assembly hall, a library, a private study area, dining hall and Sixth Form Centre as well as many well-appointed classrooms. A major refurbishment of the former boarding accommodation to include a new Library and Study Centre was completed for September 2006. There are separate buildings on the site housing the Chapel, the Music Centre, the Science Centre, Art Studios, Drama Studio, Craft Design Technology Centre and Exonian Centre. The Science Centre provides 14 laboratories and there are three fully equipped computer rooms. All departments have access to their own computers and the School has a wide, controlled access to the internet. In 2005 the school opened a new dance studio and a fitness suite to add to the existing sports facilities of a large modern well-equipped Sports Hall with its own squash courts and access to on-site floodlit all-weather sports arena, top-grade all-weather tennis/netball courts and a heated swimming pool. The playing fields, which are immediately adjacent to the School buildings are well kept and provide, in season, rugby, cricket, hockey, football, rounders and athletics areas. The Junior School, which was extended in 2007 to provide two new Mathematics classrooms, has access to all the Senior School facilities but is self-contained on the estate.

Admission. The majority of pupils enter the Junior School at 7 or 8 and the Senior School at 11 or 13. Admission is also possible at other ages where space allows and a significant number of pupils join at the age of 16 for Sixth Form Studies.

Entrance to the Junior School is by assessment in January. This includes a report from the child's previous school, classroom sessions in the company of other prospective pupils, and literacy, numeracy and general intelligence tasks.

Entrance examinations for the Senior School are held in January.

Assessment for entry to the Sixth Form at 16 is by interview and a minimum of 6 B grades at GCSE including English and Mathematics, with normally an A grade in the subjects chosen for study.

Registration Fee £100.

Fees per term (2008-2009). Junior School: £2,800 (includes lunch and text books). Senior School: £3,100 (includes text books).

Sibling discount of 10% for the second child and 20% for the third or subsequent child attending concurrently.

Scholarships and Financial Awards. (*see Scholarship Entries section*). Up to five Scholarships and five Exhibitions a year may be awarded for entrance at the age of 11 and one Scholarship at 13. Music Scholarships may be offered at 11, 12, 13 and 16. A Sixth Form Art Scholarship may be offered each year.

The School annually makes available a number of means-tested Governors' Awards. These are for external candidates joining the School at 7 and 8, 11 and 13, or in the Sixth Form, who meet the academic entry requirements and whose parents could not afford to send them to Exeter School without financial assistance. The awards may be up to a maximum of half the tuition fees but, in exceptional cases, subject to the availability of endowment funding, a free Sixth Form place may be offered. As a general guide, gross parental income will need to be below £40,000 per annum to allow consideration for a Governors' award. In addition, there are also a number of special awards made possible by donations from local benefactors for able pupils whose parents require financial assistance. The School is supported by the Ogden Trust and the Rank Foundation.

Curriculum. In the first 3 years in the Senior School all pupils take English, History, Geography, French, Mathematics, IT, Latin, Physics, Chemistry, Biology, Art, Design Technology, Drama, Music and Religious and Physical Education. In Year 9 German is introduced. After this there is a wide choice of subjects at GCSE level, including English, French, Spanish, Mathematics, dual or triple award Science, Religious Studies, Physical Education and 3 of the following: Latin, Greek, German, Spanish, Classical Civilisation, History, Geography, Music, Drama, Art, Design and Technology, and Information Technology.

Pupils enter the Sixth Form choosing from 26 different subjects for A Level study and follow whatever curriculum is appropriate to their ability and objectives, being prepared for university scholarships, university entrance and admission to other forms of further education or vocational training. Over 95% go on annually to Degree Courses.

Houses. There are nine Pupil Houses. Each is under the personal supervision of a Head of House, with whom parents are invited to keep in touch on any matter affecting their child's general development and progress throughout the school.

Religion. All pupils attend Religious Education classes, which include Sixth Form discussion groups. Sunday services are held in the School Chapel once each term. Pupils may be prepared for Confirmation which takes place annually.

Games. Rugby, Hockey, Cricket, Swimming, Athletics, Cross Country, Tennis, Badminton, Squash, Shooting, Basketball, Netball, Fencing, Cycling and Golf. Further activities are available for the Sixth Form.

Community and other Service. All pupils learn to serve the community. Many choose to take part in Social Service, helping old people and the handicapped young. There is a voluntary CCF Contingent with thriving RN, Army and RAF Sections. The CCF offers a large variety of Outdoor Activities, including Adventure Training Camps, Ten Tors Expedition Training as well as specialist courses. Pupils are encouraged to participate in the Duke of Edinburgh's Award Scheme.

Music. Pupils are taught Singing and Musical appreciation and are encouraged to learn to play Musical Instruments. More than one third of all pupils have individual lessons on at least one instrument. There are 4 Orchestras, a Choral Society which annually performs a major work in Exeter Cathedral and 4 Choirs, 3 jazz bands, and numerous smaller groups from string quartets to rock bands. There are over 30 visiting instrumental teachers. Over 20 public concerts are given each year. Different ensembles have performed regularly at the National Festival of Music for Youth at the Festival Hall, and the Schools Prom at the Royal Albert Hall.

Drama. Drama is developed both within and outside the curriculum. The School Hall with its large and well-equipped stage provides for the dual purpose of studio workshop and the regular production of plays, operas and musicals. The Drama Studio is used for smaller productions.

Art and Design. Art lessons are given to junior and senior forms. Apart from the formal disciplines of GCSE and A Level, which can be taken by those who choose, all pupils have opportunity for artistic expression in painting, print-making, photography, pottery, construction in many materials and carving wood and stone. All younger pupils learn to develop craft skills in wood, metal and plastic and to use them creatively in design work. Many then follow GCSE or A Level courses in Design and Technology. There is an annual art exhibition in July.

Expeditions. Throughout the school a large number of residential field trips and expeditions take place each year including a Third Form new pupils' Dartmoor weekend, various departmental excursions, several foreign exchanges and Duke of Edinburgh's Award expeditions. Pupils are also encouraged to compete for external expeditions and, following years of representation on its expeditions, the school has been awarded Star status by the British Schools Exploring Society (BSES). In recent summers, the school has run its own adventure trip to Costa Rica, Argentina and Chile and a canoeing trip to Peru.

Societies and Clubs. Pupils are encouraged to pursue their interests by joining one of the School Societies. Groups of enthusiasts can form new Societies or Clubs, but the following are at present available: Art, Badminton, Basketball, Canoeing, Chess, Choral Society, Christian Union, Computing, Dance, Debating, Drama, Electronics, Fencing, Music, Politics, Sailing, Shooting, Soccer and Squash.

Social. Close contact is maintained with the City and the University. Association between members of the School and the wider society outside is fostered wherever opportunity offers.

The staff believe strongly in the value of association with parents, who are invited to meetings annually throughout their sons' or daughters' time at the School. A termly lecture by a visiting speaker is provided for parents. The Friends of Exeter School, founded in 1994, exists to promote closer relations between the School, parents and those having close ties with the School.

Careers. Careers education begins with group work at the age of 13 and continues on a progressive programme until students leave the school. Careers evenings are held annually when pupils and their parents have the opportunity to consult representatives of the professions, industry and commerce. A work experience programme is organised for year 11 pupils each summer, and a scheme of mock interviews with career professionals for pupils in the Sixth Form.

Honours. Pupils regularly gain admission to Oxford and Cambridge (12 in 2007). The School encourages application to the leading universities, including the Russell Group.

Leading musicians have recently gained places at the Royal College of Music and the Royal Academy of Music.

Charitable status. Exeter School is a Registered Charity, number 1093080, and a Company Limited by Guarantee, registered in England, number 4470478. Registered Office: Victoria Park Road, Exeter, Devon EX2 4NS.

Felsted School

Felsted Essex CM6 3LL
Tel: 01371 822600 (Headmaster)
01371 822605 (Admissions Registrar)
01371 822620 (Bursar)
Fax: 01371 822697 (School)
01371 822607 (Headmaster)
e-mail: hms@felsted.org
website: www.felsted.org

The School, which was founded in 1564 by Richard, Lord Riche, today consists of three sections educating boys and girls from the age of 4 to 18. Close to both London and Cambridge, and within easy reach of Stansted Airport, the School is ideally situated in a picturesque North Essex village.

Felsted is a Church of England foundation but welcomes pupils from all Christian denominations and those from other religious traditions. The Senior School, for 13 to 18 year olds, has around 470 pupils; the majority are boarders and weekend arrangements are flexible.

The School's prospectus can be found online at www.felsted.org along with much other information and news, details of forthcoming events and location maps. Each boarding house has its own webpages, designed by pupils, and extracts from the video prospectus can be downloaded. There is also a link to the Independent Schools Inspectorate's report following the inspection in September 2007.

Governing Body:
J H Davies (*Chairman*)

C Bradley, CBE, MA
K M R Foster
The Rt Hon Sir Alan Haselhurst, MP
P G Lee, DL, FRICS
Mrs M R Chalmers
P J Cooper
S J Ahearne
Mrs J Simpson
C Daybell
Professor C Temple
P J Hutley
Mrs M Curtis
Mrs B Davey
Dr J Nicholson
C Tongue

Bursar & Clerk to the Governors: P D Watkinson, BSc, MBA

***Headmaster*: Dr Michael J Walker**, MA, PhD, CertEd, FRSA

Deputy Headmaster: D M Lauder, MA (*History*)

Second Deputies (Common Room):
P J Golden, BSocSc, MBA (*Economics & Business Studies*)
Mrs K A Megahey, BSc (*Mathematics*)

Director of Studies: Dr J M Shaw, BA, PhD (*History*)

Assistant Teachers:
N L Osborne, MA (*History, *History of Art*)
A W S Thomson, BEd (**PE*)
A M Homer, MA (*English*)
N J Spring, MA (*English; Head of Careers*)
†R L Feldman, MSc (*Mathematics*)
C J Megahey, BA (**Mathematics*)
[M Surridge, BA (*History*)] (*sabbatical*)
A D G Widdowson, BSc (*Mathematics*)
I W Gwyther, BA (*Geography*)
†D J Smith, BA (*Art*)
†M J A Sugden, MA (*Modern Languages*)
A G Chamberlain, BA (*Modern Languages*)
C R S Lee MA (**Drama, English*)
Miss A L F Simpson, BSc (*Chemistry & Biology*)
†Mrs F J Barnes, BSc (*Geography*)
†Mme B J L Chamberlain, L-ès-L (*Modern Languages*)
J D Lowry, BA, ALCM (**Music*)
B Coppel, BA (**Art*)
†Mrs F M Marshall, BSc (*History*)
N D Stannard, BA (*Religious Studies & Philosophy*)
Mrs J Balchin, BEd (*English & SENCO*)
†C S Knightley, BA (*PE*)
Miss S Hookway, BSc (*PE*)
†J S Weiner, LLB (*Economics & Business Studies*)
Mrs A L Salmon, BA (*§SEN*)
Miss E Hampson Smith, BA (*Art*)
P G Bennett, AGSM (**Academic Music*)
W A M Sanderson, MA (*Physics*)
P D Harris, BSc (*Physics*)
Ms M Valls (*Spanish*)
Mrs M Cacace, BA Hons (**Psychology*)
A W Motson, BA (*Design Technology*)
Miss N F S O'Brien, MA (*§ESL*)
Snr F Sanchez del Rio, Licenciatura (*Modern Languages, *Spanish*)
Mrs V L Smith, BSc (*§Psychology*)
S J Winter, BA Hons (**Religious Studies, History*)
A H J Spooner, CertEd (*Design Technology*)
†Mrs C M Phillips, ALA (*Learning Support*)
T J Hietzker, BSc (**Biology*)
S J Jones, MSc (**Physics*)
P S Clark, BA Hons (*Business Studies*)
Ms J K Mallett, BA (*Modern Languages*)
R Pathak, BA (**History*)
C L Watkinson, BSc Hons (**Chemistry*)
Mrs H A Murphy, MA (**Modern Languages, *French*)
T J Vignoles, BA (**English*)
The Revd J A W Brice (*Chaplain*)
Miss F V Dell, BSc (*Mathematics*)
Mrs A Gregg (*Modern Languages*)
Miss L T Glover, BSc (*Chemistry*)
M J Campbell, MSci (*Mathematics*)
Miss C A Morgan, BA (*English*)
Ms E K Rose, BA (*§Geography*)
Mrs R Grant, BA (*§Spanish*)
A S B Holt, BA Hons (*Mathematics*)
Mrs J E McArdle, BA Hons (*Business Studies*)
B R Peart, BSc Hons (*Biology*)
Miss S L Proudlove, BA Hons (*ESL*)
Miss R J Purdy, BA Hons (*English*)
Mrs A Squirrell, BA Hons (*Librarian*)
M A Pitts, BEng Hons (**Design Technology*)
A D D Murphy, BSc Hons (*Biology*)

Miss C Tye, BSc Hons (*ICT*)
Miss A H Sefton, BSc Hons (*Chemistry*)
Miss S R Bushby, MA Hons (**Classics*)
D E Lucius-Clarke, MA (*Modern Languages, *German*)
O G Brett, BA (*Music*)
G Master-Jewitt, BA (**Geography*)

Houses and Housemasters/mistresses:

Boys' Houses:
Deacon's: Charlie Knightley
Elwyn's: Michael Sugden
Gepp's: David Smith
Montgomery's: Richard Feldman
Windsor's: John Weiner

Girls' Houses:
Follyfield: Frances Barnes
Garnetts: Beatrice Chamberlain
Manor: Carolyn Phillips
Stocks's: Frances Marshall

Head of the Preparatory School: Mrs J M Burrett, BA

Roman Catholic Chaplain to Felsted: Father M Nott

Medical Officers:
Dr Malcolm Slack, MB BS
Dr Bronwen Pitt

The Houses. There are nine Houses at Felsted, a day house for boys, a day house for girls, three boarding houses for boys, two boarding houses for girls, an Upper Sixth House for boys and an Upper Sixth House for girls. Each House is under the direction of a resident Housemaster or Housemistress.

Each Housemaster/Housemistress is supported by a pastoral team comprising a resident Assistant Housemaster/Housemistress, a matron responsible for overseeing the domestic arrangements, and several House tutors.

The Curriculum. All pupils study English, English Literature, French, Mathematics and Sciences to GCSE and choose a further four subjects from the following: History, Geography, Religious Studies, German, Spanish, Latin, Classical Civilisation, Art, Music, Design & Technology, Physical Education and Computer Studies.

In the Sixth Form pupils have a choice between A Levels and the International Baccalaureate. Those studying A Levels choose four subjects to study to AS Level and then continue with either three or four subjects to A Level. The following subjects are offered: English Literature, Theatre Studies, History, History of Art, Religious Studies, Psychology, Geography, Business Studies, Economics, French, German, Spanish, Latin, Classical Civilisation, Mathematics, Further Mathematics, Physics, Chemistry, Biology, Sport & Physical Education, Art, Music, Design & Technology. An AS Level in Critical Thinking can be taken in the Upper Sixth.

For the IB pupils study six subjects and also have a course on the Theory of Knowledge, write an extended essay and have to be involved in the Creativity Action Service Programme.

Scholarships. (*see Scholarship Entries section*). Academic, Music, Drama, Art, and Design & Technology Scholarships are awarded annually up to the value of 20% of the fees for entry at 13+ and to the Sixth Form. Bursaries are available to increase the awards in case of need up to 100% of the fees in certain cases. The examinations for the 13+ Scholarships take place in May and for the Sixth Form Scholarships in November and February.

Scholarships are also awarded at 11+ at Felsted Preparatory School and these may be carried through to the Senior School.

Arkwright Foundation Scholarships are also available to talented students in Design at 16+.

All-rounder Scholarships and Foundation Awards which recognise all-round ability or specific ability in one area are available on entry at 11, 13 and 16 years old.

Registration and entry. Boys' and girls' names can be registered at any time. All those, who pass an examination at the Preparatory School at 11+, will enter the Senior School without a further need to qualify. Before admission to Felsted all pupils at other preparatory schools must pass the Common Entrance or Scholarship Examination. Entry from other schools is by Headmaster's Report and Verbal Reasoning Test, or, for Sixth Form entry, 6 GCSEs and interview.

Fees per term (2008-2009). Senior School: £7,813 boarders, £5,848 day pupils.

Preparatory School: £3,361–£4,417; Pre-Preparatory: £2,019; Boarding £5,646.

Registration fee £75.

Felsted Preparatory School, whose Head is in membership of IAPS (The Independent Association of Prep Schools), shares the same governing body as Felsted School. It has its own campus, a new teaching centre for 11–13 year-olds and a Pre-Preparatory Department. (*For further information, see entry in IAPS section.*)

Old Felstedian Society organises both social and sporting activities. The Secretary is: M A Jones, 10 Parkhill Road London E4 7ED. The Old Felstedian Liaison Master, Mr N S Hinde, would be pleased to answer queries about the Alumni and further information can be found at www.felsted.org/of

Charitable status. Felsted School is a Registered Charity, number 310870. The charity is based upon the Foundation established by Richard Lord Riche in 1564 with the objective of teaching and instructing children across a broad curriculum as ordained from time to time by its Trustees.

Fettes College

Carrington Road Edinburgh EH4 1QX
Tel: 0131 332 2281
Fax: 0131 311 6714
e-mail: enquiries@fettes.com
website: www.fettes.com

Founded in 1870 by Sir William Fettes and designed by David Bryce, Fettes College is uniquely situated in extensive grounds and woodland close to the heart of Edinburgh, and enjoys a reputation as one of the pre-eminent co-educational boarding schools in the UK. Fettes College has roughly 600 pupils aged 7–18, boarders and day pupils at a ratio of 70:30. Fettes Students are drawn from all over the British Isles and from abroad and this diverse and healthy mix of backgrounds provides a richness that contributes to the stimulating, warm and energetic community that is Fettes College.

Motto: '*Industria*'.

Governors:

A E H Salvesen (*Deputy Chairman*)
Councillor I Whyte
A E H Salvesen
The Very Revd J Harkness, CB, OBE
A A McCreath
Mrs E Ross, CBE
Mrs E J S McClelland
I Armstrong, QC
R Robson (*Convenor of the Executive Committee*)
Professor I W Campbell
Dr H W Reid
A G H Davidson
Professor D W Harding, MA, DPhil, FRSE
C K Oliver
The Hon Lord Glennie
Mrs H Douglas Miller

Clerk to the Governors: A G Fox, WS

***Headmaster*: M C B Spens**, MA Selwyn College, Cambridge

Deputy Head: Mrs H F Harrison, BA
Assistant Head (*Director of Studies*): A Shackleton, MA
Assistant Head: A F Reeves, MA
Headmaster of the Preparatory School: A A Edwards, BA Hons

Chaplain: The Revd Dr D Campbell, MTheol, CECM, MTheol, DMin
IB Coordinator: J C Fern, MA

Assistant Staff:
A Aidonis, MA, PhD
A S Alexander, MA
Mrs B J Appleson, BA
A J Armstrong, MA
Mrs J D Armstrong, BA, MSc (*Director of Music*)
H Battersby, BSc
G A Blair, MA
†Mrs S A Bruce, BSc
D Bywater, CertEd
E Comer, MA
Mrs B J Conway, BA
†Mrs C L Davies, BA
Miss E R Davies, BA
†R A Davies, BSc
D Dawson, BSc
M Delveaux, MA, PhD
D Dowey, BSc
C J du Vivier, MA
Dr K J Fairbairn, BSc, PhD
Dr R A Fellowes, BSc, PhD
Miss A H F Ferguson, BEd
J K Foot, BA
†Mrs P J M Foot, CertEd
S French, BSc, PhD
Miss S S Gilbert, BA
†D A Goodenough, GGSM, FTCL, ARCO, ALCM
D M Goude, BSc
Mrs M Goude, BSc
A M Hall, MA, PhD
†D G Hall, BEd
Mrs M D Hansen, MA
D Harrison, BSc
R H V Harrison, BA
†Mrs C M Harrison, BA
†S J Herbert, BA
Mrs T Herries, MA
P F Heuston, BSc
Mrs R L Heuston, BA
J M Hobbs, BA, PhD
†Mrs P Houston, DipEd
Mrs J A Hudson-Price, BA
R E Hughes, MA, MPhil
P M A Jenkins, MA
Miss S E Johnston, BSc
D Kennedy, BSc
Miss J Klossek, BA
Ms A Layman, BA
Mlle A M Lepers, MA
Dr S A Lewis, BSc, PhD
J A Lisher, BA
I J Loudon, MA
Señora L Lyle
Mrs M I Mackenzie, MA
Miss R MacVicar, BSc
Miss J M Maguire, MSc
Miss A A F Mair, MA
Mrs S E Masson, GGSM
D B McDowell, MA
Mrs Y E A Mitchell, BSc
J J Morris, BA
A G Morrison, BA
Mrs I W T Morton, MBA
W E Moss, BA
Mrs R C O Nicol, BA
Mrs M J Palfery, MA
D G C Parry, BA
Miss J R Pattman, MA
J D Pillinger, BSc
Miss S Rehbein, BA
Miss S-J Rennie, BSc, MSc
A B Russell, BA
Miss C E E Satow, BMus
†R F Smith, BA
B M Sneddon, BSc
A J Speedy, BA
Miss L Sutherland, BA, MFA
Miss C M Tainsh, BEd, BA
Mrs E Thomson, BA, MLitt
C S Thomson, BA
Miss H J Ure, BA
L M von Hoff, BSc
Miss M-J Walker, BSc
N C R Ward, BSc
J A Weatherby, BEd
Mrs S V Weatherly, BSc
†B G Welsh, BSc
L J Whyte, BSc, PhD
Mrs E H Young, BSc

Bursar: M A Tolhurst, MA
Finance Manager: G Burns
Foundation Director: J C Lang, BA
Director of Marketing & PR: Mrs G Gray, MA
Headmaster's Secretary: Miss J F P Shurmer
Admissions Secretary: Mrs H F Marshall
Maintenance Manager: P J Houghton
Medical Officers:
Dr G Craig, MBChB, DO, DRCOG, MRCP, MRCGP
Dr L Stevenson, MBChB, MRCGP, DRCOG
OFA Secretary: Mrs D A Beaumont
Keeper of the Register: G D C Preston, MA

Situation and Buildings. Fettes stands in a park of 85 acres on a remarkable site between the centre of Edinburgh and the Firth of Forth. Being just 20 minutes' walk to the city centre, means that Fettes students can take full advantage of the wealth of cultural resources on offer in Scotland's Capital city such as galleries, museums and theatres. Students also have every opportunity to enjoy the majestic Scottish outdoors with a full programme of trips and experiences from hill walking to canoeing, camping to white water rafting. Regular national and international school trips further broaden the experience Fettes students are offered.

The main building contains the Chapel, Library, some classrooms including the language laboratory, the Medical Centre and two Boarding Houses. The other five Boarding Houses, the Dining Hall, the Music and Art Schools, the Concert Hall, the Science and Technology Centre, the Sports Centre, Squash and Fives Courts, and the Preparatory School are situated in the grounds.

Transportation links by road, rail and air are excellent.

Organisation. There are approximately 600 pupils aged 7–18, and each member of the School is the responsibility of a Housemaster or Housemistress. There are four Houses for boys, three for girls, a brand new Upper Sixth Form house and a Preparatory School. Our new Upper Sixth Form boarding house provides individual study-bedrooms with en suite facilities for all boarders. There is a strong tutorial system for the encouragement and guidance of each pupil.

Aims. Our mission at Fettes is to develop broadly educated, confident and thoughtful individuals. The hopes and aspirations of each and every one of our students are of central importance to us, and the happy, purposeful environment of the College encourages the boys and girls to flourish and develop fully the skills and interests that they possess.

Curriculum. The academic curriculum in the Preparatory School is based on the Scottish 5–14 Programme, but with a strong element of the English and Welsh national curriculum and Independent School Examination requirements. For GCSE all students take English, Mathematics, Physics, Chemistry, Biology and ICT. Students then choose 4 subjects from: Art & Design, Business Studies, Classical Civilisation, Classical Greek, Drama, French, Geography, German, History, Mandarin, Music, PE and Spanish.

Fettes offers a very broad range of subjects in the Sixth Form with students choosing either A Levels or International Baccalaureate, therefore allowing a choice of curriculum to best suit the needs of the individual student. Over 95% of pupils gain university entry with up to 18 students securing places at Oxford and Cambridge each year.

Careers. The School is a member of the Independent Schools Careers Organisation, and a team of Staff are responsible for providing specialist advice on careers and Higher Education and for developing links with industry and commerce. The Headmaster, Housemasters and Housemistresses are also involved in this work, and parents are invited to meet the Staff at termly receptions so that they can discuss pupils' progress, future options and career plans.

Chapel. The College Chapel, situated in the heart of the School, is central to life at Fettes with the daily Chapel service forming the core of the moral and spiritual guidance offered at Fettes. Fettes has a strong Christian tradition but members of other faiths and those with no faith are warmly welcomed, and this is reflected in the tolerant and questioning character of the School.

Games. All students are involved in sports at least 4 afternoons per week. All major sports are offered at Fettes in fact there are very few sports you cannot pursue. Rugby, cricket, hockey, lacrosse, netball athletics, tennis, squash, fives, swimming, badminton, fencing, netball, basketball, volleyball are an example of what is on offer. Fettes College is very proud of the Individual and team success at school and national levels across a range of sports including rugby, fencing and cross-country. Fettes College also has excellent sporting facilities including a purpose-built sports centre, all-weather pitches, indoor Swimming Pool and courts for Fives and Squash and a newly-built shooting range.

Other activities. There is a variety of societies and clubs, and each pupil is encouraged to develop cultural interests. On Saturday evenings, in addition to lectures, plays and concerts, there are regular dances and discos, and committees of pupils, with the assistance of members of Staff, are responsible for planning and organising social events for different age groups.

Music. The College possesses a strong musical tradition, and many pupils receive instrumental tuition. In addition to the orchestras there are ensembles, a swing band, Chapel Choir and Concert Choir. A major concert is held at the end of every term.

Drama. Drama is lively and of a high standard. Each year the School Play and House plays offer great opportunities for large numbers of boys and girls to act and to participate in Lighting and Stage Management.

Art. The Art School is flourishing, and the standards of pupil attainment are very high. Regular House art competitions and gallery display of current work occur.

Combined Cadet Force, Duke of Edinburgh's Award Scheme, Outside Service. Pupils are members of the CCF for two years and may choose to extend their service while they are in the Sixth Form. There are Navy, Army and RAF Sections and a thriving Pipe Band. Training is offered in Shooting, Vehicle Engineering, Canoeing, Rock-Climbing, Skiing, Sub-Aqua and Sailing.

In the Sixth Form many pupils pursue the Gold Standard of the Duke of Edinburgh's Award Scheme, and some 70 members of the School join the Outside Service Unit which provides help for others in difficult circumstances and raises funds for Charities.

Outdoor Activities. The School aims to make full use of its proximity to the sea, the Dry Ski Slope, and the rivers and mountains of Scotland. Outdoor activities are encouraged for the enjoyment that they give and the valuable personal qualities which they help to develop. A number of members of Staff are experts in mountaineering, skiing and water sports, and all pupils have opportunities for receiving instruction in camping, canoeing, sailing, hillwalking and snow and rock climbing. There are regular expeditions abroad.

Preparatory School. The Preparatory School for 150 boys and girls aged 7 to 13 is situated in the School grounds. Boarders stay in the modern purpose-built Houses. Pupils in the Prep School share the facilities of the senior school and participate in the full range of activities enjoyed by the College as a whole. (*For further details see entry in IAPS section.*)

Admission. Personal interviews assess the promise of each individual and determine those who will gain most from a Fettes education. Entrance exams are also required for entry. Pupils may join the Preparatory School at any stage (7–13) with students normally joining the Senior School at 13 and 16. Further details are available from the Admissions Secretary.

Scholarships, Foundation Awards and Bursaries. (*see Scholarship Entries section*). Scholarships to a maximum value of 33% of the fees are available for candidates aged 11+, 13+ and 16+. Any scholarship award can be supplemented by means-tested bursaries that can cover the full cost of the fees.

General Scholarships as well as Music scholarships, Piping Scholarships, Art Scholarships and All-Rounder awards are available.

Children of members of HM Forces qualify for a 12.5% reduction in fees and Special Bursaries (Todd) are available for descendents of Old Fettesians.

Fees per term (2008-2009). Boarding £8,166, Day £5,946. The fees cover all extras except books and stationery, music lessons and subscriptions to voluntary clubs and activities.

Registration Fee £50.

Old Fettesian Association. *Liaison*: Mrs D A Beaumont, Old Fettesian Association Office, Fettes College (Telephone 0131 311 6741).

Further Details from The Headmaster, Fettes College, Edinburgh EH4 1QX (Telephone 0131 311 6701).

Charitable status. The Fettes Trust is a Registered Charity, number SC017489. Fettes aims to provide a quality education at Junior and Senior level.

Forest School

College Place Snaresbrook London E17 3PY
Tel: 020 8520 1744
Fax: 020 8520 3656
e-mail: warden@forest.org.uk
website: www.forest.org.uk

Founded in 1834 as 'The Forest Proprietary School' to 'provide a course of Education for youth, comprising classical learning, mathematics and such modern languages and other branches of science and general literature as might from time to time be introduced; combined with religious and moral instruction in accordance with the doctrine of the Church of England'. Incorporated 1947.

Motto: '*In Pectore Robur*'.

Council:
Chairman of the Governors: J W Matthews, FCA

Members of the Council:
Professor J E Banatvala, CBE, MA, MD, MRCP, FRCPath, DCH, DPH
Mrs S R Campion, MA
B M de L Cazenove, TD
D W Godfrey
G S Green, MA
G Hewitson, MA
J A Little, MA, PhD
Mrs S K Rankin, MA, PhD
G Smallbone, MA
Mrs L Marland, BEd

***Warden*: A G Boggis**, MA

Deputy Warden and Head of the Boys' School:
M Cliff Hodges, MA

Deputy Warden and Head of the Girls' School:
Mrs P A Goodman, MA

Bursar: Mrs D Coombs, BSc, MBA

* *Head of Department*
† *Housemaster/mistress*

Boys' School Assistant Staff:
A G van den Broek, MA, PhD (*Senior Master*)
*†M Gray, BA (*Senior Housemaster*)
M C V Spencer Ellis, MA (*Director of Sixth Form*)
J D Waller, BA (*Lower School Master*)

*C Barker, BSc, PhD
†P Henley-Smith, BSc, PhD
I R Honeysett, MA
†Mrs D Barker, BSc
S Turner, Essex CCC
*A R Dainton, BSc
P M Oliver, MA (*Director of Drama*)
*G Paynter, BA (*Marketing and Press Liaison*)
S C Jalowiecki, BSc
†M E Peel, BA
M J Smith, BSc (*Careers Advisor*)
†A D Ford, BA
†O E Ling, BA
P H S Corbett, MA
T C Hewitt, BA
*Mrs A E Gould, MA
Mrs H P R Miller, BA
Ms A N Berges
†M S Christie, MA
Z H Nazir, BSc, DPhil
*J Holt, BA
†S Foulds, BA
†D T Tyreman, MA
J A C Whitmee, BA
*S Firek, BSc, PhD
*Mrs G Erdil, BSc
N Dey, BSc
J Chuter, MA
*S G J Huet Deug, BEd
*P Aspery, BA
J Miller, BA
A E Foinette, MA
B Adams, BSc
I D Foakes, BA
Miss J D Cranch, BSc
J Sloan, BA
R L J Price, BSc
J J Kay, BA
*Mrs S Pearce, MSc
*V E Elad, MA
P T Baker, BA

A V Nagar, BSc
S J George, BSc
S Wiles, MA
A J Redpath, BMus
S Dindol, BA

Girls' School Assistant Staff:
Miss J Benewith, BSc (*Senior Mistress*)
Mrs J K Venditti, BEng (*Senior Housemistress*)
Mrs S M Clarke, BSc (*Assistant Director of Sixth Form*)

*Ms L E Murray, BA
N V Gray, MA
A Royall, BSc, MSc, DIC
A J Eccles, MSc
Mrs S M Harris, BA
*C D Brant, MA
*†Mrs L Bishop, BA
A H Todd, BSc, PhD
Mrs S C Keating, BEd
*Mrs T C Christie, BA
J McGurran, BA
Ms F Pereira, MA
Mrs J Donald, BSc
Miss K Skelding, BA
*†Ms C Heath, BA
†Mrs L Surowiec, MA
†Miss J Baldwin BA
Mrs M L Shirkhan, BSc
J F O'Riordan, BA
*M J Taylor, BA, MSc
G Parkyn, BSc, PhD
*M McCartney, BSc
Miss K Conroy, BSc
Miss R Lang, MA
Ms F Anwar, BA
Miss L Torence-Smith, BA
M Scates, BSc
†Mrs J McIsaac, BA
*S J Marsh, BSc, PhD
†E-W Morris, BA
Miss K Hayward, BSc
Ms V A Kelly, BSc
Miss C Risk, BSc
Miss J Stewart, BA
Mrs F Hoxha, BSc
Mrs D Graham, LRAM, GRSM
*Miss C J Spencer Ellis, BA
Miss C Rhead, MSc
Miss L Evans, BSc
Miss E Pickersgill, BA
Miss M M Duncan, MA
Miss C Mills, BA
Ms D Walsh, BA, MPhil
Miss G T M K Currie, BA
Mrs D Holland

Preparatory School:
Head of Preparatory School: Mrs E Garner, BA, MEd
Deputy Head: Mrs C P A Browne, BEd, MA

Assistant Staff:
Mrs S A Spanjar, CertEd (*Pastoral Care, Girls*)
Mrs M Healey, CertEd
E J Hickman, CertEd
Mrs L C Dalton, BA
M McCormack, DipEd
Miss S Gould, BEd, MA
M Sturgess, BSc
Miss K Elliott, BA
Mrs K Clarke, BEd
C de Jager, BPrimEd
Mrs J Chan (*English Coordinator*)

Chaplain: The Revd J G Gascoigne, MA, BPhilEd
Director of Music: J E R Sanderson, BA, BMus
SENCO: Ms N Coghlan, BA
Warden's Secretary: Miss D Bell, CertEd

There are currently 1,235 pupils in the School (510 boys in the Boys' School, 515 girls in the Girls' School, 215 boys and girls in the Preparatory School).

The three Schools share the main School campus and facilities such as Chapel, Sports Hall, Theatre and Computer Centre, but each has its own separate teaching block. The Sixth Form is then organised on co-educational lines.

Buildings. The School is situated in an open part of Epping Forest. The original building is Georgian, converted to provide libraries, recreation rooms and offices. 19th century expansion led to the building of the Gothic-style Chapel and Dining Hall. Modern classrooms and changing rooms have been built and the main Laboratory Block extended. The Deaton Theatre, seating 375, a Sports Hall, Music School, Sixth Form Centre and Computer Centre were added between 1967 and 1985. The Preparatory School is a modern block, recently extended. The Girls' School was founded in 1978, its buildings opened and dedicated in 1981. The Jenkin Wing – Art, Drama and Design facilities – was opened in 2001 and the Performing Arts Extension in 2004. The new sports complex, an ambitious project costing £5m, which includes two new swimming pools, opened in September 2006. The surrounding playing fields cover nearly 27 acres.

Organisation. The School is divided into 3 clear sections under the overall direction of the Warden: Preparatory School (ages 4–11); Boys' School (ages 11–18): Girls' School (11–18). There are 8 Houses in the Boys' School and 6 in the Girls' School.

(*See also separate Preparatory School entry in IAPS section.*)

Curriculum. Courses are designed to give a broad education as far as GCSE, each pupil taking English, Mathematics, either separate Sciences or Balanced Science, one Modern Foreign Language and other subjects depending on the individual's ability. A high priority is given to ICT throughout the School. There is a wide variety of Sixth Form courses designed to prepare pupils to enter University, Business, the Services or the Professions. The full range of AS and A2 levels are offered; all Sixth Formers take General Studies. Private tuition is available in Piano, Organ and Orchestral Instruments, and there are several Orchestras, Bands and Choirs.

Religion. Worship in the School Chapel is in accordance with the faith and practice of the Church of England. All pupils are required to attend the daily services in chapel. Religious Education is broadly based and is taught as an academic subject.

Societies. The School has a thriving Combined Cadet Force, a Voluntary Service Group and a branch of The Duke of Edinburgh's Award Scheme. Other Societies include Chess, Choral, Debating, Film, Music, Natural History, Photography, and Science. There are Badminton, Fencing, Bridge, Squash and Shooting Clubs and a specialised TV studio.

Drama. There are frequent productions and drama competitions. Music, Plays, Concerts and Lectures take place in the Theatre.

Games. The main games are Cricket, Association Football, Hockey, Netball, Athletics, and Swimming. There are Tennis Courts and Squash Courts. All pupils are expected to take part in games.

Fees per term (2008-2009). (including lunches) age 11+: £4,135; age 8–10: £3,242; age 7: £2,996; age 4–6 years: £2,690.

Admission. Examinations for pupils at 7+ and 11+ take place in January for entry in the following September. Some places are available at 16+ and occasionally at other ages.

Careers. Almost all pupils go on to Universities to take Degree Courses, including 10-12 each year to Oxford and Cambridge. Careers advice is given to all pupils.

Scholarships and Bursaries. (*see Scholarship Entries section*). Academic Scholarships, Bursaries and Music Scholarships to cover up to full fees are offered annually to pupils at 11+ and 16+. There are also Drama, Sports and Art Awards at 16+. Further fee reductions are available to children of the Clergy.

Further details may be obtained from the Warden.

Old Foresters Club. *Hon Secretary*: Dr K Duggins, c/o Forest School.

Charitable status. Forest School, Essex is a Registered Charity, number 312677. The objective of the School is Education.

Foyle and Londonderry College

Senior School: Duncreggan Road Londonderry BT48 0AW Northern Ireland
Tel: 028 7126 9321
Fax: 028 7126 9425
e-mail: info@foylelondonderry.derry.ni.sch.uk
website: www.foylenet.org/foyleandlondonderry

Junior School: Springtown Londonderry BT48 0LX
Tel: 028 7126 9321
Fax: 028 7137 2216

Foyle and Londonderry College is a Voluntary, Co-educational, Day, Grammar School. The buildings are on two campuses: Junior School (11+ to 14+) on the Springtown site and the Senior School on the Duncreggan site.

Chairman of Governors: Mr R J B Young

***Principal*: Mr W J Magill**, MA Cantab, MA NUU, CertEd Cantab

Vice-Principals:
Mr J H McNee, BA, PGCE, MPhil
Dr P P Carson, BSc, DipCompEd, MSc Ed
Mrs E L Caulfield, BA, DipEd, DipG&C, PQH

Senior Management Team:
Mr J S Goodman, BSc, LTCL, MA Ed
Mr P G Gault, BA, PGCE
Mr W M Lynn, BA, BA
Mr G S Mercer BSc, PGCE
Mrs H Eakin, BEd

Heads of Departments:

Art & Design:
Mr K F Ward, BA, PGCE

Biology:
Mrs I A Hannaway, BEd

Business Studies:
Mrs H Eakin, BEd

Careers:
Mr K J Thatcher, BA, DASE

Chemistry:
Mr K S Given, BA, PGCE

Classics:
Mr J H McNee, BA, PGCE, MPhil

Computing/Information Technology:
Mrs S McLaughlin, BEd

Technology & Design:
Mr A C Moorcroft, BEd, PGCTE

English:
Mr P G Gault, BA, PGCE

Geography:
Mrs S I Craig, BA, HDipEd

Geology:
Mr W M Lynn, BA, BA

History:
Mr S J Heasley, BA, PGCE

Home Economics:
Mrs F Feeney

Mathematics:
Mr G S Mercer, BSc, PGCE

Music:
Mrs B O'Somachain, BMus, PGCE, TTCT

Modern Languages:
Mrs E L Caulfield, BA, DipEd, DipG&C

Physics:
Mrs S M O'Connell, BSc, PGCE

Physical Education:
Mr G R McCarter, BEd, DLC (*Boys*)
Ms K Eakin, BSc, PGCE (*Girls*)

Religious Studies:
Mrs E Adair, CertEd

Administrative Staff:
Bursar: Mr N Stewart BSc
Principal's Secretary: Mrs M J Deans, BA, DLCC

Age Range. 11–18 Co-educational.

Number of Pupils. The Department of Education specifies the Admission and Enrolment numbers which are: Admission Number 130; Enrolment Number 960.

Fees per annum (2007-2008). Parents pay a Capital Fee of £15 per annum and a Parental Contribution of £105 per annum.

History. Foyle College and Londonderry High School, now Foyle and Londonderry College, have been providing education for young people in the Londonderry area and further afield for 375 years. In 1617 following the Plantation of Ulster, the Free School of Londonderry was founded by Mathias Springham, Master of the Merchant Taylors' Company, to "the honour of God and the spreading of good literature". The school remained on its site within the walls until 1814 when it moved to the fine Georgian building on Lawrence Hill, adopting the name Foyle College shortly afterwards.

The Londonderry Academical Institution, founded in 1868 by a body of influential local merchants, proved to be a vigorous rival for almost thirty years until the amalgamation of the two schools in 1896. The school then had the use of the buildings at Lawrence Hill and Academy Road.

Following the Second World War, and as a consequence of the many changes brought about by the 1947 Education Act, the Governors acquired a site at Springtown on Northland Road, overlooking the school playing fields, to build a new school. This was opened on 2nd May 1968 by His Royal Highness the Duke of Kent.

Londonderry High School also derived its existence from the merging of two independent institutions. The first of these, the Ladies' Collegiate School, was set up in 1877 at 11 Queen Street by Misses MacKillip, pioneers in the movement for the higher education of women in Ireland. The school later moved to Crawford Square and was renamed Victoria High School.

Buildings and Amenities. The Junior and Senior Schools are both well equipped, enabling staff to adopt the most effective teaching methods. In the Senior School there are six Science Laboratories plus several Computer Suites, a Technology Suite, Art and Design Suite, Music Suite, Business Studies Suite including Computer Room, Study Hall, Library, Upper Sixth Social Centre, Lower Sixth Social Centre, Sports Hall and twenty-two General Classrooms. Drama and Musical performances take place in the Assembly Hall.

In the Junior School the Library, two IT Suites and Technology Suite are well established while the Science Laboratories have been completely refurbished and a new Music Suite added. Home Economics and Art rooms have been renovated. There are fourteen General Classrooms, a fully equipped Gymnasium and Assembly Hall.

Serving the 30 acres of school grounds are two pavilions at Springtown where there are rugby pitches, cricket pitches, tennis courts and an all weather hockey and athletics ground. The Senior School has a hockey pitch and tennis courts.

The Secretary of State for Northern Ireland recently announced finance of £28 million to relocate the school, together with Ebrington Primary School, to a site formerly occupied by the army at Clooney Base in the Waterside area of the city. The new school should be operating from September 2008.

Aims of the School.

(1) To create a secure, caring, happy, healthy environment within which pupils can develop both as individuals and as members of a community.

(2) To equip each individual with appropriate skills of literacy, numeracy and oracy, and to develop full academic potential through study of a wide but integrated range of subjects.

(3) To stimulate an appreciation of aesthetic, literary, scientific, mathematical, technological, environmental, linguistic, physical and spiritual values.
(4) To provide a foundation for further study and training by creating opportunities for each pupil to:
  (a) develop a spirit of enquiry;
  (b) practice the skills needed for independent study;
  (c) make realistic career and personal decisions.
(5) To help pupils acquire qualifications appropriate to the needs of their future careers.
(6) To encourage pupils to cooperate and to appreciate the need for moral values and tolerance of others.
(7) To encourage pupils to understand and accept discipline and to develop the power of self-discipline.
(8) To provide and encourage participation in a range of recreational and cultural activities.

Framlingham College

Framlingham Woodbridge Suffolk IP13 9EY
Tel: 01728 723789
Fax: 01728 724546
e-mail: admissions@framcollege.co.uk
website: www.framlingham.suffolk.sch.uk

The School was founded in 1864 by public subscription as the Suffolk County Memorial to HRH, The Prince Consort, Albert, and was incorporated by Royal Charter.

Motto: '*Studio Sapientia Crescit.*'

Chairman of Governors: A W M Fane, MA, FCA

***Head*: Mrs G M Randall**, BA Hons, FRSA

Second Master, Deputy Head Pastoral: A N Lawrence, BEd
Deputy Head, Academic: C A Norton, MA, PGCE
Senior Master: M D Robinson, MA, BEd (*Head of History*)
Senior Master: C E Hobson, BA Hons, PGCE

Heads of Department:
Business Studies & Economics: C Caiger, BA, MSc, PGCE
Careers: R W Skitch, BSc, ACCEG, ACIB, PGCE
Design & Technology: D J Morgan, CertEd
Drama: Ms D Englert, BA Hons
EFL: Mrs K Cavalcanti, BEd, RSADipEFL
English: P R Drummond, MA
Geography: P D Barker, MA, PGCE
ICT: C Rimmer, BA Hons, MSc, PGCE
Languages: C R Thorpe, MA, PGCE, MIL
Mathematics: K R S Hoyle, BSc, PGCE
Director of Music: R W Goodrich, BA, LTCL, ABSM, PGCE
PSHE: D J Boatman, BA, PGCE
Psychology: Mrs J S Hobson, BA, PGCE
Religious Studies: J E Holland, BA
Science: Dr D Higgins, MA, PhD, PGCE
Director of Sport: J Alvis, BA Hons, PGCE

Finance Director: N J Chaplin, BA, FCCA
Operations Director: A L Payn, Chartered FCIPD
Admissions Officer: Miss E Rutterford, BA Hons
Head's Personal Assistant: Mrs A Cox

Framlingham College is a fully co-educational school that is proud of its traditions and past achievements yet has a forward-looking approach to the education of boys and girls. The school stands in a magnificent rural situation overlooking Framlingham Mere and Castle.

It has its own Preparatory School at Brandeston Hall (*see entry in IAPS section*).

Organisation. The Senior School numbers some 435 pupils of whom 265 are boarders. The flourishing Sixth Form is 196 strong. There is a fully integrated House system for day and boarding pupils with 3 girls' Houses and 4 boys' Houses.

Facilities. An imaginative buildings programme has produced an exciting range of facilities with a recent development being the Headmaster Porter Theatre, a state-of-the-art drama and music facility. Science, Technology, and Art enjoy purpose-built accommodation, and the indoor swimming pool and fitness suite enhance the superb range of sports facilities. There is a popular Sixth Form Centre and an attractive central concourse, which is used extensively for informal gatherings. We have further plans to improve our warm and friendly boarding houses and a comprehensive extension and refurbishment programme is now underway.

Curriculum. The curriculum is framed to combine the best of academic tradition with a forward looking approach which encourages independent learning. The potential Oxbridge student is carefully nurtured and stretched, and similar care is taken with those who may experience academic difficulties.

Extra-Curricular Activities. A full and varied programme of activities is provided both on and off campus.

The choice is second to none including the outward bound work of the Duke of Edinburgh's Award Scheme and the Combined Cadet Force, the cut and thrust of the Debating Society and the business world of Young Enterprise. Whether it is jewellery making or choral society, a round of golf on campus or trekking in Nepal, there is something for everyone.

Games. Framlingham College enjoys an enviable reputation for sport and fields a large number of teams.

The major games are rugby, hockey, cricket, athletics and tennis for boys, and hockey, netball, tennis and athletics for girls. There is a wide range of other sporting opportunities, including squash, soccer, badminton, basketball, rounders, swimming, archery, shooting, volleyball and table tennis. The immaculately tended grounds include four rugby pitches, three grass hockey pitches, an Astroturf, a golf course and one of the finest cricket squares in Suffolk. The facilities also include a sports hall with specialist fitness suite, a 20-metre indoor swimming pool, two squash courts, three netball courts and in the summer, 15 tennis courts.

Music and Drama. Framlingham has a very strong choral tradition, and there is a wide range of orchestras and instrumental ensembles. The College's dramatic productions enjoy a very high reputation. The main productions each year generally include one musical, a major drama and one junior play.

Religion. The College has a strong Christian foundation but students of all backgrounds are welcomed.

Admission. Common Entrance and interview form the normal means of entry to the College at 13+, but special provision is made for students for whom this is not appropriate. Entrance at 16+ is normally on the basis of GCSE results and interview or testing, but special arrangements are made for overseas students who are not following the British Curriculum. Visits from interested parties are welcomed; please contact us to make an appointment.

Scholarships. (*see Scholarship Entries section*). A variety of scholarships is available at 13+ and 16+ including Academic, Art, Design & Technology, Music, Drama, Sport and All-Rounder scholarships.

Fees per term (2008-2009). Boarding £7,291, Day £4,686.

Charitable status. Albert Memorial College is a Registered Charity, number 1114383.

Frensham Heights

Rowledge Farnham Surrey GU10 4EA
Tel: 01252 792561
Fax: 01252 794335
e-mail: headmaster@frensham-heights.org.uk
website: www.frensham-heights.org.uk

Board of Governors:

President: ¶Mr T M Aldridge QC Hon, MA (*formerly President of Special Educational Needs Tribunal*)
Vice-President: ¶Professor T Sherwood, MB, MA, FRCP, FRCR (*Emeritus Professor of Radiology, Cambridge, Fellow of Girton College*)
Chairman: Mr M J Chadwick, ACA, ATTI (*Chartered Accountant*)
Vice-Chairman: Mr M Sant (*formerly General Secretary, Independent Schools' Bursars Association*)
Treasurer: Mr D Smith, FCA (*Management Consultant*)
Mr G Buttle, MA (*formerly Headmaster Churcher's College*)
Dr J Doulton, MA, MBBS, MSc, MFPHM (*Doctor*)
Mr C Hall, LLB Hons (*Retired Solicitor*)
Mr D Haywood, MA (*formerly Headmaster City of London Freemen's School*)
Professor H Kimbell, MBE, LLB, LLM (*Solicitor and Lecturer*)
Mr A Layton, MA, QC (*barrister & author*)
¶Mrs J Read, BA, Chartered FCIPD (*Retired Personnel Management Specialist*)
Mr A J Reid (*Chief Executive, Treloar Trust*)
Mr S Seymour Marsh (*Property Developer*)
¶Mr Frank Wibaut, ARCM, Hon RAM (*International concert pianist, worldwide visiting professor, formerly director Australian National Academy of Music*)

***Headmaster*: Andrew Fisher**, BA, MEd, FRSA

Senior Management Team:

* *Head of Department*
† *Housemaster/mistress*
§ *Part-time or Visiting*

Deputy Head: Simon Pettegree, BSc
Deputy Head (*Academic*): Diana Lobban-Small, BSc, PGCE, CChem, MRSC
Bursar and Clerk to the Governors: David Armitage, MBE, MSc
Development Director: Rosellen Mates
Head of Sixth Form: Jonathan Warner, BSc, MSc, PGCE, FRGS
Head of Lower School: †Nic Hoskins, BA
Head of Middle School: Eileen Daw, BEd

*John Atkinson, BSc, PGCE, CertTheol
§Hilary Blake, CertEd, BEd
Kester Buckland, BSc
*Matthew Burns, BA, PGCE
*Barry Carr, MA, PGCE
Heather Clarke, BEd, CertEd
Russell Crew, BEng, PGCE
Sophia Colley MA, PGCE
Lynne Elgy, BA
Mark Floyer, MA, MPhil, PGCE
Rosemary Giraudet, BEd, DipEd
Kate Godeseth, BA
Lynn Goodburne, BPhil, DipLCDD
*Lisa Graham, BA, PGCE
Shelagh Harris, GGSM, ARCM, PGCE
Caron Hawkes, BEd
*Brendan Horsted, BA
Paul Hughes, BSc
Kevin Joy
§Robert Keene
§Ian King, BA, CertEd
Charlotte Knight, BSc, PGCE
Deborah Lee, BEd
*Amanda Liddle, BA
†Jeff Loomis, PhD, BSc
Hannah Lyons, BSc
§Olive Maggs BA PGCE
Rosemary McMillan, CertEd
§Carol Mallett, BEd, DipRSA
Andrew Melbourne, BSc, PGCE
Susan Millerchip, BSc, PGCE
§Nigel Milton, BA, BSc, PGCE
Fiona Morgan, BEd
†Marion Netley, BA
*Nicola O'Donnell, BA, MEd, PGCE
Nicola Pentelow, BA, DipEd, PGCE
Elizabeth Piercey, DipEd
*†Steven Powell, BSc, PGCE
Nolan Price, MA, BA
*Patricia Risley, BSc
Hugh Robertson, MBA, BSc, PGCE
*Edwin Rolles, BA, FTCL, ANSM, ARCM, CertEd Mus
§Angela Schock-Hurst, MA, BA
*Timothy Seys, BA, PGCE
Susan Slater, CertEd (*Nursery Supervisor*)
*Andy Spink, BSc, GTP
David Stevenson, BA
Alex Tekell, BEd
Karen Thompson, BSc, PGCE
†Shirley Worsfold, BEd
§Emma Wyld, BA, DipTESOL

Finance Manager: Wendy Hamilton, FCA
Theatre Manager: Sean Connor, BA
Admissions Registrar: Lynette Kerridge, BA
Domestic Bursar: Chris Hull
Secretary to the Headmaster: Lindsey Boyce
School Nurse: Sarah Burton, RGN, RM
School Counsellor: §Francesca Thorpe, BACP
Librarian: Marion Crawford, MA, ALA, PGCE
Medical Officers: Dr Jane Elliott, Dr Paul Adams

Founded in 1925 as one of the country's first co-educational boarding and day schools, Frensham Heights has always been characterised by a friendly, informal atmosphere in which the individual child feels secure and happy. As a co-educational community, the school believes in equality of the sexes; it opposes all forms of bigotry, racial, religious or social, and every effort is made to deepen understanding of human nature and behaviour and develop self-esteem.

Pupil numbers. 520 boys and girls aged 3 to 18 years. Average class size: 18.

Entry. Children entering the school at the age of 11+ sit the Frensham Heights Entrance Examination, held in January. Children entering at the age of 13+ sit the Frensham Heights Entrance Examination in January and may also take the ISEB Common Entrance Examination. A minimum of six GCSE passes at Grade C or above is required for entry to the Sixth Form with A/B grades in subjects to be studied at AS/A Level. The school holds Open Days for prospective parents. Individual appointments to visit the school may also be made through the Admissions Registrar.

Curriculum. The school has harmonised its teaching programme with that of the National Curriculum. Up to the end of Key Stage 4 (GCSE) all pupils study English Language and Literature, Mathematics, Combined Science, French, Geography or History, together with the possibility of a further humanity (Geography, Business Studies, History) or a second modern language (German or Spanish). In addition, all pupils choose between one and three creative and performing arts subjects (Art, Ceramics, Design Technology, Drama, Dance, Music, PE), a policy consistent with the School's regard for creative as well as academic intelligence. During Key Stage 3 (ages 11–14) the curriculum includes PE, RE and Information and Communication Technology (ICT). PSME is taught throughout the school. A Level subjects include most of those taught to GCSE, with the addition of Psychology and Economics. The school has a long tradition of pupils going on to study Science at university.

Academic Results. Examination results are very good. There is a strong Sixth Form, most of whom go on to further education, including Oxford and Cambridge Universities. Public examination results: A Level 100% (50% A Grades 2007); GCSE Grades A*–C (92% 2007).

Sport. The school has excellent sporting facilities which include playing fields, a swimming pool, tennis courts and an indoor sports centre. Sports include basketball, soccer, rugby, netball, hockey, cross-country running, athletics, volleyball, badminton, rounders and cricket. Annual ski and snowboarding trips take place abroad in the holidays.

Outdoor Education. Outdoor education is part of the curriculum for all pupils in Year 7 and above. Training takes place in the school's extensive adventure centre and leads to weekend and holiday expeditions in camping, climbing, caving, canoeing, scuba-diving and trekking, which are open to all members of the school. World Challenge expeditions to Borneo, Kyrgyztan, Ecuador and Tanzania.

Extra-Curricular Activities. All pupils are expected to take part in extra-curricular activities. An extensive and varied selection of activities includes sports of all sorts, art, music, dance, drama, hobbies and clubs, sailing, and the Duke of Edinburgh's Award Scheme.

Facilities. 100 acres of parkland in beautiful countryside, Performing Arts Centre, new First and Lower Schools, music school, modern science laboratories, art & design centre, ICT centre, junior and senior library, sixth form centre, photographic studio. A new Sixth Form complex opened in September 2006.

Music. Music is held in high esteem at the school and is regarded as an essential part of a person's education. It is studied by all pupils until the end of Year 9. The school has an impressive record for its choral and instrumental music. There are senior and junior choirs, three orchestras, jazz groups, and a large number of instrumental groups. Concerts are put on nationally and locally. An overseas concert tour takes place every year. The Lower School has its own European concert tour.

Boarding. Boarders are housed in small and friendly boarding houses. Each has a resident housemaster or housemistress and house tutor. There is a programme of weekend activities for the boarders, but weekly boarders may leave on Friday afternoon, returning on Sunday evening or Monday morning. The School organises a coach to London at weekends.

Religion. There are no religious services. Pupils are free to attend local churches and several pupils sing in church choirs.

Dress. There is no uniform. There is a dress code.

Welfare and Discipline. The house-staff are supported by a resident school nurse and a part-time counsellor. Every pupil has a personal tutor. The school's discipline is firmly based on good relationships between staff and pupils and reflects the values of the school, which promote a rational and caring approach. Senior pupils act as mentors to younger members of the school. A thriving School Council, consisting of elected representatives from all age groups, meets regularly to discuss matters of mutual interest and concern.

Learning Difficulties. The school is sympathetic to those with dyslexia and other specific learning difficulties and offers limited support.

Overseas Pupils. The school admits a few boarders from overseas each year and provides tuition in English as a Second Language as part of their curriculum.

Frensham Heights Lower School is situated in its new purpose-built classrooms. **The First School**, for pupils aged 3–8, is in its own recently enlarged buildings and gardens within the main school grounds. Both schools provide firm foundations in English and Mathematics, supported by a well-balanced curriculum that includes Science, French, Information Technology, Music, Drama and Dance at a level appropriate to the year group. Pupils have access to all the main school's facilities.

Fees per term (2008-2009). Nursery £16.85 per session (morning or afternoon, lunch £2.70); Reception £1,735; Years 1–2 £2,125; Years 3–4 £2,610; Years 5–6 £3,215; Years 7–8: £4,635 (day), £6,495 (boarding); Years 9–11: £4,855 (day), £7,315 (boarding); Sixth Form: £4,855 (day), £5,100 (new day pupil), £7,315 (boarding), £7,560 (new boarding pupil).

Scholarships and Bursaries. (*see Scholarship Entries section*). There are scholarships and exhibitions, limited to £750 and £400 respectively, awarded each year for exceptional ability in academic work, music, art and drama. Bursaries are awarded on the basis of a means-tested assessment.

Charitable status. Frensham Heights Educational Trust is a Registered Charity, number 312052. It exists to provide high quality education for boys and girls.

George Heriot's School

Lauriston Place Edinburgh EH3 9EQ
Tel: 0131 229 7263
Fax: 0131 229 6363
e-mail: enquiries@george-heriots.com
website: www.george-heriots.com

Heriot's Hospital was founded in 1628 to care for the fatherless sons of Edinburgh burgesses. Today it is a fully co-educational day school, deeply rooted in the Scottish tradition.

The School is attractively situated in its own grounds close to the city centre and within easy walking distance of bus and rail terminals. A number of bus routes also service the School. Edinburgh Castle forms a magnificent backdrop, and Edinburgh's flourishing financial centre, the University of Edinburgh, the College of Art, the National Library and the Royal Scottish Museum are located close by.

The original building, described as a "bijou of Scottish Renaissance Architecture", has been carefully preserved and, as a historic monument, is open at certain times to the public during school holidays. The Chapel, Council Room and Quadrangle are particularly notable.

Over the years a succession of new buildings has provided the full complement of educational facilities. The most recent additions include the purchase of an adjoining site to extend facilities. Similarly, improvements and additions have been made over the years to provide excellent sports fields and facilities at Goldenacre. The School has sole use of an outdoor centre in the Scottish Highlands.

Motto: '*I distribute chearfullie*'

Governors of George Heriot's Trust:

Chairman: M J Gilbert, CA
Vice-Chairman: Rear Admiral D M Dow, CB, DL
Finance Convener: J D M Hill, CA
Education Convener: H L Philip
Buildings Convener: N M Irons, CBE, JP, DL
Foundationers' Convener: G Sydserff, BSc
Mrs A Di Rollo
Revd R Frazer, BD, PhD
Dr P Green, BSc, PhD
F Henderson
Prof R N Ibbett, FRSE, CEng, FBCS, MIEE
Mrs K Macfarlane
Councillor M MacLaren
A Paton, MCIBS, FRSA
Dr M W J Strachan
J Thomson

Secretary and Treasurer to George Heriot's Trust: F M Simm, FCA

***Headmaster*: A G Hector**, MA

Headmaster's Secretary: Mrs E Firoozi

Head of Senior School: C D Wyllie, MA, DipEd

Depute Headteachers, Senior School:
Mrs C W Binnie, BA, DipEd
R C Dickson, MA, DipEd
Mrs M Lannon, BA
K J Ogilvie, MA
Mrs M N Williams, MA, DipRSA

Chaplain: Mrs A G Maclean, BD, DCE

Art:
*Mrs J Young, MA
Miss J R Crabtree, MA
Mrs C M Fraser, BA
Miss S L Lowrie, BA
Mrs C J McGirr, BA, PGCE
Mrs A J E Thomson, BA

Biology:
Miss A McKenzie, BSc
Ms D Barnaby, BSc
I Munro, BSc
Mrs G Lippok, DipEd
A A N Ramage, BSc
Mrs H Smith, BSc

Business Studies:
*Miss K A Macnab, MA
Miss K C Coltart, BA
Mrs A Donaldson, BA
Miss M R Green, BA
Mrs M Lannon, BA
J Payne, BA

Chemistry:
*F I McGonigal, BSc
Mrs J Blaikie, HND
J D Broadfoot, BSc, CChem, MRSC
Mrs F Donaldson, BSc
J Wilson, BSc

Classics:
Mrs A M S Jennings, MA, DipEd

Computing:
*J T Scott, BSc
C P Finlay
A Semmler, BA
Ms J McColgan, MA

Drama:
Mrs J H Douglas, BA
Miss K Henderson, MA

English:
*K Simpson, MA, LLB
R C Dickson, MA, DipEd
N H Grant, MA
Mrs G K Hay, MA
Mrs D Keohane, MA, CIM Dip
P J Lowe, MA
Mrs M C Massie, BA, MA
Dr A Neilson, MA
Mrs L M Nicol, MA
J J S Tait, MA
C D Wyllie, MA, DipEd

Geography:
*Mrs I P Robertson, MA
D Armstrong, BSc, DipEd
Mrs F Constable, MA
Mrs S E A Harris, MA
J A W Heatlie, MA, DipEd
Mrs A Hughes, MA
Mrs A MacCorquodale, BSc
K J Ogilvie, MA

History:
*M A McCabe, MA, MTh, PhD, BD
Ms A Connor, MA
D R Moffat, MA, MEd
Miss L P Robertson
A Savage
N R Seaton, MA
Miss T Peters, MA

Food, Health & Consumer Studies:
*Mrs J M Mitchell, DipHE
Miss M A Coull, BSc

Support for Learning:
*Ms V Higson, BSc, DipSpLD
Mrs G Alexander
Mrs R M Armet, MA, DipEd
Ms M Churches, MA
Mrs J Jackson, MA, MSc, PGCE, CPsych
D Thain, BEd
Mrs M N Williams, MA, DipRSA

Mathematics:
*Miss F Findlay, BSc
G A Dickson, BSc
Mrs J H Dickson, BSc
Miss F Moir, BA
D C Porteous, BSc, DipEd
P C Walker, BSc
Miss K Weir, BSc

Modern Languages:
*M G Grant, BA
Mrs C W Binnie, BA
Ms E M Brown, MA
J G Buchanan, MA, DipEd
Mrs C J M P Clarke, BA, PGDE
Mrs S Duncanson, MA
F Hédou, PGCE
Ms E R Mackie, MA
Mrs D M Mullen, BA
Mrs J M Semple, MA
Mrs J Sutherland, MA
Ms K L Temple, MA
Miss A Zeng

Music:
*G C W Brownlee, BA, LLCM, ALCM
Mrs J Buttars, BA
Mrs S C Lovell, DRSAMD
V Fleischfresser, BMus, BEd, ATCL, AACM
Mrs R S J Weir, BMus

PE/Games:
*M Mallinson, BEd
Mrs D J Barnes, BEd
Mrs N Kesterton, BEd
E Harrison, BSc
Mrs G J M McIntyre, DipPE
Mrs G Mollison, BEd
R Stevenson, BEd
K M Yuille, DipPE

Physics:
*R M Bush, BSc
Miss J Collings, BSc
Mrs M Hutton, BA
I Oliphant, BSI, PGCE
N R Short, BEd, MEd

Religious Education:
*Mrs M Campbell, BD
Mrs L Beilby, MA
Miss L Glekin, MA
Mrs A G Maclean, BD

Design & Technology:
*Mrs E L Watson-Massey, BSc
G A Laing, OND, HND, DipTechEd
I Purves, BEd
B Dalzell, BSc
D W Urquhart, HNDEng, DipTechEd, CertEdComp

Head of Junior School: D S Adams, BA, PGCE

Deputy Head of Junior School: Mrs L M Franklin, MA, PGCE

Depute Headteachers, Junior School:
Mrs M J Marquis, DipEd
Mrs H Murphy, BSc, PGCE, MEd
Mr D H Porteous, DipCert

Early Years (including Nursery):
Miss E Davidson, BEd
Ms S G Gallacher, BA, PGCE
Mrs L Gilmour, BA, PGCE
Miss R C Graham, BSc, PGCE
Miss K B Montgomery, MA, PGCE
Mrs J Naysmith, BSc, PGCE
Mrs E C Robertson, MA, PGCE (*Principal Teacher i/c Nursery*)
Miss S L Simpson, BSc, PGCE
Miss S Irvine, BEd
G Rand, MA, PGCE

Middle Primary:
Miss H Beaton, BEd
Miss C Cooke, MA, PGCE
Mrs V E J Clark, MA, PGCE
Mrs E S Clarke, DipEd, INSC
Mrs E S B Couper, DipEd
Miss E J Davidson, BA, PGCE
Miss C L Evans, BA, PGCE
N Huda, BSc, PGCE

Upper Primary:
Miss H Oliver, MA, PGCE
G Cockburn, BA
Miss V Fielding, BA, PGCE
Mrs G Happs, BEd, PGCE
Mrs N Lee, BA, BEd
Miss A Hogg, BA, PGCE
Miss L McKeown, BSc, PGCE
Miss L J Patterson, BA, PGCE
Miss C Sim, BEd
P Swierkot, BA, PGCE
B Tyler, BSc, PGCE
I J A S Woolley, DipEd

Enrichment:
Mrs R M Armet, MA, DipEd
Miss J Attenborough, BEd
Mrs A C Garden, BEd
Mrs B I S Hunt, BEd
Mrs J A Mulholland, BSc, PGCE
Mrs K S O'Hagan, BEd
Mrs P M Roberts, DipEd

Our aim is to introduce all our pupils to the broadest possible spectrum of academic, spiritual, cultural and sporting interests and experiences, which will enable them as articulate, self-reliant adults to play a full part in an ever-changing society.

Heriot's has long enjoyed a reputation for academic excellence, and we strive to help pupils to attain the highest possible level of competence. In the same spirit, every pupil is encouraged to participate in an extensive array of extra-curricular activities. We value sporting achievement, particularly in team games, and we encourage activity in art, music and design. In addition, pupils are introduced to religious, moral and philosophical concepts in the search for the answers to the more abstract questions that life poses.

The Nursery (32 children). The Nursery accommodates children in their pre-school year. It is part of the Early Years Department. Admission to the Nursery is open to all.

The Junior School (652 pupils). The 5–14 Programme has largely been adopted: particular emphasis is given to core subjects to provide a sound basis for secondary education. Art,

Drama, Modern Languages, Music and all areas of Physical Education are taught by specialists, and Junior School staff liaise closely with their secondary colleagues to provide curricular continuity throughout a pupil's time here.

A very active Junior School extra-curricular programme includes music, drama, adventure weeks and support for charities.

The Senior School (962 pupils). For the first two years a system of flexible streaming provides a broad curriculum for all. An extensive choice of subjects is available from S3 to S6 in preparation for Scottish Qualifications Agency examinations at every level. Most pupils stay on for a Sixth Year and proceed to university or other forms of tertiary education.

Our vast Senior School extra-curricular programme is designed to suit all interests and abilities, and it provides recreation, enjoyment and excellence. Pupils achieve national and international recognition in their chosen activities, and many Former Pupils have pursued their interests with similar success in adult life.

Music and drama are very strong. Performances are given annually in our two halls, our Chapel, in the adjoining Greyfriars Church, in the Usher Hall and other venues.

The CCF is active and thriving and our Duke of Edinburgh's Award Scheme is one of the largest in Scotland. The main sports are cricket, cross-country running, hockey, rowing, rugby and tennis but most other sports are available in school or at Goldenacre.

Heriot's enjoys a reputation as a caring community. The greatest importance is given to pastoral care and a sophisticated careers advisory programme is in place. The Support for Learning Department provides invaluable help to all Junior School and Senior School pupils, be it that they have a specific learning difficulty or are outstandingly gifted.

Admission. Admission (other than for Nursery) is by assessment or examination. Application for occasional places is welcome at any time, but for the main stages should normally be submitted by the end of November.

Fees per term (2008-2009). Junior School: £1,950 (P1 & P2), £2,376 (P3 to P7). Senior School: £2,937.

A limited number of Bursaries is available from P1 to S6 and there are Scholarships for entry at S1. Fatherless and motherless children may qualify for free education and other benefits through the Foundation and James Hardie Bursaries. Full information is available from the Treasurer on request.

The Heriot Club. *Secretary*: E Allan, 10 McLaren Road, Edinburgh EH9 2BH.

Charitable status. George Heriot's Trust is a Registered Charity, number SC011463. It exists to provide education for children.

George Watson's College

Colinton Road Edinburgh EH10 5EG
Tel: 0131 446 6000
Fax: 0131 446 6090
e-mail: info@gwc.org.uk
website: www.gwc.org.uk

The College was founded by George Watson, first accountant of the Bank of Scotland, who died in 1723, and opened in 1741. Transformed into a predominantly day school in 1870. Amalgamated with George Watson's Ladies College to form a co-educational school in 1974.

Motto: '*Ex corde caritas*'.

Governors:
The Education Board of the Company of Merchants of the City of Edinburgh has ultimate responsibility for the Governing of the School, but delegates responsibility to the School Governing Council.

Chairman: N Murray

Members:
I Bell
S Clark
K Dunbar
Mrs J Easson
Revd P Graham
Mrs J Hay
D Johnston
Cllr M McInnes
I A Murning
G Reid
Miss E Smith
G Wilson

Bursar: J Mills

***Principal*: G Edwards**, MA

Head of Senior School: Mrs H Wilson, BA
Deputy Head (*Guidance/Discipline*): Mrs F Denyer, MA
Deputy Head (*Timetable*): Mrs D Meiklejohn, BSc
Deputy Head (*Careers/Course Choice*): Dr R Mallinson, BSc, PhD
Deputy Head (*Curriculum*): Mrs J Urquhart, BSc
Deputy Head (*Pupil Achievement*): A Bennett, BEd

Head of Junior School: Mrs L Fleming, MA
Deputy Head: Mrs P Snell, BA, MEd

Director of Information Technology: L Smith, BSc
Examinations Coordinator: Miss E Rogers, BA

Classics:
Mrs L O'Donnell, MA
Miss D Law, MA
Mrs R Fawthrop, BA
G H Edwards, MA

Mathematics:
¶N Hopley, MA
H Gilchrist, BSc, PhD
P J Stark, BSc
K J Thomson, BSc
Mrs T Johnson, BSc
D Johnson, BSc
Mrs J Hutchinson, BSc
Mrs V Mason, BSc
C Cooke, BSc
M Neild, BSc
Mrs E Hopley, BSc
Miss L Murison, BSc
Miss S Mallett, BSc
C Sharp, BSc
Mrs J Urquhart, BSc

Physics:
G K Black, BSc, MA
R Mallinson, BSc, PhD
J Barrow, BSc, PhD
Dr H Earnshaw, BSc, PhD
J Spence, BSc
I Lawrie, MPhys
M Ramsay, BSc

Chemistry:
Mrs F Hewitt, BSc
Mrs S Floyd, BSc
Mrs D Meiklejohn, BSc
J Coull, BSc
Mrs G Wilson, BSc
Mrs E Webb, BEd
Dr F Steven, BSc, PhD

Biology:
C Gambles, BSc
Mrs I Pyper, BSc
J G Rennie, BSc
G Morgan, BA
Mrs F Graham, BSc
Miss H Croft, BSc
J Laycock, BSc

English:
Mrs L M MacKenney, BA, MA
I Jordan, BA
Miss J M Carter, MA
Miss B Dunham, BA
Miss G Mellor, BA
¶Mrs M Taylor, MA
Mrs A Giegerich, MA
R Kettley, BA
S Intihar, BEd
Mrs J Dailly, BA
Dr S Sabeti, BA, MA
Miss A Steen, MA
A Patterson, MA
M Crawford, MA

Drama:
H Paterson, DipEd
Mrs A R Porteous, DipEd
C Serrels, BA
Miss E Henderson, BA

Modern Languages (French, German, Italian, Spanish, Russian):
Mrs A Giglio, MA
R M Slater, MA
¶A Skinner, MA
Mrs S Flannery, BA
Miss E Rogers, BA
Miss E White, BA
Mrs F Denyer, MA
I Geddes, MA
R A Crawford, BA
Mrs A Allan, MA
Mrs E McCready, MA
Mrs H Wilson, MA
M Capelo

History and Modern Studies:
Mrs J Hind, MA
G L Gibb, MA
Mrs H Young, MA
Mrs D Grant, MA
Miss T Heron, MA
D Tidswell, BA, PhD
Miss L McKinstrey, BA
J Lisher, BA

P Dean, BEd
K Tait, BSc, DipTechEd
R Graham, BEng
K Hutton, BSc
Miss C Rae

Geography:
D Pyper, MA
T Young, BA
Mrs L Cooper, MA
J Cartmell, BA
Ms C Fletcher, BSc

Economics/Business Studies:
P Arlidge, BA
Miss T Wright, BA
R MacFarquhar
Mrs M Neville, BA
Miss J Graham, BA
Miss S Pettitt, BA

Religion & Philosophy:
R Travers, BD
The Revd P F Marshall, BA, BA(*Div*)
C Barrington, MA, BD
Miss C Peak, MA

Art:
W Robb, DA
Mrs C Stevenson, DA
Miss A Orr, BA
Mrs E Mackie
N Adair, BA
A Watson, BA, PhD
Miss R Birkett-Jones, BA

Information Technology:
Mrs N Tait, BSc
L M Smith, BSc
G McCartney, BSc
Miss L Callan, BSc

Technical Subjects:
R J Grant, BSc

Home Economics:
Mrs J Chalmers, BA
Mrs N Burnett, BA

Music:
D Elliott, BMus
S Griffin, BA
Mrs M Leach, DipMusEd
H Scott, DRSAMD
Miss S Buckingham, BA

PE:
I N Brown, DPE, BEd
R Mack, DPE
A M Bennett, BEd
A Donaldson, BEd
¶Mrs J Campbell, DipPE
A Ker, DipPE
Mrs E S M Batchelor, BEd
M Gifford, BEd
M Leonard, BEd
N McCallum, BEd
Mrs K McNaughton, BEd
Miss L Clement, BEd
Miss L Burton, BEd
Miss J Gray, BEd
R Snedden, BEd

Learning Support:
Dr C Weedon, BEd, MEd, PhD
Mrs A J Thornton, MA
G B Lyon, MA

Junior School:

Head: Mrs L Fleming, MA
Deputy Head: Mrs P Snell, BA, MEd
Deputy Head (*Learning & Teaching*): R Porteous, BA
Deputy Head (*Upper Primary*): G Salmond, BEd
Deputy Head (*Lower Primary*): Mrs K Wilson, BEd

Miss D F Paton, MA
Mrs R E Dickerson, DipCE
Mrs K A Grandison, MA
¶Mrs S Marshall, MA
Mrs P Walkinshaw
Mrs M Broadie, DipCE
Mrs E P Bell, MA
Mrs S Dick, LLB, CertEd
Miss R McKerchar, DipMus
I Smith, BSc
Mrs P M Scott, MA
Mrs A Reid, DipCE
Mrs K Holdgate, BSc
Miss A Robson, MA
A Macdonell, BSc
J Milligan, BA
A Forbes, BEd
A Harrison, BA
Mrs B Ferguson, DipEd
Miss L Dolby, BEd
Mrs W Elliott, BA
Miss T Eden, BA
Miss F Johnston, MA
Miss J Walker, MA
Mrs C Gregory, BEd
Mrs S Naismith, MA
E Duncan, MA
J Hutchinson, MA
Miss A Adam, BA
Mrs N M Titterington, DipCE
Mrs M Rogers, L-ès-L
Mrs J M Dickie, DipCE
Mrs S Brown, DipCE
Mrs K A McIver, MA
Miss E Smith, DipCE
Mrs C Hood, DipEd
Mrs S Brown, DipEd
Miss K Jones, BMus
Miss C Davidson, BSc
Mrs S Leslie, BA
Miss M Kay, BA
¶Mrs E E C Easton, DipCE
Miss P Stanyard, BSc
Mrs L Kemp, DipEd
Mrs H Wright, BA
Mrs F McCallum, MA
Mrs A Offer, BEd
Mrs E Thow, DipCE
Mrs E Mannion, BSc
Mrs T Spreckley, BA
Miss K Rees, DipEd
Mrs C Milligan, BCom

The College is divided into the Senior School (ages 12–18, 697 boys, 636 girls) and the Junior School, which comprises the Upper Primary Department (ages 8–12, 295 boys, 257 girls), the Lower Primary Department (ages 5–8, 193 boys, 146 girls) and the Nursery Unit (ages 3–5, 54 boys, 32 girls).

Since the present buildings were opened by HRH The Duke of Kent in 1932, extensive alterations have been carried out and additions made. Recent new building includes the Music School, special facilities for the Sixth Form, a new Art School and Technology Centre, Lower Primary, a new Nursery Unit and two Games Halls (one opened in 2008), next to the indoor Swimming Pool. There are ample recreational facilities in the adjacent grounds: in addition to the traditional winter and summer games – Rugby, Hockey (boys as well as girls), Cricket, Netball, Tennis – an extensive range of other sports is offered, including Swimming, Athletics, Rowing, Badminton, Basketball, Golf, Squash, Volleyball, Skiing, Sailing and Fencing. There are opportunities to take part in Sailing, Hill-walking and Field Work. There are School Scout and Guide Groups and a Community Service Group, a very active Duke of Edinburgh's Award Scheme and a world class Pipe Band. Normal School hours are from 8.45 to 3.30, Monday to Friday. After School Club in Junior School. Nursery Plus wrap-around and holiday care for Nursery pupils.

Organisation. The first 2 years of the Senior School have a general curriculum; after that some specialisation is allowed for the 2 years to the Scottish Certificate of Education (Standard Grade or Intermediate Grade), Scottish National Qualifications (Intermediate and Higher Grades), and in the final year fuller specialisation for University entry purposes (Advanced Highers). In Art, examinations are GCSE, AS and A Level. Pupils proceed to the full range of British Universities.

Admission. Pupils are normally admitted by interview or examination in Jan/Feb either at 3 for the Nursery Unit, or at 5 for the Junior School, or at 12 for the Senior School. Applications for Nursery places are made 16 months ahead of the start of the child's pre-school year (by 30th April). Applications for the Junior and Senior Schools are made by the preceding 30th November or as soon as possible thereafter; candidates will be considered for admission at stages other than Primary I or Secondary I, if chance vacancies arise. Special consideration is given to pupils moving into the Edinburgh area from elsewhere. In the case of candidates for S2–S6, interviews are held in the first week of February by which time it is possible to gauge what vacancies, if any, will be available in the autumn.

Fees per term (2008-2009). Tuition fees which are inclusive: £2,002 (Nursery full-time), £1,904 (P1–2), £2,295 (P3–7), £2,952 (Senior School).

Scholarships and Means-Tested Financial Assistance. We currently offer up to 9 academic scholarships and 2 music scholarships each year on entry to the Senior School ranging in value from 10% to 50% of the annual school fee. The George Watson's Family Foundation also provides means-tested financial assistance on a sliding scale based on family income, capital and other financial circumstances ranging in value from 5% to 100% of the annual school fee.

Former Pupils' Club. "The Watsonian Club", open to men & women who have attended George Watson's College, exists to foster links between former pupils and the School. It has many branches throughout Britain and overseas and a great variety of active Sports sections in Edinburgh. There are excellent modern "Club" facilities at Myreside, Myreside Road, Edinburgh, within the School grounds. Enquiries should be addressed to The Secretary of The Watsonian Club at the School. Tel No: 0131 446 6000.

Charitable status. The Merchant Company Education Board (which administers George Watson's College) is a Registered Charity, number SC009747. George Watson's College is a charity devoted to educational excellence.

Giggleswick School

Giggleswick Settle North Yorkshire BD24 0DE
Tel: 01729 893000 Headmaster's Office
01729 893012 Bursar's Office
Fax: 01729 893150
e-mail: enquiries@giggleswick.org.uk
website: www.giggleswickschool.co.uk

Giggleswick School, founded by 1512, was granted a charter by Edward VI on 26 May, 1553, at the instance of John Nowell, then Vicar of Giggleswick, and one of the King's Chaplains.

The Governing Body:
Chairman: M H O'Connell Esq, BA, FCA
Vice-Chairman: Miss L M Campbell, OBE, BEd

The Very Reverend C J Armstrong, BTh, CertEd
Dr A M Bowie, MA, DPhil
R A P Brocklehurst Esq, MA, MBA
M H Crosby Esq, MA
Dr M Dörrzapf, DPhil
J L Ellacott Esq, MA
Mrs I A Frost-Pennington
Mrs H Hancock, MA
Miss A L Hudson, MA, MRICS
D S Lowther, Esq, BA
A R Mullins, BSc, MBA, ACA
Lady Smith
¶D A Stockdale Esq, QC, MA
P J S Thompson Esq, LLB, Hon D Laws, MCI Arb

***Headmaster*: G P Boult**, BA Hons (Dunelm), PGCE

Deputy Head: N A Gemmell, BA
Assistant Head: Ms S L Williamson, BA
Director of Studies: Miss A L Wood, MA

Assistant Staff:
* *Head of Department*
† *Housemaster/mistress*

G Wigfield, CertEd
S Heap, BEd
*Mrs C Gemmell, BEd
*P Thomas, BSc
F D G Ogilvie, BEd
†A J Scholey, BSc
†Mrs E J Wharton, BA
*Mrs J E Farmer, BA
†J P Bellis, BA
*C D Knight, BA
*R Barrand, BA, PhD
†P C R Andrew, BEng, AMIEE
Mrs L M Stott
*P K Hucknall, BSc, PhD
*J Huxtable, BA
*†W S Robertson, BA
P Adams, MBA
*N M Walker, BSc, PhD
Mrs A L Coward, MA
*Mrs S Wood, BA
*Miss M M Hannah, BA
C A Meneses, BA
A Simpson, BEd
*R M Taylor, BSc
Miss E M Rowles, BA
†W N Bartlett, BA
D Morton, BA
M D Pugh, BSc
*J G Warburton
A J Pickles, BA
Miss S Clarke, BEd
*J M Curry, BSc
D P Swift, BA
Mrs K R Haynes, MA
*C D Richmond, BSc, MA
E J Hawkins, BSc
Miss J M Helm, BSc
*D C Everhart, BA, MA
Revd J E Bavington, BA
S C Griffiths, MSc
Miss R L Wilkinson, BSc
Miss J C Landon, BA
Miss H K Lindley, BA
D H Arkell, BA, LRSM
Miss J A Birch, BSc
Mrs D A Taylor, BA
D N Muckalt, BSc
J F Grissett, BA
Miss M H Bourne, BSc
M E Peek, BSc, PhD
Miss H Mannheimer

Bursar and Clerk to the Governors: G R Bowring, Esq, MA
Marketing Director: Mrs S Hird
Headmaster's Secretary & Registrar: Mrs D M Lambert

Junior School
Head: M S Brotherton, BEd Hons, NPQH

Miss J A Middleton, BA
Ms G C Sismey, BA
Miss S M Butler, ALCM
J R Mundell, LLB
A G Hiles, ABSM, GBSM
Miss P C Bagot, BA
Mrs M L Pugh, BSc
Miss D A Horsman, BEd
Miss N Slater, BA
Mrs H D Brotherton, BA
Miss A A Wimbush, BSc
Mrs J M Gardner
Mrs L Shepherd
Mrs K Hall

Headmaster's Secretary: Mrs M A Smith, BA

Giggleswick provides boarding and day education for about 380 boys and girls aged from 11–18. It also has its own Junior School for children aged 3–11. The School is situated in beautiful Yorkshire Dales' scenery, close to the borders of Cumbria and Lancashire and is an hour's drive from Leeds, Manchester and The Lakes. It can be reached from the M6 or M1 motorways or by rail via Settle or Giggleswick stations. Overseas students fly to Leeds/Bradford or Manchester Airports.

Senior School. For eleven year olds admission is usually based on performance in Giggleswick's own entrance examination. At thirteen, entrance is based on performance in the Common Entrance Examination for pupils in Preparatory Schools. However, for pupils being educated either abroad or in the maintained sector, other appropriate forms of assessment are used.

Admission direct to the Sixth Form is on the basis of reports and interviews, and is conditional upon the applicant obtaining a minimum of five GCSE passes with Grade B passes in subjects to be taken at AS/A Level. There are approximately 150 pupils in the Sixth Form. Generous Academic, Music, Art, Design & Technology, Drama, Sport and All-Rounder Scholarships are available.

Boarding. 65% of Senior School pupils are boarders and the School's routine is entirely geared to boarding education. There are seven Houses, four for boys and two for girls in Years 9–U6, with 50–60 pupils in each, and one for boys and girls in Year 7–8. The Housemaster or Housemistress is responsible for the well-being and progress of pupils in the House and is assisted by House Tutors.

Most Sixth Formers have their own Study Bedroom; other pupils share Study Bedrooms or small Study Dormitories.

Day Pupils. Day pupils are fully integrated with boarders; they arrive before Morning Assembly, share studies and use all School facilities. They have lunch and tea at School and return home after prep.

Courses of Study. From Years 7–9 the curriculum comprises English, French, Mathematics, Sciences, History, Geography, Arts (including Drawing and Ceramics), Music, Drama, Technology (including Home Economics, Graphics and Design), Religious Studies, Physical Education (Gymnastics and Swimming) and PSHE. Latin, German, Russian and Spanish are also available.

In Years 10 and 11 a pupil chooses 9 or 10 subjects leading to the GCSE examinations.

In the Sixth Form, a pupil normally studies four subjects leading to GCE AS Level and three to A2 Level examinations. The subjects available are Mathematics, Further Mathematics, Physics, Chemistry, Biology, Business Studies, English, French, German, Latin, Classical Civilisation, Spanish, Russian, History, Geography, Art, Design, Music, Economics, Theatre Studies, PE and Information Technology.

Pupils are prepared for Oxford and Cambridge University Entrance.

Religion. The religious life of the School is supervised by a full-time resident Anglican Chaplain. At their own wish pupils may be prepared for Confirmation into the Church of England. Catholic pupils are excused certain Chapel services in order to attend Mass. The School respects and allows for other religious convictions.

Health. There is a surgery in the charge of a resident SRN with a Deputy who is also an SRN. The School Doctor visits regularly 4 or 5 days a week and is available in emergencies.

Games. In the Autumn Term the main games are rugby for boys and hockey for girls and in the Spring Term hockey for boys and netball for girls. In the Summer Term the main sports are cricket for boys and tennis for girls, but athletics, swimming, and tennis are available for boys and girls. In addition, there are excellent facilities for soccer, squash, fives, golf, badminton, basketball, netball, cross-country and fell running etc. There are regular overseas tours by the sports teams. Rugby and hockey teams toured Australia in Summer 2005. A netball tour went to Grenada in February 2007 and a cricket tour to Kenya in March 2007. A Canadian Rugby and Hockey tour is planned for Summer 2008.

Outdoor Education. This is an important part of the School's extra-curricular life. All pupils have introductory courses in map reading, orienteering and camp craft, and train for the Giggleswick Certificate at the end of Year 9. Many go on to the Silver Award and some each year to the Gold. Trained and qualified members of staff lead these activities. There is a major expedition each summer climbing in the Pyrenees, Morocco, Himalayas etc.

Music. Tuition, given by four full-time musicians and a number of visiting teachers, is available in all keyboard and orchestral instruments. The Music School has excellent recital, rehearsal, teaching and practice rooms. Concerts are given by the School Orchestra, the Concert Band, Ensembles and the Choral Society. Concert tours have been undertaken in the USA, Holland and Prague.

Drama. There is a major production each year, as well as public performances of GCSE, AS and A Level work. Drama is a timetabled subject for Year 9 and the subject is offered at GCSE and A Level. The School has an extensive theatre wardrobe of its own. Drama tours are a regular feature of school life, the most recent being a Drama and Music Tour to the USA.

Art. The Art Department is fine-art-based concentrating on drawing, painting, print-making and ceramics. It boasts excellent examination results.

CCF. All pupils follow a structured course in Year 10, divided equally into military and non-military skills. The contingent has Army, RAF and Royal Marine Sections. At the end of the year, pupils may opt to leave or remain in the CCF. Advanced training is given in a variety of skills. The contingent fields strong teams for the District competitions and sends many cadets on further training at camp and on various courses.

Societies. There is a wide variety of societies. Sixth Formers have their own Social Centre.

Recent Developments. A new dining hall, a Learning and Information centre, a floodlit synthetic hockey pitch, and completely refurbished Science laboratories have recently opened. In 2004 a new Art centre was completed and work is in progress on a new Sports Hall.

Careers Advice and Staff-Parent Conferences. Two experienced Careers Advisors supplement the advice of House Staff and Heads of Academic Departments in guiding academic choices and career decisions. There is an excellent work experience programme, which includes GAP year projects. The School is a member of ISCO and uses the ISLO/Morrisby Scheme of Careers Education and guidance. Regular Staff-Parent conferences are held at School to enable discussion of pupils' past, present and future progress and needs. Parents are always welcome at other times, especially at Chapel, sports fixtures, concerts, plays, etc.

Junior School. Giggleswick Junior School stands in its own grounds on a site adjacent to the Senior School. It has its own staff but also has the advantage of specialist teachers and facilities of the Senior School. Recent improvements include a new Library, teaching and IT centre and a new Sports Hall. There is a Nursery for children aged 3 and above.

Admission is possible at any age between 3–11. At eleven, pupils transfer in the Autumn Term to the Senior School, enjoying continuity of environment, curriculum and friendships.

(*For further information see Giggleswick Junior School entry in IAPS section.*)

Entrance. Most pupils enter in the September term, but a few are admitted in January and April. Registration fee £150.

Entrance Scholarships. (*see Scholarship Section entries.*)

Fees per term (2008-2009). The fees are fully inclusive. Senior School: Boarders £5,842 (Years 7 & 8), £8,203 (Years 9–U6); Day Pupils £4,571 (Years 7 & 8), £5,615 (Years 9–U6). Junior School: Boarders £4,878, Day Pupils £1,929–£3,970.

Further details are available in the Prospectus which may be obtained from the Headmaster, to whom applications for entry should be made.

Charitable status. Giggleswick School is a Registered Charity, number 1109826. It exists to provide education for boys and girls.

The Glasgow Academy

Colebrooke Street Glasgow G12 8HE
Tel: 0141 334 8558
Fax: 0141 337 3473
e-mail: rector@theglasgowacademy.org.uk
website: www.theglasgowacademy.org.uk

Founded in May 1845, The Glasgow Academy is the oldest independent school in the west of Scotland. Its affairs are managed by the Glasgow Academicals' War Memorial Trust – formed to commemorate the 327 former pupils killed in the war of 1914–18.

It has been co-educational since 1991 when it joined forces with another West End school – Westbourne School for Girls. More recently, its mergers with Atholl Preparatory School in Milngavie and Dairsie House School in Newlands have contributed to its enduring success as a school covering the whole of west central Scotland. Parents now have a choice of three locations for their children in the popular Nursery to Prep 4 age group. Children from Atholl and Dairsie transfer to the main Academy site at Kelvinbridge at Prep 5.

Motto: '*Serva Fidem.*'

Chairman of Governors: JG Jack, MA, CA, CTA

Honorary Governors:
Sir Matthew D Goodwin, CBE, CA
Sir Angus M M Grossart, CBE, LLD, DLitt, FRSE, DL, DBA, MA, LLB, CA, FRSA, FCIBS
A L Howie, CBE
Sir Jeremy Isaacs, MA, DLitt, LLD, FRSA, FRSAMD, FGSM, Com de l'Ordre des Arts et des Lettres France, Mem Ordre pour le Mérite France
The Lord Kerr of Kinlochard, GCMG, MA, LLD St Andrews, LLD Glasgow
Dr Maurice Lindsay, CBE, TD, DLitt, FRIAS
Professor Sir Malcolm Macnaughton, MD, LLD, FRCOG, FRCP , FRSE
W M Mann, CA
Professor Sir David Mason, CBE, LLD, BDS, MD, FRCS, FDS, FRCPath, FRSE
C Miller Smith, MA, ACCA, LLD
The Very Revd Dr William J Morris, KCVO, DD, LLD
A D S Rolland, CA, FRCPS Glasgow
Dr Murray Stewart, CBE, MA, LLB, CA, DUniv, FCT, FRSA
Professor Norman Stone, MA
C W Turner, BSc, AKC

The Lord Vallance of Tummel, MSc, DSc, DTech, DBA, DEng

Nominated and Elected Governors:
Professor A Anderson, OBE, MA, PhD
Mrs M Brodie, BA
Mrs K E Brown, MBCS, CITB
B G Duncan, MRICS
J W Gilchrist, BArch, ARIAS
Mrs H Grierson, BSc, MSc, Dip AAS
Mrs E M Ker, BSc, MRPharmS
Professor C C Kidd, FRHistS, FRSE
D G Lindsay, ARICS
Dr G McLaren, MBChB
H A Millar
J W Mitchell
Professor M Siddiqui, BA, MA, PhD
I R Spinney, BA, PgDip PR, PGDip Marketing
Mrs A Swanson, LLB, DipLP
I M Veitch, FCIOBS, BAcc, CA

Secretary: T W Gemmill, LLB, NP

***Rector*: P J Brodie**, MA Oxon, MA Management of Education, Canterbury Christ Church University College

Deputy Rector: I M MacLeod, MA Oxon
Assistant Rector: Dr J Andrews, BSc Glasgow, PhD London
Assistant Rector: A L Evans, BSc Strathclyde

Heads of Department:
English: Mrs A F Watters, MA St Andrews
Mathematics: Mrs L S Moon, BSc Southhampton, CMath, FIMA, CertGuid
Classics: V W Hadcroft, BA London
Modern Languages: Mrs E M Wallace, MA Glasgow
History & Modern Studies: S M Wood, MA St Andrews
Biology: J M Shields, BSc Glasgow
Physics: S M Brunton, BSc Glasgow
Chemistry: Mrs F M Macdonald, BSc, MSc Bristol
Geography & Geology: W Robertson, BA Dunelm
Economics & Business Studies: Mrs S McKenzie, MA Glasgow, PGDip BusAdmin Strathclyde
Computing Science: Miss J E McElroy, MA Glasgow
Physical Education:
Mrs S M Crawford, DCE Jordanhill, DipPE Dunfermline, PGDip Guid Glasgow (*Head of Games*)
S W McAslan, BEd Jordanhill (*Head of PE*)
Art/Craft & Design: A de Villiers, BA London
Home Economics: Mrs M V Thomson, Dip111
Music: M B Marshall, BA Southampton, ARCO, DipMus
Outdoor Education: N C Gwynne, BSc Aberdeen
Learning Support: Mrs A A Harvie, BA Strathclyde, PGDip Ind Admin Glasgow Caledonian
Careers: Mrs E F McCallum, MA Dundee, AccC Stirling, PGDip Guid Glasgow
PSE: Mrs M T Muirhead, BA East Anglia, Dip Guid & Pastoral Care Glasgow

Preparatory School:
Head: A M Brooke, BEd Southampton
Deputy Head: R Teall, BA York

Atholl:
Head: Miss J McMorran, DCE, PGDip, DipTEFL

Dairsie:
Head: Mrs S S McKnight, DCE Jordanhill, CPE Dunfermline

Out-of-School Care:
Childcare Manager: Mrs J Thompson, HNC Childcare & Education

Chaplains:
Revd D J M Carmichael, MA, BD
Revd A Frater, BA, BD
Revd G Kirkwood, BSc, BD, PGCE
Revd S Matthews BD, MA
Revd J D Whiteford, MA, BD, Dip Soc Wk

Combined Cadet Force:
CCF Contingent Commander: Lt Col G R M Anderson
SSI: WO2 C J Duff

Administration/Finance:
General Manager: Dr W R Kerr, FCIS, FCIM, FHCIMA, PhD Strathclyde, MBA Glasgow, MSc Glasgow Caledonian
Rector's Secretary: Ms L McGowan
Administration Manager: Miss I Kovacs, BA Strathclyde
School Secretary: Mrs A M Farr
Database Coordinator/Administration Secretary: Ms C Cooke, BSc Sunderland

Development:
Director of Admissions and External Relations: M R McNaught, MA Glasgow
PA to Director of Admissions and External Relations: Mrs K McDonald

Organisation. The Preparatory School contains some 640 pupils (347 boys, 293 girls) between the ages of 3 and 11 and prepares pupils from the earliest stages for the work of the Senior School. The Senior School contains 562 pupils (298 boys, 264 girls). They are prepared for the National Qualifications at Higher at the end of Fifth or Sixth year. The Sixth Form provides courses in most subjects leading to presentation at Advanced Higher. Pupils are prepared for entrance to Oxford and Cambridge. The Academy has a fine record both at Oxford and Cambridge and at the Scottish Universities. The Academy aims to offer a unique combination of academic, musical, dramatic, sporting, extra-curricular, social and outdoor education opportunities, backed up by a comprehensive pastoral care system.

Buildings. The magnificent main building contains classrooms for the Senior School. A new purpose-built Preparatory School, open in Spring 2008, provides the most modern of facilities, and has enabled enhanced accommodation for Nursery, Kindergarten, After School Care and Senior School pupils. Physics, Chemistry and Biology are housed in separate spacious buildings. As well as an Assembly Hall, Gymnasium and Sports Hall including miniature Rifle Range, newer buildings for Music (1994) and Design (1998) considerably enhance the Academy's facilities. A comprehensive computer network linking all rooms throughout the Prep and Senior Schools enables all pupils to access the Internet, send Email or access facilities from home. The Library is the centrepiece of the main building.

Music and Drama. Music tuition is offered in a wide range of instruments. There are Senior, Junior and Theatre Choirs, a Concert Band, Pipe Band, Brass Group, Percussion Ensemble, Orchestra and various Prep School groups. Large-scale drama productions take place regularly and are supplemented by plays mounted by smaller groups.

Societies and Activities. These range from Public Speaking, Bridge, Chess and Debating Societies to a Mountaineering Club. Large numbers of pupils undertake each section of the Duke of Edinburgh's Award and there is a thriving Young Enterprise group. Residential education is an integral part of the curriculum at various stages of both the Prep and Senior schools. These experiences augment the PSE programme by promoting team building and personal and social development through outdoor challenges.

Games. All pupils, unless exempted by a medical certificate, take part in Physical Education and Games. Teams represent the school in Rugby, Hockey, Cricket, Swimming, Golf, Tennis, Athletics, Curling, Shooting and Squash. Cross-Country running is also offered as an option.

Combined Cadet Force. The Academy has a strong voluntary contingent with RN, Army, Signals and RAF Sections. In addition there is a Pipe Band.

Childcare outside school hours. The Academy provides care before and after school for its younger pupils. There is also provision for children between the ages of 3 and 12 throughout the holidays.

Entrance. Pupils may be registered at any age. The main entry points are (a) in the Preparatory School: age 3, 4 and 10; (b) in the Senior School: age 11 or 12 or for Sixth Form. Bursaries are available for S1–S6. Scholarships are available for S1 entry.

Fees per term (2008-2009). Preparatory School: £2,050/£2,225 (P1–P2), £2,260/£2,430 (P3–P5), £2,895 (P6 and Transitus). Senior School: £2,720 (S1–S2), £2,950 (S3–S5), £2,766 (S6).

Charitable status. The Glasgow Academy is a Registered Charity, number SC015638. It exists to provide education for girls and boys.

The High School of Glasgow

637 Crow Road Glasgow G13 1PL
Tel: 0141 954 9628
Fax: 0141 435 5708
e-mail: rector@hsog.co.uk
website: www.glasgowhigh.com

The new, independent, co-educational High School of Glasgow came into being at Anniesland in 1976 following a merger involving the Former Pupil Club of the High School, a maintained school previously in the State system, and Drewsteignton School in Bearsden.

Motto: '*Sursum semper*'.

Governing Body:
Honorary President: Lord Macfarlane of Bearsden, KT
Chairman: B C Adair, TD, LLB
Mrs A M B Currie, LLB
Sheriff W Dunlop, LLB
P M A Forgie, MCIBS
W G Gardiner, CA
R J A Hunter, CA
Mrs L Keith, MA, PGCE, ITQ
C M Mackie, BSc, FFA
D J Maclay, BSc, CA
J Y Miller, CA
Professor V A Muscatelli, MA, PhD, FRSA
Dr A C E Short, MBChB, FRCOG, MRCGP
G R White, BEd, MPhil
R M Williamson, MA, LLB, FRSA, FRSAMD

***Rector*: C D R Mair**, MA

Senior Deputy Rector: J O'Neill, MA

Deputy Rectors:
M A M Brown, BEd
Mrs M E R Price, MA

Staff:
* *Head of Department*

English:
*P A Toner, MA
G Baynham, BA
Miss R A Davies, MA
†Mrs G R Fergusson, MA
P D C Ford, MA
T Lyons, MA
Mrs J Muir, MA
Mrs M E R Price, MA
Miss M Sabba, BA

Mathematics:
*P F Edmond, BSc
Mrs C V M Anderson, BSc
Mrs A A Atherton, BSc
†J G MacCorquodale, BSc
P Moon, BSc
Miss N Park, BSc
Mrs M C Reid, BSc

Computer Studies:
*D L McCorkindale, BEd
N R Clarke, BSc
Mrs K M Farley, BSc
D Semple, BSc, MSc (*ICT Manager*)

Science:
A E Baillie, BSc (**Physics*)
K J A Robertson, BSc (**Chemistry*)
N M E Dougall, MSc, BSc (**Biology*)
Mrs L McGuigan, BSc
Mrs A McNeil, BSc, MSc
Dr L A A Nicholl, BSc, PhD
Mrs K S M O'Neil, BSc
Dr N J Penman, BSc, PhD
I J Smith, BSc

Modern Languages:
*M H Bennie, MA
†Mrs J M Horne, MA
N F Campbell, MA, LLB
Mrs V MacCorquodale, MA
Miss K J McAllister, BA
Mrs H O'Driscoll, BA, MA, MPhil
Mrs F B Slavin, MA

Classics:
*A H Milligan, MA
Mrs M H S Campbell, MA

Economics and Business Studies:
*A J Jensen, BA
Mrs E A Milne, BA, MCIBS

Geography and Modern Studies:
*Dr M G Davies, BA, PhD
Miss L Crothers, BSc
K F FitzGerald, BSc
Miss J A McAteer, BA
Mrs E M Paton, BSc

History:
*G K Sinclair, MA
R J Broadbent, BA, MEd (**Careers*)
J O'Neill, MA
Miss N Sutherland, MA

Art:
*P J Gilchrist, BA
Mrs C J Bell, BA
Mrs J F MacKechnie, DA

Home Economics:
*Mrs S M K Slatford, DipDomSci
Mrs C Cammidge, DipHE, MBA

Learning Support:
*Mrs R E Hamilton, BA
Miss N Park, BSc

Music:
*P S Douglas, DRSAM
L D Birch, BA, LRAM, DRSAMD
M Duncan, DRSAM
D R Fleming, BMus
Ms W MacDougall, MMus, BA, LLCM TD
N G McFarlane, BA
R McKeown, DRSAM
F Walker, BA, ARCO
Mrs J Tierney, BMus

Religion & Philosophy:
*C F Price, MTheol
Mrs M H S Campbell, MA

Physical Education:
*D N Barrett, BEd
Mrs A Cox, BEd (**Girls' PE*)
M A M Brown, BEd
K F FitzGerald, BSc
Mrs R Owen, BEd
Mrs B A Bell, DPE
C S Forsyth, DPE
Mrs M Gillan, DPE
Mrs M Jefferies, DPE
Mrs C MacKay, BEd
Mrs M Stevenson, DPE

Junior School Staff:
Head Teacher: Mrs K R Waugh, BA
Miss A M Brown, DCE (*Deputy Head*)
Mrs C Brown
Miss C E Carnall, BMus, MMus (*Head of Music*)
Mrs A J Coutts, BEd
Mrs S H Devlin, BEd
Mrs A M T Drapeau-Magee, Maîtrise, Licence (*French*)
Miss E J Eddie, BEd (*Physical Education*)
Mrs K B Freer, BA Hons
Mrs E Gibson, BEd
Mrs W Gray
Mrs C M Jaberoo, BA, MSc
Mrs J Jackson
Mrs L A Lambie
Mrs L Latimer
Mrs E McCormick
Mrs S E MacDougall
Mrs I McNeill, DA (*Art*)
Mrs J Moir
Mrs M Moreland
Mrs J O'Neill
Mrs C Ritchie
Miss I Skinner, MSc (*Principal Teacher*)

G J Walker, BSc
Mrs M Watt

Bursar: Mrs J M Simpson, BAcc, CA

Rector's Secretary: Miss L M Cook

Buildings. The Senior School occupies modern purpose-built buildings at Anniesland on the western outskirts of the city immediately adjacent to twenty-three acres of playing fields. The Junior School is in the extended and modernised former Drewsteignton School buildings in Bearsden about three miles away. New facilities opened during the last few years include a Junior School extension, a Drama Studio, a Refectory, a Fitness Centre, a Grandstand, an Information and Communications Technology building and a Science extension.

Organisation. The School is a day school with about 1,060 boys and girls. The Junior School, which includes a pre-school Kindergarten, has some 375 pupils (ages 3–10). Primary 7 pupils are included in the Senior School which has about 690 pupils (ages 11–18). A general curriculum is followed until the Third Year of the Senior School when, with the Standard Grade and Intermediate 2 examinations of the Scottish Qualifications Authority in view, a measure of choice is introduced. In Fifth Year Higher examinations are taken and in Sixth Year courses for Advanced Highers are offered. Whilst the majority of pupils are aiming for the Scottish universities, places are regularly gained at Oxford, Cambridge and other English universities.

Throughout the School, time is allocated to Art, Music, Personal, Social and Health Education, Physical Education and Religious Education. All pupils will also take courses in Computing Studies, Drama and Home Economics at various stages in their school careers.

Games. The main sports are hockey, rugby, athletics, cricket, tennis and swimming. Pupils participate in a wide variety of other sports, including badminton, basketball, netball, volleyball, golf, cross-country running and skiing.

Activities. Pupils are encouraged to participate in extra-curricular activities. Clubs and societies include debating, historical society, Scripture Union groups, computer, table tennis, chess, art, bridge, chemistry, electronics, drama and film clubs. Pupils take part in the Duke of Edinburgh's Award Scheme and the Young Enterprise Scheme, and parties regularly go on tour. There are choirs, orchestras, jazz and concert bands and a pipe band and tuition in Instrumental Music is arranged as requested. Each year there are several concerts and dramatic productions.

Admission. Entrance tests and interviews are held in January. The principal points of entry are at Kindergarten (age 4), Transitus (age 11) and First Year (age 12) but pupils are taken in at other stages as vacancies occur.

Fees per term (2008-2009). Junior School: £960–£2,544; Senior School: £2,575–£2,961.

Bursaries. The School operates a Bursary Fund to give assistance with fees in cases of need.

Former Pupils' Club. The Glasgow High School Club Limited is the former pupils' association of the old and new High Schools. Former pupils all over the world maintain an interest in the life and work of the School. *Secretary*: Murdoch C Beaton, LLB.

Charitable status. The High School of Glasgow Limited is a Registered Charity, number SC014768. It is a recognised educational charity.

Glenalmond College

Glenalmond Perth PH1 3RY
Tel: 01738 842061
Admissions Office: 01738 842056
Fax: 01738 842063
e-mail: registrar@glenalmondcollege.co.uk
website: www.glenalmondcollege.co.uk

Glenalmond College, was founded by Mr W E Gladstone and others in 1841 and opened as a School in 1847.

Motto: '*Floreat Glenalmond*'

Council:

President of Council: The Primus of the Episcopal Church in Scotland, The Most Reverend Dr Idris Jones, Bishop of Glasgow & Galloway
**Chairman of Council*: F E Gerstenberg Esq, BA, MA (*OG*)
+**Chairman of Committee of Council*: H J Morgan Esq, MA, FSI (*OG*)
C A Gladstone Esq, MA
*The Bishop of St Andrews, Dunkeld & Dunblane, The Right Reverend David Chillingworth
The Earl of Home, CVO, CBE
+*I R Wilson Esq, CBE
A H Primrose Esq, BA, LLB (*OG*)
Sheriff R A Dunlop, LLB (*OG*)
Lady Menzies, MBAOT
A C Grant Esq, BA
*D J C MacRobert Esq, LLB (*OG*)
The Right Hon Lord Kingarth, PC, BA, QC (*OG*)
C A Campbell Esq
The Rt Revd M Shaw, AKC (*OG*)
*Mrs S Bushby, Dip ACL/DMS
F E Maidment Esq, MA Cantab
*D G Sibbald Esq, BArch Hons, RIBA, ARIAS (*OG Club Secretary*)
M J Walker Esq, LLB (*OG Club Chairman*)
Dr J G Houston, MA, MD, FRCP, FRCR (*OG*)

* *Committee of Council*
\+ *Warden's Committee*
(*OG*) *Old Glenalmond*

***Warden*: G C Woods**, MA Oxon

Sub-Warden: J Owen, BSc, CertEd, MA, CSci, CChem, MRSC
Senior Mistress: Mrs M E Pitkin, BSc Hons, CPhys, MInstP
Deputy Head – Academic: Dr S Kinge, BSc, PhD
Registrar: J B M Poulter, MA, PGCE
Chaplain: The Revd G W Dove, MA Hons, MPhil, BD
Director of Development: Mrs M Marshall, MBA, MInstF Cert
Matron: Miss V Underwood, RGC, SCM
Bursar: Lt Col K H Montgomery, BSc Hons, MBA, MCMI
Secretary to the Council and Treasurer: Mrs L A Kennedy, BA, CA

Teaching Staff:
* *Head of Department*
† *Housemaster/mistress*

English:
*Mr M Watson, BA Hons, PGCE
J D Byrom, MA, PhD
Mrs A Haylock, BEd
J R Forshaw, BA Hons, PGCE
R Robinson, MA, PGCE, RSA Cert TEFL

Mathematics:
*Mrs H Yorston, BSc, MSc, PGCE
M T Jeffers, BSc, PGCE (*†Reid's*)
M Allnutt, BSc, CertEd (*Assistant Director of Studies*)
S P Erdal, BSc, PGCE
Mrs S Sinclair, BSc, PGCE (*†Lothian*)
M A Orviss MA, PGCE

Classics:
*J D Wright, MA
G W J Pounder, MA (*†Matheson's*)

Modern Languages:
*J N M Gillespie, BA, DipEd

J A Gardner, BA Hons, PGCE
J B M Poulter, MA, PGCE
P A R Shelley, BA, MPhil
I L McDonald, MA, PGCE
Mrs J Velasco, BA, PGCE (*†Cairnies*)
Mrs K Watson BA Hons (*†Home*)

Geography:
*T Rowell, BSc, MSc
S Hill, BA, PGCE (*†Patchell's*)
Mrs G Hamilton, BSc, MSc, PhD
Miss K Platt, BSc, PGCE

History:
* R R Mundill, MA, PhD, PGCE, FIHGS
J D Brett, MA Hons, PGCE
A Norton, BA, BEd

Biology:
* C I K Lallyet, BSc, PhD
C G Henderson, BSc Hons, PhD (*†Goodacre's*)
Mrs N Henderson, BSc, PGCE
Mrs S Colby, BSc, PhD, PGCE

Chemistry:
*D Armitage, BSc Hons, PGCE
J Owen, BSc, CertEd, MA, CSci, CChem, MRSC (*Sub-Warden*)
C G Henderson, BSc Hons, PhD
J Stewart, BSc, PhD, CertEd
Mrs S Colby, BSc, PhD, PGCE

Physics:
*Mrs M E Pitkin, BSc Hons, CPhys, MInstP (*Senior Housemistress*)
R Benson, BSc, PGCE
Mrs N Henderson, BSc, PGCE
S Kinge, BSc, PhD

Economics and Business Studies:
*J C Robinson, BA, PGCE
S P Erdal, BSc, PGCE
S Hamilton, BA Hons, MSc, PGCE

Drama:
C D B Youlten, BA, PGCE (†Skrine's*)
R Robinson, MA, PGCE, RSA Cert TEFL

Music:
*R D Gower, MA, FRCO, LRAM, ARCM, FRSA
B J Elrick, LLB
G Robb, DipRSAMD

Art and Design:
*Miss G MacLeod, BA Hons, PGCE
Ms P Hann, DA, CertEd
B Whitten, BA, CertEd

History of Art:
*B Whitten, BA, CertEd

Divinity:
*Revd G W Dove, MA Hons, MPhil, BD

Library:
Mrs E Mundill, MA, DipLib, ALA

Design Technology:
*A A Purdie, BSc, BEd
W G R Bain, BA, MA, PGCE

Physical Education:
*M Davies, MA, PGCE (*Director of Sport*)
Mrs J Gillespie, CertPhysEd
Miss C Bircher, BEd
Miss F J McCallum, BEd

Learning Support:
Mrs P Gower, MA, ALA, DipSpLD
Mr I Young, BSc, PGCE
Mrs N Henderson, BSc, PGCE

English as a Additional Language:
Mrs J Velasco, BA, PGCE
R Robinson, MA, PGCE, RSA Cert TEFL

The College is built on the south bank of the Almond, from the north bank of which rise the Grampians. It is about 50 miles north of Edinburgh and 10 miles from both Perth and Crieff.

The College Buildings, grouped round a cloistered quadrangle, comprise the Chapel, Hall, Library, houserooms and studies, study bedrooms, classrooms and laboratories. A separate block houses additional laboratories and a modern Theatre. A few yards away are the Art School and the Design and Technology Centre. Next to these are the Music practice rooms and a Concert Hall.

The Sports Complex consists of squash courts, a gymnasium, an indoor sports hall and a heated indoor swimming pool, fitness suite and an indoor .22 range.

The College also has a state-of-the-art Science Block and a brand new IT Resources Centre.

Houses. There are 5 houses for boys, the most recent was opened in September 2007, and 3 houses for girls. The organisation of all the Houses is the same, each having married accommodation for resident Housemaster or Housemistress. Senior boys and girls have study-bedrooms or studies of their own.

Religion. The College is an Episcopalian foundation and has a splendid Chapel. However all denominations are welcomed.

Admission. Boys and girls may be registered for admission at any time after birth and enter the College between the ages of 13 and 14 via the Common Entrance Examination or Entrance Scholarship papers. Pupils leaving Primary Schools may qualify by tests and examinations for junior entry at age 11 or 12. Girls and boys may also qualify for entry into the Lower Sixth, or at other points during their school career.

Curriculum. In the first 3 years all pupils take a wide range of subjects up to the GCSE with English, History, Geography, French, Latin or General Classics, Mathematics and the 3 Sciences as basic subjects. Greek, Spanish, German, Statistics, Electronics, Art, Music and Design/Technology are optional subjects to GCSE and beyond. Each pupil is guided by a tutor. All pupils take computer and microelectronics courses in their first year.

The Sixth Form provides specialist courses in Arts and Sciences leading to GCE AS and A2 Level. Lectures from outside speakers on social, economic and cultural subjects of topical interest take place regularly.

Economics, Business Studies, Theatre Studies, History of Art, Sports Studies and Politics are now fully established in the Sixth Form.

Careers. Over 95% of pupils qualify for entry to university; some go direct to professional careers, industry, the Services, etc. Great emphasis is placed on careers guidance: careers talks, visits and advice along with a well-stocked careers room assist pupils in their choice. Most pupils take careers aptitude tests at age 16.

The computer network with fibre optic cabling extends to all parts of the campus. ICT is available in libraries and all classrooms, and all pupils have access to e-mail and the internet within their Houses.

Art, Drama and Music. Music plays a central part in the life of the school: there is an Orchestra as well as smaller String, Woodwind and Brass Groups. A large Choir and Choral Society perform at the College, in Perth and in Edinburgh. A new Harrison and Harrison pipe organ has recently been installed. The Concert Society arranges recitals and concerts at the College; frequent visits are made to concerts in Perth and elsewhere. There are currently two Pipe Bands.

The Drama and Art departments flourish, in conjunction with the well-established Design and Technology Centre. Both Art and Music as well as Design/Technology form part of the normal curriculum and can be taken at GCSE and A Level.

Games and Recreations. Rugby (boys) and Hockey (girls) are played in the Michaelmas Term and there is a wide variety of activities to choose from in the Lent Term, including Lacrosse and Netball for girls and Hockey, Football and Cross-Country for boys, with Cricket, Athletics, Shooting, Sailing, Tennis and Golf in Summer. Shooting on the Miniature Ranges takes place during the two winter terms. There is a large indoor heated Swimming Pool and pupils are trained in personal survival and Lifesaving. Instruction in Sub-aqua and Canoeing is given. There are also Squash Courts, Tennis Courts, a nine-hole (James Braid) Golf Course, and two full-size all-weather pitches for hockey, netball and tennis.

During the Summer, pupils have the opportunity to explore the hills and the neighbouring countryside. There is also a Sailing and Windsurfing Club which uses a neighbouring loch. Weekend camping expeditions are arranged to encourage self-reliance and initiative.

Glenshee is just over an hour away and there are opportunities for skiing in the Lent Term.

Clubs and Societies. Voluntary membership of Societies such as the Dramatic, Historical, Debating and Public Speaking, Electronics, Engineering, Chess, Photographic and Film Societies is encouraged. There are Music, Opera, Computer, Mountaineering, Badminton, Fair Trade, Amnesty, Soul Space and Fishing Clubs.

Combined Cadet Force. There is a contingent of the Combined Cadet Force which has strong links with the Armed Forces and the Royal Regiment of Scotland (Black Watch Battalion) in particular. The ceremonial dress, as worn by the Pipe Band for example, is the Highland dress with the Murray of Atholl tartan.

Army and Air sections, with a Pre-Service section for Junior Pupils, are organised on the basis of the Duke of Edinburgh's Award. Shooting and Adventure Training figure prominently; pupils may also be engaged on Conservation, Community Service Work or Mountain Awareness Group.

Fees per term (2008-2009). £8,270 Boarders; £5,640 Day Pupils (for whom transport is arranged); £6,200 Junior Boarders; £4,230 Junior Day.

These fees include extras common to all pupils, such as membership of the CCF, Games, Subscriptions, journeys to matches, the use of the Golf Course, etc.

Term of Entry. Entry is normally in September. Entry in January or April can be considered where special circumstances exist.

Entrance Awards. (*see Scholarship Entries section*). Open Academic Scholarships and Exhibitions ranging in value from 10% to 25% and Music Scholarships worth up to 50% of the fees are available. Awards are also made for Art. All awards can be increased in case of need. The Examination for Scholarships is usually held in March for younger pupils and in November for entrants to the Sixth Form. All-Rounder Awards are available to 13+ applicants and are assessed in March.

'Fil Cler' Bursaries. A number of *Fil Cler* Bursaries are available for sons and daughters of Clergy. The value of these is subject to a means test; they are awarded on the result of the Common Entrance or Scholarship Examination (or special qualifying tests) and an interview.

Services Discount. There is an Award available to the sons and daughters of serving members of the Armed Forces.

Discretionary Awards. These are awarded at the discretion of the College. They are means-tested.

The Old Glenalmond Club. *Hon Secretary*: D Sibbald, 21 Ravelston Park, Edinburgh EH4 3DX.

Charitable status. Glenalmond College is a Registered Charity, number SC006123. It exists for the all-round education of Boys and Girls in the tranquillity of a rural setting.

The Grange School

Bradburns Lane Hartford Northwich Cheshire CW8 1LU
Tel: 01606 74007
Fax: 01606 784581
e-mail: office@grange.org.uk
website: www.grange.org.uk

The Grange was founded in 1933 as a Preparatory School, the Senior School opening in 1978. The School is co-educational, with 1,152 pupils from 4–18 years, and is situated in the village of Hartford, half an hour away from Chester and Manchester and eight miles from the M6 motorway.

Motto: *E Glande Robur*

Governing Body:
Chairman: Mr G Halman, FRICS
Mrs A Arthur
Mr D M Dunn, BA
Dr W J Forsyth, MBChB, MRCGP, AFOM
Mr J Hobson, MRICS
Mr C P Jackson, BSc, MIHT
Mrs K Jones, BA, ACA
Mr N Parkinson, BSc
Mr J Stamer, FRCS
Mr A Stothert
Mr C Stubbs, CEng, MIMechE, MBA
Mr R J Taylor, BSc, FCA

Clerk to the Governors & Legal Manager: Mrs R Leaitherland, BA

***Head*: Mr C P Jeffery**, BA

Deputy Head: Mr A Testard, BA
Second Deputy Head: Mrs P Duke, BA
Directors of Studies: Mr D Clapperton, BSc; Mr G Rands, BSc
Director of Sixth Form Studies: Mr D Shaw, BSc, MSc

Assistant staff:
* *Head of Department*

Mr P J Ackerley, BA (*English*)
*Mr G Addison, BSc (*Mathematics**; Physics*)
*Mrs J Woods, PGCE, VCNW (*Information Technology*)
*Mrs J Bloor, BA (*Speech & Drama*)
Mrs B A Broderick, BSc (*Chemistry; Geography*)
*Mr P Buckley, BA (*Classics*)
*Mrs V Buckley, BA (*Religious Studies*)
Miss L Burgoyne, BA (*Art*)
Miss A Bury, BA (*Art; Graphics*)
Mr C Cecchi, BA (*PE; Geography*)
Mrs M Clutterbuck, BEd (*Business Studies & Economics*)
Mrs J Corrigan, BA, CertEd (*I M Marsh*) (*PE & Games; English*)
Ms S Finnegan, BMedSci (*Biology*)
Miss J Gibbs, BSc (*Biology*)
Mr T H Giles, BA (*PE & Games*)
Mrs H Hackett, BA, MSc (*German & French*)
Mrs J Hardy-Kinsella, BA (*Drama*)
*Mrs E Heyes, MA (*German*)
*Mr R A Hibbert, BA (*Modern Languages*)
*Mr R A Hough, BA (*Religious Studies & Philosophy*)
*Mr C Howe, BSc (*Chemistry*)
Ms P H Janson, MA (*Mathematics*)
Mr D W Jones, MA (*History & Politics*)
*Mr H Kelly, MA (*English*)
*Mr D Kereszteny-Lewis, BA (*Art*)
*Mrs H Kerr, BA (*History & Politics*)
Mr M Lambert, BSc (*Mathematics*)
Mr R Latham, BA (*Religious Studies*)
Miss H Linnell, BA (*Geography*)
Miss H R Lawson, BA (*PE & Games*)
Mr B Madden, BA (*Music*)
*Mr P McAleny, BA (*Graphics*)
*Mr A J Millinchip, MA, FRCO(*CHM*) (*Music*)
*Mr A Milne, BSc, MSc (*Biology*)
Mr R Miotti, BA (*English*)
*Mr W Morrison, BA (*Economics & Business Studies*)
Mrs O Myburgh, BA (*English*)
Mrs J S Oakes, BSc (*Biology*)
Dr J R Oliver, BSc, PhD (*Biology*)
Mrs C J Osborne, BSc (*Mathematics*)
Miss K Osborne, BA (*Drama*)
*Mr J M Pearson, BA (*Geography*)
*Mrs S A Percy, BA (*French*)
*Mr S Petts, BA (*Science & Physics*)
Mrs M Plant, MA (*French & German*)
Miss J Popplestone, BSc (*History*)
Mrs K Pratt, BA (*Religious Studies*)
*Ms S Reyero-Cascallana, BA (*Spanish & French*)
Miss T Richardson, BA Hons (*Art*)
Mr D Ridley, BA (*Mathematics*)
*Mr R K Robson, BA (*History*)

Mr D Shaw, BA (*Classics*)
Mr D G Skym, MSc (*Physics*)
Mrs A Stewart (*Food & Nutrition*)
Miss J L Stockton, BA (*English*)
Mrs L Sunners, BA (*Drama*)
Mrs A B Taunton, MA (*Religious Studies*)
Mrs S Thornes, BSc (*Physics*)
Mrs P Tideswell, BA (*French*)
*Mr T W Tindale, BSc (*PE; History*)
Mr A Walne, BA (*Economics & Business Studies; Information Technology*)
Miss J Welch, BSc (*Mathematics*)
Mr S Whitehouse, BSc (*Mathematics*)
Mr R G Williams, MA (*Chemistry; Mathematics*)
Mrs C Wilson, BA, BEd (*Spanish & French*)
Mrs J L Woods, BA (*Information Technology*)

Junior School

Head of Junior School: Mr S D Bennett, BEd
Deputy Head of Junior School: Mrs K J Hill, BEd
Head of Pre-Prep: Miss A Evans, BEd
Director of Studies: Mr M Crewe-Read, BSc

Mrs F Alexander, BA
Mrs S Ball, CertEd
Mrs A Basnett, BA
Mrs L Broster-Jones, CertEd
Mrs D Bull, MEd
Mrs C Carson, CertEd
Miss L Cruddas, BA
Mrs K Dakin, BA
Mrs M Dewhurst, BEd
Miss S Dry, BEd
Mrs C Elliott, CertEd
Mr G H Evans, BEd
Miss R Ford
Mrs J Haynes, BEd
Mr D Heine, BSc
Miss V Houghton, MA, BEd
Mrs E Jones, BEd
Mrs L Jones, CertEd, BEd
Mr H Jones, BEd
Mr J P Land, BEd
Mrs Z A Pidcock, BA
Mrs R Preston, BA
Mrs G L Rosa, BA
Mr J Smart, BSc
Mrs E Stanning, BA
Miss S Vickery, BA
Miss C Winterson, BSc

Peripatetic Staff:
Mrs C Barker, BA, LGSM (*Cello*)
Mrs J Bingham, GNSM, CertEd (*Violin, Viola*)
Mrs A Boardman, BMus, LEAM (*Clarinet, Saxophone*)
Mrs M Bushnell-Wye, ARCM, LGSM, GRSM (*Clarinet, Saxophone*)
Ms A Duthie, CTABRSM (*Flute*)
Mr C Gandee, ARCM, LLCM (TD), SFLCM (*Brass*)
Mrs B Hammond, BMus, PGCE (*Piano*)
Mrs S Hoffman, BMus (*Flute*)
Mr G Hogan, BA, LRAM, LGSM, LLCM (*Keyboard, Piano*)
Mrs C Hughes, GNSM, ARCM (*Piano*)
Mrs J Martin, CT, ABRSM (*Violin*)
Mrs R Pankhurst, BMus, GRNCM, PPRNCM, LRSM (*Oboe, Bassoon*)
Mrs J Panter, GRSM, LPCL (*Violin*)
Mrs A Rogers, LGSM (*Piano*)
Mr P Smith, BMus, FTCL, FCSM, ARCM (*Singing*)
Mr S Watkiss, CT, ABRSM (*Guitar*)
Ms S Wilks, GMus, RNCM (*Singing*)
Miss R Wright, BA (*Percussion*)

Bursar: Mrs J Pointon, ACA

PA to the Head/Admissions Secretary: Miss S Dickens

The Kindergarten and Junior School (450 pupils). 1996 saw the opening of a brand new, purpose-built Kindergarten and Preparatory School for children aged 4–11. This development has brought together all the children of this age group on to one attractively landscaped eleven acre site which is within walking distance of the Senior School.

The main teaching takes place in 21 large, self-contained classrooms on two floors with the younger children located on the ground floor separated from the older children. The School has its own extensive playing fields and generous play areas while two large halls provide facilities for dining, teaching, gymnastics and school productions. Rooms are provided for specialist teaching with music having a large room next to the hall and no fewer than five individual music practice rooms. As well as a broad curriculum junior pupils study ICT and a modern language, they have regular swimming lessons and compete in sport with other schools. Close attention is given to each child's progress with two parents' evenings each year. Children learn to use computers from a young age, there is a junior orchestra and opportunities for private music and drama lessons. Extra-curricular activities are held mainly at lunch-time.

The Senior School (650 pupils). The pupils benefit from excellent extra-curricular and study facilities. There is an ambitious but realistic building programme which saw the opening of a state-of-the-art Science and Information Technology Centre in 2001. This superb facility complements such recent developments as a Modern Languages suite, including Language Laboratory and satellite television and new study and leisure facilities for the Sixth Form. A new teaching centre for the Mathematics Faculty was completed recently and a new Library and suite of classrooms opened in May 2003. A new 300 seater theatre and classroom facilities for Music and Drama was completed in August 2005.

Curriculum. Years 1, 2 and 3 follow a broad curriculum with all Third Year pupils studying two modern languages. In the Third Year pupils continue to study English, Mathematics, Biology, Chemistry, Physics, History, Geography, Classical Civilisation or Latin, Religious Studies, Information Technology, PE/Games, two Modern Languages, and select three of five practical subjects. At the end of the Third Year pupils opt for nine subjects which must include Mathematics, English, at least one science and at least one modern language. Personal and Social Education is taught in Years 1 to 5.

From the Third Year advice and assistance is available to all pupils on a wide range of career possibilities. The careers team arrange a biennial careers convention supplemented with regular visits and talks when advice is given by consultants from a variety of professions. There is a fully equipped careers room.

Pastoral Care. The School provides a disciplined, caring and secure environment in which pupils may work and play without being subjected to harm or distress, in which they may develop their personalities to the full and enjoy their time at school. The Form Teacher is the key figure in each pupil's academic and pastoral welfare and is the first point of contact with parents. The Form Teacher is supported by Heads of Year and regular meetings are held to ensure that the pastoral needs of all our pupils are met. The system is enhanced by a Peer Support scheme which allows trained senior students to listen to younger pupils' concerns.

House Activities. Each pupil is allocated to one of four Houses on entry to the school; siblings are allocated to the same House. A House Convener arranges meetings with Heads of House to discuss policy, procedure and House activities. These activities range from sporting competitions to an art and a literary competition. Each year the pupils produce their own play for the drama competition and their own repertoire for the music competition. The organisation of such activities is carried out by the pupils themselves with staff providing support and guidance. All pupils are actively encouraged to participate in the full range of activities in order to raise their self-esteem and to allow each to shine; they gain much from the experience. Junior, Intermediate and Senior House Assemblies are held on a weekly basis.

Sixth Form and Higher Education. Students take four or five subjects plus General Studies to AS Level in the Lower Sixth. They continue with three or four of those subjects plus General Studies to A2 Level in the Upper Sixth. The subjects are chosen from an extensive range with 27 presently available. All Sixth Formers participate in Games lessons, where a wide choice of activities is provided. Supplementary courses provided include Information Technology, Application of Number and Communication and ab initio language courses.

Careers guidance is given considerable emphasis in the Grange Sixth. Each student is attached to a member of the careers team and linguists are given the opportunity to undertake their work experience abroad. Almost all the students progress to higher education, with around 15% going on each year to Oxford and Cambridge.

Sixth Formers are expected to play a leading role in school life. They also participate in the extensive programme of House activities as well as in the Duke of Edinburgh's Award Scheme, outward bound courses, Young Enterprise, and the Engineering Council Award Scheme.

All students are required to participate in the execution of duties around school and there is a Sixth Form Council, run by the Head Girl and Head Boy, to coordinate the various aspects of Sixth Form life. Students have the use of their own common rooms.

Reporting to Parents. The School recognises that our pupils are best served when parents and the School work together and to this end we consider it important to report to parents fully and regularly. We encourage full discussion of the pupils' progress and well being. Each pupil receives at least two full reports per year. Each half term brings a progress report with academic grades and a profile of the pupil's extra-curricular involvement and pastoral welfare. There are two parents' evenings each year for all Junior School pupils and Years 1, 4 and Lower Sixth in the Senior School, and one for all other year groups. If parents have any concerns, they are encouraged to discuss these with the relevant staff at the earliest opportunity and the School will always contact parents and invite them to discuss issues should we feel it necessary.

Games. The School has 22 acres of sports fields. The principal games are hockey, netball, rugby, rowing, football, cricket, cross country, athletics and tennis. There are four all-weather tennis courts as well as three badminton courts.

Art, Design, Drama, Music. In addition to timetabled lessons for these subjects there are numerous opportunities to participate in extra-curricular activities.

In the music department no less than 15 peripatetic teachers provide 420 private lessons a week. There are two orchestras, jazz, string, wind and saxophone ensembles, senior choir and choral society. Cantores Roborienses, the School's senior singing group, and the Chamber Orchestra perform at the many informal concerts held during the year and at numerous public events.

Considerable emphasis is placed on Drama in the school with two part-time and two full-time members of staff and pupils participate in a number of drama festivals with a high degree of first and second placings. Over 80 private Speech and Drama lessons take place each week, with all these pupils entering Trinity-Guildhall examinations, from Junior Preliminary to Grade 8. Regular school productions take place each year with frequent theatre trips.

Religion. The School is Christian based but pupils of all faiths and none are accepted as long as they are prepared to take a full part in the life of the School. Full School Assemblies take place twice a week.

Transport. Hartford is served by two main line stations, Manchester to Chester and Crewe to Liverpool. The majority of children travel to and from school by car or by one of the eight private buses.

Admission. Kindergarten by informal assessment at the end of January; Senior School by entrance examination on the first Saturday in February; Sixth Form by interview and good GCSE results.

Pupils are also admitted at other ages as vacancies occur. Admission is gained by interview and test performance. Enquiries for admission are welcome at any time of the year and a copy of the school prospectus may be obtained by contacting the Admissions Secretary.

Open Morning. The School holds an Open Morning on the first Saturday in November when prospective parents and pupils are welcome to see the facilities available and to talk to the pupils and staff. Appointments to view the school can be made at other times by contacting the Admissions Secretary.

Fees per term (from January 2008). £2,015 (Kindergarten & Form 1); Junior School £2,175 (Forms 2–6); Senior School £2,695.

Scholarships. Several scholarships are offered for entry to the Senior School for exceptional academic ability and music. A number of Sixth Form Scholarships are awarded for outstanding academic potential after an examination held at the end of spring term preceding Sixth Form entry.

Charitable status. The Grange School is a Registered Charity, number 525918. It exists to provide high quality education for boys and girls.

Gresham's School

Cromer Road Holt Norfolk NR25 6EA
Tel: Headmaster: 01263 714500
Bursar: 01263 714503
Fax: 01263 712028
e-mail: registrar@greshams.com
website: www.greshams.com

The School was founded in 1555 by Sir John Gresham, Kt., and the endowments were placed by him under the management of the Fishmongers' Company.

Motto: '*Al Worship Be To God Only*'.

Governors:
J Cotterell (*Prime Warden of the Fishmongers' Company*)
A N G Duckworth-Chad, OBE, DL (*Chairman*)
A H Scott, DL (*Deputy Chairman*)
A Martin Smith
M Drummond, OBE, DL, Hon DSc, FCA
A Morgan
N Bankes
The Earl of Portsmouth, DL
C Spicer
The Rt Revd James Langstaff, The Lord Bishop of Lynn
Mrs R Monbiot, OBE
B Cabbell Manners
Dr G Johnson
D Copas
S Benson
C I H Mawson, FCA
Mrs A MacNicol
Dr I M Waterson, FRCP
The Hon Mrs Jeremy Soames
M H Edwards

Clerk to the Governors: K S Waters, Fishmongers' Hall, London Bridge, EC4R 9EL

***Headmaster*: P D John**, BSc, FCMI, MInstD

Deputy Head: N C Flower, BA, PGCE (*English*)
Director of Studies: Dr N J White, BSc, PhD, PGCE (*Physics*)
Head of Boarding: Mrs S Radley, BEd, CertEd (*Biology, †Edinburgh*)
Chaplain: The Revd B Roberts, BD, Dip Theol
Bursar: A Godfrey, HND, FBIFM

Assistant Staff:
* *Head of Department*
† *Housemaster/mistress*

M Abbott, BSc, PGCE (*Physics*)
Mrs C Alban, BA (*Head of Careers, Business Studies*)
Dr C M A Badger, MA, DPhil (*Chemistry*)

P Badger, BA, PGCE (* *PE, Geography*)
D Bailey, ONC/HND (*Design & Technology*)
Mrs L Barden, BA, PGCE (**French*)
G Bartle, BSc, PGCE (**Computing, Mathematics*)
J Bartlett, BSc, PGCE (*Physics*)
A Bealey, BA, PGCE (*English*)
J G Begg, MA, CertEd (**History*)
Mrs L I Betts, Cert Counselling Skills, RGN (*PSHE*)
Miss J Brenchley, BEng, PGCE (*Physics*)
G J Burnell, BA, MEd, FRGS (**Classics*)
Miss S Charlton, BA, RSACertTEFL, PGCE (*Art*)
Dr A K Cormack, BA, MA, PhD, PGCE (*English*)
S Curtis, BSc, PGCE (*Mathematics*)
Miss E Delpech, BA, PGCE (*Art*)
Mrs S L Ellis-Retter, BA, PGCE (*ESL*)
Miss C Ffoulkes-Jones, BSc, PGCE (*Biology*)
N J Fulford, BSc, PGCE (*Physics, *Electronics*)
S B Gates, BA, MA, PGCE (**Religious Studies*)
Miss F Gathercole, BA (*Biology, †Oakeley*)
M Gillingwater, MSc, BSc (*Biology, Chemistry*)
Mrs S Godfrey, BA, PGCE (*French, Spanish*)
Dr P S Gomm, MSc, PhD, FRIC, PGCE (**Chemistry*)
Dr C Hammond, MPhil, PhD (*French, Spanish*)
P J Hands, BA (**Drama*)
R Hensen, BCom, HDE (*Mathematics*)
N Humphrey, BA, PGCE (**Design Technology*)
A Jenkins, BSc, MA (*Computing*)
M H Jones, GRSM, FRCO, ARCM (**Music*)
Mrs J K Kelsey, BA, MA, LRAM, PGCE (*Music*)
P R Kelsey, BEd (*Design Technology, †Tallis*)
S Kinder, BA, PGCE (*Assistant Director of Studies, History*)
P Laidler, BSc, PGCE (**Biology*)
Mrs K Lear, BA (*Japanese*)
Mrs D Lyon, BA (*French, Spanish*)
D McKee, BA, MA, ABRSM, PGCE (*Music*)
J P B Martin, BSc (*Chemistry, †Howson's*)
M Matthams, BSc, MA, PGCE (**Physics*)
D R Miles, MA, PGCE (**Mathematics*)
Mrs J Moore (*Games, †Britten*)
Mrs M Myers, BEd, RSACert TEFL, CertSpLD (*Learning Support*)
C Nichols, BSc, PGCE (*Religious Studies*)
Miss B O'Brien, BA, PGCE (*Drama*)
C Openshaw, BA, PGCE (**Art*)
P A Paskell, BSc, BA , PGCE (**Economics*)
Mrs P F Paskell, BA, PGCE (*German*)
R H Peaver, TD, MA (*French*)
Mrs A Pitkethly, BA, PGCE (*History*)
J Quartermain, MA, MPhil, PGCE (*History*)
Dr C Rahner, MA, MPhil, PGCE (*German*)
Mrs F Read, BSc, PGCE (*Mathematics*)
F J V Retter, BA, PGCE (*Languages, †Woodlands*)
Revd B R Roberts, BD, DipTheol (*Religious Studies*)
Miss L B Roberts, BA, ARCM, AGSM, DipNCOS (*Music*)
Mrs K Robinson, BA (*English*)
Mrs L Rose, Bed, DipSpLD (**Learning Support*)
D J Rout, BSc, PGCE (**Chemistry*)
Ms T Sampy, BA (*Art*)
M Seldon, BA, MA (*English*)
A Smith, BA, PGCE (*Business Studies, Mathematics*)
Mrs J L Stickler, BEd (*Geography*)
A Stromberg, BEng, MSc, AFRIN, PGCE (*Mathematics*)
Mrs C A Thomas, BA, PGCE (**English*)
J Thomson, BEng, PGCE (*Mathematics, †Farfield*)
Mrs C van Hasselt, BA, PGCE (*English*)
M Walsh, BA, ACIB (*Economics*)
Mrs S Walsh, BA, DipRSA, PGCE (*Learning Support*)
J N Walton, CertEd (**Geography*)
Dr J Ward, BA, PhD (*English*)
P Watson, BA, PGCE (**Spanish*)
Mrs G Wiley, BA, MLitt, Cert TEFL, PGCE (*Learning Support*)

Preparatory School:

Headmaster: J H W Quick, BA Hons, PGCE

Assistant Staff:
T J Allison, MRSH
Mrs E Ashcroft, BA, PGCE (**Modern Languages*)
Mrs J Brearley, BA, Dip ELS (*Librarian, Religious Studies, English, PSHE*)
R T N Brearley, CertEd (*Senior Master, *Geography*)
G A Britton, BSc, PGCE (**Mathematics & ICT*)
P Bryant, BA, PGCE (*English*)
M Buckingham, BSc ARICS (*Mathematics*)
N P Cornell, BSc, PGCE (*Biology, Science*)
Miss S Davidson, BA, PGCE (*Physics, Science*)
Mrs J Dyble, LLB, PGCE (*Learning Support, Mathematics*)
Mrs K Fields, BEd (*†Crossways*)
S Fields, BSc, QTS (*Physics, Mathematics, †Crossways*)
Mrs H Hall (*Sport, Classroom Support*)
Mrs V Harvey-Seldon, BA (**English, *Drama*)
P A J Hawes, MEd, CertEd, FRGS (*Director of Studies, *History, Religious Studies*)
A Horsley, BA (*Science, Mathematics*)
Ms J Howard, BA (*Modern Languages, Religious Studies, Learning Support*)
D G Jackson, CertEd (*Mathematics*)
Mrs S Jamieson, BEd, PGCertSpLD (*Learning Support*)
Mrs F Kempton, BEd (**Science, Chemistry*)
Mrs G Kretchetov, MA, RSA CTEFLA (*EFL, French, Learning Support, Cultural Studies*)
P M Laycock, BA, BSc, PGCE (**Design Technology*)
Mrs S Li-Rocchi, BA, MA, PGCE (**Art*)
R J G Mansfield, BEd, MA, CertEd (*Deputy Head, English, Drama, Dance*)
Mrs P Matthams (*Sport*)
Mrs A Nash, BA, PGCE (*Modern Languages, Religious Studies*)
Mrs S O'Leary, BA (*History, English, Drama*)
Miss H E Olby, BA (*ICT*)
Mr C Ponder (*Sport, Drama*)
Mrs K Quick, BA, PGCE (*History, PSHE*)
Miss L B Roberts, BA, ARCM, AGSM, DipNCOS (*Assistant Director of Music*)
Mrs C Sankey, BA, PDSEN (*Learning Support, English*)
Mrs V Shaw, CertEd, PGCertSpLD (*Religious Studies, *Learning Support*)
N Thomas, BA, PGCE (**Modern Languages, †Kenwyn*)
Mrs S Vare, BA (*PSHE, Classics*)
Mrs K Walton (*Sport*)
Mr N Waring, BMus, MMus (**Director of Music*)
Mrs D West, BA (*English, Head of Girls' PE*)
M Williamson (*Design Technician*)
Mrs L Worrall (*Games*)
S C Worrall, BA (*Geography, Head of Boys' PE*)

Pre-Preparatory School:

Headmistress: Mrs J Davidson, DipEd Scot

Assistant Staff:
Mrs A Clear, CertEd, Cert Dyslexia SpLD
Mrs C Frewing, BA, CertEd, RCDC
Mrs K MacKenzie, BSc, PGCE
Mrs K Glennie, NatCert, CS NN
Mrs C A Burchall, BEd, MA Ed
Mrs K Kinder, BSc, PGCE
Mrs A King, CertEd
Mrs C S Mullis, BA, MPhil, PGCE
Miss J Sandford, BSc, PGCE
Miss A Scott, BEd
Mrs C Welham, MontDip

Medical Officer: Dr P Roebuck
School Counsellor: Mrs L I Betts
SSI: C C Scoles, MBE

There are 457 pupils in the Senior School, 252 boys and 205 girls, of whom 183 are in the Sixth Form, and 277 are boarders (181 weekly).

The School is situated some 4 miles from the sea near Sheringham and Blakeney, in one of the most beautiful and healthy parts of England. The School has a spacious setting in 150 acres including 50 acres of woodland. Numbered amongst its old boys are W H Auden, Benjamin Britten, Stephen Spender, Lord Reith on the Arts side, Christopher Cockerell, inventor of the hovercraft, Ian Proctor, yacht designer, Leslie Everett Baynes, who first patented swing-wing variable aircraft geometry, Sir Martin Wood of the URI scanner, and Sir James Dyson of more recent fame on the engineering side. It offers excellence in a wide range of fields, from which pupils gain an outstanding, balanced education.

Gresham's is a Church of England foundation but all religious denominations are welcomed. The School has its own Chaplain and a Counsellor who instructs new pupils and present pupils in life skills. Both are available to advise and help pupils throughout their time at Gresham's.

In the Senior School there are four boys' boarding houses and three girls' houses. After the first or second year pupils move into study bedrooms.

There has been a substantial building programme in the last two decades: Sports Hall (1983), Edinburgh Girls House (1987) and Britten Girls House (1996), English department building (1988), Junior and Senior Social Centres (1989), two all-weather Astroturf pitches (1994), the Cairns Centre for Art and Design (1990), and the Auden Theatre (1998).

Curriculum. In their first year pupils cover all the traditional subjects including separate lessons in the three sciences. Pupils may study French, German, Spanish, Latin or Japanese. Some choices are made for the 2 year GCSE course and most pupils take between 8 and 11 subjects including English, Maths, one language and 2 or 3 Sciences. In the Sixth Form pupils normally take 4 AS Level subjects and 3 A Levels (A2). The School has a particular strength in English, Mathematics and Physics and, of the Sixth Form, currently over 60% take Mathematics at A Level. Detailed careers advice is given and computerised aptitude tests, developed at Gresham's, are given to Fifth and Sixth Formers. The School's Learning Support specialists assist a small number of pupils suffering from dyslexia and related difficulties.

The School is now offering the International Baccalaureate Diploma as an alternative to A Levels. This programme may suit the intellectually ambitious.

Recreation, Music and Drama. The School has abundant playing fields. The main games are rugby football, hockey and cricket for boys, and hockey, netball, rounders and tennis for girls. Shooting, sailing, swimming, squash, badminton, cross-country running, athletics and golf are also very popular, and national and international success has been consistently achieved in shooting and sailing, and recently in hockey. A unique option also available is Forestry.

There is a flourishing CCF contingent and Duke of Edinburgh's Award section and approximately 25 gold awards are achieved each year. The School has a very strong choir which tours internationally and performs regularly in East Anglia. Six of its members have recently sung in the National Youth Choir. Art and drama are also exceptionally strong, and Drama and Theatre Studies are offered at GCSE and A level.

Entrance. Those entering at 13+ from Preparatory Schools take the Common Entrance Examination or scholarship. Tests in Maths, English and, where applicable French or German, are given to those entering from independent schools which do not prepare for Common Entrance, and from the maintained sector. Able foreign pupils are welcomed, especially into the Sixth Form.

Scholarships. (*see Scholarship Entries section*). There are several Academic Scholarships available for 13+ and Sixth Form entry. Scholarships in Music, Art, Drama and Sport are awarded for 13+ and Sixth Form entry, and All-Rounder Scholarships may also be awarded. The Fishmongers' Company sponsor 3 places annually on Sail Training trips and the Philip Newell Scholarships are available for Gap year activities.

Fees per term (2008-2009). Senior School: £8,050 (boarding), £6,180 (day). Prep School: £5,870 (boarding), £4,465 (day). Pre-Prep School: £2,225–£2,470 (day).

These are inclusive fees; no extra charge is made for laundry, games, medical attention, etc, although some areas, such as individual music tuition, attract extra charges.

Day pupils' meal charges are included in the fees. Necessary extras are very few.

Honours. In 2006 the A Level pass rate was 100% with 72.5% A and B grades. 96% of the Upper Sixth went on to university. 9.1 passes at C grade or above was the average per pupil at GCSE in 2006.

Gresham's Preparatory School is a flourishing boarding and day co-educational preparatory school of 220 pupils within half a mile of the Senior School. Its Headmaster is a member of IAPS. (*For further details see entry in IAPS section.*) There is also a Pre-Prep School of 130 pupils.

Scholarships are available at 11+ and enquiries should be directed to the Headmaster at the Preparatory School.

The Old Greshamian Club. The Club is active on behalf of present and former members of the School and it can be contacted through its Coordinator, Charlotte Martin, at Gresham's School.

Charitable status. Gresham's School is a Registered Charity, number 1105500. The School is a charitable trust for the purpose of educating children.

Guildford High School (UCST)

London Road Guildford Surrey GU1 1SJ
Tel: 01483 561440
Fax: 01483 306516
e-mail: sally.fowler@church-schools.com
website: www.guildfordhigh.surrey.sch.uk

Motto: *As one that serveth*

Established in January 1888.

Governing Body: The Council of the United Church Schools Trust

Patron: The Rt Revd The Lord Bishop of Guildford

Local Council:
Chairman: Mrs L M Keat
Mrs C Cobley
Revd R Cotton
Professor M Cox
Mr I Dyson
Mrs B Ford
Prof O Hess
Baroness Sharp of Guildford
Mr S Moffat

Staff

***Headmistress*: Mrs F J Boulton**, BSc Hons University of Wales, Cardiff, MA London (*Science*)

Deputy Heads:
Miss J L V Bowden, MA Oxford (*Religious Studies*)
Mrs R Cole, BSc Hons Exeter (*Biology*)

Director of Studies: Mr W H Saunders, BA Hons Bristol, MA St Mary's University College (*History*)

Head of Junior School: Mrs S J Phillips, BA Hons Reading

Registrar: Mrs S Fowler, BSc Birmingham

* *Head of Department*

Art & Design:
*Miss K Ballard, BA Hons Staffordshire
Mr I A Charnock, BA Hons University of Wales, Bangor, MA London
Miss N J Wright, BA Hons Westminster

Classics:
*Mr C B Buchholdt, BA Hons London
Mr P Challinor, BA Hons Liverpool, MSt Oxford
Miss S N Merali, BA Hons, MA Manchester

Design & Technology:
*Mrs S M Adilz, BSc Hons Dundee, DipArch Westminster, MA London
Mrs J M Bancroft, BA Hons OU, CertEd Madeley, Dip D&T Roehampton (*Head of Years 10 & 11, Head of Food & Textiles*)
Mrs W A Bengoechea, BEd Hons Bath (*Head of Year 7*)

Economics:
*Mrs C L Jones, BA Hons Sheffield
Mrs T Joad, BA Hons Oxford

English & Theatre Studies:
*Mr J C Baddock, BA Hons UCL
Mrs S L Glyn-Davies, BA Hons East Anglia
Mrs L D D'Arcy, MA
Ms A L Fenton, BA Hons University of Wales, Aberystwyth (*Head of Drama*)
Mrs J A Gibson, BA Hons Liverpool
Mrs K Hack, BA University of Wales, Swansea (*Deputy Head of Sixth Form*)
Mrs N J Lewis, BA Hons York
Miss F H S Mackay, BA Hons Ulster
Mrs L M Skinner, BA Hons Durham

Geography:
Miss S Edwards, BSc Hons Bristol
Dr E R Laurie, BSc Hons London, MSc London, PhD Greenwich
*Miss S P B MacDowell, MA Hons St Andrews, DMS Oxford Brookes

History:
*Mrs A Minear, BA Hons Exeter
Miss K M Sloan, BA Hons Reading
Miss K J Tromans, BA Hons Leeds

Information Technology:
Mr I T Richardson, BSc Hons Greenwich
*Mrs A Taylor, BSc Manchester Polytechnic

Mathematics:
*Mrs K M Denny, BSc Hons London
Miss A M Fairbairn, MA Oxford
Miss H Holliday, MEng Cambridge
Mr M W Holtham, BA Cambridge
Mrs E M Hudson, BSc Hons Warwick
Mrs E Mulgrew, MA Oxford
Mrs G T Rackham, BSc Hons Sheffield
Miss E Stevens, BSc London
Dr F Turner, BSc, PhD UMIST

Modern Languages:
Miss K A Buckley, BA Hons Exeter (*Head of Sixth Form*)
Mrs V Callaghan, BA Hons Portsmouth (*Head of French*)
Miss C S M Dalet, Licence d'Anglais Clermont-Ferrand
Ms P A Delatorre, BA Hons Quindio, Colombia
Mr J Gonzalez Abia, BA Hons Spain
Ms C Igoe, BSc Washington DC
Mrs C L Jones, BA Hons Sheffield
Mrs W Leighton, BSc Hons Beijing
Miss F Mellor, BA Hons Manchester
Mrs Z N Rowe, BA Hons Exeter (*Head of Spanish*)
Mrs A B Taylor, BA Hons Rome
Mrs L M Taylor, BA Hons Exeter (*Head of German*)

Music:
Mrs E M Forrest-Biggs, MA Cantab
Mr G T Jones, BMus Hons Birmingham
Mrs F J Taylor, BMus Hons RCM

Physical Education:
Miss L M Boyd, BA Hons Leeds Metropolitan
Mrs M Clifford, CertEd Neville's Cross College, Durham
*Mrs L Fitzroy-Stone, BEd Hons Bedford College
Miss R E Legg, BEd Hons De Montfort
Mrs T J Oxley, BSc Hons Birmingham
Mrs A J Whybro, BA Hons Chichester

Politics:
Mr D Cleaver, MSc Econ University of Wales, Swansea, MA Econ Manchester

Psychology:
Mrs C Benson, BA Hons Manchester
*Dr J E Boyd, BSc Newcastle, PhD London, King's College

Religious Studies:
Mrs J A Gibson, BA Hons Liverpool
Mrs A E Gillingham, BA Hons Westminster College, Oxford
Mr G Moore, BA Hons Exeter
*Mrs J A Shopland, BA Hons University of Wales, Lampeter

Science:
Mrs J Blatchford, BSc Hons Kent, MA Kingston
*Dr J E Boyd, BSc Hons Newcastle, PhD London (*Head of Biology*)
Mrs C Bulmer, BA Hons Oxford
Mrs E Carter, BSc Sheffield (*Head of Chemistry*)
Mrs R Cole, BSc Hons Exeter
Mrs D A Evans, BSc Hons Lancaster
Mrs C Gilmore, BSc Hons Bath
Dr K J Goodworth, MSc London PhD London
Mrs C R Kittow, CertEd Homerton College, Cambridge Head of Years 8 & 9
Dr L Lockett, BA Hons Oxford, MSc London, DPhil York
Dr T M Peck, BA Hons, MA, DPhil Oxford
Mrs G A Scott, BSc Hons Surrey
Mr S J Turner, BSc Hons Southampton

Junior School:
Miss S J Bauchop, BEd Hons Leicester
Mrs J A Bottomley, BA Hons Birmingham
Mrs M B Crowley, BSc Hons London
Mrs Y M Cunnane, BSc Hons University of Wales, Cardiff
Mrs J Dobell, CertEd Bradford
Mrs J M Dubery, CertEd Bristol
Mrs J E Flood, BA Hons Reading
Mrs S E Ford, MMus, BA Hons
Mrs W A Gibbs, BEd Hons Winchester
Mrs R L Hay, BEd Hons Bedford College
Mrs K E Hays, BA Hons Kent
Mrs M Kelly, CertEd Halle-Wittenberg, Germany, MA Roehampton Inst
Mrs S E Letheren, BEd Hons Kingston
Mrs E A Lloyd, BA Hons Reading
Mrs S E Marsh, BEd Hons De Montfort
Mrs K M Maycock, BA Hons Durham
Mrs K L Nanson, BEd Bedford College
Ms N A Sloane, BEd Hons Kingston
Mrs H M Stamp, BEd Hons East Anglia
Miss L Walker, BA Hons Canterbury
Miss S C Wright, BA Hons UWE

Careers:
Mrs C Cullens, BA Hons Newcastle

Library:
Mrs Y A Skene
Mrs A Hewson, BA Hons Cilip

Music Administrator:
Mrs D R G Baumann, MA Cantab, MusB Cantab

Visiting Staff:
Music:
Piano:
Mrs I Bridgmont, BMus, LTCL, ARCM
Mrs D Dawkins, LRSM, LTCL
Miss H Dives, LTCL
Mrs P M Morley, ATCL, ARCM, GRSM
Dr V C Rowe, PhD, MA, GRSM
Mrs P Topham, GMus, RNCM Hons
Mrs G Young, LRAM, ARCM, DipMT Nordoff-Robbins, Grad Dip Mus
Singing:
Mrs S M Hellec-Butcher
Miss K Walker, BMus Hons, LRAM
Head of Strings: Mrs C A Woehrel, Grad Lucerne
Violin and Viola:
Miss L Hill, LTCL, FTCL
Miss C Jackson, GGSM
Mr B Lloyd Wilson, MA, AGSM, ARCM
Mrs S Thomas, ARCM, LRAM
Cello:
Mr R Bridgmont, FTCL, ARCM, LTCL
Mrs J Meryom, BMus
Double Bass: Miss N Bailey, ARCM, LRAM
Guitar: Mr P L Howe, ARCM
Harp: Mrs J Carr, BMus
Flute:
Mrs D Ball, LTCL
Miss R E Chappell, AGSM
Mrs F J Howe, ARCM
Oboe: Miss J Lees, ARCM
Clarinet:
Miss E Cook, BSc, ARCM, PGDipMTPP
Miss C Henry, ARCM, LRAM
Bassoon: Miss R Cow, M Mus, BMus Hons
Brass: Mr L Baker
Saxophone: Mr S D West, GTCL, LTCL
Recorder, Harpsichord & Piano: Miss P Cave, LRAM, GRSM
Percussion: Mr N West, BMus
Alexander Technique: Mrs D Purrett, BSc Soc, PGCE, Dip Dr Ed, MSTAT

Bursar: Mrs G A Stead
Accounts Adminstrator: Mrs S Newman, BSc Hons Bristol, MSc LSE

PA to the Headmistress: Mrs J M Waters
Director of Marketing: Mrs A R Kearney, BA Hons Witwatersrand
Assistant Registrar: Mrs J Bak

Number of Girls. 930 Day Girls aged 4–18 years.

Guildford High School is a very successful school. We set high expectations for all with learning as our key focus. We are a community in which everyone is known, valued and feels secure. Pupils are supported and encouraged to reach their potential.

If you come to see the school, you will see that we have invested heavily in interactive whiteboards; there is now one in every classroom. The use of whiteboards, combined with discussion amongst staff and pupils, means that we have a relevant, dynamic and innovative approach to the curriculum.

We have excellent pastoral care: it is key to our happy and successful school. We have a system of Form Tutors, Heads of Year and, of course, a Deputy Head responsible for pastoral matters. When the girls arrive in Year 7, they are assigned a 'buddy' from Year 8 who will steer them through the first term and beyond.

The School has an extensive extra-curricular and curriculum-enrichment programme, encompassing sport, drama, music and much more besides.

As a result, our girls achieve outstanding success at all levels from SATs to GCSE and A Level. Last year, our A Level pass rate was 100%, with 95% of our girls achieving A and B grades. At GCSE, 91% of the results were A or A*. Most importantly, the majority of our girls went on to their first-choice university. At Key Stage 2, 96% of our girls achieved Level 5 in all three subjects.

Sixth Form. There is a strong Sixth Form and most girls take four AS Level subjects from the wide range offered and continue with 3 of these subjects to A Level. They also follow a General Studies course and a continuation course in a modern language if they are not involved in A Level or GCSE language. Virtually all girls proceed to University or to other areas of Higher Education. The Sixth Form have their own accommodation, which has been extended and refurbished as part of a major development plan.

Music. There is a lively musical tradition and girls are encouraged to play musical instruments and to join one of the orchestras, choirs or the wind bands. They are prepared for the Associated Board Music and Speech and Drama examinations.

Drama. Drama is taught as part of the curriculum. GCSE Drama is available as well as AS Theatre Studies. There are major productions every term.

The Duke of Edinburgh's Award Scheme, run jointly by parents and teachers, offers opportunities for developing character through service, skills and expeditions.

Physical Education. Lacrosse, netball, tennis, rounders, athletics, gymnastics, swimming, badminton and basketball. Sixth Formers have a wider choice and may use facilities at the University and Sports Centre.

Situation and Facilities. The school is pleasantly situated near the centre of Guildford on a bus route and close to London Road Station; frequent trains to the main station provide links over a wide area. Facilities include libraries, eleven well-equipped laboratories, whiteboards in every classroom, an Information Technology Centre, a Design Technology Centre, Art and Design Studios, a Food Technology Room, Music Rooms, Music Technology Studio, a Careers Room and Dining Hall. We opened a new £5 million Sports Hall and indoor swimming pool in October 2006.

The Junior School, which combines a warm, caring atmosphere with a stimulating environment, offers careful preparation for entry to the Senior School. A new Junior School building was opened in September 1993, as part of a major development plan.

Normal ages of entry. 4, 7 and 11 years and Sixth Form level.

Admissions. The school sets its own entrance examination. Academic standards are high.

Fees per term (2007-2008). Lower Junior £2,198, Upper Junior £2,998, Senior £3,705. Fees quoted exclude lunches. Text books and stationery are provided.

Extra Subjects. Instruments (orchestral) £150.

Scholarships and Bursaries. (*see Scholarship Entries section*). Bursaries are available at Sixth Form level.

Charitable status. The United Church Schools Trust (to which Guildford High School belongs) is a Registered Charity, number 1016538. Its aims and objectives are to provide pupils with a sound education based on and inspired by Christian principles.

The Haberdashers' Aske's Boys' School

Butterfly Lane Elstree Herts WD6 3AF
Tel: 020 8266 1700
Fax: 020 8266 1800

e-mail: office@habsboys.org.uk
website: www.habsboys.org.uk

The School was founded in 1690, its income arising from an estate left in trust to the Haberdashers' Company by Robert Aske, Citizen of London and Liveryman of the Haberdashers' Company. In 1898 it was transferred from Hoxton to Hampstead and in 1961 to Aldenham Park, Elstree, Hertfordshire.

Motto: *Serve and Obey.*

Governing Body:
The Governing Body consists of representatives of the Worshipful Company of Haberdashers, the world of education, the catchment area of the school and former pupils.

Chairman: M D G Wheldon, FRICS
Chairman of the Boys' School Committee: Mrs D J Knight
Chairman of the Girls' School Committee: A Twiston Davies

D A Hochberg MA
C M Taylor
Prof R E Susskind, OBE
N R Scarles
M Pereira-Mendoza
Miss D Finkler
N Turnbull
G Parekh

Clerk to the Governors: C M Bremner

***Headmaster*: P B Hamilton**, MA

Second Master (*Deputy Head, Academic*): S Boyes, MA
Senior Master (*Deputy Head, Pastoral*): J A Corrall, MA
Deputy Head (*Development*): Dr S Hyde, DPhil
Bursar: S B Wilson, BA, MSc, RTR
Director of External Relations: Dr P E Spence, MA, PhD

Assistant Head (*Director of Teaching*): D J Byrne, MA
Registrar: Mrs D L Robertson, BSc
Head of the Sixth Form: P H Parr, MA
Head of the Middle School: M J Cook, BEd
Head of the Junior School: Miss D J Rivlin, BA
Head of the Preparatory School: Miss Y M Mercer, BEd

Teaching Staff:

* *Head of Department*

Classics:
*R C Whiteman, MA
P H Parr, MA
Mrs S Butcher, BA
P J Stiff, BA, PhD
Mrs S L Murphy, BA
Mrs S K Wijeratna, BA
Mrs M A Carrick, BA
P D Stiff, BSc
Miss A H McKenzie, BA

Religious Studies:
*R Cawley, BA, MA
M Lloyd-Williams, BA
Mrs E J Nelson, MA
A G Stimson, MA
R C Garvey, MA

Economics and Politics:
*J Wigley, BA, PhD, MEd
R D Reid, MA, BSSc
Mrs K Shah, BSc, MPhil
C G Trinder, MA
G J Hall, MBA

English:
*M P Lemprière, BA
M J Cook, BEd
C R Bass, BA
Mrs C B Lyons, MA
T J P Norton, BA
Mrs D H Morris-Wolffe, BA
Mrs K R Pollock, MA
Miss N M Murray, BA
Tak Sang-Li, BA
A E O'Sullivan, BA

Geography:
*J Maguire, BSc
M G Day, BA
Mrs J E Beeson, BSc
Mrs A C C Baron, BSc
J A Barnes, BSc
J Hails, BSc
Mrs R M Wright, BA
R D Oldfield, BSc
Stuart Haring BA
G Kissane, BSc

History:
*R C Sloan, MA, PhD
A P A Simm, BA
N P Saddington, BA
S P H Clark, BA
I St John, BA, DPhil
Dr S Hyde, MA, DPhil
Mrs D J Bardou, BA
Dr C P Watts, PhD

Information Technology & Computing:
*I R Phillips, BSc, MA
S Yu, BSc
K M Jones, BA, MSc
Ms A J Dable, BA

Mathematics:
*I B Jacques, BA, DPhil
P A Barry, MSc, PhD, ARCS, DIC
A M Ward, BSc
P C Marx, BSc, MPhil
S D Charlwood, BSc
Mrs A Thakar, BSc
Mrs D L Robertson, BSc
R J Kingdon, BSc, MSc, CPhys, MInstP
Mrs L I Dixon, BSc
C K Whalley, BSc
Ms A Pindoria, BSc
I R Fielder, BSc
E Pauletto, BSc
Revd J Markby, MA
Dr S J Pyburn, BSc, PhD
Mrs J Letts, BSc
Mrs H M Allen, MSc
Mrs D Rhys-Brown, BSc
J B Ward, BSc, BEd
S D McKane, BSc

Modern Languages:
*R J Thompson, BA
J A Corrall, MA
J C Swallow, MA
Mrs J B Swallow, BA
M J Donaghey, BA
Mrs J Robson, BA
J A Fenn, BA, MA
Mrs E Gomez, BA
Mrs E Childerstone, BA
Miss A McKenzie, BA
M S V Bardou, BA
P Thackrey, BA
D J Byrne, MA
P Hamilton, MA

Language Assistants:
Mrs E Childerstone, BA
Mrs M C Griffiths, BA
F Chaveneau

Science:
*M J Lexton, BSc, PhD,CChem, FRSC
S Boyes, MA
D R Delpech, BSc, CBiol, MIBiol
A C Bagguley, BSc, CBiol, MIBiol
C Glanville, BSc, BA
R O Kerr, BSc
Mrs M J C Jones, BEd
Dr A D S Perera, BSc, PhD

Science Technicians:
Mrs H Ahluwalia
Mrs H Dawda
Mr R Cachuela
Mrs F Watts

Art:
*A K Keenleyside, BA
Miss L M Bird, BA
S N Todhunter, BA
Mrs J E Gleeson, CertEd
Miss L Jay (*Art Technician*)

Design & Technology:
*N P Holmes, BEd
P I Dathan, BEd
T B W Hardman, BEd
P I Roncarati, BA, MSc
G Cox (*Design Technician*)

Drama:
*T J P Norton, BA
Mrs D H Morris-Wolffe, BA
J N Cox, BA
Miss N Heinen, BA
H Silver (*Drama Technician*)

Music:
*C D Muhley, GRSM, ARCO CHM, ARCM, LRAM, FRSA
A J Simm, BA

Instrumental Staff:
Miss M B Parrington, ARCM (*Violin*)
Miss L M Rive (*Violin*)
L Gee, BA, GBSM, ABSM, HonBC (*Violin*)
Miss P Worn, LRAM, ABSM, ALCM (*Viola*)
B Bantock, BMus, PPRNCM (*Cello*)
Miss C Maguire, LRAM (*Double Bass*)
Miss S L Core, GTCL, LTCL (*Flute*)
M P Pritchard, DipRCM (*Clarinet*)
H J Legge, LRAM (*Bassoon*)
N Gibbon, BSc, LGSM (*Trumpet*)
J W Beryl (*Percussion*)
S R Topping, DipRCM, ARCM (*Pianoforte*)
Miss I C Mair, GRSM, MMus, LRAM, ARCM (*Pianoforte*)
R A Carter, FRCO CHM, FTCL, ARCM, LRAM (*Pianoforte and Organ*)
S D Lyon, GRSM, MA (*Pianoforte*)
S J Byron, BMus (*Trombone*)
D Bentley, GGSM (*French Horn*)
Mrs R Heathcote, BMus, LGSMD (*Oboe*)
Miss C Cousens, BA, FRCO (*Organ*)

Physical Education:
*R J McIntosh, BA
A F M Metcalfe, BSc (*i/c Rugby*)
K Long, BEd (*i/c Hockey*)
P D Stiff, BSc (*i/c Swimming*)
R Welsh

I C Matthews

Games:
S D Charlwood (*i/c Cricket*)
S Lowe (*i/c Athletics*)
K Long (*i/c Tennis*)
T B W Hardman (*i/c Sailing*)
A M Ward (*i/c Association Football*)
A M Ward (*i/c Golf*)

Preparatory School:
M G Brown, BSc (*Deputy Head*)
Mrs K M Francis, CertEd
Mrs C M Griggs, CertEd, DipS&D
S Lowe, BEd
Mrs S M E Herbert, BEd
Dr C A Lessons, PhD
Miss C A Grimes, BEd
S S Lipscomb, BA
M Jenkins, BA, MA
N Bowley, BSc
P D Whitby, BA
Mrs S Adat, BA
Mrs J Valente, PGCE
Miss J I Rother, BA
Miss T J Loebenberg, BEd
Miss S E McLeigh, BA
Ms A J Putt, BA

Pre-Preparatory School:
Mrs A Fielden, CertEd
Mrs H M R Pullen, BEd
Miss V G Peck, BSc
Ms N Patel, BA

Chaplain: The Revd Jane E Markby

Administrative Staff:
Bursar's PA: Mrs R Mansi
Finance Manager: P Spence
Payroll: Mrs L Meighan
Headmaster's PA: Mrs S Harkus, BA
Preparatory School Secretary: Mrs T A Kennard
Pre-Preparatory School Secretary:
School Support Director: D I Yeabsley
Examinations Officer: J A Alvarez, BSc, PhD, CPhys, FInstP
School Nurses: Ms S Carey, Mrs E A Warren, RGN, RSCN
Catering Manager: E Johnson
Buildings Manager: P J Newcombe, BA
ICT Support Director: I R Phillips, BSc, MA
Head Groundsman: D Beckley
School Shop Manager: Mrs S Lewis
Transport Manager: S T Saltmarsh
Personnel Officer: Miss R Titley
School Counsellor: Mrs A Bard

The aim of the School is the fullest possible development of the varied talents of every boy within it, and to this end a broad curriculum is provided, together with extensive facilities for the development of each boy's cultural, physical, personal and intellectual gifts. The School sets out to achieve high academic standards and sets equally high standards in cultural and other fields. In matters of behaviour a large degree of self-discipline is expected, and of mutual tolerance between members of the School community.

Organisation. The School, which is a day school, has 70 boys in the Pre-Prep (ages 5–6) and over 200 boys in the Preparatory School (ages 7–11), 300 in the Junior School (ages 11–13), 500 in the Middle School (ages 13–16) and over 300 in the Sixth Form (over 16). There are 6 Houses. The School regards pastoral care as important; all the Housemasters and Deputy Housemasters and Heads of Section have a large responsibility in this field but so also do House Tutors, the Senior Master and the Chaplain, as well as other members of the staff.

Forms. In the Pre-Prep school there are two forms in Years 1 and 2 with approximately 18 boys in each form. In the Preparatory School there are three forms in Years 3, 4, 5 and 6 each with about 18 boys. In the Main School there are 6 forms in Years 7 and 8 with approximately 25 boys in each form. There are 12 forms in Year 9 each with about 14 boys. Years 10 and 11 are divided amongst 18 forms each with 17–18 boys. The usual size of teaching groups in the Sixth Form is about 10–15.

Facilities. The School and its sister Girls' School, the Haberdashers' Aske's School for Girls, enjoy the use of a campus of over 100 acres with extensive woodlands. The playing fields surround the buildings, which in the Boys' School include the following: Assembly Hall, Dining Hall, Sixth Form Common Room, Music Auditorium, Library, special accommodation for Classics, English (including a Drama Room), History, Geography, Mathematics, Information Technology, Modern Languages including 2 Languages Laboratories, Music School, Science and Geography Centre with 19 laboratories and 8 classrooms, a Design Centre for Art, Craft and Technology, Sports Centre, Gymnasium, Indoor Swimming Bath, two Artificial Grass Pitches and Squash Courts.

The Preparatory School is situated on the same campus in a new building of its own. (*For further details, see Preparatory School entry in IAPS section.*) The Pre-Prep is situated on its own nearby campus.

The Curriculum up to the age of 13 is common for all, with no streaming or setting except in Mathematics in Year 8. From the age of 11 in addition to the usual subjects it includes three Sciences and two foreign languages (chosen from French, German, Spanish and Latin). From the age of 13, subjects are taught in sets. GCSE courses start in Year 10, when boys take ten subjects. In the Sixth Form students study four subjects to AS in the Lower Sixth, narrowing to three A2 subjects in the Upper Sixth. The School takes seriously its commitment to General Studies; this non-examined part of the curriculum occupies 10% of the week in both Upper and Lower Sixth. Boys are entered for the GCE examination at A Level at the age of 18 and are prepared for entry to degree courses at Universities. The wide scope of the School's curriculum gives ample opportunity for all its boys whether preparing for University, for a profession, for the services, or for commerce or industry. The Careers Department has its own modern facilities, and careers advice is readily available to parents and to boys.

Religious Education. The School is by tradition a Church of England school, but there are no religious barriers to entry and no quotas. It is part of the ethos of the School that all its members respect the deeply-held beliefs and faith of other members. The School Chaplain is available to, and holds responsibility for, all boys in the School of whatever faith. She prepares for Confirmation those who wish it, and there are weekly celebrations of Holy Communion and an annual Carol Service in St Albans Abbey. The morning assembly and class teaching, however, are non-denominational in character. Faith assemblies are held on Thursday mornings, and comprise separate meetings for Christians, Jews, Muslims, Hindus, Jains and Sikhs.

Physical Education. A wide variety of sports is available, including Athletics, Badminton, Basketball, Cricket, Cross-country running, Fencing, Golf, Gymnastics, Hockey, Rugby Football, Sailing, Soccer, Squash, Shooting, Swimming, Tennis, Table Tennis and Water Polo. All boys are expected to take part in physical education unless exempt on medical grounds.

Out of School Activities. The extensive range includes a period of 2 hours on Friday afternoon when boys can choose one of a large variety of activities of a service nature. This includes Community Service, both on the School campus and among those who need help in the surrounding district. It also includes the Combined Cadet Force which has Navy, Army and Air Force sections.

Music and Drama both have a prominent place in the School. The Music School has a Recital Hall and some 12 other rooms; 21 visiting instrumental teachers between them teach 500 instrumental pupils each week covering all the normal orchestral instruments together with Piano and Organ. There is a Choir of 250, and several orchestras. For Drama the facilities include a generously equipped stage and a separate Drama Room with its own lighting and stage equipment.

School Societies. School Societies and expeditionary activities in term time and holidays include Amnesty, Archery,

Art, Badminton, Bridge, Canoeing, Chess, Choral, Classical, Crosstalk, Debating, Duke of Edinburgh's Award, Dramatics, English, Football, History, Jazz, Jewish Society, Life-saving, Life Drawing, Model Railway, Modern Languages, Mountaineering, Philosophical, Photography, Politics, Puzzles and Games, Rifle, Sailing, Science, Squash, Stamp Club, Windsurfing.

The Old Haberdashers' Association. (*Hon Sec*: Tony J S Alexander) provides a focal point for boys after they have left school.

Transport. A private bus service is provided from some 109 pick-up points, to enable boys to attend the School from a wide area, and to remain for after-School activities.

Admission. Boys are admitted only at the beginning of the school year in September, except on transfer from a school in another area. They may be admitted at the age of 5 and may remain in the School until the end of the academic year in which the age of 19 is attained, subject to satisfactory progress at each stage of the course and to compliance with the School Rules currently in force. Approximately 36 boys are admitted at age 5 and a further 18 boys are admitted at age 7 each year, approximately 100 at age 11, approximately 25 at age 13 and small numbers at age 16. There are competitive examinations including written and oral tests of intelligence, literacy and numeracy at the ages of 7 and 11, held in January for admission in the following September. Applicants aged 13 also take examinations at the beginning of January and are interviewed later in the month for entry in September. At 16 admission is by GCSE and interview. An Open Day for prospective parents is held each year early in October. Registration Fee: £50.

Scholarships. (*see Scholarship Entries section*). A number of Scholarships are awarded annually to pupils entering the Main School. Music Scholarships are awarded each year to candidates showing special promise in music. Governors Bursaries are open to all pupils entering the Main School; they are based upon financial need.

Full details of all these awards are included in the prospectus available from the Registrar at the School who is glad to answer enquiries.

Alternatively you can request a prospectus on-line from our website which is: http://www.habsboys.org.uk.

Fees per term (2008-2009). Main School: £4,285; Preparatory School: £3,225–£4,285.

Piano, Organ and Orchestral Instruments (optional) £183; Orchestral classes £115; Aural classes £51.

Honours. In 2007, 40 pupils gained places at Oxford and Cambridge, and approximately 120 gained places at other Universities.

Charitable status. The Haberdashers' Aske's Charity is a Registered Charity, number 313996. It exists to promote education.

Haileybury

Hertford SG13 7NU

Tel: Reception: 01992 462507; Master: 01992 706222
Bursar: 01992 706216; Registrar: 01992 463353
Fax: 01992 470663
e-mail: registrar@haileybury.com
website: www.haileybury.com

Motto: *Fear God. Honour the King. Sursum Corda*

Visitor: The Most Revd and Rt Hon the Lord Archbishop of Canterbury

President of the Council: The Rt Revd the Lord Bishop of St Albans

Council:
R M Abel-Smith
P A Chamberlain, BSc
The Revd Canon J Cresswell, MA
C S S Drew, MA
Mrs M Evans, BA
M R B Gatenby, FCA
The Rt Revd the Bishop of Hertford
C E Holroyd, FCA
D F MacLeod, FCA
The Revd D A Moore Brooks, BA Hons, PGCE, CTM
I Much
A F Oliver, MA
A J T Pilgrim, BSc, FCA
Mrs J G Scott, BSc, PGCE
G W Staple, CB, QC (*Chairman*)
Mrs A Templeman, MA, DipTh
J D Thornton, BSc Hons, MA, CEng, MICE, MCIOB
Major General T P Toyne Sewell, DL
J Trower

Secretary and Bursar: M Halsall

***Master*: S A Westley**, MA

Second Master: R L Turnbull, MA

Director of Studies: D Wilkinson, MA, MLitt, FRSA

Senior Master: P C T Monk, MA, MBE

Senior Mistress: Ms R J Fell, MA, MEd, DipSpLD

Head of Lower School: C D Jones, MA
Asst Head of Lower School: Mrs C J Gandon, BA (*Head of Classics*)

Head of Marketing: Mrs T Macpherson-Smith, BHum

Heads of Departments:
Art: N Paterson, BA
Biology: Mrs H Woolley, BSc
Careers: E Church, MA
Chemistry: R Dexter, BSc
Classics: Mrs C J Gandon, BA (*Asst Head of Lower School*)
Design Technology: G L D Macpherson-Smith, CertEd
Drama: Mrs R C Beggs, BA
Economics: J Cohen, BSc
English: N Parkin, BA
Geography and ICT: J R G Coles, BA
Girls' Games: Miss K E Andrew, BA (*Asst Director of Sport*)
History: E R L Bond, BA
Learning Support: Mrs S Gates, BA, OCR DipSpLD
Mathematics: J R Jennings, BSc
Modern Languages: Miss C Perri
Director of Music: Q Thomas, MA, ARCO, MMus
Physical Education: D J Payne-Cook, BEd
Physics: I Findlay-Palmer, BSc
Politics: M A Perrins, BA
Psychology: Mrs E Dickens, MA
Religious Studies: Mrs A J Baker, MA
Science: I Findlay-Palmer, BSc
Director of Sport: I K George, DipPE

Ms R Adams, BA
Miss I Addyman, MA, MST
G Allen, MA
H Baxendale, BA
Dr L Bindley, PhD, MChem
R H Bishop, BSc, MA
A Box, MA
Mrs C Bradley, MA, MEng, MIEE
Mrs M J Brooking, BEd
R Charters, BA
Mrs M Conway, BSc, MSc
Dr S Cooper, PhD, BSc
T Cope, MEng
Ms C Denlegh-Maxwell, BSc
Ms N Garland, BA
Miss L Golden, BA
Miss R Goldsworthy, BA
Mrs G Griffiths, BA
D R A Harvey, MSc, DPhil
G Hessing, BSc Hons
Mrs J Howard, BSc
R Hunter, BA
C E Igolen-Robinson, BA
N Jardine, MA
Miss A Jeans, BEd
D H Longman, BA, MMus, FRCO

Dr C Loughton, BSc, PhD
K Loughton, BA, MPhil
J Marks, BA
Miss C Orford, BA
Mrs M E Pagliarulo, LAM, Equity ISTD
A T M Parker, BA
Mrs N C Payne-Cook, BSc
Mrs A J J Perrins, BA, HDE
Mrs A Petrovic, BSc
Mrs J Pilgrim, BSc Hons
S C Pinder, BA
Ms L Ramos
I J Pinnington, BA
T Reade, BSc
Miss J Schrader, MA, MEd
A N P Searson, BA
N Smith, BSc
J N Spavin
P J Stacey, PPRAM
Dr B W Thomas, MSc, DPhil
M Tookey, BSc
Ms K Watts, BA
R Williams, BSc
P R Woodburn, BSc

plus 15 Visiting Music Staff.

Academic Registrar: N Athey, MA

Senior Chaplain: Revd C R Briggs, BD, AKC

GCSE Examinations Officer: W H Flint Cahan, MA
A Level Examinations Officer: P J Greer, MA
IB Coordinator: Dr L B Pugsley, MA, PhD

Development Director: Ms H Tranter

International Students Officer: R A Wilson, BA, MA

Counsellor: Mrs J Leggatt, UKCP

Librarian: Mrs E Harvey, BA

Instructors:
WO1 (SSI) B Eales (*CCF*)
Cricket Professional: G Howarth, OBE
Rackets Professional: M Cawdron

Houses and Housemasters/mistresses:
Albans: Mrs E Alexander
Allenby: Ms R J Fell
Bartle Frere: P F Johns
Batten: A J H Head
Colvin: Mrs P Gowen
Edmonstone: S J Dixon
Hailey: Miss C Perri
Kipling: R L Matcham
Lawrence: J S Brammer
Melvill: Mrs A R B Spavin
Thomason: I E W Sanders
Trevelyan: J F Alliott
The Russell Dore Lower School: C D Jones

Registrar: Mrs E Alexander
Assistant Registrar: Dr F Hughes

Number in School. 753.

Location. Haileybury is situated approximately 20 miles due north of central London, 2 miles east of Hertford and 30 miles south of Cambridge. It is easily accessible by motorway and train to and from London and its airports. The school's 500-acre rural campus, with all its facilities and magnificent grounds on a single site, makes Haileybury unique.

History. Many of its buildings were designed by William Wilkins in the early 1800s for the East India Company's training college. The East India College was closed in 1858 after the Mutiny and re-opened as a school in 1862. During the Second World War the Imperial Service College at Windsor was amalgamated with Haileybury to become Haileybury and ISC, but to all intents and purposes our school is known simply as Haileybury. The old Imperial Service Junior School at Windsor served as Haileybury's junior school until 1997 prior to its amalgamation with Lambrook School in Bracknell to form the now thriving Lambrook Haileybury School.

Co-education. Since 1973 Haileybury has welcomed girls into its Sixth Form. In 1997 the Council took the decision to admit additionally girls aged 11 and 13 with effect from September 1998. There are girls in every year at Haileybury, making up 42% of the school roll.

Student Profile. Pupils can join at three levels: 11 year olds enter the Lower School, which has an annual intake of 48 and is a distinct unit within the Main School. The majority of pupils join the Removes at 13, while a number of girls and boys arrive at 16 to study A Levels and the International Baccalaureate Diploma. Almost 70% of pupils are boarders. Approximately 17% are from overseas.

Campus Life. Pupils joining at 11 enjoy the benefits of self-contained teaching and recreational space within the main site together with access to all the specialist facilities of the senior school. Newly refurbished, small dormitory-style boarding accommodation exists exclusively for under 13 year olds.

All accommodation for 13 to 18 year olds is centred around the Quadrangle and Houses are either recently built, or are newly refurbished older buildings to provide high-quality living and working conditions. In the Fifth Form pupils can expect to share a room, although many benefit from single accommodation, and in their final two Sixth Form years they usually enjoy a single room.

Two of the five girls' Houses have been newly built recently.

Day pupils join members of the boarding community to form houses that total roughly 55 in number. They are expected to remain in school until 6.30 pm each working day, although they are welcome to stay longer if they choose. By arrangement with their housemaster and housemistress they may stay overnight. This flexibility allows for an easy transition into boarding, an option that increasing numbers of day pupils choose.

Welfare. The provision of a stimulating, caring environment in which all pupils can thrive is at the heart of our school. This is primarily achieved through open communication with children and their parents, vigilance and common sense, underpinned by our responsibilities under The Children Act.

Children in the Lower School have the supervision, support and help of a team of tutors whose pastoral role at Haileybury is dedicated to them. Once they join a House at 13 a pupil's housemaster or housemistress undertakes prime responsibility for his or her care and should be regarded as the first point of contact for pupils and parents alike. Housemasters and housemistresses are supported by teams of tutors, each with an important pastoral role, from the teaching staff.

A full-time doctor is resident at school to attend to all medical and health education matters from the Health Centre. Together with the Chaplains and a School Counsellor, he is available to listen and counsel pupils confidentially as they grow towards maturity.

Tuition and Curriculum. Our students are taught in small groups: 16 during years 7 and 8 in the Lower School, 20 or fewer from Years 9 to 11. A Level and IB classes average about 10–12, and never exceed 15. Pupils' progress is formally monitored by means of three-weekly reports and regular tutorials. Furthermore, teachers are constantly in touch with tutors, housemasters and housemistresses to keep all involved up to date with every pupil's performance.

All pupils have ready access to computers and there is dedicated teaching in their use for younger pupils. A computer leasing scheme exists enabling families to spread costs if they are investing in their own equipment, whilst providing a range of options covering use of equipment at school and home.

In a school that is reasonably selective but not highly selective, the principles of stretching the most able and encouraging those in need of particular support apply. Pupils are 'setted' and 'fast-tracked' on grounds according to ability, where this is deemed appropriate. Years 7 and 8 study English, Mathematics, Biology, Physics, Chemistry, Design Technology, Information Technology, History, Geography, French, Latin and Classical Civilisation, Art, Drama, Religious Studies and PE. Homework is set daily and the day pupils are able to complete it with supervision before going home.

Core elements of the Year 9 programme are Mathematics, the three Sciences, English, History, Geography, French, Art, Music, Religious Studies, Technology and Physical Education. Two options are chosen from: German or Spanish, Latin, Greek, Classical Civilisation, Drama, or EFL (English as a Foreign Language). A programme of PHSE and Information Technology continues throughout the year. Weekly Religious Studies classes are part of the school curriculum.

GCSE courses begin in Year 10. Most pupils will study 10 subjects. The most able will be encouraged to take these examinations early, especially in Mathematics and Modern Languages.

In addition to the AS/A level courses, the IB (International Baccalaureate) Diploma is also offered at Sixth Form.

In the Sixth Form pupils usually choose four AS followed by 3 A Levels in the Upper Sixth from a range of 26 subjects arranged in five groups or follow the increasingly popular IB Programme. Almost all Haileybury leavers proceed to university. A full university and careers advice is continually available and the school is a member of the Independent Schools Careers Organisation.

Out of Class Activities. The principles of a rounded education demand access to rich and varied opportunities. Haileybury provides these in many ways:

Games:

The girls play Lacrosse, Hockey and Netball in the two winter terms and choose between Tennis, Athletics, Rounders and Swimming in the summer. Boys and girls have regular access to our indoor swimming pool enabling swimming to be enjoyed both as a leisure activity and as a competitive sport. The main boys' game in the Christmas term is Rugby. In the winter months there is also provision for Rackets, Squash, Basketball, Cross-Country.

Soccer and Hockey are the main games in the Easter term, and Cricket in the Summer term. In the summer there is also the option of Athletics, Tennis, Swimming, Shooting, Sailing, Rowing and Golf.

The Sports Hall provides excellent facilities for all indoor games, including two indoor tennis courts and gym. The floodlit Astroturf pitch has been resurfaced recently and provides for Tennis (12 courts) in the summer and for Hockey in the winter.

In May 2008 the school will launch a new tennis academy with 8 indoor and outdoor courts, in partnership with the Legends' Tennis Academy, a private company part funded by the Lawn Tennis Association, where free professional coaching will be available to all pupils.

Activities:

School societies and activities flourish, either in the evenings after prep or during set activity times. The Design Technology Centre offers computing, electronics, metalwork, plastics and woodwork, with an emphasis on design and 'hands-on' skills.

Drama at Haileybury has always been strong and there are usually at least 12 productions during the year. There are two venues: the Ayckbourn Theatre providing fully-equipped studio facilities and new seating, and the newly refurbished auditorium in Big School, with a computerised lighting and sound system.

The School's musical life is exceptionally lively. The musicians perform outside Haileybury regularly. The Chapel Choir and Chamber Orchestra perform annually at venues such as St John's Smiths Square, London or West Road Concert Hall, Cambridge and recent tours have included performances in Leipzig and Tuscany. The installation of our new Chapel organ has provided a magnificent focal point for music here. The Chapel Choir has reached the final of the BBC Songs of Praise Schools Choir of the Year competition in two consecutive years and was awarded Schools Choir of the Year 2005.

The Art School is an exciting and creative department producing very high standards. In a separate purpose built area, it has extensive facilities for work in fine art, design and ceramics and it stages regular exhibitions including the annual Speech Day exhibition.

A popular but voluntary CCF exists for pupils who join initially for two years in order to take advantage of the specialist courses, shooting and adventure training. There is an indoor .22 rifle range. Alternatives to the CCF are the Duke of Edinburgh's Award scheme and Community service programmes.

Admission. Pupils can join at 11, 13 and 16. 11 year olds are asked to complete tests in English, Mathematics and Reasoning to supplement references from their current school. Boys and girls joining at 13 are asked to sit Haileybury's own entrance examinations or Common Entrance. Children joining the school at 11 usually gain entry to the Main School at 13 automatically.

Sixth Form entry for girls and boys is by entrance exams and interview. The selection procedure takes place at Haileybury in the November prior to the year of entry.

There is a registration fee of £75, a deposit of £1,000 and an entrance fee of £45 for boarders, £30 for day pupils.

All enquiries and applications for admission should be addressed to the Registry team who are happy to discuss any aspect of the admissions procedure, and from whom details regarding visits and Open Days are available.

Fees per term (2008-2009). Main School: £8,435 Boarders, £6,335 Day. Lower School (11–13 year olds): £5,350 Boarders, £4,210 Day.

The fees are reviewed annually.

Books and stationery are charged as extras and there are extra charges for music lessons, private tuition and for some sports, such as rowing.

Entrance Scholarships. (*see Scholarship Entries section*). Many scholarships are available upon entrance to Haileybury. Academic and Music awards are available for 11, 13 and 16 year old entrants, All-Rounder Awards at 11 and 13, Art at 13 and 16, and Technology at 13. In addition, there are some specially founded Scholarships which are awarded as they fall vacant.

Scholarships and All-Rounder Awards can be awarded up to the value of 10% of school fees and are tenable for the whole of the pupil's career at Haileybury. No fee remission is awarded for Art or Technology Scholarships. Successful candidates will be awarded a book token to the value of £100.

Bursaries may be awarded to increase the value of any Scholarship in case of genuine financial need. Application for a bursary entails confidential disclosure of capital and income of the parents, for which purpose a form may be obtained from the Registry or Bursary.

An Additional Information brochure is issued annually in September and this provides all appropriate information regarding dates and application procedure. This can be obtained from The Registrar, Haileybury, Hertford SG13 7NU or e-mail: registrar@haileybury.com. The Registry team will be pleased to discuss with parents any aspects of the scholarship procedure.

Charitable status. Haileybury is a Registered Charity, number 310013. It exists to provide education for boys and girls.

Hampton School

Hanworth Road Hampton Middlesex TW12 3HD
Tel: 020 8979 5526
Fax: 020 8941 7368
e-mail: headmaster@hamptonschool.org.uk
registrar@hamptonschool.org.uk
website: www.hamptonschool.org.uk

Founded in the academic year of 1556/57 by Robert Hammond, a Hampton merchant, and re-established in 1612. From 1910 the School was administered by the local authority, latterly as a voluntary aided school, but in 1975 reverted to independent status.

Motto: *Praestat opes sapientia.*

The Governing Body:

Chairman: A J Roberts, CBE, BA, FRSA

Vice-Chairman: L R Llewellyn, BSc, MBA, FCMA, FRSA

P Baker, BSc, FRSA
N E Britnor, BSc, FRSA
R Davison, MA, LRPS
Mrs M Ellis
His Honour Judge S E Kramer, MA, QC
J A Livingston, MA, DIPL Arch, RIBA
A H Munday, LLB, QC
S C Naidu
J S Perry, BA
N J Spooner, Cert Arch
Mrs A Sutcliffe, MA
R M Walker, MA
The Revd D N Winterburn, BSc, MA, Vicar of Hampton

Clerk to the Governors and Bursar: M A King, BSc

***Headmaster*: B R Martin**, MA, MBA, FCMI, FRSA

Deputy Heads:
Miss P Z S Message, BSc
D J Knapman, BA, BSc, MPhil
K K Knibbs, MA

Assistant Head: Mrs E T Watson, BA

Senior Tutors:
J P Orr, MA
R J Sims, MA
A N R McBay, BSc, MSc
D R Clarke, BHum (**Physical Education*)
S A Wilkinson, MA (**Religious Studies*)

Development Director: B S Brown, BSc, MRICS, MBIFM

Registrar: Mrs S M Binns, BA, MBA

Departmental Staff:
* *Head of Department*

M G Acher, BA (**ICT*)
S R Alexander, BA, PhD (**Spanish*)
Mrs P C Allerton, BA
C G Aubrey, MA
A Banerjee, BSc
A J Bannister, BA
J W Barber, MA
C J Barnett, MA
Ms L Barrett, BA, MBA
Ms M A Barry, BA
Mrs S U Beckett, BA
B S Bett, BA, MA (**Geography*)
Miss E Biagioli, BA
C J Blachford, BA
B G Blyth, BA
J Bonea Rojas, BA
Mrs J L Boon, MA
Ms A J Boulton, BA
Ms V K Buse, BA
M A Carroll, BSc (**Design Technology*)
Mrs M Chandler, MA
F C C Chaveneau, BA
Miss H E Cheshire, BA
G H Clark, BSc
Mrs H Clarke, BSc
P A Coleman, BSc
A J Cook, MA (**History*)
Ms J Cooper, BSc
T P Cooper, BSc
J S Coulter, BSc
Ms L A Cousans, BSc
N A Coyle, BA
M P Cross, BA
Mrs P A Croucher, BA, MA (**German*)
S R Croucher, BA
C G Cullen, MA (**Counselling & Pastoral Care*)
N S Davies, BA
R J Davieson, BSc
C Dawe, BA, BMus
Miss J M Dearden, BA
K J Dempster, BA, MEd
P T K Dharmawardena, BSc, PhD
Mrs J V Dibden, BSc (**Physics*)
W Dickie, BA
I C Donald, BA (*Director of Music*)
N J Double, BSc
Miss H Felgate, BA
D J Fendley, BEng
Mrs M-W Field, BSc
N L Francis, BSc
M Franzkowiak, BEd (**Drama*)
A T W Frazer, MA (**Modern Languages*)
Ms S Garrido-Soriano, BA
Miss J L Glasson, BA
Ms C E Goddard, BA
S Gray, BSc
A D Gutteridge, MA
F A Hall, BSc (*Public Examinations*)
Mrs S Harradine, CertEd, BDA DipSpLD (**Learning Support*)
R G R Harris, MSc, PhD
Z A Higgins, BSc
S T Hill, BA, MA
Ms C M Hilland, BA, MA
Ms P A Holmes, BSc
T P Iwanowski, BSc
Ms A H Jacobs, MA (**Classics*)
C J Jeppesen, MA, MPhil
M I Johnstone, BSc, MSc
Ms C R Jordan, BMus
A W Kershaw, BSc
Miss C E King, BA, MA
P H Langton, BSc, DipEnvSci (**Biology*)
A J Lawrence, BA
T J Leary, BA, Mlitt, PhD
J J Lee, BA
A M MacDonald, BSc (**Psychology*)
I L Maclean, MA
Mrs K L Martin, MA
D Martucci, BSc, DipComp
Mrs A C McLusky, BA
C T Mills, BSc, BA (**Games*)
Ms H E Moore BA
B C Murphy, MEng
N R Newman, BA
M A J Nicholson, BA
Mrs J C Owen, BA (**Russian*)
J G Owen, BSc (**PHSE*)
S Paraskos, MA (**Economics*)
J Parrish, BA
J R Partridge, BA
M J Passey, BA
M Payne, BA, MA
D E Peel, BA
D M Perfect, BSc
Mrs J A Perkins, BA, MPhil
D E Perrin, BA
Ms L V Rawstorne, MA
Ms C H Reyner, BSc
A J Roberts, MMath (**Mathematics*)
B O Ruse, BA

J Sadler, BSc
C D Salkield, BSc
J O Sarpong, BSc
Ms C J Saunders, BA
Ms R Shellard, MPhys
R A Simpson, BA, MA (**English*)
M K Sims, BSc
J D Slater, BA
P Smith, BA, MA, MPhil
G A Stone, MA, MIL
A R Stranks, BSc
P J Talbot, BA, MA
S Timbs, BA
P G Turner, BA
R T Vyvyan, MBA (**Business Studies*)
L O Watson, MSc
S C R Whitwell, BA, PhD
H R Wiggins, BA
Mrs K A Williams, BA (**Art*)
Mrs L Wilson, BA
N D Woods BA, MEng
Ms D C Woodward, BSc
R D Worrallo, BA, MA
Mrs S C D Yoxon, MA
J W J Zablocki, BSc (**Chemistry*)

Librarian: (*to be appointed*)
School Nurse: Mrs R Cash, SRN

Hampton is a day school of around 1,100 boys aged from 11 to 18, including a Sixth Form of about 300. It offers an excellent all-round education, encouraging personal responsibility and independent thinking in an energetic, happy and well-disciplined community.

The recent Inspection found Hampton to be a highly successful school providing many areas of excellence, particularly pastoral care and moral and spiritual guidance. The Inspectors commented on how enthusiastic boys are and how proud they are of Hampton. They listed many areas of considerable strength and found no major weaknesses. The inspection confirmed the School's commitment to offering boys a happy, purposeful and challenging environment.

Hampton is academically selective and almost all boys go on to good universities, including Oxbridge. There is an excellent A Level programme including a strong emphasis on breadth of study, critical thinking, independent learning and Community Service.

An annual exchange programme offers boys the chance to visit Spain, Germany and France. Boys visit many other countries through academic and sporting initiatives and there is an extraordinary range of trips available.

Music and drama are central to the character of the school. Concerts, musicals and plays involve all age groups throughout the year. Over 400 boys learn musical instruments and The Symphony Orchestra this year will have an exchange visit to Germany; the Jazz Band toured in The Netherlands last year. A recent theatrical highlight was the joint production of Carousel (with the adjacent Lady Eleanor Holles Girls' School). A new Performing Arts Centre, to commemorate the School's 450th anniversary, is planned to complete in 2009.

Hampton has an outstanding reputation for sport and many boys represent their county or country in a wide range of sports. Particular strengths are cricket, football, rowing, rugby, tennis and chess. Hampton has produced several rowing internationals and Olympic champions and shares, with The Lady Eleanor Holles School, a boathouse on the Thames nearby.

Integrity and social conscience are encouraged implicitly through the daily interaction of boys and teachers, as well as explicitly through School Assembly, through extensive Charity, Environment and Community Service programmes and through a long standing link with Kiira College in Uganda. The School has recently become the first 'climate neutral' school by offsetting all carbon emissions.

Hampton School and The Lady Eleanor Holles School are served by 22 coach routes across south London, Surrey and Berkshire.

Buildings and Grounds. The School has been situated on its present site since 1939. Its buildings include an Assembly Hall, Dining Hall, Sports Hall, classrooms, and a full set of laboratories for the separate sciences, technology, information technology, and languages.

The School stands within its own grounds of some 25 acres, including four rugby pitches, seven football pitches, six cricket squares and six hard tennis courts.

The Garrick Building provides specialist music accommodation, a drama hall, and additional performing arts teaching rooms. The Technology Department, part of the Teaching Block opened in 2004, includes provision for practical work in metal, plastics, wood and pneumatics, as well as a drawing office, a large project space, a dark room and an applied science laboratory for electronics and control technology. The Mason Library houses a substantial stock of books and journals, supplemented by other information retrieval facilities such as CD ROM and internet links.

The Steedman Sports Hall, opened by Sir Roger Bannister in December 1987, was designed as a centre for the development of personal fitness as well as for sports training and recreation. A new set of changing rooms, Sixth Form Common Room, Combined Cadet Force rooms and further facilities were completed in February 2003.

The Alexander Centre accommodates the History Department, together with three common rooms and a quiet work room for the Careers Centre. The north side of the building houses pavilion and changing room facilities for Cricket. The Shepherd Lecture Theatre, fully equipped for multimedia presentations, seats 150 and adjoins the Alexander Centre. There are six IT laboratories within the main School building and all staff are provided with wireless linked laptop computers. Most classrooms are equipped with data projectors.

New dining rooms and kitchens were opened in September 1997. The Millennium Boathouse, shared with The Lady Eleanor Holles School, was opened by Sir Steve and Lady Redgrave in 2000. This spectacular riverside facility provides the focal point for a highly successful and popular Boat Club, whose rowing squads regularly achieve both team and individual national and regional success.

A 25-room teaching building was completed in 2000 to provide additional Science laboratories, and to house Art, Geography, Classics, Economics and Business Studies.

A Sports Pavilion and Sixth Form Centre was opened in February 2003 and a Performing Arts Centre is scheduled to be completed in 2009.

Community. Hampton School enjoys particularly strong links with two neighbouring schools, Hampton Community College (HCC) and The Lady Eleanor Holles School (LEH). These two schools participate in various activities with Hampton pupils, especially Drama and Music, Combined Cadet Force (LEH) and the very popular visiting speakers *Talk*! programme. A 'United Nations Youth & Student Association' (UNYSA) branch involves pupils meeting to discuss issues of national and international significance. Strong links are maintained with the numerous local state primary schools which provide around 70% of our First Year intake.

In addition, Hampton School has a busy Community Service Programme. All members of the Lower Sixth undertake a placement in a local primary school as part of the General Studies course, working with young children on literacy, numeracy, computing and sport. Boys in the Fourth Year and above can also opt to do weekly placements in primary schools, residential homes for the elderly, or the local Barnardos project throughout the year. Various joint activities are run with LEH, including an annual Christmas Party for the Elderly, and a trip to the Science Museum for children with special needs. Several Sixth Formers are involved in holiday schemes for children from more deprived parts of East London each summer.

Curriculum. Boys in the Lower School follow a wide syllabus including Technology, Physics, Chemistry, Biology, a Modern Language and Latin. Mandarin is currently being added. Greek, German, Russian and Spanish are optional subjects begun in the Third Year. In the Fourth and Fifth Years all boys continue to study, in addition to PE, Games and Religious Studies, English Language, English Literature, a Modern Language, Mathematics and the three sciences for GCSE. They choose 3 other subjects from Art, Drama, Geography, German, Greek, History, Latin, Music, Religious Studies, Russian, Spanish and Technology. Most of these GCSEs are taken at the end of the Fifth Year. The most able linguists and mathematicians take GCSE at the end of the Fourth Year.

The Sixth Form offers virtually free choice of A and AS Level subjects, in addition to a wide range of courses leading to A Level General Studies. Additional teaching and preparation is provided for boys seeking entrance to Oxford or Cambridge, to which around fifteen to twenty boys are admitted each year.

Games. Games and Physical Education are part of every boy's school week, though other activities are permissible alternatives in the Sixth Form. The majority of boys also take part in voluntary sport on Saturdays when representative fixtures are arranged for each age group at a range of ability levels. Generally boys are able to choose which sport to follow. In winter, the major games are Rugby, Association Football and Rowing; in summer, Cricket, Athletics and Rowing. Other sports include Tennis, Real Tennis, Squash, Sailing and Swimming.

Careers. Each boy receives advice from the careers staff at those points when subject choices should be made. The School is a member of ISCO, who provide Morrisby testing as part of the Fifth Year advice programme. A Careers Convention is held annually, there are advice evenings for parents on A Level choice and on university decision-making, and comprehensive work experience is arranged.

Pastoral Care. This is one of the strongest features of the School. A boy's form tutor is responsible in the first instance for his academic and pastoral welfare and progress, and the work of form tutors is coordinated by year heads under the direction of one of the Deputy Heads. Parents are always welcome to discuss their son's work with any of these tutors, and Parents' Evenings provide an opportunity to meet subject teachers. Year group Pastoral Forums provide parents with an opportunity to meet staff responsible for pupil welfare and to discuss a variety of pastoral issues. There is also an active Parents' Association.

Societies. The School's large CCF contingent, run jointly with The Lady Eleanor Holles School, comprises Army and RAF sections and has a programme which includes adventurous training, orienteering and gliding. Boys may also participate in the Duke of Edinburgh's Award scheme or the activities of the School's Adventure Society, which organises camps and expeditions both in the UK and overseas.

The Music Department fosters solo and ensemble performance as well as composition, and offers pupils an opportunity to perform in the School's orchestras, bands and choirs. The Joint Choral Society, with the neighbouring Lady Eleanor Holles Girls' School, gives a performance of a major choral work annually. There is at least one dramatic production each term, and an annual musical. In all these activities, as in the Community Service work, the School enjoys close cooperation with The Lady Eleanor Holles Girls' School.

A programme of visiting speakers, Talk!, holds meetings during lunchtimes most weeks and offers boys the opportunity to hear and question distinguished politicians, writers, academics and scientists.

There is also a full range of subject related and hobby societies, among which Chess, Debating, the Technology Club and the Astronomy Society are particularly strong.

Admission. Boys normally join the School in September. About 120 boys a year are admitted at 11 by the School's own entrance examination in the January of Year 6. A further 60–70 enter at 13 through the Common Entrance Examination following a pre-test in the September of Year 7. Boys are also admitted into the Sixth Form and to fill occasional vacancies at other ages at the Headmaster's discretion. Further details may be obtained from the Registrar: 020 8979 9273.

Fees per term (2008-2009). £4,290 inclusive of books and stationery.

Scholarships and Exhibitions. (*see Scholarship Entries section*). At present, at 11+ the Governors offer open academic scholarships and one Hammond Scholarship (geographically restricted). At 13+ academic scholarships and exhibitions are offered through the Common Academic Scholarship Examinations. All-Rounder and Art awards are available at 11+ and 13+.

Instrumental music scholarships are offered at both 11+ and 13+. A Choral Scholarship is available for boys of 11 with treble voices who are, or will become, choristers of the Chapel Royal at Hampton Court Palace.

The School also has a Bursary Fund, from which awards are made according to parental financial circumstances and the academic or all-round potential which their son may demonstrate. Further details of scholarships and exhibitions may be obtained from the Registrar.

Old Hamptonian Association. Leavers are entitled to life membership of this Association which provides regular communication with members and has active sporting and dramatic sections. The OHA Office is located at School and can be contacted by e-mail: oha@hamptonschool.org.uk.

Charitable status. Hampton School is a Registered Charity, number 1120005. It aims to provide a challenging and demanding education for boys of high academic promise from the widest possible variety of social backgrounds.

Harrow School

Harrow on the Hill Middlesex HA1 3HT
Tel: 020 8872 8000; 020 8872 8003 (Head Master)
Fax: 020 8423 3112 (School)
020 8872 8012 (Head Master)
e-mail: hm@harrowschool.org.uk
website: www.harrowschool.org.uk

Harrow School was founded in 1572 by John Lyon under a Royal Charter from Queen Elizabeth.

Motto: *Donorum Dei Dispensatio Fidelis.*

Visitors:
The Archbishop of Canterbury
The Bishop of London

Governors:
P M Beckwith, MA, Hon LLB
N W Stuart, CB, MA
R C Compton (*Chairman*)
General Sir Timothy Granville-Chapman, GBE, KCB, ADC, Gen
J A Strachan, BSc, FRICS
J F R Hayes, MA, FCA
W G S Massey, QC, MA
Professor D J Womersley, PhD
S J G Doggart, MA
V L Sankey, MA
Mrs J Forman Hardy, LLB
C H St J Hoare, BA
K W B Gilbert, BA, FCA
E J H Gould, MA
R C W Odey, BA
Sir Neil Chalmers
Mrs H S Crawley
Professor G Furniss, BA, PhD
M K Fosh, BA, MSI
Professor Sir David Wallace, CBE, FRS, FREng

The Hon Robert Orr-Ewing
Mrs Susan Whiddington, AB

Clerk to the Governors: A J F Stebbings, MA, 45 Pont Street, London SW1X 0BX

***Head Master*: B J Lenon**, MA

Deputy Head Master: M L Mrowiec, MA

Senior Master: A S Lee, MA, DMS

Bursar: N A Shryane, MBE, BA, MPhil

Assistant Staff:
T G Hersey, BSc
R G Collins, MA (*Registrar*)
A H M Thompson, MA
D R Elleray, BA (*Director of Boarding*)
I W Farrell, MA, DPhil (*Director of Studies*)
A Jaggs
J P M Baron, MA
C J Deacon, MA
R D Burden, BSc
J E Holland, BA, PhD, MLitt
M E Smith, MA
P G Dunbar, MA
W Snowden, BA
S J Halliday, BA
M G Tyrrell, MA
A J F Alban, BEd
P J Bieneman, BSc
P J Warfield, BA
S F MacPherson, MA
P D Hunter, MA
S P Berry, MA
A R McGregor, MA
C D Barry, BSc (*Head of Physics*)
M P Stead, MA
The Revd J E Power, BSc, BA (*Chaplain*)
C J Farrar-Bell, MA
Dr P G Davies, BSc, PhD
A D Todd, BA, MPhil (*Head of History*)
M J Tremlett, BA
N J Marchant, BEng (*Head of ICT*)
Mrs L A Moseley, BA
N C Hulme, BA, MA (*Head of Modern Languages*)
M J M Ridgway, BSc
S N Page, BEd
T J Wickson, BA, MEd, AMBDA
The Revd A R Wadsworth, MA, GTCL, LRAM (*Roman Catholic Chaplain*)
I Hammond, BSc (*Head of Mathematics*)
B J D Shaw, BA (*Head of Classics*)
E R Sie, BSc, PhD
K M Wilding, BA
N Page, BA (*Head of French*)
A K Metcalfe, BA (*Head of Geography*)
M Roberts, BSc, PhD
Mrs A L Parker-Jones, BA (*Head of Religious Studies*)
E W Higgins, BSc
S M Griffiths, BA (*Head of Design Technology*)
C S Tolman, BA (*Head of Economics*)
R J Kinghorn, BPhysEd
N D A Kemp, MSc, DPhil
C de L Mann, BSc
Miss B R Davies, BA
G H White, BSc
R Murray, BSc (*Head of Statistics*)
J Hanson, MSc
N S Keylock, MSc (*Head of Biology*)
C J A Terry, BSc
R J O'Donoghue, MA
M G J Walker, BA (*Head of German*)
F E J Wawn, MA
J Lynch, MA
R J Harvey, BA
G P J Parker-Jones, BA
S A Harrison, BSc, PhD
Miss R T Good, BA
Dr H Hitchings, BA, PhD
J L Roberts, MA
Dr M E Walsh, DPhil
Dr D R Wendelken, PhD
Mrs L Smith, BSc, BEd
Mrs V A Smit, BA
C Buys, BSc
D F Cox, BA
Dr S J Abbott, PhD
C P Bates, BSc
J C Cockburn, BA (*Head of Art*)
S C Costello, BA
Miss R L Fulton, BA (*Head of History of Art*)
Miss H Mervis, BA
I A Stroud, BA (*Head of Scuplture*)
Miss S L Mackrory, BA
S R Cooper, BEng
J S Webb, MA, MSc, MLitt
Dr A F Worrall, MA, MSc, PhD (*Head of Chemistry*)
J Kyte, BA
D R J Bell, BA (*Head of Photography*)
J N James, BA (*Head of English*)
T M Knight, BA
J J Coulson, BA (*Director of Sport*)
R J Try, BA
T M Dalton, BSc
A M Cannon, BA
Dr M T Glossop, BSc, MA, PhD

Music Staff:
D N Woodcock, MA, FRCO (*Director of Music*)
P J Evans, BA
D N Burov (*Head of Strings*)
G R M Layton, MMus, MSt (*Head of Music Technology*)
S McWilliam, LTCL (*Head of Wind Instruments and Commercial Music*)

and 27 visiting teachers

Librarian: Mrs M Knight, ALA, MIInsf.Sc
Careers Master: D F Cox
Officer Commanding CCF: Lt Col M P Stead
School Medical Officer: The Stanmore Medical Practice

Houses:
Bradbys: Mr P G Dunbar
The Grove: Mr P J Bieneman
Rendalls: Mr K M Wilding
The Park: Mr P D Hunter
West Acre: Mr M E Smith
The Knoll: Dr E R Sie
Druries: Mr D R Elleray
The Head Master's: Mr A R McGregor
Elmfield: Mr M J Tremlett
Moretons: Mr P J Evans
Newlands: Mr R D Burden
Gayton: Dr D R Wendelken

The School. Harrow is distinctive in four ways. First, we aim to achieve very good exam results for all pupils. Second, we are all-boarding. We avoid the difficulties which can arise when some pupils go home at the end of the day and others do not. We are able to put on a range of worthwhile activities at weekends which would not be possible if some pupils had gone home. Thirdly, we place a particular emphasis on a broad approach to education. We believe that some of the most valuable aspects of education can be learnt outside the classroom. Finally, we combine a long history and sense of tradition with a modern approach to the curriculum and education. Harrow is the only full boarding school in London.

Shape of the School Term. For the first two weekends all pupils are in the School and many activities are laid on. If they are able to, parents come and visit. On the third weekend all pupils go home or to friends; the weekend starts at 12 noon on Friday and ends at 9 pm on Sunday. The next two weekends are followed by a nine day half term. This pattern is repeated throughout the year.

Boarding Houses. There are eleven boarding houses, all of a similarly good standard. In all Houses boys have their own bed-sitting rooms, usually shared with one other pupil in the first and second years.

The School estates, on and around the Hill, extend to over 300 acres. They include cricket and football fields, athletics track and sports hall (with indoor swimming pool), golf course and farm.

Admission. Application for admission should be made to the Registrar. Boys are admitted between the age of 12 and 16, but most in the September before their fourteenth birthday. Most candidates take the Common Entrance Examination at their Preparatory Schools usually in the term preceding entrance to Harrow. There are also some vacancies for Sixth Form boys.

Fees per term (2008-2009). £9,335. A small number of optional charges are not covered by the consolidated fee (for private tuition in music, for example).

Entrance Scholarships. (*see Scholarship Entries section*). 25 Scholarships range in value from £500 per annum to 10% of the fee and are awarded for excellence in academic work, or music, or art, or for some other talent. These Scholarships may be supplemented up to the full fee where financial need is shown although such supplementable Scholarships are awarded only to boys of high academic or musical ability. Full particulars may be obtained from the Admissions Secretary, 1 High Street, Harrow on the Hill, Middlesex HA1 3HT.

Curriculum. Year 1 (aged 13 to 14): English Language, English Literature, Mathematics, Physics, Chemistry, Biology, Computing (Information Technology), Design Technology, History, Geography, Religious Studies, French, German, Spanish, Latin, Greek, Art, Music.

Years 2 and 3 (aged 14 to 16): up to 10 of the above subjects leading to GCSE qualification.

Years 4 and 5 (aged 16 to 18): four of the following subjects leading to AS and A Level qualifications: Mathematics, Physics, Chemistry, Biology, Design Technology, Economics, Business Studies, English, French, German, Mandarin, Spanish, Italian, Latin, Greek, History, Ancient History, Geography, Religious Studies, Art, Photography, History of Art, Music, Sports Science. Japanese and Arabic are also taught to GCSE and A Level.

At this stage students can also be prepared for the SAT tests required by American universities.

At every level students are taught to play a wide variety of sports.

Activities. All pupils take a wide range activities outside the classroom. These include:

- Music. Harrow is one of the UK's leading schools for musical education. Large numbers learn to play an instrument or sing in the School Choirs.
- Drama. The School has one of the best equipped theatres in any UK school and boys perform up to 12 plays each year.
- Sports, including soccer, swimming, rugby, cricket, athletics, cross-country running, riding, polo, fencing, rackets, tennis, fives, archery, basketball, badminton, squash, sailing, climbing. The School has its own golf course.
- Art: drawing, painting and sculpture.
- Clubs designed to foster new interests and develop skills.

Old Boys' Society. Harrow Association. *Director*: C J A Virgin, Harrow School, Harrow on the Hill, Middlesex HA1 3HP.

Charitable status. The Keepers and Governors of the Free Grammar School of John Lyon is a Registered Charity, number 310033. The aims and objectives of the Charity are to provide education for the pupils at the two schools in the Foundation, Harrow School and John Lyon School.

Headington School

Oxford OX3 7TD
Tel: 01865 759100
Admissions: 01865 759113
Fax: 01865 760268
e-mail: admissions@headington.org
website: www.headington.org

Patrons:
Sir Michael Atiyah, OM, PRS, MA
Dame Ruth Deech, DBE
Sir Christopher Paine, DM, FRCP, FRCR

Council:
Chairman: Mr R G Barnes, BSc, MBA
Mr W G Alden, MA, MBE, DL
Lady J Appleyard, BA, DipEd
Dr A Banning, MB BS, FRCP, MD, FESC
Mrs H Batchelor, BSc Hons
Mrs C Bevan, BSc Hons
Mrs T Boswood, BA
Mrs D Dance
Dr C C L Drummond, MA Oxon, PhD
Prof S Gurr, BSc, ARCS, DIC, PhD, MA
Mr C I K Harris
Mr G A Paine, JP, FCA

Company Secretary: Mr M A Clarkson, BSc Eng, MSc, ACGI, MIMechECEng, MAPM

Staff:

***Headmistress*: Mrs A Coutts**, BSc Hons, PGCE, MEd Warwick

Senior Management Team:
Deputy Heads:
Dr J Jefferies, BSc Hons, PhD Exeter (*Director of Studies*)
Mrs C Knight, BSc Strathclyde, PGCE Westminster College
Assistant Heads:
Mr R Dodds, BSc Hons Exeter, PGCE Oxford
Mr R Smith, MA Hons Aberdeen, PGCE Cantab
Bursar: Mr M A Clarkson, BSc Eng, MSc, ACGI, MAPM

Heads of Section:
Head of Sixth Form: Mrs R Kitto, MA Ed Open University, TEFL
Head of Middle School: Mrs B Dyer, BEd Hons Central School of Speech & Drama
Head of Lower School: Mrs E Bedford, BA Hons Durham, MA Oxford Brookes, PGCE Oxford, FRGS

* *Head of Department*
§ *Part-time*

English:
*Mrs J A Whitehead, BA Hons Exeter, PGCE London
Mrs N Archer, BA Hons, PGCE London (*Drama*)
Mrs J Hamilton, BA Hons, PGCE Leicester, MPhil Sheffield
Mrs K Hegarty, BA Hons, DipEd Queen's Belfast
Mr R Smith, MA Aberdeen, PGCE Cantab
Mr P Waddleton, BA Hons, MA Oxford Brookes, PGCE Westminster College, CTEFL
Mrs B Alpers, BSc, DipT NZ
§Dr D Morrish, BA Hons York, MA, DPhil Kent
§Mrs W Rooney, BA Hons Loughborough, PGCE Oxon

§Mrs V Sinclair, CertEd Froebel Inst, CELTA Oxford Brookes

Mathematics:
*Mrs R Bowen, MA Oxon, PGCE Oxon
Mrs C Knight, BSc Strathclyde, PGCE Westminster College
Mrs M Clarke, BSc Portsmouth Polytechnic, PGCE Homerton
Mrs E King, MMaths Hons Warwick, PGCE Manchester
Miss R Hudson, BA Hons Oxon, PGCE Oxon
Miss J Smart, BA Oxon, PGCE Oxon
§Mrs J Fouweather, BSc Hons, PGCE Hull
§Mrs A Hutchinson, MA Hons Glasgow, PGCE Jordanhill
Mrs S Young, BSc Bristol, BA Cantab, PGCE London

Information & Communication Technology and Business Studies:
*Mr M Howe, BA Hons, PGCE East Anglia (**ICT*)
Mrs R Kitto, MA Ed Open University, TEFL (**Business Studies*)
Mr R Demaine, BA PGCE Rhodes University
Mr M Wilson, Mus B Manchester, PGCE Christ Church Canterbury

Economics:
*Mrs M James, BA Hons London, PGCE London
Mrs N Reilly, BEd Hons Huddersfield

Modern Languages:
*Mrs J Jennings, BA Hons Oxon, PGCE Reading (*French and *German*)
Mme V Crépeau, Licence Caen, PGCE Oxford Brookes (**French and German*)
Mme C Sillah, Licence Orleans, PGCE Westminster College (*French and German*)
Mrs E Whiteley, BA Hons, PGCE London (*French and German*)
Mrs L Lechelle, PGCE Oxford Brookes (*French*)
Mme M St Germain, DEUG, City & Guilds Certificate (*French Assistant*)
Miss P Dunn, MA Oxon, PGCE Westminster College (**Spanish and French*)
Mrs C D Cruz, MCIL, PGCE London (*French and Spanish*)
Mrs G Thomas, MA, PGCE Oxford Brookes (*Spanish*)
Mrs C Casasbuenos, BSc Bogota (*Spanish Assistant*)
Mrs B Coombes (*German Assistant*)

Science:
*Mrs C Al-Sabouni, BA Hons Open University, PGCE Oxford (**Chemistry*)
Mrs J Perrin, BSc Hons UCW, MSc Open University (**Biology*)
Mr J Stephenson, BSc Hons Nottingham, PGCE Oxford (**Physics*)
§Dr H Brooks, BSc Hons, PhD, PGCE London
Mr R Dodds, BSc Hons Exeter, PGCE Oxford
Mrs J Quirk, BSc Hons Birmingham, PGCE Oxford
Dr P Smaldon, BSc University College Swansea, PhD Heriot-Watt, CertEd Moray House Edinburgh
Mrs M Rogers, BSc Hons Exeter, PGCE Oxford Brookes
Miss C Wilkinson, BA Hons Oxon, PGCE Oxford
Mrs A Coutts, BSc Hons, PGCE, MEd Warwick
Mrs J Ridley, BSc Hons Dunelm, PGCE Dunelm
Dr H Uniacke, BEng Cardiff, PhD Cardiff, PGCE Oxford
Mr J Kelly, MChem Oxon, PGCE Oxford, PGDES Oxford
Miss E Krebs BSc Hons Bristol, PGCE Oxford
Mrs H Perry BSc Hons, PGCE Cambridge
Dr E Rigney, BSc, PhD University College Dublin, PGCE Oxford
Mr P Brown, BSc Eng, PGCE Aberdeen

Classics:
*Mrs L Workman, BA Hons Durham, PGCE Queens' College Cambridge
Mrs C Hamand, BA Hons London, PGCE Birmingham
Miss L Bok, MA Amsterdam, MLitt Aberdeen, MSt Oxon, PGCE King's College London
Mr R Batten, MA Hons Cantab, PGCE

History, Politics and Law:
*Mrs S Wilkinson, BA Hons Newcastle, PGCE Oxford
§Mrs J Ormston, BA Hons UCL, PGCE London (**Politics*)
Ms J Fitch, BA Hons UCW, MA Oxford Brookes, PGCE Bristol
Mrs E Parkes, BA Hons Hull, PGCE Leicester
Mrs S Scott-Malden, BA Hons London, PGCE Oxford
§Mrs M Fraser, LLB Hons Exeter, LPC Exeter, PGCE Oxford Brookes, MA Kingston

Psychology:
Mrs K Piggott, BA Cape Town, MA Oxford Brookes, PGCE Cape Town, CTEFL, DELTA Cambridge RSA
§Mrs W Rooney, BA Hons Loughborough, PGCE Oxon
Miss H Loughran, BSc Hons Dunelm

Geography:
*Miss A Parr, BA Hons Lancaster, PGCE St Martin's College, Lancaster
Mrs E Bedford, BA Hons Durham, MA Oxford Brookes, PGCE Oxford, FRGS
Mrs L Newman, BA Hons, PGCE Exeter
Dr J Jefferies, BSc Hons, PhD Exeter, QTS
Miss L Kerr, BA Hons Kings College London, PGCE Bristol
Mrs H Brewin, BSc Hons Nottingham, PGCE Durham (**Environmental Science*)

Religious Studies:
*Mrs J Knight, MA Oxon, PGCE Winchester
Miss S Stayte, MA Oxon, PGCE Exeter, Lay Chaplain
Miss S Murphy, BMus, Grdip Tch & Lrn

Home Economics:
*Mrs J Amos, BEd Newcastle (*Food & Nutrition*)
Mrs C Stevenson, CertEd Leicester (*Food & Nutrition*)
Mrs G Thurling, CertEd UCNW (*Textiles*)
Mrs C Lamb, BA Hons UCE (*Textiles*)
Mrs M Colquhoun, BEd Hons Bath

Art and Design and Art History:
*Mr M Taylor, BA Hons Coventry
Miss L Donald, BA Hons Cranfield, MA Swansea School of Art
Mr N James, BA Hons Cheltenham & Gloucester College, PGCE Surrey
Mrs M A Taylor, DipArt Edinburgh, PGCE Birmingham
§Dr D B Morrish, BA Hons York, MA Kent, DPhil York
§Mrs A Turner, BA Hons, PGCE Reading

Physical Education:
*Miss G Hirsh, BA Hons Newcastle
Miss A Charania BSc Hons Luton, PGCE Cheltenham
Miss L Cockshott, BEd, PhyEd Bedford
Mrs J Collinson, BA Open University, CertEd Dartford
Miss A Groves, BEd Hons College of St Martin and St John, Plymouth
Mrs K Moore
Miss H Loughran, BSc Hons Dunelm
§Mrs J Roche, CertEd Bedford
Mr R Demaine, BA, PGCE Rhodes (*Director of Rowing*)

Music:
*Mr M Paine, BA Hons, ARCM, PGCE Reading
Mr J Penman, BMus, MMus, PGCE

Drama and Theatre Studies:
*Mrs C Rigby, BA Hons, MA, Rose Brufort College of Speech and Drama
Miss L Cresswell, BA Waikato, ATCL Speech & Drama (*Speech and Drama*)
Miss A Enticknap, BA Hons Roehampton Institute, PG Dip Oxford School of Drama

Ms B Dyer, BEd Hons Central School of Music & Drama
Mrs S Skipwith, MA Hons St Andrews, MSc Oxon, PGCE Oxford
Mrs S Hughes-Morgan, BA Hons Exeter, PGCE Oxford Brookes
Miss F Curtis, MA Mountview Drama School

Special Educational Needs:
*Mrs J Hamilton, BA Hons, PGCE Leicester, MPhil Sheffield, Cert Adv Prof Practice Oxford Brookes
§Mrs L Venessa, BEd Oxon, PGCE Westminster College, RSD DipSpLD, AMBDA
§Mrs S Colman, PHN, Oxford Cert SpLD, BDA Accredited

English as an Additional Language:
*Mrs V Sinclair, CertEd Froebel Inst, CELTA Oxford Brookes

Housemistresses (Boarding):
Head of Boarding: Miss T Lee, BA Hons Kent, PGCE Westminster, CPP Boarding Education, TEFL
Davenport: Mrs K Moore
Deputy: Miss A Groves, BEd Hons College of St Martin and St John, Plymouth
Napier: Miss A Charania, BSc Hons Luton, PGCE Cheltenham
Residential Matron: Mrs F Graham, RSCN, RGN
Hillstow: Mme C Sillah, Licence Orléans, PGCE Westminster College
Deputy: Miss H Loughran, BSc Hons Dunelm
Celia Marsh (*Sixth Form House*): Mrs J Wareham, BEd Hons Reading

Visiting Instrumental Music Teachers:

Piano:
Mrs M Cooper, GRSM, ARCM, PGCE (**Piano*)
Mr R Leigh-Harris, MMus, GRSM, PGCE
Mr M Leigh, BA, MA, PhD
Miss F Hedges, MA Oxon, ARCM, PGCE (*Piano, Double Bass*)
Miss K Lawrie
Mr G Howe, BA, FLCM, FNMSM, LTCL (*Piano, Theory, Technician*)
Mr M Longson, BA
Mr P Richardson, BA, MMus, LRAM (*and accompaniment*)
Ms G Fisher, ARCM, ALCM, CPPed
Ms E Kreager, BA, DPhil, CT ABRSM

Strings:
*Mr O Bonnici, Gold Medal ENM, ARCM (*Violin, Viola, Ensembles*)
Mrs V Kay (*Violoncello, Piano*)
Mr S Dunstone, MA, CertEd (*Harp, Harp Ensembles*)
Ms J Froomes, Grad Dip Mus (*Violin, Viola*)
Mrs P Terry, DipEd (*Recorder, Flute*)
Miss P Ballard, LRAM, ARCM (*Violoncello*)
Mrs E Reed, BA, MA (*Violin, Viola, Quartet*)

Woodwind:
Miss C Goble, BMus Hons (*Flute, Flute Group, *Woodwind, *Brass*)
Mrs J Cairns, GLCM, ALCM (*Clarinet, Clarinet Ensemble*)
Ms L Stott, CT ABRSM (*Saxophone, Flute, Piano*)
Mr S Cooper, GRSM, MSTAT (*Bassoon*)
Mr P Riordan, BMus, LRAM (*Oboe*)
Mrs P Terry, DipEd (*Recorder, Flute*)

Brass: Mr D McNaughton, BA Hons

Guitar:
Mr P Manhood, ACTL (*Classical*)
Mr T Perkins, LTCL (*Rock and Pop*)

Percussion and Double Bass
Mr T Dawes, BA, MSc (*Double Bass, Percussion, Bass Guitar, Jazz Ensembles*)
Mr B Twyford (*Drum Kit*)

Singing:
Mrs A Rogers, GRSM, LRAM
Mrs E Emberson, AGSM, CT ABRSM

Visiting Coaches:
Fencing: Mrs J Douglas
Rowing:
Mr R Demaine (*Director*)
Dr C Adams
Dr A Green
Miss C Murphy
Mrs N Thomas
Miss S Hughes
Miss H Loughran
Mr S Wells (*Boatman*)
Tennis: Mr J Baker, BTCA
Trampolining: Miss S Costigan, BTF
Judo: Mrs L Scarlett, BJA
Badminton: Mr I Grierson, BBA
Basketball: Mr S Cruz, BBA
Swimming: Mrs R Porter, RLSS

Admissions, Development and Marketing
Admissions Registrar: Mrs S Sowden, BSc, AKC, PGCE King's College London, Adv Dip EdMan Open
Development Director: Mr S Rainey, BA Hons Queen's Belfast
Marketing Manager: Mrs J Cowper, BA Hons Dunelm, MSt Oxon
Deputy Admissions Registrar: Mrs T Wright
Admissions Assistant: Mrs B Coombes
Development Assistant: Mrs R Fraser

Administrative Staff:
PA to the Headmistress: Mrs L Hughes
PA to the Deputy Heads: Mrs C Escreet
School Secretary: Mrs E Puddefoot
Catering Manager: Mr P Rowcliffe, AHCIMA, MISM
Clerk of Works: Mr P Mulvany
Assistant Bursar: Mrs K Hoy, BSc, ACA
Bursar's Secretary: Mrs L Painter, BSc, Mrs A Miell
Bursar's Assistants: Miss C Dean, Mrs K Jones, Mrs J Miller
Personnel Manager: Mrs S Jarvis-Foster
Swimming Pool and Sports Hall Manager: Mr G R Arman
School Staff Instructor: Mr P Dooley
Head of Grounds and Gardens: Mr D Hedger

Medical Staff:
School Doctors:
Dr G E Sacks, MB
Dr H M Merriman, MB BS, FFARCS, MRCGP, DRCOG

Sanatorium Nurses:
Mrs C Allen, RGN, RM, DipHE
Ms C Gordon, RGN
Ms Z Spring, RGN

Preparatory School

Head: Miss A J Bartlett, BEd Hons London

Bursar: Mr M A Clarkson, BSc Eng, MSc, ACGI, MIMechE, MAPM

Lower III (*10+*): Miss C Crookes, BEd Hons Exeter
Lower III (*10+*): Mrs L Smyth, BA Hons, PGCE, Dunelm
Upper II (*9+*): Miss N McConnel, BEd QTS Hons, Oxford Brookes
Upper II (*9+*): Miss J Temple, BSc Hons Bristol, PGCE Homerton College Cambridge (*Director of Studies*)
Lower II (*8+*): Mrs C Parker
Lower II (*8+*): Mrs H Clarke, BA Hons, PGCE Ripon and York St John
Form I (*7+*): Mrs C Thomson, BEd Hons, MEd Hons University of Wales (*Deputy Head*)

Form I (7+): Mrs V Kuester, BEd Hons Kingston
Transition (6+): Miss A Mills, BEd Hons Kent
Transition (6+): Mrs A Hayden, BEd Hons Southampton, CertEd Southampton LSU
Kindergarten (5+): Miss T Bramley, BA Hons Warwick
Kindergarten (5+): Miss J Reed, BA Hons Cambridge
Kindergarten (5+): Miss J Reed, BA Hons Cambridge, Head of KS1
Pre-Kindergarten (4+): Mrs R Lithgow, BSc Hons Manchester, PGCE Oxford
Pre-Kindergarten (4+): Miss A Dew, BA Hons Worcester, PGCE London
Nursery (3+): Mrs J Rawlinson, BA Open University, BEd Oxford Brookes, CertEd Bath College of Education
Physical Education: Mrs L Smith, BEd Hons Cheltenham
Head of Music: Miss S Glaisher, BA Hons Kingston
Science: Mrs J Simmonds, BSc Hons, PGCE London
French: Mrs N Walter, MA Oxon, PGCE Oxford, TEFL
ICT: Mrs K Mylrea, MA Open University, PGCE Manchester Polytechnic
Teaching Librarian: Mrs E Newton, CertEd Culham College of Education Oxford

Other Teaching Staff:
Mrs R Fleming, BA Hons Surrey, MA Oxford Brookes
Mrs R M E Ford, BPhil Hons Dunelm (*Ballet*)
Mrs D Goddard, CertEd Diploma in Council, BPhil Ed Birmingham
Mrs J Lawley, BEd Hons Bedford College
Mrs A Martin, BEd QTS Hons Warwick
Mrs N Rainbird, BA Hons, PGCE York
Mrs N Paplomatas, CertEd Westminster College
Mrs K Smith, BEd Hons Westminster College Oxford
Mrs L Tighe, BA Hons Birmingham, PGCE Roehampton
Mrs R Williamson, BA Hons, PGCE London
Mrs K Trethewey, BEd, PDSE NSW

Teaching Assistants:
Mrs R Brown, Miss S Hydar, Miss K Johnson, Mrs V Miller, Miss T Muhlberger, Mrs S Wilder, Mrs C Hilliar, Mrs D Isle, Mr R Lithgow, Miss V Lyford, Mrs L McCulloch, Mrs P Parsons, Miss A Robertson CACHE Diploma, NNEB, Mrs R Saunders, Mrs A Seneviratne

Nursery Assistant: Mrs C Parkes NNEB

Administrative Staff:
School Administrator: Mrs A Blanchard
PA to the Head: Mrs J E Kitching

After School Care:
Mrs R Brown and Mrs C Hilliar (*Supervisors*), Miss A Robertson, Miss Y Turner

Headington School Oxford is a boarding and day school for around 720 girls aged 11–18. Despite our position in the academic first division, our true strength lies in our commitment to meeting the needs of each individual pupil. Whether your daughter's strengths are academic, musical, sporting, creative or even entrepreneurial, we can provide the facilities and expertise that will enable her to develop her natural talents and to succeed.

A separate Preparatory School for girls aged 3–11, lies a short distance away. (*See Headington Preparatory School entry in IAPS section.*)

The school was founded in 1915 and moved to its current buildings in 1930. It is situated in 26 acres of grounds, one mile from the centre of Oxford and just under 60 miles from London. It is a Church of England Foundation but girls of all denominations are actively welcomed.

Facilities. A steady programme of building and upgrading has ensured excellent facilities for both living and working. The Theatre at Headington – a 240-seat professional theatre – opened in 2002 and has become the focus for a broad programme of events, ranging from music, theatre and comedy to a monologues, fashion shows and a Sixth Form lecture series. A varied programme of school productions, from student-produced plays to whole-school musicals, and from examination pieces to dance routines, is shown throughout the year. In 2003, increased demand for boarding places was met with a new boarding house for 45 pupils; other recent developments cover a broad spectrum of school life, and include an art and design centre, an additional science laboratory, and a sports hall, fitness centre and a new dining hall.

Curriculum. In the **Senior School**, the National Curriculum is broadly followed up to GCSE level. In addition all girls take a three year course in Latin, from 12–14, and take either German or Spanish for one year before they all choose their GCSE subjects. All girls take GCSE in English, French, Mathematics and Science and half or full GCSEs in Information Technology. Up to five other subjects are chosen from Geography, History, Spanish, German, Greek, Latin, Classical Studies, Religious Studies, Music, Drama, Art and Design, Food, Textiles, Physical Education. As non examination subjects girls also take Religious Studies, Personal and Social Education and Physical Education.

Most pupils stay to take A Levels at Headington and are joined by a number of new girls, some of whom will come from overseas. In the first year of the Sixth Form, girls will study four, or occasionally five, subjects to AS Level, reducing these to three for the second year. 30 subjects are currently available.

Parents are kept closely informed of their daughter's progress. Regular parent meetings are held.

Physical Education. There is a very high standard of Physical Education and the school has an inclusive approach to sport for all. Our sports facilities include 23 acres of playing fields and grounds, a 25m swimming pool, a modern gym complex including multi gym facilities, netball, hockey and tennis courts, a dedicated rowing building and a shared boat house in Oxford. The school "match" sports are hockey, netball, tennis, athletics, basketball, volleyball and swimming with teams regularly becoming County champions, and with girls playing in County and regional teams. The Headington School Boat Club, founded in 1992, is extremely active and Headington is amongst the leading girls' schools for rowing in the UK, with alumnae and current pupils frequently representing England and Great Britain at an international level. Physical Education is also available as a GCSE and A Level subject.

Music. A purpose-built music school ensures a high standard of music within the school, with a large number of girls playing a wide variety of instruments to an advanced level. Over 400 individual music lessons take place every week, and there are a number of orchestras, choirs and ensembles. The Chamber Choir regularly goes on foreign tours and full musical productions take place regularly.

Drama. The Theatre is home to the thriving drama department. There are numerous major and minor productions each year and students become involved in all aspects of theatre, from writing and producing their own plays, to lighting, costume and make-up. They may study for GCSE Drama and Theatre Studies at AS and A2 Levels. There are regular professional productions, as well as English and drama workshops.

Extra-Curricular Activities. Extra-curricular activities and clubs are vital to school life and take place at lunch time as well as after school. Over 50 clubs are on offer, including Young Enterprise and a thriving Duke of Edinburgh's Award Scheme. World Challenge expeditions were introduced in 1991, with recent trips travelling to India, Nepal, Botswana and Zambia. There is a strong tradition of community service, with numerous charity events as well as the opportunity, in the Sixth Form, to help in local hospitals, schools for the handicapped and charity shops. A Combined Cadet Force was introduced in 2001 and attracts a strong uptake. The Debating Society is also popular and very successful.

Much use is made of Headington's proximity to London, Stratford and particularly Oxford. There are regular trips for all age groups to theatres, concerts, lectures, museums and galleries, while Oxford draws many visiting speakers, who often include Headington in their itinerary.

Higher Education and Careers. All girls continue to higher education, studying for arts and science degrees in subjects as diverse as civil engineering, medicine, architecture and textiles. Detailed assistance on choice of universities is given in the Sixth Form through specialist computer programmes and careers tutors. The careers programme is in place throughout the school, with plenty of individual help as girls reach their GCSE years.

Boarding. Boarding at Headington is designed to offer maximum flexibility to parents and girls alike and there are a number of different options available. Full boarding follows the traditional format, with a full programme of weekend activities on offer, ranging from trips to London for the ballet, theatre, exhibitions or shopping to ice skating, rock climbing and indoor skiing. Weekly boarding is popular choice for parents who live within a reasonable distance, with their daughters coming home on Friday and returning to school at the end of the weekend. Flexi-boarding is a popular package whereby girls board a regular one or two nights a week and occasional boarding is for the one-off night, either to accommodate parental commitments or to allow girls to try the boarding experience.

There are four boarding houses, each with its own distinct character, run by a dedicated team of house staff. The Sixth Form houses offer a secure link between school and university, with a number of girls opting to board for the first time at this stage.

Uniform. Girls may choose from a number of options, with two styles of blue checked skirt, navy trousers, a jumper or sweatshirt and fleece, as well as a blazer for formal occasions. Girls in the Sixth Form wear their own clothes.

Entrance. Contact Sue Sowden, Admissions Registrar, to request an application form and prospectus. Entrance to the Preparatory School is taken in order of application for those aged 3–6 and, for pupils aged 7+ upwards, is subject to an interview and a short test. Entrance to the Senior School is by examination: Common Entrance Examination for 11+ and 13+, and school's examination for 12+, 14+ and 16+ ages. Early application is advised and applications should be made at least a year before the proposed date of entry.

Scholarships. (*see Scholarship Entries section*). Academic, Music, Drama, Art and Sport awards are available.

All awards carry a fixed value of £300, which may be significantly increased following voluntary means testing.

Fees per term (2008-2009). Full Boarders: 7,450 (Upper 3), £7,775 (Lower 4–Upper 6); Weekly Boarders: £6,910 (Upper 3), £7,130 (Lower 4–Upper 6); Day Girls £4,050.

Registration Fee. £75 (UK) and £125 (Overseas).

Overseas Examination Fee. £75.

Deposit. UK: £500 (day), £1,000 (boarding). Overseas: £1,500 plus £5,000 fee advance.

Charitable status. Headington School Oxford Limited is a Registered Charity, number 309678. It exists to provide quality education for girls.

Hereford Cathedral School

Old Deanery The Cathedral Close Hereford HR1 2NG
Tel: 01432 363522
Fax: 01432 363525
e-mail: enquiry@hcsch.org
website: www.hcsch.org

Founded ante 1384. No record of the School's foundation survives, although its close association with the Cathedral is indicated by Bishop Gilbert's response to the long-standing right of the Chancellor to appoint the Headmaster in a letter of 1384, and it is probable that some educational institution was always associated with the Cathedral, which was founded in 676.

Governing Body:
President: The Very Revd M Tavinor, Dean of Hereford, MA, MMus
Chairman: The Earl of Darnley, MA
Dr L Seal, MBChB, DA, DObst, RCOG
R Haydn Jones, BSc, MRICS
C D Hitchiner, LLB, ACIS
A G Silcock, MA
Mrs D Bradshaw, BA, MA
P Henchoz, BA
C R Potter, FCCA (*OH*)
C Poole, MBE, LRPS
Prof E Ellis, MA, PhD
Lady Mynors, BA
Mrs V Oliver-Davies, JP

Clerk to the Governors: S T Jones, FCMA

***Headmaster*: P A Smith**, BSc

Deputy Head: Mrs S A Price, MA

Head of Sixth Form: J R Terry, BSc

Chaplain: Canon Revd P A Row, MA

Heads of Department:

Art: C A Wilkes, BA
Biology: Dr G Mowe, BSc
Chemistry: Mrs A J Burdett, MSc
Classics: Mrs S G N de Souza, BA
Drama: Ms L D A Zammit, BEd
Economics: M R Jackson, BA
English: J B Petrie, BA
Geography: Mrs R M Floyd, BSc
History: E R Falshaw, MA
Learning Support: Mrs J M Helme, BPhil
Mathematics: P S Thornley, BA
Modern Languages: T M Lutley, BA
Music: D R Evans, MA, GBSM
PE and Games: A J Hamilton, BSc
Physics: C J Spencer, MA
Religious Studies: Mrs A E D Locke, MA
Technology: C J Howells, BA

Careers Adviser: J H Morris, DGC, MIPD, MICG
OC CCF: Lt Col A K Eames, RM
Bursar: S T Jones, FCMA
Headmaster's PA: Mrs S Gurgul
Admissions & Communications Officer: Mrs S D A Fortey
Tel: 01432 363506, e-mail: admissions@hcsch.org
School Office Administrator: Mrs L G Harding

The Junior School
Headmaster: T Wheeler, MA, BA
Deputy Headmaster: J Debenham, BEd
Head of Pre-Prep: Mrs E Lord, BEd

Assistant Staff:
P Agate, BA
Mrs E A A Ashford, CertEd
Dr I Barber, BSc
Mrs B J Batchelor, BA
T Brown, BA (*History, Geography*)
Mrs M Cadman-Davies, BA, CertEd
Mrs H Copley-May, BA Ed (*Pre-Prep Music*)
Mrs A Dale, CertEd, DipRSASpLD (*SEN*)
Miss K A Davies, BEd (*Girls' Games/Swimming*)
Mrs P Gammage, DipEd
Mrs C Goode, BEd

Mrs K Gummerson (*Art*)
T Hutchinson, BSc, CertEd (*ICT*)
Miss N Jeynes, BEd (*Mathematics*)
Miss C Lambert, BA (*French*)
Mrs S Legge, BA
Mrs K A Matthews, BA
Mrs D J Parry, BA (*English/PSE*)
Mrs S Price, LLB, PGCE
Miss A Sutton, BA (*Drama*)
M Thomas, MA, BMus (*Music*)
Dr H Tomlinson, BA, CertEd (*RE*)
S Turpin, BA
Miss H Watkins, BA
M Wilkinson, BEd
Mrs J Windows, BA (*Head of Nursery*)

Secretary: Mrs S Stick
Nurses: Mrs S Warner, RGN, Mrs J Townsend, RGN

The School is a former Direct Grant and Assisted Places School, which now operates its own Bursary scheme. It is a fully co-educational 11–18 day school of 522 pupils.

Admission. Pupils are normally admitted at the ages of 11, 13 or 16. Admission at age 11 is by sitting the Junior Entrance Examination at the School and at 13 by taking the Common Entrance Examination at the pupils' Preparatory Schools, or a Summer Entrance Examination for those not at Preparatory Schools. Suitably qualified boys and girls may be admitted at Sixth Form level, or at 12+ or 14+, if there are vacancies. The school operates a Deferred Entry scheme at 11 for 13+ entries.

Facilities. The School is situated in the lee of the Cathedral. It occupies many historic buildings and some later ones, all adapted for School use, as well as purpose-built facilities. On the main campus are, in addition to some of the main departments, eight science laboratories, a large music school, an Art, Technology and Computer Centre (that gained Hereford's first RIBA award for architecture), the Gilbert Library, the Dining Hall and the Buttery (Tuck Shop). The Zimmerman Building provides 20,000 square feet of robust working space for Classics, Modern Languages, examination/functions hall, Geography and Drama departments and the new Sixth Form Centre. The Junior School's new pre-preparatory building ("The Moat") has recently received Hereford's second RIBA award for architecture.

Sports facilities are situated on campus (gymnasium and squash courts), by the Cathedral (tennis and netball) and at Wyeside (all major games and HCS rowing club).

Curriculum. Pupils are divided on entry at 11 into 4 forms (a maximum of 20 pupils per form) for academic and pastoral purposes. Below the Sixth Form, pupils take a broad range of subjects. Option choices are made at the end of the Third year (Year 9).

In the Sixth Form pupils are prepared for A (AS/A2) Levels, for which there is a wide choice of subjects: Latin, Greek, English Literature and Language, French, Religious Studies, Classical Civilisation, Psychology, Spanish, Economics, History, Geography, Mathematics, Further Mathematics, Biology, Physics, Chemistry, Design Technology, Art, Textiles, Music and Music Technology, Theatre Studies and Physical Education. Almost all students go on to Higher Education degree courses and the vast majority to the university course of their choice.

Religious instruction throughout is in accordance with the doctrines of the Church of England. The School is privileged to have the daily use of the Cathedral for Chapel.

Sports/Activities include Rugby, Squash, Cricket, Badminton, Tennis, Hockey, Netball, Athletics, and Rowing. There is a CCF Group and a wide range of societies active within the School. The School is an Operating Authority for the Duke of Edinburgh's Award Scheme. Drama flourishes, with several productions each year. The School has a national reputation in debating.

Music. The School is also particularly strong in Music: over half the pupils receive tuition in the full range of orchestral instruments, piano, organ and classical guitar. There are two orchestras, two concert wind bands, jazz band, chamber choir and two junior choirs, recorder ensembles, and many chamber music groups. There is at least one Musical each year and operas are produced from time to time. The musical tradition is strengthened by the presence of the Cathedral Choristers (and former Cathedral choristers) in the School.

Fees per term (2008-2009). £3,336.

Extras. CCF £20 per term; DoE £30 per level; Instrumental Tuition £26.25 per hour, plus public examination fees, OH Club £15 per term, PTA £20 per term.

Scholarships. (*see Scholarship Entries section*). Cathedral choristers are members of the School from entry. They are accepted from the age of 8 as probationers following voice and educational tests held in May each year, and are educated initially at the Junior School. The Governors and the Chapter award choral scholarships jointly annually.

Bursaries. A number of bursaries are awarded competitively to able children from families of limited means.

Old Herefordian Club. *Membership Secretary*: Mrs Helen Pearson.

The Junior School. This is situated close by the main school. (*For details, please see Junior School IAPS entry*).

Charitable status. Hereford Cathedral School is a Registered Charity, number 518889. Its aims and objectives are to promote the advancement of education by acquiring, establishing, providing, conducting and carrying on residential and non-residential schools in which boys and girls of all sections of the community may receive a sound general education (including religious instruction in accordance with the doctrines of the Church of England).

Highgate School

North Road London N6 4AY
Tel: 020 8340 1524 (Office)
020 8347 3564 (Admissions)
Fax: 020 8340 7674
e-mail: office@highgateschool.org.uk
admissions@highgateschool.org.uk
website: www.highgateschool.org.uk

Highgate School was founded in 1565 by Sir Roger Cholmeley, Knight, Chief Justice of England, and confirmed by Letters Patent of Queen Elizabeth in the same year.

Motto: *Altiora in votis.*

Visitor: Her Majesty The Queen

Governors:
J F Mills, CBE, MA, BLitt (*Treasurer and Chairman*)
R M Rothenberg, MBE, BA, FCA, CTA, MAE (*Deputy Chairman*)
J H Hill, CBE, MA
Ms J Carr
M Clarke, MA, FCA
J Claughton, MA
B Davidson, MD, FRCS
The Ven M C Lawson, BA
P E Marshall, BSc, MRICS
Dr K Little, MB, BS, BSc
Miss R Langdale, LLB, M
J D Randall

Bursar and Secretary to the Foundation: J H McGeeney, MA

***Head Master*: A S Pettitt**, MA

Deputy Heads of the Foundation:
T J Lindsay, MA (*Principal Deputy Head, Senior School*)

S M James, BA, MA (*Principal of the Junior School*)

Director of Sir Roger Cholmeley's Charity: R C Wilne, MA

Director of Studies: D M Fotheringham, MA

Assistant Heads:
P R Aston, BEd
S N Brunskill, MA
S Evans, BA
J R Lewis, BA, PhD, FRGS
Mrs J F Morelle, BA
Miss L M Shelley, BA

Admissions Registrar: R C Milner, MA

Teachers:
* *Head of Department*

Art and History of Art:
Miss V Hurr, BA, MA, DipArch
Ms J E W Jammers, MA, PhD
*Mrs T A Jay, MA
Miss R F Manfield, BA
G H Tweedale, Dip AD, ATC

Classics:
*G A Waller, BA
Mrs A J Brunner, BA
D M Fotheringham, MA
P D Harrison, MA
Miss C C Nussey, BA
Miss D Picton, BA
Miss V L Smith, BA, MA

Design Technology:
*P R Aston, BEd
A B H Sursok, BA
A F Thomson, BSc
Mrs C Ward, BSc

Drama and Theatre Studies:
*M L Bowden, ARCM, FRCO, GRSM, LRAM
Ms J E Fehr, BA (**Theatre Studies*)

Economics:
D Amatt, BSc
A Golcoldas, BSc
†Miss K P Norris, BA
D Rey, BSc, MA
*J A Stenning, BA

English:
S G Appleton, MA
*G J H Catherwood, BA
R W H Fisher, BA
Miss A Gwinnell, BA
†Mrs C L Heindl, BA
Mrs K L Kramer, BA, MA, DPhil
A J Plaistowe, MA
Miss L M Shelley, MA
G C Triger, BA

Geography:
*R J Batchelor, BA, MA
D G Brandt, BA
Mrs H J Broadbent, BA
J R Lewis, BA, PhD, FRGS

History and Politics:
*Miss E M Duggan, BA, MA
A E W Grant, BA
T J Lindsay, MA
T R Livsey, BA
†D J McCombes, MA
R R X Miller, MA (**Politics*)
Mrs K B Shapiro, MA

Learning Support:
*D Jones, BA, MEd

Mathematics:
*D J Abramson, BA
†J P Bennett, MA
Miss J R Condon, MMath
P J Dawson, BA
D J T Derham, BSc
Miss H Gardiner, BA
Mrs N S Levin, MA, MBA
C P W Nairne, MMath
D Noyce, MMath
J W Partridge, BA
L A Pearce, BA
S J Williams, MMath

Modern Languages:
S J Brian, MA (**French*)
S N Brunskill, BA
Miss R Church, MA
G D C Creagh, BA (**German*)
*P Le Berre, MA
R C Milner MA
Mrs J F Morelle, BA
Miss N Y Olins, BA
Miss C Pottier, L-ès-L
I Urreaga Gorostidi, BA
†Mrs C Walker, BA
O P C Williams, BA

Music:
V J Barr, LRAM
M L Bowden, ARCM, FRCO, GRSM, LRAM
A Cannière, BM, MM
G Hanson, BMus, LRAM
†J P Murphy, GRNCM
*L S Steuart Fothringham, MA, FRCO
S P Stewart, BMus

Physical Education:
Mrs A C Evans, BA
S Evans, BA Miss S Pride, BSc
Mrs C M Rodgers, BEd, MA (*Head of Girls' Games*)
Ms L Smit, BA
N Starbrook, BSc (*Head of PE*)
†A G Tapp, BEd

Religious Education and Philosophy:
*S Bovey, BA
R N Davis, BA
Ms J T Gosney, BA (**Philosophy*)
The Revd P J J Knight, AIB, Dip Theol (*Chaplain*)

Science:
†W J Atkins, BA
R C J Atkinson, MA, MSci, PhD, DIC
K S Bains, BSc, ARCS (**Chemistry*)
A R Dabrowski, MSci
M Edwards, BA, MPhil, PhD
Mrs V C Jauncey, BSc
†K M Pullinger, BSc
M J Short, BA
D J Smith, BA, MSc, FInstP (**Physics*)
†Ms V E C Stubbs, BSc, PhD
A Z Szydlo, MSc, PhD
Miss J Tod, MSc
Ms A H Ward, BA
Mrs J C Y Welch, BSc, MSc, PhD (**Biology*)
†B S Weston, BSc, PhD

Highgate Junior School
Cholmeley House, 3 Bishopwood Road, London N6 4PL
Tel: 020 8340 9193; Fax: 020 8342 8225
e-mail: jsoffice@highgateschool.org.uk

Principal of the Junior School: S M James, BA
(*For further details, see entry in IAPS section.*)

Highgate Pre-Preparatory School
7 Bishopswood Road, London N6 4PH
Tel: 020 8340 9196; Fax: 020 8340 3442
e-mail: pre-prep@highgateschool.org.uk

Principal: Mrs S E Kennedy

There are 880 boys and girls in the Senior School. The Junior School has some 350 boys and girls, aged 7 to 12, and prepares them only for the Senior School. The Pre-Preparatory School has 130 boys and girls aged 3 to 7.

The entry to the Junior School at age 7 is fully co-educational, as is entry to the Senior School at 11+ and 13+, and girls are also admitted to the Sixth Form at age 16. In time the whole Foundation will be mixed.

Situation and Grounds. The academic centre of the main School is in the heart of old Highgate, which has retained much of its village atmosphere. In addition to the Victorian buildings, such as the Chapel, Big School and central classrooms, the pupils have the benefit of modern facilities such as Dyne House, devoted mainly to the Arts and containing a 200 seat auditorium, the Garner Building for Mathematics and Information Technology, and the Library, created in 1985 from an early 19th Century Tabernacle. A magnificent Art, Design & Technology Centre opened in 2005.

Highgate underground station, on the Northern line, is a short walk away and there is easy access to the School by car or bus. It is four miles to central London (City or West End).

A few hundred yards along Hampstead Lane in Bishopswood Road lie more than twenty acres of playing-fields together with the Mallinson Sports Centre, indoor swimming pool and other extensive sporting facilities, the dining hall, the Junior School and the Pre-Preparatory School. Hampstead Heath and Kenwood, the largest expanse of open country in London, are adjacent.

Pastoral Care. In the Senior School, pastoral care for Years 7 to 8 is organised by form, with a Head of Year in overall charge. From Year 9, each pupil is a member of a House. There are twelve Houses based on particular areas of North London. A Housemaster, helped by four tutors, is responsible for monitoring the day-to-day progress and welfare of the fifty or so pupils in his or her care and for liaising with their parents. A number of Sixth Formers act as peer counsellors.

Academic Curriculum. From 2008 the Senior School will start at age 11+; and there is a further entry at 13+. There are five or six forms in Years 7 and 8 and six or seven forms in Year 9 and the curriculum is broad. At present, in addition to the usual range of subjects, Art, Music and Design Technology are taken by all; most take Latin, and a second modern language is an option. By the time they start their GCSEs pupils have developed an appropriate pattern of work, both in the classroom and out of school. Homework is an integral part of each pupil's programme of study.

The two-year GCSE courses begin in Year 10. The core subjects, studied by all, are: English, English Literature, Mathematics, and double subject Coordinated Sciences (taught by separate teachers of Physics, Chemistry and Biology) or single award separate sciences. A further four subjects (including a modern language) are then chosen from: Art, Classical Civilisation, Design Technology, Geography, French, German, Greek, History, Latin, Music, Religious Studies, Spanish and Russian. In addition to their GCSE subjects, all pupils take Religious Education and Physical Education. Many subjects require assessed coursework and most syllabuses lead to examinations at the end of Year 11. The Edexcel IGCSE qualification is taken in Mathematics and English.

The teaching staff are experienced and well-qualified subject specialists and the teacher/pupil ratio is about 1:9. Class sizes are generally in the low twenties up to GCSE, although for some subjects they will be much smaller; in the Sixth Form classes of 6–16 are usual.

Educational resources include an extensive intranet on a large information technology network, a fully equipped audio-visual centre, satellite receiving equipment and a large, modern lending library. The use of all these is guided by trained professionals and they complement the facilities available in the academic departments, which have their own specialist teaching rooms, equipment and, where appropriate, technicians, computers and libraries. Fieldwork and visits to galleries, museums, exhibitions and lectures are an integral part of the academic programme.

When they enter Year 12, girls and boys choose four subjects from the wide range of AS and A Level courses on offer. Prospective Sixth Formers are assisted in selecting the best programme of study according to their known ability and future plans. A booklet listing the options available and containing details of the courses is published each year and given to Year 11 and their parents before those choices are made.

A feature of the General Studies programme is the fortnightly presentation by a distinguished visitor: leading men and women in politics, the arts and academic or public life come to Highgate and address the Sixth Form. In addition there is a full programme of academic extension seminars in which Sixth Formers can learn about and discuss major topics in A Level subjects which they do not study themselves.

Emphasis is placed on learning to work independently and to develop more advanced study skills. At this stage a pupil will for the first time have a number of private reading periods. A Sixth Form Common Room acts as a social and recreational base for senior pupils.

Each Sixth Former has a tutor who, in conjunction with the Housemaster, exercises supervision over general academic progress and who advises on and monitors higher education applications. Highgate is a member of the Independent Schools Careers Organisation.

Religion. Highgate has a Christian tradition but pupils from all faiths and denominations are welcome. Christian pupils attend Chapel once a week, by houses, and there are occasional voluntary celebrations of Holy Communion; Choral Evensong is sung on some Sundays, at which parents are welcome. Greek Orthodox and Roman Catholic services are also held each term and there are weekly meetings of the Jewish Circle and an assembly for those of other faiths.

Music, Drama and Art. Highgate music has a long and distinguished tradition and many former pupils are now leading composers, conductors or performers. A wide range of musical activities is designed both to encourage the beginner and to stimulate and further the skills of the talented musician.

The orchestra and concert choir are often joint ventures with Channing School, and there is also a training orchestra, a wind band and a chapel choir. There are many opportunities for playing chamber music and regular concerts are arranged, together with masterclasses, workshops and an annual house music competition.

Individual music lessons are available with specialist visiting teachers in all the main instruments and in singing. Orchestral instruments can be hired by beginners who may be offered a free term's trial of lessons. Some of the leading pupils attend the Saturday junior departments at the London music colleges.

Every encouragement is given to participate in drama, as actors, in stage management, or by assisting with sound and lighting. Major productions in recent years have included Oklahoma, Cabaret, Amadeus, Guys and Dolls, The Boyfriend, Another Country, The Merchant of Venice and Comedy of Errors. Small-scale plays are staged in most terms, some by younger pupils. A separate arts studio provides additional rehearsal and performance space. Regular visits to the professional theatre are also arranged.

The excellent new Art department has facilities for painting, print-making, life drawing, sculpture, pottery, photography, video and computer graphics. Whether taking part in formal classes or working in their free time boys and girls are encouraged to explore their own ways of expressing ideas visually. Their work is regularly exhibited, both in the department and elsewhere in the school.

Games. Highgate is exceptionally fortunate in its sports facilities. The extensive playing fields are complemented by the Mallinson Sports Centre and by courts for squash, tennis and Eton fives.

One afternoon each week is devoted to games, in which all who are physically fit take part. Teams are selected in each age group, and also practise at other times. Matches are played on Saturdays as well as during the week. The main games played are association football, cricket, Eton fives, athletics, swimming and cross-country, but a very wide range of other sports is offered at both recreational and competitive level: they include badminton, basketball, canoeing, fencing, golf, gymnastics, hockey, karate, rugby football, sailing, shooting, squash, tennis, volleyball, water polo and weight-training. Countries visited on recent tours by school teams include Holland, Spain and Germany. Many of the magnificent facilities of the fully-staffed Mallinson Sports Centre are also available for family use in the evenings, at weekends and in the holidays.

Activities. We aim to provide as many opportunities as possible in which pupils will develop qualities of self-reliance, endurance and leadership, in which they can serve the community and in which they can develop their own interests and enthusiasms. There are a large number of societies and clubs, usually meeting in the lunch-hour or after school. The School is an operating authority for the Duke of Edinburgh's Award scheme and each year many gain the bronze award and often go on to gain the silver and gold awards. There is also a Community Service scheme and an Urban Survival award scheme. One of Highgate's greatest assets is Cerrig Pryfaid, our field centre in Snowdonia with its own Warden, which is used as a base for outdoor activities and for fieldwork.

Admission. (*See the announcement, at the start of the School's entry, about future co-education.*)

Normal entry to the Junior School is at the age of 7; there are some places in other years for older girls and boys. All candidates take an entrance examination in January for entry the following September. Application should be made in writing to the Principal of the Junior School, 3 Bishopswood Road, London N6 4PL.

Enquiries about places at Highgate Pre-Preparatory School, for girls and boys aged 3 to 7, should be addressed to the Principal, 7 Bishopswood Road, London N6 4PH.

Those who enter the Senior School at 11+ are mainly from Primary Schools while those who enter at 13+ are usually from Preparatory Schools. The remainder enter from Highgate Junior School. Tests and interviews take place in January and 13+ candidates also take Common Entrance in June.

Girls and boys from other schools are also admitted to the Sixth Form at Highgate following written assessments and interviews. Only occasionally are there vacancies at other levels of the School. All enquiries concerning admission to the Senior School should be addressed to the Admissions Registrar, admissions@highgateschool.org.uk.

Fees per term (2008-2009). Senior School: £4,730; Junior School: £4,335; Pre-Preparatory School: £4,098 (Reception–Year 2), £2,050 (Nursery).

Scholarships and Bursaries. (*see Scholarship Entries section*). Foundation Scholarships, Academic and Music Awards are offered each year to those who will be under 12 and under 14 on 1st September. The examinations are held at Highgate at the time of the entry tests in January. Music candidates are auditioned and interviewed and at 13+ there is a short written test. Many will already be playing to a high standard but those with good potential should also apply. Enquiries to the Director of Music are welcomed. A number of Key Stage Awards are available at age 11, age 13 and at entry to the Sixth Form and at other stages when academic excellence is shown and sustained by a pupil. Further Bursaries are available through the Friends of Highgate School Society. Details of all awards are available from the Admissions Registrar.

Old Cholmeleian Society. Former pupils are known as Cholmeleians. Enquiries should be addressed to the Foundation Office at the School, oc@highgateschool.org.uk.

Charitable status. Sir Roger Cholmeley's School at Highgate is a Registered Charity, number 312765. The principal aims of the charity are educational, namely the maintenance of the school.

Hurstpierpoint College
A Woodard School

Hurstpierpoint West Sussex BN6 9JS
Tel: 01273 833636
Fax: 01273 835257
e-mail: info@hppc.co.uk
website: www.hppc.co.uk

Founded 1849 by Nathaniel Woodard, Canon of Manchester.
Motto: *Beati mundo corde*

Visitor:
The Rt Revd The Lord Bishop of Chichester

Provost: The Rt Revd The Bishop of Horsham

School Council:
Chairman: Rear-Admiral S Moore, CB

Members:
Professor J P Bacon, MA, MSc, PhD
Dr J R Brydie
¶R J Ebdon, BSc, MAPM, MCIOB
J C Hance, BA, FCA
Mrs B J T Hanson
M S Harrison, FCA
A Jarvis, BEd, MA, FRSA
The Revd J B A Joyce, BA, DipEd
¶J P Ruddlesdin, FCA
Mrs K E Zeeb

***Headmaster*: T J Manly**, BA, MSc

* *Head of Department*
† *Housemaster/mistress*
§ *Part-time*

Deputy Head & Head of Sixth Form: T Firth, BA
Second Deputy: J P Green, MA
Head of Middle School: R Taylor-West, BA, AKC
Chaplain: Fr Matthew Lawson, MTh

Director of Studies: Mrs K J Austin, BSc
Registrar: D C Clark, DLC
Bursar: S A Holliday, BSc, ACIB

Staff:
Mrs C Adams (*†Martlet*)
T D Asch, BA (**History*)
R Ashley, MA (**Geography*)
J O Baldwin, BSc
A C S Battison, BSc
T J Baxter, BSc, DPhil
N D D Beeby, BA (**Drama, †Chevron House*)
Ms H K Bray, BMus (*†Shield House*)
Mrs A Browne (*†St John's*)
§Mrs L A Burchell, BA
M F Clay, MBA
Miss J C Clarke, BA
Miss H L Clear, BA
B Cole, BA
Ms D B Collins
Miss R J Craig, BA
N Creed, BA
Miss R Crespo Sergio, TML Extremadura
S J Crook, BSc
§R J S Cooke, BSc
Mrs K V Doehren, BEd (**Learning Support*)
Mrs A Dunning, BSc (**Biology*)
C Eustace, MA (**Classics*)
Miss T Farrell, BA (**Art*)
D J Gabbitas, BA
§Mrs K Goddard, MA
P J Goodwin, BSc
G J Haines, BComAd
§A C Hall, BSc, BA
D M Higgins, BA (*†Woodard House*)
§Mrs H E Higgins, BA
R G Hurley, BSc (**Information Technology*)
§Mrs S Hyman, BA
Ms A Jayne, BEng (**Physics*)
Mrs J S Jedamzik, MA
E J Jeffers, BA (**German*)
R M Kift, BEd (**Director of Sport*)
Miss H Knight, BSc
M Lamb, BSc
Mrs K Lea, BSc
Mrs J Leeper, BA (*Senior Housemistress*)
T F Q Leeper, BSc (*†Crescent House*)
Miss A Lieutaud, BA, Maîtrise FLE (*†Fleur House, *French, *Spanish*)
N K Matthews, BA (*Director of Music*)
M J May, BEd (*†St John's House*)
P J McKerchar, MA, CChem, MRSC (**Science and Chemistry*)
N A M Morris, BA
Mrs R Nieuwenhuizen, BA
I D Pattison, BSc (*†Red Cross House*)
§Mrs F Pitcher, BEd
S P Poole, BEd (**Psychology*)
R H Potter, BA
§M J Pulsford, BSc
J R Rowland, BA (**Economics & Business Studies*)
I Sambles, BSc(*Ed*) (*†Eagle House*)
Miss M Schofield, BA (**Design Technology*)
J Scott, BA
§Mrs C A Shearman, BA
R L Shearman, MSc (*†Star House*)
G Spencer, BA (**Dance*)
P G Statter, BSc (**Mathematics; Director of Academic Administration*)
C B Thomson, BSc
Mrs D Treyer-Evans, BA (*Head of PR*)
Mrs K S Turner, BA (**English*)

Dr S Waugh, BA
§Mrs S Wilson
A P Wood, MA (**ERS*)

M Brigden (*Fencing Coach*)
Miss S Ivemy (*Girls' Games Coach*)
Mrs R Jutson (*Girls' Games Coach*)
P J R McKeowan (*Athletics Coach*)
Mrs L J Porter (*Mandarin Teacher*)
Mrs D Saunders (*Head of Girls' Games*)
F J Simkins (*i/c Outdoor Education & DoE Award*)
R Smith, BA (*Fitness Trainer*)
Mrs A Terry-Salter (*Ballet*)
N Turner (*Tennis Coach*)
E J Waagenaar (*Life Skills*)
C Wilson (*Hockey Coach*)

There are 16 visiting Music Teachers.

Preparatory School

Head: Mrs H J Beeby, BH, MA
Deputy Head: R P K Barnes, BA
Director of Studies: Mrs J Grubb, BA
Assistant Head (*Pastoral*): Mrs D K Stoneley, BEd (**Games/ PE & PSHE*)

Staff:
Mrs V Bacon, BEd
J R Bettridge, TCert (*Senior Housemaster; *Geography*)
Miss H K Bray, BMus
Miss S H Bucknall, BEd
T A Cattaneo, BEd, CertEd (**Mathematics*)
C de Britt, BA
Mrs S L Deelman, BSc
C Eustace, MA (**Latin*)
L Gasper, MA (**Drama*)
P J Goodwin, BSc (**Science*)
C W Goldsmith, BA
Mrs P Gordon-Stewart, BA (**English*)
M P E Grubb, BA (**Art*)
§Mrs A C Harrap, BEd
Miss R L Higham, BA
§Mrs S Hyman (*Housemistress*)
Ms H M Lowe, BSc
§Mrs A McQueen, CertEd, RSADipSpLD, AMBDA
Mrs L A Moakes, BA
V Morère, Maîtrise (**rench*)
Miss O J Newnham, BA
§Mrs F Pitcher, BEd
§Mrs C Raby, BEd, MA
M J Temple, CertEd (**History*)
M Travers, MA, GCLCM (**Music*)
D Valentine
C Wroth, DipHE (**Information Technology*)

Pre-Prep School:
Head: Mrs K M Finnegan, BEd

Staff:
Miss V Atkinson, BEd
Mrs B Carter, BEd
Ms S Jarvis, BA, LG
Mrs S Jenkins, BEd
Mrs T Mayfield, BA
Mrs C P Owen, BEd

Classroom Assistants:
Mrs K Arrowsmith, NVQ Level 2
Miss K Medhurst, NNEB
Mrs D J Reed, DPP Level 3
Miss L Taylor, Nursery Nurse

Hurstpierpoint College is a co-educational day and boarding school for boys and girls aged between 4 and 18 years. Pre-Prep, Prep and Senior Schools are linked by common values and a common academic and administrative framework, to provide a complete education. There are currently 303 boys and 198 girls. 50% of the pupils are boarders. The Preparatory School has a further 232 boys and girls and the Pre-Prep currently has 64 pupils.

Buildings and General. At the heart of the school's large country campus lie the core school buildings and Chapel arranged around two attractive quadrangles built of traditional Sussex knapped flint. Key facilities nearby including the floodlit Astroturf, art school, sports hall, music school, dance and drama studios, 250 seat theatre, indoor swimming pool and Medical Centre. Other facilities include a Learning Resources Centre and Library and fully equipped IT Centre. The extensive grounds are laid mainly to playing fields and include one of the largest and most attractive school cricket pitches in the Country. Work begins in summer 2008 on a major new extension to the classroom block, providing 15 additional classrooms and a new IT suite.

The school is truly co-educational throughout and offers boarding for boys and girls from the age of 7. Boarding is a particularly popular option at the school with many day pupils and flexi-boarders later opting to become weekly boarders. In their Upper Sixth year at Hurst, pupils join St John's House, a co-educational day and boarding house where, appropriately supervised, they enjoy greater freedoms and are encouraged to further develop their independent learning skills in preparation for university.

Chapel. As a Woodard School, Hurstpierpoint is a Christian foundation and underpinned by Christian values, although pupils of other faiths or of no faith are warmly welcomed. Pupils attend up to three assemblies during the week. The main Eucharist, which parents and friends are most welcome to attend, takes place mainly early on Friday evenings, although there are also occasional Sunday services in addition to voluntary celebrations of the Holy Communion. Pupils who wish to do so are prepared in small classes for the annual Confirmation taken by one of the Bishops of the diocese.

Curriculum. The five-day academic week is structured to allow boys and girls to study a variety of subject options that can be adapted to suit their natural ability. The entry year (Shell) gives pupils the chance to experience most of our GCSE subjects before they choose their options. It involves the study of English, History, Geography, French, German, Spanish, Latin, Mathematics, Physics, Chemistry, Biology, Religious Studies, Art, Design & Technology, Music, Drama, Physical Education, IT and PSHE. In the second (Remove) and in the third (Fifth) years students study between 8 and 11 GCSE subjects. In addition to the core subjects there are four option blocks offering a choice of 14 subjects.

The great majority of Sixth formers study four AS Levels in the Lower Sixth. The choice is wide, with 28 AS subjects to choose from. Art & Design (Photography), Business Studies, Classical Civilisation, Computing, Dance, Economics, Further Maths, Music Technology, Philosophy and Psychology are introduced in addition to the GCSE options. There is also a General Studies programme. The Upper Sixth can take a varied programme with the most able studying four or five full A Levels, whilst others build a valuable qualifications portfolio by studying a varying number of AS subjects along with at least two full A Levels.

All pupils' work is overseen by academic tutors and we take particular care to ensure that university applications are properly targeted to suit the students' aspirations and talents.

Games. The School operates a "Sport for All" policy that seeks to place pupils in games most suited to their tastes and abilities. During the first two years they are expected to take part in at least some of the major sports but thereafter a greater element of choice occurs. The major sports are Rugby, Hockey, Cricket and Athletics for boys; Hockey, Netball and Rounders for girls. Overseas tours form an important part of a wider education. In addition there are teams in Basketball, Cross Country, Football, Golf, Polo, Shooting, Squash, Swimming and

Tennis. The Sports Hall and indoor Swimming Pool provide opportunities for many other pursuits such as Aerobics, Badminton, Gymnastics, Weight Training and Water Polo, while the Outdoor Pursuits enable pupils to enjoy challenges such as Rock Climbing and Canoeing.

Service Afternoons. On Wednesdays all pupils other than the Shell (Year 9) are expected to take part in The Duke of Edinburgh's Award activities alongside the Combined Cadet Force (Army or RAF section), Community Service or Environmental Conservation.

Music. There has always been a strong musical tradition at Hurstpierpoint with an orchestra and other more specialised ensembles. A large proportion of the pupils, currently 124, take individual instrumental lessons and give frequent recitals. The Chapel Choir plays a major part in regular worship and there are several other choral groups.

Drama. The Shakespeare Society is the oldest such school society in the country and organises an annual production. Drama covers a wide range and varies from major musicals to more modest House plays and pupil directed productions. The 250 seat Bury Theatre also gives the more technically minded ample opportunity to develop stage management, lighting and sound skills.

Other Activities. The Thursday afternoon activity programme is for Shell and Remove pupils (Years 9 & 10) and include Art, Climbing, Dance, Fencing, POD Casting, Shooting, Horse Riding, Polo, Karate, Golf Range, Clay Pigeon Shooting, alongside a variety of music clubs and literary clubs. Other activities also take place during the school week.

Hurst Johnian Club. In addition to providing facilities and events for Old Pupils, the Club also assists with careers and supports the current pupils in various ways, eg Gap Year travel fund and tour sponsorship contributions. Contact the Hon Secretary, c/o Hurstpierpoint College.

Fees per term (2008-2009). Senior School: £7,725 Full Boarders; £7,310 Weekly Boarders; £5,785 Day Pupils; Flexi-boarding £6,885.

Awards. (*see Scholarship Entries section*). Scholarships and Exhibitions available at 13+ and 16+: Academic, All-Rounder, Art, Drama, Music, 'Downs' Sports, Design & Technology, and IT.

Preparatory School. *See entry in IAPS section.*

Further Details. For 13+ entry contact Mrs Sally Lloyd, Senior School Admissions Officer. For 16+ entry contact Miss Elizabeth Milne, Sixth Form Admissions Officer.

Charitable status. Hurstpierpoint College is a Registered Charity, number 1076498. It aims to provide a Christian education to boys and girls between the ages of four and eighteen in the three schools on the campus.

Hutchesons' Grammar School

21 Beaton Road Glasgow G41 4NW
Tel: 0141 423 2933
Fax: 0141 424 0251
e-mail: rector@hutchesons.org
website: www.hutchesons.org

Founded and endowed by the brothers George and Thomas Hutcheson (Deed of Mortification 1641). The School is governed by Hutchesons' Educational Trust.

Motto: *Veritas.*

Governors:
Not more than 17 in number.
Representatives of the following Bodies:
Glasgow Presbytery of the Church of Scotland (2), Senatus Academicus of Glasgow University (1), Merchants' House of Glasgow (1), Trades House of Glasgow (1), Patrons of Hutchesons' Hospital (2), Glasgow Educational Trust (1), Senate of the University of Strathclyde (1), FP Club (1), School Association (1) and not more than 9 persons co-opted by the Governors.

Chairman: A K Denholm, DUniv, FUniv, FCIBS, FInstP, FEI, SBStJ

***Rector*: Dr K M Greig**, MA Oxon, PhD Edinburgh

Senior Depute Rector: Mr M Martin, BSc Hons

Bursar: I T Keter, BA CA

Depute Rectors (Secondary School):
C Bagnall, BA Hons, MEd
Mrs J Beattie, Dip Com
J McDougall, MA Hons
Mrs L McIntosh, MA

Depute Rectors (Primary School):
Mrs L McKie, AGSM, DCE
Miss F Macphail, BA, MBA
Mrs C Hatfield, BEd

Heads of Departments:
Art: Mrs S Breckenridge, BA Hons
Biology: Mrs M J Jheeta, BSc, MS
Chemistry: P H B Uprichard, BSc
Classics: D H Gillies, BA, MSc
Computer Studies: Ms R Housley, BSc, DipCompEd
Drama: Mrs V Alderson, DipSD
Economics & Business Studies: Mr M Bergin, BSc Hons
English: A D Dunlop, BA, MEd, DipEd
Geography: C C Clarke, BSc
History: Dr R H Gaffney, MA, PhD
Home Economics: Mrs D Green, DipHEcon
Mathematics: Mrs M T Fyfe, BSc
Modern Languages: Mrs E M Bertram, MA Hons
Modern Studies: G F Broadhurst, MA
Music: E W M Trotter, BMus
Philosophy: (*to be confirmed*)
Physical Education:
Director of PE: S Lang, BEd
Head of Boys' PE: R Dewar, BEd Hons
Head of Girls' PE: Miss K McMeeking, BSc
Director of Hockey: Miss R Simpson, BEd
Physics: Dr S Lonie, BSc Hons, MSc, PhD
Religious Studies: S J Branford, MA
Technology: R W Furness, BEd

Rector's Secretary & Admissions: Mrs M E Norman

Development Director: Ms C Gillen, BA

The school has just over 1,700 pupils, with 1,150 boys and girls from 12 to 18 years at the Secondary School in Beaton Road and 550 aged 5 to 12 at the Primary School in Kingarth Street. Pupils at the Primary School move automatically to the Secondary School.

For 118 years Hutchesons' Boys' Grammar School was situated in Crown Street, but in 1960 moved to new buildings on an open site at Crossmyloof. In 1976 the Boys' School combined with the Hutchesons' Girls' Grammar School, founded in 1876, to form one co-educational establishment housed on two sites a mile apart. The Boys' School in Beaton Road became the Secondary School, with the Girls' School in Kingarth Street evolving into the Primary School. The last decade has seen substantial development on both sites, including a new Infant Block, Science Wing, Sports Hall, Library, dining room and classrooms. After acquiring the church adjoining the Beaton Road site, the School converted and extended it to form a centre for ICT and music, as well an auditorium and a multi-purpose studio/meeting room. In addition to playing fields on the Beaton Road site, the Auldhouse Sports Ground has pitches for rugby, hockey and cricket.

Admission. Pupils are normally admitted on interview at age 4/5 and by examination at age 9/10 to the Primary School or at age 11/12 to the Secondary School, but applications for vacancies at other stages are welcomed.

New pupils normally start at the beginning of the academic year, but intermediate entries are possible from time to time where circumstances dictate.

Fees per term (2008-2009). Primary £2,240–2,590, Secondary 1–2 £2,878, Secondary 3–6 £2,803. All fees from Primary 1 to Secondary 2 include books.

Financial Assistance. The School offers financially means-tested bursaries by competitive entry for entry to S1.

Religion. The School is non-denominational, but assembles most mornings for a broadly Christian service. Muslim and Jewish assemblies are also held. Religious Studies are taught in S1 and S2.

Curriculum. In the Primary School, a strong emphasis on Mathematics and Language forms the foundation for confident and successful development across the curriculum, covering Environmental Studies, Religious and Moral Education, Personal and Social Education and Health. Pupils benefit from expert teaching by specialists in Art & Craft, PE, Music, Games, ICT, and Modern Languages.

For the first two years of Secondary School, all pupils take English, a Modern Language, Latin (and another modern language in S2), History, Geography, Mathematics, three sciences, ICT, Technology, Art, Music, Drama, Physical Education and Religious Studies. They then follow more specialised courses leading to presentation for SQA Highers in S5. Most pupils continue into S6, which offers a wide range of courses, including Advanced Highers, A Levels and further Highers.

In general, pupils are prepared for universities and higher education, including Oxbridge. They are given vocational and pastoral guidance throughout the Secondary School.

Games. Rugby, Football, Hockey, Cricket, Rowing, Netball, Tennis, Golf, Badminton, Cross-Country Running and Curling, with special attention paid to Rugby, Hockey, Swimming and Athletics.

Clubs and Societies include the Debating Society, Chess, Bridge (the school is the Scottish Schools' champion), Dramatic Societies, EcoSchools, the Art Club, Computing, Film Club, Photography, Technology, Choirs, Ensembles, Orchestras, Pipe and Ceilidh Band, and Scripture Union. More than 500 pupils receive specialist instrumental and vocal tuition. There is also a very strong tradition of fund-raising for charity, community service, Young Enterprise and The Duke of Edinburgh's Award. School pupils publish the School magazine, "The Hutchesonian", every June.

Charitable status. Hutchesons' Educational Trust is a Registered Charity, number SC002922.

Hymers College

Hull East Yorkshire HU3 1LW
Tel: 01482 343555
Fax: 01482 472854
e-mail: enquiries@hymers.hull.sch.uk
website: www.hymerscollege.co.uk

Hymers College was opened in 1893, through the generosity of the late Robert Hymers, of Stokesley, Yorkshire, and in accordance with the original intention of the late Rev John Hymers, DD, FRS, Fellow of St John's College, Cambridge.

The school became fully co-educational in September 1989.

Governors:
Chairman of Governors: M de-V Roberts, FCA
R P Ashton
S Martin, MA, FCA
J H Robinson, BSc, CEng, FIChemE
J E Townend, MP, FCA
M Day, BA Hons, ACA
Mrs D Fisher, LLB
Professor L E Frostick, BSc, PhD, FGS, CGeol, FRGS, CGeog, FRSA
R Laucht, BA, ACMA
Mrs P Locker BA Hons, BA Open
J R Wheldon, MRICS
Mrs P M Wilkinson, BA, JP, SRN
Mrs B E Elliott, MSc, BN, RGN, RSCN, RHV, NNDNCert
Mrs G Greendale
Cllr J G Robinson, BA
D J Stone, BA
S G West, BA
P J E Wildsmith, LLB
M C S Hall, BSc
P A B Beecroft, MA, MBA

***Headmaster*: D C Elstone**, MA Ed Mgt

Deputy Head (*Academic*): T P O'Byrne, BMus
Deputy Head (*Pastoral*): Mrs C R Gravelle, BA

Bursar and Clerk to the Governors: G D Noble, BA, CDipAF, FIMgt, FInstAM, MInstD

Senior Teachers:
J G Bell, MA (*Head of Science*)
Mrs S A Atkinson, CertEd (*Head of Junior School*)
T P O'Byrne, BMus (*Deputy Head – Academic*)
Mrs C R Gravelle, BA (*Deputy Head – Pastoral Care*)

Teachers:
* *Head of Department*

*C Aldred, MA
Mrs S Atkinson, CertEd
Ms D Bache, BA
Miss S E Baines, BA
Mrs J M Brown, BA
Mrs D Bushby, LRAM
Revd M J Bushby, BSc, MA
A D Cadle, BSc
Ms L Catlin, BA
*P Cook, BA
Mrs C Copeland, BSc
J Denton, MA
Mrs J Dex, CertEd
P C Doyle, BSc
Mrs J I Duffield, BA
Mrs R Elstone, MA
Mrs A Exley, BA
N Exley, BA
Mrs P V Ferguson, MA
*C J Fitzpatrick, BA Ed
Mrs N Foster, BSc
I Franklin, BSc, PhD
*C Gaynor-Smith, BA
*Mrs N Gibson, DEUG Lic Lyon
Mrs Z L Gillett, BSc
A Gittens, BA
*J Gravelle, BSc
D Guy, BA
Mrs S Guy, BA
Miss K Halliwell, MChem
D Harrison, MA
D Hickman, BSc
Mrs S F Hood, BA
Mrs H Jackson, BSc
Dr J M Jarvis, BSc
M Jones, BSc
J R Kennedy, BA
G Lansdell, BEd
Mrs S Lord, BA
*D McPherson, BA
M McTeare, BA
P Meadway, BSc
D A Merrick, BSc
*Mrs C Mitchell, BA
*I Nicholls, BA
C O'Donnell, BA
Mrs S O'Reilly, BSc
A Penny, GRNCM, ARNCM
*G Prescott, MA
*M Pybus, BMus
R Quick, ALCM, ARCM
A Raspin, BSc
Mrs L Raymond
*P J Roberts, MA
M Sharp, GLCM, ALCM
Mrs S E Sinkler, BPharm
*Ms F A Stanyon, BA
R J Summers, BSc
J Swinney, BSc
Mrs J Tapley, BEd
N A Taylor, BA
*S Taylor, BA, MEd
D Thompson, BSc
Miss D J Wallis, BA
Mrs L A Walmsley, BA
S J Walmsley, BA
Mrs A Webb, BA
A Whittaker, BA
R K Wooldridge, BSc
Miss L Wright, MSc
J Wynn, BA
*A G Young, BA

Number of Pupils. 970.

The Junior School has 228 pupils aged 8–11 and is staffed by specialist teachers. There is a full range of academic and sporting activities.

Admission is by competitive examination at ages eight and nine. Most pupils proceed at age eleven into the Senior School by a competitive examination taken also by pupils from other schools. Almost all pupils qualify for the Sixth Form through GCSE results. Pupils from other schools are admitted to the Sixth Form on the basis of good GCSE results.

Pupils are prepared for the GCSE in a broad curriculum including music, business-related subjects, computer studies, technology and the crafts.

There is a full range of courses leading to AS and Advanced Level examinations, and special preparation is given for Oxford and Cambridge entrance.

Facilities. The buildings consist of 35 classrooms, 11 specialist laboratories, a 30-booth language laboratory, extensive ICT facilities, audio-visual room, art rooms, theatre, Design/Technology Centre and a music centre containing teaching, practice and recital rooms, a gymnasium and very large sports hall. A new Junior School building contains 9 classrooms and specialist rooms for music, DT, art, ICT and science, along with a library, hall and changing rooms. The grounds, which extend for over 40 acres, include a newly built all-weather hockey pitch and 12 tennis courts. A swimming pool/sports centre opened in November 2004.

Extra-Curricular Activities. All pupils are strongly encouraged to participate in the very wide range of extra-curricular activities. The main school games are rugby, cricket, hockey, netball, tennis and athletics There are also school teams in swimming and fencing. The school regularly competes at national level in these sports and provides members of county and national teams. Many pupils take part in the Duke of Edinburgh's Award Scheme and the school has an impressive track record in Young Enterprise. Other clubs include ACF, chess, modelling, debating, photography, community service and Christian Union. Drama is particularly strong, with several productions a year. Music is a major school activity; there are three full orchestras, a large choir, and several chamber and "academy" groups in each part of the school. Individual tuition is available in most instruments.

Fees per term (2008-2009). (including text-books) Senior School £2,640; Junior School £2,196–£2,319. Hymers Bursaries are awarded at ages 8, 9, 11 and 16.

The Old Hymerians Association, c/o Headmaster, Hymers College, Hull HU3 1LW.

Charitable status. Hymers College is a Registered Charity, number 529820-R. Its aims and objectives are education.

Ipswich School

Henley Road Ipswich Suffolk IP1 3SG
Tel: 01473 408300
Fax: 01473 400058
e-mail: registrar@ipswich.suffolk.sch.uk
website: www.ipswich.suffolk.sch.uk

The School was founded about 1390 by the Ipswich Merchant Guild of Corpus Christi. Its first Charter was granted by Henry VIII and this was confirmed by Queen Elizabeth I. In 1852 the School moved into new buildings, to which extensive additions and improvements have since been made.

Motto: *Semper Eadem.*

Visitor: Her Majesty The Queen

Governing Body:
K Daniels, ACII, FPMI (*Chairman*)
D E Barker, MBE
D E Bertram-Ralph
C D Brown, MA
G Byrne Hill, MA
J A Caudle, LLB
D A Chivers, BA, DipPM
W D Coe, BSc, ACA
The Revd Dr G M W Cook, MSc, PhD, FIBiol, FRSC
D J Defoe, BSc, PGCE
Professor L A Dobrée, BSc, MSc, RN, RM, CertEd
Dr J L H Foster, MA, MSc, PhD
The Bishop of St Edmundsbury and Ipswich (*ex officio*)
J W Poulter, MA
A C Seagers, BA
Ms M J Smith, BA, PGCE, MPhil
N H H Smith, MA, FCA
H E Staunton, BA, FCA
Dr D J Stone, MA, PhD
Professor C M Temple, BSc, MA, DPhil, CPsychol, AsFBPS
Dr D Thakerar, MBBS, LRCP, MRCS, DOccMed
Mrs C H Willcox, MSc Econ (*Vice-Chairman*)
M G Wood, BA, FCMA

***Headmaster*: I G Galbraith**, MA

Deputy Head: D Ayling, MA
Head of Sixth Form: W G B Stansbury, MA
Head of Middle School: A D Brown, MA
Head of Lower School: D F Walsh, MA
Director of Studies: Miss J C Limrick, BSc
Chaplain: The Revd D J Warnes, MA

Heads of Houses:
M J Bannan, BSc
S J Blunden, BA
Mrs N M Brown, BA
Dr N K Notcutt, BSc
A K Golding, MA
P R Gray, BA

Heads of Department:
Mrs Z Austin, MA (*Psychology*)
A J Burnett, BA (*English*)
A M Calver, BSc (*Careers*)
R L Clayton, BEd (*Physical Education*)
M J Core, BSc (*Mathematics*)
J R C Cox, MA (*Classics*)
Mrs M O Davis, BEd (*Art and Design*)
S J Duncombe, BA (*Design Technology*)
Mrs K Galbraith, MA (*History*)
P M Godsell, BSc, PhD (*Biology*)
D J P Halford-Thompson, BSc (*Chemistry & Science*)
J E G Halls (*Games*)
A D Leach, MA, BMus, ARCO, LRAM (*Music*)
J A C Phillips, BEng, MEd (*ICT*)
J A Thompson, MA (*Modern Languages*)
Q R Thurtle, BTech (*Physics*)
S J Tidball, MA (*Economics & Business Studies*)
Ms T Walker, BA (*Religious Studies*)
Mrs L Ward, BEd (*Drama*)
R G Welbourne, BA, FRGS (*Geography*)

Head of Preparatory School: Mrs J M Jones, BA

Bursar: P V Boughton
Registrar: Mrs Y M Morton
Headmaster's Secretary: Mrs S Dawson

Ipswich School occupies an attractive site adjacent to Christchurch Park. The cricket field lies within the perimeter of the school buildings and other playing fields of 30 acres are ten minutes' walk from the school.

There are 790 pupils in the Senior School (11–18), including 45 boarders. Of these, 225 boys and girls are in the Sixth Form. There are 300 pupils in the co-educational Preparatory School (3–11). The Senior School became co-educational in 1997.

The Boarding House stands in its own grounds a short distance from the school. There is a choice of full or weekly boarding for pupils in the Senior School. Day pupils may become boarders temporarily or permanently if there is space and if the need arises.

All academic subjects have been housed in new or refurbished rooms in the last few years and visitors comment on the quality of the buildings, which are grouped around one of the school's playing fields.

The Preparatory School is housed in new, purpose-built accommodation opened in 2006 on an adjacent campus; it benefits from all the amenities of the Senior School including the Sports Hall, Swimming Pool, Performing Arts Centre and Playing Fields. (*For further details, see entry in IAPS section.*)

Admission. Pupils entering the Preparatory School must show language and number skills appropriate to their age. The main entry to the Senior School at 11 is by examination in English, Mathematics and a Reasoning test, taken in early February. At 13, more pupils enter the Senior School, taking the Common Entrance Examination or the school's own Entrance and Scholarship Examination. Admission to the Sixth Form for girls and boys from other schools is by attainment of the required grades at GCSE, a report from the previous Head and an interview in November. Application forms may be obtained from the Registrar. A registration fee of £50 is payable (£25 for brothers or sisters).

Religious Education. There is religious education throughout the age range and weekly chapel services for different sections of the school; pupils normally attend one Sunday service a term at which their parents are also most welcome.

Careers. Computer analyses of interests and aptitudes complement carefully planned advice about GCSE and A Level choices, higher education and professional training.

Curriculum. In the Preparatory School pupils study English, Mathematics, French, ICT, History, Geography, RE, Science, Music, PE, Art and Design Technology.

Senior School pupils follow a common curriculum in the first two years with a choice between French and Spanish. An option including Latin, Classical Civilisation, German and Russian is introduced in the third year. Mathematics, English, one or more Modern Foreign Languages, and either separate or coordinated Sciences are taken by all pupils to GCSE level. Apart from these compulsory subjects, pupils are examined in 3 or 4 other subjects chosen from French, Latin, History, Geography, German, Russian, Spanish, Drama, Design and Technology, Classical Civilisation, Art and Design, Religious Studies and Music.

In the Sixth Form AS and A Level subjects are chosen from the following:

Mathematics, Further Mathematics, Physics, Chemistry, Biology, Latin, Classical Civilisation, Economics, Business Studies, Art, Design Technology, Music, History, Geography, English, French, German, Russian, Spanish, Psychology, PE, Philosophy of Religion and Ethics.

In addition to their A Level studies, all Sixth Formers participate in an Enrichment Programme composed of group work and conferences designed to complement and broaden the conventional curriculum. Students are also able to gain qualifications in a range of subjects such as Critical Thinking, ICT, Mandarin, Politics, Law and Spanish.

Societies and Activities. All are encouraged to participate in a variety of extra-curricular activities which take place in lunchtimes, after school, at weekends and during the holidays. One afternoon a week is devoted to community service, conservation work, CCF (Army and RAF contingents) and a variety of sports and indoor pursuits. Sixth Formers may participate in the school's International Leadership Programme at this time.

Drama in the school is particularly strong; continuous activity in this sphere maintains a succession of productions throughout the year, in all age groups. Productions in 2007–2008 included: Death of a Salesman, Inherit the Wind, Five Arrive in Suffolk, The Learned Ladies, Lady Lollipop, The Samson Riddle, Lord Arthur Savile's Crime.

Individual lessons are given in all branches of Music, and there are good opportunities for music-making, including Choral Society, Chapel Choir, Chamber Orchestra, Symphony Orchestra, Second Orchestra, Concert Bands, Jazz Bands and Rock Groups. In addition there are lunchtime recitals, formal and informal concerts, instrumental competitions, choir tours, and concert visits which pupils are encouraged to attend. Outside the school, concerts are given at Snape Maltings and at parish churches in Suffolk.

The Duke of Edinburgh's Award Scheme, Young Enterprise and the Community Sports Leader Award Scheme are run within the school.

Games. The main team games for boys are Rugby football, hockey and cricket and for girls, hockey, netball and rounders. Alternatives for many in the Senior School include athletics, cross-country, golf, tennis, Eton fives, soccer, squash, polygym, sailing, badminton and swimming; also windsurfing which is carried out on nearby Alton Water. Skiing parties travel overseas each year.

The Mermagen Sports Hall provides facilities for a wide range of indoor sports and is part of a complex which includes a Cricket Gallery, whose indoor nets function as a centre of excellence for the county as well as the school. There is a heated indoor swimming pool, three covered Eton fives courts, two squash courts and a twenty-two station fitness suite.

Fees per term (2008-2009). Day: £3,451 Senior School; £3,148 Lower School; £2,635 Preparatory School; £2,367 Pre-Preparatory Department.

Boarding (inclusive of tuition fees): Full Boarding: £6,053 Senior School; £5,296 Lower School; Weekly Boarding: £5,682 Senior School; £5,056 Lower School.

Scholarships. (*see Scholarship Entries section*). Queen's and Foundation Scholarships are available at 11 and 13, carrying up to half remission of tuition fees. Scholarships and Exhibitions may be awarded for music or art as well as for academic excellence and a Sports Scholarship is offered at 13+. Academic, Music and All-Rounder Scholarships are available for external entrants to the Sixth Form. Outstanding students intending to study Maths or a Physics related degree at University and currently at a state school may apply for an Ogden Trust Science Scholarship in the Sixth Form; awards are up to 100% of fees. Students intending to study Design Technology and Maths in the Sixth Form may apply for an Arkwright Scholarship. All awards may be held by day pupils or boarders and may be supplemented by bursaries in case of need.

Bursaries. These are available on a means-tested basis, up to full fee remission, for entry at 11, 13 and 16.

Leaving Exhibitions. Six endowed Exhibitions of £100 each and Rigaud Prizes of £50.

The Old Ipswichian Club. Annual dinners are held in London in April and Ipswich in December. There are clubs for cricket, fives and golf. Teams are fielded against the school in several sports and the Club holds a number of social events each year.

Charitable status. Ipswich School is a Registered Charity, number 310493. It exists for the purpose of educating children.

The John Lyon School

Middle Road Harrow Middlesex HA2 0HN

Tel: 020 8872 8400
Fax: 020 8872 8455
e-mail: enquiries@johnlyon.org
website: www.johnlyon.org

The John Lyon School was established as a Day School in 1876 under the Statutes made by the Governors of Harrow School, in pursuance of the Public Schools Act, 1868.

Motto: *Stet Fortuna Domus.*

Foundation Governors: The Governors of Harrow School

Governors:
Dr Owain Arwel Hughes, OBE (*Chairman*)
M J C Christelow
D A Crehan
J R Davies
Prof A de Mello
J Dunston
A Fraser, MBE
P R Harrison
J F R Hayes
A McClaran
Mrs S Symonds

Clerk to the Governors: A J F Stebbings, 45 Pont Street, London SW1X 0BX

***Headmaster*: K J Riley**, BA, MEd

Bursar: N J Marten, MCMI

Academic Deputy Head: S Miles, BMus, ARCO, ARCM, AMusLCM

Pastoral Deputy Head: D A Rimmer, BSc, MSc

Assistant Staff:
S J K Andon, BA, MSc
Mrs A L Armstrong, BA (*History*)
L D Budd, BA, MA
P M Clarke, BA, MSc (*Learning Strategies*)
Dr A L M Clayton, BSc, PhD (*Biology*)
C J Clews, BA
R L Cobb, BEd, BA (*Economics*)
P J Cowie, BA
O Damree, BSc
T P Dennehy, BA
R A Freeborn, BSc, MSc (*ICT*)
L R Garwood, BA
Miss D Gibbs, BA (*Drama; Head of Sixth Form*)
W I N Griffith, BA
Mrs L Gupta, LLB (*Chemistry*)
G Haines, BA, BEd (*Psychology*)
Miss E Headd, BSc
Ms L C Holmqvist, BA, MA
Ms L Hope (*Art and Design*)
J L Irvine, MA
A L Jones, BSc
S J Leach, BSc, MSc (*Physical Education*)
Miss V L Levinge, BA
A S Ling, BSc
C K Longhurst, BA
T Mahon, BSc, MA
P A Matthews, BSc, MA (*Geography*)
Mrs J Morris, BA, MBA (*Modern Languages*)
J Orme, BSc
I R Parker, BSc (*Head of Upper School*)
N H Parsons, BA
Mrs L S Plummer, BA
S Rana, BMedSc (*Science*)
Miss J Rowley Jones, MusB
A Roy, BA (*English*)
Ms C Seymour, BSc, BEd
Ms K F Syed, BEd, MSci
Miss L A Twist, BA
Mrs U Varsani, BA
M W Vickery, BEng
D P Vosper Singleton, MMath
W R J Waite, BSc (*Mathematics*)
Ms P Waldron, BA (*Head of Oldfield & Lower School*)
D F Weedon, MA
A S Westlake, BA, BA (*Religious Studies*)
Miss A M Wilby, BA, MMus (*Music*)
A P Wright, BA

Part-Time:
Miss V M L Balavan, Licence LLCE
Mrs F Brown, BA
Ms B Guyomard, BA, MA
Mrs E J Ingham, BSc, MSc
Mrs E J Marden, BA
Mrs E McMillan, BSc
Mrs C A Wickson, BA

Visiting Music Staff:
K Bache, ARCM, LGSM (*trumpet*)
R Boyle, AGSM (*guitar, guitar ensemble*)
Mrs A Chancellor, MA, DipRCM, LRAM (*viola, violin*)
J Clarkson (*voice*)
H Clement-Evans, GRNCM, PPRNCM (*oboe, saxophone*)
Miss S Crisp, BMus Hons TCM (*violin*)
V E Davies, BMus (*horn, euphonium, trombone*)
L Evans (*bass guitar, Rock Jam Sessions*)
Miss L Friend (*flute*)
A Gerolemou, BMus Hons (*electric guitar*)
C Grey, MA, BMus, LRAM (*piano, jazz band, Junior Strings, Grade V Theory, Musician in Residence*)
Miss G Harvey, BMus Hons (*saxophone, saxophone ensemble*)
W Kristiansen, BMus, LRAM (*electric guitar*)
Miss E May, BMus, LRAM (*cello*)
R Marshall (*drums & percussion, electric guitar*)
M McLaughlin, DipTCL (*drums & percussion*)
R Russell, MMus, BMus (*clarinet*)
Ms K Stagg, MMus, LLCM (*clarinet*)

PA to the Headmaster: Mrs H S Cade

There are 580 boys in the School, all day boys.

Admission. The School is open to boys residing within reasonable travelling distance.

There are places each September for boys who will be over 11 and under 12 on their entry into the school. An entrance examination is set in January.

In addition, places are available each September for boys to enter the third form. They must be over 13 and under 14. An entrance examination takes place in January. There are also places available in the Sixth Form for boys who have five A grades at GCSE.

Registration Fee: £75.

Fees per term (2008-2009). £4,215, payable in advance, which covers the cost of all textbooks and stationery.

Curriculum. The School Curriculum at present includes Religious Studies, English, History, Geography, Economics, French, German, Spanish, Italian, Latin, Mathematics, Chemistry, Physics, Biology, Art and Design, Music, Drama, Computer Studies, Government and Politics, Psychology and PE. Religious teaching is non-denominational.

Examinations. Boys are prepared for GCSE. In the Sixth Form four subjects are normally chosen to be studied for AS level in the first year leading to three (or four) A2 levels in the second.

Scholarships. (*see Scholarship Entries section*). *Governors' Scholarships*: Academic and All-Rounder Scholarships will be awarded to outstanding boys entering through the School Entrance Examinations at 11+ and 13+. Additional Academic Scholarships are available to Sixth Form entrants on the basis of outstanding performance at GCSE.

Art & Design, Drama, Music and Sports Scholarships are available at 11+, 13+ and 16+.

Bursaries. Bursaries up to the value of 95% of the fees are available, subject to financial assessment.

Term of Entry. Normal entry date is in the September term.

School Buildings. The School Buildings are on the West side of Harrow Hill and include the usual facilities. Regular additions have been made. In 1973 a wing was built as part of a Development Plan, allowing for the reorganisation and modernisation of existing buildings, which was completed in 1974. In 1981 Oldfield House was built to accommodate the first two years and in 1989 a new assembly hall/theatre/classroom complex called the Lyon Building came into use. A Sports Complex comprising an indoor swimming pool and sports hall was opened by HRH The Duke of Edinburgh in February 1997. Recent developments include a new Sixth Form centre, a Drama studio, a computerised language laboratory, and a modern library. A new Science block opens in September 2008.

Games. The School playing fields are within 10 minutes' walk on the south side of the Hill. In addition, the School is able to use the Harrow School Athletic Track, Golf Course and Tennis Courts.

The main games are Association Football and Cross-country in the Winter Terms, Cricket and Athletics in the Summer Term, supported by Badminton, Tennis, Basketball, Archery, Shotokan-Karate and other games. PE and Swimming are in the curriculum.

Out of School Activities. Boys are strongly encouraged to play an active part in a wide range of activities. There is a School Orchestra, a Junior Orchestra, a Wind Band, a Jazz Band, large and small choirs. Drama, as well as being taught in the curriculum, is developed through House and School Plays. There is the normal range of School Clubs and Societies.

The School takes an active part in the Duke of Edinburgh's Award Scheme and has a full-time Activities Coordinator. It also uses the Young Enterprise Scheme so that boys can gain early experience of running a small company. Most Lower Sixth Formers take part in a week's residential leadership course in Scotland.

Community Service has been developed through various projects which are undertaken to help the old and the handicapped in the Harrow Area. Each year the school devotes considerable time to fund-raising for a Charity chosen by the boys.

Careers. Advice on Careers is given by the Careers Staff. The School is a member of the Independent Schools Careers Organisation. Specialist advice concerning entrance to Higher Education is given.

The Old Lyonian Association. The Old Lyonians' Association, which was founded in 1902, has always been a strong support to the School. All boys on leaving the school from the Sixth Form become life members of the Association. The Association has its own ground and pavilion at 74 Pinner View, Harrow, and its President is Mr M Christelow.

Entries to Universities. The second year Sixth Form on average consists of 75 boys who will usually apply for Degree courses at leading Universities and of these the great majority are successful. A steady stream of boys is sent to Oxford, Cambridge and London.

Charitable status. The Keepers and Governors of the free Grammar School of John Lyon is a Registered Charity, number 310033. The purpose of the charity is the education of boys living within reach of Harrow between the ages of 11–18.

Kelly College

Tavistock Devon PL19 0HZ
Tel: 01822 813100
Fax: 01822 612050
e-mail: headmaster@kellycollege.com
admissions@kellycollege.com
website: www.kellycollege.com

Kelly College was founded in 1877 by Admiral Benedictus Marwood Kelly.

Motto: *Fortiter occupa portum.*

Governors:

Chairman: D R Milford
Vice-Chairman: Dr W J Rea, DPhil

The Rt Revd The Lord Bishop of Exeter
Prof P F W Preece
Rear Admiral R J Ibbotson, DSC
Prebendary R Carlton
Capt M C Clapp, CB, RN
Mrs E Loosmore
Dr H J Ball
M W Kelham
N R Bomford
The Baroness Fookes of Plymouth, DBE, DL
D M Vine
Brig I McNeill
S J Carder
Colonel G E W Raikes, MBE
District Judge C J Tromans
K Hollinshead

***Headmaster*: Dr G R W Hawley**, BSc Durham, PhD Durham

Second Master: D J Wilson, MA (*English*)
Assistant Head (*Academic*): P Smith, BA (*Religious Studies*)
Assistant Head (*Staff*): Ms T B Ridge, MA (*Religious Studies; Head of Faculty, Humanities*)
Assistant Head (*Pastoral*): Mrs L B Huish, BEd (*History and Religious Studies*)
Assistant Head (*Pastoral*): R B J Huish, BEd (*Biology*)

Housemasters/mistresses:
School House: D Tomalin, BSc, MA (*Mathematics, Economics & Business,*)
Courtenay House: R J Stanyer, BSc, BEd (**ICT*)
Newton House: Miss R Callard, BSc (*Physical Education*)
Marwood House: D R Bott, BA (*History*)
Russell House: Mrs R Morel, BA (*French*)
Conway House: B G C Donnelly, BSc (*Biology*), Mrs S Donnelly, BSc, MPhil, Mrs T A Bratt, BA (*English*)

Assistant Staff:
Mrs C Allen, BA (*Learning Support*)
Mrs J Asmussen, StExFS (*German*)
R A Brew (*Director of Swimming*)
Mrs M Bridger, BA (*English*)
F Bué, BA (*French*)
Mrs S E Bury, BA (*ESL*)
G C Collard, BEd (**DT*)
Mrs D Collard, BEd (*DT*)
Mrs M J Collier, BA, LRAM (*French and Spanish*)
D Cummins, BA (*Director of Sport, *Physical Education*)
Mrs S M de Glanville, CertEd (*Mathematics*)
Mrs F L Dunn, BA (*Physical Education*)
Miss M S Fuentes, Licenciada (*Spanish*)
N Geere, BA (*Mathematics*)
Mrs R A Gibbs, BA (*English*)
Mrs J Gratton, BA, MSc (*Learning Support*)
Mrs S J Gray, BSc (*Chemistry*)
A Halls, BA (*Artist in Residence*)
I J A Hardy, BSc (**Mathematics*)
Mrs V J Lanyon Jones, CertEd, AMBDA (*Learning Development Coordinator*)
Mr M F Latimer, MA, MSt (**Modern Languages*)
I R Lazenbury, BEng (**Physics*)
I Leaman, BSc, (**BTEC, Physical Education*)
C J Limb, BA (**English*)
Miss C Luton (*Language Assistant*)
A Makepeace, BSc (*ICT*)
S Martin, MA, BSc (**Geography*)
Mrs V McCarty, CertEd, ALAM (*Speech and Drama*)
R McDermott, BEng (**Science, Physics; Head of Faculty, Science, Mathematics and ICT*)
D Page, BA, MA (*History*)
Mrs N Pang (*Industrial Fellow*)
Miss R H Plumptre, BA (*Learning Support*)

Mrs L Pitts-Tucker (*Learning Support*)
A Ratcliffe, BSc (**Chemistry*)
T Ryder, BA (*Geography*)
Mrs A G Shephard, BA, MIMgt (**Economics and Business*)
Mrs H Simpson, BSc (*Mathematics*)
Miss E Smith, BA, MA (*English; *Drama*)
Mrs S Speakman (*Netball and Rounders*)
Mrs A Stokes, BA (**Art & Design; Head of Faculty, Practical & Performing Subjects*)
S Thomson, BSc, (*Physical Education*)
Mrs S Thomas, BA (*Art & Design*)
D C Turnbull, BA (*Design & Technology*)
A Westlake, BA (*DT Assistant*)
Miss N Woodroffe, BSc (*Physical Education*)

Music Department:
A M Wilson, BMus (*Director of Music*)
Ms M Brindle, BA, PGCert, PGDip (*Violin*)
D Gray, LTCL (*Brass*)
Mrs S Houghton, CertEd, ARCM (*Flute*)
R King (*Guitar*)
J Lewington, LTCL, ARCM (*Singing*)
Mrs O Loewendahl, BMus (*'Cello*)
Mrs M Mazur-Park, BMus, LTCL (*Piano*)
S Smith, CertEd (*Clarinet, Saxophone*)
T Ryder, BA (*Classical Guitar*)

Bursar: Miss A Hedrich, MA, MSt, ACA

Registrar: Mrs C Greensted, MBA, DipM ACIM
Tel: 01822 813193; Fax: 01822 612050; e-mail: registrar@kellycollege.com

Medical Officer: Dr M Eggleton

Headmaster's Secretary: Mrs S C Harding

Kelly College offers a co-educational boarding, weekly boarding and day education for boys and girls aged 11–18. It is a small and friendly school of about 370 pupils of whom half are boarders. The school balances a good academic schooling with a strong commitment to a whole range of extra-curricular activities, be they musical, artistic or sporting. The College plays a significant part in the cultural and intellectual life of the local community. The location of the school next to the Dartmoor National Park naturally enhances the strong 'outdoors' tradition of team games and adventure training.

The school has a happy atmosphere within a disciplined framework, where the care of others, good manners and self-respect are important values. Kelleians typically are contributors and, whilst the school maintains high academic standards throughout, the admission process looks at the whole person and welcomes a range of talents and abilities.

Small class sizes ensure individual attention, and a committed staff seek to work with parents to achieve the personal goals of each pupil, whether that be a place at Oxford, International sporting representation, or a chosen career path.

All pupils are part of one of the Houses, which is their 'home from home' in the case of the boarders and their working base for day pupils. Boarders and day pupils are integrated throughout the school. Each pupil is cared for by a Housemaster or Housemistress and a tutor who oversees their academic progress and personal development.

Site and Buildings. Kelly College occupies a beautiful site on one bank and hillside of the Tavy valley looking out over the Dartmoor National Park on the edge of Tavistock, Devon. The buildings comprise the School Chapel, Assembly Hall, Performing Arts Centre (opened in 2007), Central Dining Hall, Library and ICT Centre, Art and Design Studios, Technology workshops, Science Laboratories, a heated indoor Swimming Pool, Gymnasium, covered Fives and Squash Courts, Floodlit all-weather surface for Hockey and Tennis, Armoury and Miniature Rifle Range. There is also a residential Adventure Training Centre, including a high-ropes course and trapeze jump. The school has its own Trout and Salmon fishing.

All pupils joining the school at 11 (Year 7) are part of Conway House for two years before progressing on to the senior houses. From 13 (Year 9), there are two Senior Girls' Boarding and Day houses, two Senior Boys' Boarding and Day Houses, and a Senior Mixed Day House (opened in September 2002).

School Structure and Admission Procedures. There are normally two forms in the First and Second form. Admission at age 11 (Year 7) is by school examination in the preceding February. There is an additional form from the Third Form. Admission at age 13 (Year 9) is by the College Entrance or by the Common Entrance Examination. Entrance to the Sixth form is on the basis of GCSE predictions. A report from the present school is required and all candidates for entry have a formal interview with the Headmaster.

Term of Entry. Pupils may also be accepted in January and April.

Entrance Scholarships, Exhibitions and Awards. (*see Scholarship Entries section*). All scholarships and exhibitions are competitive on entry to the school. Awards may be awarded at ages 11, 13, and 16 in the following areas: Academic, All-rounder, Art, Drama, Design & Technology, ICT (13+ only), Music, Sport, Swimming and Triathlon. At 11, for entry into the First Form (Year 7), candidates sit an additional General Paper and, in the case of 'performance' awards, are assessed as part of the routine admissions process. At 13, for entry into the Third Form (Year 9), candidates sit the Scholarship papers in February/March, and/or, in the case of 'performance' awards, are assessed on a visit to the school. Sixth form Scholarships are awarded on the basis of GCSE results. Awards of 10% discount of the school fees are available to sons and daughters of Old Kelleians and up to 20% for members of the Forces.

Curriculum. The Lower School curriculum (Years 7–9) introduces pupils to a broad range of subjects in line with the National Curriculum. In Year 9 pupils begin to study a second modern language. All pupils at Kelly study for the International/European Computer Driving Licence, which they may complete as early as the end of the fourth year in the school.

The GCSE curriculum at Kelly is quite flexible and aims to stretch each pupil appropriately. The core subjects are Mathematics, English, Biology, Chemistry, Physics, Religious Studies (short course), ICT (ECDL qualification) and a Language. The range of option subjects includes Art, Design & Technology, Drama, French, Geography, German, History, Music, Physical Education, Religious Studies and Spanish.

Pupils entering the Sixth Form need to possess 6 GCSE passes and at least 47–52 GCSE points to study 4 AS Levels, with at least 5 GCSE points in each of English and Mathematics. Most pupils at Kelly study for 4 AS Levels in the Lower Sixth year, but in exceptional circumstances some study five or three subjects. A Level option subjects include Art & Design, Biology, Chemistry, Design & Technology, Drama & Theatre Studies, Economics and Business, English Literature, French, Geography, German, History, ICT, Mathematics, Further Mathematics, Music, Physical Education, Physics, Religious Studies and Spanish. Tuition in Latin or Greek with a private tutor can be arranged at an additional cost. All pupils in the Lower Sixth year receive tuition in Public Speaking. An Oxbridge Entrance class is taught by the Headmaster for part of the Lower and Upper Sixth years.

Combined Cadet Force. All Third Form (Year 9) and Fourth Form (Year 10) pupils follow the Duke of Edinburgh's Award Scheme as part of their CCF commitment and can join the Royal Naval, Royal Air Force or the Army Section. The CCF has a strong emphasis on Adventure Training and there are opportunities for sailing, kayaking, sub-aqua diving, orienteering, small-bore shooting and abseiling; many of which are available on site or nearby on Dartmoor. The College, originally founded as it was for the 'sons of Naval Officers and other Gentlemen', enjoys strong links with the Royal Navy at

Dartmouth and pupils have the opportunity to visit our affiliated ship, HMS Argyll, when she is in port.

Cultural and Academic Societies and Activities. All boys and girls are encouraged to explore new interests and to make the most of their spare time. Societies and Activities include Literary and Debating, Current Affairs, Drama, Dance, Choral, Music, Football, Computing, Photography, Chess, Bridge, Fine Arts, Surfing and Textiles.

Kelly has a strong music department. Kelleians can learn a broad range of musical instruments from the Organ to the Electric Guitar. The school hosts a Concert Society which is open to pupils and members of the local community alike; and the Senior Orchestra and Senior Choir join with the local Choral Society and Orchestra to put on major concerts. There is also a Junior Choir and Junior Orchestra, plus a number of music ensembles.

There is a strong tradition of Public Speaking and debating and many of the pupils study for LAMDA qualifications. The School Hall is fully equipped for theatrical productions, and there are a number of House and School plays each year. A Performing Arts Centre opened in July 2007.

Sport. Kelly has a strong sporting tradition and has probably produced more Olympians and Internationals than any other school of its size. The major sports for girls are Hockey, Netball, Tennis, Athletics and Swimming; and for boys are Rugby, Hockey, Cricket, Athletics and Swimming. Many other sports are available in the school, Aerobics, Climbing, Cross-Country, Golf, Riding, Rugby and Winchester Fives, Squash, Basketball, Sailing, Surfing, Tennis and Soccer.

Dress. The school uniform for girls consists of a school kilt, white blouse and school blazer. Boys wear a blue shirt, grey flannel trousers and school blazer.

Fees per term (2008-2009). Full boarding: £6,600–£7,800; Weekly boarding: £5,900–£7,250; Day Pupils: £3,600–£4,450. Music lessons are among the voluntary extras, which are kept to a minimum.

Kelly International Study Centre (KISC). The Study Centre opened in September 2005, providing a one-year pre-Sixth Form course. For details, contact the Registrar at the College.

Application. A prospectus and further details are available from the Registrar, who will be pleased to arrange visits to the school.

Old Kelleian Club: The OK Secretary, The Registry, Kelly College, Tavistock, Devon PL19 0HZ.

Charitable status. Kelly College is a Registered Charity, number 306716. It is a day and boarding school for boys and girls, which also grants maintenance allowances and the provision of assistance for higher education by means of Scholarships, Exhibitions and Means Tested Bursaries.

Kelvinside Academy

33 Kirklee Road Glasgow G12 0SW
Tel: 0141 357 3376
Fax: 0141 357 5401
e-mail: rector@kelvinsideacademy.org.uk
website: www.kelvinsideacademy.org.uk

The Academy was founded in 1878. Since May 1921, it has been controlled by the Kelvinside Academy War Memorial Trust, which was formed in memory of the Academicals who gave their lives in the War of 1914–18. The affairs of the Trust are managed by a Board of Governors, mainly composed of Academicals and parents.

Motto: ΑΙΕΝ ΑΡΙΣΤΕΥΕΙΝ

The Governing Body:
Chairman: D G W Stewart, BSc

Mrs G Buchanan, DBO
T L Craig, MBIM
Mrs M Eadie, RGN
W Frame, LLB, FRICS, FCIArb
A W H H MacLeod, BSc, FCMI
N J McNeill, CA
Mrs A Rushforth, RGN, SCM
C Rutherford, MCIBS, MBA
J Turnbull, BSc Hons
C Kerr, BSc
D McGillivray, LLB, NP (*President KAC*)

Secretary to the Governors: D Pocock

***Rector*: John L Broadfoot**, BA, MEd

Senior School Staff:
I D Lindsay, BSc, BA, DipEd (*Deputy Rector*)
C Dallas, BSc
A J Gilliland, BSc (*Director of Studies*)
P R Billinghurst, BSc, PhD
Mrs J Cunningham, BMus Hons
R W J Moir, BEd
A G Mulholland, BSc
D J Wilson, BEd
Miss S Crichton, BMus
J Gilius, MA
Mrs J B Shields, MA
Mrs G T Ali, MA
J I O Cuthbertson, BSc
Miss A M Dal'Santo, BA
Mrs A Schneeberger, MA
N Fischbacher, BEng
Mrs H Jephson, MA
I Nicholson, BSc
S Connor, BEng
Ms C Alonso-Bartol, MA
Miss J L Carswell, BA
S Klimowicz, MA
C Lawson, BEd
Mrs A Mullan, BA Hons
Miss K Leckie, BSc Hons
I Leighton, BSc Hons
Miss F Donald, BA Hons
Mrs F Whittle, BMus
Miss K Watt, BA Hons
Mrs D Macgregor, BSc
Miss B Davison, BA
Mrs J Hardy, MA
Mrs N Mathews, BA
Mrs J Rynn, BSc Hons
Miss L Semple, BSc
Mrs E Whatley-Marshall, MA
Miss K Hopkin, MA
Mrs A Tough, BSc
N Reid, BSc
Miss L Bruce, BSc
Mrs J Clark, BA

Chaplain: (*to be appointed*)
Bursar: D Pocock
Assistant Bursar: Mrs M Bennett, MA

Head of Junior School: A Dickenson, MA Hons

Junior School Staff:
Mrs M Jeffrey, DPE
Mrs G Whittaker, CertEd
Mrs L Woore, DPE
Mrs P Campbell, BEd
Mrs A Stevenson, BEd
Mrs R E Porter, BEd
Mrs L L McColl, BEd
Miss E Samson, BEd
Mrs B Deutsch, MA
Mrs S Paterson, BEd Hons
Mrs J S Maclean, BEd Hons
Mrs S Rodger, BEd Hons
I Forrest, MA
Mrs F Kennedy, BEd
N Armet, BSc
Miss I Munro, BA
Miss E Laird, BSc

Nursery School Staff:
Ms T Monks, BEd Hons (*Nursery Leader*)
Mrs S Garner (*Nursery Nurse*)
Miss K Macfarlane (*Nursery Nurse*)
Miss K Yule (*Nursery Nurse*)
Miss K MacIntyre (*Nursery Nurse*)

Instrumental Music:
J Hawkins
L Birch
Ms M Campbell
Ms A Gow
Miss L Gowens
A Douglas
Ms J McCreath
Ms R Guerrier
Ms M Houlihan
Ms G Carlin
Ms A Gordon

Registrar: Mrs L Andonovic, MA
SSI: Capt D Simpson
Drama: Mrs J Speculand, Mrs E Lannigan

Kelvinside Academy is a co-educational day school for some 640 pupils, aged 3 to 18.

The main building is in neo-classical style and Grade A listed but has been extensively modernised within. Further buildings and extensions provide excellent facilities for all subjects and interests, and are symptomatic of the school's progressive approach. Recent additions include state-of-the-art IT and multimedia suites, floodlit all-weather hockey pitch, and Theatre.

Curriculum. Junior School pupils (from J1) benefit from specialist input in Art, Music, PE and Modern Languages. The Senior Prep (P7) year is a transitional year with a core curriculum taught by the class teacher but science, languages, art, music and PE are delivered by secondary specialists. Computing is a core compulsory subject up to S4.

Senior 3 and 4 pupils follow 8 Standard Grade/Intermediate courses, followed by Higher and Advanced Higher courses in Senior 5 and 6.

The maximum class size at any stage of the school is 20.

Combined Cadet Force. The hugely popular CCF is compulsory for one year in Senior 3. Pupils embark upon the Duke of Edinburgh's Award Scheme at this stage.

Games. Rugby and hockey are the principal team games in the winter terms with athletics, tennis and cricket in the summer. A range of additional sports and games, from football to golf and squash, is offered.

Activities. A rich programme of extra-curricular and House activities contributes significantly to the broad educational experience enjoyed by all pupils.

The Expressive Arts. Music, drama, dance and the visual arts have a central role in both the curriculum and the co-curriculum.

Fees per term (2008-2009). Nursery £806–£1,990, Junior School £1,889–£2,820 (all-inclusive*), Senior School £2,920–£3,098 (all-inclusive*).

*Also includes Activities Week (Junior 5–Senior 3).

Admission is by interview and entrance test.

Scholarships. Scholarships are offered annually to those about to enter the **Senior 1** year. Pupils already at the school are eligible to compete.

Bursaries. Assistance with fees is available in cases of financial need.

Charitable status. The Kelvinside Academy War Memorial Trust is a Registered Charity, number SC003962. The purpose of the Trust is to run a combined primary and secondary day school in memory of those former pupils of the school who gave their lives in the war of 1914–18.

Kent College

Canterbury Kent CT2 9DT
Tel: 01227 763231
Fax: 01227 787450
e-mail: registrar@kentcollege.co.uk
website: www.kentcollege.com

The School was founded in 1885 and occupies an idyllic semi-rural site overlooking the historic City of Canterbury. In 1920 it was acquired by the Board of Management for Methodist Residential Schools. Its Junior School is situated a mile away at Harbledown.

Kent College has been fully co-educational since 1973. The Senior School (11–18 years) has some 460 boys and girls, approximately one-third boarding and two-thirds day, 160 of whom are in the Sixth Form. There are around 220 pupils in total in the Junior School, Infant Department and Nursery section (*see Infant & Junior School IAPS entry*).

The school's Christian heritage continues to inform all its policies and objectives, including its outstanding pastoral tradition, but it happily welcomes pupils of all faiths, or none. A strong international element in its boarding population adds cultural richness and diversity.

Motto: *Lux tua via mea*

Visitor: The President of the Methodist Conference

Administrative Governors:
¶G A W Connolly, LLB, FRAeS (*Chairman*)
Dr D McGibney, FRCP, FFPM (*Vice-Chairman*)
Mrs H J Brian, RGN
Miss J Charlesworth, MA
Mrs A V Davis, MA, PGCE, MIL
J Earl, ACIB, MIBA
S Earl, BA, BSc, MRICS
D J Endersby
J M Harte, ACA, MBA
Revd J Hellyer, BSc, MA
¶D F Lander, MRTPI
M G Lang, Dip Agric CQSW
A S Masters, BA
Miss J E Neville, JP, BA, RN, RNT
G Russell, MA, DipTheol
¶D Shipton, CertEd, Dip MEd (MA)
N W Thorne, BEd, MSc, FRGS, FRSA
P G F Turner, BSc, MBA, MRICS
¶H F B Weeks

¶ *Old Canterburian*

***Head Master*: Dr D Lamper**, EdD, MA, AKC

Deputy Head Master: J N G Waltho, MA
Senior Teacher and Coordinator of Boarding: Mrs J Gray, BA
Director of Studies: *J S Williams, MA
Senior Master: *T J Williams, BEd, MEID
Head of Sixth Form: *G Letley, BA
Head of Middle School: *J Burnage, BSc
Head of Lower School: *Mrs C A Baker, CertEd
Head of Year 7: Mrs K L McGibney, BA
Chaplain: Revd Dr P Glass
Marketing Manager: M D Conolly, MA

Teaching Staff:
* *Head of Department*
† *Boarding House Parent*

A J Frost, MA
J M Coles, BA, MA
R B Grayson, BSc
Mrs F C Hart, BA, MA
*S Worth, MA, CPhys, MInstP
R E J Van Hinsbergh, BA
A P Spight, BSc
Mrs B Alonso-Harris, Lda
*M F Sochacki, MA, MSc
*D R Montague, BSc, MA
†*Mrs H Goddard, BA
*S A Fell, BA
C D T McGarrity, BSc, BA, PhD
Mrs C Balsdon, BA
*Mrs G Bunyan, BEd
*Mrs C MacLaren, BA, MCILIP, PGCert (Hum)
Ms J Van Deelen, MA
Ms P Bax, Lda
Mrs S Collins, BEd
Miss A Bennett, BA
Mrs L Brissenden, MA
*C S McIntosh, BEd, MA
Mrs K Plumb, BA, MA, AdvDipSN
P H Bourdillon, BA
Mrs J Spencer, GRSM Hons, LRAM
G Gape, BSc
†*C A Joy, BEd
*G Noble, BA
Ms C Langlands, BA
P Dyer, BEd
*Mrs E Humphreys, BLaw
†*Ms E Jameson, BA
*A McCarthy, BSc
*H Jones, Dip Dramatic Art
Mrs B C Ingham, BSc
J W Watton, BSc
Mrs J Webber, MA
†C Daly, BSc
D R Mathews, BSc
C P Dawn, BSc
Mrs A Haines, BSc
*S D Gant, BA
Mrs E S W Smiley, MA
*Ms M Hancock, BA
D Laslett, BA
A Clark, BA
*S Wiles, BSc
J Copland, CELTA, TEFL
T Gardner, BA
Mrs R Rutland, BSc
E Young, BSC, MSC
P Dingle, MA

Infant and Junior School

Head Master: A J Carter, BEd

Assistant Heads:
T M Baldwin, BEd
Mrs A Tingey, BEd
Mrs J Parker, BA(Ed)

Mrs J McRae, CertEd, BDA Dip
Mrs M Laslett, CertEd
C P Sweet, BA
Mrs R L Fitzgerald, BEd
Mrs R Pryce, BEd
Mrs C Balsdon, BA
Mrs H Fairhurst, CertEd, MEd, MA
Mrs G Griffin, BA(Ed)
Mrs K Carter, BEd
Mrs M Baker, CertEd, DipMusEd
Mrs J Laird, BSc
Mrs S Rogers, BA
Miss A Bennett, BA
Mrs J Spencer, GRSM, LRAM
Mrs S Cronin, BSc
Mrs E Shopland, BA
Mrs A Appiah, BEd
Miss K Spillett, BA
Mrs B Garratt, MEd
H Pearce, BSc
Miss G Moxon, BA
D Corrigan, BSc, MSc
Mrs R Taylor, BSc
Ms S Freeborough, BEd
Mrs J Jenner, BA

Medical Officers:
Dr M Richardson, MBBS, DA
Dr J B Thompson, MBBS, MRCGP, DRCOG, DFFP

Secretary to the Governors and Bursar: (*to be appointed*)
Registrar: Mrs J Simpson
Head Master's PA: Mrs D Beaumont
Old Canterburian Liaison Officer: G D Colson, BA, MSc, PhD

Facilities. As well as the core buildings where the majority of teaching is carried out, the school has four boarding houses, two for boys and two for girls. The school Chapel has been skilfully adapted to serve additionally as a Theatre.

The school has recently completed a £3.5 million development project which has resulted in refurbished laboratories, a new Library, ICT suite, eight-room teaching block, new Medical Centre, Day Common Rooms, Music School and new staff social and working facilities.

A floodlit all-weather sports pitch is used for Hockey in the Autumn and Spring Terms and for Tennis in the Summer. The availability of this pitch brings a number of district and regional tournaments to the school and is a major factor in the school's success in Hockey. In addition there is a large and well-equipped Sports Hall which caters for a variety of indoor sports as well as having Dance and Gymnastic studios.

Close to the main campus is the school Farm (and further land for playing fields and recreational purposes) which is managed by a Farm Manager who runs a Young Farmers' Club that regularly achieves success in The Kent County Show.

The estate at the nearby Junior School is particularly beautiful. The house was owned by Sidney Cooper RA who created the garden there. It is an ideal environment in which young children can flourish.

Curriculum. The curriculum is aligned to the National Curriculum but a greater range of subjects is provided. All pupils are normally expected to take at least one European language at GCSE. It is not the aim to specialise in any one group of subjects but to provide a balanced curriculum which will give full opportunity for every boy and girl to get a good grounding of general knowledge and later to develop particular gifts to a high standard.

Twenty-two subjects are currently offered at AS/A2 level.

Dyslexia Unit. The school makes provision for a number of dyslexic children of appropriate ability. There is a special unit with very well qualified staff and all staff are trained so that the school offers an understanding approach to children with this difficulty. The objective is to integrate pupils into the mainstream curriculum and activity of the school whilst giving them appropriate support within the Dyslexia Unit.

International Study Centre. A major attraction for overseas students is the school's ISC where specialist tuition in small groups is given to those pupils whose English language skills need enhancement prior to their integration into the mainstream curriculum.

Pastoral Care. All pupils are placed in the care of a Tutor who works closely with the Houseparent and Year Head, liaising with the Head Master on the one hand and parents on the other. Opportunities are arranged several times a year to enable parents to meet staff and in addition the Head Master and all staff are willing to meet parents by arrangement.

Religion. Although the School is controlled by the Board of Management for Methodist Residential Schools, boys and girls of all denominations or none are accepted. During the week all pupils attend Morning Assembly. Confirmation classes are arranged in the Spring Term and a joint Confirmation Service for Methodists and Anglicans is held in the School Chapel early in the Summer Term.

Games and Activities. The school possesses 28 acres of playing fields and a floodlit all-weather hockey pitch. The major games for boys are Rugby, Hockey, Tennis and Cricket and for girls Netball, Hockey, Tennis and Rounders. Boys' Hockey is a particular strength. The U18 team were national champions in 2004 and the U16 team have been national champions for four out of the last seven years. The U13 team achieved the same success in 2003. There are also school fixtures in Athletics, Basketball and Cross-Country.

Senior pupils take part in various forms of community service in the City and the school also has its own Duke of Edinburgh's Award group. There is a full range of optional school activities, including Art, Chess, Pottery, CDT, Photography, Riding and Farming. The School has its own farm with plenty of livestock to provide all-year-round interest.

Music and Drama. Music and drama play an important part in the life of the school.

There are three choirs, two orchestras, a jazz band, rock groups and a variety of other specialist ensembles and singing groups. Many concerts are given each year, including the annual Carol Service in Canterbury Cathedral, and the school is developing the tradition of holding one celebrity recital each year. The school is a centre of musical excellence in the area and its new Music Department, opened in 2006, offers outstanding facilities which are attracting many talented young musicians.

The main school play is eagerly awaited each year and usually involves both actors and musicians. Recent productions include works by Oscar Wilde, Cole Porter, Lionel Bart, Shakespeare and Chaucer.

Dance is popular, not only as part of the musical numbers in plays, but in shows where our dancers perform works choreographed by teachers and pupils.

Admission. The usual age of admission to the Senior School is 11 years. The Entrance Examination takes place in the Spring Term for admission the following September. There is another entry at age 13 and places are also available in the Sixth Form for those wishing to follow A Level courses. There are occasional vacancies at other levels.

Fees per term (2008-2009). Day Pupils £4,596–£4,729; Boarders: £7,876–£7,983 (full), £7,540–£7,647 (weekly). International Study Centre: £8,942–£9,074.

Entrance Scholarships. (*see Scholarship Entries section*). The school awards academic, music, sport and art scholarships to pupils for entry into Years 7, 9 and 12. Year 7 and 9 academic scholarships are awarded as a result of performance in our Entrance Test, usually held in the Spring Term, for entry the following September. Sixth Form academic scholarships are awarded on the basis of existing performance, a detailed report from the Head of Year or current school, and confirmation of high levels of performance in the final GCSEs. Music, sport and art scholarships are awarded in conjunction with the

Entrance Test and appropriate separate performance assessments at Kent College.

Scholarships normally carry a value equivalent to a percentage remission of the fees which would vary according to circumstances but would not exceed a maximum of 50% of fees and would be at the discretion of the Head Master. Full particulars may be obtained from the Registrar.

Honours. Most school leavers go on to university and a number of pupils secure offers of places at Oxford and Cambridge colleges each year.

Charitable status. Kent College, Canterbury is a Registered Charity, number 307844. The School was founded to provide education within a supportive Christian environment and is a member of the Methodist Independent Schools' Group.

Kimbolton School

Kimbolton Huntingdon Cambs PE28 0EA
Tel: 01480 860505
Fax: 01480 860386
e-mail: headmaster@kimbolton.cambs.sch.uk
website: www.kimbolton.cambs.sch.uk

The School was founded in 1600 and was awarded Direct Grant status as a boys' day and boarding school in 1945. Day Girls were first admitted in 1976. The Preparatory School (ages 4–11) and the Senior School are fully co-educational with day boys and girls (4–18) and boarding boys and girls (11–18). As a result of the withdrawal of the Direct Grant the School assumed fully independent status in 1978. There are 322 pupils in the Prep School (168 girls and 154 boys) and 603 pupils in the Senior School (62 boarders, 243 day girls, 298 day boys).

Motto: *Spes Durat Avorum.*

Governing Body:
C Paull (*Chairman*)
J Bridge, OBE (*Vice-Chairman*)

P Aylott
C R Boyes
Mrs J Doyle
Mrs S Duberly
J Gray
Mrs D Hellett
Dr T P Hynes
Mrs K Lancaster
S J F Page
G R Peace
M J Pitt
P Seabrook
A Semple
Mrs P W Silby
A P Weale

***Headmaster*: J Belbin**, BA, FRSA

Deputy Headmaster: M J Eddon, BSc

Second Deputy Head: Ms S Hutchinson, BA

Director of Studies: C J Bates, MA

Head of Sixth Form: A J Bamford, MA

S Ball, MA
Mrs L Bamford, MA
Miss A V Barnett, BA
Mrs A J Bates, BA
A Beal, BSc, MSc
Mrs C E Bennett, BSc
M Bennett, BA, RAS, PDip
Dr R Blindt, BSc, PhD
Miss D Bright, MPhil
Mrs D Brough, BA
Miss S J Bull, BSc
Mrs K Chaplin, BA
D Conerney, BA
K J Curtis, BSc, CPhys, MInstP
E C Drysdale, BSc
Mrs C C Elliott, BA
Mrs C E Firby, MA
Mrs E Forbes, RSA DipSpLD
Miss E Fowler, BEng
J Garland, BA
D Gibbs, MA
M Gilbert, BEd
B Goakes, BA
Dr C Grant, BA, PhD
A Gray, BSc
J D Greening, MA
Mrs L A Hadden, BA
O Hall, BA
Mrs J Hart, CertEd
Mrs S Hart, DipLib
S E C Henson, BEd
Mrs C M Hobbs, CertEd
C J W Horricks, BA
T Hutchinson, BEng
A Jessup, BSc, MA
Miss C Kennedy, MA
R E Knell, BA
A S Lawless, BSc
Mrs E Lawless, BSc
Miss T Lloyd, BSc
Miss H M E Morrell, BSc
J Newsam, MA
Miss H F O Perry, BSc
S K Pollard, MA
Mrs R Priest
Ms D V Robinson, BA
Mrs A M Rushton, BSc
Mrs C Sarkies, BA, MA
J R Saunders, BA
Mrs E Simons, BA
W J Skinner, MA
K Spencer, BEd
Miss A C Stewart, BA
Mrs C Stokes, BEd
Mrs L J Stone, BEd
Mrs C Vincent-Bennett
R Walker, BA
T Webley, BSc
T Webster
S Whitlock, MA
S Wilson, BA
Dr S P Yallup, MSc, PhD

School Chaplain: Mrs L N Bland, BEd

Prep School:

Head: R Wells, BEd, BA

Deputy: O Stokes, BEd

Director of Studies: Mrs F Y Williams, MA

Miss L Bainbridge, NNEB
Mrs A Barber, BSc
Mrs H Belbin, BEd
Miss A Berry, BEd
Mrs P Binham, BSc
A Bull, BEd
Mrs H Cardwell, BEd
Mrs J Cole, BA
Mrs S Eddon, LRAM, GRSM
Mrs J Edwards, BEd
Mrs A Farrer, NNEB
Mrs T Garzarolli, BSc
Mrs E J Hartwell, BA
Miss M Jenns, BSc
Mrs A Knell, NNEB
Mrs J Laino, NNEB
M Myers, BA
Mrs P Neale, BA
Mrs E L Prew, BEd
Mrs L E Reeves, DipEd
Miss K Rogers, BA
Mrs Z Sheffield, BA
Miss K Umpleby, BSc
Mrs C Wood, BA
Mrs D Woodward, BA

Bursar & Clerk to the Governors: E F P Valletta, MBIFM

Mission Statement. Within a friendly, caring environment, Kimbolton pupils are encouraged to develop the social responsibility and independence of thought to equip them for the challenges of a changing world.

Everyone has talent; the School aims to provide the opportunity for each individual to excel so that success can be celebrated and self-esteem enhanced.

Buildings. The main school building is Kimbolton Castle, once the home of Queen Katharine of Aragon and for three centuries the home of the Dukes of Manchester, and now, with its Vanbrugh front and Pellegrini murals, a building of considerable beauty and architectural importance. There is also on permanent display in the Castle, a fine collection of portraits including some by Lely, Pellegrini, Zoffany and Mengs, and the former Staterooms are study areas for senior pupils. The Chapel, located in the Castle, is used each day for prayers. In the grounds, the Mews and the Robert Adam Gatehouse have been adapted for school use. There are two large classroom blocks, one of which houses the Mathematics, Geography, Biology and Food Technology Departments. The Donaldson Laboratories for Physics and Chemistry contain 8 laboratories. The Design Technology Centre is modern and well-equipped, as is the ICT Centre. The School has a fine all-weather hockey pitch and has plans for a second. The Lewis Hall caters for the performing arts and daily assemblies and provides modern theatre and concert facilities.

A large sports complex, incorporating squash courts, gymnasium, sports hall, multi-gym and changing rooms stands in the Castle's parkland. Closer to the Castle itself, lie a modern Art Centre, new Library and an indoor swimming pool which was opened by the Duke of Gloucester in 2000, as part of the

School's quatercentenary celebration. A new, state-of-the-art teaching and learning centre, The Queen Katharine Building, opened in September 2008.

The Prep School has recently undergone a major rebuilding programme providing new classrooms, changing rooms and a hall for music and drama. There is also a gymnasium and specialist science and information technology rooms. The 4–7 age range is housed in the purpose-built Aragon House which opened in 1999.

One boarding house for girls and one boarding house for boys stand adjacent to the grounds in the picturesque Kimbolton High Street.

Organisation. The Prep School admits children at the age of 4 or 7 (day pupils only) who are expected to complete their education in the Senior School. Entry at other ages is sometimes possible. The relationship between the Prep and Senior Schools is a close one and contributes to the strong 'family' atmosphere of the whole School. Entry into the Senior School at the age of 11 is open to boarders and day pupils and there is a significant 13+ entry (via Common Entrance or internal Kimbolton exam).

In addition to the boarding houses, there are four senior houses and one junior house. Housemasters/mistresses, assisted by tutors, look after the general well-being and progress of their charges.

Work. For the first two years in the Senior School there are four parallel forms; in the third, fourth and fifth years there are five smaller forms and sets for some subjects. Boys and girls entering at 13 join one of the five Third Forms. An option scheme is introduced in the Fourth Form. In the Sixth Form specialisation occurs, and pupils will usually study four AS subjects from the following list: English, History, Geography, French, Spanish, Maths, Further Maths, Physics, Chemistry, Biology, Music, Art, History of Art, Food Technology, Design Technology, Theatre Studies, Sports Studies, Economics, Business Studies and Politics. All Sixth Formers sit at least AS General Studies having followed a 'Preparation for Life' series of lectures, seminars and debates. In the Upper Sixth pupils usually continue with three subjects to A2 Level.

Almost all leavers go on to University or to Further Education. In 2008, almost 10% of the Upper Sixth received offers from Oxbridge.

Religious Teaching. Morning prayers are held every morning in the School Chapel, and every pupil in the first three years has two periods of RE teaching each week. Sunday Services are held in the Chapel and occasionally the School worships in the Parish Church.

Games and other activities. The School owns over 120 acres of land, more than 20 of which are laid out as playing fields. The major sports for boys are Association Football, Hockey and Cricket. For girls the main sports are Hockey, Netball and Tennis. Other sports include Athletics, Swimming, Golf, Fitness Training, Rifle Shooting, Clay Pigeon Shooting, Squash, Badminton, Basketball and Rounders. Swimming is popular with before school sessions and numerous age group galas. Extensive use is also made by the Sailing Club of nearby Grafham Water, both for recreational sailing and inter-school matches. Canoeing is popular and a team competes in the 125-mile Devizes–Westminster challenge. The Equestrian Club competes in around twenty fixtures during the course of the year.

The School contingent of the CCF is a voluntary, keen and efficient body, divided into Navy, Army and RAF Sections; Community Service is an alternative. There is a successful Duke of Edinburgh's Award scheme with a growing number of participants.

Music and Drama play an important part in the life of the School. There is a Choral Society, two orchestras, several bands, and ensemble groups. The School Dramatic Society stages plays or musicals each term.

There are many other activities and societies, such as debating, public speaking, Young Enterprise, photography, chess, pottery and philosophy.

Careers. Advice can be sought at any time by pupils or their parents from the Careers Staff, three of whom specialise in university entrance. There is a well-stocked Careers Room, and the School is a member of the Independent Schools Careers Organisation. Fifth formers take the Morrisby careers tests administered by ISCO.

Dress. Boys wear blazers and grey flannels (shorts until the final year in the Prep School). The girls' uniform includes a standard skirt, blouse and blazer. Sixth Formers wear a black suit.

Admission. (*see Scholarship Entries section*). Correspondence about entry, whether to the Prep School or to the Senior School, should be addressed to the Registrar. The School Entrance examinations at 11+ are held in February when a number of Entrance Scholarships may be awarded. Tests for entry into the Prep School are also held in February. Entry at 13+ is usually by the Common Entrance Examination in June, when a number of scholarships are awarded. The William Ingram Awards are for those at 13+ with strengths in music, art or games. Entry into the Sixth Form is based on interview and GCSE results. There are a number of Sixth Form Scholarships and Exhibitions.

There is a bursary scheme for deserving candidates. Two Sir Brian Corby bursaries, available for pupils entering the Sixth Form from state schools, cover up to 100% of fees and may include extras.

Arrangements can be made for overseas candidates to take the entrance examination at their own schools.

Fees per term (2008-2009). £2,410 (Aragon House), £3,070 (Prep School), £3,755 (Senior Day), £6,220 (Senior Boarding).

The fees are inclusive of lunches and there is no charge for laundry, books, stationery or examination entries.

There is a reduction of 2½% from tuition fees when siblings attend at the same time.

Music Tuition Fee. For individual lessons £168–£188 per term. (A term's notice must be given in writing before a pupil discontinues music lessons.)

Registration Fee. A fee of £70 should be sent when the registration form is completed. This is not returnable.

Term of Entry. Most pupils enter at the start of the School year in September, but entry in other terms is also possible.

Old Kimboltonians Association. All correspondence to: The Secretary, OKA, Kimbolton School, Kimbolton, Huntingdon, Cambs PE28 0EA.

Charitable status. Kimbolton School Foundation is a Registered Charity, number 1098586.

King Edward VI School
Southampton

Kellett Road Southampton SO15 7UQ
Tel: 023 8070 4561
Fax: 023 8070 5937
e-mail: registrar@kes.hants.sch.uk
website: www.kes.hants.sch.uk

King Edward VI School was founded in 1553, under Letters Patent of King Edward VI, by the will of the Revd William Capon, Master of Jesus College, Cambridge, and Rector of St. Mary's, Southampton. The original Royal Charter, bearing the date 4th June 1553, is preserved in the School. The first Head Master was appointed in 1554.

Governors:
B E Gay (*Chairman*)

P W Brazier, BSC, FCIOB (*Vice-Chairman*)

The Lord Lieutenant for the County of Hampshire
Dr Y Binge, MBChB
Dr R B Buchanan, FRCP, FRCR, MBBS
D A Creal, FCA
A J L Dodds, MA Cantab
J R-H Martin
Councillor T Matthews
M H Mayes, MSc, MA, MBA, MRICS
A J Morgan, MA Oxon, FCA, ATII
Councillor A Samuels, BA Cantab
Mrs S Saunders-Davies
A L Thomas, MA, PhD
Mrs E Thompson, BSc Hons, MC Optom
R H Thornback
K St J Wiseman, MA
J B Young, BSc, MPhil, FCA

Bursar and Clerk to the Governors: R V Maher, BA Econ, ACA

***Head Master*: A J Thould**, MA

Deputy Head Masters:
P A Hartley, BSc
R T Courtney, MA

Registrar: R J Putt, BSc

Assistant Staff:
J C Allen, BA
R W Allen, BSc
Ms S L Allen, MA
S J B Ayers, BA
Mrs E M S Backen, MA
S H Barker, MA
Miss J M Barron, BA
Mrs L M Bates, BSc
J Bell, BA
Frl J Bihlmaier
Mrs P E Burrows, MSc
Miss C Campbell, BA
A J Cherry, BA
Mrs J M Cole, BA
Mrs M Cottrell-Ferrat, BA
K P Coundley, MA
H M Coverdale, BSc
R J Cross, BSc
N D Culver, MA
G T Darby, BA
A J Davies, BSc, PhD
Mrs H Dean, BSc, PhD
Miss E C K Dee, BA
N J Diver, MA
Miss L M Doyle, BSc
D M Dykes
Mrs M E England, BSc, PhD
Mrs S Evans, BA
K A Fitzpatrick
J M Foyle, BSc
Mrs H Freemantle, MA, LLCM, ALCM
S D Gamblin, BSc, PhD
A W Gilbert, BA
C E Giles, BA
Ms R M Greenwood, MA
M C Hall, BA, ARCO, ATCL
S G Hall, BSc
J C Halls, BA
Mrs J M Hardwick, BA
G P Havers, BSc
Mrs L C Henderson, BEd
L J Herklots, BSc
Srta M R Herrero
Mrs A Hipwell, BA
S R Hoskins, BSc, PhD
G S Hunt, BSc
Mrs J M Hutton, BA
N J James, BA, PhD
Mrs J V Jones, BA
P D Jones, BA
P G Kay-Kujawski, BA
D G Kelly, BA
L J Kelsey, MA
Mrs S King, BEd
M G Kukla, MA
Miss E M Ladislao, BA
O J Leaman, BMus
K N Lindsay, BSc
Miss M Lindebringhs, BA
M W Long, DipAD
Mrs N Lovegrove, BSc
N J Mason, MA
Miss A Matysiak, MA
Mrs E Mayes, MA
Mlle E Mazella
Mrs L S D Millar, BSc
M G Mixer, BSocSc
Mrs N A Moxon, BA
C D Murphy, BSc, MPhil
Miss S Noble, BA
Mlle C Notelet
Miss C F Noyes, BSc
R G Patten, BA
Miss A H Payne, BA
Miss C A Peachment, BSc
G L Piggott, BA
Revd J G Poppleton, BA, DipRS
A L Powell, BSc
D A Price, BA, MIBiol
Mrs J Price, BA
G T Purves, MPhys, PhD
Mrs J Ribi, BA
Miss V A Ridley
P J Robinson, BEng
Mrs S Rugge-Price, MA
A J Schofield, MA
Mrs E L Sheppard, BSc
P Sheppard, BSc
Mrs K S Skipwith, BSc
R S Simm, BSc
J H H Singleton, BSc
S J Smart, BA, MPhil
P B Tasker, BSc
Mrs E J Thomas, BSc
Miss S C Thompson, BEd
C E G W Thom, BA
T H Tofts, MA, DipPhil
A Turner, BSc
M A Walter, BSc, MPhil
R J Wilkinson, BSc, PhD
F Winter, BSc
R J L Wood, BEd
Miss K J Yerbury, BSc

There are about 970 pupils in the School, of whom over 260 are in the Sixth Form.

Admission. An entrance examination is held in the Spring Term for boys and girls seeking to enter the First Form at age 11 in the following September. Applications from able underage candidates will also be considered. In addition, admission into the Third Form takes place at age 13. Smaller numbers of entrants are accepted into the other school years if there is space, provided the applicants are of suitable academic ability. Boys and girls are also admitted to the Sixth Form.

Registration for entry may be made at any time on a form obtainable from the Registrar, who can supply current information about fees, bursaries and scholarships.

In order to qualify for entrance to the Sixth Form a boy or girl will normally be required to have grade B or above in six subjects at GCSE, including English Language and Mathematics, and the subjects to be studied at A Level, but A grades in French, German and Spanish.

Class sizes average 22; the average size of Sixth Form sets is 11.

Curriculum. All pupils follow a common course in the first two years: this includes French or German or Spanish with Latin, Mathematics, General Science and an Extended Studies programme. In years 3, 4 and 5 all pupils study eight 'core' subjects to GCSE: Biology, Chemistry, English Language, English Literature, a Modern Foreign Language, Mathematics, Religious Studies and Physics. In addition there is a range of 'option' subjects: Art, Design and Technology, Economics, Geography, German, Greek, History, Music, PE, Sports Studies, Theatre Studies and Spanish. The syllabus leading to the GCSE Examinations, in which most pupils take eleven subjects, is designed to avoid any premature specialisation. In the Sixth Form, students may either take 3 Advanced Level subjects along with one AS course or four full Advanced Level subjects. In addition, all have an afternoon of games in both years and follow a Foundations Studies programme in the Upper Sixth Year.

On entering the First Year pupils join a form of about 22, with a Form Tutor responsible for their general welfare and progress. The other years are organised on a system of pastoral groups of about 16. Each group has its own Year Head. In addition there is a Head of Lower School who has general responsibility for the first three years; a Head of Upper School and a Director of the Sixth Form have similar responsibilities in their respective areas.

Our aim is to provide a congenial atmosphere and a disciplined environment in which able pupils can develop as individuals.

School Activities. 10% of a student's timetable is devoted to physical education. Games are regarded as forming an integral part of life at King Edward's, and none is excused from taking part except on medical grounds. The major sports played in the three terms are rugby, hockey, cricket and tennis for boys; and netball, hockey, tennis and rounders for girls; other sporting activities include athletics, basketball, badminton, fencing, squash, swimming and a number of other games. The School has a large sports hall and a fully equipped fitness studio and an all-weather pitch for Hockey and similar games which provides twelve Tennis Courts in Summer. There are a further 33 acres of off-site sports fields which include a second astro-pitch and floodlit netball and tennis courts.

A considerable range of societies meets during lunchtime, after school, at weekends and in school holidays, catering for pupils of all ages and many differing tastes. All are encouraged to join some of these societies, in order to gain the greatest advantage from their time at the School.

In addition to a large number of sporting teams representing the School, there are such activities as charitable and community work, drama, debating, chess, Duke of Edinburgh's Award Scheme, International Expeditions, sailing, collectors' clubs and music. The School has flourishing choirs, as well as orchestras and a large number of smaller instrumental groups. Art and Design and Technology occupy up-to-date premises. The studios and workshops are usually open during lunchtimes and after school. The science laboratories have been recently refurbished and the Sixth Form Centre has been extended. The School has a 250-seat Theatre.

Fees per term (2008-2009). £3,495. The full fee can be reduced in appropriate cases by the award of Bursaries and Scholarships. Scholarships are available on entry at age 11 and age 13 and further Scholarships may be awarded during a pupil's career in the School. Some Scholarships are awarded for proficiency in the Creative Arts. Foundation Bursaries are available at age 11, 13 and into the Sixth Form.

Charitable status. King Edward VI School Southampton is a Registered Charity, number 1088030. The object of the Charity is the provision and conduct in or near the City of Southampton of a school for boys and girls.

King Edward VII and Queen Mary School

Lytham

Clifton Drive South Lytham Lancs FY8 1DT
Tel: 01253 784100
Fax: 01253 784150
e-mail: admin@keqms.co.uk
website: www.keqms.co.uk

The Lytham Schools Foundation was established after a great flood in 1719. King Edward VII School (for boys) was opened in 1908 and Queen Mary School (for girls) in 1930; both were Direct Grant Grammar Schools and with the withdrawal of the Grant became independent. The two schools merged to form a new school with a co-educational intake in September 1999. In September 2003 the school moved to one site with a multi-million pound development of facilities on its 35-acre campus.

Motto: *Sublimis ab unda.*

The Governing Body includes representatives of the Trust Managers of the Foundation and of the Universities of Lancashire, Liverpool and Manchester, together with co-optative members.

Governing Body:

Chairman: Mr D A Webb
Vice-Chairman: Mrs J M Towers, LLB

Mrs L Beddows, FREC
Mr W J Bennett, CEng, FICE, FIHT
Revd A Clitherow, BA, MPhil
Mr W G Cowburn, DipArch
Mr P M Gibbons, FCA
Mr M E Gunson, FCA, FRSA, FFA, FIAB, MIMgt
Mr R N Hardy, LLB
Dr S D A Hayes, MBChB
Miss J E Hilton, MLitt, BA
The Revd Canon G I Hurst, BA
The Revd D M Porter, BTh
Mrs D L Raymond, BSc, MRAeS
The Revd D Welch, MA Oxon
Mr E T Woodfine, RD, BA

Clerk to the Governors and Bursar: Mrs C Fox, ACA, BSc

Staff:

***Principal*: Mr R J Karling**, MA Edinburgh, MBA Leicester

Vice-Principal: Mr G A Little, BSc Leeds

Assistant Principal / Head of Sixth Form: Mr M G Stephenson, BA Oxford

Assistant Principal / Director of Pastoral Care: Mrs J A Cooper, BSc Salford

Assistant Principal / Director of Learning and Teaching: Mrs P A Lenney, BSc Leeds

Art:
*Mr C Wildon, DipAD Wolverhampton College of Art, ATD Birmingham
Miss S Lukasiewiecz, DipAD, ATC Sheffield College

Business Studies/Economics:
*Mr J A Liggett, BSc Cardiff

Design and Technology:
*Mr P F Klenk, BA Loughborough
Mr C K Hill, CertEd Birmingham, BA Loughborough

English:
*Mr N Walker, MA Oxford
Mrs K E Busby, BA Liverpool
Mr I R Clarke, BEd Newcastle, MA Lancaster
Mrs F M Withers, BA Hull
Mr K Maund, BA Wales

Food Technology:
Mrs V Nuttall, BA Open University, CertEd Keele

Geography:
*Mrs J A Cooper, BSc Salford
Mr G A Little, BSc Leeds
Mrs J I K Rimmer, BA London, FRGS

History:
*Mr I D Cowlishaw, BA London
Mrs D Ward, BA Bangor, MA Lancaster
Mrs J Trohear, MA Glasgow

Information Technology:
*Mr B Smith, BSc UMIST

Mathematics:
*Mr T Dawson, BSc LSE, MA Open University
Mr P Butterworth, BSc Lancaster
Mr K C Dawson, BSc Manchester Polytechnic
Mr P M Rudd, BSc Bangor

Modern Languages:
*Mr J G Finney, BA Nottingham
Mr R P Chester, BA Leeds
Miss E S A Hall, MA Oxford
Mr M G Stephenson, BA Oxford
Mrs F M Winterflood, BA Reading
Mrs A Boyes, BA Central Lancs (*French conversation*)
Mrs F Riley, CertEd Central Lancs (*French conversation*)
Mrs M Jones (*German conversation*)

Music:
*Mr J Pennington, BMus London, ARCM, ARCO, ALCM, DipRCM
Mrs C E Hanlon, BMus Sheffield

Physical Education:
*Mrs K Hanham, BEd Sussex
Mrs R A Morris, BEd De Montfort
Mrs B Storey, CertEdPE Bishop Lonsdale College, Derby
Mr A E Watt, BA Manchester Metropolitan
Mrs A Roberts, BA Leeds Metropolitan
Mr S Clarke, BA Liverpool John Moores

Psychology:
Mr S Collings, BA Marshall University USA, MSc Chichester

Sociology:
Mrs D Ward, BA Bangor, MA Lancaster

Religious Studies:
*Mrs J I Pybon, BA Newcastle
Mr N J Horan, BA Lancaster

Science:
*Mrs P A Lenney, BSc Leeds
Mrs J M Denver, BEd Nottingham College of Education
Dr J H Lees, BSc Liverpool, PhD Loughborough
*Dr C Jessop, BSc, PhD York
Mrs G Merrick, BSc York
Mr S Matthews, BSc Liverpool John Moores
*Mr J M Turner, BSc Sheffield, MSc Salford, CPhys, MInstP
Dr A Fielder, BA Oxford, PhD Oxford

Careers: Mrs S M Hampson, BA Leeds, DCG

Librarian: Mrs J Browell

Learning Support Coordinator: Mrs J Klenk, BA London, PGCE SpLD Edinburgh, AMBDA
Learning Support Assistants:
Mrs J Ingle, BA Lancaster
Mrs M Guminski, BSc, PGCE

Admissions Secretary: Mrs J Hothersall
Office Manager & PA to the Principal: Mrs Jill Butterfield

Facilities. The School stands on an impressive 35 acre site overlooking the Irish Sea. The buildings include a magnificent new Library, eight Science laboratories, Art Studio, specialist rooms for Music and Design Technology and a state-of-the-art Multimedia Language Laboratory. The whole campus is networked with broadband internet access and there are three newly equipped Information and Communication Technology suites. A fitness suite, sports hall and international standard artificial sports ground complement the facilities provided by the extensive playing fields. A major redevelopment of the School site was completed in the Autumn of 2003, including a purpose-built Preparatory School, a new teaching block for senior pupils, a new dining room and kitchens, and much enhancement and upgrading of the facilities.

Organisation. There are 450 day boys and girls in the Senior School. On site, there is also a co-educational Preparatory School for children from 2 to 11 years.

Curriculum. The broadly based curriculum, leading to GCSE after five years, comprises the following subjects: Art, Design and Technology, English Language and Literature, Drama, French, German, Geography, Mathematics, Music, Physical Education, Religious Education, Spanish and the Sciences. All pupils take part in Games. Most pupils enter the Sixth Form: a full range of AS and A2 subjects, including General Studies, is available in very varied combinations. There is a choice of 24 AS/A2 subjects, including the further options beyond GCSE of Business Studies, Further Mathematics, Psychology, Sociology, Sport Studies and Theatre Studies. Students are prepared for university, entry to the professions and careers in industrial and commercial life. The School offers comprehensive careers education and guidance on university choices.

Games and Activities. Cricket, hockey, netball and rugby are the main sports, but considerable choice is available including athletics, badminton, basketball, cross-country, golf, tennis, swimming and sailing. Extra-curricular activities include The Duke of Edinburgh's Award, mountain biking, canoeing, fell-walking and skiing, aerobics, choir, gymnastics, orchestra and swing band, public speaking and table tennis. Recent productions have included Cabaret, West Side Story, The Crucible, The Mikado, The Sound of Music and Les Misérables.

In recent years there have been regular sports tours in the UK and abroad to Holland, Italy and New Zealand, expeditions to Norway, India and Namibia, skiing in the Alps and Vermont, cultural trips to Normandy and the World War battlefields, student exchanges with France, Germany and the Czech Republic, art and music tours, and an international science symposium.

Admission. Admission to the Senior School is by examination for all pupils, aged 11, held each year in January. Pupils may also be admitted at other ages. Application Forms for admission and further details will be sent on request.

Fees per term (2008-2009). Senior School £2,600; Preparatory School £1,800.

Scholarships. A number of Scholarships and Bursaries are offered on the results of the Senior Entrance Examination and include auditions for Music and Sport Scholarships. Awards are also available at Sixth Form level.

Charitable status. The Lytham Schools Foundation is a Registered Charity, number 526315. Its aim is to provide a well-balanced academic education catering for the talents, needs and interests of each individual pupil.

King Edward's School
Bath

North Road Bath BA2 6HU

Tel:	Senior School: 01225 464313
	Junior School: 01225 463218
	Pre-Prep School: 01225 421681
Fax:	Senior School: 01225 481363
	Junior School: 01225 442178
	Pre-Prep School: 01225 428006
e-mail:	headmaster@kesbath.com
website:	www.kesbath.com

King Edward's School was founded in 1552 by King Edward VI. Originally a Grammar School, the School was fully independent until 1920, when it accepted Direct Grant status, reverting to full independence in 1976. King Edward's is fully co-educational, with girls and boys from age 3–18.

King Edward's School is a busy day school, with a proud record of sustained academic achievement (98% of its pupils regularly proceed to universities and institutions of higher education). It is also committed to providing the broadest possible range of opportunities for all its pupils and a multiplicity of extra-curricular activities, trips and expeditions are on offer. The School has a strong commitment to sport, both recreational and competitive, and the arts flourish, with the Annual Arts Festival providing a showcase for talented pupils in art, music and drama.

There are currently 682 pupils in the Senior School (including a Sixth Form of 214), 187 pupils in the Junior School, and 96 pupils in the Nursery and Pre-Prep.

For over 400 years, the School occupied various premises in the city centre, but in 1961 the Senior School moved to a fine fourteen-acre site on North Road, on the south-eastern slopes of the city. This site has been extensively developed in recent years and now boasts superb facilities. The Junior School moved into outstanding new premises here in 1990.

The Pre-Prep School is situated in an elegant Victorian house on the western side of the city.

Chairman of Governors: A Greening

***Headmaster*: Mr M Boden**, MA

Second Master: Mr M J Horrocks-Taylor, BSc, MEd
Director of Administration: Mr A R Monks, MSc

Deputy Head, Academic: Mr T D Burroughs
Deputy Head, Pastoral: Ms C Losse
Head of Lower School: Mr D J Chapman, BA
Head of Middle School: Mr A M Bougeard, MA
Head of Sixth Form: *Mr P H Simonds, BSc

Mr N P C Barnes, MA
Mrs R Barghout, MA
Mrs W Bederman, BA
*Mr S Bolderow, BA, MSt
*Mrs P M Bougeard, MA
Miss S Buxton, BA
* Mrs J Chapman, BA
Mrs S Cooper, MA
Miss T Costanza, BSc
Mrs J Crouch, BSc
Mr C Cunningham, BA
Mr M A Cunliffe, MA
*Mrs S M Curtis, BA, MPhil
§Mrs M N Davis, MA
Miss R Davies, BA
Mr R J S Drury, BA
Dr A M Fewell, PhD, BSc
Mrs C M Finch, BA
Mrs L Formela-Osborne, BEd
Mr S C Frost, BSc
Mrs L Gwilliam, BSc
Mrs E Grainger, BA
*Miss E Gurney, BA
Mr D Hall, BA
Mr M Hawker, BEd
*Mr R Haynes, MA
*Mr B Heywood, BSc
Mr J Holdaway, BEng
*Mr R Hughes, ALCM, BMus
Miss Z Kayacan, BA
*Dr G J F Kilroy, MA, PhD
*Mr T W L Laney, BSc
Mrs B Lang, BSc
Mr P J McComish, BSc
Mr T G Medhurst, BEd
*Mr D Middlebrough, BA
Mrs T Minty, BA
Mrs N Morris, BA
*Dr L H Newman, MSc, PhD
Mr H Nilsson, BA
*Mr M R Pell, BA
Mr N D Purcell, BA, MA
Mrs A S Ransom, BA
Miss J K Riding, BEd
§Mrs F Rothwell, CertEd
Mr M Ruxton, BSc
*Mr W R Satterthwaite, MA
*Mrs J Scott-Palmer, BSc
Ms Selvey, MA
Miss V Stevens, BA
Miss H Stewart, BDes
Mr R Thomas, BA, MA
Mr J E G Tidball, BSc
*Mr A W Trim, BA
Miss H Tully BSc
*Mr A I M Vass, MA
Mr N A Vile, BSc
Miss J Village, BA
Mr D Viñales, MA
Mr D J Walker, BA
MISS a Ward, BSc
§Mrs A White, BA
§Mrs J Wilcox, BSc
Mrs Willoughby, MSc
§Mr M Wood, MA
Mr D Wright, BSc

Senior School Chaplain: (*to be appointed*)
Director of Music: Mr R Hughes, BMus, ALCM
Deputy Director of Music: Mr R J S Drury, BA
Head of Careers Education and Guidance: Mr J Turner, BA
Head of Operations & Finance: Ms J I Rowell, MBA, BSc
Registrar: Ms A Rashid
Head's Secretary: Mrs A L Plumbridge
School Nurse: (*to be appointed*)
School Librarian: Mrs L Denton, BA, MA, MLS
School Accountant: Mrs N Rowlands, AAT
Resources Administrator/Fees and Bursaries Advisor: Miss J Prestidge
Development Office: Mrs C Davies, BA
Marketing Office: Mrs J Acklam, BSc Hons

Junior School
Head of Junior School: Mr G Taylor, BA
Deputy Head: (*to be appointed*)
Director of Studies: Mr J Bond, BA Hons, PGCE

Mrs R Barrett, MA Hons, PGCE
Mr P Borg
Mr S Carr, BEd Hons
Miss L Chapman, MA, PGCE
Mr J Corp, BSc Hons, PGCE
Mrs M Edwards, BMus Hons, MA, PGCE
Mr M Howarth
Ms Lucia Sdao
Mrs C Lewis, CertEd
Mr A J MacFarlan, BA Hons
Mrs E MacFarlan, BEd Hons
Mrs G Oliver CertEd
Mr D J Orchard, BSc Hons PGCE
Mr J Roberts-Wray, BA Hons PGCE
Mrs A Sellick, BSc Hons PGCE
Mrs C Sharpe, LLB Hons, PGCE

Junior School Administrator: Mrs R Goulding

Pre-Prep School Staff:
Head of Pre-Prep & Nursery: Mrs J Gilbert, BEd
Deputy Head: Mrs D Bright, BA Hons QTS
Mrs C Alexander-Jupp, CertEd, CTh
Mr S Boydell, BA Hons, PGCE
Mrs S Dowty, BA QTS
Mrs C Ford, LTCL, PGCE
Ms L Williams, BSc, PGCE

Pre-Prep Administrator: Mrs T Claridge

Buildings. The Senior School is housed in a complex of buildings arranged in three adjoining groups. Nethersole, dating from 1830, is in the process of being completely refurbished. The second floor now provides accommodation for Psychology and Economics and Business Studies. The rest of Nethersole is scheduled to be refurbished during 2008 when Classics, History and Religious Studies will have their own departmental areas. The Main Building comprises a Music block, the Wroughton Theatre, Physics and Chemistry laboratories and classrooms, a Biology laboratory, a Geography block, and a Mathematics block. Starting in the Summer of 2007 new laboratories and classrooms are to be built on the site between the Sports Hall and Main Teaching block. This building will house the Biology Department with 3 new biology laboratories and preparation room; the Geography Department; a new ICT laboratory; and a Modern Languages suite which will include two dedicated Modern Language Laboratories. The developments include a new IT suite for the Art, Design and Technology Centre. The Willett Hall with adjoining kitchens and servery functions as a dining hall and lecture hall. The Holbeche Centre houses a Sixth Form Centre with adjoining kitchen, an extended and modernised Careers and Higher Education Centre, a new, state-of-the-art Drama Studio and Art Gallery, purpose-built Library and various tutorial rooms. There is also a magnificent Sports Hall, together with an artificial playing surface for hockey and tennis.

The pavilion at Bathampton, completed in March 1998, is surrounded by 17 acres of playing fields and newly added Club House.

Admission. While half the pupils come from the City of Bath or its immediate environs, nearly half are resident in the counties of Gloucestershire, Somerset and Wiltshire – a wide catchment area made possible by excellent public transport services and coaches organised by the parents.

Methods of Entry. To the *Nursery and Pre-Prep*: From the age of 3, according to the availability of places. There is no assessment on entry.

To the *Junior School*: From the age of 7 by assessment and interview. The main entry is in Year 3 and Year 5 at the age of 7 or 9 but other vacancies may occur at age 8 or 10.

To the *Senior School*:

(1) From our own Junior School, by passing the Senior School Entrance Examination for 11 year-olds.
(2) Pupils from other Primary and Preparatory Schools may be offered fee-paying places on the results of the same examination, held in January of each year.
(3) Older pupils may enter the Senior School, if and where places are available, by sitting an Entrance Examination appropriate to their age.
(4) Students may also seek direct entry into the Sixth Form. Such students are expected to acquire a sound set of GCSE passes before transfer for advanced study. Applicants are interviewed and a reference is sought from their present school.

Application forms and further information concerning entry are obtainable from the Registrar, who will arrange prior visits to see the School. Open Days are held in the Autumn Term.

Fees per term (2008-2009). Senior School: £3,380–£3,420; Junior School: £2,670; Pre-Prep School £2,500; Nursery (full-time) £2,050.

Scholarships. Scholarships to a maximum of £500 per annum are awarded at Year 7, either for academic excellence or for outstanding talent in drama, music and sport. Students who perform outstandingly at GCSE may also receive a Scholarship award. Further details are obtainable from the Admissions Secretary.

Bursaries. Income-related entrance Bursaries may be awarded to children entering Years 7 and 12, whose parents are unable to pay the full fee. A general Bursary fund is also available to assist parents during times of unforeseen family circumstances, when they may find themselves unable to fund full school fees. Further details are obtainable from the Bursaries Administrator.

Curriculum. The School is committed to breadth in education. Seventeen subjects are taught up to GCSE level. A very flexible choice system is introduced in Year 10 so that no doors need be closed before entry into the Sixth Form. All students study all three sciences to GCSE at the Double or Triple Award.

The AS/A2 subjects on offer are English Literature, French, German, Spanish, Latin, History, Economics, Business Studies, Geography, Mathematics, Further Mathematics, Physics, Chemistry, Biology, Design and Technology, Religious Studies, Theatre Studies, Classical Civilisation, ICT, Philosophy, Psychology, Politics, Sport Studies, Art, Photography and Music; and they may be combined in a variety of ways. Pupils are encouraged also to enter for A Level General Studies.

Boys and girls are prepared for all forms of Higher Education, especially for Universities and for entry into the Services. The School has a proud tradition of sending a significant proportion of its students to the best universities in the land.

Music and Drama. There is a healthy and developing musical tradition in the School. Many instrumental and choral groups afford opportunities to explore differing musical styles. There are Senior, Intermediate and Junior orchestras, Early Music Groups, a Baroque Group, a Blues Guitar Group, a Brass Group, a Concert Orchestra, a Choir and a Swing Band. The School is a centre for the examinations of the Associated Board of the Royal Schools of Music and these are held termly. Music is an enjoyable and highly participative activity.

The School has an outstanding dramatic tradition, with two or more major productions a year. The splendid Wroughton Theatre, supported by a full-time technical manager, provides an outstanding facility for productions and concerts of every kind. There is in addition a brand new purpose-built Drama Studio.

Art. Housed in an extended and modernised custom-built suite of studios, the Art Department is a centre of excellence, with a fine tradition within the School and the Bath area. Teaching covers fine art, drawing and painting, ceramics and three-dimensional work, printmaking and photography. Art History and critical studies are taught as an integral part of the course and field trips and visits to galleries along with links to practising artists, are encouraged. Sixth Form Art Tours are planned annually. Every year students are prepared for interview at Art School and related courses.

Games. The main playing fields at Bathampton, comprising 17 acres, are attractively situated at one end of the Limpley Stoke valley, about a mile from the School. An All Weather Synthetic Pitch on the main School site has proved to be invaluable for hockey and tennis, and as an intensively used practice area for all games.

The major games are Rugby Football, Hockey, Cricket and Netball. Minor sports include Aerobics, Athletics, Cross-Country, Tennis, Swimming, Soccer, Shooting, Rounders, Fencing, Judo, Badminton, Squash, Golf, Basketball, Dance, Gymnastics, Table Tennis, Trampolining and Rock-climbing. Each boy or girl has a full games session per week and has ample opportunities to represent the School or to participate in a wide range of inter-Form activities.

Activities. In Year 9, pupils may opt to join the School CCF, founded in 1896 and the oldest in the West Country. The contingent has a fine record of success in regional and national competitions. The CCF provides many opportunities for adventure training and leadership and there is an Annual Easter and Summer Camp. Each year a number of students win scholarships or cadetships in different branches of the armed services. Students can also participate in the Duke of Edinburgh's Award Scheme.

There is also a strong tradition of mountain walking and adventure training for pupils with trips to Dartmoor, the Welsh mountains and abroad each year. The School enters the Ten Tors Competition each year.

School Societies and Clubs. Pupils are actively encouraged to engage in the many out-of-school activities which supplement their more formal education. A wealth of Societies and Clubs caters for every interest and for every age group. An organised programme of Outdoor Pursuits functions throughout the year. Frequent opportunities for travel abroad, especially during the Easter vacation, are provided by School tours or exchanges conducted by members of Staff. All pupils in Years 7–10 are involved in a residential trip during Activities Week in the Summer Term.

Pastoral Care is exercised by Form Teachers and Prefects up to Year 11, by Tutors in the Sixth Form, and is coordinated by the Heads of Lower School, Middle School and Sixth Form. The School prides itself on its family atmosphere and the excellent relationships between pupils of all ages and staff. Advice on Careers and entry to Higher Education is readily available. Parents meet Staff at regular intervals to discuss academic progress, or at social functions. Many of the latter are organised by very active parents' committees.

Dress. Boys in the Main School wear a dark blue blazer and flannels. Younger girls wear a Lindsay tartan kilt, a white open-neck blouse and the school blazer, whilst Middle School girls wear a grey skirt or grey trousers. In the Sixth Form, boys and girls wear suits of their own choosing, appropriate for formal work. Girls may wear trouser suits.

Junior School. The Junior School is an integral part of the foundation and is governed by the same Board. It joins with the Senior School in major events, such as the Founder's Day Service in Bath Abbey, and shares various games facilities. The curriculum is organised in close consultation with the Senior School and the Pre-Prep to ensure that education provided is continuous and progressive from the age of 3 to 18.

Its curriculum comprises English, Mathematics, Science, DT, History, Geography, Art, Music, Religious Education, Physical Education, French, ICT taught to all years and Learning Skills, including Philosophy.

All children learn the violin in Year 3 and recorder in Year 4. Well over half of the children learn additional instruments under the tutelage of a strong peripatetic music staff. French is taught throughout the School while purpose-built facilities in Art, Science, Technology and IT, coupled with specialist teaching, ensure high standards of achievement in those areas. The Junior School has developed a reputation in the past few years for dramatic productions of the highest quality and a drama club, which runs throughout the year, is always a popular choice. This School is a very busy one renowned for its extra-curricular activities programme. The wide variety of activities on offer include table tennis, gymnastics, fencing, judo, street dance, golf, challenge club, environmental club, computer, chess, art and animation. This is not to mention the various musical and instrumental groups and the many opportunities to play rugby, football, hockey, netball, cricket, basketball, tennis, rounders and athletics. All children throughout the School also go swimming at the pool at Bath University. A large number of competitive fixtures are played against other schools in a wide variety of sports and activities and each year group has their own programme of fixtures. Frequent educational trips are arranged in and around the local area and during the summer Activities Week; residential trips for Years 2–6 include destinations such as France and Devon. Sporting tours also take place;

in the last two years there has been a rugby tour to Scotland, a netball tour to Jersey and a joint tour to Oxford.

The House system plays a central role in the life of the School. All children belong to one of four Houses and take part in many events and competitions during the year. These include football, rugby, golf, general knowledge, hockey, unihoc, netball, swimming, tennis, cricket, drama, table tennis, music and a festival of public speaking.

The main entry is at the age of 7 or 9 but other vacancies may occur at 8 or 10. Applications should be made direct to the Junior School Administrator.

Pre-Prep School. The aim of the school is to provide a balanced and planned programme of learning for all children which takes into account their individual developmental stage and enables their personal and intellectual growth. Children are encouraged to develop academic abilities as well as personal qualities such as enthusiasm, self-motivation, persistence, empathy with other people and social skills which are vital for success in life.

The curriculum is designed to develop well-motivated, independent learners, who find learning fun, who take a pride in well-produced work, who strive for high personal achievement and who have a confident and positive response to all the new experiences they encounter.

A wide variety of extra-curricular activities comprising physical education and games skills (PEGS), short tennis, speech and drama, piano, violin and music workshops, judo, French, dance and recorders, are offered to children during each academic year in addition to the broad and balanced curriculum.

The Nursery which takes girls and boys from 3, has its own self-contained unit and playground to cater specifically for the needs of the very young child. Structured play offers children rich opportunities for controlling and shaping what they do. Children may stay all day or attend separate morning or afternoon sessions. The Pre-Prep caters for children from 3 to 7. Children in Reception work on both the Foundation Stage Curriculum and Level 1 of the National Curriculum.

Applications should be made to the Admissions Secretary.

Honours. In 2007 students have once again performed extremely well at A Level, with a pass rate of 99.7, and an impressive 58.4% of all entries being awarded an A grade. Students excelled in every subject area, with 95% of grades being A–C: 86% were graded at A/B. Nearly a third of all candidates achieved A grades in all their subjects with nearly 40% gaining at least three grade As. This success has meant that the vast majority of students have gained entry at the university of their choice, and seven pupils have gained entry to Oxford or Cambridge. At GCSE 72.9% of all entries were graded A* or A and just over a third of all students got nothing less than an A in all of their subjects. One pupil gained 11 A*s and five pupils gains 10 A*s. All pupils (100%) gained five or more GCSEs at A* to C grade.

The Association of Old Edwardians of Bath. c/o The Development Office.

Charitable status. King Edward's School at Bath is a Registered Charity, number 310227. It is a charitable trust for the purpose of educating children.

King Edward's School
Birmingham

Edgbaston Park Road Birmingham B15 2UA
Tel: 0121 472 1672
Fax: 0121 415 4327
e-mail: office@kes.bham.sch.uk
website: www.kes.bham.sch.uk

King Edward's School, Birmingham, was founded in 1552 and occupied a position in the centre of the city until 1936 when it moved to its present 45 acre site in Edgbaston, surrounded by a golf course, lake and nature reserve and adjacent to the University. It is an independent day school with about 840 boys aged 11 to 18. Approximately 30 boys in each year receive financial assistance with fees from Scholarships and the Assisted Places Scheme. The school belongs to the Foundation of the Schools of King Edward VI in Birmingham (two independent and five grammar schools), and its sister-school, King Edward VI High School for Girls, is on the same campus. Academically one of the leading schools in the country, King Edward's is also renowned for the scale of its provision and its excellence in sport, music, drama, outdoor pursuits and trips and expeditions.

Motto: '*Domine, Salvum fac Regem*'.

Governing Body:
S G Campbell (*Chairman*)
M D Stirling (*Vice-Chairman*)

Mrs G Ball
P Burns
P A Christopher
Mrs M M England
Mrs S Grant
D Holmes
Professor T Norris
M B Squires
A W J Stevens
Mrs A Tonks
R V Wharton

Acting Secretary to the Governors: J Collins

Bursar: J Bone

***Chief Master*: J A Claughton**, MA

Deputy Chief Master: G Andronov, BSc

Assistant Head (*Administration and Pupil Discipline*): K D Phillips, BA
Assistant Head (*Pupil Welfare/Health & Safety*): J C Howard, BEd
Assistant Head (*Teaching and Learning*): M Roden, BSc

Assistant Teachers:
M D Stead, BA
R W Symonds, BSc
S Birch, BEd
D C Dewar, BSc
S E Lampard, BSc
R T Bridges, MA, PhD
J R R Emery, MA
S F Owen, MA
T F P Hosty, BA, PhD
J A Cumberland, MA
R N Lye, BA
L W Evans, BA
J P Davies, MA
J C S Burns, MA
Mrs J E Durman, BEd
Mrs C M Southworth, BA
L M Roll, BA
T Mason, BSc
E J Milton, BA
M N A Ostrowicz, BSc
B M Spencer, BA
C D Boardman, BSc
S J Tinley, BSc
Miss C M L Tudor, BA
J Porter, BSc
T A McMullan, BSc
The Revd D H Raynor, MA, MLitt
J G Evans, MSc, PhD
M J Monks, GRSM
R W James, BA
S L Stacey, MA
T F Cross, BSc
R J Deeley, MA
D J Ash, MA
M Daniel, BSc, DPhil
Miss C R Bubb, BA
C W Walker, CertEd
Ms R Leaver, MEng
J P Smith, BA
P B Evans, BMus
R E Turner, BA, MPhil
Ms D E McMillan, BSc
P A Balkham, BA
D M Witcombe, MSc
I J Connor, BSc
R D Davies, BSc
Ms S-L Jones, BSc
J M Pitt, BA
R M Brookes, MChem, DPhil
A T Dean, MChem
J L Amann, BA, PhD
Ms E K Sigston, BA
A Hayes, BSc
Ms J L Putt
P W L Golightly, BA
Mrs S Thorpe, BSc, MEd
Miss J L Parkinson, BA, MSc
M J Bartlett, BA
Miss J Helm, BA
Mrs H K Stokes, BA, MA
A D Melvill, BA

F L Howes, BA
Mrs P J R Esnault, MA
Miss S Khan, BA
M Green, MChem

Part-time Teachers:
P E Bridle, MBE, GRSM, LRAM
P H Lambie, MA
Mrs J R E Herbert, LLAM, ALAM
Miss P Asher, BA
Mrs A Ostrowicz, BA
G Galloway, PhD, MPhilEd
Mrs G Cook, BA
Mrs G Gardiner, BSc, MSc
Mrs G Hudson, BEd
Mrs G E Savage, BA
G A Worthington, MA
Mrs H J Cochrane, BA

Librarian: Ms J Allen, BA

School Medical Officer: Dr M Forrest, MBChB, DRCOG, MRCGP

Admission. The names of candidates must be registered at the School before the closing date as stated in the prospectus. Evidence of date of birth and a recent photograph must be produced when the name of a candidate is registered for the examination.

Term of Entry. Autumn term only.

Admission Examination. Most boys enter the school at 11+, although a small number join at 13+. In addition, applications at 16+ to enter the Sixth Form are encouraged. At both 11+ and 13+ candidates take papers in Mathematics, English and Reasoning at a level appropriate to the National Curriculum. A large number of pupils are also interviewed as part of the admissions process. At 16+ all candidates take an entry paper in four chosen subjects and are interviewed.

Scholarships at 11+ and 13+. (*see Scholarship Entries section*). Up to twelve academic scholarships of between one-half and one-fifth fees per annum are offered.

Music Scholarships are also available.

Scholarships at 16+. `Betts Scholarships' of value up to half fees for boys studying Science and Mathematics subjects at A level, one Finnemore Scholarship for boys studying Arts subjects at A level of up to half fees.

Fees per term (2008-2009). £2,990.

The Assisted Places Scheme offers means-tested support to up to 20 boys a year. The scheme targets primarily 11+ entrants but 16+ entrants will also be eligible to apply.

Academic Success. In 2007 85% of all A Levels were passed at A or B grade. Almost all leavers go on to University, some after a GAP year. Over 30 pupils a year are accepted to read Medicine.

Curriculum. *Lower School*: The following subjects are studied by all boys to the end of the third year: English, Mathematics, French, Geography, History, Physics, Chemistry, Biology, (General Science in first year), Latin, Art, Design, Drama, PE and Religious Studies. Music is a compulsory subject to the end of the second year. In addition, boys are required to undertake familiarisation courses in Information Technology. In the Fourth and Fifth year all boys study Mathematics, English, French and either Physics, Chemistry, Biology plus 3 other optional subjects, or Dual Award Science plus 4 other optional subjects, which are taken to GCSE. All boys study German, Spanish or Classical Greek in the third year and may take their choice to GCSE and beyond.

Sixth Form: In the Divisions (First Year Sixth) boys choose four from the following subjects for study to AS Level of which three (sometimes four) are carried through to A Level: Art and Design, Biology, Chemistry, Classical Civilisation, Design & Technology, Economics or Business Studies, English Literature, French, Further Mathematics, Geography, German, Greek, History, Latin, Mathematics with Mechanics, Mathematics with Statistics, Music, Physics, Spanish, Religious Studies.

In addition, all boys take an A Level in General Studies.

The aim is to produce a broad and well-balanced education, but that involves more than just preparation for examinations. For example, PE and games are compulsory for all, there is an extensive provision for General Studies in the Sixth Form and, above all, for all pupils Friday afternoon is set aside for the pursuit of non-academic activities: CCF, Leadership, service in the community, outdoor pursuits, Art, computer programming etc.

Music and Drama. The school has a very rich musical and dramatic life. Many of the musical groups and theatrical productions take place jointly with King Edward VI High School for Girls. There are ten different musical groups and choirs. Each year the school's major concert is performed in Symphony Hall, Birmingham and there is also a large musical production each year.

Games. Rugby, Cricket, Hockey, and Athletics are the major team games in the school. However, many other games prosper including archery, badminton, basketball, chess, cross-country, cycling, fencing, Fives, golf, kayaking, squash, swimming, table tennis, tennis, water polo. The School has extensive playing fields for all these activities plus its own swimming pool, double Astroturf, all-weather athletics track, sports hall, 2 gymnasia and squash courts.

Societies and Clubs. The school has a very wide range of clubs and societies including Christian Union, Islamic Society, Literary Society, Classical and Junior Classical Societies, Historical and Junior Historical Societies, Living History Society, Economics Society, Musical Society, Senior and Junior Dramatic Societies, Shakespeare Society, Art Society, Geographical Society, Debating and Junior Debating Societies, Scientific Society, Biological Society, Mathematical Society, Meteorological Society, Modern Language Society, Chess Club, Photographic Section, School Chronicle, Film Society, Hard Rock Society.

CCF, Outdoor Pursuits and Expeditions. The Royal Naval, RAF and Army Sections of the Combined Cadet Force are very popular amongst pupils. In addition, the Duke of Edinburgh's Award Scheme has grown substantially in recent years, so that the majority of pupils in the third year gain the Bronze Award and about 20 each year gain the Gold Award. All of this forms part of a strong tradition of trips and expeditions, ranging from cycling and caving and walking and skiing trips, to language trips to Europe to major expeditions to Honduras, Venezuela, Peru, Egypt, Morocco. There have also been very successful rugby tours to Australia and South Africa.

Forms and Houses. In the first five years there are five forms in each year, with an average of 24 pupils. In the Sixth Form, forms are on average 12 in number, and often comprise pupils together from the Lower and Upper Sixth. There are 8 houses and the house system continues to provide an important element of pastoral support and competition, not only in sport, but also in music.

Charitable status. The Schools of King Edward VI in Birmingham is a Registered Charity, number 529051. The purpose of the Foundation is to educate children and young persons living in or around the City of Birmingham.

King Edward's School
Witley

Wormley Nr Godalming Surrey GU8 5SG
Tel: 01428 686700
01428 686735 Admissions
Fax: 01428 682850
01428 685260 Admissions
e-mail: info@kesw.surrey.sch.uk
website: www.kesw.surrey.sch.uk

The School was founded in 1553 by King Edward VI with the title of Bridewell Royal Hospital. Originally housed at the Bridewell Palace, which was given under Royal Charter to the City of London, the School moved to Witley in 1867, simultaneously changing its name. It became co-educational again in 1952 and will accommodate approximately 500 pupils, equally divided between boys and girls. The School provides both boarding and day education for children between the ages of 11 and 19 years. There are a substantial number of bursaries available to help boys and girls whose home circumstances make boarding a particular need.

Treasurer and Chairman of Governors: P K Estlin, BSc

***Headmaster*: P Kerr Fulton-Peebles**, MA (*Economics, Geography*)

Senior Deputy Head: S J Pugh, MA

Academic Staff:
* *Head of Department*
† *Housemaster/mistress*

R J Bird, BSc (*Development Director*)
Mrs S C Bird, BSc (*Science*)
Miss E Bateman, BSc (*Economics & Business Studies*)
Mr M J Blackamore, BA (*History*)
Miss S Brown, BA (*Modern Languages*)
N Budden, BSc, MA (**Modern Languages*)
Miss J A Carlsonn, BA (*Geography*)
Mrs C A Cox, BSc (*Mathematics*)
J G Culbert, BSc (*Science, Physics*)
Mrs J Curran, BA (*English*)
B Doherty, BA (*Art, Photography*)
N R Fellows, MA (**History, Staff Development Coordinator*)
K B Forster, BA (*Modern Languages, Careers Coordinator*)
Dr E K Foshaugen, BA, MPhil (*Religious Studies*)
D G Galbraith, BSc (**Science,Chemistry*)
Mrs K M Goundry, BA (*Food & Textiles Technology, †Queen's*)
Mrs C E Green, BA (*English & Drama, Language & Literacy Coordinator*)
P Head, BSc (*Mathematics*)
Miss C D Hedges, BSc (*Modern Languages*)
Mrs A E Hill, BSc (**Biology, †Tudor*)
A N K Johnson, BSc, MSc (*ICT, D & T/ICT*)
Mrs S J Lane, BSc (*Biology*)
Miss A M Kuczaj, BA (*Games*)
J Langan, BA (**English*)
W Marr, BComm (*Physical Education, †Edward*)
Miss M McCuish, BSc (**Mathematics*)
R Meanwell, BSc (*Physics*)
Mrs C J Meharg, BA (*Deputy Head-IB Coordinator, Modern Languages*)
Mrs J Millington, BA (*Deputy Head-Pastoral, Key Skills Coordinator, Religious Studies*)
Revd R W E Millington, BA, DipTh (*Chaplain, Student Counsellor*)
N H Mott, BA, MA (*Head of Sixth Form, English & Drama*)
Mrs P V Nash, BEd (*Science, Design Technology*)
Mrs L Nikolaou, BA (**Learning Support*)
T Norton (*Assistant Chaplain*)
Miss J A Patton, BSc (*Mathematics, †Elizabeth*)
Mrs G A Pedlar, BA (*English*)
S C Pedlar, GRNCM
D Pennell, BEd (*Physical Education*)
S D Pentreath, BSc (*Science, Chemistry, †QMH*)
G M Phillips, BA (*Assistant Head-Marketing, Economics*)
M C Phillips, BA (*Geography, †Grafton*)
D K Poulter, BSc (*Deputy Head-Co-curriculum, Geography*)
S J Pugh, MA (*Senior Deputy Head, Director of Studies, Classics*)
S P Rigney, BA (*Design and Technology, HE Coordinator, Examinations Officer*)
J N I Secker, BA (*Modern Languages, Scholars' Tutor, Video Conferencing Mentor*)
Miss L E Smith, BSc (*Science*)
Mrs C Tee, BA (*Food Technology*)
Mrs A J Tinsley, CertEd (**Design & Technology*)
S L Todd, BSc (*Director of Games*)
P J Towler, BA (**Classics*)
B J Turner, MA (**ICT, Mathematics*)
Mrs J S Turner, CertEd (*Library & Resources*)
Miss K S Warburton, BA (*Design and Technology, †Ridley*)
Ms C Waterhouse, BA, NDD (*Art*)
Mrs B Waters, BEd (*German*)
J Webster, BSc (*Mathematics, †Wakefield*)
Mrs H A White, BSc (*Mathematics*)
T D Woodhead, BA, LTCL, ARCO, ALCM (**Director of Music*)

Houses and Housemasters/Housemistresses:

Queen Mary House (*Junior Boys*): S D Pentreath
Copeland House (*Junior Girls*): Mrs R Evans

Senior Paired Houses:
Ridley (*Boys*): Miss K S Warburton and *St Bridget's* (*Girls*): Mrs S Norton
Wakefield (*Boys*): J Webster and *Elizabeth* (*Girls*): Miss J A Patton
Edward (*Boys*): W Marr and *Tudor* (*Girls*): Mrs A E Hill
Grafton (*Boys*): M C Phillips and *Queen's* (*Girls*): Mrs K M Goundry

Medical Officer: P R Wilks, MA, MB, BChir

Bursar: P J Luard

Headmaster's Secretary: Mrs K Stevenson

King Edward's School is situated in a well-wooded site of over 100 acres near the Surrey-Sussex-Hampshire border, and is easily accessible by both road and rail. The buildings include the School Chapel, Charter Hall (a modern assembly hall with stage and concert platforms), the Warburg Science School with 9 full-sized laboratories, and well-equipped ancillary rooms, a Mathematics and Computing Block, both Technology and Home Technology Centres, an Art Centre (equipped for Photography, Pottery and Sculpture), an Exhibition Hall, the Countess of Munster Music School including a Concert Hall and Music Library, the Gerald Coke Library & Information Centre, a Sports Centre, a new all-weather playing surface for hockey and tennis, a Dance and Drama Studio, an Indoor Swimming Pool, hardplaying and playing fields provision for Cricket, Football, Hockey (boys and girls) and Athletics, and courts for Tennis, Squash and Netball. From the Third Form upwards boys and girls live in eight modern, purpose-built paired houses where the accommodation and study areas are completely separate but everyone can come together in the shared communal facilities on the ground floor. The unique paired houses allow boys and girls to mix naturally, and are particularly valued by parents whose sons and daughters attend the school and can be placed in adjacent accommodation. The houses are upgraded continually and there are new washroom and shower facilities throughout.

There are 450 pupils in the school, approximately a third of whom are day pupils.

The generous staffing ratio and the exceptional pastoral care provision in the School make possible a wide-ranging curriculum, and a real opportunity to live a full life. More than 20 subjects are available at AS and A2 Level. The International Baccalaureate Programme, introduced in 2004, is studied by 40% of the Sixth Form. Both the pupils whose interests are academic and those whose bent is less academic find a wide choice of subjects open to them. The great majority of our pupils proceed to the Sixth Form and subsequently to higher education.

Places in the School are open to everyone, but it is always kept in mind that the School is a charity whose first purpose is to meet the needs of children who have a particular need for boarding education. Such children are of both sexes, of differing abilities and from every walk of life, and the School seeks to draw as widely as it can to make up its community. It is thus co-educational by conviction, believing that the richer potential of a co-educational environment is desirable for most pupils, and significantly so for the children with whom it is especially concerned.

The School was founded as a result of Christian concern, and it still aims to provide a full education that has a Christian setting, within a caring community. The centre of its spiritual life is the Chapel, where the services are under the direction of the Chaplains, who in turn call on the help of many staff and pupils. Services vary in character although they are based upon the worship of the Church of England. Children who wish to do so can join church membership classes which culminate in a Confirmation Service for those wishing to become members of the Church of England. All pupils attend Chapel Services.

Admission. Children are normally admitted either at 11+ (following an entrance examination), at 13+ (following an entrance examination and Common Entrance), or at 16+, based on GCSE results, but if there is room they may be admitted at other times, and occasionally a child who should clearly be working alongside older children is admitted at 10+.

Fees per term (2008-2009). Boarders: £7,490, including all boarding and tuition fees, books and games equipment, and the provision of school uniform and games clothing, and for third, fourth and fifth formers a laptop computer.

Day Pupils: £5,380, including meals and uniform. Individual music tuition in piano, organ, singing and all orchestral instruments is provided at less than cost to all who are prepared to take the trouble to profit from skilled teaching. Over 200 such lessons are given weekly, and the musical side of the School flourishes accordingly.

Bursaries. Some of the pupils may be given bursaries by the Governors. The number and size of the bursaries will depend upon the endowment income available, and they are given at the Governors' absolute discretion. Awards are reviewed annually with regard to parental circumstances and to school fees. They may be given in conjunction with Local Education Authority grants or help from a charitable trust. It is hoped that there will always be as many pupils in the School whose parents are unable to contribute substantially towards the education provided as there are those whose parents are paying full fees from their own resources. The basis on which bursaries are awarded is a combination of the need of the pupil for boarding education, the means of the parent, the support available from other sources, and the contribution that the pupil can make to the school community. It is emphasized that these are not scholarships which a pupil wins by his or her own merits, but a distribution of endowment income to those who need it most.

Scholarships. Academic, art and music scholarships, supplementable according to boarding and financial need as described above for bursaries, are offered at 11+, 13+ or 16+ for entry to the Sixth Form. A discount of 10% of full fees is available to children from service families.

Charitable status. King Edward's School, Witley is a Registered Charity, number 311997. The foundation exists to provide boarding education for families whose circumstances make boarding a particular need, though the excellent facilities and the high standards of academic achievement and pastoral care make it attractive also to any family looking for boarding education.

King Henry VIII School
(Part of the Coventry School Foundation)

Warwick Road Coventry CV3 6AQ

Tel: 024 7627 1111
Fax: 024 7627 1188
e-mail: info@khviii.com
website: www.khviii.com

"*Success, responsibility and enjoyment – these are our prime aims*" George Fisher, Headmaster.

There are 486 boys and 437 girls in the Senior School, and 149 boys and 97 girls in the Prep School. The school is entirely a day school.

King Henry VIII School was founded under Letters Patent of King Henry VIII, dated 23 July 1545 by John Hales, Clerk of the Hanaper to the King. Today it is an independent, co-educational day school of a high academic standing. The school is represented on the Headmasters' Conference and on the Association of Governing Bodies of Independent Schools. The governing body is the Coventry School Foundation, on which are represented Sir Thomas White's Charity, the Coventry Church Charities, Coventry General Charities and Birmingham, Coventry, Oxford and Warwick Universities. There are also several co-opted Governors.

Chairman of Governors: Mr Brendan Connor

Senior School

***Headmaster*: Mr George Fisher**, MA

Deputy Heads:
Mr Simon Bird, MA, DipEd, NPQH, FRGS
Miss Ann Weitzel, MA, NPQH

Assistant Head: Mr Warren Honey, BSc

Teaching Staff:
Dr Simon Ainge, BSc (*Head of Chemistry*)
Mrs Mary Aldenton, BEd (*Religious Studies*)
Mr Tom Andrews, BSc (*Mathematics*)
Mr Conn Anson-O'Connell, BA (*Head of Modern Foreign Languages*)
Mr Matthew Blake, MPhys (*Physics; Coordinator for the Academically Able*)
Mr Ben S Bramley, BSc Hons (*Biology*)
Mr Michael Browning, BSc, MSc, PhD, PGCE (*Chemistry*)
Mr David Butler, MSc, MICE, CEng (*Head of Boys' Cross-Country; Physics*)
Mrs Jan Butler, BA (*Music; Key Skills Coordinator/ Complementary Studies*)
Mr James Carlyle, BA (*Geography; Games*)
Mr Andrew Carman, BA (*Economics & Business Studies; Events Coordinator; Calendar*)
Mrs Anna Clegg, BA (*Modern Foreign Languages*)
Miss Cindy Colwell, MA (*Modern Foreign Languages; Coordinator for German*)
Mr John Cooper, MA (*Head of Mathematics*)
Miss Michele Cuthbert, BSc, HDipEd, WITS (*Physics; Marking Project Coordinator*)
Ms Ana Djordjevic, PhD, BA, PGCE (*Classics*)
Mr Niall Doherty, BA, LTCL (*Director of Music*)
Mr Doug Drane, MEd, HNC (*Design Technology*)
Ms Clare Farmer, BSc (*Mathematics; Assistant Head of Years 10 & 11*)
Mrs Tracy Ferguson, BSc (*ICT; Deputy Head of Holland's House*)
Miss Kate Fisher, BSc (*Chemistry; Assistant Head of White's House; Student Voice Coordinator; Cross-Country*)
Mr Peter Forse, BA (*Head of Sixth Form; History*)
Mr Colin Foster, BA, PhD, CChem, MRSC (*Mathematics*)
Mr Peter Geall, BA (*Head of Classics*)
Miss Christina Gottwald (*Modern Foreign Languages Maternity Leave Cover*)
Mr John Grundy, BEd (*Head of CDT; Buildings*)
Dr David Hayton, BSc (*Science Coordinator; Head of Physics; Timetabler; Invigilation and Cover Scheduler*)
Mrs Anna Heathcote, BA (*Food Technology*)
Mr John Henderson, BA (*Art*)
Mrs Julie Holland, BA (*History; Coventrian Magazine*)
Mrs Dorinda Holt, BA, DipEd (*Modern Foreign Languages; Spanish*)

Dr Tim Honeywill, MMaths, PhD (*Maths*)
Mrs Fiona Horne, BSc (*Food Technology*)
Mrs Linda Horton, MA (*Biology; Chemistry; Games; Head of Year 7*)
Mr Robert Howard, BA (*Head of Geography; Head of Sherwyn's House*)
Mr James Hunt, BA (*English; Games; Head of Hales' House*)
Mrs Karen Hunt, BEd (*Food Technology*)
Mrs Kathryn Hunt, BSc (*Mathematics*)
Mr Peter Huxford, MA (*Head of History, Head of Year 9*)
Mr Nicholas Jones, BA (*Classics*)
Mr Peter Manning, MA (*Head of Psychology; Religious Studies*)
Mrs Rachel Mason, BSc (*Head of A Level PE; Head of Girls' Hockey/Games*)
Mrs Jaynita Mattu, BSc (*ICT; Webalumnus; Intranet*)
Mr Antony McAlister, BEd (*PE & Games; Head of Boys' Hockey*)
Dr Mary McKenzie, MA (*Head of English*)
Miss Victoria McNaney, BA Hons, CertEd (*Modern Foreign Languages*)
Mr Nick Meynell, BA (*Head of Economics and Business Studies*)
Mrs Pip Milton, BSc (*Biology*)
Mr Peter Milton, BA (*Geography, Head of White's House*)
Mrs Anne Morris, MA, BD (*Classics*)
Mrs Debra Morris, BA (*Art*)
Miss Sarah Mould, BA (*Head of Art; Publicity Officer*)
Mrs Pam Nicholls, BSc (*Mathematics*)
Dr Donna Norman, BSc (*Head of Biology*)
Mr Francis O'Reilly, BA (*History*)
Mrs Gill Othen, BA (*Head of Drama; English*)
Mrs Kulwinder Pabla, MSc (*Chemistry; PA Link*)
Mr Andrew Parker, BEd (*Head of Boys' PE and Games*)
Dr Noel Phillips, BSc (*Chemistry; Sound System; Coordinator for Reporting*)
Mrs Dolores Pittaway, MA, PG Dip (*Learning Support Coordinator*)
Mrs Amanda Pontin, CertEd (*Head of Girls' PE and Games; Deputy Head of Hales' House*)
Mrs Annemarie Powell, BA (*English; Junior Drama*)
Dr Michael Purslove, BSc (*Physics*)
Dr Michael Reddish, LLM (*Head of Law; Critical Thinking; Oxbridge Coordinator*)
Ms Sally Ridley, BA, MBA (*Head of ICT*)
Dr Tajinder Sanghera, MA (*English; Teacher i/c of Debating & Public Speaking*)
Mrs Helen L Savage, BEd Hons (*English*)
Mr Shaun Schofield, BSc (*Biology; Games*)
Mrs Barbara Seagrave, CertEd (*Girls' Games*)
Mrs Fiona Singer, MA, MEd (*Modern Foreign Languages; Latin*)
Mr Toby Smith, MA, PhD (*Religious Studies; Games*)
Mrs Chris Spriggs, BSc (*Assistant Head of Sixth Form; Geography*)
Dr Robert Stephen, BA, BD, MTh, FSA Scot (*Religious Studies*)
Mr Ian Stickels, BA (*Modern Foreign Languages*)
Mr Sukhbir Tandy (*Design Technology*)
Mrs Mary Tynan, BSc (*Mathematics; Charities and Community Link*)
Mrs Anne Wade, BSc, MA, CBiol, ML (*Biology; Director of Outdoor Pursuits*)
Dr Sarah Wah, MA (*English*)
Mr Ieuan Weir, BA (*Head of Religious Studies; Head of Year 8*)
Mr Simon Westmancoat, BA (*Assistant Head of Music*)
Mrs Lisa Whiteman (*Dance*)
Mr Chris Wilde, BA (*Modern Languages; Games*)
Mr Steve Wilkes, BEd (*Physical Education; English; Head of Holland's House*)

Administrative Staff:
Bursar: Mr Vince Iwanek, OBE
School Administrator: Mrs Julie Goodwin
Headmaster's PA/Admissions Secretary: Mrs Amanda Skinner
Examinations Officer: Mrs Belinda Leslie
Careers Advisor: Mrs Sally Pike
School Nurse: Mrs Cally Lawrie, BSc Nursing
School Network Manager: Mr Tim Lees
Office Manager: Mrs Jacky Matthews
Librarian: Mr Rob Phillips, BSc Hons
Assistant Librarian: Mrs Joy Schofield

Prep School

Headmaster: Mr Nicholas Lovell, BA Hons, PGCE
Deputy Headteacher: Mrs Anne Wilson, BEd
Assistant Head: Mrs Helen Higginson, BSc, MA
Director of Studies: Mr Steven Dhaliwal, BEd, MSc

Teaching Staff:
Mrs Rachel Avlonti, BEd Hons
Mrs Claire Bradley, BA
Mr Julian Brown, BEd Hons
Miss Gill Beck, BEd
Mrs Jane Coles, CertEd, BPhil, MSc
Mrs Viv Cooper, BEd
Mr Steve Dhaliwal, BEd, MSc
Mrs Jacqueline Garland, CertEd
Mr Colin Groom, JP, CertEd
Mr Steve Hall, BA
Mrs Jane Halliday, BA
Mrs Julia Halstead, BA
Mrs Helen Harvey, BA
Mr Brian Hewetson, BA
Mrs Barbara Hunt, BEd Hons
Mrs Anna Johnson, BA
Miss Sian Jones, BA Ed
Mrs Lynn Keller, BSc Hons, PGCE
Mr Lau Langkilde
Mrs Jayne Legate, BSc
Mrs Dot Monnington
Mrs Ruth Morris, BA Hons, PGCE
Mr Ken Pearson, BEd
Mrs Pauline Pepper, BEd, MA
Mr Keith Rawlins, BEd
Mr Phil Savage, BA
Mr David Senyk, BA Ed, BPhil, STB
Mrs Jill Sutherland, BA, QTS
Mrs Karen Wormald, BEd Hons
Miss Kate Wozencroft, HND, BEd Hons

Administrative Staff:
Bursar: Mr Vince Iwanek, OBE
School Administrator: Mrs Julie Goodwin
Prep School Secretary: Mrs Lesley Batson
School Secretary: Mrs Dianne Wyhinny
School Nurse: Mrs Cally Lawrie, BSc Nursing
Librarian: Mr Rob Phillips, BSc Hons
Assistant Librarian: Mrs Joy Schofield

Facilities. The school moved to its present extensive site in a pleasant part of Coventry in 1885. The Governors have continually improved, extended and restored the buildings which are well equipped to cope with the demands of an up-to-date, relevant and challenging curriculum. The school has extensive playing fields, some of which are located on the main site. Other playing fields are five minutes away by minibus.

The Governors have committed themselves to a major building programme at the school. A new Prep School, Art facility, Sixth Form Centre and Sports Hall have recently been completed. Both Senior and Prep Schools have a first rate computer network which is available to all pupils. A six-lane, 25m swimming pool (and fitness suite) is planned for 2008.

Curriculum. The curriculum is broad and balanced, integrating National Curriculum principles and practices where appropriate. The Senior School curriculum provides courses leading to the GCSE examinations and GCE AS and A levels. Subjects available currently are Art, Biology, Business Studies, Chemistry, Classical Civilisation, Computing, Technology, Drama and Theatre Studies, Economics, English, French, Geography, German, Greek, History, Information and Communication Technology, Latin, Law, Mathematics, Music, Psychology, Physics, Religious Studies and Spanish. Physical Education and Sport are also considered to be a vital part of the curriculum and are available as an AS and A2 level option. All students follow a carefully structured PSHE course.

Courses in Key Skills/Complementary Studies and Critical Thinking are offered in the Sixth Form.

Examination results at all levels are excellent.

Games. Rugby, Hockey, Netball, Basketball, Cross-Country Running, Athletics, Rounders, Tennis, Cricket, Swimming, Golf, Orienteering and Fencing. Prep School games include Tag Rugby, Swimming, Soccer, Rounders, Athletics, Cricket and Cross-Country Running. In 1986 the Governors took into use the largest artificial turf games area in the country, used mainly for hockey, but providing an additional 24 tennis courts in the summer. This facility is shared with Bablake School.

Extra-Curricular Activities. The School is noted for the excellence of its sport, music, drama, debating, public speaking and outdoor pursuits. All pupils are encouraged to make a contribution to the extra-curricular life of the school. The School has close connections with many universities including Oxford and Cambridge. The Coventry School Foundation owns an extensive property near Fougères in the Normandy region of France, and all pupils will spend at least one week there during the second year in the Senior school.

Admission. Admission is via the School's own Entrance Examination, held annually in January for entrance the following September. The normal age of entry is 11, but there are smaller additional intakes at other ages (12 and 13) and also at Sixth Form level. All enquiries about admission to the school should be addressed to the Headmaster.

Scholarships. The Governors award annually a number (not fixed) of entrance bursaries and scholarships. Full details regarding financial assistance are available from the Headmaster at the school.

Old Coventrians Association. Contact: Mrs Pam Thomas; e-mail: webALUMNUS@khviii.com; website: www.khviii.com.

Fees per term (2008-2009). Senior School £2,793; Prep School £2,115.

Prep School. The Prep School enjoys excellent facilities adjoining the main site which include a Library, an ICT room with networked PCs, an Art and Design room, a Science room and a Music room. Children are accepted by competitive examination from 7+ to 11+. The emphasis is on a broad education based upon the National Curriculum and children are prepared for the Entrance Examination for entry to the Senior School.

(*For further information about the Prep School, see entry in IAPS section.*)

Charitable status. Coventry School Foundation is a Registered Charity, number 528961. Its aim is to advance the education of boys and girls by the provision of a school or schools in or near the City of Coventry.

King William's College

Castletown Isle of Man IM9 1TP
Tel: 01624 820428
Fax: 01624 820401
e-mail: principal@kwc.sch.im
website: www.kwc.im

King William's College owes its foundation to Dr Isaac Barrow, Bishop of Sodor and Man from 1663 to 1671, who established an Educational Trust in 1668. The funds of the Trust were augmented by public subscription and the College was opened in 1833 and named after King William IV, 'The Sailor King'.

In 1991, the College merged with the Isle of Man's other independent school, The Buchan School, Castletown, which had been founded by Lady Laura Buchan in 1875 to provide education for young ladies. The Buchan School has been reformed as the junior section of the College for boys and girls up to age 11. (*For further details of The Buchan School, see entry in IAPS section*).

The Isle of Man, being internally self-governing, has a very favourable tax structure and the independence of College would not be affected by changes in UK legislation.

Motto: '*Assiduitate, non desidia.*'

***Principal*: Dr Sarah J Welch**, MA, PhD

Head of Senior School: Miss R J Corlett, BA

* *Head of Department*
† *House Parent*

J M Allegro, BA
Mrs M Bailey-Barnes, BA (**Spanish*)
Mrs E J Ballantyne, BSc
A W Beadle, BEd
M G Bowles, BA (**Design & Technology*)
Mrs K E Brew, BEng
Miss C L Broadbent, BA
J H Buchanan, BA (**History, Director of Studies*)
S N Cope, BA (**Geography*)
Miss E R Cowen, BA
M C Crabtree, BSc
Mrs D J Currie, BA
C Davidson, MA
Mrs B Dunn, BEd (*Director of Sport*)
Mrs I E Ferrier, MA (**German, Head of CAS*)
Dr R P Filho, BA, MA, D-ès-L (*Registrar, Director of IB*)
Mrs S L Filho, BA (**Theatre Arts*)
Miss J R Forrest, BA
Miss C Ganzo Perez, BA
Miss N F Gardner, BA
Mrs E J Green, BMus, ARCM (*Director of Music*)
Miss F Heckel, MA (**French, Head of Modern Languages*)
Miss S Hills, BSc
Mrs A B Holden, MSc

K Holder, MA
Dr C E Humphreys-Jones, BA, PhD (**English*)
R D Humphreys-Jones, BSc (**Physics, Head of Fifth Form*)
L Ilott, BEd
S P Kelly, BA (**Art*)
B T Lockyer, MA
Mrs Z A McAndry (*†School House*)
A A Maree, BA (*Head of Boarding, †Colbourne House*)
D M C Matthews, BSc (**Mathematics*)
G E Moore, BMus
Revd T H Mordecai, MA (*Chaplain*)
Mrs A L Morgans, BA Ed, BSc (*Head of Sixth Form*)
Dr P H Morgans, BSc, PhD (**Science*)
Miss H E Morton, BEd (*Head of Fourth Form*)
R Riekert, BComm (**Economics*)
Miss B Saxon, BSc, MEd
Mrs A M Schreiber, MA
Mrs V L Stevenson, BSc
A D Ulyett, BSc
Mrs B Van Rhyn, BA
P Verschueren, MSc
Miss M Zahkna, MSc

Part-time Staff:
A Carter Johnson, MA
Miss S Havet
Mrs N A Litton, CertEd
Mrs J Munro, BA
Mrs S A Ross, BEd

School Medical Officer: Dr J E Brewis, MBChB
Personal Assistant to the Principal: Mrs S J Craine

The College is set in superb countryside on the edge of Castletown Bay and adjacent to Ronaldsway Airport. The Isle of Man is approximately 33 miles long and 13 miles wide and is an area of diverse and beautiful scenery. The Isle of Man is an unusually safe environment with a very low crime rate.

There are approximately 375 pupils at College and a further 200 pupils at the Preparatory School. There is also a Nursery School for 2 to 4 year olds on the Buchan site. Both King William's College and The Buchan School are fully co-educational.

Entry. New pupils are accepted at any time, but most begin at the start of the September Term. Boys and girls are admitted to the Preparatory School up to the age of 11 at which point transfer to King William's College is automatic. Pupils at both Schools follow the National Curriculum in slightly augmented form. The entry to College, including Sixth Form level, is by Head's report and, where possible, by interview.

Organisation. The school is divided into three sections: Fourth Form (National Curriculum Years 7 & 8), Fifth Form (Years 9, 10 & 11) and Sixth Form (Years 12 & 13). Each section is led by a Head of Year, assisted by a team of tutors who monitor the academic progress and deal with all day-to day matters relating to the pupils in their charge. In addition, all pupils are placed in one of three co-educational Houses for internal competitive purposes, but which do provide an important element of continuity throughout a pupil's career at the School.

Boarders. There are two houses: one for boys and the other for girls. The living and sleeping accommodation is arranged principally in study-bedrooms for senior pupils with junior pupils sharing dormitories in small groups. Each House has its own Houseparent who is responsible for the pastoral welfare of the pupils. He or she is assisted by two or three tutors, of whom at least two are resident.

Chapel. The College is a Church of England foundation but pupils of all denominations attend Chapel; the spirit of the services is distinctly ecumenical.

Curriculum. The curriculum is designed to provide a broad balanced and challenging form of study for all pupils. At 11 and 12 pupils take English, Mathematics, French, Science, History, Geography, Technology (including Information Technology and Food Technology), Art, Music, Drama, Religious Studies, Physical Education and PSHE. At 13 there is the opportunity to study from a choice of Creative Subjects, PE, Spanish or Latin. A year later, a selection of up to ten subjects is made for GCSE.

In the Sixth Form King William's College offers the **International Baccalaureate**. Students choose 6 subjects, normally 3 at higher level and 3 at standard level, which must include their first language, a second language, a science, a social science and Mathematics. In addition, students write an extended essay (a research piece of 4,000 words), follow a course in the Theory of Knowledge (practical philosophy) and spend the equivalent of one half day a week on some form of creative aesthetic activity or active community service (e.g. Duke of Edinburgh's Award fulfils this requirement).

Music and Drama. There are excellent facilities for drama with House plays and at least one major school production each year, together with regular coaching in Speech and Drama. There are Junior and Senior Bands and Choirs, and a very flourishing Chapel Choir. The House Music competition is one of the many focal points of House activity.

Games. The College has a strong tradition and a fine reputation in the major games of rugby, hockey and cricket. There are regular fixtures with Isle of Man schools and schools in other parts of the British Isles. Netball, athletics, soccer, cross-country and swimming all flourish and there are both House and College competitions. Senior pupils may opt to play golf on the magnificent adjoining Castletown Golf Links or to sail as their major summer sport. There are approximately thirty acres of first class playing fields, an indoor heated swimming pool which is in use throughout the year, a miniature rifle range, a gymnasium for basketball and badminton with an indoor cricket net, hard and grass tennis courts, two squash courts and a sand dressed all-weather pitch.

Other Activities. There is a wide range of societies and activities to complement academic life. The Duke of Edinburgh's Award Scheme flourishes and expeditions are undertaken regularly both on the Island and further afield. There is a thriving Combined Cadet Force and Social Services group. There are strong links with the Armed Services who help regularly with Cadet training. There are regular skiing trips, choir tours and educational trips to the UK and abroad.

Travel. King William's College is easily accessible from the UK and from abroad. Some boarders come by sea from Heysham or Liverpool using the regular service to Douglas but the majority of boarding pupils and parents come by air from the British Isles and much further afield. There are direct flights to London, Belfast, Dublin, Liverpool, Manchester, Bristol and other UK cities. Boarding House staff are fully experienced in arranging international flights and younger pupils are met at the airport.

Health. The health of all pupils is in the care of the School Doctor. There is a sanatorium supervised by a qualified nursing sister and high standards of medical care are available at Noble's Hospital in Douglas.

Fees per term (2008-2009). Day: £3,906 (Years 7 & 8), £4,877 (Years 9–11), £5,553 (Years 12 & 13). Boarding Fee: £2,535 in addition to Day Fee.

A reduction of one-third of the fee for boarders and one half of the fee for day pupils is allowed to children of clergy holding a benefice or Bishop's licence and residing in the Isle of Man. There is a similar arrangement for children of Methodist Ministers. A reduction of 15% is allowed for serving members of HM Forces.

A reduction of 10% is made for the second child, 30% for the third and 50% for the fourth.

Scholarships. (*see Scholarship Entries section*). There is a variety of Scholarships for pupils entering Years 7 and for Sixth Form entry.

Music Scholarships, Performing Arts and Sports Awards are available for pupils aged over 11.

A bursary fund is available to assist with school fees in cases of need.

Further details of the school and a prospectus may be obtained from the Registrar's office to which applications for entry should also be made.

Charitable status. King William's College is a Manx Registered Charity, number 615 and is operated as a Company limited by guarantee.

King's College School

Wimbledon Common London SW19 4TT
Tel: 020 8255 5300
Fax: 020 8255 5309 (Porters' Lodge)
020 8255 5379 (Senior Common Room)
020 8255 5359 (Head Master's Study)
e-mail: admissions@kcs.org.uk
headmaster@kcs.org.uk
website: www.kcs.org.uk

King's College School was founded as the junior department of King's College in 1829. According to the resolutions adopted at the preliminary meeting of founders in 1828, "the system is to comprise religious and moral instruction, classical learning, history, modern languages, mathematics, natural philosophy, etc., and to be so conducted as to provide in the most effectual manner for the two great objects of education the communication of general knowledge, and specific preparation for particular professions". In 1897 it was removed from the Strand to its present site on Wimbledon Common.

Motto: *Sancte et Sapienter.*

Governing Body:

Visitor: The Archbishop of Canterbury

Chairman of the Governing Body:
J M Jarvis, QC, MA

Prof M L Brown, MA, PhD
The Rt Revd Thomas Butler, BSc, MSc, PhD, CEng, MIEE, Bishop of Southwark
Mrs F R Cahill, BA
O L Carlstrand, BSc, CEng, MICE
A J M Chamberlain, MA, FIA
T A Clark, MA, MSc
P Evitt, MA
T A I Fitzpatrick,
P Fraser, PhD
B Gidoomal, CBE, CCMI, FRSA
G W James, MA
H M G King
Sir Peter Lampl, OBE, MA, MSc
P F G Levelle
R S Luddington, MA, MPhil
R G Mathews, FCA, CTA
Sir Trevor McDonald, OBE
Mrs P Reed-Boswell, CertEd
D R J Silver, MA
G D Slaughter, MA
D G Tilles, BSc, FCMA, ASIP
Mrs C van Tulleken, BA

***Head Master*: A D Halls**, MA, FRSA

Second Master: D J Grossel, MA

Third Master: K N Hawney, BSc

Senior Masters/Mistresses:
B J Driver, MA
Miss H L McKissack, MA

Undermasters:
M D Allen, MA
R J Mitchell, MA
M P Stables, BA
N P Tetley, BA

Chaplain: The Revd Mrs L R F Collins, BD, AKC, MTh
Assistant Chaplain: The Revd T J E Marwood, MA

Senior School

P Lloyd, BSc, PhD (*Head of Science*)

R C Clark, BSc, PhD (*Head of Biology*)
Dr J E Blythe, BSc, PhD
Dr S A Brown, BSc, PhD
N E Edwards, MSc (*Head of Examinations*)
E H Johnson, MSc
P M Lavender, BSc (*Head of University Entrance, USA admissions*)

A M Hayes, BSc, PhD (*Head of Chemistry*)
I M Davies, MA
S Foot, BSc
Miss H L McKissack, BSc, MA
R J Mitchell, MA

R W M Hughes, MSc (*Head of Physics*)
G E D Bennett, MA
G Cawley, BSc
E W M Kittoe, BSc
D J Lavender, MA, ALCM (*Head of Careers*)

C M Jackson, MA (*Head of Classics*)
G E Bennett, BA (*Head of Sixth Form*)
J R Carroll, MA (*Head of Maclear House*)
Miss V R Casemore, BA
T B Hayward, MA
Miss C L Tedd, MA

W P Brierly, BSc (*Head of Economics & Business Studies*)
Miss S-A Gosher, BCom
A G Hepworth, BSc
Mrs L A High, MA
Mrs C J Shandro, BA

T F Wayman, BA, MPhil (*Head of English*)
M D Allen, MA (*Teaching & Learning*)
Miss L J Drayton, BA
Miss A V Eilert, MA
Mrs J N Hammond, BA (*Head of PSHE*)
Miss S Kaba, BA
F S McKeown, BA, PhD
Miss K L Robinson, MA, MPhil
P S Swan, BA (*Head of Drama & Theatre Studies*)
J L B Trapmore, MA
Mrs J J Whitaker, BA

P C Guinness, MSc (*Head of Geography*)
M J Chambers, BSc (*Head of Major House*)
J A Galloway, BA (*Head of Alverstone House*)

A W Thomas, MA (*Head of History*)
Miss R M Davis, BA (*Coordinator of Educational Visits, Exchanges & Development*)
Miss S H Fitzmaurice, BA
D J Grossel, MA
J G Lawrence, MA, MLitt (*Director of Co-curricular Education*)
Miss M-H Quaradeghini, MA (*Head of Kingsley House*)
J G Ryan, BA
N P Tetley, BA (*Director of IB*)

Ms C A Ramgoolam, HDipEd (BEd) (*ICT Coordinator*)

S J Nye, BSc (*Head of Mathematics*)
E B S Bowles, MEng
B J Driver, BA, ARCO

K N Hawney, BSc
T P Howland, BA
G C McGinn, CertEd
R J Pagnamenta, MA, MEng
M P Stables, BA (*Director of Studies*)
Miss C M Szekely, BSc
C J Thomas, BEng
Miss S Walker, BEng

S Tint, MA, FCIL (*Head of Modern Languages*)
B P Andrews, BA
R P Bailey, MA
Mrs C R Butler, MA
H Chapman, MA
Miss A V Eilert, MA (*Coordinator of Chinese Studies*)
C C D Fowler, BA
Ms L Hardwick, MA
Dr E Keyes, PhD
Ms M-Z Li, MPhil
Miss K Long, MA
S Marshall-Taylor, BA (*Head of Glenesk House*)
Mrs D McBride, Graduate Political Sciences (International), Florence University
Mrs H M Mulcahy, BA
Miss R C Peel, BA
Mrs J E Purslow, MA
J M A Ross, BA
A R J Swigg, BA

Dr G M Bamford, BSc, PhD (*Head of Psychology*)
D G Kokott, BA

M J Storey, BA, PhD (*Head of Religious Studies*)
R R Carnighan, MA, MPhil
Revd Mrs L R F Collins, BD, AKC, MTh
Mrs L A Ogilvie, MA
J T Sprague, BA, MA

Mrs E Goodchild, BSc, DipSpLD (*Head of Learning Support*)
Mrs A Tingle, BA

Junior School
Tel: 020 8255 5335; Fax: 020 8255 5339;
e-mail: jsadmissions@kcs.org.uk; HMJSsec@kcs.org.uk

Headmaster: Dr G A Silverlock, BEd Hons, MLitt, PhD

Deputy Head (*Pastoral*): Mrs H J Morren, MA

Deputy Head (*Curriculum*): D Jones, BA

R Anderson, BSc
C R M Andrews, BSc (*Professional Tutor; Head of Science*)
Miss V J Attié, BA
A Baker, BEd
J C Barnwell, BA
Mrs S L Beazley, BA (*Head of Rushmere*)
Miss C M Bitaud, BA
Mrs J Blight, BA
P K Brady, BA
R Brambley, BA (*Head of Mathematics*)
E D Brooks, BA (*Head of PSHE*)
M R Bryan, BA (*Head of Classics*)
Miss N Chilko, BEd/BA (*Head of Stuart House*)
Miss S V D Coke, BA (*Head of Drama*)
M P Culverhouse, BA
Miss L Cunningham, BA
Mrs S J de Montfort, BTheol
Miss S C Dore, BA
Miss L S Gillard, MA, ATC (*Head of Art & Design*)
Mrs O M E Hamilton, MA (*Head of Religious Studies*)
R Hammond, CertEd (*Head of Tudor House*)
J E A Hipkiss, BSc (*Head of Norman House*)
Miss F C Hutchison, BA
Miss T J Leach, BA (*Head of Windsor*)
Mrs J C Lewis, BA
Mrs G A McGee, BSc, CTC (*ITC Coordinator*)
Mrs S J Martineau Walker, BA
I D Morris, BA (*Examinations Officer*)
P Nash, BA (*Head of Keyboards*)
M L Nixon, BMus
M W G Robinson, MA (*Head of Learning Enrichment, English*)
Mrs P Saunders, BSc
M A Stevenson, MA (*Head of Music in Junior School*)
E T Watkins, BA (*Head of History*)
J Streatfeild, BA (*Head of Geography*)
Miss P J Whitwell, MA (*Head of Modern Languages*)
T S Young, BA (*Head of PE & Games*)

Senior and Junior Schools

D G Phillips, MA (*Director of Music*)
P A Hatch, BMus (*Assistant Director of Music*)
R J H Krippner, BMus (*School Organist*)
R Lorraine, MA (Composer), MMus, PhD
M L Nixon, BMus (*Head of Keyboards*)
L Silvera, BMus (*Head of Strings*)
A G S Skinner, BA
M A Stevenson, MA (*Head of Music in Junior School*)

R A Carswell, MA (*Head of Art*)
Miss L S Gillard, MA, ATC (*Head of Junior School ADT*)
Miss S C Dore, BA
S J Martineau Walker, BA
N Pollen, MA

Miss D Langenberg, BA (*Head of Design Technology*)
J D Broderick, BA
A R Pleace, BSc

L B D Kane, BSc (*Head of Games & PE Department*)
T S Young, BA (*Head of KCJS Games & PE*)
J C Barnwell, BA
M J Blackburn, BA (*Director of Rugby*)
M P Culverhouse, BA
C J Grimble, BA (*Head of Rowing*)
J S Reyburn, BSc
M V Thompson, BSc

CCF Instructor: N P Brett

Administrative Staff:
Bursar: A T Hawksley, MA, FCA
Head Master's PA: Mrs R Ingram, BA
Junior School Headmaster's PA: Mrs S E C Richards
Junior School Admissions/School Secretary: Mrs J N Worth
Librarian: Miss H J Pugh, BA, ALA
Junior School Librarian: Mrs A Beddoe
Human Resources Officer: Mrs L Kinloch, MCIPD

Organisation. KCS is a day school for boys. The School consists of a Senior School, which boys enter at 13, and a Junior School, which educates boys aged 7 to 13 in preparation for entry to the Senior School. On entry to the Senior School boys are placed in one of the six Houses. Every boy has a Tutor who is responsible for his progress and welfare throughout his school career.

Admission. Entrance to the Senior School is through the Common Entrance Examination or the KCS Scholarship Examination. Candidates should normally be registered by their tenth birthday, and will be assessed at 11+ with a view to advising parents on their suitability as candidates for KCS at 13+. A number of places are available each year for entry to the Sixth Form. Preliminary enquiries about entry should be made to the Registration Secretary.

Junior School. Entrance examinations, graded according to the ages of the boys, are held in the January of the year of entry. Enquiries should be made to the Junior School Secretary. (*For further details of the Junior School refer to entry in IAPS section.*)

Scholarships. (*see Scholarship Entries section*). In the case of financial need further contributions to fees may be provided by the bursary fund (see below). Up to 15 Scholarships, with varying values up to 20% of the full tuition fee, may be awarded. One of the scholarships may be awarded to a boy offering Greek who shows particular promise as a classical linguist; two others may be awarded to boys who show particular promise in modern languages or science. The number of Scholarships awarded in any year will vary according to the quality of the candidates. There are separate additional prizes to recognise outstanding ability in the Humanities, Mathematics and English. Up to 6 Music Scholarships, with varying values up to 20% of the full tuition fee, may be awarded to boys of high musical ability. Two Art & Design Scholarships may be awarded, with a value up to 20% of the full tuition fee. Candidates for all these awards must be under 14 years of age on 1 September of the year in which they sit the examination. One Organ Scholarship is available in the Sixth Form. Further information on all scholarships is available from the Registration Secretary.

Bursaries. The School has its own bursary fund through which it can offer assistance with fees in case of established need. (Boys already in the School take preference in the award of bursaries.) Awards may be made to boys entering either the Junior School at 11+ or the Senior School at 13+ or 16+.

Registration. A non-refundable fee of £100 is charged.

Tuition Fees per term (2008-2009). Senior School £5,150. Junior School: £4,115–£4,640. Individual music tuition is charged separately.

Curriculum. The Middle School provides a 3-year course to the GCSE. In the first year (Fourth Form) boys follow a common curriculum. In the Lower and Upper Fifths the core subjects are English, French, Mathematics, Biology, Physics, Chemistry, PSHE and PE, with options from Art, Design & Technology, Greek, German, Geography, History, Italian, Latin, Mandarin, Music, Religious Studies, Spanish and Russian.

The Sixth Form. The Sixth Form is housed in College Court, a sixth form centre with teaching and seminar rooms, recreation and study areas. College Court also houses the Careers Department as well as the Economics Department. College Court links with Collyer Hall (the theatre/concert/assembly hall) and the Cotman Art Gallery.

Sixth Form Curriculum. All boys now study the International Baccalaureate. After several years offering both A Levels and the IB, the School took this decision on academic and philosophical grounds and in the light of the gradual tarnishing of the reputation of A Level.

Boys following the IB take 6 papers: literature; a modern language; a science; mathematics; a humanity (eg History, Geography, Psychology, Politics, History of Art or Economics); and either a creative subject, a classical language or another of the first five categories. Three or four of these subjects are taken at Higher Level, the rest at Standard Level. In addition they take a course in the Theory of Knowledge and their contribution to extra-curricular activities through Creativity, Action & Service is also assessed.

Every sixth former also participates in a wider educational programme of classes, lectures and activities, which include spiritual and moral issues, a full programme of games and an afternoon devoted to extra-curricular activities.

Religious Education. KCS is an Anglican foundation but welcomes boys from all churches and faiths. The practice of other faiths is encouraged. The School has a Chaplaincy through which boys are prepared for confirmation and there is a Chapel for voluntary worship and communion.

Music. There is a purpose-built Music School. Four orchestras, three choirs and two wind bands, as well as various smaller groups and jazz groups, perform a number of major choral and orchestral works each year. Some 40% of the boys have individual music lessons at the School.

Games. After an introduction to a range of games in their first year, boys have a free choice of termly sports. The games programme includes athletics, badminton, basketball, cricket, cross-country running, fencing, fives, hockey, karate, rowing, rugby, sailing, shooting, soccer, squash, swimming, tennis and water polo. The School has its own indoor heated swimming pool. The sports hall has a floor area providing 4 badminton courts, as well as volley and basketball, indoor tennis and cricket nets, together with a fitness training room and four squash courts. There is an all-weather surface for hockey and tennis at the West Barnes Lane ground. The School's boathouse is on the Tideway at Putney Bridge.

School societies and activities. Every boy is encouraged to take part in extra-curricular activities. Societies meet in the two extended lunch breaks and after school. Friday school finishes early to allow boys to participate in a range of activities like the CCF and voluntary service. There are active drama and debating societies, together with a wide range of other societies.

Numbers. In the Senior School 770; in the Junior School 450.

Honours. Places at Oxford and Cambridge for 2008: 40.

Charitable status. King's College School is a Registered Charity, number 310024. It exists to provide education for children.

King's College
A Woodard School

South Road Taunton Somerset TA1 3LA
Tel: Headmaster: 01823 328210
Bursar: 01823 328100
Fax: 01823 328202
e-mail: admissions@kings-taunton.co.uk
website: www.kings-taunton.co.uk

A Woodard school, Canon Nathaniel Woodard renamed the school King's College in memory of King Alfred, when he bought it in 1879, but its historical links go back to the medieval grammar school which was founded by Bishop Fox of Winchester in 1522.

King's College, Taunton is an independent co-educational boarding and day school for 430 boys and girls aged 13–18 years.

Situated on the outskirts of Taunton, the county town of Somerset, on a splendid 100-acre site, King's College offers high academic standards, a friendly and caring day and boarding community, and has an enviable reputation for music, drama and sport. Kindness, consideration for others, honesty and self-discipline are the values which King's hopes will provide its pupils with the inner resources not just for school, but for life.

Motto: *Fortis et Fidelis*

Provost: The Rt Revd J D G Kirkham, MA

School Council:
M C Mowat, Esq, FCA (*Chairman and Custos*)
G J Mulder, Esq (*Vice-Custos*)
R D V Knight, Esq, MA
A H Beadles, Esq, MA
Mrs L H Eliot, MA
R M Excell, Esq
Sir H W Farrington, MRICS
The Revd D J M Jasper, BA, DipTh
R D V Knight, Esq, MA
P J LeRoy, Esq, MA, DipEd
R D A Lloyd, Esq, BSc, MRICS
R I W Marfell, Esq, FCA

Dr R A K Mott, BA, PhD
Mrs R Price

***Headmaster*: R R Biggs**, BSc Cape Town, MA Oxon

Chaplain: The Revd M Smith, BA, DipTh

Deputy Heads:
R R Currie, BA
Mrs K L McSwiggan, BA

Assistant Teachers:
* *Head of Department*
† *Housemaster/mistress*

C J Albery, BMus (*Director of Music*)
M J Bakewell, BA
Mrs J E Brossard, BA
Mrs L S Cashmore, BA
Mrs J M Chadwick, BA
D J Cole, BSc (**Induction*)
Mrs K E Cole, BA (**Learning Support*)
Mrs P Corke, BA
Mrs J M Currie, LLB, Cert TEFL
P A Dossett, BSc (**Chemistry*)
Miss G Fagan, MA (*†Meynell*)
Miss K J Fergusson, BA, MMus
Miss C H Flood, BA (**Geography*)
S B Gray, MA (*Director of Studies*)
Mrs J A Gresswell, BSc (**Physics*)
N S Gresswell (*†King Alfred*)
J H Griffiths, BTech (*†Tuckwell*)
J W Grindle, BSc, BEd
Miss R L Grove, BSc, MPhys, AMInstP
Miss S J Harvey BSc (*Co-Director of Sport*)
T J Haynes, BA
Miss I S Hobday, BSc (*Senior Tutor*)
C K Holmes, BA (*†Woodard*)
A R Hopwood, BSc (*Administrative Master*)
Mrs M A Hudson, RGN, RMN (*†Carpenter*)
A Jones, BA (*Co-Director of Sport*)
M M Lang, BSc, MPhil (**ICT*)
J A Lee, BA (*Senior Tutor*)
Dr B Lewis, BSc, PhD (*Senior Master*)
P D Lewis, BSc
R Llewellyn-Eaton, MA
O H Lloyd, BA (*†Bishop Fox*)
I R Lundie, MA (**Design Technology*)
Ms C N Mackenzie, BA, DipAD
A P McKegney, BA (**Business Education*)
Mrs K M Mulligan, BA, RSA Dip
Miss R L Nutt, BA
Dr R H C Poland, BSc PhD (**Science*)
M A Polley, MA (**Classics*)
J K Round, MA (**Mathematics*)
P J Scanlan, MA (**History, †Taylor*)
Mrs M J Scanlan, RGN (*†Taylor*)
J A Scott, BSc (**Biology*)
Mrs A M Sheehan, Connecticut University (**Drama*)
Mrs L D Wrobel, BA
G Wrobel BSc

CCF:
P J Belfield, BSc
Lt Col T K W Hart, BA
S Sgt R Mason (*SSI*)

Medical Officers:
Dr Y L Duthie, MB BS, DCH, MRCGP
Dr P L B Squire, MB BS, MRCGP
Dr A F C Fulford, MBChB, DRCOG, MRCGP

Bursar: J C Boal, BA, BPhil
Director of Marketing: Mrs J M Hake
Admissions Registrar: Mrs B Lancey
ICT Manager: A R Hopwood

King's College, Taunton, delivers success at all ages whilst offering a friendly, happy and safe living and working environment. The school provides an extraordinary breadth of opportunities to pupils and has very high academic standards. King's is well placed in national exam results league tables and also enjoys the highest levels of achievement in sports, art, drama and music. The school is the current holder of the BBC Songs of Praise Senior School Choir of the Year title, as well as the Rosslyn Park 7s Rugby Cup – a taste of the breadth of opportunity available to pupils.

King's College has produced a large number of Oxbridge entrants over the years and is well regarded by the top universities in the UK. Pupils can join the Third Form (Year 9) at 13, going on to take GCSE exams, or in the Sixth Form (Year 12) at 16 or 17 to study for A Levels. The school is blessed with highly-qualified and committed members of staff who see their role as ensuring the happiness and successful development of each individual member of the school community. The word community is very prominent at King's: Boarders and day pupils benefit from a strong Christian ethos: an environment where self-respect and kindness to others are highly-regarded qualities.

Admission. All entries are made through the Headmaster. Pupils normally enter at 13 years in the Michaelmas term and are admitted via Common Entrance or the Scholarship Examination.

The registration fee is £60.

Fees per term (2008-2009). Boarders £7,795, Day Pupils £5,070. The fees are inclusive of all extra charges of general application.

Scholarships. (*see Scholarship Entries section*).

Old Aluredian's Association. *Secretary*: Dr R H C Poland, BSc, King's College, South Road, Taunton, TA1 3LA.

Charitable status. Woodard Schools Taunton Ltd is a Registered Charity, number 1103346. King's College exists to provide high quality education for boys and girls aged 13–18.

The King's Hospital

Palmerstown Dublin 20 Ireland
Tel: 00 353 1 643 6500
Fax: 00 353 1 623 0349
e-mail: kingshospitaladmissions@ireland.com
website: www.kingshospital.ie

Chairman of Governors: Mr Michael Brown

***Headmistress*: Frances J Hill**, MEd, BA, HDipEd

Deputy Head: Glascott Symes, MA, HDipEd

Assistant Heads:
John Rafter, BA, BSc, HDipEd (*Games & Recreations*)
Siobhán Daly, BA Mod, HDipEd (*Academic Affairs*)
John Aiken, BA, HDipEd (*Pastoral Care*)

Chaplain: The Revd Peter Campion, MPhil, MA, PGCE

Heads of Departments:
Detta Brennan, Dip Fine Arts, Dip ADT (*Art*)
Mark Campion, BA, HDipEd (*Mathematics*)
The Reverend Peter Campion, MPhil, MA, PGCE (*Religious Education*)
Norma Clarke, BA, HDipEd (*Business*)
Andrew Deacon, BA, HDipEd (*English*)
Barbara Fuller, MSc, BA, AdvDipEd, HDipEd, DipEd (*Special Education Needs*)
Paul Huggard, BA, HDipEd, HDSGC (*Geography*)
John Huggard, BA, HDipEd (*History*)
Emma Ryan, BSc QTS (*Physical Education*)
Marita McGeady, HEcT Hons, DipSocSc (*Home Economics*)
Jane Morrow, BA, HDipEd (*SPHE*)

Dymphna Morris, BA Hons, DipComp (*Information Technology*)
Michelle Murray, MEd Mgt, BA Special, HDipEd (*Irish*)
Patrick O'Shea, BTechEd (*Design and Communication Technology*)
Aileen Polke, BA, HDipEd (*Modern Language*)
Helen Roycroft, BA, Dip PRII (*Music*)
Jane Salter, BSc Hons, HDipEd (*Science*)
Susan Tanner, BSc, HDipEd, HDCG (*Career Guidance*)
Cormac Ua Bruadair, BA Hons, HDipEd (*Transition Year*)

Housemasters/mistresses:
Bluecoat (*Sixth Form boy boarders*): Raymond McIlreavy, MEd, BA, HDipEd
Bluecoat (*Sixth Form girl boarders*): Lorna McGinn, MA, BA Hons, HDSGC
Grace (*Girl boarders*): Rachelle van Zyl, BComm Hons, HDipEd
Mercer (*Girl boarders*): Caroline Brady, BEd Hons
Ormonde (*Boy boarders*): Niall Mahon, BSc, HDipEd
Morgan (*Boy boarders*): Cormac Ua Bruadair, BA Hons, HDipEd
Bluecoat (*Sixth Form day pupils*): Dermot Kelleher, AdvDipPhysEd
Swift (*Middle School day pupils*): Paul Huggard, BA, HDipEd, HDSGC
Stuart (*Middle School day pupils*): John Huggard, BA, HDipEd
Blackhall (*Middle School day pupils*): Andrew Deacon, BA, HDipEd
Desmond (*Middle School day pupils*): Noel Cunningham, MSc, BSc, HDipEnvirEng, HDipEd
Ivory (*First Form day pupils*): Peter O'Boyle, BA, GradCertEd, DipCat

Bursar: Ronald Wynne

Secretary to the Headmistress: Lorraine Walker

Age Range. 11–18 Co-educational.

Number of Pupils. 706: Boarders: 160 Boys, 186 Girls; Day: 195 Boys, 165 Girls.

The King's Hospital, one of the oldest boarding schools in Ireland, was founded in 1669 as The Hospital and Free School of King Charles II. In 1971 the School moved from the centre of Dublin to its present, modern setting in spacious, scenic grounds of over 100 acres on the banks of the River Liffey in Palmerstown. A Church of Ireland (Anglican), co-educational secondary school with 700 pupils, the majority of whom are boarders, the King's Hospital attracts pupils from all over Ireland as well as from overseas.

The King's Hospital believes that every child should achieve his or her true potential intellectually and socially, through personal endeavour and the encouragement and support of our staff, parents and governors. Through our academic, pastoral and extra-curricular programmes, we strive to develop core values of:

- a love of learning which makes all study a discovery and a joy, and which leads to standards of academic excellence appropriate to each child's ability;
- a Christian conscience and awareness which enables our pupils to develop a personal faith in God, to lead fulfilling lives which will enrich the communities in which they live, to uphold truth and show respect for others as well as for themselves, and to accept responsibility for their own actions;
- a sense of duty and loyalty which encourages participation in, and commitment to, every aspect of school life.

Academic. Most pupils pursue a 6 year course on entering the school at the age of 12. The first three years lead to the Junior Certificate Examination, followed by a Transition Year and the final two years are devoted to the Leaving Certificate Examination. Streaming is not a policy at The King's Hospital and the consistently high level of academic achievement is a reflection of the manner in which the School has always adapted to the ever-evolving education process and the ever-changing needs of its pupils by providing a comprehensive and progressive range of subjects, extensive specialist facilities and a highly qualified teaching staff.

The specialist facilities range from laboratories, workshops and computers to technical equipment and instruments, with Computer/PowerPoint facilities in many classrooms. A highly trained and well-equipped Special Needs department is available for both gifted children and those with learning difficulties. Media technology in the Harden Library provides access to national and international databases for project work as well as a computerised resource centre for information and guidance on careers.

Extra-Curricular. In addition to academic pursuits, The King's Hospital is renowned for its unrivalled choice of recreational activities. Pupils are encouraged to participate and all have the opportunity to represent the School at various levels in the activities of their choice.

An ultra-modern Sports Hall and Gymnasium, incorporating a fully equipped computerised fitness centre, a 25 metre indoor heated swimming pool and a floodlit astroturf pitch are among the outstanding facilities providing ample opportunity for Rugby, Hockey, Athletics, Swimming, Canoeing, Rowing, Cricket, Soccer, Basketball, Badminton and Tennis.

The promotion of cultural activities is catered for through Arts and Crafts, Choirs, Orchestras and Drama and Musical productions. A dedicated Performing Arts Centre is a recently built facility with the School's Assembly Hall/Theatre also upgraded significantly.

A diverse array of recreational activities is covered with clubs and societies, a Student Council, social works and European Studies, theatre and concert trips and trips abroad, both sporting and cultural.

Pastoral. Cooperation and mutual respect between pupils and staff, as well as a specified code of behaviour, are central to the daily life of the School. There are ten houses whose Housemaster or Housemistress has specific responsibility for the general welfare and development of pupils under his or her care. The diverse aspects of health education are included in the School's programme and there is 24 hour nursing care and a counsellor available. Worship, according to the rites of the Church of Ireland and led by the resident Chaplain, is an integral part of daily life and pupils gain an understanding and respect for all religious persuasions.

The Future. A vision for the future of the School is embodied in an ever-evolving School Plan and the Board of Governors is committed to constantly implementing the development strategies within that plan. The School's ambitious development programme is designed to maintain its position as one of Ireland's leading educational institutions. The building of a new Form 6 Bluecoat House was completed in February 2008 – a tremendous addition to the Senior School costing €8 million. The King's Hospital is a school firmly rooted in tradition while continuing to be at the cutting edge of modern education.

Fees per term (2008-2009). Boarders €4,450, Day €1,815.

King's School
Bruton

Bruton Somerset BA10 0ED
Tel: 01749 814200
Fax: 01749 813426
e-mail: office@kingsbruton.com
website: www.kingsbruton.com

The School was founded in 1519 by Richard Fitzjames, Bishop of London, John Fitzjames, his nephew, Attorney-

General, afterwards Chief Justice of the King's Bench, and John Edmonds, DD, Chancellor of St Paul's. It was closed in 1538 on the suppression of the Monasteries, and re-founded by Edward VI in 1550.

Motto: *Deo Juvante.*

Governors:
Air Chief Marshal Sir Peter Squire, GCB, DFC, AFC, DSc, FRAeS (*Senior Warden*)
I M Argyle, Esq, BEd
R I Case, Esq, CBE, DL, FREng, FRAeS, MSc (*Chairman of Finance*)
Professor W P H Duffus, BVSc, MA, PhD, MRCVS
R Gallannaugh, Esq, ARIBA
General Sir Alex Harley, KBE, CB
K L Lawes, Esq, FCA
Mrs A L Lee, RGN, RNT, BEd, MA
Mrs S McKenzie
Mrs E M McLoughlin, CBE
S R Oxenbridge, Esq
P J Phillips, Esq, FIPA
D E Prince, Esq, BA
R R Williams, Esq, ACIB
E W Thomas, Esq, BA

Clerk to the Governors: Col S G Adlington

***Headmaster*: N M Lashbrook**, BA Hertford College, Oxford

Deputy Headmaster: G J Evans, BSc Econ
Second Deputy Head: Mrs A Grant, BA
Director of Studies: A Kok, BEng, CEng
Director of Boarding: R J P Lowry, BA

Teaching Staff:
* *Head of Department*
† *Housemaster/mistress*

M F Parr, MA, DipLit (**Classics*)
N G Watts, MA (*†Old House*)
S J F Atkinson, BSc (**Biology*)
E J Tickner, BA (**Modern Languages*)
R J P Lowry, BA (*Director of Boarding*)
D J Friend, BSc (**ICT*)
S W Spilsbury, BEdTech (**Art*)
A Atkinson, BSc, PhD (**Physics*)
M J Middlehurst, BA
D R Barns-Graham, MA (**Chemistry*)
C H M Oulton, MA (*†Blackford House*)
T Fletcher, BA (**History*)
Revd N H Wilson-Brown, BSc (*Chaplain*)
G E Jenkins, BA, PhD (**Director of Music, OC CCF*)
D Warren, BA (**Geography*)
C A Barrow, BA (**Director of Sport*)
Ms M H King, BA (**Theatre Studies*)
J B Slingo, BSc (**Economics & Business Studies*)
Mrs G de Mora, BSc (**Mathematics*)
Miss R A Vigers, BSc (*†Arion House, *Food Science*)
Mrs A L Ashworth, BSc (*†Wellesley House*)
Mrs L J Bray, BA
Mrs S E Duncan, BSc (*Theatre Manager*)
Mrs J M Lashbrook, BA (**PSE*)
G A Tresidder, BA, MA, PhD (**Careers*)
Miss L J S Vickery, BSc (**Girls' Games*)
R S Hamilton, BEd (*†Lyon House*)
Dr J C Shepherd, BSc, PhD (*†Priory House*)
T R N Walker, MA
D J Gorodi, GRSM, LRAM (*Assistant Director of Music*)
W R Dawe, BA (*†New House*)
Mrs A Sherrard, BA (**Learning Support Unit*)
D R Cowley, BEd (**Design and Technology*)
Miss S F Huebner, MA
Dr S D Osborne, BSc, MSc, PhD
Mrs M C Startin, BA (**English*)
Mrs P G Atkinson, BSc
Miss J J Hill, BSc
Ms A F Turnbull, BEd
Miss M Roebuck, BSc
Mrs C Tickner, BA
Mrs S L Wilson-Brown, BEd
Mrs D T Paulley
Mrs A M Allen, DipSpLD
Mrs A Maistrello, BA
Miss S Jorgensen-Hull
M Helm

Assistant Music Staff:
Mrs S Whitfield, BA, ARCM (*Piano & Theory*)
P Caunce (*Violin/Viola*)
K R Schooley, MISM (*Percussion & Drum Kit*)
P Kelly (*Guitar*)
Mrs J Whitteridge, FTCL, AGSM, ARCM, Cert Ed (*Bassoon*)
G Austin, ARCM (*Brass*)
D Bertie, BA, FTCL, DipMus (*Trumpet*)
R Shipley, BSc, MMus, CT ABRSM, LRSM (*Clarinet & Saxophone*)
P Lambton (*Clarinet & Saxophone*)
Mrs B Jenkinson, MA, BMus, GRSM, LRAM, ARCM, PGCE (*Piano*)
Miss M Marton (*Singing*)
D Slater, MA (*Organ*)
M Walker (*Piano*)
Mrs J Brown, BA, AGSM (*Singing*)
Mrs A McBride, CertEd (*Oboe*)
Ms R Zagni (*Cello*)
M Nightingale (*Recorder*)

Bursar: Ms P L Bremner, MA, PGDip
Development Director: R J Claas
Marketing Manager: Mrs A Crowcombe
Registrar: Miss V J Helmer, MA
Assistant Registrar: Mrs C S E Oulton
Headmaster's PA: Mrs S L Carpenter
Examinations Officer: Mrs M D Edwards
Bursar's PA: Mrs J I M Bennett
School Administrator: Mrs J L Deaney
School Receptionist: Mrs C A Hunt

Medical Officers:
Dr M H Player, BSc, MB BS, DRCOG, MRCGP
Dr L H Chambers, MB BS, DRCOG
Dr U Naumann, FRG, DRCOG, MRCGP
Dr N Gompertz, BSc, MBChB, MRCP
Dr S Franks, ChB, MB, MRCGP

Hazlegrove (King's Bruton Preparatory School)
Sparkford, Yeovil, Somerset BA22 7JA
Telephone: 01963 440314 (*Headmaster and Secretary*)
Fax: 01963 440569
e-mail: office@hazlegrove.co.uk
website: www.hazlegrove.co.uk

Headmaster: R B Fenwick, MA

Deputy Head: M Davis, BEd Hons
Head of Pre-Prep Department: Miss E Lee, BEd Hons
Assistant Head (Admin): C J Smith, CertEd (**ICT*)
Assistant Head (Academic): Mrs A Hughes, MA Hons (**RE*)
Headmaster's Secretary: Mrs S Newton
Admissions Secretary: Mrs F O'Neill

Number of Pupils. 331. Boarders: 66 girls, 152 boys. Day: 35 girls, 78 boys. Sixth Form: 150.

Pastoral Care. When pupils first arrive at King's, they are welcomed into a genuinely caring community, where individuals and individuality are valued. At the centre of this community are the boarding houses which are in the care of a Housemaster or Housemistress who has overall responsibility for each pupil and who is that pupil's first and last supporter throughout his or her time at King's. In addition, pupils have their own tutor, who will keep an eye on academic progress, ensure that any problems are resolved, and offer advice and friendship. Housemasters, housemistress, matrons, tutors and senior pupils all work to ensure that each new pupil settles in quickly and successfully.

From the very beginning our pupils lead busy lives, full of work, activities and friends. The modest size of the School is a particular strength; in a community where everyone is known, pupils cannot remain annonymous.

We believe that close communication between school and parents is very important, and the Housemaster/Housemistress will be the first point of contact for parents, who are kept informed of progress through reports and also informal contacts.

Day pupils are fully integrated into the life of the boarding houses and it is often hard to dislodge them from King's. They will frequently stay late into the evenings and come into school at weekends. For them, and for our many boarders, the friendships they build at King's become of great value to them, both while they are at school and after they have moved on.

Co-education. Girls have been admitted since 1969 to Sixth Form courses subject to GCSE level success, either as boarders or day girls. Junior girls from age 13 have been welcomed since 1997 when Arion House was opened.

Buildings. The oldest portion of the Buildings dates from the early part of the 16th century. This, with numerous additions and alterations, forms Old House. New House was begun in 1872, and has been considerably extended since. Priory House is situated in adjacent property acquired in 1942. Lyon House was opened in September, 1954, and extended in 1976 and 1986, and Blackford House in September 1960. Wellesley was opened in 1984 and Arion in 1997. There is a Medical Centre, staffed by a Sister-in-Charge. The Memorial Hall, built by Old Brutonians after the First World War, incorporates a classroom wing, a recital and meeting room and the refurbished and extended Music School. A development programme, completed in 1979, included the extension of the Music School, a large Sports Hall with a theatre-cum-cinema in the same building, and the self-service Dining Hall, built in 1974, which has classrooms and the Norton Library on the first floor. A classroom block, Chemistry, Maths and Modern Languages, lead to the splendid Design Centre opened in 1989 and incorporating all facilities for Design, Technology, Art and Information Technology. An extension to the Design Centre housing a Physics Department and extended Computive facilities was opened in September 1994. A synthetic playing surface for hockey and tennis was opened in September 1995. A new Science Centre for Biology, Chemistry and Home Economics was opened in September 1999 and a new Library/ Learning Centre built in 2004. All the boarding houses have been fully refurbished in the last seven years. 2007 saw the completion of a Sixth Form Social Centre and a third girls' boarding house. The Basil Wright Reception Centre was opened in September 2008.

Curriculum. King's is divided into Upper and Lower Sixth, Fifth, Fourth and Third forms. The subjects taught include RS, English, History, Geography, Philosophy & Ethics, Economics, Business Studies, Mathematics, Further Mathematics, Physics, Chemistry, Biology, Latin, Theatre Studies, French, German, Spanish, Italian, Music, Music Technology, Art, Technology, PE, Information Technology, Drama and PSHE. National Curriculum GCSE courses are followed up to the Fifth Form, after which, in the Sixth Form, pupils are able to specialise for subjects at A Level, for entry to Universities, the Services and other Careers.

Games. The main school sports are Cricket, Rugby Football, Hockey and Netball. There is a wide variety of other sports available as options. Rugby is played in the Christmas Term, Hockey in the Easter Term; Cross-Country Running for both girls and boys takes place in both. Athletics and Tennis are encouraged in the Summer Term. Girls play hockey in the Christmas term and Netball in the Easter term. There are 2 main playing fields, 17 Tennis Courts, 2 Squash Courts, 2 Fives Courts, a heated open-air Swimming Pool and a Sports Hall. A Hard-Play area with 2 All-Weather Hockey Pitches is well used. A new synthetic playing surface for hockey and tennis was completed in September 1995. A Physical Education course is provided for all pupils. Judo, Basketball, Badminton, Fencing and Golf are also part of the School sports provision.

There is a Combined Cadet Force which all boys and girls are expected to join for a definite period, after which they can undertake other forms of Service in the community. An RAF Section and a RN Section also flourish. There is an excellent Rifle Range, and Army ranges are nearby. A Leadership Training Area was opened in 1984. Many pupils are also engaged in the Duke of Edinburgh's Award Scheme.

Music. Vocal and Instrumental Music has for many years been one of the strong features in education at the School, and pupils are strongly encouraged to learn and appreciate music. Frequent concerts are given by Choir, Orchestra, Dance, Jazz and Military bands. The Music School, built in 1979, was refurbished during 1992.

Societies and other activities. One afternoon a week and time on two other days is devoted to a wide range of activities, including Acting, Archaeology, Archery, Art, Bee-Keeping, Chess, Debating, Electronics, Horse Riding, Modelling, Music, Printing, Photography. Design, Technology, Art and Computing are all provided in the Design Centre. The Societies make external visits; exchanges and School journeys abroad are arranged and Lecturers on a wide range of subjects are invited to the School. A Community Service activity provides help in the town and the neighbourhood. The Friends' Association provides Travel Scholarships as well as various extra amenities.

Worship. Assembly takes place in the Memorial Hall. On Sundays and Thursday mornings the School worships in the large parish church of St Mary, Bruton. Pupils are prepared by the Chaplain for Confirmation in the Autumn Term. There is a flourishing Christian fellowship group and many Bible study groups.

Scholarships. (*see Scholarship Entries section*). Scholarships are awarded annually for competition.

Careers. Careers and Higher Education materials are readily available in the library and via the school intranet. Most of our pupils go on to university so the main thrust of the work of the Careers Department is aimed at university application. Younger pupils are well briefed on the importance of topics such as subject choice, CV writing and work experience. Psychometric testing and consequent advice is available for fifth formers.

Admission. No child is admitted to the Senior School before age 13. Entry is via the Common Entrance or Scholarship Examinations.

Fees per term (2008-2009). Boarders £7,997, Day £5,808.

The fees are inclusive of necessary extras, eg Medical Attendance, Games.

The Preparatory School is at Hazlegrove House, Sparkford, 9 miles from Bruton, and takes pupils from age $2^1/_2$–13. The fullest cooperation and continuity are ensured between the Preparatory and Senior School, boys and girls passing from one to the other having obtained a pass in Common Entrance.

(*For further details, see Hazlegrove's entry in IAPS section.*)

Old Brutonian Association. An edition of the Old Brutonians Register 1911–1979 was printed in 1980. Contact about the Old Brutonian Association can be made to D J C Hindley, JP, MA, at the school.

Charitable status. King's, Bruton is a Registered Charity, number 1071997. It exists to provide education for boys and girls from 13–18.

The King's School
Canterbury

Canterbury Kent CT1 2ES
Tel: 01227 595501
Bursar: 01227 595544
Admissions: 01227 595579
Fax: 01227 595595
e-mail: headmaster@kings-school.co.uk
website: www.kings-school.co.uk

The origins of King's stand with the arrival of St Augustine in 597 AD. His foundation, centred on monastic life in his abbey in Canterbury, combined worship, prayer and education, a tradition which has been continuously followed ever since. In 1541, the Abbey Foundation was re-formulated under King Henry VIII. The Abbey was translated to become Canterbury Cathedral and the school to become the King's School. Thus it is that the Headmaster, Lower Master and scholars of King's are part of the Cathedral Foundation.

Visitor: The Lord Archbishop of Canterbury

Governors:

Chairman: The Dean of Canterbury, The Very Revd R A Willis, BA, DipTh, FRSA
Vice-Chairman: Mrs M Berg, MSc Econ, MA
Dr C R Prior, DPhil, PhD
¶P J Stone, MA
The Revd R Marsh, BD, MA, AKC, CertEd
¶Prof S J Gurr, BSc, ARCS, DIC, PhD, MA
Dr O Rackham, OBE, MA, PhD
The Ven S Watson, Archdeacon of Canterbury
The Revd Canon E F Condry, BA, BLitt, DPhil, MBA
¶A Stewart
Mrs E McKendrick, BA
The Revd Canon D C Edwards
¶N S L Lyons, MA
R De Haan, CBE, DL
The Revd Canon C P Irvine

Clerk to the Governors: R C A Bagley, LLB

Governors Emeriti:
The Very Revd J A Simpson, OBE, MA, DD
¶The Very Revd D L Edwards, DD
Sir Peter Ramsbotham, GCMG, GCVO
The Lady Kingsdown
¶Sir Robert Horton, LLD, BSc, SM, DCL, FIChemE, CMgt
The Lady Lloyd, OBE, MA

***Headmaster*: N Clements**, MA, BSc

Headmaster's PA: Mrs S A Sutton

Deputy Heads:
P B Taylor, BA (*Lower Master*)
G R Cocksworth, BA, MA (*Director of Studies*)
Mrs P A Wakeham, BA (*Senior Mistress*)

Head of Sixth Form: R N Warnick, MA
Head of Middle School: Dr H R O Maltby, MA, DPhil
Head of Lower School: R P Cook, BSc

Bursar: R Nelson-Gracie, FCA, FCMI
Estates Bursar: G R H Merryweather, BSc

Registrar: R I Reilly, BA, MSc

Senior Tutor: M J Miles, MA
Head of Careers: J R Parker, BSc

Senior Chaplain: The Revd C F Arvidsson, DipTheol
Assistant Chaplain: The Revd Dr J I Bentley, BTech, MSc, PhD

Librarian: Mrs S A L Gray, BSc Econ, MCLIP

Medical Officers:
Dr W Lloyd Hughes, MB BS
Dr J Fegent, MB BS

Art:
*D Cameron, BA
P J Chaundy, BA
Mrs C P Coleman, BA
Mrs J Taylor-Goodman, BA, MA

Classics:
Miss H P Isaksen, BA
R P Mew, MA, ALCM
†Mrs J A Richards, MA
*Miss J Taylor, BA

Design:
M J Franks, BEd
*K E J Martin, BA
G J Swindley, BSc

Drama:
*G E Sinclair, AGSM
Mrs R J Beattie, BA
Miss K J Dover, BEd

Economics:
*†Mrs B Cocksworth, BSc
†Mrs L A Horn, BSc
R W Ninham, MA
Mrs R J Whitehead, MA

English:
Mrs J M Cook, BA
C H Downer, BA
M T Gardner, BA
*A J W Lyons, BA, MA, FRSA
†Dr C E Pidoux, MA, PhD, ALCM
Mrs C J Shearer, BA
J Soderholm, BA, MA, PhD
G P Tyndall, BA
Mrs A L Young, MA

Geography:
†S E Anderson, BA
†N L Phillis, MA
R I Reilly, BA, MSc
*R P Sanderson, BA
Mrs P Wakeham, BA
†Mrs S M Webber, NDip

History:
Miss C E Anderson, BA
S J Graham, MA
*R M Hooper, MA
H R O Maltby, MA, DPhil
*T Purser, BA, MSt, PhD (*from January 09*)
P B Taylor, BA

History of Art:
*D J Felton, MA
Miss D M Francis, BA

ICT
†A J Holland, BSc
Ms N Ahmed, BA, PhD

Mathematics:
M Cox, BA, MEng, Dip ITEC
†M P H Dath, L-ès-ScM, M-ès-ScM
J P E Dickson, BSc
†P W Fox, MSc
Mrs J Gorman, BSc
A McFall, BSc
*S P Ocock, BA
G E Powell, BSc, PhD

R N Warnick, MA

Modern Languages:
*T J Armstrong, MA
Mme M-D Bradburn, BA
Mrs A Browne, LSc
*M Bruna, Ldo
Miss Z T Crawshaw, MA
Mrs D Davis, MA
Mrs M B Garcés-Ramón, BA
Mrs N Geoffroy, L-ès-ScEd
T I Jennings, MA
D A Leitch, BA
M J Miles, MA
†C P Newbury, BA
Mme M Rodes, L-ès-L
Miss F Zanardi, MA

Music:
*H J P Ionascu, BMus, ARCM (*Director of Music*)
W M Bersey, BMus, LTCL (*Assistant Director of Music*)
C Metters, ARCM, Hon ARCM, Hon RAM (*Head of Orchestral Studies*)
A Pollock, MA (*Head of Strings*)
K Abbott, DipRCM (*Head of Brass*)
S J R Matthews, MA
N Todd, BA

Politics:
Mrs D J Ardley, BA

Physical Education:
Miss K Bradley, BSc
Miss S J Clark, BEd
T Hill, BSc
*R A L Singfield, BEd, FRSA

Religious Studies and Philosophy:
The Revd C F Arvidsson, DipTheol
G R Cocksworth, BA, MA
Miss C A Hall, BA
†J W Outram, BA
*Mrs J M Reid, BEd, MPhil
M D Wilson, BA

Science:

Biology:
†J M Hutchings, BA
M J W Smiley, BSc
†M J Thornby, BSc
Mrs J A Watson, MSc
Mrs J H Wharfe, BSc
*S J Winrow-Campbell, BSc

Chemistry:
*D M Arnott, BSc, PhD
R P Cook, BSc
S P Hermes, MChem
D A Scott, BSc, MA
A R Stewart, MChem, PhD
E Sykes, BSc

Physics:
Miss C M Astin, MA, LTCL
*Miss L M Comber BSc
Mrs E S Ladd, BEng
J S G Ling, BEng, PhD
S J Ripley, BSc, PhD
D M Tanton, MA, MSc, PhD

Geology:
*R Churcher, BSc

Houses and Housemasters/mistresses:

School House: M J Thornby
The Grange: M P H Dath
Walpole: Mrs S M Webber
Meister Omers: C P Newbury
Marlowe (day): S E Anderson
Luxmoore: Dr C E Pidoux
Galpin's: J M Hutchings
Linacre: J W Outram
Tradescant: N L Phillis
Broughton: Mrs A K Arvidsson
Mitchinson's (day): P W Fox
Jervis: Mrs L A Horn
Harvey: Mrs B Cocksworth
Bailey (Sixth Form): Mrs J A Richards
Carlyon (day): A J Holland

The Junior King's School
Milner Court, Sturry, Nr Canterbury, CT2 0AY.
Tel: 01227 714000

Headmaster: P M Wells, BEd

(*For further details see King's Junior School entry in IAPS section.*)

Religion. The school's Christian tradition is at its heart and there is a desire to foster Christian virtues of love and justice, faith and courage, hope and perseverance. Of course, pupils and staff comprise individuals of different faiths and beliefs but there is a desire to aspire to Christian values. In the Cathedral, and in other places of worship, school services and prayers regularly take place.

Numbers and Organisation. There are currently 783 pupils on the school roll, 425 boys and 358 girls, 609 of which are boarders (78%). There are 6 boys' boarding houses, 6 girls' boarding houses and 3 day houses. Junior King's, the prep school of King's, occupies a site on the River Stour, in Sturry, 3 miles from Canterbury. There are currently 401 pupils at Junior King's, 219 boys and 182 girls, of which 73 are boarders (18%).

The Senior School occupies various sites around the Cathedral and its Precincts. Many teaching departments and the majority of houses are in the beautiful ancient buildings around the Green Court, on the north side of the Cathedral. To the east of the Cathedral, the St Augustine's site is home to 5 boarding houses and the magnificent school library. There are 2 major sites for sport, Birley's and Blore's, each with extensive sports facilities.

Academic Life. The curriculum at King's is based upon strong academic roots. It emphasises and relies upon what is best in traditional independent school education: scholarly excellence supported by a caring pastoral and tutorial system, and a wide-ranging co-curricular programme. However, it is continually adapting and reacting to the changing demands of modern education: new subjects are added, new teaching techniques adopted, and there is an increasing awareness of the need to provide programmes of study that match individual needs and skills.

The curriculum is divided into three units: the Lower School (Shells, Year 9), an introductory year; the Middle School (Removes and Fifths, Years 10 and 11), working to GCSEs; and the Sixth Form (6b and 6a, Years 12 and 13), taking AS and A Levels.

Music and Drama. The strongest encouragement is given to music and drama, and many entrance awards for music are available. Details are given in the Scholarships Section.

King's Week, the School's own festival of Music and Drama, attracts thousands of visitors each summer.

Sport and Outdoor Education. The major games are Rugby Football, Football, Netball, Tennis, Lacrosse, Fencing, Hockey, Athletics, Cricket, Rowing, Swimming and Sailing. Good facilities exist for all the usual sports. A new Recreation Centre includes Swimming Pool, Squash Courts and Sports Hall. The Maurice Milner Hall is specifically equipped for Fencing.

Cultural recreation and hobbies are encouraged through some 25 societies managed (with advice) by the boys and girls themselves, and through a programme of "Activities" which occupies one afternoon each week. Many of these "Activities" are linked to the Duke of Edinburgh's Award Scheme and pupils are encouraged to gain the Bronze Award in their second (Remove) year. Lectures and recitals by distinguished visitors take place each term.

CCF, Social Service, Adventure Training and The Duke of Edinburgh's Award. Membership of the Combined Cadet Force is voluntary. The Social Service unit cooperates with kindred bodies in Canterbury. Bronze and Gold awards in The Duke of Edinburgh's Award Scheme may be taken.

Admission. Application should be made to the Admissions Secretary. It is advisable to register pupils at an early age. Admission is normally through the Common Entrance Examination or, if academically able, through the School's own Scholarship Examination. The age of entry is about 13.

Fees per term (2008-2009). Senior School: £9,210 for boarders and £6,805 for day pupils. Junior School: £6,260 for boarders and £2,720–£4,610 for day pupils.

Entrance Scholarships and other awards. (*see Scholarship Entries section*). Up to 20 King's Scholarships can be awarded if candidates of sufficient merit present themselves. The examination is held annually in March and is open to boys and girls under the age of 14 on 1st September. The awards may be up to 25% of the annual fee in every year (more in the case of need). Up to 12 Music Scholarships are offered each year in February, and Art and Sports Scholarships and Awards are offered in March. Pupils entering the Sixth Form may compete for academic scholarships which will be offered as a result of the entrance examination in November. Music and Art scholarships will also be offered for competition in November.

Leaving Gifts and Closed Awards. The School has a number of these.

Some 25 offers of admission to Oxford and Cambridge are received each year.

OKS (Old King's Scholars). *Secretary*: G S Allan, BSc, ARICS, 8 Dornford Gardens, Coulsdon, Surrey CR5 1JW.

The King's Society exists for all parents, past and present. A termly programme of social and cultural events is open to all members.

Charitable status. The King's School of the Cathedral Church of Canterbury is a Registered Charity, number 307942. It exists to provide education for boys and girls.

The King's School
Chester

Chester CH4 7QL
Tel: 01244 689500
Fax: 01244 689501
e-mail: info@kingschester.co.uk
website: www.kingschester.co.uk

The School was founded AD 1541 by King Henry VIII, in conjunction with the Cathedral Church of Chester. It was reorganised under the Endowed Schools Act in 1873, and by subsequent schemes of the Ministry of Education. The School is now Independent. The aim of the School is to prepare pupils for admission to Universities and the professions, and at the same time provide a liberal education.

Motto: '*Rex Dedit, Benedicat Deus.*'

Patron: His Grace the Duke of Westminster, KG, OBE, TD, DL

Governors:
K James, FCA (*Chairman*)
The Rt Revd the Lord Bishop of Chester
The Very Revd the Dean of Chester
The Rt Worshipful the Lord Mayor of Chester
M J P Cooke, FCA, MSIDip, AIIMR
J C Davies, MSc, CEng, FICE, MCIOB, MIWM
Revd Canon T J Dennis, MA, PhD
Professor J A J Gowlett, MA, PhD
D S Hempsall, MA, PhD, FRSA
K Hassett, BA, MSc
P M H Jessop, BA
Mrs E M Johnson, JP
Mrs K Kerr, MBA, BA
N Kirk, DipM, FCIM, ACIB
Mrs J Lea, LLB (*Deputy Chairman*)
Dr D Pawson, BSc, PhD
Mrs R J Phillipson, BA, FCIPD
S Preston, MA Cantab, CDir
J K Shanklin, BSc, FGS, CGeol
R A Storrar
Revd I M Thomas, MA
J N C Tweddle, BSc

Clerk to the Governors: S P Cross, LLB
Ex officio: CAOKS President

***Headmaster:* C D Ramsey**, MA, late scholar of Corpus Christi, Cambridge

Second Master: J A Hargreaves, MA

Director of Studies: B R F Routledge, MA
Head of Sixth Form & Careers: T R Hughes, MA, MPhil
Head of Middle School: M J Harle, BSc
Head of Lower School: R G Wheeler, BA
Learning Development Coordinator: Mrs D Hearne, BA, MEd, PG Cert SpLD, AMBDA

Assistant staff:
* *Head of Department*

Art and Design:
*S Downey, BA
Mrs A L Hollingworth, BA
Miss L Black, BA

Biology:
*T Keeley, BSc, MIBiol
R D J Elmore, BSc, MIBiol, CBS
Ms J E Meredith, BSc, MIBiol
Mrs P Housden, BEd
Ms H M Davies, MSc

Chemistry:
*A Cook, BSc, PhD
M J Harle, BSc
Mrs K L Russon, BSc
Mrs J E Jepson, BSc
Dr C A Gleave, BSc, PhD
Dr J R Macnab, BSc, PhD

Classics:
*P S Fentem, MA
M J P Punnett, MA
Mrs S H Gareh, BA, MA
H R Holt, MA

Design Technology:
*K M Lloyd, MA
Miss E Hodgson, BA
I Reid, BEd

Economics:
*S D Walton, BA, MSc
Ms S Roberts, BA
Miss E M Rowley, BSocSc

English:
*T P Heavisides, MA
B R F Routledge, MA
J A Hargreaves, MA
R G Wheeler, BA
Dr A M McMahon, MA, DPhil
Mrs D Hearne, BA
Ms E L Wood, BA
Mrs H C Lydon, BA

Geography:
*J H King, MA, MSc
T R Hughes, BA
Mrs R H Aldridge, BA

History & Politics:
*S Neal, BA
P G Neal, BA
Mrs G K Chadwick, BA
J C Heap, BA

Information Technology:
*D G Lavender, BSc
M R Tiller, BA

Mathematics:
*Mrs K Crewe-Read, BSc
Mrs C A Hill, MA, MSc
S J Parry, BA
C J Canty, BSc
Mrs L Beresford, BA
S D Bibby, BSc
Miss S C Roberts, BA
Mrs C Lanceley, BSc
Mrs A Ignata, BSc
Mrs S Cooper, BSc

Modern Languages:
*P D Shannon, MA
Mme F Vergnaud, MA
Mrs K L Shapland, MA
Miss J M Ledsham, BA
Mrs K J Thurlow-Wood, BA
Miss V Allan, BA
M Sabio
Mrs E J Shannon, L-ès-L, Maîtrise
Mrs A J Rourke, BA

Music:
*J E Millard, BA
Miss K Z Andrews, BMus, MA
C J Wharton, BA (*Music Technology & Drums*)
Mrs V L S Yearsley, BMus
S A Rushforth (*Head of Strings*)
Mrs S E Tyson, MA (*Woodwind, Voice*)
Mrs V L Ierston, LTCL (*Piano & Flute*)
P D Oliver, BMus, LTCL (*Guitar*)
Miss R Jones, GMus, RNCM, LRAM, ARCM, FLCM (*Piano*)
Mrs J Riekert, ATCL (*Flute*)
Mrs H Hopkins, DipABRSM (*Woodwind, Theory & Piano*)
Mr T Wyss, ARCM, LRAM, LTCL (*Brass*)
Mrs F Cooke, MA, LRAM (*Voice*)
G Macey, ATCL (*Woodwind*)
Miss C Barker, BA (*Cello*)
Miss J Vernon, BMus (*Brass*)
Mrs N Smalley (*Violin & Viola*)
M Owens, BA (*Double Bass & Bass Guitar*)
Mrs J Holmes, BA (*Oboe*)
D Ortiz, BMus (*Brass*)
A Parker, MA (*Saxophone*)
A Stamatakis-Brown, BMus (*Piano and Jazz piano*)

Personal & Social Education:
*Ms J E Meredith, BSc, MIBiol

Physical Education:
*R Lunn, BEd
C Morris, BEd
B Horne, BSc (*Director of Football*)
Mrs K Jones, BA (*Head of Girls' PE*)
R I D Hornby, BA
Ms J Huck, BA
Mrs C Sumner, BA

Physics:
*D Yalland, BSc
P A Bradley, BSc, PhD
N Heritage, MSc, PhD, MInstP, CPhys
S Bosworth, MA, DPhil, FRAS
Mrs J E Jepson, BSc
B Horne, BSc
G S Andrews, BEng
Ms H M Davies, MSc

Religious Studies:
*M G Loach, MA
R A Parry, BSc
M S Lee, BA

Junior School:
Head: S A Malone, BEd
Deputy Head: A Griffiths, BA
Director of Studies: T W Griffin, BA

Assistant Staff:
Miss J M Anderson, BA, CertEd
Miss N Arkle, BA
Mrs K Dickson, BA
H J Duncalf, BEd
Miss J Evans, BA
Mrs V M Gibson, BA
Miss J M Hartley, BA
K A Hollingworth, BEd
Mrs C Jones, CertEd
Mrs M D O'Leary, BA
D M O'Neil, BSc
Mrs B A Roberts GRNCM
Mrs D L Rudd, BA
Miss K A Savage, BA
Mrs S Tomlinson, BEd
Miss S E Wells, BEd

Administration and Support Staff:

Bursar: Mrs P Hopkinson, BSc, ACA
Management Accountant: Mrs K Houghton, ACMA
Estates Manager: M A Wright
Director of Marketing: Mrs V M Titmuss, BA
Examinations Officer: R D J Elmore, BSc, CBiol, MIBiol, CBS
Web Services Manager: P A Bradley, BSc, PhD
Headmaster's PA: Mrs A M E Wilson, BA
Registrar: Miss B A Roberts
School Secretary: Mrs F Bell, BEd
Music School Secretary: Mrs D Bainbridge
Receptionist: Mrs J F Booth
Junior School Secretary: Mrs S L Whitta, BA
Junior School Receptionist: Mrs S Johnson
Care Scheme Supervisor: Mrs L Hornby
School Nurse: Sister S J Catherall, RGN
Senior Librarian & Archivist: Mrs H Holyoak, BSc, MCLIP
Network Manager: J Bellis
Catering Manager: S Beasley
Head Groundsman: A Roberts
Master in Charge of Rowing: R A Parry, BSc
Boatman: J R Blackwell
Contingent Commander, CCF: Sqn Ldr K L Shapland, MA
OC Army Section, CCF: Capt A Joseph, BEM
OC RAF Section, CCF: Flt Lt G H Shapland
Duke of Edinburgh's Award Coordinator: Mrs S H Gareh, BA, MA
Educational Visits Coordinator: R I D Hornby, BA

Organisation. The School, which at present numbers 945, consists of (i) a Junior School for pupils aged 7 to 11 years, which is housed in a separate building, but is run in collaboration with (ii) the Upper School.

Admission. Boys and girls are admitted to the Upper School aged between 11 and 12, and may remain till the end of the year in which they become 18. Pupils in the Junior School normally move into the Upper School at the age of 11, but must pass the Upper School entrance examination before doing so. Boys and girls are admitted to the Sixth Form on the basis of GCSE results.

The Entrance Examinations for the Junior and Upper Schools are held in the Lent Term. Applications are made on a form obtainable from the School and on the website.

Academic. The subjects offered for study in the Sixth Form are – on the Arts side: Art, Business Studies, Classical Studies, Economics, English, English Language, French, Geography, German, History, Latin, Music, Music Technology, Philosophy, Politics, Religious Studies, Spanish; and on the Science side: Biology, Chemistry, Computing, Further Mathematics, Mathematics, Physics, Sports Science and Technology. It is possible to take most combinations of subjects at AS and A Level. All pupils in the Sixth Form take four subjects at AS Level but may drop to three subjects at A Level if they wish.

Spiritual life. The School is part of the Cathedral Foundation and regularly holds its own services in the Cathedral. Spiritual assemblies are held each week and there are two, pupil-led Christian Unions.

Music. Music is part of the general curriculum for all pupils up to the age of 14. After this music may be taken at GCSE and A Level. Private tuition in orchestral instruments, piano and organ is available. There are many musical ensembles and choral groups including the Schola Cantorum which leads the worship in Cathedral services.

Cadet Corps. There is a CCF contingent which welcomes cadets from other schools. The CCF gives pupils opportunities to develop leadership skills and to undertake adventurous training.

Outdoor Education. Opportunities are provided both within and outside the curriculum for outdoor education, and all pupils in each of the first three years of the senior school spend some days away at centres specialising in outdoor activities. In addition many pupils participate in the Duke of Edinburgh's Award Scheme at all levels.

Games. Soccer, Rugby, Hockey, Cricket, Rowing, Swimming, Badminton, Basketball, Athletics, Netball, Tennis, Squash, Golf, Rounders.

Buildings. Formerly situated adjacent to the Cathedral, the school moved into new buildings in 1960 situated in rural surroundings nearly 2 miles from the centre of Chester. Though the Junior and Upper Schools are on the same site of 32 acres, they are housed in separate buildings each having its own playing fields. On 22 June 1960 the new school was formally declared open by Her Majesty Queen Elizabeth the Queen Mother. In 1964 a new indoor Swimming Pool and Pavilion were opened.

More new buildings were added in the 1980s starting with a workshop opened in 1984. On 17 May 1989 Her Royal Highness the Princess Margaret formally opened a development consisting of ten new classrooms, four new laboratories, a music school, an art room, a Sixth Form centre, sports hall, general purposes room for the Junior School, new kitchen, tutorial rooms and offices. In September 1989 the Senior School went from two to three form entry.

In 1994 an extension to the Junior School buildings was completed and from September 1994 boys were admitted at 7. In 1998 girls were admitted to the Sixth Form. In January 2000 a new Library/IT Centre was opened.

In September 2003 the school became co-educational throughout and the senior school moved to four-form entry. A major building programme has taken place over the last five years. An all-weather playing surface for hockey and football is now in use and the art and technology studios have been considerably enlarged and improved. A new Music School opened in April 2005.

Chester Association of Old King's Scholars. The School has what is believed to be the country's oldest former pupils' association, started in 1866, and the association is a very flourishing and active body. The present Hon Secretary is Adrian Ackroyd, 5 St Christopher's Close, Chester CH3 5BP (Tel: 01244 390819; e-mail: adrian.ackroyd@kingsonline.org.uk).

Fees per term (2008-2009). Tuition: Upper School £3,154, Junior School £2,417. The School offers a small number of bursaries annually.

Scholarships. *At 11+*: Academic scholarships are offered to 11+ candidates on the results of the Entrance Examination. The value of these awards is of the order of £250–£400 in the first year only. Scholars carry the title 'King's Scholar' throughout their time at the school.

Tenable in the Sixth Form: (1) One Alfred McAlpine Scholarship of £1,000; (2) One Keith Oates Scholarship of £1,000.

Tenable at Universities: (1) One Old King's Scholars Exhibition of £150 pa for 3 years; (2) One Robert Platt Exhibition of £100 pa for 3 years; (3) One John Churton Exhibition of £100 pa for 3 years; (4) One William Denson Haswell Exhibition of £100 pa for 3 years; (5) Two Exhibitions of £100 pa for 3 years awarded by the King's School Parents' Association.

Charitable status. The King's School, Chester is a Registered Charity, number 525934. The aim of the charity is to provide a sound education to all boys and girls who can benefit from it regardless of their economic and social background.

The King's School
Ely

Ely Cambs CB7 4DB
Tel: Head: 01353 660701
Bursar: 01353 660700
Fax: Head: 01353 667485
Bursar: 01353 662187
e-mail: enquiries@kings-ely.cambs.sch.uk
website: www.kingsschoolely.co.uk

The school traces its origins back to the 7th century AD and the foundation of the abbey church at Ely. In 1541 Henry VIII reconstituted the school by royal charter; hence its name. Its statutes were confirmed by Elizabeth I and Charles II. Since 1879 the school has been a registered charity.

Henry VIII stipulated that up to twelve senior boys should be King's Scholars, and in 1973 they were joined by twelve girls, at the request of HM Queen Elizabeth II. The King's and Queen's Scholars, together with the Head, are members of the Foundation of Ely Cathedral – an indication of the strong links between school and Cathedral. The magnificent Cathedral is used, in effect, as the school chapel for regular worship, and the school educates the Cathedral choristers.

The school still uses many of Ely's medieval monastic buildings – as boarding houses, as classrooms and as the dining hall. The 14th century Porta, the great gateway to the monastery, has been converted into a magnificent new Senior School library. Other new buildings show the continuing and substantial investment in modern facilities: the renovated Georgian villa that now houses the Nursery and Pre-Prep section of King's Acremont; a splendidly refurbished senior Art Department; a Technology Centre; a senior Music School and Recital Hall and a self-contained, two-storey accommodation including seven classrooms and a science laboratory for Years 7 and 8, which opened in 2003.

The school is fully co-educational from the ages of 2½ to 18. The total roll is about 950 and more than a quarter of pupils over the age of eight are boarders. The King's School Ely has a reputation as an exceptionally friendly and welcoming school. Its pupils represent a wide range of ability and interests, from the highly academic to those with predominantly practical or creative talents. The school turns out young people who are considerate, adaptable and self-confident but free of arrogance – and who are often delighted to acknowledge that they have exceeded their own and their parents' expectations.

Visitor: The Rt Revd The Bishop of Ely

Governors:
Chairman: R P Slogrove
Vice-Chairman: Professor Clara Taylor, FRAM, FRSA, LRAM
Chairman of Executive and Finance Committee: Mrs J A Swann, LLB, ACA, MABRP
Mrs B Aspinall
Mrs M Benfield, JP
The Lord Browne of Madingley, FRS, FREng
The Very Revd Dr Michael Chandler, Dean of Ely
B D Fraser, BSc, MBA
A J Morbey
C B Morris, FRICS
R Phillips, QC
The Revd Canon David Pritchard, BA, FRCO, LTCL
Miss S E Rawlings, MA
Dr N Richardson MA
Mrs S Rowland, BA

***Head*: Mrs S E Freestone**, MEd, GRSM, LRAM, ARCM, FRSA

Deputy Head of Senior School: G Parry, BSc, PhD, PGCE
Deputy Head (Academic): I G Young, BSc, PhD, PGCE
Deputy Head (Development): Mrs F A Blake, BA, PGCE

Head of Junior School: R J Whymark, BA Ed
Deputy Head of Junior School: S J Buck, BSc, PGCE

Head of King's Acremont: Dr L Brereton, BSc, PhD, PGCE
Head of Nursery and Deputy Head of King's Acremont: Mrs M Brogan, CertEd

Bursar: S Mitchell, BA, MA
Chaplain: The Revd T P Humphry, BA, MA
Medical Officer: A S Douglas, BMedSci, BM, BS, DRCOG, SPCert
Executive Assistant to the Head: Mrs C Margree
Admissions Secretary: Mrs D Burton

Assistant Staff, Senior School:
J R Atkinson, MA
Miss C Bond, HBA
D Burke, BSc, PGCE
P G Carberry, BEd
S G Cavill, BSc, PGCE
Miss A C Charlton, BEd
G Couper-Marsh, BSc, PGCE
P A H Coutts, MA, PGCE
Miss R Crabtree, MA, PGCE
F J L Dale, CertEd, MA, DipTEFL
F Danes, BA, PGCE

K R Daniel, BA, PGCE
Miss M P Day, BA, LRAM, MTC
R P Emms, BA, PGCE
M C D Ewan, BEng, PGCE
Mrs L Goosen, BA, PGCE
G P L Griggs, BMus, MA, GRNCM, FRCO, PGCE
M W Hall, BSc, PGCE
O Hancock
M G Hawes, BA, PGCE
S Heath, BA, PGCE
D J Hodgson, BSc, PGCE
J Houlston, BMus
B S Jackson, BEng, PGCE
D Kittson, HND, CertEd, FETC, ACIS, PACA
Miss S E Knibb, BA, PGCE
P A Lott, BSc, PGCE
Mrs J P Mackay, BSc
Miss P McClanahan, BA
Mrs N McIntyre, MA, BA, PGCE
J A Mascall, BSc, MSc, PGCE, CPhys, MInstP
I A McWhinney, BSc
S Merrell, BA, TCert
S L Murfitt, BA, PGATC
Mrs T Murfitt, MA
M C Nicholas
P B North, BA
Mrs M P C Payeras-Cifre, MA
Dr W K Pitt, BEd, PhD
N J Reckless, MA, PGCE
Mrs L Reid, MA, FRCO
J Rees, BA, MA, PGCE
Mrs A J Rhodes, BA, MA
J W Riley, MA, CertEd
K Shaw, BSc
Ms C P Skeels, BSc, DPhil, PGCE
Ms G Smith, MA, MTh, PGCE
Mrs J Cuttress, BA, PGCE
Mrs S Stirrup, BEd, MA
A J Thomas, MEd, BA, PGCE
Mrs J R Thomas, MA, PGCE
A Thompson, BSc, MSc, PGCE
N A Tooth, BSc, PGCE
Mrs H Williamson
Miss H A Wright, BEd, CertEd
F K Young, BA, PGCE

Assistant Staff, Junior School:
Mrs M Acton, L-ès-L, PGCE
D A Boothroyd, BEd
Mrs R J Chapman, BEd
Mrs J Currah, BEd
E J Davis, BA, BA, PGCE, MA
Ms M Delaveau, BA, CPLP2, PGCE
Mrs E Diss, BA, PGCE, DipSpLD
Miss C L Duncan, BA, PGCE
Mrs P Foulds, BEd
Miss M R Haigh, CertEd
Miss A E Kippax, BSc, HND, DipSpLD
J A Lowery, BA, PGCE
Mrs C Middleton, BSc, PGCE, MEd
R M Oliver, BSc, PGCE
N M Ovens, BA, CertEd
D M Parratt, BEd
Mrs K Pearce, BA, PGCE
Mrs A R Pearson, CertEd
Mrs B A Pope, CertEd
N Porter-Thaw, LTCL, DipTCL
R F Powell, BA, CertEd
Mrs K Prior, SpLDDip, CertEd
Mrs L H F Roberts, BSc, PGCE
Dr S I Robinson, MEd, BA, BEd
Mrs J C Schaniel, BA, MSc
Mrs N Sivier, GMus, LGSM
Miss K Sudbury, BEd, MA
Mrs A Sutherland, CertEd
N Tetley, BA, PhD, PGCE
Mrs N Van Wright, BFA
Miss R Watkins, BEd
Ms R Watkins, MEd, BEd
M A Wilkinson, BA, PGCE
Mrs A J Wilson, BEd

Assistant Staff, King's Acremont:
Mrs C M Burgess, BA, PGCE
Miss S Clements, BA
Mrs C M Cooper, CertEd
Mrs K Furness, BA, PGCE
Mrs G Heard, BSc, PGCE
Ms J H Lyall, BA, PGCE
Mrs K Wylie, BTec Dip
Mrs A G Wynn, BEd

In addition 26 visiting music teachers.

Organisation. The school is divided into four parts: King's Acremont, the Nursery and Pre-Prep for children from 2½ years of age to Year 2, standing in its own grounds at Acremont House; King's Junior School for Years 3–8; King's Senior School for Years 9–13 and King's International.

The Nursery and Pre-Prep curriculum at King's Acremont introduces children to systematic planned learning. Teaching starts from where each child is, in terms of experience and development, not from a pre-determined idea of where they should be. Children are encouraged to express what they have experienced in their growth and learning – in their own way and at an appropriate pace – to help them absorb and consolidate their experience. Teaching is mainly on a class-teacher basis.

The curriculum in the Nursery and Reception classes is geared towards the Foundation Stage laid down by the Government through the Qualifications & Curriculum Authority. Children in Years 1 and 2 follow – and indeed go beyond – the National Curriculum at Key Stage 1. The areas of learning covered in the Pre-Prep are: Personal, Social and Emotional Development, Communication, Language and Literacy, Mathematical Development, Knowledge and Understanding of the World, Physical Development and Creative Development. French begins in the Reception class.

During Year 2 there is constant liaison with Year 3 staff in the Junior School to ensure that children are fully prepared for the next stage of their education. The move to the Junior School for Year 3 (at age 7+) ensures continuity of teaching of the Key Stage 2 curriculum.

King's Acremont offers working parents the option of an 8 am Breakfast Club, After School Care until 6 pm and Holiday Club.

The Junior School curriculum is planned to give pupils both breadth and depth in their total learning experience. Subject specialists coordinate the work of each department and ensure progression from year to year, though for the youngest pupils teaching is still mainly on a class-teacher basis. From Year 7 all teaching is by subject teachers. Year groups are usually taught in classes based on general ability. Pupils' progress is monitored week by week and reported regularly to parents.

All foundation subjects are covered in every year, and the whole curriculum is compulsory. French is taught to all years; the more able pupils study Latin from Year 6. German and Spanish are introduced in Year 8. Information Technology and Technology begin in Year 4. There are specialist teaching rooms for Art, Design & Technology, Information Technology, a Drama studio and a specialist Music Suite. Years 7 and 8 are taught in a classroom block with its own Science laboratory and IT suite, opened in 2003.

During the school day all children are divided among four co-educational houses for pastoral and competitive purposes; each of these houses is staffed by male and female members of the teaching staff. King's Junior School has one co-educational boarding house and one for the boy choristers of Ely Cathedral who are all pupils of King's Junior School. There is a wide range of extra-curricular opportunities both at lunch times and after school.

The Senior School curriculum. The amount of academic choice that pupils can exercise grows as they move through the Senior School: options in the Sixth Form are very flexible, and the sets are often small. Up to GCSE (Year 11) there is a compulsory core of English, Mathematics, Religious Studies and Sciences. In addition every pupil chooses up to four option subjects from: Art, Business Studies, Classical Civilisation, Design & Technology (Resistant Material Technology, Food and Nutrition), Drama, English as a Foreign Language, French, Geography, German, History, Latin, Music, Physical Education, Spanish.

The entry qualification for the Sixth Form is not less than six C grades with B grades in subjects selected for A Level. Twenty-seven AS/A2 Level subjects are offered in Years 12 and 13.

Extra-Curricular Activities. Music, art, drama, outdoor pursuits, sports, practical hobbies and interests – all are catered for in a large range of lunchtime and after-hours activities.

The Ely Scheme. All pupils in Year 9 are introduced to the school's distinctive outdoor pursuits programme, the Ely Scheme, which provides a training in practical and personal skills and in teamwork, initiative and leadership. For some pupils it leads on to the Duke of Edinburgh's Award Scheme or to specialised activities such as climbing.

Art, Drama and Music. Music is strong, as one would expect in a school that is so closely linked to the Cathedral. There is a full programme of performances for school and public audiences, and regular tours overseas. Nearly half of all pupils have personal tuition in a musical instrument; many learn two or even three. Well-equipped art rooms inspire painting, sculpture, ceramics and textiles. All parts of the school present plays every year in addition to productions by year or ad-hoc groups.

Games. The main sports are rowing, rugby, soccer, netball, hockey and cricket. Athletics, badminton, basketball, tennis, sailing, squash, swimming, golf and horse-riding are also available. All pupils are encouraged to take part in team games, and there is a full programme of fixtures against other schools.

Religious Worship. The Junior and Senior Schools worship regularly in Ely Cathedral. Other services weekly are also in accordance with the principles of the Church of England. The Bishop conducts a confirmation service for pupils in the Lent term. However, all denominations (or none) are warmly welcome.

Exeats. Boarders are granted weekend exeats on the written request of a parent or guardian. Weekly boarding is increasingly popular.

Admission. Application forms can be obtained from the Admissions Secretary. Admission to King's Acremont is by interview; to King's Junior School by interview and qualifying examination; and to King's Senior School at 13+ by the school's entrance examination or an equivalent. A £65 fee is payable at first registration. Pupils may enter the school at any time, although an Autumn start is recommended; and they may stay at the school until the year in which they become 19.

Scholarships and Exhibitions. (*see Scholarship Entries section*). Scholarships and Exhibitions up to a cumulative total of 25% (15% in King's Junior School) of fees are awarded for achievement and potential in academic work, music, art, design & technology, drama and sports.

Choristerships are available for both boys and girls. The school supports the music of Ely Cathedral by providing discounts for choristers, ex-choristers and members of Ely Cathedral Girls' Choir. Additional bursary support may be available to new pupils over the age of eleven, whose parents are unable to pay the full tuition fee.

Fees per term (2008-2009). *King's Acremont Nursery and Pre-Prep*: Nursery places are booked by the session (morning or afternoon) and the day of the week; full care for five days a week would be £2,260. The fee for Pre-Prep Reception – Year 2 is £2,435 (no boarding). Pre- and after-school care and holiday club are available at extra charge.

King's Junior School: Years 3 and 4: £3,440 (day); £5,490 (boarding); Years 5 to 8: £3,760 (day); £5,795 (boarding). There is no Saturday morning school for Years 3 and 4. There is an optional programme on Saturday mornings for pupils in Years 5 and 6. From Year 7 Saturday morning school is a compulsory part of the school week.

King's Senior School: Years 9 to 13: £5,190 (day); £7,510 (boarding).

Flexi-boarding: It may be possible to offer overnight accommodation for day pupils on an occasional basis at a cost of £30 per night. The cost of extended flexi-boarding will be quoted in advance upon application to the Bursar.

Concessions: for children of the clergy or of members of the armed services a 10% discount is available. Bursaries may be awarded in cases of financial need.

Old Eleans. Former pupils receive news of the school and of their contemporaries and are invited annually to events.

Charitable status. The King's School, Ely is a Registered Charity, number 802427. Its aims and objectives are to offer excellence in education to day and boarding pupils.

The King's School
Gloucester

Pitt Street Gloucester GL1 2BG
Tel: 01452 337337
Fax: 01452 337314
e-mail: office@thekingsschool.co.uk
website: www.thekingsschool.co.uk

The King's School, Gloucester is one of the seven famous Cathedral Schools established by Henry VIII in 1541. It has grown over the centuries into the leading provider of Independent education in the area, with around 500 pupils, girls and boys aged three to eighteen. Sport, Music and Drama play a huge part in school life and Academic results are testimony to King's reputation for achieving the best out of every pupil.

In the most recent School Inspection, the inspectors were unstinting in their praise of King's "all round-education".

The school is a fully co-educational day school drawing its pupils from the surrounding areas.

Motto: *Via Crucis via Lucis.*

Governing Body:

Chairman: The Very Revd N Bury, MA, Dean of Gloucester

Canon G Bridgewater, BA
Canon N Heavisides, MA
Canon M Irving, BEd
Canon C Thomson, MA
Reverend Canon D Hoyle
Mrs A Cadbury, OBE, JP, DL
Miss C Holme, JP, LLB
Mr C Major, LLB
Mr J H Smith, BSc, DipEd
Mr T Heal, FRICS
Mr P Lachecki, BSc
Mr J Holroyd, CB, CVO, MA
Mrs S White, MA
Mrs J C Gazard, MA, CertEd
Mr P Markey, BSc
Mr C Collier
Mr P Lapping
Mr M Warton

***Headmaster*: A K J Macnaughton**, MA

Deputy Head (*Academic*): Mr D J Evans, MA
Deputy Head (*Pastoral*): Miss V S Scholes, BEd, MBA

* *Head of Department*

English & Drama:
*Dr M C Craddock, BA, PhD
Mrs L Harrison, BA
Mr A K J Macnaughton, MA
Mrs A J Stafford, BEd
Miss L Gibbs, BA
Mrs P Blair, BA
Mr B H Sandell, BA

Mathematics:
Mr P Goldbrum, MSc
Mrs S Rodford, BEd
Mr J Hand, BA
Mrs S Miskin, BA
Mr N Stewart, BSc

Modern Languages:
*Mr P Arnison, BA
Mr P J Irving, BA
Miss A F Williams, BA
Mrs H Cleland, MA

Geography:
*Miss C J Barber, BA
Mr W Joyce, BSc

History:
*Miss Helen Colson, BA
Mrs S J Hobbs, MA
Mr D J Evans, MA

Classics:
*Mr P O'Brien, MA
Mrs P Fayter, BA

Religious Studies:
*Mr J M Webster, MA, BD (*Chaplain*)
Mr D J Griffiths, BEd, DipRS

Economics & Business Studies:
*Mr D A Lloyd, BSc Econ
Mr M Evetts, BA

Art, Design & Technology:
*Miss C Billingsley, BA
Miss L A Lewis, BA
Mr J S Collins, BA
Miss H Grice, BA

Science:
*Mr A G Moore, BSc
Mr S Harrison, MA
Mrs B J Rouan-North, BSc
Miss V Scholes, BSc
Miss R A Nelson, BSc
Mr P Timmis, BSc

Music:
*Mr D Harris, DipRCM, GRSM
Mrs D Osborne, BA
Mrs J D Fenn, BEd
Mr L E Robson, BEd
Mrs M J Phillips, BA
Miss T J Kelson, BA

Physical Education:
*Mr A J Phillips, BA

Psychology:
Mrs L Sutton

Junior School:
Head of Junior School: Mr C W Dickie, BEd

Director of Studies: Mrs E I Tuffill, BA

Mrs C J Hadfield, BEd
Mrs C A McKane, BA
Mrs S E Jelf, NNEB
Miss H E Powell, BA
Mr J D Ward, BSc
Miss S Linton, BA
Mrs H M McVittie, BA
Mrs P Williams, NNEB
Mr S P Williams, BSc
Mrs C M Griffiths, BEd
Mrs S A Falkus, NNEB
Mrs H M Balmer, NVQ111
Mrs R Woodliffe

Learning Support:
*Mrs M Connell
Mrs J Rochfort, BEd

Library Support:
Mrs R Stickland, CertEd
Mrs A Youldon, BSc, Dip Inf Sc

After School Care:
Mrs G Southgate
Mrs T Jennings

Personal & Social Education: *Mr D J Griffiths, BEd
Careers: Ms A Williams, BA

Music Department (Instrumental and Singing Teachers):
Mrs A Adiri, BMus (*Violin*)
Miss J Beddoe, LTCL, ATCL (*Clarinet and Saxophone*)
Mrs C Burton, BA (*Piano*)
Mr R A Burton, GBSH, ARCS, ABSM (*Singing*)
Mrs C Carter, BA (*Piano*)
Mrs J Gibbons, BMus, LTCL, CertEd (*Flute*)
Mr R Goode, ALCM (*Classical and Rock Guitar*)
Mr I Russell (*Brass*)
Mrs E Platten (*Singing*)
Ms J Tomlinson, LRAM, RAMProfCert (*Cello*)
Mr J Trim, BMus, MMus, LRAM (*Violin and String Groups*)
Mr G Watson (*Drum Kit*)

Bursar: Mrs N Mosley, BA, ACA
Estates Manager: Mrs C Savage, MA, MRICS, MBIFM
Registrar: Mrs S Bird, BA

Medical Centre Staff:
Dr I Jarvis, MB, BCh
Sister J Dunne, RGN

Structure of the School. The school provides a day education for boys and girls aged 3–18 years. The most common ages for entry are at 3, 11, 13 and 16 years. There are 500 pupils in total, including a thriving Sixth Form of about 80 pupils.

For administrative purposes, the school is divided into the following sections:

Junior School: aged 3–11 (incorporating Wardle House, ages 3–5).

Senior School: aged 11–18.

Junior School (including the Nursery). The Junior School is staffed by class teachers chosen for their expertise in working with young children. There is a close liaison with the specialist teachers in the senior school to ensure continuity in teaching and the curriculum. The Head of the Junior School is responsible to the Headmaster of King's School for the day to day running of the Junior School. The Junior School shares a common site with the Senior School and benefits from use of the Technology Centre, ICT Suite, Gymnasium and Dining Hall, as well as taking part in full school assemblies in the Cathedral. After school care is available.

Senior School. The transition from class teaching to subject based set teaching is carried out gradually to enable the pupils to feel secure in their educational environment. Pastoral care is form-based with Tutors and Year Heads monitoring the progress of each pupil and liaising closely with parents.

The Senior School is based round the Cathedral buildings with their attractive gardens. Whilst the classrooms afford a sense of history and good learning, as well as having outlooks over the Cathedral Close, the laboratories and Technology suite are housed in modern buildings and are equipped to cope with current curriculum demands. The school playing fields, home to premiership cricket squares and Rugby pitches, are nearby at Archdeacon Meadow. Here, other facilities are available including indoor swimming pool, gym, and tennis courts.

The school is proud of its tradition of personal discipline which is based on mutual respect and self esteem. The relationship between pupils and staff is at the same time friendly and well defined. A coordinator of Personal and Social Education oversees the cross curricular themes essential to the development of the whole person in this challenging world.

The Sixth Form Centre in Dulverton House provides an academic and social focus for senior students.

The Curriculum. Heads of Department ensure continuity for the teaching of their subjects from the earliest years, in itself an unusual opportunity.

Formal teaching of modern foreign languages begins at the age of 7 in the Junior School, although is introduced through conversation and song from the Nursery upwards.

A full range of choices at GCSE is available and whilst the National Curriculum is offered, it is by no means compulsory. Every attempt is made to encourage the individual interests and enthusiasms of pupils through a flexible curriculum. Pupils may still opt for Classics as well as Technology. Information Technology is taught at all levels and to all pupils as an essential cross curricular skill. Physical Education and Business Studies are also offered at GCSE level as well as at A Level. Many pupils take GCSE Music and/or Religious Studies at an early stage in their time at the school. Support is offered to pupils with Learning difficulties through a fully staffed Learning Support Department.

In the Sixth Form there is a very wide range of academic subjects, around 25 in total. All members of the Sixth Form follow courses in ICT, General Studies and Critical Thinking, and all aspire to university entrance.

There is a strong Careers Department which deals with university entrance as well as work experience, careers experience and Service scholarships and cadetships. The school is a member school of the Independent Schools Careers Organisation.

Games and Activities. A full range of games is available with the main games being Rugby, Hockey and Cricket for boys and Hockey, Netball, Tennis and Rounders for girls. Senior pupils are able to participate in a whole range of minor games including Squash and Badminton, and Athletics is also available. A well-equipped Gymnasium at The Riverside Centre, at Archdeacon Meadow, provides the focus for Physical Education; Dance and Drama are fully integrated in the curriculum. Swimming lessons are an important part of the curriculum throughout the school, the annual House swimming gala being a very competitive event.

The school's main playing field, Archdeacon Meadow, hosts the County Cricket Festival each year. The King's School is a Junior Academy of Gloucestershire County Cricket Club and a Partnership School with the Gloucester and England RFU Junior Academy.

Its proximity to Kingsholm and its special relationship with Gloucester Rugby Football Club has enabled the school to become a centre of excellence in the sport. Overseas sports tours are held regularly for boys and girls.

The school offers the Duke of Edinburgh's Award scheme, a comprehensive outdoor pursuits programme and a wide range of clubs and societies. Annual overseas expeditions go as far afield as Ecuador and Mongolia.

Music and the Performing Arts. There is a strong tradition of musical excellence as befits a Cathedral Choir School, where all pupils are encouraged appreciate music. A good proportion of the school receives instrumental tuition and the various choirs, orchestras and ensembles play regularly in the Cathedral, and in the local region. Music Technology includes DAT, MIDI, multitrack, synthesis, sequencing and music publishing. The school is a Choir School and as such provides the trebles for the Cathedral choir, and has a number of music scholarships and bursaries endowed for that purpose. As well as providing a succession of Oxbridge organ scholars, the school provides a full range of musical activities.

Dance and Drama are very popular at the school and productions are arranged in the school hall, the Cathedral, and in local theatres. Both are features of the curriculum throughout the school. The summer Performing Arts Festival has recently become a featured climax to the school year.

Religious Worship. Whilst pupils from all denominations are warmly welcomed, the religious services are in accordance with the principles of the Church of England. Most days start with an Assembly, usually in the Cathedral and of a nature to suit each age group. A strong chaplaincy team, led by the School Chaplain, supports the spiritual development of pupils and staff alike.

Admission. To the Junior School this is through a Taster Day and low-key assessment of each child. Senior School: entrance tests are given for each pupil. At key entry points: 11+ or 13+ examinations, Common Entrance Examination or other tests appropriate to a child's previous education.

Fees per term (2008-2009). These are staged according to age. Junior School £1,995–£3,920; Senior School £4,135–£4,780.

Scholarships. (*see Scholarship Entries section*). Cathedral Choristerships receive a Scholarship worth 75% of tuition fees. Academic scholarships and exhibitions are awarded at ages 11+, 13+ and for the Sixth Form. Music awards are available to instrumental players of ability and potential. Sports, Art and Drama Awards and Governors' Bursaries are also available.

King's School Society. *Hon Sec*: c/o King's School, Gloucester GL1 2BG.

Charitable status. The King's School of the Cathedral Church of Gloucester is a Registered Charity, number 1080641. It exists to provide for the education of Cathedral Choristers and others, within a co-educational environment.

The King's School
Macclesfield

Macclesfield Cheshire SK10 1DA
Tel: 01625 260000
Fax: 01625 260022
e-mail: mail@kingsmac.co.uk
website: www.kingsmac.co.uk

Situated in rolling Cheshire countryside on the edge of the Peak District, the School was founded by the Will of Sir John Percyvale in 1502. The school offers an academic education through a unique combination of mixed and single sex education. The school places a high emphasis on extra-curricular activities and prides itself on pastoral care.

Patron: The Rt Hon The Earl of Derby, MC

Chairman of the Governors: F M Burdekin

***Head of Foundation*: S Coyne**, BSc, PhD, MEd

Senior Staff:

Deputy Headmaster: D J Pook, BA, ThM

Principal of Boys: I J Robertson, BSc
Principal of Girls: Mrs S E Spence, BA
Principal of Juniors: G J Shaw, BA
Principal of Sixth Form: T H Andrew, BA

Vice-Principal of Sixth Form (Acting): Mrs R Roberts, BA
Vice-Principal of Boys: P M Edgerton, MA
Vice-Principal of Girls: Mrs V B White, BEd, MA
Vice-Principal of Juniors: Mrs A Lea, BMus
Vice-Principal (Infants): Mrs E L Warburton, BEd
Senior Teacher (Admissions): Mrs C A Harrison, BSc
Senior Teacher (Staff Development): Mrs V B White, BEd, MA

Director of Finance: J M Spencer-Pickup

Miss M Acharya, BA
Mrs L F Adams, BA
Mrs R A Agour, BA
Z Ahmed, BSc
P J Atkinson, DipTeaching
Mrs V F A Atkins, BSc
Mrs D C Baker, BA
Dr G N Banner, BA, MA, PhD
Mrs D M Barker, BEd
Mrs J T Barratt, GTCL Hons, LTCL (Pft)
J P Bartle, BSc
Mrs J Beesley, BA
Mrs C H Bingham, BSc
Mrs L Booker, MMedSci, BA
Mrs H L Broadley, BSc
Mrs J E Brown, BSc
M J Brown, MSc, BSc
D T Browne, BA
Mrs C Buckley, HND
Mrs M Byrne, BA
S A Carpenter, BSc
Mrs J Cole, BA
P J Colville, BSc, MSc
Mrs R H Cookson, BA
Mrs V Costello, BA
Dr L Craig, BA, PhD
Dr G Crawley, BSc, PhD
Mrs R E Crowley, BSc
Mrs L Cunliffe, BSc
I E Dalgleish, BA
Mrs K Darch, BA
R G Davenport, BA, MA
Miss L C Derby, BA
J A Dodd, BSc
Mrs A Eardley, BA
Miss K E Easby, BA, MA
Dr J A Fitzgerald, BSc, MSc, PhD
Mrs M A F Gartside, BSc
D Gee, CertEd
A K Green, BA
Mrs G Green, BA
Mrs K Griffin, MA
P F Halewood, CertEd
A Hallatt, BA
Mrs J Hankinson, TCert
D M Harbord, CertEd, BA
Dr S J Hartnett, DPhil, BSc
Mrs L E Hewitson, BA, MSc
Dr C P Hollis, PhD, BSc Hons, CPhys, MInstP
Mrs M Holmes, BA
M T Houghton, BA
P Illingworth, BSc, CPhys, MInstP
Miss D Inman, BA
Mrs A M Johnson, BA
Mrs L M Johnston, CertEd
Dr I Lancaster, BSc, MSc, PhD
G Laurence, MA
Mrs J Locke, BSc
Mrs R E Maddocks, BA
D R Marshall, BSc
C J Maudsley, BSc
A McInnes, DipPE
Miss M McMaster, BSc, MPhil
Mrs A E Mitchell, BSc
Miss J A I Morris, BA
Ms C A Morton, BA, MEd
P Murray, BA
J Nichols, BEd
T G North, BSc
C O'Donnell, BSc
Mrs E P Olsen, BA
Mrs S E Ord, BA
Dr L C Palazzo, BA, MA, PhD
Mrs J H Panton, BA
D C Parkes, BA
Miss N Partington, BA, NNEB
M Patey-Ford, BA
Dr J R Pattison, PhD, BSc
P J Percival, BSc
Dr J M Pinkham, BSc, PhD
A S Puddephatt, BA
Mrs C L Pyatt, GRSM, LRAM
A P Reeve, BA
A Rice, BA
C A Richards, BSc
Mrs R A Richards, BA
Miss A E Rivers, BSc
Miss E Schué, BA
M T R Seccombe, BSc
Miss A Sheen, BSc
Miss E Smith, BA
Mrs N Squares, BMus, MA
J Street, BSc
Mrs J T Sykes, CertEd
Ms G Taylor, BA
Mrs Z Taylor, BA
Mrs C P Thompson, BA
P A Thompson, BSc
F Walker, LLAM, CertEd

Miss S H Waller, BSc
Miss L C Watkins, BSc
Mrs K Wells, BA
Dr J M West, BSc, MSc, PhD
Mrs C Whelpton, BSc
Mrs F A M Williams, BA
P Williams, BA

Number in School. Infants 3–7: 63 boys, 68 girls. Juniors 7–11: 132 boys, 87 girls. Boys (11–16) 497; Girls (11–16) 364. Sixth Form: 122 boys, 114 girls. Total: 1,447.

Organisation and Curriculum. The Foundation is organised in four Divisions: on one site, a Junior Division (co-educational 3–11) and a Girls' Division (11–16); on the other, a Boys' Division (11–16) and a Sixth Form (co-educational 16–18). Each Division is run by a Principal, who is responsible for day-to-day organisation, and the pupils in the 11–16 divisions of the school are taught separately but undertake a number of joint extra-curricular activities (eg music, drama, trips abroad etc.)

The Foundation has one Board of Governors, one Head and one Deputy Head who manage the school and plan regularly with the Division Principals to carry out the aims and objectives of the school. Girls and boys from 3–18 enjoy the same opportunities.

The curriculum is rich throughout all year groups offering pupils of all ages choice and a breadth of experience.

Pastoral care is a high priority. The divisional structure is key enabling each unit to be small and operate as a community.

Students are assigned to a personal tutor responsible for a group of 10 or so pupils throughout their Sixth Form course. Any justifiable combination of available A and AS Level subjects may be pursued, complemented by General Studies and Recreational Activity. In addition to compulsory core units in General Studies, students choose from a wide range of options designed to extend their breadth of cultural interest and intellectual inquiry, whilst Recreational Activities are designed to encourage the positive use of leisure time and offers initial experience in sports and activities new to the individual. Pupils are also prepared for University Entrance Examinations where appropriate.

Arts and Craft. Well equipped art rooms and workshops are also available for use by the members of the Art Club and Craft Societies outside the timetable.

Music. Over 400 pupils receive tuition in the full range of orchestral instruments, the Piano, Organ, Classical Guitar and Singing. An introductory tuition scheme enables all new entrants to assess their talent. There are three orchestras, a Concert-band, a Jazz band and three Choirs, which provide regular performing experience. The Foundation Choir was the first BBC, Songs of Praise, Choir of the Year in 2003. Pupils regularly enter music profession in addition to those pursuing academic training.

Drama. Theatre Studies is an important creative option at GCSE and A level and covers all aspects of the theatre. Great importance is attached to the regular school plays and musicals, which involve large numbers of pupils and enjoy a distinguished reputation. Pupils regularly take examinations in performance and public speaking.

Games. All pupils take part in games and athletic activity appropriate to the season. Junior School sports include Soccer, Cricket, Netball, Hockey, Tennis, Athletics and a wide range of individual games. In the Senior School, boys' sports include Rugby, Hockey, Cross-Country, Squash, Badminton, Cricket, Tennis, Athletics, Swimming and Basketball; the girls' sports include Hockey, Netball, Tennis, Football and Athletics. In addition there is a varied programme of sports in the Sixth Form, including soccer and such activities as Hill Walking, Caving and Rock Climbing which are actively pursued by boys and girls.

Outdoor Pursuits. There is a regular programme of training in the skills of hill walking and camping for all pupils. In addition, numerous expeditions are arranged in the many favourable areas near the school and also abroad. Sailing and orienteering are popular and the Duke of Edinburgh's Award scheme attracts 60 pupils each year.

Clubs and Societies. There is a wide range of other clubs catering for most interests and hobbies.

Fees per term (2008-2009). Senior School £2,785, Junior School £2,200, Infants Department £1,930. All fees are payable in advance on or before the first day of term.

Financial Support. (*see Scholarship Entries section*). Bursaries are available for entry at 11, 13 and 16. In addition seven or more Scholarships are given on performance in the Entrance Examination. Academic, music and organ scholarships are available in the Sixth Form. Funds are available to assist pupils attending courses and field trips and to help in cases of urgent need. Leaving Awards are granted from funds held in trust by the Governors.

Admissions. Admission is normally in September each year through competitive examination for boys and girls aged 7, 8 9, 10, 11 and 13 years, held during the previous February. Girls and boys are admitted to the Sixth Form subject to academic attainment, interview and course requirement. Admission arrangements are advertised and also available on request.

Intermediate admission, eg for new arrivals in the area, is possible.

Former Pupils' Association. *Hon Secretary*: c/o The King's School, Macclesfield, SK10 1DA. A gazette and register of names is published regularly.

Visit the Website. The award-winning website is found at www.kingsmac.co.uk.

Charitable status. The King's School, Macclesfield is a Registered Charity, number 525921. It exists for the education of boys and girls between the ages of 3 and 18.

King's School
Rochester

Satis House Boley Hill Rochester Kent ME1 1TE
Tel: 01634 888555
Fax: 01634 888505
e-mail: walker@kings-school-rochester.co.uk
website: www.kings-school-rochester.co.uk

The School traces its history to 604 AD, when St Justus, the first Bishop of Rochester, formed a school in connection with his Cathedral; it was reconstituted and endowed by Henry VIII as the King's School in 1541. The School has been fully co-educational since 1993.

Patron: The Lord Bishop of Rochester

Governors:
Chairman: The Very Revd A Newman, BSc, MPhil
Vice-Chairman: The Revd D Crabtree, BSc(Econ)

The Ven P H D Lock, AKC
The Revd Canon Dr P Hesketh, PhD, BD, AKC
The Revd Canon J Kerr, CertEd, MA
E L Darwin, MA, CEng, FICE
Miss L M Grosse, LLB
J W Lord, FCA, ATII
M J Chesterfield
J K Daffarn, FRICS
C R Shepherd, BEng, CEng, FICE, FRSA
Dr K R Dimond, BSc, PhD, CEng, MIEE
R W Hoile, MS, FRCS
Dr A Ward, MA, PhD, FSA
N A Sampson, MA
Miss D S Webster, MA, BEd

***Head Master*: Dr I R Walker**, BA, PhD, LTh, ABIA, FCollP, FRSA

Headmaster, Senior School: K Jones, MA

Director of Studies: Miss N Steel, BSc

Senior Teacher: Mrs C M Laws, BA

Chaplain: The Revd J A Thackray, BSc, ACIB

Assistant Staff:
N C M Abrams, BSc
B H Aspinall, BSc
I Barratt, BA
Mrs S Carver, BEd
Miss J E Chapman, BSc
Mrs B M Clarke, Maîtrise
M E Drury, BSc, MA
Mrs J Fenner, BA
M Dunton, BSc
Miss A V Gardener, BA
Miss J A Gillick, BA
R J Gosden, BA
C J Halsall, MA, MLitt, DipRSA, DipSocAnth, DMS Ed
C M Hoile, BA
Mrs C M Laws, BA
M Lewins, BA
Mr A Martinez, BA
N J McMillan, BSc
Miss S C K Otaki, MA
C H Page, BA
Miss A J Pine, BSc
K Ranglall, BA, MSc
B W Richter, BA
A J Robson, BA
Mrs L A Rogers, BA
W E Smith, BA
Miss N Steel, BSc
S Taranczuk, FRCO, MMus
Mrs M Thandi, BA, MA
R J Urquhart, MA
Mr J Waite, BSc
P W Wallace, BA
T R Walsh, MPhil, BA
Miss E Weavers, BA, MSci
C J White, MSc
Mrs S N Wright, BA

Mrs Xu Guo, BA, PGCE (*Librarian*)

Preparatory School
Headmaster: R P Overend, BA, FTCL, ARCM, FRSA

Deputy Headmaster & Director of Studies: P N Medhurst, BA, MA

Chaplain:

Assistant Staff:
J Downer, CertEd
I Flanagan, MPhil, BA, UED
Mrs C Green, BA
Mrs J L Grieves, BA
Mrs N J Heddershaw, BEd
Mrs J M Hines, BA
Mrs R C Kennedy, BA
A B Knight, BSc
Mrs M M Lapthorn, BSc, DIRPS
O Mahenga, BSc(Ed)
G J Mitchell, BA
G N Moore, BA, CertEd
A K Rumley, BSc, BA
Frau B Wagner
Mrs S Walsh, BA
F Wiesner

Educational Support Team:
Coordinator: C J Steward, BA, RSA, DipSpLD, CertTESOL

Visiting Educational Support Staff:
Mrs A Boyle, BEd, CertSpLD
Mrs C Keep, DipSpLD
Mrs T Jelfs, BEd

Visiting TEFL Staff:
Mrs J Aers, BA, CELTA
Mrs C Halsall, BA, DipEd, RSA, DipTEFL
Mrs J Squires, CertTESOL, RSA, CertSpLD

Pre-Preparatory School
Headmistress: Mrs A M Parkins, MA, CertEd

Deputy Headmistress: Mrs G J Singfield, MA, CertEd

Second Deputy/Early Years Coordinator: Miss R Dines, BEd

Assistant Staff:
Mrs C A Brown, CertEd
Mrs L J Green, BA
Mrs S Khela, BEd
Mrs M Malsher, CertEd
Mrs G A Newman, BA
Miss A I Parker, CertEd
Mrs H J Pemberton, BA, CertEd
Mrs R Phillips, CertEd
Mrs J Tyson, CertEd

Classroom Assistants:
Mrs F Blair
Miss A Booth, BTecDip
Mrs J Cross
Mrs E Franquiera, CLANSA
Mrs T Gilbert, DipRCSLT
Mrs M Harris, SRN
Mrs D Helmore, CACHE
Mrs K New
Mrs B Sheridan
Mrs C Simpson, SRN
Mrs J Smith, RNMH
Mrs N Woodward, NNEB

Honorary Chaplain: The Revd C M Haydon, CertEd

Educational Support Coordinator:
Mrs A Fisher, DipEd, RSA, DipSpLD

Visiting Educational Support Staff:
Mrs S Millward, CertEd, RSA, DipSpLD
Mrs P Weston, CertEd

The European Initiative
Director: C J Halsall, MA, MLitt, DipRSA, DipSocAnth, DMS(Ed)
Junior Director: Frau K Neubauer, Lehramt an Grundschulen, Erziehungswissenschaftliche (Fäkultält der Friedrich-Alexander-Universität Erlangen-Nürnberg)

Assistant Staff:
F Wiesner (Pedagogical University, Zwickau)
B Wagner (Leipzig University)

Music Department

Senior School Director of Music:
S Taranczuk, BMus, MMus, FRCO

Preparatory School Director of Music & Head of Strings:
Mrs J M Hines, BA

Head of Woodwind: G R Vinall, BA, LRAM (*Clarinet*)

Visiting Music Staff:
W D Bass, BA (*Cello*)
A Bunker, GGSM (*Brass*)
M P Clements, MA (*Academic Music*)
Mrs J M Colman, LTCL (*Bass, Piano*)
Miss A Floyd, AGSM (*Singing*)
Mrs M Gofman, Vladivostrok diplomas (*Piano*)
Mrs G Hayward-Ravenscroft, LTCL, ALCM (*Kindermusik, Singing*)
M Hines, AGSM (*Bassoon*)
Mrs B Hanson, LTCL (*Oboe*)
J Harrison, CertEd (*PCET*) (*Flute*)
Miss R K Otaki, GTCL, LTCL (*Singing*)
R M Sayer, ARCM, LRAM, FTCL, Dip RCM (*Organ*)
R J Scarff, GTCL, LTCL (*Percussion*)
Mrs J A Smith, LRAM, LTCL, LMusA (*Piano*)
Mrs S Thorpe, DipTCL (*Violin/Viola*)
Miss C Wakeman, BMus (*Guitar*)
R Wilson, BMus (*Violin/Viola*)

Cathedral Organist and Director of Music:
R M Sayer, ARCM, LRAM, FTCL, DipRCM

Finance Director and Clerk to the Governors:
G Longton, BSc, FCMA

Estates & Property Director: A B Nicholls

Personnel Director: R V Hubbard

Registrar: Mrs L Davies

Medical Officer: Dr F A Yeates, MB BS, DRCOG
Nursing Sister: Mrs S C Darby, BA, RGN, RM

The School is situated close to the Cathedral and Castle in the centre of the city and in a secluded conservation area; it enjoys the open spaces of the Precincts, the Vines and the Paddock, which is one of the School's playing fields. The other playing field, the Alps, is 10 minutes from the School.

The Main School dates from the mid-nineteenth century but the School also has a number of fine listed buildings from the eighteenth century, and considerable extensions of more recent date. Recent additions include a £3 million Conference Centre and dining facility, a girls' boarding house, and a Pre-Prep building and Sports Hall. An indoor swimming pool was opened in 1997 and a leading edge computer-based language laboratory was opened in 2007.

The School numbers about 700 pupils, of whom over 60 are boarders. The School is fully co-educational and divided into a Pre-Preparatory School of 116 (+28 in nursery) pupils (4–8 years), a Preparatory School of 210 pupils (8–13 years) and a Senior School of 306 pupils (13–18 years); this provides 3 units of an intimate size, which are regarded as a single community working closely together. While catering for the whole of a pupil's career from 3 to 18, there is a large entry of pupils at 11 and 13 who bring experience from other backgrounds, and enjoy the advantages of coming into a stable community with a strong family atmosphere.

The boarders, some of whom are weekly, play an important part in the life of the School. Although a minority, they are a large enough part of the School to make a very significant contribution of their own, and enjoy a more intimate atmosphere than is possible in a larger boarding community.

King's is the Cathedral School. The Dean and Chapter are ex officio Governors, the Headmaster and King's Scholars are members of the Cathedral Foundation, and the Cathedral Choristers are members of the Preparatory School. The School uses the Cathedral for worship.

Work. In the Pre-Preparatory School, the pupils follow a four year curriculum of Maths, Science, English, Divinity, Geography, History, Information Technology, Art and Craft, Design & Technology, Music, and Physical Education. Daily spoken German lessons taught by native German teachers form part of the curriculum from the age of 4.

In the Preparatory School, the syllabus covers Divinity, English, History, Geography, Mathematics, Information Technology, Science (Physics, Chemistry and Biology), Latin, French, Art, Music, Physical Education, General Studies, and Design & Technology.

In the Senior School, all pupils continue with the same range for the first year. In the Fifth forms, a core of subjects is continued and pupils add a balanced choice of options in preparation for the GCSE and IGCSE examinations at the end of the two-year course.

In the Sixth Form, a wide range of AS and A Level subjects are available. Normally a pupil studies for 4 AS and then 3 A Level subjects, and, in addition, undertakes a programme of General Studies.

All Sixth formers, who wish to, go on to university or other further education, and are encouraged to think carefully about their ultimate careers. Careers Talks are given by outside speakers during the GCSE year, and the advice of specialist careers advisers and the careers teachers is available at all stages.

Activities. The School aims to develop pupils through a wide range of activities, both within the School programme and outside it.

There is a large CCF contingent, with Army, Navy and Air Force sections. Strong Service connections locally give particularly wide scope for CCF activities.

Pupils also undertake a variety of activities in Community Service, and participate in the Duke of Edinburgh's Award Scheme.

Out of School there is a range of over 20 school societies in all three parts of the School, and in the holidays there is a strong tradition of annual cultural and outdoor expeditions in this country and abroad for Preparatory and Senior School pupils.

Art, Drama and Music. The School sets great store by the Arts, and uses the comparative proximity to London to take pupils to art exhibitions, concerts and the theatre. The School stages major drama productions each year, recently Little Shop of Horrors, In Holland Stands a House and The Dresser have been the main presentations. There is a strong musical tradition enhanced by visiting music staff, and pupils are encouraged to learn instruments. In addition to concerts in the School and the Cathedral, the Orchestra gives a number of outside performances each year, some by invitation. The choral tradition is strengthened by the presence of the Cathedral choristers in the School who regularly undertake overseas tours.

Games. The boys' games are Rugby, Hockey, Football (Preparatory School) and Cricket and for girls' Hockey, Netball and Tennis. Other team sport options are Rowing, Athletics, Cross Country, Fencing, Tennis and Swimming, and there are opportunities in addition for Squash, Badminton and Sailing. Physical Education is a regular part of the School curriculum and all pupils are required to take part in games. 80% represent the School competitively.

Religious Education and Worship. Although there is no denominational requirement for entry to the School, religious instruction is in accordance with the principles of the Church of England. All three parts of the School begin the day with an assembly or chapel service, some of which are held in the Cathedral.

Admission. Pupils can enter the School at any age from 3 to 18. Entrance to the Senior School is either by Common Entrance at 13 or by the School's own examination for pupils who have not been prepared for Common Entrance.

Sixth Form entry is on the basis of interview and School report, together with satisfactory GCSE results (a minimum of 5 A*–C passes, and grade requirements for A Level courses).

Choristers. Choristerships to Rochester Cathedral (8+/9+) from Cathedral and School are awarded to boys following voice trials and a satisfactory performance in the Preparatory School Entrance Examination. Under normal circumstances the choristership will continue until a boy transfers to the Senior School or until he leaves the choir.

Scholarships. (*see Scholarship Entries section*). ***Senior School***: Up to five Major King's Scholarships (30%) and five Minor King's Scholarships (15%) may be awarded annually. Major Scholarships may be up to 75% of tuition fees (means tested above 30%). At least five scholarships are for pupils from the maintained sector.

Up to five Music Scholarships of up to 30% of tuition fees, and means-tested up to 75%, may be awarded annually on the basis of interview and practical test. An Organ Scholarship of up to 30% of tuition fees, means-tested up to 75%, may be awarded when a vacancy occurs. One Choral Scholarship (£2,500 per annum) and one Music Scholarship (£3,000) are occasionally available.

Governors Exhibitions: These academic awards are available to pupils and may be of value up to 100% of fees. All are means tested using the same assessment as originally applied to the Government Assisted Places Scheme which they replace.

Preparatory School: Five King's Exhibitions at 11+ of 30% of tuition fees, means-tested up to 75%, are available. Two are for pupils from a maintained Primary School.

Details of all awards may be obtained from the Headmaster. Additional means-tested bursaries may be available.

Remissions. Children over the age of 8 of Church of England ministers are given a 10% reduction in tuition fees, means-tested beyond.

Children over the age of 8 of Service Personnel are given a 20% reduction in tuition fees for the first two years and a 10% reduction in the following two years.

Where parents have three or more children at the school a reduction after the second child of 10% of the youngest child's fees.

Fees per term (2008-2009). Senior School: Boarders £8,460, Day Pupils £5,030. Preparatory School: Boarders £5,990, Day Pupils £3,430–£3,890. Pre-Preparatory School: £2,174–£2,880 (Day only).

Charitable status. King's School, Rochester is a Registered Charity, number 1084266. It is a charitable trust for the purpose of educating children.

The King's School
Tynemouth
A Woodard School

Huntington Place Tynemouth Tyne and Wear NE30 4RF
Tel: 0191 258 5995
Fax: 0191 296 3826
e-mail: admissions@kings-tynemouth.co.uk
website: www.kings-tynemouth.org.uk

Motto: *Moribus Civilis*

Governing Body: The Provost and Fellows of the Society of S S Mary and Aidan of York

President: The Rt Revd Anthony Russell, DPhil, Bishop of Ely
Visitor: The Rt Revd The Bishop of Newcastle

School Council:
D R Bilton, BSc, CEng, MIEE, AMI, MechE (*Chairman*)
D E T Nicholson, MA
A M Conn, MA, ACA
F S McNamara, BA
His Hon Judge J E Evans, BA
I A Angus, BSc, ARICS
Dr A E Colver, BSc, MRCGP
D Hodgson, BSc, FIChemE, CEng, MIOSH
R Lofthouse, BTech, PhD, CChem, MRSC
Mrs P F Craggs, LLB, MBA
Revd G Lowson, BEd, DipTh
Mrs D Parfitt, BSc
Revd Canon B D Clover, MA, LTCL

***Headmaster*: P J S Cantwell**, BA, PGCE

Deputy Head, Academic: M Heywood, BA, PGCE
Deputy Head, Pastoral: E M George, BA, MBA(Ed)
Head of Sixth Form: M C Long, BSc, PGCE

Assistant Masters and Mistresses:
D Wager, BSc, DipEd
S J Pettitt, BEd, MLitt
W Ryan, CertEd
B J Wood, BSc, CertEd
C Moore, BA, PGCE
V Gordon, BSc, PGCE
B J Gibson, CertEd
J Limer, CertEd
J H Taylor, MA, DipTh, PGCE
C Johnston, BEd
D H Waters, MA, PGCE
P R McCall, BA, PGCE
Mrs C A Rix, BSc, PGCE
K Rix, BA, PGCE
A C Fowler, BEd
P C Hadwin, BSc, PGCE
G R Dickson, BA, MA, PGCE
Revd W D Miller, BA (*Chaplain*)
Mrs J H Marsh, DipEd
A Cutting, BA
P A Baxter, BA
Mrs I M Nicholson, BEd, MA
P Angel, MA, BSc, PGCE
Miss V E Hansen, BEd, BA
Miss C E Taylor, BA, PGCE
P J Nicholson, BA, PGCE
R A Marriott, BA, PGCE
Miss J L Brady, BA (*Librarian*)
A ul Haq, BSc, PGCE
Mrs J N Liddie, BA, PGCE
Dr M H Brookes, BSc, PhD, PGCE
H C Morris, BA
Mrs S E Smith, BA, PGCE
Miss L Scurfield, BA, PGCE
Ms D Summerson-Fenwick, BA, MA, PGCE
Mrs C E Green, BA, PGCE
C Leather, BA, PGCE
Mrs M J Turnbull, BEd, PGCE
Miss J Patterson, BEd, PGCE
Miss L Gordon, BSc, PGCE
Mrs D Wallace, BA, BSc Econ, MEd
Mrs S Brookes, BA, PGCE
Mrs H Hamilton, BSc, PGCE
Mrs P Laws, BA, PGCE
Mrs A Richardson, CertEd, DipSpLD
D E Boardman, BSc, PGCE
G Bradley, BSc, PGCE
P G Clarke, BA, PGCE
Mrs C Dunn, CertEd, BA, MEd
Mrs L D Herron, BA, PGCE
A Antoranz, BA, PGCE
P Thompson, BA, PGCE
Miss R Murphy, BSc, PGCE
Miss C M Smith, BA, PGCE

Junior School including Kindergarten:
D J Littlefield, MA, BEd (*Head of Junior School*)
Miss K Benson, BEd (*Deputy Head of Junior School*)
D W Lilly, BEd
A J Russell, BEd
Mrs H C Baines, BSc, PGCE
Mrs J M Large, BSc, PGCE
Mrs C A Spencer, BEd
Mrs S A Porteous, BA, PGCE
Mrs M A Went, CertEd, DipSpLD
Miss J Quinn, BSc, PGCE
Miss H N Boyle, BTec (*Nursery Nurse*)
Mrs J A Ray, BEd
Mrs K M Adams, CertEd
Mrs S Boutwood, BMus, GRNCM, PGCE
Mrs S L Brandrith, CertEd

Bursar and Clerk to the Governors: J Scott-Batey, BEd, FCA

The King's School Former Pupils' Association: J Brown

Alumni Development Officer: Mrs K E Bilton, BSc

General. The King's School, founded in 1860, is the largest school of the Woodard Corporation. It is an Independent Day School for boys and girls aged 4–18. There are approximately 870 pupils in the School: 80 pupils in the Kindergarten (4+ to 7); 150 pupils in the Junior School (7 to 10+); and 620 pupils in the Senior School (11+ to 18) with a Sixth Form of 180. All three sections of The King's School work closely together and enjoy many of the same facilities.

King's endeavours to educate 'the whole person' and so the excellence of our classroom teaching and GCSE and A level results is complemented by a wide range of extra-curricular activities both sporting and cultural. Teaching is in small groups and all pupils are known individually.

As a day school King's aims for a close partnership with parents.

King's is a Christian school and the School Chapel is at its centre, providing a powerful symbol of the School's values and aims.

The School enjoys a remarkably fortunate location: it is situated on the North East coast in the beautiful village of Tynemouth, on direct bus and metro routes from Newcastle and the surrounding areas. There are also private coaches travelling from south of the River Tyne.

Senior School Curriculum. The School aims to give pupils a broad education in general, and in particular to prepare them for public examinations and for entry into Universities (including Oxbridge) and other establishments of Further Education.

In the first three years all pupils follow a common curriculum consisting of: English, Mathematics, History, Geography, French, Science, Art, Music, Drama, Religious Education, Design/Technology, ICT and Physical Education. German and Spanish are introduced in the Year 8.

In Years 10 and 11 pupils are prepared for a wide range of GCSE options. All pupils in Year 11 have a period of work experience immediately after the GCSE examinations.

In the Sixth Form most pupils take four AS-Level subjects, followed by three or four A2-Level subjects in the second year. Practically any combination of subjects is possible and there is no arts-science barrier.

King's maintains excellent links with Industry and is greatly indebted to parents and the thriving Former Pupils' Association for their assistance in this field.

Careers and University Application. Careers education and guidance are provided from Year 9 onwards. The vast majority of Sixth-Formers proceed to degree courses and expert advice is given on University applications.

Games and Physical Education. The programme of games and physical education is designed to provide every pupil with an opportunity to gain satisfaction from participation in sport. King's has busy fixture lists and maintains a high standard at Rugby, Cricket, Tennis and Hockey (the major team games) as well as at Athletics, Gymnastics, Cross-Country Running, Netball, Squash, Soccer, Basketball and Badminton. Facilities are also provided for Golf, Sailing, Canoeing, Swimming, Fencing, Archery and Trampolining.

The School has a magnificent new sports centre and also its own playing fields at Priors Park, virtually adjacent to the main campus. King's fosters close links with local Rugby, Cricket and Tennis Clubs.

Many pupils win selection at county and national level.

Activities. Music and Drama are exceptionally strong at King's as are the numerous other clubs and societies which include: Art; Bridge; Christian Fellowship; Computers; Chess; Dance; Debating; Orienteering; Table Tennis; Science; Stained Glass, Young Engineers, Young Enterprise.

Many pupils are involved in the Duke of Edinburgh's Award Scheme and in Community Service. The School organises annual skiing, mountaineering, climbing, and adventurous trips; visits to the Inverclyde National Sports Centre and the Outward Bound Mountain Centre at Ullswater; and a Summer Camp. The King's School has a field centre at Alnham in Northumberland, which is used as a base for field study work and for Duke of Edinburgh's Award Scheme activities.

Junior School (including Kindergarten). The Junior School (4+ to 10+ years) is staffed by class teachers specially qualified for work with younger children, though there is close liaison with the specialist teachers in the Senior School to ensure continuity in teaching and the curriculum. The Head of the Junior School is responsible to the Headmaster of The King's School for the day-to-day running of the Junior School.

The Junior School shares a common site with the Senior School and although housed in separate accommodation with its own classrooms, Library, Design & Technology room and ICT centre, it makes full use of the school chapel, cafeteria, sports centre, laboratories, workshops, playing fields and field centre.

Admissions. Prospectus and Registration forms can be obtained from the Admissions Office.

All entries are made through the Headmaster. Pupils are admitted to the Kindergarten on the basis of an interview; and to the Junior and Senior Schools on the basis of performance in the School's examinations in English and Mathematics and an interview with the Headmaster. The main intakes to the Senior School are at 11+ and 13+. For entry at Sixth Form level a minimum of 14 points at GCSE is normally expected in addition to a satisfactory report from a pupil's current Head.

Fees per term (2008-2009). Senior School £2,951; Junior School £2,342.

Scholarships and Bursaries. Scholarships (including those for Art and Music) are offered for entry to the Senior School at 11+, 13+ and Sixth Form level. Bursaries are available by application to the Headmaster.

Charitable status. The King's School Tynemouth Limited is a Registered Charity, number 269665. It exists to promote education.

The King's School
Worcester

5 College Green Worcester WR1 2LL
Tel: 01905 721700 (School Office)
01905 721721 (Bursar)
Fax: 01905 721710
e-mail: info@ksw.org.uk
website: www.ksw.org.uk

A Cathedral School appears to have existed at Worcester virtually continuously since the 7th century. In its present form, however, The King's School dates from its refoundation by King Henry VIII in 1541, after the suppression of the Cathedral Priory and its school. In 1884 the School was reorganised as an Independent School and in 1944 the Cathedral Choir School was amalgamated with The King's School.

Visitor: The Lord Bishop of Worcester

The Governing Body:
D T Howell, Esq, BSc Eng, FCA (*Chairman*)
The Very Revd P G Atkinson
Mrs K L Brookes, MA
H B Carslake, Esq, BA, LLB
Dr K J Clarke, MA Oxon
Professor M Clarke, CBE, MA, DL
W A Comyn, Esq, FCA
R M Dancey, Esq, MA
S J Doughty, Esq, BSc, FICE, CEng, FIHT
D L Green, Esq
Dr J A Harvey, GNSM, LRAM, PGCE, ILTM, FRSA
D R Mills, Esq
The Hon Lady Morrison
Revd Canon Dr A Petterson
Mrs I Taylor, MA Cantab, FCA

Clerk to the Governors and Bursar: J G Bartholomew, MBA, AIMBM, PIIA

***Headmaster*: T H Keyes**, MA

Senior Deputy Head: Miss S E Hincks, MA
Second Deputy Head: R Chapman, BSc
Director of Studies: R C Baum, MA

Assistant Staff:
* *Head of Department*
§ *Part-time*

Art:
*Mrs E R Hand, BA
C Haywood, BA
Mrs R Terry, BA, MA
Miss L Folwell, BA
§B Wang, BA
R Gilbert, BA, MA

Biology:
*M Parkin, MA, PhD
Mrs R Worth, BSc
S M Bain, BSc, MSc
Mrs N Essenhigh, BSc
M J Newby, BEd
Miss L Lawson Pratt, MA

Careers:
*B Griffiths, BTech

Chemistry:
*R P Geary, BSc, CChem, MRSC
J T Wheeler, BSc, CChem, MRSC
M C Poole, BSc, PhD
§Mrs C E Battrum, MA
R James, BSc, PhD

Classics:
*R N G Stone, MA
T H Keyes, MA
Mrs E Shepherd, MA
Mrs S C Bradley, BA
Mrs P Grundy, BA

Design and Technology:
*C Wilson, BA
Miss J Cooke, BA
E Lummas, BA
A Deichen, BA

Key Skills:
*Mrs E Allen-Back, MA

Drama & Theatre Studies:
*S M Atkins, BA
Mrs T D Marskell, CertEd
Mrs L Guy, BA
A J M Maund, MA

Economics & Business Studies:
*R P Mason, BA
§Mrs L Martyn-Smith, BSocSc
Miss E Gittings, BA

English:
*A J M Maund, MA
S Le Marchand, BA
Mrs S P Griffiths, BA
R J Davis, BA
Mrs S H Le Marchand, BA
D P Iddon, BA
§Mrs K Adam, BA
A K Macnaughton, MA
Mrs L Guy, BA
Mrs E Allen-Back, MA
Mrs L Walmsley, BA

Geography:
*S C Cuthbertson, BA
A W Longley, BA
Mrs L M Ghaye, BEd, MA
Mrs F L Short, BA
D N M Orr, BA
Miss C Lea, BSc

History:
*P T Gwilliam, BA, MPhil
Mrs C F Roslington, BA
T R Sharp, MA
Mrs N Sears, BA
Miss J Mosely, BA

Information Technology:
*J M Roslington, BSc, CPhys, MInstP, MIITT
Mrs J C Vivian, CertEd
J D Manthorp, BA

Mathematics:
*Mrs A Hines, BSc
M J Roberts, BSc
B Griffiths, BTech
D G Willmer, MSc, PhD
Mrs C M Cox, MA, MSc
Mrs P A Edwards, BA, MSc
Mrs M M Longley, BEd
§Miss A-M Simpson, BSc
§Mrs D Salkeld, BSc
Mrs L Brighton, BEd
A J Knowles, BSc

Modern Languages:
*R A Ball, MA
Mrs K Appleby, BA
J L Owen, BA
M D Rudge, BA
C A Gallantree-Smith, BA
Mrs C Painter, BA
Miss S E Hincks, MA
Mrs R M Rutter, BA
Miss S Hirner, BA

Music:
*D E Brookshaw, BMus, FRCO
Mrs V J Gunter, GTCL, LTCL
G M Gunter, GTCL, LTCL
§C J B Allsop, BA, MA
and 24 visiting teachers

PE & Games:
J J Mason, BSc (*Director of Sport*)
A A D Gillgrass, BA (*Head of Boys' Games*)
Mrs F L Short, BA (*Head of Girls' Games*)
Miss O Beveridge, BEd
S M Bain, BSc, MSc
D P Iddon, BA
Mrs T D Marskell, CertEd
Mrs M M Longley, BEd
§Mrs J D Clark, BEd
C Atkinson, BSc
J Chalmers

Physics:
*D J Haddock, MA, DPhil Oxon
I C Robinson, BSc
R C Baum, MA
Mrs S K Stone, BEng
Mrs L E Haddock, BSc

Religious Studies:
*Revd M R Dorsett, BA, MTh, PhD, CertTheol (*Chaplain*)
D A Jones, MTh

PSE:
*D A Jones, MTh

Headmaster's Secretary: Mrs C Swainston
Registrar: Mrs V Peckston
Medical Officer: Dr M Smith, MBChB
Sister: Mrs C F Furber, RGN, DipN

The King's Junior Schools:

King's St Alban's
Head: R Bellfield, BEd
Deputy Head: W Toleman, BA

§Mrs A D Walton, CertEd
§Mrs L A Jackson, MA
§Mrs C Woodcock, BA, CertEd
§Mrs N Cain, BA
Mrs K Kear-Wood, BSc
§Mrs J Pitts, BEd
§Mrs V Martin, CertEd, DipRSA SpLD
§Mrs M A Keyes, MA
D Braithwaite, BEd
Mrs R Duke, BA
§J T Walton, CertEd, FRGS
§Mrs J Leach, BEd, DPSE
J M Bailey, BEd
Miss F Dolphin, BSc
Mrs H Heggerty, BA
Mrs A Hind, BSc
I Fry, PGCE
Ms E Wyatt, BSc

Registrar: Mrs A Bellfield
Secretary: Mrs T Pearman
Tel: 01905 354906; Fax: 01905 763075

King's Hawford
Head: J M Turner, BEd Hons, DipEd, ACP
Deputy Head: A Hymer, BA

Mrs S Roscoe, CertEd
§Mrs J M Tune, BSc
§Mrs G M Wales, BA
R B Cook, BSc
Mrs C Rawnsley, BA
Mrs J Bayliss, BSc
Mrs C Knight, BEd
Mrs J Redman, BEd
§R Forrester-Walker
Mrs D Goodayle, BEd
Mrs L Cross, BSc
J Broderick, BEd
§D Peters, BMus
Mrs G Turner, CertEd
A R Drenth, BA

Pre-Prep:
Head: Mrs P M Bradley, BEd
Mrs J N Willis, BA Ed
Mrs C A Griffin, BA
Mrs L C N Baxter, BSc
Mrs J Farmer, BEd
Mrs G Riley, BSc
Mrs J Wilson, BEd
§Mrs H Fowler, BA

Headmaster's Secretary: Mrs W Mason
Tel: 01905 451292; Fax: 01905 756502; e-mail: Hawford@ksw.org.uk
School Secretary: Miss S Freeman
Hawford Matron: Mrs F Geary, RGN

The School still occupies its original site south of the Cathedral. The buildings are grouped around College Green and the School Gardens. They range in date from the 14th century College Hall and Edgar Tower through the 17th and 18th century buildings surrounding College Green, to a range of modern, purpose-built accommodation, much of which has been constructed in the last twenty years. Recent additions in a continuing development programme include a new library located in the heart of the school, the John Moore Theatre, new teaching and science provision for the Junior School on site, the refurbishment of the Sports Hall, a covered Swimming Pool, new, upgraded House accommodation. There are new centres for English and Mathematics and a new Music School was opened in April 2003. A Languages Computer Centre with the latest software for the teaching of French, German and Spanish has been established.

There are two Junior Schools. King's St Alban's stands in its own grounds on the edge of the main school site, offering education from 7–11. King's Hawford is in a spacious rural setting just to the north of the city and offers education from 2–11.

Numbers and Admission. The school is fully co-educational. King's St Alban's has about 180 pupils. King's Hawford has about 300 pupils. The Senior School has about 900 pupils, including 230 in the Sixth Form.

Entrance to the school is by the Junior Entrance Test at 7, 8 or 9, or by the School's Examination at 11, 12 and 13. Boys and girls also join the School at Sixth Form level; this entry is by test, interview and GCSE results.

Term of Entry. Pupils are normally admitted annually in September.

Religion. The School has an historic connection with the Cathedral. Religious education, given in accordance with the Christian faith, is non-denominational. Pupils of all denominations and faiths are welcomed.

Curriculum. Pupils are prepared for the GCSE, and A, AS and Advanced Extension papers, and for Higher Education, the Services, the professions, industry and commerce. The curriculum is designed to give all pupils a general education and to postpone specialisation for as long as possible. Further details will be found in the Prospectus.

Games. The major sports are Rugby, Netball, Hockey, Football, Rowing and Cricket. Other sports include Tennis, Athletics, Cross Country, Badminton, Rounders, Fencing, Squash, Golf, Swimming, Sailing and Canoeing. PE and games are compulsory for all; a wide choice is offered to Sixth Formers. The school has been awarded the Sportsmark Gold award.

Other Activities. The school has a Choral Society and two other Choirs, 3 Orchestras and a Wind Band; there are at least 20 concerts each year. There are more than a dozen dramatic productions each year, including two or three major School plays, one of which is usually a Musical. The School takes part in the Duke of Edinburgh's Award Scheme; there is a CCF and a Welfare and Community Service group. Young Enterprise companies in the Sixth Form are well subscribed and highly successful. A large number of societies and groups cater for a wide variety of other out-of-school activities and interests. The School has an Outdoor Activities Centre in the Black Mountains which is widely used both during the term and in the holidays. The Himalayan Club takes about 25 pupils on expeditions each year to Nepal or India.

Scholarships. (*see Scholarship Entries section*). Both Music and Academic Scholarships are available at 11+, 13+ and 16+ in the Senior School, value up to one third of tuition fees. Academic scholarships at 11+ are awarded on the basis of the Entrance Test; at 13 + on the Entrance Test and an interview; at 16+ on the basis of an aptitude test and interview, along with a report from the candidate's school. Full details are available from the Registrar. Scholarships are available at 7+ and 8+, value up to one third of tuition fees (tenable only while in the Junior Schools) and are awarded to candidates of outstanding academic or musical ability. Bursaries of up to one third of the cost of tuition may be granted to candidates who face financial hardship.

Those in receipt of a combination of scholarships/bursary will only receive a maximum of one half of tuition fees.

Fees per term (2008-2009). Senior School £3,408; Junior School £2,195–£2,962.

Chorister Scholarships. Entry to the Choir is by means of Voice and Academic Tests which are held at various times throughout the year. A high vocal and musical standard is naturally required and boys must also have sufficient intellectual ability to hold their own in the Choir and the School. Boys should be 7–9 years old at the time of entry.

The **Prospectus** and information about Entrance Tests, Awards and Chorister Scholarships can be obtained from the Registrar.

Charitable status. The King's School Worcester is a Registered Charity, number 1098236. It exists to provide high quality education for boys and girls.

Kingston Grammar School

London Road Kingston-upon-Thames Surrey KT2 6PY
Tel: 020 8546 5875
Fax: 020 8547 1499
e-mail: head@kgs.org.uk
website: www.kgs.org.uk

A school is believed to have existed in the Lovekyn Chantry Chapel since the fourteenth century. However in 1561, Queen Elizabeth I, in response to a humble petition from the Burghers of Kingston, signed Letters Patent establishing the "Free Grammar School of Queen Elizabeth to endure for ever". In 1944 the School accepted Direct Grant Status and became fully Independent in 1976. Two years later the School went Co-educational, initially with girls in the Sixth Form, but in the following year joining in the Preparatory and First Forms, to progress through the School. There are still close links with the Royal Borough of Kingston upon Thames, but no residential qualification for entry to the School, which now numbers around 450 boys and 350 girls.

Motto: *Bene agere ac laetari.*

Governing Body:
J A Elvidge, MA, LLB (*Chairman*)
A Clinch, FCIMA, FACA (*Vice-Chairman*)
Professor G Cunningham, MA, DPhil (*Vice-Chairman*)
D Baker, ARICS
Professor F M Brennan, BSc, PhD
Mrs S Fowler, CEng, BSc, MCIBSE
M Green, MA
Mrs L C Jones, MA, AICA
D J Ott, BSc, UED
B J W Rourke, FCA
Dr P Smith, OBE, MBChB
J S Tapp
D U Thompson, JP, BA, MMS, ACEA
Mrs H Webster, LLB

***Headmaster*: C D Baxter**, MA Oxon, FRSA

* *Head of Department*

Principal Deputy Head: M M Hall, MA, BA (*Economics*)
Second Deputy Head: Miss V S Pownall, BA (*Geography, *PSHE*)
Assistant Head: M Jones, BA, MEd (*French*)
Assistant Head: N Bond, BA (*English*)
Assistant Head: Miss D M Williams, BSc (*Geography*)

Staff:
Mrs T C Airley, BA (*Preparatory Form*)
Mrs R Allen, BA (**Director of Drama*)
Miss H L Anderson, MChem (*Chemistry*)
Miss L S Andrews, BSc (*Mathematics*)
Mrs J Barkey, BA (*Art*)
R L Barker, BA (*Director of Careers and Enterprise*)
A J Beard, BA (*History, Head of Fifth Form*)
M Behnoudnia, BSc (*Physics*)
Miss N Bell, BSc (*PE, *Sports Studies, Games*)
S W Bell, BA (*Drama*)
Mrs J M A Bowen, BSc (*Mathematics*)
T A Braine, MA (*Design Technology*)
Miss A E Brown, BEd (*Sports Studies, *Girls' Hockey, *PE*)
Miss P Browne, BA (*Geography*)
D G Buttanshaw, BEd (*PE, Mathematics, *Boys' and Girls' Hockey*)
Miss L Collison, BSc (*Mathematics*)
Mrs H B Cook, BSc (*Mathematics*)
P J Cooper, MSc (**Mathematics*)
Mrs S J Corcoran, BEd (**Learning Support*)
Mrs A Crampin, BSc, PhD (*Physics*)
Miss P V Crothers BA (*French, German, Head of Second Form*)
J M Davies, MA (**History*)
I Deepchand, BSc (**Physics*)
W G Dunlop, BA (*English, *CCF, Head of Preparatory and First Form*)
J A Dyson, BA (**Art*)
Miss S K Ellis, BA (**IT, Assistant Head of Sixth Form*)
D Farr, BA (*Design Technology*)
J M Fenton, BA (*Religious Studies*)
N S Forsyth, BSc (*Biology*)
Mrs S Garside, BA, MA (*English*)
Miss R L Gladwyn, BA (*English*)
Ms N S Goul-Wheeker, BA (*Classics*)
M S Grant, BA, MA (*History, Head of Fourth Form*)
C Greenaway (**Rowing*)
G A Greenwood, BSc (*Chemistry*)
W R Gurney, BSc (*Mathematics*)
Miss C M Hall, BSc (**Science, *Chemistry*)
Miss R Hay, BA, MFA (*Art*)
Mrs N L Hempstead, L-ès-L (*French, Spanish*)
Mrs M J Horrocks, BA (**French, *Spanish*)
Mrs E M Hyde, MA (*Assistant Director of Music*)
C A Jackson, MA, FRCO, ARAM (**Director of Music*)
M P Joyce, BA (*History*)
R King, BA, MA (**Psychology*)
A M Langdon, BA, PhD (*Mathematics, Assistant Head of Sixth Form*)
Miss F J Little, MA (**English, Gifted and Talented Coordinator*)
Miss H Lycitt, BA (**Religious Studies*)
N E MacKay, BA (*French, Spanish, Head of Third Form*)
Miss C Mara, BSc (*PE, *Netball, *Tennis*)
Miss B A McDonald, BA, MA (**Classics*)
V R Muir, BSc (**Biology*)
C C Muller, BA (*Classics, Head of Sixth Form*)
Mrs E J O'Reilly, BA (*French, Spanish*)
Mrs S Osborn, BSc, AIMA (*Mathematics*)

J H Renwick, BA (*Religious Studies*)
P J Ricketts, MA (**Economics, *Business Studies*)
S R J Robertson, BA (*Geography*)
M J C Rodgers, BSc, MSc (*Biology*)
J A Royce, MPhil, BEd (*Director of Sport*)
Mrs T M Russell, Mag Phil (**German*)
J E K Schofield, BSc (*Business Studies, *Cricket, *Soccer*)
Mrs M E Serjeant, BA, DipLib (**Librarian*)
Miss R J Sharp, BA (*French and Spanish*)
C R Smalman-Smith, BA (*Mathematics, Rowing*)
J S Smith, BA, MPhil (*English*)
D A R Sorley, BA (*History, *Politics*)
Miss E M F Stadler, BA (*French, German*)
S R Steele, BEd (**Design Technology*)
D L Thomson, BSc (*Chemistry*)
Miss E K Varley, BA (*English*)
D Vermeulen, BA (*History*)
Mrs V Ward, BEd (*Design Technology*)
P R Williams, BA (*Biology*)
M P Williamson, BEd (*Physical Education, *Boys' Hockey*)
L H Winning, MChem, DPhil (*Chemistry*)
G R M Yates, BA, MA (**Geography, Director of Teaching and Professional Development*)

Bursar and Clerk to the Governors: E N Lang, BA, ACA
Property Manager: R Osgood
Development Director: Ms L Weston, BA
Headmaster's Secretary: Mrs C Pink
Registrar: Mrs H Smith

Buildings. Starting with the medieval Lovekyn Chapel, the site of Kingston Grammar School has been developed over 400 years to include modern classroom and laboratory facilities. Major recent developments have seen the building of a Library, Studio and Seminar Room, and an Art/Technology Centre with an art gallery. Kitchen and dining facilities have been upgraded, and all three Science departments extended/refurbished. The Chapel has been restored as a recital/lecture room, a new History Department building was opened in 1997 and an Information and Communication Technology Centre with a school wide network was installed in 1998. A multi media Modern Languages Centre opened in 1999. In 2002 the school acquired additional land, which has been developed to include a Performing Arts Centre with a Theatre, new Music and Drama Departments, Sixth Form social and study areas and additional classrooms. The school is easily accessible by road and rail links to Kingston. The 22 acre sports ground includes an indoor games area, pavilions, cricket nets, netball courts, two all-weather pitches plus practice area and boat house.

Entry to the School. Admission to the School is by examination: at 10+ and 11+ candidates sit the School's own examination in January for entry the following September; at 13+ candidates sit the Independent Schools Common Entrance Examination in June for entry the following September or the School's own Examination for non-Common Entrance candidates. A large number of girls and boys are also admitted to the Sixth Form.

Term of Entry. Apart from occasional vacancies pupils enter in September.

Fees per term (2008-2009). The basic fee is £4,229 for pupils in the Preparatory Year (entry at 10+), and £4,343 for pupils in the Main School (11+ and above); this covers all charges except examination fees and lunch.

Scholarships and Bursaries. (*see Scholarship Entries section*). The Governors award Scholarships (on academic merit) at 11+, 13+ and 16+, and a number of Bursaries (according to parental means) to pupils entering the School at 11+, 13+ and 16+. Music, Art and Sports awards are also available.

Curriculum. The academic curriculum through to GCSE emphasises a proper balance between varied disciplines and range of intellectual experience, with all taking Maths, English, the three sciences and at least one modern language as part of 9 or 10 GCSE subjects. Maths GCSE may be taken early by able candidates. Full careers information and counselling are given, though pupils are encouraged to view academic pursuit as a desirable end in itself, using a profiling process to develop their commitment to study. In the Sixth Form, students choose at least 4 AS Level subjects in the First Year Sixth and 3 or more subjects for A Level, as well as undertaking a Research exercise, following a course on Questions of Value and Thinking and conferences on international themes. Almost 100% of the Sixth elect to proceed to higher education, including Oxford and Cambridge Universities.

Care. A pupil's form tutor is responsible for welfare and progress. Heads of Year coordinate the work of form tutors. There is a qualified nurse and a School Counsellor visits one day a week to support any pupils who do not feel they are fulfilling themselves in school. Parents' meetings are held annually and pupils receive two written reports per year, in addition to twice termly grade cards. Pastoral evenings are also held, where parents can discuss with each other and staff the difficulties and anxieties faced by young adults.

Games. The school Sports Ground is beautifully situated at Thames Ditton, by the River Thames opposite Hampton Court Palace. Kingston Grammar School prides itself on the large number of pupils who represent Great Britain in Hockey and Rowing.

Hockey (in both winter terms) and Rowing (all the year round) are 'main games'. Cricket (boys) and Tennis (girls) are the 'main games' in the summer. The School also has representative sides in Soccer, Athletics, Cross-Country, Shooting, Tennis and Netball.

Societies. A large number of School Societies provides for the interests of pupils of all ages. They range from Chess and Debating, to Natural History, Shooting and Young Enterprise. The Duke of Edinburgh's Award Scheme is popular and overseas travel is a regular feature of many activities. The Music Department has a vigorous programme of concerts and tours to such places as France, Germany, Canada and America.

Combined Cadet Force. The CCF is divided into Army and RAF Sections. A variety of activities ranging from shooting and flying to Outward Bound and Adventurous Training take place. Camps are held in school holidays and pupils attend courses in a variety of subjects. This is an entirely voluntary activity which pupils may take up in the Third Form.

Careers. The Careers Staff assist pupils in their choice of options at all levels, and give advice on possible future careers. They are in close touch with employers in professions, commerce and industry, and all fifth formers undertake a period of work experience after their GCSE examinations. An annual Careers Convention is held at the school. Particular attention is given to advice on entry to the Universities to which the majority of Sixth Form students go. The School is in membership of the Independent School Careers Organisation and pupils are able to take advantage of several computer assessment programs.

Parents' and Staff Association. The Association exists to further the interests of the School in the broadest possible way and does much to strengthen the links between staff, parents and students. The Sherriff Club (rowing), The Ditton Field Society (cricket, soccer, netball, tennis, hockey), Music Society, and Drama & Dance Society also support school activities.

The Old Kingstonian Association likewise does much to foster a spirit of unity and cooperation. All students are eligible to join on leaving the School.

Honours. An average of 8 or 9 places are gained each year at Oxbridge.

Charitable status. Kingston Grammar School is a Registered Charity, number 1078461, and a Company Limited by Guarantee, registered in England, number 3883748. It exists to enable children to adapt their talents to meet the needs of an ever changing world, whilst holding fast to the principles of self reliance, a sense of responsibility and a determination to seize opportunity.

Kingswood School

Lansdown Bath Somerset BA1 5RG
Tel: 01225 734210
Fax: 01225 734305
e-mail: enquiries@kingswood.bath.sch.uk
website: www.kingswood.bath.sch.uk

Kingswood is an independent, co-educational, Christian-based school represented on HMC. It was founded by John Wesley in 1748 and moved to its present 218-acre site overlooking Bath in 1851. Kingswood combines academic excellence with a concern for the development of each individual's talents. Boarders and day pupils are fully integrated within a happy and caring community environment. There are 644 pupils (366 boys and 278 girls) at the Senior School and 321 pupils at the Prep School.

Motto: *In via Recta Celeriter*

Chairman of the Governing Body: The Revd R Lansley

Hon Secretary to the Governors: Mr P Sadler, FCCA

***Headmaster*: Mr S A Morris**, MA

Senior Deputy Head: Mr G P Lloyd, MA, MSc

Deputy Head (*Academic*): Mrs S C Dawson, BEd

Deputy Head (*Pastoral*) & Chaplain: The Revd M L Wilkinson, MA

Bursar: Mr P Sadler, FCCA

Development Director: Ms A Carlton-Porter

Registrar: Mrs D W Patterson

Full-time Teaching Staff (Senior School):
Mr J C Allison, BEd
Mrs A L Baker, BA Hons, PGDip, PGCE
Mrs K J Barry, BA Hons, PGCE
Miss N J Beale, MA
Miss R J Bleathman, BA
Mrs L J Bradbury, BA, MA
Miss N E Brett, BSc Hons, PGCE
Mrs C Brown, BA Hons, PGCE
Mr S J Burgon, BEd, LTCL
Mr R E Burton, BSc
Miss A Y Conway, BSc Hons, PGCE
Mrs J Cook, CertEd
Miss A M Cooper, BSc Ed Hons
Mrs L J Court, BA, PGCE
Mrs S Cunliffe, CertEd
Mrs S Dakin, MA Hons, PGCE
Mr J W Davies, BA
Mr R J Duke, MA, PGCE
Dr M D Fletcher, PhD
Mr S J Forrester, MA, PGCE
Mrs S Fountain, MA
Mrs K E Fox, BA Hons, PGCE
Mr J R Garforth, MA, BSc
Mr A E Haines, BA
Mr D T Harding, BA
Mr J P Hills, BA Hons, PGCE
Mrs A Hirst, BA Hons, PGCE
Mr P J Hollywell, BA
Mr D P Hughes, BA Hons, PGCE
Mrs M Hutchison, MA, PGCE
Mrs D J Jenner, BA
Ms K Keen, BL, PGCE
Mr P P G MacDonald, BA Hons
Mr C J Main, BA Hons, PGCE
Mr R Mainwaring, BA, ALCM
Mrs J L Mainwaring, MA, PGCE
Mr J Matthews, BA
Mrs A Matthews, BSc, PGCE
Mr G J Musto, BSc, MPhil
Mr G D Opie, BEd
Mrs J R Opie, BA
Mrs M K Patterson, BSc, MSc, PGCE
Miss U J Paver, BA
Mr I J Prior, BA Hons, MTL
Mr C J Redman, BA, MEng, PGCE
Mr T P R Reeman, BA Hons, PGCE
Mr M Sealy, GRSM, FRCO CHM, ARCM
Mrs C M Sergeant, BA Hons, PGCE
Dr N M H Sheffrin, BSc, PhD
Ms B M Slevin, MA, PGCE
Mr S R Snowden, BA
Miss M E Telford, MA, PGCE
Mr W T Vaughan, BEng, PGCE
Mr M J Westcott, BEd
Mr C B Woodgate, MA
Miss A T Wright, BEd

Part-time Teaching Staff (Senior School):
Mrs F E Best, MA, CChem, MRSC
Mrs M L Brennan, BEd Hons
Mrs M L Brown, BSc
Mrs V Gibson, BSocSc, PGCE
Mrs L Heseltine, BA
Mrs S J Marshall, BA, PGCE
Mrs R H Murchison, BA Ed
Mrs J Reeman, BEd
Mrs R M Todd, BA Hons, PGCE
Mrs D Westcott, BEd

Kingswood Preparatory School

Headmaster: Mr M Cornah, CertEd

Deputy Head: Mr P Dixon, BEd Hons, MA(Ed), NPQH

Head of Pre-Prep: Mrs G Hull, MA, CertEd

Head of Foundation Stage: Mrs J Jones, CertEd

Housemaster, High Vinnalls: Mr P Titley, BEd Hons, BTec

Full-time Teaching Staff:
Miss C Breeze, BA Hons, PGCE
Mrs S Butcher, MA, PGCE
Miss S Caden, CertEd
Mrs K Caisley, BEd
Mr M Callahan, BScEcon Hons, PGCE
Mrs J Cook, CertEd
Mrs J Cross, BA, PGCE
Miss M Diaz, BA Hons, PGCE, TESOL
Mrs J Dix, BA Hons, PCGE
Miss K Elliott, BA Hons, MSc, PGCE
Mrs K Fox, BA Hons, PGCE
Mrs C Frey, CertEd
Miss S Gaskin, BSc Hons, PGCE
Mrs S Gilmore, BA QTS
Miss J Hammond, BA Hons, ITE Primary, BTec
Mrs S Higgins, BEd Hons
Mrs M McGlynn, BA Hons, PGCE
Mrs M Newman
Mr I Shrubsole, ASA
Mrs L Stokes, RTP/BA

Part-time Teaching Staff:
Mrs E Bennett, BTech
Mrs M Burke, RGN
Mr J Chitson, BSc, PGCE
Mrs C Cutter
Mrs S French, NNEB
Mrs J Gowans, NNEB
Mrs R Green, BEd Hons
Mrs A Hirst, BA Hons, ITE Primary, PGCE
Mrs C Holtam, CertEd
Mr J Hull
Mrs J Humphrey
Mrs E McKenzie
Mrs J Mason, BEd
Mrs E Masters, NNEB
Mrs S Moss, BTech
Miss S Paradise
Mrs Y Robinson
Mrs J Scott
Mrs K Simpson, NNEB
Mrs A Titley, BSc Hons, ACMA
Mrs I Turner, DAC Dip BS
Mrs C Ward, BSc, PGCE
Mrs H Ward, BA Hons, ATC
Mrs K Wilkinson
Mrs M Wright, BSEd

Visiting Music Staff (Senior & Prep):
Mr C Bissex, BA (*Voice*)
Mr A Bull (*Drums*)
Mrs C Burden (*Piano*)
Mrs S Burnett (*Recorder, Clarinet, Saxophone*)
Mr A Cheshire (*French Horn*)
Mrs T Dicker, LWCMD (*Cello*)
Mr R Dorrell, MA, BMus (*Brass*)
Mr A Foister (*Brass*)
Mrs V Hammond, GRSM, LRAM (*Oboe*)
Mr G Harrup, BA, LGSM (*Electric Guitar*)
Mrs J Hobbs, BMus, LRAM, LTCL (*Piano*)
Mrs C Hollywell (*Voice*)
Mr A Jenner, ALCM (*Guitar*)
Mr D Kniveton, BA, LTCL (*Flute*)
Mrs S Lane (*Piano*)

Miss N Lemmy (*Voice*)
Mrs V Miche (*Violin*)
Mr K Morgan (*Saxophone*)
Mrs J Phillips (*Voice*)
Mrs A Salamonsen, MMus (*Violin*)
Mrs L Sealy (*Voice*)
Mr J Scott (*Drums*)
Mr D Seymour, ARCM (*Piano*)
Mrs C Seymour (*Violin*)
Dr D V Shepard, BSc, PhD, PGDip, Mtpp (*Clarinet, Saxophone*)
Mr N Thorne, MA (*Piano*)
Mrs P J Wendzina, CertEd (*Piano*)
Mrs A Witton (*Piano*)

Medical Officer: Dr T J Harris, MD, MCh, MRCOG

Site and Buildings. Kingswood occupies 218 acres of superb parkland overlooking the world heritage City of Bath and within easy reach of the M4 and M5 motorways, as well as rail and air links. In addition to the beautiful main Victorian buildings, there is a state of the art Theatre, a spacious multi-roomed sixth-form centre, a series of specialist centres for ICT, DT, Art and a Music School with its own recording studio. All departments have well-resourced areas and the Mathematics Department and all but two of the eleven science laboratories have recently been refurbished. There are seven houses for boarding and day pupils, a beautiful Chapel and excellent sporting facilities, including a Sports Hall, indoor swimming pool, two floodlit astroturfs, and extensive playing fields. The School also has its own Prep School in a Georgian mansion and award-winning modern buildings in a separate section of the parkland. A brand new library was opened in September 2006.

Curriculum. Kingswood wants its students to develop lively, enquiring and well-informed minds and the high standard of attainment reached by its pupils has been highly praised. From 11 to 13 pupils follow a broad and balanced curriculum. Each pupil has a tutor to supervise progress and to offer advice and encouragement. At 14 the pupils choose at least eight and up to twelve GCSE subjects to develop their particular talents whilst maintaining a broad range of skills. They are also encouraged to develop independent learning plans which they work on with their tutors. Most sixth formers specialise in at least three or four subjects and all participate in a General Studies programme. Sixteen subjects are offered at GCSE level as well as over twenty at AS/A2 level, including Politics, Business Studies, Sports Studies, Theatre Studies and Critical Thinking.

Organisation. *Preparatory*: Kingswood draws its pupils from a wide variety of schools but it also has its own prep school for boarders and day pupils. Kingswood Prep School caters for c335 boys and girls between the ages of 3 and 11, and offers a variety of activities alongside the academic curriculum. A new boarding house for boys and girls aged 7–11 opened in September 1998. This "family-based" unit of c20 boarders is cared for by houseparents who also teach at the school. Children from the prep school are expected to move on to Kingswood but parents are advised if children are felt to be academically unsuitable for the Senior School.

Westwood: Kingswood operates a junior house for boys and girls aged 11–13. This is designed to settle new pupils into the school at 11+ or 12+ and provide the special environment that the younger pupils require before going into the senior houses. In effect, it means the pupils enjoy the atmosphere associated with a prep school whilst also enjoying all the facilities of a senior school. Sixth formers are specially selected to act as elder "brothers/sisters" and prefects to your younger pupils. The house is run by four resident house staff, together with assistant house staff.

Senior Houses: From the age of 13+ pupils are assigned to one of six houses, three for boys and three for girls, each under a resident Housemaster or Housemistress and assisted by other teaching staff. The houses ensure a good and friendly environment and there are also shared social areas in the centre of school. It would be normal to have c180–200 in the sixth form, which has its own special building.

Houses. The seven houses are all very distinctive and five are set within their own grounds. Emphasis is placed on creating a family atmosphere in each house and the pastoral care provided has been judged as exceptional. Tutors monitor each pupil's progress and welfare. The school has a number of houses and flats for single and married staff. Half of the staff at the senior school live on the campus which cultivates exceptionally good relationships between teachers and students.

Sports and Games. The sporting and leisure activities programmes have around 70 activities with particular emphasis on sport, drama, music, art and outdoor pursuits. Sporting activities include athletics, badminton, basketball, cricket, cross-country, fencing, golf, hockey, netball, rugby, swimming and tennis. Other activities range from the Duke of Edinburgh's Award Scheme to Computing, from Orienteering to Photography, and Bird Watching to Dance Express. Regular group activities in the instrumental field include orchestra, jazz band, string group and wind band. There are also junior and senior choirs and a large-scale choral society and an extensive performance programme. Over 50% of the school are involved in extra music lessons. At least four dramatic productions take place each year.

Health. The well-equipped School Medical Centre is under the supervision of a fully qualified resident Sister and the School Medical Officer.

Religious Activities. Kingswood welcomes pupils from all denominations. In addition to regular morning worship, there is a wide variety of guest speakers and the Christian Fellowship organises its own events. There are regular fund-raising activities for charities and a Community Service programme. Every year a joint Methodist-Anglican Confirmation service is held and there are special services in Bath Abbey for the whole school Carol Service and for Commemoration Day.

Careers. From the earliest possible age we encourage students to participate in all decisions affecting their future. Kingswood subscribes to the Independent Schools Careers Organisation and has links with local career guidance organisations. Our programme of work experience, followed by all members of Lower Sixth, is aimed at providing experience of the entire process of job application, interview and work itself, and we have established close links with local employers to make all this possible. For the ages 16 to 18 a programme of discussions with visiting employers is reinforced by personal guidance from the Sixth Form Tutor and the Head of Careers.

Leavers. It is normal for all of our Sixth Form pupils to go on to university courses, around 90% to the place of their first choice.

Fees per term (2008-2009). £3,475 (day), £6,469–£7,749 (full boarding), £5,651–£7,001 (weekly boarding).

TEFL teaching is provided for students who do not speak English as their first language – this is invoiced separately as required.

Entry Requirements. Entry is based on Kingswood's entrance examination, the report of the previous school and a personal interview. Candidates at 13+ may also enter by Common Entrance papers where spaces permit (priority to boarding applicants). Entry to the Sixth Form is by a minimum of six or more GCSE passes – four at Grade B plus two at Grade C, plus school report and interview. (Most applicants achieve more than the minimum entry grades.) There are normally around 25 places available due to the extended facilities available at Sixth Form level.

Scholarships. (*see Scholarship Entries section*). Academic and Special Talent scholarships of value up to a maximum of 50% of the full fees are available annually to pupils entering Years 7, 9 (boarders only) and Lower Sixth. Special Talent scholarships are awarded for excellence in a particular field such as music and sport. A number of bursaries are also awarded annually at the discretion of the Headmaster and the Governors. Further details of scholarships can be obtained from the Director of Admissions or on the school website.

Charitable status. Kingswood School is a Registered Charity, number 309148. Founded by John Wesley, it maintains its Methodist tradition in providing preparatory and secondary education.

Kirkham Grammar School

Ribby Road Kirkham Preston Lancashire PR4 2BH
Tel: 01772 671079
Fax: 01772 672747
e-mail: info@kirkhamgrammar.co.uk
website: www.kirkhamgrammar.co.uk

Kirkham Grammar School, founded in 1549, is a co-educational independent School of 990 pupils aged between 3 and 18. The Senior School of 700 pupils, 65 of whom are boarders, incorporates a Sixth Form of 170, and the Pre-School, Infants and Junior School for day pupils, with 290+ on roll, is housed in splendid purpose-built accommodation. The Headmaster is a member of HMC and a member of the Boarding Schools Association. The school fees are competitive; forces personnel are offered a reduction in the boarding element of the fees; scholarships, exhibitions and bursaries are available at 11+ and 16+. The recently refurbished Boarding House is pleasant and comfortable and is run under the personal supervision of the Boarding Housemaster and his wife, whose residence is attached to the boarding wing of the School.

As well as excellent academic results and a good Oxbridge entry record, Kirkham Grammar School prides itself on turning out rounded, well-balanced and confident young people, the vast majority of whom continue their education at University. The School has a strong Christian ethos, with an emphasis on care for the individual, traditional family values, good manners and sound discipline. It is a friendly close-knit community where staff and pupils work particularly closely together.

Sited amid 30 acres of its own grounds, Kirkham Grammar School boasts some excellent facilities, which include a large multi-purpose hall, a superb floodlit all-weather pitch, a Sixth Form Centre, an outstanding Technology Centre and Languages Centre, built in partnership with BAE SYSTEMS, and a magnificent Dining Complex. Most recently the School has built a new Science Centre alongside a new extended classroom block incorporating interactive facilities and also a new Performing Arts Centre.

An impressive range of extra-curricular activities is offered by a School renowned for its sporting prowess, but with strength across the board in music, art, drama, a strong and popular Combined Cadet Force Unit and a flourishing House System.

Chairman of Governors: Mr S Fulford-Brown

***Headmaster*: Mr D R Walker**, MA Cantab, PGCE

Deputy Headmaster: Dr R Luker, BA Hons, MA, PhD, PGCE

Deputy Head (Pastoral): Mrs J E Taylor, BA, CertEd, AdvDip SEN

Director of Studies & Head of Sixth Form: Mr A R Long, MA Oxon, PGCE

Senior Teacher: Mr R J Watson, BA Hons, PGCE

Director of ICT & Technology: Mr M J Hancock, BEd Hons, MA, MBA

Heads of Year:
Sixth Form: Mr A R Long, MA Oxon, PGCE
Assistant Heads of Sixth Form:
Mr M Gaddes, MA, PGCE
Mrs J Stanbury, BA Hons, PGCE
Middle School (Fourth & Fifth Years): Mr M A Whalley, BEd Hons, MEd
Assistant Head of Middle School: Mrs A Walker, BA, PGCE
Third Year: Mr S F Duncan, BA Hons
Second Year: Mrs D F Airey, BEd Hons, BDA, TEFL
First Year: Mrs K C O'Flaherty, BA Hons, PGCE

Heads of Departments:
Art: Mr S P Gardiner, BA Hons
Biology: Mrs M E Scott, BSc Hons, PGCE
Business Studies: Mrs F M Lang, BA Hons, PGCE
Design & Technology: Mr D Gardner, BEng, PGCE
Drama: Ms J E Barrie, BA Hons, PGCE
English: Mr C J Hawkes, BA Hons, MA, PGCE
Geography: Mr I M Scott, BA Hons, PGCE (*also OC CCF*)
History: Mr T P Miller, BA Hons, PGCE
ICT: Mr R J Browning, BSc Hons, ACCE, PGCE
Latin: Mrs S P Long, BA Hons, PGCE
Learning Support: Mrs D F Airey, BEd Hons, BDA, TEFL
Librarian: Mrs C Copland, ALA
Mathematics: Miss S R Howe, BSc, PGCE
Modern Foreign Languages: Mr W R McDowell, BA Hons, PGCE
Director of Music: Mr A C Barratt, BA Hons, GRSM, LRAM, MTC
Director of Physical Education & Games: Mr M A Whalley, BEd Hons, MEd
Girls' Physical Education & Games: Mrs K H Benter, BEd
Physics: Mr M Gaddes, MA, PGCE
Politics: Mr M P Melling, BA Hons, MA Ed, PGCE
Psychology: Mrs J Stanbury, BA Hons, PGCE
Religious Studies: Mr A E Trenhaile, BA Hons, PGCE
Science & Chemistry: Dr A C Hall, PhD, Grad RIC

Houses & Housemistresses/Housemasters:
Kirkham House: Mrs J M Glover, BEd Hons
Fylde House: Mr P T Reeves, BSc Hons, PGCE
School House: Mr M Marmion, BEd, MA (*Head of Boarding*)
Preston House: Dr A B Rollins, BSc Hons, PhD, PGCE (*Health & Safety Officer*)

Bursar: Mrs C E Brown

Headmaster's PA/Registrar: Mrs C M Seed

Matron: Mrs D Heyes

Junior School:
Headmistress of Junior School: Mrs A S Roberts, BEd
Deputy Headmaster: Mr B Edgar, BEd
Head of Infant Department: Mrs P Edgar BEd Hons
Nursery Manager: Mrs C Lawton, NNEB

Headmistress's Secretaries: Mrs M Horrocks, Mrs A Giddings

Aims. The School's academic aim is to encourage pupils to extend themselves to achieve the best results of which they are capable in order to acquire the necessary qualifications for entry to higher education or the career they wish to follow. Outside the academic sphere, our objective is to introduce pupils to as wide a range as possible of cultural, sporting and creative activities and to encourage them to participate in those which appeal to them. The School aims to foster an ethos which encourages leadership, self discipline, good manners, cheerful, friendly and supportive relationships and to promote Christian teaching and values within the framework of 'one family'.

Academic Programme. The courses lead to GCSE, A Level and AS Level. In the first three years, the basic subjects studied are English, French, Mathematics, German, Geography, History, Physics, Chemistry, Biology, Music, Art, Drama, ICT, Design and Technology, and Religious Studies. The first stage of specialisation takes place on entering the fourth form where the core subjects of English, Mathematics, Physics/Chemistry/Biology and French/German are taught in sets, and there is a further choice of subjects from three option blocks, which include: Art, Design and Technology (Product Design; Graphic Products; Systems), Music, Business Studies, Drama, Geography, History, ICT, Religious Studies, German, Latin and Physical Education.

In the Sixth Form, A and AS Level subjects are chosen from the following: English, Maths, Further Maths, Biology, Chemistry, Physics, French, German, Art, Music, Design Technology, Geography, History, Psychology, ICT, Politics, Theatre Studies, Religious Studies, Business Studies, Physical Education, Electronics (AS only).

In addition all Sixth Formers follow a programme of General Studies and many voluntarily continue in the CCF and/or take up the Duke of Edinburgh's Award, Young Enterprise or Community Service. Extra tuition is provided for Oxbridge candidates.

Sport. The School has a long and strong sporting tradition and offers the following sports: Rugby, hockey, cricket, athletics, tennis, netball, badminton, squash, swimming and rounders.

Music. There is a very active musical life at the School, with regular Concerts both at lunchtime and in the evening, providing a platform for the Orchestra, Ensembles and Soloists. The School is noted for its fine Choral traditions.

Other Activities. There is a strong Combined Cadet Force contingent, with Army and RAF sections. A large number of societies cater for a wide range of interests including drama, debating, Duke of Edinburgh's Award, chess, animal ark, public speaking, German, Italian, philately, climbing, French, Internet and music. A comprehensive careers service is available through the Careers Teachers. The School is an active member of ISCO and is also served by Careerlink.

Admission to Senior School. Four form entry. Pupils are usually admitted at 11 years after passing the entrance examination held in January each year. Admissions to the School in other year groups, especially the Sixth Form, are possible. Day/Boarding applications should be made to the Headmaster who will be glad to provide further details.

Fees per term (2008-2009). Day (excluding lunches): £2,720 (Senior School), £2,040 (Junior School), £2,040 (Pre School).

These Fees cover tuition, use of class, text and library books, school stationery, scientific equipment, games apparatus.

Senior School Boarding (in addition to the Day fee): £2,215 (full boarding); £2,104 (weekly boarding).

Scholarships and Bursaries. The School offers an impressive number of Scholarships, Exhibitions and Bursaries which are detailed in a Scholarship Booklet available from the Registrar.

Junior School (3–11 years). The Junior School, which comprises a Pre-School, an Infant Department and a Junior Department, is an integral part of the School under the same Board of Governors. The work is organised in close consultation with the Senior School to ensure that education in its broadest sense is continuous and progressive from the age of 3 to 18.

The curriculum is broadly based and balanced. The core subjects: English, Maths and Science will be given priority as set in the National Curriculum. History, Geography, RE, Music, ICT, Design and Technology, PE and Games will be studied as pure subjects and also as they relate to one another in a cross-curricular manner.

Application should be made direct to the Junior School Secretary, from whom a separate prospectus may be obtained.

Old Kirkhamians Association. For further details contact the Development Manager.

Charitable status. The Kirkham Educational Foundation is a Registered Charity, number 526721. The object of the Charity shall be the provision in or near Kirkham of a day and boarding school for boys and girls.

Lancing College

A Woodard School

Lancing West Sussex BN15 0RW
Tel: 01273 452213
Fax: 01273 464720
e-mail: admissions@lancing.org.uk
website: www.lancingcollege.co.uk

Founded in 1848 by the Revd Nathaniel Woodard, Lancing College is the first of the Schools of the Woodard Foundation.

Motto: *Beati mundo corde.*

Governing Body:
The Provost and the Directors of Lancing College Ltd

Visitor: The Rt Revd The Lord Bishop of Chichester

Governing Body:
Chairman: R M Reeve, MA

S J O Gurney, FCA
N A O Bennett, MA
D L Godfray, FCII
G Wedlake, LLB
Dr H O Brunjes, BSc, MB BS, DRCOG
Prof M M Edwards, JP, BSc, PhD
P Bowden, LLM
R H Stapleton, FRICS
The Rt Revd L G Urwin, OGS
Professor H Smith
Mrs J L Robinson, BA, PGCE
C P Baron, MA, LLM
I Maxwell-Scott

Bursar and Clerk to the Governing Body: Mrs P Bulman, FCA

***Head Master*: J W J Gillespie**, MA

Second Master: J S McCullough, MA
Deputy Head: Mrs H R Dugdale, MA
Assistant Head (*Pastoral*): D E Austin, BSc
Assistant Head (*Director of Studies*): S W Cornford, MA, PhD
President of the Common Room:
Registrar and Director of Marketing: R J Tomlinson, MA
Director of Extra-Curricular Activities: C P Foster, MA
Chaplain: The Revd Roger Marsh, BD, MA, AKC, CertEd
Director of Development: I R McLean, CFRE

Assistant Staff:
A D B Arnold, MA (*Classics, PSHE*)
D E Austin, BSc (*Physics*)
T S Auty, BA (*Photography, Art*)
D G Barker, MA, PhD (*Head of Classics*)
A J Betts, BA, PhD, MIL (*French*)
A K Black, MA, BLitt (*English*)
N A Brookes, MSc (*Mathematics*)
A M Chappell, BSc (*Biology, Chemistry*)
A R Coakes, BA, MSc (*Design & Technology*)
D S Connolly, BA (*History, Classical Civilisation*)
S W Cornford, MA, PhD (*English*)
D N Cox, MA, FRCO, FTCL, LRAM, ARCM (*Joint Head of Music*)
C P E Crowe, BEd (*Director of Sport*)
P Dale, MSc, MIBiol (*Head of Biology*)
D G Davies, BA, ALCM (*Head of Spanish*)
M F Day, BSc, PhD, MIBiol (*Biology*)

C J Doidge, MA (*French, Spanish*)
Miss N C Dragonetti, BA (*Music*)
Mrs H R Dugdale, MA (*English, PSHE*)
J R J East, BSc (*Mathematics*)
C P Foster, MA (*Head of Geography*)
J A Grime (*Geography*)
D J Harman, MA (*English*)
Ms J Hayward-Voss, BA (*Head of Business Studies*)
Miss K Holden, BSc (*Design & Technology*)
Miss L Jakubikova (*Spanish, French, Italian*)
P D Kennedy, MA , PhD (*Physics*)
D A Kerney, MA, PhD (*Head of History*)
M Kuhn, BA, MES (*German, Italian*)
Mrs K Lindfield, HND (*Art*)
D N Mann, BSSc (*Head of PE, Biology*)
Mrs S D Marchant, BA, MCLIP (*Librarian*)
The Revd R P Marsh, BD, MA, AKC (*RS , Classics*)
Mrs M A Martindale, MA, MLitt (*English*)
T J Meierdirk, BFA (*Head of Design & Technology*)
J S McCullough, MA (*Mathematics*)
C Metcalf, DLC (*PE, Mathematics*)
Miss M R Mitchell (*French, Spanish*)
C M Mole, BSc (*PE, PSHE*)
Mrs C R Mole (*Economics, Business Studies*)
I Morgan-Williams, GMus, RNCM (*Joint Head of Music*)
S R Norris, BSc, PhD (*Chemistry*)
Mrs C E Palmer, MA (*History*)
M S W Palmer, BA, PhD, MIL (*Head of Modern Languages, German, Italian*)
Miss C M Parkinson, BA (*English, History, RS, PSHE*)
P G Polden, BSc, PhD (*Mathematics*)
G A Preston, BSc, PhD (*Head of Science, Physics*)
Miss C M Pringle, BA (*Head of Art*)
P C Richardson, MA (*Head of RS, Drama, History*)
O R Ridley, BA (*Head of English*)
Mrs H M Robinson, BSc (*Chemistry*)
G S Sampson, MA (*Head of French*)
Mrs J M Scullion, BA (*Learning Support*)
J L Sherrell, MA (*Head of Economics*)
M J H Smith, BA (*Head of Drama, Religious Studies*)
Ms H A Stevenson, BLib, MCLIP (*Assistant Librarian*)
Mrs A Stone (*PE*)
Mrs J O Such, MA, MSc (*Head of Mathematics*)
Mrs W A Swarbrick, MSc (*Physics, Chemistry*)
Mrs A W Tritton, BSc, MA, FRGS (*Geography, PSHE*)
Miss K E Vaughan, BA (*Art*)
S J Ward, MMath, MPhil (*Mathematics*)
J J Whitton, MA, BBusSc (*Economics, Mathematics*)
M W Wilkes, BA (*Biology*)
D J Wilks, MA (*History*)
A P Williamson, MA (*Head of Chemistry*)

Houses & Housemasters/mistresses:

Boys:
Head's: Mr A M Chappell
Second's: Mr D S Connolly
School: Dr A J Betts
Gibbs': Mr M J H Smith
Teme: Dr S R Norris

Girls:
Field's: Mrs H R Dugdale
Sankey's: Miss N C Dragonetti
Manor: Mrs A Stone
Handford (*Sixth Form*): Mrs C E Palmer

Head Master's Secretary: Mrs H L Betts, BSc
Admissions Officer: Mrs G S Prichard
OL Development Officer and OL Secretary: Catherine Reeve, BA

Medical Officers:
Dr N S Lyons, MB BS
Dr R M MacLintock, MB BS, FRCGP, DRCOG
Dr H Bentley, MB BS, MRCGP, DA, DRCOG
Dr C Huckstep, MB BS, DRCOG, DCH

There are about 510 pupils in the school, accommodated in nine houses.

Location. The School stands on a spur of the Downs, overlooking the sea to the south and the Weald to the north, in grounds of some 550 acres, which include the College Farm.

By train, Lancing is 10 minutes from Brighton, 30 minutes from Gatwick Airport and 75 minutes from central London.

Buildings and Facilities. The main school buildings, faced with Sussex flint, are grouped around two quadrangles on the lines of an Oxford or Cambridge College.

The great Chapel, open to visitors every day, has the largest rose window built since the Middle Ages.

The College has extensive laboratories, a purpose-built Music School, a theatre, which was completely refurbished in 2004, and a modern Design and Technology Centre with computerised design and engineering facilities. There are over 330 private studies for boys and girls, many of which are study-bedrooms. There is a sports hall, indoor swimming pool and a miniature shooting range. Sporting facilities also include Squash and Fives courts and an all-weather surface and full-sized astroturf hockey pitch. A new library and information centre was opened in March 2000, a new girls' boarding house in September 2002 and a girls' day house in September 2006.

Admission. Boys and girls are normally admitted at the beginning of the Autumn Term in their fourteenth year. Admission is made on the result of either the Entrance Scholarship, the Common Entrance Examination or by private testing. A registration fee of £75 is paid when a child's name is entered in the admission register. Entries should be made via the Registrar, who will assign a House, following as far as possible the wishes of the parents. After a pupil has joined the School, parents usually correspond with the Housemaster or Housemistress directly.

Sixth Form Entry. Applications for entry should be made to the Registrar. Testing takes place in November or by private arrangement.

Curriculum. Designed as far as possible to suit every pupil's potential, the curriculum provides the training required for entry to the Universities and to a wide range of professions.

In a pupil's first three years the curriculum provides a broad, balanced education without premature specialisation. The total of subjects taken at GCSE is limited to about nine or ten, the object being to promote excellence in whatever is studied and to lay firm foundations for the Sixth Form years.

The following subjects are studied in the Lower School: English Language and Literature, Religious Knowledge, Mathematics, Physics, Chemistry, Biology, French, Spanish or German, Geography, History, Physical Education, Music, Art, Design and Technology, Latin or Classical Civilisation, Greek and Drama.

In the Sixth Form there is a choice of 24 subjects which can be studied to A or AS level, together with a General Studies course in the Lower Sixth.

A close connection has been established with schools in Germany and Spain, with which individual and group exchanges are arranged.

Tutorial System. In addition to their Housemaster or Housemistress there are pastoral Tutors attached to each House, and each pupil chooses another member of staff as an Academic Tutor at the end of the first year at the College. The Academic Tutors' main functions are to supervise academic progress and to encourage general reading and worthwhile spare time activities. A pupil keeps the same Tutor until he or she moves into the Sixth Form, where this function is taken over by an Academic Tutor chosen from one of the specialist teachers.

Music and Art form an important part of the education of all pupils. There is a large number of orchestras, bands, ensembles and choirs. Organ and Choral awards to Oxford and Cambridge and Colleges of Music are frequently won. There is a full programme of extra-curricular **Drama**. A new **Art School** opened in Autumn 2008. The **Design and Technology** Centre, adjacent to the Science School, provides for a wide range of technical and creative work.

Other Activities. Boys and girls in their first year are given the opportunity to sample the many activities on offer at the College. A well-organised extra-curricular programme is followed by all pupils, under the supervision of the Director of Extra-Curricular Activities.

Participation in extra-curricular activities is strongly encouraged and there is a vast range on offer. Up to twelve plays are produced each year and pupils are able to write and perform their own plays and to learn stagecraft.

In the Advent term the main sports are Association Football for boys and Hockey for girls; in the Lent term Football and Hockey for boys and Netball for girls. Squash, Fives, Badminton, Basketball, Cross Country and Shooting (the College has indoor and open ranges) take place during both terms for boys and girls. Some Rugby is played in the Lent term. Cricket, Tennis, Sailing, Athletics, Rounders and Swimming (indoor heated pool) take place in the Summer term.

There is a CCF contingent (with Army and RAF sections) and the School takes part in the Duke of Edinburgh's Award scheme. There is also a flourishing Social Service group, which works in the local community. Pupils help to run a small farm (including sheep, goats, pigs, alpacas and chickens) under the supervision of the Farm Manager.

Links have been established with local industries and pupils are involved in business experience through the Young Enterprise scheme.

Careers and Higher Education. A member of staff is responsible for careers and there is a well equipped Careers Library. Over 98% of pupils go on to Universities, and about 10% to Oxford and Cambridge. Careers lectures and visits are arranged throughout the year, and pupils also attend work experience courses arranged by the Independent Schools Careers Organisation.

Scholarships and Exhibitions. (*see Scholarship Entries section*). Candidates for the following awards must be under 14 years of age on 1st September in the year of the examination. The age of the candidate is taken into account in making awards. A candidate may enter for more than one type of award, and account may be taken of musical or artistic proficiency in a candidate for a non-musical award; but no one may hold more than one type of award, except in an honorary capacity.

(1) A number of Open Scholarships ranging in value from £1,000 per year to half of the annual boarding fee.
(2) Three or four Music Scholarships ranging in value up to half the annual boarding fee. Scholarships may be offered to pupils from schools where the time for Music is less than in some others, and where a candidate may have less musical experience but greater potential.
    One Professor W K Stanton Music Scholarship of up to half the boarding fee for a Chorister from Salisbury Cathedral School, or failing that any Cathedral School. A Stanton Exhibition may also be awarded.
(3) A number of scholarships in Art, Drama and Sport, ranging in value up to a quarter of the annual boarding fee.
(4) A number of Ken Shearwood Awards, ranging in value up to a fifth of the annual boarding fee, are made to pupils of all-round ability and potential who have made outstanding contributions to their present schools.

Entry Forms for Academic, Art, Music, Drama, Sport and All-Rounder (Ken Shearwood) awards are obtainable from the Admissions Officer, Lancing College, Lancing, West Sussex BN15 0RW. These forms must be returned to her with a photocopy of the candidate's birth certificate.

Sixth Form Awards (Boys and Girls). Scholarships are available for new entrants to the Sixth Form with special proficiency in Academic Subjects or Music. There is also one Organ Scholarship. The candidate's general ability to contribute to the life of a boarding school community will also be taken into account. A small number of Scholarships is also available internally on the strength of GCSE results.

The value of all Entrance Scholarships may be augmented by bursaries up to a maximum of two-thirds of the annual fee, according to parental circumstances.

Fees per term (2008-2009). Boarding £8,570 (£25,710 per annum). Day £5,950 (£17,850 per annum).

The School Fees, which cover all obligatory extras, including medical attention, are payable termly in advance. The only other items of expense are purely optional extras, books, and charges of a strictly personal character.

A scheme exists for the payment in advance of a single composition fee to cover a pupil's education during his/her time in the School. Particulars may be obtained from the Bursar.

Charitable status. Lancing College is a Registered Charity, number 1076483. It exists to provide education for boys and girls.

Latymer Upper School

King Street Hammersmith London W6 9LR
Tel: 0845 638 5800
Fax: 020 8748 5212
e-mail: registrar@latymer-upper.org
website: www.latymer-upper.org

The Latymer Foundation owes its origin to the will of Edward Latymer, dated 1624. It is a Day School of 1,080 pupils, of whom 340 are in the co-educational Sixth Form. The School moved to full co-education in September 2004, with entry at 11+ for girls as well as boys.

There are also 165 pupils in the co-educational Latymer Prep School which shares the same grounds. (*Please see entry in IAPS section.*)

Chairman of Governors: Professor R N Perham, MA, PhD, ScD, FRS

Co-opted Governors:
Mrs R Caleb-Landy
I S Elliott, Esq, BA
Dr W A D Griffiths, MB, MA, BChir, MD, FRCP
J Graham, Esq, MA Cantab
S Hodges, Esq, MA
Ms R Radcliffe, CBE, MA, MPhil, FIMC
Mrs S Salmon, BA, FCIPD
Wm C Smith, Esq, OBE, JP
B J Southcott, Esq, BSc, AIIMR, ASI
P Taylor, Esq, BSc
T A Woolley, Esq, MA
N L Woolner, Esq, DipArch, RIBA, ARAIA, FRSA
J Wotton, Esq, MA

Ex officio Governor: The Revd Simon Downham, LLB, DipMin, MA

Clerk to the Governors: S Porter, Esq

***Head*: P J Winter**, MA Wadham College Oxford

Deputy Heads:
A L Hirst, MA Fitzwilliam College Cambridge (*Premises and Resources*)
A R Matthews, BA Sidney Sussex College Cambridge (*Academic*)
Miss A Tomlinson, BSc University College Cardiff, MA Open University (*Staff Welfare and Development*)

Assistant Heads:
C D Chivers, MA King's College Cambridge (*Sixth Form*)
K Spencer, BSc Hull, MA Cincinnati, USA (*Middle School*)
Mrs N Varma, BSc, MSc Warwick (*Lower School*)
R B Niblett, BA Liverpool (*Co-curricular*)

Heads of Year:
M G Holmes, BA Bristol (*Head of Upper Sixth*)
Mrs S J Markowska, BA Westfield College London (*Head of Lower Sixth*)
J Payne, BSc Auckland (*Head of Year 11*)
Ms C-M Goldsworthy, BA Aberystwyth, Duncan of Jordanstone School of Art (*Head of Year 10*)
Ms G Attenborough-Cox, MA St Andrews (*Head of Year 9*)
Mrs R B Field, BSc Canterbury NZ (*Head of Year 8*)
G Cooper, BSc Port Elizabeth SA (*Head of Year 7*)

Assistant Staff:

Art & Design:
D Mumby, BA Wolverhampton (*Head of Art & Design*)
Miss J Clarke, BA Canterbury
D Flynn, BDes Visual Dublin, MA Brighton
Ms J Hillis-Maidment, BA Exeter College of Art, MA London Institute
Ms C-M Goldsworthy, BA Aberystwyth, Duncan of Jordanstone School of Art (*Head of Year 10*)

Biology:
Miss S Bishop, BSc Massey University NZ (*Head of Biology*)
J Bossé, BSc, BEd Moncton University, New Brunswick, Canada
Mrs Z Brown, BA St Anne's College Oxford
G M Hardy, BSc Cardiff, PhD Emmanuel College Cambridge
Mrs R O'Brien, BA Jesus College Cambridge
N R Orton, JP, BSc London, CBiol, FLS, MIBiol
Ms C Hopley, BSc Cape Town SA

Chemistry:
B Chaplin, BSc Portsmouth, PhD Reading (*Head of Science*)
J M Beyers, BSc, BEng Stellenbosch SA, BEd Cape Town
Miss H Davis, MSc University College London
E Forbes, MSc Edinburgh
R Savva, BSc Bedford College London
Dr D Shah, BSc University College London, DPhil Oxford
M J Teskey, BSc Birmingham

Classics:
M Lewis, BA Durham (*Head of Classics*)
Mrs B M Dutrieu, BA Cardiff
M G Holmes, BA Bristol (*Head of Upper Sixth*)
Miss K Playfair, BA Christ's College Cambridge
M J Smith, MA Sidney Sussex College Cambridge

Design & Technology:
J Clark, DipTech, MA Brunel (*Head of Design & Technology*)
D Baker, BArch Newcastle
Miss S Ip, BA De Montfort
Ms J Selby, BA Sir John Cass School of Art

Economics & Business Studies:
M Wallace, BSc Birmingham (*Head of Economics & Business Studies*)
C Ben Nathan, BA Exeter, MBA Middlesex
N Sennett, BA Reading
Miss A Tomlinson, BSc University College Cardiff, MA Open University (*Deputy Head*)

Computing/IT:
M D Chandler, MEd Tech Brunel (*Head of Computing & IT*)
Mrs J Price, BA Huddersfield
M Shields, BSc Warwick

Drama:
J Joseph, BA London (*Director of Drama*)
Miss S Boulton, BA, MA Central School of Speech and Drama
Ms S Fowler, BA Aberystwyth

English:
Mrs R Babuta, BA King's College London, MLitt St John's College Oxford (*Head of English*)
Mrs S M T Adams, BA Birmingham, MA Surrey
T Biddle, BA Queens' College Cambridge, MA King's College London
C D Chivers, MA King's College Cambridge (*Assistant Head Sixth Form*)
B Cooper, BA, MPhil, PhD Downing College Cambridge
Mrs C Douglas, BA Warwick
Mrs S J Markowska, BA Westfield College London (*Head of Upper Sixth*)
A Merchant, BA Lady Margaret Hall Oxford
W Newhouse, BA Exeter, MA Sussex
Ms A Smith, BA Sidney Sussex College Cambridge

Geography:
M C Ashby, MSc King's College London, FRGS (*Head of Geography*)
Miss E Coates, BA St Edmund Hall Oxford
Ms G Attenborough-Cox, MA St Andrews
A L Hirst, MA Fitzwilliam College Cambridge (*Deputy Head*)
K Spencer, BSc Hull, MA Cincinnati, USA (*Assistant Head Middle School*)
J A Wilson, BA Open University (*Examinations Officer*)

History & Political Studies:
J White, MA Selwyn College Cambridge (*Head of History*)
B J Bladon, BA King's College London
J P Foynes, BA, MA King's College London
J S Gilbert, MA Wadham College Oxford (*Head of Politics*)
Ms L Harding-Wyatt, BA Warwick
R Holder, MA Sussex
S Hole, BA Trinity Hall Cambridge
A R Matthews, BA Sidney Sussex College Cambridge (*Deputy Head*)
R N Orme, MA Gonville & Caius College Cambridge (*Head of History of Art*)

History of Art:
R N Orme, MA Gonville & Caius College Cambridge (*Head of History of Art*)
Ms A Ford, BA Christ's College Cambridge, MA Courtauld Insititute London

Learning Support:
Ms J Heywood, BSc LSE
Ms C Ellis, BA Sussex

Mathematics:
P MacMahon, BA Emmanuel College Cambridge, MSc Open University (*Head of Mathematics*)
Mrs N Alishaw, BSc Kent, MSc Imperial College London
Miss T Andrew, BA Mansfield College Oxford
S Cheung, BSc Imperial College London, MSc University College London
G Cooper, BSc Port Elizabeth SA (*Head of Year 7*)
Mrs R B Field, BSc Canterbury NZ (*Head of Year 8*)
M Finnemore, BSc Imperial College London
Mrs M Kazi-Fornari, MA Hertford College Oxford
Dr R Nanayakkara, PhD Imperial College London, MMath Warwick
J Payne, BSc Auckland (*Head of Year 11*)
O J Rose, BSc Queen Mary College London
Mrs N Varma, BSc, MSc Warwick

Modern Languages:
A J Rees, BA Swansea (*Head of Modern Languages*)
Mrs C Amodio-Johnson Lecce

Mrs M Bell, BA Southampton, MA London (*Head of Spanish*)
D Gysin, BA King's College London
Mrs C Healy, BA Durham (*Head of German*)
Mrs A-C Hetherington, MA Robinson College Cambridge
Mrs G Gauthier, BA Université Paul Valéry, Montpellier
Ms D Kendall, BA Leeds
Mrs S-A Parra, BA Liverpool, MA Surrey
M Russell, BA St Catherine's College Oxford
S N Ware, MA Brasenose College Oxford, MBA South Bank (*Head of Careers*)
Miss K Whiting, BA Durham
Srta V Rodriguez de Nova, BA Universidad Autónoma Madrid, MA Birkbeck

Music:
T Henwood, MA Exeter College Oxford, ARCO, FRSA (*Director of Music*)
P Drumm, BMus Bangor, MA York, DPhil Sussex
M Laflin, BA Keble College Oxford
R B Niblett, BA Liverpool

Physical Education & Games:
P Kirk, BSc Loughborough (*Head of PE & Games*)
P Gibson, BA Wolverhampton (*Head of Soccer*)
Ms T Hill, BEd Massey University NZ
K Paradise, MSc Brunel
Miss R Rank, BSc Exeter
Ms H Taylor, BSc Cheltenham & Gloucester College (*Head of Girls' PE & Games*)

Physics:
Dr J Rogers, BSc, MSc Bristol, PhD Cranfield Institute (*Head of Physics*)
J Hunt, BSc Manchester
J Ryan, BSc, MSc Queen Mary College London
M Twomey, MEng Bristol
S Whitehead, BSc University of Western Sydney

Religious Studies & Philosophy:
K Noakes, MA Corpus Christi College Cambridge, MA Theol Manchester (*Head of Religious Studies & Philosophy*)
Ms M Pyne, BA King's College London
Ms A Strhan, BA King's College Cambridge, MA Sussex
Ms L Summers, BA Bristol
P Wizonski, BA King's College London, MA London

Language Assistants:
Mme V Brian, Université de Rouen
Mlle H Butz, Université de Lille
Herr R Diesel, Technische Universität Berlin
Srta V Rodriguez de Nova, BA Universidad Autónoma Madrid
Snr J Soldevila

Visiting Music Staff:
P Jacobs, ARAM, LRAM, ARCM, ARCO, GRSM (*Head of Keyboard*)
Miss M Sugars, GBSM (*Head of Woodwind and Brass*)
R Thompson-Clarke, BA, Dip RS (*Head of Strings*)
Ms L Abbott, BMus, LTCL (*Violin & Viola*)
Ms R Biggins, BA (*Saxophone*)
Ms R Buxton, BMus RCM, LGSM (*Clarinet*)
G Caldecott, GRNCM (*Piano*)
S Coleman, MMus (*Electric & Bass Guitar*)
Ms M Drower, ARCM (*Singing*)
Ms R Fuller (*Piano*)
S Gibson, BMus (*Percussion*)
G Hunt (*Piano*)
Ms P Ismay, ARCM (*Clarinet*)
Ms G James (*Double Bass*)
Miss F Jellard, BA (*Singing*)
S Kalonaris, GRSM (*Electric & Bass Guitar*)
C Lacey, LRAM (*Flute*)
T Marsden, BMus (*Percussion*)
Ms C Philpot, ARCM (*Oboe*)
D Porter-Thomas (*Singing*)
D Prophet, BA, AD WCMP, PG Dip RCM (*Trombone*)
C Ramirez, ARCM (*Guitar*)
Miss S Rose, GRSM, ARCM, LGSM (*Piano*)
G Ross, BA Cantab (*Piano*)
H Rowntree, BMus RCM (*Trumpet*)
Ms J Snell, LRAM (*Violin & Viola*)
Miss J Staniforth, GRSM, LRAM (*Bassoon*)
Ms O Travers, BA, LRAM (*Piano*)
Miss A Whittlesea, BMus, LRAM (*Recorder*)
C Wood, LRAM, ARCM (*Piano*)

Administrative Staff:
Finance Director: J Tyrwhitt, MA, FCA
Facilities Manager: T Fisher
Head's Secretary: Ms E Curlet
Registrar: Mrs C Sutherland-Hawes
Theatre Manager: J Vernon
Office Manager: Mrs C Kava
Network Administrator: D Stanford, BSc
Librarian: C E Appleton, ALA
School Doctor: M Kaplan, MBBS, MRCGP, DPD, DFFP, LRCP, MRCS
School Nurse: Mrs J Wilson, RGN

Co-education. Latymer's Sixth Form has been co-educational since 1996. 11+ entry is open to girls and boys.

Admissions. This is by competitive examination and interview at 11 and 13. Past papers are published and sent to those who register. Details of Open Days and Entry are obtainable from the Registrar. Entry to the Sixth Form is based on interview and conditional offers at GCSE.

Preparatory School. Pupils sit the 11+ Entrance Exam for the Upper School from Latymer Prep School. (*For further details see entry in IAPS section.*)

Fees per term (2008-2009). £4,490.

Scholarships. (*see Scholarship Entries section*). A substantial number of Scholarships and Awards are available in addition to substantial means-tested Bursaries.

Curriculum. A full range of academic subjects is offered at GCSE and AS and A2 Level. Languages include French, German, Spanish and Italian (European Work Experience and exchanges are run every year), Latin and Greek. Science is taught as separate subjects by subject specialists from Year 7. Form sizes in the Lower School of around 22 and smaller teaching group sizes ensure the personal attention of staff.

Pastoral Care. The School has a strong tradition of excellent pastoral care. There are three Divisions (Lower School, Middle School, Sixth Form) and each Division is led by an Assistant Head. A Head of Year is responsible for the pupils in each year. Teams of Form Tutors deliver a coherent PSHE programme which promotes involvement in the community, charity work, and the personal, social and academic development of the Form.

Sixth Form. The large co-educational Sixth Form offers around thirty-five A Level choices; students opt to take four or five subjects at AS and three or four at A2 Level. Students have the opportunity to undertake work experience in Paris or Berlin and receive extensive Careers and Higher Education guidance. All students expect to go on to University or Art College; more than 1 in 10 go to Oxbridge each year. The Sixth Form has use of new Common Room facilities as well as a University and Careers Centre.

Music and Drama. These activities play a large part in the life of the School. The Latymer Arts Centre houses music practice rooms and a 300-seat Theatre in addition to increased facilities for Art. In April 2008 a new Performing Arts Centre opened housing a 100-seat recital hall, music classrooms and more practice rooms and a dance/drama studio. There are several orchestras and bands and two major concerts each term.

There are five major drama productions each year, and opportunities for all pupils to perform in events.

Sport. There are excellent facilities for sport. The School has a Boat House on site with direct river access, as well as a large sports hall and an indoor swimming pool in the grounds. There are playing fields at Wood Lane near the BBC (recently redeveloped to include a new pavilion and changing rooms and an all-weather, floodlit playing surface). The emphasis is on involvement, participation and choice. School teams enjoy great success in the major sports of rugby, soccer, netball, hockey, rowing, cricket and athletics. Other sports such as karate, swimming and golf cater for individual interests. The School maintains excellent fixture lists for all major sports.

Extra-Curricular Activities. There is a wide range of clubs and societies at lunch time and after school. In addition, every pupil has the opportunity to have residential experience and to take part in outdoor pursuits as part of the annual School Activities Week. A very active Parents' Gild ensures that nobody is excluded from an activity for financial reasons. The Duke of Edinburgh's Award Scheme flourishes with a number of students achieving the Gold Award each year.

Charitable status. The Latymer Foundation is a Registered Charity, number 312714. It exists to provide education for children.

The Grammar School at Leeds

Alwoodley Gates Harrogate Road Leeds LS17 8GS
Tel: 0113 229 1552
Fax: 0113 228 5111
e-mail: enquiries@gsal.org.uk
website: www.gsal.org.uk

The Grammar School at Leeds is a selective, independent, day school for girls and boys aged 3 to 18, and is the result of a merger between Leeds Grammar School (founded in 1552) and Leeds Girls' High School (founded in 1876).

As individual schools, they have a long-established and proven pedigree in developing well-rounded, mature young men and women ready to embrace further education and to face the world as confident, caring citizens.

The Junior and Senior schools are located in extensive, leafy grounds at Alwoodley Gates in north Leeds. Rose Court Nursery and Pre-Prep is housed in newly expanded premises in Headingley.

Governors:
Professor D Sugden, PhD (*Chairman*)
Mr D W Richardson, CBE, FRICS (*Vice-Chairman*)
Mr P N Sparling, LL.B (*Vice-Chairman*)
Mrs E E Bailey, BChD, LDS, RCS, DOrthRCS
Mr A Barker, OBE, FCA
Mr D P A Gravells, JP, MBA
Mr C Greenhalgh, CBE, DL
Mr P D Lawrence
Professor C M Leigh, PhD
Miss B Neale, BSc
Mr J Parkinson, BA
Mrs A F B Portlock, BA, FCA
Mr E Ziff
Mr I Jones

Teaching Staff:

***Head and Chief Executive*: Mark Bailey**, PhD Corpus Christi, Cambridge, FRHistS

Dean/Director of Human Resources: Sue Fishburn
Senior Deputy Headmaster: Peter Jolly

Director of Operations: Gregg Butt
Deputy Head (*Systems*): Eric R Medway
Deputy Head (*Academic*): Tim Kirk
Director of Finance: David Naylor
Director of External Relations: Rachel Kerr
Development Manager: Browen Ashton

Head of Sixth Form: Christine Jagger
Head of Upper Sixth: Carol Heatley
Head of Lower Sixth: Paul Rushworth
Head of Year11: Maureen Kelbrick
Head of Year10: Paul Lunn
Head of Year 9: Chris Freeman
Head of Year 8: Ruth Rothwell
Head of Year 7: Geoff Thompson

Head of Junior School: Sue Fishburn (*Acting*)
Head of Pre-Prep: Anne Pickering

Heads of Department:

Art, Design and Technology: Amanda Tait
Biology: Mark Smith
Chemistry: Kim McDougall
Classics: David Pritchard
Computing: Angela Eckersley
Critical Thinking: Ellis Gregory
Drama: Antoinette Keylock
Economic Studies: Christopher Law
English: Jenny Bolton
Food Technology: Yvonne Wilson
French: Nawel Herbrechter
Geography: Simon Knowles
German: Emma Whittaker
Historical Studies: Graham Seel
ICT: Rob Evans
Instrumental Studies: Andrew Wheeler
International Baccalaureate: Mark Humphries
Languages: Duncan Moynihan
Mathematics: Andrew Ashworth Jones
Music: Katie Staggs
Physics: Dr Mark Cramoysan
Politics: Andrew Stodolny
Religious Studies: Helen Stiles
Science: Dr Ian Hotchkiss
Spanish: Rowan Reed-Purvis
Sport: Paul Morris

Admissions: Angela Boult
Headmaster's Secretary: Judy Watker

Structure. Once physical merger is complete, what has become known as the 'diamond model' will be adopted, whereby classes will be fully co-educational from age three to eleven and again in the Sixth Form. Between the ages of eleven and sixteen, boys and girls will be taught separately, but enjoy mixed extra-curricular and pastoral activities. Pupils will therefore have both the social benefits of co-education and the academic benefits of single-sex teaching in the adolescent years.

Junior School pupils will progress to Senior School, in most cases automatically. From September 2008 Senior School begins with Year 7. Pupils entering at 10 or 11 join Year 6 or Year 7 which comprise the Lower School section. Years 8 and 9 form the Middle School, and Years 10 and 11 the Upper School.

Pastoral Care. Heads of Section are responsible for the progress of pupils in their part of the school, and give guidance and advice where necessary.

The Form Tutor is directly responsible for the progress of every boy and girl in his or her care.

The School is divided into Houses, four in the Junior School and eight in the Senior School. Each house is under the charge of a Housemaster, assisted by House Tutors. Form Tutors, Housemasters and Heads of Section work closely with the

Headmaster and Parents to ensure the well-being of every boy and girl.

Religion. The School has a Chaplain and its own Chaplaincy centre which serves as a focus for worship and pastoral care. Although an Anglican foundation, the School welcomes boys and girls of all faiths and separate meetings are held for Jewish, Muslim, Hindu and Sikh pupils.

Facilities. The Grammar School at Leeds occupies a modern, purpose-built site whose facilities are unrivalled anywhere in the country. They include:

- Specialist suites of teaching rooms for all subjects with the necessary support systems for each faculty.
- Centres for each section of the School, with generous common rooms, locker and cloakroom areas.
- A large assembly hall.
- A newly extended Junior School, having its own identity, specialist resources and operating an independent timetable.
- A library incorporating multimedia facilities.
- IT centre with three inter-locking suites.
- A dedicated art, design and technology unit with computer aided design suite.
- Seventeen specialist science laboratories.
- A fully resourced music school.
- Theatre with fully-equipped lighting gantry.
- A new Food Technology Suite.
- Extensive playing fields with changing facilities and hospitality areas.
- A large indoor sports complex with 2 sports halls, climbing wall, squash courts, conditioning room, a 25m swimming pool of competition standard.
- Extensive grounds with pitches, tennis courts, athletics track.
- Large play and recreation areas for each section of the School.
- Refectory for breakfast, lunch and snacks.
- Provision for a wide variety of indoor and outdoor extra-curricular pursuits.
- Conservation areas.
- A versatile Chaplaincy Centre.
- A new Sixth Form Centre with its own cafeteria, study area and IT and leisure facilities.

Curriculum. Rose Court Nursery and Pre-Prep establishes the foundation for a long and rewarding education – pursuing a broad and balanced curriculum, which builds upon the natural aptitudes, learning skills and interests of each child, whilst enabling each to develop at his/her own pace. We use our own schemes of work, broadly based upon the early years of the National Curriculum, but refined by our own expertise and experience.

In the Junior School pupils concentrate upon the core subjects of English, Mathematics and Science. History, Geography, French/German, Religious Studies, Music, Art and Technology are also taught.

Pupils follow a broad curriculum, including two foreign languages in Years 7–9.

At the end of Year 11 pupils are presented for the GCSE examination.

In the Sixth Form, where students choose to study up to 5 AS and 3 A2 Level subjects. Students are encouraged to choose a broad range of subjects. From 2008 (subject to authorisation), students will also have the option of studying for the new IB Diploma.

Games. Rugby Football, Cricket, Athletics, Swimming, Tennis, Basketball, Badminton, Cross-Country, Volleyball, Hockey, Netball, Rounders, Squash, and Soccer. There is a running track, a swimming pool and a sports centre, including squash courts.

Other Activities. The School's many clubs and societies offer pupils the opportunity to participate in a wide range of out-of-school activities from Mountaineering and Skiing to Choral Singing, Dancing and Drama. There are regular tours and visits abroad and there are long-established exchanges with French and German schools.

The School has an extensive Arts Programme which covers music, film, drama, debating and creative art and includes visiting groups with national reputation as well as the students' own contributions.

The School provides a contingent of the CCF (Army & RAF sections), and has a Scout Troop, with Cub Pack and Venture Scout Unit. The School participates in the Duke of Edinburgh's Award Scheme and Community Service is compulsory in the Sixth Form.

Admission. The entrance procedure takes place in the Lent term for entry the following September and is based upon an examination, an interview and school report. Very young boys and girls are assessed through a series of observed activities. The usual points of entry are 3+ for Nursery, 4+ for Reception, 7+ for Junior School and 11+ for Senior School, although applications can be made at any time for any age. Entry to the Sixth Form is based upon the attainment of good GCSE grades.

Details of the entrance procedure together with copies of sample papers are available from the Headmaster's Secretary.

Fees per term (2008-2009). £3,198 Senior School, £2,388 Junior School, £2,190 Rose Court Nursery & Pre-Prep.

Scholarships and Bursaries. A number of means-tested bursaries (some full fee) are currently awarded each year to pupils entering the school at 11+ and 16+ (Sixth Form). A limited number of modest scholarships are awarded according to academic merit. In exceptional circumstances, financial support is sometimes available for fee-paying parents who find themselves in difficulty.

Old Leodiensian Association (Leeds Grammar School) and Old Girls (Leeds Girls' High School). Lively and active, c/o Bronwen Ashton, The Development Office, The Grammar School at Leeds, Alwoodley Gates, Harrogate Road, Leeds LS17 8GS.

Charitable status. The Grammar School at Leeds is a Registered Charity, number 1048304. It exists for the advancement of education and training for boys and girls.

Leicester Grammar School

London Road Great Glen Leicester LE8 9DJ
Tel: 0116 222 0400
Fax: 0116 222 0510
e-mail: admissions@leicestergrammar.org.uk
website: www.leicestergrammar.org.uk

Leicester Grammar School was founded in 1981 as an independent, selective, co-educational day school to offer able children in the city and county a first-class academic education. Its founders sought to create a school which would maintain the standards and traditions of the city's former grammar schools lost through reorganisation and develop them to meet the demands of a rapidly changing environment. The School moved to a new state-of-the-art building on the south-east side of Leicester in September 2008.

Governors:
I D Patterson, LLB (*Chairman*)
C J Castleman (*Vice-Chairman, Finance*)
G G Bodiwala, MBBS, MS, FICS, FICA
The Hon Mrs A Brooks
Mrs A Eggleston
The Very Revd V F Faull, MA, MA
P F Goffin
N P T Hall
M J Holley, MA
K J Julian, MA

Dr D H Khoosal, MB, BCh, LLM RCS, LLM RCP, FRCPsych
Mrs N Lynch
D V M Mitchell
Mrs T Rist
P L Rose, BA, FCA
Prof J Saker, BSc, MSc
Dr J J A Scott, BSc, PhD
The Rt Revd T Stevens, MA
Prof B H Swanick, BEng, PhD, FIEE, CEng, MInstMC (*Vice-Chairman, Academic*)

Business Director: Mrs A Shakespeare, MA Fitzwilliam, Cantab, ACA, FCA

***Headmaster*: C P M King**, MA Dunelm

Deputy Head (*Curriculum*): T R Cawston, BSc Leicester (*Mathematics*)
Deputy Head (*Pastoral*): Mrs A Ewington, MA Nottingham, CBiol, MIBiol (*Biology*)

Assistant staff:
T Ahmad, MA Punjab (*Art*)
T P Allen, BA Kent (*Head of Sixth Form; History; Politics*)
Mrs J A P Barrow, BEd Liverpool (*Design & Technology*)
R Berry, MA Cantab (*Geography*)
Miss A Binks, BSc Hons Loughborough (*Physical Education*)
L Christie, BA Leeds (*English*)
F W Clayton, BA Wolverhampton (*Religious Studies*)
Miss J Coote, BSc UWI Cardiff, MSc MMU (*Physical Education*)
Dr D M Crawford, BA, DPhil Oxon (*Head of Mathematics*)
Mrs M E Cush, BSc UMIST (*Chemistry*)
Mrs A J Davies, MA De Montfort (*Art*)
N G P Donnelly, BA Leicester (*Geography; DofE Award*)
A N Duffield, BSc UCW Cardiff, MIBiol (*Head of Biology*)
Dr S Ewers, BSc Bristol, PhD (*Biology*)
S Faire, BSc Surrey (*Mathematics*)
Dr C W Fearon, BSc Liverpool, PhD Birmingham (*Biology*)
Mrs A Fraser, BA Sussex (*German*)
D W Gee, C&G Tech Cert Nottingham (*Head of Design & Technology*)
M J Gower, BA Leicester (*Head of Geography; Health & Safety Officer*)
Mrs A L Griffin, MA Loughborough (*Head of Drama*)
†J M Griffin, MA Cantab (*Deputy Head of English*)
Mrs H A Griffiths, GNSM (*Music*)
P M Handford, MA Oxon (*Chemistry*)
Mrs B A Harper, BA Warwick (*Head of History*)
S J Harrison, BA Keele (*English*)
A H J Harrop, MA Oxon (*Head of Classics; Examinations Officer*)
Mrs W E Harvey, BA Hons Loughborough College of Art & Design (*Design & Technology*)
S Hayhoe, BA Coventry, MEd (*Head of ICT*)
Ms S Haywood, BEd Worcester College (*Art*)
Mrs M Higginson, MA Toronto (*English*)
Mrs K B Hinshelwood, BA Reading (*Academic Support*)
C W Howe, BEd, CNAA Crewe & Alsager College (*Director of Physical Education*)
Miss N Hughes, BA London (*English*)
G Inchley, BSc Hull, MSc Bristol (*Mathematics; Young Enterprise Coordinator*)
C James, MA Cambridge (*Mathematics*)
R W S Kidd, BA Ulster, MA Ulster (*Head of English*)
R I Longson, BA UCW Aberystwyth, DipCG, MICG (*Head of Careers; History*)
D M Lupton, BA Exeter (*French and Spanish*)
D W Maddock, BA Bristol Polytechnic, MA Leeds Polytechnic (*Head of Art*)
D McCann, BEd Leicester (*Physical Education*)
P Moore-Friis, BA De Montfort (*Economics*)
Miss J Mould, BEd Bedford College of HE (*Head of Girls' Physical Education; English*)
N Murray, BSc Imperial, MA, MSc Sheffield Hallam (*Mathematics*)
Mrs E C Nisbet, BEd Trent Polytechnic (*Food Technology*)
Mrs H D Painter, CertEd Dunelm, DipEd Leics (*Head of Preparatory Department*)
Mrs B J Panton, MA Edinburgh (*Classics*)
C D Paterson, MA Cantab (*Classics; Master of Choristers; Curriculum Coordinator*)
Miss A M Patterson, BSc Sunderland Polytechnic (*Chemistry; Housemistress of Duke's*)
N C Perry, MA Oxon (*Chemistry*)
Mrs K Pollard, BSc Loughborough (*Mathematics*)
L Potter (*Head of Lower School; Physical Education*)
Mrs E Pottinger, MA Edinburgh (*History*)
Mrs A Price, BSc Edinburgh (*Physics; Staff Development Coordinator; SMT Secretary*)
P T G Reeves, BSc Manchester (*Head of Physics*)
J G Robinson, BA Newcastle (*Head of Modern Languages*)
D E A Roebuck, BSc UCW Swansea, CChem, FRSC, FRSA (*Head of Science; Head of Chemistry*)
Mrs S J Sains, MA Oxon (*Mathematics*)
B H Shaw, GRSM, ARCM, LRAM (*Head of Instrumental Studies; Director of External Relations*)
Ms M Sian, BA Middlesex (*Design & Technology; ICT*)
Mrs C L Stevenson, BA Lancaster (*French and Spanish; Housemistress of Judges*)
T A Thacker, BEd, CNAA Crewe & Alsager College (*Head of Boys' Games; Head of Years 10 & 11*)
J S Thomason, BSc UCW Bangor (*Assessment Coordinator; Biology*)
Dr A Vassiliou-Abson, BA Athens, MPhil Birmingham, PhD Birmingham (*Classics*)
Mrs B Wallwork, BEd Cantab (*Mathematics*)
M D Wheeler, BSc, PhD Bristol (*Physics*)
Dr D M T Whittle, BMus, PhD Nottingham (*Director of Music*)
Miss A L Williamson, BSc Loughborough (*Physical Education; Geography; Head of Year 9*)
D R Willis, BSc, CNAA Portsmouth Polytechnic (*Science; Housemaster of Vice Chancellor's; Senior Housemaster*)
Dr S G Yeomans, BA QM College, MA Loughborough, PhD Loughborough (*Politics*)
Mrs C M Young, BA Birmingham (*Head of Religious Studies; Pastoral Programme Coordinator*)

Visiting music staff:
J Cherry, DRSAMD, DipRAM, LRAM
Miss A de Graeve, BA
J Gilchrist, BA
K L Hall, GRSM, LRAM, LTCL
C Jeans, LRAM (*Brass Coordinator*)
D McHarg
Miss D Morgan, BMus
D Morris, LRAM
P J Nuttall, BA
Miss G E Print, BA (*String Coordinator*)
M Todd, Dip Kons Luzern

Headmistress, Junior School: Mrs M Redfearn, BA Hons

There are 706 day pupils in the School (307 girls, 399 boys), of whom 194 are in the Sixth Form. A further 288 pupils, aged 3–11, attend Leicester Grammar Junior School at Evington Hall.

Admission. An entrance examination is held in the Lent Term for boys and girls seeking to enter the Preparatory (10+) and Year 7 (11+) forms in the following September. Papers are taken in verbal reasoning, English and Mathematics. In addition admission into Years 9 and 10 takes place at ages 13 and 14 and there is provision for direct entry into the Sixth Form, offers of a place being conditional upon the GCSE grades gained. The normal entry requirement to the Sixth Form is two A and four B grade passes at GCSE. Visitors are always welcome to make an appointment to see the school and meet the Headmaster. All applications are handled by the School Secretary, from whom all Registration forms are obtainable. Candidates at all levels may be called for an interview.

Scholarships. (*see Scholarship Entries section*). Academic, music, art and sports scholarships are offered to the outstanding candidates on examination and the School has some funds available for bursaries. It has always been the policy of governors to try to ensure that children capable of benefiting from education at the School should not be prevented by financial considerations from entry.

Curriculum. Class sizes are about 20 to 24 in the first three years; the average size of a GCSE group is 19, of a Sixth Form group 12.

All pupils in the first three years (and those entering the preparatory form) follow a balanced curriculum covering the National Curriculum core and foundation subjects, Religious Studies and Latin (Classical Studies in the preparatory form). Classes are split into smaller groups for the creative and technological subjects, so that all pupils can gain practical experience, whether in the School's ICT suite or on its extensive range of musical instruments. From Year 8 the three science subjects, Biology, Chemistry and Physics, are taught separately. There is no streaming and setting occurs only for Mathematics and French. In Year 9 an element of choice is introduced and pupils must opt from a choice of third languages and from a list of five creative subjects.

In Years 4 and 5 pupils prepare for GCSE examinations in ten subjects, as well as doing PE/Games. All study a 'core' of five subjects: English Language and Literature, Mathematics, French and Chemistry. The range of 'options' includes Art, Biology, Chemistry, Classical Civilisation, Design and Technology, Drama, French, Geography, German, Greek, Religious Studies, History, Latin, Music, Physics, Spanish and PE.

Students in the Sixth Form normally study 4 AS levels leading to 3 or more A levels from a choice of 19 subjects, including Further Mathematics, Economics, Physical Education, Politics, Computer Studies and Theatre Studies. There is no rigid division between arts and science sides. To ensure that breadth of education does not suffer, a broadly based cultural general studies course leads on to A level General Studies. The school has an excellent record of success at public examinations and university admissions, including Oxbridge. The Careers Department is very active in giving help and advice to students.

School activities. A broad range and variety of activities complements the academic curriculum. Participation rates are high.

Music, drama and sport form an integral part of life at LGS. Every pupil in the First Year learns a musical instrument and a high proportion continue afterwards with private weekly lessons. The School Orchestra gives two major concerts a year, whilst a training orchestra, a jazz band, a dance band, recorder groups and various chamber ensembles explore other avenues. The School Choir is the resident choir for the Crown Court Services and tours regularly. Links are strong with the Leicestershire School of Music orchestras and several pupils play in national orchestras. Senior and junior drama clubs function throughout the year, a major play or musical and a junior play are staged regularly and house drama extends the opportunity to act to most pupils.

Games are seen as an important means not only of promoting health and fitness but also of inspiring self-confidence. Major winter games are hockey, netball and rugby and in summer athletics, cricket and tennis. Opportunities occur for individuals to follow their interest in badminton, basketball, squash, golf, table tennis, gymnastics, dance, sailing and cross-country running whilst swimming is an integral part of the PE programme. The School's own facilities are extensive and meet all modern standards for sport. Teams represent the School in the main games at all age groups and several students achieve recognition at county or even national level. The school is proud of the fact that it is one of only eight other schools to have been awarded the Sportsmark Gold with Distinction, for the quality of the delivery of sport within the school.

Societies and clubs complement these activities, ranging from chess to the Duke of Edinburgh's Award scheme, history and Lit Soc to model aeroplanes, debating to art, design and technology, for which the workshop and art rooms are usually open during lunchtimes and after school.

Religion. The school espouses the principles of the Church of England, teaching the Christian faith, its values and standards of personal conduct, but also prides itself on welcoming children of all faiths, who play a full part in the life of the community. Very strong links exist with Leicester Cathedral and there is a flourishing Guild of Servers and cathedral clergy participate in school life and prepare confirmation candidates.

Pastoral Care. Responsibility for a wide-ranging system of pastoral care and for the creation of the caring, friendly and disciplined environment, resides in four Heads of School, assisted by form teachers, personal tutors and a very active house system.

Junior School. Entry to the Junior School is by interview and, where appropriate, examination, at 3+, 4+, 7+ and into other school years, when places are available. Pupils are prepared for entry to the Senior School. A balanced curriculum is followed covering National Curriculum Key Stages 1 and 2 and beyond; French (from 5 years), classical studies and ICT are also taught. A wide range of activities complements the academic curriculum, with a strong stress on music and a rapidly growing games programme. The School is a Christian foundation and lays great emphasis upon the pastoral care of young children. (*See also Junior School entry in IAPS section.*)

Fees per term (from April 2008). Senior School £3,040; Junior School £2,380 (from Sept 2008).

Old Leicestrians Association. All correspondence to the Secretary, c/o the School.

Charitable status. Leicester Grammar School Trust is a Registered Charity, number 510809. Its aims and objectives are to promote and provide for the advancement of education and in connection therewith to conduct, carry on, acquire and develop in the United Kingdom or elsewhere a School or Schools to be run according to the principles of the Church of England for the education of students and children of either sex or both sexes.

Leighton Park School

Shinfield Road Reading Berkshire RG2 7ED
Tel: 0118 987 9600
Fax: 0118 987 9625
e-mail: admissions@leightonpark.com
website: www.leightonpark.com

Governors:
Paul High (*Chairman*)

Mark Allsopp	Naomi Iliff
Jonathan Bowen	Marshall Leopold
Glynne Butt	Judi Marling
Andrew Clark	Andrew Morgan
Adrian Dixon	Tony Stoller
Martin Forster	Elizabeth Whitehouse
Paul High	Stephen Wright

***Head*: John H Dunston**, MA Cantab, ACIL, FRSA

Deputy Head: Elizabeth Thomas, BA Hons Lancaster, NPQH

Bursar: (*to be appointed*)

Senior Master: John N Allinson, BA Liverpool

Director of Studies: Nigel Williams, BA Bristol, MA London

Teaching Staff:
* *Head of Department*
§ *Part-time*
† *Head of House*

Roger Aylward, BSc (*History, PE, Games; †Fryer House*)
§Kathy Baldwin (*Mandarin*)
Irene Bell, MA Cantab (**Physics*)
Julian Berrow, BA (*§Modern Foreign Languages*)
Philippa Bleach, BA (*History*)
Zenon Bowrey, BA (**Economics & Business Studies*)
David Bradford, CertEd, MA Ed (**Design Technology*)
Peter Bulteel, BA (*PE & Games*)
§Clive Burns (*Design Technology*)
Simon Cain, BSc (*Biology, Physics, Games; †School House*)
Ruth Carter, BSc, MA (*Mathematics*)
Kathryn Cunningham, BSc (*Chemistry & Biochemistry*)
§Deborah Duggan, BA (*Modern Foreign Languages*)
Jon Emerson, MA Oxon (**Science*)
§Rosemary Few, BEd (*Individual Learning Centre*)
Kate Findlay, BA (*History*)
Simon Gifford (**English*)
§Karen Gracie-Langrick, MA (**History, Ancient History, *PSHE*)
Richard Griffiths, BSc (**History, Games*)
Geoff Harnett, MA Cantab (*Modern Foreign Languages; †Grove House*)
Jane Ireland, BA (*Individual Learning Centre*)
Jane Kennedy, BEd (*Modern Foreign Languages*)
§Tariq Khan, BSc (*Chemistry*)
Adél Kiss, BSc, BEd (*Mathematics*)
Richard Lade, BSc (*Design Technology, ICT*)
Ann Line, BA (*English*)
Ken Lovesy, MA Oxon (*English*)
Jakki Marr, BEd (*PE, Games*)
Jackie Marsh, BEd (**Individual Learning Centre*)
§Rachael Martin, BEd (*Mathematics, Individual Learning Centre*)
Paula Masters, BA (*Beliefs & Values*)
Mair Mayers, BA (*Mathematics*)
Rachel Mayne, BSc (*Science*)
§Chris Mitchell, BA (*Assistant Director of Music*)
Marjory Morris, CertEd (*English; Director of Sixth Form*)
Pablo Gorostidi Perez, BA (*Spanish*)
§Claire Reeves, BSc (*Geography*)
§Angela Rigby, BA, BSc, MSc (*ICT*)
Elaine Rimmer, BA (**Art, Careers, Games*)
Premnath Samyrao, MSc, MEd (*Mathematics*)
§Pablo Gorostidi Perez (*Spanish*)
Rosemary Scales, MA, BA (*Director of Music*)
Mark Simmons, BEd (**PE, Games; †Field House*)
Graham Smith, BA (*Games, Weekend Activities Coordinator; †Reckitt House*)
Christine Smyth, BSc, MSc (**Geography*)
§Juliet Straw, BA (*Beliefs & Values*)
Yun Yun Tang, BA, MA (*Mandarin*)
Helen Taylor, BSc (**Biology*)
Geraint Thomas (**Drama*)
§Lindsey Thompson, BSc, PhD (*Science*)
Michael Ward, BEd, MA (**Information Technology*)
Sherilynn Wass, BSc, PhD (*Science*)
Michael Whiteman, BA (*Music*)
Nicola Williams, BEd (**PE, Games*)
Simon Williams, BA (**Art*)
Françoise Wilson, BA, MA (**Modern Foreign Languages*)
John Woodings, BA (*English*)
Sue Wright, Dip TEFL (**ESL*)
§Damon Young, BA (*Drama*)

Librarian: Chris Routh, MA, BA

Admissions Coordinator: Sabine Wattez
Head's PA: Linda Hay

Leighton Park is a forward-looking, co-educational day and boarding school for 470 pupils aged 11-18, set in sixty acres of attractive parkland, about a mile south of Reading town centre.

Our commitment to academic excellence is balanced by our commitment to the development of every individual, deriving from our Quaker heritage. You will find at Leighton Park outstanding teaching and excellent academic results. The last ISI inspection stated, "Leighton Park is highly successful in providing an education of good quality in a strongly Quaker ethos. Pupils achieve well academically in relation to their abilities, while experiencing rich opportunities for their personal and social development".

For eight successive years, A Level students have achieved a pass rate of 96% or above (99% in 2006) with an average of three or more passes each. 39% of all passes were Grade A.

At GCSE, 95% of pupils in 2007 achieved five or more passes at Grade A*-C, with 90% of all passes at Grade C or higher; 48% A*/A.

Curriculum. In Years 7 and 8 pupils follow a broad curriculum, which extends well beyond the National Curriculum. Mandarin has been introduced in Year 7. Year 9 pupils are expected to follow a full GCSE course of nine or ten subjects, comprising both compulsory and optional subjects. In the Sixth Form, a wide range of examination courses is complemented by a broad programme, including Mandarin, Critical Thinking, Film Studies, European Computer Driving License and Dance. A team of qualified specialists works with pupils for whom English is an additional language, and the Individual Learning Centre for those with identifiable learning needs.

Leighton Park is a candidate school for the International Baccalaureate Diploma.

Facilities. Excellent facilities and resources include a Science and Technology Centre, an ICT Centre, a Drama Studio, a splendid Library and dedicated Individual Learning Centre. The dining centre offers a first-rate choice of meals (breakfast, lunch and tea). A new Sixth Form Centre opened in 2006 and a new Mathematics block in 2007.

Ethos and Pastoral Care. Within Leighton Park's distinctive Quaker ethos, pupils of many faiths and backgrounds flourish in an atmosphere of tolerance, harmony and understanding. They know they will be challenged in their work to achieve the highest standards of excellence.

Boarding and Day Boarding. We offer a highly flexible approach to boarding with full, weekly and day boarding options to suit a family and pupil's needs. The five houses provide a comfortable base in which all pupils, whether day or boarding, genuinely feel at home. Day pupils and boarders both have individual study facilities in the houses. Day pupils are welcome for breakfast and to stay for tea, prep and hobbies, included in the fees. Flexi-boarding is available.

Sport. Sport plays an important role in life at Leighton Park with many individual and team performances reaching county and national level. First rate coaching and superb facilities – which include a heated indoor swimming pool, floodlit astroturf pitch, 16 tennis courts and a cricket square – ensure that talented and enthusiastic pupils can develop their sporting abilities to the full. 2007 Hockey and Rugby tour to South Africa.

Music. Music has for a long time been one of Leighton Park's particular strengths with around half the pupils learning instruments and performing a wide range of styles. Our facilities for practice and performance include a suite of ten practice rooms, a digital recording studio, a suite of Apple Macs, recital room and concert hall.

Opportunities to perform include almost weekly concerts and foreign tours, in 2006 to France, Switzerland and Italy and a 2008 tour to Scandinavia.

Hobbies and other activities. Pupils can participate in an enormous variety of activities both during the week and at weekends, before and after school. The Duke of Edinburgh's Award Scheme is well established and Lower Sixth pupils run their own company in the Young Enterprise programme. In keeping with our Quaker perspective many Leighton Park pupils are involved in Community Service.

Careers. Pupils have access to the well-resourced Careers Library as well as networked computer software to help them research and evaluate their options. All Year 10 and Lower Sixth pupils complete a week of work experience and there are many other occasions when career alternatives or gap year possibilities can be explored. Thorough preparation for entry to university is given.

Entry to the school is by exam and interview, with an additional English test where appropriate. Pupils are normally admitted at one of three points: Year 7 (age 11); Year 9 (age 13), and the Sixth Form. Entry to the Sixth Form requires 6 GCSEs.

Fees per term (2008-2009). Full Boarding £6,870–£8,085; Weekly Boarding £6,040–£7,100; Day £4,500–£5,300.

Scholarships. (*see Scholarship Entries section*). Several Major Awards (up to 25% of fees) and Minor Awards (15% or 10% of fees) are made each year for academic work, music, art and sport. Bursaries may be available on a means-tested basis. Additional awards may be made by the David Lean Foundation.

Old Leightonians. Website: www.oldleightonians.org.

Charitable status. The Leighton Park Trust is a Registered Charity, number 309144. It exists to provide education for young people.

The Leys School

Cambridge CB2 7AD
Tel: 01223 508900
Fax: 01223 505303
e-mail: office@theleys.net
website: www.theleys.net

The Leys is situated less than half a mile from the centre of the university city of Cambridge, close to the River Cam and Grantchester Meadows. The School was founded in 1875 on the initiative of a group of leading Methodists to provide a liberal Christian education, establishing a tradition which has continued unbroken to this day. The School was incorporated as a Charitable Trust in 1878. All the buildings are grouped around the playing field and lie within the estate originally acquired for the purpose; there is a second extensive playing field nearby.

The Leys is a friendly, caring and happy community, large enough to offer many opportunities, but not so large as to lose sight of the individual. The School is fully co-educational; of a total of over 540 pupils, 190 are in the Sixth Form. Girls and boys are accommodated in separate houses. 50% of the pupils are boarders; the remainder, whether home boarders or day pupils, sleep at home but otherwise are able to enjoy all the opportunities of boarding school life.

Motto: '*In Fide Fiducia.*'

Governors:

Chairman: Professor E Ebsworth, CBE, PhD, SCD, FRSC, FRSE

N J M Abbott, MA
Mrs J Allison, BA
Mrs P Appafram
Mrs H Arthur
M D Beazor, BA
S G Benson, MA
¶M A Bishop, MA
Mrs A Brunner
J D Callin, FRICS, FRVA
C Clough
Mrs C Crawford, BA
Revd Dr P C Graves, THM
Mrs J W Harding, BA
¶R B Haryott, BSc, CEng, FICE
C R B Hewitson
R A Johnson, MA
C M Kidman, LIOB, JP
Revd Dr P Luscombe, MA
Mrs M E Mackay
Mrs E L Mimpriss
D Page
G Russell, MA
R C Sadler, FRICS
¶A V Silverton, BSc, FSI
¶D C W Unwin, MA, ACA
R D H Walker, MA, PhD
R B Webster, FCA
Mrs S Wilkes, BA, PhD, FSA

***Headmaster*: Mr M Slater**, MA

Deputy Headmaster: A W Jessop, MA, PhD

Assistant Teachers:
J H Aylmer, MA
A S Erby, BSc
M A Brown, BSc
P White, BEd
E M W George, BEd
R Adamson, BSc, PhD
R A D Hill, BA
D J Nye, BSc
P A Mathieu, BA
Mrs P B Davis, BA, MPhil
Mrs S Schilperoort, BSc, MA
Mrs C E Wiedermann, MA
Mrs P J Jessop, BEd
C I A Fraser, MA, MCMI, FRSA
Mrs A P Muston, BEd
W J Earl, BSc
J M J Deveson, BMus, MMus
G K Howe, BSc, MSc
Revd C J Meharry, BEd
D K Fernandes, BSc
A P Harmsworth, MA
Mrs C L Howe, BA, PhD
D R Bell, MA
S H Dorman, BA, MPhil
G J Deudney, BSc, BEd
P M Davies, BSc
M A Egan, BSc
§Mrs C J Ilman
§Mrs P C A Taylor, BA, MEd
Mrs J Stobbart, BA
Miss C E Battison, BA
Miss C Brocklehurst, BSc
M Gale, BEd
R A Hall, BA, MA, ARCO
Miss P Lees, BA
A C R Long, MA
J Norton, BA
Miss E Prosser, BSc
T Reed, MA, MSc
Mrs E R Culshaw, MA
Ms J F Kedie, BA
S A Newlove, BSc, PhD
Miss R L Pike, BA
R W Tillett, BA
S G Wilson, BSc
B A Barton, BA
A J Welby, MA
Mrs J A Jennett, BSc
Miss C J Keyser, BSc
S Hancock, MA
S N Leader, BA
N R Born, MA
N J Dix-Pincott, MA
Mrs V Llewellyn, BA, MSc
Miss L C Earl, BA
A J McGarry, MA
G F Stentiford, BSc, MSc
Miss J P E Cooke, BA
Mr A S Phoenix Holland, BA
D J Wilson, BA, PhD
T P Dunn, BA, MSc
Miss R Taylor, MA
Mr J Fawcett, MA
Miss E Walsh

Housemasters:
School House: S H Dorman
West House: W J Earl
North A House: C I A Fraser
East House: C J Meharry
Barker House: G J Deudney
Bisseker House: R W Tillett

Housemistresses:
Granta House: Mrs C L Howe
Dale House: Miss C E Battison
Fen House: Mrs S Schilperoort
Barrett House: Mrs E R Culshaw
Moulton House: Miss A Macpherson

Director of Studies: S G Wilson
Careers Adviser: Mrs S Vallance Goode
Bursar: P D McKeown, BA
Director of Development: Mrs N S Bryant, BSc
Director of Admissions: Miss J C Muir, MSc, BA
Director of Marketing: J D R Benson, CIM
Higher Education Coordinator: M A Egan
Examinations Officer: Mrs C Maskell
Head of Outdoor Education: R S McAlinden
Chaplain: Revd C J Meharry
Medical Officer: A J Stewart, MB, BCh

Nursing Staff:
Sister M A Williams, SRN, SCM
Sister G Woolley, RN
Sister P Sherman, RN
Facilities Manager: N Keen
Sports Hall Manager: P Terry
Headmaster's PA: Mrs S M Inskipp
Administration Manager: Mrs J A Cooper, BA
Database Officer: Mrs D V Butterworth

Buildings and Facilities. There is a continuing development programme involving all areas of the School. A state-of-the-art Music School was opened in 2005. There is an excellent Humanities Building with first-class facilities for Geography, History, Classics and Divinity together with a Museum and Archives Centre, and an award-winning Design Centre, which contains workshops (metal, plastic and wood), Art School, Ceramics Studio, Electronics Workshop, Computer Centre, School Press, together with facilities for Design, Photography, Cookery and an Exhibition Centre. A Sports Hall and all-weather pitch were built in 1995. The Sports Hall was extended and a second Astroturf pitch was built this year. A new climbing wall was constructed in summer 2007. Other major buildings include the Theatre, the Science Building and the Queen's Building, comprising classrooms and a drama studio used for both teaching and performances. There are 40 acres of playing fields, an indoor heated swimming pool open all the year, a boat house on the Cam, and synthetic grass tennis courts. A radical re-designing and refurbishment of all boarding houses began in summer 2006, with the aim of providing the most comfortable and homely of boarding facilities. The School Library underwent a major refurbishment this year.

Admission. Admission for girls and boys is mainly at 11+, 13+ and 16+. Registration may be made at any time beforehand. Entrance tests and Scholarship Examinations for 11+ and 13+ entry are held in the January prior to entry. Places in the Sixth Form are available for both girls and boys who have successfully completed their GCSE or equivalent courses elsewhere. Application for admission should be made to the Director of Admissions in the first instance.

Scholarships. (*see Scholarship Entries section*). Academic Scholarships are available for entry at 11, 13 and for entry to the Sixth Form at 16. Scholarships are also available for entry at 13 in Music, Art, Design Technology, Sport, Drama and All Rounder, and for entry to the Sixth Form at 16 in Music, Art, Sport and Drama. The Scholarship Examinations at 11 and 13 take place in the Spring Term and the Sixth Form Scholarship takes place in the November of the year prior to entry. Awards may be up to 30% of the fees payable. Further particulars may be obtained from the Director of Admissions. The School also participates in the Arkwright Scholarship Scheme, which is an external examination offering Scholarships for those wishing to take Design and Technology in the Sixth Form and who are aiming to read Engineering, Technology or other Design-related subjects in Higher Education.

Curriculum. The academic curriculum broadly conforms to the National Curriculum but is not restricted by it. Each pupil has an Academic tutor who, in conjunction with the Director of Studies and the Housemaster or Housemistress, works to tailor the pupil's programme to suit the needs of the individual wherever possible. Pupils follow a broad programme in the first three years (years 7, 8 and 9). At the end of Year 9 they choose three from a wide range of GCSE options to add to the basic core of English Language/Literature, Mathematics, separate Sciences, Religious Studies and a Modern Foreign Language. The GCSE examinations are normally taken at the end of Year 11. Religious Education and Physical Education are taught throughout the School.

In the Sixth Form, a similar option scheme operates with pupils choosing from a total of 23 subjects to take normally 4 AS Levels in the LVI and 3 at A2 in the following year.

There is considerable flexibility of combinations possible at both levels, and choices are made after consultation between parents, tutors, careers staff and subject teachers.

About 95% of the A level candidates proceed to degree courses. A Reading Party for potential Oxford and Cambridge candidates is held during the Summer Term.

Personal and Social Education forms an integral part of the curriculum at all levels. In the Sixth Form this is supplemented by a Festival in the Autumn Term that draws on the cultural resources of Cambridge University and the city as a whole.

The Chapel. The School Chapel is at the heart of the community in every sense. From the time of its Methodist foundation The Leys has been firmly based on non-sectarian Christian principles. It welcomes boys and girls of all denominations and religions, encouraging them to see the relevance of a personal faith of their own. Religious Education forms part of the curriculum. Preparation is also given for Church membership, and a combined confirmation service is held.

Physical Education. The physical education/games programme aims at introducing a wide variety of physical activities. Sports available are Rugby, Hockey, Cricket, Tennis, Athletics, Netball, Badminton, Basketball, Fencing, Fives, Gymnastics, Golf, Rowing, Sailing, Karate, Dance, Shooting, Climbing, Clay-pigeon Shooting, Squash, Swimming, Volleyball, Water Polo. Outdoor activities such as Camping, Orienteering, Canoeing, and Climbing are also encouraged through CCF and the Duke of Edinburgh's Award. PE is offered at GCSE and A level. The School has close links with many Cambridge University Sports Clubs, with the Sixth Form competing in University Leagues.

Careers. In the Lower School, careers guidance forms part of the PSHE programme and is carried out by tutors and members of the Careers Department. Year 9 are supported in their option choices by tutors and Careers staff and are introduced to the Careers Library .Year 11 take the Preview Careers Selection Programme. It matches pupils' interests and abilities to appropriate career fields and is followed up by two individual interviews with career specialists. Year 11 pupils are also encouraged to participate in the Work Experience scheme. Support continues into the Sixth Form with all Lower Sixth being interviewed by Careers staff. An annual Careers Forum is organised in the Lent term, enabling students to investigate various career paths before embarking on their UCAS applications.

Societies. All are encouraged to participate in out-of-school activities of their choice. These range from Literary, Philosophical, Scientific, Mathematical, Languages, Debating, Music and Drama societies to any of the activities available in the Design Centre, which are available after School and at weekends. The life of the School is enriched by its proximity to Cambridge; distinguished visiting speakers are available, and pupils are encouraged to go to plays, concerts and lectures in the town.

Combined Cadet Force. Except in special circumstances, pupils in Year 10 join the CCF (Army or Navy section) and also follow the Duke of Edinburgh's Award scheme. CCF camps take place annually, and an Adventure Training week is also undertaken at Easter. There is a miniature range, and a Rifle Club exists for small-bore shooting. The School is an authorised centre for the organisation of activities within the Duke of Edinburgh's Award scheme and pupils work towards the Bronze, Silver or Gold awards in the four sections: community service, expeditions, physical recreation and skills or hobbies.

Fees per term (2008-2009). Years 7 and 8: £5,750 Boarders; £3,715 Day Pupils.

Years 9 to Sixth Form: £7,980 Boarders; £6,000 Home Boarders; £5,210 Day Pupils.

St Faith's Preparatory School is part of the same Foundation. It was founded in 1884 and acquired by the Governors of The Leys in 1938. There are 500 boys and girls, aged 4–13 years. The buildings, which include the Keynes Building opened in 2006, stand in 10 acres of grounds. Full particulars may be obtained from the Headmaster of St Faith's, Mr S Drew, BA. (*For further details, see entry in IAPS section.*)

The Old Leysian Union. *Secretary*: J C Harding, MA, The Leys School, Cambridge CB2 7AD. Handbook and Directory, twentieth edition, 1991.

Charitable status. The Leys School, Cambridge is a Registered Charity, number 311436. It aims to enable boys and girls to develop fully their individual potential within a School community firmly based on Christian principles.

Liverpool College

Queen's Drive Mossley Hill Liverpool L18 8BG
Tel: 0151 724 4000; 0151 724 1611 (Admissions)
Fax: 0151 729 0105
e-mail: admin@liverpoolcollege.org.uk
website: www.liverpoolcollege.org.uk

Motto: *Non solum ingenii, verum etiam virtutis.*

Visitor: The Bishop of Liverpool

President: The Rt Hon The Earl of Derby, DL

The Revd Canon Dr D C Gray, CBE, TD, PhD, MPhil, AKC, FRHistS
The Rt Hon The Lord Hunt of Wirral, PC, MBE
The Rt Revd Nigel McCulloch, MA
District Judge R A McCullagh, MA
H M Alty Esq, MBChB, BDS, FDS, RCS
J H D Williams, MA
His Honour Judge G M Clifton
B S Clarke Esq
L Holden Esq, DL, LLB
C C Hubbard Esq
I N Lightbody Esq
J D Robertson Esq
R L Sington Esq

Governors:
Mrs B M Greenberg (*Chairman*)
N Ashbridge (*Deputy Chairman*)
G N Wood, QC (*Deputy Chairman*)
P Barlow, MA
Mrs E Bramley
Mrs S Hilditch
M G Jones
J D A Leith
Professor P N Love, CBE, DL
J W Lowe Esq, FCA (*Joint Honorary Treasurer*)
Mrs I Maddison, JP
Mrs M Mason, BSc
Dr A M Miller
J R Sumner Esq, FCA (*Joint Honorary Treasurer*)

***Principal*: Hans van Mourik Broekman**, MA Hons

Deputy Head (*Curriculum*): S P Downes, BSc, PhD, MBA

Deputy Head (*Administration*): M Halton, MA

Finance Bursar: A A Blackhurst

Chaplain: G A Hayes, BA

Registrar: Mrs S Loveridge

Staff:
M Alexander, BA
C Ashbrook BA
E J Atkins, BA PhD
DJ Bishop, BMus
S Brady, BA
E Cain, CertEd
J V Callacher, BEd
P Cartwright, BEd
A S J Celine, BSc
K-M Corrie, BSc
B C Donnelly, BEd
S Doran, BA
J M Everett, BSc
H Finch, MA
A Fox, BSc
A Gammon, BEd
N W Griffith, BA
P Gunawardena, BSc
D Hall, BSc
J Hall, BA
L A Hamilton, BSc
N Hannah, BSc
J G Hutchinson, BA
R Kelly, BA
M M Lawrenson, MA
S Lines, BSc
H Lock, MA
B Martin, BSc
R McAlea, MA
K L McCaughey, MA
L M Miller, BSc
E Nixon, MA
M O'Donoghue, BA
D A O'Leary, BA
E Othen, MA, MPhil
K Reid, BA
B Roberts, BEng
T Rooney, BA
A P Ryan, GRSM, ARMCM
L Townley, BA
T J Traynor, BEng
M R Ward, BA
G P Wilson, MA
G A Wright, BA

Prep and Pre-Prep

Head: S Buglass, MEd

Deputy Head: W G Kendall, CertEd

Head of Pre-Prep: Mrs G Gannon, BEd

J Anderson, BSc
H Boyle, NNEB
D A Buglass, CertEd
R Charnock
B Chew, BA
P A Davey, CertEd
S E Glaze, BEd
C Hegarty, BA
R Kerr, NNEB
E L Lewis, NNEB
D McClements, BEd
G M McGuinness, NNEB
E McLennon, BA
S J Nelson, BEd
M H Oakes, BEd
J Poole, NNEB
A F Russell-Moore, BSc
J Saunders, BSc
L Strong, BEd
K J Taylor, BEd
J Tegg, BSc
K A Ward, BEd
N Ward, BA
F Wright, BA

Campus and Buildings. The College is situated 4 miles south of the city centre, in 26 acres of wooded grounds and playing fields, adjacent to extensive parkland, and situated in the South Liverpool conservation area. It is easily accessible by public transport or by one of the College buses.

Founded in 1840, the College has expanded and upgraded the buildings and facilities to keep abreast of curricular developments and to create the optimum environment for a modem multi-faith and multi-cultural educational community.

The Preparatory School occupies its own self-contained site within the College grounds (*see entry in IAPS section*) and the Pre-Prep and Nursery has recently been extended and provided with a well-equipped outdoor play area.

A floodlit synthetic pitch has been added to the extensive playing fields, and a Sports Centre with a fully equipped gymnasium, an aerobics/dance studio and facilities for indoor cricket, basketball and tennis was opened by HRH Princess Anne in 1999.

Organisation. There are at present 362 day girls and 515 day boys in the school. The College provides a complete and continuous course of education for boys and girls from 3 to 18 years of age in the Preparatory School (3–11) and in Upper School (11–18). Each of the schools has its own Head and staff, but additional specialist teaching is provided in the Prep school in Music, Sport and Modern Languages.

Admission. The main points of entry are at ages 3, 5, 7, 11 and 16 by assessment and/or examination, although pupils are admitted at other ages. Tours of the College may be booked through the Registrar.

Scholarships. Academic Scholarships, Music, Art, Drama and Sport Scholarships are offered, as are Bursaries for children of Clergy of any religion and of members of the Armed Forces.

The Curriculum. The curriculum retains an emphasis on a rigorous training in academic subjects while allowing scope for individual preferences. The curriculum to GCSE includes

English Language and Literature, Latin, French, Spanish, Mathematics, Physics, Chemistry, Biology, Business Studies, Information and Communication Technology, CDT, Drama, Art, Music and Physical Education.

Sixth Form. The majority of pupils proceed into the Sixth Form and nearly all (99%) go on to Universities or pursue other specialist areas, eg Arts, Drama. There is a regular entry to Oxford and Cambridge. While retaining their role as an integral senior part of the community and being required to take some responsibility for the running of the school in a prefectorial capacity, the Sixth Formers enjoy greater freedom and independence. They have separate study rooms, common rooms and a café. The International Baccalaureate Diploma Programme is to be introduced in 2008, and subjects offered at Higher and Standard Levels will include English, Mathematics, French, Spanish, Latin, Biology, Chemistry, Physics, Design Technology, Geography, History, Economics, Business and Management, Visual Arts, Theatre Arts and Music.

Careers. Careers advice and guidance is provided throughout the school by a team of staff with particular experience and expertise in this field. There is a full and active Careers programme of both general instruction and individual, specialist counselling, and a well-stocked Careers room. The College is a member of ISCO. The Head of Careers arranges work experience and work shadowing for Year 11 and Year 12 students within their potential career fields. Particular attention is paid to preparation for University entrance.

Religious Education. All faiths are respected and, although the Chapel remains a focus for Christian worship, assemblies are provided for those of other faiths.

Pastoral Care and House System. The College is divided into four Houses, each with its own Housemaster or Housemistress and Tutors. Pupils join one of the school Houses on entry and continue in it throughout their school career. Close contact is established and maintained between staff and pupils within the Houses. House activities include music, sport and drama. Alongside the Houses and providing a firm infrastructure for academic and pastoral support and guidance is a Tutorial system by year group. Form Tutors and Heads of Year monitor each pupil's progress and give regular advice on a personal and individual basis.

Medical Care. First aid is provided by a team of fully-qualified first aiders.

Reporting. Regular consultations are held with parents to review each pupil's progress and achievement in terms of both ability and effort and in relation to his or her potential: appointments may be made with the Form Tutor or Heads of Year if parents have cause for concern about any aspect of their child's progress.

Sport. For boys the main sports are Rugby, Football, Hockey and Cricket. The main sports for girls are Hockey, Netball, Tennis and Rounders. For both boys and girls, cross-country races are held in the Lent term and Athletics in the Summer. There are many other sports and options.

Music. The College has a strong tradition of excellence in Music. All pupils receive tuition in Music as part of the normal curriculum and many learn at least one musical instrument, including the organ. There are orchestras, bands and other instrumental groups for all ages within the school. Concerts are given regularly on both competitive and informal bases. Myriad Jazz, based at the College, offers a Youth Jazz Orchestra for the Merseyside area.

Drama. Drama is taught to all pupils up to Year 9. They may then wish to choose a course in Drama for GCSE or IBDP Theatre Arts. School plays and other dramatic productions are staged regularly and as many pupils as possible are encouraged to participate. There is also a House Drama Competition, for which responsibility rests entirely with the members of each House. Staff and pupils in the Art, Music and Drama departments combine to produce a Performing Arts' Evening for parents, guests and students at the end of each school year.

Activities and Societies. There are more than thirty Societies currently operating: these cover many aspects of pupils' interests from Computing to Classics, from Chess to Debating. Teams from the College regularly participate in Debating competitions, among them the Observer Mace and Cambridge Union. Pupils participate in a Community Service Project from Year 9. Over 120 pupils take part in The Duke of Edinburgh's Award Scheme.

Activity holidays, Adventure Training and trips abroad which combine recreation and education are organised regularly.

After School Clubs. After School Clubs are provided for children aged 3–11, enabling them to remain on the school premises under qualified supervision until 6.00 pm each day.

Combined Cadet Force. The voluntary Combined Cadet Force is one of the largest in the UK and has RN, Army and RAF sections: pupils spend 2 years in one of these sections after a year of pre-CCF training. About 50% volunteer for a further two years.

Fees per term (2008-2009). Upper School £2,865, Preparatory School £2,330, Pre-Prep and Nursery £1,805. Reductions for brothers and sisters also apply.

Old Lerpoolians. The school fosters and maintains connections with former pupils through the Old Lerpoolian Society and holds regular functions and reunions. Information may be obtained from the College office, Tel: 0151 724 4000.

Charitable status. Liverpool College is a Registered Charity, number 526682. It exists to provide education for boys and girls.

Llandovery College
(Coleg Llanymddyfri)

Queensway Llandovery Carmarthenshire SA20 0EE
Tel: Reception: 01550 723000
Bursary: 01550 723044
Bursar: 01550 723043
Fax: Bursary: 01550 723047
Reception: 01550 723002
e-mail: mail@llandoverycollege.com
website: www.llandoverycollege.com

Llandovery College sits in over 50 acres of grounds in the beautiful Towy Valley, Wales. The College, endowed by Thomas Phillips in 1847, remains true to its founding values of providing a well-rounded classical and liberal education in a rural setting. Sport, cultural activities and outward bound remain part of the curriculum.

Clerk to the Trustees: Mr T D Williams, BA, FCCA

***Warden*: Mr I M Hunt**, BA, PGCE

Deputy Warden: Mr J G Davies, PGCE, MA Oxon
Bursar: Mr T D Williams, BA, FCCA

Senior School Staff:
Mr B R Banks, BA (*English, Head of Sixth Form, Housemaster Ty Ddewi*)
Mr T J Bayley, BSc (*Biology, Head of Boarding*)
Mr D Bentham, BA Hons, PGCE (*Head of Art*)
Ms L Burgess, BA (*Head of Modern Languages*)
Mr T J Cannock, MA (*Head of Classics*)
Mrs S E Collins, MA Hons, PGCE (*Head of English*)
Revd M Cottam, KMD, DMS, FTC Agric, NDA (*Chaplain*)
Miss D Crichton, BSc, PGCE (*Head of Science*)
Mr P Davies, DipPE (*Head of Rugby*)
Major D Drinkall, BSc (*Head of Outdoor Pursuits, SS1*)
Miss F Earle, BA, PGCE (*Head of Drama*)
Mrs S Finn, BSc, MSc, PGCE (*Head of Mathematics, Head of Careers*)
Miss L Grey, BA, PGCE (*Teacher of Welsh*)
Miss A Hewes, MA Hons, PGCE (*French, Spanish*)
Major C N H Jennings, BSc, PGCE (*Biology, Chemistry, CCF*)
Mrs J Jiang (*Chinese language assistant*)
Mrs S A Jones, CertEd (*Welsh*)
Mr T Jones, MEd (*Head of Business Studies*)
Mrs J D Kendrick, JP, CertEd (*EFL*)
Miss E Lewis, BA, PGCE (*Head of Music, Housemistress Ty Llanofer*)
Mrs J Livings, BEd Hons (*Head of Learning Support*)
Miss K Marshall, BSc, PGCE(*Head of Girls Games, Assistant Housemistress Ty Teilo*)
Mr J M McHale, BA, BTh, PGCE (*Head of Religious Studies*)
A W Morgan, MA, PGCE (*Head of Welsh, Teacher of Business Studies*)
V A Price, BSc, PGCE (*Head of Physics, Examinations Officer*)
Mrs D A Rockey, BSc, PGCE (*Head of Biology, Director of Studies*)
Dr J Rockey, BSc, MSc, PhD (*Head of ICT*)
Mr N Shaw, BSc, PGCE (*Mathematics, Physics, Housemaster*)
Mrs C Spackman, BA, PGCE (*Mathematics*)
Mr P Spowage, BEd (*Design & Technology*)
Mr N A Watts, AdDip, CertEd, MEd (*Head of Design & Technology, Senior Master*)
Ms J Weavers, BA (*Housemistress Ty Teilo*)
Mr A Webster, BA (*History, Housemaster Ty Llandingat*)
Mrs H Whittle, BA, PGCE (*Drama*)
Mr M Williams, BEd Hons (*Director of Sport*)

Prep School Staff:
Acting Headteacher: Mr A Thomas, BSc Hons, PGCE

Mrs P D Bullions, BEd
Mrs K Pemble, BEd
Mrs J Webster, BA, PGCE (*Housemistress Ty Llandingat*)
Classroom Assistants:
Mrs J Dewland
Ms L Morgan

School Medical Officers:
Dr J Richards, MB, BCh
Dr R W Salt, MB, BCh
Dr M J M Boulter, MA, MB BS

Medical Staff:
School Nurse: Mrs A Anwyl-Williams, RN
Mrs J Sanger, RGN RSCN
Mrs A R Jones, RGN RMN ONC

Alumni:
Sir David John (*former Chairman, BOC Group*)
Peter Morgan (*former Director General, Institute of Directors*)
Major General P M Davies (*Former Chief Executive, RSPCA*)
Cerith Rees
Rhydian Roberts
Craig Quinnell
Alun Wyn Jones
Gwyn Jones
Cliff Jones
A M Rees
Vivian Jenkins

Age Range. 3–18.

Number of Pupils. 314: 192 boys, 122 girls; 172 day pupils, 142 boarders.

Progress and Tradition. Since opening its doors in 1848, the College has been the vanguard of educational development. Our aim is to respond positively to the changing needs of society while retaining a commitment to standards and values that are both honourable and endurable. After 150 years, Llandovery College remains the school of choice for those wanting the widest and most fulfilling of educational experience.

Location. The College is set amidst the beautiful countryside of mid Wales in the small, safe market town of Llandovery on the edge of the Brecon Beacons.

Recent Developments. In recent years over £3 million has been invested in new buildings and in the refurbishment of teaching and boarding accommodation. Additions include a floodlit, all-weather pitch, the preparatory school, a new ICT department, a Welsh language centre, medical centre and a boating lake. A state-of-the-art teaching centre opened in 2006.

Curriculum. The College provides a broad, rounded education to all pupils. Standards are high but individuals are respected and rewarded for their overall contribution to College life. Learning support is highly regarded. The College offers more than 22 subjects at GCSE and A Level. Progress reports are issued every half term. The staff:pupil ratio is better than 1:10 and examination results are good.

School Life. Uniform is worn during the working day. Houses arranged by age group and sex with a co-educational house for younger boarders, aged 9–13. Head Boy and Girl appointed by the Warden, House Prefects by House Parents, School Prefects voted for by pupils and appointed by Senior Staff. Religion: Church in Wales. Exchange schemes with schools in France, America and South Africa. Pupils are allowed to bring own car, bike, and motorbike. High quality food is served from a modern kitchen in the Great Hall, built at the turn of the Century.

Sports. Rugby, hockey, cricket, netball, tennis, squash, badminton, fencing, swimming, horse-riding, basketball, athletics and golf. PE may be taken up and including A Level. The College has a long, distinguished reputation in sport, particularly Rugby. Rugby is played in first and second terms finishing with the 7s season. 42 Full Welsh Internationals are former pupils. National representatives in rugby, shooting, athletics and cross-country running. 17 International honours in the last year alone. Hockey is played in the first term and netball and hockey in the second. There are overseas sports tours every two years. Girls and the boys' fixtures lists are impressive, competing against the best schools in the UK. The College has its own 9-hole golf course. Riding and swimming are offered at nearby locations.

Activities. Pupils take bronze, silver and gold Duke of Edinburgh's Award (15+ Gold Awards each year). CCF compulsory for 2 years, optional thereafter. CCF field days are held throughout the year and annual camps take place in the Easter and summer holidays. Many extra-curricular clubs, eg choir, public speaking, orchestra, music, welsh, art, chess. Young enterprise schemes. Considerable emphasis on outdoor pursuits. Superb countryside within striking distance of the

College lends itself to outward-bound activities such as rock climbing, canoeing, hill walking and fishing. Outdoor pursuits trips organised recently include trips to Morocco, Kenya, Russia and Patagonia.

Discipline. Discipline and standards are set at the same level as one would expect in a caring, traditional family. Smoking, drinking and drug taking are forbidden and punishments of varying degrees are applied to match the level of offence committed. Pastoral and disciplining policy are operated through a system of individual tutors, house staff and school prefects.

The Arts. Music and Drama are strong and involve most pupils. There is an annual programme of visiting artists and lecturers. LAMDA exams are taken by prep school pupils who also have the option of ballet lessons. School productions each year including, recently A Midsummer Night's Dream, Joseph, Amadeus, Fiddler on the Roof, Les Misérables, The Sound of Music. Art, Design, Pottery and Photography are offered and enjoy high levels of participation. Over 40% of pupils learn a musical instrument or have singing lessons. Most instruments can be taught privately or by members of the music department. ABRSM instrumental & singing exams can be taken. Musical groups include a school choir, orchestra, swing band, chapel choir, girls choir, senior choir and other ensemble groups.

Boarding. Sixth Formers have their own study bedrooms or share with one other. Houses cater for 50 or less. Resident qualified nurse and a new purpose-built medical centre. Junior houses have dormitories. Houses arranged by age group and sex with a co-educational house for younger boarders, aged 9–13. Laundry services provided. Two Exeat weekends per term. Visits to local market town allowed. Campus is friendly, mixing across age groups and after school socialising in boarding life is vibrant. Sixth Formers have their own common room equipped with TV, games and comfortable seating. ICT Centre and Library opens late every night for studying. Lively and varied weekend programme of activities. Lessons on Saturday mornings.

Careers Service. Comprehensive Careers Service support for pupils with regular visits by the Regional Director of the Independent Schools Careers Organisation, the Forces Liaison Officers and the West Wales Careers Service. Well equipped to give advice on higher education.

Admission. Main entry ages are 3, 7, 11, 13, 16 however pupils are welcome at other entry levels. 5% are children of former pupils. Entrance Examinations are usually sat at the College using our own papers. Several exam sessions between January and July. Prep school entrants are invited to spend a day at the school for assessment. Six GCSEs at grade C or above required for Sixth Form entry.

Scholarships and Bursaries. (*see Scholarship Entries section*). Thomas Phillips Scholars may receive 100% of boarding or day fees for their entire education. This is a means-tested scholarship for academically-able Welsh children. Non means-tested scholarships are available for academic, musical, artistic, dramatic and sporting ability/potential. Exhibitions are awarded on the same grounds but for smaller sums. Scholarships and Exhibitions are contractual agreements and the benefits will be withdrawn if the pupil fails to maintain their enthusiasm for the scholarship activities. In cases of financial hardship a parent may be offered a bursary based on particular circumstances.

Fees per term (2008-2009). Senior School: Day £4,270, Boarding £6,313, Overseas £6,918. Preparatory School: Day: £1,950 (Pre-Prep), £2,040 (Prep); Boarding £4,083.

Charitable status. Llandovery College is a Registered Charity, number 1111878. It exists for the purpose of educating children from the age of 3 to 18.

Lomond School

10 Stafford Street Helensburgh Argyll and Bute G84 9JX
Tel: 01436 672476
Fax: 01436 678320
e-mail: admin@lomond-school.org
website: www.lomond-school.org

Lomond is a co-educational day and boarding school for pupils aged from 3 to 18 years. The original foundations date from 1845 and the current roll is 592 pupils, including 70 boarders who are housed in a brand new building with en-suite study bedrooms completed in March 2003. A new main building was opened in October 1998 and facilities and examination results are superb.

Twenty five miles from Glasgow, Europe's City of Culture in 1990, Helensburgh is situated on the north bank of the Firth of Clyde in a quiet residential setting and with immediate access to mountain, sea and loch – ideal for outdoor activities.

Board of Governors:
Chairman: Mrs C Dobson, BSc, MSI
Vice-Chairman: Mr D M Mitchell, CA
Mr C M Burnet, CA
Dr T D Dunlop, MBChB
Dr J M Girkin, BA Oxon, PhD
Mr A J D Hope, LLB
Mrs T Kelbie, BA, PGCE
Mr A D Livingstone, BSc, DipEd
Mr T Smith, BSc Hons, MEd
Mrs A Stanley-Whyte, LLB Hons, Dip LP, NP
Mr F Thornton, BA, CA

Staff:

***Headmaster*: Mr A D Macdonald**, MA Hons Cantab, DipEd

Depute Headmaster: Mr W G MacKenzie, MA Hons, MPhil, MLitt, CertEd
Assistant Headmistress: Miss N Dudley, MA Hons Oxon, DipEd
Assistant Headmaster: Mr A Minnis, MA Hons, PGCE, Cert PP
Head of Primary: G Calder, MA Hons, PGCE

Subject Teachers – Secondary:
§ *Part-time Staff*

Art & Design:
Mrs B Croft, BA Hons, CertEd
§Miss D Wood, BA Hons, CertEd

Business Studies:
§Mrs C McElhill, BA Hons, CertEd

Drama:
§Mrs A Ritchie, MA, PGCE

English:
Dr M E Everett, BA Hons, PhD, DipEd
Dr R Russell, MA Hons, DipEd, MEd, PhD
Mrs P Wales, MA Hons
Mrs M McKillop, MA Hons, MPhil, PGCE

Geography:
Mr G M Taylor, BSc, MSc, DipEd, Comp CertEd
Mr R Ledingham, MA Hons, PGCE

Graphic Communication:
Miss K Mason, BA Hons, PGCE

History:
Mrs S Guy, MA Hons, PGCE
Mr A Minnis, MA Hons, PGCE
Miss E Travena, MA Hons, PGCE

ICT:
Mr S J Kilday, DipTechEd, DipComp

Learning Support:
Mr H Hunter, BA, DipLS
§Mrs C Greaves, BSc Hons, PGCE
§Mrs J Baird, DipEd

Mathematics:
Mr G Macleod, BSc Hons, MEd, CMath, PGCE
Mr A Laceby, BA, DipMath, PGCE
Miss G Molland, BSc Hons, DipEd
§Mrs E Cameron, BSc Hons, DipEd

Modern Languages:
Mr A Greig, MA Hons, DipEd
Miss N Dudley, MA Hons Oxon, DipEd
Mrs A E Robertson, MA, CertEd
§Mrs J Robertson, BEd
Miss E Clarke, BA Hons, PGCE
§Miss I Skowranski, MA Hons, PGCE

Modern Studies:
Mrs S Guy, MA Hons, PGCE
Miss E Travena, MA Hons, PGCE

Music:
Mrs A Lyon, DRSAMD, CertEd
Mr I MacDonald, DipMusEd, CertEd

Physical Education:
Mrs M G Taylor, BEd
Mr D Fitzgerald, BEd Hons
Mrs J Fitzgerald, BEd

Religious Education:
§Mrs A Ritchie, MA, CertEd

Science
Dr A E Tully, BSc Hons, PhD, PGCE
Mr C Butler, BSc Hons, DipEd
Mr D L Dodson, BSc Hons, DipEd
Miss M Ward, BSc Hons, PGCE
Mrs E Hunter, BSc Hons, MEd, CertEd
Mrs C Normand, BSc Hons, PGCE

Careers Advisor:
Mrs J Barrett-Bunnage, MA Hons, PG Dip CG

Class Teachers – Transitus:
Mrs J Brown, CertPEd
Mrs C Greig, BA Jt Hons, CertEd, DipEdTech
Mrs J Fullarton, BEd

Class Teachers – Clarendon:
Mr G Calder, MA Hons, PGCE
§Mrs S Gardiner, DipPE, CertEd
Mrs V Cassels, MA Hons, MA, BSc, DipEnvDev, PGCE
Mrs J Macleod, BEd Hons, MEd
Mr O Carter, BA Hons, QTS Ed & Prof Studies with PE
Mrs V McLatchie, BEd
Miss S Murphy, MA Hons, PGCE
Miss A Springett, BSc Hons, PGCE
Miss L Boyd, BSc Hons, PGCE
Mrs L Robertson, DipEd

Nursery/Pre-School Group:
Mrs J Reynolds, CertEd
Ms A Goram, SNNEB
Ms L Lovell, SPA Childcare
Mrs J McArthur, SNNEB
Mrs H Windsor, SNNEB

Mrs J Ferguson (*Clarendon Assistant*)
Mrs J Marrison (*Clarendon Assistant*)
Mrs F Reid, SNNEB (*Clarendon Assistant*)
Mrs G Thomas (*Clarendon Assistant*)

Aims of the School. Lomond has a proud academic tradition and 90% of the Sixth Form will leave to attend University or College. However, it aims to get the best from every pupil regardless of talent and successfully caters for the 'average' youngster as well as those with high ability. It believes strongly in developing the whole person and instilling a 'do it' philosophy.

Class sizes average fifteen and there is a close monitoring of all pupils both academically and for extra-curricular input. The school has the distinct advantage of selecting the best features of the Scottish and English examination systems. Pupils sit Scottish Certificate of Education S grade and Higher examinations in Senior 4 and Senior 5 before sitting A levels in the Sixth Form. Maintaining both breadth and depth in senior years enables there to be a flexible approach to individual needs which means that a complete range of ability is successfully catered for.

Extra-curricular. The philosophy of the school looks to involvement in the extensive extra-curricular programme from every pupil. It is expected that pupils will take part in the main sports of rugby, hockey, and athletics and in the Duke of Edinburgh's Award Scheme. There are teams for football, cricket and tennis and a wide variety of activities are strongly represented. Fixtures against other schools take place every weekend and there is a very extensive outdoor education programme. Music and drama are also strong and a plethora of pupils have achieved success at the highest level.

Some distinctive aspects. Nine staff hold outdoor education qualifications and the extensive Duke of Edinburgh's Award Scheme programme leads to participation in such events as the Lomond Challenge Triathlon (a national event) and the Scottish Islands Peaks Race. A week long 'Outward Bound' programme has been developed for the school which concentrates on leadership and teamwork skills. There are annual wilderness expeditions.

The Traditional Music Scholarship has led to the school developing an international reputation in this area of expertise.

The international dimension is significant not only with long established exchanges and work experience abroad but also due to special arrangements that have encouraged pupils from abroad to study at Lomond which broadens the outlook of the school's pupils and leads to greater international understanding.

State-of-the-art boarding, sporting and teaching facilities.

Entry and Scholarships. Academic scholarships are available at Senior 1, Senior 5 and Senior 6 and are worth 25%–50% of tuition fees as are the Traditional Music scholarships. Significant Service bursaries restrict payment to £690 per term.

Admission is by examination in English and Mathematics for 11–13 year olds. For younger pupils placement in classes is the main requirement whilst for senior pupils reports and examination results are given due weighting.

Fees per term (2008-2009). Tuition: £895 (Nursery), £1,375 (Junior 1), £2,015 (Junior 2), £2,355 (Junior 3–5), £2,570 (Transitus), £2,720 (Transitus 2), £2,805 (Senior School).

Boarding (in addition to Tuition Fees): £3,195 (full), £45 (daily per night).

A levy of £50 per pupil per term is payable along with tuition fees.

Charitable status. Lomond School Ltd is a Registered Charity, number SC007957. It exists to provide education for boys and girls.

Lord Wandsworth College

Long Sutton Hook Hampshire RG29 1TB
Tel: 01256 862201 (Main Office)
01256 860348 (Headmaster)
01256 860200 (Admissions)
Fax: 01256 860363
e-mail: info@lordwandsworth.org
website: www.lordwandsworth.org

Lord Wandsworth College is a co-educational secondary school for 530 pupils between the ages of 11 and 18. There are approximately 215 weekly boarders, 50 full boarders and 265 day pupils.

Motto: '*Vincit Perseverantia.*'

President: Sir Humphrey Prideaux, OBE, DL, MA

Chairman of Governors: R G Janaway

The Governing Body consists of 12 governors.

***Headmaster*: I G Power**, MA

Deputy Heads:
Dr T Johnson, BSc
S L Badger, MA

Foundation Registrar: (*to be appointed*)

Bursar: A C Usborne, BSc

Assistant Staff:
Mrs V Allan, BA
Miss B Anderson, BA
Mrs S Badger, MA
P Y Booth, BA
Mrs J Campbell, BSc
Mrs L Chapple, BSc
E Coetzer, BA
Mrs D Croft, BA
M Curran, BSc
Dr M R Eldridge, BSc, PhD
A L Eysele, BSc
Mrs C D Eysele, BA
Mrs L Faulkner, MA, BSc
P Finan, BSc
P M Gilliam, BSc
A O F Hamilton, MA
C C Hicks, MA
T C Hicks, BA
D P Ibbotson, BSc
C Irvine, BSc
I S Kerr, MA
R J Kimber, BSc
Mrs P Kimber, MA
Revd S Leyshon
Miss C Liggins, BA
C Lovelock, Bed
Mrs R Lovelock, BSc
Mrs S Ludlow, BSc
A Lumsden, BSc
D O C Machin, BA
Miss S Mactier, BA
S P Matthews, BA
G A McKinnon, BA
Mrs J M McKinnon, BA
G J Mobbs, BA
A Murray, MA
Mrs G R Neighbour
B Noithip, BA
D C Pering, MA
M Perriss, MA
Mrs L D Power, BA
C H Radmann, BA
Mrs L A Radmann, BA
Mrs N Reeson, BA
Mrs S Richardson, BA
T R Richardson, BA Hons Ed
Mrs P Sandham, BSc
T J Shedden, BA
Miss M Sinclair-Smith, BA
G R Smith, BA
Mrs H Tomlinson, BA
E Walker, BSc
R G Walters, BSc
D L Widdowson, BSc
A Williams, BSc
Mrs C J Wisdom, CertEd, RSA DipSpLD
C Wiskin

Librarian: Mrs S Brown

Director of Admissions & Marketing: Mrs M Hicks

Development Director: Mrs K Chernyshov

Headmaster's Secretary: Mrs P Gray

Medical Officers:
Dr R Assadourian, MB BS, BSc Hons, MRCGP, DRCOG, DFFP
Dr C Shand, MB BS, LMSSA, MRCGP, DRCOG, DFFP

Location and accessibility. The school is fortunate in that, although it occupies a magnificent rural setting on the edge of the rolling North Hampshire/Surrey border, it has excellent communications, being five miles from Junction 5 of the M3 and under an hour from London. Access to main line trains and all major airports is quick and easy.

Many pupils come from the surrounding towns and villages around Farnham, Alton, Fleet, Basingstoke, Guildford and Reading, and there is a well-established tradition of such children weekly boarding although living relatively close-by.

History. Lord Wandsworth died in 1912 and left a large sum of money for the foundation of a school. The College that bears his name now occupies a 1,200 acre site. The Lord Wandsworth Foundation awards a number of places annually to children who have lost the support of one or both parents through death, divorce or separation with priority to those who have lost a parent through death.

Mission statement. Lord Wandsworth College is a non-denominational foundation which fosters the intellectual, moral and spiritual development of all the young people in its care. It strives to ensure that each pupil realises his or her full potential within a stimulating environment which emphasises concern for others.

The outstanding features of the school are

- that almost all academic staff live on campus allowing them to provide a high level of pastoral care;
- that all pupils, whether day, weekly or full boarding, belong to one of the eight boarding houses and are fully integrated into the social life of the school;
- that the school is purpose-built with an outstanding range of facilities for both academic and extra-curricular activities;
- that the school is an unusually unpretentious, caring community. It is a happy and relaxed community.

Curriculum. The aim of the curriculum is to provide a full and flexible range of subjects to fit the needs of each individual. The school's policy is to follow closely the National Curriculum.

Subjects taught to GCSE are: English (Language and Literature), French, Geography, Mathematics, History, Latin, Classical Civilisation, Drama, Physics, Chemistry, Biology, Spanish, German, Art, Music, Design & Technology and Religious Studies.

Most pupils continue into the Sixth Form where the subjects taught to AS and A2 Level are: English, History, Geography, Economics, Business Studies, Classical Civilisation, Music, Latin, French, Spanish, German, Physics, Chemistry, Biology, Mathematics, Further Mathematics, Art, Design, Theatre Studies, PE, Religious Studies, Music Technology and Psychology.

ICT. There has been, and continues to be, significant investment into IT provision. There is a wireless networked system across the whole school.

Games. The school lays great store by its games involvement and has a local and national reputation for many of its pursuits. The main boys' games are rugby, hockey and cricket and for girls hockey, netball and tennis. In addition swimming, athletics, squash, badminton, basketball, golf, cross-country running and canoeing all take place and provide teams which represent the school.

Drama. Drama has a high profile within the school and several shows are staged each year. There is a musical production every other year as well as showcases, reviews and workshops. Pupils are encouraged to participate in all fields of drama either acting, writing, set design, lighting, stage management, prop-making or sound.

Music. There is a large variety of instrumental ensembles, including an orchestra, swing band and many chamber and rock groups. Pupils sing in two choirs. Tuition is available in singing, all orchestral instruments, piano, organ, percussion and guitar. Musicians regularly perform formally and informally both within school and at local venues.

Other activities. There is an extensive extra-curricular programme. Some of the activities on offer are: Cookery, Soccer, Roller Hockey, Chess, Pottery, Drama clubs, Mountain Biking, Horticulture, Archery, Dance, Photography, School newspaper, Life-saving, Self-defence, Scuba-diving, Debating and Climbing.

The Duke of Edinburgh's Award Scheme is thriving and the College has its own licence to run the scheme. There is an active CCF programme for Year 10 pupils and above which has an Army and Air Force Section. All Sixth Form pupils take part in a Community Service programme.

Organisation. There is a two or three form entry at age 11. For the first two years all pupils are in the co-educational Junior House which has its own buildings and sports fields. At 13 there is another entry, mainly from children who have taken Common Entrance. All houses are in the charge of Houseparents assisted by a team of tutors and matrons.

Fees per term (2008-2009). (*see Scholarship Entries section*). Senior Full Boarders £7,918, Senior Weekly Boarders £7,538, Senior Day Pupils £5,618, Junior Boarders £7,142, Junior Day Pupils £5,333.

Charitable status. Lord Wandsworth College Trust is a Registered Charity, number 272050. It exists to provide education for boys and girls.

Loretto School

Musselburgh Near Edinburgh East Lothian EH21 7RE

Tel: School: 0131 653 4444
Headmaster: 0131 653 4441
Admissions: 0131 653 4455
Fax: School: 0131 653 4445
Admissions: 0131 653 4456
e-mail: admissions@loretto.com
website: www.loretto.com

Loretto has flourished as a school since its establishment in 1827, 6 miles from Edinburgh, on the banks of the River Esk and surrounded by the beautiful countryside of East Lothian. It is a non-denominational, co-educational boarding and day school and provides for full and flexi boarders, as well as for day pupils, with a distinctive emphasis on the full development of the individual through academic, intellectual, sporting, musical, dramatic and artistic pursuits in a fine, secure environment. Loretto's distinctive ethos fosters in its pupils a quiet confidence in themselves and a spirit of readiness to succeed in the changing world beyond school. Loretto is a small community where staff and pupils know each other personally. Classes are deliberately small so that proper individual attention is possible; recent examination results have been outstanding. Boys and girls take part in a very wide range of activities. Its pupils, from 3 to 18 years, are known and valued for themselves and are expected to respect and support each other. The School makes fullest use of its proximity to Edinburgh, enabling pupils to take advantage of the music, drama, museums and art galleries, as well as giving opportunities for sport and leisure in this capital city. To the east lie the golf courses which provide the fairway for The Golf Academy at Loretto.

Governors:
R L Martin, QC (*Chairman*)
P Arthur (*Vice-Chairman*)
M Black
Mrs A Brobbel
D Christie
Mrs S Geddes
Lt Col S J M Graham
M Hinton
R J Semple
M Simmers
Mrs A Swanson
R D G Walker
W Waterhouse

Clerk and Secretary: R M Urquhart WS, 16 Heriot Row, Edinburgh EH3 6HR

***Headmaster*: P A Hogan**, BCom, PGCE, MA, FRSA

Headmaster of Junior School: R G Selley, BEd (*Business Studies*)

Staff:
* *Head of Department*
† *Housemaster/mistress*

Miss J Addis, BA Hons (*English*)
D Allott, BA, BA, PGCE (**Classics*)
M J Baker, MA (*Physics*)
Mrs M Bonner, BA Hons, MA, PGCE, DIS (**Art*)
A J R Brown, BA, MA (**English*)
M T Brown, BMus Hons, MMus (*Music*)
Mrs A Buchanan, BA (*Art*)
J D Burnet, MA (**Modern Languages*)
D A Burton, BEd (*Director of Sport*)
Miss C Cadzow, BDes Hons (*Art, Ceramics*)
Miss E Chisholm, BSc, PGCE (*Mathematics*)
W E Coleman, MMus (*Director of Music*)
Mr B Cooper, MA Hons (*Director of Studies;History and Politics*)
Mrs C A Cursiter, MA (*Modern Languages*)
W D Dickinson, BEd (*†Schoolhouse; Geography*)
Mrs J Dunford (*Head Librarian*)
P S Dunn, BSc (*Mathematics; Careers Adviser*)
J M Elder, BA, MLitt (**History and Politics; Further Education Adviser*)
K N Erskine, BSc (**Information Technology*)
Ms S Feria (*Modern Languages*)
Mrs J Fletcher, BSc, PGCE (*Biology; *Girls' Games; †Balcarres*)
Dr Ian Fox, Cert Sec Ed (*Physics, Mathematics*)
Mrs M Galloway, MA Hons (*Modern Languages*)
Miss C A Hartley, BSc, MSc, PGCE (*Biology*)
J Karolyi, PGCE (*Modern Languages*)
Revd A F C Keulemans, BEd (*Chaplain*)
Mrs C Lekkas, BSc Hons, DipTEFL/TESOL (*ESL*)
Dr D Levey, BSc, PhD (*Mathematics*)
S J M Lowe, MA (*Director of Expressive Arts; Modern Languages*)
S Lucas, MLitt (**Support Learning*)
H M MacLean, BSc (*Geography; Deputy Head*)
Mrs K McLean (*†Holm*)
D McLean-Steel, BA (**Drama; English*)
G McSkimming, BSc, PGCE (**Physics*)
Mrs E Middlemass, MA, PGCE (*Assistant Head, Senior School Pastoral Care; English and Drama*)
P Middleton, BA, PGCE (*English; Assistant†Hope*)
P Middleton, MA (*ESL*)
Mrs R Newlands, BSc (*Support for Learning*)
Mrs A Peak, BA Hons, PGCE (*Head of Geography*)
D Pierce, BSc Hons, PGCE (**Mathematics*)
Pipe Major C Pryde (*Piping*)
D H Rossouw, BSc (*†Hope; Sports Coach*)
Ms H Scanlon, BA PGDipILS (*Assistant Librarian*)
Mrs J Scott (*Support for Learning*)
Dr M G Topping, BSc Hons, PhD (*Biology*)
J R Torrance, MA (**Biology*)
R I Valentine (*Director of Golf; Assistant†Seton*)
Ms S Ward, BSc, PGCE (**Chemistry*)
R P Whait, BSc (*Director of Activities;*Business Studies*)
G W Young, BSc (*Physics; †Seton*)
Miss J Young (*ESL*)

Houses and Housemasters/Housemistresses:

Boys Boarding:
Hope House: D H Rossouw
Seton House: G W Young

Girls Boarding:
Balcarres House: Mrs J Fletcher
Holm House: Mrs K McLean

Day (Boys and Girls):
Schoolhouse: W D Dickinson

Junior Boarding:
Newfield House: D Pearce

Bursar: A Lawson, BA, CA
Director of Admissions: Miss F Stevenson
Director of Marketing: Mrs B Lamotte

Junior School
Headmaster: R G Selley, BEd

Staff:
Mrs J Brown (*After School Club*)
Mrs K Brown (*Classroom Assistant*)
Mrs E Burgess, BEd Hons
J P Clark, BEd
Mrs C Davies (*Science*)
Mrs N Dinwoodie (*Nursery Nurse*)
Ms E Donald, MA Hons, PGCE
Mrs A Gauld, DCE, ACE (*Nursery Teacher*)
Mrs S Gold (*Year 3*)
K Hutchison, DipTMus (**Music*)
Miss S A Kettlewell, BA (*Art & Drama*)
Mrs J O'Raw (*Nursery Assistant*)
D J Pearce, BSc (*Mathematics*)
Mrs M Reeves, BSc (*Learning Support*)
Ms K Reid, PGDE Primary
Mrs S Scott, BEd
Mrs E Karolyi, MA Hons, PGCE
Miss K Seabra, BEd
Ms E Shaw, BA (*Nursery Teacher*)
Mrs F Torrance, MA (*English; Year 6*)
Ms C Ward, BA (*French; Year 7*)
Mrs L M Watson, MEd (*Deputy Head; Head of Early Years*)

The Senior School consists of 340 boys and girls with over 70% of pupils boarding.

Academic. An excellent staff/pupil ratio ensures an environment that stimulates, supports and nurtures the potential in everyone. The academic programme aims to challenge pupils and to recognise and reward effort and attainment. A full range of curricular subjects – humanities; drama, music and art; languages and sciences; ICT and business; physical education – is offered. The depth, breadth and quality of a Loretto education encourages each pupil to achieve his or her personal best and to enjoy doing so. Pupils are prepared for success in IGCSE, GCSE, AS, Advanced Extension Awards and A Level and for a choice of good university careers thereafter. The School is also running the AQA Extension Project Scheme which contributes to UCAS points. In 2007 Over half of all A Levels sat were at grade A. 97% of GCSEs were at A–C grades. 14 members of the UVI (a cohort of 47 pupils) achieved straight A grades.

Virtually all pupils go on to higher education.

The facilities keep abreast of changing national academic demands, with modern, well-equipped specialist areas in languages, art and design, music, drama and the sciences. The Communication and Resource Centre provides a traditional library as well as a computer network which can be accessed from academic departments and Houses. All pupils become familiar both with modern technology and with books, to facilitate independent learning, essential for success in Higher Education and beyond. The Support for Learning department assists the academically gifted as well as those who have a learning difficulty or those who simply want to improve essential study skills.

Pastoral Care. There are six houses where full and flexi boarders and day pupils can relax "at home", socialise and develop their studies under the experienced supervision of dedicated resident pastoral teams. The House structure is: 4 boarding houses (2 for Sixth Form and 2 for Third, Fourth and Fifth Form), 1 Junior boarding house (boy and girl) and 1 day house (boy and girl). There is excellent pastoral care, nurturing an atmosphere of mutual care and support in which children mature at their own pace and older pupils are encouraged to take responsibility, not just for themselves, but for their young housemates.

Younger pupils sleep in small dormitories, while sixth formers have individual study bedrooms.

The day pupils at Loretto have access to the same broad and full education provided for boarders, and are able to take full advantage of the facilities of a boarding school, while returning home to sleep.

All academic staff are involved in the boarding houses and so staff are always on hand to guide and encourage. The aim is always to ensure that the well-being and development of every pupil is closely and sympathetically monitored. An excellent programme of personal, social and health education is an integral part of the curriculum.

Health. A medical centre staffed twenty-four hours a day by professional nurses, with a daily doctor's surgery, monitors health issues closely and supports the residential matron in each House. In addition, a counsellor visits the School each week.

Music, Drama and Art. Loretto is well known for the excellent quality of its Expressive Arts. Pupils are encouraged to enjoy the creative arts and to develop their individual talents. A purpose-built Music School enables a very high proportion to learn individual instruments or to take voice lessons and there is a range of concerts, recitals and performances both in School and in venues in Edinburgh and East Lothian. The choir and orchestra practise weekly. All pupils enjoy whole School choral singing in chapel, while performance music extends from rock, through jazz to classical music. The Loretto Pipe Band competes successfully in national competitions and has a busy schedule of appearances. A theatre is the base for much drama work, with performances – both musical and dramatic – each term involving pupils of all ages. The theatre facilities have been refurbished to provide performance areas and technical facilities to the highest specifications. There is also a newly equipped studio theatre and state-of-the-art recording studio. The Art department offers drawing, painting, mixed media, ceramics, photography, sculpture and lino-printing. The School's art gallery allows pupil work to be displayed as well as housing outside exhibitions that encourage experimentation with different techniques and styles.

Games and Activities. Pupils are encouraged to enjoy exercise and to develop their skills. The Golf Academy at Loretto is fast becoming known as the best independent golfing school in Britain, with on-site facilities and professional coaching. Provision is also made for rugby, hockey, lacrosse, athletics, cricket, tennis, squash, fives, badminton, swimming, shooting, and basketball, to name but a few. A well-equipped fitness centre, squash courts and an astroturf pitch are also on site. Riding, sailing, skiing and snowboarding are available using excellent local facilities. Team games are important: boys play rugby, hockey and cricket; girls, hockey, lacrosse and netball. There is an extensive range of fixtures for both boys and girls at all levels. Participation in the Duke of Edinburgh's Award scheme is strong and the Combined Cadet Force offers additional experience of a range of skills and challenges. A full programme of activities, from karate to hip hop dance, operates each day and all weekend.

Sixth Form. Preparing its pupils for the world beyond school is something that Loretto takes very seriously. Loretto's Sixth Form is structured to encourage boys and girls to take more responsibility for their work and the organisation of their time. Academic tutors and mentors are there at every step to provide encouragement and guidance. There is a richer options programme to enable them to enjoy concerts, theatres, lectures and social time in Edinburgh and to organise social evenings and supper parties within school. The focus turns more fully to the world beyond school, career choices are prepared for by a structured programme of guidance; work experience, Young Enterprise and an Understanding Industry Conference, broaden horizons and encourage pupils to learn their strengths. There is a teamworking programme and life skills courses. Dedicated staff help with university applications procedure and a programme of careers talks guide them to consider a range of choices. Many outside speakers come to talk to the sixth form on a wide range of topics.

Religion. Services are held in the School Chapel every week. The services are non-denominational and boys and girls are prepared for confirmation in both the Church of England and the Church of Scotland; they are confirmed at a combined service held in the Chapel. Whole School singing is a long-standing tradition at Loretto and continues to be memorable.

Developments. A Loretto Foundation has been established to provide for the mid to long-term future of the School. A major programme of development has taken place to give six new science laboratories, four new classrooms, a further Art room and ICT room, a lecture theatre, and a state-of-the-art recording studio, all equipped to a very high standard. There is also an ongoing programme of refurbishment in the houses.

Uniform. The uniform is practical and comfortable. Formal dress on Sundays is the kilt for boys and girls. Ordinary School dress is charcoal trousers for boys, navy skirts for girls, with white shirts and the distinctive red jacket.

Entrance Examination. Boys and girls are required to pass either the Common Entrance Examination or the Open Assessment Examination in English, Mathematics and Verbal Reasoning before being admitted, as well as an interview. Entrance for the Lower Sixth is based on interview and assessment in English, Mathematics and Verbal Reasoning at the School; places are then offered subject to a satisfactory performance at GCSE/Standard Grade.

Junior School. 'The Nippers' enjoy many of the facilities of the Senior School, such as the playing fields, Theatre, Sports Hall, Swimming Pool, Music School and Chapel. The boys and girls are under closer adult supervision than in the Senior School but in other respects the system is similar. There are just over 200 boys and girls aged between 3 and 12. The majority are day pupils, but occasional, weekly and full boarding are all encouraged. *(For further details, see entry in IAPS Section.)*

Fees per term (2008-2009). Full Boarding: Senior School £5,325–£8,150, Junior School £5,325. Weekly Boarding in the Junior School £4,825.

These fees include all the expenses of board, lodging, laundry, most text books (though in the sixth form text books may have to be purchased), stationery, games material, medical attendance and medicine, CCF, transport to matches and internal school entertainments.

Day Fees (including meals): Senior School £3,995–£5,540; Junior School £1,895–£3,820.

Optional Expenses. These will be kept to a minimum, but include individual voice and instrumental music lessons; extra-curricular visits and expeditions.

Scholarships. (*see Scholarship Entries section*). The Second and Third Form Academic Scholarships are usually held in February/March and are taken at Loretto. There are also All-Rounder, Music, Drama, Art, Golf and Sports scholarships in recognition of outstanding general, musical, sporting or artistic promise. There are scholarships for Sixth Form entrants from both private and state sectors; these are usually taken in November, although, if funds permit, they will be awarded throughout the year.

Leaving Scholarships. A number of awards are given to assist with university education to those who have 'deserved well of Loretto' in recognition of their loyalty and service to the School.

Old Lorettonian Society. *Hon Secretary*: Mr N G C McDowall, Loretto School, Musselburgh.

Charitable status. Loretto School is a Registered Charity, number SC013978. It exists in order to educate young people in mind, body and spirit.

Loughborough Grammar School

Burton Walks Loughborough Leicestershire LE11 2DU
Tel: 01509 233233/233258
Fax: 01509 218436
e-mail: registrar@lesgrammar.org
website: www.lesgrammar.org

Loughborough Grammar School was founded in 1495 by Thomas Burton, Merchant of the Staple of Calais, though it is probable that the Trustees of the Town Charity were managing a free school well before that date. The School is itself part of a larger 'family' known as the Loughborough Endowed Schools. Situated in the spacious and attractive grounds surrounding the Grammar School are Loughborough High School for Girls (*see GSA entry*) and Fairfield School, our co-educational Preparatory School (*see IAPS entry*). Links between all three are very strong.

Motto: *Vires acquirit eundo.*

Governing Body:
Chairman: H M Pearson, BA Econ, LLB, ACIS
Vice-Chairman: A D Emson, BPharm, MRPharmS

Non-Executive Vice-Chairmen:
G P Fothergill, BA, FCIM
Dr P J B Hubner, MB, FRCP, DCH, FACC, FESC
Professor J Feather, BLitt, MA, PhD, FLA

Nominative Governors:
A J Bowen, MA Cambridge
Professor D Robertson, MA, PhD Oxford

Co-optative Governors:
Professor S F Brown, OBE, DSc, FREng
Dr A de Bono, MA, MB, BChir, MFOM
Mrs M Gershlick, RGN, DipNEd
D Godfrey, BSc, CEng, FIEE
The Lady Gretton, JP, Lord-Lieutenant of Leicestershire
Dr J E Hammond, BDS
I A Hawtin, BA, MA
P M Jackson, FIMI
A M Kershaw
W M Moss, D Univ Hon
M Mulla, BSc, MSc, MIM
Mrs J G E Page, JP
Mrs C Wales

Foundation Secretary & Treasurer: K D Shaw, MBE, MSc, FCIS

***Headmaster*: P B Fisher**, MA Christ Church, Oxford

Deputy Headmaster: J S Weitzel, BSc
Director of Studies & Deputy Headmaster: T G Willmott, BSc, PhD
Head of Main School: C L Davies, CEd, BA
Head of Sixth Form: C G Walker, MA, PhD
Under Master: P S Sergeant, BEd, MPhil
Chaplain: Revd Canon A J S Cox, MA
Professional Development Officer: D W Steele, BSc
Registrar/Marketing: Mrs D P Briers
Headmaster's PA: Mrs K Rajput

Assistant Staff:
W Atkins, BSc
Miss N Bahl, BSc
Mrs H Baker, BEd
R J Ball, BSc, PhD
A W G Ballentyne, MA, MLitt, AssocRHS
Miss E Bancroft, BA
Mrs D C Barrett, BSc, PhD

Mrs H Beardsworth, BA
Ms S Bell, BA
R Bhattacharyya, BA
C W Blackman, BA
M S E Broadley, BA
Dr K Buckley, MA, PhD, BA
P D Bunting, MA
M D Butcher, BSc, MSc
Mrs R M Butterfield, MA, MLitt
Miss K Cartwright, BEng
Miss L Christie, BA
J Clarke
Miss S Cleveley, BSc
Mrs H J Coles, BA
C V Collington, BA
Mrs R L Cooch, BSc
Miss P Cumine, BA, MA
R E Davies, BSc, MSc
M Dawkins, BA, MA
A J Dossett, BSc
R Doyle, BSc
Dr N M A Ebden
S Else, BA, MPhil, PhD
D L Evans, BSc
Miss E Faircliffe
C B Faust, BSc, MEd, CChem, FRSC
C J Feakes, BSc, MSc
Mrs H Fisher, BA, MA
Mrs R French, BEd
P Gacs, MA
M I Gidley
M Green, BSc, PhD
R T Griffiths, BA
A J Haigh, MA
S D Hatfield, BEng
R J Head, BA
R C Healey, PhD, BEng
C S Herbert, BSc
Mrs M C Herring, BSc
G L Horvath, BSc
J E Hunt, MA
P Jackson, BSc

Mrs H E James, BA
Miss S Jenkins, BA
M R Jennings, BA
Mrs D Kaur, BA
R F Kerr, MA
N Khan, BSc, MSc
Mrs E Lax, BA, LTCL
R L Lightfoot, BA, MA
N Lipotov, PhD
A Lloyd, BSc
Mrs N Vicente-Lorente
Dr C Luke
P M Marlow, BSc
B K McCabe, MA
J Mellors, BA
R Michalak, BA
D J Miles, BSc
Miss Z Mir, LLB
Mrs V Morandi
T D Morse, BSc, MSc
A Moreton, BA
A Morris, BA
Mrs C Nelson, ATD, MA
D S Northwood, MA
Miss J E Orr, BA
Mrs D Outwin-Flinders, BEd
R B Parish, BSc, MSc
J S Parton, MA
M Peake, BA
N Pollock, BA
Mrs A Quigley, BA
J M Rees, MA, PhD
M J Rundle, BEd
J P Salter, BSc
P Smith, BEd, MA
D M Starkings, BSc, BA
R Statham, BSc
G I Sutcliffe, BA
Mrs V Thompson, BA
H T Tunnicliffe, BEd
P Viccars, BA
Miss H Walters, MA
A D Waters, PhD
Mrs A Whitehead, BA
R C Wright, BEd

Music:
A J Mitchell, BA, LLCM (*Director of LES Music School*)
Dr P J Underwood, MA, MMus, PhD, FRCO CHM, FTCL, LRAM, ARCM, ADCM (*Head of Senior Curriculum*)
T H Lax, LRAM, CertEd (*Head of Performance Studies*)
Mrs A McGee, GTCL Hons, LTCL (*Head of Junior Music*)
Dr A Bean, BMus Hons, PGCE, LRAM, AMusD (*GCSE/AS/A2 & Instrumental-Piano*)
Mrs E Foulds, GRSM Hons, LRAM, PGCE (*KS3 and Instrumental-Piano*)
Miss C Revell, BMus Hons (*KS1, KS2, KS3*)
Mrs E Lax, BA, LTCL, CertEd (*Year 6, LGS Music & KS3*)

Visiting Music Teachers:
Mr J Bean, LRAM, CertEd, LGSM MT (*Cello*)
Miss J Bevan, BMus, LTCL, PGCE (*Flute, Clarinet*)
Mr J Boyd, DipMus (*Guitar*)
Mrs K Burns, BA Hons, LLCM, ALCM (*Violin, Viola*)
Mr D Cowan, MA FRCO (*Piano, Organ*)
Dr J Dalton-Pawle, EdD, ALCM, LGSM (*Piano, Clarinet, Saxophone, Voice*)
Mrs S Douglas, ARCM, ABSM, CertEd (*Clarinet, Saxophone*)
Mrs J Fraser-Burton JP, BA (*Voice*)
Miss E French, BA Hons, MMus, LRAM, LRSM (*Piano, Accompanist*)
Mr A Geary, GLCM Hons, LLCM (*Percussion*)
Miss J Gilchrist, BA Hons, DipMus, PGCE (*Harp*)
Mrs A Gillies-Loach, GMus, LRSM, LTCL (*Flute*)
Mr C L Groom, PSM (*Brass*)
Mr D Hinson
Mrs L Holleworth, MA (*Violin*)
Mr M Johnson, CertMusEd TCL, LTCL, FVCM Hons, Hon VCM CT (*Guitar*)
Miss J Kirkwood, BMus Hons, AdvPGDip Music (*Flute*)
Mrs C Lee, LRAM, ProfCert RAM (*Violin, Viola, Piano*)
Miss V Locock, LRAM (*Piano*)
Miss V Moore, BA Hons, PGDip (*Saxophone, Clarinet*)
Mrs A Parker, BA Hons, ABRSM (*Piano, Flute*)
Miss F Richardson, LRAM (*Guitar*)
Mr A Thomas, MMus, BMus (*Guitar*)
Mrs E Thomas, GRSM, ARCM Piano, ARCM Oboe, PGCE (*Piano, Oboe, Bassoon, Saxophone, Clarinet*)
Mrs M Usher, GRNCM, ARNCM (*Percussion*)

Head of Careers: D R Bishop, BSc, MSc, CPhys, MInstP
Librarian: Mrs V Bunn, ALA
Commanding Officer, CCF: Wing Commander P S Sergeant, BEd, MPhil, RAFVR(T)
School Staff Instructor, CCF: M A Cooper
Estates Manager: T Allardice
Medical Officer: Dr A Taylor, MBChB, MRCGP, DSSP
School Nurses: Mrs J Bryan, Mrs N Krarup

There are just over 1,000 boys in the School, including 50 boarders.

The School moved to its present site of some 27 acres in 1852 and is situated away from the centre of the town in attractive grounds, which contain the beautiful avenues of trees knows as Burton Walks. At its centre is a handsome Victorian College quadrangle. There has been an impressive development programme in recent years and a new Music School serving the Grammar School, High School and Fairfield opened in September 2006.

Admission. Entry to the School is by examination at 10+, 11+, 13+ and Common Entrance. Sixth Form entry is dependent on interview with the Headmaster and other senior staff and GCSE results. Entry at other year groups is possible.

Boarding Arrangements. Boys are admitted at the age of 10 or over to Denton House (the Junior House) and at 14 they move to School House. Termly and Weekly boarding is available.

Fees per term (2008-2009). Day £3,126 (includes books and stationery). Boarding (includes laundry, board, medical attendance): £5,604 (full), £4,938 (weekly).

Scholarships. (*see Scholarship Entries section*). There are a number of Scholarships at 10+, 11+ and 13+. Choral and instrumental scholarships are also awarded at 10+, 11+, 13+ and Sixth Form. There are also a number of bursaries, depending on parental means, as well as School Assisted Places.

Foundation Bursaries. The Governors have introduced a replacement to the Government Assisted Places.

Religious Teaching. The School is undenominational, though there is a strong Christian tradition. The Chaplain is available for boys at any convenient time. On Wednesdays, Boarders attend the School Chapel, and on request are prepared for Confirmation by the Chaplain.

Curriculum. The aim of the School is to give good general education to GCSE with greater specialisation afterwards. In Year 6, boys follow a curriculum similar to that of their last year of junior school; subjects included are English, Mathematics, Art, Sciences, Drama, Design and Technology, Geography, IT, History, Music, PE, RE. In Year 7, all boys study English, Mathematics, French, History, Geography, Latin, Music, ICT and three Sciences. Additionally, all boys have lessons in RE, PE, PSHE and Games. In Year 8, Design and Technology and Classical Civilisation are introduced and in Year 9 pupils make some choices from their existing subjects and can also include Drama, German, Spanish and/or Greek. All pupils take a half GCSE in Computing/IT at the end of Year 9.

In Years 10 and 11, for GCSE, boys study English Language and Literature, Mathematics and a modern Foreign Language, and in addition they choose five subjects from an extensive options list. Some more able boys study a tenth subject.

The Sixth Form contains 270 boys. In Year 12, boys study 4 subjects to AS Level and in Year 13 they will take 3 or 4 of them to A2 Level. A wide range of subjects and combinations is available, along with General Studies, Critical Thinking, Games and other activities. There are some joint teaching lessons with the Girls' High School.

Games. The school has an excellent First Eleven field and a junior field of over 13 acres within its precinct and within two miles are well equipped playing fields extending to nearly 70 acres.

The school runs teams in Rugby, Soccer, Hockey, Cricket, Athletics, Tennis, Cross Country, Swimming, Badminton, Fencing and Squash. In addition there is a Sailing and Canoe Club and Karting. The School prides itself in an array of mind sports, with teams in Bridge, Chess, Go and Chinese Chess.

Combined Cadet Force. There is an efficient and keen CCF of about 350 boys from Year 10 onwards, run on a voluntary basis, with 17 Officers and the SSI. Boys have the choice of joining the RAF, Army or Naval Sections, and there is a highly proficient Signals Section with a transmitting room. A new purpose built CCF building has recently been opened. Many varied and adventurous courses are available to members.

Scouts. There is a flourishing Scout Troop with 1 Scouter and 35 boys.

Duke of Edinburgh's Award Scheme. Over 250 boys and girls from our sister school, Loughborough High, are actively involved in the scheme and each year a large number earn gold, silver and bronze awards.

Music. (Joint with the Girls' High School): 3 Choirs, 2 Orchestras, Big Band, 2 Concert Bands, Swing Band and numerous smaller instrumental ensembles take place in an outstanding new purpose-built Music School.

Drama. The School has a fine Studio/Theatre and all boys in Years 6, 7 and 8 participate in a dramatic production. After that, there are productions for other age groups in conjunction with the Girls' High School each term.

Careers. Careers advisors are available to inform boys on options for their futures, with special regard to University or Professional careers. The School is a member of the Independent Schools Careers Organisation.

Academic Successes. Over the last 15 years, 1992–2008, an average of 15 boys per year have gained admission to Oxford and Cambridge, and over 98% each year began degree courses at Universities.

Old Loughburians. All pupils of the school become members of the Association. Correspondence should be addressed to Mr D Wood at the School.

Charitable status. Loughborough Endowed Schools is a Registered Charity, number 1081765, and a Company Limited by Guarantee, registered in England, number 4038033. Registered Office: 3 Burton Walks, Loughborough, Leics LE11 2DU.

Magdalen College School
Oxford

Oxford OX4 1DZ
Tel: 01865 242191
Fax: 01865 240379
e-mail: admissions@mcsoxford.org
website: www.mcsoxford.org

Founded in 1480 by William of Waynflete as part of Magdalen College, the school has a lengthy list of prestigious old boys. Cardinal Wolsey was an early Master and St Thomas More, Richard Hooker, William Tyndale, Ivor Novello, Basil Blackwell, Jim Rosenthal, Nigel Starmer-Smith, Tim Hunt, John Caird and Sam Mendes are among the school's alumni. The College choristers have been full members of the School since at least the early 19th century.

In 1987 the School was given separate legal existence by the College as a Company limited by guarantee with charitable status wholly owned by the College. In 2004, the School was the eighth best independent school of any type in the UK. The School was chosen by *The Sunday Times* as their independent school of the year in November 2004.

Motto: *Sicut Lilium.*

Visitor: The Rt Revd The Lord Bishop of Winchester

Governors:
J Palmer (*Chairman*)
M Allingham, MA, PhD
J Baker, QC (*Deputy Chairman*)
B J Bellhouse, MA, DPhil
Mrs W E Hart
T M Knowles
J D Martin
F Nizami, DPhil
G Pye
N P Record
Professor J A C Smith
Professor B J Sutton, MA, DPhil
Mrs J Townsend, MA, MSc
Sir Michael Wheeler-Booth, KCB

***Master*: T R Hands**, BA, AKC, DPhil

Usher: S D A Griffiths, BA (*Classics*)

Teaching Staff:
* *Head of Department*

A Baker-Munton, MA (**Modern Languages*)
D S Barr, BA, MA (*English, *Drama*)
Mrs L Barr, BA, MA (*Mathematics, Classics*)
D Bebbington, BSc, DPhil (*Chemistry*)
J A Brown, MA (**Physics*)
A C Buckoke, BSc (**Technology*)
Miss S Cameron, BA (*Art*)
M Coatsworth, MA (*Head of Junior School*)
M J Collins, MA (*History*)
A C Cooper, MSc, BA (*Professional Tutor, Mathematics*)
C Corr, BA (**ICT*)
K H Cousineau, BSc (*Physics*)
J D Cullen, MA (**Director of Music*)
A C W Dixon, BA (**Learning Support, Geography*)
Mrs L D Earnshaw, MA (**Mathematics*)
T B Earnshaw, MA, MPhil (*Senior Administrator, Classics*)
Miss J A Ellis, GRSM, LRAM, MTC (*Head of Junior School Music*)
P J Emms, BA (*Modern Languages*)
Ms N C C Ferguson, MA (*Junior School*)
N J Fraser, MA (*Academic Deputy, French*)
Mrs M-J Gago, BA (**Spanish*)
R G Gilbert, BA (**Cricket*)
M Gray, BA (*English*)
Mrs S Groves, MBiol (**Biology*)
R Hemingway, BA (**History*)
N Hewlett, BSc (**Geography*)
Miss B A Hudson, MChem (*Chemistry*)
Mrs S D Johnson, MSc, BA (*Biology*)
H Jones, BA (*History*)
Mrs M Jones-Christodoulou, BSc (*Head of Lower School, Physics*)
Dr T Khimyak, MSc, PhD (*Chemistry*)

Miss J A Kirk, BEd (*PSHCE, Junior School*)
A I Kostyanovsky, BA (*Theology*)
Miss E J Liddiard, BA (*Geography*)
Mrs G E Lydford, BSc (**Chemistry*)
B Macdonald, BA, MA (*Examinations Officer, ICT*)
Mrs H McLean (*Librarian*)
P J McDonald, MA (**Classics*)
R S Milne, BA (**English*)
St J E J Mitchard, BA, MA (*Special Educational Needs*)
J O Morris, MA (*Head of Sixth Form, History*)
R J Naylor, BA (*Art*)
C E Newbury, BA (*Junior School Director of Studies*)
Y W Ooi, BA, BMBCh (*Biology*)
C Pearson, BSc, DPhil (*Biology*)
M Penton, BA (**Director of Sport*)
J F Place, BA (*Junior School*)
Sra V Pradas, BA (*Spanish*)
J D Price, BSc (*Head of Hockey*)
Mrs F J Pritchard, BA (**Art*)
Mrs B Riddiford, MA (*English*)
M J P Saunders, MChem (*Chemistry*)
P A Shrimpton, MA, MEd, PhD (*Mathematics, *Careers*)
T E Skipwith, BSc (*Head of Middle School, Biology*)
D A Smith, MA, PhD (*Director of Studies, Mathematics, Physics*)
P D Smith, MA, LTCL (*Music*)
S A Spowart, BA (*Classics*)
Mrs E Stapleton, BHum (*Deputy Head of Junior School*)
Mrs M-R Staton, L-ès-L (*French*)
Miss C E Steele, BA (*Child Protection Officer, Junior School*)
Miss Z Tayler, BA, MSc (*Mathematics*)
Mrs S L Toovey, BA (*English*)
J Unwin, BA (**Philosophy*)
J A Watts, BA (*French*)
B White, BA (*Mathematics*)
E J White, BSc (*Geography*)

Assistant Music Staff:
Miss M Ackrill (*Flute*)
Ms K Bailey (*Saxophone*)
Dr E M Baird (*Violin*)
Ms A Bendy (*Guitar*)
Ms E H Churcher (*Piano*)
S Cutting (*Trumpet*)
T Dawes (*Double Bass, Bass Guitar, Drums*)
Miss J A Ellis (*Violin*)
K Fairbairn (*Percussion, Drums*)
Dr J Faultless (*Horn*)
Miss G Fisher (*Piano*)
J Hill (*Clarinet*)
M R Jones (*Piano*)
Ms C Lane (*Singing*)
Mrs S Lynn (*Violin*)
P Manhood (*Guiltar*)
J Newell (*Organ*)
M Picket (*Piano*)
W Purefoy (*Singing*)
B P Skipp (*Oboe*)
R K Stevens (*Brass*)
Dr J P Whitworth (*Guitar*)
S J Wilson (*Cello*)
G Williams (*Bassoon*)

Clerk to the Governors and Bursar: Dr N Carter

Master's PA: Mrs L D Beaumont

Registrar: Miss E Williams, BA

Numbers. There are 697 day boys in the School. The Sixth Form numbers 155. The main entry points are at 7, 9, 11 and 13. Up to 18 boys are taken at 7, a further 18 or so at 9, and about 72 at the age of 11. Up to 25 boys are taken at 13. A limited number of pupils join the School directly into the Sixth Form. Almost all pupils go on to higher education when they leave.

Pastoral. From 7–11, boys are in form groups of approximately 18. Their form teacher is responsible for day-to-day care, pastoral welfare and academic progress. Boys from age 11 are allocated to one of the six Houses. Houses are divided into four Houserooms. A Housemaster or Tutor in charge of each section is responsible for the pastoral and academic welfare of pupils in his Houseroom. The Heads of Departments, SENCO, Chaplain and Matron also play their part in the pastoral organisation of the school.

Buildings. The school buildings include a Chapel and Theatre, Library, Classrooms, Science Laboratories, Music School and Art Department. New Science Laboratories were opened in 1991 and totally refurbished in 2001. A Technology Department opened in 1992. The expanded Junior School was opened in 1993, and new changing rooms and English Department in 1996. New classrooms, Lecture Theatre, Careers Centre and a Sixth Form Centre were opened in September 1998. In June 2001, a £2m Sports Complex was opened. In 2002, additional science laboratories were provided as well as a new ICT centre. In 2005, the school opened its new Sir Basil Blackwell library. In 2007, the school began construction of a new building to house a modern refectory, art and design, senior common room and porter's lodge. This will be completed in the summer of 2008.

Organisation and Curriculum. All boys study a core of subjects to GCSE level, consisting of English, French, Maths and Science. In addition, there is a wide variety of options taken by pupils in their GCSE years including Latin and Greek, Geography, German, Spanish, History, Computing and Art. Most GCSEs are taken in the Fifth Form although a few may be taken earlier. There is no streaming and very little setting.

Mixed Arts and Science subject combinations are common and a boy's AS and A2 Levels are complemented by a wide range of 'minor' (general studies) courses.

Most boys in the Sixth Form take 4 AS and 3 A2s, but a significant proportion take 4 or even 5 AS and A2 subjects.

Careers. There is a well-equipped Careers Room, and there is a team of Careers Staff. Careers Aptitude Tests are offered to all boys in the Fifth Form, and there is a weekly lecture in the Sixth Form.

Games and Societies. In addition to Physical Education which is taught in the curriculum, games play a major part in the School. Major sports are Rugby in the Michaelmas Term, Hockey and Rowing in Hilary, and Cricket, Rowing and Tennis in the Trinity Term. Other sports include Basketball, Football, Fencing, Cross-Country, Sailing and Athletics. There are Army, Navy and Air Force sections of the CCF and a Community Service Organisation. Many boys participate in the Duke of Edinburgh's Award Scheme. Girls from Oxford High School and Headington School participate in the CCF.

The main playing field, surrounded by the River Cherwell, adjoins the grounds of School House and covers 11 acres. An additional playing field of 13 acres with its own pavilion and changing rooms has been developed at Sandford-on-Thames, three miles from the school. The school also has use of the Magdalen College sports fields one mile from the school.

Music is extremely important in the School and there is a large Choral Society, a Madrigal Group, Senior and Junior Orchestras, a Jazz Band and other ensembles. Many pupils are involved in Drama and there are several productions in the year. There are many other societies and clubs covering cultural and recreational activities. The main school concert is held annually in The Sheldonian Theatre.

Fees per term (2008-2009). Dayboys: £3,856 (aged 9–18); £3,756 (7 and 8 year olds). They are payable in advance and are inclusive of text-books and stationery. The Registration Fee (non-returnable) is currently £50.

Admission and Scholarships. (*see Scholarship Entries section*). Admission at ages 7, 9 and 11 is by a School Entrance Examination held in January or February each year.

Admission at age 13 is by the Common Entrance Examination for candidates at Preparatory Schools and by a School Entrance Examination held in March each year for candidates at maintained schools. Up to 16 Academic scholarships are awarded each year at age 13, a number of Music Scholarships, Games Scholarships and Art Scholarships are awarded to candidates under 14 on 1st September of the year of entry. All scholarships are worth up to £300, beyond which they can be means-tested.

In special circumstances awards of bursaries may also be made.

A limited number of boys are admitted each year directly into the Sixth Form after interview and school report. Offers are conditional on good GCSE grades.

Candidates can be registered at any age.

Full particulars can be obtained from the Registrar.

Term of Entry. Boys enter the School in September. Exceptionally, for example if parents move into the Oxford area, other arrangements can be made.

Choristerships and Exhibitions. There are 16 Choristerships. Entry is by Voice Trial and candidates should normally be between the ages of 7 and 9. For a Chorister two-thirds of the tuition fee is remitted. All enquiries about Choristerships should be addressed to the Informator Choristarum, Magdalen College, Oxford. Choristers normally continue at the School after their voices have broken. In deserving cases, further financial help may be available.

Honours. In the 10 years 1998–2007 inclusive 158 places have been gained at Oxford and Cambridge universities, and 541 places at other universities, from an average Sixth Form year group of 70.

Old Waynfletes. *Secretary*: D R Dunsmore, 12 Owlington Close, Botley, Oxford OX2 9DP.

Charitable status. Magdalen College School Oxford Limited is a Registered Charity, number 295785. Its aims and objectives are to promote and provide for the education of children.

Malvern College

College Road Malvern Worcestershire WR14 3DF
Tel: 01684 581500
Fax: 01684 581617
e-mail: enquiry@malcol.org
website: www.malcol.org

Malvern College was founded in 1862, opened in 1865 and was incorporated by Royal Charter in 1929. Malvern College is co-educational. The Senior School takes pupils from the age of 13 through to 18. The Preparatory School takes pupils from 3 to 13 (*see IAPS entry*).

Motto: '*Sapiens qui prospicit*.'

Ten members of the Council may be nominated, one each by the Lords-Lieutenant of the Counties of Gloucestershire, Herefordshire and Worcestershire, by the Vice-Chancellors of the Universities of Oxford, Cambridge and Birmingham, by the Service Boards of the Navy, Army and Air Force, and by the Headmaster and Teaching Staff. Ten members are elected by the Governors, and between six and ten are appointed by the Council.

President and Visitor: The Lord Bishop of Worcester

Council:
Lord MacLaurin of Knebworth (*Chairman*)
Mrs C Campbell (*Vice-Chairman*)
R K Black (*Treasurer*)

Dr N Bampos
S P Bennett
P G Brough
P J Cartwright
Professor K J Davey, OBE
Mrs R Dawes, JP
G W Davies
Mrs J Edwards-Clark
F R R Francis
Mrs L Gullifer
Ms J M Hampson
S M Hill
Mrs G Hylson-Smith
G E Jones
The Very Revd R Lewis
S R Lister
K U Madden
W H Moore
D G Robertson
J D Roseman
Dr C W O Stoecker
Mrs J Thompstone
R T H Wilson

Clerk to the Council and Bursar: I Barron

***Head*: A R Clark**, MA Cantab

Deputy Head: Dr R A Lister, BA, MTS, PhD
Director of Studies: J A Gauci, BA

Teaching Staff:
R E Allen, BSc, MPhil
Mrs H R Andrews, BA
Mrs S K Angling, MA
Miss A S L Appleby, BA
Mrs L M Atkins, BA
A R Bannister, BA
Mrs I P M Bijl, BA
P A Blair, MA
J P Burns, BA
Mrs N J Cage, BA
P J Chappell, BA
Mrs A Clark, BSc
M Cleal, BA
Mrs J Cockbill, MA
Miss J F Collot, BA
J D Cox, BSc
M M Cox, BEd
G M Cramp, BSc
Miss J A Danks, BMus
W R Davidson, MA
S Doidge, BSc
M C Frayn, BA
P Godsland, MA (*Senior Master*)
Mrs S Godsland, BA
P J Gray, MA
A J Grundy, BA
C Hall, BSc, CBiol, MIBiol
Mrs L M Hallett, BA
H Hardingham, BA
Miss S D Hardy, BSc
M A T Harris, MA
Mrs A M Higgins, BA
S C Holroyd
Dr S J Holroyd, BA
R A Hookham, BA
R Huguenin, BA
Dr P Jackson, BSc, PhD
R A Jackson, BSc
Miss C M Jones, MA
Miss L B Jones, BA
J P Knee, MA
R G Lacey, BSc
Mrs A L Lafferty, BA (*Senior Mistress*)
The Revd A P Law, DipTh
M G Lloyd, BSc
J R Mace, BA
Mrs R E Mace, MTheol, MPhil
Mrs M C Maskell, MChem
Mrs D M McCarry, BA
S P McDade, ARAM
R W Morgan, BSc
T P Newman, BSc
T M Newsholme, BA
D T Oliver, BA, MPhil
Mrs M B O'Reilly, MA
Mrs F C Packham, BSc
K R C Packham, BA
M A L Phillips, MA, FRCO, ARCM
Mrs A Pilfold, BSc
Miss L R Pugh, BA
Mrs V E Rice, BA
Mrs P D Richardson, BA
T Roberts, BA
J Rodriguez, PGCE
J A O Russell, BSc, BA
Mrs S F Schott, BA (*Senior Tutor*)
Mrs A-I Sharp, BA
Dr D Sibthorpe, BSc, MSc, PhD
I D Sloan, BMus, ARCM
A Smith, MA
R J Smith, BEd
S R Spanyol, FTCL, ARCM, LTCL
Dr R P Stafford, BSc, PhD
Mrs B J Stokes, BA
J C Stotesbury, BSc
E D E Thomas, MA
Mrs J C A Thomas, BEd, RSASpLD
R G Thurlow, MA (*Careers*)
Mrs R Turner, MA
C P J Wastie, MSc
Dr N V Watson, BA, PhD
M J Weaver, BA
Mrs P G R Webb
Mrs C Wedelich-Niedzwiedz, BMus
A J Wharton, BTh Hons
P Wickes, BSc
R N Willatt, MSc
Dr R B Winwood, MSc, PhD

Chaplain: The Revd A P Law

Registrar: Mrs S R Jackson, BSc

Medical Officers:
Sarah D Roberts, MBChB, MRCGP
G F J Henry, DRCOG, MRCGP

Boarding Houses:
J A O Russell (*School House*)
A J Wharton (*Number 1*)
R G Lacey (*Number 2*)
Mrs F C Packham (*Number 3*)
Mrs A I Sharp (*Number 4*)

T P Newman (*Number 5*)
Mrs N J Cage (*Number 6*)
P J Gray (*Number 7*)
Mrs P D Richardson (*Number 8*)
P Wickes (*Number 9*)

Malvern College is particularly fortunate in its location. Situated on the lower slopes of the Malvern Hills and close to the centre of Great Malvern, the main College campus commands striking views across the Severn Plain towards the Cotswolds.

Founded in 1865, the College offers co-education from the age of 3 to 18. There are currently some 777 pupils in the school, 177 of whom are in the Preparatory School with its Pre-Prep Department. At age 13+ pupils join the senior part of the school where there are four girls' houses and six boys' houses, all of which also take day pupils. The school is justly proud of its high academic standards and of its pastoral care. There are 308 pupils in the Sixth Form, of whom about half study for the International Baccalaureate and half for A Levels.

Further details of the School are available in the Prospectus which may be obtained by contacting the Registrar or by visiting the website at www.malcol.org.

Curriculum. In the Foundation Year (Year 9), pupils study a wide variety of subjects. Nearly all are introduced to a second modern foreign language. All pupils study debating, computer literacy and creative ICT as well as a compulsory PE course. The object of this year (as in co-curricular activities) is to show pupils as much as possible of what the College has to offer. On entering the Remove (Year 10), pupils choose their GCSE or IGCSE subjects, to be taken at the end of the Hundred (Year 11). In French and Latin the top set takes GCSE at the end of the Remove. The compulsory subjects are English (plus English Literature, for almost all pupils), Mathematics, Double Award Science and French (or English as a foreign language). Most pupils take a short course GCSE in Religious Studies in Year 10. Pupils also choose optional subjects from Art and Design, Drama, Geography, German, History, Italian, Latin, Music, Physical Education, Spanish and Technology. Greek is available for those who began it in the Foundation Year. A Separate Sciences option enables pupils to extend the core Double Award Science to the three separate science GCSEs. Pupils choose either three or four options, according to their academic ability. Pupils decide on their choices in consultation with their Tutors, Housemasters/Housemistresses and parents.

In the Sixth Form, pupils can choose to study either A Levels or the International Baccalaureate. In the IB, combinations of the following subjects are offered: Art & Design, Biology, Business Management, Chemistry, Economics, English, Ecosystems and Societies, French, German, Geography, Greek, History, Italian, Latin, Mathematics, Further Mathematics, Music, Physics, Spanish, Technology, Theatre and Sport & Exercise Science. All pupils take the valuable Theory of Knowledge Course. A Levels are available in all of the subjects listed above for the IB (except Ecosystems and Societies and Italian) and also in Theatre Studies, Classical Civilisation, Politics and Religious Studies. Pupils take four AS subjects in the Lower Sixth and most drop to three subjects at A Level. The timetable allows many different combinations, although a pupil's choice is carefully monitored.

Pastoral Care. In addition to their Housemaster/Housemistress and House Tutor, all pupils have a Form Tutor who shares the responsibility for their overall personal development and well-being. Members of the Sixth Form choose their own Tutor. There is also a full-time Chaplain. In addition, pupils have (free) access to school counsellors.

Health Care. There is a modern and well-equipped Medical Centre staffed 24 hours a day by Registered Nurses.

Coaches. During the school year there are three half-term holidays and about five leave-out weekends. On these occasions, school coaches are run to Exeter, Guildford, London Paddington, and Knutsford, according to demand. Coaches to Heathrow and Birmingham airports run at the start of half term and the end of term.

Activities. The School has a strong tradition of expedition training and outdoor pursuits, including rock-climbing, kayaking, sailing, mountaineering (Summer and Winter, UK and Abroad). Opportunities exist for the use of the College's cottage in the Brecon Beacons. Expeditions go annually to Scotland and have also gone to Iceland, the Alps, Kashmir, Scandinavia, Malta and China in the school holidays. Many of these activities, are integral within the voluntary CCF (which has RM, Army and RAF sections) and Duke of Edinburgh's Award Scheme. There is also a flourishing Community Service Organisation.

Art. The modern, purpose-built and spacious Arts Centre has outstanding facilities for Painting, Drawing, Printmaking (including etching), Ceramics, Photography and 3-Dimensional Design.

Careers. In the GCSE year pupils sit the Futurewise/Morrisby careers guidance tests which assess ability, personality, aptitude and interests. An in-depth interview with an experienced ISCO careers advisor helps pupils to make sensible and informed choices about their future. All pupils in the Lower Sixth are encouraged to spend at least one week in the holidays on work experience. Pupils are given advice on choice of course at University by the Head of Careers, Sixth Form Tutor and Housemaster/Housemistress. Malvern College is a member of the Independent Schools Careers Organisation (ISCO).

Design and Technology. The well-equipped Technology Centre ensures that pupils have the opportunity to develop their knowledge and skills through project work in this exciting subject. Facilities include Food and Textiles Technology, Resistant Materials, Computer Aided Design and Manufacture, Systems and Control Technology.

Drama. Drama is promoted actively throughout the College. It features in the timetable, where it is a popular option at GCSE level, and at higher level where it attracts candidates as part of the IB and A Level Programme. Drama is also a lively and thriving extra-curricular activity, with many productions being presented over the year in the school's well-equipped and versatile theatre. Recent presentations include *West Side Story*, *Don Quixote*, *Macbeth*, *Coram Boy* and Terry Pratchett's *Mort*. Regular trips are arranged to see productions at Stratford, Birmingham and other theatres in the vicinity.

Physical Education. *Curriculum*: Year 9 – All students follow four activities from the National Curriculum with the girls being taught Games (Hockey, Netball and Tennis/Rounders), Athletics, Swimming and either Gymnastics or Dance. The boys are taught Games (Football, Rugby, Hockey, Cricket and Tennis), Athletics, Swimming and Orienteering. Years 10 and 11 – All students follow two compulsory water-based units at Key Stage 4, Lifesaving and Personal Survival, and a further compulsory unit in Health and Fitness. In addition, there is a wide ranging option programme including all activities taught at Key Stage 3 plus others which include Rackets, Fives, Cricket, Lacrosse, Squash, Badminton, Basketball and Volleyball. Those students opting for a full GCSE in Physical Education are assessed in 4 activities and follow the AQA GCSE specification. Many students go on to study the OCR Physical Education specification at A Level or Sport & Exercise Science within the IB Diploma.

Facilities include an Astro-turf pitch, Squash/Rackets/Fives courts, Shooting range, Multi-gym and the new Sports Hall and Swimming pool are due for completion September 2009.

Co-Curricular Activities. In addition to the activities mentioned in the curriculum section, pupils have the opportunity to take part in such additional activities as sailing, fencing, aerobics, cross-country, golf, kayaking, taekwondo, archery, pilates and streetdance.

Music. Malvern has a strong musical tradition. The well-equipped Music School (24 practice rooms, 3 large rehearsal rooms) includes a recording studio and a music technology laboratory. Attached to the Music School is St Edmund's Hall, a 150-seat recital hall with a fine Steinway piano. Pupils of all standards are encouraged both instrumentally and vocally, and regular performances (internal, at local venues, and internationally) are given by orchestras, bands, chamber groups and choirs. The Music Department works closely with the Drama Department and musicals are produced regularly.

Admission. Most pupils are admitted between their thirteenth and fourteenth birthdays and may qualify for admission to the school by a satisfactory performance in either the Common Entrance Examination or the annual Scholarship Examination. Boys and Girls are also able to secure entry at 13+ by sitting tests at the end of Year 6 under the College's secured places scheme. Special arrangements are made for pupils who wish to enter from schools which do not prepare pupils for Common Entrance.

Pupils are also admitted to the Sixth Form at 16 on the basis of GCSEs, interviews and tests.

Application for admission should be made to the Registrar.

Scholarships. (*see Scholarship Entries section*). The school offers a generous number of Scholarships and Exhibitions at 13+ each year, varying in value according to merit and financial circumstances up to 50% of the current fees. These awards are given for pupils with academic ability or special talent in Art, Drama, Music (both instrumental and choral), Sport or Technology.

Candidates for 13+ Scholarships must be under 14 years of age on 1 September in the year of the examination but there is no age limit for Exhibitions.

Fees per term (2008-2009). Senior School: Boarding £8,633–£9,211; Day £5,721–£5,899.

An acceptance fee is payable 20 months before entry and is refunded as a deduction from the final account.

The Malvernian Society. On leaving, Malvernians retain contact with the College by joining the Malvernian Society and/or through the College website. They also become members of the OM Club which organises various teams and a number of social functions. Secretary of the Malvernian Society: M Eglington (Tel: 01684 581517).

The Downs, Malvern College Preparatory School is situated on the west side of the Malvern Hills and prepares boys and girls primarily for entry to the senior part of the College. Entries are welcomed at all ages and those who qualify to join the school from age 11 are guaranteed entry to the Senior School at 13. (*For further details, please see IAPS section*).

Charitable status. Malvern College is a Registered Charity, number 527578. It is a charity established for the purpose of educating children.

The Manchester Grammar School

Old Hall Lane Manchester M13 0XT
Tel: 0161 224 7201
Fax: 0161 257 2446
e-mail: general@mgs.org
website: www.mgs.org

The Manchester Grammar School was founded in 1515 to promote 'godliness and good learning' and it has endeavoured throughout its history to remain true to these principles, while adapting to changing times. It is now an independent boys' day school with around 1,500 pupils. Almost all leavers go on to university, about a quarter of them going to Oxford or Cambridge. Over 140 qualified teaching staff provide all pupils with a broad curriculum and rich extra-curricular opportunities.

The tradition of offering places to clever pupils regardless of their background is maintained by MGS bursaries. More than 200 pupils in the school are fee-assisted. They come both from primary and preparatory schools and represent a wide variety of cultural, ethnic and religious backgrounds. Many undertake a long daily journey.

Motto: *Sapere Aude (Dare to be wise)*

Co-optative Governors:
M I Davis (*Deputy Chairman*)
A M Dean (*Treasurer*)
J B Diggines
B Dixon, CBE
Ms F M S Goodey, CBE, DL
W T Hall
Professor T A Hinchliffe
C G Kenyon, CBE (*Chairman*)
Ms J Kingsley
Mrs J Luca
Dr P Mason
A Ruia
J P Wainwright
E M Watkins

Ex officio Governors:
The Dean of Manchester
The President of Corpus Christi College, Oxford
The Lord Mayor of Manchester

Representative Governors:
Manchester University: Mrs D Chambers
Cambridge University: Professor D A Cardwell
Oxford University: Dr T Watt

Bursar and Clerk to the Governors: Mrs G M Batchelor, BSc

***High Master*: C Ray**, BA, PhD, FRSA, CPhys

Deputy High Master: S V Leeming, BSc, CChem, MRSC, CSci
Surmaster: N J Munday, MA
Senior Master: N A Sheldon, MA, BSc, MPhil, CStat, MBCS, CEng, CITP
Head of Sixth Form: P A M Thompson, BA, DPhil, MA Ed
Head of Middle School: A N Smith, BA
Head of Lower School: Mrs S C James, BA
Head of Junior Section: Mrs L A Hamilton, BEd
Head of Co-Curricular: J W Mangnall, MA
Director of Development: I Thorpe, MA

Academic Staff:
T Ahmed, BSc
R Alderson, MA
Miss R E Aldred, BMus, GRNCM
Mrs J K Allinson, MA, BA
P N A Baylis, BA
G Blackwell, BA
J Blair, BSc
P L Bowen-Walker, BSc, PhD, CBiol, MIBiol, MCoT, Cert FPA
R C Bradford, BSc, PhD, MInstP, CPhys
Ms E Brewer, BA
D J Bristow, MA, MA, MEd
D Brown, BD, STM, MLitt
C Buckley, BSc
S J Burch, BSc, PhD, MIBiol
N T Burin, BSc, AFIMA
A P Burrows, BSc, PhD
Mrs H Butchart, BA, LTCL
Ms J M Byrne, BA, PhD
Ms S E Byrne, BA
J A Cantrell, MA, PhD
R M Carey, MA
G E Chandler, MA
E C F Cittanova, L-ès-L, L-ès-L, M-ès-L, DEA
M P A Coffey, MA
J T Coller, BA
S G Cranshaw, BA, PhD
Miss A F Crofts, BA
Miss S M F Cross
H S Crowther, BSc, CMath, FIMA, CSci
Mrs A Curry, BSc
G G Curtis, MA
Mrs E R Dalton, L-ès-L
R A H Dean, BA
Mrs J Dobbs, BA
A P Dobson, BA, MA
S J Duffy, BSc, MIBiol, CBiol
D Dyson, BA
B S Edwards, MA
Mrs L Ennos, BA, MA
M Ellis, BSc, DPhil
D Farr, MA
C C Figes, BSc
Miss F A Forsyth, MA
S Foster, BA, MA
D E Francis, MusB, GRNCM, ARNCM, LRAM, LTCL, ATCL
P W Freeman, BSc, MSc
R J Frost, MA, MRSC
J C Gibb, MA
R D Gilbert, BA
J Hargreaves, BA
G W M Harrison, BA
A R T Hern, BA, MPhil
M S R Hesketh, BSc, MSc
Miss P J Higgins, BSc
Mrs H L Howard, BA
Mrs H M Hughes, BSc
S J F Hunt, MA
A C Hunter, BSc, MSc, PhD

Miss A Jacinto, BA
Mrs S C James, BA
D Jeys, BSc, MA
S P Jones, BA
R N Kelly, BA, MA, MPhil
I Z Khan, BSc
Miss M A Koontz-Garboden, MA
C Lawrence, BSc
Ms E Loh, BSc, MSc, PhD
Mrs N A Loughlin, BSc
Miss M A S Lowe, BA, MPhil
R Lunn, BEd
R I A Martin, BA, PhD
N J Matthews, BSc
Miss E E Mayer, BA
Miss H McNally, BSc
G Mc Rory, BA
Mrs L Merlo, BA
Mrs C Metcalfe, BA
G J Morris, BSc
D Moss, MA
Mrs L J Murphywood, BA
Ms L E Nelson, BA, MA
D Noble, BA
Mrs S J van der Ouderaa, MA
C J Owen, BA
Mrs A J Parkinson, L-ès-L, M-ès-L
T J Pattison, BSc, MIMA, CMath
Mrs S Paulson, BA
A C Pickwick, BSc, MSc, FRAS, MInstP, MBCS
J Potts, BSc
D Preston, MA, MSc
E R Prestwich, BA, BPhil
Miss F C Roberts, MChem
Miss H E Sargeant, BA, MA
Miss H D Sayers, BEd, MA
Miss R L Sharkey, BA
N J Sharples, BA, MA
Mrs J R M Shaw, BA
J E Sheils, BSc
J H Shoard, MA
P Shufflebottom, BA
R W Simpson, BA
A M Smith, MA
A N Smith, BA
Mrs J L Smith, BA
N D Smith, BA
Mrs L Speed, Mosc Dip
S P G Spratling, BA
Mrs P Squires, BSc, PhD
J P Stanley, MA
Mrs R J Stanley, MA
M G P Strother, BA, MPhil
R I Tabick, MA
D M Taylor, BA
Ms S Taylor, BA
C P Thom, MA
Mrs E M Thornber, BA, MPhil
B Townsend, BA
J N Tucker, BA
M L Warnes, BSc, PhD, FRES
N Warrack, MA, MA
P J Wheeler, BSc
Ms B S Weichert, MSc, PhD
Mrs J A Whittell, BA
Miss A Wicking, BA
R Wild, BSc
Miss L J Wilkinson, BSc
N G Williams, BA
Miss R G Williams, BA, DPhil
Ms C A Worth, BA, MA
Miss J T Yuen, BA

Medical Officer: Dr J L Burn, FRCP, FRCPCH
Secretary to the High Master: Lorraine Coen
Admissions Secretary: Kath Heathcote
Communications Manager: Sally Rogers

Registration and Entry. Boys may be registered at any time prior to the assessment procedure in their year of proposed entry, which is normally at age 9 or 11. Entry to the Sixth Form follows interview and appropriate qualifications. Current details are available from the Admissions Secretary.

Tuition Fees per term (2008-2009). £2,992.

Bursaries. The Governing Body awards means-tested bursaries.

Junior Section. The School opens to boys aged from 9 in September 2008.

Senior School Organisation and Curriculum. The eight unstreamed forms in each of the first two years follow the same broad curriculum, comprising English, Mathematics, a modern foreign language, Classics (including Latin) History, Geography, Science (General Science in Year 7 and separate sciences in Year 8), Religious Studies, ICT, Music, Art & Design, Drama, PE, Swimming and Games. Pupils then proceed to make GCSE choices, typically taking ten subjects, including Mathematics, English, a language and one or more science subjects.

In the Sixth Form boys have a choice of studying either A Levels or the International Baccalaureate; in addition all students participate in the School's own non-examined enrichment programme.

Pastoral Care. Each form in the school is looked after by a Form Tutor, who is one of the form's subject teachers. The Form Tutor is responsible, with the appropriate senior members of staff, for the academic and general progress of each pupil. Regular written reports are supplemented by Parents' Evenings. The School Medical Room is staffed by a part-time doctor and two full-time Nursing staff. The older pupils selected as prefects are encouraged to help younger pupils in running societies and other co-curricular activities.

Creative Arts. All pupils experience Music, Art & Design and Drama within the curriculum, but each of these areas offers activities to large numbers of pupils during the lunch-hour and after school. There are choirs, orchestras and instrumental tuition; plays, drama workshops and musicals; clubs for art, pottery, and computer design. There are regular exhibitions and public performances both in school and in public venues.

Sport. All boys take part in timetabled games and the school produces successful teams in most sports. There is a gymnasium and a heated indoor swimming pool. A sports hall was opened in March 1997 by Michael Atherton, Captain of Cricket at the School, Cambridge University and England. Older boys have a wide choice of sporting activity within the timetable, with some groups travelling to use facilities outside the school.

Outdoor Pursuits. The school has a long tradition of camping and trekking and there are numerous weekend and holiday excursions. Four annual camps cater for the full age range and offer a wide choice of activities. In recent years expeditions have visited the Alps, the Pyrenees, Morocco and Scandinavia.

Foreign Visits. Many trips abroad are organised each year, providing enjoyable holidays of broad educational value. Destinations include France, Germany, Spain, Russia, Italy, Greece, Mexico, Tunisia, India and China.

Societies and Activities. There are over 50 societies catering for most interests, Chess and Bridge Clubs, and a school newspaper produced by pupils.

Prizes and Scholarships. In addition to bursaries, funds are provided for grants to help deserving pupils with the expense of a range of extra-curricular activities. Prizes are awarded in all subjects in the curriculum.

Old Mancunians' Association and MGS Parents' Society. The Old Boys' Association has many regional sections. There is an annual Old Boys' Dinner in Manchester. The Development Office Manager is Mrs C M Pemberton who can be reached at the School.

The MGS Parents' Society has a membership of parents and friends and exists to support school activities and promote a programme of social events.

Charitable status. The Manchester Grammar School is a Registered Charity, number 529909. The aim of the School is to prepare able boys from the Manchester area, regardless of their financial background, to proceed to university and make a positive contribution to society in their adult life.

Marlborough College

Marlborough Wiltshire SN8 1PA

Tel:	Main Switchboard: 01672 892200
	The Master: 01672 892400
	The Bursar: 01672 892390
	Admissions: 01672 892300
Fax:	Main No: 01672 892207
	The Master: 01672 892407
e-mail:	master@marlboroughcollege.org
	admissions@marlboroughcollege.org
website:	www.marlboroughcollege.org

Founded 1843. Incorporated by Royal Charter.

Visitor: The Archbishop of Canterbury

Council:
President: The Rt Revd The Lord Bishop of Salisbury
Sir Hayden Phillips, GCB, DL (*Chairman*)
Sir Roger Hurn
Dr C P M Heath
P A F Figgis (*Chairman of Finance Committee*)
R C H Jeens
Sir Christopher Gent
The Venerable Sheila Watson
Major General A S Ritchie, CBE
I D Coull
J P Hornby
R J H Fleck
A C V Evans
P J Manser, CBE, DL
Sir Richard Sykes, DSc, FRS, FMedSci

Clerk to the Council: W F Wyldbore-Smith, DL

***Master*: N A Sampson**, MA

Deputy Head: R B Pick, BSc
Director of Studies: A Gist, BA, MA
Senior Master: J P Rothwell, MA
Senior Admissions Tutor: C A Fraser, MA
Head of Boarding: Lady Cayley, MA

Assistant Staff:
* *Head of Department*
† *Housemasters/mistresses*

Ms C C Russell, BA
A J Brown, MA (*†Littlefield*)
J N Copp, BEd (*Director of Summer School*)
A S Eales, BMus
A D McKnight, BSc (*†Turner House*)
Revd D J Dales, MA, BD, FRHistSoc
N G Hamilton, BA, PhD, ATC
Ms J J McFarlane, BA DPhil
N M Allott, BSc
J A Genton, MA (**Science*)
M J Ponsford, BA, PhD (**Academic Enrichment*)
P G M Ford, MA
J D C Hicks, BA, ATC (**Design and Technology*)
A K J Yearsley, BA PhD
D Allen, BA, MA
N R Cleminson, MA
A B D Harrison, BSc (**Mathematics*)
Mrs P J Harrison, BSc
K J D Richards, MA (**Geography*)
P R Adams, BEd
I G Crabbe, MA, FRCO, ARCM
J F Lloyd, BA, MPhil (**Classics*)
M W McVeigh, BSc, MA (*†C2*)
V J Stokes, BA, ATC (**Art*)
S J Ellis, BSc
S C Clayton, BA
S M D Dempster, BA (*†C3*)
R T Markham, MA (**Art History, IB Coordinator*)
M Conlen, BSc
A J Arkwright, BA
Mrs L F W Ford, MA
P N Keighley, BEng (**Business Studies*)
E G Nobes, MA (**Careers*)
Mrs R L T Bruce, BA
N E Briers, BEd (*Director of Sport*)
Mrs C A Walsh, BSc (*†New Court*)
T J Gibbon, MA
Mrs S L J Greenwood, BSc
N J L Moore, BSc, MA (*†Barton Hill*)
T J W Ridley, GRSM, LRAM, PhD
C E Barclay, BSc, FRAS (*Director of the Observatory*)
M A Gow, BA
T E Hare, MA
R D A Lamont, BA (**English*)
N Nelson-Piercy, BA (*†B1House*)
W D L Nicholas, BEng (*†Summerfield*)
Mrs L J Richards, BSc, PhD (**Biology*)
G B Shearn, BSc (**ICT*)
T G R Marvin, MA (*†Preshute*)
J H Parnham, BA, MA
N O R Rosedale, BSc (**Outdoor Activities*)
Miss C Toomer, GGSM
Mrs J A Hodgson, BA (*†Morris House*)
M B Blossom, BA
J A Hodgson, BSc
Miss R D Kettle, BSc
O T Moelwyn-Hughes, BA, LLB, MSt (**Politics*)
P J O'Sullivan, BA
K G A Smith, BA
R Tong
T A Kiggell, MA
Mrs H A M Cox, BSc
B H Miller, BSc (*†C1*)
R A Sandall, BCom, BA
P A Finn, BA
Mrs S J Auty, BEng, CEng, MIChemE
P V Hampson, BSc
Mrs R F Horton, MA
Mrs K J Kiggell, MA
M K Druett, MPhys
J G Hobby, BA
Mrs S A Finn, BA
D G Roberts, MSc, PhD (**Physics*)
L W G Walters, BA
Mrs H Wilson, BSc
Mrs V R Hawthorn, BA, Dip SpLD, AMCollT
Mrs A T Woodford, BA
J P Carroll, BEd
R A Cockett, MA (**Modern Languages*)
Mrs V J Seanor, BSc
S R Hawthorn, BSc
Mrs J McFarland, BSc (*†Elmhurst*)
Mrs J L M North, BA (*†Mill Mead*)
Miss I M Painter, BA
S G Quinn, BSc
Dr G Doyle, BSc, MSc, PhD, DIC, CChem, MRSC (**Chemistry*)
C L Harrison, BSc
G D M Lane, BSc
J J Lyon-Taylor, BSc
Miss P A Thorpe, BA
Miss L Rowlands, BSc (**Girls' Games*)
Miss A C Langdale, BSc
Miss K J Hockley, MA
Miss E J Rayner, BA
Ms J A Potter, BA, MPhil, PhD (**History*)
Mrs C E Page, MA, BA (**Learning Support & Study Skills*)
G M Turner, BSc
Miss D L Goodger, BSc
N O P Gordon, MA
P N Morley-Fletcher, BA
Mrs S A Richardson, BA
Miss A K Fraser, BA, MPhil
Miss R L Heywood, BA
D Kenworthy, BA, MFA (**Drama*)
J P Goldsmith, BA

Bursar: D S Williamson, BA
Senior Chaplain: Revd J G W Dickie, MA, BLitt (**Religious Studies*)
Medical Officers:
Dr R W Hook, MB BS, MRCGP, DRCOG
Dr S Hanson, MB BS, MRCGP, DCH

Librarian: Mrs L Pilkington, BSc, MSc
Archivist: T E Rogers, BSc, PhD
Master's Secretary: Mrs S Nicholas

There are approximately 872 boys and girls in the 14 houses in the College. The College is fully co-educational, 13 being the normal age of entry for both girls and boys. A limited number of boys and girls are admitted to the Sixth Form.

Registration. For entry to the school at 13+ registrations are accepted no earlier than four years before entry. Registrations for entry at 16+ are accepted at any time.

There has been a significant change in the procedure for admission to the school at 13+ from September 2009. The College no longer operates a policy which gives preference to those who register early and whose children then go on to pass the Common Entrance examination. We shall now aim to assess all applicants 20 months ahead of entry and offer places accordingly. After this date a small number of able candidates may still win a place in the school by being accepted onto the Master's List. All applicants to the school must either take the Academic Scholarship or the Common Entrance examination. Please see our website for details of this new policy: www.marlboroughcollege.org.

The 13+ Scholarship examination is in February/March of the year of entry and the Sixth Form Scholarship examination is in the November before entry.

Scholarships. (*see Scholarship Entries section*). Scholarships range in value up to 25% of full fees. Augmentation above 25% is available on the basis of need. At least twenty awards are available at 13+, including Music, Art and Sport, and at least six for Sixth Form entry. From time to time there are a number of other special categories of scholarship based upon parental occupation and particular abilities. Two means-tested scholarships/bursaries are worth 100% of full fees; one of these is the College Organ Scholarship. Anniversary Bursaries, which are subject to a means test, offer up to 85% reduction of school fees: these awards are based upon strengths in academic work, sport, art or music. A number of Children of Clergy Bursaries are awarded on interview and consultation, in addition to the automatic 15% reduction for all Children of Clergy.

Applications and enquiries about entries and scholarships should be addressed to The Senior Admissions Tutor.

Universities & Careers. Nearly all pupils who come to Marlborough go on into the Sixth Form and virtually all proceed to degree courses. Twenty-seven A and AS Level subjects are available in almost any combination in the large Sixth Form, plus additional courses. From September 2009, the International Baccalaureate will be introduced as an alternative to A Levels: pupils will be invited to choose between the two offerings. The Careers Department is modern and well-equipped, and assists Housemasters and Housemistresses in advising boys and girls and their parents as to careers and university choices, in addition to gap year projects.

Extra Curricular. Good games facilities are available with a modern Sports Hall, indoor swimming pool, spacious playing fields, two all-weather pitches, an athletics track and numerous tennis courts. The main games are athletics, hockey, rugby, tennis, cricket and netball; alternative games include lacrosse, soccer, rackets, fives, shooting, swimming and squash. There is a strong Outdoor Activities Department, which offers the Duke of Edinburgh's Award as well as climbing, canoeing, sub-aqua and orienteering; the CCF covers adventure training as part of its basic course, with specialist leadership training to a high standard. School Societies offering activities at different levels enable interests to be nurtured and, for those who enjoy country pursuits, the River Kennet and two trout lakes provide fishing.

Music. Nearly half the boys and girls play a musical instrument. There are three school orchestras, a wind band, a chamber orchestra, a brass band, Chapel Choir and a choral society; also numerous small instrumental and choral groups.

Drama. There are over fifteen productions each year, including two school plays, Junior productions and a house drama festival. Many are produced and directed by pupils. The Sixth Form curriculum includes Theatre Studies and Drama is an option at GCSE.

Art and Design. All pupils study Art in their first year and many go on to take the subject at GCSE, AS and A Level. The new Art School was opened in November 2005 and the department believes that all pupils can acquire a good standard of visual literacy across a variety of artistic disciplines. A new purpose-built centre houses Design, which is taught throughout the school.

Fees per term (2008-2009). £9,230 Boarding; £6,930 Day Pupils.

The Marlburian Club, Marlborough College. *Hon Secretary*: M C W Evans, Esq.

Charitable status. Marlborough College is a Registered Charity, number 309486 incorporated by Royal Charter to provide education.

Merchant Taylors' Boys' School
Crosby

Liverpool Road Crosby Liverpool L23 0QP
Tel: 0151 928 9323 (Headmaster)
0151 928 5770 (Bursar)
0151 949 9333 (Admissions Office)
Fax: 0151 949 9300
e-mail: info@merchanttaylors.com
website: www.merchanttaylors.com

The Boys' School was founded in 1620 by John Harrison, Citizen and Merchant Taylor of London. In 1878 the School was transferred to its present site.

Motto: '*Concordia parvae res crescunt*'

Governors:
Chairman: L C Coligan, Esq, BA
Chairman of Finance: F C Mercer, Esq, JP, FCA
Prof P W J Batey, BSc, MCB, PhD, FRTPI, FRSA
P J R Evans, Esq, FCA
Mrs S M I Hetherington, JP
Dr M I Hughes, MBChB
D R Jacks, Esq, LLB
Mrs V A P Johnson, BEd
P G Magill, Esq, MSc, CFIPD
Mrs D F Shackleton, MA, FCIH, FRSA, MAPM
Dr R Thind, MB BS, DMRD, FRCR
R J Walker, Esq, CEng, MIMechE

Bursar and Clerk to the Governors: P S Gaunt, MA, FCA

***Headmaster*: David Cook**, BA, MA

Deputy Headmasters:
D A C Blower, MA
D N Craig, MA, MEd, PGCE

Head of Sixth Form: J P Farrell, BSc, MA, PGCE
Head of Middle School: Mrs D Knaggs, BSc, PGCE
Head of Lower School: J E Turner, BA, MA
Director of Music: D Holroyd, GMus, RNCM, PPRNCM, ARCO
Chaplain: Revd D A Smith, BA

Teachers:
J C Ashcroft, BA, MA
J Benbow, BSc, PGCE
A P Boardman, BA, MA
Mrs A C Byrne, BSc, PGCE
Mrs M Casaus, MA, PGCE
P J Cooper, BSc, PGCE
D Chandler, BMus Hons
K R Connor, MEng
P J Cooper, BSc
D E Cowling, BSc, PhD

J Dore, BSc
Mrs S A Dunning, BA
J P Farrell, BSc, MA
Miss C Ferris, BSc, PGCE
S G Fletcher, BSc, MSc, PGCE
S J Freedman, BSc, CBiol, MIBiol
Dr J S Gill, BA, MPhil, PhD
J B Green, BA, PGCE
Mrs I Grek, BA, PGCE
C A Hall, BA, MSc
Mrs L M Harkins, BA
A G Heap, BSc, MSc
T W Hildrey, BSc
D W Hivey, BSc, PGCE
N A Hunt, BA
J C Irlam, BSc
P A Irvine, BEd
S J Kay, MA, PGCE
P A Lally, BA
P Little
I W McIntosh, MA
I D McKie, CertEd
Dr N Myers, BA, PhD
Dr A J Patchett, BSc, PhD
Miss S A Patel, BA
Mrs E C Peacock, BA
Mrs K E Plummer, BA
Mrs E Rea, BA, ALA
F J Rubia Castro, BA
Mrs K L Siddle, BEd, PGCE
M A C Slemen, BEd, DipPE
P R Spears, BA
M Stanley, BA, MA, PGCE
G T Stiff, BA
S P Sutcliffe, BA, MA
I Wallace, MA
M Whalley
Miss T Wilkinson, BA
J H Williams, BA
S J Williams, BSc
Mrs V A Winrow, BSc, PGCE
Mrs R J Wright, BSc, PGCE

Junior School:
Head: Mrs J E Thomas, BEd, MEd
Deputy Head: D K J Youngson, BA

Mrs B P J Ashcroft, BEd, PGCE, BGDE
Mrs A Davies, CertEd
D I Lyon, BA
Mrs L Rogers, BEd
Miss E A Trought
P A Wardle, BEd
Mrs H White, BA
Mrs A Wynne, BEd

Admissions: Mrs P Saffer
Headmaster's Secretary: Mrs M Delaney

The senior boys' school consists of about 643 boys, 180 of whom are in the Sixth Form. In addition there is a junior boys' School with about 154 boys between the ages of seven and eleven.

The school has a reputation for academic excellence and the majority of our leavers proceed to degree courses at Russell Group universities including Oxford and Cambridge. The emphasis throughout is very much on developing learners who are able to increasingly work independently and who have a genuine curiosity in their studies.

Curriculum. In the first three years of the Lower School boys study a wide variety of national curriculum subjects including separate sciences as well as the opportunity to pick up extra modern and ancient languages. They gradually specialise in the Middle School where there is the flexibility to study between 8 and 11 GCSEs including an accelerated IGCSE mathematics course. A weekly "enrichment" afternoon provides opportunities for co-curricular activities and educational visits.

In the Sixth Form the following subjects are available at A Level: Mathematics, Further Mathematics, Physics, Chemistry, Biology, Latin, Greek, Classical Civilisation, English Language, English Literature, History, Geography, Economics, French, German, Spanish, Design and Technology, Art & Design, Music, Theatre Studies and Physical Education. In addition, all boys in the Sixth Form will have an opportunity to follow a course in General Studies.

Games. Games played are Rugby Football, Cricket, Tennis, Hockey, Athletics, Cross Country and Rowing. There are Wind Surfing and Sailing Clubs, a gymnasium and indoor swimming pool, an Astroturf all-weather surface and six tennis courts. All boys are expected to participate in one of the many games options available throughout their time at the School.

School Societies. A wide range of activities and interests is covered by School Societies.

Music and Drama. About 150 boys receive weekly instrumental tuition and there is a subsidised scheme for beginners on orchestral instruments. There is a School Choral Society, Junior School Choir, Senior Concert Band and Jazz Band, all of which perform frequently inside and outside the School, in addition to a number of smaller ensembles.

There are 9 visiting specialist music teachers and close links in Music with our sister school, Merchant Taylors' Girls' School. There are also close links with the Girls' School in Drama, which now forms an integral part of the Upper School curriculum as well as being a major extra-curricular activity.

Combined Cadet Force. The School has a voluntary contingent of the Combined Cadet Force with Army, Navy and RAF Sections. There are around 220 members of the CCF, many of whom are girls from our sister school.

Admission. Boys are admitted to the Junior School at age 7 and to the Main School at 11, 13 or after GCSE. Some Assisted Places are available at 11.

Fees per term (2008-2009). Tuition: Senior School £2,727; Junior School £2,004.

Old Boys. There is an active Old Boys' Association (The Old Crosbeians) whose Secretary may be contacted via the School and from whom a handbook/register may be obtained.

Charitable status. Merchant Taylors' School is a Registered Charity, number 526681. It exists to provide education for local boys.

Merchant Taylors' School

Sandy Lodge Northwood Middlesex HA6 2HT
Tel: Head Master's PA: 01923 821850
Reception: 01923 820644
Admissions Secretary: 01923 845514
Bursar: 01923 825669
Fax: 01923 845522
e-mail: info@mtsn.org.uk
website: www.mtsn.org.uk

Motto: '*Concordia parvae res crescunt.*'

The Governors of the School:
Chairman: Sir Geoffrey Holland, KCB, MA Oxford, Hon LLD Sheffield, CIMgt
R J Brooman
G F Brown
Baroness Elizabeth Butler-Sloss, GBE
M C Clarke, MA Cambridge, FCA
R C G Gillott
J A J Price
Dr J H S Sichel, MB BS London
Sir Michael Tomlinson
P H Watkins

***Head Master*: S N Wright**, MA Queens' College, Cambridge

Second Master: T R Stubbs, BSc, PhD, CBiol, MIBiol
Development Director: C A Massi, BA
Senior Master: C R Evans-Evans, BA, MEd
Director of Studies: J G Taylor, MA
Deputy Head, Communications: C E Roseblade, BA
Registrar: A J Booth, MA
Head of Sixth Form: M Bond, BA
Chaplain: The Reverend R D E Bolton, MA

Assistant Staff:

Art & Design:
J C P Otley, MA (*Head of Art and Design*)
Ms A D Badar, BA
Miss H C Blowes, BA
J G Woodman, BA

Biology:
M T W Filtness, MA (*Head of Biology*)
Mrs H English, BA (*Head of Personal Education, Head of Psychology*)
C W Gray, BSc
T C H Greenaway, BSc (*Head of Lower School*)
Dr T R Stubbs, BSc, PhD, CBiol, MIBiol (*Second Master*)
Dr A Walker-Taylor, MA, PhD (*Head of DoE Award Scheme*)

Chemistry:
A J W Horrox, MA (*Head of Chemistry, President of SCR*)
Dr J S Braithwaite, BSc, PhD
D L Brewis, MA
C P Overton, MSc, MA, CChem, ARCS, FRSC
Mrs F A Rashid, BSc (*Head of Science*)

Classics:
M C Husbands, MA (*Head of Classics*)
M F Drury, MA
M R Jacobs, BA (*Head of Andrewes House*)
Miss L R Nicholas, MA (*Oxbridge Coordinator*)

Design & Technology:
J B Coleman, CertEd, MA (*Head of Design & Technology*)
A S Bannister, BSc (*Head of Walter House*)
N J Kyriacou, BEd (*Head of Spenser House*)
G M Stephenson, BSc (*Head of Mulcaster House*)

Economics & Politics:
A H Ellams, MA (*Head of Economics & Politics*)
C Chong, MPhil
D Howell, BA, MSc
C P Sowden, BA, MSc
M Tanweer, BA (*Head of Careers*)
Miss H F Thompson, BA, MSc, MA

English:
D A Lawrence, MA (*Head of English*)
P M Capel, BA (*Learning Support Coordinator*)
Dr A R Doyle, DPhil, MA
D Garnet, BA (*Director of Drama*)
J L Hartley, MA (*Enrichment Coordinator*)
S J Morris, BA
C E Roseblade, BA (*Deputy Head, Communications*)
Ms L V Smith, MA
J W Struthers, BA (*Assistant Head of Sixth Form*)
C J Taylor, BA (*Second in English*)

Geography:
Mrs S A Riddleston, BA (*Head of Geography*)
G P Colley, CertEd (*CO CCF*)
C T Tracey, BSc
D W Trebble, BA (*Staff Tutor*)
S W Turner, BSc

History:
S W Stott, MA (*Head of History*)
M Bond, MA (*Head of Sixth Form*)
A J Booth, MA (*Registrar*)
J G Brown, MA (*School Archivist, Head of General Studies, Governing Body SCR Representative*)
A R Lock, MA (*Head of Middle School*)
Mrs E F Marshall, BA
J G Taylor, MA (*Director of Studies*)
S N Wright, MA (*Headmaster*)

Information Systems:
C P Hirst, MA, BSc (*Head of Academic ICT*)
J Beck (*Network Technician*)
P Gregory (*Technical Services Manager*)
P A T Gregory (*ICT Technician*)
C E Roseblade, BA (*Deputy Head, Communications*)
I Rudling (*Webmaster*)
J A Sagnella (*Network Technician*)
M J Scott, BA

Learning Support:
P M Capel, BA (*Learning Support Coordinator*)
Mrs G M Kantor, BA

Library:
Mrs Y F Steward, BA (*Senior Librarian*)
Miss J Jacobs, BA (*Second Librarian*)
Mrs P J Jones, BA

Mathematics:
J D G Slator, MA (*Head of Mathematics*)
Mrs N Bigden, BSc
R G Cranston, BA
Miss H Croft, BSc (*Second in Mathematics*)
M F Illing, MA
D C Lowry, BA
S L Rowlands, BA
Mrs F S Teskey, BSc
P D Wild, BSc, MSc (*Senior Head of House, Head of White House*)

Modern Languages:
S N Hollands, MA (*Head of Modern Languages*)
Ms M E Broncano, MA (*Head of Spanish*)
Mrs M C R Castro, BA (*Spanish*)
Miss R G Haye, DEUG (*French & Spanish*)
Mrs A S Lock, BA (*French and Italian*)
Mrs K T Kenny, MA (*Head of DofE Award Scheme*)
Ms H McCann, MA (*Italian*)
Miss H E McCullough, BA (*Head of German*)
R M McGinlay, MA (*Head of French*)
J M S Rippier, BA (*French*)
T P Rocher, L-ès-L (*French*)
Mrs C E Udell, MA (*German*)
F R Vignal, DipHE (*French and Spanish*)

Music:
R N Hobson, MA, ARCO (*Director of Music*)
S J Couldridge, DipTCL
Mrs J H Stubbs, BMus, ARCO, ALCM (*Assistant Head of Middle School*)

Physical Education:
C M J Lehane, BA (*Director of Sport & Head of PE*)
R Briggs, BSc
J P Cowan, BSc (*Head of Academic PE, Head of Hockey*)
C R Evans-Evans, BA, MEd (*Senior Master*)

Physics:
N G Blight, MA (*Head of Physics*)
Dr A R H Clarke, MA, DPhil (*Assistant Director of Studies*)
N J D Hillier, BA, MSc
N P Migallo, BSc
M J Milsom, BSc
Ms L A Slator, BSc (*Examinations Officer*)

Psychology:
Mrs H M English, BA (*Head of Psychology, Head of Personal Education*)

Religious Studies:
The Reverend R D E Bolton, MA, Cert Theol, FRSA (*School Chaplain*)
Mrs E F Marshall, BA

School Counsellor: A J C Dickinson, BA, MEd, ALCP

Visiting Teachers:
J Atkins, DipRAM (*Trumpet*)
G Boyd, DipMus (*Double Bass*)
S Byron, BMus Hons RCM (*Trombone*)
Miss S Clark, MA, LRSM, ARCM, DipRCM, CTABRSM (*Piano*)
Mrs N S Coleman, CertEd (*Flute*)
Miss K Cormican, GTCL, PDOT (*Violin*)
Mr G Cracknell, LRAM (*Violin*)
A Francis, LRAM (*Clarinet*)

J Francis (*Saxophone & Clarinet*)
Ms N Hawkins (*Guitar*)
D Hester, LTCL, DipTCL (*Bassoon*)
C Hooker, LRAM, ARAM (*Oboe*)
Mrs F Jones, LRAM (*Violin*)
D Lewis, LRAM (*Brass*)
Mrs N Manington, BMus LGSM (*Piano*)
N Martin (*Percussion*)
B O'Doherty, LRAM, Prof Cert Hons (*Guitar*)
D Saunderson, GGSM (*Singing*)
M Smith, GRSM Hons, LRAM, ARCM (*Piano*)
Mrs M Stone, MMus (*Piano*)
Mrs N Tait, LRAM Hons (*Cello*)
S Yalden (*Percussion*)

Sports:
M Baggs (*Graduate Assistant*)
G Davies (*Rugby*)
H C Latchman (*Cricket*)
F Lombard (*Rugby*)
J Rayden (*Fencing*)
K Remfrey (*Judo*)
J Shaw (*Hockey and Tennis*)
S Singh (*Hockey*)
C Visagie (*Rugby*)
R Worrell (*Squash*)
M Khalifa (*Squash*)

Bursar: G R H Ralphs
Development Director: C A Massi
Head Master's PA: Mrs C Herbert
Admissions Secretary: Mrs K Kaye
Bursar's Secretary: Mrs S Enright

The School has enjoyed a distinguished history since its foundation by the Merchant Taylors' Company in 1561. It was one of the nine original Public Schools as defined by the 1868 Act and its pupils have achieved distinction throughout its history. The school enjoys close links with the Company who, to this day, constitutes its Governing Body. In 1933 the School moved from central London to its present superb, rural setting of 250 acres at Sandy Lodge, Northwood. We are within easy reach of parents in Buckinghamshire, Hertfordshire, Middlesex and North-West London by car, train or school coach service, as well as a mere half hour by tube from Baker Street.

There are 839 boys in the School.

All pupils have an individual tutor who looks after them throughout their school career in small House tutor groups. They are encouraged to find activities at which they can excel, to have confidence in their abilities and to gain self-knowledge as well as knowledge. The academic achievements of the School are first-rate and are achieved in an humane, civilised and relatively unpressured atmosphere. We place a great emphasis on encouraging boys to organise many activities themselves and to take responsibility for others.

Admission. Entry to the School at 11+, 13+ and 16+ is by the School's own Entrance Examinations and interview.

Scholarships and Bursaries. (*see Scholarship Entries section*). 11+ entry: Up to five Scholarships available, each with a maximum value of 30% of the fee.

13+ entry: Eleven scholarships are available, the largest up to the value of 30% of the fee.

For both these age groups bursaries are available depending upon proven financial need. These can also be used to increase the value of the Scholarship.

16+ entry: One Scholarship up to the value of 15% of the fee, plus one Exhibition up to the value of 5% of the fee.

Lower Sixth Internal Exhibitions: Eight Exhibitions may be awarded for boys going into the Lower Sixth up to the value of 5% of the School fee.

Music Scholarship Examination: The awards in music offered annually to boys at 11, 13 and 16 include one Scholarship of up to 25% of the fees, one Scholarship of up to 15%, and two exhibitions of up to 10% of the fees. All award holders receive free instrumental and/or singing tuition. Additional awards of free tuition may be made if there are candidates of sufficient merit.

Bursaries: Other bursaries are available to assist in cases of special hardship.

Other Awards: There is a generous variety of awards open to Sixth Formers for travel, Outward Bound and Sail Training, as well as leaving scholarships to assist at University.

Scholarships at Oxford and Cambridge Universities. At the end of their first undergraduate year, old boys are eligible for election to a maximum of three Sir Thomas White Scholarships at St John's College, Oxford, a Matthew Hale Scholarship at Queen's College, Oxford and a Parkin & Stuart Scholarship for Science or Mathematics at Pembroke College, Cambridge.

Curriculum and Organisation. The curriculum in years 7, 8 and 9 (Thirds, Upper Thirds and Fourths) is a broad one: Art and Design, Biology, Chemistry, Design and Technology, Drama, English, French, Geography, History, ICT, Latin, Mathematics, Music, Physical Education, Physics, PSHE and Religious Studies. Greek, German, Spanish or Italian are started when 13+ boys enter the school. All boys take nine or ten GCSEs, chosen from a wide range of subjects, including Music, Drama and ICT. Boys are entered for the IGCSE in Mathematics and English. A student entering the Lower Sixth embarks upon a two year course in which all boys study four subjects to AS Level, followed by three subjects at A2 for most (some continue with four). In addition, all boys do AS General Studies. An extensive choice of options is available and an enriching General Studies programme includes courses in Japanese and Mandarin.

Music. Any boy who wishes to can learn an instrument. A wide range of orchestral and vocal ensembles give frequent concerts throughout the year, and there is a dedicated Music School.

Free tuition for one year is available for selected boys who wish to start learning an orchestral instrument.

Games and Physical Education. Magnificent playing fields over 55 acres are dedicated to the playing of Rugby, Cricket, Soccer, Hockey, Cross-Country and Golf. There are Fives, Squash and Tennis Courts; also, an athletics track and floodlit, all-weather pitch. The Sports Hall accommodates four badminton courts, a multi-gym, a climbing wall, a fencing piste and indoor cricket nets. The school's lakes provide a marvellous facility for our Sailing Club, canoeing and windsurfing. Physical Education is compulsory for all pupils and all pupils learn to swim. There is an indoor swimming pool and Water Polo is offered. Coaching in Fencing, Basketball, Judo and Karate is excellent and boys enjoy national success in these sports.

Service Sections. The School has a Contingent of the Combined Cadet Force with RN, Army, and RAF Sections. The CCF includes girls from St Helen's School, Northwood. There is a Rifle Range for the use of the Contingent, and we send a team to Bisley every year. The Duke of Edinburgh's Award Scheme allows boys to achieve Bronze, Silver and Gold Awards, and the Community Service Group which provides an opportunity for a wide range of activities in the local area. All boys in Years 10 and 11 take part in the CCF, The Duke of Edinburgh's Award Scheme or Community Service teams.

The School places great emphasis on charitable endeavour and the boys run a great many societies to support good causes. A special feature of the school's charity work is PHAB, a week-long residential holiday for handicapped children held every Easter and organised by Sixth Form boys together with the girls of St Helen's School.

School Societies. There is a large number of School Societies covering a wide field of interests and activities.

Careers. There is a strong Careers Advisory Service, which organises annual Careers and Higher Education Conventions at the School and a range of work experience.

House and Tutorial Systems. The School is divided into eight Houses. Each House is under the care of a Head of House and a team of Tutors, who are responsible for the pastoral care of boys in that House.

Fees per term (2008-2009). £4,760. These cover not only tuition and games but also lunch. There is a registration fee of £50; admission fee deposits will subsequently be charged.

Term of entry. September unless there are very special circumstances.

Charitable status. Merchant Taylors' School Charitable Trust is a Registered Charity, number 1063740. It exists to provide a first-class all-round education for boys, irrespective of their background.

Merchiston Castle School

Colinton Edinburgh EH13 0PU
Tel: 0131 312 2200
Headmaster: 0131 312 2203
Director of Admissions: 0131 312 2201
Fax: 0131 441 6060
e-mail: headmaster@merchiston.co.uk
website: www.merchiston.co.uk

The School was established in 1833 and moved in 1930 from the centre of the city out to its present spacious and attractive site, bordered by the Water of Leith and close to the Pentland Hills.

Motto: *Ready Ay Ready.*

Governors:
Chairman: J M Gourlay, BCom, CA
The Hon Lord Hodge, QC, BA, LLB
A E Corstorphine
R E M Irving, MA, DPhil
M N Donaldson, MSc
C M A Lugton, MA
W M Biggart, BA
D J Biggar, OBE
H P G Maule, MA
R W L Legget, MBA, CA
Mrs A J B Loudon, MA, CA
G R T Baird
Prof Lorraine Waterhouse, BA, MSW
G F Barnet, LLB
P K Young, BSc, MRICS
Mrs N C D Kuenssberg, CBE
R M Ridley, MA

Secretary to the Governors and Bursar: D G Smith, BCom, CA
President of the Merchistonian Club: S P Abram

***Headmaster*: A R Hunter**, BA Manchester

Deputy Heads:
F N Rickard, BA Hull, ACCEG (*English*)
T F West, MA Edinburgh (*English*)

Director of Studies: Mrs M Muetzelfeldt, BSc London (*Mathematics*)

Housemasters:
Evans: K J A Anderson, MTh St Andrews (*Religious Studies, PSE, Chaplaincy*)
Rogerson West: R D Heathcote, BSc Nottingham, PGCE Liverpool (*Head of Geography*)
Sixth Form Day House: I H Mitchell, BA Hons Strathclyde, PhD Imperial College (*Physics*)
Rogerson East: Prof J Palacios, Buenos Aires (*Spanish*)
Chalmers East: J M V Cordingley, MA London (*Head of Art*)
Chalmers West: P K Rossiter, MA Oxford (*Director of Music, Chaplaincy, Head of Middle School*)
Pringle Form III: R C Lucas, MEng Aston, MA Sheffield (*Mathematics*)
Pringle Forms II + I: P K Hall, MA Oxford (*English, Head of Junior School*)

Assistant Staff:
J Rainy Brown, BSc Edinburgh (*Chemistry, Mathematics*)
M C L Gill, BSc, PhD Edinburgh (*Head of Science*)
J R Hart, BSc Aberdeen (*Biology*)
J C O Vaughan, BSc Edinburgh (*Mathematics*)
P S Williams, BA Leicester (*English, Assistant Head of Department*)
Mrs C A Watson, BA Manchester (*English, Head of Learning Support*)
Mrs M V Prini-Garcia, L-ès-L Madrid (*Classical Languages, Spanish, Head of Careers, CPO*)
A Hambling (*Master i/c Shooting & Transport*)
T J Lawson, BA Sheffield, PhD Edinburgh, FSA Scot (*Geography*)
C W Swan, CertEd Loughborough (*PE*)
D M Turner, MA Oxford, ARCO (*Music, ICT*)
A C N Millard, MA Aberdeen (*Geography*)
S J Horrocks, MA Cambridge (*French, Spanish, ESOL*)
P Corbett, MA St Andrews (*Head of Languages, French, Latin*)
Miss F M Blakeman, DipDes Napier (*Art & Design*)
Revd A S Macpherson, MA Glasgow (*Religious Studies, Chaplaincy*)
S Campbell, BSc Glasgow (*Mathematics, Assistant Head of Department*)
N J Mortimer, MA, DPhil Oxford (*Head of English, Religious Studies, Assistant Head Academic*)
F Geisler, LA SII/I Bochum (*German, ESOL*)
Mrs F Horrocks, BA Pretoria (*French*)
Mrs M B Watson, BSc Glasgow (*Mathematics, ICT*)
Miss C A Walker, BA Edinburgh (*EFL*)
R A Charman, BA Canterbury (*Mathematics, Head of Physical Education, Director of Sport*)
Mrs J M Williams, BA Leicester (*Librarian, Deputy CPO*)
M E Appleson, BA Leeds Metropolitan (*Director of Rugby, History, Physical Education, Learning Support*)
F P J Main, BEd Edinburgh (*Design Technology*)
R P Nicholls, BSc Durham (*Head of Physics, Head of Electronics*)
K G Pettigrew, BSc Edinburgh, PhD (*Head of Chemistry, Physics*)
Miss S M Twyford, BSc Glasgow, MSc Strathclyde, PhD Glasgow (*Physics, Coordinator of Junior Curriculum*)
Ms R Cohen, DRSAMD (*Music*)
R J Armstrong, BEng Edinburgh (*Physics*)
T S Wilkinson, BSc Kingston, PhD Lancaster (*Chemistry*)
N G D Blair, BA Queen's University, MA Edinburgh (*Religious Studies, English, Chaplaincy*)
M J Caves BSc Belfast (*Mathematics, Rugby Coach*)
M S King, BSc Bristol, PGCE Cambs (*Head of Biology*)
Mrs B G Hunter, BEd Exeter (*Art & Design*)
Miss S J Godfrey, MA Hons Edinburgh, PGCE York (*English, Classical Civilisation*)
Mrs N G Hairs, BA Hons Kent, PGCE Loughborough (*Junior School Teacher*)
J B Bisset, MA Hons Aberdeen, PGCE Edinburgh (*Director of ICT Services, Head of ICT*)
D D J Cartwright, BSc Edinburgh (*Junior Science, Chemistry*)
Miss C L McShane, BA Oxford (*Probationer Teacher of English*)
I H Mitchell, BA Hons Strathclyde, PhD Imperial College (*Physics*)
Miss J R Vaughan, BA Newcastle (*Junior School Teacher*)

Mrs M Hsu-McWilliam, BA Tamkang, MSc Edinburgh (*Mandarin*)
P D R Osborne, BEd Natal (*Director of Junior Sport, Asst Housemaster I & II Forms*)
G Campbell, MA Aberdeen (*Master i/c Pipe Bands*)
A E N Brown, BA New South Wales (*History*)
W J J Clayton, MA Edinburgh (*Economics*)
Mrs A Almeida de Palacios, UCA Buenos Aires (*Spanish*)
A C Dickson, BEd Edinburgh (*Design & Technology*)
J P W Dixon, MA Cambridge (*Head of History*)
M Du Coudray (*Tennis Academy Coach*)
A D Ewing (*School Staff Instructor*)
M R Hillier, BA Cambridge (*History*)
Mrs M H Knights, MA Lyon (*Head of Languages, French*)
Mrs I Stewart, BEd Glasgow (*Junior Learning Support*)
P M Shaw, BSc, MPhil London (*Physics*)
P J Deakin, BA Durham, PGCE Cambridge (*Head of Geography*)
S Thompson, MA Hons Edinburgh, PGCE Cambridge (*History*)
Ms K Tully BSc Edinburgh, MPhil Edinburgh, PGDE Edinburgh (*Biology*)
Ms F Vian, PhD Parma (*Mathematics*)
Miss J C Kane, MA Edinburgh, PGDE Edinburgh (*Junior School Teacher*)

Student Helpers:
Megan Laing, Wynberg Girls' High School, Cape Town
Charles Fairfield-Smith, Canberra Grammar School, Australia
Angus Lockhart, The Southport School, Australia
David Owen, Lindisfarne College, New Zealand

Medical Officers:
Dr T McMillan, MBChB, MRCGP, DRCOG
Dr D A Reid, BSc, MBChB, MRCGP, DipSEM

Medical Staff:
Ms L Moussa, RGN, BSc, PGC
Mrs J L Bisset, MA, BA, RGN
Mrs S Collis, SRN
Mrs J N Fisher, RGN
Mrs F G McKenzie

CCF: SSI WOl A Hambling MISM

Administration:
Headmaster's PA: Mrs S Dow
Director of Admissions: Mrs C A Rickard
Director of Marketing: Miss G A Cordiner
Master of Works: D M Stenhouse

There are 430 boys in the School, of whom 295 are boarders.

Admission. The normal ages of entry are 8–14 and 16, though from time to time there may be vacancies at other ages. Entry at 8–10 is by assessment and interview; at 11 or 12 by means of the Merchiston entrance examinations; entry at 13 by the Common Entrance or Merchiston entrance examinations. Entry to the Sixth Form at 16 depends on a successful showing in the GCSE or Standard Grades as well as on interview and a report from the previous school. There are approximately 140 in the Sixth Form. There are a number of prestigious Open Entrance Scholarships (see Scholarships section below). Entry is possible in all three terms where vacancies permit.

A prospectus and further details may be obtained from the Director of Admissions. Prospective parents are encouraged to visit the School. Information is also found on our website: www.merchiston.co.uk.

Courses of study. In the Lower School the curriculum comprises English, Mathematics, Biology, Chemistry, Physics, History, French, Latin, German, Spanish, Geography, Religious Studies, Art, Music, PE, Electronics, Design, and Information Technology.

In the Middle School a 2-year course leading to the GCSE is followed, consisting of a core curriculum: English, English Literature, Mathematics, a foreign language (French, German, Spanish), Chemistry, and a wide range of option subjects, including History, a second foreign language, Electronics, Physics, Biology, Information Technology, Geography, Mandarin, Latin, Religious Studies, Art, Design and Music. Most boys take 9 subjects.

In the Lower Sixth most boys study 4 subjects at AS Level or a mixture of Highers and AS Level. In Upper Sixth, boys study generally 3 subjects to A2. The A Levels include English, Mathematics, Biology, Chemistry, Physics, French, German, Spanish, History, Geography, Information Technology, Latin, Modern Studies (Higher only), Music, plus Design and Art. In addition to his main subjects each boy follows a General Studies course offering Presentation Skills, Mandarin, Moral and Social Studies and Careers Guidance. Classes are small throughout the School and all subjects are setted by ability. The School prepares boys for entry to Oxford and Cambridge.

The School makes provision for specialist ESOL teaching for foreign students.

Learning Support Provision. Boys with learning difficulties, including dyslexia, namely 3–4 able pupils per annum, enjoy successful careers at Merchiston. Our aim is to enhance self-esteem through genuine praise. We encourage each pupil to find success in his area of strength, whether inside or outside the classroom. The objective is that all pupils have access to a wide and varied curriculum, and that as a result each discovers his own personal strengths and talents, and enjoys the resulting success. All are expected to follow mainstream GCSE courses.

Houses. Each of the boarding Houses caters for a particular age group and the atmosphere and activities are tailored accordingly. The Housemaster and his House Tutors pay special attention to the care of the individual and to the development of both his studies and interests.

Day boys. The life of day boys is fully integrated with that of the boarders.

Games. The principal games are rugby, played in the Autumn and Lent Terms, and in the Summer cricket and athletics. Launched in 2007 The Tennis Academy provides specialised coaching and a full training and sports science programme. There is a large indoor heated swimming pool and a sports hall, and there are good facilities for other sports including tennis, squash, fives, shooting, sailing, skiing, basketball, fencing, badminton, golf, hockey and curling.

Music. Music plays an important part in the life of the School. Tuition is available in all keyboard and orchestral instruments and currently about one quarter of the School is learning a musical instrument, and two choirs flourish. There is also a School orchestra, a close harmony group, a jazz band and two pipe bands. The choir and instrumentalists frequently go on tour, eg USA, Far East, Europe.

Drama. There is at least one major play production a term, with frequent House plays or drama workshop productions in a well-equipped, purpose-built theatre.

Art, Craft, Design and Technology, and Ceramics. The art and design centre offers both within the curriculum and in the pupil's free time scope for painting, pottery, metalwork, woodwork and design work. Courses within the curriculum or in free time in Computing and Electronics are also available.

Societies. There is a wide variety of clubs including chess, debating, electronics, and photography. Visits to theatres, concerts and exhibitions are a frequent part of a boy's life at Merchiston.

CCF. All boys join the CCF for a period of three terms, after which point participation is voluntary. This includes outward bound activities such as climbing, hillwalking, canoeing and camping. The School is also very active in community service work.

Girls. The School does not take girls but has a special relationship as brother/sister school with St George's School for Girls, Edinburgh and Kilgraston School in Perthshire. This includes joint expeditions, concerts, tours, seminars, debating, social events and study courses. Merchiston operates a joint fees scheme with Kilgraston School.

Careers advice. A qualified careers adviser leads a team of trained staff to supplement the advice of the Academic Management Team, Housemasters and House Tutors. Pupils attend lessons in careers as part of their Personal and Social Education Programme in the Senior School and all Fifth Form pupils take the Morrisby Careers Aptitude test. The School is a member of the ISCO. A designated careers research centre is located in the library complex.

Links with parents. There are regular parent/staff meetings and parents are fully briefed and consulted with regard to all academic and career decisions. There is also a parents' forum, which holds regular meetings.

Health. There is a medical centre in the charge of the School Nursing Sisters and the School Doctor visits regularly.

Fees per term (2008-2009). Junior School: Boarders £5,195, Day boys £3,665; Forms 2 and 3 Boarders £5,980, Day boys £4,225. Senior School: Forms 4 and above Boarders £7,920, Day boys £5,735.

Siblings, Forces, Clergy and Teaching Profession fee reductions are available.

Scholarships. (*see Scholarship Entries section*). Mostly at 13+. The main categories are academic, all-rounder and music. There are Prep School Awards for boys entering from prep schools, a Technology Award, and a Community Scholarship for boys living in the Edinburgh postcode area. Additional Awards for overseas students include European, Kenyan and Hong Kong. Laidlaw Scholarships launched in 2008.

Academic Scholarships and All-Rounder Awards grant honour to the recipient and may, in addition, carry a fee concession. The level of concession awarded depends upon a boy's ability, the number of awards made in each year, and financial need. Some means-tested bursaries are also available.

Further details can be obtained from the Director of Admissions.

Old boys. The Secretary of The Merchistonian Club, c/o the School. Former pupils include: The Rt Hon John MacGregor, MP; Peter Burt, former Chief Executive, Bank of Scotland; John Jeffrey, OBE (ex Scotland XV).

Charitable status. Merchiston Castle School is a Registered Charity, number SC016580. It aims to give each boy in his way the capacity and confidence to live in an uncertain world and to make that life as rich as possible; more specifically to encourage him to work hard and to take pride in achievement, to think independently, to face up to challenges, to accept responsibility, to show concern for others and to develop wider skills and interests.

Methodist College

1 Malone Road Belfast Co Antrim BT9 6BY
Northern Ireland
Tel: 028 9020 5205
Fax: 028 9020 5229
e-mail: school@methody.org
website: www.methody.org

Methodist College was founded in 1865 to provide a public school for pupils of all denominations. It was opened in 1868 and has grown to be a very large grammar school with relatively small boarding departments for both boys and girls and with 2 preparatory schools. The Board of Governors consists of 15 members elected by the Conference of the Methodist Church in Ireland (including *ex officio* the President and Secretary of the Church) 6 members appointed by the Department of Education, Northern Ireland, 3 elected parent representatives and 3 elected teacher representatives.

Motto: *Deus Nobiscum.*

Chairman: J McGarry, ACII, CDipAF, FBIBA

Honorary Treasurer: J Mulholland, BSc, CEng, FICE, FIEI, FCJWEM

Honorary Secretaries:
The Revd D P Ker, BA, BD, MTh
Dame M Uprichard

***Principal*: J S W Naismith**, MA

Senior Vice-Principal: Mrs M P White, BA

Vice-Principal: D R S Gallagher, BSc, MEd, PhD

Head of Senior School: W J Slater, BEng
Head of Middle School: M A Cinnamond, BA
Head of Junior School: S E Roulston, MA, MEd
Head of Pastoral Care: (*to be appointed*)
Director of Studies: M A McCullough, BA

Heads of Faculty:

Creative & Performing Arts: Ms A Moore, BA
English: Mrs H D Collier, BA, PhD
Environment & Society: Mrs N F M Gallagher, BEd, MA
Languages: A R Dempsie, MA, PhD
Mathematics: A Craig, BSc
Physical Education, Games & Recreational Activities: T D Creighton, BEd
Science & Technology: B R Wheeler, BSc, PhD

Head of Preparatory Department: (*to be appointed*)

Director of Music: Mrs R M E McCartney, BMus, MBE

Director of Services: J Robinson, FCMA, MIMgt

Principal's Secretary: Mrs R Wheeler

The School is situated in 14 acres of grounds immediately adjacent to the Queen's University of Belfast. There are 40 acres of playing fields at Pirrie Park, just over a mile away, and a further 12 acres at Deramore Park, at about the same distance, and a newly-constructed Boat House for the Rowing Club on the river Lagan within half-a-mile of the School.

The premises comprise the original College Building, opened in 1868, part of which is used for the accommodation of boy boarders; McArthur Hall, opened in 1891 as a hall of residence for girl boarders; the Whitla Hall and capable of seating 800; the Chapel of Unity, built to celebrate the Centenary in 1968; and a fine range of buildings for day school purposes of which three quarters have been built since the Second World War. There are new computer, technology and Science suites; a music department with rooms for individual practice and a range of instruments that includes 2 pipe organs; a fine library; a new Sports Hall; a new Art Department; 2 gymnasia and an indoor swimming pool; and a large number of teaching rooms most of which are adapted for specialist teaching of particular subjects. A Sixth Form Centre, with provision for recreational activities, private study and tutorial teaching, was opened in 1972.

Curriculum. With its staff of about 140 full-time teachers the College provides education from the age of 5 to the age of 19 for both boys and girls. In the grammar school, courses lead to the GCSE and AS and A2 level examinations. English and English Literature, Latin, Classical Civilisation, Greek, French, German, Spanish, Russian, Religious Studies, History, Geography, Economics, Political Studies, Mathematics, Physics, Chemistry, Biology, Home Economics, Computer Studies, Technology, Geology, Music, Art, History of Art, Psychology, Drama, ICT are offered in the examinations, and it is possible to arrange for pupils from overseas to be examined in their local languages. A wide-ranging selection of 'general studies' is available to Sixth Form pupils alongside their specialist examination work. Religious and Physical Education, Games, Drama, Music and a wide variety of activities ensure that the education given is not limited to intellectual matters and that every kind of talent has an opportunity for development. Students are prepared for universities in Ireland and Great Britain, for colleges of education and for other forms of professional and vocational training for which a high level of general education is a prerequisite. In recent years about 95% of all leavers have proceeded to degree courses in universities. Each year there is a high success rate of entry to Oxbridge Colleges.

Forms. By reason of its size the School is in a position to offer a wide choice of courses in the senior forms. Advice about these choices in relation to possible careers is given to all pupils by specially trained teachers. Each pupil's progress is kept under review, not only by his or her Tutor, but also by the Head of Form, an experienced teacher in charge of the year group. Each pupil has the opportunity to gain full benefit from the activities the College offers. Careful consideration is given each year to the precise placing of pupils in the next form and parents are consulted where options are to be exercised. Full reports are furnished twice per year and an internal reporting system ensures regular contact with parents throughout the year. The Heads of Form, Heads of Faculty and Heads of Department deal with disciplinary problems, and problems arising from failure on the part of the pupils to work as they should.

Games. Rugby Football, Cricket, Rowing, Hockey, Tennis, Netball, Athletics are among the outdoor activities available. The College has an outstanding record in competitive sport and its former pupils include many notable international players. A heated indoor pool is in daily use at the main School. A new astroturf hockey pitch has been laid.

Activities. Music and drama are particularly strong. Each year there are 5 or 6 dramatic productions, ranging from large-scale to small and experimental, and involving pupils of all ages. There are 5 choirs, 2 orchestras, a band with some 100 players, and a large number of smaller instrumental groups. In addition to regular recitals in the College, there are major public performances throughout the year, culminating in the Easter Concert which is held in the Waterfront Concert Hall in Belfast. Since 1993, the Senior Girls' Choir has been twice Northern Ireland 'Choir of the Year', has been runner-up in the Sainsbury's UK Choir of the Year competition and in 1998 was the overall winner of the Sainsbury's Choir of the Year title, the first school choir to do so. Another record was achieved in this prestigious competition by the Senior Girls' Choir in 2002 who became the first choir in any category to win the overall competition twice. The Chapel Choir (a mixed choir of 35 voices) won the Songs of Praise National Competition and the UTV Choir of the Year.

There are some 35 clubs and societies which meet regularly: from Chess, in which the College has an outstanding record, to Community Service, Conservation, Electronics, Angling and Debating.

Pupils now have the opportunity to discuss issues with staff on Form Councils, Sixth Form Forum and ultimately the School Council.

Model United Nations is offered to all year groups. The College organises a conference in the Autumn attracting participants from Europe and America.

In January 2003, a delegation of 18 students won the prestigious Yale Mun Competition.

The College received The British Council's International Award in 2005.

Calendar. The School session opens at the beginning of September, and ends in the last week of June. Holidays totalling about 4 weeks are divided between Christmas and Easter in the way that best suits each year's calendar. Long weekends are granted at Hallowe'en and at mid-term.

School House. Boys are accommodated to a maximum number of 90 as boarders in the charge of the Senior Resident Master, who is assisted by his deputy, several resident masters, 2 matrons, a nurse, and domestic staff.

McArthur Hall. Girls are accommodated to a maximum number of 70 as boarders in the charge of the Lady Warden, who is assisted by her deputy, several resident mistresses, a matron, a nurse and domestic staff. The very handsome building provides a gracious environment.

Senior boys and girls have individual cubicles and private study places. All boarders are the particular concern of the School Doctor, the Chaplain and his lady assistant. The recreational facilities of a large school are available when day pupils are not present.

Downey House Preparatory School was founded in 1933. There are some 300 pupils and a staff of 16 teachers. The School is in the grounds of the main playing fields at Pirrie Park and the pupils have the full use of these facilities.

Fullerton House Preparatory School received its name in 1950 when the preparatory department of the Grammar School was moved to separate premises in the campus. There are some 300 pupils and a staff of 16 teachers. Facilities for physical education, swimming and dining are provided in the main College.

The 2 preparatory schools have been allowed to build up their own individual traditions whilst sharing resources. Under the general supervision of the Principal and Governors, the Head of the Preparatory Department has been given as large a measure of autonomy as possible.

Boarders under 11 years of age attend one or other of the preparatory schools.

Fees per annum (2008-2009). Boarding Fees: Preparatory Department £7,500, Secondary Department £8,360.

Tuition Fees: Preparatory Department £3,435, Secondary Department £140, Non-EEA Nationals £6,410.

Tuition Fees include Capital Fee of £140.

Scholarships. Entrance scholarships of £400 pa are available for first year boarders, and details of these and other awards are available from the Principal's Secretary. There is provision on the Foundation for the children of Ministers of the Methodist Church in Ireland.

Admission. Local pupils are admitted to the Preparatory Schools from the age of 5. Children whose parents are working overseas are admitted as boarders from the age of 8; otherwise it is preferred that boarders enter at 11. The main entry to the grammar school is at 11, for most pupils, on the basis of the Northern Ireland transfer procedure. Application must, however, always be made direct to the College and the choice of pupils admitted rests with the College and not with the local authorities. It is the College's policy to do its utmost to accommodate at later stages the children of parents moving to Northern Ireland, and senior boys and girls who have outstripped the resources of their present schools. Except in such cases, application for the admission of day pupils should be made not less than 6 months before the prospective entry, and for boarders, as early as possible.

Entry is possible in all three terms following application, possible interview and an admissions test.

Charitable status. Methodist College Belfast is a Registered Charity, number X45039A. Its aims are to provide education for boarders and day pupils irrespective of their denomination.

Mill Hill School

The Ridgeway Mill Hill London NW7 1QS
Tel: 020 8959 1221 (Admissions)
Fax: 020 8906 2614
e-mail: registrations@millhill.org.uk
website: www.millhill.org.uk

Motto: *Et virtutem et musas.*

Court of Governors:

Chairman: Prof M R E Proctor, ScD
Prof J E Banatvala, CBE, MA, MD, FRCP, FRCPath, FMedSci
Dr R G Chapman, BSc, MB BS, FRCGP
Dr A P Craig, MB BS, DRCOG
Mrs C G Erskine-Murray, BA
Mrs S E Freestone, MEd, GRSM, LRAM, ARCM
N D Marcou, Esq
G Nosworthy, Esq
Miss J M Taylor, BSc, DipEd
G O Vero, Esq, FCA

Clerk to the Court: R L Axworthy, BA, PhD, PGCE, Cert Acc

***Headmaster*: Dr D Luckett**, BA, DPhil

Deputy Head: Mrs J Sanchez, BSc (*also Geography*)
Deputy Head (*External Relations*): P J P McDonough, MA, ACP (*also History*)
Deputy Head (*Academic*): A C Gaylor, BA (*also Mathematics*)

Assistant Head (*Pastoral*): N Gregory, BA
Assistant Head (*Academic*): Mrs M Atkins, BSc

Bursar: B D Fraser, BsBA, MBA

Chaplain: Revd A J Keep, MA

Assistant Teachers:
† *Housemaster/Housemistress*

Art & Design:
A D Ross, MA (*Head of Art*)
Miss V C Dempster, MA
Ms N Mirzoeff, BA

Business Education:
Miss L H Sharples, BA (*Head of Business Education; also Co-Director of Sixth Form*)
Mrs V G Miner, MSc
M S Smith, BA

Classics:
A Homer, BA (*Head of Classics*)
†S T Plummer, BA

Design Technology:
H Barnes, BA (*Head of Design Technology*)
Ms B D Banks, BEd

English & Drama:
R W Searby, BA (*Head of English*)
D S Proudlock, BA (*Head of Drama*)
†D T Bingham, BA (*also Head of Careers*)
Miss E Curtis-Rouse, BA
C Green, BA
†Miss L J Farrant, BA
J M Lewis, MA (*Director of Studies*)
Ms S J Owen, BA
Mrs S Stagg, LLB
Mrs E E Worsdale, BA
S Pulham, BA (*Head of EAL*)
Mrs S Isaacs, BEd

Geography:
N R Hodgson, MA (*Head of Geography*)
†J R Monaghan, BSc
D R Woodrow, BA (*also Director of Sport*)

History & Politics:
M Dickinson, MA (*Head of History*)
J D Rees, BA, AKC
T Hardy, BA
S D Parrish, BA (*also Coordinator of Activities*)
Miss H O'Connell, BA

Information Technology:
M J Northen, BA (*Head of IT*)
M E Jennings, BSc
Mrs P Newsome, BSc (*Head of Careers*)

Mathematics:
G Docherty, BSc
R P Cross, BSc, CMath, MIMA
K P Bulman, BSc (*Head of Mathematics*)
P J Kwok, BSc
†A H Slade, BA
T Trhlik
H S Cartz, MSc

Modern Languages:
†P R Lawson, MA
A H Armstrong, BA, PhD
†Miss C J Lewis, BA
Miss K Skoudy, Maîtrise LEA (*Head of Modern Languages & Spanish*)
†P M Durán, BA
Miss T M G Villalón, BEd
Ms A Thomas, M-ès-L
S E O'Neill, BA (*Head of German & European Section*)

Music:
R P Allain, BMus, FTCL (*Director of Music*)
M P Kemp, BMus, ARCM

Visiting Instrumental Teachers:
J Bradford, BA, BMus, LGSM, LLCM, ALCM, AdvDip KIB, Cert Berklee (*guitars*)
J Fleeman, GCLCM, AdvCert GSMD (*percussion*)
O Gledhill, MA Mtpp (*violoncello*)
T Gray, BA Hons (*guitar*)
P Jaekel, GRSM, LRAM, ARCO (*piano*)
Mrs H Kearns, BA Hons, LTCL (*pianoforte*), LTCL (*flute*) (*piano*)
Miss K Kelly, ALCM, LTCL (*flute*)
L Kelly, ALCM, LTCL (*trumpet*)
K Kyle, BMus Hons, LRAM, PGDipRAM (*voice*)
A Martin, AGSM (*percussion*)
P Nathaniel, GGSMD (*saxophone, clarinet*)
Miss C Philpot, BRSM (*oboe*)
A Poole, BSc (*double bass, guitar*)

Physical Education:
Miss S Reynolds, BSc (*Head of PE and Girls' Games*)
Miss R Martin, BEd
J H Kingstone, BSc
D M Halford, PGA (*Director of Golf*)
G A Byrnes, BA

Sciences:
†D S Hughes, BSc (*Head of Science & Biology*)
J G W Watson, BSc (*Head of Chemistry*)
P H Thonemann, MA, MPhil (*also Head of Complementary Studies*)
T J Chilton, BSc, MA
Dr E J M Evesham, BSc, PhD, CBiol, FIBiol (*Head of PSHRE*)
D H Fawcett, BSc (*also Mathematics*)
Dr S Radojevic, BSc
Miss S Whitehead, BSc
D Bennett, BSc
†A Luke, MA
G M Turner, BSc
R N R Wallace, BSc
Dr S V Baker, BSc
D A Webster, BEng (*Head of Science & Physics*)
G N Saint, BSc

Learning Support:
Miss L Silverman, BA, Dip SpLD (*Head of Learning Support*)

Officer Commanding CCF: Major J Monaghan, BSc

Medical Officer: Dr S V Thwaites, MB BS, MRCG, DO, RCOG

Nursing Staff:
Mrs Valerie Beynon, RGN
Mrs Jane Simpson, RGN

Belmont, Mill Hill Preparatory School
The Ridgeway, Mill Hill, London NW7 4ED
Tel: 020 8906 7270; Fax: 020 8906 3519
e-mail: office@belmontschool.com;
website: www.belmontschool.com

Head: Mrs L C Duncan, BSc, PGCE

Deputy Head (Curriculum): L Roberts, BA, PGCE
Deputy Head (Pastoral): Mrs C A Adler, BA, DipDysInst

Head of Upper School: C Cole, BA, PGCE

Head of Lower School: Miss C Froud, BEd

Director of Activities: J Fleet

Heads of Department:
J McNulty, BA, PGCE (*Art*)
J Clement, BA, PGCE (*Classics*)
Mrs V McSween, BEd (*Design Technology*)
M Russo, BA, DipEd (*English*)
Mrs C McRill, BA, PGCE (*French*)
A Hayward, BSc, PGCE (*Geography*)
R S Pace, BA, MA, MAT (*History*)
Mrs A Gritz, BSc (*ICT*)
Miss G Carpenter, BA, PGCE (*Music*)
G Rumbell, BA
D W Elder, CertEd (*Physical Education*)
Mrs H Lawson, BA, PGCE (*RE, PSE*)
Mrs J Fisher, BSc, PGCE (*Science*)
J Buoy, BEd (*Educational Visits Coordinator*)
C Cole, BA, PGCE (*English*)

Subject Teachers:
J Buoy, BEd (*Mathematics, Games*)
Mrs B Ahmed, BA, MA (*French*)
T Brandt, MA, PGCE (*Mathematics, Science, PE*)
C Hoban, BMus, TEFL (*Music, Games*)
Mrs M Clarke, BA, PGCE (*French*)
A W T Haigh, BSc, PGCE (*Science*)
Mrs A Skipper-Jones, BA (*PE, Games*)
J Ince, BA (*English*)
Miss J Harrison, BSc, PGCE (*Mathematics*)
Miss G Carpenter, BA, PGCE (*Music, Games*)
Mrs P Bloom, BEd (*Girls' PE*)

Special Needs Coordinator: Mrs B Russo, BA, PGCE

Lower School Tutors:
R Baker, BEd
Miss A Cohen, BA, PGCE
Miss J Swailes, BA
Mrs E Pendred, BA, PGCE
L Smith, HED
Miss M Sevani, BA, MA
Mrs M L Slade, BEd
Mrs K Sahoo, MA (*Teaching Assistant*)
Mrs S Roberts
Miss K Wilkinson, BA, PGCE

Support Teachers:
Mrs S Lewin, RSADipSpLD
Mrs E Shepherd, CertEd, RSADipSpLD, AMBDA
Mrs H Hardy, BA, PGCE
Mrs N Harris, BSc, PGCE, DipIT

School Counsellor: Mrs S Sawyer
Librarian: Mrs L Mason, BA, MCILIP
Matron: Mrs R Corbett, RGN

ICT Technician: Dr J White, PhD, BSc
Laboratory Technician: A Smith
Head's PA: Mrs G Ellen

Grimsdell, Mill Hill Pre-Preparatory School
Winterstoke House, Wills Grove, Mill Hill, London NW7 1QR
Tel: 020 8959 6884; Fax: 020 8959 4626
e-mail: office@grimsdell.org.uk;
website: www.grimsdell.org.uk

Head: Mrs P E R Bennett-Mills, CertEd

Deputy Head: Mrs A Attree, CertEd (*also Special Needs Coordinator, DT Coordinator*)

Senior Teacher: Mrs T Weeks, BA Hons, PGCE (*Year 2 Coordinator; English Coordinator*)

Assistant Staff:
Miss S Butt, BEd (*Mathematics Coordinator*)
Mrs A Cotsen, BEd (*ICT Coordinator*)
Mrs P Fraser, CertEd (*History Coordinator*)
Miss S French, BA Hons, PGCE (*Nursery Teacher, PSHME Coordinator*)
Miss C Holliday, BA (*Art Coordinator*)
Mrs S Kirk, BEd Hons (*Science Coordinator, Year 1 Coordinator*)
Mrs N Maraney, BA Hons (*Music Coordinator part-time*)
Mrs B Myburgh, BPrimEd (SA) (*Design & Technology Coordinator*)
Mrs P Raghunath, BEd Hons
Ms V Suarez-Rivas, BEd Hons, PGCE (*PE Coordinator*)
Mrs J Sutcliffe, MontDip (*Early Years Coordinator, Geography Coordinator*)
Miss J Warden, BMus Hons, PGCE (*RE Coordinator*)

Mill Hill was founded by Samuel Favell (1760–1830) and Revd John Pye Smith (1774–1851) as a grammar school for the sons of Protestant dissenters and opened in 1807. Freedom of conscience, as well as sound learning, has been Mill Hill's "charter" and the policy of the School from its foundation has been one of wide tolerance. In September 1997 the School became fully co-educational.

Location. The School is part of Mill Hill village and is situated in a conservation area, on the borders of Hertfordshire and Middlesex, approximately 12 miles from the centre of London. Set in 120 acres of parkland originally formed by the famous botanist Peter Collinson, the grounds provide a spacious setting for the academic buildings, boarding and day houses and offer extensive facilities for sports and activities.

Buildings. Mill Hill combines a rich traditional heritage with modern educational facilities. The present School was designed by Sir William Tite, architect of the Royal Exchange and opened in 1826. Since the late 19th century numerous buildings have been added, including the Chapel, Library, Assembly Hall, Music School and Science Block. Other additions include the Art and Design Technology Centre, a modern Sports Hall, a Sixth Form Centre, the Piper library and learning resources centre, a multimedia language centre, two networked IT suites, a music technology centre including a hard disk recording studio, a theatre, a studio theatre, an indoor swimming pool and 3 Eton Fives Courts.

As well as these facilities, a brand new academic teaching block has recently been opened. This houses 25 new classrooms with libraries, seminar rooms, and departmental offices for the Geography, History, Business Education, Classics, RE and Modern Languages departments.

Houses. There are 720 pupils in the School (500 boys, 220 girls in 2008) of whom around 160 are boarders. There are 3 boarding Houses and 7 day Houses. Day pupils take a full part in the activities of the School.

Admission. Application may be made as early as parents wish. The majority of boys and girls enter at the age of 13.

Candidates are selected on the basis of interviews, examination and a Head's confidential reference; successful candidates are given unconditional offers in February for entry in September while others qualify by taking the Scholarship Examination, held annually in January. Pupils not sitting the Scholarship Examination are required to sit the School's own Entrance Examinations which are held in January.

There are two other methods of entry:

(a) A limited number of places are available at 14+. Candidates are selected on the basis of interview, performance in the 14+ Entrance Examination (which is held in January) and a Head's confidential reference.

(b) Sixth Form Entry. Admission to the Sixth Form is open to both boys and girls, from the UK and abroad. Entry requirements are 5 GCSE passes at minimum Grade B plus 2 at Grade C or above, or equivalent qualifications for overseas pupils. More detailed entry requirements for specific AS courses are given in the School's Sixth Form Curriculum Guide. Candidates unable to offer the number of subjects required (eg some overseas candidates) will be considered on their individual academic merit.

Selection is by interview at the School (there are no examinations) and by reference from the candidate's present school. Offers made are conditional on meeting the entry requirements detailed above. Scholarships are awarded on the basis of examinations and interviews in January.

Curriculum. Every effort is made to avoid premature specialisation and in the Lower School all pupils follow a broad curriculum. Pupils are setted separately for core subjects, so that they are able to move at a speed best suited to their ability in different subjects. GCSE French may be taken in the second year, but all other subjects are taken in the third year, in the Fifth Form. Entry to the Sixth Form, from Fifth Form pupils already in the School, is conditional upon a minimum of 5 Grade B and 2 Grade C passes at GCSE.

In the Lower Sixth pupils take a one-year course to AS Level in four subjects. In the Upper Sixth they continue with three of these to A Level. There is a wide range of subject combinations and pupils are specially prepared in all subjects for Oxford and Cambridge entrance.

A Level studies take up approximately 75% of the timetable. In addition Sixth Formers take courses in PSRE and Complementary Studies.

Modern Languages. Mill Hill places emphasis on proficiency in the use of Modern Languages in a vocational context. Full use is made of satellite television and other audio-visual methods. About 20% of the second year take GCSE French one year early and continue in the Fifth Form with AS level. Irrespective of Sixth Form specialisation, many choose to take AS levels in French, German and Spanish. Thus a good number of pupils, including Mathematicians and Scientists are competent in their use of a foreign language by the time they leave school. All pupils studying French, German or Spanish are encouraged and helped to spend extended study time abroad under the *European Initiative*.

The European Initiative. One of the distinctive features of the Mill Hill School Foundation is that it provides pupils with an education that is firmly set within a contemporary European context. Over the last 30 years the School has pioneered a number of initiatives, such as seminars, exchange visits, work and GAP year placements in Europe. The range of exchange visits is well established: all first year pupils visit France, Germany or Spain for a three-day stay; there are also term-time exchanges at different ages with schools in Rouen, Nantes, Agen, Almeria and Goslar. Every year, over 40% of Mill Hill pupils engage in study visits or exchanges to continental Europe. In 1997 the European Initiative was recognised by the Central Bureau and Council of Europe by the granting of the European Curriculum Award.

Up to 25 students from the European Continent spend one or two years at Mill Hill. The School also participates in an annual residential seminar week, where pupils and staff from European schools live and learn with Millhillians. Pupils can expect therefore to have first-hand experience of living and working with Europeans together with opportunities to gain qualifications which will enhance a European-based career.

Tutors. Each pupil has a tutor who is responsible for his/her academic progress and pastoral care, and who writes an end-of-term report. Parents are also invited to parents' meetings which are held at least once a year for each year group.

Careers and Higher Education. The School is a member of the Independent Schools Careers Organisation (ISCO) and the Careers and Higher Education Department, based in the Piper Library, provides a comprehensive range of literature on careers and higher education and Gap Year opportunities. The Head of Careers and Higher Education and his team are able to offer advice on these areas, to help with organising work experience, and provide links to a wide range of external agencies. There is a hugely successful annual ISCO Careers Fair held at Mill Hill for local schools.

Most pupils in the Fifth Form sit a professionally administered academic and careers guidance test; this helps to identify suitable potential careers areas, which in turn enables informed decisions to be made regarding AS level subject choices. All pupils discuss the test report with their tutor, and a consultation with a professional careers guidance counsellor is also available on request. In the Sixth Form there is a comprehensive higher education guidance programme, which involves parents as well as pupils.

There are numerous opportunities for work experience during school holidays – both in the UK and in other European countries.

Music. The School offers a wide range of curricular and extra-curricular musical activities, including choirs, chamber and full orchestras, wind band and other ensembles. Concerts are given regularly by pupils and visiting professional performers. Pupils are encouraged to perform their own work in regular informal concerts. Individual tuition in most instruments, including voice, is available and instruments may be hired through the School. Free instrumental tuition is available at the discretion of the Headmaster, on the recommendation of the Director of Music. The Music School includes a hard disk recording studio. The Choir tours regularly and visits have included New York, Venice, Florence and Edinburgh. CDs of a professional standard are produced on a regular basis.

Art and DT. Pupils in the Lower School study Art and Design Technology and are also encouraged to study Art out of School hours when in addition to normal practical work there are facilities for Oil Painting, Pottery, Modelling, Casting, Printing and Wood Engraving. The Art and Technology Block provides facilities for these activities, and for Wood and Metal Work and Design Realisation.

Drama. There is a strong tradition of drama at Mill Hill and in addition to regular School and House plays an annual House Drama Competition is held. Theatre Studies is an option at both GCSE and A Level. The two theatres are superbly equipped and offer at least 3 productions each term. In recent years pupils have enjoyed considerable critical success on the Edinburgh Festival Fringe.

Sport. Every pupil, regardless of physical ability, is encouraged to participate in both individual sports and team games. The major sports for boys are Rugby, Hockey and Cricket and for girls are Hockey, Netball and Tennis. Other opportunities include Aerobics, Athletics, Badminton, Basketball, Cross-country, Eton Fives, Golf, Karate, Sailing, Soccer, Squash and Volleyball. Competition and excellence are valued and the level of professional coaching skills is exceptional. The school has an indoor swimming pool, 3 Eton Fives Courts, shooting range, all-weather pitch and Sports Hall, with multi-gym and a range of indoor sports facilities. There are strong links with Saracens RFC and special bursaries are available in the Sixth Form for gifted rugby players. Pupils are given the opportunity of participating in overseas sports tours. Sports tours for boys and girls have included countries, such as Barbados, Australia, Fiji, New Zealand and Canada. Recent tours for girls include hockey in South Africa and netball in Barbados and for the first time the school ran a tennis tour in 2007 to La Manga, Spain.

Extra-Curricular Activities. First year pupils are introduced to the range of minor sports (as above) and aspects of adventure training. All pupils are also offered a range of other activities such as debating, drama, modelling, pottery, photography, chess and computing. On Friday afternoons pupils have a choice between CCF (Army, RAF and Navy), Community Service, and Orchestra. In addition, many Societies exist to cater for a variety of out-of-school interests and, in particular, the Fifth Form undertake a week's "Challenge of Leadership" course in the summer after GCSE examinations.

Fees per term (2008-2009). £8,006 for Boarders and £5,067 for Day Pupils which includes the games fee and the cost of most text books and stationery.

Scholarships and Bursaries. Scholarships, which attract a maximum of 25% fee remission, are available to pupils showing exceptional talent in a variety of areas both in the classroom and on the sports field. In addition to major Awards, there are a number of minor Awards or Exhibitions also on offer. The Headmaster, Deputy Headmaster (External) or the Assistant Registrar are happy to advise parents and feeder schools about any of these Awards.

Bursaries are available for those entrants able to demonstrate a financial need. Parents will be asked to complete a detailed statement of their financial circumstances. Applicants for Bursaries will be selected in the normal way. A new initiative is the provision of full fee Bursaries for a limited number of Lower Sixth entrants. It is possible for bursary funds to be used to top up Scholarship Awards. As with scholarship queries, the Headmaster, Deputy Headmaster (External) or the Assistant Registrar are happy to offer advice.

There are also a number of special scholarships and bursaries for the children of Old Millhillians, Christian Ministers, members of the Armed Forces and the Diplomatic Services.

For further information on both scholarships and bursaries please see the school's website www.millhill.org.uk.

Charitable status. The Mill Hill School Foundation is a Registered Charity, number 1064758. It exists for the education of boys and girls.

Millfield

Street Somerset BA16 0YD
Tel: 01458 442291
Fax: 01458 447276
e-mail: admissions@millfieldschool.com
website: www.millfieldschool.com

The School was founded in 1935 by R J O Meyer with the philanthropic aim of using its resources to generate places for boys who were gifted but not wealthy. A substantial expansion took place in the 1960s when the School became co-educational. C R M Atkinson became Headmaster in 1971, and carried out a major building programme that established modern purpose-built facilities throughout the academic and recreational areas of the School, including a prize-winning Library and Resources Centre and a large Fine Arts Centre, completed in 1992, a year after his death. Recent improvements to the campus include a purpose-built Mathematics Centre, 500-seat Theatre and Dining Hall. Nine new boarding houses have been opened since 2003. A new Design & Technology building with high-tech equipment was completed in 2005 and a new Music School complex housing a 350-seat Concert Hall was completed in September 2006. The main part of the School is surrounded by over 100 acres of parkland and playing fields, which includes an equestrian centre, stabling for 50 horses, a 50m Olympic swimming pool and an indoor tennis centre.

Governors:

Chairman: A E White, CBE, DL

The Rt Revd Paul Barber, MA
Dr R Clark
Mrs C Cripps
Mrs J E Derbyshire
C J Driver
G O Edwards, CBE
R M Mawditt, OBE
A Patel
B Rigby, CBE
D W A Rosser
Mrs A Sexton
R S Trafford

Clerk to the Governors: S R Morley

***Headmaster*: Mr Craig Considine**, MEd

Bursar: D A P Oddie, MBE, FCMA

Deputy Headmaster: R Decamp, BSc, MA

Second Deputy: F J Clough, BSc, PhD

Tutor for Admissions: C G Coates, BA, DMS

* *Head of Department*
† *Houseparent*

Art, Design & Technology:
*L A Green, MA
J L Batchelor, BA
J C M Clements, MA
Miss C Flohr, BA
D Harper, DipAD
Ms S G Key, MA
Mrs A L Kinch, BSc
S A M Lewis-Williams, BA
Mrs M J Nimmo, BA
Miss N C Ritzaki, BA
R W Smith, BEd
Miss J S Wallace-Mason, BA
Mrs B J Waterhouse, CertEd

Biology:
*Mrs J A Frampton, BSc
†G J Bailey, BSc
Mrs A E Brade, BSc
Miss R E J Corke, BSc
J M P Hallows, BSc
K F Hawksworth, BSc
†Miss N H Kightley, MSc
Mrs L McEwen, BSc
G T Shayler, BEng
G B Smith, MSc, PhD
Z R Watkins, BSc, PhD
Miss J Weal, BSc
S J Whittle, BSc

Business Studies:
*N E Williams, BA, MPhil
J J C Britain, BComm
Miss A Burnett, BA
N A Chamberlain, BSc
†Ms K L Davies, MA, MBA
Mrs C C Essam, CertEd
M P Mills, MSc, LLB
Mrs M A Nash, MA
R J Owlett, BA
†A Shaw, BA
G E O Stanford, MA, MBA

Chemistry:
*C J Middleton, BSc, MRSC
A Angelosanto, BSc
Miss T Bolt, MSc
C A Hedgecock, MA
E T Jones, BSc
Miss S L Legg, BSc
†C I Page, BSc
M A Perry, BSc, PhD
M S Woodward, BSc, PhD, MRSC

Computing & IT:
*Mrs S J Bishop, MSc
G R Cottell, BSc
Mrs S J Edwards, BSc
Mrs S A Etherington, BEd, MSc
E E Williams, MEng

Drama:
A C Boyd-Williams, BA
M E Cooper, BA
Mrs R Johnson, BEd

Economics:
*N R Driver, BSc
J M G Andrews, BA
J A Brimacombe, BSc
S A Briston, BA
A M Goodenough, BSc
B M Sneddon, BSc

English and Media:
*S M MacAlpine, BA, MSc
J M Brown, BA
†R H I Bullock, BEd
Mrs C Byrne, MA, MEd
S B Cole, BA
Mrs A J Gray, BA
Mrs H Heriz-Smith, BA
J M Hill, BA, MTheol
M D J Lewis, BA
M M Milton, MA
J C Shaw, MA
Mrs S A Skinner, MEd
M A Speyers, MA
D J Trevis, BA, MEd

Geography:
*C Lane, MA
Mrs M J Angelosanto, BA
Miss N J A Batchelder, BA, MSc
†P R Cookson, MEd

†T J Greenhill, BSc
T B Kingsford, BA
Mrs N S Lewis-Williams, BA
A R Woods, BA

History:
*N A T Eatough, BA
D E Askham, BA
D W Burton, MA, DPhil
D W Carr,BA
Mrs T J Crouch, BA
P A Kelly, BA
C A Mantell, BA
P S Rolf, BA
†J N Whiskerd, BA
†Miss C L Witt, BA

Languages:
*Mrs L J Wilson, BA
J A Bishop, BA
Miss C Bowring, BA
Mrs K S Boyd-Williams, MA
S M Coase, MA
Mrs S M Dye, BA
R J Essam, MA
A S Fraser, MA
†N J Gabb, BEd
W R Harper-Holdcroft, MA
Mrs M N Harwood, MA
Miss S M V McAllister, BA
Mrs A V J Phillips, BA
Mlle P Rouprich, L-ès-L
†C J Skinner, BA, PhD
J R Taylor, BA
C W Tudsbery-Turner, BA
Mrs B E Wood, BA
Ms R Zhao, MA

Learning Support Centre:
*Mrs D M Morrison, MA, DipEd Spec Ed
Mrs S E Coates, BA
M J Cole-Edwardes, BA
Miss E A Dando, BA
P R Harland, BA
†R J Mylne, BEd
Mrs S Small, BA
Mrs J A Szymkow, BA

Mathematics:
*Miss C C Fiddes, BA, PhD
Ms T A Allen, BSc
†T P Akhurst, BEd
Miss S L Attwood, BSc
Mrs H J Bevan, CertEd
Mrs J Brimacombe, BSc
B P Brooks, MA, PhD
R J Furlong, BSc, MEd
L C Glaser, BSc, MA
M G Godfrey, MA
Miss V J Harkness, BEd, MA
Mrs N A Jones, BSc
Mrs L A Kelly, MA
†J T Knight, BA
Miss C O'Doherty, BSc
J J Rix, MA
Miss L Shephard, BSc
Mrs M P Speed, BSc
J Williams, BSc
Mrs S M Woods, BSc

Music:
*B P H Charles, BA
†A R Barker, ARCM, MA
A H Dearden, LTCL, GTCL
Mrs E M Fraser, MPhil, PhD
C J Hughes, AGSM, MA
M A Rhind-Tutt, ARCM, GRSM, MA
†L G Sheills, ARCM

Physical Education:
Mrs J A Boyd, BEd
†R M Ellison, BEd
C D Gange, BSc
†D J Hacker, HND
Miss E L Hadfield, BSc
G N Jennings, BSc
†J A Mallett, BSc
Miss L-J Marsh, BSc
Miss S Mead, BSc

Physics:
*M A Lewis, BSc
J B Allen, BSc
Miss A C M Brown, BA
S P Houghton, BA
K Leonard, BSc
R L C Lowndes-Northcott, BSc
C J Ridler, MPhys
E J Sanchez, BSc
Mrs D E Tinker, BSc

Religious Studies:
*Miss L F Jackson, BA
M Day, BA
Revd P C A Harbridge, BA, LLB (*Chaplain*)
†D H Landrock, BEd
P G Neeve, BA

Millfield English Language School:
*†R L Orton, MA
S J Dye, MA
Miss K L Murray, BA, BSc
†G S Orton, MSc

Houses and Houseparents:

Boarding Houses:
Abbey House: Mr and Mrs J N Whiskerd
Acacia House: Mr and Mrs D J Hacker
Butleigh: Mr and Mrs A Shaw
Etonhurst: Mr and Mrs T P Akhurst
Holmcroft: Dr and Mrs C J Skinner
Joan's Kitchen: Mr and Mrs R J Mylne
Keen's Elm: Mr and Mrs C I Page
Kernick: Mr and Mrs D H Landrock
Kingweston: Mr and Mrs T J Greenhill
Martins: Mr and Mrs N J Gabb
Millfield: Mr A R Barker
Orchards: Mr and Mrs R M Ellison
Portway: Ms K L Davies
St Anne's: J T Knight
Shapwick: Mr and Mrs J A Mallett
Southfield: Mr and Mrs R L Orton
Walton: Mr G J Bailey
Warner: Mr and Mrs L G Sheills

Day Houses, Boys:
Cookson: Mr P R Cookson
Bullock: Mr R H I Bullock
Skinner:

Day Houses, Girls:
Witt: Miss C L Witt
Kightley: Miss N H Kightley

Coaches:

Athletics:
K Holmes, Senior England Coach – Throws
A Lerwill, Senior Coach – Jumps

Chess: M Turner, MA, Grand Master

Cricket:
M R Davis, NCA Advanced Coach
R Keates, Assistant Coach
W Durston, Assistant Coach

Dance:
Miss J Peach, ARAD, AISTD, Major Teaching Cert Dir (*Ballet*)
Mrs D Court, ARAD (*Ballet*)
Miss G Wright, AISTD (*Dance*)

Fencing:
Prof N Golding, BAF Diploma, South West Coach
Mrs S Benny, BAF Advanced and County Coach

Golf:
Director: Miss K Nicholls (LET)
Mr S Wells, Assistant Golf Professional

Hockey:
R Keates, Level II HA coach
W Durston, Assistant Coach

Judo & Self Defence:
M Benney, Black Belt (*Judo*)
M Brock, Black Belt (*Judo*)
P Hacker, Black Belt (*Karate*)

Lacrosse: Mrs G Heavyside, Scotland & GB Player

Modern Pentathlon:
Director: D Wilsher, National Coordinator (Youth) MPAGB

Netball:
Mrs C Mitchell, Assistant Coach Level II
Mrs G Heavyside

Outdoor Activities: P Bond (MLA)

Riding:
Director: D O Anholt, BHSI
Assistant Director: Miss K Fontaine, BSHI

Polo: R Horne, HPA Instructor

Squash:
J Barrington, SRA National Coach, Former Men's World Professional Champion
I Thomas, Intermediate Level III SRA Coach

Swimming:
Director: J Finck, Australia Gold Licence Coach
Miss E Collings, Assistant Coach, Level 2 ASA
E Sinclair, Assistant Coach, Level 3 ASA

Tennis:
Director: A A Simcox, Member of Professional Tennis Coaches' Association
Miss J Sinkins, Assistant Coach, PCA Part 3
P R Thomas, Assistant Coach, CCA Part 2
R Woolright, Assistant Coach, DCA Part 1

Trampolining:
Mrs C Mitchell, Level 3
Mrs J Stevens, Level 4

The School is fully co-educational with 780 boys and 470 girls; there are 950 boarders.

Housing. There are 18 single-sex, vertically aged Boarding Houses situated in or near the School; three lie in surrounding villages. All Houses have resident assistants. Most Sixth Formers, except in rare circumstances, have their own rooms whilst younger pupils share either in pairs or fours.

Boarding is best described as full time, but exeat weekends can be taken, four in the first term and three in the second and third terms.

Day pupils are grouped in 5 houses, attached to boarding houses for house competitions, and are fully assimilated into School life.

The Curriculum. The academic programme is consistent with the broad principles laid down in the National Curriculum pre-16. Thus those moving to Millfield from a wide range of independent preparatory and maintained secondary schools should find both common academic ground and unrivalled choice for GCSE, Vocational Courses and AS/A2 Level.

All pupils entering the Third Year (at age 13), regardless of ability, study English, Mathematics, three Sciences, at least one language, Design and Technology, ICT, Geography, History, Religious Studies, Physical Education, Art and Music. The pupil teacher ratio is 7.64:1 and the average class size is 8.70. A five-year course in Personal and Social Education is also included within the curriculum. Each pupil is involved in conservation at the School's 40 acre conservation centre at Worley Hill.

In the Fourth and Fifth Years, all pupils follow courses leading to GCSEs in the core subjects of English, Mathematics, Science and a Modern Language. In addition, there is a wide choice of options: Arabic, Art, Business Studies, Economics, Design & Technology, French, Geography, German, Product Design, History, ICT, Italian, Japanese, Latin, Mandarin, Music, Physical Education, Religious Studies and Spanish. The Learning Support Centre provides individual support for all pupils in need of this.

At Sixth Form level, over 40 subjects are on offer which lead to AS and A2 qualifications. These include Accounting, Art, Biology, Business Studies, Chemistry, Classical Greek, Computing, Critical Thinking, Economics, English Language and Literature, French, Further Mathematics, Geography, German, Government & Politics, History, ICT, Italian, Latin, Law, Mathematics, Media Studies, Music, Music Technology, Philosophy, Physical Education, Photography, Physics, Product Design, Psychology, Religious Studies, Spanish, Theatre Studies and World Development. Also on offer are the vocational courses of Double A Level Leisure Studies (equivalent to a two A Level course), BTEC National Diploma in Art & Design (equivalent to a three A Level course), BTEC National Certificate in Sport (equivalent to 2 A Level courses), the Leith Cookery Course and the British Horse Society Advanced Instructors Certificate (BHSAIC). Most students choose four AS level subjects in the Lower Sixth and then take three of these to the full A level in the Upper Sixth. All Lower Sixth pupils follow an Enrichment Programme. AS/A2 Level General Studies, AS/A2 level, is offered on an optional basis.

The curriculum offers breadth, depth and flexibility in course choice. Pupils are also prepared for the Advanced Extension Awards and STEP papers, Arabic, Japanese and Mandarin Certificates, Scholastic Aptitude tests for American Universities. EAL and Language Development Study Support is available at all levels.

Every pupil is guided through his or her school career by a Group Tutor. Each Tutor cares for between 10 and 14 pupils within a House, taking a close personal interest in each and maintaining regular contact with parents on academic matters.

Games and Activities. Junior pupils are generally required to play the team game of the term; senior boys and girls choose from the following games: Archery, Athletics, Badminton, Basketball, Canoeing, Chess, Climbing, Cricket, Croquet, Cross Country, Fencing, Fitness Training, Golf, Hockey, Judo, Karate, Modern Pentathlon, Polo, Riding, Sailing, Shooting, Skiing, Squash, Swimming, Table Tennis, Tennis, Trampolining, Volleyball.

In addition to the above options, boys may choose Rugby or Football, and girls may opt for Aerobics, Ballet, Dance, Netball, Rounders or Yoga.

In addition to games all pupils take part in the School's Activities Programme; they can choose from more than 80 activities, ranging from archery to Zulu beadwork – encompassing ceramic painting, croquet, dance, juggling, film clubs, octopush, photography, rock guitar and Ultimate Frisbee along the way.

Fees per term (2008-2009). Boarding £8,700, Day £5,940.

Scholarships and Bursaries. A number of scholarships are available each year for excellence in academic studies, music, art and sport. All-rounder awards are also available for multi-talented individuals. Bursaries are available as an additional support for families in financial need. Further details of all these awards may be obtained from the Tutor for Admissions.

Charitable status. Millfield is a Registered Charity, number 310283. Its aim is to provide independent boarding and day education for boys and girls, and to maintain an extensive system of bursary aid to gifted pupils or those in financial need.

Monkton Senior

Monkton Combe Bath Somerset BA2 7HG
Tel: 01225 721102
Fax: 01225 721181
e-mail: admissions@monkton.org.uk
website: www.monktoncombeschool.com

Monkton was founded in 1868, and today is one of the best known smaller Independent Schools in the country. The School's aim has always been to provide a broad education designed to enable boys and girls to develop all their potential to the full, with an emphasis on high academic standards. The School's tradition is unashamedly Christian, and every effort is made to relate Christian belief and worship to the needs of daily life.

Patrons:
Prof R J Berry, MA, DSc, FIBiol, FRSE
G Coates
The Baroness Cox of Queensbury, SRN, BScSoc, BSc Econ, FRCN, PhD Hon
The Rt Revd I P M Cundy, MA
The Rt Revd T Dudley-Smith, OBE, MA, MLitt
L E Ellis, Esq, MA, AFIMA
P W Lee, Esq, CBE, MA, DL
R D Spear, Esq, JP, MA
Lady Stanley, BSc, MSW

Governors:
Chairman: S Wilsher, BA Econ
Vice-Chairman: Bishop J F Perry, MPhil, LTh, Hon D Univ
Mrs J M Argyle
R S Baldock, MA Cantab

Mrs J Brooks, BA, DipSocSi, CQSW
Canon Mrs K A Holt, OBE, BA
Rear Admiral C A Johnstone-Burt, OBE, MA, FCIPD, RN
The Ven D S K Kajumba, BA, HND, Dip Theol, Dip IMBM
Prof M R B Keighley, MB BS, MS, FRCS, FEWI
Dr B W Martin, BSc Hons, PhD
J G W Matthews, MB, BAO, MCh, FRCS
J E Metters, MA, FCA
J R Myers, BEng Hons
A D Owen, OBE, MA, Hon DSc Aston, D Univ UCE
P C Poulsom
T S Sanderson, MA, MSc Econ

***Principal*: R P Backhouse**, MA

Deputy Head: T J Dewes, MA, BA

Assistant Heads:
Mrs R H Garrod, BEd
Mrs L M Vaughan, BA

SMT Houseparent: P Marais, BSc, MEd (*Clarendon House*)

Director of Studies: J B Morley, BA

Assistant Staff:
† *Houseparent*

M C Garrod, BSc
N D Botton, MA
J C Bradby, MA
Mrs A K Bossom, BA
P G Bossom, MA
D M Merricks, BEd, MA
Mrs J R T Gabe, DipRCM, ARCM Perf
Mrs A Mills, BEd
B J Newman, BMus, FRCO, LRAM
P R Clark
T F Hardisty, BA
A D McPhee, BA, DipTEFL
Miss D W Clark, RGN
S K Skews, LTCL
Mrs A J Weller, BSc
J J Smith, BA (*†Farm House*)
Mrs D Smith (*†Farm House*)
P R Wickens, BSc
Mrs C S Morley, BEd
S R Harris, CertEd, MA
Mrs S H Harris, BSc, ACII, Dip IM (*†Eddystone House*)
Mrs S Vercher, Lic
Miss E M-L L Arnaudet, Lic DEA
D P J Tobias, BA
M B Abington, BSc
Mrs R M Glasgow, BA (*†Nutfield House*)
A W R Glasgow (*†Nutfield House*)
Mrs S C Dimond, BSc, MSc
G P Reay, BSc
Mrs L Marais (*†Clarendon House*)
S J Call, BSc (*†Grove Grange House*)
Mrs H Call, BPharm, MRPharmS (*†Grove Grange House*)
Mrs H K Wilkinson, BA (*†Hill House*)
A C Clarke, BA, MA, MBA
Mrs J A Hildreth, BA, MDes
Mr J Shone (*†School House*)
Mrs O Shone (*†School House*)
Miss V Armand-Smith
Ms M C Bensted, BA
R Campbell, MSc
S Chilcott, MEng, MSc
Mrs M Egan, BA
Mrs E Gibson, BA
Mrs J Pring, BA
D Sixsmith, BA
S Wilkinson, BSc (*†Hill House*)
M Parfitt, BA
Ms C R Maidment, BA
Revd Dr W P Olhausen, MA, PhD (*Chaplain*)
D H J Bryson, BSc, PGCE
J P C Sertin, BA, PGCE
Miss C Dodds, BSc, PGCE
Miss D Sellers, BA, PGCE

ESL Staff:
T J Evans, BA

Learning Support:
Mrs F J Davies, BA, Dip Dys
Mrs F C Dodds

Visiting Music Staff:
D C Date, Hon FLCM, GGSM, ARCM, ARCO (*piano*)
P Skelton, BA, LRAM (*piano*)
D Pagett, GRNCM, PGdipRNCM (*saxophone & clarinet*)
J Scott (*percussion*)
D Kelleher (*electric guitar*)
Mrs G M Davies, LWCMD, LTCL (*singing*)
Miss A Higgs (*brass*)
Mrs J F Finch, ALCM, LTCL (*oboe & bassoon*)
W Lynn, MA (*bass & acoustic guitar*)
Miss Y Nieuwerf, GMus, LRSM (*flute*)
Miss C Gainford, BMus, GRNCM (*bassoon*)
Mrs V Hammond (*oboe*)
H Hetherington, BA Hons (*singing*)
Miss A E Higgs (*lower brass*)
Miss L Stocks (*cello*)
Miss J Walker, BMus (*singing*)

Headmaster of Preparatory School: C J Stafford, BA

Head of Pre-Preparatory: Mrs K Morrell, BEd

Medical Officers:
Dr N A Gough, MB BS, MRCP, MRCGP, DRCOG, MRCS
Dr L Paterson, MA, MB BS

Company Secretary and Bursar: Mrs A C Cracknell, BSc, ACA

Development Director: Dr A L Kerbey, MA, PhD

Situation. The geographical situation is delightful; the Senior School faces south across the Valley, or Combe, from which the place takes its name, about 200 feet above sea level, while the Preparatory School is at the top of the hill above, some 400 feet higher, with magnificent views over Avon and Wiltshire.

Organisation. The Pre-Prep, Prep and Senior Schools each have their own Heads and the Principal of the Senior School has overall responsibility for the three schools. However, they share the same Board of Governors and there are close links between them. About half of the Senior School pupils come from the Preparatory School; the rest from Preparatory Schools all over the country, State Maintained Schools or from abroad. The Senior School went fully co-educational and merged with Clarendon School, Bedford, in September 1992. The Preparatory School went co-educational in September 1993.

(*For further details see Monkton Preparatory entry in IAPS section.*)

Numbers. *Preparatory School*: There are 352 pupils of whom 50 board and 123 are in the Pre-Prep.

Senior School: There are 359 pupils (234 boys, 125 girls), of whom 212 are boarders. The Sixth Form numbers 152.

Admission. *Preparatory School*. The main entry is at age 7, 8 or 9 but every effort is made to accept boys and girls who wish to join at age 10 or 11. Some scholarships are offered. The majority of pupils from the Pre-Prep go on to the Prep school.

Senior School. There is a one-form entry at 11 by means of report and interview and papers in English, Mathematics and a Reasoning Test. The main entry is at age 13 by means of the

Common Entrance or Scholarship Examinations. Candidates from State Schools and schools abroad are admitted on the basis of report and interview and papers in English, Mathematics and a Reasoning Test. Entry direct into the Sixth Form is encouraged. Admission is on the basis of report, interviews and a Reasoning Test, and is conditional on not fewer than 5 subjects at grade C or better in GCSE, normally with an average of B/C across all GCSE subjects taken.

Buildings. The Senior School's buildings are of Bath or Cotswold Dale stone. They have been steadily extended and modernised to meet the changing needs of the School. In recent years two new girls' Houses have been built and the boys' Houses have undergone major upgrading and refurbishing.

A new Information Technology Centre, a Sixth Form Centre, a Sports Centre, a Swimming Centre, and a Drama Studio have recently been opened. The Library has been extensively refurbished to provide a modern Learning Resource Centreand a state-of-the-art Maths & Science centre has just been opened.

The School has extensive playing fields, a newly refurbished Astroturf all-weather playing area for Hockey and Tennis, Boathouses on the River Avon, 3 Netball Courts, 14 Tennis Courts, a covered Rifle Range, a Rowing Tank, a heated outdoor Swimming Pool, 2 Squash Courts, a Sports Centre and a 25m indoor Swimming Centre and Fitness Centre.

The Monkton Campaign was launched during 1995 to assist in the further development of the School over the next few years. Over £2 million has been raised in the first phase and fund-raising for the second phase is now well under way.

Chapel. There is a full-time resident Anglican Chaplain. The Chapel itself stands in the centre of the School and has recently been extended and completely refurbished. A short service or assembly is held every morning and a School Service, at which parents are welcome, each Sunday. There is a Confirmation Service each year. Pupils of other than Anglican tradition are welcomed to Communion Services.

Houses. The four boys' Houses, the two girls' Houses and the Junior House for 11 and 12 year olds are all under the care of Houseparents, who together with their tutorial teams of colleagues are responsible for the boys' and girls' general welfare.

Day Pupils are fully integrated into the boarding houses and the total life of the School and are encouraged but not obliged to stay until the end of evening prep. Senior pupils are given opportunities for responsibility as School or House Prefects during their sixth-form careers.

Tutor System. Each pupil has a Tutor, normally a member of staff of his or her own choice, who keeps in touch with parents and provides guidance and advice over every aspect of School life and over making choices for the future.

Curriculum. Our aim is to provide a broadly based curriculum in the years leading to GCSE. The curriculum reflects the spirit and fundamental goals of the National Curriculum. Those who show particular ability in French or Mathematics may proceed to work more advanced than GCSE before the end of Year 11. Personal, Social and Health Education and Physical Education are included.

In Years 7, 8 and 9 all pupils study English, Mathematics and the Sciences with a foundation course comprising at least one Foreign Language, Art, the Classics, Design Technology, Geography, History, Information Technology, Music, PE and Religious Studies. In Years 10 and 11 all pupils take IGCSE English, Mathematics, and Coordinated Dual Award Science (Biology, Chemistry and Physics). English Literature is taught alongside English to the top three sets. Pupils choose four other subjects from Art, Business Studies with IT, Classical Civilisation, Design Technology, Drama, French, Geography, History, Latin, Music, Religious Studies, Spanish and Sports Studies. Extra English is available as an option for those with particular needs in this subject.

Most pupils stay on for two years in the Sixth Form. The subjects at present offered at AS/A2 Level are: Art, Biology, Business Studies, Chemistry, Critical Thinking, Design Technology, English Literature, English Language, French, Further Mathematics, Geography, History, Mathematics, Music, Photography, Physics, Psychology, Religious Studies, Spanish, Sports Studies and Theatre Studies. Most pupils entering Year 12 study four subjects for one year to AS and continue with three to full A Level. Pupils also attend courses on world religions, the family, personal finance, self-presentation and interview technique. A notable feature of the Sixth Form programme is the wide variety of lectures and presentations delivered by visiting speakers prominent in their field.

Careers Advice and Staff/Parent Meetings. An experienced Careers Teacher works closely with Tutors in advising pupils. There is also a member of staff responsible for advice on higher education. Parents, Old Monktonians and local people are invited to help pupils in their thinking about careers. The School belongs to the Independent Schools Careers Organisation which arranges Aptitude and Interest tests. Annual staff/parent meetings are held at the School to discuss pupils' progress. Parents are of course always welcome at other times.

University Entrance. The great majority of leavers go on to degree courses at Universities and Colleges of Higher Education. Last year 98% of leavers went to their first choice university.

Games. Those with particular abilities are encouraged to aim for excellence, but we also believe that regular games and exercise are important for all, helping to build a healthy lifestyle for the future and fostering leadership, teamwork and cooperation.

The major sports for boys are: in the Michaelmas Term, Rugby; in the Lent Term, Hockey or Rowing; in the Summer Term, Cricket, Rowing or Tennis. Boys choose either to row or to play Hockey and Cricket, but are allowed to alter their choice during their time at the School. Younger boys are normally required to play the major game of each term but as they become more senior they are allowed a greater degree of choice.

The major sports for girls are: in the Michaelmas Term, Hockey; in the Lent Term, Netball or Rowing; in the Summer Term, Tennis or Rowing. Representative teams are fielded in all these sports. As with the boys, the choice becomes more extended as girls become more senior.

There are also School teams in Athletics, Basketball, Cross-Country, Football, Judo, Squash and Shooting.

CCF and Community Service. There are sections for all three Services, besides various specialist activities such as Venture Section (through which the Duke of Edinburgh's Award scheme is offered) and car maintenance. There is also an active Community Service group.

Leisure Activities. Monkton encourages as many worthwhile leisure pursuits as possible. Between 35 and 40 different activities are offered; up to the age of 15 pupils are expected to be involved in at least one. All the facilities of the School, including the Art and DT Departments, Music Rooms and ICT Centre are available to pupils during their free time. The Choir, Orchestra, Big Band and other less formal music groups play an important part in the School's life and tuition is available in all orchestral instruments. About 45% of the members of the School take music lessons. There is a major School dramatic production in the Michaelmas Term. The School is conveniently close to Bath and Bristol for taking parties to concerts and theatres. Some 30 clubs and societies figure on the School List, ranging from the Bridge Club to the Literary Society and the Christian Union. Bible Study groups meet weekly.

Health. The School Medical Officer visits regularly and all boarders are required to register with him. The Medical Centre is under the care of a fully qualified Sister and Assistant who provide a 24-hour service.

Catering. All pupils take their meals in the Dining Hall, with cafeteria service.

Dress. The Clothes List is kept as simple as possible. All required items can be purchased in the School Shop.

Scholarships. (*see Scholarship Entries section*). Four Anniversary Awards are offered at the age of 11 for open competition each year. They range in value from 25% to 10% of the appropriate fee.

At least ten Scholarships or Exhibitions, including at least two for Music, at least one for Art, at least one for Drama and at least two for Sport are offered at the age of 13 for open competition each year. These range in value from 35% to 10% of the appropriate fee.

At least four Scholarships are offered at age 16 for open competition to two candidates from other schools and two to candidates from Monkton Combe for entry into the Lower Sixth each year. Academic, musical or sporting merit will be taken into account in making such awards. They range in value from 25% to 10% of the appropriate fee.

There is a limited number of Bursaries to enable pupils to come to Monkton Combe who would otherwise be unable to do so on financial grounds.

The Governors are prepared to make a remission of up to one-third of the fee to a limited number of children of Clergy and Missionaries, on proof of need.

Fees per term (2008-2009). Senior: £5,999–£8,178 (boarders); £4,251–£5,524 (day pupils). Preparatory: £5,718–£5,999 (boarders); £3,316–£4,251 (day pupils). Pre-Prep: £2,290–£2,480.

Old Monktonian Club. The Monkton Combe School Register has been fully revised and updated. Details from the Development Office at the School.

Charitable status. Monkton Combe School is a Registered Charity, number 1057185, and a Company Limited by Guarantee, registered in England, number 3228456. Its aims and objectives are to provide education for girls and boys combined with sound religious training on Protestant and Evangelical principles in accordance with the doctrines of The Church of England.

Monmouth School

Almshouse Street Monmouth Monmouthshire NP25 3XP
Tel: 01600 713143
Fax: 01600 772701
e-mail: enquiries@monmouthschool.org
website: www.habs-monmouth.org

The School was founded in 1614, by William Jones, a merchant of the City of London and a Liveryman of the Worshipful Company of Haberdashers, who was born near Monmouth and bequeathed a large sum of money to found a school and almshouses in the town. The School has derived immense advantage from this unusual association with the City of London.

The School is controlled by a Board of Governors appointed variously by the Haberdashers' Company, the Universities of Oxford, Cambridge and Wales, and local representative bodies.

Motto: *Serve and Obey.*

Chairman of the Governors: J B S Swallow, MA, FCA

Ex officio: The Master of the Worshipful Company of Haberdashers

[1]J A Ackroyd
M Anderson
Dr M G Archer
Dr P E G Baird
[1]Professor P Blood
[1]Mrs H M Bosanquet
[1]Councillor W A L Crump
Canon E J S Hiscocks
[1]D J Hitchcock
Miss H Hutton
[1]Mrs L Kelway-Bamber
A M Kerr (*Chairman of the Monmouth School Committee*)
[1]Mrs G B Kerton-Johnson
A D Kirk
Mrs M A Molyneux
[1]Mrs T Pike
[1]J E G Prevett
Revd Dr J T Rigney
Mrs M Wetherell

[1] *Member of the Monmouth School Committee*

***Headmaster*: S G Connors**, BA, PhD

Second Master: M J Orton, BSc
Director of Studies: A J Winter, BSc, PhD
Head of Sixth Form: H F Tatham, MA

Assistant Staff:
* *Head of Department*
† *Housemaster/Housemistress*

Mrs P Ackroyd, BA
D C Adams, MA
Mrs S G Atherton, BA
Miss K H Balnaves, MA (**Religious Education*)
Miss E K Barson, BSc, MSc
Miss A R Beak, BA
J C Bevan, CertEd (*†New House*)
Miss R A Blacklaws, MA (**Drama*)
J A D Blackham, BA
J Boiling, BA (*†Town House*)
R C Boyle, BSc (**Design Technology, †School House*)
Mrs A R Callicott, CertEd
M D Clarke, BSc, PhD
A N Cochran, BSc, MSc, CEng, MIEE
A S Collins, BA, DipSocAnthropology
R J Corbett, BA
J P Danks, BSc, DPhil (**Chemistry*)
A J Dawson, BSc, MSc
P Dennis-Jones, MA
J Despontin, BSc
Mrs P Dollins, BMus
G Dunn, BSc, MSc
M J Dutton, BA, BEd, MA, PhD (**English*)
S J Edwards, BA (**Modern Languages*)
Miss B H Evans, BA
J N Exton, DipAD, ATC (**Art*)
Mrs S J Exton, BA
A V Francis, BSc, PhD (**Biology*)
N J R Goodson, BSc, CertEd
P M Griffin, BA
Miss S Harpagès, L-ès-L
Mrs C J Hartley, BSc
M H G Hayter, MA
J M Harrison, BA, PhD (**History*)
R S Harry (*Visiting Fellow*)
J J Hartley, MA (**Geography*)
J C Hatton, BA
A Hawley, BA
D G Hope, BA (**Classics, †Chapel House*)
Mrs L A Hope (**ICT*)
R Howe, BA (*†Monmouth House*)
P C Hunt, GRNCM, LLCM (*†Wye House*)
P D Jefferies, BSc
A J Jones, BA (*†St James House*)
D K Jones, BSc (*†Weirhead House*)
D F Lawson, BA, CRE (*Director of Music*)
Miss G S Lee, BA, MA
A J S Macdonald, BSc
K J Madsen, BA (**Economics, †Tudor House*)
D J McGladdery, BEd, MA, DipTheol Min
S M F McQuitty, BSc (*†Severn House*)
K A Moseley, BSc, PhD, FRES (**Physics*)
D Mather, BA (**Spanish*)
J A T McEwan, BA
M J Orton, BSc
A K Peace, BSc
D J Pearson, BSc
Mrs S Phillips, BEd
Mrs F P Sanders, CertEd

P Sanders, MA, MSc (**Mathematics*)
M J Stubbs, BA
M J Tamplin, BSc (*†Hereford House*)
K-A Tiebosch, BA
A J Tribe, BA
P D Vaughan-Smith, BA
D M Vickers, BEd (*Director of Physical Education*)
Mrs J Walker, BEd (*†Dean House*)
A J White, BA
D Williams, BSc (*†Glendower House*)
A J Winter, BSc, PhD

Chaplain: Revd G R Knight, MTh, MTheol, HND

The Grange (Preparatory Department)

Head: Mrs E G Thomas, BA
Deputy Head: Mrs S L Wilderspin, CertEd

D Webb, BEd
P N Morris, BEd
Mrs J A Osborne, BEd
D F Gould, BSc, PGCE
K J Shepherd, BA
D G Murray, MA
Mrs S M Jones, BEd
D Hayden, MA
Ms J Morse, BA
Mrs K Noel

Bursar: Mr N G R James, BA, MIPD

Medical Officer: S H D Shaw, BA, BM

There are approximately 589 boys in the Senior School, of whom 141 are boarders. **The Grange**, the School's Preparatory Department, caters for over 100 dayboys aged 7 to 11, with boarding available at age 10. (*For further details see entry in IAPS section.*)

Situation and Buildings. The School was founded in 1614 by William Jones and is one of the schools of the Worshipful Company of Haberdashers. A generous endowment enables the School to provide superb facilities and an excellent academic education whilst keeping fees at a reasonable level. There are many scholarships and bursaries and the Haberdashers' Assisted Places Scheme, which replaced the Government scheme in 1998, ensures that an education at Monmouth School can be available to boys who will benefit from it, irrespective of their parents' income.

The School is enriched by close cooperation with Haberdashers' Monmouth School for Girls in many areas of school life, especially at Sixth Form level.

The School is set in the delightful landscape of the Wye Valley and much use is made of the surrounding countryside for expeditions and other outward-bound activities. There is a strong tradition of music and drama as well as of excellence in sport. A new sports complex was opened in Autumn 1999, a studio theatre in January 2001 and additional outdoor facilities, including an all-weather pitch, in Autumn 2001. The Blake Theatre (500 seats) was completed in Summer 2004. Other recent developments have included greatly expanded ICT facilities and refurbished boarding houses and classroom blocks. The Sixth Form has a dedicated Sixth Form Centre.

Boarding. The boarding community forms the core of the School. Junior boarders (10–12 year olds) are accommodated in St James' House for their first few years and benefit from the care of a dedicated house team who also provide an ambitious and popular programme of extra-curricular activities, tailored to the interests of the age group.

There are four senior boarding houses for boys between 13 and 18. The School has a flexible boarding policy which provides a considerable degree of freedom for families to make boarding arrangements which fit in with their lives, but which encourages boys to take full advantage of the many sporting, cultural and extra-curricular activities for which the School is renowned.

Admission. The main admission points are 7, 10, 11, 13 and 16, but other stages will be considered if places are available. Candidates aged 7 and 11 sit the School's own entrance tests. At 13, candidates take either the Common Entrance Examination, the School's own Foundation Scholarship Examination or its 13+ examination. Entrants to the Sixth Form are accepted either after sitting the Sixth Form Scholarship Examination or on the basis of GCSE results (or equivalent).

Candidates from overseas are welcome. Those whose first language is not English take a preliminary test of proficiency in English before proceeding to the appropriate entrance test.

The School accepts pupils with Dyslexia or similar specific learning difficulties. They are taught in mainstream lessons and additional study support is available.

Curriculum. The curriculum is designed to provide both flexibility and breadth and to be in step with the National Curriculum without being constrained by it. Those in Forms I and II (Years 7 and 8) study a wide range of subjects including Latin, French and combined Science. In Form III (Year 9) the three Sciences are taught separately and pupils have the option of starting Greek.

Pupils normally take nine or ten GCSE subjects, four or five of which are of their own choosing. There is a cross-curricular ICT scheme to enable pupils to make full use of the School's extensive facilities.

In the Sixth Form a range of approximately 32 AS subjects is offered along with an enrichment programme which includes the ICT course, Clait Plus. This programme and many of the AS subjects are offered in cooperation with Haberdashers' Monmouth School for Girls.

A particular feature of the curriculum is the extensive range of Modern Languages. French is taught at all levels and Spanish and German are available from Form II. The Welsh Club enables boys to study Welsh for GCSE and Russian is also available at AS/A level.

The Chapel. The School is an Anglican foundation and the Chapel plays an important part in its life. All pupils attend Chapel at least once each week and there is a weekly service for boarders. A varied programme of preachers is organised, including clergy and lay people of many denominations. The Bishop of Monmouth officiates at the annual Confirmation Service.

Games. The main sports are rugby, rowing, cricket and soccer. Many other sports are also available at a highly competitive level including athletics, cross-country running, golf, sailing, squash and swimming. Several members of staff have international sporting honours and pupils regularly gain places to represent Wales in a variety of sports.

Activities. There is an extensive programme of activities throughout the School. Pupils in Form IV and above may join the CCF (Army and RAF sections) which enjoy excellent links with locally based regular and territorial forces. Community Service is a popular option and many boys participate in the Duke of Edinburgh's Award Scheme. There is a very strong musical tradition with many pupils taking part in choirs, orchestras and bands which achieve high levels of success in competitions, and play to appreciative audiences locally and on the regular overseas tours which take place. School musicians have performed alongside professional musicians at such venues as St David's Hall, Cardiff and on national television. Drama is also strong and good opportunities are provided for participation at all levels. A wide range of School clubs and Societies further enriches the life of the School.

Fees per term (2008-2009). Boarding (including tuition) £6,289; Day £3,735; The Grange: Boarding £5,197, Day £2,643.

Entrance Scholarships. (*see Scholarship Entries section*). Scholarships are available on the basis of performance in the Year 7 Entry Assessments (11+), Foundation Scholarship Examination (13+) and Sixth Form Examination (16+). Bursaries and the Haberdashers' Assisted Places Scheme can also provide up to 100% remission of fees, in certain circumstances.

Old Monmothians. Past members of the School are eligible to join the Old Monmothian Club, which enjoys a close relationship with the School. The Membership Secretary is Henry Toulouse, 3 Monkswell Close, Monmouth NP25 3PH.

Charitable status. William Jones's Schools Foundation is a Registered Charity, number 525616. Its aims and objectives are to provide an all-round education for boys and girls at reasonable fees; also to carry out the Founder's intention that local boys qualifying for entry should not be prevented from attending the School by lack of funds.

Morrison's Academy

Ferntower Road Crieff Perthshire PH7 3AN
Tel: 01764 653885
Fax: 01764 655411
e-mail: principal@morrisonsacademy.org
website: www.morrisonsacademy.org

Morrison's Academy Boys' School was opened in 1860 with a Girls' Department in 1861, an arrangement which continued until 1889 when a separate school for Girls was opened within the ten acres of the original site. In 1979 these two schools were brought together to become the one Morrison's Academy. The original foundation was possible through the generosity of Thomas Mo(r)rison, a native of Muthill who became a builder in Edinburgh and who in 1813 executed a Trust Deed directing that the fee of the reversion of his estate should be used to found and erect 'an institution calculated to promote the interests of mankind, having particular regard to the Education of Youth and the diffusion of useful knowledge . . . A new Institution which may bear my name and preserve the remembrance of my good intentions for the welfare and happiness of my fellow men'.

Motto: *Ad summa tendendum : Striving for the highest*

Board of Governors:
Chairman: R Mickel, LLB, WS
Vice-Chairman: J Haggart, BSc

Members:
G Berrie, FCII
A Burdon-Cooper, MA, LLB, FRSA
H Campbell, BSc, CEng, MICE, MI Struct E
Mrs E AGilmour, MA Hons
D A Glen, BAcc, CA, CTA
Dr K M Greig, MA, PhD
Professor W S Hanson, BA, PhD, FSA, FSA (*Scot*)
Professor J S Henley, BSc(*Eng*) PhD
Dr A Jackson, BSc, PhD
L Johnston
S Logie, BA
Mrs F R Sharp, MA
Dr P Wright, MA, PhD, FRSC

Clerk to Governors: J C Andrew, LLB Hons, Dip LP, NP

Staff:

***Rector*: G S H Pengelley**, BA

Admissions Secretary: Mrs A Ross

Head of Primary: A R Robertson, DipEd

Assistant Rectors:
A J Law, MA
Mrs A F Allan, BA
D A L MacKenzie, BSc

Bursar: A U Beaton, MSc, FCIPD, MCMI

Teaching Staff:

* *Head of Department*

Art:
*Miss P M McQue, MA
S Jewell, BD, MD

Business Studies:
*H McMillan, DipCom
Mrs E M Fraser, BA, DipCom

Computer Studies:
*D Hamilton, BSc, MSc, CEng, MBCS
Mrs P Boal, BSc

CDT/RME/PSD:
R G McDermott, MEd, BEd

English:
*P G O'Kane, MA
Mrs A F Allan, BA
Mrs T Lafferty, BEd
Mrs D D Riddell, MA

Geography:
*D L Allan, MA
R S Anderson, MA

History:
*P J Lovegrove, MA
M J Clayton, MA

Home Economics:
Mrs S S Farnan, Dip DSC

Mathematics:
*I K O Barnett, BSc Hons
D A L Mackenzie, BSc
A M Jack, BSc

Heads of Year:
Mrs A F Allan, BA
Mrs E M Fraser, BA, DipCom
L T Howell, BA
Mrs M T O'Kane, BSc
Miss A McCluskey, MA

Primary School:
Head of Primary: A R Robertson, DipEd
Depute Head, Primary: Mrs L S Anderson, BEd
Ms M M Anderson, BEd
I P Barr, MA
G Chater, BA
Mrs A Dickinson, LLB
Miss F Harvey, BEd
Mrs G M Lauchlan, MA
Mrs J A Longmuir, DipEd
Mrs C Marchbank, BA
Miss K McCain, BDes Hons

Mrs M T O'Kane, BSc

Modern Languages:
*E Coffey, MA
A J Law, MA
Miss M A Lines, MA, MLitt
Miss A McCluskey, MA

Music:
H A Duthie, MA, FRCO, DipEd (*Director of Music*)
Mrs J M Taylor, BA (*Head of Primary School Music*)
Mrs S Smart, BA

Physical Education:
*D N F Pennie, MA
L T Howell, BA
Mrs J Lee, BEd
Miss E J McCormick, BEd
Miss D J Nesbitt, BEd

Science:
*J B Beedie, BSc
G Guile, BSc
S Hill, BEng, MSc
M McKeever, BSc
Dr M A Kihlken, PhD, Msci
Mrs A S Taylor, BSc

Learning Support (Primary and Secondary):
Mrs G S Wilkie, MA
Mrs C Jones, BSc

The School. Morrison's Academy is an integral part of the community in Crieff and comprises a 10 acre main campus supplemented by 45 acres of sports fields, main hall, after-school club and nursery housed in a spacious building a short walk from the main campus. The school provides education for 520 boys and girls from 3 to 18 years.

The well-equipped Nursery can accommodate 30 children from 3 to 5 years in an impressive Victorian villa and the dedicated staff stimulate learning in the early years. The Nursery was recently inspected by HMIE/Care Commission and received a glowing report, where all areas received "very good" indicators. The Nursery and After-School Club together offer care from 8.00 am to 6.00 pm.

The Primary School, housed in a separate building on the main campus, educates 170 pupils in small classes. Transfer between primary and secondary is helped by our Transitional Year (P7), which provides teaching in the primary school by a class teacher supplemented by lessons in the secondary school taught by subject specialists.

The Secondary School has 330 pupils studying towards Scottish Qualifications and entry to universities in Scotland, the rest of the UK and abroad. Academic expectations and achievements are high and small groups encourage individual learning and development. Over ninety-five percent of our S6 go on to university.

Staff and pupils mix easily and the scale of the school allows for every individual to be known and valued by all.

Situation. Morrison's Academy is situated in the market town of Crieff on the edge of the Scottish Highlands in Perthshire. Strathearn is a beautiful area of mountains, rivers, lochs and rich agricultural land. Day pupils attend from the local area and travel from Perth, Pitlochry, Dunkeld, Auchterarder, Stirling and Dunblane.

Curriculum. Pupils in Primary and lower Secondary follow broadly the Scottish 5–14 programme of study, leading in upper Secondary to Intermediate and then to Higher and Advanced Higher National Qualifications. Emphasis is placed upon academic achievement, while the pupils are also always encouraged to develop broad skills and interests outside the classroom. Extra curricular activities are extensive and Morrison's Academy makes good use of its glorious location.

Houses. All pupils are placed in one of the four houses named after local families: Campbells, Drummonds, Grahams and Murrays. There is healthy, competitive rivalry between the houses and senior pupils are encouraged to take charge of teams for sporting, music, debating and other events.

Games and Activities. Morrison's Academy encourages pupils to participate in a wide range of extra curricular activities and sports. All pupils use the playing fields and facilities on the main campus or walk to the 45 acres of playing fields and pavilions at Dallerie. Main sports are rugby, hockey, cricket, tennis and athletics. From upper primary fixtures against other schools take place, generally on Saturday mornings. Other sporting activities include soccer, basketball, netball, swimming, athletics, golf, weight training, sailing, short tennis, skiing, climbing, karate and more. To complement the sporting activities, pupils are active in The Duke of Edinburgh's Award Scheme, the Combined Cadet Force, drama, music, debating, chess, Pipe and Drum Band, environment group, Young Enterprise, charity fund-raising, Christian groups, highland dancing and more. Pupils are challenged to make the most of their time and all within the wonderful environment of Perthshire.

Fees per term (2008-2009). Day: Primary £1,977–£2,816, Secondary £2,991.

The fees include tuition, textbooks, stationery, external examination fees, sports and curriculum-related travel.

Admission Procedure. Admission to the school is by entrance test and school report and/or exam results and entrance interview. The school's main entrance testing/interview days are at the end of February and beginning of March, for entry to the academic year commencing the following August.

For a prospectus pack and any queries please contact the Admissions Secretary.

Scholarships and Bursaries. (*see Scholarship Entries section*).

Charitable status. Morrison's Academy is a Registered Charity, number SC000458. The school is a recognised charity providing education.

Mount St Mary's College

Spinkhill Nr Sheffield Derbyshire S21 3YL
Tel: 01246 433388
Fax: 01246 435511
e-mail: headmaster@msmcollege.com
website: www.msmcollege.com

Mount St Mary's College was founded in 1842 by the Society of Jesus in order to provide educational facilities for the growing Catholic population of the country. The manor of Spinkhill in N E Derbyshire was the first home of the College and round this nucleus the present school has been built. The Elizabethan manor of Barlborough Hall, some $1^1/_4$ miles distant, is the home of the Junior Department of the College.

Numbers: College 390. Junior Department 3–11 years: 250. Boarders, Weekly Boarders and Day Pupils (girls and boys) are accepted at the College.

Motto: *Sine Macula.*

Governing Body:
Chairman: Sir N Adsetts, OBE

J Bergin
A Cooper
Father M Beattie
R Gilbert
Mrs H Massarella
T Wragg
Mrs L Penny
D Wesmoreland
J Kelly

Members:
The Very Revd M Holman
The Very Revd J Twist
Brother A Harrison

***Headmaster*: L E McKell**, MA Hons, MEd

Deputy Head: F Thompson, MA Cantab, MPhil
Director of Studies: Mrs M Smith
Business & Development Director: D Cotterill
Chaplain: E Pike

Assistant Staff:
* *Head of Department*
† *Housemaster/mistress*

P Abell, BSc Hons (*Mathematics*)
Dr V E Argent, BEd, BA, MA, DipSpNeeds, TEFL, DipSpLD (**Learning Support*)
G G Brammer, BEd Hons (*Head of Lower School, Geography*)
Mrs J Burkinshaw MA (*English*)
R Carey, BA (*EAL*)
Mrs R Powell, BEd Hons (**Girls' Games, Geography*)
M Forbes-Jones, BTh (*Religious Studies/Chaplaincy*)
J M Fry, BSc, ARSM (*Physics & Geography*)
Ms J Gabbitas (*†Hopkins*)
I Garbett, BA
Miss H Gonzalez-Florido (**Modern Languages*)
M Greene, BA (*English and Drama*)
D Griffiths, BA Hons, PGCE (**PE*)
Mrs G Kocura-Hackett, BA (*Drama*)
J Harvey-Tsakiropoulou, BA (*Modern Languages*)
S Haslehurst, MA (*Head of Sixth Form, *History, Asst †Loyola*)
Mrs G Hazlehurst, BSc (*Head of Middle School, PSE Coordinator, *Geography*)
Ms A Hoskin, BSc (*Games, PE*)
P Hulse, MA Dist, BA Hons (*ICT Coordinator, *Classics*)
R Ives, BSc (*Physics*)
Mrs S Johnson, BA (*Modern Languages*)
G F Kirrane, BA (*History*)
Mrs L Kitchener, BMus, MA (*Director of Music*)
M Krlic, BSc (**Business Studies*)
Mrs L A Lovatt-Jones, BA, MA, CertEd, LSDC (*Art & Design Technology*)
Mrs H McKell, BA (*English*)
R McMillan, BTheol (*Religious Studies, Assistant Chaplain*)
M Miller, BSc, MSc (**Mathematics*)
A P Mulkerrins, BSc Hons (**Biology, Staff Development Officer*)
Dr M B Murray, PhD, ARIC (**Chemistry*)
B Naughton, BSc (**Science*)
Mrs B D Owers, BA (*Modern Languages*)
G Powell, BSA Cert Boarding Education (*CCF*)
Mrs M Ridley, BSc, MSc (*Biology*)

P Scott, BEd , MEd (*Director of Sport*)
S Slater, MA
Mrs M Smith (*Director of Studies, *English & Drama*)
S Steed, BA (*Mathematics*)
J Stephenson, BTheol Hons (**Religious Studies, Philosophy, Head of Syntax Year 11*)
D Toerien, BA
Mrs J Toerien, MA (*Science*)
R Totterdell, BA (*Geography*)
R Wareham, BSc (**Boys' Games*)
G Wilks, BSc (*Business Studies*)
I M Wilson, BEd (*ICT*)
C White BA (*DT & Art*)
P Woodhouse, BA (* *Art &Design Technology*)
Mrs C Woodward, BSc (*Biology*)

Headmaster's Secretary: Mrs S Badger
Medical Officers: Dr Palmer, Dr Gardner
School Nurse: Mrs M Gibson
CCF: Sqn Ldr J M Fry, Maj G Powell, MISM

Barlborough Hall School:
Headteacher: Mrs W Parkinson, BEd

Mount St Mary's is a co-educational independent boarding and day school in membership of HMC, BSA and AGBIS. Entry to the College is at age 11 and to the Junior Department at Barlborough Hall at age 3+. Pupils at Mount St Mary's are prepared for GCSE, AS and A levels and University entry, including Oxbridge. Entry into the Sixth Form is based upon school reports and GCSE results.

Aims. Mount St Mary's College is a Jesuit foundation inspired by the ideals of St Ignatius of Loyola. The College seeks to develop the whole person with Christ as the model for human life and encourages an appreciation of the needs of others both in the College community and the world at large. Mount St Mary's prepares its pupils for an active life commitment through the development of 'a faith that promotes justice'. The College seeks to produce young men and young women for others. Though essentially a Catholic college, pupils of other religious denominations are welcomed.

Special Features. Mount St Mary's College is well known for its family atmosphere. The level of participation of former pupils, called Old Mountaineers, in the life of the College affirms this. Relationships between pupils and teachers are friendly and there are few disciplinary problems. Pupils benefit from the close interest and encouragement which they receive throughout their time at the College and parental involvement is particularly encouraged.

Situation. The College is situated in its own extensive estate of playing fields and parkland and is easily reached from the M1 motorway, junction 30, or from Chesterfield and Sheffield, both of which are about 8 miles away. School minibuses run from Sheffield and other local towns.

Organisation. The College is organised into Lower, Middle and Upper schools, each under its own Head of School, responsible for overseeing academic progress, pastoral care, recreation and discipline. Heads of School work closely with the Deputy Head and Director of Studies.

Boarders are located in one of the boarding areas under the care of a resident boarding housemaster or housemistress, assisted by resident assistant boarding staff. Each boarding house caters for pupils of approximately the same age although girl boarders have separate boarding accommodation across the age range. The majority of pupils are housed in en-suite rooms, some of which are 2-3 sharing and some of which are single rooms.

Curriculum. The curriculum for the first three years (11–13) broadly follows National Curriculum at KS3 with opportunity to pursue a second foreign language and Latin. The KS3 tests in Mathematics, Science and English are taken at the end of the third year (Year 9). The standard GCSE package is 9 GCSEs, although more or less is negotiable according to ability; this includes a core of English, Mathematics, a foreign language and Science. Other subjects are chosen from a range of options. In the Sixth Form pupils follow AS Levels in the Lower Sixth (usually four), leading to three A Levels at the end of Upper Sixth year. In keeping with the school's Ignatian ethos, all pupils follow a Religious Studies course at every stage. Various special interest subjects are offered in the Sixth Form such as Astronomy and Amateur Radio. Specialist tuition is available in a variety of musical instruments. Assesment and monitoring of work is built into the tutorial system and reports are sent to parents four times per year. Academic excellence and breadth of knowledge are characteristics of Jesuit education and the curriculum is constantly reviewed to ensure that the widest opportunities are available to each pupil.

Religion. Mount St Mary's college is a Catholic school and, more distinctively, a Jesuit school. However, pupils of other than Catholic denominations are welcomed. Ignatian principles inform the College's work in fostering a realistic knowledge, love and acceptance of self and of the world in which we live and this underpins our main objective: the formation of young men and young women for others. There are school masses, year masses and other liturgical celebrations regularly throughout the school year, as well as retreats and pilgrimages. Religious Education is a part of the curriculum to GCSE and either as an examination or non-examination option in the Sixth Form. The community service programme provides opportunities for Sixth Formers to work with people who have special needs and the College maintains a strong link with Jesuit missions in different parts of the world, finding ways and means to further the work of the Society in this area. Pupils have the opportunity to be involved in gap year projects supported by the Society of Jesus. Pupils and their parents are expected to recognise and endorse the religious commitment of the College.

Games. The College has extensive playing fields for rugby, hockey, cricket and football. Rugby, for which the College has a strong regional and national reputation, is the major boys' sport. Cricket facilities are excellent with all-weather practice wickets and indoor practice nets. The main girls' sport in the winter term is hockey, for which there is a floodlit all-weather hockey pitch. A new pavilion and floodlit international standard athletics track were opened in 2007, and there is a full-time Level 4 Athletics Coach. Other sports include swimming, tennis, basketball, volleyball, badminton, shooting, netball, and football. The nearby Rother Valley Country Park and Derbyshire Peak District are used for sailing, canoeing, windsurfing and hill-walking. There is also a scuba-diving club.

Art, Drama and Music. There are many opportunities to be involved in the Arts within the school, both within the curriculum and as part of the extra-curricular activities. Within the art department pupils can study fine art, textiles, resistant materials within the workshop and photography. On Saturday mornings activities are run involving sculpture, art and photography.

Pupils are encouraged to take up a musical instrument, and can participate in a wide number of musical activities, ranging from three choirs and a barber shop to orchestras, wind band, jazz band and many ensembles. Drama is strong in the College, and several Senior and Junior productions are put on every year.

Combined Cadet Force and other Extra-Curricular Activities. All pupils in Year 10 and Year 11 participate in the Combined Cadet Force, in the Army or RAF section. They can continue to be a member, on selection, in the Sixth Form. The CCF gives opportunities for external leadership courses and adventurous training and fulfilling Duke of Edinburgh's Award options. There are extensive opportunities for extra-curricular activities at lunchtime, after school and on Saturday mornings. Pupils can pursue interests in drama, music, sports, the Duke of Edinburgh's Award and other clubs and societies.

Facilities. Among the facilities available are a Drama Studio, Observatory, Radio Station, ICT suite of three fully-equipped rooms, Music School with practice rooms and Recital Hall, College Theatre, Library with ICT facilities, Fitness Centre, heated indoor swimming pool, Sports Hall, Rifle Range, Outdoor Pursuits Centre, all-weather tennis courts and 30 acres of games fields. An Olympic standard athletics track was opened in 2007.

Admissions. At 11+ pupils enter via the College entrance examination, taken early in the Spring term at the College. At other ages, pupils are accepted on the basis of school reports, with College entry tests as appropriate and in the Sixth Form, pupils are accepted on the basis of GCSE results, or their equivalent.

Fees per term (2008-2009). Full Boarders: £6,230 (Years 9–13), £4,720 (Years 7 and 8). Weekly Boarders: £5,380 (Years 9–13), £4,000 (Years 7 and 8). Day Pupils: £3,260 (Years 9–13), £2,815 (Years 7 and 8). Barlborough Hall: £2,500 (Day Pupils), £1,750 (Pre-Prep).

Scholarships. Academic scholarships are awarded at 11+ on the basis of the entrance examination. Music, Art and other scholarships are also available and the College will be happy to provide further information on these. In keeping with the College's ethos, bursaries are awarded in cases of demonstrable need. The Old Mountaineers offer post-graduate scholarships to former pupils of the College and applications are considered annually for these.

Prospectus. This may be obtained by writing to the Headmaster's Secretary at the College and parents are always encouraged to visit Mount St Mary's College or its Junior School.

Charitable status. The Society of Jesus Trust of 1929 for Roman Catholic Purposes is a Registered Charity, number 230165. Mount St Mary's was founded in 1842 to provide an education for children.

Newcastle-under-Lyme School
(Newcastle-under-Lyme Endowed Schools Charity)

Mount Pleasant Newcastle-under-Lyme Staffordshire ST5 1DB
Tel: 01782 631197
Fax: 01782 632582
e-mail: info@nuls.org.uk
website: www.nuls.org.uk

Newcastle-under-Lyme School, which attracts pupils from a large area of North Staffordshire, South Cheshire and North Shropshire, is a co-educational day school for 1,125 pupils aged 3–18. The present School was formed in 1981 through the amalgamation of Newcastle High School and the Orme Girls' School, two schools which were endowed as a single foundation in 1872 under an educational charity scheme for children in Newcastle which has its roots in the 1600s. The two schools enjoyed a reputation for scholarship and for service to the community throughout North Staffordshire, a reputation which has continued with the formation of Newcastle-under-Lyme School. The School is also well known for its high standards in sport, music and drama, which play a major part in the extra-curricular life of the School. The preparatory department, Orme House, is adjacent to the Senior School and has some 350 pupils aged 3–11.

Governing Body:

Ex Officio Governor:
The Mayor of the Borough of Newcastle-under-Lyme

Nominative Governors:
Appointed by:

The Council of the University of Keele:
Professor R Cocks

The Newcastle-under-Lyme Endowed Schools Parents' Association:
P T Mills, BEd

The Committee of the Old Boys' Association of Newcastle High School:
A Curzon

The Committee of the Old Girls' Association of the Orme Girls' School:
Mrs K Miller

Co-optative Governors:
L J Bassett
I R Cheetham, FRICS
T M Davis, BSc, MSc
Mrs R M King, LLB (*Vice-Chairman*)
P Moxon, OBE, DL
Mrs J Nicholas, BSc
T J O'Neill, CEng, MBA, MSc, MIEE, PhD
J P Wenger (*Chairman of Governors*)

Associate Governors:
W H P Evans, ACIB
A T Gough
Mrs M E Leese
Mrs R J Morrey
R Nadin
J S Rushton, BSc, FCA, CISA

Bursar: A D Simpson

***Principal*: N A Rugg**, MA

Vice-Principals:
A P Jeffreys, MA
G A Cappi, MA

English:
*P M Cash, BA, MPhil
Mrs J Betts-Nicholson, BA
Miss F Charles, BA
S Durrant, BA
Mrs B A Godridge, BA
Mrs B Joughin, BA
O J A Leech, BA
R Lench, BA

History:
*D Dunlop, BA, PhD
D A Cawdron, BA
Mrs J A Simms, BA, MSc
Mrs S J Stockdale, BSc

Mathematics:
*Miss J M Griffiths, BSc
Mrs C M Barber, BSc
D T Buckley, BSc
M Byrom, BSc
Mrs J C Cliff, BSc
Mrs J A Cryer, BSc
Mrs H Goodall, BSc
J Sillitoe, BSc

ICT:
*S Luck, BSc

Chemistry:
*M S Snell, BSc
Mrs M M Atkins, BScTech (*Director of HE & Careers*)
P Calder, BSc, MSc, MEd
Miss J Galvin, BSc
G Moore, BSc, PhD

Physics:
*Mrs S Bremner, BSc, PhD
A Fishburne, MEng
S Rimmington, BSc
Mrs P Woodcock, BSc

Biology:
*N J Simms, BSc
N C Carter, BSc
Miss R Kane, BSc
D R Pepper, BSc, PhD

Geography:
*T P Jowitt, BSc
I J Cartwright, BEd, MA (*Director of Admissions*)
D P Sherratt, BA
Mrs F P E Williams, BA

Modern Languages:
*D L Brayford, MA, MEd
Mrs H Bayley, BA
C Diaz, BA
Mrs M Isherwood, BA
D G Murtagh, BA
Mrs K H Tan, BA
Mrs D A Woodcock, BA

Religious Studies:
*R W Bridges, BSc

Classics:
*Ms T A Thomas, BA

G Tankard, MA

Economics:
*D N Hartshorne, BSc Econ
Mrs J A Kelt, BSc Econ (*Senior Mistress*)

Art:
*P Dare, BA
P G Dawson, CertEd
Miss L Herian, BA
Mrs S Parkinson, BA

Design and Technology:
*Mrs S Hancock, BEng
D Patrick, BA

Home Economics:
*Mrs J Machin
Mrs N G Swindells, BEd

Textiles:
*Mrs B W Jones, TCert

Physical Education (Girls):
*Miss E A Webb, BEd, MEd
Mrs D Glenn, BEd
Mrs J Pointon, BEd
Mrs P Smith

Physical Education (Boys):
*G M Chesterman, BSocSc
G M Breen
S A Robson, BEd

Careers:
*Mrs B Joughin, BA

Music:
*T Sagar, MA
D G McGarry, DLM
Mrs C Hughes, BA, MusEd
Mrs M Potter, GGSM, ARCM, PGCE

Swimming: P J Butler, FISTC, AIST LS

Orme House Preparatory Department:
Head Teacher: N Vernon , BSc, MA
Acting Deputy Head: G Lewis, BEd
Head of Pre-Prep: Mrs A Burgess, BA
Nursery Manager: Mrs A Smith, NNEB, NEBS

Mrs C Deakes, BA
Mrs H Dickson, CertEd
Mrs H Eady
Mrs A Farnsworth
Mrs J Grisdale, BEd
Mrs P Hodson, CertEd
Mrs L Moss, BA
Mrs S Nixon, BEd
Mrs J M Parker, BA
Mrs J S Roberts, BEd
Miss F Scott, LLB
Miss C K M Shipton, BA
Miss J Stanton, BEd
Mrs K Tapp, BA
Mrs J Ward, BEd

Librarian: Miss W F Butler, BA, MA, DipLib, MCLIP

Buildings and Grounds. Set in 30 acres of grounds, the School is pleasantly situated on high ground in a quiet conservation area close to the centre of Newcastle-under-Lyme. The original buildings still form part of the School and extensions have been added from time to time. A fine dining hall was opened in one of the wings of the original building, part of the continuing programme of development and refurbishment which was begun when the School reverted to full independence in 1981. The Millennium Sixth Form Centre opened in March 2000 affording spacious new accommodation for senior students. In addition to the well equipped classrooms and Science laboratories, the School has Language laboratories, workshops, a Music School, an Art and Design Centre, two libraries, a gymnasium, and a Sports Centre which includes a sports hall, a weights room and an indoor swimming pool. Computers are accessible in subject areas and in four modern laboratories, where machines are linked on a network basis. There are also tennis and netball courts and extensive playing fields, providing pitches for cricket, rugby and hockey, adjacent to the School. An all-weather pitch with floodlighting was opened in March 2002.

Organisation. The School is organised in two sections: a nursery (2004), pre-preparatory (2004) and preparatory department, Orme House, which was opened in 1982 and which has 300+ pupils in the age range 3 to 11 and the Senior School, with approximately 400 boys and 400 girls. The Sixth Form numbers more than 225 students.

Form Tutors and Heads of Year have particular responsibility for the pastoral welfare of the pupils in their charge.

In the First and Second Forms boys and girls have their own inter-form and inter-house competitions, with separate Junior assemblies. This structure gives to the junior forms a separate identity within the Senior School. The Senior House structure, which extends from Form 3 upwards, consists of four co-educational houses.

Curriculum. A broad curriculum in the first five years has English (Language and Literature), Mathematics, Biology, Chemistry, Physics, and French as core subjects. All pupils also take Latin, History, Geography, Religious Education, Music, Art, Home Economics, Design and Technology, ICT, PE, Swimming and Games; German and Spanish are introduced as option subjects in the Third Form. Pupils have the option of taking Biology, Chemistry and Physics as a double award GCSE or as three separate GCSEs in the Fourth and Fifth Forms.

Pupils take nine or ten GCSEs and the great majority will proceed to take four AS Levels, in addition to General Studies or Critical Thinking in the Lower Sixth Form. Three or four of these subjects will be continued in the Upper Sixth as A2 qualifications.

Optional choices in the Sixth Form include A Level Business Studies, Economics, British Government and Politics, Philosophy and Theatre Studies, in addition to AS Levels in the subjects available at GCSE. All pupils follow a course in Critical Thinking or General Studies and take the NEAB examination at A Level. Pupils are also prepared for Oxford and Cambridge Entrance.

Extra Curricular Activities. The main school games are Rugby, Cricket, Hockey, Athletics, Tennis and Cross-Country for the boys and Hockey, Athletics, Netball, Tennis and Rounders for the girls. Swimming, Waterpolo, Life Saving and Synchronised Swimming also feature strongly and there are usually opportunities for Shooting, Squash, Aerobics, Basketball, Badminton, Golf and other physical activities in the Sixth Form.

There are also strong traditions in both Music and Drama and standards are very high. More than 300 pupils receive instrumental tuition and there are a number of concerts in each year with major performances being given in local churches and in the Victoria Concert Hall in Hanley. There are several major drama productions each year including one each at Senior, Middle and Junior School levels.

The flourishing Combined Cadet Force has naval, army and airforce sections and there is also a large Scout troop, which enrols both boys and girls. Pupils also participate in the Duke of Edinburgh's Award Scheme.

Clubs and Societies meet during the lunch hour and after school.

Careers. The School places much emphasis on the importance of careers guidance, both in the GCSE years and in the preparation for tertiary education. The School is an all-in member of the ISCO Careers Guidance Scheme, through which all pupils in the Fifth Form receive a careers report based on tests of ability, personality and aptitude. Pupils receive full advice on applications to Universities and other Institutes of Higher Education.

Honours. Between 1987 and 2007 259 of our students gained places at Oxford and Cambridge, while in 2007, some 95% of all Upper Sixth leavers gained entry to degree courses in Higher Education.

Admissions. Entry to the Nursery is on a first-come first-served basis. Entry to the Pre-Prep, Prep Department and the first three forms of the Senior School is by examination/assessment only, normally at the ages of 7, 11 and 13. A few candidates are also admitted at 8, 9, 10, 12 and 14. The entrance examinations for these age groups are usually held in January and February for entry in the following September but pupils moving into the area may be considered at other times.

Entry at Sixth Form level is by interview and GCSE qualifications.

Registration forms, and copies of the Prospectus, are available on request.

Scholarships and Bursaries. (*see Scholarship Entries section*). Governors' scholarships are awarded annually on the results of the entrance examination at 11+. Academic and

Sports Scholarships are also available for entry at 13+. Scholarships are also awarded in Mathematical Sciences and in Physics for the Sixth Form, on the results of Scholarship Examinations.

The Governors have established a Bursary Scheme to assist parents with school fees.

Further details may be obtained from the Principal.

Fees per term (2008-2009). Senior School £2,747; Preparatory School £2,384; Pre-Preparatory School £2,140; Nursery £36 per day (£19.50 per session).

Charitable status. Newcastle-under-Lyme Endowed Schools Charity is a Registered Charity, number 528591. The object of the Schools Charity shall be the provision and conduct in or near Newcastle-under-Lyme of a day or a day and boarding school or schools for boys and girls.

Norwich School

70 The Close Norwich NR1 4DD
Tel: 01603 728430
Fax: 01603 728490
e-mail: enquiries@norwich-school.org.uk
website: www.norwich-school.org.uk

Norwich School is a co-educational day school for pupils aged seven to eighteen. Set in the Cathedral Close, the School is an historic place. The exact date at which it came into being is unknown, but its origins can be traced back to the foundation of the Cathedral in 1096. In 1547 it was re-founded by Edward VI.

In 2007–8 there were approximately 840 pupils: 680 in the Senior School (age 11–18) and 160 in the Lower School (age 7–11) (*see Norwich School, Lower School IAPS entry*); around one-third of the Sixth Form are girls.

With the introduction of full co-education from September 2008, the School is expected to grow to approximately 1000 pupils during the next five years.

Cathedral Choristers are members of the school.

Motto: '*Praemia virtutis honores*'

Council of Management:

Co-optative Governors:
G H C Copeman, CBE, DL (*Chairman*)
T J Gould, MA (*Vice-Chairman*)
C H Bradley-Watson, BSc, MRICS
N J Fischl, MA
Mrs A Fry, MA
E J H Gould, MA
Mrs A Green BSc
A D Jeakings, FCMA
A Knowles, MDes
Mrs E McLoughlin, BArch, RIBA
Mrs M C G Phillips, BA
Dr N P V Richardson, MA, PhD
P J E Smith, MA, FIA
E P Witton, ACIB
Miss T Yates, BA

Representative Governors:
Professor C Andrew, MA, University of Cambridge
N P Blair, Worshipful Company of Dyers
J R Chambers, FCA, Worshipful Company of Dyers
The Revd Canon JM Haselock, BA, BPhil, MA, Dean & Chapter
Professor K Heywood, BSc, PhD, University of East Anglia
R A Leuchars, BSc, Worshipful Company of Dyers
P N Mirfield, BCL, MA, BA, University of Oxford
The Very Revd Graham Smith, BA, Dean of Norwich

***Head Master*: J B Hawkins**, MA Oxon

Principal Deputy Head: P A Todd, MA Cantab
Academic Deputy Head: N M Plater, MA Oxon
Senior Master: G D Sumner, BEd
Under Master: P D Goddard, BEd
Director of Studies: Dr D N Farr, BA, PhD, FRHS (*Head of History*)
Senior Mistress: Mrs N J Hill, BSc
Bursar: B D G Delacave, ACA

Teaching Staff:
Miss K E Adams, BA
Dr C E Adkins, MA, PhD
P E R Badger, BSc (*Head of Chemistry*)
C A Banham, BA, MSc
M D Barber, BA (*Head of Modern Languages*)
D P Bateman, BSc (*Head of Politics; Housemaster, Valpy*)
Miss A L J Batty, BA, MA
R H Bedford-Payne, BA (*Housemaster, Nelson*)
T D Berwick, BSc
Dr M Bhaduri, BSc, MSc, PhD
Mrs R M Bolton, BSc
Miss A E Boyt, BA (*News Coordinator, Tutor for Girls – 6th Form*)
Miss S Brankin, MA
R A Bunting (*Head of Boys' Games*)
Mrs L L Butcher, BSc (*Chief Examinations Officer*)
Miss C Chaumont, L-ès-L Maitrîse
A J Christie, BA
Ms S A Chuter, BEd, MSc (*Head of Girls' Sports*)
A S Crocker, BA (*Coordinator of Art*)
W H J Croston, BA (*Head of Careers*)
A P Curtis, BA
Mrs K E Curtis, BA (*part-time*)
E C Dowdeswell, GRSM, ARCM (*Director of Music*)
G M Downes, BA (*Housemaster, Brooke*)
Mrs F L Ellington, BA (*Housemaster, Parker*)
R H Ellson, MA
Miss V L Fincham, BA, MA
A L Fisher, BA
J C Fisher, BSc (*Housemaster, Repton*)
A Fullwood, MA (*Head of English*)
R C Gardiner, BSc (*Head of Economics, Head of Cultural Studies*)
S J Gibbons (*Director of Sport*)
I M Grisewood, BA (*Housemaster, School House*)
F P A Hanique, BA
G A Hanlon, BSc (*Housemaster, Coke*)
T J Hill, BSc (*Head of ICT*)
Dr A P Hinsley, BSc, PhD
C Hooper, BA (*Head of Sixth Form*)
E D Hopkins, BA
Dr J C Hopper, BSc, PhD (*Head of Biology*)
Miss A J Hurrell, BA
T G Hutchings, MA, MPhil
M James, MA (*Head of Drama*)
A M Jarvis, BSc, MA (*part-time*)
S A Kettley, MA (*Head of Classics, Oxbridge Coordinator*)
Mr T J Leveridge, MA (*Head of Geography*)
Miss M E Ling, BSc
Mrs N B Looker, BA (*part-time*)
B W Mack, BSc
F J Mclvor, MA (*Senior Tutor, Head of Meno*)
Miss C L Meddins, BA
Miss T M Mounter, BA (*Tutor for Girls – 4th Form*)
M Mulligan, BA, MPhil (*Head of Philosophy & Critical Thinking*)
Dr P Muskett, BSc, PhD
I R Passam, BA (*Head of Art & Design*)
R W Peters, BA (*Head of Mathematics*)
Mrs C M Pywell, BSc (*part-time*)
M Ramshaw, BSc
Ms N J Ravenscroft, MA (*part-time*)

Mrs E Reed, BA (*part-time*)
Dr G Richardson, BSc, PhD
Mrs D Saywack, MA, MA (*Head of Religious Studies, Tutor for Girls – 5th Form*)
Miss L Slade, BA
Mrs P R Staufenberg, MA (*part-time*)
M G Thompson, BSc
Mrs J V Turner, BA (*part-time*)
Dr M Venables, MA, PhD (*Head of Science, Head of Physics*)
J E R Waite, CertEd (*Coordinator of Internal Examinations*)
J W Walker, BEd (*part-time*)
T J Watts, LLB
Mrs S Wortley, AGSM, GGSM, CertEd (*part-time*)

Lower School
Master of the Lower School: J K Ingham, BA
Second Master: R A Love, BSc
Director of Studies: R E Hambleton, BSc, MA
I K Blaxall, BEd
T J Brook, MSc
C C G Cordy, BA
Mrs N B Dunnett, BA (*Music*)
P M Embling, CertEd (*part-time*)
Mrs I R G Grote, 1st & 2nd Staatsexamen
J S G Worton, BSc
Mrs G E Wright, BEd

Head Master's PA: Mrs K E Moore
Registrar: Mrs V A Gaskin, BSc
Lower School Secretary: Mrs J S Payton
School Secretary: Ms J A Algar
Common Room Secretary: Mrs J M Raath
Secretary to Head of Sixth Form: Mrs E Reed, BA
Music School Coordinator: Mrs S Wortley, AGSM, GGSM, CertEd
Deputy to the Examinations Officer: Mrs S L Bate, BEd
Assistant to the Examinations Officer: Mrs J Powell, BA

Medical Officer: Dr J C Bennett
School Nurses:
Mrs C Bennett, RGN, ONC
Miss C Castle, RGN

Archivist: Dr P D T Cattermole, BSc, PhD

Norwich School's style and values are traditional but pertinent to today's young people, based firmly on academic excellence and Christian principles. The School provides an education of considerable breadth and depth within a disciplined, happy and caring environment. All pupils are urged to be ambitious in their studies and activities; good results are expected and celebrated. Through inspirational teaching and a challenging and distinctive curriculum, Norwich School engenders love for learning and appreciation of scholarship.

Admission. The main points of entry are at ages 7, 11, 13 and 16. There may be small numbers of places available at other ages. Application for admission should be made to the Head Master on the form obtainable from the Registrar.

Fees per term (2008-2009). Senior School £3,506; Lower School £3,294.

Faith and Worship. Members of the Senior School meet in the Cathedral every morning. Services and assemblies provide precious opportunities for corporate gathering and worship. The Christian tradition of the School provides a framework for its spiritual life. Pupils of all faiths are welcomed and it is not the School's intention to proselytize or indoctrinate. It is felt right, however, that all pupils should receive grounding in the liturgy and traditions of Christian worship so that they are acquainted with the faith heritage of the School and the Cathedral that it regularly visits. Familiarity with prayers, hymns and Biblical texts provides pupils with a spiritual vocabulary and a vehicle through which to encounter important ethical and spiritual questions. The School aims to provide pupils with a secure basis from which they can embark upon their own journeys into faith.

Teaching and Learning. Good scholarship is held in high regard at Norwich School. Those pupils who exhibit strong academic ability and the desire to read, learn and express their opinions are at the heart of school activity. Inspirational teaching using imaginative methods and content is fostered throughout the School. Fundamental to all teaching and learning at Norwich School is the shared belief that a well-educated person who loves to learn and is able to think critically and creatively is more likely to lead a fulfilling and positive life. Education is perceived as a worthwhile end in itself.

Pastoral Care and Discipline. The School aims to sustain a friendly atmosphere with genuine trust and respectful camaraderie between pupils and staff. There is firm discipline within that caring environment, enabling pupils to feel secure within clearly defined parameters.

In practical terms, each pupil's welfare is the responsibility of their tutor in whom the parents have a main point of contact for pastoral matters.

The Senior School (age 11–16). There is a distinctive curriculum for the 11 to 14 age group, elements of which are sustained throughout the GCSE years. Alongside the traditional range of subjects is the Meno Programme: approximately six periods per week that incorporate exotic languages such as Hebrew, Mandarin and Hieroglyphics – as well as philosophy, thinking and relaxation skills. There are practical elements where learning takes place outdoors – to learn, for example, about ecology and food production by experience on school land. Site visits to the North Norfolk coast and other areas of the county are programmed into the year so that different academic subjects such as Art, Biology, Geography and History can combine resources on project work. The aim is to aid learning through varied experiences and stimuli and to excite the pupils about the learning process.

The Sixth Form. Almost all Sixth Form pupils go to university upon leaving Norwich School. There is a long track record of success in large numbers gaining entrance to Oxford, Cambridge and the other top academic institutions. All boys and girls are encouraged to excel in their A Level studies and to be committed to sporting, cultural and extra-curricular activity.

The Advice Team, led by the Head of Sixth Form, tailors a programme of University and career preparation for each pupil and monitors their success from Lower Sixth to A Level results day – and beyond where necessary.

Creative and Performing Arts. The music department is very popular with pupils, welcoming and encouraging boys and girls of all levels of ability to explore their musical creativity. Over 60% of all pupils make music regularly. There are more than twenty-five specialist teachers and various orchestras, ensembles, bands, choirs and groups. Performances at all levels and ages regularly take place within the School, the Cathedral and in the wider community.

Drama facilities include the purpose-designed Blake Studio. Pupils also have the privilege of performing at some of the finest venues in Norwich: the Senior Play traditionally is performed in the Maddermarket Theatre; other productions take place in the Puppet Theatre, the Lower School and the Cathedral; major musicals are staged at the Playhouse.

Art and Design are well-resourced and, in recent years, several talented artists and designers from the School have gained places at the top Art Colleges.

Sport. Norwich School is unusual among day schools in providing two games sessions each week and fixtures on many Saturdays. Games and sport are perceived as vital aspects of the curriculum.

The major games for boys are rugby, cricket and hockey; and for girls, netball, hockey and rounders. There are strong fixture lists in each of these sports. Boys and girls are able to take up a broad range of other sports including swimming, netball, cross-country running, fencing, lacrosse, rowing, sailing, self-defence, soccer, shooting and badminton – among others.

Activities and Trips. The intellectual life is enhanced by an array of stimulating activities. There is a Debating Society, a Politics Forum and the Thomas Browne Society for the presentation of philosophical papers and intellectual discussion. Many academic departments run clubs to allow pupils to gain a wider experience of their subjects. The School Consultative Committee allows elected pupils to discuss school issues directly with the Head Master.

The variety of clubs and societies is continually changing as new teachers and pupils bring their own particular interests to the School. Debating, creative writing, philosophy, Amnesty International, yoga, the Duke of Edinburgh's Award, conservation, chess, cookery and film clubs are on the list at the time of writing. Music, drama and the practical arts all provide further extra-curricular opportunities.

Overseas visits broaden the experience of many pupils. The Modern Languages Department runs exchanges to France, Germany and Liechtenstein. Recent cultural, sporting or adventurous trips have gone to Austria, Canada, China, Ecuador, Egypt, Greece, Holland, Iceland, India, Israel, Russia and Turkey.

Scholarships and Bursaries. (*see Scholarship Entries section*). Scholarships are awarded to pupils with outstanding ability and flair, which the school assesses by examination, interview or audition. The financial value of a scholarship will be 20% of the annual tuition fee – irrespective of parental means. Scholarships are awarded in four categories: Academic; Music; Sport; and Art, Design or Drama.

Academic and Music scholarships are awarded at 11+, 13+ and Sixth Form entry. Sport and Art, Design or Drama scholarships are awarded only at Sixth Form entry. Pupils may apply for more than one scholarship, although the maximum financial benefit that can be cumulated is 40% of the school fees.

We set aside generous bursarial funds to enable boys and girls to come to Norwich School who would not be able to do so without financial help. All bursaries are means-tested and can result in a reduction in fees of up to 100%; there is a sliding scale dependent on family income and finances.

As a general rule, it is unlikely that a bursary will be awarded when family income is greater than four times the school fees. It is possible, indeed not unusual, for a bursary holder to have a scholarship. In such circumstances, 20% of the fees would be covered by the scholarship; any bursary funding further to this would, of course, be means-tested.

To supplement the School's bursary provision, the Worshipful Company of Dyers, through its charitable trust, is able to give financial support to a pupil with all-round talent in both L4 and L6. The criteria for the Dyers' Bursary Scheme are similar to those outlined above and potential applicants should simply register interest in bursarial assistance on the application form.

In addition to the above arrangements, the school has an association with the Ogden Trust which is able to give financial support to selected Sixth Form pupils who join us from the state sector with primary academic strengths in mathematics or the applied sciences. The Trust's financial criteria are similar to our own.

Cathedral Choristers hold Chorister Bursaries to the value of 50% of fees. Further assistance in cases of need is possible.

Lower School. *For further details, see entry for Norwich School, The Lower School in the IAPS section.*

Old Norvicensians. All enquiries should be made to Mrs R Lightfoot, Norwich School, 71a The Close, Norwich NR1 4DD.

Charitable status. Norwich School is a Registered Charity, number 311280. It exists solely to provide education.

Nottingham High School

Waverley Mount Nottingham NG7 4ED
Tel: 0115 978 6056
Fax: 0115 979 2202
e-mail: info@nottinghamhigh.co.uk
website: www.nottinghamhigh.co.uk

Motto: '*Lauda Finem*'

This School was founded in 1513 by Agnes Mellers, widow of Richard Mellers, sometime Mayor of Nottingham. The first Charter was given by Henry VIII, and supplementary Charters were given by Philip and Mary, and by Queen Elizabeth. The School, which remains independent, is now administered under the terms of a scheme issued by the Charity Commissioners.

Governing Body:
The Lord Lieutenant of Nottinghamshire
The Lord Mayor of Nottingham
Two Representatives of the City Council
One Representative of the Nottinghamshire County Council
Four Representatives of the Universities
Eleven Co-optative Members

Chairman of the Governors: N V Tamplin, FCA

Clerk to the Governors: A B Palfreman, MA, 84 Friar Lane, Nottingham

***Headmaster*: K D Fear**, BA Southampton

Deputy Headmaster: P G Sibly, BSc, PhD, ARCM University College, London
Deputy Headmaster (*Academic*): D M Williamson, BA Durham, MA York, FRGS
Senior Master: J L Wilkinson, MA St Andrews
Director of Finance and Estates: R Dunmore, BA, ACA

Academic Staff:
* *Head of Department*

G J Lewin, MSc, ARCS, DIC (**Science, *Physics*)
J F W Knifton, MA, (*French*)
D A Slack, BSc, PhD (**Information and Communications Technology*)
R G Willan, BA (**Geography*)
R Kilby, BSc (**Mathematics*)
J A Cook, BSc (**Biology*)
G Douglas, LTCL (*Music*)
P G Morris, BA (*Physics*)
A D Holding, BA (**General Studies*)
W P J Ruff, MA (**English*)
A F Wood, BSc, PhD (*Chemistry; Director of Studies*)
K P Brierley, BSc (*Chemistry*)
M T Cleverley, BSc (*Chemistry*)
A S Winter, BA (*French*)
R J Clarke, BSc (*Mathematics*)
C P Sedgewick, MA (*Geography*)
J T Swain, MA, PhD, FRHistS (*History*)
Revd S Krzeminski, BTh (**Religious Education, Philosophy*)
S L Williams, BA, MA (*History*)
K C Clayton, BSc (*Biology*)
S Barber, BA (**French*)
Miss S Willan, BA (*Religious Education, Philosophy*)
Mrs C Y Fletcher, BSc, PhD (*Biology*)
M D Smith, BEd (**Physical Education*)
J Lamb, BSc (*Mathematics, Careers*)
A V Martin, BA, DipPsych (**Psychology*)
Mrs M O Mills, BSc (*Mathematics*)
M I Saperia, BSc (*Biology*)
D B Thomas, BEd (*Design Technology*)
R A Gilbert, BA (*Chemistry*)

D Hecht (Studienassessor) (**German*)
G J Martin, MA (*English*)
G Whitehead, MA (*German*)
J E Rayfield, BMus (**Music*)
P J Cramp, BA (**Economics*)
N Highfield, CertEd (*Physical Education*)
Mrs A Griffin, BA (*German*)
I F Thorpe, BEd (*Design Technology*)
I P Spedding, BSc (*Mathematics*)
J G Allen, BA, MSc (*Mathematics*)
D S Gill, BSc, PhD (*Physics*)
Mrs K M Costante, MA (*Chemistry*)
Mrs E E Barr, BA (**Art*) (*maternity leave*)
D J Poole, MA (*Economics*)
Mrs W Davies, BA (*Geography*)
Mrs B Kruger (*German Assistant*)
Mrs K A Mitchell, MPhil, PhD (*English*)
M M Jackson, BA (**Spanish*)
P Dowsett, BA (**History*)
Mrs A R G Lemon, BA (*Geography*)
Mrs C O'Brien, BA, OCR CertSpLD (**Learning Support Coordinator*)
Mrs S D Hills, BA (*Religious Education*)
A N Leech, BA (*Art*)
S A Barr-Smith, BSc (*Mathematics*)
R Grant, BA (**Classics*)
Miss M Kirbyshire, BA (*Art*)
W Perry, BSc (*Physics*)
Miss C Sourbuts, BSc (*Mathematics*)
Mrs M Wadsley, BA (*English*)
S Whitehead, BEd (*Physical Education*)
Mrs C D Torr, MA (*Biology*)
W A Burn, BA (*English*)
R M A Batchelor, BSc (*Mathematics*)
D P Brumby, BSc (*Mathematics*)
J P Kennedy, MPhys (*Physics*)
Mrs A Paunovic, PhD, BA (*Classics*)
Ms S Culshaw, CertEd (*ICT Assistant*)
F A Rosas (*Spanish Assistant*)
Ms C Sanford, BA, MA (*English*)
A Swithinbank, MA (*Classics*)
Mrs J Poole, BSc (*Biology*)
K Heath, BSc (**Chemistry*)
Miss H Robertson, MSc (*Chemistry*)
S Boswell, BSc (*Physical Education*)
Mrs M Hubbard, BSc (*Psychology*)
Miss L Gritti, MSci (*Physics*)
Miss A Dubois, MA (*French Assistante*)
K W Leutfeld, BMus, MA (*Music*)

School Nurse: Ms S Jacob, RGN
Headmaster's PA: Mrs K Holdsworth
Librarian: Mrs D Gair

Junior School

Headmaster: A R Earnshaw, BA, QTS
Deputy Head: E Jones, BA
Mrs A P Eastwood, CertEd
Mrs L Y Harrison, BA
Mrs M Sweeney, BA
Mrs H Whittamore, BA, QTS
I W Bevell, GRSM, LRAM
Miss J Abell, BA
C Dixon, BA
Mrs G K Sethi, BA, MA

Fees per term (2008-2009). Tuition: Senior School £3,358, Junior School £2,674.

Admission. Entrance Examinations are held in January or February each year. Applicants for the Junior School should be between the ages of 7 and 11 years, and for the Senior School between 11 and 12 years on 1 September of the year of entry.

Organisation and Curriculum. There are 986 day boys, of whom 143 are in the Junior School and 210 in the Sixth Form. The Junior School (*see entry in IAPS section*) caters for boys who intend to complete their education in the Senior School.

The Senior School course leads to examinations at GCSE in the normal range of subjects. Boys in the Sixth Form are prepared for the AS and A2 Papers of the GCE, and for 'STEP'. The range of subjects is wide – Latin; Classical Studies; Modern Languages; English; History; Economics; Politics; Design Technology, Geography; Mathematics; Physics; Chemistry; Biology; Music; Art; Philosophy; Psychology; Classical Greek; Music Technology; Spanish.

Entrance Scholarships. (*see Scholarship Entries section*). An Entrance Examination is held in January each year for the award of Entrance Scholarships. An additional school fund provides entrance bursaries for boys who receive grants according to their parents' means. Bursaries are also available each year from the HSBC Bank and from the Ogden Trust for Sixth Form entry.

Games. The Playing Fields, covering 20 acres, are situated about a mile and a half from the School with excellent pavilion facilities. There are also indoor cricket nets at the school. The School games, in which all boys are expected to take part unless medically exempted, are Rugby Football (Association Football in the Junior School) and Athletics in the winter, and Cricket or Tennis in the summer. Other alternatives provided for senior boys include Cross Country, Squash, Hockey, Association Football, Badminton, Golf, Shooting and Basketball. Swimming forms part of the Physical Education programme.

Combined Cadet Force. The School maintains a contingent of the CCF based on voluntary recruitment and consisting of Navy, Army and Air Force sections. There is a small bore range, and the School enters teams for various national competitions.

Societies. Individual interests and hobbies are catered for by a wide range of Societies which meet in the lunch break or at the end of afternoon school. These include Drama, Modern Languages, Mathematics, Chemistry, Biology, English, Politics, Arts, Music and Debating Societies, the Chess Club, the Bridge Club, Christian Union, and the Scout Troop. Over 120 boys a year participate in the Duke of Edinburgh's Award Scheme. The Community Action Group, the Explorer Scouts and other Societies meet jointly with the neighbouring Nottingham Girls' High School.

Music. Apart from elementary instruction in Music in the lower forms, and more advanced studies for GCSE and A Level, tuition is offered by 3 full-time and 18 part-time teachers in the full range of orchestral instruments. There are 2 School orchestras of 50 and 30 players, 2 Choirs, a concert band (wind) of 50, a Training Band and Big Band and choral and orchestral concerts are given each year. Four instrumental bursaries, covering fee tuition on one instrument, are available to boys entering Year 7.

Honours. 10 Places at Oxford and Cambridge.

The Old Nottinghamians Society owns a substantial Social Centre at its sports ground. The Hon Secretary is Mr R J Dunmore, Nottingham High School, Waverley Mount, Nottingham NG7 4ED. (Tel: 0115 845 2210).

Charitable status. The Foundation of the Nottingham High School is a Registered Charity, number 528236. It exists to provide education for boys between the ages of 7 and 18 years.

Oakham School

Chapel Close Oakham Rutland LE15 6DT
Tel: 01572 758500
Admissions: 01572 758758
Fax: 01572 758595

e-mail: admissions@oakham.rutland.sch.uk
website: www.oakham.rutland.sch.uk

Motto: '*Quasi Cursores Vitai Lampada Tradunt*'

Trustees:
Chairman: Dr S E Blaza

Hereditary Trustee: W F B Johnson

Ex officio:
The Rt Revd The Lord Bishop of Peterborough
The Lord Lieutenant of Rutland, Dr L Howard, OBE, JP
The Very Revd The Dean of Peterborough

Representatives of the Governors of the Foundation:
Mrs K S Blank
Sir Clifford Boulton, GCB, DL, MA
Mrs P A G Corah
T F Hart MA
Col J M K Weir, OBE, TD, FRICS, DL

Co-optative:
J H Arkell, MA
D J Blezard, MA
P S Douty
Mrs G M Harris, MHCIMA
P O Lawson, BSc, CITP, MBCS, DipMus
Dr D L Smith, MA, PhD, PGCE, FRHistS
M T D Squires
M J Swallow
M G Wilson

Bursar and Clerk to the Trustees: L Rao, MA

***Headmaster*: Dr J A F Spence**, BA, PhD

Deputy Head: B A H Figgis, BA

Second Deputy: Mrs J M D West, BSc, SRD, DipRSA

Master of the Lower School 'Jerwoods': V J Harvey, BSc

Senior Members of Staff:
Director of Studies: I Robson, MA
Head of Upper School: R S Williams, BSc, MBA, MEd
Head of Middle School: Mrs S J Gomm, BSc
Director of IB: Mrs S Lorenz-Weir, MA
Registrar: J Wills, DipEd
Marketing Director: Mrs L Penny
Foundation Director: A C Welch, BEd

Heads of Department:
Activities: K Townsley, BA
Careers: Mrs A L Lewis, MA
Creative Arts: S L Poppy, BA
Business and Economics: P Nutter, BA
English: M M Fairweather, MA
Geography: H A Collison, BSc, MPhil
History: J N J Roberts, MA
ICT: K L Slingsby, MA, ARCO
Languages: S T Glynn, MA
Mathematics: D A Harrow, MA
Music: P Davis, MA
Religious Education: Dr D J Sheppard, MA
Science: J A Chilton, PhD
Sport: I Simpson, BSc

Senior Chaplain: The Revd A C V Aldous, BA

Housemasters/mistresses:

Lower School:
Ancaster: Mrs S A Wragg, BSc
Lincoln: Mrs J R Welch, BEd
Peterborough: S B Foster, GRSM
Sargants: M Durose, BSc

Middle School:
Barrow: A J Williams, BSc
Buchanans: Mrs M Nicholls, BA
Chapmans: C B Dawson, BA
Clipsham: G E Doodes, MA
Gunthorpe: Miss M E Grimley, BEd
Hambleton: Mrs S M Healey, BSc
Haywoods: D M Taylor, BA
Rushebrookes: Mrs T Drummond, GRSM, LRAM
Stevens: Mrs A M Lear, BA, MCLIP
Wharflands: N S Paddock, BSocSc

Upper School:
Round House: Mrs L E Asher-Roche, BSc
School House: D J Jackson, BA

History. In 1584 Archdeacon Robert Johnson of Leicester, founded "as many free schools in Rutland as there were market towns therein; one at Oakham, another at Uppingham". Having its roots in the late 16th century but its eyes firmly fixed on the demands being made on young people in the early 21st century, Oakham both respects traditions and seeks innovative solutions to contemporary challenges.

Today, Oakham School is genuinely co-educational with 1,080 pupils (543 Boys, 537 Girls) aged 10–18 and with a 50:50 ratio of boarders to day pupils. The overall staff:pupil ratio is 1:7.

Facilities. Oakham's facilities include one of the best school libraries in the country, science laboratories, an information and communication technology centre, an art and design centre, a theatre and a music school. Sports facilities are extensive with superbly maintained fields, two all-weather pitches, one of which is floodlit, and a sports complex with an indoor swimming pool, squash courts, fives courts and fitness centre.

Organisation and Curriculum. There are four Lower School houses (age 10–13) and ten for the Middle/Upper School (age 13–17), whilst separate houses for pupils in their final year enable them to lead a less restrictive life and to organise their own commitments to a greater degree. All pupils have a Tutor, who is responsible for supervising their work, and a Housemaster or Housemistress.

Lower School pupils study English, mathematics, French (and in Year 8 a second modern language: Spanish or German), science, history, geography, religious education, information and communication technology and a series of creative arts courses; most pupils take Latin.

For most Middle School pupils, the established ten subject curriculum will be appropriate: English, English Literature, Mathematics, Double Award Science, History, Geography, French, a second language and a Creative Arts subject. However, there will be some whose particular needs and strengths will be better served by a variation on this pattern and the School offers several options which may include a third language, additional Creative Arts subjects, ICT, Classical Civilisation and PE, or short courses in Religious Education, Citizenship and ICT.

Following GCSE, Upper School pupils may opt either for the AS/A2 course or the International Baccalaureate. AS/A2 students normally take four AS Level subjects following on to at least three A2 levels. Subjects available are art and design, biology, business studies, chemistry, classical civilisation, computing, critical and contextual studies, design and technology, economics, English, ethics and philosophy of religion, French, geography, German, history, Greek, Latin, mathematics, further mathematics, music, physics, politics, Spanish, PE and sport studies, and theatre studies. The International Baccalaureate programme has a similar range of subjects.

Music. Over 40% of pupils learn a musical instrument and almost half the school are involved in practical music making through participation in choirs, bands, orchestras, and drama productions. Talented pupils have gained places in the

National Children's Wind Sinfonia, the National Children's Orchestra and National Youth Music Theatre and the Chamber Choir recently reached the national finals of BBC Radio 3 Choir of the Year competition.

Drama plays an important part in the life of the School with several productions each year. A majority of pupils at all levels takes part in at least one dramatic production a year.

Art, Design and Technology. The Richard Bull Centre offers a wide range of creative activities, including painting, pottery, sculpture, textiles, work in wood, metal and plastics, jewellery making, print-making, computer aided design, electronics, home economics and photography.

Sport and Activities. Over 30 sports are offered, including rugby, soccer, hockey, cricket, athletics, swimming, shooting, tennis, squash, fives, badminton, basketball, netball, fencing, lacrosse, golf and sailing. Many clubs and societies flourish. Oakham is the first institution worldwide to achieve 1,000 Duke of Edinburgh's Award gold medallists. There is a well-developed community service programme and thriving Combined Cadet Force.

Entry. (*see Scholarship Entries section*). Normal entry points are 10+, 11+, 13+ and 16+. Pupils are accepted mainly in September at the start of the academic year, but a few places may be available for January entry. Full admissions information is available from the Registrar.

Fees per term (2008-2009). Lower School (age 10–13): £7,120 (full boarding), £6,050 (day boarding), £4,520 (day).

Middle and Upper Schools (age 13+): £8,350 (full boarding), £7,100 (day boarding), £4,990 (day).

2007 Honours. 9 places at Oxford or Cambridge. In 2007, Out of a 100% pass rate, 78% of our A Level candidates gained grades A or B. 98.6% of Oakham International Baccalaureate candidates gained their diploma, of which 90% achieved the equivalent of A Level AB passes. GCSE pass rate was 97.5% with 58.4% of candidates achieving A or A* grades. 99%+ of leavers go to University or College.

Charitable status. Oakham School is a Registered Charity, number 527825. It exists for the purpose of education.

Oldham Hulme Grammar Schools

Chamber Road Oldham Lancs OL8 4BX
Tel: 0161 624 4497 (boys)
0161 624 2523 (girls)
0161 624 2947 (kindergarten)
e-mail: boysinfo@hulmegrammarschools.org.uk
girlsinfo@hulmegrammarschools.org.uk
website: www.hulme-grammar.oldham.sch.uk

The school, founded in 1611, was reconstituted in the 19th century under the Endowed Schools Act. The main buildings of The Oldham Hulme Grammar Schools were opened in 1895 on a commanding south-west facing site overlooking the city of Manchester.

Motto: *Fide sed cui Vide.*

Patron: The Lord Clitheroe of Downham

The Governing Body:
Chairman: Mrs R Brierley, JP, BA contactable via the Schools' Bursar/Clerk to the Governors
Vice-Chairman: Mr D J Illingworth, BA, FCA
Honorary Treasurer: Mr J E Halliwell

Co-optative Governors:
Mr J Broadbent, BSc, MRICS
Dr K Buckley, MBChB
Mr R S Illingworth
Mr A Milnes
Mr V A J Srivastava, LLB
Mrs V Stocker, LLB
Mr M Taylor, BA, MEd
Mr A P Wild, OBE
Mr G Winterbottom

Representative Governors, Metropolitan Borough of Oldham:
Mrs J Capener
Mrs B M Jackson
Mr P M Buckley, BSc, ACG1

Clerk to the Governors and Bursar: R W Flower, BSc

***Principal*: Dr Paul G Neeson**, BSc, PhD

* *Head of Department*
† *Housemaster/mistress*

Deputy Principal – Boys: P T Byrne, BSc London
Deputy Principal – Girls: Miss S E Shepherd, BA London
Deputy Principal – Sixth Form: J C Budding, BEd Sheffield Hallam (*†Assheton House*)
Director of Studies: N G H James, MA York
Director of Pupil Development: Mrs C A Wilkinson, BSc Liverpool

Teaching Staff:
S P Adamson, MA Manchester (*English, Duke of Edinburgh's Award Scheme*)
Mrs B J Allwood, BA, MA Oxford (**German, Examinations Assistant*)
S Baty, GRSM, ARMCM (*Music*)
Mrs S E Beard, BA York (*Chemistry*)
D F Beirne, BA Cardiff (*Modern Languages*)
Dr P M Beagon, MA, DPhil Oxford (**Classics*)
J M Bibby, BSc Wales (*Chemistry, Physics*)
Mrs N Bibi, BSc Manchester (*Mathematics*)
P D Bolton, BSc Sheffield Hallam (*Physical Education, Games*)
Mrs N Breen, BA Manchester, MA Lancaster (*History*)
Miss J C Brown, BA Liverpool (*Physical Education, Head of Year 7*)
Mrs R Chester, BSc Hull (*Biology, Head of Middle School and Year 11*)
N J Chesterton, BA Leeds (*Physical Education and Games*)
Ms J Shepley Clarke, BA Durham (*English, Duke of Edinburgh's Award Scheme*)
G W Conroy, CertEd Leeds (*Physical Education, Games*)
T M J Cotton, BEd MMU (*Design Technology*)
Miss L J Cowan, MA Dundee (*History and Geography, Head of Year 8*)
A J Coyle, BEng Brighton (*Physics, Technology*)
Mrs C E Crebbin, BMus Huddersfield (*Music*)
C M B Crossley, BA Oxon (*English, School Public Relations Officer, Newsletter Editor*)
Miss E Crozier, BA Cambridge (*English*)
D J Dalziel, BSc London, PG Dip Leeds (*Biology, Head of Middle School*)
Mrs C Davies, BA Kent (**Drama, Careers*)
Mrs R Dixon, BA Liverpool, LRAM (**Music*)
M N Dowthwaite, BA Manchester (**History, Examinations Officer, School Functions Officer*)
Miss C W Duffy, BA Aberystwyth, M Phil Aberystwyth (**History*)
Mrs C A Eliot, BA Heriot Watt (*Home Economics, PSHE Coordinator*)
Miss H A Fitzgerald, BA Manchester (*Art*)
P Galloway, BSc UMIST (**Physics*)
O M Gandolfi, BSc, MSc, Bangor (*Biology*)
M J C Garnett, BA East Anglia (*Modern Languages*)
Mrs H Garside, BA North Wales (*Modern Languages*)
Miss J V Graystock, BA Liverpool (**Art*)
Mrs K L Gregson, BSc Lancaster (*Biology, *General Studies, Deputy Head of Sixth Form*)
Mrs R Hall, BA Birmingham, MTh Nottingham (*Religious Studies, Community Action*)
Mrs E Harris, BA Liverpool (*Physical Education*)

M Harris, BA Lanchester (**Modern Languages*)
Mrs J Harrison, BSc Durham (*Mathematics, Examinations Officer*)
J M Harrison, APS Sheffield Polytechnic, MPhil Newcastle Polytechnic (**Physics*)
Mrs C Headdock, BA London (*Modern Languages, English, Special Needs Coordinator*)
Miss S C Hennelly, BA Edge Hill (*Politics*)
G Hepworth, BSc Leeds (**Mathematics*)
J R Hesten, BA Manchester (*Physics, Biology*)
Mrs L Hewitt, CertEd Coventry College of Education (*Mathematics*)
E F Hilditch, BD, St Andrews, PhD Nottingham (**Religious Studies and Philosophy*)
Mrs D Howarth, BSc Manchester Metropolitan (**Home Economics*)
G Hulme, ARCO, LTCL (*Director of Music*)
Mrs F J Kenney, BSc Manchester (*Home Economics*)
Mrs T A Kershaw, BA Salford (*Modern Languages*)
Miss J P Knighton, BEd Leeds Metropolitan (**Physical Education*)
Mrs A J Kremnitzer, BSc Aberdeen (*Chemistry, Physics, Website Management*)
Mrs J A Lamb, BSc Liverpool (**Mathematics*)
P Langdon, BEd Manchester Metropolitan (**Information Technology*)
Mrs J Leach, BA Hull (*English*)
D Ledson, BA Humberside (**Information and Communication Technology*)
M G Lefley, BSc, PG Dip Liverpool, CMath MIMA (*Mathematics*)
T A Leng, BA Leeds (*History*)
M Lomas, BA Manchester (*Modern Languages*)
Mrs D Maders, BSc Leeds (*Chemistry, Physics, Careers*)
C J D Mairs, MA Edinburgh (**English*)
A H Marshall, BSc Hull (*Geography, Head of Lower School*)
Mrs S G Massey, BMus Huddersfield (*Music, Head of Year 8*)
Mrs J McCarthy, MA, PG Dip Liverpool (*Art, Design Technology, Head of Year 7*)
Ms E Mills, BA Manchester (*English*)
S McRoyall, BA Sunderland (**Art*)
Mrs H J Murray, BA Durham (**French*)
Mrs A M Newby, BSc Brunel (**Design Technology*)
Mrs C A Parker, CertEd Manchester Polytechnic (*Biology*)
Mrs B A Parkinson, BSc Liverpool (*Geography, Careers*)
A Peacocke, BA Glamorgan (*Geography, Head of Year 9, †Hulme House*)
Miss H R Plews, BA Liverpool, M Phil Cantab (**Classics*)
Mrs P T Ramotowski, BSc London, BA Open (*Biology*)
S G Rawlings, BEng Aston (*Mathematics, Physics*)
D R A Rees, BSc Bradford (*Business Studies, Head of Year 10*)
Mrs A G Robinson, BSc Romania, MSc Manchester (*Physics*)
Mrs A Sheldon, BA Manchester Metropolitan (*Mathematics*)
G R Sims, BA Open (*Information and Communication Technology, Head of Year 11*)
A D Smith, BSc Salford (*Mathematics*)
Miss J M Solomon, BSc Manchester (*Chemistry*)
J P Spalding, BSc Manchester (*Mathematics, †Platt House*)
Mrs S Standring, BA Open, BSc Bolton Institute, MSc Manchester (*Psychology*)
Mrs J Sullivan, BSc Salford (**Chemistry*)
P J Sutherland, BA Hull, PhD Bradford (**Geography, Induction Coordinator, †Lees House*)
Mr C R Sykes, BA Manchester, MA Manchester (*Classics, History*)
Miss J L Thomas, MA Cardiff School of Art & Design, BEd Homerton Cambridge (*Art*)
Mrs S Titmuss, BA Manchester (*History, Government and Politics*)
Mrs S M Toole, BSc London (**Biology, Charity Coordinator*)
Mrs J Travis, DipM (*Higher Education and Careers, Business Studies, PSHE Coordinator Year 7–11*)
G L Wailes, BA Sheffield (**Business Studies and Economics, Young Enterprise*)
Mrs S A Watt, BA Manchester MA Leeds (**Geography*)
Mrs D Y Wheldrick, BA Preston Polytechnic (*Information Technology, Head of Year 10*)
Mrs J C Wood, BA Leeds (**Religious Studies, Head of Lower School*)
Miss M J Wood, BA Huddersfield (**Learning Support*)
P F Wood, CertEd St John's College, York (*Director of Physical Education*)

Estcourt Preparatory School:
Head: Mrs W Maitland, BSc Sheffield
Mrs T Bradley, BEd Chester College
Mrs Z Fleming, CertEd Edge Hill College
Mrs A D Pearson, CertEd Chester College
Mrs E M T Schofield, BEd Oxford, CNAA

Hulme Court Preparatory School:
Head: D Washington, BEd Wales
T Collins, CertEd Hopwood Hall College
P S Coulson, BSc Edge Hill College
A J Halliwell, BEd Manchester, CertEd Manchester
Mrs C Kershaw, BEd Manchester
Miss S E Oates, LTCL, LGSM, CertEd Reading
M Turner, BSc Wolverhampton

Hulme Kindergarten:
Head: Mrs A S Richards BSc Leeds
Miss C Barnett, BA Edge Hill
Mrs E Brocklehurst BA Exeter, ABRSM
Miss A A Done BA Manchester Metropolitan
Miss C Fergusson, NVQ
Miss C Gamwell, NVQ
Mrs B Humphreys, NNEB, HNC
Mrs M Marland, CertEd Oldham
Miss H A Rodgers, BA Bradford College
Ms A Smith, BSc Bolton Institute
Mrs J Wood, BEd Manchester

Visiting Music Teachers:
A Asquith, GBSM, LTCL (*Bassoon*)
D Brown, GRNCM (*Cello*)
Mrs V Eastham, MA, FTCL, LRSM (*Piano*)
Miss S Gamba, BA RNCM, MMus, PPRNCM (*Clarinet & Saxophone*)
Dr R Gibbon, GMus, RNCM, ATCL (*Clarinet & Saxophone*)
Ms S Gibbon, GRNCM (*Violin & Viola*)
K Heggie, GRNCM (*Guitar*)
C Holmes, MusB, GRSM, ARMCM (*Piano*)
Mrs E Taylor (*Singing & Piano*)
Mrs J Kent, CTABRSM (*Horn*)
Miss J Lyons, BMus, PPRNCM (*Clarinet & Saxophone*)
Miss P McMillan, BMUS RNCM ALCM (*Percussion*)
Miss M Rayner, GRNCM, PPRNCM (*Flute*)
Mrs K Small, BA Mus, GRNCM (*Clarinet and Saxophone*)
Mrs S Walker, GRSM, PPRCM (*Flute*)
Miss J Wilson, GRSM, PPRCM (*Oboe*)

PA to the Principal: Mrs D Webb

Since the 1970s there has been a gradual development of the Schools facilities and these now include a refurbished indoor heated swimming pool and sports hall, improved Sixth Form facilities as well as specially designed music rooms, new computer rooms and additional laboratories. The Centenary Library was opened in 1997 and this contains a state-of-the-art ICT resources area, and a new Art Block will be opened in September 2007.

There are a total of 1,268 pupils within the Oldham Hulme family of schools and we are proud to offer outstanding levels of education for each stage of the child's development. Hulme Kindergarten has 108 pupils and provides nursery and infant education for boys and girls. When they reach the age of 7 they continue their studies at the preparatory schools: Hulme Court which has 130 boys and Estcourt which has 93 girls. Following an entrance examination at the age of 11, pupils may progress to the senior schools: Hulme Grammar School for Boys which has 404 pupils and Hulme Grammar School for Girls which has 330 pupils. Most students will continue their studies in the co-educational Sixth form which has 203 pupils.

The schools primary aim is to provide a caring, friendly and lively school environment that fosters a desire to learn and at all times, pupils are encouraged to think and work independently.

With a reputation for academic excellence and outstanding extra-curricular activities, pupils benefit from the right environment which enables them to achieve their full potential in life so that they go on to become successful, happy and confident young men and women.

The Hulme family of schools value academic achievement and standards are high. Consequently there is an excellent record of examination success at GCSE and A Level. Pupils are taught within small classes by a team of dedicated, well qualified staff.

The schools also offer an excellent pastoral care system which guides and supports pupils, promoting their personal development within the wider school community.

The comprehensive careers education programme on offer widens each pupil's understanding of the opportunities available in the changing world of work, while equipping them with the skills to manage their future career.

A stimulating range of extra-curricular activities provides opportunities for fun, challenge, initiative, leadership and service, while activities within the wider community encourage active involvement and promote a genuine concern for the needs for others.

To support working parents, Kindergarten offers a before and after school club which provides registered childcare, and during the school holidays there is a holiday club.

The school's coach service provides transport for pupils from many areas within Rochdale, Heywood, Middleton, Royton, Shaw, Chadderton, Tameside and Oldham.

Fees per term (2008-2009). Hulme Kindergarten £1,671, Preparatory Schools £1,883, Senior Schools £2,622.

A number of bursaries are awarded annually to pupils entering at the ages of 11 and 16. These awards are based on parental income and academic ability and will remain in place for the time in school subject to satisfactory progress by the pupil.

Charitable status. The Oldham Hulme Grammar Schools is a Registered Charity, number 526636. It exists to provide a balanced academic education for pupils aged 3 to 18.

The Oratory School

Woodcote Reading Berkshire RG8 0PJ
Tel: 01491 683500
Fax: 01491 680020
e-mail: enquiries@oratory.co.uk
website: www.oratory.co.uk

The Oratory School was founded in 1859, by the Venerable John Henry, Cardinal Newman, at the request of a group of eminent Catholic laymen. The Chaplain apart, the School is administered and staffed entirely by laymen.

Motto: '*Cor ad cor loquitur*'

President: Rt Hon Sir Igor Judge

Vice-Presidents:
His Eminence Cardinal William W Baum
M F S Chapman, TD, MA, DipEC
J J Eyston, MA, FRICS, KSG
The Most Revd Vincent Nichols, MA, STL, PhL, MEd

Chairman: M H R Hasslacher
Vice-Chairman: C J Sehmer, FCA

The Governors:
B F H Bettesworth, FRICS, ACIArb
The Very Revd R Byrne, BD, AKC, Cong Orat
Mrs M Cochrane
Professor P W Evans, MA, PhD
F J Fitzherbert-Brockholes, MA
C J French
H H Judge
K A D Hornby, BA Hons
N R Purnell, MA, QC
The Revd J N Saward, MA, MLitt
M W Stilwell
Lt Col T E Thorneycroft
T A H Tyler, OBE, BA

Clerk to the Governors: A F Bradshaw, DMS, MCIM, FInstLM

***Head Master*: C I Dytor**, MC, MA

Second Master: J D Nicholson, BSc, PhD

Senior Master: P L Tomlinson, MFA

Chaplain: The Rt Revd Mgr A F M Conlon, STB

Academic Staff:
* *Head of Department*
† *Housemaster*
§ *Part-time*

S Bosher (*Design and Technology; CCF*)
S A Bowles, BSc, PhD (*Chemistry*)
J A Brooke, BA, MA (*English*)
P W Brown, BSc (*Physics*)
A N Callan, BSc (**Biology; Chemistry*)
I A N Campbell, BSc (*Physics*)
T N Danks, BSc, PhD (**Chemistry*)
D R Dixon, MBA (*Business Studies*)
P J Easton, BSc (*Biology*)
G R Evans, BA (*French; Spanish*)
C W Fothergill, BA, MA(*Ed*) (**Classical Civilisation; History*)
G W Fox, ACP (*§Art*)
Mrs H R Fox, BA (*Art*)
D J Froggatt, BSc (*Geography*)
O P Garner, BA (*French; Italian*)
O C Godfrey, BA (**Drama*)
M H Green, MEd, MBE, FRSA, MRAES (**Design and Technology; Lower Master*)
G F Halpin, BSc (*Geography; Business Studies; †FitzAlan*)
I Hart, BSc, PhD (**Physics*)
T J Hennessy, BSc (*Mathematics; †St John*)
A A Hill, MA, AIL (**Classics; Examinations Officer*)
N C Jones, BA, ARCO (**Academic Music*)
S Jones, BA (**English*)
I P Jordan, BEd (**Physical Education & Games; Mathematics*)
K Laughton, BA, AIL (**Modern Languages*)
G J Lyke, BSc (*Mathematics*)
K E MacNab, BA (*Religious Education*)
I C McLean, MA, MSc (*Chemistry*)
J McNamara, MA, FRCO (**Director of Music*)
Miss E Michalopoulou, MA (*Classics*)
Miss N A Mihai, BSc (*Mathematics*)
Mrs D A Nash, MA (**Religious Education; Head of Sixth Form*)

Mrs S M Nicholson, BA (*English*)
R A O'Sullivan, BA (*English*)
C N B Pohl, BA (**History; English*)
P E Poynter, BA (*Geography*)
M A Smith, MA (*Director of Studies*)
A N Stroker, BA, MA, PhD (*English; †Faber*)
P A Thomas, BA, MA(*Ed*) (*Economics; †St Philip House*)
Mrs E S Thomas, BA, MA(*Ed*) (*§Curriculum Support*)
G Timuri, BSc (*Mathematics*)
P L Tomlinson, MFA (**Art; Senior Master*)
S C B Tomlinson, BSc (*Physical Education and Games*)
N E Topham (*Physical Education; CCF Admin Officer*)
H Upton, MA (**German; French*)
A J Wilson, BSc (*Physical Education and Games; †Norris*)
R B Womersley, BEd (*Ancient History; History; Geography*)
J M S Woodcock, MSc (**Mathematics*)

Curriculum Support:
Mrs K Hamilton-Bowker, DipSpLD
Mrs D Redfern BA

Music Staff:
C Caiger (*Guitar*)
A Chamberlain, BMus (*Brass*)
Mrs Hilary Cox, BMus, PGCE (*Singing*)
J Donnelly (*Drums/Percussion*)
Mrs S L Dytor, ARCM (*Violin*)
G Howarth, BSc, MA (*Brass*)
R H Herford, MA, GRNCM (*Singing*)
D Horniblow (*Clarinet*)
L Ingram (*Chanter & Bagppipes*)
C C King, FRICS (*Drums & Percussion*)
Miss E V Krivenko, MMus Dip (*Piano*)
Mrs C Lancaster, BMus, MMus, PGDip (*Cello*)
Mrs K E Laughton, BA (*Saxophone*)
S Nisbett, LTCL (*Guitar*)
Miss J Schloss, BMus, MMus Dip (*Piano and Accompanist*)
Mrs K Tavener, BA, ARCM (*Piano*)
Mrs E Tugwell (*Bassoon*)
J Underwood (*Electric & Bass Guitar*)

School Health Centre:
Dr S A Richards, MA, MB, BChir, DCH (*Medical Officer*)
Mrs P Codner, MSc, RGN, RM (*Health Centre Sister*)
Mrs J E Tomlinson, SEN (*Staff Nurse*)
Mrs M Naylor, RGN RM
Mrs J Richmond, RGN
Mrs S Hester, SRN, RSCN, SCM, HV Cert

Non-Teaching Staff:
A F Bradshaw, DMS, MCIM, FInstLM (*Bursar*)
Mrs S A Waghorn (*Head Master's PA*)
Mrs M Lee (*School Secretary*)
Mrs G Munoz (*Reception*)
Mrs J Crowther (*Reception*)
Mrs E Henderson (*Common Room Secretary*)
Mrs L Coupland (*Marketing and Public Relations*)
Mrs C Macnab (*Librarian*)
M Sixsmith, BSc, MPhil (**Computer Services*)
§A K Tinkel, MA (*Archivist*)

Sports Centre Staff:
M Eadle (*Professional/Sports Centre Manager*)
B D Sayer (*Junior Real Tennis Professional*)
T Huelin (*Sports Centre Assistant*)

Number in School. There are 400 boys: 225 boarding and 175 day boys.

The School is situated in an area of outstanding natural beauty in grounds of 400 acres, in South Oxfordshire. There are four Senior Houses (13–18) and one Junior House (11–13). Each House is run by a married Housemaster and staffed by a House team, which includes a Housemother. There is at least one other adult in each Boarding House and over three-quarters of the staff live on-site – vital today for the delivery of a comprehensive education.

The Head Master is pursuing a nine-year building programme to upgrade and to re-shape the school. Two academic departments and two new new state-of-the-art boarding houses have been constructed. The rest of the the academic facilities are being refurbished and upgraded.

Organisation. Four Senior Houses and the Junior House offer living facilities for 400 boys, both day and boarding. Particular care is taken to provide an environment which facilitates the assimilation of new boys.

Health. The School Medical Centre is under the supervision of a fully qualified resident Sister and the School Medical Officer visits once a week.

Admission. Boys enter at age 13 through the Scholarship or Common Entrance Examinations, or at 11 by informal interview and exam. A small number of boys are received directly into the Sixth Form.

Religious Education. Catholic spirituality pervades the school in an unobtrusive and unaggressive way. It is at the heart of the school and to be an Oratorian is something special. Respect for the individual within the larger framework of this society is the hallmark of this Oratorian ethos. There is a Resident Chaplain who looks after the needs of both boys and staff.

Studies. Boys are prepared for A levels and GCSE. A wide range of subjects is offered in the Sixth Form. There is no rigid division into Arts and Science subjects; almost any combination of subjects can be taken.

Games. In addition to the main games – Rugby Football, Soccer, Cricket and Rowing – boys take part in Athletics, Cross-Country Running, Swimming, Tennis, Badminton, Basketball, Squash, Golf, Canoeing, Sailing and Real Tennis. There is a nine-hole golf course on the 400-acre site and a four-lane indoor shooting range. Awarded Independent School of the Year for Sport 2008 by The Daily Telegraph & Norwich Union for commitment to sport at all levels and for encouraging boys into national and international teams.

CCF. There is a flourishing contingent of the CCF which, in addition to the Army section, includes the following sub-sections: RN, RAF, REME, Signals, Adventure Training. The Duke of Edinburgh's Award Scheme is operated. The school ranks in the top five shooting schools in the country with some team members shooting for Great Britain.

Extra-curricular activities. There are frequent theatre outings, visits to museums and art galleries, careers visits, as well as talks and lectures given in the School by visiting speakers. There is a wide range of clubs and societies, and a Young Enterprise Scheme. Every holiday there is a major trip abroad.

Optional Extras. Instrumental Music, coaching in Real Tennis, Lawn Tennis, Squash and Golf.

Careers Guidance. The Head of Sixth Form provides guidance for boys in their choice of future occupation.

The School is a member of ISCO.

Fees per term (2008-2009). Boarders: £8,215 (Junior House £5,875); Day Boys: £5,935 (Junior House £4,365).

The fees include board, tuition, consolidated extras, and games. An optional insurance scheme is in operation which covers remission of fees in the event of a boy's absence through illness. A full term's notice of withdrawal is required; failing such notice a term's fees are payable. There may be a reduction for younger brothers and sons of old boys.

Scholarships. (*see Scholarship Entries section*). A number of Academic Scholarships and Exhibitions, and Awards in Music, Art and Sport, are offered.

The Preparatory School is at 'Great Oaks', a property situated in grounds of 45 acres on the same ridge of the Chilterns, about 2 miles from the Main School, between Cray's Pond and Pangbourne. This is co-educational. (*For further details, see entry in IAPS section.*)

The Oratory School Society. *Chairman and Correspondent*: Mr R A Cox, 38 Home Park Road, Wimbledon Park, London SW19 7HN.

Charitable status. The Oratory School Association is a Registered Charity, number 309112. It is a charitable trust dedicated to continuing the aims of its Founder, The Venerable John Henry, Cardinal Newman.

Oundle School

Oundle Peterborough PE8 4GH
Tel: 01832 277120 (Headmaster)
01832 277125 (Admissions)
01832 277112 (Second Master & Director of Studie s)
01832 277116 (Undermaster)
01832 277101 (Bursar)
Fax: 01832 277128
e-mail: registrar@oundleschool.org uk
website: www.oundleschool.org.uk

Oundle School was established by the Grocers' Company with the object of providing a liberal education in accordance with the principles of the Church of England.

The aims of the School are: to give its pupils a sense of belonging, expecting them to contribute to the community; to enable its pupils to reach their full academic and intellectual potential; to ensure that they have a sense of accomplishment; and above all to provide them with an overall view of life and sense of values.

Motto: '*God Grant Grace*'

Governing Body:

[1]Sir Toby Frere, KCB (*Chairman*)
¶Mr I L Schmiegelow
Mr J P Sabben-Clare
Mrs G Monk
Miss J Gough
His Honour Judge Simon Coltart
[1]¶Mr A S Dalton
¶Mr J N Cheatle
¶Mr I McAlpine, OBE, DL
Mr P R Hutton, OBE
[1]Mr J G Tregoning
Dr P Rogerson
The Countess Howe
¶Mr D C L Miller
[1]Mr P M Bostelmann (*Master of The Grocers' Company*)
Mr J P H S Scott (*Second Warden*)
Mr R Ringrose (*Third Warden*)

[1] *Member of the Court of The Grocers' Company*
¶ *Old Oundelian*

Secretary to the Governing Body and Bursar: J H O'Hare, OBE, MBA, BSc

***Headmaster*: C M P Bush**, MA

Second Master: R I Briggs, MA
Undermaster: R J Page, BEd
Director of Educational Development: P P Couzens, BSc, ARCS, AFIMA
Director of Studies: M A R Collier, MA
Senior Mistress: Mrs A M Page, MA
Senior Chaplain: The Revd I C Browne, MA
Head of Laxton: P S C King, BSc, MSc
Registrar: G Phillips, BA

Medical Officers:
Dr D Clayton, MBChB, DRCOG, DCH
Dr R Wilmot, MBChB, DRCOG

* *Head of Department*

Art:
R J Page, BEd
Mrs S J Hipple, BA, BEd
*J D Oddie, BA
M A Case, BA
Miss G C Pontifex, BA, MA

Biology:
J Hunt, BSc, PhD
P S C King, Bsc, MSc
W F Holmström, BSc, PhD
Mrs M A Holmström, BSc, MSc
*A E Langsdale, BSc, MSc
Dr P J Rowe, PhD
Miss V G Bateson, BA
W W Gough, BSc

Chemistry:
R J McKim, PhD, CChem, MRS, FRAS
R F Hammond, BSc
M A Stephen, BSc, PhD
W E Buckley, BSc (*Proctor*)
*D J Evans, BSc
D J Higgins, MBiochem, PhD
M J Bessent, MChem, PhD, AMRSC
C E Penhale, BSc
C J Quiddington, MChem, PhD
Miss C Leung, BSc

Classics:
Mrs M P R James, MA
K R Hannis, MA
Mrs D L Watt, MA
*S J Chambers, MA
N J Aubury, BA
T J Morrison, BA
Miss C L Westran, BA

Design and Technology:
*C D Humphreys, BA (*Freeman of the City of London*)
D A Vincent, CAP, BTS, CAPET
B A Dayment, BA
R H Lowndes, BSc, MEng

Drama:
A D Martens, BA
Ms K A Francis, BA
*A J H Boag, BA (*Director of the Stahl Theatre*)
*M Burlington, BA

Economics:
A P Ireson, MA (*Examinations Officer*)
J Röhrborn, MA
*E M Tweedie, BA
Mrs F L Quiddington, BEcon, MT

Educational Support:
*Mrs V C Lacey, BA
Mrs V Nunn, BEd
Mrs J M T Clay, BA
Mrs C M Redding, BA, MA
A Lacey, BA

English:
Mrs M K Smedley, BA (*Publisher*)
N J T Wood, BA
Mrs J T Coles, BA
A D Martens, BA
*T P Hipperson, MA
B Raudnitz, MA
A J Sherwin, MA
L V Court, BA
Mrs H M Wells, BA
Miss L V Burden, BA
C A Davies, BA

Geography:
J R Wake, CertEd
J M Taylor, MA
Mrs M S Turner, BA
G Phillips, BA (*Registrar*)
Mrs J H Briggs, BSc
C W Symes, BSc
*J R Hammond-Chambers, BA

Government and Politics:
*J D C Gillings, BA
D R K Robb, MA
E M Tweedie, BA

History:
*C R Pendrill, MA
P J Pedley, BA
R N Mather, MA
I D Clark, BA
M A R Collier, MA (*Director of Studies*)
M P H von Habsburg-Lothringen, MA, MLitt
S R L Clayton, BA
A J Brighton, BA
Mrs C R Hempsall, BA

Information Technology:
*R J Cunniffe, BSc (*Head of Academic ICT*)
R Banerjee, BSc
I Peacock (*Director of Computing*)
R J Newman, BSc, DipComp (*Network Manager*)
J D A Willington, MA
J D Holmes
D Holmes, BSc
A Jolley, MCSA
P Jeffs
R Clayton

Mathematics:
P P Couzens, BSc, ARCS, AFIMA (*Director of Educational Development*)
A Butterworth, BSc
D A Turner, BSc
R Atkins, BSc
N D Turnbull, BA
D B Meisner, BA, MSc, PhD (*Assistant Director of Studies*)
D P Raftery, BSc
K Hayward-Bradley, MA
E J Clark, BA
A R Hunt, BA
*N P Hamshaw, BA
S G Dale, MEng, MA
Miss C Leung, BSc

Modern Languages:
S T Forge, MA
S D Johnston, BA
Mrs S R Worthington, BA (*Head of French*)
P J Lewins, MA
Mrs N M Mola, BA (*Head of Spanish*)
M P Bolger, BA
Mrs A M Page, MA (*Senior Mistress*)
Mrs C R Gent, MA (*Head of Careers*)
B Béjoint, L-ès-L
J Röhrborn, MA
Mlle G M Morin-Skinner, L-ès-FLE, L-ès-LCE
Mlle S Fonteneau, L-ès-L
S C Kent, BA (*Head of Mandarin Chinese; Head of Higher Education*)
T D Watson, MA (*Head of German*)
Mrs E Archibald
Miss H F P Machin, BA
C ben Nacef, BA
*Miss S Davidson

Physical Education and Games:
*C J Olver (WLIHE) (*Head of PE*)
Mrs M Layden, CertEd
Miss R S Goatly, BA
Miss G Evans, FISTC
G Terrett, BA
A J Cowley
*Miss L Barnwell, BSc (*Head of Girls' Games*)
*J R Husbands (*Director of Sport*)
G J P A Maitre, BSc, MSc (*Head of Rowing*)
M J G King, BSc (*Sports Assistant*)
Miss S Langford, BSc (*Sports Assistant*)
Miss E J Slones, BSc (*Sports Assistant*)

Physics:
*M N Wells, MA
A B Burrows, MA Ed, BSc
P C Clark, BSc, ARCS (*Head of Science*)
Mrs L E Kirk, BSc
Mrs T E Raftery, BSc
M J Meatyard, BSc
H Roberts, BSc
Mrs J E Lane, BSc
Miss M Shea, BSc

Psychology:
B McDowell, BSc, PhD (*Webmaster*)
P J W Dyer, MPhil, PhD
*S R Heath, BA, MSc
Mrs T E Raftery, BSc

Religious Studies:
Mrs V Nunn, BEd
The Revd I C Browne, MA
*Mrs A E Meisner, BA
D R H Edwardson, BSc, BA
R S Ambrose, BA
B T Deane, BA

Library:
Mrs L Guirlando, BA, MSc, MCILIP
Mrs S Marsden, MCILIP

The Music School:

Director of Music: A P Forbes, BA, LRAM
Organist: J C Arkell, MA, FRCO, FTCL, FLCM, FRSA
Head of Choral Studies: A G Tighe, BA
Head of Woodwind: D P Milsted, BA, LTCL
Head of Brass: Mrs A Hudson, GRNCM, PPRNCM
Head of Keyboard: A Hone, BMus, ARCM, ARCO
Head of Strings: A P Gibbon, GRNCM
Academic Music: Mrs S L Ratchford, BA

and 34 peripatetic teachers

Houses and Housemasters/Housemistresses:
Bramston: Mr D R K Robb
Crosby: Mr D R H Edwardson
Dryden: Mrs V Nunn
Fisher: Mr N J T Wood
Grafton: Mr A B Burrows
Kirkeby: Mrs D L Watt
Laundimer: Dr B McDowell
Laxton: Mr P S C King
New House: Mrs M Layden
Sanderson: Mr D A Turner
School House: Dr J Hunt
Sidney: Mr C W Symes
St Anthony: Mr I D Clark
Wyatt: Mrs L E Kirk
The Berrystead: Dr W F Holmström

Bursar: J H O'Hare, OBE, MBA, BSc
Finance Manager:
Estates Bursar: R M C Tremellen, BSc, RICS

Headmaster's Personal Assistant: Mrs P Barr
Second Master's Secretary: Mrs T Heath
Undermaster's Secretary: Mrs R Wood
Director of Studies' Secretary: Mrs T Heath
Bursar's Secretary: Mrs K Worth

Introduction. Oundle School originated from the bequest of Sir William Laxton, a native of Oundle, to the Grocers' Company in 1556 and became fully co-educational in September 1990. It is, perhaps, unique in that the buildings are spread throughout the attractive market town of Oundle and its pupils mix with the town community as they go about their daily business.

Number of pupils (2007–2008). Boarders: 510 boys and 333 girls. Day Pupils: 131 boys and 119 girls.

Admission. Most boarding pupils sit the June Common Entrance Examination or the Oundle Scholarship Examination at thirteen before joining in September. The majority of day pupils, together with candidates for the junior boarding house, The Berrystead, join the School at eleven having taken English, Mathematics, Science and Verbal Reasoning tests. A small number of places are available for entry at other stages, including at Sixth Form level.

Facilities. Academic departments are situated in the Cloisters, the Needham building, the Sir Peter Scott building the Gascoigne building, Old Dryden and SciTec, Oundle's hugely ambitious and spectacular science building, with its extensive 'green' credentials, recently opened in June 2007. The teaching areas are very well equipped; the Information Technology Centre includes three fully-equipped computer rooms and there are 'cluster networks' around the School. Electronic whiteboards and computer-driven projectors feature in most teaching rooms and the Modern Languages Department is equipped with two state of the art language laboratories.

Art, Music, Drama and Design Technology are all very strong and are well provided for. The long tradition of the Oundle Workshops continues, incorporating courses and projects in Engineering and Industrial Technology and pupils design and construct sports cars in the Patrick Centre. Facilities in Music include the Frobenius Organ and an electronic Music Studio. The Art Studios are large and airy and well equipped and the department includes the Yarrow Gallery. The Drama Department is centred on the Rudolph Stahl Theatre, a cleverly converted chapel in the middle of the town, where numerous productions of both the School and visiting companies take place.

The Chapel was built as a memorial shortly after the Great War and its East windows, designed by John Piper and installed in 1956. Thirty-two stained glass windows by Mark Angus were added in 2005 and compliment Piper's original vision. Religious instruction accords with the Church of England.

The Sports Hall complex includes a forty three metre long swimming pool, five Squash courts, a large and extensively equipped fitness suite, Physical Education classrooms and four new Fives courts were added in 2006.

Since 1990, when the renovation of boys' houses, Fisher and Crosby was completed and two new girls' houses, Kirkeby and Wyatt, were built, other girls' houses have been created. Dryden House was renovated and has taken girls since 1993; New House from 1997 and Sanderson from 2001. An extension to Laundimer House was added in 2000. An extension and other improvements to Laxton were completed in 2005. A continuous cycle of renovation and refurbishment of Houses is in operation. The fifteen houses are distinct communities partially defined by the fact that the pupils dine in separate house dining rooms.

Academic Curriculum. Third Formers (Year 9) take a general course consisting of English, Mathematics, French, Latin, Physics, Chemistry, Biology, History, Geography, Religious Studies, Art, Design and Technology, PE, Music, Drama, ICT, and German or Spanish or Greek. The First and Second Form curriculum is similar.

The traditional importance of Science and Technology in the Oundle Education is still maintained with all pupils being taught the three sciences to GCSE (both single subject and Dual Award on offer) and all Third Formers spending time in the Design and Technology Department. Computing and Microelectronics are available at all levels.

Pupils take English, Mathematics, Physics, Chemistry and Biology as the core of their GCSE curriculum and choose a further five subjects from Art, Computing, Design and Technology, Drama, Electronics, French, Geography, German, Greek, History, Latin, Music, Religious Studies, Spanish and Sports Science. Mandarin Chinese and Arabic are available as additional subjects.

In the Sixth Form AS and A Levels are offered in Art, Biology, Chemistry, Classical Civilisation, Design Technology, Economics, Electronics, English Literature, French, Geography, Greek, Government and Politics, History, Information Technology, Latin, Mathematics, Further Mathematics, Music, Physics, Psychology, Religious Studies, Russian, Spanish, Sports Science and Theatre Studies. The majority of these are assessed as A Levels, though Economics, German and Physics can be assessed by the Cambridge International Examinations Pre U qualification. Pupils have the option of taking just an AS Level in one of their four subjects. Studies in the Sixth Form are enhanced by pupils opting for one or two of a range of non-examined extension courses, which include Arabic, Critical Thinking, Global Perspectives, Mandarin Chinese, Music Performance and Science Research Projects. In the Upper Sixth they take a General Studies course which is based around invited speakers.

Honours. 99% of Upper Sixth Former pupils go on to higher education at good universities and in the last six years the number of places obtained at Oxford and Cambridge has averaged 24.

Sport. The main school sports are Rugby, Hockey, Cricket, Rowing, Netball and Tennis, but others available include Aerobics, Athletics, Badminton, Clay Shooting, Cross-Country, Cycling, Fencing, Fives, Golf, Horse-riding, Sailing, Shooting, Soccer, Squash, Swimming and Volleyball. A second Astroturf hockey pitch has been added to the School's extensive sporting facilities.

Activities. A full range of activities take place and these are intended to be an integral part of the wider school curriculum. Events in Drama and Music feature prominently in the School calendar, and Art Exhibitions are held regularly in the Yarrow Gallery. A large number of Societies meet on a regular basis. Links have been established with schools in France, Germany, Spain, Hungary, the Czech Republic, Russia, China, America and Australia, with annual Exchanges taking place. Pupils are able to participate in the very large number of expeditions and trips in the UK and abroad. There is a flourishing CCF comprising Army, Navy, RAF, Fire and Adventure Training sections and a thriving Duke of Edinburgh's Award scheme is in operation. Community Action plays an important part in school life and contributes significantly to the wider community. Much time and energy are devoted to fund-raising activities in support of national charities, international aid programmes and holidays run at Oundle for MENCAP and inner-city children.

Entrance Scholarships. (*see Scholarship Entries section*). An extensive series of entrance Scholarships is offered each year to thirteen year olds, including Art, Drama, Technology, General Scholarships (Stainforth and Conradi) and Music awards. In addition, a small number of scholarships are available to eleven year-old boys and girls, and at sixteen to new lower sixth entrants. Full details are available from the School.

Fees per term (2008-2009). Boarders: Berrystead Year 1 £6,430; Berrystead Year 2 £7,465; Years 3–7 £8,450.

Day Pupils: Year 1 £4,180; Year 2 £4,855, Years 3–7 £5,505.

Details of extras are given in the School prospectus. The registration fee is £75.

Laxton Junior caters for 4 to 11 year old boys and girls. It moved to a new purpose-built facility in September 2002, increasing in size to have a two-form intake. (*For further details, see entry in IAPS section.*)

Charitable status. Oundle School is a Registered Charity, number 309921.

Pangbourne College

Pangbourne Reading Berkshire RG8 8LA
Tel: 0118 984 2101
Fax: 0118 984 1239
e-mail: registrar@pangcoll.co.uk
website: www.pangbournecollege.com

Pangbourne College was founded in 1917 by Sir Thomas Devitt of the Devitt & Moore Company to train boys for a career at sea. It is now a modern, friendly, boarding and day school for about 400 girls and boys aged 11 to 18, offering good academic results, first-class sports coaching and an excellent system of caring for the development of each individual pupil.

Motto: '*Fortiter ac Fideliter*'

***Headmaster*: T J C Garnier**, BSc Bristol, PGCE

Second Master: G Pike, MA Oxon, PGCE

Chaplain: The Revd B J Cunningham, MA Oxford

Bursar: R Obbard

Location and Facilities. Set in fine grounds of 240 acres and a mile from Pangbourne village, neighbouring the town of Reading, the College combines a country environment with easy access to London and Heathrow. The extensive school facilities include the exciting new Chapel opened March 2000, electronics and science laboratories, a recently refurbished library, art and music schools and an impressive design and technology centre. The performing arts centre contains a school hall/theatre with fly tower. The fully equipped sports hall, astroturf hockey pitch, spacious playing fields, and boathouses on the River Thames provide excellent sporting facilities. Pupils are accommodated in six fully refurbished or new houses. After the first year they share study bedrooms and have single rooms in the Sixth Form. An additional, new girls' boarding house is to be opened in 2007. Meals are taken in a central dining hall. Most academic staff live on the campus in College houses and there is an extremely strong community spirit. The College is to introduce the International Baccalaureate to run alongside their existing A Level programme in September 2008.

Admission. Children normally enter the Junior House (Dunbar) at 11+ through an interview and the College entrance examination. They are joined by more boys and girls at age 13 through the Common Entrance or Scholarship Examinations. Sixth Form entry is based on interview, a satisfactory report from the previous school and good examination results. A Prospectus and Registration Form may be obtained from the Registrar who is always pleased to arrange visits to the College.

Scholarships. (*see Scholarship Entries section*).

Junior House. A new Junior House, Dunbar, opened in September 2005 offering excellent, purpose-built accommodation and common room areas for 11 and 12 year old pupils in the heart of the College. Fully integrated into the academic, cultural and social life, these pupils enjoy full use of all the Senior School's facilities and its specialist teaching. Pupils transfer automatically to the Senior School without further examination.

Academic Study. The curriculum of the Lower School (11 to 16) is based on the National Curriculum ideal of a broad and balanced education, although we do not enter pupils for the Standard Assessment Tests at 14, using instead our own assessment and reporting system. The majority follow a mainstream curriculum covering all the core and foundation subjects of the National Curriculum: English, Mathematics, the Sciences, Design Technology, French, German, History, Geography, Art, Drama, Music, Religious Studies, Physical Education, and ICT. A Learning Support Unit, staffed by specialist teachers, is available to help.

At Sixth Form level there is a choice of 22 A Levels. To complement these specialised A Level courses, all follow a stimulating General Studies course, which includes a Study Skills component.

The College is proud of the quality of its academic and pastoral support system, and each child is guided by a Tutor, a Housemaster/Housemistress and the Director of Studies.

Careers. While the College pursues a deliberate policy of recruiting a broad spectrum of academic ability, it looks for talent of various kinds, believing that its task is to enable each individual to make the very best of his or her potential, no matter where strengths lie.

The Director of Sixth Form Studies and the Careers Adviser work closely with the individual's Tutor to ensure that wise, informed choices are made in the well-equipped Careers Room. The result is that, while some students will go on to Oxford or Cambridge, the majority will proceed to degree courses at other universities prior to a wide variety of exciting careers.

Games. For a small school Pangbourne has an outstanding reputation for sport, particularly at National levels in several games. The College has won Henley Regatta four times making it one of the top rowing schools in the world. In the recent past it has dominated independent school judo, there is a strong tradition of successful rugby and the girls enjoy county success in hockey (Berkshire Cup Winners, 2007). Sports offered include athletics, basketball, cricket, cross-country, golf, hockey, judo, netball, polo, riding, rounders, rowing, rugby, sailing, shooting, soccer, squash, swimming, tennis.

Adventure Training. The College has always placed great emphasis on teamwork and leadership. There is a full programme of adventure training built into the curriculum from the first form, with weekend and holiday expeditions. Every two years a major expedition abroad is organised. Boys and girls can join the CCF which has Army, Royal Navy and Royal Marine Sections. The College is the current holder of the prestigious Pringle Cup. Snowdonia in April and a sea-voyage in the summer holidays are regular features. The school has been chosen by HMS Ocean (Navy's latest helicopter carrier) to be their affiliated school. A new comprehensive high and low Ropes Course is used for leadership training. Third Form pupils are entered for the bronze Duke of Edinburgh's Award.

Music and Drama. Pangbourne has a long tradition of excellence in Music and Drama. The Music School has its own Recital Room, ideal for internal concerts, and also a newly appointed Recording Studio. The College Choirs, Choral Society, Orchestra, Swing Band and Marching Band perform regularly within and outside the College. The Choir undertakes a biennial continental tour and more than a third of the school have individual instrument tuition. Drama has an exciting and flourishing tradition and we have a fine theatre fully equipped with computerised lighting and sound systems. School productions run throughout the year at every level.

Activities. There is a full programme of activities in those afternoons when pupils are not involved in school sport.

Fees per term (2007-2008). At age 11 and 12: Boarders £5,648; Part Boarders £4,982; Day Pupils £3,974. At 13 and above: Boarders £7,780; Part Boarders £6,845; Day Pupils £5,457. These fees are inclusive of medical attendance, games and most textbooks, and there are no obligatory extras.

Charitable status. Pangbourne College Limited is a Registered Charity, number 309096. The objective is to provide an excellent all-round education for boys and girls between the ages of 11 to 18.

The Perse Upper School

Hills Road Cambridge CB2 8QF
Tel: 01223 403800
Fax: 01223 403810
e-mail: office@perse.co.uk
website: www.perse.co.uk

The Perse School is Cambridge's oldest secondary school, founded in 1615 by Dr Stephen Perse, a Fellow of Gonville and Caius College. The school still maintains close links with both Gonville and Caius and with Cambridge University.

The Perse Upper School is an independent day school for pupils aged 11–18 and has run a successful co-educational Sixth Form since 1995. It will begin the transition to full co-education by admitting both boys and girls at 11+ and 13+ in 2010.

Governing Body:

Representing the University of Cambridge:
Dr K J R Edwards, BSc, MA, PhD (*Chairman*)
Dr PA Lyon, MA, PhD

Representing Gonville & Caius College:
Professor D S H Abulafia, MA, PhD, LittD
Professor R J Evans, MA, DPhil, LittD, FBA, FRSL, FRHistS
Representing Trinity College:
Dr A G Weeds, MA, ScD, PhD (*OP*) (*Vice-Chairman*)

Co-opted:
Professor A W Barrell, DBA, FRSA
A S Cheeseman, CEng, FIMC, MIM
Dr J T Green, MA, PhD
F Harris, BSc
Dr J R Haylock, BSc, LLD (*OP*)
D E Hollest
W E Kirby, BSc
M P H Pooles, QC, LLB (*OP*)
R M Rainey, CertEd
Councillor J E Reynolds
C L Ricks, MA
Dr P C D Southern, MA, PhD
R S Trafford, MA
S A Woodward

Bursar & Clerk to the Governors: G A Ellison, MA

***Headmaster*: E C Elliott**, MA

Deputy Heads:
Deputy Head (*Staff*): D R Cross, BA
Deputy Head (*Pupils*): L Playfair, BA, MA
Deputy Head (*Curriculum*): Dr C J Pyle, BA, PhD

Senior Staff:
Director of Sport: S M Ball, BSc
Director of Qualifications and Progression: J N Green, MA
Director of Music: G A Richards, BA
Director of Co-Curriculum: J Southworth, BSc, MSc
Director of Marketing and Admissions: S V Wilson, BA
Head of Biology: Dr C Buchanan, BSc PhD
Head of Science, Head of Chemistry: J C Burrows, MA
Head of Psychology: D Clarke, BA
Head of Mathematics: D F Daniels, BSc
Head of Classics: M R T Donnelly, MA
Head of Technology: D Gant, MA
Head of English & Drama: C E J Green, MA
Head of Girls: G F Hague, BSc
Head of Lower School: M Jelley, BA
Head of Geography: D S King, BSc
Head of Philosophy and Religious Studies, Chaplain: B R L Kinsey, MA, BD, MTh
Head of Modern Languages: M P Nierinck, BA
Head of Business Studies: A J Peploe, BA
Head of Economics, Politics: C A Proud, BA
Head of French: J B Pullen, BA
Head of Learning Support: A Redshaw, BA, MSc
Head of History: A J Roberts, MA
Head of IT: M C Thurston, BEd, MIITTed
Head of Physics: Dr D M Tricker, MA, PhD
Head of Middle School: E W Wiseman, MEng
Head of Art and Design: C M Wood, BA

The Perse Preparatory School:
Headmaster: G R P Jones, BMus
Deputy Head: D E J Adams, BEd, ACP, CertEd

The Perse Pelican Nursery and Pre-Preparatory School:
Headmistress: P M Oates, BEd
Deputy Head: A Watts, BEd

The number of pupils in the Upper School in September 2008 will be approximately 695, including 90 girls in the co-educational Sixth Form.

Admission. The school welcomes applications at 11+ (boys), 13+ (boys) and 16+ (boys and girls). The Upper School is moving towards full co-education and will admit girls at 11+ and 13+ from 2010.

At 11+ and 13+ candidates are examined in Mathematics, English and Verbal/Non-Verbal Reasoning, and given an interview. Candidates at 16+ are interviewed and given offers based on their GCSE results.

Facilities. Located a little over 2 miles from the centre of Cambridge, The Perse Upper School occupies 27 acres of land including extensive grass playing fields. We have invested over £11m in new facilities over the last decade to give the school the best possible facilities including a purpose-built sports hall, a music centre and state-of-the-art science labs. We will be constructing a new teaching block incorporating a library, a learning resources centre and a suite of ICT rooms in 2009.

Education. The Perse has been a pioneer of International GCSEs in Mathematics and the Sciences, recognising that these courses are in many ways a better preparation for further study than conventional GCSEs. Post-16, we believe in flexibility and choice and offer the new Pre-U qualification as an alternative to A Level in some subjects.

To ensure balanced intellectual development, a broad based curriculum is offered with equal weighting given to Arts, Humanities and Science subjects. In the first five years, all pupils study English Language, English Literature, Philosophy and Religious Studies, Maths, Biology, Chemistry, Physics and a modern language. This compulsory core is supplemented by a number of optional subjects. As they mature, pupils make their own guided subject choices.

To give pupils a head start in an increasingly global world, they have the opportunity to develop their linguistic skills – French, German, Spanish, Portuguese, Mandarin, Russian, Arabic and Japanese – and improve their cultural awareness through our links with schools overseas, pupil exchanges and tours.

The Perse is committed to offering a broad classical education, and pupils can choose to follow courses in Latin, Greek and Classical Civilisation which are supplemented by overseas study trips.

Nearly 30 A Level and Pre-U subjects are on offer in the Sixth Form and pupils can choose to study up to 5. They may either specialise in the Arts or Sciences or create a more diverse programme by mixing disciplines.

The success of our approach is reflected in our academic results and in the university offers our pupils receive. In a typical year, some 90 per cent of the Sixth Form will secure an A or B grade at A Level and over 20 per cent will gain places at either Oxford or Cambridge Universities.

There is a full range of sport to cater for most interests. Main sports are rugby, hockey, cricket and netball. Other sports offered are badminton, rowing, aerobics, shooting, basketball, football, squash, fitness training, climbing, tennis and athletics.

At the heart of the extra-curricular life of the school are the many societies that either have strong subject links or arise out of a group of pupils having a common interest. The result is a vibrant range of societies including natural History, Juggling, Climbing, Debating, Lego Robotics, Psychology and Young Enterprise.

Fees per term (2008-2009). Upper School £4,123.

Scholarships. In 2007, the school publicly launched their 'Access to Excellence Campaign', the aim of which is to make the all-round education that The Perse School offers accessible to more children from a broad range of backgrounds. Its objective is to raise pledges for £3 million by December 2008. This funding will be used to establish an expendable bursary endowment and to fund a capital project at each of the three Schools. The key outcome of the campaign will be to enable The Perse School to double the number of bursary pupils over the next decade. The Upper school currently awards a number of scholarships (Academic, Science/Engineering, Music and Art) and bursaries (including hardship bursaries up to 100%) each year. For details please refer to the school's website.

The Perse Preparatory School is a co-educational preparatory school on a separate site for pupils aged between 7 and 11. Tel: 01223 568270; e-mail: prep@perse.co.uk. (*See The Perse Preparatory School entry in IAPS section.*)

The Perse Pelican Nursery and Pre-Preparatory School is for children aged 3 to 7. Tel: 01223 403940; e-mail: pelican@perse.co.uk. (*See The Perse Pelican Nursery and Pre-Preparatory School entry in IAPS section.*)

Old Persean Society. Alumni Officer, The Old Persean Society, The Perse Upper School, Hills Road, Cambridge CB2 8QF.

Charitable status. The Perse School is a Registered Charity, number 1120654, and a Company Limited by Guarantee, registered in England and Wales, number 5977683, for the education of children.

Plymouth College

Ford Park Plymouth Devon PL4 6RN
Tel: 01752 203245 (Headmaster and Admissions)
01752 203300 (School Office)
01752 203242 (Bursar)
Fax: 01752 203246; 01752 205920 (Headmaster)
e-mail: mail@plymouthcollege.com
website: www.plymouthcollege.com

The School was formed by the amalgamation in 1896 of Mannamead School, Plymouth, founded in 1854, and Plymouth College, founded in 1877. It is now a co-educational school. In 2004 the school merged with St Dunstan's Abbey to form one school, Plymouth College.

Governing Body:
Sir Robert Hicks (*Chairman*)
P H Lowson, FCA (*Vice-Chairman*)

The Rt Revd J Ford, The Bishop of Plymouth
Commodore S R Lister
C Lindsay, Exeter University
Professor M Watkins PhD, MN, RN, RMN, Plymouth University

Revd R J Carlton
M Downward, MA
Mrs N S Duncan, LLB
Miss V Harman
Mrs R Hattersley
Cdr C Howeson, RN
P Jones
D W Luke
Mrs J McKinnel, DipLSN, RGN, RMN, SCM, DipHV
Mrs A Mills ACIS, MCIPD
Mrs J Paull
C J Robinson, MA
T E J Savery, MA, LLB
B L Spear, MRICS
Revd D Waller
Miss L P Stevenson, BVetMed, MRCVS
B E Walton, MA
D R Woodgate, MBA

Bursar and Clerk to the Governors: D W J Baylis, OBE, MA, MSc, MCMI (*Senior & Junior School*)

***Headmaster*: Dr S J Wormleighton**, BEd, PhD

Deputy Head: Miss S J Dunn, BSc Exeter

Director of Studies: C R Compton, BA Scholar Exeter College Oxford

Assistant Staff:
A J Lewis, BA Open, CertEd Carnegie College (*Director of PE*)
Mrs S Knight, BEd Hons Sheffield (*Senior Teacher*)
M P R Rose, MA Hertford College Oxford
M A H Bradfield, BA Peterhouse Cambridge
K C Boots, BA Wales, MEd Exeter, AMBDA (*Head of Learning Support*)
J P Gregory, BA Birmingham (*Head of Economics & Business Studies*)
M E Hodges, BA London (*Head of Geography*)
C J Sillitoe, MPhil, MRSC, CChem
J W Hocking, BSc Open, BEd Exeter (*Head of Design Technology*)
Mrs W E Marshall, BSc Kent
R Chapman, BEd College of St Mark & St John
Dr S Jordan, PhD Dundee (*Head of Biology*)
C J Hambly, BSc Manchester (*Head of Chemistry*)
Mrs Z P Thurston, BSc Exeter
Miss A C Blunden, BA Exeter (*Head of Girls Games*)
Mrs L E S Clark, BA Open (*Senior Teacher*)
G A Ashfield, BA Open
M Tippetts, BA Exeter (*Boarding Housemaster*)
Mrs H J Owen, BA College of St Mark & St John
Miss E D Tremaine, BEd De Montfort
J Shields, BSc Hull (*Head of Sixth Form*)
R J Prichard, MA London (*Head of English*)
A N Longden, BSc Plymouth
L C Mellor, BA Bristol (*Head of History*)
Mrs P M Brockbank, CertEd (*Head of EFL Department*)
R P Robinson, MA Queen's College Cambridge (*Head of Careers*)
Mrs B C Robinson, BA, CNNA
R G Palmer, BA
Mrs E Wright, BA UCL
Miss F Venon
Dr A Hawker, BSc Plymouth
A Miller, BSc, PhD Bristol
Miss E Williams, BA Greenwich
P J Cragg, BSc Open, AMInstP
R L Edwards, BA Wales (*Head of Rugby*)
D A Jones, BSc Birmingham (*Head of Mathematics*)
Miss C Wells, BA Durham
D J Whiteley, BSc Imperial College
Miss A Hamilton, BA Plymouth (*Director of Music*)

P J Randall, BA Oxford Brookes (*Head of French*)
S Vorster, BCom Port Elizabeth
Miss S Kerr, BEng Brunel
Miss M Labrousse, Licence d'Anglais Bretagne Occidentale
D J Roberts, MA Northumbria, BA Leeds
Miss R Swaysland, BMus King's, LRAM
Miss L M Odendaal, BA Stellenbosch
D J Martin, BA Warwick (*Head of Religious Studies*)
R S Groves
Miss L M Russo, MSci Imperial College
A R Carr, MA St Andrews
N Hunt, MA Pembroke College Cambridge, MSc London, FRGS

Part-time Staff:
Miss P J Anderson, MA Emmanuel College Cambridge (*Head of Classics*)
Mrs C F T Henderson, MA St Hugh's College Oxford
S J A Terry, BA Magdalene College Cambridge
Mrs T K Shields, MSc Leeds
Mrs G C Brown, BA London
Mrs J E Hansford, BEd Reading
Mr C G Nicol, Diploma Duncan of Jordanstone College of Art (*Head of Art*)
Miss A Green, BA Exeter
Mrs V J Wilden, BA Plymouth
C Childs, MSc Imperial College, BSc Sussex
Mrs P R Russell-Copp, BPhil Exeter, BEd TESOL
Mrs M Reynolds, BA Durham
Mrs J B Pope, BA St Anne's College Oxford
Miss N Clarke, BA Plymouth

Examinations Secretary: Mrs P Taylor

School Nurse: Mrs K Compton, RGN, MEd, CertEd

Headmaster's Secretary & Admissions: Mrs S L Lambie

Junior School:
Plymouth College Junior School
St Dunstan's Abbey
The Millfields
Plymouth PL1 3JL

Headmaster: C D M Gatherer, BA

Numbers. Currently there are 570 pupils in the school (170 in the Sixth Form) and of these 230 are girls.

Buildings. The Senior School stands on high ground in Plymouth. The buildings include Science Laboratories (extended in 1957 and 1984), Art and Craft rooms including extensive facilities for pottery, photography and print-making, the Dining Hall, an Assembly Hall in which concerts and plays are performed (1974). A well-equipped Design and Technology Block was opened in 1979. The grounds in Ford Park include a Small-bore Rifle Range and a Squash Court. Games are also played on 2 other fields to which the pupils are transported by coach. The Sports Hall was opened in 1986 and a new library was opened in 1996. An astro-surface was built in 1999. A new swimming pool, heated and indoor, was opened in 2001. In 2004 a new hospitality suite and Music School opened. In 2005 a dedicated Sixth Form Centre was opened.

The Junior School at The Millfields is approximately half a mile from the Senior School and has its own playing field and sports hall.

Organisation. Below the Sixth Form there is some setting so that pupils may proceed at a pace best suited to their abilities. Pupils are organised in 4 Houses. Each pupil is under the supervision of a Tutor and Head of Year. In Years 7–10 Form Prefects are appointed. There is a Chaplaincy team which also has a pastoral responsibility for all pupils. Every pupil is expected to play a full part in games and other school activities outside the classroom.

English (Language and Literature), French, Mathematics, Physics, Chemistry and Biology are taken by all to GCSE. Normally three more are chosen by the pupils.

Sixth Form. The Sixth Form is based on tutor groups with about twelve in each group. Pupils study usually four AS Levels leading to 3 or 4 A Levels and most prepare for General Studies as well. The tutor keeps a pastoral and academic watch on the pupils' performance. Most standard A Levels are available.

Sixth Formers are prepared for the Universities, the Services and the Professions; help is given by the Careers Teacher for almost any career, often with the assistance of the Independent Schools' Careers Organisation.

Games. Rugby, Cricket, Hockey and Netball are the major sports. There is also Athletics, Badminton, Basketball, Cross-country Running, Sailing, Shooting, Squash, Swimming and Tennis. Games are compulsory but more senior pupils have a wide range of options available to them.

School Activities. Pupils take part in a wide range of activities. There is a contingent of the CCF with Navy, Army and Air Force Sections. There is also The Duke of Edinburgh's Award Scheme as well as Ten Tors and pupils in Year 10 participate in a JSLA scheme with local primary schools. School Societies cover a wide range of activities. A School Yearbook is published annually.

Music. There is an excellent school choir which performs in public. The orchestra, fed from a junior wind band, Swing Band and a string group, plays both light and serious music. Various chamber ensembles are formed ad hoc. The choir and a madrigal group perform a variety of music from church to popular as occasion demands. The School provides tuition on all orchestral instruments, including percussion. Guitar and piano lessons are also offered. There are annual music scholarships.

Boarders. In the Senior School there are 3 Boarding Houses, one for boys and one for girls (40 in each). They are situated close to the school field and are equipped with small dormitories, sickroom, common rooms and games rooms. Meals are taken in the Dining Hall, supplied by a modern, well-equipped kitchen. There is also a separate boarding house on The Millfields site for the elite swimmers.

Admission. (*see Scholarship Entries section*). Admission to the Senior School is normally based on the College Entrance Examination for boys and girls over $10^1/_2$ and under 12 on 31 August of the year of entry, but it is also possible to enter at 13 via the Common Entrance Examination or a Year 9 Scholarship/Entrance test. Occasional vacancies are available at other ages. Application forms may be obtained from the Headmaster.

Admission to the Junior School is from the age of 3+. Application should be made direct to the Secretary to the Headmaster of the Junior School.

Fees per term (2008-2009). Junior School: Infant Department: Kindergarten £1,900, Reception £2,200, Years 1 & 2 £2,400. Junior Department: Years 3–6 £2,550.

Senior School: Day: Years 7–8 £3,450, Years 9–11 £3,635, Sixth Form £3,720. Full Boarding: Years 7–8 £6,790, Years 9–11 £6,975, Sixth Form £7,060. Weekly Boarding: Years 7–8 £6,750, Years 9–11 £6,935, Sixth Form £7,020.

These fees include books, stationery and games. Music lessons and lunches are extra.

Charitable status. Plymouth College is a Registered Charity, number 1105544. Its aim is to provide private education for boys and girls.

Pocklington School

West Green Pocklington York YO42 2NJ
Tel: 01759 321200
Fax: 01759 306366

e-mail: enquiry@pocklingtonschool.com
website: www.pocklingtonschool.com

Motto: '*Virtute et Veritate*'

Pocklington School aims to provide an education which is broad and humane, characterised by a combination of rigour and enjoyment, to contribute to fullness of life for each boy and girl. The school was founded by John Dolman in 1514 as part of a guild whose aims encompassed support for the poor and sick of the parish as well as the foundation of a school "for the bringing up of youth in virtue and learning". The foundation was thus based on a commitment to the value of education and to the creation of opportunity for those who would take their place in a society which was finding itself increasingly in need of an expansion of education. Today there is in the school a similar commitment to quality of education and the upholding of high standards in all facets of life.

The school values its Christian foundation: pupils and staff comprise individuals of different faiths and beliefs but there is a desire to aspire to Christian values.

Governors:
R E Haynes, MA (*Chairman*)
C M Oughtred, MA (*Vice-Chairman*)

Mrs J Atkinson
Dr H R L Beadle, MA, DPhil
J L Burley, BSc, MRICS
D G Buttery, BA
S C Elliott, BSc PGCE
J A Farmer, FCA
Lord Halifax, JP, DL
Revd J Harrison, MA
Mrs N Jennings
Rt Hon G Knight, MP
J S Lee, MA
Ms D Nott, BA
Mrs S M Ougtred, BSc
Mrs P J Peacock
Revd C J Simmons, MA
T A Stephenson, MA, FCA
Dr A J Warren, MA, DPhil Oxon, FRHS

Life Patrons:
K Applebee, OBE, MA
Mrs J S Carver, DL
Rt Hon D M Davis, MP
R Fenton, OBE
J L Mackinlay, FCA, FCMA
D V Southwell
Major General H G Woods, CB, MBE, MC

Clerk to the Governors and Bursar: P S Bennett, BSc

***Headmaster*: M E Ronan**, BA

Deputy Head: A M Dawes, BSc
Director of Studies: R Smith, BSc
Deputy Director of Studies: Mrs C L Bracken, MSc
Head of Lower School: Dr D B Dyson, BSc, PhD, GRSC
Bursar: P S Bennett, BSc
Bursar's Secretary: Miss C Nicholls
Accountant: Mrs J L Knott
Estates Manager: R S Denton
Residential & Commercial Manager: A D'Arcy MHCIMA, CertEd
OP Association Secretary: Mrs R J Dare
Marketing Officer: Mrs M Stefanini, BA, DipM, ACIM
PA to Headmaster & Administration Manager: Mrs J M Whatford
Admissions Secretary: Mrs F A Lambert

* *Head of Department*

English and Drama:
*Miss L J Powell, MA
*A W J Heaven, BHum, MA, CFPS SpLD
Mrs A J Bond, BEd
Mrs E J Cunningham, BA
Mrs A K V Hallam, BA
Mrs F B de L Marshall, BA
Mrs E M Edwards, BEd
Mrs D A Henderson, BA
M P Newhouse, CertEd

Mathematics:
*J F Cullen, BSc
Mrs C L Bracken, MSc
Mrs L Deadman, BEd
T M Loten, BA
Mrs T J Randell, BSc
I C Sheppard, BSc
R Smith, BSc
Mrs H V Towner, BSc

Modern Languages:
*P M H L Dare, BA
Miss S L Allen, BA
D A Galloway, MA
S C Nesom, BA
Mrs M R Peel, BA
Miss C J Postlethwaite, BA
Miss N C Whatford, BA

Science:
Biology:
*M J Butcher, BSc
Dr K J Clow, PhD, BSc
A M Dawes, BSc
R J Peel, BA

Chemistry:
*Mrs S J Pratt, BSc (*Head of Coordinated Science*)
M R Evans, BSc (*Senior Master*)
Dr D B Dyson, BSc, PhD, GRSC
P R Horne, BEd
Dr K J Winstanley, BSc, PhD

Physics:
*G Binks, BSc
D W Hutchings, BSc
S D Ward, BSc
R Smith, BSc

Psychology:
*Dr S McNamee, BSc, PhD (*Director of Sixth Form*)
Mrs R Anderton, BSc
Mrs L L Hutchinson, BSc

Classics:
I J Andrews, BA
Miss C J Blake, BA

Art:
*P Edwards, BA, MA
Mrs T Hopkins
D E Swales, BA
Mrs C M W Swann, BA

Design:
*D Wagstaff, MA
S D Ellis, BA

ICT:
Miss H T McIntyre, BA
S Spruyt, BA
Mrs M S Wilson, BA, MSc

Music:
*M Kettlewell, BA, ATCL
Mrs H J Kneeshaw, MMus
T E W Taylor, MA
Mrs C V Allan, GRNCM
M A Currey, BA, ACTL
J Diver, BSc LRSM
D J Hardy
Mrs K E Hart, GRNCM, ARMCM
K Holbrough, GLCM
I F Huntingford, ACLM
Miss C M Jowett, BA
P Judge, MA, PGTC
Mrs K Ledger, BA
Mrs K Meinardi, LRSM, DipConsMusic Rome
D Saint John
I C Sharp, BMus, GRSM, ARMCM
M Smith, BA
M E Stier, LRAM, DipLCM

Economics and Business Studies and Politics:
*N A J Tomaszewski, BA
P J Donaldson, BA
D Watton, BA

History:
*J M Webb, MA
Mrs J Fell, MA
J A Taylor, BA

Geography:
*I McDougall, MA
R P Bond, BEd
Mrs A L G Cosby, BSc
J Sykes, BSc

PE:
*A E Towner, BA
S A Houltham, BPhEd, BTchg
G M Kilsby, CertEd
Miss S A Metcalfe BSc
Mrs M Newhouse, CertEd

Religious Studies:
*M J Davies, BA
The Revd Jim Roberts, BA
Miss H M Young, BA

Sport:
D Byas (*Director of Coaching and Development*)
Mrs M Newhouse, CertEd (*Director of Games*)
Mrs J E Danby, CertEd
Mrs S Harris, BEd
G M Kilsby, CertEd
Mrs J S Kilsby

Careers:
Dr R Farrar, PhD, BSc, PG Dip CG

English as a Foreign Language, Guardianship:
Mrs S E Bosworth, BA

Learning Support:
Mrs L Deadman, BEd
Mrs B Wilson, CertEd

Librarian: Mrs A J Edwards, BA
Chaplain: The Revd Jim Roberts, BA

Director of Activities: M Kettlewell, BA, ACTL

Director of Boarding: T E W Taylor, MA
Boarding Houses:
Fenwick-Smith: T M Loten

Dolman: T E W Taylor
Faircote: Mrs A K V Hallam
St John's: A E Towner
Orchard: Mrs J E Midwinter

Day Houses:
Dolman:
Mrs H V Towner (*Lower School*)
D A Galloway (*Middle School*)
M Davies (*Sixth Form*)
Gruggen:
I J Andrews (*Lower School*)
Mrs C M W Swann (*Middle School*)
Miss H T McIntyre (*Sixth Form*)
Hutton:
Mrs M Newhouse (*Lower School*)
(*to be appointed*) (*Middle School*)
D W Hutchings (*Sixth Form*)
Wilberforce:
Miss C J Blake (*Lower School*)
Mrs M R Peel (*Middle School*)
N A J Tomaszewski (*Sixth Form*)

Number of Pupils (2007–08). There are 848 pupils in the school (460 boys, 388 girls) of whom 170 (89 boys, 81 girls) are at Lyndhurst School (School Years 3–6). These numbers include 134 boarders, in three senior houses (School Years 9–13) and two junior houses (School Years 5–8).

Lyndhurst School, for pupils aged from 7 to 11 years, is on the same site as the Senior School. (*For further details, see entry in IAPS section.*)

Curriculum. Pocklington's curriculum has been developed to motivate and stretch pupils. Following foundations at Lyndhurst and in the Lower School, there are wide-ranging options in Year 9 and GCSE. Sixth Form AS and A2 subjects offer a diverse selection of subjects and combinations. There is excellent careers and university advice. Music, drama and art thrive, as do sport, outdoor education, community service, the CCF and other extra-curricular activities. The main sports are athletics, badminton, basketball, cricket, cross-country, fencing, football, hockey, netball, rounders, rugby, squash, swimming and tennis.

Location, Campus and Development. The school is set in extensive grounds on the edge of Pocklington, a market town 12 miles east of York. Emphasis is given to the importance of an attractive, high quality learning environment. There are very good facilities with an extensive long-term development programme well underway.

Admission is subject to vacancy and to a satisfactory entry exam result and school report. Interviews may also be held. Year 9 applicants sit either a Senior School entry exam or Common Entrance. Sixth Form applicants should have gained at least 4 B grades and 2 C grades at GCSE. Subject to these entry criteria, the school seeks to admit candidates who will benefit from what it has to offer and whom it will be able to support. Children with mild learning difficulties can be supported, as can those who will in due course seek entry to the most demanding university courses.

Scholarships and Exhibitions. (*see Scholarship Entries section*).

Fees per term (2008-2009). Day £3,517, Boarding £6,297, 5-Day Boarding £5,960, Day Boarding (2–5 nights per week) £250–£600.

Charitable status. Pocklington School is a Registered Charity, number 529834.

Portora Royal School

Enniskillen Co Fermanagh BT74 7HA Northern Ireland
Tel: 028 6632 2658
Fax: 028 6632 8668
e-mail: info@portora.enniskillen.ni.sch.uk
website: www.portoraroyal.co.uk

Founded 1608.

The School buildings were first at the village of Ballybalfour, not far from Enniskillen. In the year 1641 they were removed to Enniskillen itself. The School was removed to new buildings on Portora Hill in 1777, these buildings forming the central block of the old school buildings. Since 1990 all teaching and sporting facilities have been either renovated or rebuilt, and extended. This includes four new Science Laboratories, new Technology and Information Technology suites, an Art & Design Centre, and a Sixth Form Centre. In its earlier days the government of the School was in the hands of the King and the Viceroy, but since the year 1890, the School has been governed and managed under Scheme No 34 framed under the Irish Educational Endowments Act (1885) and subsequent amending schemes framed under the Act.

Governing Body:

Rt Revd M G St A Jackson, MA, PhD, DPhil (*Chairman*)
S B Morrow, OBE, BAgr (*Vice-Chairman*)
H J W Logan, BSc, FSM (*Hon Secretary*)
P M C Little, BSc
J Kerr, CertEd
J N Morton, MA Ed, MA, BA, BS Sc, DASE (*Headmaster*) (*ex officio*)
Mrs M Cooper, LLB
R F Toner, BA, FCA
Revd Precentor B Courtney, MA, BD
W I L Kennedy, BSc Econ
Mrs D Frazer, MEd, DipDomSc
A I A Crawford
M Coalter, BA, Dip MCIM (*Parent Governor*)
Mrs B Johnston, MSc, BA
N McClements, BA, ACA
J Dickie
G M T Moore
Dr N S J Baxter, QPM, BA Hons, MA Dist, PhQ
J A Styles, FGA
Mrs S McElroy, BEd (*Parent Governor*)
S Balmer (*Parent Governor*)
Miss N M Heap, BA, MSc, PGCE (*Teacher Governor*)
R G McNeill, BSc, CertEd (*Teacher Governor*)
Mrs R E S Maxwell, MSc, PGCE (*Teacher Governor*)

***Headmaster*: J N Morton**, MA Ed, MA, BA, BS Sc, DASE, PQH NI, MIHR

Deputy Headmaster: R H Northridge, BA
Vice-Principal: T R Smith, BEd, DipEd, GradIED, FTC Prod Eng
Senior Teacher: R G McNeill, BSc, DipEd
Chaplain: Revd G West, BA, BTh
Bursar: Mrs A Stronge, ACA, MIATI

Assistant Masters:
D K Dempster, MSc, BA, PGCE, MILAM
R J Stewart, MSc, PGCE
†J J R Clarke, BEd, PGCE
†S J Gaston, BA, PGCE
Miss N M Heap, BA, MSc, PGCE
D J McLaughlin-Borlace, BA, MSc, PGCE
W R Sloane, BSc, PGCE
†Mrs R E S Maxwell, MSc, BSc Econ, PGCE
Miss C Doherty, BA, PGCE
Mrs C M Peel, MA, BEd
R J Mason, BSc, PGCE
Mrs J E Goodall, BA, BAI, PGCE
†Mrs C Condell, BSc, PGCE
D J Holland, BSc, PGCE
I C Hodgson, BA, PGCE
C Bersot, MA, CAPES

R McKeague, BSc, HDipEd
Miss R Hogg, PhD, BMedSc, PGCE
D H S Wilson, PhD, BSc, PGCE
F G McHugh, BA, PGCE
Miss H Gibson, MA, PGCE
P McCallum, MA, BA, PGCE
Miss J M Lagan, BA, PGCE
B O'Shea, MA, BA, PGCE
Miss L V Vincent, BA, PGCE
F Hoeritzauer, BA, PGCE
T J M Smith, BA, PGCE
J McCallister, PhD, BSc, PGCE
J R McClure, BEd
B Bellinger, BA, PCGE
Mrs S McCordick, BSc, PGCE

Numbers. 490 boys.

Situation. The School is situated on an elevated site of 70 acres, on the shores of Lough Erne. Pupils are encouraged to take full advantage of this superb site and the wide area of unspoilt countryside.

The School Buildings. Tuition: a large classroom block, 5 Science Laboratories, Library, Music Centre, Art & Design Centre, Gymnasium, Engineering Laboratory, Technology and Computer Laboratories, and Sixth Form Centre.

Religious Teaching and Practice. All pupils have at least 2 periods of Divinity a week.

Curriculum and Examinations. Years 8–10 follow a broad course of general education in the National Curriculum. They choose up to 9 or 10 subjects for study to GCSE level. The range to A level is comprehensive, from the academic to the artistic and technical. University Scholarship work is also undertaken.

Games and Activities. A very wide range of outdoor pursuits is followed which take advantage of the School's superb natural environment of rivers, lakes, mountains and forests. Rugby, rowing and cricket are the main team sports. The school has a Gymnasium and heated Swimming Pool, and an all-weather running track. Music and Drama flourish with public performances at least twice each year. Amongst the other clubs and societies are the Electronic Society, Debating Society and Chess Club.

Fees per annum. Tuition: £3,167 (Years 8–12), £4,110 (Year 13–14). Capital Fee: £42. Pupils whose parents are EC Nationals do not pay tuition fees.

The Portsmouth Grammar School

High Street Portsmouth Hants PO1 2LN
Tel: 023 9236 0036
Fax: 023 9236 4256
e-mail: admissions@pgs.org.uk
website: www.pgs.org.uk

The School was founded in 1732 by Dr William Smith, Mayor of Portsmouth and Physician to its Garrison, MD of Leiden, and a member of Christ Church, Oxford, to which he left land in trust for the foundation of Portsmouth's first established school.

Motto: '*Praemia Virtutis Honores*'

Governing Body:
Chairman: D K Bawtree, CB, DL, BSc Eng, CEng, FIEE, FIMechE
Vice-Chairman: Mrs M Scott, BSc
I A Carruthers
W J B Cha
Mrs J Cockcroft, RGN, FPC, CertEd
M R Coffin, BA Econ, FCA
N Iliffe, FRICS, MCIArb
Air Chief Marshal Sir Richard Johns, GCB, CBE, LVO, FRAeS, RAF
B S Larkman, BSc, ACIB
Rear Admiral N D Latham, MSc, CEng, FIMarEST, MIMechE
Mrs Susan Marks, MA
Professor C B R Pelling, MA, DPhil
M J Pipes, MA, MBA, FInstP
F S K Privett, LLB
Mrs S Quail, BA
Mrs S Resouly, BSc, MRPharmS
Cmdre D G Steel RN, BA, FCIPD, FCILT, ADC
P F J Tobin, MA, FRSA
The Right Worshipful The Lord Mayor of Portsmouth
The Dean of Portsmouth, The Very Revd D Brindley, BD, MTh, MPhil, AKC

Clerk to the Governors and Bursar: D J Kent

***Headmaster*: J E Priory**, MA

Second Master: S J Mills, MA
Second Deputy (*Director of Studies*): N J Weaver, BA, MA
Assistant Head (*Head of Sixth Form*): Miss L E Péchard, MA
Senior Teacher: Mrs C Giles, BSc

Upper School Staff:
* *Head of Department/Subject*
† *Head of House*

Art & Design:
*G C Whitehead, MA
Mrs L Ashton, BA
Miss A Dyer, BA (*Deputy Head of Middle School*)
S P H Willcocks, BA (*Deputy Head Whitcombe House*)

Careers:
*A R Hogg, BA

Classics:
*B P Lister, BA
J R Deeks, BA
Mrs B Richards, BA Wales, BA London

Design and Technology:
*L A Ansell, BSc, MA
M J Kirby, BSc, PGCE (*General Studies Coordinator*)
Ms S J Green, BSc (*†Summers House*)
Mrs W Whitaker, CertEd

Drama and Theatre Studies:
*M B Smith, BA, MA (*Director of Drama*)
D R Hampshire, BSc, BA, ARCS, CBiol, MIBiol (*Senior Teacher, Head of Middle School*)
Mrs E E Bell, BA (*President of the Common Room*)
J Robinson (*Director in Residence*)
Miss G Meadows, BEd (*Deputy Head Years 9–11*)

Economics and Business Studies:
*R Dolan
D T Doyle, BA (*Deputy Head Smith House, Languages Coordinator*)
S Quinn, BA, PGCE
Miss D A S Tabtab, MSc (*†Hawkey House*)
Mrs A T Wickson, BA, ACA

English:
*Mrs C Jepson, BA
J E Burkinshaw, BA
Miss E Callen
J Dunne, BA, MA (*Head of Publications*)
Mrs E E Bell, BA (*President of the Common Room*)
J J Elphick-Smith, MA (*Senior Teacher, †Latter House, Librarian*)
B C Hart, BA, MA, QTS
Miss L Kirby, BA (*General Studies Coordinator*)
Miss G Meadows, BEd (*Deputy Head Years 9–11*)

T McCarthy, BA
Mrs M Mitchell, BA (*Senior Teacher, Registrar*)
M P Richardson, BA, MA, PGCE

Ethics:
Revd A K Burtt, BA, MA, LTh (*Chaplain*)
Dr R J I Richmond, MA, PhD (*Charities Coordinator*)

Geography:
*Miss S Stewart, BSc, MEd
J P Baker, BSc, MA Ed, FRGS, FGS
S J Curwood, BEd (**Cricket*)
Mrs C Giles, BSc (*Senior Teacher, Professional Development*)
S J Mills, MA (*Second Master*)
Ms F J Nicholson, BSc, MPH

Geology:
J P Baker, TD, BSc, MA Ed, FRGS, FGS

Government & Politics:
*S Lemieux, MA

History:
*S Lemieux, MA
Miss F E A Bush, BA (*†Whitcombe House*)
J A Cooper, MA
Dr P W Galliver, BA, MA, MPhil (*Senior Teacher, UCAS Coordinator*)
S E Palmer, BA, PGCE, DipSpLD
Miss L E Péchard, MA (*Assistant Head, Head of Sixth Form*)

History of Art:
S P H Willcocks, BA (*Deputy Head Whitcombe House*)

International Baccalaureate:
S Taylor (*Director of IB*)

Information Technology:
*A H Harrison, BSc

Learning Support:
*Mrs J M Okell, BSc, DipSpLD, AMBDA
J K Edwards, BSc

Mathematics:
*M H McCall, MA, PhD
D P Ager, MSc, BSc
J D Baker, BSc
N F C Blewett, BEd, MPEA, DipSP (*Senior Teacher, Surmaster*)
S J Dean, BEd (*Deputy Head Sixth Form*)
J R C Gillies, BSc (*Deputy Head Latter House*)
A H Harrison, BSc
J Jackson, BSc
J F Kensall, BEd
D Mountford, BA, MSc, PhD
Miss R Nash
Mrs J M Okell, BSc, DipSpLD, AMBDA (*SENCO*)
Miss K Penry
Miss J Read, BSc
P Robinson
L J Ronaldson, MA, PhD
A J Spender, BEd

Modern Languages:
*N G Waters, BA (*Senior Teacher, Head of Years 9–11*)
Miss C L Coward, BA (**German, Assistant Head Modern Languages*)
D T Doyle, BA (*Deputy Head Smith House, Languages Coordinator*)
A J Goodwin, BA, MPhil
Mrs C A Gozalbez-Guerola, BA (**French*)
A R Hogg, BA
Mrs L Nogueira-Paché, LicSc, MA
S Page, BA (**Spanish*)
S Quandte, PG Cert, Dip
Mrs B Richards, BA Wales, BA London
Mrs M A Stubbs
Mrs I Wellman-Hewett

Music:
*A M Cleary, BA (*Director of Music*)
Mrs Y R Hall, MA (**Academic Music*)
Miss S Heath
Miss K Kingsley, GRSM, LRAM (**Keyboard Skills*)

Physical Education:
*C J Dossett, BSc, MSc (*Senior Teacher, Director of Sport*)
J P Baker, TD, BSc, MA Ed, FRGS, FGS
M Bartlett, BSc, PGCE (**Hockey*)
N F C Blewett, BEd, MPEA, DipSP (*Senior Teacher, Surmaster*)
B J Cooper, BA
N L Cooper, BPhEd
S J Curwood, BEd (**Cricket*)
Mrs A J Day, BEd (**Athletics*)
M W Earley (*Games Assistant*)
J R C Gillies, BSc (*Deputy Head Latter House*)
S D Hawkswell, BA (*†Barton House*)
J K Herbert, BSc (*Sixth Form Coordinator*)
Miss A C Howarth, BSc
J E Law, MA, FRSA (*Hockey Coach*)
Miss H Linnett, BSc (*Deputy Head Years 9–11*)
S J Mills, MA (*Second Master*)
Miss L E Péchard, MA (*Assistant Head, Head of Sixth Form*)
H Prentice, BA, PGCE
Mrs D F Spencer
Miss S Stewart, BSc, MEd

Philosophy and Religious Studies:
*Dr R J I Richmond, PhD, MA (*Charities Coordinator*)
Revd A K Burtt, BA, MA, LTh (*Chaplain*)
Mrs A S Carter, BA
J L Cathie, BA

Portsmouth Curriculum:
Mrs E E Bell, BA (*President of the Common Room*)
Revd A K Burtt, BA, MA, LTh (*Chaplain*)
Miss F E A Bush, BA (*†Whitcombe House*)
Mrs C Giles, BSc (*Senior Teacher, Professional Development*)
Mrs J M Okell, BSc, DipSpLD, AMBDA
Mr J E Priory, MA

Psychology:
*Miss A J Wood, BA, PGCE
S M Pakes, BA

Science:
*B C Goad, BA, PGCE (**Physics*)
Miss E J Cox, MSc, CPhys, MInstP (*†Grant House*)
Mrs M G Bates, BSc
S G Disley, BSc
J C Dunne, BSc, AMIBiol
Mrs H Harris, BSc (*†Eastwood House*)
J K Herbert, BSc (*Sixth Form Coordinator*)
M R Howson, BSc, PhD, CChem, MRSC (**Chemistry*)
P E Nials, BSc, MA Ed, CBiol, MIBiol, CertCouns (*Senior Teacher, *PHE*)
Dr P O'Neil, BSc, PhD
R V Puchades, BSc
K L Sparkes, BSc, PGCE
Ms A C Stephenson, BSc
M R Taylor, BSc
Miss E-J Toland, MSc, MA (**Biology*)
Mrs J M H Tyldesley, BSc
Dr V Vincent, BSc, PhD (*Deputy Head Sixth Form*)

Librarian: Mrs J C J Godfree, MA, DipLib
Archivist: Mrs C R I Smith, BA, MAr Ad

School Medical Officers:
Dr C Foley
Dr A Scott-Brown
Dr M L Saunders

Personal Assistant to Headmaster: Miss J E Moody
Admissions Secretary: Mrs G M Williams

Junior School

Head of Junior School: Mrs P S Foster, CertEd
Deputy Head: A P N Rowley, BSc, PGCE
Assistant Head: Mrs E R Day, BA, CertEd

R Ainsworth, BSc, PGCE	Mrs R Mills, BEd
Mrs J Albuery, BEd	Mrs C Minall, BA Hons, PGCE
Mrs H Carroll, BA, PGCE	Mrs F Nash, BEd Hons
Miss C S Chambers, BEd	Mrs D J Payne, BEd
Mrs J Crossley, CertEd	G D Payne, BEd
Miss N Davies, BA Hons, QTS	Miss J People, BEd Hons
Mrs C L Dean, BA, PGCE	E J P Sharkey, BA
Mrs S Dipple, BSc, CertEd	Mrs E Sharrock, BMus, LRMA
Mrs J Ellis, BEd	B W Sheldrick, BA
G Evans, BA	Mrs S J Sheldrick, BEd
Mrs C Houselander, CertEd	Mrs M Smith, BSc, CertEd
Mrs J E Ingamells, ARCM	Mrs P Stirling, BA Hons, PGCE
Miss D H Jennings, BA, MA, ALCM, LTCL, MusEd, PGCE	Mrs B E Tilling, BSc, PGCE
Mrs L Johnson, BEd, PGDip Early Years (*Head of Nursery*)	Miss K Turner, BA PGCE
I Jones, BEd	Mrs S P Tyacke, BEd
Miss V Jubb, BA, PGCE	Miss L Vinsen, BA, PGCE
Mrs J E Low, BEd	J Wadge, BA, PGCE
Miss R McGibben, BA Hons	M F Warin, BA, PGCE
	Miss P Watkins, BA Hons
	I Webber, BA Ed

Headmistress's PA: Mrs J Potter
Junior School Admissions Secretary: Mrs G Bull, BA
Junior School Secretary: Mrs P Kaznowski

The School, formerly on the Direct Grant List, assumed full independent status in 1976. It is co-educational throughout. There are 1,102 pupils in the Senior School and 503 pupils in the Junior School. There are no boarders.

The Nursery School opened in September 2001and offers outstanding provision for boys and girls from 2½ years old.

The Junior School numbers 503 boys and girls aged 4–11. It is a thriving, dynamic and popular institution, committed to giving Portsmouth pupils the best possible start to their educational lives. The main ages of entry are 4 and 7 by assessment tests held in January. Occasionally there are places available for intermediate entry. (*For further details see entry in IAPS section.*)

Although promotion to the Senior School is not automatic, it is normal for pupils to move there when they are 11.

Senior School. Admission is by the School's Entrance Assessment at 11 and at 13, chiefly by Common Entrance. All entrants at 13+ are pre-tested at 11+ to accommodate demand for places. Pupils are admitted at other ages, should vacancies occur, subject to assessments and satisfactory reports from previous schools. Admission to the Sixth Form, which numbers 289, is subject to satisfactory standard at GCSE and interview.

Curriculum. Pupils are educated for life as well as public examinations, through initiatives such as The Portsmouth Curriculum in Year 7 and the wide-ranging General Studies Programme in the Sixth Form. The curriculum aims to give a general education and to defer specialisation. After GCSE, pupils enter the Sixth Form, which seeks to prepare pupils for the challenges of a rigorous university education and subsequent competitive employment. Pupils generally select 4 subjects to take to A2 Level from: Art, Biology, Business Studies, Chemistry, Classical Civilisation, Design and Technology, Drama, Economics, Electronics, English Literature, French, Geography, Geology, German, Government and Politics, Greek, History of Art, History, Latin, Mathematics, Further Mathematics, Music, Physical Education, Psychology, Religious Studies and Spanish. The General Studies Programme is mainly taught by outside professionals and is aimed at widening personal and academic horizons as well as offering some further academic opportunities, such as AS Critical Thinking. The Sixth Form prepares candidates for entry to Higher Education, and the Careers Department provides close relations with various forms of employment. The school plans to offer the International Baccalaureate Diploma from September 2009 in addition to A Level.

Religion. The School has always been closely connected with Portsmouth Cathedral. However, Religious Instruction, given in accordance with the principles of the Christian faith, remains, in accordance with a long tradition of latitudinarianism, non-denominational. The School has a Chaplain.

Pastoral Care. Pastoral Care is of paramount importance. Pupils are allocated to one of four Houses on entry. Heads of House and their House Tutors are responsible for the pastoral and academic welfare of all pupils, supported by Heads of Years 7–8, 9–11 and Sixth Form, and provide a focal point for communication between teaching staff and parents. Particular emphasis is placed on the triangular relationship between pupil, parents and teaching staff, including a programme of telephone calls from tutors to new parents in which all senior staff and the Headmaster have a monitoring role.

Games. Rugby football, rugby sevens, netball, hockey and cross-country are the main games in Winter and Spring, cricket, tennis, athletics and rounders in the Summer Term. Cross-country running, squash, judo, badminton, basketball, aerobics, swimming and sailing are also available. The School has enjoyed national success in recent years in sports such as hockey, netball, athletics, cricket and rounders and was Runner Up in The Daily Telegraph Sports Awards 2007 for independent schools.

Other Activities. The Combined Cadet Force (which has Army, Navy and RAF Sections) is of particular significance, having produced 3 VCs *inter alia*. There are opportunities for Adventurous Training, Ten Tors and participation in the Duke of Edinburgh's Award Scheme as well as for service to the local community and charity work. Drama flourishes at all levels and Portsmouth's New Theatre Royal and Kings Theatres provide young performers and technicians with a professional venue for major school productions. Many societies cater for a considerable range of extra-curricular interests. Various holiday activities and visits are encouraged and include many foreign tours for bands, orchestras, choirs and ensembles. The School has a flourishing exchange scheme with French, German and Spanish schools. Sports teams have recently gone on tour to South Africa and Australia.

Fees per term (2008-2009). Senior School: £3,630. Junior School: £2,329–£2,582. (Fees quoted include direct debit discount.)

Scholarships and Bursaries. (*see Scholarship Entries section*). Scholarships are chiefly available for entry at 11 and 13. Full details are available on the website.

Buildings. Nothing remains of the former Schoolroom, destroyed when the present Junior School, now Grade II listed, was erected on the site of the town fortifications. The Lower Junior School and Senior Schools occupy a unique range of former Barrack buildings in an historic location in the High Street: these are now also listed throughout. In the last decade of the twentieth century there was an emphasis on new buildings: a Music School and Sports Hall (1989), a modern theatre (1990), a sports pavilion (1992) and a Sixth Form Centre (1995). A comprehensive refurbishment of the older buildings was also undertaken including science laboratories (1996 and 1997) and an IT Suite generously equipped by IBM (1998). The most recent acquisition has been the fine Cambridge

House Barracks, which not only doubles the space available for teaching and pastoral care, but also gives the School ownership of a harmonious group of historic buildings. Conversion of the Gate House has provided custom-designed drama facilities, and No 10, The High Street, provides a superb Art Gallery. In a major Development Project (2004–2005), the Library has been expanded and refurbished; a new all-weather pitch has been created on the School's playing fields at Hilsea; a state-of-the-art science laboratory has been opened, and a new dining and theatre complex developed.

Honours. Over 99% of Sixth Formers transfer to University each year, the very large majority to their first-choice university. 18 pupils took up places at Oxford and Cambridge in 2006. Sportsmen include England Cricket Captain Wally Hammond and Athletics International Roger Black. Military distinction in abundance, including 3 VCs (one the first VC submariner), several Admirals, Generals and Air Marshals. Medicine is also a continuing theme – from pioneer opthalmologist James Ware to Viagra researcher Ian Osterloh. Arts are well and diversely represented: dramatist Simon Gray, poet Christopher Logue, novelist James Clavell, cathedral organist Christopher Walsh and pop singer, Paul Jones. Civil Servants and Judges and barristers galore, plus entrepreneur industrialist Alan Bristow.

Old Portmuthian Club. This maintains links with former pupils not least by holding reunions in Portsmouth, London and Oxford, and is enhanced by its relationship with the School's Development Office.

Charitable status. The Portsmouth Grammar School is a Registered Charity, number 1063732. It exists to provide education for boys and girls.

Prior Park College

Bath Somerset BA2 5AH
Tel: 01225 835353
Fax: 01225 835753
e-mail: info@priorpark.co.uk
website: www.priorparkschools.co.uk

Prior Park College is a fully co-educational Catholic Boarding and Day School. Founded in 1830 by Bishop Baines, it was under the control of the Bishops of Clifton until 1924, when it passed to the Congregation of Christian Brothers. Since 1981 Prior Park has been under lay management and has more than doubled in size and is completely co-educational. Prior Park is a friendly, thriving community of approximately 550 pupils with a strong boarding community, excellent academic standards and a strong devotion to educating the whole person.

The College is housed in magnificent Palladian architecture, built by John Wood for Ralph Allen, with glorious views of the World Heritage City of Bath. The 57-acre site combines an elegant setting for boarding and day education with access to Bath and its numerous cultural attractions. Proximity to the M4 and M5 motorways places the College within easy reach of London, the Midlands, the South-West and Wales. Good rail links and proximity to Bristol, Heathrow and Gatwick international airports allow easy transfer for our international students.

Motto: '*Deo Duce, Deo Luce*'

Patrons:
His Eminence Cardinal Cormac Murphy-O'Connor, PhL, STL
The Rt Revd Declan Lang, BA
The Revd Monsignor Canon R J Twomey, VF
The Rt Hon the Lord Patten of Barnes
F J F Lyons, KSG
Miss J Bisgood, CBE
Sir Cameron Mackintosh
Col R S C Dowden, JP, DL, KCSG
C J B Davy, CB
D R Hayes

Governors:
Sister Jane Livesey, CJ, MA Cantab (*Chair*)
E W Cussen, BSc, FRICS (*Vice-Chair*)
Sir Neil Butterfield
Mrs G Chapman, BEd, MCIPD
Dr R Gliddon, BSc, PhD
Miss A Grayson, DipEd
Mrs B Huntley, BEd
Sister Andrea Le Guevel, MA, MPhil
C W Long, MA, CMG
Fr W M McLoughlin, PhL, BD, MTh, OSM
A J Owen, LLB, FCA
A M Pitt, MA, FCA
Commodore C B York, FCMI, Royal Navy
Mrs M M Rae, MSc, PH, DipEd, FFPH, FRIPH
Rear Admiral N J F Raby, OBE

Bursar & Clerk to the Governors: Col M J Vacher, OBE, FCMI

***Headmaster*: Dr Giles Mercer**, MA, KSG, FRSA

Deputy Headmaster: Mr D G Clarke, BSc
Second Deputy Head: Mrs S Ashby, BSc, AdvDipEd
Academic Deputy Head: Mr T J Simons, BSc, BA
Chaplain: Father Malcolm Smeaton, BSc
Director of Admissions & Marketing: Dr Margaret Ruxton, BSc, PhD
Headmaster's PA: Ms D Miller (*Dee@priorpark.co.uk*)

Assistant Staff:
Miss R Atkinson, BA, MA (*Modern Languages*)
Mr M Blaikley, BA (*Mathematics*)
Mrs K Bond, BA (*Design Technology*)
Mrs L Brierley, BA (*OC Royal Navy Section CCF; Housemistress, Fielding*)
Mr T Brierley, BSc (*Head of Mathematics; Bronze DofE*)
Mr S Burt, BSc (*Head of Geography*)
Mrs C Byron, BSc (*Mathematics*)
Mrs L Collison, BA (*Head of History*)
Mr S Capon, BEd (*Director of PE and Sport*)
Miss R Chambers, BA, MA (*English*)
Mr K Chard, BSc (*Head of Chemistry*)
Miss J Clark, BA (*PE & Sports studies*)
Mr E Clements, BA, MSc (*Economics/Business Studies*)
Mrs W Cornish, BEd (*Head of Learning Development Programme*)
Mrs H Cronk, BSc (*EAL*)
Miss C Cummins, BA (*Theology; Housemistress, St Mary's*)
Miss L Dawson, BA (*History*)
Mr S Dorey, BSc (*Physics; Officer i/c Naval Section CCF; Gold DofE*)
Mrs J C Eatwell, BSc (*Head of Economics and Business Studies; Head of Careers*)
Mrs N Fahey, BA (*Learning Development Programme*)
Mr M Fisher, MA (*Head of Classics*)
Mrs C Ford, BA, Dip CG (*Careers*)
Mrs S Forshaw, BSc (*Chemistry; Assistant to the Academic Deputy Head*)
Mrs R Fox (*Drama & Theatre Studies*)
Mr J C Fry, BA (*Economics and Business Studies; Housemaster, Allen*)
Mrs H Goodman, BA (*Theology*)
Mr A J R Haines, BA (*ICT Manager; Music*)
Miss R Haf Jones, BA (*Drama*)
Mr A S Hall, BEd (*Head of Boys' Games*)
Miss L Hellberg, BA (*Art*)
Mrs A Holbrook; Dip Lib (*Library*)
Mrs C Hutchings, BMus, PGCE (*Music*)
Miss L Justine, BA (*French*)

Mrs J Klinpikuln, BEd (*EAL*)
Mr D Langley, BA (*Director of Drama and Theatre Studies*)
Ms J Law, BSc (*Mathematics; Examinations Officer*)
Ms C Maggs, BA (*Spanish; Housemistress, English House*)
Mrs A Mallon, MA (*French*)
Mr T B C Maxwell, BA (*Head of Theology*)
Mrs K E McCarey, BA (*Geography*)
Miss E Meehan, BA (*Classics*)
Mrs M E Mudie, BSc (*Science*)
Mr R Panayides (*Sports*)
Miss T Penfold, BA (*Design Technology*)
Mrs C M Pepler, BA (*Head of Sixth Form; French*)
Miss L Perry, BA (*Modern Languages*)
Mr G Pruett, BEd (*Housemaster, Roche House; Head of Rugby; Geography*)
Mrs L Pruett, BSc (*2nd i/c Mathematics*)
Dr C Roberts, BA, PhD (*Head of Modern Languages*)
Mr R P Robertson, MA, ARCO (*Director of Music*)
Mr J Rutter, BA (*Head of Design Technology*)
Mr D M Sackett, BA (*Housemaster, Baines; Music*)
Miss C Saunders, BA (*English*)
Mr V Shannon, BSc (*Science; Housemaster, Burton*)
Dr G Smith, BSc, PhD (*Housemaster, Clifford; Chemistry*)
Mrs A Spelman, BA (*English*)
Mr N Tattersfield, MA (*Head of English*)
Mr P Thompson, BA (*English and Theology; Deputy Head of Sixth Form*)
Dr R Trott, BSc, PhD (*Biology; OC Army Section, CCF*)
Mrs K Trott, BSc (*Biology; PE and Sports Studies*)
Mrs C Walker, BA (*Classics*)
Dr R L Wells, BSc, PhD (*Head of Science; Head of Biology*)
Dr S A Wilcock, BSc, PhD (*Head of Physics, i/c timetable*)
Dr R J Willmott, BA, MA, PhD (*Philosophy*)
Mr D F Wood, BA (*Head of Art*)

Music Staff:
Mr G Austin, ARCM (*Brass*)
Mr P Badley, PPRNCM (*Voice*)
Ms L Campbell (*Double Bass*)
Miss A Carroll, MA (*Voice*)
Mrs A Caunce, GRSM, LTCL, ARCM (*Piano*)
Mrs J Finch, ALCM, LTCL (*Oboe*)
Miss C Gainford, BMus, GRNCM (*Bassoon/woodwind*)
Mr A Haines, BA (*Bass Guitar*)
Mr G Harrup, BA Hons, LGSM (*Acoustic/Electric Guitar*)
Mrs A Hickmore (*Voice*)
Miss A Kazimierczuk (*Voice*)
Mrs M Konigsfeldt, GRSM, ARCM (*Piano*)
Mr J Lambert, MA, BMus (*Piano*)
Mr J Law, Dip ABRSM (*Piano*)
Mrs J Mason-Smith, BA, ABSM, ALCM (*Flute*)
Mr D Pagett, GRNCM, PG Dip RNCM (*Clarinet/Saxophone*)
Ms S Power, BEd (*Cello*)
Ms A Townley, AGSM (*Violin/viola*)
Mr R Webb, BMus, PGCE (*Trumpet*)
Mrs I Windsor, LRSM, LTCL, BA Hons (*Piano*)
Mr P Woodburn (*Drums/percussion*)
Mr Roland Robertson, MA, ARCO (*Director of Music*)
Mr D Sackett, BA (*Assistant Director of Music*)
Mrs C Hutchings, BMus, PGCE (*Junior Music/singing*)
Ms S West, BMus (*Music Secretary*)

Houses and Housemasters/mistresses:
Baines (*Junior House*): David Sackett
Burton (*Senior day boys*): Vincent Shannon
Clifford (*Senior day boys*): Graham Smith
English (*Senior day girls*): Claire Maggs
Fielding (*Senior day girls*): Louise Brierley
St Mary's (*Senior boarding girls*): Charlotte Cummins
Allen (*Senior boarding boys*): Jonathan Fry
Roche (*Senior boarding boys*): Giles Pruett

Higher Education and Careers Advisor: Mrs C Ford

Theatre Technician: Mr J Powell
Infirmary:
Medical Officer: Dr I Batterham
Sister i/c Infirmary: Mrs R Cole, RGN
Mrs S Taylor, RGN
Mrs F Whittington, RGN

Structure of the School. Prior Park is a friendly, thriving community of approximately 550 pupils. The annual two or three form entry of day pupils aged 11–13 makes up our co-educational Baines Junior House. A further two forms enter the school at 13, when we admit both boarders and day pupils. Each boy and girl between 13 and 18 is a member of a boarding or day single-sex Senior House. Year groups also meet regularly for assemblies.

Objects of the College. The College provides an outstanding education, within the framework of a caring Catholic community which warmly welcomes members of other denominations. Our resident Chaplain serves the needs of the whole community and great importance is attached to the commitment of all staff to the ethos of the school. Pastoral care is perceived by the current parent body to be outstanding and great efforts are made to ensure that all pupils are nurtured and supported. A Personal Development Programme aims to equip all our pupils with information and guidance specifically addressing contemporary moral issues and problems. The School makes great efforts to developing the full potential of all its pupils, according to their individual abilities, with particular emphasis being placed on each pupil's academic progress. Through all aspects of College life, through community service, and through shared experiences in sport, music and drama, we engender self-respect and respect for others. We strive to equip our young people with the vitally important communication and other skills which will allow them to leave the College as confident young adults, ready to negotiate successfully the next stage of their lives.

Buildings and Grounds. The Houses, Administration and College Chapel are to be found in the fine 18th century architecture grouped around Ralph Allen's celebrated Palladian Mansion. A major programme of modernisation has enhanced the accommodation for residential staff and their families, and added to the attractive environment for the residential community. Boarding and day accommodation of high quality is provided for all girls in The Priory and All Saints at the eastern end of the estate. A major refurbishment programme of boys' boarding accommodation has provided comfortable study bedrooms, quiet areas and recreational rooms. A rolling programme of refurbishment continues.

Academic teaching is provided in modern classrooms. Seven renovated Science laboratories, an Art Centre, and a well-equipped Design Technology Centre provide a stimulating environment for practical work. ICT provision includes several suites of computers in the library, the new ICT Centre, Design Technology Department and the Houses. ICT provision is also made within departments.

An elegant library, with over 11,000 volumes and a full-time librarian and assistant, enhances private research and independent learning.

Curriculum. The academic curriculum conforms to and goes beyond the requirements of the National Curriculum. Core subjects to GCSE are Mathematics, English, the Sciences, a Modern Language and Religious Studies. The curriculum in Year 7–9 is broad. Great care is taken to ensure that careful guidance is given to pupils in Year 9 and Year 11 when GCSE and AS/A2 choices are being made. The Academic Deputy, his assistant and the Housestaff work with pupils and their parents to tailor a programme which reflects the strength and interests of the individual. The majority of pupils will study 10 GCSE subjects and 4AS/A2 subjects in the Lower Sixth, dropping to 3 A2 in the Upper Sixth.

We currently offer 23 AS/A2 courses and there is considerable flexibility of combinations at both GCSE and A level.

Virtually all Sixth Form students proceed to Degree course at Universities, Medical Schools or other Higher Education Institutions, with the majority gaining places at their first-choice university.

A Sixth Form Enrichment programme of visiting lecturers, UCAS and Oxbridge preparation ensures a broad education at Sixth Form level.

Music. The College, under Director of Music Roland Robertson, has a highly deserved reputation for musical excellence. Two chapel choirs provide high quality music for the weekly sung Mass in the glorious surroundings of the Chapel of Our Lady of the Snows. The John Wood Chapel, within Prior Park Mansion, offers a further concert and rehearsal venue for the very many musicians in the school.

The Music Department, also in the Mansion, houses a recording studio and teaching and practice rooms. Around half the pupils learn a musical instrument, and there are several thriving orchestras, chamber groups and bands as well as a large and ambitious Choral Society, annual competitions and festivals. Prior Park musicians go on to Oxbridge and major conservatoires and play in NYO, NCO, NYC etc.

Performing Arts. Drama productions (around 20 a year), Dance, Debating and Public Speaking all feature prominently in the life of the school. The Julian Slade Theatre is a wonderful setting for this extensive and diverse performing arts programme. It has been extended to provide a Dance Studio and further teaching and technical support areas.

Physical Education and Games. Physical Education is included in the curriculum. Games are an important part of school life. Main school games are Rugby, Hockey, Cricket, Tennis for boys; Hockey, Netball, Tennis for girls. Provision is made for Swimming, Badminton, Cross-Country, Soccer, Volleyball, Basketball, Table Tennis, Fencing, Athletics and Rounders.

Sports facilities include a Gymnasium and fitness centre. A new Sports Hall is planned. An Astroturf, refurbished pavilion, netball and tennis courts as well as extensive rugby, hockey and cricket pitches are all on site. An entirely renovated and extended swimming pool and changing room complex opened in 2005.

Activities Programme. The voluntary Combined Cadet Force includes Navy and Army Sections including a Signals Platoon and Advanced Infantry. Adventure training takes place both in the UK and overseas. Cadets are encouraged to participate in the Service and Contingent Camps and Courses.

The Duke of Edinburgh's Award Scheme operates at all levels up to Gold Award. Volunteers may work on the four sections; service, physical recreation and skills, expeditions or hobbies.

The College operates its own Community Service Programme involving extensive work in the local community. A Young Enterprise scheme allows pupils the opportunity to compete successfully at a national level against other schools.

Boarders and day pupils alike partake of a wide range of activities including arts and crafts, sports, electronics, Radio Club, chess, golf, aerobics, Scrabble, cross-country running, model engineering, dance and a whole host of challenging events. Poetry and literary groups have won national awards. Public speaking and debating thrive.

Charity work is strongly encouraged, both in the form of fund-raising and visits to homes, hospitals and schools. A biennial charity week raises thousands of pounds.

Careers. Our careers programme combines the traditional strength of the House system with the benefits of a specialised central careers department. Every boy and girl will have individual careers guidance from their Housemaster or Housemistress through the five years from Form 4 (Year 9) to Upper Sixth, with particular support at the three critical stages of choice for GCSE, A Level, and university entrance. At the same time, specialist and technical advice is available from the Head of Careers and Head of Higher Education and a Careers professional, who provide detailed information and guidance via a programme of year assemblies for pupils and evening meetings for parents.

In Lower 5 (Year 10) pupils use KUDOS – a careers guidance programme – and a day of seminars, involving problem solving and business simulations, is organised. In Upper 5 (Year 11) pupils can take Morrisby Tests and are encouraged to undertake work experience. Sixth Form pupils are offered careers seminars, attend careers interviews with business and professional interviewers and have the opportunity to attend a Gap Year Fair and a Careers Fair.

Admission and Scholarships. (*see Scholarship Entries section*). Main points of admission are at 11+, 13+ and 16+ but pupils may transfer into the College at 12 and 14 if places are available. Early registrations are encouraged. Prospective families are encouraged to visit the College on Open Days or on an individual visit.

Entrance and scholarship examinations for 11+ and 13+ take place in January and March prior to entry in September. 16+ scholarship examinations and interviews take place in November/December. Please contact the Director of Admissions & Marketing for the relevant entrance/scholarship admission booklet.

Academic scholarships are available at 11+, 13+ and 16+. Art, All-Rounder, Music and Sporting Excellence awards are available at 11+, 13+ and 16+. Drama awards are available at 13+ and 16+. All awards carry with them a fee remission of up to 50% of the appropriate fee.

Fees per term (2008-2009). Boarding £7,446; Day 13+ £4,129; Day 11+ £3,706.

Prior Park Preparatory School. The Preparatory School is situated at Cricklade, Wiltshire, 35 miles from Prior Park and within easy reach of Swindon train station and the M4. It has ample boarding and recreational facilities for 180 boys and girls aged 7–13+. In addition, the adjacent nursery and preparatory school offer a wonderful educational environment for day children up to the age of six. Extra-curricular activity is an important element and the school has excellent standards in Music, Drama and Sport.

Headmaster: Mr G B Hobern, BA Hons.

For further details, see entry in IAPS section.

The Paragon School, Bath – Junior School of Prior Park College. The Paragon School is now part of Prior Park Educational Trust. Housed in an impressive Georgian mansion, the co-educational school for 3–11 years is set in beautiful wooded grounds only a few minutes drive from Prior Park College. A broad and balanced curriculum is delivered within a happy, caring environment.

Headmaster: Mr Titus Mills, BA Hons.

For further details, see entry in IAPS section.

Charitable status. Prior Park Educational Trust is a Registered Charity, number 281242.

Queen Elizabeth Grammar School
Wakefield

154 Northgate Wakefield West Yorkshire WF1 3QX
Tel: 01924 373943
Fax: 01924 231603
e-mail: office@qegsss.org.uk
website: www.wgsf.org.uk

The 'Free Grammar School of Queen Elizabeth at Wakefield' is supposed to be the descendant of a school existing in Wakefield in the 13th century, and was founded by Royal Charter in 1591, at the 'humble suit made unto us by the inhabitants of the Town and Parish of Wakefield'. The endowment is largely due to the munificence of George Savile, Esquire, of Haselden Hall, and his sons George Savile and Thomas Savile, whose names may still be read on the exterior of the old school.

Motto: '*Turpe nescire*'

Governing Body:
The Governing Body is the Wakefield Grammar School Foundation, consisting of 15 co-opted Governors and 6 nominated Governors (representatives of the Universities of Sheffield, Leeds, Huddersfield and York; Wakefield Cathedral and mid-Yorkshire Chamber of Commerce and Industry).

Spokesman: Mrs Megan Waugh

Clerk to the Governors: L Perry, BA, ACMA

***Headmaster*: M R Gibbons**, BA, AKC

Deputy Headmaster: J Slack, BSc, MA(Ed)
Academic Deputy (*Director of Studies*): L A Hallwood, BSc
Assistant Head: J T Palin, BEng
Assistant Head (*Pastoral*): L A Francis, BA

T Barker, BSc
A J Barraclough, BSc
D T Benn, BTech
R Bidmead, BA
D A Binney, BA
J R Birkinshaw, BTech
T A Brunt, PhD, MA
D Bunnell, BSc
D M Burrows, BSc
J P Cholewa, BEd, MA
S Clark, PhD, MChem
Mrs H L Cowan, BA
S E Davies, BA, MA
Ms J Dieckhöner-Kelly, BA
S L Dowson, BEd
D R Dryland, BA
P L Dryland, BA, ATC
M C Fascione, BSc
Mrs L J Firth, BA
Mrs A J Fitzsimons, BA, MA
M Fitzsimons, BA
K Fortas, BA
T H Gibb, BA
D N Gratrick, BSc
J Greenwood, BSc
J Holt, BSc
Mrs E M Jenkins, BSc
O K Lambert, BA
O Leask, BA
Dr J N Lord, PhD, BSc
Mrs V Macklam, BSc
P Mason, BSc
Mrs E Matthews, BA
Mrs E McGlone, BA
P McWilliam, BSc, MPhil
M J O'Connor, BA
Mrs C L Palin, BA
M C Parsons, BEd
K J Payne, MA
A T Pesterfield, BSc
G Pickersgill, BSc
Mrs S Powell, BSc
Mrs F D Preston, BMus, LTCL
J P Preston, BEd
A M Rees, BA
A N Rhodes, PhD
N Rigby, MA
R M Rylance, BA
R G Sewell, BA
Mrs H M Sheard, BSc
T Spencer, BA, MSc
P W Sutcliffe, BA
P Tamblyn, MA
G D Tingle, BA
Mrs L van der Schans, BA
Miss C J Walker, MA
D Waters, BA
C R Winborn, MA
M I Wood, BA

Headmaster's PA: Mrs H C Smith

Junior School
Head: Mrs L Gray, MA
Deputy Headmaster: I Shuttleworth, BSc

Mrs C A Blacker, BEd
C Cheffins, BEd, MEd
Mrs J S Clayton, ARCM, GRSM
Mrs A Coombes, BEd
J R Coughlan, BEd
Mrs K E Cousins, BEd, LTCL
G N Crowther, CertEd
N E Davies, MA
A Ferguson, BA
Mrs B D Lindley, BEd
Mrs P R Perkin, CertEd
Mrs L I Randall, Cert.Ed
R Ribeiro, BSc
Mrs D J Rogers, BEd
J S Wood, BA
D R Wright, BSc, MEd

Head's Secretary: Mrs C Denison

Visiting Music Staff:
D Allen, MSc, GCLCM, Grand Dip
C J Bacon, GMus
Mrs S T Bacon, GMus
Mrs K Baker, BMus
Mrs L Berwin, LRAM, GRSM
P Bingham
R Blanchard
J Clayton, ARCM, GRSM
P Francis, GDJCM
J Gibson, GRNCM
Mrs C Hall, DCLCM, LTCL
Mrs E Hambleton, GNSM, LRAM
D Heathcoate, BSc, PhD, PG Dip Perf
G B S Hirst, LRAM, ARCM, LTCL
A Holmes, BA, LTCL, CertEd
G Lewis
Mrs J D Maunsell, GBSM, ABSM, LTCL
D Mitchell, BMus, MA
T Moore, BMus, MA
I Naylor, BMus
M J Roberts, LGSM, DPLM
E Spencer, BA
J Storer
D Waller

Queen Elizabeth Grammar School has a long and proud tradition of achievement and exists to provide an excellent education for your son. There are approximately 990 boys in the school (junior 260 and senior 730).

The Headmaster is responsible to the Governors for both the Senior and the Junior Schools. Under his general supervision the Junior School (for boys of 7–11 years of age) is separately housed and administered by its own Head, who is a member of IAPS. (*For full details, see Junior School entry in IAPS section.*)

Situation and Buildings. The school is situated on Northgate near the centre of Wakefield. It is within walking distance of Wakefield Westgate Station and is convenient for all road links including the M1 and M62 motorways. The main building has been used by the school since 1854. Over the years, the school has expanded greatly, but its core remains the distinguished Early Gothic Revival building, whose architectural merits have been accentuated by extensive stone cleaning and renovation. A gradual programme of building has matched the school's expansion with additions and improvements taking place in all areas. Developments include the Queen's Building named in honour of Her Majesty the Queen who visited the school in 1992 to mark the school's Quatercentenary, a new Language Suite and new Sports Hall. In 2005 a new Theatre, Learning Resources Centre and English Department were opened along with a Sixth Form Centre.

The Junior School is housed in its own building and enjoys its own specialist facilities; Art Room, DT Room, Hall, ICT Room, Library, Music Room and Science Laboratory.

Curriculum. In the Senior School all boys follow a wide ranging common curriculum including various subject options from which they choose their GCSE subjects taken for examination at the end of Year 11. In the Sixth Form boys study subjects in a variety of combinations, following 4 subjects to AS and continuing 3 to A2 level. All in the Sixth Form also follow a General Studies course as an additional subject. An increasing number of subjects in the Sixth Form can be studied with pupils of our sister school, Wakefield Girls' High School.

Religion. The school is a Christian Foundation and maintains close links with Wakefield Cathedral for whom it educates choral scholars, but there is no denominational bias in either teaching or morning assemblies, and those who practise religions other than Christianity are warmly welcomed into the school.

Pastoral Care. A thoughtful programme of induction for new pupils, including a special activities week in the Yorkshire

Dales, is administered by the Head of Year 7. Thereafter boys are supervised by individual Heads of Year who coordinate teams of Form Tutors responsible for the progress and development of the boys in their care. A full PSHE programme is delivered and an expert Careers Department offers careful advice on all subject and university choices.

Physical Education and Games. Physical Education is an integral part of the school curriculum throughout the school. The school has some 37 acres of playing fields, with excellent rugby and hockey pitches in the Winter, with four cricket squares, an all-weather athletics track and access to 16 tennis courts in the Summer. The school has a six-badminton-court-size sports hall and fully equipped fitness room. January 2006 saw the addition to the sports facilities of a sand-dressed, all-weather surface, together with three new acrylic show courts for tennis.

The major games for Winter are rugby, hockey and cross-country. In the Summer term cricket, athletics and tennis predominate. All major sports are played to a high level, with boys regularly reaching county and, currently, international level.

Table tennis, basketball, golf, swimming, weight-training, squash and badminton exist at club level, either at lunchtime or after school. Regular competitions take place with other schools.

There is an annual ski trip and the school has a flourishing outdoor pursuits club, where activities are organised weekly during term time and as expeditions during vacations.

Music and Drama. The school has a full programme of musical and dramatic activities, many operating in conjunction with Wakefield Girls' High School. There is a major production each Autumn and Spring. There are in addition other productions and performances throughout the year.

There is at least one concert each term, designed to reflect the range of musical activity, which is wide and varied, ranging from madrigals through orchestral music to jazz and rock. Activities taking place throughout the year include two orchestras, two concert bands, two swing bands, junior and chamber choirs, together with many smaller groups and chamber ensembles. There is a large team of visiting instrumental staff, and close links with Wakefield Cathedral, where some events take place. A music scholarship is available each year on entry to the Sixth Form.

Clubs and Societies. These include Art, Chess, Christian Union, Classics, Debating, Drama, Geography, History, Literature, Photography, Angling, Bridge, Fell Walking, Film, Modelling, Table Tennis and Science. The various music groups include brass, woodwind, string ensembles and choirs. The school also participates in the Duke of Edinburgh's Award Scheme, which is extremely popular and undertakes many exciting expeditions. There is also a significant programme of charity collections and related activities.

Entrance. Entry into the Junior School is usually at 7 although places are retained for entry at 8, 9 and 10. Places depend on performance in the entrance tests held in February, and enquiries for entry at this level should be made to the Head of the Junior School (01924 373821).

There is a 5-form entry annually into the Senior School. Entry into the Senior School is possible from any kind of school and is normally:

(a) at 11 after a satisfactory performance in the entrance examinations held early in January or as a result of good academic performance in the Junior School.

(b) at 13 from Preparatory Schools after a satisfactory performance in the Common Entrance Examination.

(c) at 16 from any school after a satisfactory performance in the GCSE examinations and interview.

Enquiries about entrance to the Senior School at these or at other ages should be made to the Secretary for Admissions.

Fees per term (2008-2009). Senior School: £3,033. Junior School: £2,275–£2,404.

Scholarships, Bursaries, etc. The Governors award each year a limited number of scholarships to boys entering the Senior School at 11. Means and asset-tested awards are also available under the Wakefield Grammar Schools' Foundation Awards Scheme. Enquiries about these awards should be made for the Junior School to the Headmaster of the Junior School, and for the Senior School to the Secretary for Admissions.

Choral Scholarships are provided for boys in the Wakefield Cathedral Choir, and enquiry about these should be made either to the Precentor of Wakefield Cathedral, or to the Headmaster of the Junior School.

The Old Savilians Society. President: Mr N Rigby
The Parents Association. Chairman: Mrs K Harrison
The Friends of Queen Elizabeth Grammar School. Chairman: Mrs M Jackson
The Sports Association. Chairman: Mrs H Smith
can all be contacted through the School.

Charitable status. The Wakefield Grammar School Foundation is a Registered Charity, number 1088415.

Queen Elizabeth's Grammar School
Blackburn

Blackburn Lancs BB2 6DF

Tel: 01254 686300 (Headmaster)
01254 686303 (Bursar)
Fax: 01254 692314
e-mail: headmaster@qegs.blackburn.sch.uk
website: www.qegs.blackburn.sch.uk

Blackburn Grammar School was originally a Chantry School founded in 1509 by Thomas, the Second Earl of Derby, and associated with the Parish Church of Blackburn; it was disendowed in the reign of Edward VI, and re-established and constituted a Corporation by Royal Charter in 1567 by Queen Elizabeth. It is now administered by a scheme under the Charitable Trusts Acts dated 1910.

Motto: '*Disce Prodesse*'

Chairman of Governors: J C Barker, LLB

***Headmaster*: S A Corns**, MA

Deputy Headmasters:
J Cave, MA
D Hopkinson, BSc (*Acting*)

Heads of Departments:
Art: T D Birtwistle, BA
Biology: P R Taylor, BSc
Careers: S R Northin, BEd
Chemistry: A Sagar, BSc
Classics: D Westworth, MA
Complementary Studies: Mrs M Foxley, CertEd, PGDip
Design Technology: J R Hart, BEd
Drama: Miss J V St Jean, BA
Early Years: Mrs K A Marshall, BA
Economics: T R Glover, MA
English: Mrs K L Perkins, BA, MA
Geography: A E Young, MA
History: A L Thorpe, MA
ICT: M J McCann, JP, BA, DipPSE
Junior School: Miss A C Wharmby, BEd
Mathematics: A N Holman, BA, MA
Modern Languages: A M Rose, BA
Music: G R Hill, JP, BA, MLitt
Physical Education: M E Butler, BA, PhD
Physics: Mrs P Wild, BSc
Politics: D Hopkinson, BSc
Psychology & General Studies: P J Lowe, BSc

Religious Studies: A F Priory, BA, MA

Assistant Staff:

Miss C J Abrey, BA	A C Keay, CertEd
Mrs A Adam, NNEB	Ms K L Lawrence, BA Ed
Mrs R Arkwright, DipAD, ATC	B Lead, BA, MPhil
L Barré, BA	Mrs G Lees, NVQ
Miss A M Berry, BA	M J Lockwood, BA, MA
Miss K A Blount, MA	J B Morgan, BA
P K Broadhurst, BSc	R W Nicolson, BSc, MSc
Dr A M Brown, MA, PhD	Mrs S A Nowell, BA
A Buckingham, BEd	Mrs A Nuttall, BEC, NNEB
A J Clare, BEd	Miss F Pook, BSc, MSc
R L R Cooper, BA	M W Russell, BSc, MA
Mrs R J Cox, BA	Dr Z M Saunders, BSc, PhD
Mrs L M Crabtree, MA	Mrs G L Simpson, BEd
Mrs R A Deacon, BA, MA	M A Sirkett, BEd
M J Dearden, BSc, PhD	S A Smith, BSc
Miss P J Disley, BSc	J Steel, BSc, PhD
Miss N J Eggleston, BA	Mrs J E Taberner, BSc
C P J Evans, MA	Mrs R M Tattersall, BA
Mrs C Y Gammon, BSc	Mrs K Taylor, BEd
J F Grogan, BA	S J Taylor, BSc
P Hargreaves, BSc	Mrs A E Trafford, BA
S P Heald, BA	Miss R M Wildman, BA
M D Hindle, BSc	Miss D Wilkinson, BA
Miss M E Jordan, BA, MA, LCCI	Miss P C Williams, BSocSc
Mrs E L Kay, BEd	P H Wooldridge, BSc
	Miss K S Wrathmell, BA, MA

Bursar: J Ranford, ACMA
Director of Marketing and Development: P B Lloyd, BA, MBA, FCIM
Headmaster's Personal Assistant: Mrs D M Tate
Librarian: Mrs V Dewhurst, BA
School Nurse: Miss C Hargreaves

There are 762 pupils, of whom 136 are in the Junior Department, aged 3–11, and the Sixth Form numbers about 154. The School has been fully co-educational since 2001. Many pupils are bussed in from a large catchment area.

The Junior School curriculum includes English, Mathematics, Religious Education, Geography, History, Science, Art & Craft, Physical Education, and Music with optional tuition in most instruments.

Boys and girls join the Main School at the age of 11 with a few places at 13+ CE stage and follow a full range of academic and practical subjects up to GCSE.

Boys and girls who enter the Sixth Form have a wide choice of Advanced courses, including Classics, Modern Languages, English, History, Geography, Economics, Politics, Music, Art, Mathematics, and the Sciences, by means of which pupils are prepared for the universities, the professions and industry.

The School is a non-denominational, Christian school. There is daily worship. Religious instruction forms part of the ordinary teaching of all pupils, except those whose parents express a wish in writing to the contrary.

The School was rebuilt on a new site, facing Corporation Park, in 1884. In 1987 Her Majesty The Queen opened the £3.4 million Queen's Wing, which besides providing classrooms also incorporates a library and a language laboratory. A new sports hall was built on the sports fields at Lammack and in October 1990, on the school site, a new 25m swimming pool with sophisticated electronic timing facilities was opened. In 1995 a £1.5 million purpose-built Centre, Singleton House, was completed for the Sixth Form. Since the turn of the century, a new Early Years Department and a Modern Languages laboratory have come on stream, the Brian Mercer Physics Laboratory has opened, the Biology and Mathematics departments have been completely updated and refurbished in 2008, and there has been a number of major enhancements to the Junior School facilities.

The main School games are Association Football and Cricket, though Tennis, Rugby, Swimming, Netball and Basketball are among the many other physical activities provided. The 13 acres of playing fields are situated at Lammack, a short distance from the School. They have been extensively developed and improved, including new netball and tennis courts in 2005.

Out-of-school activities are provided for by various societies – for example Debating, Dramatic, Chess, Geographical and Sailing. A School play and a musical are produced publicly each year while the Choral Society and School Orchestra present several concerts. Instruction in the playing of orchestral instruments is provided.

There are educational visits abroad and exchanges with schools in France and Germany.

Fees per term (2008-2009). Main School £2,943, Junior School £2,121, Early Years £1,667. The School offers Bursaries.

Charitable status. Queen Elizabeth's Grammar School is a Registered Charity, number 1041220. It exists to provide quality education for boys and girls.

Queen Elizabeth's Hospital

Berkeley Place Clifton Bristol BS8 1JX
Tel: 0117 930 3040
Fax: 0117 929 3106
e-mail: headmaster@qehbristol.co.uk
juniors@qehbristol.co.uk (Junior School)
website: www.qehbristol.co.uk

Patron: Her Majesty The Queen

By his Will dated 10 April 1586, John Carr, a Bristol merchant, founded Queen Elizabeth's Hospital, a bluecoat school in Bristol on the lines of Christ's Hospital which was already flourishing in London. The Charter was granted to the School by Queen Elizabeth I in 1590. Originally composed entirely of boarders, the School continued so until 1920 when foundation day boys were admitted. Direct Grant status was accorded in 1945. The School is now independent and day only.

Motto: '*Dum tempus habemus operemur bonum.*'

Governing Body:
N Tyrrell, BA (*Chairman*)
J G Mason (*Vice-Chairman*)

Professor R D Adams	J G Pickard, BSc
G Bird, ACII	H Roberts
A J Brackin, BA, FCA	Mrs G Rowcliffe, BEd
H L M Bothamley	C Russell-Smith, BSc, FRICS
D Ellis	Mrs M Shutt, JP
P N Gibson	D A Smart
N A Mitchell, MSc, FRAeS	
A J Morsley, BSc	

Bursar: J W Parker, MIMgt

Staff:

***Headmaster*: S W Holliday**, MA

Deputy Head (*Operations*): S P Ryan, BSocSc
Deputy Head (*Pastoral*): D M Bateson, MA
Director of Studies: J G Sykes, BSc

P M Amor, BA	A C M Clements, BSc
S Albon, BSc	C B Conquest, BEd
Mrs F Bean, BEd, MA	S M Cook, MSc
Mrs L Benson, BEd	Mrs S Cosgrove, BSc
C Brotherton, BA	Miss A Calvert, BA
J F Brown, BSc	P Davies, BSc
Ms P Cawte, BA	Mrs M Dimes, BSc

R Dixon, BSc
Ms B Dullroy, BEd
T Dunn, BSc
W J Earp, MA
W R Ellis, BSc
T Fewster, BSc
Mrs A G Gardner, MA, BEd
E Gent, BA
M Hale, BSc
D Harris, BSc
R Harris, BA
B Hollis, BSc
A Hughes, BA
Mrs N Hunter, BSc
Dr J Jönsson, MSc, PhD
P M Jones, BA
R J Jones, BMus, FRCO, LRAM
P E Joslin, BEd
P J Kirby, BA
H L Kyle, BSc, PhD
A G Lewis-Barned, BEd
Ms S Maltin, BA
J E Martin BA
R Martineau, MEng
J R Matthews, BEd
S McGlynn, BA
Miss N Morgan, BA
P R Murray, BA
M Owen, BSc
J D Perkins, MA
W G Plowden, BA
Mrs S Pole, BA
Mrs A Powell-Wiffen, BSc
Mrs J Rostrup, BSc
Miss J Sharrock, BA
Mrs C E Steen, BA
Mrs R Steven, BA
Mrs F Waite-Taylor, BA
Mrs P Warford, BA
Miss C J Winchester, BA

Junior School:
Headteacher: M J Morris, BA

Visiting Teachers:
Miss K Bagshawe, BMus
K Figes
Mrs C Garland, ATCL, LAMDA
C Khajavi, BA Mus
Ms K Latham
S Lewins
Miss I McLean, BMus
A Stewart
Miss A White, BMus

Chaplain: The Revd S B Taylor, BA
Headmaster's Secretary: Mrs E Davies
Librarian: Ms L Casserley

Admission. There are 560 boys in the Senior School, ranging in age from 11 to 18. Entrance examinations for both 11+ and 13+ applicants are held in January each year.

Term of Entry. Usually September.

Entrance Scholarships. (*see Scholarship Entries section*). A few scholarships are offered at 11+ and 13+. These are awarded purely on academic merit for outstanding achievement in the entrance procedures and may also carry with them generous assistance for applicants whose parents' means are limited.

Assisted Places. There are many School assisted places available. The School has a substantial foundation income and is able to give generous support to parents whose means are limited.

Music Scholarships. Music scholarships are available at 11+ and 13+.

Buildings. The School was originally close by the City Centre but moved to new premises on Brandon Hill in 1847. A major building and improvement programme included the building of the QEH Theatre (1990), refurbishment of the Art School (2000), new Mathematics rooms and heavy investment in ICT (2004). An 80-strong Junior School has been opened (2007) along with completion of a new Sixth Form Centre (2007). In 2008, a multi-million pound development programme, in conjunction with Bristol City Football Club, sees completion of pitches on 23 acres of recently acquired land at the Sports Ground at Failand. Extensive new Science facilities are to be developed in the near future.

Curriculum. Boys are prepared for the GCSE (IGCSE in Mathematics and English) and GCE A Level, and for university entrance. The usual school subjects are offered at GCSE Level, and the AS/A2 Level subjects are: English Literature, English Language, Theatre Studies, Economics, Latin, Classical Civilisation, History, Geography, French, German, Spanish, Art, Music, Mathematics, Further Mathematics, Physics, Chemistry, Biology, PE and Sport, Business Studies, ICT, Ethics and Philosophy, Politics and Psychology.

Music. There is a School Orchestra, Choir, Brass Group and Wind Band. Music is included in the timetable for all the junior forms. GCSE and A Level music is part of the School curriculum, and tuition is arranged for a wide range of instruments. The Choir and Instrumentalists perform regularly and also undertake joint ventures with the independent girls' schools in Bristol.

Art. The Department is well equipped and offers ceramics, screen printing, photography and computer imaging.

Religious Studies. The School is a Christian one which welcomes boys of all faiths. Religious Studies is part of the curriculum and boys attend two services a year in Bristol Cathedral.

Games. Rugby, Football, Athletics, Cricket, Hockey, Swimming, Tennis, Badminton, Sailing, Squash, Fencing, Judo, Climbing and Mountain Biking. A large number of boys also participate in The Duke of Edinburgh's Award and Ten Tors.

Dress. Boys wear either grey flannel trousers and a blazer or a plain dark suit. Traditional bluecoat uniform is worn on special occasions.

General. All parents are encouraged to join the Friends of Queen Elizabeth's Hospital, a society whose aim is to promote a close relationship between parents and staff and to further the welfare of the School. There is a flourishing Old Boys' Society (Secretary: Mr N Coombes), which holds regular meetings and circulates a newsletter. A panel of Old Boys, formed from all professions, and working with the Head of Careers, is available to give advice on careers to boys.

The School has long been known in Bristol as The City School and its links with the Lord Mayor and Corporation are strong. Boys read the lessons and sing in the Lord Mayor's Chapel, and groups are in attendance for such occasions as Mayor-making and Council Prayers.

The central position of the School, close to the University, the Art Gallery and Museum, the Central Library, the Bristol Old Vic and the Colston Hall, affords ready access to a wide range of cultural facilities which boys are encouraged to use.

Junior School. 80 Day Boys aged 7–11.

The Junior School of Queen Elizabeth's Hospital is an extremely well-resourced all-boys' school, unique to Bristol. It opened in 2007 in a fine refurbished Georgian terrace adjacent to the Senior School. Whilst having many of its own on-site facilities, it also shares some with the Senior School, particularly the Dining Hall, Theatre, Science and extensive Sports Ground. It also shares the strong ethos and values of the Senior School, whilst retaining its own identity.

Entry is by test at seven years with the main purpose being to prepare boys for the Senior School. There is one form per year group and the School offers an enjoyable and enriched educational experience in a wide range of subjects taught by specialists, some from the Senior School. Many clubs and after-school activities are available, designed especially to appeal to boys.

Being small, the Junior School focuses on each boy's personal qualities, fostering a love of learning whilst nurturing the interests and talents of each one. Every boy leaves recognising himself as a lifelong learner, moving on with ease and confidence to secondary education secure in numeracy and literacy.

Like its Senior School, which is renowned nationally for high achievement, the QEH Junior School aims to be a happy place with strong pastoral care, academic excellence, and high standards in drama, sport and music.

Fees per term (2008-2009). Senior School £3,184, Junior School £1,995. Fees include educational visits, textbooks and stationery.

Charitable status. Queen Elizabeth's Hospital is a Registered Charity, number 1104871, and a Company Limited by

Guarantee, number 5164477. Queen Elizabeth's Hospital has existed since 1590 to provide an education for boys.

Queen's College
Taunton

Trull Road Taunton Somerset TA1 4QS
Tel: 01823 272559 School Office
01823 340830 Admissions
Fax: 01823 338430
e-mail: admissions@queenscollege.org.uk
website: www.queenscollege.org.uk

Queen's College is one of the South West's leading independent day and boarding co-educational schools and has a consistent record of high academic achievement. Queen's' expertise also shows in music, drama and the arts. Please see the school website for further details.

The college has a well-deserved reputation for the quality of its teaching and all pupils are cared for in small tutor groups. The staff works untiringly to encourage students to develop their personal skills and abilities. The class sizes are well below the national average thus helping to develop a friendly, supportive environment.

Queen's operates a very strong co-curricular programme including a wide variety of sports and considerable emphasis is placed on participation in the Duke of Edinburgh's Award Scheme. All students take Bronze, many go on to Silver and to date, over 300 Sixth Form students have achieved their Gold Awards.

The college is controlled by the Board of Management for Methodist Residential Schools and receives pupils of all denominations.

Motto: '*Non scholae sed vitae discimus*' (*We learn not for school but for life*)

Visitor: The President of the Methodist Conference.

Governors:
Chairman: J N Birkett, FCIB, MSI

B M Butt, FCA
Revd F J Carne
D R Evans, MA
Mrs J A Forsyth, MA, BA, FRSA
Capt P M Gowen, RN
Mrs M Hannam
N Harvey, BA, MP
P Hughes
R James, BA
S A Lawson
P Madhavan, Dip NB Surg, FRCS Ed Tr & Orth
I McIntyre
L Oldham, FDSRCS, BDS, LDS, RCS
Mrs D Perreau
M F Powell, BSc, FRICS, FAAV
G Russell, MA
Mrs A St John Gray, BA Hons, MA, JP
Maj Gen M F L Shellard, CBE
G Slocum
Revd B D Thompson

Honorary Governor: The President of the Old Queenians' Association

***Headmaster*: Christopher J Alcock**, BSc Durham, FRGS

Chaplain: Revd Robert J Blackhall, BSc, BA

Financial Director & Clerk to Governors: Richard J Abolins, BSc, ACA

* *Head of Department*
† *House Parents*

Senior Leadership Group:
Deputy Headmaster: Marcus K Paul, MA (*English*)
Assistant Head – Pastoral: Mrs Gill Watson, BEd (*Chemistry and Science Education*)
Director of Studies: Graham H Warner, BSc (**Mathematics*)
Director of Marketing and Communications: Keith Wheatley, BA (*Law and American Studies*)
Director of Co-Curriculum: Simon Ross, BA (**Geography*)
Head of Sixth Form: David Cooke, BSc, MEd (*Biology*)

Senior School

Teaching Staff:
Miss Donna Ashman, BA (*History, Examinations Office*)
Ralph Bates, BEd (*English*)
Geoffrey Bisson, BA (**History*)
Mrs Kay Bloxham, BEd, MA (*Dance and Physical Education*)
Roger Bowden, BEd (*Mathematics*)
Mrs Jennifer Brierley, BA (*English*)
Miss Marta Carankova (*EFL*)
John Chidgey, BA (**Modern Languages*)
†Mrs Rebecca Cole, BSc (*Food Technology*)
Paul De Jaeger, BSc (*Geography*)
Miss Pauline Ellis, BA (*Art*)
Mrs Jane Evans (*Performance Studies*)
Stephen Evans, BA (**Theatre Studies*)
Mrs Terri Fisher, BA (*Modern Languages*)
Michael Fletcher, BSc (*Ceramics*)
†Mrs Amanda Free, BA (*Learning Support*)
†Andrew Free, BA, DipSpPsych (**Director of Physical Education and Games*)
Andrew Garton, BA (*Music and ICT*)
Mrs Cherry Grant, CertEd, (*Learning Support*)
Mrs Donna Greenow, BSc (*Modern Languages*)
Mrs Lindsay Hall, BA (**English*)
Angus Hamilton, BA (**Religious Studies*)
†Miss Claire Harrison, BSc (*Biology*)
Miss Julie Harrison, BEd (**Girls' Physical Education and Games*)
David Hedges, BA (*Music*)
Ian Henden, BSc (*Chemistry*)
Mrs Lisa Henden, BSc (*Biology*)
Ben House (*Physical Education and Games*)
Timothy Jolliff, MA (**Chemistry*)
Byron Lewis, BSc (**Design Technology*)
Mrs Caroline Lewis, BH (*Physical Education and Games*)
Ms Kate Littlewood, MA, Cert SpLD (**Learning Support*)
Mrs Grace Mainstone, BA, LRSM, LTCL (**EFL*)
Miss Sarah Male, BA (*Modern Languages*)
Miss Lisa Manley, BA (*Physical Education and Games*)
†Philip Mann, MNASC (**Boys' Physical Education and Games*)
Miss Gemma Mansfield, BA (*Religious Studies*)
†Damian Marshman, BSc (*Mathematics*)
John Marston, BA (*Theatre Studies*)
†Mrs Carole Mason, BEd (*Mathematics*)
†Christopher Monks, BSc (*Mathematics*)
†Ian Morrell, BEd (*Design Technology, Careers*)
Mrs Virginia Murray, BA (*French*)
Mark Neenan, BEd (*Geography*)
Nicholas O'Donnell, BEng (**Physics*)
Mrs Valerie Orme-Dawson, BA (*EFL*)
Adrian Palmer, BA, Cchem, MRSC (*Science*)
Mrs Pamela Pawley, BA (*Mathematics*)
Mrs Sheila Platt (*Mathematics*)
Miles Quick, BA (**Music*)
Mrs Lynda Rixon, BSc (*Economics & Business Studies*)
Mrs Nicola Ross, BA (*Manager, Learning Resource Centres*)
Mrs Laura Schofield, MA (*Modern Languages*)
Jon Shepherd, BSc (**Biology*)
Miss Melissa Smith, BSc (*History*)
Nigel Smith, BSc (*Physics*)
Leslie Stevens, BSc, BSc (**ICT, Physics*)
Tristan Stone BSc (*Mathematics*)
Mrs Sophie Turpin, BA (*Mandarin*)
Peter Vicary, BSc (**Business Studies*)
Mrs Sue Wedge-Thomas, BSc (*Biology*)

Mrs Claire Western, BA (**Art*)
Dick Wilde, BEd (*Physical Education and Games*)
Mrs Sharon Wilde, BA (*Physical Education and English*)

PA to the Headmaster: Mrs Wendy Harding
Admissions Secretary: Mrs Anne Slocum
Office Administrator: Miss Judith Poole
School Secretary: Mrs Cathy Carter
Sixth Form Administrator: Mrs Penny Bates

Junior School, Pre-Prep and Nursery

Headmaster: Justin M Backhouse, BEd

Junior School Teaching Staff:
Mrs Linda Alcock, BA
Mrs Sarah Beats, BA
Mrs Patricia Camera, CertEd
Andrew Clark, BA
Philip Dudman, BA
Mrs Gill Harrison, BEd, RSA Dip SpLD
Miss Samantha Horner, BEd
Mrs Belinda Hoskins, BEd
Mrs Sue Marston, BA, LAMDA Gold Medallist
Mrs Annie Mason, DipEd
Mrs Vicky Miller, DipEd
†Christopher Monks, BSc
Mrs Shirley Nickerson, CertEd, RSA DipSpLD, AMBDA
Mrs Valerie Orme-Dawson, BA
Andrew Owen, BA
Mrs Janet Proud, Dip Teaching Assistant
Miss Johanna Read, BEd
Miss Sarah Scutt, BA, MA
Mrs Catherine Stirzaker, NNEB
Terence Stirzaker, CertEd
Mrs Anne Wade, BA
Mrs Penny Walker, BSc
Mrs Anthea Watkins, CertEd, RSA Dip SpLD
Miss Margaret Way, LRAM, LGSM, ALAM Gold Medallist AM
Dick Wilde, BEd
Mrs Sharon Wilde, BA

Pre-Prep and Nursery Staff:

Head: Mrs Janet Williams, BEd, CertEd, NNEB

Mrs Dawn Coram, NVQ3, DPP, STC
Mrs Jill Fear, BEd
Miss Christina Hardwick, BTEC Early Years
Miss Elizabeth Hayes, NNEB, DPQS (*Head of Nursery*)
Mrs Anne Higgins
Mrs Clare Hood, BEd
Mrs Rachel Hoyle, NVQ Level 2
Mrs Susan Hutt, Dip Child Care CACHE
Mrs Rebecca Milby BSc
Mrs Vanessa Monks, BA
Mrs Sarah Silverwood, NVQ2
Mrs Theresa Underwood, BSc
Mrs Sarah Warner, BEd

Secretary to Headmaster and Head of Pre-Prep & Nursery: Ms Julie Cameron
Assistant Secretary: Mrs Sarah Musgrave

Medical Staff:
Dr David Downs, BSc, MBChB, DRCOG, MRCGP
Dr Gabrielle de Cothi, MBChB, DRCOG, MRCGP
Mrs Lyn Dimery, SRN, SCN
Mrs Susan Parratt, RGN
Mrs Judith Barry, RN, RM, DipHE Health Studies
Mrs Helen Backhouse, RGN (*Junior School*)
Miss Rebecca Morgan (*Resident Matron, Junior School*)

Number of Pupils. The Queen's College Pre-Preparatory, Junior and Senior co-educational schools are based on the same site with some facilities shared: continuity of education is assured.

The Senior school (11 to 18 years) has 571 pupils of whom 152 are boarders. The Junior school (7 to 11 years) has 178 pupils, of whom 14 board and the Pre-Prep school has a total of 49 pupils (none of whom are boarders). The full College complement of pupils is therefore 798. Nursery pupils are additional, attendance being a mix of full and part time.

Situation and Buildings. Queen's College was founded in 1843 within Taunton's Castle walls but was relocated to the south western outskirts of Taunton three years later when the present main school buildings were constructed. It is in a good situation with fine views of the Quantock and Blackdown Hills, within easy reach of Exmoor and Dartmoor, just a mile and a half from Taunton town centre, easily accessible by road or rail, junction 25 of M5 is 2 miles away and serviced by Bristol International and Exeter Airports.

The 1846 original Grade II* listed building contained a School House, the School Hall and a Dining Room. Later a Junior School was added, an indoor heated Swimming Pool and a Music Department.

Over the last twenty years there has been an extensive building programme which has included: nine classrooms for the Junior school, applied science, computer and electronics centre, design area, new changing rooms, day girl and day boy accommodation, enlargement and modernisation of girl and boy boarding houses, school hall for the Junior school, new music school, concert/assembly hall for the Senior school and DT block. Latest additions are a new Art & Drama building; Leisure and Performing Arts Centres; a new Science Block and major expansion of Pre-Prep facilities.

Organisation. At Queen's College continuity of education is assured from the Nursery, through Pre-Preparatory, the Junior school, the Senior school and then into the Sixth Form.

There are two day boy houses and two day girl houses and each has a House Master/Mistress and Tutor for each year group. There are two boys' boarding houses and two girls' boarding houses and each is in the care of House Parents, together with a resident assistant House Master/Mistress. Tutors are attached to each house and are responsible for academic progress. They guide each student through GCSE and A Level choices and in conjunction with one of the Careers Masters and the Director of Studies, the tutor advises them on university selection and choice of career.

Curriculum. Pupils in the first three years of Senior School follow a broad, common curriculum. This provides them with a sound base in the arts, sciences, humanities and technology based subjects as well as games and PSHE. They are streamed and taught as a form for most subjects and are setted for mathematics, English and French. At GCSE there is a common core of English language and literature, mathematics, three sciences, French and religious studies. Pupils then choose three option subjects.

In the Lower Sixth pupils choose 4 AS Level subjects and in the Upper Sixth the majority take three subjects to A2 Level. Throughout the Sixth Form some periods of curriculum time are devoted to a general studies course that includes RE, PSHE and key skills.

Co-Curriculum. In addition to games, music and drama, pupils are encouraged to participate in a range of activities including debating, public speaking, general knowledge quizzes, ICT, chess, photography, robotic design, electronics, bridge and dressmaking. There are also a number of academic societies. Outdoor pursuits such as canoeing, canoe polo and rock climbing are popular and participation in the Duke of Edinburgh's Award Scheme is a particular feature of Queen's. Over 300 Queen's College pupils have now achieved their Gold Award.

Music. The music staff provides teaching cover for keyboard, strings, brass, woodwind, percussion and singing, and give lessons to 25% of Senior School pupils, 50% of Junior School pupils and 40% of Pre-Prep pupils.

The purpose-built Music Department is comprised of :

- classroom
- 6 large teaching rooms
- 5 practice rooms
- electronic studio for keyboard studies
- audio studio for computer-based composition (GCSE and A Level)
- instrument store with individual lockers of varying sizes

The Music Department also uses the Performing Arts Centre in the main building for rehearsals and small concerts. The Queen's Hall (which adjoins the Music Department) has a 350-seat multi-purpose auditorium with 2-manual pipe organ and Steinway Concert Grand Piano.

Musical organisations:

- Chapel Choir – assemblies and Sunday Services
- First Orchestra – two rehearsals each week
- Middle School Orchestra
- Wind Band
- Chamber Orchestra (Strings)
- Madrigal Group

Also a wide variety of small ensembles and chamber groups for strings, brass, woodwind with or without piano. A number of concerts are staged each year.

Drama. There is a very active drama programme throughout the college with the Senior school Drama department providing courses from Year 7 to Year 13, the department aims to involve all those wishing to develop their co-curricular and academic interests.

In the Senior school, productions take place once a term. There is a main school production at the end of the Autumn term, Sixth Form and Middle School plays at the end of the Spring term, and a Lower school play at the end of the Summer term. Major productions and concerts take place in the Queen's Hall and the new Performing Arts Centre stages smaller scale concerts and plays.

Students are offered Theatre courses at GCSE, AS and A2 Level. Theatre visits are arranged on a regular basis and for those studying the subject at GCSE and A Level the visits form part of their course.

PE/Games. The 30 acre playing fields of Queen's are both extensive and adaptable. In the Autumn term the grass area provides 5 rugby pitches which are also used for sevens in the Spring term.

In the Summer there are 3 cricket squares, 2 grass volleyball courts, a 400 metre athletics track and numerous rounders pitches.

The two Astroturf pitches are used very frequently – daily for hockey in the Autumn and Spring terms – and are of such quality that Queen's has often been called upon to host County hockey tournaments. Both pitches are converted to tennis courts in the Summer, giving a total of 24 tennis courts.

The hard court surface in the middle of the field is used for netball in the Spring term and for tennis in the Autumn and Summer terms. Alongside this area are cricket nets for use in the Summer term.

The Sports Hall is used for the following activities: gymnastics, trampolining, basketball, badminton, volleyball, indoor hockey and indoor tennis. There is a squash court and a fully-equipped fitness centre adjoining the Sports Hall. Within the complex is an indoor heated pool that is used at various times for swimming from Pre-Prep through to Sixth Form lessons. Team swimming, canoeing, canoe polo and sub aqua are regular activities throughout the year.

Admission. Education at Queen's can start at 3 years on entry to the Nursery. The majority of pupils join the Pre-Preparatory school from the age of 4 years. Junior school pupils start at age 7. Entrance is by examination and those who are successful in gaining places to the Junior school make satisfactory transfer to the Senior school. There are places for boys and girls at the age of 13 from Preparatory schools who take the Common Entrance examination. A number enter the Sixth Form direct on GCSE Level results.

Scholarships. (*see Scholarship Entries section*). *Academic Scholarships*: Worth up to 50% of fees for students of proven academic ability in one or more subjects. Day and boarding scholarships for students aged 8+, 11+, 13+ and 16+ on 1st September in year of entry.

Music Scholarships: Worth up to 50% of fees for the most gifted scholars. Offers of up to 8 scholarships for talented musicians aged 10+, 11+, 12+ and 13+ at the projected time of entry to the College. Three Sixth Form entry scholarships are also available plus an Organ award.

Drama Scholarships: Worth up to 50% of fees for the students of best ability. Queen's College offers up to 6 scholarships for talented students with proven drama ability aged 11+ and 13+ at the projected time of entry to the college. Sixth Form scholarships included.

Art Scholarships: Worth up to 50% of fees for the most talented scholars. Scholarships are for talented students with an existing standard and potential for considerable development. Candidates to be aged 11+ or 13+ at projected time of entry to the college. Sixth Form scholarships included. Art scholarships are awarded as part of the Academic scholarship and are based on portfolio and interview.

Sport Scholarships: Worth up to 50% of fees for the students of best ability. Queen's College offers up to 6 scholarships for talented students with proven sports ability aged 11+ and 13+ at the projected time of entry to the college. Sixth Form scholarships included.

Awards: Sixth Form November; 10+, 11+ and 12+ January; 13+ March.

Fees per term (2008-2009). Pre-Preparatory School £1,545–£1,590 (day pupils only); Junior Day Pupils £1,885–£3,105; Junior Boarders £3,185–£4,845; Senior Day Pupils £3,905–£4,435; Senior Boarders £5,885–£6,915. These fees include all necessary expenses: books, stationery etc.

Charitable status. Queen's College, Taunton is a Registered Charity, number 310208. The College is a leading Charitable Trust in the field of Junior and Secondary education.

Radley College

Abingdon Oxfordshire OX14 2HR
Tel: 01235 543127 (Warden)
01235 543122 (Bursar)
01235 543174 (Admissions)
01235 543000 (General Enquiries)
Fax: 01235 543106
website: www.radley.org.uk

St Peter's College, Radley, was founded by the Rev William Sewell, Fellow of Exeter College, Oxford, to provide an independent school education on the principles of the Church of England. It was opened on 9 June 1847, and incorporated by Royal Charter in 1890. It stands in a park of some 700 acres.

Motto: '*Sicut Serpentes, sicut Columbae*'

Visitor: The Rt Revd The Lord Bishop of Oxford

Chairman: Lord Wilson of Dinton, GCB, MA, LLB

Council:
C G Clarke, FCA (*Vice-Chairman*)
I A Balding, LVO
M E Hodgson, MA, FRICS
D A Peck, MA
T O Seymour, MA
M J W Rushton, MA
Sir Tim Rice
S W B Whitworth, MA
Rt Revd A J Russell, DPhil
A W M Fane, MA, FCA
N J Henderson, MA, FRCS
D C S Smellie, MA
A P G Holmes, MA
Mrs D J Pluck, FCA
G A Kaye, BSc
Mrs E McKendrick, BA
W S H Laidlaw, MA

***Warden*: A W McPhail**, MA

Sub-Warden & Director of Studies: A E Reekes, MA

Senior Masters:
C R Barker, BA
M J S Hopkins, BA

Teaching Staff:
M J Harris, MA
C W Hastings, MA
M F Dean, BA
A C Wallis, BSc, PhD
G Wiseman, BA
J C Nye, MA
J F leManac'h, BA
†B J Holden, MA, BTech (*D Social*)
M R Wright, BSc
J R Summerly, BA, PhD
Mrs J A Wright, BA
M P Horsey, CertEd
J F C Nash, MA
P W Gamble, MA
I P Ellis, BA, DipRASchls
R E Schofield, MA
S Barlass, BA
†A J McChesney, BSc (*F Social*)
C M Bedford, BA, PhD
Mrs M E H Craig, MA
†N Murphy, MA (*K Social*)
I S Yorston, MA
†R M C Greed, BSc (*B Social*)
†H D Hammond, BSc (*G Social*)
W O C Matthews, BA
†T R G Ryder, BA, MFA (*A Social*)
†D C K Edwards, MA (*H Social*)
Mrs G M Gurney, MSc
†R A King, BSc, MRSC, CChem (*E Social*)
S A Thorn, BSc, PhD
†J M Sparks, BSc (*C Social*)
S A Hall, BA, MPhil, PhD
N L Haggett, MBE, BEd
Mrs B L M Haggett, ATD, DipSLD
†M K T Hindley, MA, LLB (*J Social*)
M R Jewell, BA
E J Wolstenholme, BSc, PhD
R Johnson, BSc
J R W Beasley, MA
C R Martin, BA
I K Campbell, BA
Mrs S Pullen-Campbell, BA
Mrs M C Hart, BA
B R Knox, BEd
R D Shaw, MA
P M Fernandez, MA
Ms E D Murtagh, BA
P M Teale, MMath
D W S Roques, MA
K A Mosedale, MA, MSc
Miss K J Lean, BA
H Crump, LLB
S H Dalrymple, BA
S Kerr, BA
S A Graham, BA, MA
K Halliday, BSc, PhD
J F Adams, BA
R P Malpass, BA, PhD
D J C Vaccaro, MA
R M Lowe, BA
A M Lowe, BSc, PhD
G H S May, MA
G R King, BA
D J Pullen, BSc
R K McMahon, MA, MPhil, DPhil
H G C Clarke, BA
C J Ellott, BA, LLB
J E Gearing, BA
D S Borthwick, DPhil, MChem
Mrs G C Porter, MA, MSc
O H Langton, MA
Miss T Scammell, BA, MPhil
Mrs N J King, BA
Ms E E N Danis, BA
E W Brooke, DPhil, MChem
G J A Hughes, BA, MSc, PhD
D J Palmer, MPhys
S R Giddens, BSc, MSc, PhD
T C Lawson, BA
A C Jackson, BA
C J Lee, BA
C E R Scott-Malden, BA, MA
P R Wallace, BSc, MPhil, DPhil
Mrs C C A de Bono, BA
A D Cunningham, MA, PhD
A C Shouler, BA

Chaplain: The Revd T D Mullins, BA
Assistant Chaplain: The Revd T J E Fernyhough, BA
Librarian: Mrs C D Sargent, MA, ALA

Music:
Precentor: S D J Clarke, MA, ARCO
A J A Williams, MMus, DipRAM, GRSM, LRAM
Miss S-L Naylor, MA
T M Morris, MA, DPhil, FRCO

There are 30 peripatetic music staff.

Bursar and Secretary: A Ashton, MA
Medical Officer: Dr J N B Moore, BSc, MB BS, DRCOG, MRCGP

Old Radleian Society Secretary: J K Mullard, BA
Foundation Director: A L Robinson
Registrar: Mrs E H Barker, BA

General Arrangements. There are 665 boys in the School. On admission, boys enter one of the 10 houses known as Socials. All are close together within the grounds. All meals are served in Hall on a cafeteria system.

Admission to the School. Boys are admitted between the ages of 13 and 14 in the Michaelmas Term, and qualify by taking either the Common Entrance Examination, our own extrance exam, or the Entrance Scholarship Examination. Registration starts at birth and registration forms can be obtained from the Registrar. All entries are made centrally. A registration fee of £100 is payable when a boy's name is entered. This fee is not returnable and registration does not guarantee a place in the School. Three years before a boy is due to come, a Final Acceptance Form will be sent to parents for whose sons a place can be guaranteed. These forms are sent out in date order of registration. An Entrance Fee of £700 (part refundable against first term's account) is payable on acceptance. A few places are sometimes available for entry to the Sixth Form. Details are available on our website.

Entrance Awards. (*see Scholarship Entries section*). Up to twelve Academic Scholarships are awarded each year. In addition All-Rounder, Music, Drama and Art Awards are offered. All awards may be supplemented by a means-tested bursary. Details of all awards are available from our Website or the Registrar.

Further means-tested Bursaires are available for boys who would otherwise be unable to come to Radley.

Work. In the Shells, Removes and Fifth Forms a broad curriculum is followed. There is some choice at GCSE with boys generally taking 9 or 10 subjects.

In the Sixth Form a boy can specialise in a combination of Classics, French, Spanish, German, Theatre Studies, English, History, Religious Studies, Geography, Geology, Biology, Chemistry, Physics, Mathematics, Economics, Politics, Economics and Business Studies, Music, Art or Design, leading to AS/A2 examinations.

Careers. Advice and assistance is available to all boys on a wide range of career possibilities through the Director of Careers. The School is a member of ISCO (The Independent Schools Careers Organisation) and close connections are maintained with the professions, with firms and with the Services. Visits and talks by experts in these fields are a special feature.

Games. In the Michaelmas term Rugby Football is the major school game. In the other 2 terms the 'wet-bobs' row; the 'dry-bobs' play Hockey (the major game) and Soccer in the Lent term, Cricket (the major game), Athletics and Tennis in the Summer. There are also numerous minor sports which involve boys in competition with other schools.

The playing fields are close to the main buildings.

The College has its own boathouse, and the use of a stretch of the river Thames between Sandford and Abingdon. The VIII's compete in regattas and Head of the River races.

There are two all-weather Hockey Pitches, an Athletics Track, 5 Squash Courts, a new Real Tennis Court, a Rackets Court, 2 covered Fives Courts, 20 Hard Tennis Courts and a 9-hole golf course. There is a large, well-equipped Gymnasium and an indoor, heated Swimming Pool attached to a multi-purpose Sports Hall.

CCF. All boys, in their fourth term, join the Radley College Contingent, Combined Cadet Force (Army, Navy and Air Sections). They work for the Proficiency examination, which takes 3 terms. When they have passed Proficiency and done a week's Corps Camp in the holidays they either stay on in a special section for further training or join one of the many Community Action Projects on offer.

Fees per term (2008-2009). £8,820 (inclusive of medical attendance). Lessons in Pianoforte and other musical instruments are given at a charge of £24.71 a lesson. There is available a system of insurance against loss of fees caused by illness, accident, or infection. Particulars can be obtained from the Bursar.

Charitable status. St Peter's College, Radley is a Registered Charity, number 309243. It exists for the purpose of the education of youth in general knowledge and literature and particularly and especially in the doctrines and principles of the Church of England.

Ratcliffe College

Fosse Way Ratcliffe on the Wreake Leicester
Leicestershire LE7 4SG
Tel: 01509 817000 School Office
01509 817072/817031 Registrar
Fax: 01509 817004
e-mail: registrar@ratcliffe.leics.sch.uk
website: www.ratcliffecollege.com

Ratcliffe College is a co-educational Catholic day and boarding school. The School was founded in 1844 and opened in 1847; the original buildings by A W Pugin were erected with funds provided by Lady Mary Arundel of Wardour, who also bequeathed money for subsequent extensions.

Motto: '*Legis plenitudo charitas*'

Governing Body:
Consists of two members of the Board of Directors of the Company Limited by Guarantee which owns the College (Ratcliffe College Ltd), together with up to 10 additional governors, appointed by the Directors, who hold office for a period.

Present additional governors:
Dr Colin Draycott (*Chairman*)
Mr Richard W Gamble (*Vice Chairman & Director*)
Fr Antonio Belsito (*Director*)
Mrs Mary Espinasse
Mrs Mary Goldstraw
Dr David S Jolliffe, CB, FRCP
Mr Enzo Lallo
Mr Louis Massarella
Miss Louise McKenna
Mrs Anne De Rijk
Mr Paul Rudd
Mrs Joan Smidowicz

***Headmaster*: Mr Peter Farrar**, MA

Senior Deputy Head: Mrs J P Clayfield, BSc
Second Deputy Head: Mr J Reddin, BSc, MSc
Director of Finance: Mr D Robson, ACA

Teaching Staff:
* *Head of Department*

Mrs J Ackerley, BA (*English*)
Mrs L Arnold, BSc, MPhil (*ICT*)
Miss C Axcell, BSc (*Mathematics*)
Mr M Balmbra, BSc (*Physical Education, Geography, OC CCF*)
Mrs G Bell, BA, DipEdSEN (*Learning Support, Art, Careers Coordinator**)
Mrs M-J Bisson, BSc (*French*)
Dr M Burns, BSc, MSc, PhD (*Science*)
Mrs K Burton, BA (*Home Economics**)
Mr J Cantrill, BA (*History*)
Miss M Casas-Ojeda, BA, MA (*Spanish*)
Mrs C Caven-Henrys, AISTD (*Drama, Dance*)
Mr A Chorley, MSc (*Physics*)
Dr J Clarke, BSc, PhD (*Chemistry*)
Mrs S Clarke, BA, QTS (*Mathematics*)
Miss S Clegg, BA (*Art & Design**)
Mrs J Cluley, BEd, CertEd (*SENCO**)
Mrs K Cooper, BA (*English, Media Studies*)
Mrs P Curran, CertEd (*Junior Department*)
Mrs S Cushing, BA (*Languages**)
Mr M Darlington, BSc (*Physics*)
Mrs J Dorn, BA (*Languages*)
Mrs A Dungey, BSc (*Science*)
Mr A Dziemianko, BSc (*Head of Year, Geography*)
Mrs L Eccles, BA (*Languages*)
Mrs A Etty, BSc (*Junior Department*)
Mrs C Farrar, CertEd (*Junior Department*)
Mrs F Featherstone, NVQ 3 (*Nursery Nurse*)
Miss A Gennard, BA (*Junior Department French*)
Mrs C Gerighty, BSc (*PSHCE Coordinator*, Languages*)
Fr S Giles, IC (*Rector*)
Miss C Gregory, BA (*Media Studies**)
Mr G Higham, BSc (*Mathematics**)
Mr R Hughes, BA, QTS (*Physical Education, Learning Support*)
Miss C Jeyes, NNEB (*Nursery Nurse*)
Mr M Jones, BA (*Head of Year, Director of Music**)
Mr M Kaye, BA (*Physical Education*)
Miss J Kearns, BA (*Junior Department*)
Mr M Lambert, BSc (*Geography**)
Mrs M Lee, BPhil Ed, NPQH (*School Chaplain*)
Mrs F Lodder, BA, MA (*History*)
Mr J Maingot, BA (*English**)
Mrs M Markham, BA (*Junior Department*)
Mr P McCrindell, BA (*Head of Year, Languages*)
Mr H Midgley, BA, MEd (*Curriculum Coordinator, ICT**)
Mr S Ottewell, BA, QTS (*Religious Studies*)
Miss P Phillipson, BA (*Junior Department*)
Mrs S Rankine, BEd (*Head of Nursery School**)
Mrs C Rigby, BA (*Head of Junior Department*)
Mrs S Roberts, BA (*Physical Education*)
Dr A Robinson, BSc, PhD (*Science*)
Miss M Schlotfeldt, BA (*English, EAL*)
Mrs J Schofield, BSc (*Science**)
Mr A Seth, BSc (*Design and Technology*)
Mr G Sharpe, BA, MBA (*Assistant Head, Science*)
Mrs P Sharpe, Dip OT (*Head of Girls' Boarding*)
Mr M Sherwood, BA (*Physical Education*)
Mr M Sleath, BSc (*Head of Year, Mathematics*)
Mrs H Smith, BSc (*Mathematics*)
Mr P Spencer, ACIB Banking Dip (*Economics & Business Studies**)
Dr S Standen, BSc, PhD (*Chemistry*)
Mrs A Taylor, BEd (*Director of Sport**)
Mr N Taylor, BEd (*Head of Boys' Boarding, Physical Education*)
Mrs G Thomas-Atkinson, BA (*Physical Education*)
Mr D Turner, BEd (*Junior Department*)
Mr N Walsh, LLB (*Religious Studies**)
Mr S Waterhouse, BMus (*Music*)
Mrs E Waters, BEd (*Nursery School, Junior Department*)
Mrs P Watson, BA (*Head of Year, Religious Studies*)
Mrs L Whieldon, BA (*English*)
Mrs M Williams, BA (*Librarian*)
Mr E Woodcock, BA, MSc (*Physical Education*)
Mrs S Worsnop, BSc (*Head of Year, Mathematics*)
Miss A Wright, BA (*Art & Design*)

Medical Officer: Dr T Jennings

Senior Nursing Sisters:
Mrs D Warburton, RGN
Mrs E Weston, RGN

Age Range. 3–18.

Number of Pupils. 648: 373 boys, 275 girls. Sixth Form: 131. Boarders: 94.

Aims. The vision of the College is to educate young people in the spirit of the Gospel and the traditions of the Catholic Church, seeking to nurture the God-given talents and potential of each individual, so that each one may become a confident, responsible and useful member of society. Whilst Ratcliffe is a Catholic school, it welcomes children of other denominations and faiths, whose parents feel they can share in and benefit from the school's ideals and environment.

Location. Ratcliffe College is set in over 100 acres of rolling parkland on the A46, seven miles north of Leicester. It is easily accessible by road and benefits from being free of congestion at peak times. The M1/M6 motorways, main line railway stations and airports of Birmingham and Nottingham-East Midlands are all within easy travelling distance. For day pupils, school buses operate daily from Leicester, Loughborough and Nottingham.

Site and Buildings. The main Senior School buildings surround a quadrangle and contain the Administration offices, Church, Dining Hall, Library, Medical Centre, Computer Rooms and Common Rooms, together with a number of subject departments. In addition, there is a Music Department with Concert Hall; a fully-appointed Theatre; a Science Block with additional classrooms for Home Economics. Sporting facilities include extensive playing fields, floodlit all-weather hockey pitch and the sports centre comprises sports changing room, swimming pool and sports hall with fitness room. A complex of recently refurbished buildings nearby provide departmental bases for Geography, Modern Languages and Mathematics. Modernised Boys' and Girls' boarding accommodation is situated on the upper floor of the main building, in separate wings, with individual study bedrooms for older pupils.

The Rosmini Sixth Form Centre, named after Fr Antonio Rosmini the founder of the Rosminian Order, opened for use by pupils and staff in January 2007. With an upper floor wholly dedicated to independent academic study with full IT accessibility and ground floor areas providing for social and extra-curricular usage, the Centre provides a flagship modern setting for Sixth Formers.

The Junior Department is situated in the Newman Building close to the Senior School. The Nursery School is located in purpose-built accommodation nearby on the campus.

Organisation. The College is divided into 3 sections: Senior School (11–18 year olds), Junior Department (5–11 year olds), Nursery School (3–5 year olds). The sections are closely integrated, allowing continuity of education from 3 to 18. Boarding girls and boys are accommodated in separate wings of the main Senior School building, under the supervision of a resident Housemistress/Housemaster. There is a strong emphasis on pastoral care for all pupils. The teacher : pupil ratio in the Senior School is 1 : 20 (The Sixth Form is a much lower ratio).

Curriculum. In the Nursery School, the emphasis is on early literacy, numeracy and the development of personal and social skills, all of which contribute to a child's knowledge, understanding and skills in other areas of learning. Programmes of study are based on the DCSF early learning goals, but extend well beyond these guidelines to develop a child's interests, talents, outlook and general knowledge of the world.

The Junior department offers small class sizes, well-resourced classrooms, a clear focus on the National Curriculum, extended school day and an extra-curricular activities programme. Pupils learn French and subjects like PE, Music, History and Geography are emphasised, whilst pupils use the Senior School facilities for ICT, Drama, Music, Sport and Science.

In the Senior School a broad and balanced curriculum is followed, which aims to identify and provide for individual needs. Most pupils take at least nine GCSEs. All pupils study a core of subjects consisting of English (Language and Literature or Drama or Media), Mathematics, Religious Studies, a modern Foreign Language and Science (Double or Triple Award). This is augmented by up to three further option subjects. In the Sixth Form, most pupils choose 4 AS levels in Year 12 and 3 A2 levels in Year 13. In addition to A level work, pupils take a complementary studies course, which incorporates a general studies programme including preparation for university and careers guidance, study skills and moral and ethical studies.

Games. The playing fields cover over 100 acres which surround the College buildings. All pupils participate in Games, the major sports being Cricket, Hockey, Rugby, Tennis and Athletics for boys and Hockey, Netball, Rounders, Tennis and Athletics for girls.

Extra-Curricular Activities. Pupils' talents and interests are developed through an extensive programme on weekdays and at weekends. As well as many sporting opportunities, 25% of pupils learn a musical instrument and there are many musical groups including brass ensemble, orchestra and choirs. Many pupils are involved in school productions and film making and other media activities are popular. The Combined Cadet Force and the Duke of Edinburgh's Award Scheme both flourish. Pupils are encouraged to be caring and have consideration for others through Chaplaincy groups and Voluntary Service.

Admissions. *Nursery School*: Entry is by school report (if applicable) and informal assessment.

Junior Department: Entry is by school report and assessment for Years 1–4 or entrance examinations (papers in English, Mathematics, Verbal Reasoning) for entry to Years 5 and 6.

Senior School: Entry is normally at 11+, 12+, 13+ and 14+. Entry is normally by school report and successful performance in the entrance examinations, either Common Entrance or the College's own examinations (papers in English, Mathematics and Verbal Reasoning).

Sixth Form: Entry is based on interview, school report and successful performance in GCSE examinations.

Scholarships and Bursaries. (*see Scholarship Entries section*). Academic scholarships are offered on entry to Year 7, Year 9 and the Sixth Form. Some bursaries are available on entry to Year 7.

At 11+, all candidates take the normal entrance examination papers in Mathematics, English and Verbal Reasoning and those obtaining the best results will be recommended to the Headmaster for a scholarship.

At 13+, candidates take papers in English, Mathematics, Science, History, French and Verbal Reasoning; those obtaining the best results will be recommended to the Headmaster for a scholarship. Pupils already at the College may enter for the awards as internal candidates.

Scholarships into the Sixth Form are awarded for academic excellence and are based on GCSE results. Pupils already at the College are also eligible for these awards.

There are two Music Choral awards and a small number of additional awards are available at the Headmaster's discretion.

Scholarships are reviewed annually and, provided good scholastic and discipline standards are maintained, remain with the pupil throughout his or her school career.

Fees per term (2008-2009). Full Boarding (Years 6–13) £6,282; Weekly Boarding (Years 6–8) £5,066. Fees are subject to such termly increase as may prove necessary.

Day Fees: £2,230–£2,537 (Nursery aged 3–5); £2,537–£2,986 (Years 1 to 5); £3,316–£4,166 (Years 6 to 13).

Additional charges are made for: private Music lessons at £180 per term for 10 half-hour sessions (for individual tuition for each instrument); EFL (English as a Foreign Language) at £345 per term for 10 one-hour lessons. Where additional teaching of Learning Skills is required and agreed with parents, this will be charged at £33 per lesson. There is a registration fee of £75 (£100 overseas) and a deposit of £250 for UK students and £500 for students from overseas.

Charitable status. Ratcliffe College is a Registered Charity, number 1115975, for the education of children.

Reading Blue Coat School

Holme Park Sonning Berks RG4 6SU
Tel: 0118 944 1005
Fax: 0118 944 2690
e-mail: lab@blue-coat.reading.sch.uk
website: www.blue-coat.reading.sch.uk

The School was founded in 1646 by Richard Aldworth, a merchant of London and Reading, and a Governor of Christ's Hospital. There are 669 pupils (aged 11–18) including a co-educational Sixth Form. The School is situated in 46 acres of grounds and riverside woods near the village of Sonning, four miles east of Reading.

Visitors to Trustees:
Vice-Chancellor of the University of Oxford
President of St John's College, Oxford
Warden of All Souls' College, Oxford

Chairman of Governors: B S Walsh

***Headmaster*: M J Windsor**, MA, BA Hons, PGCE

Second Master: A P Colpus, BSc Hons, PGCE
Deputy Head, Staff Development: Mrs A J Bawden, BA, PGCE
Deputy Head, Academic Development: P C K Rowe, MEd, MA, PGCE
Deputy Head, Pupil Development: R S Slatford, MA, CertEd, BSc Hons, PGCE

Mrs S M Adams, BA, PGCE
M J Baker, BA, PGCE
Miss K E Bayliss, BA
Mrs L J Bennett, BEd Hons
Mrs J M Blair, BA, PGCE
P S Bodinetz, BA, PGCE
J Bowler, BA, PGCE, LTCL, ARCM
J P Brown, BSc, PGCE
J D Bruce, BSc, Dip EIA, PGCE
L A C Busfield, BSc
O J Clayson, BA Hons, PGCE
Mrs J A Coates, BSc, PGCE
S J Cook, CertEd, BA
D N Cottrell, CertEd
M R Crowther, BA Hons, PGCE
Mrs C Dance, BA Ed Hons
Dr S M Dimmick, BSc, DipEd, MSc, PhD
D J Draper, MA, BA Hons, PGCE
Dr A C Dutton, PhD, BA Hons
Mrs R Edsall, BA, PGCE
R N Ennis, BA, PGCE
R Field, BA, PGCE
D Fisher, MA Ed, DipEd, BSc
D Gandy, BSc Hons
Miss L Griffin, BMus, MA, PGCE
Mrs S A Head, MA
Miss A Hobbs, BA Hons, PGCE
I P Holleley, BA
E R Hooper, MA, BA, DipEd, GDIESE
Miss J Hope, BSc Hons, PGCE
Miss N Johnson, MSc, BSc Hons, PGCE
P Kiddell, BA Hons, PGCE
Mrs K S Lambert, BA, PGCE
N Lee, MA, BA, PGCE
Mrs P J Leonard, BA, PGCE
T J Lewis, MEng, BA
A J Maddocks, BA
Dr K J Magill, MPhil, BA, PGCE, PhD
Miss M F Maltby, BA, PGCE
Miss E M Marshall, BA, PGCE
N T P Matenga, BSc, Dip Teaching
S McCluskey, BSc Hons, PGCE
H J McGough, BSc Hons
Revd Dr D W McHardy, PhD, BA (*Chaplain*)
D C Montague, MA, BA Hons, PGCE
Mrs H J Oliver, BA Hons, PGCE
Miss J Pasco, BA Hons, PGCE
Mrs P Y Pemberton, BA Hons, PGCE, Dip SpLD, AMBDA
A M Pett, BSc, PGCE
A D Phillips, BSc Hons, PGCE
E A C Rattray, BA Hons, CPGS
S R Roberts, BSc, PGCE
Mrs C Ross, BA, PGCE
Mrs C Rule, BA Hons, OCR SpLD Diploma
S W Sadler, BA Hons
D L Salmon, MA, ComputingDip, PGCE
Dr F B Santos, BSc, MSc, PhD
D H R Selvester, BA, PGCE
Mrs J Shabani, BA, PGCE
R I Shuttleworth, BSc Hons, PGCE
Mrs J P Smith, BSc, PGCE
M Syddall, BA Hons, TESOL Cert
J D Tindall, BSc, Master of Teaching Sydney
G C Turner, BSc, PGCE
Mrs J M Turton, BSc, PGCE
Miss T van der Werff, MA, PGCE
Mr W Voice, BA Hons, PGCE
T C Walford, BSc, PGCE
R J Wallis, BA, PGCE
Miss N Watmough, BMus Hons, PGCE
P D Wise, BSc Hons, PGCE
S Yates, BSc Hons, PGCE
Mrs J F Zambon, BA Hons, PGCE

Bursar: J G E Jacob, BSc Hons, MIMgt
Headmaster's Secretary: Mrs L A Bell
Admissions Secretary: Mrs V M Frost
School Nurse: Mrs G F Montgomery, RGN
Sports Centre Manager: C Bate
Archivist: P J van Went, MA, CertEd

Aims. The School aims to provide a stimulating and friendly atmosphere in which each pupil can realise his or her full intellectual, physical and creative potential. Pupils are encouraged to be self-reliant and adaptable and we hope that they will learn the basis of good citizenship founded on honesty, fairness and understanding of the needs of others.

Our School is a Church of England Foundation, and emphasis is placed on Christian values and standards. Confirmation classes are taken by the Chaplain.

Buildings. A continuous programme of improvement has been undertaken in recent years. This has seen the building of the Roddy Messer Building, which contains the English and Geography Departments, the Senior Common Room and Administrative Offices. Facilities for the teaching of Music and the IT Centre have been extended and the Sixth Form has moved into a new Sixth Form Centre. All year groups enjoy common room facilities. The Edelston Library, audio-visual learning resource centre and sixth form study areas were relocated in the splendour of School House in the Summer 2001. An 11 laboratory Science Centre was opened in October 2001 to accommodate the teaching of the principal sciences including geology. A Sports Hall/School Hall, incorporating indoor facilities for climbing, tennis, badminton, hockey, soccer, cricket, and a fitness centre was opened in April 2004. This project also includes a new dining hall and kitchens. In the past year additional playing fields, with space dedicated to an environmental study area, have been acquired; a new cricket pavilion has been built and the swimming pool has been covered with a retractable roof.

Curriculum. The first and second years provide a broad foundation, with a wide variety of subjects, including two foreign languages, Latin, Classics, Music, Art, Information Technology, Design Technology and Religious Studies. In the Year 3 there is some provision for choice with the introduction of Drama. In the Year 4 subjects are chosen for GCSE courses with English, Mathematics, the Sciences and a language being compulsory. All boys follow a GCSE short course in both RS and ICT. A wide range of subjects is offered at AS and A2 Level, with most pupils going on to University including Oxford and Cambridge.

Sixth Form. The co-educational Sixth Form Centre accommodates over 200 students. Girls are fully integrated into all activities. In addition to the examination courses, all Sixth Formers follow a compulsory General Studies and Critical Thinking course to A Level.

Games and Activities. A wide range of sports and activities is offered within the curriculum. From the Fourth Year, pupils may choose their sport and regular school fixtures are arranged. Full advantage is taken of the River Thames and rowing is a popular sport for both boys and girls. The main boys' games are Rugby and Hockey in the Christmas Term, Soccer and Hockey in the Easter Term, and Cricket and Athletics in the Summer Term. Girls play Netball, Rounders and Hockey. Other sporting activities include Fencing, Squash, Basketball, Tennis, Real Tennis, Golf, Table Tennis, Climbing, Swimming, Scuba Diving and Sailing.

The Cadet Force is voluntary with Army, RAF and RN Sections. Camping and adventure training activities take place during holidays and at weekends. There is a wide range in the Activities Programme which includes the Duke of Edinburgh's Award, overseas expeditions, community service and sports leadership.

Music and Drama enjoy a high profile in the life of the School. Well over a third of the pupils receive individual instrumental lessons and pupils are encouraged to join in activities such as the Choir, Orchestra, Wind Band, Brass Group, Jazz and Swing Bands. Concerts, plays and musicals are presented regularly.

Admissions. The main entry is in September at 11+ by entrance examination taken the previous January. Entry at other levels is by examination and interview and is subject to vacancies. Entry to the Sixth Form for girls and boys is by GCSE results, assessment and interview.

The Foundation makes provision for awards of scholarships and bursaries, including academic, music and art awards, based on merit and need. Foundation Scholarships up to 100% of fees are available according to financial need.

Fees per term (2008-2009). £3,780.

Charitable status. The Reading Blue Coat School is a Registered Charity, number 1087839. Its aim is the provision of secondary education for pupils aged 11 to 18.

Reed's School

Cobham Surrey KT11 2ES
Tel: 01932 869001
Fax: 01932 869046
e-mail: admissions@reeds.surrey.sch.uk
website: www.reeds.surrey.sch.uk

Reed's is a boarding and day school for boys with girls in the Sixth Form, founded by Andrew Reed in 1813 and incorporated by Act of Parliament in 1845 under the presidency of the Archbishop of Canterbury, the Duke of Wellington and the Marquis of Salisbury. When the School was founded, its facilities were reserved for boys whose fathers had died. In 1958 the School expanded and all boys became eligible for entrance. Sixth Form girls became eligible for entrance in the 1980s. Foundation awards are still granted each year to boys and Sixth Form girls who have lost the support of one or both of their parents.

Patron: Her Majesty The Queen

Presidents:
G M Nissen, CBE
Viscount Bridgeman

Governors:
I Plenderleith, CBE (*Chairman*)

Mrs I M Barker
U D Barnett
D R Blomfield, BSc
D H A C Caddy, FCA
J W Flecker, MA
M A Grenier, MA
C R Hawkins
Professor J N Hay, PhD, FRSC
A R Merry, FRICS
J W Murray, BA
Mrs L F Napier, FSI
Mrs A F Noakes
T D Page, MA
P D Reed
Miss K Richardson, MA
R Stewart, FCIB
P H H Verstage, BCom Hons
M Wheeler, BCom, FCA

Secretary to the Governors & Bursar: A D Bott, FCCA

***Headmaster*: D W Jarrett**, MA

Deputy Headmaster: G D Spawforth, MA
Senior Housemaster: P R Kemp, BA
Head of Sixth Form: I A Clapp, BEd
Director of Studies: D J Atkins, BA
Director of Sport & Activities: †A R W Balls, BEd
Chaplain: The Revd A J Clarke, MA

Assistant Staff:
* *Head of Department*
† *Housemaster*

Miss A M Abad, MA (*Spanish*)
Mrs D Adwent, BEd
J Bacchi-Andreoli, MA
D Bevan, MA
†A J Blackman, MA
S M Bramwell, BA (*French*)
Mrs J Brewster, BSc (*Chemistry*)
I B Carnegie, MA (*Director of Music*)
†I A Clapp, BEd
C E Cole, BA (*Printing*)
D J Crowther, BSc
P P Davies, MA (*History*)
J K Ditchburn, BA
†M R Dunn, HND
B J Edwards, BA (*Physical Education*)
Ms N R Evans, BA
Ms M Fitzgerald, BA (*Librarian*)
Mrs M Francis, BA
W Gatti, BA (*English*)
B J Goodrich, MSc (*Geography*)
D H Hamilton, BA
T A Harrison, MSc (*Mathematics*)
Mrs J G Hart, BA (*Psychology*)
G S Hart, HEd
N I Heather, MSc (*ICT*)
P Jenkins, LRCM
Miss A N Johnson, MA, FRSA (*Art*)
E B H Jones, BA
Mrs C Kemp, BA
†P R Kemp, BEd
M G Kerrison, BA
Mrs K A Lambert, BSc
Mrs J A Lawrence, BA
Mrs S L Leslie, BA (*Learning Support*)
L G Michael, BA (*Drama*)
P L Millington, BSc (*Design Technology*)
Mrs T A Millington, BEd (*Religious Studies*)
T P W Murdoch, BA
J W A Norman, BA
Mrs L Paterson (*Biology*)
Mrs A L Prior, BSc
L Pytel, BA
Miss A D Rawlings, BSc
Mrs A J Rollinson
J A Rollinson, BSc
C Sandison-Smith, MA (*Modern Languages*)
Mrs S Shoosmith
T P Silk, BA (*Media Studies*)
Ms C F St Gallay, BA
Ms R Stone, MA
D Thompson, BSc (*Physics, *Science*)
C S Thomson, BA (*Classics*)
Miss E J Tuck, BA
†M C Vernon, BSc
Mrs V Wakefield, BSc
A J Waller, BA
J M Wallis, MEng
T Webb, BA
S Whiteley, BA (*Economics & Business Studies*)
Mrs L Williams, BA

Visiting Music Teachers:
A Bernardi (*Strings*)
J Dalgleish (*Piano*)
J Dunning (*Guitar*)
S James (*Guitar*)
K Garrett (*Jazz Piano*)
D Hawkins (*Guitar/Bass*)
R Willey (*Trombone*)
J Jaggard (*Oboe*)
J Calderbank (*Clarinet, Saxophone, Piano*)
J Shaddock (*Trumpet*)
E Spevok (*Drums*)
J Fryer (*Saxophone*)
J Turner (*Drums*)
P Von Wielligh (*Flute*)
D Deam (*Voice*)

Development Director: R M Garrett, BA
Headmaster's Secretary: Mrs A Gregg
Registrar: R M C Gilliat, MA

Admissions Secretary: Mrs P F Gilliat
Medical Officer: R Draper, MBChB, DCH, DRCOG, DA, MRCGP

The School is situated near Esher in 40 acres of heath and woodland. It can be reached in 30 minutes by train from Waterloo and is within half an hour's drive of both Heathrow and Gatwick Airports.

To the original buildings have been added in the last 15 years a Sixth Form House, Chemistry laboratories and Computer Centre, two artificial turf hockey pitches, a swimming pool and sports complex, a new library, a new teaching block for the Physics and Mathematics departments, a Music School, an Indoor Tennis Centre, new Biology, Geography and History departments, an extension to the Day Pupil Centre and an extension to the Sixth Form House which incorporates a lecture theatre.

There are 575 pupils, just under 20% of whom are boarders, divided among 5 senior houses, Blathwayt, Bristowe, Capel, Mullens and School House, and one junior house, the Close, for those under 13. There is also a separate Sixth Form House. Admission at the age of 13 is normally by the Common Entrance examination; admission at the age of 11 or 12 is by means of the School's own examination, normally taken at the School. There is admission into the Sixth Form for boys and girls.

The School admits Dutch pupils, who are integrated into the School's academic, games and activities programmes. They follow a Dutch curriculum in Dutch and Mathematics and follow the Reed's curriculum for all other subjects.

Pupils are prepared for GCSE and GCE, AS and A Levels for University Entrance, and for entry to the Services, professions and industry. The games are Rugby, Cricket, Hockey, Athletics, Tennis, Swimming, Squash, Netball and Basketball. The School has its own Combined Cadet Force with RAF and Army sections. The Duke of Edinburgh's Award can also be undertaken at Bronze, Silver and Gold levels. Special scholarships may be awarded for tennis, skiing and golf.

Pupils are all involved in a wide-ranging Activities Curriculum. There is also a broad range of Inter-House competitions. There is a School Choral Society, a Chapel Choir, an Orchestra, a Jazz Orchestra and various ensembles.

Religious instruction, which promotes religious tolerance, is in accordance with the principles of the Church of England. An annual Confirmation Service is held in the School Chapel for which pupils are prepared by the Chaplain. Pupils of all denominations are accepted into the School and are expected to attend chapel.

The National Curriculum is broadly followed in Years 7 to 9 and early specialisation is avoided. There is a Careers Team which advises pupils and arranges suitable visits and interviews and gives advice on University degree courses. The School is a member of the Independent Schools Careers Organisation.

The main responsibility for each pupil is undertaken by his or her Housemaster, supported by a Tutor. The health of the pupils is in the care of the School Doctor, and a State Registered Nurse is in charge of the Medical Centre.

Fees per term (2008-2009). Day Pupils (including meals): £4,664 (Years 7 & 8), £5,883 (Years 9–13). Boarders: £6,219 (Years 7 & 8), £7,717 (Years 9–13). All boarders may exercise a weekly boarding option. There are no compulsory extras.

Scholarships. (*see Scholarship Entries section*). All applications should be made to the Registrar, Reed's School (01932 869001).

Charitable status. The London Orphan Asylum (Reed's School) is a Registered Charity, number 312008. Its aims and objectives are to provide boarding education for pupils who have lost the support of one or both parents.

Reigate Grammar School

Reigate Road Reigate Surrey RH2 0QS
Tel: 01737 222231
Fax: 01737 224201
e-mail: info@reigategrammar.org
website: www.reigategrammar.org

Governing Body:

Chairman: Mr A Walker
Vice-Chairmen:
Professor C Jennings
Mrs J Langham

Mr R Bacon
Dr Y Burne
Sir Colin Chandler
Professor F Cotter
Mr K Crombie
Professor I Dennis
Mr W Dunnet
Mrs J Forbat
Mrs A George
Mr R Hails
Mr D Hall
Dr K Knapp
Mrs J Oliphant
Mr W Siegle
Mr R Woodhouse

***Headmaster*: D S Thomas**, MA Oxford

Senior Deputy Head: Mrs M A Collins, BEng Bristol
Deputy Head (*Development*): A J Manfield, BSc Bristol
Deputy Head (*Pastoral*): E M Wesson, BA Cambridge, MA Cantab
Deputy Head (*Staff*): G Sanderson, BA Oxford

Assistant Head (*Assessment*): Miss V Godbold, BA Hull

Head of Sixth Form: D G Bader, BSc Bath
Head of Upper School: P G Stephens, BSc Aberystwyth
Head of Third Form: M S Russell, BEd Bulmershe College
Head of Second Form: Mrs E L Bader, BEd Worcester
Head of First Form: Miss S L Kümpel, BA Leeds

Chaplain and Head of PSHE: P J R Chesteron, BA Open, CertEd St Luke's

Assistant Staff:
* *Head of Department*
§ *part-time*

Art:
W H Edwards, BA Staffordshire Polytechnic
Mrs S J T Genillard, ATC Goldsmiths College, London
Miss R Mansfield, BA Southampton Inst of Art & Design
Mrs R Robinson, BA Brighton
*P F Tinney, BA, Goldsmiths College, London

Biology:
§S L Lawson, BSc, PhD Plymouth
§Mrs A K Mayor, BSc Queen Mary College, London
Miss G Palmieri, BSc Reading
A M Proudfoot, BSc Durham, PhD East Anglia
P G Stephens, BSc Aberystwyth

Chemistry:
Miss M Egan-Smith, BSc Lancaster
Mrs G Hanlan, BSc Royal Holloway College, London
Mrs R Hood, BA Cambridge
*C R Lawrence, PhD Cambridge
J M Sergeant, BSc King's College, London

Classics:
M J Buzzacott, BA Durham (**Careers*)
H G Ingham, BA Oxford
Mrs J Jakeways, MA St Andrews
*S J M Wakefield, BA, AKC, PhD London

Design and Technology:
M D Hallpike, CertEd Crewe and Alsager College
*R A Rooth, DipEd Loughborough College

Drama:
*Miss S Branston, BA Wales
§Mrs L Lobb, BA Nottingham
§Mrs J Rance, BA Open
D Jackson, BA Middlesex

Economics and Business Studies:
M H Benton, BA Anglia
*P A Flanagan, BA East Anglia, MSc Birkbeck
A J Manfield, BSc Bristol
Mrs P A Tucker, BA Brighton

English:
S T Chevalier, MA Oxford
Miss K Knoesen, BA RAU South Africa
*Mrs G M Penfold, BA York
Miss A M Powers, MA Sheffield
R A Riggs, BA King's College, London
Mrs K Scaglione, BA Keele
Mrs P A Smith, BA London

Food Technology:
Mrs E L Bader, BEd Worcester College of HE

Geography:
*M G Cline, BA Southampton
S A Collins, BA Durham (*Outdoor Training*)
Mrs G C Dexter, BA Queen's, Belfast
Miss V Godbold, BA Hull
Mrs G L Hodges, BSc Birmingham
§Mrs V L Ramsden, BA Nottingham

History & Politics:
Miss C Green, BA East Anglia
Mrs L Goldsmith, MA, PhD London
Mrs F A Gunning, MA Oxford (*History*)
N Hughan, BA Southampton
Miss A R O'Dwyer, MSc Edinburgh (*Politics*)
§Mrs C J Peats, BA Nottingham
G Sanderson, BA Oxford
§Mrs A S Thomas, MA, PhD Edinburgh
E M Wesson, MA Cambridge

ICT:
Miss G Adams, BA Brighton
*N Stokes, BSc Surrey

Mathematics:
D G Bader, BSc Bath
Mrs F G Buzzacott, BSc Exeter
*A R D Davies, BSc Bristol
Mrs F Grant, BEd Bulmershe College
P I Rollitt, MSc King's College, London
M S Russell, BEd Bulmershe College
Mrs L J Stephens, BEd Cambridge
J Farrelly, BA Nottingham
Mrs S M Taylor, BSc Exeter

Modern Languages:
R D Appleton, BA Durham (*Modern Languages, *Spanish*)
Miss J C Ball, BA Lampeter
Miss S Bellaoui, BA La Sorbonne, Paris
Miss S L Kümpel, BA Leeds
§C G Coughlan, BEd Anglia, AIL
D C R Jones, MA Oxford
Mrs J R Manfield, BA Bristol (*French*)
Miss M Sowa, BA Kent (*German*)
Mrs J Spencer Ellis, BA Hull
Ms B Thomas, BA Bristol

Music:
*S J Rushby, BA Surrey
N J Lobb, BA Bretton Hall

PE & Sport Studies:
§Mrs C Cline, BSc St Mary's College, Twickenham
§Mrs A J Davies, BEd Brighton Polytechnic
Miss L H Eades, BSc Brighton
Mrs E J Mitchell, BEd Exeter (*Girls' PE*)
C S Nicholson, BSc Loughborough (*General Studies; *Boys' PE*)
A K Reid, BEd St Luke's College, Exeter (*Director of Sport*)
A J Whiteley, BEd Loughborough College (*Sports Studies; Director of Activities*)
Mrs D S L Trewinnard, BA Chichester
D Cooper, BA Exeter

Physics:
Mrs M A Collins, BEng Bristol
§Mrs S M Garcia, BSc Queen's, Ontario, BEd Kingston
*A McGilchrist, MEng UMIST
Mrs D Pricopie, Baccalaureat Diploma Romania
A Reid, BSc King's College, London
P Saunders, BEng Southampton

Religion and Philosophy:
A A Powell, BD, AKC London
*N C Roberts, BA, AKC London
T Wright, BA Durham, MA Cambridge
A Cullen, BA Cambridge

Learning Support:
§Mrs K F Capper
*Mrs B Desclos

Bursar & Clerk to the Board of Governors: J Jensen-Humphreys, ACA, FCA
Project Manager: D F Aburn, MBIFM, IMBM
Headmaster's Secretary: Mrs C A Harrison
IT Manager: G Redfern, BSc

Reigate Grammar School is a co-educational day school for pupils aged 11 to 18.

The school was founded in 1675 as a free school for boys. It became an independent Grammar School during the nineteenth century, but after the 1944 Education Act it came under the control of Surrey County Council. On the abolition of the direct grant in 1976, RGS reverted to independent status. At the same time girls were admitted for the first time, initially in the Sixth Form only, but throughout the school from 1993. The school now numbers 860 pupils, of whom 230 are in the Sixth Form. In September 2003, the school merged with Reigate St Mary's Preparatory and Choir School (*see entry in IAPS section*), which provides education to 300 boys and girls aged from 3 to 11.

The school is situated in the historic market town of Reigate, just outside the M25 yet with easy transport links into London, Surrey and Sussex. Pupils come from a wide geographical area and from across the social spectrum, thanks to the school's own Assisted Place system, and to the generous support of the Peter Harrison Trust which provides substantial financial support each year. Around 50% of pupils come from primary schools, the remainder coming from the preparatory sector.

The Governors have invested considerable sums in new buildings in recent years, including a new Dining Hall and kitchens, Sixth Form Centre, Drama Studio, and Music School. A new indoor swimming pool is due to open in September 2008. In addition to the main school site, the sports ground at Hartswood, two miles from the school, provides some 32 acres of playing fields and a floodlit all-weather astroturf pitch.

Organisation. The school is divided into five sections: First Form, Second Form, Third Form, Upper School (Fourth and Fifth Forms), and Sixth Form. The welfare of pupils is overseen by the Heads of Sections and Heads of Year.

Curriculum. The range of subjects on offer is traditional in the early years, but allowing for a broadening of options in the Sixth Form. Prior to GCSE, all pupils study a core curriculum of Mathematics, English, Science, one or two Modern Languages (French, German or Spanish), Latin, History,

Geography, Religious Studies, ICT, Art, Design Technology, Food Technology, Music, Drama, PE and Games. Most pupils take ten GCSEs, chosen from the above, with the added options of Sports Studies and Greek. Both Dual Award Science and the separate sciences are offered.

Most pupils stay on into the Sixth Form and take four subjects to A2 level. No modules are set in the Lower Sixth. Subjects available include all of the above, with the added options of Business Studies, Economics, Politics and Philosophy and Ethics. Further details are available on the website.

Extra-curricular activities. Reigate Grammar School has a strong tradition of excellence in a wide variety of extra-curricular activities, including an enviable reputation in sport, music and drama; large numbers of pupils participate in the CCF and in the Duke of Edinburgh's Award Scheme and last year the school raised some £22,000 for charities. The main sports are rugby, hockey and cricket for boys, and hockey, netball and rounders for girls, but other sports on offer include athletics, badminton, basketball, gymnastics, football, squash, swimming and tennis. There are several musical groups which rehearse regularly, including two orchestras, a Swing Band and three choirs, and there are frequent concerts both inside and outside the school, including tours overseas. The Drama department presents at least one major production each term, sometimes in collaboration with the music department.

Admissions. Pupils are normally admitted to the School at the ages of 11, 13 or 16, although vacancies may occasionally occur at other ages. There is a registration fee of £50. Except for entry to the Sixth Form, all candidates sit an entrance examination in January or November. All those who perform well in the examination are invited for an interview. All enquiries concerning admission to the school should be addressed to the Headmaster.

Fees per term (2008-2009). Tuition £4,286. Sibling discounts are available.

Scholarships. The school offers a wide range of scholarships and bursaries, aimed at enabling parents who might not normally be able to consider an independent school to send their child to Reigate Grammar School. All scholarships are means-tested, with fee remission of up to 100%. These include Academic scholarships, Music scholarships and a small number of All-Rounder awards (Ragg Scholarships) which are available at age 11 and 13 for pupils who show potential in at least two extra-curricular areas. Sports Scholarships are available for Sixth Form entry.

Reigate Grammar School Assisted Places may also be available, dependent on parental income and assets, and candidates living in Reigate and Banstead may be eligible for a Harrison Scholarship, which is also means-tested and made available through the generosity of the Peter Harrison Foundation. Further details are available from the Bursar.

Junior School. Reigate St Mary's Preparatory and Choir School (*see entry in IAPS section*) is the junior and nursery school of RGS. It numbers approximately 300 pupils aged 3 to 11 and is one of the few choir schools in the country not attached at a cathedral or college.

Charitable status. Reigate Grammar School is a Registered Charity, number 1081898. Its aim is to provide high-quality education for boys and girls.

Rendcomb College

Cirencester Gloucestershire GL7 7HA
Tel: 01285 831213
Fax: 01285 831331
e-mail: info@rendcomb.gloucs.sch.uk
website: www.rendcombcollege.co.uk

Rendcomb College was founded in 1920 by Noel Wills. It is a member of the Association of Governing Bodies of Independent Schools and the Headmaster is a member of The Headmasters' Conference. A new Junior School opened in September 2000 (further details at the end of the entry).

The Governors:
Sir Michael Angus, DL (*Chairman*)
Professor C J Arnison
D P J Cairns, FRICS
P N H Gibbs, MA
Dr R Hawley, CBE
Mrs P Hornby
P Lacey
Mrs A J Layton
S D E Parsons
The Ven H S Ringrose
H C W Robinson, BA, DipFM
A T K Smail, SCA
A Snow
Mrs F Symondson
Major M T N H Wills, DL
R H Wills

***Headmaster*: G Holden**, MA St Andrews, FRSA

Deputy Headmaster: D Baker, BA (*History*)
Assistant Head: Mrs D Dodd, BA Victoria University, NZ (*English; Theatre Studies*)
Director of Studies: C J Wood, MA Exeter College, Oxford, CChem, MRSC (*Chemistry*)
Head of Science: C Vuolo, BSc London (*Biology; Head of PE*)
Director of Sport: M Slark, BA Hull (*Business Studies*)
Director of Activities: Mrs S Scarisbrick, DEd
Director of Music: R Raby, GMus Hons
Director of American Studies: Mrs S Scarisbrick, DEd

Housemasters/Housemistresses:
Park House:
H Marsden, BA (*PE; Mathematics*)
Dr R Marsden, DPhil (*Head of Sixth Form*)
Stable House:
P Bevans, BSc (*Physics*)
Mrs M Bevans
Lawn House:
Mrs V A Hayward, BA Birmingham (*French*)
Mr D Hayward
Old Rectory:
A St J Brealy, BA St Andrews (*Geography; Mathematics*)
Mrs A Brealy, BA Hons, PGCE
Godman House:
Mrs R E Fielding, BA Exeter (*Head of German*)
Dr S Fielding

* *Head of Department*

Miss S Bell (*PE & Games*)
Mrs S R Blackwell, DipAD St Martin's School of Art, London (**Art*)
P Brooke, BA Hons (*English*)
S Clark, BSc, PGCE (**Mathematics*)
Mrs J Collishaw (*EFL & Spanish*)
D Essenhigh (*PE & Games*)
M Ford, BSc, MSc Bristol, PGCE Liverpool (**Physics; Head of External Exams*)
Mrs C Forshaw, BSc Loughborough, CertEd (*Mathematics*)
Miss C Franklin, BSc Hons Bristol (**Geography*)
Mrs F Garnet-Lawson, BA Hons Cambridge (*Business Studies*)
Mrs J Gibson, BSc Edinburgh, CChem, MRSC (**Chemistry; Physics; ICT*)
M H Graham, MA Gonville and Caius College, Cambridge (**History; Librarian*)
Mrs L Gregory, BSc Hons UMIST (*Mathematics*)
Mrs G Harford, BSc Hons (*Psychology*)
Miss M Harries, BA Hons Manchester (*English*)
Miss C Hockley, BA Hons (*Art & Design*)
Mrs B Hughes, BA Hons Gloucester (**Design & Technology*)
Miss K Hughes (*PE & Games*)
Revd C Jefferson, MA St Peter's College, Oxford (*Chaplain; RE; PSHE*)
P Jennings, BA Sheffield (**English*)

Mrs M Kinson, BA (*History*)
J McKelvey, BA Hons Durham (*Assistant Director of Music*)
Mrs S Mills, BA Hons Ripon & York St John (*Drama*)
B L North, BA Liverpool (**French*)
Miss E Roffe, BA Hons Bristol (*Art*)
J H Stutchbury, BSc York (*Biology*)
Mrs J D Stutchbury, BA Leeds (**EFL*)
Mrs S M Westhead, CertEd Sussex (*Learning Support; *PSHE*)
Mrs S White, BA (*German*)
A Wilkes, BSc (*Mathematics; ICT*)
Mrs E Young, BA, RSADipTEFL (*EFL*)

Junior School:
Head: M Watson, MA, BEd Hons
Deputy Head: Anne Haas, BEd Hons

J Arnold, BEd Hons
Mrs F Auster, BSc, Cert Learning Support
Mrs A Barker, BA Hons, PGCE
Mrs A Brealy, BA Hons, PGCE
P Colls, MA, BMus, ARCM, LTCL
Mrs J Hill, BEd Hons
Miss K Hunter, BEd Hons
A Lawrence, BA Hons, PGCE
Mrs B Lee, BA Hons, PGCE, Hornsby Dip SLD
Mrs J Lee-Browne, LDAD, BS Dip, PGCE
Mrs M Moore, MA, PGCE
Miss M Pavia, BSc Hons, PGCE
Mrs L Watson, BEd
Mrs R Watson, BA Hons, PGCE

Nursery Staff:
Miss S Langstaff, NNEB Norland Dip
Miss S Botha, BMus RAD, TCert, IDTA
Miss R Flint, DCE Norland Dip

Games Coaches:
Miss S Bell
N Ferreira
Ms J Greenberg

Classroom Assistants:
Mrs N McKenna
Mrs J Major
Mrs K Cairns
Mrs K Burnip

Bursar: Lt Col The Hon J F A Grey, MIMgt
Headmaster's PA: Mrs C Johnson
Junior School Headmaster's Secretary: Miss D Freegard
Admissions Registrar: Mrs A Slark, BA Hons
Marketing: Mrs L Holden, BA Hons
Bursar's Secretary: Mrs C Endersby
Finance Manager: Mrs S Watkins
Finance Assistant: Mrs S Thomson
Medical Officer: Dr S W Drysdale, MBChB, MRCP
Sister: Mrs J Pritchard, GRN
Assistant Sister: Mrs J Hunt, GRN
Nurse: Mrs R Jardine

Visiting Music Staff:
P Anderson (*Brass*)
Mrs M Brownbill (*Voice*)
J Carter (*Piano*)
P Colls (*Voice*)
P Cordell (*Electric Guitar*)
Mrs S Day (*Piano*)
P Dunn (*Acoustic Guitar*)
Miss C Hansford (*Oboe, Bassoon*)
Ms R Howego (*Cello*)
Mrs N Phillips (*Voice*)
Mrs D Stirling (*Strings*)
G Watson (*Drums*)

Situation and Buildings. Rendcomb overlooks the River Churn in the heart of the Cotswolds, five miles from Cirencester and ten miles from Cheltenham on the A435. It is easily accessible from the M4, A40 and M5. The College is set in 200 acres of parkland rich in wildlife.

Numbers. There are 157 boys and 127 girls from 11 to 18 years, who either fully board, weekly board or are day pupils. Flexible boarding is available.

Admission. Pupils normally join at 11, 13 or 16 to enter the Sixth Form. The entrance examination for entry at 11 is taken at Rendcomb and comprises three papers: English, Mathematics and Verbal Reasoning. At 13, pupils are admitted by Common Entrance or Rendcomb Examination and at 16 by interview, school reports and GCSE results.

Character. Rendcomb is the right size for everyone to grow in confidence and ability. The College week is designed to combine academic studies with a wide variety of activities and sports.

We encourage pupils to achieve the best possible academic results and to find out what they are good at. We want them to care for other people and their surroundings, and to enter the world of work, of marriage and of family life, with confidence and sensitivity.

Rendcomb provides a stable, disciplined and structured way of life to sustain hard work, with fine opportunities for developing talent outside the classroom. Facilities for study and leisure are superb, helping prepare students for University and independent living.

Curriculum. Pupils are prepared for GCSE, AS and A2 level examinations and for university entrance. They go on to a wide range of careers in the professions and services, commerce and industry, and in agriculture.

In the first two years there is a broad course of studies including Religious Studies, English, French, History, Mathematics, German, Geography, Music, Art, Spanish, Design & Technology, General Science, Drama, Games, PE, ICT and PSHE.

In the third year, Science is studied as separate subjects and all pupils study a short course GCSE in ICT.

In the fourth and fifth years pupils are offered a range of options and most take ten subjects at GCSE.

AS Level courses are provided in English, History, French, German, Geography, Business Studies, Mathematics, Further Mathematics, Physics, Chemistry, Biology, Psychology, Art, Music, Theatre Studies, and PE. Most pupils take four AS levels. Three of these are continued in the second year of the Sixth Form to A2 level.

University Entrance. A high level of academic achievement is maintained, and in recent years over 95% of leavers have gone on to a Higher Education.

Careers. There is a Careers Room which offers comprehensive current information on both careers and higher education and experienced staff are available for further information, consultation and advice.

Careers advice is available for all pupils throughout their stay at Rendcomb. It is particularly important when selecting subjects for GCSE and A level. Rendcomb uses the Centigrade System as part of the Higher Education Applications Procedure to assist Lower Sixth Form pupils in selecting universities and degree courses. All pupils will take part in an extensive cultural enrichment programme during their time in the Sixth Form.

Religious Education. Church Services take place on Sundays and during the week in the fine 16th Century Parish Church, which also serves as the church for the small village of Rendcomb. Pupils are required to attend a short service on two days in the week and boarders attend a Morning Service on Sunday. There is an annual Confirmation and the Chaplain is available as a listening ear to all members of the school.

Music, Art and Drama. The Arts Centre stands at the centre of the school site. It is equipped for Art, Music, Design, Pottery and Textiles.

Art is taught to all pupils for at least three of their years at Rendcomb and they may use the facilities at other times as an activity or for recreation. A special studio is dedicated to pupils studying A Level Art and professional artists teach alongside the Head of Art to provide balanced, relevant and up to date teaching. Visits are undertaken to a wide range of art galleries.

There is a high standard of instrumental and choral performance. Individual tuition is available in all instruments and voice. There are many opportunities to play and sing throughout the year at Rendcomb and at other venues.

Plays are staged in the well-equipped fine Victorian Orangery including portable tiered seating. The Rendcomb site also lends itself to producing open air plays during the summer term. All kinds of productions are staged at Rendcomb from full scale performances involving large numbers of pupils and staff to the regular junior play, small plays and reviews produced by pupils. Recent productions include *Les Misérables*, *Jesus Christ Superstar*, *Amadeus* and *Back to the 80s*. There are also performances by visiting companies and frequent trips to theatres in London, Stratford, Bristol, Oxford and Cheltenham.

Drama is offered at GCSE and Theatre Studies may be studied at A2 and AS Level.

Sport. The games fields are excellent and a large majority of members of the school represent Rendcomb at one or more sports in their age group. Recent tours include a Rugby Tour to Venice and a Hockey and Cricket Tour to Barbados.

An all-weather playing surface represents an important training advantage in hockey and tennis at Rendcomb; it complements the seven hard and one grass tennis courts already in use. There are two squash courts, four badminton courts in the sports hall, a heated open-air swimming pool and climbing wall. Football, archery, clay pigeon shooting and horse-riding are also popular.

Living Accommodation. Rendcomb has excellent accommodation for both boarders and day pupils. Most pupils in the Fourth Form and above have a comfortable single study bedroom and there are spacious Common Rooms and excellent social facilities. Sixth formers enjoy their own centre, with TV, Satellite TV, video, games room, dance area and bar.

Scholarships. (*see Scholarship Entries section*). There are a number of valuable scholarships available at all ages of entry for pupils with special academic, artistic, dramatic, musical or sporting abilities.

For further details and information about Scholarships apply to the Admissions Registrar, Rendcomb College, Cirencester, Glos GL7 7HA. Tel: 01285 831213.

Fees per term (2008-2009). Senior School: Boarding £5,848–£7,582, Day £4,190–£5,655.

Junior School: Day £1,815–£2,925.

Fees are payable termly in advance, by the first day of term. The Governors reserve the right to charge interest at up to 2% per month on fees not paid by this date. For information on monthly and other payment schemes please contact the Bursar.

The premium for a pupil's personal accident insurance scheme is included.

The registration fee is £35.

The Junior School. The Junior School opened in September 2000 and now has classes for three to eleven year olds.

For pupils in Nursery and Reception, the Curriculum is based on an extension of the Government's learning goals including social, emotional and physical development. Junior 1 and 2 are largely class teacher taught with Junior 3 to 6 operating a degree of subject specialism. A wide range of subjects are taught including ICT, Drama and French.

All pupils have the opportunity to represent the school in a variety of sporting fixtures and to participate in Music and Drama productions.

Each pupil's development is closely monitored and reports, grade cards and teacher meetings provide regular feedback to parents.

After-school clubs run Monday to Thursday, from Judo to Band, Nature Club to Computer Club. The use of College facilities by the Junior School, from the Astroturf to the Multimedia Suite, raises the standard of activities. The Junior School also has its own facilities including an adventure playground.

Enquiries should be directed to the Admissions Registrar on 01285 831213.

Charitable status. Rendcomb College is a Registered Charity, number 1115884. The aims and objectives of the Charity are the provision of boarding and day independent education.

Repton School

Repton Derbyshire DE65 6FH
Tel: 01283 559220 (Headmaster)
01283 559200 (School)
Fax: 01283 559210 (School)
01283 559223 (Headmaster)
e-mail: registrar@repton.org.uk
website: www.repton.org.uk

Repton School was founded in 1557 under the Will of Sir John Port, of Etwall, Derbyshire. His executors purchased the remains of the Augustinian Priory which had been established in the village in the 12th century and the central features of the School buildings are still the Priory and Cloister Garth.

The School is now governed by a scheme drawn up under the Endowed Schools' Act in 1874 and subsequently amended.

Repton is 8 miles from Derby and 4 from Burton-on-Trent. The School is co-educational at all levels. There are at present 593 pupils on the roll: 457 boarders (253 boys, 204 girls) and 136 day pupils (70 boys, 66 girls).

Motto: '*Porta vacat culpa*'

Governors:

[1]The Earl of Loudoun
[1]The Earl of Carnarvon
[1]Lord Gerard
The heir of the late Miss A Harper-Crewe
J M Fry (*Chairman*)
J K Bather, JP
Dr K J Dell, MA, DPhil, PhD
R A Litchfield, ACMA
M G Gilbert, BSc, FCA
Mrs J E Stephen, BSc
R J R Owen, MA
P M Village, LLB, QC
Mrs A E Hill, JP
D R Ashby, BSc, MBA, MRICS
Revd M Ludlow
Miss D Pulverer, BA, MSc
R Bates, BSc, FCOptom
Sir Henry Every, Bt, FCA
Miss C J Blackshaw, BA, FRAeS, MBAC
Prof A M Buchan, MA, FRCP, FMedSci
Dr M Tozer BSc, MEd, PhD
M R H Wimbush, BSc
R M Kirkland, BSc, FCIOB

[1] *Hereditary Governors*

***Headmaster*: R A Holroyd**, MA late Scholar of Christ Church, Oxford

Deputy Head (*Pastoral*): Mrs S A B Tennant, MA late Scholar of Somerville College, Oxford
Deputy Head (*Academic*): T C Owen, MA late Exhibitioner of St Edmund Hall, Oxford
Chaplain: The Revd A J Watkinson, BA Keble College, Oxford

* *Head of Department*

Classics:
*D S Newman, MA Magdalen College, Oxford
R G Embery, BA Durham
J E L Dahl, MA Jesus College, Cambridge
Mrs S A B Tennant, MA late Scholar of Somerville College, Oxford

Modern Languages:
*T B Blain, MA, MEd late Exhibitioner of Corpus Christi College, Cambridge
Mrs S L Checketts, BA Cardiff (*Head of Spanish*)
Mrs M J Blain, BA Leicester
N J Kew, BA Bath
K I R McCallum, BA South Bank
Miss N Reyner, MA
M Stones, BA Birmingham
Mrs C Suarez Pardo, BEd Madrid

English:
*I W McClary, MA St Andrews
Mrs L H Bordoli, BEd Bedford College of HE
Mrs K A Dahl, BA Newcastle
S Earwicker, BA, MPhil Manchester
J M J Hill, BA Birmingham
J G Golding, BA London
Miss V L Kinmond, MA Bristol
F P Watson, BA Liverpool

Drama:
*J C Sentance, BA Goldsmiths College, London (*Director of Drama*)
J M G Levesley, BA Hull

History:
*Dr N F Pitts, BA Leeds, PhD East Anglia
J Plowright, MA Peterhouse, Cambridge
W G Odell, MA St Andrews
T C Owen, MA late Exhibitioner of St Edmund Hall, Oxford

Geography:
*Miss N J Collins, BA Jesus College, Cambridge
Mrs R E Thompson, BA Homerton College, Cambridge
Miss R L Randle, MA Leeds, UK & McMaster Univ, Canada

Economics:
*C M Keep, MA Queen's College, Cambridge
M M Carrington, BSc Hull
Mrs M K Court, BA Durham
M L Jones, BA Nottingham Trent
T H Naylor, BSc Reading
D A Exley, BSc York

Mathematics:
*M A Sanderson, BSc Sheffield, LRSM
G B Attwood, BA Durham, MSc Sheffield, CMath, FIMA (*Director of General Studies*)
Mrs S J Beckett, BEd Homerton College, Cambridge
P V Goodhead, BA Pembroke College, Oxford
P J Griffiths, MSc RMCS, Shrivenham
A F Mylward, MA Magdalen College, Oxford
Miss N M Oborn, BA Exeter
Mrs S M Q Nield, BA York

Ethical & Religious Studies:
*J H Fox, BA Surrey
Mrs E J Sacker, BA Leeds
The Revd A J Watkinson, BA Keble College, Oxford

Science:
Dr H G Gould, BSc UMIST, PhD, CPhys, MInstP (**Physics*)
Dr S Ingleston, BSc, PhD Nottingham *(*Biology*)
D Morris, BSc Manchester (**Chemistry*)
P N Bradburn, BSc Birmingham
Mrs V R Cosford, BSc Hull
J C Driver, BSc Sheffield
Miss C A M Horne, BSc London
R Humphries, BEng Lancaster, MSc Cranfield
Mrs C E Goodhead, BSc Sheffield
G Lawrence, MA, MEd Downing College, Cambridge
Mrs J Rushton-Jones, BSc Imperial College, London
A J Smith, BSc Loughborough

Music:
*J Bowley, MA King's College, Cambridge, ARCM (*Director of Music*)
J Drinkwater, BA Pembroke College, Cambridge
R Fairbrother, BA Open
N J Firth, GBSM (*Brass*)
D J Francis, BA York
Mrs C Palmer, LTCL, GTCL, FTCL (*Keyboard*)

Art:
*J H Bournon, BA Wimbledon School of Art (*Director of Art*)
Mrs A J Benson, BA, MA Wolverhampton
Miss E Strange, MFA Glasgow
E J Weeldon, BA Wolverhampton
Mrs J Weeldon, BA Nottingham
I Whitfield, MA Royal College of Art, London

Information Technology:
*F J Rule, BSc Birmingham
L G Alderman, BSc Nottingham Trent (*Network Manager*)
A C Cooke, BA Leeds Metropolitan

Design and Technology:
*I Setterington, BEd Loughborough
Miss G Hill, BA Nottingham Trent

Physical Education:
*S J Clague, BSc Crewe and Alsager College of HE
Mrs D M Newman, BEd Bedford College of HE
R S Thompson, BA Manchester (*Director of Sport*)

Learning Support:
*N G Bennett, BEd Saint Luke's College, Exeter
Mrs M A Mylward, CertEd (*Head of ESL*)

Librarian: P J Stevens, BA Southampton, PGDipLis, ALA

Careers Staff:
Mrs M J Blain, BA,
assisted by:
T H Naylor, BSc

Boys' Boarding Houses:
School House: F P Watson
The Priory: J G Golding
The Orchard: A J Smith
Latham House: J E L Dahl
The Cross: S Earwicker
New House: W G Odell

Girls' Boarding Houses:
The Abbey: Mrs C E Goodhead
The Garden: Mrs V R Cosford
Field House: P J Griffiths & Mrs J Griffiths
The Mitre: Mrs D M Newman & D S Newman

Medical Officers: Newhall Surgery
Bursar: C P Bilson, MA, MBA Jesus College, Cambridge
Finance Bursar: Mrs P A Sharratt, FCCA
Registrar: Mrs C Hanneford-Smith
Director of Marketing and Development: Mrs C M Twigg
Headmaster's Secretary: Miss J J Taylor

Admission. Pupils are usually admitted at 13+ (Year 9) and 16+ (Year 12) but exceptions may be made in other years subject to places being available. Application for admission should be made to the Headmaster. There is a registration fee of £80. Candidates must normally have passed the Common Entrance Examination at their preparatory schools, but there is also an entrance examination for candidates not being prepared for the CEE.

Fees per term (2008-2009). Boarders £8,375; Day pupils £6,215. Additional expenses (for books, stationery, pocket money, etc) need not, after the first term, exceed £150 per term.

There is a Bursary Fund from which grants in the form of remissions from full fees may in certain circumstances be made. No remission of fees can be made on account of absence.

Scholarships. (*see Scholarship Entries section*). Academic scholarships and exhibitions are awarded annually after a competitive examination, senior in November, junior in May. The value of an award may be increased where need is shown. *C B Fry Awards*: A number of awards are made annually to candidates exhibiting outstanding all round leadership potential.

Art, Design Technology, Drama, Information Technology, Music and Sport scholarships are also offered to candidates showing outstanding potential.

In addition, there are nominated foundation scholarships and endowment fund bursaries.

Curriculum. The curriculum in Year 9 is very broad so that pupils are able to make an informed choice of GCSE subjects at the beginning of Year 10.

All pupils study Mathematics, English, French and Science to GCSE. Science is offered as a dual award GCSE; the more able pupils are entered for examination in the three separate sciences. Pupils also take GCSEs in three or four optional subjects; these are chosen from Art, Design and Technology, Business Studies, Information and Communication Technology, Drama, German, Spanish, Greek, Latin, Classical Civilisation, Geography, History, Music, Religious Studies and PE.

In the Lower Sixth form, the majority of pupils have the opportunity to study up to four AS Level courses and in the Upper Sixth continue with three of these through to A Level.

AS Level courses are offered in all subjects available to GCSE, plus Economics.

Potential Oxbridge candidates are identified by the end of their second term in the Sixth Form, and are prepared for interview.

Chapel services are those of the Church of England, and boarders are expected to attend a service every Sunday unless specially excused. A Confirmation is held each year.

Other activities. Every opportunity and encouragement is given to pupils to develop their creative interests in art, music, drama and design technology. Facilities include dedicated Art, Drama and Music Schools, Studio Theatre and a recently completed Textiles Studio. There are numerous School societies, covering a wide variety of interests.

Games and sports. Cricket, football, hockey (three astroturf pitches – 2 water-based, 1 sand), netball, rugby, fives, squash rackets, tennis (2 indoor courts and 14 hard courts), cross-country running, athletics, sailing, climbing, canoeing, swimming, golf and horse riding. Ample facilities are provided for physical education including a Sports Hall, a Gymnasium and an Indoor Swimming Pool.

Combined Cadet Force. The School maintains a contingent of the Combined Cadet Force and every pupil is a member for 1 year. After that pupils may remain in the CCF to take part in The Duke of Edinburgh's Award scheme or specialise as instructors. Sixth Formers have the additional choice of Community Service.

Houses. All pupils belong to a house, which is regarded as their home in their time at school. The housemaster or housemistress, who has overall responsibility for a pupil's work and development, lives in the house and all meals are taken within the houses.

Old Reptonian Society. All boys and girls who leave Repton become members of the Old Reptonian Society which has branches all over the country. Annual dinners and other regional social functions provide an opportunity for them to maintain and renew old friendships. Old Reptonian football, cricket and other sporting clubs are also keenly supported, and provide opportunities for young players to enjoy amateur sport at its best. Repton has been a frequent winner of the Arthur Dunn Cup and has also won the Cricketer Cup twice. The Secretary of the Old Reptonian Society is M Stones, c/o Repton School.

Repton Preparatory School and Pre-Preparatory School are situated at Foremarke Hall, about 1½ miles from the main school. There are at present 74 boarders and 253 day boys and girls, plus 117 pre-prep day boys and girls. Pupils are currently taken from age 2½ and prepared for entrance to Repton and other schools. Academic Scholarships are offered and the examination is in January.

Further particulars may be obtained from The Headmaster, Foremarke Hall, Milton, Derbyshire DE65 6EJ. (*See Foremarke Hall's entry in IAPS section.*)

Charitable status. Repton School is a Registered Charity, number 1093166. It exists to provide high quality education for boys and girls.

Robert Gordon's College

Schoolhill Aberdeen AB10 1FE
Tel: 01224 646346
Fax: 01224 630301
e-mail: enquiries@rgc.aberdeen.sch.uk
website: www.rgc.aberdeen.sch.uk

Motto: '*Omni nunc arte magistra*'

The College was founded as a residential establishment in 1729 by Robert Gordon, a member of a well-known Aberdeenshire family, who made his fortune as a merchant in the Baltic ports. In 1881 it was converted into a Day School, but a boarding facility was re-established for a very small number of pupils from 1937 to 1995. Formerly a grant-aided school in receipt of a Direct Grant from the Scottish Education Department, the College became a fully independent school on 1st August, 1985, though retaining its statutory link with The Aberdeen Educational Endowments Scheme 1958 (amended 1985). It has been fully co-educational since 1992.

Governors:
Convener of Aberdeen City Council (ex officio) and representative of the following bodies:

Aberdeen City Council (3), University of Aberdeen (2), Aberdeen Presbytery of the Church of Scotland (2), Aberdeen Endowments Trust (2), Gordonian Association (2), Seven Incorporated Trades of Aberdeen, Trades Unions, Chamber of Commerce, and not less than 4 nor more than 6 co-opted members.

Chairman of Governors: Colin A B Crosby, OBE, LLB, CA

***Head of College*: Hugh Ouston**, MA, DipEd

Deputy Head of College: Jennifer M S Montgomery, MA, DipEd
College Secretary: Robert M Leggate, MA, CA

Deputy Heads (Secondary):
Michael S Elder, MA
Carol Oliver, BA
Philip J Skingley, BA, MEd
William Smit, BSc

Departments:
* *Head of Department*
‡ *Principal Teacher* (*Learning*)

Art:
*Andrew L Hopps, BA
Fraser Beaton, DA
Fiona Michie, DA
Patrick McKenzie Smith, BA

Biology:
*David Strang, BSc
David A Horne, BSc
Alexandra Hendry, BSc, MSc
Gail E Clark, BSc
Wendy MacGregor, BSc
Jessica Power, BSc, BEd
Tracy Reid, BSc
Peter Shand, BSc, PhD

Business Studies:
*Andrew Slater, DipComm, DipM, ASCA, BA
Jackie Farquhar, BA
Scott McKenzie, BA
Valerie Ingram, BA

Chemistry:
*Robert Graham, BSc, PhD
Kevin S Cowie, BSc
John Duncan, BSc
‡Jane Kennedy, BSc, PhD
Christopher Spracklin, BSc, PhD
Sarah Coates, MSc
(*to be appointed*)

Classics:
*Allan M Bicket MA, MLitt
Craig Galbraith, MA, MLitt, PhD
Veronique Oldham, Lic Phil Class
(*to be appointed*)

Computing Studies:
*Fiona M Currie, BSc
Sarah Johnson, BSc
Lorna Hawthorn, BSc

Drama:
(*to be appointed*)

English:
(*to be appointed*)
‡Francesca McKenzie, MA
Shona M Bruce, MA, MEd
Michael S Elder, MA
Claire McGowan, BA
Roderick W Richmond, MA, DipEd
Jill Smith, MA
Elizabeth Templeton, MA
Fiona Wilson, MA
Shirley Cummings, MA
Claire McEwen, MA

Geography:
*Jennifer Gray, MA, PhD
Anna Nicoll, BSc
Samantha Watson, MA
Fiona Stone, MSc

History and Modern Studies:
*Robin Fish, MA
Noel Shearer, MA
Philip J Skingley, BA, MEd
Margaret Hogg, BA
Anne Gilks, BA, PhD
(*to be appointed*)

Mathematics:
*Vicky Fletcher, BSc
Karen O'Brien, BSc
Donna Ellis, BSc
Arthur Jamieson, BSc
Rebecca Lynch, MA

Guidance (Principal Teachers):
Sheila Sanderson, BA
Phyllis Thomson, MA
Kevin Cowie, BSc
Shona Bruce, MA, MEd
John Thomson, BSc
Colin Filer, BEd
Daniel Montgomery, MA, DipEd

Elaine Pascoe, BEd
Fiona M Robertson, MA
Eileen Smith, MA
‡Lorna Taylor, MA
Shirley Mackenzie
Roy Wakeford, BSc

Modern Languages:
*Thomas C Cumming, MA, DipEd
Kerry Joss, MA
Derek A Harley, MA, DipEd
‡Pamela McGregor, MA, DipEd
Daniel Montgomery, MA, DipEd
Catherine Richmond, MA, DipEd
Phyllis Thomson, MA
Ulrike Plasberg, BA
Judit Moscoso, MA
Carol Oliver, BA

Music:
Kevin Haggart, BMus, MM
Rhonda E McColgan, LTCL
Kevin Cormack
P Louise A Counsell, AGSM
Rachel Mackison, GRSM
Lydia Thom, LTCL
(*to be appointed*)

Physical Education:
*Andrew G Dougall, DPE
*Sheila McNaught, BEd
Richard Anderson, BA
Kirsten Hastie, BEd
Colin B Filer, BEd
James Lamont, BEd
David Swanson, DPE
Stacey Lamont, BEd
Swimming Teacher: Sandra Inglis, DPE

Physics:
*Stuart Farmer, BSc
‡Graham P Sangster, BSc
Sheila B Sanderson, BA
John Thomson, BSc
Craig McEwan, BEng
Michael Walker, MSc, PhD

Religious Education:
(*to be appointed*)
Lesley Ross, MA
Teresa Watson, MA

Technology:
*David McLaren, DipTechEd
Colin J Lavery, BSc, DipTechEd
Joseph Leiper, BEng
Heather Smith, BSc, PhD
Roy Wakeford, BSc

Scott McKenzie, BA
Gail Clark, BSc
Guidance/Careers (*Principal Teacher*): Fraser Beaton, DA
Development Director: Frances Loughrey, MA
Data & Research Coordinator: Isabel Mitchell
Office & Events Coordinator: Julia Smith
Network Manager: Gordon Crosher
Admin Systems Supervisor: Louise McBay
Administration/Exams: Roderick Richmond, MA, DipEd (*Principal Teacher*)
Health & Safety Coordinator: Stuart W Robertson, MA (*Principal Teacher*)
Support for Learning: Sheila Sanderson, BA; Fiona Brown, MA
Marketing Manager: (*to be appointed*)
School Nurse: Janet Murdoch, RGN
Publications: Fiona Reid, BA
School Librarian: Elaine Brazendale, MA, MCILIP
Assistant Librarian: Jennifer Strang, MSc
Archivist: Penny Hartley, BA
Duke of Edinburgh's Award Manager: David Horne, BSc
House Competition Coordinator: Walter Craig, MA, DipEd
Personal Assistant to Head of College: Ann Gannon
Senior School Receptionist: Fiona McKay

Junior School:
Head of Junior School: Mollie Mennie, DPE, MBS, DipEd
Deputy Heads:
Sally-Ann Johnson, BEd
Varie Macleod, BEd

Class Teachers:
Helen Crichton, BEd
Sophie Main, BEd
Karen Miller, BEd
Norma Murray, BSc
Matthew Northcroft, BEd
Claire Rae, BSc
Susan Rust, MA
Lorraine Wright, BA
Heather Crowther, BEd
Susan Jamieson, MA
Ingrid Stanyer, BA
Sally Kinsey, BA
Maureen Drummond, DipEd
Anne McDonald, DipEd
Vivien Scott, BEd
Samara McIntyre, MA
Andrew Lewis, BSc, MSc
Robert Cowie, BA

Class Assistants:
Fiona Coull, BSc RGN
Moira Craig, Dip DomSc
Lesley Dougall, DipEd
Pauline Greenhalgh
Diane Legg
Sylvia Macdonald, RGN, DipHen
Elisabeth Macdougall
Moira Murray, BA

Music: Rosemary Elliott-Jones, LTCL
Swimming: Janet Johnson, Sandra Inglis
PE/Games:
Carolyn Armstrong, BEd
Shirley Blake, BEd
Support for Learning: Hilary Esson, BEd
ICT Coordinator: Caireen McDonald, BA
French: Katherine Smith, MA
Art: Caroline Chinn, DA
Science:
Carol Hendry, MA
Tracy J Geddes, MA
Librarian: Alison Lloyd-Wiggins, BA, CLIP

Nursery Teacher: Ailsa Reid, BEd

Nursery Nurses:
Fiona McRae, BA
Anne Marie Gove, NNEB
Deborah Browne, NNEB

After School Club Supervisor: Aimee Bainbridge, BEd
Secretary to Head of Junior School: Dorothy Hardie, BA
Junior School Receptionists: Julie Adams, Coleen Manson
Admin Assistant: Lesley Cameron, MA

Admission. The College is divided into two sections: the Junior School (Primary, Classes 1–7) 400 pupils and the Senior School (Secondary, Forms 1–6) 1,050 pupils. The normal stages of entry are to Primary 1, Primary 6 and Secondary 1.

Entry to Primary 1 (age 4½–5½ years) is by interview held in February, and to Primary 6 (age 9½–10½ years) by Entrance Test held in February.

Entry to Secondary 1 is by an Entrance Examination held in January.

Entry at other stages depends upon vacancies arising, and the offer of a place is subject to satisfactory performance in an Entrance Test and interview.

Nursery. There is also a Nursery Unit (age 3–5) for some 35 children.

Fees per term (2008-2009). Nursery: £2,067. Junior School: £1,900 (P1–2), £2,592 (P3–7). Senior School: £2,983. These fees are inclusive and cover Games. Pupils provide their own books.

Bursaries. A significant number of bursaries are awarded to pupils entering SI on the basis of performance in the Entrance Examination and of financial need. Scholarships are awarded to pupils entering the Sixth Year. In total some 20% of pupils in the secondary department receive financial help.

Buildings. The centre block was erected in 1732, but there have been many modern additions. The College is fully equipped with Assembly Hall, Library, Laboratories, Art Rooms, Computing areas and Workshops. There are two Gymnasia and a Swimming Pool at the School. A new playing field was opened in 1992 on a 40-acre site 3m from the school incorporating first-class accommodation and facilities, including a water-based hockey pitch and an astroturf all-weather sports surface. A five-storey teaching block, incorporating a Dining Hall, was opened in 1994, and a new Library and Information Centre in 2000. Further expansion is planned into buildings to be purchased from The Robert Gordon University, including a new Junior School, opening in 2009, and new Music and Drama facilities.

Curriculum. In the Junior School the usual subjects of the primary curriculum are covered, with specialist teachers in Art, French, Computing, Music, Science and Physical Education. The first 2 years of the Senior School have a general curriculum; after that some specialisation is permitted, and courses are provided in Classics (Latin, Greek and Classical Studies), English, Mathematics, Physics, Chemistry, Biology, Human Biology, Modern Languages (French, German, Italian, Spanish), History, Geography, Modern Studies, Music, Art, Drama, Religious Studies, Computer Studies, Information Systems, Technical Subjects (Technological Studies, Graphic Communication), Economics, Accounting and Finance, and Business Management. Pupils are prepared for the Scottish Qualifications Authority examinations which lead directly to university entrance. All pupils have classes in Religious Education and Physical Education. Special courses are run for Sixth Year on entrepreneurship, philosophy, leadership, psychology, sociology, ceramics, photography, electronics, word processing, electronic publishing, survival cooking, Spanish, Japanese, Chinese (Mandarin), Scots Law and European Computer Driving Licence (ECDL).

Examination results are among the best in Scotland, with 96% annually going on to University, some 20% of these beyond Scotland.

Games. Rugby, Hockey (boys and girls), Cricket, Netball, Tennis, Athletics, Cross-Country Running. A wide range of other sports is offered, including Badminton, Basketball, Volleyball, Golf, Squash, Skiing, Swimming, Orienteering, Hill-Walking, Kayaking and Football.

Extra-Curricular Activities. There is a Contingent of the Combined Cadet Force (Army and RAF sections) and a Pipe Band. Participation in the Duke of Edinburgh's Award Scheme is consistently strong. The Choirs, Concert Band and Orchestras play a prominent part in the life of the School, as do a Literary and Debating Society, which meets weekly, and a Dramatic Society, which presents a variety of performances. Many other clubs and societies flourish, making over 60 in all. A very large proportion of pupils undertake The Duke of Edinburgh's Award.

Charitable status. Robert Gordon's College is a Registered Charity, number SC000123. It exists to provide education for boys and girls.

Rossall School

Fleetwood Lancs FY7 8JW
Tel: 01253 774201
Fax: 01253 772052
e-mail: enquiries@rossallcorporation.co.uk
website: www.rossallschool.org.uk

Motto: '*Mens agitat molem*'

Rossall School was founded in 1844 on the coast of Lancashire. It is incorporated by Royal Charter, granted in 1890, and is under the management of a Council.

Life Governors:
The Earl of Derby, President of Corporation
¶Mr R P Shepherd, DL
Mrs H N Trapnell

Governors:
¶Mr D S Stockton (*Chairman*)
¶Mr A N Stephenson, MA (*Vice-Chairman*)

Mrs A E Bott, JP
¶Mr CC Fayle, BScEng, MIMechE
¶Mr M J Reece, MA
The Rt Revd Robert Ladds, SSC, BEd, The Bishop of Whitby
¶Mr J Parr
Mrs C Preston, BSc, ARICS
Mr M Craven
Dr R W F Oakley
¶Mr J A R Prestwich, FCA
The Revd Cannon P Warren, MA
¶Dr H O Fajemirokun
Mr D O Winterbottom, MA, BPhil
Mr H H Aird, MA
Mr M R Moseley
Mr J J Butler, MA
¶Mr C Littler
¶Mr S James
Colonel S Davies

¶ *Old Pupil*

Secretary to the Corporation and Council: Mr B E Clark, MBE

***Headmaster*: Dr Stephen C Winkley**, MA, DPhil

* *Head of Department*
† *Housemaster/mistress*
§ *Part-time*

First Deputy Head: Mr F Q Livingstone, MA Cantab
Deputy Head (*Curriculum*): Mr C Egdell, BSc, PGCE (**ICT, Physics*)
Senior Teacher (*Pastoral*): Mrs K M Lee, MA, CertEd (*Director of Sport & Activities*)
Senior Mistress: Mrs J C Briggs, BA (**English*)

Assistant Staff:
Mr J C Roberts, BA, , PGCE, CertTEFL, FRGS (**Geography*)
†Mrs A Jurczak, CertEd, DipRE (*SENCO*)
Mr M G Roberts, BSc, PGCE (*Science*)
Miss J Mercer, BSc, PGCE (*Science*)
†Mr S L Corrie, BMus (*Assistant Director of Music*)
Mrs S J Cross, BA, PGCE (*English*)
Dr D Dohmen, DPhil, PGCE (*Modern Languages, IB Coordinator*)
Mrs E L Williams, BSc, PGCE (**Girls' Games*)

†Mr J L Riding, BEng, PGCE (*Science*)
Mrs J Nichol, BA, PGCE (**Modern Languages*)
Mrs S Holder-Williams, MA, RSADipPA (**Art*)
Mr J McCafferty, BSc, PGCE (**Mathematics*)
†Mrs K Griffiths, BSc, PGCE (*Chemistry*)
Mr C Ashworth, BSc, PGCE (*Chemistry*)
Revd S Cooper, BSc, DipHE Theology (*Chaplain*)
Mr D Wright, BA, PGCE (*Economics & Business Studies*)
Mr A Fairhurst, BA, PGCE (*Geography*)
Mr K Sullivan, BSc Hons, PGCE (*Science*)
Mrs S Alonso, UGDFL, AIOL, CertEd (*Spanish*)
§Mr R W F Oakley, PhD, BSc (*Physics*)
§Mrs L Furniss (*Mathematics*)
§Mr S P Hoffman, BA (**Economics & Business Studies*)
Mr P Jurczak, BA, MTh (**Religious Studies*)
§Mrs K Anderson, BA, PGCE, PGDipSpLD (*SEN*)
Mrs S Byrne, BSc, PGCE (*Mathematics*)
Mrs L Heap, BA (*Art*)
Mr D Hall, BA Hons, PGCE (*History*)
Mr L Hodgetts, BA Hons (**Design & Technology*)
Mr M Metcalfe, BSc, PGCE (*Biology*)
Mr I Moore, BA, PGCE, TESOL (*English, ICT, Art*)
Mrs R Barker, BA, CertTEFL (*English*)
Miss I H Riley, BA, CertTEFL (*English*)
Mr A Carter, BA, PGCE (*Business Studies*)
§Mrs N Sinclair (*Mathematics*)
Mr T McNab, BA, PGCE (*English*)
Mr A Williams, BSc, PGCE (**Boys' Games*)
Mr T Root, BSc, PGCE (*Geography*)
Mr P Addison, BA, MA, PGCE (*Media Studies*)
§Miss M Welch (*Independent Listener*)
Mr T Birchall (*Mathematics*)
Ms S Unsworth (*Mathematics*)
Mr L Thomsen (*Mathematics*)
Mrs C Wolstencroft (*English*)
Mrs M Young (*Director of Music*)
Mr G Emmett (**History*)

Houses/Houseparents:
Anchor House: Mr & Mrs C Parsons
Dolphin House: Mrs A Jurczak
Lugard Boys House: Mr M Clinton-Baker
Lugard Girls House: Miss J Mercer
Maltese Cross House: Mr & Mrs S Hoffman
Mitre & Fleur de Lys House: Mr S L Corrie
Pelican House: Mr J Riding
Rose House: Mrs K Griffiths and Mr Griffiths
Spread Eagle House: Mr & Mrs J McCleary

Instrumental Music:
Mr G Banks (*brass*)
Mr P Kirk (*clarinet, saxophone*)
Mr A G Keeling (*flute, guitar, composition*)
Mr M Yarwood (*music technology, percussion*)
Mr G Baker (*piano*)
Mrs R E Birchall (*piano*)
Mrs G Carleston (*strings*)
Mrs J Turner (*voice*)
Mrs K Matthews (*voice*)

Finance Director: Mr D Swaine
Registrar: Mrs L Smith
Examinations Officer: Mr R Asher, BSc, PGCE
Head, International Study Centre: Mr D Rose, BA, MA, CertTEFL
Medical Officer: Dr P G Carpenter, MBChB, MRCGP, DRCOG, FPA

Academic Curriculum. All entrants are expected to take a broad based curriculum prior to GCSE. At this stage pupils study English Language, English Literature, Maths, IGCSE Triple Sciences and a Modern Foreign Language (French, German and Spanish: SEN students possibly excepted); there is then a choice of three options taken from History, Geography, Religious Studies, Art, DT, PE, Music and ICT.

In the Sixth Form the International Baccalaureate, A Levels and the BTEC National Diploma in Design are offered. At AS/A2 all the subjects at GCSE are on the curriculum, with separate sciences, Media Studies, Economics and Philosophy also on offer. There is a similar wide range of subjects offered within the IB, where Psychology and Business Studies are also taught. Much emphasis in the IB is also placed upon the 'Core', the teaching of the Theory of Knowledge, the Extended Essay and the Creativity, Action, Service component.

Some 95% of the Upper Sixth follow on into Higher Education both at home and abroad. Special arrangements are made for those seeking entry to Oxbridge and specialist institutions abroad.

The Arts, Science and Technology. Arts Week in the Lent Term is the main school showcase for the performing and visual arts. There are performances ranging from individual instrumental competitions through to plays and concerts. They involve all pupils across the Junior and Senior Schools and the International Study Centre. The Music Department, housed in the Thomas Beecham Music School, provides the basis for individual instrumental tuition. The Chapel Choir sings weekly choral services in the magnificent Chapel of St John the Baptist. There are other choral groups, a junior and senior orchestra, a jazz group, etc. The Drama Department produce both Senior and Junior Plays in the Michaelmas and Lent Terms, with many informal productions particularly associated with Arts Week.

The newly refurbished Art and Design Technology departments offer extensive art and design facilities within purpose-built art and design workshops containing state-of-the-art tooling image making machinery.

The School's Astronomy and Space Science Centre incorporates an observatory, permanent planetarium, lecture theatre and classroom suite. This is not only used within the school for curriculum teaching but is also available for outside use. The Science Department is well used with some 50%+ of students following science at 16+. Within the school grounds there are 3 Sites of Scientific Interest, which are maintained by staff and students. The sea, beach and dunes in front of the school are similar sources for study.

The IT provision is also housed primarily within the Science area with 300+ state-of-the-art machines available through the working day and beyond both in the IT suite and in departments around the campus. The machines are part of a secure wireless network. The Junior School and International Study Centre have their own provision.

The House System. All pupils are members of a House. At age 15 there are four boys' mixed day and boarding houses (two primarily boarding and two primarily day), a girls' boarding house and one girls' day house. All boarding boys and girls entering at 11+ are in Anchor House, which has its own residential unit. (The International Study Centre also has a boys' and girls' house.) Houseparents have responsibility for each pupil's welfare and are supported by deputies, tutors, medical, careers staff, etc.

Religious Instruction. Rossall was founded as 'the Northern Church of England School' and Chapel remains central to the well-being of the community. Pupils of all faiths are encouraged to share in this community.

Games. 45 acres of playing field and a gymnasium, floodlit Astroturf and indoor 25 metre swimming pool, along with squash, tennis, and fives courts allow all pupils to pursue a sporting interest. The boys mainly play rugby, hockey, cricket, football and basketball, with the girls playing hockey, netball, cricket, rounders and tennis. All pupils are taught to play the unique game of Rossall Hockey on the sandy beach owned by the School. There are full programmes of competitive fixtures against other schools and clubs. House matches occur in all major games, including football, cross-country in the Lent

Term. Archery, athletics, shooting, golf, horse-riding and many other activities are offered.

The CCF. Rossall proudly lays claim to having the oldest CCF in the country. Currently most of Years 9–11 are in either the Army, Navy or Air Force contingents. In Year 9 all cadets will follow the Bronze Duke of Edinburgh's Award, progress to Silver and Gold is optional. All cadets also have the chance to follow the BTEC Service award within the corps, the equivalent to 4 GCSEs this is completed entirely within CCF time. The school has a shooting range, keeps boats on the Wyre and there is opportunity to fly at RAF Woodvale.

Activities and Clubs. Rossall's Master in Charge of Weekend Activities is responsible for the overall running and supervision of activities and clubs. Time is set aside after school 4 days a week and at weekends for activities and clubs which operate over the 3 terms. Clubs and activities include but are not limited to: The Literary Society, PhysSoc, Choir, Sports, and bi-half termly excursions.

Admission. Any term in the year for boys and girls aged 11+ and 13+, September preferably at 16+ or 17+. All applications for entrance should be made to the Headmaster. On registration a fee of £50 will be charged to UK applicants and £120 to international applicants. Applicants will be put in touch with a Housemaster or Housemistress as soon as appropriate.

Fees per term (2008-2009). Day £2,030–£4,315; Full Boarding £5,520–£8,830; Weekly Boarding £4,907–£7,740.

Scholarships and Bursaries. (*see Scholarship Entries section*). All enquiries about Scholarships and Bursaries and other awards should be addressed to the Headmaster.

The Trapnell Scholarship (up to full fees) and the Jackson Scholarship (85% of fees) are awarded annually to those of very high academic and all-rounder ability. A further award (up to full fees), the Lugard Bequest, is offered to a child of a regular officer from the Duke of Lancaster's Regiment. Open Scholarships (up to 50% fees) are offered at 11+, 13+ and Sixth Form entrance. They are awarded for academic, music and sport. Free musical tuition is also awarded for outstanding instrumentalists.

Substantial bursaries continue to be awarded to children of the clergy and those in the armed forces.

Rossall Junior School. Rossall has its own Junior School for children aged 7–11 situated within the same grounds. There is also a Nursery and Infants School for day boys and girls aged 2–7.

Access. Motorway: 15 minutes from M55 (spur off M6). Railway: Blackpool North (6 miles). Air: Manchester International Airport (55 miles by road).

The Rossallian Club. Secretary: Jen Booth c/o Rossall School. This Former Pupils Club keeps a record of more than 5,000 members and coordinates the activities of eight Branches. A Newsletter is published twice each year.

Charitable Status. The Corporation of Rossall School is a Registered Charity, number 526685. It aims to provide a sound Christian education for boys and girls.

Rougemont School

Llantarnam Hall Malpas Road Newport South Wales NP20 6QB
Tel: 01633 820800
Fax: 01633 855598
e-mail: registrar@rsch.co.uk
website: www.rougemontschool.co.uk

President: Mr I S Burge

Governors:
Chairman: Mr I G Short
Vice-Chairman: Mr D Blayney, LLB
Mrs J Clark, BA, PGCE
Mr R Pugsley, MSc, FCCA
Dr R M Reynolds, BSc, DipEd
Mr T Rose, CBE, BSc, CEng, FIChemE
Mrs S Routledge, BPharm, MRPharmS
Mr J A Shewring, FCA
Miss J Sollis, BA, AKC
Mr M Tebbutt
Mrs A C Thomas, JP, SRN, SCM
Prof D Fone, MB BS, MD, FFPH, FRGS, MRCGP, DCH, DRCOG

***Headmaster*: Dr Jonathan Tribbick**, BA, LLB, PGCE, FCMI, JP

* *Head of Department*
§ *Part-time*

Deputy Head of Senior School: Mr J Worth, BA, PGCE (*Geography*)
Academic Registrar: Mr M James, MA Ed, BEd, BA, BSc, CBiol, MIBiol (*Biology*)
Assistant Head, Director of Studies: Mr R Carnevale, MA Ed, BSc, PGCE (**Physics*)
Assistant Head, Head of Sixth Form: Mrs E Ferrand, BEd (**Extra Mural Progamme, Mathematics*)
Head of Junior School: Mrs L Turner, BEd (*English*)
Head of Infants' School: Mrs N Rice, BA, PGCE
Finance Manager: Mrs H Perry, FCCA
Operations Manager: Mr C Whitney

Senior School:
Mr A Akram, BSc, PGCE (*Chemistry, House Tutor*)
Mrs S Ashton, BSc, PGCE (*§Mathematics*)
Mr K Bell, BA, PGCE (**Physical Education*)
Mrs K Benson-Dugdale, BMus, MA, QTS, PGEM (*Higher Education Advisor, *Music*)
Mr D Cobb, BSc, PGCE (**Biology*)
Miss C Dugdale, BA, PGCE (*§Games, History, Religious Studies*)
Mrs S Eley, BA, PGCE (*§Dyslexia Dept*)
Mrs S Elson, LLB (*§Latin, Religious Studies*)
Mrs R Garrod, BA, PGCE (*History*)
Mr L Godfrey, BSc, PGCE (*Mathematics, House Tutor*)
Mrs J Goodwin, BSc (*Physics, House Tutor, Pupil Performance Coordinator*)
Mr J Hardwick, BSc, PGCE (*Biology, Chemistry*)
Mrs J Harris, CertEd, Dip Theol (**Religious Studies, PSE*)
Miss R Hayes, BA, PGCE (*Design & Technology, ICT*)
Mrs F Heirene, BA (*Assistant Librarian*)
Ms C Hughson, BA, MSc (*Librarian*)
Mr M Jenkins, MA Cantab, PGCE (**History*)
Mr I Kelly, BA, PGCE (**Professional Development, Senior Mentor, *German*)
Mrs J Lloyd, BA, PGCE (**English*)
Miss L Meredith, BSc, PGCE (*Physical Education*)
Mr L Mintowt-Czyz, BA, BTec, PGCE (**Art*)
Mrs D Morgan, BA, PGCE (**Modern Languages*)
Mrs D Moore, BA, PGCE (**Drama, Media Studies*)
Mrs S Morgan, MSc, BSc, PGCE, Cert Lit/Dyslexia (*Dyslexia Dept*)
Mrs S Munro, DEUG, Licence, PGCE (*French*)
Mrs A Page, BSc Econ, PGCE (*Economics & Business Studies*)
Miss K Page, BSc, PGCE (*Physical Education*)
Miss L Parr, BA, PGCE (*Art*)
Mr F Pearce, BSc, PGCE, DipComp (**ICT*)
Mr G Prothero, BA, Cert PE (*Senior Tutor Y10–11, French, German, PE*)
Mr A Rees, BA, PGCE (*Physical Education, DofE Award Scheme*)
Mr A Richards, BSc, PGCE (*Mathematics, ICT, House Tutor*)
Mrs S Roberts, BSc, PGCE (**Mathematics*)
Miss A Robst, BA, PGCE (*English, ICT, Editor School Magazine*)

Mrs P Rogers, BSc, PGCE (**Geography*)
Mr A Scarfi, BA, PGCE (*English*)
Mrs C Sims, BA, PGCE, AMBDA (*Dyslexia Dept*)
Mr H Singer, BA, PGCE (*Senior Tutor Yrs 7–9, *Design & Technology*)
Mrs L Thickins, BA, PGCE (*English, Media Studies*)
Mrs T van der Linde, BSc, PGCE (**Chemistry, Pupil Performance Coordinator*)
Mrs R Taylor, BA, PGCE, AMBDA (*English, Dyslexia Dept*)

Junior School:
Mrs J Bolwell, CertEd (*Deputy Head*)
Mrs R Carroll, BA, PGCE (*Class Teacher*)
Mr C Dobbins, BMus, DipMus, LRSM, PGCE (*Music*)
Mrs K Galloway, KS2 (*Classroom Assistant*)
Mrs J Greenaway, CertEd (*Class Teacher*)
Miss L Hallas, BA, PGCE (*English*)
Mrs A Jenkins, BSc (*§Science*)
Mrs R Jenkins, BEd (*Class Teacher*)
Mr P McMahon, BA, PGCE (*Mathematics*)
Mrs C Poore, BEd (*Science, Mathematics, Geography, KS2 Coordinator*)
Mrs K Williams, BEd (*Class Teacher*)
Mr S Rowlands, BA, QTS (*Class Teacher*)
Mrs C Richards, BA, QTS (*Class Teacher*)

Infants' School:
Mrs H Ashill, NNEB (*Nursery Nurse*)
Mrs A Burridge, BSc, PGCE (*Class Helper*)
Mrs A Exley (*Class Helper*)
Mrs J Farouzan, NNEB (*Pre-Reception Supervisor*)
Mrs S Hotchkiss, BA, QTS (*Y2 Class Teacher*)
Mrs S Jones, BA, PGCE (*§Music*)
Mrs L McLoughlin (*Class Helper*)
Mrs T Mountford, BEd (*Reception Class Teacher*)
Mrs N Noor, BA, PGCE (*Y2 Class Teacher*)
Mrs R Payne, NNEB (*Nursery Nurse*)
Miss G Rees, BA (*Reception Class Teacher*)
Miss Z Rees, NNEB (*Nursery Nurse*)
Mrs C Townsend, NVQ (*Pre-Reception Supervisor*)
Miss M Verrier, BA, QTS (*Y1 Class Teacher*)

Registrar: Mrs D Lunt

Rougemont was founded in a house of that name immediately after the First World War as a co-educational day school taking children through to grammar school entrance at 11. It moved to Nant Coch House just after the Second World War and grew to about 200 pupils.

In 1974 the school was re-founded as a Charitable Trust. Since then it has bought extensive new buildings and has 696 pupils on role in the Infant School (Nursery to Year 2), Junior School (Years 3–8) and Senior School (Years 9–13).

The Junior and Senior Schools moved to a new site at Llantarnam Hall, a large Victorian mansion set in 50 acres of grounds, between 1992 and 1995, with the Infant School joining them in April 2004. The grounds have been landscaped to provide playing fields and an extensive building programme has taken place on the site. During 1998 a Liberal Arts area including Sports Hall, Music suite and Drama Studio was completed. In 1999 a new classroom block and library was completed and in 2000 additional classrooms together with Art studio were built.

Admission to the Infant, Junior and Senior Schools is by interview and examination. Entry to the Sixth Form is dependent on GCSE results.

The following paragraphs refer to the Senior School although peripatetic specialists work in both and there is some inter-change of teachers.

Curriculum. Pupils follow a wide syllabus to age 14. For the two years to GCSE pupils study nine subjects of which English Language and Literature, Mathematics, a language, science and a humanities subject are normally compulsory. 18 subjects are available.

Sixth Form. 17 AS/A2 levels are available. Sixth Form pupils have their own common room and study area. Sixth Form pupils can also study AS level Critical Thinking and take part in a range of extra-curricular activities and games.

Religion. Rougemont School has no direct affiliation to a Christian Church or denomination. However, the religious instruction, corporate worship and moral value system of the School is based on that of the broad tradition of the mainstream Christian Churches.

Careers. The School belongs to the Independent Schools Careers Organisation. The Senior teachers advise on all aspects of further education and careers.

Music. In addition to specialist teachers of music a large number of peripatetic teachers cover the range of orchestral instruments. There are choirs and instrumental ensembles for all ages.

Drama. In addition to the Infant School's Spring Festival and the Senior School Eisteddfod, one major play and one musical event take place each year.

Elocution and Dance. Visiting staff hold weekly classes for LADA courses, ballet and modern dance.

Sport. The School has developed a high standard of performance in most major sports. There is a wide fixtures programme for both boys and girls, as well as the opportunity to participate in numerous coaching courses.

Clubs. A wide variety of extra-curricular activities and clubs is available at lunch time and after school, as is supervised prep.

Duke of Edinburgh's Award Scheme. This is a very successful activity within the school and over 60 pupils have gained the Gold Award in the last twenty years.

Fees per term (2008-2009). Infant School £1,960–£2,060; Junior School £2,360; Senior School £2,700–£3,080.

Scholarships. An annual scholarship examination is held for entry to Year 7. A limited number of means-tested bursaries is offered from Year 7 upwards.

Further information. A prospectus and other details are available from the Registrar (Tel: 01633 820800, e-mail: debra.lunt@rsch.co.uk).

Charitable status. Rougemont School is a Registered Charity, number 532341. It exists to provide education for boys and girls.

The Royal Belfast Academical Institution

College Square East, Belfast, Co Antrim BT1 6DL
Northern Ireland
Tel: 028 9024 0461
Fax: 028 9023 7464
e-mail: prinsec@rbai.belfast.ni.sch.uk
website: www.rbai.org.uk

RBAI is a non-denominational school which welcomes pupils from widely varied social backgrounds in Belfast and from areas up to 40 miles outside the city.

The School is under the management of a Board of Governors constituted under a scheme authorised by the Privy Council in Ireland. Twenty-four Governors are elected by members of the Institution, 3 are co-opted, and there are 2 parent and 2 teacher Governors.

Founded in 1810, the Institution was until 1849 a College as well as a School and had Faculties of Arts and Medicine; on the foundation of the Queen's College, now The Queen's University of Belfast, it became a School offering grammar school courses.

Motto: '*Quaerere Verum*'

Board of Governors:
Chairman: Sir Kenneth Bloomfield, KCB, MA, LLD
Vice-Chairman: A W Kinnaird, OBE, BAgr, BSc, FRICS

***Principal*: Miss J Williamson**, MA Oxon, NPQH

Secretary to the Governors and Registrar: K J Wilson, BSc Econ, FCA

Vice-Principals:
C A McKinstry, BEd, PGDipGC
B J Todd, BA, MEd, PGCE

Dean: E T Foster, BA, MLitt, PGCE

Preparatory Department: Inchmarlo
Head Master: W A O Armstrong, BA

The School occupies an 8-acre site in the centre of the City on which its first buildings were erected; major recent additions provide modern and specialised facilities. In addition to 50 classrooms, there are 17 specialist laboratories, Art Suite, Technology and Design Centre, Music suite, a Careers room, a Computer department, a new Sports Hall, fitness suite, gymnasium, indoor heated swimming pool, a Common Hall with extensive stage facilities, a Dining Hall and library. The award-winning Christ Church building, opened by Prince Charles in September 2003, houses the new library and ICT Centre of Excellence. There is a Boat House on the River Lagan.

For the first 3 years boys follow a common curriculum: in the fourth year certain options are introduced, and at the end of the fifth year boys sit the examination for the Northern Ireland GCSE. Subjects studied at A Level in the Sixth Form include Art, Biology, Business Studies, E Chemistry, Economics, English, French , German, Geography, Government and Politics, Greek, ICT, Latin, Mathematics, Media Studies, Modern History, Music, PE, Physics, Psychology, Spanish and Technology.

Football, Hockey and Rugby are played in the winter; Athletics, Cricket and Tennis occupy the summer months; Badminton, Fencing, Rowing, Shooting, Squash and Swimming (including Water Polo and Life-saving) take place throughout the year. Teams representing the School take part not only in matches and activities within the Province, but also in events open to all Schools in the United Kingdom. There are numerous Clubs and Societies, a School Orchestra, Choir and Band, a contingent of the Combined Cadet Force, Scout and Explorer Scout units and a Community Service Group.

Over 95% of each year's leavers go on to universities or to full-time courses in other institutions of higher or further education. In addition to a large number of prizes throughout the School, endowed Scholarships are offered in the Sixth Form which are tenable for travel or at University.

Candidates for admission to the Main School should be under 12 on 1 July of the year of admission and applications must be received by mid-February. Boys who are regarded by the Department of Education for Northern Ireland as qualified for grammar school education have their Tuition Fee paid by their local Education and Library Board. There is an annual capital fee of £760. Scholarships are awarded by the School to boys whose work shows outstanding progress during their School career.

Preparatory Department. This is set in 6 acres of ground in South Belfast. Admission is mainly at 4, but can be at any age depending on availability of places. The Annual Fee for P1–P3 is £2,650, and for P4–P7 £3,050.

Old Instonians' Association. *Hon Sec*: D Jardin, 5 Elmwood Pk, Lisburn, Co Antrim BT27 4AX.

Charitable status. The Royal Belfast Academical Institution is a Registered Charity, number XN45554.

The Royal Grammar School
Guildford

High Street Guildford Surrey GU1 3BB
Tel: Headmaster: 01483 880608
School Office: 01483 880600
Fax: 01483 306127
e-mail: office@rgs-guildford.co.uk
website: www.rgs-guildford.co.uk

The Royal Grammar School has occupied its fine Tudor buildings in Guildford's High Street for nearly five centuries. It was founded by Robert Beckingham in 1509 and established by King Edward VI's Charter of 1552, which decreed that there should be '. . . one Grammar School in Guildford . . . for the Education, Institution and Instruction of Boys and Youths in Grammar at all future times for ever to endure'. Among the first in the country to be purpose-built, the original buildings contain a remarkable Chained Library, which is now the Headmaster's Study.

Governing Body:
Chairman: H J Pearson, OBE, MA, PhD, CMath, FIMA
Vice-Chairman: J McCann, BMus, ACIB
Professor G R Bird, MA, PhD
F Bouwers, BA, DipArch
Mrs C Cobley
¶D J Counsell, FCA
Mrs S K Creedy, MA
His Honour Judge Critchlow, LLB, FCIArb
The Reverend R L Cotton, MA, DipTh
P D Harmer, BA
B Hartop, BSc
A D Jenkins, MA
The Mayor of Guildford
The Earl of Onslow, High Steward of Guildford
M Nicholson, OBE
P G Peel, FCA
Mrs J S Rice, ACMA
Mrs C Rimmer
¶J E Rule, FCA
G Sutton, MD, MA Cantab, FRCP, FACC

Governor Emeritus: ¶J F Brown

Bursar and Deputy Clerk to the Governors: I C A Watson, BA, MSc

***Headmaster*: J M Cox**, BSc, PhD

Deputy Heads:
M W Hoskins, BA, MA
G T Williams, MA

Director of Studies: J A Simpson, BEd, MIBiol, AdDipEd, MSc, MPhil, CBiol

Assistant Staff:
S M Adams, BA
S W Armstrong, MA
E J Badham, ARCS, BSc, CBiol, MIBiol
A H S Barras, BA, MA, PhD
Mrs S Barrass, BSc
Miss C L Bell, MA
S G Black, MMath
Mrs J Bodmer, BSc, PhD, MBA
Mrs M C Booth, BEd
E J P Bradnock, BA
M A Burbidge, BSc
E K D Bush, MA
¶R C Bustin, BSc
J A Casale, BSc, MBA
D H Chambers, BMus, PCASS
W D Cowx, BSc, MSc
A M J Curtis, MA
Mrs H Curtis, BA
G T Davies, MPhys, PhD
¶A C Dodd, BA, MA
A H Dubois, BSc
P J Dunscombe, BSc
C J Eldridge, BA, MPhil
J Gent, BSc
Miss H Golding, MMath
Mrs M R Goodman, BA
N W Gough, BSc, MSc

C J Grace, BA, MA, LTCL, AMusLCM
Mrs K Handley, BSc
L M Holland, BSc
P J Hosier, BA, MEd
D M Hoyle, BEng
Mrs S F Hudson, BSc, MSc
M R Jenkins, BSc
M J Jennings, BA
J B Kelly, BA, MA, MA RCA
G M Knight, BA
K J Knight, BSc, MSc
M E Lambert, BA, MA
W S Lau, MChem
O C Lawson, BSc
Mrs S J Lingard, BSc
Ms E López García, MPhil, MA, BA
A R Lowe, BA
¶A J Mackowski, BA
Miss F Y Marcus, BA
Mrs E D McIntyre, MA
R B Meadowcroft, BA, MA
Miss C J S Moorehead, MA, FRGS
Miss A Murray-Bruce, BA, MA, CIM
M W Nash BA
P G Nathan, BA
L W O'Brien, BA
M O'Malley, BA
D Patel, BSc, PhD
M G Paterson, BA, MEd, MPhil
Mrs S J Perrett, BA Perrett,
J W Pressley, MA
M R F Royds, BEng
A N Rozier, BA
J R Saxton, MA
¶J-M Saxton, BA
G E Schofield, BEd, MA
R A Sears, BA
R E J Seymour, BEd, FRGS
T W Shimell, MChem
S B R Shore, BEd
A F Smith BA, MA, MA
Mrs C E Smith, BA
K Stagno, BSc, PhD
R Stark, BEd
S G Thornhill, MA, DPhil
O M Torri, BA
Miss J Wardle, BA
¶A P Way, BA
¶A J Welch, BA
Revd J P Whitaker, MA
P H White, MA
Mrs D Whitehead, BTech
N E Wild, BA
I Wilkes, BEd
A U Woodman, BSc
D J Woolcott, BA
S J H Yetman, BSc

Admissions Registrar: Mrs S Dowell, MA

The Royal Grammar School of the 21st century is a day school for around 900 boys, some 250 of whom are in the Sixth Form. The age range is 11 to 18.

Buildings and Facilities. The School occupies a large site in the centre of Guildford. As well as the Chained Library, the Old Buildings contain the Sixth Form Common Room and the Music and Art departments. The New Building, opened in 1965, contains Great Hall, the Careers Centre, the Library, the Dining Hall and kitchens, the Language Laboratory and a large number of classrooms and laboratories. A continuous programme of building development has recently provided a Drama Studio, excellent facilities for Science and Technology, a Sculpture Studio and a large Resources Centre and Study Area. A new Sports and Outdoor Activity Centre with an all weather outdoor training area, an Auditorium and a new Art block have all opened in the last three years. New music facilities and a Sixth Form Centre were completed in 2007.

Curriculum. The Royal Grammar School has an established reputation for academic excellence. Virtually all its Sixth Formers comfortably pass at least three A Levels and gain entry to higher education. About a quarter of them go on to Oxford and Cambridge.

The School's day is from 8.45 am to 4.00 pm. There are no lessons on Saturdays.

In the first three years (Years 7, 8 and 9 nationally), all boys follow a common curriculum embodying the programmes of study for Key Stage 3 of the National Curriculum. The subjects studied are English, French or Spanish, Geography, History, Latin, Maths, Information Technology, RE, PE, Art, Music and Science with Technology, which includes aspects of Astronomy, Earth Science, and Biotechnology. In the third year (Year 9) all boys choose between Spanish, German and Greek and study the separate sciences and Technology.

In the fourth and fifth years (Years 10 and 11) all boys follow a broad and balanced curriculum and take at least nine GCSEs which include English, Maths, French and Science. In addition, all boys take RE, PE and Games. A course in Study Skills, Problem Solving and Personal, Social and Health Education is taught through a timetabled tutorial programme. After the GCSE examinations, all boys participate in the work experience programme.

In the Sixth Form, in addition to the subjects already mentioned, boys may take Classical Civilisation, Further Mathematics, Electronic Systems, Economics, Politics, Drama and Theatre Studies and PE through to A Level. Although many boys prefer a predominantly Maths/Science or Arts choice of subjects, there is no Arts/Science barrier, and more or less any combination is possible. There is an enterprising programme of Sixth Form General Studies organised in conjunction with two local girls' schools.

Religion. The Royal Grammar School is not a specifically religious foundation, but Religious Education (non-denominational) is naturally an integral part of the School's curriculum. RE periods are compulsory at all levels in the School, although parents with conscientious objections may ask the Headmaster for alternative arrangements to be made. The school day normally begins with an Assembly at which every boy is required to be present. The short Act of Worship which features twice a week within Assembly is a Christian one. The School also holds annually its own Carol Service, Commemoration Service and Remembrance Service. The School is closely linked with Holy Trinity Church, a few yards down the High Street.

Pastoral Care. Each boy's progress through the School is monitored with care, and there is a system of regular checks involving the Careers Department in conjunction with a boy's parents. Below the Sixth Form a boy is looked after mainly by his Form Tutor; in the Sixth Form there is a system of tutor groups. Boys in the Fourth Form upwards are also encouraged to choose a personal tutor. All boys belong to one of the six Houses, which exist mainly to provide a framework for competitive sport, but which also give further pastoral care opportunities.

Extra-Curricular Activities. Clubs and Societies flourish. Activities include Bridge, Chess, Computing, Debating, Electronics, Model Railway, History, Geography and Philosophy. There is a Scout Group, a Combined Cadet Force contingent of Army, Navy and RAF sections, and the Duke of Edinburgh's Award Scheme. Many boys play musical instruments and there is a School Orchestra, a Big Band, a variety of instrumental groups and a strong Choral Society. There are frequent opportunities for boys throughout the school to participate in dramatic productions.

Games. The School's principal games are rugby, hockey and cricket, although as boys move up the School their sporting options widen considerably. Sports available include tennis, swimming, cross-country running, shooting, sailing, athletics, golf, squash, basketball, football, fencing and badminton.

Admission. Boys may be considered for entry to the Royal Grammar School at any age between 11 and 18. The usual ages of entry, however, are at 11, 13 and 16 into the Sixth Form. Applicants at 11 take the School's entrance examination early in the year of entry; those for 13 entry take the Common Entrance examination after 11 or 12+ assessment.

New boys are admitted in September of each year.

The Headmaster is pleased to meet parents, arrange for them to see the School, and discuss the possibility of their son's entry to the School. Appointments may be made through the Registrar, who will supply the School's prospectus on request.

Fees per term (2008-2009). £4,033 (plus £180 lunch) inclusive of all tuition, stationery and loan of necessary books.

Scholarships. (*see Scholarship Entries section*). Details of Scholarships and Bursaries are also available from the Registrar.

Preparatory Department. Lanesborough (*see entry in IAPS section*) is the preparatory department of the RGS.

Old Boys. The Membership Secretary of the Old Guildfordians' Association is D H B Jones, BSc, who can be contacted at the School.

Charitable status. The King Edward VI Royal Grammar School, Guildford is a Registered Charity, number 312028. It exists to provide education for boys from 11 to 18.

Royal Grammar School
Newcastle upon Tyne

Eskdale Terrace Newcastle-upon-Tyne NE2 4DX
Tel: 0191 281 5711
Fax: 0191 212 0392
e-mail: admissions@rgs.newcastle.sch.uk
website: www.rgs.newcastle.sch.uk

The Royal Grammar School was founded and endowed in 1545 by Thomas Horsley, and by virtue of a Charter granted in 1600 by Queen Elizabeth it became 'the Free Grammar School of Queen Elizabeth in Newcastle upon Tyne'. For over 450 years and on six different sites the School has been of major educational importance in Newcastle and in the North East as a whole. It has valued its close links with the city and region, and its Governing Body consists largely of representatives of Local Authorities and Universities.

The School benefits from its central position, being within easy walking distance of the Civic and City Centres and of Newcastle's two Universities, and linked with the whole region by easily accessible rail, bus and metro services.

The School is a Day School and moved towards full co-education in 2006 with places being allocated to boys and girls at all entry points (7+, 9+, 11+, 16+). There are about 1,250 pupils, including 1,050 in the Senior School (age 11–18) and 200 in the Junior School (age 7–11).

Governors:
Chairman: D L Taylor, MA
Vice-Chairman: P A Walker. BA
A J Applegarth, BA
Mrs L R Bird
P A Campbell, MA
Dr S Cholerton, BSc, PhD
N A H Fenwick, MA
J C Fitzpatrick, BA, FCA, ACI Arb
Professor E W N Glover, MA, PhD, CPhys, FInstP, ILTM
A Hobson, MA
Professor A C Hurlbert, BA, MA, PhD, MD
D Marshall, BSc, MSc, PGCE
Dr K J Neill, MBBS, FRCA
Councillor A W Purdue, BA, MLitt, FRHist
Professor E Ritchie, BA, PhD
Dr K E Spence, PhD, DipArch
S E Wood, LLB
R D Armstrong, PhD, DSc

Clerk to the Governors and Bursar: R J Metcalfe, MA, FBIFM

***Headmaster*: B St J Trafford**, MA, MEd, PhD, FRSA

Second Master: A A Bird, BMus, MEd, LRAM

Assistant Staff:

* *Head of Department*

Art:
*K Egan-Fowler, BA
Mrs C Egan-Fowler, BEd
Mrs S M Elliott, DipEd
G P Mason, BA
P Edwards, BA

Biology:
*Mrs S F Hutchinson, BSc
Dr M H Bell, BSc, PhD
P J Heath, BSc
Mrs J A Malpas, BSc (*Assistant Head of Lower School*)
Ms R E Clements, BSc
C J H Wancke, BSc
§Dr C J Murgatroyd, BSc, D Phil

Chemistry:
Dr A J Pulham, BA, DPhil (**Science*)
*R W Wiggins, BSc
Dr D J Lawson, BA
T Kelso, BSc
Miss N Brennan, BSc
Dr J Henshaw, BSc, PhD
Dr E A Sconce, BSc, PhD

Classics:
*E H T Noy Scott, BA (*Head of Year 11*)
T C Clark, BA (*Head of Lower School*)
J B Mutton, BA, MA
Mrs P Coningham, BA, MA
Miss C E Garrow, BA
S Robertson, MA

Economics/Politics:
*P Shelley, BA, MSc
R C M Loxley, BSc, MEd (*Director of Studies*)
*J D Neil, MPhil (*Politics*)
W M Scott, BSc
M J Smalley, BA, QTS

English:
*Dr S J Barker, BA, PhD
A R D King, BA, MA
Dr C Goulding, BA, MLitt, PhD
Dr H Jones-Lee, BA, DPhil (*Senior Mistress*)
J D Hughes, BA
Mrs K J Keown, BA
§S C Masters, BA, MA

Geography:
*D A Wilson, BSc
Miss S J Longville, BA (*Assistant Head of Middle School*)
Mrs R J L Laws, MA (*Assistant Head of Careers*)
M G Downie, BA (*Head of Careers*)

History:
*S E Tilbrook, BA
D C Greenhalgh, BA, MA
*J Ferstenberg, BA (*Head of RE, Personal Development Studies*)
O L Edwards, BA
S P Wright, BA, MA
A S W Davies, BA, MSt

Mathematics:
*T E Keenan, BSc, MSc
A Delvin, BSc, MSc
Dr J Argyle, BSc, MSc, PhD
P M Heptinstall, BSc, PhD
J A Smith, BSc
H Rashid, BSc, MSc
Mrs E Temple, BSc
W Gibson, MA
S D Watkins, BSc (*Head of Middle School*)
G D Dunn, BSc
A Snedden, BSc

Modern Languages:
*Miss K E Sykes, BA
Miss S Demoulin, DEUG (**French*)
Mrs C L Diaz-Crossley, BA (**German*)
Mrs L M Boucaud, BA
§Mrs C Dixon, BA
M S Bailie, BA, MA
Mrs C A M O'Hanlon, BA
Miss J Budd, BA
M Metcalf, BA, MPhil
Miss E L Hayes, BA
§Mrs S J Huntley, BA

Music & Performing Arts:
*N T Parker, BA (*Director*)
T W S Rhodes, BMus, RCM (*Assistant Head of Music*)
Mrs G M Blazey, BMus, MA (*Head of Junior School Music*)
D M Key, MMus, BA
Miss R A Irving, BA

Philosophy:
*H H H Baker, MA (*Third Master; Head of Upper School*)

Physical Education:
*P J Ponton, BA, DLC
F Dickinson, BEd
D W Smith, BEd (*Senior Master*)
P D Taylor, CertEd, DipPE
A G Brown, BSc
Miss A J Bryson, BSc
Miss C E O'Brien, BSc
§R V MacKay, BSc

Physics:
*E T Rispin, BSc
A N Baker, BSc
J L Camm, BSc
P Wilson, BSc, MSc
Dr M B A Read, MA, MPhil, PhD

Psychology:
*D J Merritt, MA (*Counsellor*)
Mrs C M B Stewart, BSc, MA

Design & Technology:
*I Goldsborough, BEd, MSc
Mrs C A Pipes, BA
P M Warne, MEng

Junior School:
R J Craig, BEd (*Headmaster*)
J K Wilkinson, BEd (*Deputy Head*)
Mrs C Biggins, BA
J A Pollock, CertEd
Mrs B Joy, CertEd
Dr A J Spencer, BSc, PhD

Mrs K Wall, BA
Miss R M Carson, BA
Miss L M Harrison, BA
Mrs S G Owens, BEd, MA
§G Scrafton, BA

School Medical Officers:
Dr M A Borthwick, MB BS, MRCGP
Dr J A Browell, MBChB, MRCGP

Admissions Secretary: Mrs J M Glendon

Curriculum. The aim of the curriculum up to Year 11 is to offer a general education, culminating in GCSE in a wide range of subjects. All pupils study English (Language and Literature), a Modern Language, Mathematics, Biology, Physics and Chemistry to this level and three further examination subjects are taken at GCSE level from Art, Classical Studies, Economics, Geography, German, Greek, History, Latin, Music, Spanish, Design & Technology and Drama. Additionally there is a programme of Art, Drama, Music and Technology for all in Years 7 to 9.

Sixth Formers will normally choose 4 subjects for study to AS Level in the Lower Sixth, and in the Upper Sixth 3 subjects to A Level, most combinations from the following list being possible: Art, Biology, Chemistry, Classical Civilisation, Economics, English, French, Geography, German, Greek, History, Latin, Mathematics, Further Mathematics, Music, Physics, Politics, Psychology, Spanish, Technology. Philosophy, Performance Studies and Film Studies are among subjects available as an AS in the Lower Sixth. There is a substantial course of General Studies available.

Almost all sixth-formers go on to University, and success in gaining entry at Oxford and Cambridge, and medical schools, has been an outstanding feature of the school's record.

Physical Education. All pupils are required to take part in a Physical Education programme which, up to Year 10, includes Rugby, Football, Cross-Country, Cricket, Athletics, Gymnastics, Hockey, Netball, Tennis, Swimming. At the upper end of the School a wider range of activities is offered: in addition to the above pupils may opt for Badminton, Basketball, Climbing, Fencing, Fitness training, Karate, Orienteering, Squash, Tennis, Table Tennis, Volleyball and Dance. A wide range of activities is available to all through voluntary membership of various Sports Clubs.

Activities. Art, Drama and Music are strong features in the life of the School, all of them overflowing from scheduled lessons into spare-time activity. There are some 30 music groups and ensembles ranging from choirs and orchestras to bands, jazz ensembles, rock groups and an early music consort. There are a number of productions in the theatre each term. Numerous societies meet in the lunch-break or after school, some linked with school work but many developing from private enthusiasms. There is a thriving Duke of Edinburgh's Award scheme. There is an entirely voluntary Combined Cadet Force Contingent. Annual overseas visits include ski-parties, sporting tours, Classics trips, visits to art galleries and to the battlefields of World War I.

Supervision and Pastoral Care. Each pupil is within the care of (a) Form Supervisor and (b) Tutor. The latter will normally be associated with the pupil throughout their school career, and the aim is to forge a personal link with pupils and their families.

The Careers programme begins in Year 9; in Year 11 and the 6th Form every possible care is taken to advise each pupil individually about Careers and Higher Education.

The School's Medical Officers are available regularly for consultation; there is also a School Counsellor.

Buildings. Some of the School's buildings date from 1907 and are described by Pevsner as "friendly neo-Early-Georgian". Recent years have seen many developments and improvements, including the rebuilding of the indoor swimming pool in 1990, the opening in February 1996 of a new Sports Centre, a new Science and Technology Centre which opened in 1997, and new Maths and ICT departments in 1998. A new Junior School extension opened in 2005 and a Performing Arts Centre opened in September 2006.

Junior School. Years 3 and 4 of the Junior School are separately housed in Lambton Road opposite the Senior School playing fields. Years 5 and 6 are housed in a new extension on the main school site. Junior School pupils use the Sports Centre, Swimming Pool, games fields and dining hall. English and Mathematics are taught by Form Teachers, while Environmental Studies, French, Science, Religious Education, Music, Art and Physical Activities are taken by specialists.

Entrance. Entry is by examination. Application forms are available from the Admissions Secretary.

Junior School at 7+ and 9+. Prospective pupils attend an Assessment Day in January when they take part in a number of activities and sit a number of short tests.

Senior School at 11+. The Senior School examination is held each January for prospective pupils who will be 11 on 1 September of the year in which entry is desired. Applications by 15 December (later application at School's discretion).

Sixth Form at 16+. Applicants are considered for direct entry to the Sixth Form if their GCSE results are likely to form an adequate basis. All external candidates are interviewed and a reference is sought from the previous/current school.

Each year a small number of places may be available at entry points other than the main ones listed. Please contact the Admissions Secretary for details.

Term of Entry. Autumn, although a small number of places may become available throughout the year.

Fees per term (2008-2009). Senior School £2,933, Junior School £2,472.

Bursaries. Some bursaries, awarded on the basis of parental income, are offered. They include those awarded by the Ogden Trust, which may cover all fees and expenses depending on parental income. Details are available from the Bursar.

Charitable status. The Newcastle upon Tyne Royal Grammar School is a Registered Charity, number 1114424.

RGS Worcester and The Alice Ottley School

Upper Tything Worcester WR1 1HP
Tel: 01905 613391
Fax: 01905 726892
e-mail: office@rgsw.org.uk
website: www.rgsao.org

The Royal Grammar School Worcester was founded ante 1291, received its Elizabethan Charter in 1561 and was granted its 'Royal' title by Queen Victoria in 1869. The Alice Ottley School was founded in 1883 as Worcester High School for Girls. The two schools merged to form RGSAO in September 2007.

Board of Governors:
Chairman: R A Ingles
I L Carmichael
R G Fry
R F Ham
C W Parr
S J Shaw
T G Walker
F H Briggs
D E Long
J Q S Poole
J Preedy

Bursar & Clerk to the Governors: Commander M J Sime, CDipAF, FICM

***Headmaster*: A R Rattue**, MA

Second Master: P J Lee, BA

Senior Master: N W Lowson, BA

Deputy Head (*Pastoral*): Rebecca Appleyard, BA

Assistant Heads:
S C Brough, BEd (*Middle School*)
G W Hughes, BEd (*Lower School*)
S J Richards, BSc (*Academic*)
M J Ridout, BA, MSc (*Academic*)
H Sykes, BSc (*Sixth Form*)

Teaching Staff:
S N Alexander, BA
A J Barr, BSc
S M Bee, BA
D Beer, PhD
R N Berry, BSc
S Blincoe-Deval, BSc, MSc
Miss R S Briggs, BSc
R D Burt, MA
Mrs G Cartwright, BSc
Mrs S C Coggins, BSc
Mrs S Cooper, BD
D J Cotterill, BEd
Mrs P Cunnington, BA
T S Curtis, BA
Miss K M Dale, BEd
Mrs D A Dawson, BEd
Mrs C E de Trafford, PhD
Mrs A Dimond, MA (*SEN*)
Miss E Dovey, MA
Mrs D Drew, BA
Miss C Duckworth, BSc
Miss E Dukes, BA
Miss J Dutfield, BA
P J Ehlers, MA, PhD
Mrs A Fitch, CPE
Mrs A J Freeman, BA
J C Friend, BSc
R T Gibson, MA
Mrs J Glover, BSc
H Groves, MA
T J B Hallett, BA, MPhil
M Hamilton, BA
Mrs D Harkness, BA
Miss S Hearne, BA
M H Henderson, MA
Miss J Holwill, BSc
R J Houchin, BA
M Howard, B.Tech
S D Howells, BA
J L Howgate, BA
Mrs C Hunter, BA
Mrs V C James, MA
Mrs L Kettle, MA, MSocSci, BEd
Mrs E W Kilburn, BA
Miss J E Marsh, BA
Mrs S A Mather, BA
M Matthews, BA
R J Michael, BA
A R Millington, BSc, CBiol, MIBiol
J D Moffatt, BA
P H Mullins, BSc, PhD
P J Newport, BA
Mrs S Nicholls, BA
S J Osmond, MA
P J O'Sullivan, BSc
Mrs A Park, BA
Miss S E Partridge, BSc
Miss E Ponfield, BA
D J Powell, BSc
Mrs F Pryce, MA
Mrs K M W Rahim, BA
M D Ralfe, MA
P Roberts, BA, ALA
Mrs C Shepherd, MA
J M Shorrocks, BSc, BA
H Smith, PhD
R C Tarry, BSc
B Taylor, BSc
Mrs L Taylor, BSc
I Venables, BA
M H Vetch, MA
Mrs E L Walker, BA
J N Waller, MA
Mrs D Warman, BA
J G Wilderspin, BSc, ARCO
M D Wilkinson, BSc
Ms G M Williams, BSc
M P Williams, BEd CPhys, MInstP
S Wishart, BA
A N Wood, BSc
C N Wright, BA

Junior School: RGS The Grange

Headmaster: T R Lowe, BA

Deputy Heads:
Mrs J Stowe, CertEd (*Pre-Prep*)
M Turner, BA (*Prep*)

Junior School Staff:
Mrs B Ashby, Cert Ed
T C Barnes, MSc
Mrs H L Baverstock, BA
Mrs V Bradley, BA, SpLD
Mrs J B Brown, BEd
Miss E M Bussey, BEd
Miss L Carlile, BSc
Mrs S Coleman, BA
Mrs M J Corrie, GTCL, LTCL, ALCM
Mrs M C Egginton, BSc
Miss N Evans, BA
Miss R K Glinka, BSc
Mrs A Halliwell, BEd
Mrs A E Parish, BEd
Mrs C Roberts, BA
L M Satchwell, BA
R Scase, PhD
Miss N Shaw, BA
Mrs H Stevens, NVQ3 (*Nursery*)
A M Sinton, BEd
Mrs T A Turner, BA
S Wintle, BEd
Mrs A M Webb, BTEC (*Nursery*)
Mrs P White, BEd
J L Wickson, BA
M Wood, BA
Mrs M Yarnold, BEd
Mrs R Young, BA

Junior School: Springfield

Headmistress: Mrs M Lloyd, BEd CNAA

Junior School Staff:
Mrs P M Arr, CertEd
Mrs D Bennett, NVQ3
Mrs C Carr, CertEd
Mrs A Myers, BSc
Mrs S Salisbury, BEd
Mrs E Teece, CertEd
Mrs J Walker, BEd
Mrs A Webster, BEd
Mrs G Williams, BEd
Mrs E Wilkins, BEd

Situation and Buildings. The Senior School is situated a few minutes' walk from the centre of the City and is convenient for rail and bus stations. The Headmaster's office is housed in the Grade II* listed Britannia House, and there are several other historic buildings on the site, including the RGS Main Block, dating from 1868. Educational facilities are outstanding: there are two Sports Halls, specialist Art, ICT, Technology and Textiles rooms, a theatre, library, Science Block, music technology room, and a lecture theatre, as well as several assembly halls. The playing fields and boathouse are close by and the School has good use of the local swimming pool. A full-size, floodlit all-weather pitch was opened in November 2007 and a state-of-the-art fitness centre in April 2008. A new Dance Studio plus changing facilities and two new Science Laboratories will be ready for September 2008.

There are two co-educational Junior Schools. RGS The Grange (*see IAPS entry*) is set in 40 acres of grounds to the north of the city and has recently opened a 16 classroom, £4.5 million Prep School extension to complement the original Victorian building that houses the Pre-Prep. Springfield is housed in a beautiful Georgian building in the centre of the nearby Britannia Square, close to the senior school and the city centre. It is secluded and secure, and benefits from its close proximity to the Senior School.

Organisation. The Senior School population is c940 (400 girls and 540 boys). The Senior School is divided into three sections – Lower (Years 7 and 8), Middle (Years 9, 10 and 11) and Sixth Form – with an Assistant Head responsible for each. The basic unit is the form, and the form tutor, under the Head of Year, is responsible for all day to day matters relating to the pupils in their charge. In addition all pupils are placed in Houses which exist mainly for internal competitive purposes, but which do provide an important element of continuity throughout a pupil's career at the School. Both Junior Schools admit pupils from the age of two and a half, and most proceed to the Senior School at the age of eleven, into Year 7. RGS The Grange and Springfield are both well known for the high standard of their pastoral care and for stretching the brightest children. Learning Support is particularly well organized.

Aims. A high level of academic achievement is sought within a caring and civilised society. By placing emphasis on a wide range of sporting, artistic and extra-curricular activities, we aim to extend our pupils in as many ways as possible. Overall, we offer a balanced and challenging education which will stand our pupils in good stead in their future careers and within the community at large.

Curriculum. Pupils follow a common curriculum for the first three years in the Senior School which includes the usual academic subjects, plus IT, Design Technology, Music, Drama and PE. The GCSE option arrangements (Years 10 and 11) allow a wide choice, subject to final selection, giving a balanced curriculum which does not prejudice subsequent career decisions. Normally 9–10 subjects are studied: English, Mathematics, a Modern Foreign Language and Sciences being setted and compulsory, plus three from French, German, Latin, Spanish, Geography, History, RE, Drama, Art, Music, Textiles, Design Technology. Most members of the Sixth Form study four subjects to AS Level and at least three to A2 Level. In addition to those subjects studied at GCSE Level, PE, ICT, Classical Civilisation, Business Studies, Economics and Politics may be taken up.

Careers. The School is a member of ISCO; the well-equipped Careers Rooms are readily available and the Head of Careers is responsible for ensuring that all pupils receive basic careers education, and subsequently, access to all the necessary information and experience on which a sound decision may be made regarding future career and Further or Higher Education.

Physical Activities. The School aims to satisfy a wide range of sporting interests and abilities. For boys, Rugby Football, Association Football, Cricket and Athletics are the main activities. Girls take Netball, Hockey and Lacrosse in the winter and spring, and Athletics, Tennis and Rounders during the summer Term. Cross-Country Running, Swimming and Rowing have a full programme of fixtures. Gymnastics, Trampolining, Basketball and Badminton share priority in the Sports Halls throughout the year, and high quality cricket coaching is given throughout the winter months.

Outdoor Pursuits. Combined Cadet Force and The Duke of Edinburgh's Award Scheme: all pupils may choose to join one or the other at the end of Year 9. The strong CCF comprises Royal Navy, Army and Air Force sections. Good opportunities exist for attachments to regular units in UK and abroad, for flying training, for leadership training and for Adventure Training. Those who choose The Duke of Edinburgh's Award Scheme may work for the Bronze, Silver and Gold Awards, and undertake adventure training and community service.

Other Activities. There is a wide range of clubs and societies. All Lower School pupils receive drama lessons as part of the curriculum and school productions take place each term. School music is also strong: in particular, there is a fine organ, a Big Band, several brass ensembles, two choirs, several smaller vocal ensembles and a very popular Jazz Band. The School fosters a range of international links including regular exchanges with schools in France, Germany, Spain and China. The School has strong links with schools in the developing world via the World Challenge Organisation, and the school community raises large sums for a range of local, national and international charities every year.

September Admission. This is by our own examination held in February, mainly at 11+ but also at 12+ and 13+. Pupils are also admitted into the Sixth Form on the basis of a test, interview and GCSE results. Exceptionally, pupils may also be examined and admitted at any time of the year. Admission to the Junior School is by assessment from age 6+ and by classroom visit before this age.

Fees per term (2008-2009). £1,648–£3,012.

Scholarships and Bursaries. Scholarships are offered for academic achievement as well as for music and art of up to 33% remission of fees. Bursaries of up to 100% are also available according to parental means and academic potential. Further details can be obtained from the Registrars at the schools.

Charitable status. RGS Worcester and The Alice Ottley School is a Registered Charity, number 1120644. The aim of the charity is the education of boys and girls.

The Royal Hospital School

Holbrook Ipswich Suffolk IP9 2RX
Tel: 01473 326200
Fax: 01473 326213
e-mail: admissions@royalhospitalschool.org
website: www.royalhospitalschool.org

The Royal Hospital School is a co-educational full boarding and day school with 665 pupils aged 11 to 18. Founded at Greenwich in 1712 by the Crown Charity, Greenwich Hospital, it moved to its present 200-acre estate overlooking the River Stour in 1933. The School is magnificently situated and well equipped. A multi-million pound development programme features a new Music School and refurbished of all ten boarding houses.

Visitor: HRH The Duke of York

Director of Greenwich Hospital: M Sands

Chairman of Governors: B Burns

***Headmaster*: H W Blackett**, MA

Deputy Headmaster: I S Wilmshurst, MA
Bursar: D Charlton, MBA
Marketing Director: Mrs S Braybrooke, BA
Admissions Officer: Mrs S Toner
Chaplain: Revd Dr C E Stewart, BSc, BD, MTh
Director of Studies: J Allday, PhD
Senior Mistress: Mrs H Anthony, BA
Senior Master: M L March, JP, BEd
Head of Sixth Form: Mrs S E M Godfrey, BA
Head of Middle School: Miss F Kennedy, BA
Head of Lower School: A R Evans, MA

Teaching Staff:
Mrs C Allday
M J Barraclough, BA
Miss M-C Bigot, MA
C D Boughton
Miss S J Bourhill, CertEd
M A Callow, BSc, MA, CBiol, MIBiol
C J Chick, BSc
Mrs D M Clayton, DipEd
D J Cousins, BA
P H Crompton, GRNCM
P A Cuddihy, BSc
Miss A J Derricott, BA
A R Doyle, DPhil
J R Dugdale, BEd
S P Durrant, BA
P C Du Toit, BComm/ HDE
R G Encinas
Mrs G Evans, MA
Mrs H Evans, BA, Hornsby DipSpLD
L G Frost BEd, BSc, MA
Mrs J Fuschillo, CertEd
Mrs R M M Gladwell, BSc, MA
M H Godfrey, BSc Econ
C M Graham, BSc
Mrs A J Grant, BA
P Hall, MA
D P Hardman, BA
Mrs D R Hardman, MA
D W Hawkley, MA
N J Hele, BA
Mrs C J Herbert, BSc
J C Herbert, BSc Econ, MA
Mrs J Hewitt, BA
Mrs S J Hirst, BEd
Mrs D K Hitchen, BA
B Hocking, BEd, MCollP
Miss L Hubl
M K Jeffery, BSc
R B Jones, ARCM
A Kupersmith
Mrs R Leefe, DipEd
A J Loveland, BSc Eng, ACGI, MA
P Madge, BA
Mrs N Mann, MA
R J Mann, BA
S E Maunder, BA
P McCaffery, BMus, LRAM, ARCM, LTCL
L R Menday, Dip Psych Sport, AIST
I J Mitchell, BA
C F Morgan, BA
P G Mussett, BSc
Ms S L Nicholls, BA
Mrs P G Noble
A Nutton
Mrs A Pearson, BEd
J F Pooley, BEd
A Quentin, BSc
G D Ravenhall, BA, ATD
C A Rennison, BSc
S R Robertson, MA
Mrs A E Skitch, BSc
D P Simmons, BEd
I V Simmons, BA
J Snoddon, MBE, MSM
P A Surzyn, BSc
Mrs S L Tansley, BA
L Thompson, BEd
T D Topley
R Trowern, BSc
Miss R van Zee
S R Warr, MA, ACP
Mrs M Z H Warren, BSc
C J White, MA
R Whitman
Mrs J Wilby, BA
A J Wilding, Bed
A P Wynn, BA

Boarding Houses. A major refurbishment programme of all 6 boys and 4 girls boarding houses is underway. Younger pupils are accommodated in four-bedded rooms and older pupils have double or single studies, which, in the new houses, are en suite. In the Upper Sixth both boys and girls join Nelson House, where they learn to live more independently in preparation for university.

Curriculum. The School follows National Curriculum. At age eleven there are usually four forms, rising to five or six by Year Nine. The average class size is 18 but will not exceed 22. Pupils are streamed and in many cases setted for subjects. All pupils follow GCSE in a minimum of 8 subjects with most taking 9 or 10. Sixth Form students follow AS and A2 courses from a wide range of options as well as General Studies.

Sport and Leisure. The facilities include a nine-hole golf course, ninety-six acres of playing fields, a sports hall, heated indoor swimming pool, squash courts, and an all-weather sports surface. The School has a strong sailing tradition – every pupil has the opportunity to learn to sail – with extensive sailing facilities on the River Stour, a fleet of dinghies on the adjacent Alton Water Reservoir, as well as yachts and dinghies. The main sports are rugby, hockey, netball, cricket, athletics, cross-country, rounders, football, tennis, riding and swimming. The swimming pool also offers opportunities for canoeing and sub-aqua.

Music and Drama. The School has a particularly strong musical tradition. Almost half the pupils are involved in music on a regular basis. The Chapel is of cathedral proportions and has one of the finest organs in England, much used by pupils as well as professional performers. Peripatetic teachers offer tuition in a wide range of instruments and the choir and chamber choir perform both nationally and internationally. A new Music School houses a recital hall, 16 specialist rooms, a technical suite and "rock room". As well as drama in the curriculum, productions are often combined with the music department for whole school performances and there is a full programme of plays, competitions and festivals each year.

CCF and Community Service. All pupils join the Combined Cadet Force in Year 9 and are able to choose between Army, Naval, RAF and Royal Marine Sections. The emphasis is on adventurous training and personal development. More that 300 pupils take part in the The Duke of Edinburgh's Award Scheme and 100 of these to Gold Award. Staff and pupils operate the Holbrook Auxiliary Coastguard Station and there is a thriving St John Ambulance Brigade unit. The Community Action Team is actively involved in a wide range of activities teaching pupils the importance of giving something back to the community in which they live.

Religion. The Chapel holds over 1,000 people and the school day begins with an act of worship. Inter-denominational services are held and the Chaplain prepares candidates for Confirmation annually.

Careers guidance. From Year 9 onwards there is a continuous service both inside and outside the curriculum. All pupils take part in a Personal, Social and Health Education course and are offered advice by the careers masters and outside specialists.

Further Education. 97% of pupils go on to university and the School is proud of its links with HM Forces, especially the Royal Navy.

Travel. The school provides the services of an international coordinator to oversee the travel arrangements of pupils living overseas. Transport at the beginning and end of the school day is provide for day pupils living in certain areas.

Admission. Entry to the School is at 11, 13 and 16 with small numbers joining at 12 and 14. The entrance examination takes place at the end of January or pupils may take the Common Entrance Examination. Entry into the Sixth Form is as a result of gaining an average of 5.0 points at GCSE from at least 8 subjects (A*=8, C=5) following an interview with the Headmaster and senior staff.

Fees per term (2008-2009). Boarding £6,556, Day £3,507. Fees include all school uniform, sports clothing, accommodation, food and tuition. For eligible services families fees are set at 10% above forces MOD Continuity of Education Allowance (CEA).

Scholarships. (*see Scholarship Entries section*). Scholarships are awarded annually, at the Headmaster discretion, for academic excellence, musical or artistic talent, sport and for sailing to pupils entering the Lower School and Sixth Form.

Bursaries. The parent charity, Greenwich Hospital, awards a limited number of means-tested bursaries to the children and grandchildren of seafarers.

Charitable status. The Royal Hospital School is owned by Greenwich Hospital which is a Crown Charity. The School exists to provide education for boys and girls aged from 11 to 18.

Royal Russell School

Coombe Lane Croydon Surrey CR9 5BX
Tel: 020 8657 4433
Fax: 020 8657 0207
e-mail: headmaster@royalrussell.croydon.sch.uk
website: www.royalrussell.co.uk

The Royal Russell School is a co-educational, boarding and day school, founded in 1853 by members of the textile trade. Set in 100 acres of woodland, it enjoys very easy access to London, the South, and the airports at Gatwick and Heathrow. There are nearly 840 pupils of whom 155 are in the Sixth Form and 300 in the Preparatory School.

Motto: *Non Sibi Sed Omnibus*

Patron: Her Majesty The Queen

President: R P Green

Past President: F D Furlonger

Vice-Presidents:
A F C Miller
J P B Hecks
P E Reynolds

Board of Governors and Trustees:

Chairman: K Young
Deputy Chairman: B J Welch

Mrs A D Greenwood
P J McCombie
R N Martin
C T Shorter
Mrs P Lloyd
Dr D J Begley
Mrs S M Loughlin
S Kolesar
R Stanley
R Wong
A Merriman
Dr A Fernandes
Mrs E Brown
J Penny

Senior School

***Headmaster*: J R Jennings**, BSc Queen Mary College, London, PhD, MIBiol, FRSA

Deputy Head – Pastoral: Mrs S Thomas-Webb, BA Leeds, MA OU

Deputy Head – Administration: D J Selby, BA Durham

Director of Studies: G R Moseley, BEd, MA

Assistant Staff:
* *Head of Department*
† *Housemaster/Housemistress*
§ *Part-time*

†J Piggin, BA (**History*)
†M J Tanner, BSc, MA (**Geology, Marketing Director*)

N A Marshall, BEd (**Biology*)
Mrs A R Roseweir, BSc
K W Owens, DipAD (**Art & Design*)
†I O'Brien, CertEd (**PE*)
†Miss K J Palenski, BA MA
Miss M P Latessa, DLing, RSA Cert TEFLA (**EFL*)
Mrs M J Clower, BA, ALA (*Librarian*)
Mrs S J Dodsworth, BA, Essex (**Information Technology Coordinator*)
H R Sutton, BA, ARCM, MEd (*Director of Music*)
Mrs R J Gedney, BA
†S J Keable-Elliott, BA (**Politics*)
†S J Greaves, BSc (*Examinations Officer*)
†Miss M J Davenport, BA
§N R Lupton, BA
Mrs K E Howard, MA, MSc (**Learning Support*)
P J Endersby, BSc (**Science*)
P C Cook, BSc
†Mrs J Kirby-Jones, CertEd, DipEd (**Food Technology*)
M G Riches, MA
A W Moore, BA
§S P Mohan, BSc, MSc
Mrs S M Culbert, MA, MA EdMan, DipM (**Careers and PHSE, Joint Head of Sixth Form*)
M L Stanley, BA, MBA EdMan (**Mathematics*)
Mrs D I Pepperdine, BA
Miss F S Cassim, BA
G Parmar, Cert/Dip CDT & IT
Miss L Cacace, BSc
Mrs A Mawer, BA (**Modern Languages*)
A J Wylie, BA (**Geography*)
Mrs G Missan, BSc, BA (**Spanish*)
†Mrs S M Strutt, BSc
H J Dunlop, BA, MA
§Mrs G Smith, CertEd
Miss C A Roe, BSc
J S Baron, BSc (**Chemistry, Joint Head of Sixth Form*)
C P Dear, BA (**Media Studies*)
M C Finch, BEd (**Design Technology*)
Miss L T Hicks, BA (**Girls' Physical Education*)
N P Rocca, BA (**Business Studies*)
§Mrs G M Brinded, BEd
Mrs S J Addis, CertEd
§Mrs A Armstrong, BA
J I Bueno
E S Hutchinson, BA
§Mrs S Milton-Thompson, BSc
§Mrs M Womack, GMus
Revd S J Padfield, MA, BA
S Watkins, BSc
Ms D Baldwin, BA
Ms E Cripps, CertEd (**Drama*)
Miss S Calvet, FLE
Miss L Faulkner, BA
D Jewiss, BEd
Mrs L Smith, BSc, MA
Miss C Flannery, BA
Ms C Allison, BEd, MA, MA (**English*)
Mrs F Taylor, GIBiol

Houses and Housestaff:

Boarding:
Cambridge: J Piggin
Oxford: S Greaves
Queen's: Miss M Davenport

Day:
Buchanan: Mrs J Kirby-Jones
Keable: E Hutchinson
Madden: M J Tanner
Reade: Miss K J Palenski
St Andrews: S Keable-Elliott
Hollenden: Mrs S Strutt

Preparatory School
Headmaster: D Goodwin, BSc Hons City, MA Ed Southampton, PGCE London
Director of Studies: Mrs K Ingrams, BA, DipRSA, PGCE

Mrs A Gavin, CertEd
A G C Adams, LTCL
Mrs R Coker, BEd
D Naidoo, HrDipEd
Mrs S McPherson, BA
R Hoyle, BEd, MA, PhD
P Venier, BEd
C Holmes, BSc, BA, PGCE
Mrs J Bennett, BA, PGCE
Mrs F Rizvi, BA, MA, PGCE
Mrs L Soyvural, BAGA

Pre-Preparatory Department
Head of Pre-Prep: Miss A Easter, BA

Mrs C Trim, CertEd
Mrs S Fladgate, BEd
Miss J Lingley, BA, PGCE
Mrs P Francis, CertEd
Mrs A King, BEd
Mrs H Walsh, CertEd
Mrs A Netherway, BSc, PGCE
Ms S Wilson, MA, BEd

Learning Support: Mrs K Howard, MA, MSc

Bursar: P Barlow

Medical Officer: Dr S A Shaikh, MB BS, DRCOG, MRCGP
Medical Centre Sister-in-Charge: Mrs S Smith, RSCN
Boys' Matron: Mrs K Rhodes
Girls' Matron: Miss D Cripps

Number in School. In the Senior School there are 560 pupils: 135 boarders, 425 day pupils. Of these, 314 are boys, 246 girls. In the Preparatory School there are 285 pupils: 162 boys and 123 girls.

Admission. Most pupils enter the school in the Autumn term at the age of 3, 4+, 7, 11 or 13. Space permitting pupils may be considered and admitted at other ages and there is a direct entry into the Sixth Form.

Religion. The school's religious affiliation is to the Church of England but pupils of all persuasions are welcome. Our approach to daily life is founded on Christian principles and we try to maintain an atmosphere of mutual respect, affection and understanding.

The resident Chaplain is responsible for the conduct of all services and the teaching of Religious Education throughout the school. Weekly Chapel assemblies allow a brief act of worship and an opportunity to share ideas and concerns. The Sunday service is compulsory for those boarders at school, and the voluntary Eucharists are specifically for those with a Christian commitment. Enquiries regarding Confirmation to the Church of England are encouraged.

Curriculum. The keynote of curriculum organisation is flexibility and there is close alignment with the requirements of the National Curriculum. In the early years everyone follows a curriculum designed to give a sound foundation across a broad range of subjects. Equipped with this experience pupils are helped in selecting their GCSE examination subjects from a wide range including Information Technology and Drama. Great care is taken to achieve balance in each pupil's timetable and to ensure that an appropriate number of subjects is studied.

A high proportion of pupils continue to the Sixth Form where, typically, four subjects are studied in Year 12 with three continuing into Year 13. At present A Level courses available are Mathematics, Further Mathematics, Information Technology, History, Geography, Geology, Physics, Chemistry, Biology, English, Business Studies, Politics, French, Spanish, Drama and Theatre Arts, Media Studies, Art and Design, Design and Technology, Music, Food Technology and Physical Education.

It is our expectation that all pupils will leave the Sixth Form to go onto higher education and we regularly secure places at Oxford and Cambridge for our strongest students.

Facilities. The School lies in 100 acres of grounds providing excellent academic and sporting facilities for all age groups.

Recent new-build and refurbishment programmes have transformed the boarding houses and provided a purpose-built School Library and Sixth Form Study Centre.

In summer 2004, the extension to our Sports Hall was opened to provide a Sports Centre with an additional Gymnasium and changing facilities.

Other recent improvements have included a new Swimming Pool, six Computer Laboratories, a Food Technology room, a CDT Centre and a Language Laboratory.

A detached Science building contains six modern and very well equipped laboratories.

Our next major project is an ambitious new Music and Performing Arts Centre.

Careers. The Head of Careers coordinates Careers advice, giving individual counselling and helping with all University applications. The School is a member of the Independent Schools Careers Organisation whose services are available to all pupils. Towards the end of the Summer Term work experience placements are organised for those who have completed GCSE examinations, and members of the Lower Sixth participate in organised visits to Universities and Colleges.

Organisation. The Senior School is divided into nine Houses each of approximately 60 pupils, 2 boarding and 3 day for boys, 1 boarding and 3 day for girls. Each House has its own premises, Housemaster or Housemistress and assistant House Tutors. All Sixth Formers are accommodated in single or double study bedrooms, fully carpeted and newly furnished. The members of the school fall into three categories: full boarders, weekly boarders and day pupils. It is expected that all pupils should be able and encouraged to participate as fully as possible in the extra-curricular life of the school, becoming involved in evening and weekend activities, irrespective of their status. Supervised homework sessions are provided for day pupils participating in evening activities and they attend supper with the boarders. Tutors play a vital pastoral and academic role, monitoring overall progress and development.

Games. The main games are hockey, cricket, soccer, netball, tennis and athletics. There are four hard tennis courts, a gymnasium, a Sports Hall, a heated indoor swimming pool and a small bore rifle range. Badminton, basketball, volleyball and judo are popular. It is possible to go riding.

Music, Drama and Art. Music in the Senior School is in the hands of the Director of Music whilst the Assistant Director of Music concentrates on the Prep School. They are assisted by a large number of visiting teachers. There is a Senior School Orchestra and smaller wind, brass and string ensembles. Choral Society, Chapel Choir and Preparatory School Choir and Orchestra meet and perform regularly. A new Prep School Music Centre has recently opened.

Drama is taught as part of the Creative Studies programme in the lower school and is available at GCSE and A level where pupils make use of our Drama Studio.

Instruction is offered in a wide range of Artistic techniques using a variety of materials – paint, ink, screen printing, ceramics and pottery.

Clubs and Activities. Computer, Young Engineers, Art, Drama, Dance, Pottery and Chess Clubs are very popular and meet regularly.

There is a flourishing voluntary CCF unit. There are regular camps and weekend activities and The Duke of Edinburgh's Award Scheme operates. The school's involvement in Model United Nations programmes is unique in this country. The annual October conference attracts 400 student delegates from all over the world.

Preparatory School. The aim in the Preparatory School is to prepare pupils as thoroughly as possible for entry to the Senior School. The Kindergarten and the Pre-Preparatory Sections provide a happy, secure and purposeful environment for those just starting school and during the early years of schooling. (*For full details please see our entry in the IAPS section.*)

Scholarships. A number of scholarships are available each year to pupils aged 11+ to 13+ who show particular academic promise. Sixth Form scholarships are also awarded annually. Special awards are available to members of the Armed Forces.

For further details or an appointment to visit the school apply to the Headmaster.

Fees per term (2008-2009). Senior School: £8,370 (senior boarders), £6,190 (Year 7 & 8 boarders); £4,230 (day pupils inclusive of lunch and supper). Preparatory School: £3,125 (day pupils inclusive of lunch and supper). Pre-Preparatory: day pupils £2,560 (full day inclusive of lunch); £1,125 (half day).

Charitable status. Russell School Trust is a Registered Charity, number 271907. It exists solely for the education of boys and girls.

Rugby School

Rugby Warwickshire CV22 5EH

Tel: 01788 556216 (Head Master)
01788 556261 (Bursar)
01788 556274 (Registrar)
Fax: 01788 556219 (Head Master)
01788 556267 (Bursar)
01788 556277 (Registrar)
e-mail: head@rugbyschool.net (Head Master)
bursar@rugbyschool.net (Bursar)
registry@rugbyschool.net (Registrar)
website: www.rugbyschool.net

Motto: '*Orando Laborando*'

Rugby School was founded in the year 1567 by Lawrence Sheriff, native of Rugby, one of the Gentlemen of the Princess Elizabeth, a Grocer and Second Warden of the Grocers' Company. The School was endowed with estates in the neighbourhood of Rugby and in London. In 1750 the School moved to its present site on the edge of Rugby town. Between 1809 and 1814 the Head Master's House, School House and the Old Quad were built. Under Dr Arnold and subsequent Head Masters, including two later Archbishops of Canterbury, Rugby was influential in establishing the pattern of independent education throughout the country.

There are currently 784 pupils (443 boys and 341 girls) of whom 130 are day pupils.

Rugby values scholarship, team work in games, music and drama, and qualities of leadership and self-reliance in the pupils. Rugby prides itself on a sharp edge of academic excellence but its aim, as a fully co-educational school, is to encourage cooperation, seeing a wide range of enterprises through to their conclusion, an awareness of the wider world and a lively approach to a very broad range of opportunity. The boys and girls who come to Rugby are expected to have a go at a variety of things. As they leave they should feel ready for (almost) anything; that they have stretched themselves and have been asked to do a great deal; and finally that along the way life at Rugby has been fun.

Governing Body:

W M T Fowle, Esq, CBE (*Chairman*)
C H E Imray, Esq, FRCF
The Lord Lieutenant of the County of Warwick, M Dunne, Esq, JP
Mrs P A Williams, BA, ACA
The Rt Revd the Lord Bishop of Birmingham, D A Urquhart
Professor R H Friend, FRS
M J Mansell, Esq, LLB Hons
Dame Fiona Caldicott, DBE, FRCP

R W A Swannell, Esq, FCA
Lady S McFarlane, MCSP
T R Cookson, Esq
R W B Williams, Esq
Mrs L Holmes, BA
R Hingley, Esq
B N Habib, BA
J P Parry

Bursar and Clerk to the Governing Body: G Lydiatt, BSc, FCCA

Medical Officer: Dr P J Kilvert, BSc, MB BS, DRCOG, DCH

***Head Master*: P S J Derham**, MA

Deputy Head: Mrs S K Fletcher, MA

Assistant Heads:
N D Jarvis, BA, MA
E D Hester, BA
D A Shinkfield, BSc

Registrar: Mrs H A Morrish, MA

Assistant Teaching Staff:

Chaplaincy:
The Revd R M Horner, BSc (*Chaplain*)
Miss L Greatwood, BSc Hons

Classics:
Miss C Le Hur, BA (*Head of Department*)
Mrs E M Beesley, MA
T J Day, BA
Miss K Howitt, BA
M J Pappenheim, BA
H W F Price, MA

Design:
C P John, BA, FRSA (*Director of the Design Centre*)
A D Bradbury, BA, AIIP (*Head of Photography & Graphics*)
P A Byrne, BA (*Head of D & T*)
R B Drennan, DSD, CDS (*Director of Theatre Productions, Head of Media*)
M Howard, DipAD (*Head of Art*)
Miss S Start, BA Hons (*Head of Drama & Theatre Studies*)
Mrs N Cannock, BSc
Mrs S E Phillips, BA (*Ceramics*)
Miss J Rayner, BA
P D Richard, BSc
M R Williams, BA
R Witcombe, BSc

Economics and Business Studies:
A J Darby, BA (*Head of Department*)
J A H Lewis, BA
P J Rosser, BA
M Semmence, BA
H G Steele-Bodger, MA

English:
A Fletcher, MA (*Head of Department*)
Mrs B C Almond
Mrs E M Barlow, BA
Mrs E M Beesley, MA
J B Cunningham-Batt, BA
Mrs L McIlwraith, BA
Mrs E E Moyle, MA
A J Naylor, BA
A T Shaw, PhD, MA
R J Smith, BA

Geography:
J C Evans, BA (*Head of Department*)
Mrs A J V Moreland, BEd
Mrs S A Rosser, BEd
A E Smith, BSc, MPhil, PhD, FRMetS, FRGS

History:
T Beaumont, BA (*Head of Department*)
E A Beesley, BA, PhD
P S J Derham, MA
P W Dewey, BA
Mrs S K Fletcher, MA
K Hollings, BA
J D Muston, MA, MPhil, DPhil
Mrs A Naylor, BA

Information Technology:
Miss L Dixon, BSc (*Head of Department*)
C A Burton, BSc, PhD, MIITT
T E Rennoldson, BSc
Mrs A Tooke, BSc

Mathematics:
P Jewell, BSc (*Head of Department*)
J W L Hind, MA (*Second in Department*)
P K Bell
C J Edwards, MA
G J Hedges, MA
M A Hennings, BA
E D Hester, BA
Miss P M Hopkins, MEng
J E Ingram
D A Shinkfield, BSc
K Twentyman, BEng

Modern Languages:
David Gillett, BA (*Head of Department*)
Mrs W J Corvi, BEd
N D Jarvis, BA, MA
Mrs R Kayada, BA
Mrs A C Leamon, BA, MA, PhD
A M Maguire, BA
Mrs C A M O'Mahoney, BA
J C Smith, MA, DPhil
J A Swiffen, BA
Mrs C Williams, L-ès-L, M-ès-L

Music:
R Dunster-Sigtermans, MA, BMus, FRCO, ARCM (*Director of Music*)
D McIlwraith (*Assistant Director of Music*)
T W Bentham, BA (*Head of Brass*)
Mrs A Brogaard (*Violinist in Residence*)
R F Colley, MA, DipRAM, LRAM, ARCM (*Composer in Residence*)
D Eno, BMus
M C Martin, BMus, LTCL (*Music Studio & Cello*)
C P Woodhead, MA

Physical Education:
F J Hemming-Allen, BEd, MEd (*Head of Physical Education*)
S J Brown, BSc (*Director of Boys' Games*)
Mrs L Hampton, MSc, BEd (*Director of Girls' Games*)
Mrs A J V Moreland, BEd

Politics:
P Teeton, BA (*Head of Department*)
R D R Ray, BSc Econ, FRGS

Science:
N A Fisher, BSc, MSc, CPhys, MInstP (*Head of Science*)
M A Monteith, BSc (*Head of Biology*)
A G Davies, BSc (*Head of Physics*)
T M White, BSc (*Head of Chemistry*)
Mrs N Cannock, BSc
R Dhanda, BSc
C Douglas, BEd
Miss G Gammons, BSc
N Hampton, MA, PhD
S Ingleston, PhD, BSc
J H G Jarvis, BSc, MSc

R B McGuirk, BSc
N J Morse, BSc, PhD, CChem, MRSC
J Norris, BA Hons
P D Richard BSc
P J Robinson, BSc, PhD, CPhys, MInstP
Mrs C Shelley, BEd
J L Taylor, BA, BPhil, DPhil
Mrs A Tooke, BSc

Careers and Higher Education: Mrs J C Phelps
Rackets Professional: P J Rosser, BA
Sports Centre: H D P Bennett (*Manager*)

Houses and Housemasters/mistresses:

Boarding Houses (boys):
Cotton: Mr Matt Williams
Kilbracken: Dr Justin Muston
Michell: Dr Neil Hampton
School Field: Dr Ed Beesley
School House: Dr Nick Morse
Sheriff: Mr Henry Price
Whitelaw: Dr Andrew Smith

Day Boy House:
Town: Mr Jerry Lewis

Boarding Houses (girls):
Bradley: Mrs Monica Barlow
Dean: Mrs Chantal Williams
Griffin: Mrs Anne Naylor
Rupert Brooke: Mrs Colette O'Mahoney
Stanley (*Sixth Form only*): Mrs Carlien Shelley
Tudor: Mrs Sally Rosser

Day Girl House:
Southfield: Mrs Lizzie Beesley

Junior Day House (boys and girls):
Marshall: Mr Barrie Cunningham-Batt

Director of Development: Mrs K Wilson

Situation. Rugby is situated near the junction of the M1 and M6 motorways and is not far from the M40. It is just one hour by hourly rail service from London (Euston) and is close to Birmingham International Airport as well as being within easy reach of Heathrow. Though the School is close to the countryside and has a 150-acre campus with a full range of facilities and games fields, it is essentially a town school and has the practical advantages of links with industry and opportunities for experience and service in the wider world.

Facilities. The main classroom block, the Macready Theatre, the Chapel, the Temple Reading Room and Gymnasium were designed by William Butterfield and to these have been added further buildings of architectural distinction, among them the Temple Speech Room and the Science Schools.

Since then there have followed new Science Laboratories, a Multimedia Language Laboratory, IT Centre, a state-of-the-art Design Centre, housing Art, Design and Technology, History of Art, Photography and a professional standard TV studio for Media.

Other developments include a Sports Centre, opened by HRH The Duchess of Kent in 1990, and recently extended to include a new cafeteria, seminar room and extensive fitness suite. There are floodlit astroturf pitches and hard courts for hockey, tennis and netball. The Lewis Gallery, a new art and design exhibition space, is proving very popular with professional artists throughout the Midlands.

The School is fully networked. All pupils have a laptop computer for use in the classroom and all classrooms are equipped with Promethean Boards.

Boarding Houses. All boarding houses undergo a continuous programme of improvement. Houses provide small dormitories of 4 to 6 in the first one or two years and study-bedrooms thereafter. Meals are eaten in House Dining Halls.

GCSE. All the usual subjects are offered as well as German, Spanish, Latin, Greek, Design, Art and Music.

AS/A2. AS/A2 Level is offered in all the GCSE subjects as well as in Economics, Electronics (AS), Music Technology (AS), Oriental Studies, Religious Studies, Business Studies, English Language, Media Studies (AS), PE, Italian (AS), Japanese (AS), Theatre Studies, History of Art, Politics, Philosophy (AS) and a newly accredited course 'Perspectives in Science' – an Extended Project which includes philosophy, ethics and the history of science (AS). Other EPs include Business Ethics and Enterprise, Classical History and Culture, Culture and Identity, Digital Innovation, The Global Environment, Oriental Studies, Performance and Engineering Technology. All boys and girls go on to Higher Education and about 20 go on to Oxford or Cambridge each year.

There are several learned societies and each academic department invites distinguished speakers to the School. Recent speakers include Lord Hurd, Terry Waite, and Fergal Keane.

Spiritual life. The experience of holiness, an understanding of right and wrong, and respect for the worth of each human being are the bonds of community. These values are learned in every part of our lives, but the School Chapel and the activities connected with it are a particular focus.

There are two full-time chaplains, one male and one female, who involve themselves with all the School's activities. On Mondays, Wednesdays and Fridays the School day begins with a ten-minute service in Chapel. On Sundays there is usually a morning service for the majority of the pupils, often with a guest preacher.

There is an active Christian Union, and a weekly service of meditation with Holy Communion, both of which are optional for the pupils. Members of faiths other than Christian are encouraged to attend worship and instruction within their own faith.

Sport. Sports include Athletics, Badminton, Basketball, Cricket, Cross-country, Fencing, Football, Golf, Gymnastics, Hockey, Judo, Netball, Polo, Rackets, Riding, Rugby, Sailing, Squash, Sub Aqua, Swimming and Tennis.

Activities. All boys and girls are encouraged to undertake a full programme of extra-curricular activities. The School aims to ensure that music touches the lives of all pupils as well as catering for outstanding musicians. With School, House and visiting productions and a very well-equipped theatre, drama is well to the fore. Other activities include Ballet, Canoeing, Camping, CCF, Choirs, Climbing, Duke of Edinburgh's Award, First Aid, Orienteering, Pottery, Sculpture, Target and Clay-pigeon shooting, Silver-smithing, Social Service, Television Production and School Journalism. The aim is to give all boys and girls a wide variety of experience so that they can excel in a few things but understand and develop some appreciation of most areas.

Entry. Entry for boys and girls is at 13+ by Common Entrance, Scholarship, or – for those from schools which do not prepare for Common Entrance – by interview, report and specially designed tests. All 13+ boarding applicants attend a pre-assessment interview and test five terms before they join the School, following which conditional places are offered subject to passing Common Entrance with an average of at least 55%. Day pupil places are offered two years before entry, following an interview and a computerised test, and are also subject to success at Common Entrance.

Boys and girls also enter the Sixth Form on the basis of written examinations in their proposed A level subjects, interviews and a report from the current school, or by scholarship.

The Junior Department. At age 11 boys and girls enter Marshall House as day pupils by taking a computerised test. Foundation Scholarships are available at this stage. There is one class of 11-year-olds and one of 12-year-olds. Classes run from 8.45 am to 4.00 pm. A full programme of extra-curricular activities is offered, most of it based on the Senior School's extensive facilities. All of the teaching is done by staff from the Senior School but Marshall House has its own Head.

Scholarships. (*see Scholarship Entries section*).

Fees per term (2008-2009). The consolidated termly fee for boys and girls: £8,845 (boarding), £5,510 (day). Junior Department: £3,285 (Marshall House).

Optional charge for instrumental or singing tuition: £235.

Further Information. Full information about the School's aims, its academic curriculum, facilities and activities will be found in the School's prospectus. Enquiries and applications should be made in the first instance to the Registrar who will be pleased to arrange for parents to visit the School and to meet members of the staff and the Head Master.

'The freedom, sophistication and civilisation of Rugby struck me as absolutely miraculous. I just loved my time there.' (Robert Hardy, actor).

Charitable status. The Governing Body of Rugby School is a Registered Charity, number 528752. It exists to provide education for young people.

Rydal Penrhos School

Pwllycrochan Avenue Colwyn Bay North Wales LL29 7BT
Tel: 01492 530155
Fax: 01492 531872
e-mail: info@rydal-penrhos.com
website: www.rydal-penrhos.com

Rydal Penrhos is a unique educational experience. Located on the edge of the Snowdonia National Park and close to the Bay of Colwyn, its programmes of sports, outdoor activities from rock climbing to sailing are exceptional. Full or weekly boarding and day education are encompassed within spectacular buildings and grounds. To this we add a rigorous academic programme which offers both A Levels and the International Baccalaureate in the Sixth Form.

Motto: '*Veritas Scientia Fides' (Truth Knowledge Faith)*

The Governors:
Chairman: The Revd Philip Barnett
Vice-Chairman: Mrs M E Davies, BA, JP

***Headmaster*: P A Lee-Browne**, MA

Vice-Principal: P J Bendall, BSc

Chaplain: The Revd K Tewkesbury, MTh (Oxon)

Director of Finance: K Baines

Situation and Buildings. The School is built on rising ground within the conservation area of Colwyn Bay, a small rural town overlooking the Irish Sea. The Snowdonia National Park with the many opportunities it affords for extensive and exciting extra-curricular activities is within easy reach. The School is easily accessible via excellent transport provision including the A55 Express Way, regular rail services and Manchester Airport (1 hour's drive).

The excellent teaching accommodation includes 9 laboratories, dedicated study areas for senior pupils, specialist Art, Music and Design Technology Centres, a Lecture Theatre and a drama studio. There is a new state-of-the-art Library and Resources Centre and a new Information Technology suite. The new Sports Hall and astroturf pitches enhance the already extensive sporting facilities.

Boarders are accommodated in fine houses which are separate from the main buildings. The residential facilities are of a superior quality and comprise mainly single, double and triple bedrooms. The Preparatory School (Lyndon Preparatory) which takes boarders from 7 years (day pupils from 2½ years) is on an adjacent site. Success within boarding has resulted in the school becoming one of the fastest-growing boarding schools in the UK.

Numbers and Organisation. There are 471 pupils in the Senior School (including the Sixth Form), 271 boys (100 boarders) and 200 girls (71 boarders). There are 5 boarding houses for boys and 2 boarding houses for girls. Each house is supervised by resident house-parents with the assistance of a team of tutors and matrons. The houses are fully self-contained although pupils use a central dining hall.

Religious Aims. Rydal Penrhos is a Methodist foundation although pupils are interdenominational. Prayers are held daily with boarders attending a Sunday service. There are wide ranging styles of worship and once a month pupils are encouraged to attend a local church of their own faith.

Curriculum. It is fundamental to school policy that whilst the National Curriculum is shadowed, it is also supplemented to afford extra opportunities and choices to the pupils. The extended day and boarding tradition allows pupils more breadth and depth to their study.

On entry to Year 7, pupils study Art & Design, Biology, Chemistry, Physics, English, Food & Nutrition, French, German, Geography, History, Drama, ICT, Latin, Mathematics, Religious Studies, Music, Physical Education, Design & Technology and Personal and Social Education. Welsh is being introduced in September 2007.

Years 10 and 11 constitute Key Stage 4 (KS4) of the National Curriculum and in Year 10 the core subjects are English and English Literature, Mathematics, Science (Dual Award), a modern foreign language and Religious Studies. In addition, the majority of pupils will choose three further subjects from the following: Art & Design, Business Studies, Design Technology, Drama, a second foreign language, Food & Nutrition, Geography, History, ICT, Latin, Music, Physical Education, and Textiles to complete their GCSE options. During KS4, all pupils participate fully in both Physical Education and a Personal and Social Education programme. A GCSE in Welsh is also available.

The Sixth Form. The Sixth Form at Rydal Penrhos is particularly strong. In January 2008, a new dedicated Sixth Form Centre was opened named 'The Ferguson Centre'. This modern facility homes a study and social centre for our growing Sixth Form to support them in their goals and achievements while at Rydal Penrhos. Students can choose to do A Levels or the International Baccalaureate. Pupils are expected to have Grade C or above in at least 5 subjects at GCSE before entering the Sixth Form. With a wide range of options available, pupils have the advantage of choosing courses which reflect their own particular strengths and interests.

Options at A Level include Art & Design, Biology, Business Studies, Chemistry, Design Technology, Drama & Theatre Studies, Economics, English Literature, French, Further Mathematics, Geography, German, History, Home Economics, Information & Communication Technology, Mathematics, Music Technology, Physical Education, Physics and Religious Studies.

Options for the International Baccalaureate include English (A1 & A2), French (B), German (A1 & B), Spanish (Ab Initio), History, Geography, Economics, Biology, Chemistry, Physics, Mathematics (SL & HL), Mathematical Studies, Visual Arts (SL & HL), Music (SL & HL), Theatre Arts (SL & HL), Psychology (SL & HL), Environmental Systems & Societies (SL & HL) Theory of Knowledge (TOK) and Creative, Active & Social Service Programme (CAS).

Additionally, it is possible for Sixth Formers to gather key skills in Communication, ICT and Application of Numbers. Each Sixth Former also participates in a range of outdoor pursuits and has one hour per week with their personal tutor.

Sports and Activities. All pupils undertake a balanced programme of both sporting and non-sporting extra-curricular activity. The aim is to provide a wide variety of opportunities to learn various skills and to suit different aptitudes. The importance of competitive sport is recognised. Principal games include Rugby, Cricket, Netball, Hockey, Athletics and Tennis. In addition there are ample facilities for Swimming, Squash, Volleyball and Gymnastics. Pupils compete with success at both national and international level.

The School's coastal location within a few miles of Snowdonia National Park allows for a full programme of adventurous activities, including mountaineering, climbing and canoeing. The Duke of Edinburgh's Award is very well supported by pupils. The School has a strong reputation for sailing, and is recognised by the RYA (Royal Yachting Association) as a training centre. The School hosts and organises national sailing events.

The Arts. The School has a fine tradition in both Music and Drama and pupils are actively encouraged to develop an enthusiasm for the performing arts. Tuition across the widest possible range of musical instruments is available and there is a particularly active choir.

The Arts Centre and the Design Technology Centre both add to the school's wide-ranging facilities.

Careers. Professional staff are responsible for advising on Careers and Higher Education, and the school has a well-equipped Careers Centre to support this function. All pupils in Year 11 have access to work experience and the School holds a regular Careers Convention and Industrial Conference. Mock Interviews are arranged with local businesses and the professional community and pupils have regular personal tutorials.

Admission. Pupils can be admitted at the beginning of any term after their 11th birthday although the largest entry is in September. Entry is normally via the School's Entrance Examination or equivalent tests.

Educational Awards & Bursaries. (*see Scholarship Entries section*). A limited number of means-tested Bursaries and Awards are available for able students and are awarded annually by examination for excellence in academic studies, music and sport. These are available for entry into Year 7 and Sixth Form. Children of Methodist and Anglican Ministers are admitted at substantially reduced fees and Forces Bursaries are available.

Fees per term (2008-2009). Boarding £6,450–£7,740, Weekly Boarding £5,805–£6,965, Day Pupils £3,315–£3,540. New Sixth Form entrants: Boarding £7,960, Weekly Boarding £7,185, Day £4,730.

Lyndon Preparatory School. This is situated close to the Senior School and is therefore able to share its facilities. Teaching between the two parts of the School is also closely coordinated.

(*For further details see Lyndon Preparatory School entry in IAPS section.*)

Charitable status. Rydal Penrhos is a Registered Charity, number 525752. The aim of the charity is the education of young people.

Ryde School with Upper Chine

Queen's Road Ryde Isle of Wight PO33 3BE
Tel: 01983 562229
Fax: 01983 564714
e-mail: school.office@rydeschool.org.uk
website: www.rydeschool.org.uk

Ryde School was founded in 1921 by William Laxon McIsaac and moved to its present site in 1928. In 1994, it was joined by Upper Chine School.

The School is fully co-educational at all levels. There are some 530 pupils between the ages of 11 and 18 in the Senior School, and some 265 aged 3 to 11 in the Junior School which shares part of the same site. (*See Junior School entry in IAPS section.*) There are full and weekly boarders who board on the Bembridge site (see below). The remainder are day pupils from the Island, with a small handful commuting on a daily basis from the Portsmouth area.

Motto: '*Ut Prosim*'

Visitor: The Right Revd Dr Kenneth Stevenson, Bishop of Portsmouth

Governors:
Chairman: R J Fox, MA, CMath, FIMA
Vice-Chairman: I J Rawlinson, OBE
Hereditary Governor: A McIsaac, MA, DPhil

Sir Guy Acland, Bt LVO, DL
The Venerable Caroline Baston
Mrs E Bladon
R W Bradbury, MA
Ms C R Clark
Dr R D Gill-Garrison, BA, BSc
Ms J Lees-Spalding, MA
Dr C J Martin, BSc, MBA, DPhil, FIChemE
Mrs P E F Partridge, MBChB
Miss C E Pepys, SRN, RSCN, SCM
D M T Rhodes, FRICS
R J Scarratt
P Tobin, MA, FRSA
H B Verey

Clerk to the Governors: P C Taylor, JP, FCA

***Headmaster*: Dr N J England**, MA, DPhil

Deputy Head: D E J J Lloyd, BSc, PGCE

Senior Teachers:
K J Dubbins, BEd (*Head of Year 9; Contingent Commander CCF*)
Mrs S E Evans, BA (*Director of Drama*)
B W Penn, BSc, CBiol, PGCE (*Director of Studies*)

Senior School:
Mrs M Armstrong, BA, PGCE (*Head of Year 7*)
S R Baxter, BA, PGCE (*Head of Sixth Form*)
Ms K Bishop, BSc, PGCE (*Head of Psychology*)
N Brady, BA, PGCE (*Head of Economics & Business Studies*)
P K Bridge, BA, PGCE
K G Bridgeman, MA (*Head of Science*)
Miss S Broyé, BA, MA, PGCE
T Bull, BA
Mrs M E Burgess, BSc, PGCE (*Head of Geography*)
Miss A Drinkwater, BEd, MA (*Head of Girls' Games & PE*)
Miss J A Dyer, BA, PGCE
Miss E Edmunds, BA, QTS
M J Glasbey, BSc, PGCE (*Head of Year 11; Head of CDT*)
P K Griffiths, MA, PGCE
A Grubb, BMus, PGCE (*Director of Music*)
Mrs T A Hall, BA, PGCE (*Head of Modern Languages*)
Mrs R A Hamar, BA (*Librarian*)
Miss J Hillyard, BA, PGCE
R Hoare, BA, QTS
K J Hothersall, CChem, MRSC
P A Johnson, BSc, BA, PGCE (*Head of Mathematics*)
A Johnston, BA (*Head of ICT*)
Mrs R Jones, BA, PGCE
Revd J Leggett (*Chaplain*)
Mrs A M Limon, BA, QTS (*Head of Learning Support*)
K Long, BEd (*Head of Boys' Games*)
Ms H McComb, BA, PGCE (*Head of RE*)
S M Mead, BEd (*Head of Year 10*)
J H Mitchell, BHum, PGCE (*Head of Academic PE*)
A P Munn, MA, CertEd
C M Ody, BA, PGCE (*Head of Year 8; Head of PSHE*)
Mrs P A Parry, BA, MA, CertEd
Mrs S Patel, BSc, MSc, HNC, FIMLS, PGCE, MA
Revd J Peek, BSc, BA
A Penalva, CertEd
M Postelnyak, MA, DPhil
Mrs B Preston, CertEd
Mrs S R Prewer, BEd (*Examinations Officer*)

R W E Salisbury, BA, PGCE
Mrs J Sheridan, BA, CertEd
A L Smith, BSc, PGCE
P J Stott, BA, PGCE (*Head of History and Politics*)
Miss A Sutton (*Head of Boarding*)
Mrs B Sutton, CertEd
C Sutton, BA, PGCE (*Head of Art*)
G Taylor, MA, PGCE (*Head of English*)
C G S Trevallion, BSc, PGCE (*Head of Biology and Environmental Science*)
Mrs R Tweddle, GTCL, LTCL (*Choral Director*)
Mrs C Vince, BA, PGCE
Mrs K Vowell, BSc, PGCE (*Head of Chemistry*)
Mrs L L Waldron, BA, PGCE
H Wilkie, BA, CertEd
M J Windsor, BSc, PGCE
Mrs M A Woodhams, MA, PGCE

Junior School
Head: H Edwards, BSc, PGCE
Director of Studies: R A Hutchins, BEd, CertEd

M Bowes, BEd
Mrs A Bull
Miss C Burroughs, MA, MPhil (*Librarian*)
Mrs L J Dickinson
P Dickinson
Mrs J Edwards, BSc, PGCE
A Gallerwood, GA
Mrs G Gallerwood, BA
Ms J McKay, BEd
Miss D J Meadows, BEd, CertEd (*Senior Teacher*)
Mrs A Selby
Mrs D Shepherd, CertEd
K Smith, AMusLCM, CertEd
Mrs H Vann, BA
Mrs K Woodward, BA

'FIVEWAYS' Nursery and Pre-Prep:
Head: Mrs S A Davies, BEd

Mrs N Bell, NNEB
Miss K Clarke, NNEB
Miss S Crocker, BTech (*Nursery Nurse*)
Mrs G Elsom
Miss D Gillam, BEd
Miss S Glover, NNEB
Mrs D Grubb, BA, PGCE
Mrs S Hawker, BA, CertEd
Mrs V J Jones, BEd
Mrs S Lea, NTD
Miss V Lovell, BEd
Mrs J Mortimer, BEd
Miss N Noott, BA
Mrs P Ong, DipPP

Situation and Buildings. The School stands in its own grounds of 17 acres in Ryde overlooking the Solent, and is easily accessible from all parts of the Island and the near mainland. It is within walking distance of the terminals which link Ryde to Portsmouth by hovercraft (10 minutes) or catamaran (15 minutes). In recent years there have been many additions to the School buildings. Since 1989, a programme of new building and conversion has provided an Art and Design Centre, a Sports Hall, a Music School, a new classroom block for languages, a new Science Block, a Sixth Form Centre, a new teaching block of eight Senior School classrooms and a library. In 2004 a Junior School Hall and Learning Support Department was opened.

Organisation and Curriculum. The School aims to provide a good all-round education based upon Christian principles, and enjoys an enviable reputation on the Island for high standards both inside and outside the classroom.

In the Junior School strong emphasis is laid on basic skills and on proficiency in reading, writing and number work. Pupils are prepared in this way for entry into the Senior School, and, following a recommendation from the Head of the Junior School, they are offered places in the Senior School at the age of 11.

The programme of work in the Senior School is designed to provide as broad an education as possible up to the end of Year 11. The subjects taught to GCSE level are English, English Literature, Mathematics, Physics, Chemistry, Biology, French, Spanish, Geography, History, Religious Education, Business Studies, ICT, Art, Music, Physical Education, Drama and Craft, Design and Technology. All pupils also follow a programme of Religious Education, Health Education and Games.

In the Sixth Form pupils are normally required to select three or four subjects at AS/A2 level from a wide choice. In addition, pupils may follow a General Studies course, designed to add breadth to their academic studies. Courses lead to entrance to universities, the Services, industry and the professions. The Careers Department provides advice and guidance to all pupils.

Tutorial System. Each pupil has a tutor who is responsible for his or her academic and personal progress and general pastoral welfare. The tutorial system encourages close contact with parents, which is further reinforced by parents' meetings which are held at regular intervals. The School aims to maintain sound discipline and good manners within a traditionally friendly atmosphere.

Games. The main games in the Senior School are rugby football, hockey, cricket and athletics for the boys, and netball, hockey and athletics for the girls. In the Junior School, Association football is also played. Other games include basketball, squash, golf, swimming and tennis. Regular matches are arranged at all levels against teams both on the Island and the mainland.

Music and Drama. The Music School incorporates practice and teaching facilities and a well-equipped recording studio. The School has a flourishing choral tradition, with opportunities for participation in a variety of choirs and instrumental groups. Concerts and musical plays are performed in both Senior and Junior Schools, and concert tours abroad have taken place in recent years. Full-length plays are produced each year by both Senior and Junior Schools, and special attention is given in the English lessons of the younger forms to speaking, lecturing and acting. Public speaking is a particular strength. In addition to a newly refurbished theatre and a smaller studio theatre on the Ryde site, the School now enjoys the use of the Ryde Town Theatre.

Activities. There are many societies which cater for a wide range of individual interests. The School has a contingent of the Combined Cadet Force with Royal Navy and Royal Air Force sections. Sailing, canoeing, gliding, and other forms of venture training are strongly encouraged. There is a flourishing Duke of Edinburgh's Award scheme. Holiday visits and expeditions are regularly arranged, and there are opportunities for exchange visits with schools on the continent.

Boarding. Boarding for both boys and girls is available for pupils on the Bembridge campus which offers approximately one hundred acres of playing fields and woodland overlooking Whitecliff Bay and Culver Cliff, some six miles from Ryde. Transport is provided to and from Ryde for the school day.

Fees per term (from January 2008). Tuition: Nursery: £1,430 (full day), £790 (half day); Pre-Prep £1,595–£2,260; Junior School £2,725; Senior School £3,015.

Boarding (excluding tuition): Senior School: £3,150 (full), £2,760 (weekly).

Scholarships and Bursaries. (*see Scholarship Entries section*). The School offers a number of Ryde Assisted Places. These are awarded to suitable candidates from outside the school. These places are means tested. Some scholarships are also awarded on merit.

Charitable status. Ryde School is a Registered Charity, number 307409. The aims and objectives of the Charity are the education of boys and girls.

St Albans School

Abbey Gateway St Albans Herts AL3 4HB
Tel: 01727 855521
Fax: 01727 843447
e-mail: hm@st-albans-school.org.uk
website: www.st-albans.herts.sch.uk

The origins of the School date back, according to tradition, to the monastic foundation of 948, and there is firm evidence of an established and flourishing school soon after the Conquest. Following the Dissolution, the last abbot, Richard Boreman, sought a private Act of Parliament to establish a Free School. Charters, granted to the Town Corporation by Edward VI and Elizabeth I, together with endowments by Sir Nicholas Bacon from the sale of wine licences, secured the School's continuance.

Visitor: The Rt Revd The Lord Bishop of St Albans

Governors:
Chairman: I F Jennings

The Mayor of St Albans
The Dean of St Albans
The President of the Old Albanian Club
J Barber, PhD
A S Barnes
R Blossom, BSc, CertEd
N K Brook
M J Collins, MA, DPhil
Mrs H M Crookston, BSc
G R Dale, MA, MCIPD, FRSA
P J Dredge
S P Eames
B S Kent, BA
D C Lindsell, MA, FCA
A R M Little, MA
Mrs J Mark, BA
Mr C McIntyre, BA
Prof R C Munton, BA, PhD, ACSS
Cllr G Myland
D Pepper, FRICS, FICPD
Mrs R Phillips

Bursar and Clerk to the Governors: D Todd, MA, FCA

***Headmaster*: A R Grant**, MA, FRSA

Second Master: R D W Laithwaite, BA
Director of Studies: M E Davies, MA
Senior Tutor: A P S Talbot, BA
Head of Middle School: P R Byrom, MSc
Head of Lower School: P W Taylor, BEd
Senior Master: P P Wade-Wright, BSc

Assistant staff:
R J Alton, MPhys
Mrs K M Bailey, BSc, PhD
B S Balden, MA
Miss S J Banfield, BSc
A J Bateman, BA
E J Beavington, BSc
I J Black, MA
Mrs C C Bolton, BA
D A Brunskill, MA
G J Calvert, BEd
A J W Carman, BSc
N J Cassidy, BA
I Charlesworth, MA
B T Clark, BA
Mrs E W Davies, BA
R Dear, MA
J P Dray, MA, DPhil
R G Egglesfield, BA
Ms C R E Fenn, BA
A W G Ford, BA
A M Godfrey, BA
C P A Gould, BSc
Mrs M-C Gould, BSc
Mrs V H Graveson, BA
Miss J M Grieveson, BA
Mrs R Hardy, MA
G C Higby, MA, PhD
Mrs J Higgins, BA, ARCM
C C Hudson, BSc
C J Humphreys, BSc
T N Jenkins, BA, MFA
A K Jolly, BA
Miss K Kaur-Lillian, MA
D H Kerry, BSc
M J Langston, BSc
E J Logan, BA
Mrs T Maisey, BA
T J Martin, BA
D K McCord, BMus, ARCM
P McGrath, BA
Mrs P M Mills, MA
I Murray, BA
Miss J J M Nelson, BSc
D M L Payne, MA
M A Pedroz, MA
Mrs D S Percival, MA, MIL
Miss D Porovic, MSci
Ms A V Rhead, MA
Mrs L R Reid, BSc
Mrs G Renz, MA, MPhil
D C Richards, BCom, MBA
D M Rowland, MA
J R Russ, BA
I M Shillcock, BSc, PhD
G L Smithson, BSc
Mrs L L Stanbury, BSc
P Stewart, MA
D J Stone, BA
M R Stout, BMus
Mrs M O Stratton, MSc
Mrs J H Swain, MA
D Swanson, RADA
R E Tanner, DPhil, BSc
Mrs D Walker, MSc
G J Walker, BA
D Whitehead, BA
Miss L J Wilkinson, BA
P G Yates, A CertEd

Chaplain: The Revd Dr C D Pines, MB BS, MA
Medical Officer:
OC CCF: Major K J Everitt

Visiting Staff:

Poet-in-Residence: J D Mole, MA

Music:
P A Bainbridge, DipRCM, ARCM
N Buick, DipMus, RSAM
A Crompton, GRNCM, FTCL, ARCM, LTCL
T G Goodman, DipMus
S Laffy
Mrs V Parker, GRSM, ARCM
Mrs R Runcie, LRAM, ARCM
Miss J E Simmons, BMus, GGSM
Ms C Vince, GRSM, LTCL
M Vishnick, LLCM, ALCM
N Woodhouse, FLCM, LTCL, LLCM, ALCM

St Albans is a day school of about 780 pupils which, after being for many years part of the Direct Grant System, reverted to full independence. Girls were admitted into the Sixth Form in September 1991. Its atmosphere and ethos derive from its long tradition and its geographical position near the city centre of St Albans in close proximity to the Abbey and overlooking the site of the Roman City of Verulamium. Whilst maintaining a high standard of academic achievement, it offers wide opportunities for development in other fields, and a strong emphasis is laid upon the responsible use of individual talents in the service of the community.

Buildings. For more than 3 centuries the School was in the Lady Chapel of the Abbey. It moved in 1871 into the Monastery Gatehouse, a building of considerable historic and architectural interest where teaching still continues. Since 1900 extensive additions have been made, including, most recently, the award-winning Hall, the Language Laboratory, Library, Art School and IT, Design and Technology Centre, new Science laboratories and a well-equipped fitness centre. A nearby building has recently been converted for use as a fully-equipped Drama Centre.

The School has close historical ties with the Abbey, and by permission of the Dean the nave of the Abbey is used regularly for morning prayers.

Admission. The majority of boys enter at the age of 11 or 13 but there are also entries at 16, when girls are also admitted; candidates are accepted occasionally at other ages. For the main entry at 11 an examination in basic subjects is held at the School each year, normally in January, and parents of interested candidates should write to the School for a prospectus and application form. Candidates at 13 enter through the Common Entrance examination, and conditional offers of places are normally made about one year before entry, following a preliminary assessment. Ideally parents should apply to the School at least 2 years in advance for entry at 13.

Pupils are admitted only at the start of the Autumn Term unless there are exceptional circumstances.

Enquiries about entry should be addressed to the Headmaster's Personal Assistant.

Fees per term (2008-2009). £4,135.

Bursaries and Scholarships. (*see Scholarship Entries section*). Some assistance with tuition fees may be available in cases of proven need from the School's own endowments. Such Bursaries are conditional upon an annual means test and will be awarded according to a balance of merit and need. Numerous scholarships, worth up to 50% of fees, are awarded on academic merit at each age of entry, and Scholarships in Art and Music are offered to existing pupils or new entrants at 13+ who show exceptional talent. Internal Bursaries from a fund established to the memory of John Clough, a former Director of Music, are awarded annually to pupils who show musical talent.

Curriculum. The curriculum for the first three years is largely a common one, and covers a wide range. All boys study two languages and three sciences, and devote some part of their timetable to Art, Drama, Music, ICT and CDT. Mathematics GCSE is taken at the end of the fourth year, and in the fourth and fifth years a system of compulsory subjects and options leads in most cases to the taking of at least a further eight GCSEs. In the Sixth Form most pupils study four subjects at AS level in the Lower Sixth Form and three or four A2s in the Upper Sixth. In addition, all pupils take General Studies either as an AS or a full A level and are prepared for an AS in Critical Thinking. The choice is wide, and the flexibility of the timetable makes it possible for almost any combination of available subjects to be offered.

Virtually all Sixth Form leavers go on to universities or other forms of higher education, a good proportion to Oxford or Cambridge.

Out-of-school activities cover a wide range, and there are clubs and societies to cater for most interests. Several of these are run in conjunction with other schools. Musical activities are many and varied and include regular concerts and recitals by the School Choir, Choral Society and ensembles and by professional artists. Plays are produced 3 or 4 times a year either in the New Hall, the Drama Centre Studio, the English Centre Studio Theatre or in the Open-air Theatre, and there is ample opportunity for creative work in the Art school, the Workshops or the Printing Press. There is a strong contingent of the CCF with sections representing the Army and RAF. Other groups train under the Duke of Edinburgh's Award Scheme and do various forms of social service and conservation work in and around the city of St Albans. The School owns a Field Centre in Wales which is used for research and recreation in holidays, as part of the Lower School curriculum and as a base for field studies and reading parties. The School also owns a working 400 acre farm within 3 miles of the school where new playing fields, extending to 45 acres, were opened in 2002 by HRH The Duke of Gloucester. The new grounds include an Astroturf all-weather pitch and a superb state-of-the-art pavilion.

Games. The main games are Rugby Football, Hockey, Cross-country, Cricket, Tennis and Athletics, with a range of other sports, which includes Association Football, Squash, Shooting, Sailing, Swimming, Orienteering, Basketball, Golf and Table Tennis. The playing fields are within easy reach of the School, and the spacious and pleasant lawns on the School site, stretching down to the River Ver, provide room for Tennis Courts, Cricket Nets and a Shooting Range.

Old Albanian Club. Information about the Old Albanian Club may be obtained from its secretary: R L Cook, 1 Pondswick Close, St Albans (Tel: 01727 836877).

Charitable status. St Albans School is Registered Charity, number 1092932, and a Company Limited by Guarantee, number 4400125. The aims and objectives are to provide an excellent education whereby pupils can achieve the highest standard of academic success, according to ability, and develop their character and personality so as to become caring and self-disciplined adults.

St Aloysius' College

45 Hill Street Glasgow G3 6RJ
Tel: 0141 332 3190
Fax: 0141 353 0426
e-mail: mail@staloysius.org
website: www.staloysius.org

Motto: *ad majora natus sum* (I am born for greater things).

Board of Governors:
President: Rev Michael Holman, SJ (Jesuit Provincial)
Chairman: Mr David Boyce
Mrs Maureen Brogan
Dr Harry Burns
Mrs Elaine Cameron
Dr Francis Dunn
Mrs Linda Eadie
Fr Peter Griffiths, SJ
Mr Greg Hannah
Rev Alan Harrison, SJ
Ms Ruth Holgate
Mr John Hylands
Professor Bartholomew J McGettrick

Bursar and Clerk to the Board: Mrs Kathleen Sweeney, FCCA

***Head Master*: Mr John Stoer**, BA

Depute Head Master: Mr Ronald Renton, MA, MPhil

Assistant Headmaster: Mr J Phillip Crampsey BEd

Administrative Officer: Mr Robert Cleary, MA

Head of Junior School: Dr Aileen Brady, BSc Hons

Head of Early Years: Mrs Marie Forbes, DipEd

Secretary to the Head Master: Mrs Lesley Adam

St Aloysius' College, founded in 1859 and sited in Glasgow city centre, is a Roman Catholic independent school under the Trusteeship of the Society of Jesus.

The school is fully co-educational at all stages (Kindergarten to S6) with a total roll of over 1,300, drawn from a wide catchment area including Strathclyde and beyond.

Jesuit education is inspired by the vision of St Ignatius Loyola (1491–1556) in which God reveals his love for us in all things. As a Jesuit school, the aim of St Aloysius' College is the formation of men and women for others, people of competence, conscience and compassion.

Entrance. Entrance to the school is by open examination at S1 and P7 and by interview and assessment at P1 and Kindergarten. There may be places in intermediate years from time to time.

Buildings. The Senior School occupies buildings from 1840, 1866, 1908 and 1926. A new £3.7m maths, science and technology building was opened in 2002. The Junior School is accommodated in an award-winning building opened in 1998. Playing fields are located four miles away.

Curriculum. The Junior School and lower years of the Senior School follow internally devised courses which are suitable for academically able children. All Junior School pupils study French and science from Kindergarten and P1. Intermediate II is taken at the end of S4 and pupils take five Highers in S5. A wide range of Advanced Higher, A Level and other courses are available in S6.

Co-Curricular Activities. The main sports are Rugby, Hockey, Athletics and Cross Country. Pupils are extensively involved in community service and charity work. There is a wide range of co-curricular activities.

Fees per annum (2008-2009). £6,120–£8,010.

Bursaries are available on consideration of parents' income.

Charitable status. St Aloysius' College is part of the wider work of the British Jesuit Province which is a Registered Charity, number 230165.

St Bede's College

Alexandra Park Manchester M16 8HX
Tel: 0161 226 3323 (Senior School)
0161 226 7156 (Preparatory School)
Fax: 0161 226 3813 (Senior School)
0161 227 0487 (Preparatory School)
e-mail: head@stbedescollege.co.uk
enquiries@stbedescollege.co.uk
prep@stbedescollege.co.uk
website: www.stbedescollege.co.uk

Motto: '*Nunquam otio torpebat*'

St Bede's was founded in 1876 by Bishop Herbert Vaughan, who later, as Cardinal Archbishop of Westminster, went on to found Westminster Cathedral. From small beginnings the College has grown and changed whilst remaining faithful to Bishop Vaughan's ideals. Over 500 priests have received their early training at the College; although the number of priests on the staff has been reduced in recent years our religious faith remains central to the life of the College.

Throughout the many changes that have taken place since its formation the College has remained true to its founder's intention: to provide a thorough academic education for Catholic children, in an atmosphere of stability, care and concern.

We therefore seek the highest standards of performance so that pupils are stretched to, but never beyond, their personal limit. The provision of this education within a Catholic environment remains one of the chief characteristics of the College. High expectations of personal behaviour and discipline are rooted in our faith.

The College was one of the first Catholic schools in the country to enter the Direct Grant system. St Bede's was the only school which opted to retain that independence when the Catholic secondary schools in Manchester were re-organised in 1976.

The Governors introduced co-education in 1984, so that they could offer girls from Greater Manchester and beyond the benefits of a Catholic Grammar School education.

Governors:
Chairman: Rt Revd Mgr M R Quinlan, DCL
Vice-Chairman: H B Ellwood, PhL, BA, RIBA

Rt Revd Mgr J Allen, STL, PhL
Rt Revd T J Brain, Bishop of Salford
A Carr, LLB
Rt Revd Mgr T Dodgeon, MA
Mrs L Edwards
Mrs C Finnigan, LLB
M Gillespie
His Honour Gerard Humphries
G Lanigan, FCA
A J Keegan, BA
Dr Susan O'Driscoll, BSc, MB BS
K O'Flynn, MB, BCh, BAO, FRCS, FRCS Urol
Revd T Hopkins
Revd P McMahon
M Quinn, BA

Bursar & Secretary to Governors: J L Fletcher, FCA

***Headmaster*: M L Barber**, MA, MSc

Senior Management Team:
Headmaster: M L Barber, MA, MSc
Deputy Head: Mrs R A Meehan, GRSM
Deputy Head & Director of Studies: M Bartlett, MA
Deputy Head: D Kearney, BA
Assistant Head: J Bowden, BA
Examinations Secretary: I Service, MA
Assistant Head (Head of Chemistry): Mrs S Pike, BSc
Head of Economics & Business Studies: K McKeogh, MA, MBA

Assistant Staff:
* *Head of Department*

Art:
*Mrs J Hudson, BA
Mrs S Dittman, BA
H Peers, BA
H Weiss, BEd (*Head of Lower School*)

Business Studies/Economics:
*K McKeogh, MA MBA
D Grierson, MA (*Head of Lower Sixth*)
P Glancy, BA
Miss M Delaney, BA (*Assistant Head of Upper Fifth*)
M Gallagher, BEd

Classics:
*P B Maree, BA
J Gibson, MA (*Teacher in charge of Assessments*)
J Dumbill, BA

Drama:
*Mrs N Alderson, BA

English:
*J M Berry , BA
Mrs M Hazell, BA (*Second in Department*)
Mrs N Alderson, BA (*Head of Drama*)
Miss F Cochran, BA
B Peden, MA (*Head of Upper Fifth*)
Miss H Jordan, BA (*Head of Upper Sixth*)
Mrs S Norton, MA

Geography:
*Miss J C Tomkinson, BA
Mrs M Vidouris, BA (*Assistant Head of Lower School*)
H Weiss, BEd (*Head of Lower School*)
K Rafferty, BEd
P J C Loader, BSc

Geology:
*P J C Loader, BSc

History:
*P G Griffin, BA
J Bowden, BA(*Assistant Head*)
M Bartlett, MA (*Deputy Head & Director of Studies*)
Mrs M Harter, BA (*Head of Upper Fourth*)
T Fisher, CertEd
P Wilcock, MA

ICT:
*P McDaid, BSc
S Fallon, BEd
Mrs C Earles (*Network Manager*)

Mathematics:
*D McCotter, BSc
*Dr A Dando, BSc, PhD
S Bargery, BSc
M Cahill, MSc
I Service, MA (*Examinations Secretary*)
C Wright, BSc
Mrs C Brewer, BA
Mrs D Lawson, BSc, MSc

Modern Languages:
*P Lee, MA

French:
Mrs S de Castro, BA (*Teacher in charge of French*)
P Lee, MA
G Walker, MA
Mrs C Casson, BA
Miss M B O'Neill, BA
Miss M McMackin, BA
Miss R Evans, BA
Spanish:
*Mrs J Wallwork, BA
Mrs C Casson, BA
Miss M McMackin, BA
German:
*P Lee, MA
Miss R Evans, BA

Music:
*Mrs R Meehan, GRSM (*Deputy Head*)
Miss R Darby, BMus

PE:
*K Rafferty, BEd (*Head of Boys' PE*)
*T Fisher, CertEd (*Cricket*)
*S Fallon, BEd (*Football*)
Mrs N McCormick, BEd (*Head of Girls' PE*)
Mrs M Andrews, CertEd
Mrs E O'Neal, BEd
Mrs N Lavorini, BEd

Politics:
*Mrs R Lockett, BA (*Teacher in Charge of Careers*)

Religion:
*M Campion, BA
D Kearney, BA (*Deputy Head*)
Mrs E Meakin, BA
Mrs M Andrews, CertEd
Miss M Curry, BSc

Science:
*J Martin, BSc
Physics:
*J Martin, BSc
Mrs C Aspinall, BSc
N O'Hagan, BSc
Chemistry:
*Mrs S Pike, BSc (*Assistant Head*)
Mrs S Quirk, BSc (*Head of Lower School Science*)
Miss P Brammer, BSc
Mrs D Lawson, BSc, MSc
Biology:
*Miss C Hennity, BSc
M Nally, BSc
Dr S Powell, BSc, PhD
P Gill, BSc
Dr M Smedley, BSc, PhD

Technology:
*A Hennigan, BEd
J Lalley, BSc
Mrs M Collins, BEd

EAL and Dyslexia Support:
Mrs S Alexopoulos

Preparatory School:
Headmaster: P Hales, BA, DASE

Medical Officer: Dr M Cunningham

Headmaster's Secretary: Mrs M M Duff

Admission. The rapid growth of recent years enables us to offer 920 senior school places (260 of them in the Sixth Form).

Most pupils enter St Bede's at 11+ by taking the College Entrance Examination. Of those who apply, approximately one quarter are admitted. There are occasional vacancies in other age groups, and there is an additional intake of students from outside the College into the Sixth Form each year.

The College Entrance Examination takes place in January and is open to Catholic boys and girls who will not have reached the age of 12 by 31st August in the year of the examination. Christians of other denominations are also welcomed. Details of the examination and copies of past papers may be obtained from the Headmaster's Secretary. Occasional vacancies occur in other years. There is also direct entry to the Sixth Form for boys and girls who expect to obtain good GCSE results. Interviews are held from the beginning of the Easter Term.

Sixth Form Scholarships. Each year the Governors provide a number of scholarships and bursaries for Catholic boys or girls from other schools, who would like to enter the Sixth Form at St Bede's. The scholarships are awarded both on the basis of interview and performance in an examination which is held in January and according to financial need. Further details may be obtained from the Headmaster's Secretary.

Music Scholarships. The Governors award at least one half fee Music Scholarship to a pupil entering the Upper Third. Details of the award may be obtained from the Headmaster's Secretary.

St Bede's Educational Trust. St Bede's College Educational Trust awards a large number of bursaries to Catholic pupils of good academic ability who can demonstrate financial need. At present one third of pupils are in receipt of means-tested bursaries.

Curriculum. Curriculum provision is constantly being refined to improve the education offered to all pupils. It is supported by the most modern facilities, including recently built technology rooms, a new 17,000 volume library and four ICT suites.

A common Lower school curriculum offers all expected subjects together with Latin, ICT, Technology, ample PE/Games and pastoral time. In the Middle School three subjects are chosen from German, Greek, Spanish, Latin, Economics, Business Studies, ICT, Design & Technology, Art and Music for a one year course to further enhance GCSE options.

At GCSE, 9 or 10 subjects are taken from a choice of 21 which are available in any combination.

Students must usually achieve 7 GCSE passes (grades A*–C) to be admitted to the Sixth Form where they usually take four subjects to AS Level in the Lower Sixth and three A2 subjects in the Upper Sixth. The 30 subjects available can be combined in any way and no group exceeds 12 students for A Level.

All Sixth Form students in addition have pastoral time, General Religion lessons and preparation for General Studies.

Music. In the early years there is curricular music time to provide a thorough theoretical introduction to the subject as well as plenty of practical experience. The pupils thus learn to read music fluently and study the lives and music of the major composers.

Music is an option at both GCSE and A Level.

Instrumental tuition is available in string, woodwind and brass instruments. In addition, specialist tuition in electric guitar and drum kit is offered. There is a full programme of evening concerts.

Art. Art is a flourishing area of cultural expression. Textiles and photography are particular areas of expertise along with fine art. A specialist sixth form art studio housed separately gives these students a better opportunity to study the subject at a more mature level. In 2003 full computer-aided provision was added to the art suites. All pupils take Art in the Lower School and the subject is a very popular GCSE and A Level choice.

Drama. We stage two productions each year in late November and March. There are also one act plays for younger pupils and occasionally some open-air productions. Every two years we stage a drama festival, which is particularly successful in encouraging participants from all levels at the College.

Games. The Physical Education curriculum includes Badminton, Basketball, Netball, Volleyball, Cross Country, Gymnastics, Rounders, Cricket, Tennis, Athletics, Rugby, Soccer and Aerobics. We have extensive facilities which include a modern Sports Hall, 13 acres of playing fields and tennis and netball courts. On any Saturday there may be over three hundred pupils representing the College and 20 members of staff on duty, supported by large numbers of parents. A floodlit, all-weather surface for soccer, hockey and tennis was opened in October 2003.

ICT. There are 163 networked computers, both in departments and in four dedicated air-conditioned computer suites. Broadband internet access, an intranet allowing students to access the school network from home and all-day access to ICT are all available. Digital projectors are to be found in all departments and there is access to interactive whiteboards. All students receive teaching in ICT skills in their first year. Thereafter, the subject is delivered in a cross-curricular manner. A state-of-the-art language laboratory was completed in January 2005.

Other Activities. A wide range of expeditions and excursions are organised each year as part of our programme of activities.

There are regular trips and exchanges (including France, Spain, Cuba, Czech Republic, Poland, Russia, Italy and Germany in the last 2 years) to the Continent. Other extra-curricular activities include: Debating and Public Speaking, Drama, Theatre Visits, Orchestra and Choir, Chess, Photography, Community Service, Geological Society, Computing Group, Scientific Societies, Orienteering, United Nations Group, Politics Group, Quizzes and Art Club.

Fees per term (2008-2009). Senior School £2,665, Preparatory School £1,793.

Careers Education. The Careers Room with its library contains an extensive range of literature on Careers and higher education opportunities and is open every day and manned by two members of staff with responsibility for careers guidance. We make extensive use of computer based information sources and in particular the Prestel Database.

Every two years a Careers Convention is organised for pupils from Upper Fourth to Sixth Form and for senior pupils a higher education conference is organised every February.

Honours. 58 Oxford and Cambridge offers in the last 4 years.

Preparatory School. St Bede's College Preparatory School, a co-educational day school for pupils aged 4–11, was founded in 1985. The school has the same Governing Body as the College. There are some 234 pupils with 11 full-time and 12 part-time staff. The Prep School is situated within the main College campus and has full use of College facilities.

Charitable status. St Bede's College Limited is a Registered Charity, number 700808. Its aims and objectives are the advancement and provision of education on behalf of St Bede's College.

St Bede's Senior School

Upper Dicker East Sussex BN27 3QH
Tel: 01323 843252
Fax: 01323 442628
e-mail: school.office@stbedesschool.org
website: www.stbedesschool.org

Founded in 1978 St Bede's is a Charitable Educational Trust administered by a Board of Governors. It owes its existence in part to the success and vitality of St Bede's Preparatory School in Eastbourne, one of the first boys' Preparatory Schools to become fully co-educational and now one of the largest co-educational Preparatory Schools in the country.

St Bede's has grown from an initial 22 students to 850. Of these – 350 are boarders (full and weekly boarders), 500 are day students, 288 are Sixth Formers, 60 per cent are boys and 40 per cent are girls.

In September 2007 the School opened two innovative and award winning boarding houses and in November the new Multi-Purpose Hall began to be used. The hall is used for School Assemblies, examinations and many sports including basketball, badminton, cricket, football, netball and tennis. A new performing arts centre, in a beautiful setting next to the lake, was completed in 2006, providing new studio space for both drama and dance. In addition, new tennis courts have been built. St Bede's buildings are friendly, in enviable settings and a far cry from the overbearing, institutional character of much school architecture.

The School takes great pride in the variety of its students and the outstanding range of opportunities available to them. It is primarily a boarding school and is, therefore, organised with the aim of providing a happy and challenging atmosphere for those who are resident seven days a week. Thus a positive programme of weekend activities is always provided.

Governors:
Maj-Gen A L Meier, CB, OBE (*Chairman*)
C J Bean
Mrs S Bottomley
Dr A Bull
J D Courtney
J East
Mrs S Huang
T MacGibbon
T Martin-Jenkins
Lady Newton
D L Summers
W D Troy
Ms L Whistler

***Headmaster*: S W Cole**, BA University of Auckland, DipT Auckland College of Education, DipEd Admin, UNITEC

Second Master: D G Newton, BA
Assistant Headmaster: A R Hammond, BA Hons
Director of Studies: Mrs S A Quinn, BSc Hons
Senior Master: R Frame, BA Hons
Senior Teacher: M Rimmington, BSc, Dip Ind St
Senior Housemaster: Mrs L M Belrhiti, BEd

Faculty Heads:
Mathematics: P J Wilkinson, BSc
Languages: Mrs L Belhriti, BEd, Dip EFL
Humanities: G Parfitt, MBA
Arts: D T Graham, BA
Science: M Costley, BSc

Houses and Housemasters/mistresses:

Boarding Houses:
Crossways: Mrs M Waterhouse
Camberlot Hall: N Hatton
Dorms House: S Gough
Dorter House: Mrs L M Belhriti
The Stud House: A Walker

Day Houses:
Dicker House: R Mills
Knights House: Dr A Carroll
Deis Houses: E Dickie
Charleston: Miss S Muxworthy
Bloomsbury: Mrs S M'Timet

Aims and General Information. The purpose that guides our school is quite uncomplicated; it is simply that we wish our boys and girls to leave with their spirits and confidence high, aware of what they have achieved and can do in the future and proud of themselves. That self-confidence will be founded on each young person being valued for what they themselves achieve and the security that goes with succeeding not only in activities, academic and extra-curricular, but also socially. Thus St Bede's provides a very wide-ranging programme, both academically and in its extra-curricular activities, and maintains a teacher / student ratio of 1 : 8. All this means St Bede's can tailor programmes to the individual's needs to an unusually high degree.

Much is made of the merits or otherwise of co-educational schools. The St Bede's experience leads us to believe certain simple advantages are to be found in co-education. Boys and girls remain boys and girls, but a balance between the sexes, both in students and staff, does wonders in producing a relaxed but lively atmosphere.

St Bede's enjoys an enviable reputation internationally. Currently 22% of our students are from 40 different countries.

Curriculum. During the first year in the School students follow a very wide introductory course which includes the following subjects: Art and Design, Classics, Dance, Design & Technology, Drama, English, Geography, History, Home Economics, ICT, Mathematics, Modern Languages, Music, Physical Education, Science, SHAPE.

In the Fifth Form (Year 10) most students begin 2 year courses leading to the GCSE (Key Stage 4) examinations. Students usually follow 8, 9 or 10 subjects at GCSE; Mathematics and English are compulsory subjects. Potential courses include: Art and Design, Biology, Business Studies, Chemistry, Citizenship Studies, Communication Key Skills, Dance, Design & Technology, Drama, Geography, History, Home Economics, Environmental Science, Information Technology, Latin and Greek, Modern Languages (French, Spanish, German, Italian), Music, Performing Arts (Dance), Physical Education, Physics, Religious Studies, Rural and Agricultural Science, Science (Double Award), Science (Single Award). Some IGCSEs are also offered.

It is possible to provide courses to suit most individuals and students have a free choice of six (or more subjects depending on the timetable) from those that are not compulsory. During the first three years those with particular needs, such as those with any form of Dyslexia and those who are non-native speakers of English, can follow organised programmes within the timetable taught by suitably qualified teachers.

In the Sixth Form students can follow the traditional three or four A Level courses or a combined programme of A and AS Levels which can provide a broader education. Most GCSE subjects are offered at AS and A2 Level plus Accounting, Economics, Film Studies, Government & Politics, History of Art, Certificate in Professional Cookery, Media Studies, Statistics and Theatre Studies. Equine Studies NVQ Level 1 and 2, Creative Skills – Fashion Certificate are also offered outside the curriculum. All Sixth Formers take part in a wide-ranging and challenging General Studies programme offering cultural and religious studies, current affairs, career advice and an innovative programme of guest speakers.

Vocation provision: Applied A Levels: Performing Arts, Art, Business Studies, BTEC National Certificate in Sport, National Award in Music Performance.

St Bede's also runs the Legat Professional Dance Course which is fully integrated with the academic programme.

Current class sizes average 16 up to GCSE level and 10 at A and AS Level.

Club Activities Programme including Games. The extensive programme includes the many sporting and games playing opportunities open to students, The Army Cadet Force, The Duke of Edinburgh's Award Scheme, numerous outdoor pursuits and a daily programme of activities within the fields of Art, Drama, Music, Journalism, Science, Technology, Engineering and Social Service. In all there are currently over 140 Club Activities running each week and an average daily choice from 40 options. All students are obliged to take part daily. Games and Sports include Aerobics, Archery, Athletics, Badminton, Basketball, Canoeing, Climbing, Cricket, Cross-Country, Dry-Skiing, Fishing, Football, Golf (the School has its own practice course), Hockey, Judo, Dance, Netball, Orienteering, Photography, Riding (the School has its own stables), Rounders, Rugby, Scrabble, Squash, Swimming, Table Tennis, Target Rifle Shooting, Tennis and Volleyball.

Pastoral Care. There are three boys' boarding houses and two girls' houses, the numbers in each house varying between 40 and 70, with three resident staff in each. An appropriately selected tutor provides a mentor for each student during their time at the School. These tutors are responsible for ensuring that each student's academic and social well-being is carefully looked after. Tutors act in liaison with Housemasters and Housemistresses and are readily available for discussions with parents. All parents have several formal opportunities each year to meet those who teach or otherwise look after their sons or daughters.

Religion. The School shares the Village Church with the local community. Confirmation classes are available, if requested. All students attend weekly meetings in the church which are appropriate to boys and girls of all religions and are of outstanding variety. We do not wish to impose any singular religious observance on our students but would rather either that their existing faith is further strengthened by their being full members of the congregation of local churches or that they grow to appreciate and value the importance of a strong spiritual life through the thoughtful and varied programme of 'School Meetings'. There is a choice of four types of observance on Sundays: the Multi-Religious School Meeting, Church of England, Roman Catholic and Free Church.

Admission. The normal age of entry to the School is between 12½ and 14 years. The Common Entrance Examination, our own Scholarship Examination and Entry Tests are primarily used to determine a student's placing within sets and streams. It is unusual for any student who has been interviewed and has received a satisfactory report from his or her present school to be refused admission. Places are open each year to those wishing to join the School as Sixth Formers and at other levels in the School.

Scholarships and Bursaries. (*see Scholarship Entries section*). A number of Scholarships and Bursaries are awarded each year based on performance in the Open Scholarship Examination held annually in February. This examination is suitable for boys and girls of any educational background. Candidates should be over 12½ years and under 14 years on 1st September of the year in which they sit the Scholarship Examination. In addition to academic scholarships awards can be made to those who show particular promise in the fields of Art, Music, Drama, Dance and Sport. Interview and recommendation from the Head of a boy's or girl's present school play an important part in deciding to whom awards should be made. Certain Scholarships may be awarded to those entering the Sixth Form. Bursaries are available for children of service families.

Fees per term (2008-2009). Full and Weekly Boarders £7,780; Day Pupils £4,785.

Charitable status. St Bede's School Trust Sussex is a Registered Charity, number 278950. It exists to provide quality education.

St Bees School

St Bees Cumbria CA27 0DS

Tel: 01946 828000

Fax: 01946 823657

e-mail: mailbox@st-bees-school.co.uk

website: www.st-bees-school.org

Motto: '*Expecta Dominum*'

Founded by Edmund Grindal, Archbishop of Canterbury, in 1583. Now conducted as a co-educational independent school under a scheme approved by The Charity Commission.

Governors:

Chairman: W Lowther, Esq, CBE, OBE, DL, JP
Deputy Chairman: D G Beeby, Esq, FCA

J A Cropper, Esq, BA, FCA, The Lord Lieutenant of Cumbria
Professor H F Woods, BSc, BM, BCh, DPhil, FRCP
Mrs A Metcalfe-Gibson
N A Halfpenny, Esq, BSc, MSc, MIMgt
M P T Hart, Esq, FRICS, DipQS
G R Smith, Esq, BSc, DL
Mrs C T McKay
C R C Tetley, Esq, BA
Mrs M A I Creed
J H Hunter, Esq
A P Fox, Esq
A J Wills, Esq
C Woodhouse, Esq
M Rigby, Esq
Sir D Hart

***Head*: Mr P J Capes**, BSc, MA

Deputy Head: J W Rowlands, MA
Deputy Head (*Academic*): F A Winzor, BMet, PhD

Assistant Masters/Mistresses:

† *Housemaster/mistress*

H M Turpin, GNSM
H L Lewis, Cert Ed
Mrs G F Hudson, MA
Miss J L Dyer, BSc
J M Mellor, BA
J D Evans, MA
Mrs J A Bell, LLCM
Mrs S L Bromiley, BA
Mrs J A Carnegie, BA
Mrs W Mellor
M A Williams, BA
Mrs S J Williams, BA (*†Bega House*)
M K Midwood, BA
Mrs J Skeen, BSc
S McNee, BA
Mrs C M Dearden, CertEd
M Ollis, BA
Mrs S J Evans, BEd
Mrs C O Reed, BSc
T H Bell, BSc
M J George, BA
Miss R C Richards, BSc
S G Morrison, BSc (*†Grindal House*)
Mrs J C Malan, BA (*†Lonsdale House*)
Mrs E R Mullen, MA, BA
Mrs S G A Ollis, BA
B R Allen, BA (*†School House*)
Mrs V Smart, BSc, PhD
R A Young, BSc, MSc, PhD
Mrs V E Rowe, BA (*†Abbots Court*)
D A Rowe, BEd (*†Abbots Court*)
Mrs M France, BSc
R B Bardsley, BA
Miss B Lavin Campo, BA
Ms A F Considine, BA
Mrs C M Mauger, BEd
S W Taylor, BSc

Chaplain: Revd L F Nowen, BTh

Medical Officers:
G J Ironside, MBChB, MRCGP, DRCOG
S E Megan, BMedSci, BM BS, MRCCP, DRCOG, DCH

Bursar: G Stokes
Director of Marketing and Admissions: Mrs H C Miller
Head's Secretary: Mrs E M Smith

Situation and Buildings. The School stands in 150 acres of the attractive Valley of St. Bees, half a mile from a fine sandy beach and on the western edge of the Lake District National Park.

The principal older buildings, including the Chapel, Library, Art & Design Department, Gymnasium and Swimming Pool are of St. Bees sandstone and are situated on a raised terrace overlooking the main playing fields. The original school-room, which dates from 1587, now forms one side of a quadrangle and is used as the dining hall.

More recent developments include a fully refurbished Music School with extensive teaching and practice facilities, plus a basement studio which houses a 24-track digital recording studio, a new Sixth Form Centre and a totally retiled indoor swimming pool and changing rooms.

Organisation. There are 300 pupils aged 11–18, and each member of the School is the responsibility of a Housemaster or Housemistress and a personal tutor. There are three Houses for boys and two for girls. All senior boarders have study bedrooms while junior boarders share a room with up to four occupants. Boys and girls who live within commuting distance of the School are accepted as day pupils and the School also admits weekly boarders. The School operates an extensive bus service.

Religion. The Chapel stands at the centre of the School buildings and there are short services on certain weekdays before morning school. The Vicar of the Parish is the Chaplain and on some Sundays the boarders attend Morning Service in the Parish Church, The Priory.

Aims. The purpose of the School is to provide an education based on Christian principles, which will enable each pupil to develop his or her individual talents to the full. Particular emphasis is placed on academic excellence, good personal relationships and strong pastoral care. Thriving artistic, dramatic and musical traditions coupled with a wide range of sporting facilities help to avoid any narrow specialisation.

Curriculum. The curriculum provides GCSE courses in English, Latin, French, Spanish, History, Geography, Mathematics, Physics, Chemistry, Biology, Information Technology, Home Economics, Art, Physical Education and Music; option systems permit pupils to select the combination of subjects best suited to their abilities. Most members of the Sixth Form will study four subjects at AS Level and three at A2 Level together with a Key Skills and General Studies programme. Virtually all proceed to higher education. There is a highly successful Dyslexia and Learning Support Unit and Specialist EFL tuition is also provided.

Careers. The School has developed good links with the locally-based Careers Offices. Members of the Staff are responsible for providing specialist advice on careers and higher education and for developing links with industry and commerce. The Head, Housemasters and Housemistresses are also involved in this work and there is regular contact between parents and staff so that progress, future options and career plans can be discussed.

Games. The major sports for boys are Rugby Football, Cricket and Athletics. The girls play Hockey and Rugby 7s and are given a wide choice of games, including Tennis and Athletics, during the Summer Term. The School provides many County and Regional Representatives in all major sports. A large number of other sports flourish; the School has its own Golf Course, indoor heated Swimming Pool, large multi-purpose Sports Hall, and courts for Eton Fives, Squash Rackets, Tennis and Badminton.

Other Activities. There is a wide variety of societies and clubs, for example Young Enterprise, Debating and Public Speaking, and each pupil is encouraged to develop cultural interests. The School offers an extensive and varied weekend programme for boarders. Recently these have included weekend trips to London, theatre excursions to Stratford, days out to York, Glasgow, Edinburgh and Newcastle, beside the usual cinema, ten-pin bowling etc. activities.

Music. The School possesses a strong musical tradition and a large proportion of the pupils receive tuition in an instrument. In addition to the Orchestra and Choir there are strings, brass and woodwind ensembles. Keyboard players have access to a Willis organ. The Choir and instrumentalists perform regularly at the School and in the locality. There are close links with drama.

Drama. Drama is part of the junior curriculum and each year there are several productions involving all age groups.

Combined Cadet Force. Pupils are members of the CCF for two years and may choose to extend their service while they are in the Fifth or Sixth Form. There are Army and RAF Sections and all cadets receive instruction in Shooting. The Duke of Edinburgh's Award scheme can be taken through to Gold whilst pupils are cadets. Advanced courses are available in Leadership Training. Courses in flying and pilot training are also arranged.

Outdoor Activities. The School makes full use of its unique location between the Lakeland Fells and the sea and outdoor activities are encouraged for the enjoyment that they give and the valuable personal qualities which they help to develop. Adventure Training is part of the curriculum for junior pupils. Some members of staff are experts in mountaineering and water sports and all pupils have opportunities to receive instruction in camping, canoeing, hill walking, orienteering and rock climbing. There are annual skiing parties to Europe.

Admission. Candidates for entry at age 11 or 13 sit the Scholarship and Entrance Examination in early March. Boys and girls from Preparatory Schools take the Common Entrance Examination for entry to the School at age 11 or 13. Entry to the Sixth Form is dependent on interview, school report and the gaining of a minimum of five GCSE passes. The Head is prepared to give individual consideration to candidates entering at other ages.

Scholarships and Bursaries. (*see Scholarship Entries section*). Junior Scholarships up to 40% of the fees are available to pupils who are entering the First Form and are under the age of 12 on 1st September and to pupils entering the Third Form who are under the age of 14 on 1st September. Music Scholarships up to 40% of the fees are available at the ages of 11, 13 and 16. Academic Scholarships with Art and Sports Awards are available to pupils entering the Sixth Form.

The School also offers a limited number of means-tested Bursaries.

Fees per term (2008-2009). Senior: £7,715 (full boarding), £6,582 (weekly boarding), £4,624 (day). Junior: £5,595 (full boarding), £4,592 (weekly boarding), £3,581 (day).

Registration. A fee of £30 is payable at the time of registration.

Further Particulars from The Director of Marketing and Admissions, St Bees School, St Bees, Cumbria, CA27 0DS. Tel: 01946 828010; Fax: 01946 828011; e-mail: helen.miller@st-bees-school.co.uk

Former Pupils. The St Beghian Society Secretary: c/o St Bees School, St Bees, Cumbria. Tel: 01946 828000. Handbook and Register of Members. Latest Edition 2000.

Charitable status. St Bees School is a Registered Charity, number 526858. It exists to provide high quality education for boys and girls.

St Benedict's School

54 Eaton Rise Ealing London W5 2ES
Tel: 020 8862 2000 (School Office)
020 8862 2010 (Headmaster's Office)
Fax: 020 8862 2199
e-mail: headmaster@stbenedicts.org.uk
website: www.stbenedictsealing.org.uk

Motto: '*A minimis incipe*'

The School traces its history back to the foundation of the English Benedictine Community of St Gregory at Douai in 1606. St Benedict's was founded in 1902 by Abbot Hugh Edmund Ford to provide a Catholic education in London incorporating the Benedictine ethos. The School occupies a lovely site in West London, with outstanding sports facilities a mile away. The total number of pupils on role is 892 of which 609 are in the Senior School (186 in Sixth Form, including 38 girls), 261 in the Junior School and 22 in the Nursery. Boarders are not accepted. From September 2007 the Junior School has admitted girls and the Senior School will be admitting girls from September 2008.

Governing Body: The Abbot & Community of Ealing Abbey, assisted by a lay Advisory Body.

***Headmaster*: Mr C J Cleugh**, BSc, MSc (*also Chemistry*)

Deputy Headmasters:
Dr C Ferrario, MA, PhD (*also Geography*)
Dom Thomas Stapleford, BA (*also Religious Education*)

Director of Studies: Mrs P Lightfoot, BSc (*also Economics*)

Bursar: Mrs C de Cintra, BA, ACA (Tel: 020 8862 2183)

Teaching Staff:
* *Head of Department*

Art & Design Technology:
R Pereira, BA (*Director of Art*)
C Lethaby, BA
Miss K Linton, BA
Miss E Nicholau, BA (*Head of Design Technology*)

Classics:
*R A Hardman, BA
Sr T Geach, BA
T E McBratney, MA (*Lower Fourth Division Head, Year 8*)

Drama:
*Ms K M Ravenscroft, BEd
J Padden, BA

Economics & Business Studies:
*I Simpson, BSc Econ
Mrs P Lightfoot, BSc (*Director of Studies*)
P McCarthy, BBs

English:
*M Watts, MA
Mrs J Greenhough, BA, MA
Miss E Dibb, BA (*Upper Fourth Division Head, Year 9*)
Miss J Euvrard, BA
Mrs A Lewer, BA (*SEN Coordinator*)
Miss C Malcolm, BA
Miss S O'Shea, MA, HDipEd (*Deputy Director of Sixth Form, Year 13*)

Geography:
*Miss C Ferrario, BA, MA
Miss A Buckland-Wright, MA
Dr C Ferrario, MA, PhD (*Deputy Headmaster*)
P J Halsall, BA (*Head of Middle School*)
Miss N Shaw, BSc (*Upper Fifth Division Head, Year 11*)

Government & Politics:
*C Wilks, BSc, MA

History:
*R J Nonhebel, BA
A Heald, BA
M Jennings, LLBA, MA (*CCF*)
Miss C Thompson, BA
C Wilks, BSc, MA

ICT:
*D Barnes, BA
D M K Brown, MA, BSc (*Third Form Division Head, Year 7*)

Mathematics:
*S Scicinski, BSc, MSc
R Anghaee, MSc, BSc
Miss K Barteková, MSc
C S Gasiorek, BEd, MSc (*Lower Fifth Division Head, Year 10*)
M Nalewajko, MA, MEd (*Marketing Director*)

A Rees, BA (*Middle Manager Staff Cover; DofE Award*)

Modern Languages:
*Dr T J Ennis, PhD, BA, MA
Mrs L E Brooks, BA (*Head of PSHCE*)
Miss T Correia, BA
Miss A Davis, BA
Mrs O Kirtchuk, BA
Miss F G MacTaggart, MA (*Director of Sixth Form*)
P A F Thomas, MA (*Senior Leader Co-curriculum*)

Music:
*Mrs J Pashby, BA, PGDipRCM (*Director of Music*)
C Eastwood, BA
S Pashby, BMus

Physical Education & Games:
*M E Knights (*Director of Sport*)
E Conway
J Coulson, BA, MA (*Head of Boys' PE and Games*)
Miss G Dunlea, BA, MA (*Head of Girls' PE and Games*)
R Finch, BA (*Head of Academic PE*)
A Maclennan, BSc (*Head of Rugby*)
P I Telisca, BA

Religious Education & Sociology:
*P Allott, BA, BA (*Deputy Director of Sixth Form, Year 12*)
Dom A Bevan, OSB, BA, BD, ACA, MA
Ms G T Comyn, BRSc (*Head of Sociology*)
J P Foley, BA (*Head of Upper School*)
S Gayle, BA, MA
Ms A McGibbon, BA
A J Murphy, BA, BD, MA
Dom Thomas Stapleford, BA (*Deputy Headmaster*)

Science:
*I H Latif, BSc (*Director of Science; Head of Chemistry*)
Mrs A Hayes, BEd (*Head of Biology*)
C Bowles, MPhys (*Head of Physics*)
S Codrington, BSc (*Biology*)
Miss Y Drought, BSc (*Biology*)
Mrs C Wall, BSc (*Biology*)
C J Cleugh, BSc, MSc (*Headmaster*)
S Gobin, BSc (*Chemistry*)
C Windmill, BSc, ARCS (*Chemistry; Assessment Leader*)
V Cooke, MSc (*Physics; KS3 Science Coordinator; DofE Award*)
N H Hull, BSc, MSc, MA (*Physics; Senior Leader Examinations & Data*)

Special Educational Needs:
Mrs A Lewer, BA (*SEN Coordinator*)
Mrs K Cullen, BA

CCF:
B Spivey, BSc, MRes (*Contingent Commander*)
M Jennings, LLBA, MA

Assistant Music Staff:
Miss C Beard, BMus, LRAM (*Flute*)
D Field, GLCM, MMus (*Brass*)
B Gale, BA, PPRNCM (*Drum Kit*)
Miss E Jackson, GMus, ARCM (*Violin*)
P Jaekel, GRSM, LRAM (*Piano*)
Ms K Mlynar, BMus (*Saxophone*)
A Pledge, FRCO, LRAM (*Piano*)
J Preiss, MMus (*Acoustic and Electric Guitar*)
Mrs A Rayner (*Singing*)
Ms E Sheriden, BMus, PGCert (*Clarinet & Saxophone*)
J Smale (*Drum Kit, Percussion*)
E Stewart (*Electric Guitar*)
Miss R Stockland, BMus, AGSMD (*Singing*)
L Taliotis, BA, DipRAM (*Singing*)
S Trentham, BA, PGDip, ABSM (*Cello*)

Administration:
PA to Bursar: Mrs H Mortemore
Senior Accounts Assistant: Mrs J Bharij
Accounts Assistants: Mrs B Downey, Mrs H Shah, Ms G Nelson
Properties Manager: R Ferrett, MACIOB, MRICS
Assistant Properties Manager: H Keep
Health & Safety Coordinator: M Bridgford
Headmaster's PA: Mrs D Simmons (Tel: 020 8862 2010)
Senior Receptionist: Mrs A de Berg
Registrar: Mrs M Moore (Tel: 020 8862 2254)
Examinations Officer: Mrs J Wallace
School Secretary: Mrs A Brown
Assistant to Headmaster's PA: Miss T Henry
School Nurse: Mrs S Varnava, RGN
Librarian: Mrs S Mortimer
Assistant Librarian

ICT Services Manager: M Ferns, BA
ICT Network Manager: J Hatch
ICT Support Analysts: A Williams, A Cooper, S de Allie

Laboratory Technicians:
Mrs B Khamoo, BSc (*Biology*)
S Wall (*Chemistry*)
Mrs M Moore-Saxton (*Physics*)
S Le Geyt (*Art, Design and Technology*)

Old Priorian Association: P Fagan, President, c/o The School

Admission to the School is in September at the age of 11, by interview and special examination. Admission to the Sixth Form is subject to good GCSE results. Application for admission should be made to the Headmaster. Registration Fee: £50.

Religion. A specifically Christian and Catholic atmosphere is fostered through contact with the Monastery. There are regular periods for liturgy, both formal in the Abbey Church and informal in small groups. However the School welcomes pupils of other denominations and faiths.

Curriculum. In the Senior School, for the first year all pupils follow a common curriculum including Latin, ADT, French and Music. In the second year additional languages are offered, German or Spanish. Pupils normally take between 9 and 11 GCSE subjects. A wide choice of subjects is available at AS and A Level. Pupils are also prepared for Oxford and Cambridge entrance, where there is an impressive record.

Religious Studies are undertaken by all in every year. The Sixth Form is large, nearly 200, and almost all proceed to University or further education.

Physical Education and Games are part of the curriculum throughout the School. Rugby and cricket are the two principal games for boys and netball and swimming are being introduced for girls. Other sports are also promoted, particularly rowing, tennis, swimming (for boys also), athletics, karate, volleyball and table tennis. The School has 15 acres of playing fields nearby at Perivale. A new state-of-the-art Pavilion and changing rooms were completed in April 2005.

School activities are too many to mention but include Combined Cadet Force, The Duke of Edinburgh's Award Scheme, and over 60 lunchtime or after-school clubs and societies. Drama is strong with annual major productions. The Musical tradition is firm; almost any instrument can be learnt and activities include choirs, wind band, samba band and two orchestras. Public concerts are held several times each term. Art is outstanding, with a large number of pupils passing from the Sixth Form to Art Colleges each year. Considerable use is made of opportunities available in London for visits to concerts, theatres, museums and art galleries. In the nature of a wholly day school, contact with parents is frequent and regular.

Careers. There is a Careers Centre with experienced careers staff and some work experience in appropriate fields is organised. Close contact is enjoyed with the Services.

Honours. We continue to have a strong Oxbridge entry each year.

Fees per term (2008-2009). Tuition fees: Senior School £3,820, Junior School £3,360.

Charitable status. St Benedict's is a Registered Charity, number 242715. Its aim is to promote the Christian and Catholic education of young people.

St Columba's College

Whitechurch Dublin 16 Ireland
Tel: 00 353 1 490 6791 (Warden's Office)
00 353 1 493 2860 (Bursar's Office)
Fax: 00 353 1 493 6655
e-mail: admin@stcolumbas.ie
website: www.stcolumbas.ie

Motto: '*Prudentes Sicut Serpentes et Simplices Sicut Columbae*'

St Columba's College was founded in 1843 by the Revd William Sewell, the Lord Primate, the Earl of Dunraven and others. The College was incorporated by Royal Charter in 1913.

Visitor: The Right Revd A E T Harper, OBE, BA, Archbishop of Armagh and Primate of All Ireland

Fellows:
The Most Revd J Neill, MA, LLD, Archbishop of Dublin
H D Thompson, MA, BAgricSc
Mrs A C Kennedy
J R E Bewley (*Chairman*)
Dr Brian L Bond, BA, BAI, PhD, CEng, FIEI, MICE, ACIArb
Mrs Ann Budd, MA, HDipEd
J N White, FIAVI
C D S Shiell, FCIS
R H Simpson, BBS, FCA
Mrs K M Erwin, MA
R C C Johnson, MSc
Dr M O Moore, BA, MA, PhD, FTCD
P Myerscough
G D Crampton, MA, BBS
Dr M Redmond Ussher, BCM, LLM, PhD
J Bailey, MA
I Roberts, BA, BAI, CEng, FIEI, FIStructE, FICE
M Ridley, MA
P Kemp

***Warden*: Dr L J Haslett**, BA, DPhil, PGCE

Sub-Warden: J M Girdham, BA, HDipEd

Bursar: Mrs S Gibbs, MA, MSc, HDipEd

Assistant Staff:
* *Head of Department*
† *Housemaster/mistress*

The Revd M R Heaney, MA, HDipEd, DCG, CMIGC (*Chaplain*)
P J Jackson, BSc, HDipEd (**Science, Director of Boys' Boarding*)
F H Morris, BA, HDipEd (**Modern Languages, Senior Housemaster*)
J R Brett, MA, MSt, HDipEd (**Classics, Senior Tutor, Librarian*)
P R Watts, DipArt, HDipADE (**Art*)
D C Sherwood, MA, HDipEd (**Geography, Master i/c Sport and Extra-Curricular Activities*)
B A Redmond, BTech, DipID (**Technology*)
G R Bannister, MA, PhD, HDipEd (**Irish*)
L Canning, BA, HDipEd (*†Stackallan*)
Miss A Maybury, BA, HDipEd (**SPHE*)
J J Stone, BSc, PhD, HDipEd (**Drama, Transition Year Coordinator*)
Dr M Singleton, BSc, MSc, PhD, HDipEd (*Registrar, Director of Studies, *Physics*)
P G McCarthy, MA, HDipEd (**Business Studies, Classical Studies*)
Mrs D Sherwood (*†Iona*)
Ms S McEneaney, BA, PGCE
Mrs F G Heffernan, PGCert (*SLD*), CertEd, ACLD, ILSA, AMBDA (**Learning Support*)
Mrs A Stone, BA, HDipEd (*†Hollypark*)
Miss D Cullen, BEd (*†Beresford*)
D Higgins, MA, HDipEd (*†Glen*)
Mrs G Malone-Brady, MA, LRAM, ARCM, LRSM (*Director of Music*)
P Cron, MA, NDip (**Boys' Games*)
Mrs M D Haslett, BA, MPhil, PGCE (**History*)
Ms S-J Lawson BEd (**Girls' Games*)
Ms K Hennessey, BSc
R Swift, BA, HDipEd
N Coldrick, BSc
S Crombie, BSc (*Director of ICT*)
Ms R Howell, BA, HDipEd
H Jones, BScEd (*Guidance and Careers*)
Ms A Kilfeather, BA, HDipEd
M Patterson, BSc, PGCE (**Mathematics, †Tibradden*)
M O'Shaughnessy, MA
B Finn, MA, HDipEd
E Jameson, MA, HDipEd
Dr U Riemenschneider, MSc, PhD
Ms J Robinson, BA, HDipEd
Ms A Stokes, MA, HDipEd

A Grundy, MA Mus, HonVCM, FTCL, LRSM, ALCM (*Guitar*)
Ms S Taylor, MBA, BA, LTCL (*Piano & Theory*)
L McGuinness, LRAM (*Voice*)
P Barley, MA, MMus, FRCO, ARAM (*Organ*)
Ms S O'Regan, BMus, LRSM, MA Mus (*Voice*)
Ms K Snowe, LRSM, ALCM (*Piano*)
P Hughes (*Clarinet/Saxophone*)
Ms A Murnaghan, BA Mus, LRAM (*Cello, Piano, Theory*)
Ms B Baginska, BA (*Violin, Piano*)
F Hughes, BA Mus, FTCL, ALCM (*Organ*)
Ms T Lawlor, ALCM, LLCM (*Guitar*)

Accountant: N Grannell, FCA
Admissions Secretary: Ms N Crisp
Warden's Secretary: Ms E Bainton
Medical Officer: Dr A Khourie
Infirmary Sister: Mrs L Hanna, RGN

The College is a co-educational boarding school, with a number of day pupils, of about 300 pupils. It is situated on the slopes of the Dublin Mountains about 7 miles south of the city overlooking Dublin Bay in an estate of 138 acres. Much of this comprises playing fields, a 9-hole golf course and a deer park.

Having occupied its present site for over 150 years, the College combines the best of architecture old and new. Recent additions include a new Library and Reading Room, a Sports Hall, a Computer Centre, a Careers Library and an Arts Centre. Two completely new boarding houses and four classrooms opened in 2004. A new Music School was opened in 2008. A second astroturf hockey pitch was also added.

Admission. Application for admission should be made to the Warden. There is a registration fee of €100. There are two junior Houses for entrants between the ages of 11 and 13 years. An assessment day is held for 11/12 year old entrants in October prior to the year of entry. Entry is determined by a number of factors, including family association, geographical spread (including Northern Ireland, the UK and overseas), date of registration and an understanding of the values which underpin the College. Entrants from Preparatory Schools take the Common Entrance Examination.

Curriculum. In the Upper School, a wide choice of subjects and a large number of courses are available for the Irish Leaving Certificate. This examination keeps many options open for third-level colleges. It is the qualifying examination for entry to Irish universities and is acceptable (with requisite grades) to the faculties of all British universities. The Irish Junior Certificate is taken in the third form. A compulsory Transition Year programme follows the Junior Certificate.

Religious Teaching. Chapel services and religious instruction are based upon the liturgy and doctrine of the Church of Ireland. Boys and girls of other denominations and faiths are included.

Other Activities. Music, Art, Pottery and Technical Graphics (which are part of the curriculum in the Lower School) and Drama, Debating, Photography, Computers and various other clubs and societies function at all levels.

Games and Pursuits. Rugby Football, Hockey, Cricket, Athletics, Cross-country Running, Tennis, Badminton, Basketball, Golf, Swimming, Canoeing, Hill-walking, Orienteering, Horse-riding, Sailing, Aerobics and Fishing.

Fees per term (2008-2009). Senior House: €3,945 Day Pupils, €4,710 Day Boarding, €6,965 Boarding. Junior House: €3,290 Day Pupils, €3,930 Day Boarding, €5,805 Boarding.

The above fees are expressed in Euros. Fees may be paid in the Sterling equivalent.

Entrance Scholarships. Junior and senior awards are made at age 12 and 15 (i.e. entry to Form I and Form III). Entrance exhibitions are sometimes awarded to candidates for entry to Form II through the Common Entrance Examination. Generous discounts are available for the sons and daughters of the Clergy of the Church of Ireland. Old Columban and sibling discounts are also available. Details on request.

Leaving Scholarship. Norman Scholarships, for two years or more at all university colleges in Britain and Ireland, are open to the sons and daughters of Clergy of the Church of Ireland.

St Columba's Former Pupils' Society. Old Columban Society. *Hon Secretary*: J M Girdham, St Columba's College.

Charitable status. St Columba's College is a Registered Charity, number 4024. Its aims and objectives are the provision of Secondary Education facilities.

St Columba's College

King Harry Lane St Albans Hertfordshire AL3 4AW
Tel: 01727 855185
Fax: 01727 892024
e-mail: admissions@st-columbas.herts.sch.uk
website: www.stcolumbascollege.net

St Columba's College has been a school in the tradition of the Brothers of the Sacred Heart (New England Province) since 1955 and is a Roman Catholic, selective boys' school, but with about half of its pupils coming from other denominations and faiths. Brothers and lay teachers (now in the majority) work together with pupils and parents to provide a Christian education based on traditional values, balancing a friendly community with sound discipline and academic rigour.

The College and its Preparatory Department stand in their own grounds overlooking the picturesque vale of St Albans and the Roman settlement of Verulamium. In the last few years extensive improvements have been made to Science, English and Drama, Sixth Form, Preparatory and Pre-Preparatory facilities.

Motto: '*cor ad cor loquitur*'

Trustee and Dean: Br R Hetu, SC, BA

Governors:
Chairman: Mrs G Cummings, JP
Vice-Chairman: K Rudd, Esq

Professor J Cilliers, MBA, PhD, CEng, CSci, FIChemE, FIMMM
Mrs D Garfield, BSc , PGCE
C Hancock, FCIOB, FCSD, MBIAT, MBEng, MAPS
Mrs J Harrison, BEd
Mrs A P M Hartnett, LLB
The Revd Canon Stephen Lake, BTh
Br Ivy Leblanc, SC
Br Joseph Rocco, SC
C Thorpe, MBA, BA, FCIM, FRSA
A Yates, BSc, ACA

Bursar & Clerk to the Governors: Neville De Lord, BSc

***Headmaster*: David Buxton**, MA

Deputy Headmaster: D Shannon-Little, CertEd, BA
Academic Deputy Head: I T Nash, BSc
Head of Sixth Form: S Robins, BSc
Head of Preparatory: E Brown, BEd, MA
Pastoral Deputy: I Ioannou, BEd
Academic Deputy: Mrs M Shannon-Little, BEd
Head of Pre-Preparatory: Mrs R Loveman, BSc
Senior Master & Director of Admissions: A K Smith, CertEd, DLC

Chaplain: Fr T Edgar, BD, AKC, STD

Heads of House:
Charles: S D'Souza BSc
Guertin: R McCann, BA
Joseph: B Alway, BSc
McClancy: P J Baker, BSc
Stanislaus: R J Byrne, BSc
Vandebilt: A Colville, BA

* *Head of Department*

Art:
*J Tatham, BA
Miss E Sleigh, BA
Mrs J Golding, HND (*Art Technician*)

Careers:
*M Grant, MA, PhD

Classics:
*J Lidiard, BA Oxon
M Grant, MA, PhD
A Smith, MA Oxon

Critical Thinking:
S Jones, BA, CTS (*Department Coordinator*)
Mrs M Adair, MA Oxon

Design Technology:
*P Heaton, BSc
Miss V Risianova, BA
Mr G Edward, DMS, HNC (*DT Technician*)

Economics:
*Mrs K Healer, MA Cantab, LLB
J Turner, BA
Mrs J Greaves, BSc

English & Drama:
*E Waters, BA
J Ashmore, BEd, MA
Miss A MacFarlane, BA
Mrs C Gwynn, BEd
Mrs M Lawson, BEd
D Shannon-Little, BA

Geography:
*Mrs J A Fletcher, BA, FRGS
Mrs S Hassall, BSc
M D Lyons, BSc
M Mashiri, BA

History:
*Mrs C Powesland, BA
R J Byrne, BSc
Mrs M James, BA, MSt
R McCann, BA
K Roberts, MA

Information & Communications Technology:
*S M Leadbetter, MA
Mrs R Mason, BA
Br P Vaillancourt, SC, MA
J Lagrue, BSc (*Network Manager*)
L Dow (*Assistant Manager*)
Mrs M Cooper (*ICT Technician*)

Learning Support:
A L G Nevard, BSc, OCR Dip SpLD

Library/Media:
Mrs S Mathieson, Dip Lib (*Head Librarian*)
Mrs S Clarke

Mrs C Hart
Mrs J Foster, BA

Mathematics:
*I Devereux, BEd
Mrs K Parsons, BSc
Mrs A Cunningham, BSc
Mrs M Dattani, CertEd
C Jewell, MSc, PhD
Mrs N Rowlands, BSc
A Wilkins, BA
I T Nash, BSc

Modern Foreign Languages:
Ms S Jasieczek, BA (**French*)
Mrs I Jones, BA (**German*)
Mrs I Yates, BA (**Spanish*)
M Camara, LLB
A Colville, BA
D Gaze, MA
Miss L Jones, BA
Miss C Kyle, BA

Music:
Mrs P MacKenzie, MA Oxon (*Director of Music*)
J Woodhall, ALCM, LTCL

The Music Department is assisted by visiting instrumental teachers.

Physical Education:
M P Swales, BA (*Director of Sport*)
B Alway, BSc
K Boland, BA
A Leighton-Scott, BA
A Lowles, BEd

Politics:
*R McKenzie, BA
S Robins, BSc

Religious Education:
*Ms L Cronin, BA
Mrs M Adair, MA Oxon
E Castle-Campbell, BA
S Jones, BA, CTS
Mrs J Spruce, BA
Miss C Treacy, BA

Science:
*Mrs M Walker, BSc
M Connor, BSc (**Biology*)
J G Sapsford, BSc (**Chemistry*)
Miss K Stanbridge, BSc, PhD (**Physics*)
S D'Souza, BSc
P J Baker, BSc
R Baker-Glenn, MA Cantab, PhD
Mrs M Mester, BSc
Mrs S H Payne, BSc
Ms H Foucault, MSc

Science Technicians:
Mrs J Dewar, BSc
Mrs E Green, BSc
Ms V Sullivan, BSc, PhD
Ms E Walls, BSc, PhD
Mrs E Webb, BSc
Mrs R Wright, BSc

Sociology:
N Hogan, BA (*Department Coordinator*)
T O'Donnell, BA

Preparatory Department:
Mrs P Almond, BA
Mrs L Bills, BA Music LGSM (**Music*)
Mrs S Brandt, BA (**PSHE*)
Miss D Harvey, MA (**Science*)
Mrs S Burgon, BA (**Art and Design*)
Mrs U Kelly, BSc (**Mathematics*)
E Lowe, BSc (**PE and Games*)
Mrs H McLeod, MA, ALA (*Head Librarian*)
I Martin, BSc (**ICT*)
Mrs N Sells, BA
N Smart, BSocSci, DipT
C Stevens, BEd (**Geography*)
Mrs D Sumpter, BA (**Learning Support*)
Mrs M Turner
R Webster, BEd
Mrs M Willcock, BEd (**English*)

Pre-Prep Department:
Mrs E Rigby (*Pre-Prep 1 Derry*)
Miss C Harding, BEd (*Pre-Prep 1 Kells*)
Mrs L Brown, BEd (*Pre-Prep 2 Derry*)
Mrs L Latham, BA (*Pre-Prep 2 Kells*)
Miss K Leahy, BA (*Pre-Prep 3*)
Mrs M Streeter, BEd (*Pre-Prep 3*)
Mrs P Knox, DipEd (*Music*)
Mrs G Lewis, BEd

Teaching Assistants:
Mrs D Brown
Mrs J Cubis
Mrs M Hull
Mrs M Scott
Mrs K Walker
Mrs C Whittaker, BA
Mrs A Wynn-Owen

Administration:
College Accounts: Mrs F Armand, BA, MBA
Marketing Coordinator: Mrs C Tominey
Headmaster's PA: Mrs R Crowley
College Administrator: Mrs C Wood
College Secretary: Mrs M Richardson
Head of Prep Department's PA: Mrs C Talbot
Prep Department Secretary: Mrs O Cumine
Registrar: Br D Bessette, SC, BA
Examinations Officer: Mrs T Bovington
College Nurse Manager: Mrs G O'Sullivan, RGN
College Nurse: Mrs C Newton, RGN
Counsellor: Dr J Catty, MA Oxon, DPhil, FPC, BACP
NLP Study Skills Trainer: Mrs J Whitelam, MA
CO CCF: Ft Lt S D Leadbetter, MA

Entry. The College admits boys from 4–18. Currently there are 200 boys in the Preparatory Department (including the Pre-Prep Department), aged 4–11, and 645 boys in the Senior School, aged 11–18. The main entry for the Senior School is at 11, by Entrance Test and interview, with a significantly smaller group being offered by deferred entry at 13+.

Scholarships. Academic Scholarships are awarded at 11, 13 and for the Sixth Form. Additionally, the College offers two Music Scholarships each year and means-tested Bursaries.

The Curriculum. This is kept as broad as possible up to GCSE, pupils usually taking 9 subjects from the traditional range of Arts and Science options. There are 22 A Level (A2) subjects for pupils to choose from, many of them also available as a fourth option up to AS. Sixth Form education is complemented by a Key Skills course which aims to develop further the pupils' abilities in ICT, communication and numeracy. A Critical Thinking course is also undertaken. Almost all of the Sixth Form go on to universities, including Oxford and Cambridge.

Careers. A full-time Head of Careers and Higher Education works from a fully-equipped Careers Centre to ensure that all students receive high-quality guidance in order to make informed decisions about subject choices and university courses with subsequent career options in mind.

Pastoral Care. St Columba's is a Roman Catholic foundation welcoming students from all traditions. The spiritual and moral well-being of our pupils is a matter of primary importance for all of our staff, the majority being tutors. The six Housemasters and their teams are supported by a Ministry Team and Counsellor. Relations between the College and parents are open – a strength of the Foundation – and they are in regular contact with each other in monitoring the progress of the boys. The College seeks to nurture the academic and personal talents of each individual.

Sport. All boys participate, and the College has a strong sporting reputation. A rich variety of sports is available, including Rugby, Basketball, Soccer, Tennis, Cricket, Athletics, Swimming and Cross Country. For Sixth Form boys, not selected for the major sports, an even wider range of activities is available. Facilities include a large gymnasium and sports field on site. The Sports Department makes extensive use of soccer and rugby pitches, an athletics track, swimming pool and a golf course which are all immediately adjacent to the College site.

Extended and Extra-Curricular Activities. The College offers a mix of activities both at lunch-time and after school. These include sports clubs, such as archery and lacrosse, drama, art, chess, computing, Young Enterprise and many others, as well as a variety of academic and social clubs. There is a number of music ensembles, including a choir, orchestra and jazz band and four choirs of hand-bell ringers.

CCF. The Combined Cadet Force includes an Army and an RAF section. A full-time SSI (School Staff Instructor) is employed and the sections now include girls from The Princess

Helena College, Hitchin and Loreto College, St Albans. The Duke of Edinburgh's Award Scheme comes under the same management.

Preparatory Department. The Preparatory Department is on the same site as the College and shares many of its facilities. The College has a strong family atmosphere, providing a secure and purposeful environment in which expectations are high. It admits boys only, by examination and interview, into the Pre-Preparatory and Preparatory phases. In their final year, most Preparatory Department pupils are offered unconditional places at St Columba's College, following recommendations by Prep Department staff.

Fees per term (2008-2009). Senior School £3,339; Prep 2–4 £2,982, Prep 1 £2,732, Pre-Prep £2,640.

Charitable status. St Columba's College and Preparatory School is a Registered Charity, number 1088480. It exists to provide a well-rounded Roman Catholic education for pupils from 4–18 years of age.

St Columba's School

Duchal Road Kilmacolm Inverclyde PA13 4AU
Tel: 01505 872238
Fax: 01505 873995
e-mail: secretary@st-columbas.org
website: www.st-columbas.org

Junior School:
Knockbuckle Road Kilmacolm Inverclyde PA13 4EQ
Tel: 01505 872768
e-mail: juniorsecretary@st-columbas.org

Founded in 1897, St Columba's School is a non-denominational, co-educational day school for pupils aged 3–18. The School currently has just under 730 pupils with around 346 at Senior School. It is situated in the small rural community of Kilmacolm, surrounded by delightful countryside and located only 7 miles from Glasgow Airport.

Motto: *Orare Laborare Literisque Studere*

Governing Body:

Honorary President: The Rt Hon Lord Lang of Monkton, DL

Honorary Vice-Presidents:
Geoffrey C C Duncan, BL, NP
John C Ritchie
Dr Helen M Laird, OBE, MA, PhD, DL
Ron M Kennedy, TD, FCCII, FLIA

Board of Directors:
David Ward, MA, DUniv (*Chairman*)
Hugh M Currie, BSc, CEng, MICE (*Deputy Chairman*)
Nicola Anderson, MCSP
Thomas Anderson, LLB
Mrs Sara Bishop
Russell Crichton, BSc, MCIBS, FSI
Graham Cunning, BAcc, CA
Dr Aileen Findlay, BSc, MBChB Ed, MRCGP
James McAlpine
Colin McClatchie
George Morris, LLB, MBA
Paul Yacoubian, BAcc, CA

***Rector*: Mr D G Girdwood**, BSc St Andrews, MEd Stirling, SQH

Senior Depute Rector: Mrs J Wallace, DipPE Dunfermline, DipSEN

Head of Junior School: Mrs D L Cook, DCE Jordanhill, ITQ, DipAdPrStudies, DipEdMan Strathclyde

Depute Rector: Mrs J E Stevens, BEd Aberdeen

Depute Rector: Mr M J McLaughlin, MA Greenwich, BA Thames

Depute Head of Junior School: Mrs D Hecht, DCE Jordanhill

Senior Master: Mr C S Clark, BEd Glasgow

Company Secretary: Mr A D Gallacher, CA

Rector's PA: Mrs Dorothy Motherwell

Heads of House:
Strathgryffe: Mrs N Smith, MA Glasgow
Kilallan: Mr G Robertson, MA Glasgow
Craigmarloch: Mrs J Scott, BA Edinburgh, DipSL
Duchal: Mrs V Reilly, MA Edinburgh

Senior School Teaching Staff:
* *Head of Faculty*

Ancient & Modern Languages:
*Mr C Ure, MA Glasgow
Mrs E A Hunter, MA Glasgow
Mrs V Reilly, MA Edinburgh
Ms P Rennie, MA Glasgow
Mrs N Smith, MA Glasgow
Mrs E Carey, MA Glasgow, BA Open, DipIndAdmin
Mrs A Holt, MA St Andrews

Design:
*Mrs H Beall, BA Reading
Mrs M R Robinson, BA Glasgow School of Art
Mrs H Macdonald, DipDomSc Glasgow West of Scotland Coll, DipSecEd Jordanhill
Mr A Morrison, BEd Strathclyde
Mr T Boag, DipTechEd Jordanhill

English:
*Mr G McNicol, BA Hertfordshire
Mrs V Kennedy, BA Stirling
Mrs J E Stevens, BEd Aberdeen
Mrs A Moran, MA Glasgow
Mr G Smith, MA Glasgow
Mr C Eckford, MA Glasgow
Mr M J McLaughlin, MA Greenwich, BA Thames

Humanities:
*Mrs L T Eadie, BEd Aberdeen
Mrs M McCaffer, BSc Glasgow, DRLP, DIRM
Mr G Robertson, MA Glasgow
Mrs J Scott, BA Edinburgh, DipSL
Dr C Gilmour, BA, PhD Stirling

Business Studies:
(*to be appointed*)

Mathematics & ICT:
*Mrs F I Bruce, BSc Glasgow
Mr C S Clark, BEd Glasgow
Mrs J Judd, BSc Paisley
Mr A Walkey, BSc, MSc Glasgow
Mrs N Gardner, BA, MPA Indiana

Music:
*Ms Y Carey, DipMusEd Glasgow
Mrs A G Sutherland, DipEd, LTCL (Piano), LTCL (Voice)
Mrs J Mitchell, MA Sheffield, GTCL, LTCL (Piano)

Physical Education:
*Mr B A Manson, DipPE Jordanhill
*Mrs C Marr, MBE, DipPE I M Marsh College of PE
Mrs J Bellew, BEd Dunfermline
Mrs L Urie, BEd Dunfermline
Mr G Steel, BEd Strathclyde
Mrs G Green, BEd Heriot-Watt

Science:

Biology:
*Mrs P Nicoll, BEd Notre Dame

Mrs E Wilson, BSc Paisley
Mrs J Andrew, BSc, DipEd Dundee
Chemistry:
*Mrs T Munro, BSc Paisley, PGDipComp Jordanhill
Mr G L McLean, BSc, DipEd Stirling
Physics:
*Mr I Weir, BSc Paisley, MBA Strathclyde
Dr I Spencer, BSc, PhD Glasgow

Junior School Teaching Staff:
Mrs J Andrews, BA King Alfred's, MA(Ed) Open
Miss G Beggs, BEd Dundee
Mrs E M Black, DCE Jordanhill
Mrs M Blackie, DCE Jordanhill
Mrs M S Campbell DCE Jordanhill
Mrs Y Campbell, DCE Hamilton
Mrs E Corbett, BEd Jordanhill
Mrs I Evans, DCE Jordanhill, ALCM
Mrs J Flinders, BA London
Mrs C Gillies, MA Glasgow
Mrs G Henderson, BA Paisley
Mrs L Hunter, BA Glasgow Caledonian
Mr A MacKay, BEd Strathclyde
Mrs F MacFarlane, BEd Strathclyde
Mrs A Moore, DCE Craigie
Mrs K Paterson, DCE Jordanhill
Mrs S Robertson, DipEd Jordanhill
Mrs S Swinnerton, DCE Craigie

The School has an excellent academic record with a consistently high ranking in league tables and nearly all students go on to university. However, just as important as academic excellence are the personal attributes and qualities developed within the pupils. The ultimate goal is to produce self-confident, mature individuals, able to balance personal fulfilment with consideration for others and to play a full role in society. A distinguishing feature of St Columba's is the intimacy of the atmosphere whereby every teacher knows each pupil by name. St Columba's was awarded Investor in People status in 2007.

Facilities. The School buildings and sports facilities are located within a quarter of a mile radius of each other. Over the past decade major investments have resulted in St Columba's being extremely well equipped and resourced. A major extension to the Senior School is planned for the immediate future.

Sports facilities include: gym area for gymnastics and dance, large purpose-built sports hall including fitness suite, all-weather floodlit hockey/tennis ground, access to three rugby pitches and a large playing field used for athletics and cross-country running.

The School has a dedicated transport service and an after-school care facility.

Curriculum. St Columba's School follows the Scottish Curriculum at all stages. Junior School pupils are taught French, music and PE by specialist staff. Transitus (P7) is a transitional year with core curriculum taught by the class teacher and science, languages, art, music and PE delivered by specialist secondary teachers. Pupils in SIV are presented for Standard Grade/Intermediate 2 examinations followed by Higher Grade and Advanced Higher Grade examinations in SV and SVI.

Games. Rugby, hockey, tennis, athletics, badminton, gymnastics, swimming, volleyball, basketball, soccer, dance (girls), orienteering. Optional: netball, squash, cricket, golf, skiing/snowboarding, curling, yoga, weight-training.

Extra-Curricular. In both Junior and Senior Schools, the importance of extra-curricular activities is strongly emphasised. The School offers over 20 clubs including The Duke of Edinburgh's Award, debating, public speaking, sport, chess, school magazine, drama, music (choirs, orchestras, ensembles, pipe band, jazz band) etc. Individual tuition may be taken in many instruments plus Diction. Public performances and school shows are arranged on a regular basis.

From SIII upwards, The Duke of Edinburgh's Award Scheme attracts very large numbers with its emphasis on skills, service, sport and the expedition section at bronze, silver and gold level.

There is a very strong tradition of fund-raising for charity and community service within the School.

St Columba's has strong links with schools in Australia and Canada and has annual exchanges between students for periods of time.

Organisation. The school is broken up into four Houses for both pastoral and competitive purposes. Each house has a Head of House as well as pupil Captain and Vice-Captain. Career guidance is supported by ISCO.

Admission. Entry to St Columba's is by a combination of entry test, interview and, where applicable, a report from the applicant's previous school. An open week is held in November and entrance tests are held in January. The main entry points are Junior 1 and Transitus however pupils are taken in at other stages as places become available.

Fees per term (2008-2009). Nursery £730, Prep £973, J1 & J2 £2,073, J3 £2,267, J4 £2,397, J5 and J6 £2,527, Trans & SI £2,807, SII £2,897, SIII–SV £2,807, SVI £2,827.

A number of bursary places, ranging from 10–100% of fees, are available for new applicants entering Transitus (P7), SV to study Highers and SVI to study Advanced Highers.

Charitable status. St Columba's School is a Registered Charity, number SC012598. It exists to provide education for pupils.

St Dunstan's College

Stanstead Road London SE6 4TY
Tel: 020 8516 7200
Fax: 020 8516 7300
e-mail: hm@sdmail.org.uk
website: www.stdunstans.org.uk
intranet: www.sdonline.org.uk

Motto: '*Albam Exorna*'

The College was founded in the 15th century in the Parish of St Dunstan-in-the-East, part of the Tower Ward of the City of London. In 1888 the school was refounded in Catford, South East London. It became co-educational in 1995.

Governors:
Chairman of the Governors: ¶Sir Paul Judge, MA, MBA, LLD Hon

Deputy Chairman: P L Coling, Esq, FRICS

Mrs V Alexander
C R Berry, Esq
P Forbes, Esq
¶P W France, Esq
¶Very Revd John Hall, Dean of Westminster
Mrs L Kiernan, MA, DipEd
K L Marshall, Esq, RD, FICS, ACII
Revd B Olivier
Mrs C Price, MA, FRSA
¶F A Robinson, Esq, BSc, MPhil, Dip TS, FRTPI, CMILT
Mrs A Thompson
¶C L Watts, Esq

¶ *Old Dunstonian*

Clerk to the Governors and Bursar: Colonel N Wallace

Senior School Academic Staff:

***Headmistress*: Mrs J D Davies**, BSc

Deputy Head: S D Thorogood, BA
Head of Sixth Form: A W Johnston, MA

Head of Middle School: Mrs E G Emes, BSc, MSc
Head of Lower School: B Harrild, BA

* *Head of Department*

Miss C E Acker, BA
N M Adriano, BA
Mrs S E Algeo, MA, BA
Miss C Amery, BA, MA
D J Atkinson, BA
Mrs J Atkinson, GRSM, NCOS
R Austin, BSc
Mrs H S Baptiste, BSc
Miss G L Barlow, BSc
*J W Bennie, BSc
S G Blache, MA
*R R D Bodenham, BSc
Miss C L Brady, BA
J G Brown, BA
Miss C M Buchanan, BA
Ms M M Callaghan, BA
*A B Chadwick, BA
Mrs A E Chandler, BA, MA
R Cliff, BA, MA
R W Davies, BA
Miss H Eastmond, BEd
J P H Elmes, MA
M H Freakes, BSc
*P A Glavin, BA
*P Glyne-Thomas, BA
*P M Gobey, GRSM, ARCO CHM, ARCM
Mrs S Hearn, BSc
*W J Holroyd, BA, AKC
Miss K Jefferson, BA
Ms F C Kasper, MA
A J C Kinnear, BEd
*J P Kitchingman, BSc
*Mrs I Lambert, Leipzig Univ
R W Lea, BA, BEd
*C R Leeder, BSc
Miss T S Lessem, BA
Ms J J Lettman, CertEd
J A R Loudon, BA
Mrs D S Malpart, BSc
*B J P May, BA
Dr S M C McClellan, PhD
Ms D K Mitchell, MA
Ms G Z Moody, BSc
*Miss A L Morrell, BA
M J Muchall, BA
J M Newman, BA
Miss J O'Connor, BA
*C J Osborne, BEd
*M F Patel, BSc, PhD
*G S Phillips, BSc, MSc
*Mrs K A Plummer, BA
Ms J Reeves, BA
*Mrs V C Salin, MA
Ms K Sawyer, BA
*Miss F L Scarantino, BA
*A D Sharp, MA
Miss L Smith, BSc
N R Taylor
Miss E C Topp, MSc
Mrs J L van der Valk, BA
*Mrs A Vieira, BA, MSc
Miss D M Warren, BEng
D J Webb, BA
Mrs J V Williams, BEd
M Workman, BA

Headmistress's Personal Assistant: Mrs P Phillips
Marketing Officer: Miss J Goldsmith
Junior School Secretary/Registrar: Mrs R Scard
College Doctor: Dr D G Thompson

Buildings. The College is located in mainly Victorian buildings on a 15-acre site three minutes' walk from Catford and Catford Bridge railway stations. Facilities include an imposing Great Hall, a well-equipped Learning Resource Centre, a drama theatre, three state-of-the-art ICT suites and newly-refurbished chemistry laboratories. To complement extensive playing fields on site, St Dunstan's has a sports hall, fully-equipped gym, floodlit netball/tennis courts, rugby fives courts and an indoor swimming pool, recently modernised to a very high standard.

Organisation and Curriculum. The College educates boys and girls from the ages of 3 to 18. The Junior School comprises a nursery class for 20 children (3+), a Pre-Prep Department for 100 children aged 4–7 and a Prep Department of 175 children aged 7–11.

In the Junior School great emphasis is placed on letting children learn in a friendly caring and stimulating environment. Pupils study a broad curriculum and participate in a wide variety of extra-curricular activities. The Head of the Junior School is a member of IAPS (*see entry in IAPS section*).

The Senior School, with a total of 620 pupils, comprises a Lower School (Years 7–9), a Middle School (Years 10 and 11) and a Sixth Form. A considerable choice of subjects is on offer – English, French, German, Spanish, Italian, Latin, Classical Civilisation, History, Geography, Religious Studies, Economics, Business Studies, Mathematics, Physics, Chemistry, Biology, DT, ICT, Physical Education, Music, Art & Design, Drama and Personal, Social and Health Education (PHSE).

The College is also a registered test centre for the European Computer Driving Licence and all pupils are expected to gain their licence while in the Lower or Middle School.

In the Sixth Form students can choose whether to study for AS/A2 Levels or for the International Baccalaureate Diploma. The College received accreditation from the IBO in 2004 and the first cohort of students began studying for the Diploma in September 2005. Virtually all students proceed to Higher Education.

The College is a vibrant community with a friendly atmosphere. It values cultural diversity and has a reputation for excellent pastoral care.

Pupils have the opportunity to join a wide range of extra-curricular activities to develop their special interests and personal strengths, for example:

- A thriving Combined Cadet Force
- The Duke of Edinburgh's Award Scheme – among London schools, the College has very strong numbers of pupils involved at all Award levels
- Community service – every year the College supports a range of British and overseas charities and local organisations
- The Armstrong Society (Science)
- Modern Languages Society
- Debating Society
- Christian Forum
- Literary Society
- Puzzle Club
- Drama Club
- Chess Club
- Electronic Workshop

Music. Pupils from all parts of the school participate in a variety of choirs, orchestras and instrumental groups and music clubs.

Sport. The chief sports are cricket, rugby, soccer, netball, hockey, rounders and swimming. Students also have opportunities to take part in cross-country running, fives, tennis, basketball, badminton, sailing, golf and fitness training.

Entrance. The main entrance points are at the age of 3, 4, 7, 11, 13 or 16. Admission to the College is competitive in all years with the exception of the Nursery, and depends on academic ability and the demonstration of potential. At 11+ and 13+ an Entrance Examination is held annually in January.

Entrance Scholarships. Scholarships are offered for academic merit and excellence in Music, Sports, Art and Design and Drama. A small number of means-tested bursaries are available.

Fees per term (2008-2009). The consolidated fees (including lunch) are: Nursery £2,306; Junior School £2,936–£3,838; Senior School £4,058.

Old Dunstonian Association. The ODA has over 3,700 members. All pupils subscribe to the ODA while at school and automatically become life members when they leave.

St Dunstan's College Family Society. This parent-run fund-raising body works to support the educational, social and extra-curricular activities of the school for the benefit of all pupils. All parents are automatically members of the Family Society.

Charitable status. St Dunstan's College is a Registered Charity, number 1094290.

St Edmund's College
and St Hugh's School

Old Hall Green Ware Herts SG11 1DS
Tel: 01920 821504
Fax: 01920 823011
e-mail: admissions@stedmundscollege.org
website: www.stedmundscollege.org

Motto: '*Avita pro Fide*'

Located on a beautiful 400 acre site in the East Hertfordshire countryside, St Edmund's College is an Independent, fully co-educational, day and boarding school for pupils aged 3 to 18 (boarding from 11 years). As England's oldest Catholic School, founded in 1568, St Edmund's welcomes not only Catholics, but students from all faiths and denominations, who appreciate the values of a Catholic education.

Situated between London and Cambridge, the College is easily accessible by road and rail and is conveniently located near to London's Stansted Airport. There is an extensive bus service for students with routes spanning North London, Enfield, Essex and most of Hertfordshire.

The College's wonderful Catholic heritage continues to provide inspiration to its 800 pupils today, as it delivers its main objective, unchanged for over 400 years; to foster the spiritual, intellectual, physical and emotional development of every person in its community.

Patron and President: Cardinal Cormac Murphy-O'Connor, STL, PhL

Governors:
Chairman: J Gillham, BA
Deputy Chairman: P J Mitton, MSc
The Very Revd Canon M Brockie, JCL
The Revd Monsignor J P Curry, STB
D B A Hirst, FCA, KSG, KGCHS, FCA, JP
M Hutchison, FCA
Mrs M Lynch, BSc, ARCS, NPQH
Dr F MacIntosh, MA, MRCP, MFPM
Mrs P Newton, BSc, DipArch, FFB, RIBA, MBAE, DHS
N Ransley, MA, MEd
Sister J Sinclair, BSc, SHCJ
Revd Dr J Sweeney, CP, BD, BA, Mth, PhD, MA

Director of Finance & Administration and Clerk to the Governors: B A Tomlinson, BA, ACMA

***Headmaster*: C P Long**, BA

Deputy Head & Registrar: Mrs J Neal, BA
Assistant Head (*Community Life*): A D Petty, BA, FRSA
Assistant Head (*Director of Studies*): A Celano, BSc, MEd
Chaplain: The Revd M P A Pinot de Moira
Head of Sixth Form: Mrs M McCann, BA (*English*)

* *Head of Department*
† *Housemaster/Head of House*

Mrs J Ball, CertEd (*†Pole, *Physical Education*)
Mrs L Blackburn, BA (*International Department*)
C R J Breese BA, MPhil (*Media Studies, English*)
Mrs G A Burrows, BA (*Mathematics*)
N Cattermole, BEd (*Physical Education*)
Miss E Cobb BSc (*Sports Studies, Physical Education*)
D R Davies, BSc (**Business Studies*)
Mrs P Davies, CertEd (*†Poynter, Religious Education*)
Mrs A De Bell (*Drama*)
A A Drew, BSc, CPhys, FRAS, FRSM (*Physics*)
Miss A Dunning, BA (*Modern Foreign Languages*)
H Evans, BSc (**Science*)
Mrs E Franco, MA (*Modern Foreign Languages*)
K Fry, BSc, MSc (**ICT*)
D A Gallie, KM, BEd (*†Challoner, *Religious Education, Head of Boarding, College Archivist, Custodian Douay Museum*)
Mrs A Goring, CertEd (*English*)
Mrs S Gribbin, BA (*Librarian*)
Dr R G Hacksley, BA, PhD (*Coordinator for Gifted & Talented*)
K Hall, MA (*Biology, Examinations Officer*)
Miss K M Hallgate, BSc (*Geography*)
J Hayes, MA (*English*)
J Hounsell, BSc, BCA, DipT (*Mathematics*)
N D Howard, BA, LTCL, FRCO (*Music*)
Miss C Hugo, CertEd, Dip RSA (*Director, International Department*)
Mrs M Inglessis, BA, MA (*Psychology*)
Miss S Jackson, BA (*History, Careers Coordinator*)
Mrs V L Jefferies, BA, MA, MA (**Languages*)
Mrs E Johnstone, BA (*Languages*)
Mrs M T King, BEd, CertEd (**Art, Design & Technology, Head of Girls' Boarding*)
G D Lewis, BA (*Physical Education*)
Mrs R M Lewis, BA (**Design & Technology PSHE Coordinator*)
R M Lewis, BEd (*Geography*)
Mrs S Miller, CertEd, DipSpLD (*Special Needs Coordinator*)
S Mohana Esq, MSc, BEd (*Mathematics*)
R Moore, MA (**English*)
Mrs J Morley, BA, HHD (*Art, Design &Technology*)
J W Morley, BA (**Geography, Activities Coordinator*)
A L Moss, BEd, CertEd (*†Douglass, Chemistry*)
Miss J Parker, BSc (*Biology*)
Miss P M Peirce, BD, AKC (*Religious Education*)
Miss L Robb, BA (*Business Studies, ICT*)
Mrs K Salter-Kay, GTCL, LTCL, ALCM (*Director of Music*)
K Sarpong, BSc, MSc (**Chemistry*)
A Simmonds, BA, MA (*English*)
Miss M C Simon (*Languages*)
A J Sleight, BEd, CPhys, MInstP (**Physics*)
J R Stypinski, BA (**History*)
Mrs S Theroulde-O'Neill, MA (*Modern Foreign Languages*)
J Vaughan-Shaw, BA (*Classics*)
A Watson, BA (*Biology*)
G West, BSc (*†Talbot, Mathematics*)
Mrs R A K West, BEd (**Mathematics*)
Mrs C Wilkin, BSc (*Mathematics*)

Learning Support Assistants:
Mrs J Gentle
Mrs J Rasmussen

St Hugh's:
Head: Mrs J Hart, BEd, MSc, Adv Dip RE
Director of Studies: Mrs S E Mills, BEd
Director of Music: Dr F J F McLauchlan, MA, PhD

Miss R Bibby, BA
Miss A Blakey, BA
Mrs E Brooks, DipCE, AdvDipEd
Miss E Docherty, BA
G Duddy, BEd
Miss H Dutton, BA
Mrs Y Elliott, BA
G Goodfellow, BA
C M Jenkinson, BEd
Miss C Lane, BA Ed
Mrs A Loran, BA
Mrs C Mitton, BEd
Ms S O'Callaghan, BEd
Mrs D Steel
Mrs P Wheldal, CertEd

Library: Mrs S Gribbin, BA
Information Technology Manager: S Winfield

Admission. Pupils are mainly admitted at the ages of 3, 5, 7, 11, and 16, although entry may be considered at other ages if there are spaces available.

Scholarships and Bursaries. (*see Scholarship Entries section*). The College offers Academic, Art, Sport, Music and All-Rounder Scholarships to the value of a maximum of 50% of the fees. Applications should be made to the Headmaster. Means-tested Bursaries are also available at 11+, of up to 100% of fees.

Fees per term (2008-2009). Day Pupils: £2,810–£4,450; Weekly Boarders: £5,730–£6,525; Full Boarders: £6,315–£7,220; all depending on age of the pupil. There are reductions for families of HM Forces and for siblings.

Curriculum. All pupils follow the National Curriculum. At the end of NC Year 11, pupils take GCSE examinations in all courses that they have followed, usually more than is required by the National Curriculum.

In Rhetoric (Sixth Form) students will study four AS Levels in the Lower Sixth and 3 or 4 A2s in the Upper Sixth. Tuition is provided for entry to Oxford, Cambridge and other Universities.

Religious Instruction. St Edmund's is a College for all those who appreciate the values of a Catholic Education. All students receive instruction in Christian doctrine and practice from lay teachers. GCSE Religious Studies, AS and A2 Theology and the Catholic Teaching on Bioethics Diploma are entered. Importance is attached to the liturgical life of the College and the practical expression of faith. All faiths and denominations are welcomed.

Sport and Extra-Curricular Activities. Great importance is attached to sport and physical education throughout the College. All pupils are required to participate in a variety of sports on two afternoons a week. The major sports for boys are football, rugby, cricket and athletics, while for girls they are hockey, netball, rounders and athletics. The other sports available are cross-country, tennis, swimming, basketball, badminton, volleyball and squash. A floodlit artificial pitch, large sports hall, indoor swimming pool, tennis and squash courts, fitness room, together with 400 acres of grounds provide excellent facilities.

There are many extra-curricular activities including regular concerts and drama productions. The CCF (RAF and Army sections), Community Service and The Duke of Edinburgh's Award Scheme play a prominent part in developing a self-reliant and confident individual. Time is also set apart for the many clubs and social activities that take place.

Careers. There is a Careers teacher and Careers Library. The College is a member of the Independent Schools Careers Organisation. Careers advice is available to pupils from the age of 13. There are regular careers lectures and visits to industry and Universities. Work experience is organised for the Lower Sixth.

St Hugh's School, the Prep School, is situated on the same estate. It consists of a Nursery, Infants and Junior School for pupils from 3 to 11, which feeds into the Senior School at 11. The pupils are able to make use of many of the amenities of the Senior School such as the Refectory, Chapel, Swimming Pool and Sports Hall. There is no boarding at St Hugh's.

Charitable status. St Edmund's College, Ware is a Registered Charity, number 311073. It aims to provide a Catholic Education for students of all faiths between the ages of 3 and 18.

St Edmund's School

Canterbury

Canterbury Kent CT2 8HU
Tel: 01227 475600
Fax: 01227 471083
e-mail: info@stedmunds.org.uk
website: www.stedmunds.org.uk

Motto: '*Fungar Vice Cotis*'

The School, which is named after the great scholar-saint, St Edmund, Archbishop of Canterbury 1234–1240, was founded in 1749 and was transferred from London in 1855, mainly through the munificence of the Revd Dr Samuel Warneford, to its present 60 acre site on an out-lying spur of the Downs, a mile from Canterbury. It commands a marvellous view of the Cathedral and the city of Canterbury, and is only 5 miles distant from the sea. The 1855 main building, constructed of Kentish ragstone, is praised in Pevsner's *The Buildings of England*. Many other buildings have been added and there has been considerable development in recent years, including a new Junior School in 1998 and a new Music School in 2005.

The school is owned by St Edmund's School Canterbury, a charitable company limited by guarantee, registered in England and Wales.

Patron: The Lord Archbishop of Canterbury

Governors:
Chairman: M C W Terry, Esq, FCA
P F Atkins, Esq, ACIB
J P W Coleman, Esq
Dr P Eichorn, MD
Mrs M Griffin, FRSA, PhD
The Rev N Genders
Miss P Holmes, BA, PGCME, MSc
The Revd Canon Christopher Irvine
Mrs M L Lacamp, CertEd London, DipRSA
N Lewis, Esq, FCA, ACIB
Mrs P Stewart, FRSA
Councillor P A Todd
Col P R M Whittington, FCMI
Mrs A A Williamson, JP, BSc, FRSA (*Vice-Chairman*)

***Headmaster*: Mr Jeremy Gladwin**, BSc Dunelm

Master of the Junior School: Mr R G Bacon, BA Dunelm, PGCE

Head of Pre-Prep School: Mrs J Frampton-Fell, BA Hons Kent

Chaplain: The Revd Dr I A Terry, PhD MA St Mary's Twickenham, BA Dunelm, PGCE

Head of Finance and Estates: Mrs M T Stannard, FCA

Deputy Head: Mr D E Knight, BA Hons Leeds

Assistant Deputy Head & Director of Studies: Mrs J E Mander, BSc Hons Nottingham, FEDA

Assistant Staff:

1 *Department serving both Senior & Junior Schools*
* *Head of Department*
† *Housemaster/Houseparent*

1 *Art*:
Mrs A A Slater-Williams, BA Hons Glasgow School of Art, PGCE
Miss Z J Fountain, BA Hons Staffs
Mr N J Hodge, BTec National Diploma Blackburn College, BA Hons Sheffield Hallam, PGCE
Miss S C Passmore, MA Birmingham

Business Studies:
Mr R N Comfort, BSc Hons Wales (†Owen*)

Classics:
*Mr I F Thompson, MA Cantab, LRAM

Curriculum Support:
Mrs S Williams, BA Hons Nottingham, RSA DipSpLD, DipTEFL

Drama and Theatre Studies:
Mr M Sell, NCDT Acc Diploma ALRA, PGCE (*Director*)
Miss E Sears, BA Hons Central School, PGCE (*Head of GCSE*)

1 *English*:
*Mr J P Dagley, MA Oxon, MA Kent
Mr M J Brewer, BA Hons Christ Church, PGCE
Mr I F Narburgh, MA Edinburgh
Mrs M G Robinson, MA Kent, PGCE
Miss E Sears, BA Hons Central School, PGCE
Mrs J C Wilkinson, MEd Bristol

EAL:
Ms H E Theakston, TESOL Trinity College

Film Studies:
*Mrs M G Robinson, MA Kent, PGCE
Miss E Sears, BA Hons Central School, PGCE

Geography:
*Mr I P Urey, BA Hons Nottingham, MSc Imperial College
Mr T J Sheahan, BEd Hons Kent, CertEd

History:
*Mr R A Robinson, BA Hons
Mr D E Knight, BA Hons Leeds

[1]*ICT Coordinator*:
Mrs J J Mitchard, BSc Hons London

[1]*Mathematics*:
*Mrs J E Mander, BSc Hons Nottingham, Cert EdMan
Mr C D Barnard, BEd London
Mr A W J Middleton, BA Hons Kent
Mr L A Millard, BSc Hons Loughborough
Mrs J J Mitchard, BSc Hons London
Mrs A J Potter, BA Hons York, PGCE

Modern Languages and European Studies:
*Mr T J Barnett, BA Hons Southampton
Mrs D F Micheloud, LL Fribourg, DipMG
Mrs S C Newton, BA Hons Nottingham, PGCE
Ms S Thelliez, FLE Littoral, PGCE
Mr I F Thompson, MA Cantab, LRAM

[1]*Music*:
*Mr C McDade, BA Hons Huddersfield, PGCE Bath, LTCL
Dr A R Braddy, PhD Goldsmiths, MA City, BA Hons, ABSM (*Head of Strings, †Warneford*)
Mr S J Payne, BA Hons, MA, ARCM, LTCL, ARCO (*Head of Academic Music*)
Mr R Underwood, BA Hons Middlesex (*Head of Percussion and Music Technology*)

Visiting Music Staff:
Mr K Abbott, Dip RCM (*French Horn*)
Mr S Bailey, MMus (*Piano*)
Mrs H Cleobury, ARCM (*Piano*)
Mr A Cunningham (*Clarinet/Saxophone*)
Dr A Delacour, PhD, BMus Hons (*Bass Guitar*)
Miss E de la Porte, ARCM, LRSM (*Piano*)
Ms R. Davies (*Violin*)
Miss S Desbruslais, BA Hons, LRAM (*Flute*)
Dr D A Flood, MA, FRCOChM, Hon FGCM (*Piano*)
Ms S Geering, LLB, BMus (*Piano*)
Mr R Hall, MAMus (*Piano*)
Mr J Hazelby (*Bass & Electric Guitar*)
Mrs J Jaggard, AGSM, Dip NCOS (*Oboe*)
Mrs K Lewis, BA, ARCM (*Voice*)
Mr G Mann, BA Hons (*Percussion*)
Miss M Morley, BA Hons, DipOrchStudies (*Harp*)
Miss R A Rathbone, BA Hons, LRAM (*Flute*)
Mr C Reid, BA, Cert AdvSt RAM (*Trombone*)
Mr M Rogers, ARAM, LRAM (*Violin*)
Mrs K Shave, ARAM, LRAM (*Violin*)
Mr P Smith, PGCE (*Recorder*)
Mrs K Upton, LRAM, ARCM (*Trumpet*)
Miss J Vohralik, MA, ARCM (*Cello*)
Ms H Ward, BA, LTCL, ALCM (*Piano*)
Mrs D Wassell, GRSM, ARCM, CertEd, PGCE (*Violin*)
Mr S J Wassell, ARCM, LTCL, CertEd (*Low Brass*)
Ms F Whiteley, LRAM (*Violin*)
Mr N Wright, GMus Hons, RNCM, FRCO (*Piano*)
Mrs S Wyver, MA (*Bassoon*)

[1]*Physical Education*:
*Mrs J C Wilkinson, MEd Bristol
Miss T M Cliff, CertEd Sussex (*†Watson*)
Mr A R Jones, BSc Sheffield
Mr J R Maylam
Mr L Millard, BSc Hons Loughborough
Mr M J Walker (*Lent term only*)

Psychology:
*Dr C F Sotillo, MA, PhD Edinburgh

[1]*Religious Studies*:
*Mr M J Brewer, BA Hons Christ Church, PGCE
The Revd Dr I A Terry, PhD MA St Mary's Twickenham, BA Dunelm, PGCE

[1]*Science*:
*Dr L J Ashby, BSc, PhD London
Miss R E Hummerstone, BSc Hons Surrey (*KS3 Coordinator*)

Biology:
*Mrs K M E Barnard, BEd London, MISTC
Mr J M Clapp, BSc Hons, MA Reading
Mr C J Mount, BA Hons, MSc Cantab, PGCE

Chemistry:
*Dr L J Ashby, BSc, PhD London
Mrs K M E Barnard, BEd London, MISTC
Mr P A Bold, BSc Kent, PGCE
Mr P I O'Connor, BSc Kent, MA York
Mr D G Whitehouse, BSc Nottingham

Physics:
Dr J C Horn, BSc, PhD Leeds (†Wagner*)
Miss R E Hummerstone, BSc Hons Surrey
Mr D G Whitehouse, BSc Hons Nottingham

[1]*Technology (Design, Graphics, Food)*:
*Ms K Lloyd, MSc Christ Church
Mr P Gadenne, MCSD
Mr S R Lund, CertEd Loughborough

Additional Responsibilities:
Careers Adviser: Ms K Lloyd, MSc Christ Church
Public Examinations Officer: Mr D G Whitehouse, BSc Nottingham
Hall Manager: Mr M G S Hawkins, MA, MSc Cantab
Hall Technical Director: Mr G N Hawkins, BSc London, ARCS
Higher Education Adviser: Mr J P Dagley, MA Oxon
Officer Commanding CCF: Lt Col C D Barnard, BEd London
President of Common Room: Mr T J Barnett, BA Hons Southampton
President of Games: Mr D E Knight, BA Hons Leeds

Junior School

Second Master: Mr R A Austen, BEd Hons Bulmershe (*Mathematics*)
Senior Master: Mr T Hooley, MA Cantab (**Latin, English, Mathematics*)
Director of Studies: Mrs E A Swallow, MA, BEd Dunelm (*Form 7*)
Head of Lower School: Mrs L V Richardson, BA QTS Hons (*Form 5*)

Preparatory:
Mrs C Barnes, BEd Hons London (*Lower School Curriculum Support*)
Mrs A Buckingham, BA Natal (*Form 4*)
Mr S Buckingham, BEd Natal (*Games*)
Mrs J Burden, BA Ed Christ Church (*Form 6, Science*)
Mrs R H Kroiter, BA Hons Liverpool, DipTEFL (*EFL, French, Mathematics*)
Mr J Lambert, BA Hons Liverpool, PGCE, ATCL (**Junior School Music*)
Mrs C M Lawrence, BA Christ Church (**English*)
Mrs C McCabe, BA Bedford (*PE*)
Mrs H Millard, BSc Loughborough, PGCE (*Girls' Games*)
Mr D G C Parry, BA Hons London (*French, Latin*)
Mr T J Pearce, ACertCM Christ Church (**Geography, Religious Studies*)
Mr C Penn (*Head of Boys' Games, PE, †School House*)

Mr M Reames, BSc Virginia, MA, PPTL (**Mathematics*)
Mrs L Relf, BA Ed Hons Exeter (**PE and Girls' Games*)
Mr E J Southey, CertEd Dartford (**History*)
Mrs H R Surridge, BA Hons Kent (*Form 4*)
Mrs H M Thompson, BEd Birmingham (*Form 3*)
Mrs J Vafidis, BEd Christ Church, CETHIC (*Curriculum Support*)
Mr M G B Walters, BA Hons London (**French*)
Mrs M Yearsley, BA Hons (*Form 5*)

Master of Choristers:
Dr D A Flood, MA Oxon, FRCO ChM (*Cathedral Organist*)

Pre-Prep School

Abingdon House:
Mrs L Bradley (*Bumble Bees*)
Mrs C Futcher, BMus, PGCE (*Performing Arts*)
Mrs R George, NNEB (*Ladybirds*)
Mrs A Gibson, CertEd (*Dragonflies*)
Mrs A J Johnson, BEd Leeds (*Honey Bees*)
Mrs H Millard (*Grasshoppers*)
Mrs A Pearce, CertEd (*Grasshoppers*)

Teaching Assistants:
Miss E Day (*Ladybirds*)
Mrs S Geeves (*Bumble Bees*)
Mrs C Lawlor (*Honey Bees*)
Mrs M Stanley (*Ladybirds*)
Mrs V Wisker (*Grasshoppers*)
Miss A Webster (*Dragonflies*)

CCF: SSI M Ferguson
Librarian: Mrs L Humphreys
Medical Officer: Dr G. Manson
Headmaster's PA: Ms E Ottaway
Junior School Master's Secretary: Mrs Y King

From its inception St Edmund's has maintained the highest in educational standards for all its pupils and, to this day, it retains its rooted traditions of purposeful endeavour and a high quality of caring. It has been able to build continuously on its Christian foundation whilst developing into an exciting but well-ordered school of some 560 boys and girls.

The school enjoys a commanding site at the top of St Thomas' Hill overlooking the city and cathedral of Canterbury and adjoining the University of Kent. Behind its magnificent facade there lies a happy and busy boarding and day community which is committed to excellence in all that it undertakes, and which is large enough to provide a rich variety of opportunities, yet small enough to maintain the strong family ethos for which it has become renowned. The gifted academic, the talented artist, the promising musician, the devotee of sport, as well as those who are still identifying their talents, all find support and skilled teaching to cultivate their aptitudes to the fullest extent. Pupils are very much encouraged to develop their individuality and to do so in an atmosphere of civilised tolerance towards others.

Whilst the school is modern in facilities and forward looking in its curriculum, great stress is laid on such traditional virtues as courtesy, honesty, self-discipline and smartness of dress.

Organisation. The junior and senior schools are very closely integrated, sharing many of the same facilities, and affording continuity of education throughout the age range of 3 to 18. The Junior School, which educates the choristers of Canterbury Cathedral, has about 35 boarding and weekly boarding boys and girls, 130 day boys and 90 day girls. The Senior School (13 years and upwards) contains about 45 boarding boys, 160 day boys, 35 boarding girls and 90 day girls.

The Senior School is divided into four Houses: Baker, Wagner, Warneford and Watson, the respective Housemasters each being assisted by a team of Deputies and Tutors.

The Chapel. All pupils attend at least two of the morning services a week. There is a variety of Sunday services, attendance at most of which is voluntary. Parents are always welcome, especially to the regular family communions. Confirmation is conducted annually by the Archbishop of Canterbury (as Patron of the School) or by the Bishop of Dover acting on his behalf; the candidates are prepared by the School Chaplain. The school carol service is held in Canterbury Cathedral, by kind permission of the Dean and Chapter.

Academic Organisation. In the Junior School, including the Pre-Preparatory School, the curriculum provides a firm foundation in all academic subjects in line with the National Curriculum requirements. French and Latin are also taught in the Junior School. All pupils are prepared for entrance to senior school(s) with the most able given the opportunity for Senior School Scholarships.

In the first year of the Senior School (Year 9) pupils follow a core curriculum in English, Mathematics, French, Physics, Chemistry, Biology, History, Geography, Art, Music, Information Technology, Religious Education, PSHE, Physical Education, and Technology. Drama and Latin are options.

GCSE core subjects are: English, English Literature, French, Mathematics and dual award Sciences. Options include Latin, Spanish, History, Geography, Art (Ceramics), Art (Drawing and Painting), Technology: Resistant Materials, Food Technology, Graphic Products, ICT, Music, Drama and Religious Studies.

The following subjects are offered for AS/A2 Level examinations: Art and Design, Biology, Business Studies, Ceramics, Chemistry, Design and Technology, English Literature, Film Studies, French, German, Geography, History, Mathematics and Further Mathematics, Music, Music Technology, PE, Photography, Physics, Psychology and Theatre Studies.

Pupils in the Lower Sixth are expected to study four AS Levels, most then proceeding to three A2 subjects in the Upper Sixth. A non-examined General Studies programme is an integral part of the Sixth Form curriculum.

Comprehensive reports are sent regularly throughout the school year. A system of interim reports, as well as regular parents' meetings, ensures close communication with parents.

Buildings and Facilities. Over the past twenty years there have been extensive additions to and modernisation of the school's buildings and facilities: a new Junior School building, a new Sixth Form Centre, the main hall with tiered auditorium and exhibition area, the splendid sports hall, the technology department, additional classrooms and major extensions to the science, art, information technology, music, and pre-prep departments, as well as the conversion of all Senior School boarding accommodation to study-bedrooms and refurbishment of Junior boarding premises. A new music school opened in 2005.

Careers and Higher Education. The school is affiliated to the Independent Schools Careers Organisation and the Careers Research and Advisory Centre. Pupils have the opportunity to undergo careers aptitude testing in the GCSE year, and all pupils are assisted in finding a placement for a week or more of work experience in the GCSE year. The careers and higher education staff give all possible help in the finding of suitable careers and in selecting appropriate universities and colleges of further education. Most A Level candidates go on to degree courses after leaving school; others join Art or Music colleges.

Music. There is a continuous programme of music tuition from the age of 3. A very high standard of music is maintained and there are numerous ensembles, both large and small. 60% of pupils learn at least one instrument. Tuition is given in piano, organ and all orchestral instruments. Parents are invited to join the flourishing choral society. Music scholars benefit from an exciting programme of seminars and London concerts (of which full details may be obtained from the Director of Music). A number of pupils attend conservatoires on a Saturday morning.

Sport. Association football, hockey, cricket, athletics, tennis, squash and (for girls) netball and rounders are the principal sports but there are opportunities for many other forms of exercise, including cross-country running, golf, badminton, basketball, volleyball, swimming, fencing, weight training and sailing. The large playing fields adjoin the school buildings. There is an open-air heated swimming pool. The sports hall is well-equipped and includes a multi-gym room. There are eight tennis courts (both hard and grass), a small golf course and a rifle range. The school has access to the climbing wall, the gym and the astroturf pitches at the University of Kent.

Activities. For those in the first four years of Senior School one afternoon a week is given over specifically to a broad range of activities. A number involve helping the local community, while other pupils learn new skills, eg bridge, golf, fencing, electronics, Japanese, yoga, radio work or photography. Over 80 different activities have been offered during the last four years.

In the second year all Senior School pupils join the Combined Cadet Force, a highly successful unit commanded by a member of the teaching staff and administered by an ex-soldier. There is an annual camp in the summer and an adventurous training camp at Easter, attendance at which is voluntary. Cadets may remain in the CCF for the duration of their school career if they wish, and are encouraged to do so if contemplating a career in the armed forces.

Pupils may also participate in The Duke of Edinburgh's Award Scheme and the British Association of Young Scientists. There are regular ski and field trips, choir and music tours, sports tours and many other one-off trips.

In Junior School, too, there is a diverse range of extra-curricular activities, many of which draw on the school's excellent facilities for sport, music and drama. As part of the adventurous training programme there is an annual adventure course in the Hebrides and a Year 8 outdoor activities week in the South of France.

Health. The school Medical Centre is staffed by state registered nurses at all times. The health of the boys and girls of both Junior and Senior Schools is supervised by a senior local general practitioner under the NHS. A counselling service is available.

Junior School. The Master of the Junior School is a member of IAPS. The Junior School is also in membership of CSA (Choir Schools' Association) and prepares boys and girls for the Senior School. Passage into the Senior School is determined by performance over the two preceding years. The Junior School is self-contained and has its own classrooms, boarding premises, playing fields, etc. Applications for admission should be addressed to The Master of the Junior School. (*See entry in IAPS section.*)

Choristers. The 27 choristers of Canterbury Cathedral are all members of the Junior School. They board in the Choir House (in the Cathedral Precincts) in the care of Houseparents appointed by the school. All their choral training is undertaken in the Cathedral by the Organist; the remainder of their education takes place at St Edmund's. Admission is by voice trial and academic test. Enquiries should be addressed to the Master of the Junior School or to the Cathedral Organist.

Admission to Senior School. Entry at 13 from preparatory schools is through the Common Entrance Examination. Candidates from other schools will be tested appropriately or may be accepted on the basis of school reports. There is also a large entry of pupils into the Sixth Form, usually on the basis of interview and GCSE grade estimates from their present school.

Admission to Junior School. Entry at any age from 3–12. Candidates aged 8 and above will sit entrance tests and all prospective pupils will be interviewed or attend an assessment day.

Chorister Admission. St Edmund's is the school of the Canterbury Cathedral choristers. For details of the voice trials please contact the Master's Secretary.

Fees per term (2008-2009). Senior School: Boarders £8,019; Day pupils £5,178.

Junior School: Boarders £5,606, Weekly Boarders £5,108, Choristers £5,514, Day pupils £3,947. Pre-Prep: £2,419–£2,796, Nursery £1,794 (mornings only £1,025).

Music fees: £195 (10 lessons). Extras have been kept to the minimum.

Entrance Scholarships. (*see Scholarship Entries section*). The school offers various awards at 11+, 13+ and 16+ each year. Academic, Music, Art, Drama and Sport scholarships of up to half fees are offered. Full details are available from the School Secretary.

Bursaries and Fee Concessions. Bursaries and fee concessions are available to the sons and daughters of clergymen serving the Anglican Communion, members of the armed forces and diplomatic personnel; third child discount. The School was originally founded to provide a free education for the fatherless sons of the clergy of the Church of England and the Church in Wales and still accepts applications from boys and girls for Foundationer status. Applications should be made to the Headmaster.

The St Edmund's Society (for former pupils). *Secretary*: Mr M C Harvey.

Charitable status. St Edmund's School Canterbury is a Registered Charity, number 1056382. It exists to educate the children in its care.

St Edward's, Oxford

Oxford OX2 7NN
Tel: Warden: 01865 319323
Bursar: 01865 319321
Registrar: 01865 319200
Fax: 01865 319242
e-mail: wardensec@stedwards.oxon.sch.uk
website: www.stedwards.oxon.sch.uk

St Edward's, Oxford was founded in 1863 by the Revd Thomas Chamberlain. Originally the School buildings were in New Inn Hall Street, Oxford. In 1873 it was removed to Summertown, and the present School was built by the Revd A B Simeon.

Motto: '*Pietas Parentum*'

Visitor:
The Rt Revd The Lord Bishop of Oxford

Governing Body:
M P Stanfield, Esq (*Chairman*)
H W Bolland, Esq, BA
Mrs T Camilleri, MA
G Fenton, Esq
E J H Gould, Esq, MA
The Revd R G Griffith-Jones, MA
M G Hay, Esq, BA, PhD, MBA
Mrs A Holloway, BM, MRCGP
C I M Jones, Esq, MA, FRSA
Kenneth MacRitchie, Esq, MA, BD, LLB
P M Oppenheimer, Esq, MA
Mrs J M Peach, MA, DPhil
R G P Pillai, MB BS, FRCS
Sir Bob Reid
D A Roe, Esq, DLitt, MA, PhD
Mrs K A Ross, BA

***Warden*: Andrew F Trotman**, MA

Sub-Warden: Thomas A James, BSc, MSc

Director of Studies: Sarah J Kerr-Dineen, MA

Senior Tutor: Ian R M Rowley, MA, ALCM

Chaplain: Revd E Charles Kerr, MA, MTh

Director of Sports and Activities: Keith J Shindler, MA, MSc

Director of Cultural Activities: Anthony J Kerr-Dineen, MA

Assistant Teachers:

Vaughan Abigail, BA
Laura K Allen, BSc
Simon R Arnold, BA
Andrew Ashworth-Jones, BSc
James Askew, BA, MA
Lucy R D Baddeley, MA
Julian V Baker, BSc
Charles F Baggs, BSc
John A Bament, BA
K Naveed D Barakzai, BSc
Philip N Barras, MA
O Stuart Bartholomew, MAJames L Boyd, BA
Phoebe Brookes, BA, MA
Susan F Buchan, BA, MEng
Mark J Burkitt, BSc, PhD
Revd Ruth KF Bushyager, MSci, BA
Henry Chitsenga, BSc
Jason E Clapham, MA, MSc
Paul W Clarke, Dip LAMDA
Tom H G Copeland, BSc
Florence M C Corran, BA, MPhil
Neville C Creed, MA
R Jane Crudass, BSc
Andrew J Dalgleish, BSc, MSc
Gabriele Damiani, BMus, ARCO
Rebecca L Davies, BA
Andrew J Davis, BSc, PhD, FRGS
Charmian M Downer, BA, RSADipSpLD
Rebecca E Drury, BSc
Jesse R Elzinga, BA, MSt
Mercedes Fages Agudo, BA
Lewis Faulkner, BA
David Finamore, BSc
Maria Fleming, MMath
Robert E Fletcher, BA, MA, MLitt
Laura S Gallacher, BA
Sheila D Greaves, DMS, DipSpLD
Mark J Hanslip, BEd
Leonie Hillier, BA
A Patricia Hinde, BEd, MA
Tova Holmes, BFA
Richard W J Howitt, BSc
Robert McA Hughes, BMus, LTCL
Edmund T Hunt, BA, MA
Nicola F Hunter, BA
Huw J Jones, MSc
Kirsty R Jones, BA
Jonathan T Lambe, BA
Margaret Lloyd, BSc
Peter Lloyd-Jones, DipFA
Linda A Lyne, MA
Lucy Maycock, BA, DipRADA
Jonathan W J Mitchell, MA
David S Moore, BSc, PhD, AKC, CChem, MRSC
Garrett E Nagle, MA, DPhil
Einar M Olive, BSc
Tabatha J Palmer, BA
Matthew Parker, MA, MSc
David J C Perkins, BA, MA, PhD
Nicola J S Perkins, BSc
Gareth R Playfair, MA
Christopher T Pollitt, BA
Ben J Pyper, DipAD
Oliver L Richards, MA
Peter J B Rudge, BA, BA
Charlotte S Schofield, MA
Mark I Sellen, BA, MMus, ARCM
Joanna M Sephton, BA
Joanna L Shindler, BSc, MSc
Nicoletta M Simborowski, MA
John R McK Simpson, BEng
Karima Soutsane, BA, MA, PhD
Bethany Steer, BA
Mark A Stephenson, MA
Alastair M Summers, BSc
Mark J Taylor, BA
Joseph W Tomlinson, MSc, DPhil
Mary R Trotman, MA
Lorraine R Turley, BA
Philip R Waghorn, BSc, MSc
Kerry F Walsh, BA
Bella K Wethey, BA
A John Wiggins, MA
Kendall A Williams, BSc, PhD

Houses and Housemasters/Housemistresses:

Cowell's: Nicholas H Coram-Wright, MA
Sing's: David P Corran, BA
Field House: J Richard Murray, BA, MA
Macnamara's: Sarah L Sephton, BEng
Apsley: Richard T F Pleming, MA
Tilly's: Philip A Jolley, BA, BEd
Segar's: David R Gibbon, BSc, BSc
Kendall: James E B Cope, BA, MA
Oakthorpe: Judy Young, BSc
Corfe: Susan A Norton, BA
Avenue: Rachel Bellamy, BA, MA

Administrative Officers:
Bursar: Stephen Withers Green, MA, ACA
Registrar: Sarah K Munden, BEd
Development Director: Jane Rogers, MSc, BA
Examinations Officer: W Michael Boswell, MA
Librarian: Marian O Oyedoh, MSc, BSc

Medical Officers:
Dr Roisin McCloskey, MBChB, MRCGP
Dr Matthew Cheetham, MB, MS
Dr Bridget Geer, MBChB, MRCGP, DRCOG

Ethos. The education offered at St Edward's is designed to promote the all-round development of the children in its care. It is our objective that each pupil will leave the school with the qualities, skills and qualifications necessary for a fulfilling life. To that end, St Edward's offers a genuinely broad education to a wide range of pupils of varying talents within a boarding context which allows time for pupils and teachers to benefit from the impressive resources in and out of the classroom.

History and Development. Founded in 1863, St Edward's moved to its present site of over 100 acres in North Oxford in 1873. The School roll is c650 boys and girls, of whom about three-quarters are full-time boarders. Pupils live in one of the 11 houses (4 for girls, 7 for boys), and in addition to having the run of extensive playing fields, they benefit from the use of our facilities, including the Chapel, Library, Common Rooms, Sports Hall and Sports complex (including pool and 4 indoor tennis courts), a new Performing Arts Centre, astroturfs, golf course and the river. A new Science building opens in September 2008.

Pastoral Care. Our network of pastoral care lies at the heart of what we try to achieve. Each pupil is in the direct care of a Housemaster or Housemistress who communicates regularly with a team of tutors, some of whom are resident in the House. Pupils' academic progress is carefully and systematically monitored by academic tutors who meet their charges in tutor periods, as well as in house. A great deal of pastoral work is done by subject teachers, music, drama and games coaches, and we lay emphasis on good communication. We aim that pupils learn to take responsibility for their actions and to note their consequences: this is the basis of our attitude to discipline.

Academic Work. We aim that all pupils may proceed to University, if that is their choice. This implies a wide curriculum and St Edward's offers most subjects. We lay emphasis on independent learning and this is achieved through good practice in teaching and learning and through the comprehensive tutorial system, with its important aspects of self-assessment. In 2007 over three-quarters of all A Level presentations resulted in an A or B pass, and over 60% A* and A grades at GCSE. On average 10% of the Sixth Form gain offers from Oxford and Cambridge Universities. Shells (Year 9) follow a wide common course, with a choice to be made from Spanish, German, Ancient Greek or Arabic, and two of these for the ablest linguists. The Fourth and Fifth Forms follow courses leading to 9 GCSEs. In the Lower Sixth, pupils are expected to take 4 or 5 AS Levels and proceed to at least 3 A Levels. From September 2008, Sixth Form pupils may choose to follow the International Baccalaureate Diploma Programme in place of A Levels. We provide learning support for pupils who are mildly dyslexic or dyscalculic.

Higher Education and Careers. The Department is staffed by two teachers, and draws on the expertise of ISCO for Careers advice and psychometric testing. It runs sessions on the University application procedure and interviews, as well as a highly participative 'Team Challenge' conference. There is a programme of work experience for Fifth form pupils, and Lower Sixth pupils take part in the Young Enterprise Scheme. Younger pupils take part in whole-day careers activities.

Music, Drama and the Arts. The Arts are highly valued at St Edward's. The Music Department delivers about 600 lessons every week, taught by a team of 40 visiting specialists. The main school groups include the Orchestra, Chamber Orchestra, Chapel Choir, Chamber Choir, St Edward's Singers, Concert Band, Big Band, Jazz Band and various Chamber Music groups. There are around 60 concerts a year, with regular foreign tours. The Drama department is flourishing: main school productions, including musicals, are complemented by devised pieces, House plays, Shell plays and a rapidly expanding Speech and Drama programme. The Art Department is strong and vibrant, benefiting from recently enhanced facilities and the stream of visiting exhibitions to The North Wall. Large numbers of pupils go on to Art related courses at University. The Dance programme is extensive, with over 30 classes every week – covering styles from ballet to cheerleading – generating a range of material for the dance shows. In addition, the cutting-edge programming of the award-winning North Wall Performing Arts Centre enriches the cultural life of both the school and the wider community, placing St Edward's right at the forefront of development in Arts education.

Sport, Games and Activities. A very wide variety of sports, games and activities is on offer. We compete at the highest level in several sports and can boast of county and national representatives. We also encourage all our pupils to participate and to enjoy playing at more modest levels. We have fielded as many as 27 teams on one day – over 400 children representing the School. These sports, games and activities include Rugby, Football, Hockey, Cricket, Rowing, Athletics, Netball, Squash, Swimming, Tennis, Cross-Country running, Sailing, Clay Pigeon Shooting, Golf, Soccer, Judo Basketball, Canoeing, Rock-climbing, Chess, Bridge, Debating, and Community Service. We operate a Combined Cadet Force with Navy, Army and RAF sections, and offer all levels of the Duke of Edinburgh's Award Scheme.

Admission to the School. Registration forms can be obtained from the Registrar. There is a registration fee of £75. Places in the School, conditional upon performance in the entrance exam, are offered 18 months before entry at 13+. Boys and girls are expected to take the Common Entrance Examination or Scholarship in their last Summer term at their Preparatory School. Separate assessment arrangements can be made for applicants from schools not preparing candidates for the Common Entrance Examination. Lower Sixth scholarship and entrance examinations are held in November prior to entry; offers of places in the sixth form are subject to good performance at GCSE (at least six B grades and above) and a satisfactory report from the previous school.

Scholarships. (*see Scholarship Entries section*). Open Scholarships and Exhibitions are assessed by examination and interview. As well as Academic Scholarships, Music, Art and Sports Scholarships are available at both 13+ and 16+ entry. In addition All-Rounder, Drama and Dance Scholarships are available at 13+.

Bursaries. There are three Widening Access bursaries available each year: two at 13+ and one at 16+. There is also one bursary for the children of serving RAF personnel and the school may offer bursaries of up to 30% of current boarding fees for children of clergy and university dons at the Warden's discretion.

Fees per term (2008-2009). Boarding, Tuition and Maintenance £9,005; Day Pupils (including subscriptions and meals) £7,203.

Charitable status. St Edward's, Oxford is a Registered Charity, number 309681. The aims and objectives of the School are to provide education for pupils between the ages of 13 and 18.

St George's College

Weybridge Surrey KT15 2QS
Tel: 01932 839300
Fax: 01932 839301
e-mail: contact@st-georges-college.co.uk
website: www.st-georges-college.co.uk

Founded by the Josephite Community in 1869 in Croydon, the College moved in 1884 to its present attractive grounds of 100 acres on Woburn Hill, Weybridge. Within its particular family orientated ethos, the College seeks to encourage a wide, balanced Christian education in the Catholic tradition encouraging excellence and achievement across a broad spectrum of academic, sporting and extra-curricular activities. Almost all pupils move on to higher education, gaining places at a wide range of institutions including Oxford and Cambridge. The College is co-educational throughout the school.

Motto: '*Amore et Labore*'

Governing Body:
Chairman: Mrs K Quint

Governors:

Mr K Alexander	Mr M J G Henderson
Mrs S Borg	Mr S Howard
Fr A Cadwallader, CJ	Mr P Morgan
Mrs M Hackett	Revd W M Muir, CJ
Revd R D Hamilton, CJ	Mrs S Wood

Clerk to the Governors and Bursar: Mr P J Fletcher, ACIS

***Headmaster*: Mr J A Peake**, MA Oxon, PGCE

Deputy Headmaster: Mr M A Saxon, BA, MA, PGCE (*History*)
Director of Studies: Ms F M May, MA, BA, PGCE (*English*)
Curriculum Coordinator: Mr A M Gunning, BA, PGCE (*Geography*)

Mrs J A Andrew, MA Oxon, PGCE (*Physics*)
Ms S Arif (*Mathematics*)
Fr Martin Ashcroft (*Josephite Chaplain*)
Mr M J Barham, BA Hons, PGCE (*History, Assistant i/c Careers*)
Mrs A L Barnett, BSc, PGCE (*Chemistry*)
Mrs M Bigwood, BSc, HDE (*Mathematics*)
Mr A M Blyth, MSc, BA, PGCE (*Mathematics*)
Mrs J M Bourne, BA, PGCE (*Physical Education, Games*)
Mr D J Bradford , BHum, PGCE (*Mathematics, i/c Examinations*)
Miss C A Butler, BA, PGCE (*Art*)
Ms A Byrne, BSc, PGCE (*Physical Education, Games*)
Mrs T Castledine, BA Oxon, RAM, MA, ARCO (*Music*)
Mr J P R Chesterton, BSc, PGCE (*Geography, Physical Education, Games*)
Miss T A Cooke, BSc, MSc, PGCE (*Physical Education, i/c Girls' Games, Head of Middle School*)
Miss L M Cooper, BA Hons, PGCE (*Music*)
Mr M J Crean, BA, PGCE (*Physical Education, Games, Head of Rugby*)
Mr J M Cunningham, BA, PGCE (*Religious Studies, PSE Coordinator*)
Mrs J Davies, CertEd, PGCE (*Academic Support*)
Mr J E Davies, BA, PGCE (*Head of Geography*)
Mr T Deive, BA, PGCE (*Languages*)
Mrs V L Diprose, BA Hons, PGCE (*Spanish*)
Dr J V Drayton, BSc, PhD (*Head of Chemistry*)
Miss E Drysdale, BA Hons, PGCE (*Art*)
Mr P S Ellwood, BA, PGCE (*History*)
Mrs V G Emad, BA Hons, PGCE (*Art*)
Mr M Fitzgerald (*Games*)
Miss S Frawley, MA, MPhil (*English, i/c Oxbridge Entrance*)

Ms P L George, BEd, BA, MA (*Head of Religious Studies & Philosophy*)
Mr W Glover, BA, MEd, PGCE (*Head of Economics & Business Studies*)
Mr S H Graham, BSc (*Chemistry, Head of Stirling House*)
Mrs C F Grant, BA, PGCE (*History, Head of Southcote House*)
Miss E Grigsby, BSc, PGCE (*Maths*)
Mr P Graves, BSc, PGCE (*Languages, Head of Co-Curricular*)
Mr R P Grimmer, BSc, PGCE (*Physics*)
Mr A M Gunning, BA, PGCE (*Curriculum Coordinator, Geography*)
Mrs G Hale, Deug LL France (*Languages*)
Miss S Hall, BSc, PGCE (*Geography, Head of Second Year*)
Miss E A L Hare, MA, PGCE (*Drama*)
Mr M T Harrison, BSc Hons, GTP, QTS (*Physical Education, Games, i/c Cricket*)
Ms C Hulf, BA Hons (*Rowing*)
Mrs S M Knights, BSc, PGCE (*Geography, Head of Careers*)
Mr P C Lamb, MA, PGCE (*Languages*)
Mrs M A Lamey, BSc (*Physics, Head of Sixth Form*)
Miss L C Lever, BA, PGCE (*Languages*)
Mr J J Lewis, BA, PGCE (*English*)
Miss K Maguire, BSc Hons, PGCE (*Biology, Head of Fifth Year*)
Miss S J Marlow, BA, PGCE (*Geography, Head of Third Year*)
Ms F M May, MA, BA, PGCE (*Director of Studies, English*)
Br Michael, CJ (*French*)
Mrs A M Morison, BA Hons, PGCE (*Drama*)
Mrs S L Morris, BSc (*ICT*)
Mr R Nayman, BA, PGCE (*Head of Languages*)
Mrs A O'Brien, BSc Hons, PGCE (*Economics & Business Studies*)
Mr G Oliver, MA Hons, PGCE, MEng (*Head of Mathematics*)
Mr M Parnham, BEd Hons, CertEd (*Head of Technology*)
Miss V A Quinn, BEd Hons (*English*)
Mr A J Reynolds, BA, PGCE (*Director of Sport, i/c Rugby, i/c Activities*)
Mrs S Rowlatt, BA Hons, MA, PGCE, DipLE (*Head of English, i/c 'The Georgian'*)
Mr M A Saxon, BA, MA, PGCE (*Deputy Head, History*)
Mr M A Schofield, MA (*Head of Drama*)
Mrs J M Sciortino Nowlan, BA Hons, PGCE, MPhil (*Religious Studies*)
Mrs M C Scragg, BA Oxon, PGCE (*Biology*)
Mrs I Seymour, BSc, MSc, GTP (*Mathematics*)
Dr H A Shaw, PhD, BSc, PGCE (*Chemistry*)
Mr M T Stather, BSc Hons, PGCE (*Biology, Assistant Examinations Officer*)
Mr D N Strange (*Music – Head of Strings*)
Mr T Sweeney, MA (*Head of Art*)
Mr K Taggart, BEng, PGCE (*Head of Physics*)
Dr C A Taylor, PhD, MSc, BSc, PGCE (*Physics*)
Ms E Thomson, HSc, HDE (*Mathematics*)
Mrs C S Thorne, BSc, CertEd (*Biology*)
Mr M P Tiley, MA (*Head of History*)
Mrs S H Turner, MA, BA, PGCE (*Religious Studies*)
Mr N Waight, BA, PGCE (*English*)
Mr S C Walford, BA, PGCE (*English*)
Mr G P Walters, BSc (*Biology, i/c Rowing, Head of Petre House*)
Mr A B Watters, BA, Dip BA, PGCE (*Philosophy, Politics*)
Mrs J B Weaver, BA Hons, PGCE (*Food Technology*)
Mrs S E Wedgwood , BA, PGCE (*History*)
Mrs F Wheat, MA (*College Chaplain*)
Mrs K Wilkinson, BSc, PGCE (*Physics*)
Mr J Williams, BA, BSc, PGCE (*Hockey*)
Mr S J Woolnough, BA, PGCE (*Languages*)
Mrs K York, BSc, PGCE (*Head of Biology*)

Librarian: Mrs I Monem
Library Assistant: Mrs B Wing
Library Assistant: Ms J Bungay
Marketing Executive: Mrs B Roberts
Headmaster's Secretary: Mrs C A Greenwood, BA
Matron: Mrs A Sweeney, BSc School Nursing, RGN

There are approximately 850 boys and girls in the school.

Admission. Entry is normally at age 11 (First Year), 13 (Third Year) or 16 (Sixth Form). Students are accepted in September each year. Entry is also possible during an academic year if a place is available.

Admissions details may be obtained from the Headmaster's Secretary.

Entrance Scholarships. (*see Scholarship Entries section*). Academic Scholarships are awarded at 11, 13 and for the Sixth Form. Additionally, the College offers Music, Drama, Sport and Art Scholarships.

Bursaries. The College has its own in-house Assisted Places Scheme. Further information is available from the Bursar.

Facilities. Recent refurbishment has provided modern facilities for Music, Languages, English, Mathematics, Theatre and Technology. There is an extensive Arts Centre, an impressive library, a Sixth Form Study Centre (renovated in 2006) and a large indoor Sports Hall with an adjacent fitness training room. The College has 19 tennis courts, including three international standard grass courts, clay courts and an impressive four-court Indoor Tennis Centre. In addition there are three new Resource rooms, networked computers, floodlit netball courts, an all-weather athletics track and two astroturf hockey pitches. The College Boat Club is situated nearby on the Thames.

The Curriculum. This is kept as broad as possible up to GCSE, with a balance between Arts and Science subjects. Students usually take a maximum of 10 GCSEs, A level candidates may choose from over 20 subjects. The vast majority of the Sixth Form go on to Russell Group universities including Oxford and Cambridge.

Careers. Guidance is given throughout a student's career but particularly in making GCSE, A level and university choices. The Careers Coordinator has a modern well stocked Careers Room and makes effective use of COA testing, portfolios, work experience, trial interviews, Challenge of Industry days and computer software.

Art. The Art Department attracts large numbers of students at GCSE and A level who achieve consistently high results in public examinations. A large proportion of A level candidates successfully apply to Art Colleges, often each receiving several offers in this highly competitive field.

Music. Music plays a vital part in school life. There is a wide range of music-making encompassing early music, madrigal groups, jazz, rock, African Drumming as well as more traditional ensembles, orchestras and wind bands. The choir and orchestra give regular performances (including radio broadcasts), and tour Europe annually. Tuition is available on all orchestral instruments from a team of 36 visiting specialists who teach over 400 students each week. Students play in youth orchestras including the NYO and have gained scholarships to the major conservatoires.

Responsibility and Service. Many boys and girls are engaged in the care for the elderly at home or in old people's homes, as well as the mentally and physically handicapped. Each Easter and Summer groups of Sixth Formers accompany handicapped people on visits to Lourdes. Students find these activities a rewarding exercise in Christian service. The Prefect system and the mentor system offer positions of responsibility to the oldest students. The Duke of Edinburgh's Award Scheme is encouraged and there is a flourishing College Council.

Pastoral Care. The spiritual, moral and academic wellbeing of the students is the concern of every member of staff at the College. Nearly all staff act as Group Tutors with particular responsibility for the daily care of their students and for forging links with parents. Each Year Group is led by a Head of Year, and the Chaplain has a general pastoral role. All groups have a day of retreat away each year. The College also has four Houses to which the students are affiliated and all students have one period per week as part of their PSE programme.

Extra Curricular Activities. There is a very wide range of clubs and societies taking place both at lunchtime and after school. In addition to music and sport, a broad range of interests is catered for such as the Science Club, Cookery, Young Enterprise, Philosophy and Model Clubs.

Sport. All students participate and there is a variety of sports: rugby, hockey, netball, cricket, tennis, rowing, and rounders, plus a wide range of other activities such as golf, athletics, badminton, basketball and cross-country. Each student has the opportunity to develop his or her own talents in small coaching groups. The College has its own boat house on the Thames, nineteen tennis courts (including four indoor), two floodlit artificial pitches with viewing stand, floodlit netball courts, six artificial cricket nets, one main pavilion and two smaller cricket pavilions, eight rugby pitches. The College has access to the Junior School heated swimming pool. All facilities are of a very high standard in an attractive setting. Overseas tours to Holland and Malta have been completed recently by hockey and cricket teams. Attendance at national hockey finals is an annual event and the College hosts a very popular U18 Hockey Sixes every year. International honours have recently been gained in hockey, cricket, rowing and tennis.

Junior School. St George's College Junior School is located nearby in Thames Street, Weybridge, and is co-educational, catering for boys and girls from 3 to 11.

(*For further details, please see Junior School entry in IAPS section.*)

Fees per term (2008-2009). First and Second Forms £3,870; Third–Sixth Form £4,455. Lunches £200.

Charitable status. St George's College Weybridge is a Registered Charity, number 1017853, and a Company Limited by Guarantee. The aims and objectives of the Charity are the Christian education of young people.

St John's School

Leatherhead Surrey KT22 8SP
Tel: 01372 373000 Switchboard
01372 385441 Headmaster
01372 385446 Bursar
Fax: 01372 386606
e-mail: secretary@stjohns.surrey.sch.uk
website: www.stjohnsleatherhead.co.uk

Founded 1851. Royal Charter, 1922.

St John's School was founded in North London in 1851 for the education of the sons of Anglican clergy. The move to Leatherhead was made in 1872 and a Royal Charter was granted in 1922. The School has grown to over 470 pupils, including Foundationers, sons and daughters of clergy, and is co-educational in the Sixth Form.

Motto: '*Quae sursum sunt quaerite*' "Seek those things which are above."

Patron: HRH The Duchess of Gloucester, GCVO

Visitor: The Lord Archbishop of Canterbury, DD

The Council:

Chairman: P C F Hickson, MA, FCA

A M Airey, LLB (*OJ*)
T Beckh, MA
P A Crossley, BA, BArch, RIBA (*OJ*)
The Rt Revd The Bishop of Dorking
P G Gardner, FRICS (*OJ*)
R M Gordon Clark, LLB (*OJ*)
Mrs J Grant Peterkin, BA
The Rt Revd The Bishop of Guildford
Mrs J Harris, BA
H J Malins, CBE, MP (*OJ*)
A J Peake, FCA (*OJ*)
C Richardson, MBA, MA, FSI
L F Speller
Mrs C Swabey
P H Thorne, BA (*OJ*)
S A Westley, MA, MIMgt
D J Woodhead, BA, FRSA

Bursar and Secretary to the Council: Mrs J V Maynard, BA, DMS

***Headmaster*: Mr Nicholas J R Haddock**, MBE, MA St Edmund Hall, Oxford, FRGS

Deputy Headmaster: M Mortimer, BA
Deputy Head (Academic): M W Clarke, BSc
Director of Studies: J Nuttall, BSc, MSc, PhD, BPhil

Assistant Staff:
* *Head of Department*
† *Housemaster/mistress*

P C Noble, BSc
P F Lutton, MA, ARCO, ARCM
A B Gale, BSc, CPhys, MInstP
A J Phillips, BA
*A P King, BA, FSA
*Mrs D J Burgess, BSc
*Mrs L S Culm, BEd, DipRSA SpLD
Miss J A Belfrage, MA
*R C B Clark, BA, MBA
*Mrs S Harmon, MA
*†P M Goodyer, BA
*M Rogers, BSc
†R W L Allan, BA
†J A Lockwood, BEd, MA
*J M Thorne, MA, MSt
†A Bass, BEd
*P Reilly, BSc, MA, PhD
*N T Whitmore, MA
†Mrs M A Arnal, BA, MSc
*T Lauze, BA
*J Ward, BSc
*†N Smith, BA, DRSA, MD
*Q Wiseman, BA
*T L Hadcroft, BA, MSc
*R Davidson, BA
Ms J Fowler, BSc
R J Gregory, BSc
*J A Passam, BA
Miss L J Bond, BSc
Dr J H Chandler, BSc, DPhil
A R Houston, BSc
†N Johnston-Jones, BA
J Kidd, BA, MA
G Macmillan, BA
*N S Platt, BA Ed
M Sartorius, BA
S Briggs, MIED, CertEd
*Miss M Hennebry, BA, MSc
Miss P Parrouty, BA
J P Sutcliffe, MMus
P Thomas, BSc
Miss P Whittingham, BSc
*The Revd C Case, BA, MTheol
*J Davies, BSc
C Evans, BA
G Hicks, BA
Miss T King, BA, MA
*M Probert, BA
S Reid, BA,MA
A Vargas, BA

Houses & Housemasters/mistresses:

Boarding Houses (Boys):
West: P M Goodyer
East: J A Lockwood
Churchill: N Smith

Day Houses (Boys):
North: R W L Allan
Surrey: N Johnston-Jones
Montgomery: A Bass

Day & Boarding (Girls):
South: Mrs M A Arnal

Marketing & Commercial Manager: Miss C M Buckingham, BSc
Librarian & Archivist: Mrs S Todd, BA, MA Ed, MCLIP
Medical Officer: Dr J B Close, FRCGP, MRCP UK
Medical Centre Sister: Mrs C Cannon, RGN

Boarding. Full and weekly boarding places are available.

Houses. There are three boarding houses (West, East and Churchill) and three day houses (North, Surrey and Montgomery) for boys. There is one day and boarding house (South) for girls, which comprises Hallaton and the Fairfield building opened in September 2004.

Buildings. The School occupies a 50-acre site in Leatherhead within easy reach of the M25. The original 19th Century buildings form an open cloistered quadrangle, comprising the boarding and day houses, the oak-panelled dining hall, and the Chapel. Extensive development of the site has included an Art Centre and Music School, superbly equipped DT workshops, a Communications Centre, including an extensive ICT suite, a Multimedia Studio, a Sixth Form Study Centre and an astroturf pitch. Recent developments include a Performing Arts Centre, a Sixth Form Social Centre, and Fairfield, an additional building for Sixth Form girls complete with en-suite accommodation. Future development of a new Classroom block is planned for 2008/09.

Religion. As a Church of England Foundation, St John's has always had a special place for worship in the life of the School, and is particularly fortunate in its fine modern Chapel.

Curriculum. On entry into the Fourth Form, all pupils study English, Mathematics, Religious Education, French, Spanish, Physics, Chemistry, Biology, Geography, History, Information and Communication Technology, Art, Design and Technology, Music, Physical Education (including Health Education) and either Latin or Classical Civilisation.

In the second year, pupils will study English (including Literature), Mathematics, a Modern Foreign Language (French or Spanish), Science (Physics, Chemistry and Biology) and three other subjects to GCSE. In addition, all pupils will continue with Information and Communication Technology and a non-examined Religious Education course. The other subjects studied to GCSE include a second Modern Language, History, Geography, Religious Studies, Latin, Information and Communication Technology, Physical Education, Design and Technology, Art and Music.

In the first year of the Sixth Form, pupils will begin their Advanced Subsidiary course, generally choosing four subjects. A wide range of choices is possible from the following subjects: Art, Biology, Business Studies, Chemistry, Design and Technology, Drama and Theatre Studies, Economics, English Literature, French, Geography, History, Information and Communication Technology, Latin, Mathematics, Further Mathematics, Music, Music Technology, Physics, Psychology, Religious Studies, Spanish and Sport and Physical Education.

In the second year of the Sixth Form, pupils will generally continue three of their subjects to Advanced Level.

Over the first four terms of the Sixth Form, pupils will follow a General Studies programme. This includes a range of talks from outside speakers, aimed at encouraging an interest in different aspects of culture and society, and a course on entry to Higher Education.

Music. There is a strong musical tradition. The Chapel Choir contributes effectively to the worship in Chapel and travels widely at home and abroad. Many boys and girls study musical instruments and are encouraged to participate in the School orchestra, wind band, string quartets, choral society, chamber choir, jazz band and rock groups. There are regular informal concerts to encourage informal performance.

Art and Design Technology. As well as providing the facilities for pursuing the academic curriculum, the Art and Design facilities and the Technology workshops are used extensively in co-curricular activities.

Drama. Drama plays an important part in the life of the School, with most boys and girls taking to the stage at some point during the year. Up to nine productions, including School and House plays, are staged each year.

Information and Communication Technology. There is a school-wide network of computers (in excess of 400) and other ICT resources that support many activities and areas of school life. Interactive Whiteboards in every classroom provide an invaluable resource for curricular and co-curricular activities of all descriptions. Computers, including those found in four dedicated ICT classrooms, the Sixth Form Study Centre and the Houses, both Boarding and Day, are available for use throughout the School both during and outside the School day. Pupils and staff have widespread access to the internet for research and preparation.

Debating. The School competes in national and regional competitions and other inter-school events. There are inter-House competitions at junior and senior level each year.

Careers. All boys and girls are advised on their Advanced Level and Higher Education courses. ISCO careers aptitude tests are offered, as are regular careers evenings and visits. There is a work experience programme and an annual 'Challenge of Business Management' conference.

Sport. Cricket, Rugby and Football are the major sports for boys, with Hockey and Netball for girls. Many other sports flourish, including Tennis, Fives, Squash, Swimming, Sailing, Badminton, Table Tennis, Athletics, Volleyball, Basketball, Cross-Country and Shooting.

Combined Cadet Force. The contingent comprises RN, Army and RAF sections. All boys enter the CCF in the Summer Term of their first year. They stay in their chosen service for at least four terms. During this time, cadets train for the Services Proficiency Certificates and the various stages of the Duke of Edinburgh's Award Scheme. Field Days, annual camps and courses are an integral feature of CCF training. Adventure Training expeditions take place each year in more remote areas of the country. After the period of compulsory service, boys elect to continue in the CCF or move to the Community Service Unit. Girls may opt to join the CCF in the Sixth Form. Cadets also achieve notable successes in the BTEC Diploma in Public Service.

Admission. Boys are required to take the Common Entrance Examination, unless they have previously satisfied the Examiners in the Scholarship Examination. No boy is admitted under the age of 13 or over 14 years except in special circumstances. The Prospectus and Application Forms may be obtained from the Headmaster's Secretary. Academic, Music, Art, Sport and All Rounder Scholarships are available, along with Bursaries.

For Sixth Form admission, boys and girls have interviews in the November before their entry into the Sixth Form. There are Academic, Music, Art, Sport and All Rounder Scholarships available at this stage. Day and Boarding places are available. Details of Open Days and admission may be obtained from the Headmaster's Secretary.

Foundationerships. In accordance with the Foundation of St John's, places are available for sons and daughters of Anglican clergy who are resident in any Diocese of the Church of England or the Church in Wales and who are engaged in the Ministry of the Church. These Foundationerships are awarded on the result of the Common Entrance or Scholarship Examination, or Sixth Form entry tests.

Term of Entry. The only term for entry, except in special circumstances, is the Autumn term.

Scholarships. A number of scholarship awards are made to candidates who demonstrate excellence in their particular discipline at 13+ and 16+ as follows:

Academic: 13+ Common Academic Scholarship Examination Papers. 16+ is assessed on predicted GCSE results, interview and references.

All-Rounder: Assessed by general character, academic ability, leadership qualities and a level of excellence in one or more areas of Art, Drama, Music or Sport.

Art, Music, Sport: Assessed by audition/assessment and interview together with supporting references.

Scholarship assessments take place in January/February prior to entry for 13+.

Dates:
Music: 26 January 2009
Academic: 23, 24 and 25 February 2009
Art: 25 February 2009
All-Rounder: 26 February 2009
Sport: 27 February 2009

Assessments take place in November prior to entry for 16+.

The value of a scholarship may be supplemented by a means-tested Bursary.

For further details, please contact the Headmaster's Secretary, St John's School, Epsom Road, Leatherhead, Surrey KT22 8SP. Tel: 01372 385441; Fax: 01372 386606; e-mail: secretary@stjohns.surrey.sch.uk.

Fees per term (2008-2009). Boarding £7,960; Day £5,790.

Old Johnian Society. Contact the Secretary, Richard Francis, at the School, on 01372 385450.

Charitable status. St John's School is a Registered Charity, number 312064. It exists to provide a first class education for children.

St Lawrence College

Ramsgate Kent CT11 7AE
Tel: 01843 572900 (Headmaster)
01843 572912 (Junior School)
01843 587666 (Bursar and General Office)
01843 572931 (Registrar)
Fax: 01843 572901 (Headmaster)
01843 572913 (Junior School)
01843 572915 (Bursar and General Office)
01843 572901 (Registrar)
e-mail: hm@slcuk.com (Headmaster)
hjs@slcuk.com (Junior School)
bursar@slcuk.com (Bursar and General Office)
ah@slcuk.com (Registrar)
website: www.slcuk.com

Co-educational, Day: age 3–18 years, Boarding: age 7–18 years.

The Council:

President: ¶Sir Kirby Laing, MA, FREng

Vice-Presidents:
The Baroness Cox, BSc, MSc, FRCN
¶Sir Martin Laing, CBE, MA, FRICS
G H Mungeam, MA, DPhil
S Webley, MA

Chairman: The Revd Canon Nigel M Walker

Members:
M G Macdonald, MA, LLM
¶M Iliff, MSc
A T Emby, FCA
Mrs G E Page
Mrs A E Driver, BA
J B Guyatt, MA
¶B J W Isaac, Esq
D W Taylor, MA Oxon, PGCE, FRSA
D C Chaplin, BA
Mrs A G Burgess, TCNFF, ACP
Mrs M F Youlten, BSc, PGCE
¶N G Marchant
Revd B Griffiths, BA, Dip Th

¶ *Old Lawrentians*

Clerk to the Governors and Bursar: J P Marshall, Esq

***Headmaster*: Revd M Aitken**, BA Hons Durham, Cert Theol Fitzwilliam College, Cambridge, FRSA

Deputy Head: Dr E B Gill, BSc, PhD London, CChem, MRSC (*Chemistry*)
Director of Studies: I D Dawbarn, BA York, MSc Oxon
Chaplain: Revd Steven Lee, BA Durham, DipHE Bristol
Senior Academic Tutor: Dr D A Scales, BA Durham, PhD Cantab (*Head of Classics*)
Registrar: Miss A Hall, CertEd Cambridge Inst of Ed, NPQH

Heads of Department:
I M Anderson, MA St Andrews (*Head of Economics, Coordinator of International Students, Psychology, Mathematics*)
P Binks, BA Sunderland (*Head of Art & Design*)
G A Bryant, MA London (*Business Studies, Mathematics*)
Dr T A Clarke, BSc Durham, MSc London, PhD Liverpool (*Head of Biology*)
Mrs G Crouch, BA Hons, CertEd (*Head of Religious Studies*)
I D Dawbarn, BA York, MSc Oxon (*Careers, Mathematics*)
Mrs J Denton, BA Hons Manchester, PGCE Manchester, Cert SpLD (*Head of Learning Support*)
P W Graham, BA Exeter (*Head of Modern Languages, French, Spanish*)
Mrs J A Green, PGCE Bath (*Head of Home Economics*)
Mrs G C Harris, BSc Liverpool (*Chemistry, Mathematics, Science, Head of PSE*)
Mrs J Löcsei-Campbell, BSc, BA, BEd (*German, Head of Psychology*)
Mrs A J Fletcher, BEd, CertEd, Dip TEFLA (*Head of EAL*)
Miss A Monk, BSc Cardiff (*Head of Chemistry*)
T Moulton, BA Leeds (*Head of History, Classics*)
Dr C J Ransom, BSc, PhD, MA, AKC, PGCE (*Head of Physics and Science*)
M T Single, BA Hons Loughborough (*Head of Design Technology*)
P M Stubbings, BMus Manchester, Prix d'Excellence-Cum Laude Amsterdam (*Director of Music*)
Miss V M Vasey, BA London (*Head of English*)
Mr N Watts, BA Hons Brighton, QTS (*Head of Geography*)
R B Wilkening, BA London, MA Kent (*Head of ICT*)
Mrs W J Wilkening, BSc York (*Head of Mathematics*)

Houses and Housemasters/mistresses:
Lodge: M T Single, BA Hons Loughborough (*Head of Design Technology*)
Tower: P R Murray, MA Glasgow (*Classics*)
Newlands: N O S Jones, BA OU (*Geography; Head of Games and PE*)
Bellerby: Mrs A E Bailey, BEd, MA Sussex (*PE and Games*)
Laing: Miss P M Savill, BA OU (*Mathematics*)
Kirby House (*Middle School*): R E Muncey, BEd Soton (*English, Religious Studies*)
Kirby House Boarding (*Middle School*): T Moulton, BA Leeds (*Head of History, Classics*)

Junior School
Head: S J E Whittle, BA Hons, PGCE
Deputy Head: S C Bithel-Vaughan, BA (*English, ICT, History*)

Number of Pupils. Senior School: 333: 204 boys (127 boarders, 77 day), 129 girls (63 boarders, 66 day).

Junior School: 10 boarders, 184 day pupils (of whom 38 attend the Nursery).

Who we are. Walk through the historic arch at St Lawrence College and you will immediately feel at home. The school welcomes students from all over the world to this most beautiful site in Ramsgate, Kent. Recently modernised rooms and dormitories provide some of the best boarding accommodation in the Country.

Outstanding results are achieved by the most academic students who progress to many of the top universities. The school is also highly regarded as a centre of excellence for 'value added': students who need additional support perform well beyond expectation.

The school has stunningly beautiful surroundings and outstanding sports facilities. The buildings reflect the nature of the school: steeped in history and tradition, yet modern, creative and forward-thinking. The Main building has a striking 19th Century facade dating back to 1884 which sits alongside the glorious Chapel which was completed in 1927. The magnificent Kirby House, opened in January 2007, is home to our 11–13 year olds. The architecturally striking and imaginatively designed building has a spacious glass atrium and virtual library at its centre. Throughout the school, the lively, professional approach to education and an innovative curriculum provide a challenging and stimulating framework for teaching and learning, but most of all, the school really takes care of its pupils.

At St Lawrence College our aim is to encourage a real intellectual curiosity about life; there is a disciplined working environment which promotes good manners and respect. The deeply rooted Christian ethos remains to the fore. This produces a particular atmosphere within our school. It is enhanced by the size of the community which allows every pupil to be known personally by the staff. The exciting mixture of local children from the South East of England, sharing their education with others from all around the world, in a co-educational setting, produces a hopeful vision for the future.

The school is close to the Channel Tunnel and the port of Dover and has excellent transport links to London and Europe, being only 1½ hours from Gatwick and 2 hours from Heathrow and within 3 miles of Kent International Airport.

Selecting a school can be one of the most important decisions we have to make and we therefore encourage parents and prospective pupils to visit the school if at all possible and to ask the following question. Are these the kind of role models, companions and possibly life-long friends that I would like for my child? We are confident that you will say 'Yes'. The school is justifiably proud that St Lawrence students leave as confident, compassionate and capable adults.

Exam Results. In 2007 86.2% of GCSE candidates achieved grade C or above in 5 or more subjects and the total pass rate at A/AS Level was 96.5%.

Admissions. *Junior School*: An initial parental tour with the Headmaster will be followed by a pupil visit. A taster morning as a follow up allows the prospective pupil to be assessed in numeracy, literacy and reasoning, as well as getting to know the school from the inside.

Senior School: At 11+ admissions are based on an Interview with the Headmaster. A copy of a recent school report will also be required. Testing will be carried out where appropriate.

At 13+ the offer of a place will be dependent on the Common Entrance Examination, GCSE predications and/or an assessment of a recent school report.

At 16+ the offer of a place will be dependent on a minimum of 5 GCSEs passes.

EU and Overseas Students will be admitted on the basis of current performance, references and a short language test as interviews are not always possible. Our special EFL centre will assess and integrate overseas pupils into the curriculum by offering a range of English teaching options, including an intensive English course, which is charged as an extra at £600 per term.

Fees per term (2008-2009). Boarders £7,764, Day £4,547. Fees are due and payable before the commencement of the relevant school term.

Individual Private Tuition: £39.90 per hour. Individual Instrumental Music: £199.50 per term (10 half-hour sessions).

Siblings. St Lawrence College offers generous sibling allowances. For the academic year 2008/09 these rates will be 10% of the fee rate for the second child, 35% for the third child and 50% for the fourth and subsequent children, providing no other financial benefit in respect of fees is received by the parent in respect of children at the College (excluding Scholarships) above or in addition to the foregoing sibling allowance – the foregoing arrangement for siblings does not apply to the Nursery or Junior School.

Bursaries. In accordance with tradition children of Clergy and Missionaries and of serving members of HM Forces will be considered for bursaries. Parents in HM Forces pay the MOD CEA (Continuity of Education Allowance) plus 10% of our main boarding and tuition fees.

Bursaries may be awarded to new or existing pupils of the College and pupils who have been awarded a scholarship which requires supplementing. Parents may apply to the Governors' Bursary Committee for assistance and will be required to complete a confidential grant application form.

Scholarships. (*see Scholarship Entries section*). The value of Academic Scholarships will range from 10% to 50% of the fees. Music Scholarships can be awarded in the Senior School and range in value from 10% to 50%. They can be awarded in conjunction with the academic scholarships. Sports Scholarships are also available in the Junior and Senior Schools and range from 10% to 25%. Scholarship exams are held in November and March although late applicants will be considered.

Charitable status. The Corporation of St Lawrence College is a Registered Charity, number 307921. It exists to provide education for children.

St Mary's College

Crosby Merseyside L23 5TW
Tel: 0151 924 3926
Fax: 0151 932 0363
e-mail: principalsmc@stmarys.lpool.sch.uk
website: www.stmaryscrosby.co.uk

St Mary's College was opened by the Christian Brothers in 1919 at the invitation of Archbishop Whiteside of Liverpool, who felt it was of paramount importance that the Catholic boys of this locality should have the benefits of Grammar School education. The school has been fully co-educational since September 1989.

Motto: '*Fidem Vita Fateri*'

Governors:
Chairman: H Hitchen, FCA

T Bates
P Burns, LLB
Mrs L Byrne
P Keith
Mrs G Mackay
Councillor Mrs P M Parry
Mrs P Old, LLB
M McKenna, LLB
B Hicks, BA, MA, NPQH, MEd
M Mansour, BSc Pharm
J Sankey
K Williams

***Principal*: M Kennedy**, BSc, MA, NPQH, CChem, MRSC

Deputy Head: G Prendergast, BSc

Bursar: H Ewins, BA, CMC

Senior Teachers:
T Lane, BSc, PhD
D Magill, BA
Mrs K Lane, BEd (*Head of Lower School*)

Assistant Teachers:
* *Head of Department*

Miss N Addy, BSc (**Fourth Year*)
J Armstrong, BA
Mrs B Baden, BA
Mrs D Barbosa, MPhil
Mrs S Bartolo, BEd
Mrs L Bennett, BEd
Mrs J A Burt, BA, BSc
A Byers, BA (**Fifth Year*)
Mrs C Cahill, BSc
Miss N Caton, BSc (**Girls' PE & Games*)
Mrs E Connolly, BA (**English*)
L Doherty, BEd
P Duffy, MPhil (**Religious Studies*)
R W Duxfield, BSc (**Physics*)
S C Emery, BA (**Music & Third Year*)
Mrs B Fletcher, BA
Mrs E Ford, BA
Mrs C Gibbon, BEd

D Gough, BA, MA
J J Hayes, BA
Mrs C Hearty, BEd
Mrs C Hyland, BA (**First Year*)
M Ireland, BEng, MSc
R S Johnston, BSc (**Biology*)
Mrs M C Jones, BA, PhD
Mrs A Jordan, BSc
Mrs C Killen, BEd
J G King, BEd, MDes (**Design & Technology*)
Mr D Linley, MA
Mrs C MacKenzie, MA (**Chemistry*)
P E McColgan, MA (**Careers*)
Mrs M McKean, BA (**Modern Foreign Languages*)
Mrs M A Murphy, BA
M Murphy, BSc
P Nagington, BEd, MDes (**Second Year*)
Mrs J Nuttall, BA, MSc
Miss H Orrett, BA
D Phillips, BA
H Piotr, BSc (**Geography*)
P N Richardson, BA (**Classics*)
N C Rothnie, BA (**History*)
H Sage, BSc
Miss J Simpson, BA (**Business Studies & General Studies*)
G Smoult, BA
C Sweatman, BA, PGCE
Mrs J Thomas, BSc (**Mathematics*)
N Vagianos, BSc, MBA (**Information Technology*)
Mrs A Whelan, MA (**Art*)
D Williams, BA (**Boys' PE & Games*)
Miss S Wilson, BEng
Miss A Yates, PhD, MA, BA

Preparatory Department:
Head: M Collins, CertEd, DipMgt
Deputy Head: Mrs A Daniels, BA Hons, PGCE
Head of Infant Department: Mrs A M Chambers, CertEd
Head of Nursery: Mrs A Haigh, BEd

Assistant Teachers:
N Antrobus, BA Hons QTS
Miss J Batisti, BSc Hons QTS
G Bates, BA, PGCE
Mrs C Doyle, IELTS, C&G TCert
Mrs L Gallagher, CertEd
M Hewlett, CertEd
J B Mitchell, BEd
J Moran, BEd
N J Webster, CertEd

Claremont House:
Mrs A Haigh, BEd
Mrs A Fielding, NNEB

Numbers. There are 581 pupils in the Senior School and 195 in the Preparatory Department. There are no boarders.

Preparatory Department. Open to boys and girls up to the age of 11. There is an Early Years Unit (0–4) comprising baby unit and kindergarten. Pupils are admitted to the Preparatory Department after an interview at 4, 5 and 6 years of age and by examination in the other year groups. An agreement must be signed by the parent or guardian undertaking that the pupil shall attend until the end of the School year in which he or she attains the age of 11. Admission to the Preparatory Department does not guarantee admission to the Senior School; this may be obtained only by passing the Entrance Examination.

The Mount has a strong family atmosphere, providing a secure and lively environment in which expectations are high. The school takes what is best from the National Curriculum and follows an enhanced programme with greater emphasis on the 3 Rs and fostering self-discipline.

Sciences play an important part in the curriculum. Sport and Music are particularly strong. Tutoring in a wide range of musical instruments is provided. French and Spanish are taught in small groups from Year 1.

The Head of the Preparatory Department, Mr M Collins, will be pleased to meet you and show you round.

Senior School. Fully co-educational, the Senior School admits pupils at 11 both from The Mount and from Primary Schools over a wide area. An Entrance Examination is held in January each year. Generally speaking, pupils must be between the ages of 10½ and 12 on 1 September of the year in which they wish to enter the School. There is also a 13+ entry. A Registration Fee of £40 is payable with the form of application for admission.

The **Curriculum in the Senior School** includes English Language and Literature, French, German, Spanish, History, Geography, Classical Studies, Latin, Physics, Chemistry, Biology, Mathematics, Information Technology, Art, Music, Drama, Design and Technology and Physical Education. A broad curriculum of 14 subjects is followed for the first 3 years. In the Fourth and Fifth Years, pupils normally take 10 subjects at GCSE, including either single Sciences or Core plus Additional Science, and all pupils study for GCSE Religious Studies and a Euro-qualification in Information Technology. In the Sixth Form there are Advanced courses in all the subjects mentioned above. Psychology, Business Studies, Theology and Drama may also be taken to A Level and all Sixth Formers take A Level General Studies. The Sixth Form options system is flexible allowing combinations of 3 or 4 A Levels.

St Mary's is a pioneer school on Merseyside in the inclusion of **orchestral music** as a normal feature of the School curriculum. All pupils are given the opportunity to play an orchestral instrument. The School Band and Orchestra give an annual Concert in the Liverpool Philharmonic Hall, win regional contests and undertake tours abroad.

Religious Education. Religious Education is a core subject through to GCSE. In the Sixth Form there is the option of Christian Theology A Level. General Religious Education in the Sixth Form is integrated with social work for the handicapped and deprived.

Careers. The College works in partnership with the Independent Schools Careers Organisation. Arrangements are made each year for interviews for Fifth Formers to which parents are invited. Sixth Formers are interviewed several times to help them choose appropriate courses at University or in Higher Education. Advice is given to Third Year pupils in choosing options.

Games. Games periods provide opportunities for Rugby, Cricket, Hockey, Netball, Squash, Golf, Cross-Country, Tennis and Basketball. The main games for girls are Netball and Hockey. There is an adjacent modern Sports Centre.

Activities. Some 40 extra-curricular activities and societies are available, including the Duke of Edinburgh's Award Scheme.

Combined Cadet Force. There is a very active Combined Cadet Force which contains Army and Air Force sections. Membership of the Combined Cadet Force is voluntary.

Fees per term (2008-2009). Senior School £2,687; Preparatory Department £1,726–£1,829.

Open Academic Scholarships. There are up to six Open Scholarships based on performance in the College Entrance Examination, worth up to half fees. The awards are based on academic merit alone and are currently irrespective of income. There is also a small number of Art, Music and Sports Scholarships.

There are also School Assisted Places, known as Edmund Rice Junior Scholarships, at 11+. These are income-related and are open to pupils whose parents' joint income would have brought them within the Government scheme.

Sixth Form Scholarships. Edmund Rice Scholarships (worth approximately 10% of fees) are available on merit, and are awarded on the basis of a Scholarship Examination in January.

Charitable status. St Mary's College Crosby Trust Limited is a Registered Charity, number 1110311. The aims and objectives of the Charity are to advance religious and other charitable works.

St Paul's School

Lonsdale Road Barnes London SW13 9JT
Tel: 020 8748 9162

Fax: 020 8746 5353
e-mail: hmsec@stpaulsschool.org.uk
website: www.stpaulsschool.org.uk

St Paul's School was founded in AD 1509, by John Colet, DD, Dean of St Paul's. An ancient Grammar School had previously existed for many centuries in connection with St Paul's Cathedral, and was probably absorbed by Colet into his new foundation. Colet laid down in the original statutes, still preserved at Mercers' Hall, that there should be 'taught in the scole children of all Nacions and Countres indifferently to the Noumber of a CLIII', the number of the Miraculous Draught of Fishes. There are still 153 Foundation Scholars, in a school of 850 pupils, in addition to about 440 pupils in the Preparatory School. Colet appointed 'the most honest and faithfull fellowshipp of the Mercers of London' as Governors of his School. The Governing Body has been extended to include 6 University Governors and other nominees. The School was moved from its original site adjoining the Cathedral to West Kensington in 1884 and to its present position on the River Thames at Barnes in 1968. A history of the school entitled 'A miraculous draught of fishes' by A H Mead was published in 1990.

Motto: '*Fide et literis*'

Governors:

Chairman: ¶Alderman Sir Alexander Graham, GBE, DCL
Deputy Chairman: Professor R E Pounder, MA, MD, DSc Med, FRCP

Master of the Mercers' Company:
F C G Hohler, Esq

Appointed by the Mercers' Company:
Dr M Bailey
¶R C Cunis, Esq
L Dorfman, Esq
Alderman Sir Robert Finch
Ms Alison Macleod
¶Professor the Lord McColl of Dulwich, CBE
A W Morgan, Esq
The Hon H W Palmer
Ms Jo Rickard
¶A Summers, Esq
¶Sir Nigel Thompson, KCMG, CBE
The Earl St Aldwyn

Appointed by the Mercers' Company in consultation with the University of Oxford:
¶Professor C P Mayer, MA, MPhil, DPhil

Appointed by the Mercers' Company in consultation with the University of Cambridge:
Dr C Y Barlow, PhD

Appointed by the Mercers' Company in consultation with the University of London:
Professor R E Pounder, MA, MD, DSc Med, FRCP (*and Deputy Chairman*)

Clerk to the Governors: Mrs M McGregor

***High Master*: G M Stephen**, BA, PhD, FRSA

Surmaster: R G Jaine, MA, FRGS

Director of Studies: P Woodruff, MA, MSc

Undermasters:
T A Peters, BSc (*Senior Tutor*)
E A du Toit, BPE
P J King, MA
A J Mayfield, BSc, MSc, DPhil
A G Wilson, BA

Housemaster: P A Collinson, MA

Art:
§T P M E Flint, MA
Mrs P C Holmes, BA, UED
*N W Hunter, BA Hons, MEd
§Mrs S E W Hunter, MEd
§Miss E Stravoravdi, MA
I J Tiley, MA, ATC

Classics:
D J Cairns, MA
§J N Davie, MA, BLitt
J T Harrison, BA (*PSHE/ Citizenship*)
*P D Hills, MPhil, PhD
P J King, MA
S A May, MA (*Archivist*)
A G Wilson, BA

Drama
T Y Benyon, MA (*also English*)
*E J T Williams, MA (*also Modern Languages*)

Economics and Politics:
P R K Bird, BA
E A du Toit, BPE
G L Boss, BA
*M R Mikdadi, BSc, MSc, MBA
S P Schmitt, BSc
D C Thaw, MA, BD

English:
A J Broughton, MA
P R J Hudson, MA, PhD
J S Lowden, MA
Miss J McLaren, MA
B J O'Keeffe, MA
J A Sutcliffe, BA, PhD
*J C Venning, MA

Geography:
A P D Isaac, BSc, MSc
R G Jaine, MA, FRGS
P S Littlewood, BSc, MSc, FRGS (*General Studies*)
Mrs S M Nichol, BA, MSc
*J R Williams, MA

History:
C Dean, MA (*University Entrance*)
*M G Howat, BA
M K Lawson, BA, DPhil
Mrs S Mackenzie, BSc, MA
Ms H L Pike, BA
N J Sanderson, MA

Learning Support Coordinator:
Miss J A Isnardi-Bruno, BA

Mathematics:
D P Eves, MEng, PhD
B R Girvan, BA, MEng
M L Harvey, BSc
G Leversha, MA, PhD
A J Mayfield, BSc, MSc, DPhil
T C I Morland, MA, CMath, MIMA
P W Motion, BSc
T A Peters, BSc
P Robson, BSc
M J R Slay, BA, MSc
J M Stone, BA
*O L C Toller, MA
P Woodruff, MA, MSc

Modern Languages:
†P A Collinson, MA
P J C Davies, MA (*Spanish*)
Miss E Garner, BA
D J M Hempstead, BA, MPhil (*French*)
Mrs E D J Hess, MA, MLitt
Miss D Hinnah, BA
Miss E J James, BA
Miss L Lapaire, BA
G C Larlham, BA
Ms J M Newitt, BA
*P S Vanni, MA
S J Wood, BA

Music:
*P W Gritton, MA, LRAM
R A Hepburn, BA, MA
R D A Wedderburn, MA, ARAM, GRSM

Physical Education:
J R Blurton, BSc
A G J Fraser
W T D Hanson, BA
*R G Harrison, BSc
A W Pearce, DipPE
J B H Reed, BA, MSc, DPhil
S Tulley

Religious Studies:
*Revd P L F Allsop, MA
J I Griffiths, BA, MPhil

Sciences:
H W T Adams, BA
J R Bennett, DPhil
W J B Burnett, BSc, PhD (*Biology*)
S J Clarke, MChem
D P Gamblin, MChem, DPhil
A Gardam, MSc, PhD, CEng, FIMechE
Miss L Hasell, BA
S Holmes, MPhys, DPhil
Mrs A Jeffery, BSc (*Chemistry*)
N A Lamb, BSc, PhD
T Lowes, MChem
G S Miller, BSc, MA, MInstP, CPhys
I Poots, BSc, PhD, CChem, MRSC (*Science*)
S J Roberts, MA
C A P Sammut, BSc, MSc
Miss C M Tucker, BSc
K P Zetie, MA, DPhil, MSc, MInstP, CPhys (*Physics*)

Technology:
O V Avni, BSc, ARCS (*Electronics*)
R A Barker, BA, MA (*Computing*)
P F Bullett, MA, PhD, MEd (*Director, Technological Studies*)

K M Campbell, BEd (**Design Technology*)
O J Rokison, MEng
A E Goodridge, BA
D R Smith, MA (**Director of ICT*)

Chaplain: Revd P L F Allsop
Finance Director: I E S May, FCMA, BSc, FPC
Operations Director: D J Imrie, MA
Medical Officer: Dr O G Evans, BSc, MBBS, MRCP
Counsellor: Dr R Bor, CPsychol, AFBPsS, UKCP
Librarian: Mrs A M Aslett, BA, ALA

Colet Court (St Paul's Preparatory School)
Tel: 020 8748 3461
Fax: 020 8746 5357
e-mail: HMsecCC@stpaulsschool.org.uk

Headmaster: T A Meunier, MA, CChem, FRSC

Deputy Headmaster: C G Howes, MA
Director of Studies: Miss A J Gordon, BA
Director of Administration: A P C Fuggle, MA
Head of Juniors: S R K Bailey, BA
Senior Tutor: J Barlow, BSc

Miss S Amaslidis, MA
Mrs J R Baldock, CertEd
P J Berg, ARCM, FRCO
Mrs K Kean, BA
K M Campbell, BEd
D Carroll, BA
Miss J Clough, BA
D M Edwards, BEd
T M Frost, BA
I Gamble, BSc
Miss C H Gill, BA
A E Goodridge, BA
Mrs B A Gordon, BA
N W Groom, BA
T J Harbord, CertEd
Mrs S E J Harrison, BSc
Miss A L Hillyer, BA
Mrs E Howe, BA
N E L Howe, BEd
Mrs A James, BEd
Miss D Lamb, BA
I St J Maynard, BEd
Miss C McCabe, BSc
M McRill, BTech, PhD, CBiol, MIBiol, NPQH
M Mews, BSc
Mme V C M Nolk, L-ès-L
G E Nava, BSc
Mrs J S Olney, BEd
C A Porter, BA
J A J Renshaw, BA
P H Reutenauer, L-ès-L
Miss A Rushman, BSc
Mrs W K Seigel, CertEd
G Tsaknakis, BSc

Admission. Application for Admission to St Paul's is to be made on a form to be obtained from the Admissions Office. Candidates at 13+ take the Common Entrance Examination in June prior to entry in September. A few Sixth Form places are also available.

There is a registration fee of £150.

A Deposit of one third of the termly day fee is required when a parent accepts the offer of a place for his son after interview. The Deposit will be returnable if the boy fails to reach the necessary standard in the entrance examination or when the final account has been cleared after the boy leaves St Paul's.

Fees per term (2008-2009). The Basic Fee is £5,507. This covers Tuition, Games, Loan Books, Stationery, Libraries, Medical Inspection, a careers aptitude test in the GCSE year, certain School publications and Lunch, which all boys are required to attend. Charges are made for the purchase of some books (which become the personal property of boys) and Public Examination Fees.

There are facilities for up to 50 boarders (ages 13 to 18) and boarding is flexible allowing boys to go home at weekends as they wish. The Boarding Fee is £2,656 in addition to the Basic Fee.

Bursaries. A number of bursaries are available whereby the school maintains the spirit of the former Government Assisted Places scheme. The bursaries are means-tested and boys joining Colet Court at 10+ or 11+, or St Paul's at 13+ or 16+ are eligible.

Foundation Scholarships. (*see Scholarship Entries section*).

Other Scholarships. Music: A number of Foundation Music Scholarships are available at St Paul's each year. Candidates are expected to have attained at least grade VI on their principal instrument. A Dennis Brain Memorial Scholarship is available from time to time and a Sharp scholarship for entry to St Paul's at 16+. South Square Choral Awards are offered each year in conjunction with Colet Court for treble voices of age 8, 9 or 10.

South Square Art Scholarships: One or more scholarships are available each year to boys who have taken GCSE to assist them in following a career in practical art. These scholarships can be awarded for the candidate's A Level course at St Paul's.

Arkwright Scholarships: The School is a member of the Arkwright Scholarship Scheme which offers financial assistance to sixth-formers who intend to pursue a career in Engineering, Technology, or other Design-related subjects.

Leaving Scholarships or Awards. A number of Prize Grants and Exhibitions (including the Lord Campden's exhibitions, founded in 1625 by Baptist Hicks, Viscount Campden) are given by the Governors every year to boys proceeding to Oxford or Cambridge or to any other place of further education.

Curriculum. All boys follow a broadly based course up to GCSE. Thereafter in the Eighth Form, AS and A level subjects are so arranged that boys can combine a wide range of Arts and Science subjects if they so wish. Boys take four or five AS level subjects followed by three or four A level subjects.

Games. Games offered include: Athletics, Cricket, Fencing, Fives, Golf, Judo, Rackets, Rowing, Rugby, Sailing, Soccer, Squash, Swimming and Tennis (hard and grass).

The School has its own Swimming Pool, Fencing Salle, Tennis, Squash, Fives and Rackets Courts, and its own Boat House. The Games Centre also comprises a Sports Hall and Gymnasium. The Sports Hall is equipped for Tennis, Badminton, Basketball and indoor Cricket nets. There are Cricket and Rackets Professionals.

Music. Tuition is available in piano, organ, harpsichord, all the standard orchestral instruments, jazz, bagpipes and the Alexander Technique. There are three choirs, two orchestras, several jazz bands and a wealth of small ensembles. New purpose built Music School and Recital Hall opened in Autumn 1999.

School Societies. There is a wide choice of more than 30 Societies, including Musical, Artistic and Dramatic activities, Debating, Historical and Scientific Societies, Politics and Economics, Bridge, Chess, Natural History, Photography, European Society, a Christian Union and Social Service.

The Preparatory School (Colet Court) adjoins St Paul's School. (*For details see entry in IAPS section.*)

Charitable status. St Paul's School is a Registered Charity, number 1119619. The object of the charity is to promote the education of boys in Greater London.

St Peter's School

Clifton York YO30 6AB
Tel: 01904 527300
Fax: 01904 527302
e-mail: enquiries@st-peters.york.sch.uk
website: www.st-peters.york.sch.uk

Founded in 627AD, St Peter's is one of Europe's oldest schools. It provides both outstanding boarding and day education for boys and girls from 13 to 18. St Peter's School has an unrivalled record of academic achievement in the North of England. Its adjacent Prep School, St Olave's, admits boarding and day boys and girls from 8 to 13 and Clifton Pre-prep School admits day girls and boys from 3 to 8.

Motto: '*Super antiquas vias*'

Governors:
J D Pike (*Chairman*)

M Bainbridge
R Barrett
Mrs C Blenkin
J Burdass
Professor R A Butlin
D Dickson
Canon J Fletcher
Lady Emma Ingilby
Mrs D N Jagger
Professor P V Lamarque
Mrs M Loffill
Mr J C Morris
Mr P Netherwood
Mrs V M Rose
P N Shepherd
G B Smalley
Mrs C E Wesley

Clerk to the Governors: Mrs K Hodges

***Head Master*: R I Smyth**, MA Emmanuel College, Cambridge

Deputy Headmaster: Mrs M C Wyke, BSc, PGCE
Senior Teacher: M C Lawrence, MA
Director of Studies: D J Watkinson, BSc
Senior Chaplain: The Revd J Daly, BA, MA, MTh

Heads of Departments:
Art: J Darmody, BA
Biology: M C Lawrence, MA
Careers: Mrs P Bollands, BA, PGDip LSE, MBA, CertEd, MCIPD
Chemistry: P D Northfield, BSc, CChem, FRSC
Classics: M Adams, MA
Drama: T Coker, MPhil, PhD
Economics/Business Studies: A Severn, BA
English: Miss E K G McFarlane, BA
Geography: D M Paterson, BA
Government & Politics: P C Taylor, BA
History: A J Craig, MA Cantab, PhD
Information Technology: P Hynard
Mathematics: D J Spencer, BSc
Modern Languages: C A Hodsdon, BA
Director of Music: A P Wright, BMus, LRAM
Physical Education & Games: S J Williams, BEd
Physics: D K Morris, BSc
PSHE: J Whitehouse, BEd
Religious Studies: The Revd J Daly, MA
Technology: J Whitehouse, BEd

All other St Peter's academic staff are listed on the school website.

Houses and Housemasters/mistresses:

Girls' Boarding Houses:
Dronfield: Mr and Mrs R J P Trevett
The Rise: Mr and Mrs C W Hall

Boys' Boarding Houses:
Linton: Mr and Mrs M Hall
The Manor: Mr & Mrs P C Taylor

Day Houses:
Clifton: M J Grant
Grove: P J Stephen
Queen's: S J Gwilliam
School House: Dr A J Craig
Temple: Mrs J M Houghton
Hope: Mrs S M Watkinson

The Prep School (St Olave's)
Master: A Falconer, BA, MBA

Deputy Head: Mrs S Jackson, BA
Senior Master: C W R Lawrence, BSc
Director of Studies: Mrs L Garner, MA
Head of Boarding: Mrs S L Bennett, BSc
Chaplain: J M Dodsworth, MA

All other St Olave's academic staff are listed on the school website.

St Olave's Houses and Housemasters/mistresses:

Junior Boarding:
Wentworth: Mrs S L Bennett

Day Houses:
Ainsty: Miss S-J Fell
Alcuin: Mrs S E Rose
Elmet: Mrs F J Stasiak
Fairfax: Mrs C F J Round
York: N B Savage

Clifton Pre-prep School
Headteacher: Mrs P M Arkley, MA, BSc, CertEd

Assistant Heads:
Mrs G D Spaven, CertEd
C Tidswell, BEd

Nursery:
Mrs F Bonas, BA, NNEB

All other Clifton Pre-prep academic staff are listed on the school website.

Administrative Staff:
Bursar: Miss P J Lacy, ACA
Head Master's Secretary: Mrs J Green
Medical Officer: Dr D S Kemp, MB BS, MRCGP, DRCOG
Librarian: Ms P Chandler, MA

St Peter's is co-educational with 550 boys and girls. There are 350 girls and boys in the Junior Prep School, St Olave's, and a further 150 boys and girls in Clifton Pre-prep School. There are 200 boarders housed in five boarding houses and all St Peter's day pupils belong to a day house, all of which are on the campus.

Buildings & Facilities. The School occupies an impressive 47-acre site with playing fields stretching down to the River Ouse close to the centre of York.

There is a large sports centre and a recent development has provided the most up-to-date conditions for the teaching of science, computing, design and technology. There is also a drama centre, music school, outstanding art department and a superb library.

Entrance. Pupils are admitted through the School's entrance examinations held at the end of January for both 13+ and 16+. St Olave's entrance examinations are held in January (8+) and February (10+ and 11+) and pupils can enter in any of the years. Clifton Pre-prep school entrance is by assessment in March.

Means-tested Bursaries for those who will qualify for more than 50% of the fees are also available.

Scholarships. (*see Scholarship Entries section*). Honorary academic scholarships and music awards for instrumental tuition are available.

Curriculum. A very broad middle school curriculum including ICT, Music, PE, Design & Technology, and courses in personal and social education.

Nearly all pupils proceed into the Sixth Form, and A Level courses in all subjects studied for GCSE and in Economics, Politics, Business Studies, Further Mathematics and PE are available.

Academic and pastoral care. A comprehensive house and tutorial system with interim assessments and reports during the term ensure the close scrutiny by all the teaching staff of pupils' academic and general development.

Religious education and worship. Religious Studies are part of the curriculum, and Chapel is seen as an opportunity for pupils to be made aware of the School's Christian heritage.

Careers and university entrance. The School is an 'all-in' member of the Independent Schools Careers Organisation. Careers staff are available for consultation, maintaining an extensive library relating to careers and higher education and organising a full programme of events for the Sixth Form.

Games and Physical Education. Physical education is part of the curriculum. There is an extensive games programme and excellent sports facilities. Rugby football, netball, hockey, cricket and rowing are major sports, and many other options including swimming, athletics, cross-country, shooting, basketball, climbing, squash, badminton, tennis, association football, fencing, golf, trampoline and weight-training.

Combined Cadet Force. A flourishing and voluntary CCF contingent, with army and air sections, allows the pursuit of many activities including a full programme of camps, expeditions and courses.

The Duke of Edinburgh's Award is also on offer with expedition training for all levels as part of the activities programme.

Music. Musical ability is encouraged throughout the School. There is an orchestra, bands, choirs, choral society and over 10 smaller groups, with concerts a regular feature of the school year as well tours abroad.

Tuition in all instruments is provided, and GCSE and A Level music courses.

Art. Drawing, painting, print-making, ceramics and sculpture may all be taken up both in and out of school hours in an outstanding department.

Drama. The School has two theatres: the Memorial Hall and the smaller, more flexible Drama Centre. There are various productions through the year giving opportunities both for acting and back-stage skills.

Clubs and societies. Many societies flourish including chess, debating, discussion groups, etc. Use outside school hours of such facilities as workshops, computer department and art studio is encouraged.

Travel and expeditions. Recent holiday opportunities, which are regularly available, have included skiing trips, trekking in Morocco, hill-walking and climbing in Snowdonia and the Scottish Highlands and expeditions abroad.

The Friends of St Peter's. Parents are encouraged to join the Friends, a society whose aim is to promote a close relationship between parents and staff and to further the welfare of the School.

The Old Peterites. The honorary secretary of the Old Peterites' Club is: P J Netherwood, Tel: 01904 422863 or via the school's website.

Fees per term (2008-2009). Full Boarding £7,165, Day Boarding £5,225, Day £4,450.

These fees cover all costs (including books and stationery) except individual music lessons and external examination fees.

Further information. Prospectuses for St Olave's, Clifton Pre-prep and St Peter's, containing full details of the three schools' entry requirements, are available on request: tel: 01904 527300, e-mail: enquiries@st-peters.york.sch.uk, or via the website: www.st-peters.york.sch.uk.

(*See also entries for St Olave's School and Clifton Pre-preparatory School in IAPS section.*)

Charitable status. St Peter's School York is a Registered Charity, number 529740. Its aims are to promote education.

Seaford College

Petworth

Lavington Park Petworth West Sussex GU28 0NB
Tel: 01798 867392
Fax: 01798 867606
e-mail: jmackay@seaford.org
website: www.seaford.org

The College was founded in 1884 at Seaford in East Sussex and moved to Lavington Park at the foot of the South Downs in 1946. The grounds cover some 400 acres and include extensive sports facilities and scope for future developments. The campus includes a superb Art and Design department, a Sixth Form Centre, purpose-built boarding houses, a Junior House incorporating classrooms and boarding facilities, and a new state-of-the-art Maths and Science block, and recently the stable block has been refurbished for the new music suite.

Seaford is controlled by an Independent non-profit making Charitable Trust approved by the Department of Education and the Charity Commissioners and is administered by the College Board of Governors.

Motto: *Ad Alta – To The Heights*

Governing Body:
G Sinclair (*Chairman*)
D Avery
N V Bevan, MA, JP
J H Crosland
Mrs P Hadley
Mrs A Harris-Shaw
N Lacey
A G Mason
Mrs J Peel
R Venables Kyrke

***Headmaster*: T J Mullins**, MBA, BA

Deputy Head: J R Hall, BSc
Academic Deputy Head: Mrs B Jinks, BA Jt Hons, MA, NPQH

Teaching Staff:
* *Head of Department*

Art & Design:
*A G Grantham-Smith, BA, PG Dip ArtEd
Mrs K Grantham-Smith, BA (*Photography*)
B Murphy, BA (*Ceramics*)
A Kirkton, BA Hons

Business Studies:
T Clark, BEd

Classics:
T Farmer, BA Hons (*Deputy Head of Junior School*)

Design Technology:
*D Shaw, BEd
S R Parry, BSc

Drama:
*Dr J Askew, BA Hons

EFL:
J Scoular, BA, TEFL

English:
*L McBratney, MA, BA
P R Jennings, MA Oxon
P Harvey, BEd
Mrs P White, BA, PG DipSpLD
A Phillips, BA QTS
A Carlton-Oatley, MA, AVCM (*Library*)
Miss M Munt (*Media Studies*)
Mrs J Gargon, BA Hons

Geography:
*N Q Angier, BSc, MA
C Pearson, BA Hons, PGCE
K R Woodcock, BSc

History:
*T D Phillips, BA
Mrs J A Gregory, BEd (*Assistant Head*)
R Stather, BA (*Head of Junior School*)

Information Technology:
*D Crook, BA
P Bain, BA

LAMDA:
Mrs P Trower, BA
Mrs S Arnold

Learning Support:
*N Foster, BA, Hornsby Dip
Mrs M Gilbert
Ms A Jensen, DipSpLD
Miss J Lorimer-Green, DipSpLD
Mrs E Barden, BA, PGCE
Mrs P A Angier, BA, Dip CG, DipSpLD
Mrs S Stafford, BEd
T E Warren, BSc Econ, FCIT, FILT, MInstTA
Mrs L Ferris

Mathematics:
*S Kettlewell, BA
Mrs Brinzan-Motoc, BA, PGCE
Mrs B Jinks, MA, BA, NPQH
Miss J Gramsma, BEd
Mrs K Miliam, BSc, PGCE
P A Wilson, BA Hons, PGCE
Miss E Geraghty, BSc, PGCE

Modern Languages:
*N Kyte (*Spanish*)
Mrs H Farmer, BA
Mrs S Weekes, BA Hons, PGCE
Ms H Martin, PGCE (*French*)
Mrs J Linford, BA (*Spanish*)

Psychology:
Mrs C Greenhouse, BSc Hons, PGCE

Music:
D Read, BMus, MMus, FRCO, DipEd (*Director of Music*)
Mrs J Hawkins, PGCE, BMus (*Asst Dir of Music*)

Physical Education:
*J Thompson, BA Hons, PGCE
Miss E Teague, BA Hons QTS
T W Gregory, BEd
W Cuthbertson (*Marketing & PR*)
Mrs D Strange (*Coach, Head of Year 9*)
A Cook, BA, PGCE
M McNeil, EHA Level 2 (*Hockey Coach*)
C Sayell (*Adventure Training Coordinator*)
N McFarlane (*Golf Professional*)

Religious Studies:
*R Bailey, BA, MPhil (*Head of Year 11*)

Science:
*Dr V Davis, BSc, PhD (*Science*)
D Coulson, BEng Hons, MEng, CEng, PGCE (**Chemistry, Head of Sixth Form*)
P Nazir, BSc, PGCE (**Physics*)
Mrs G Pasteiner, BSc (**Biology, Head of Year 10*)
J R Hall, BSc
Mrs J Wright, BSc, PhD, PGCE
J Batts, BSc, MSc, PGCE
Dr N Harris, BSc, PhD

Careers/Exams:
D C Garrard, BA

CCF:
Major RC Lowry CFM
WO2 S Gerrard

Chaplain: Revd M Gilbert
Bursar: Mrs A Lemon van de Kooij
Headmaster's Secretary: Mrs C Mullins
Admissions Secretary: Mrs J Mackay-Smith

Pupils. Seaford College offers options of Full Boarding, Weekly, 4-Day and Day facilities to girls and boys aged 10 to 18. There are 520 pupils at the College with over 100 in the Sixth Form. There are two boys houses and two girls houses and a junior house for both girls and boys aged 10–13.

Aims. Seaford College's aim is to provide an all-round education that equips students with the skills needed to function in the commercial world after leaving their academic studies. The College takes students with a range of abilities and aims to provide the greatest possible 'value-added' for their given abilities. Streaming children in core subjects allows them to work at their own speed and makes them aware of others skills and shortcomings.

Academic. The Junior House (incorporating Years 6, 7 and 8) offers a wide ranging curriculum which includes core subjects of English, Mathematics, Science, a language, Information Technology and extra English, as well as all the usual topics of Geography, History, Art and DT etc.

Years 10 and 11 lead up to the GCSE examinations. Students study the core subjects of English Literature, English Language, Mathematics and Double Science and then choose four other syllabuses to follow from a comprehensive list of subjects which include: Art, Business Studies, Ceramics, Drama, Design and Technology, Geography, French, History, Music, Physical Education, Spanish.

All students in these forms also study Information Technology and Religious Studies and take part in the College sports.

The A Level subject list is comprehensive with new subjects, such as Textiles, added to the curriculum in 2005. In the Lower Sixth students follow a College set curriculum and choose four subjects to study for the first year at the end of which pupils sit AS examinations. They usually then choose to continue with three subjects through to A Level. Over and above this in their first year students will undertake to achieve the Duke of Edinburgh's Silver Award. In the Upper Sixth year students will concentrate on their three A Level subjects.

Music. Music is an important part of Seaford's life. The College boasts an internationally renowned College Chapel Choir who have been requested to visit countries such as Ecuador, America and Russia to sing at Ambassadors' Christmas parties or raise money for underprivileged children; they have recorded several CDs and their recordings are often heard on radio stations. The College also has an orchestra and offers lessons for all instruments. Music can be studied at GCSE and AS level.

Sports. With superb facilities available in the grounds, and staff that have coached and played at international level, the College has a reputation for sporting excellence. Facilities include: six rugby pitches, eight tennis courts, squash courts, pool, a water based all-weather hockey pitch, a large indoor sports hall that allows tennis and hockey to be played all year round, and a 9-hole golf course and driving range.

Art. The College has an excellent Art department which allows students to exercise their talents to the fullest extent in every aspect of art and design, whether it is ceramics, textiles, fine art or any other medium they wish to use. Many pupils from Seaford go on to study at design school and work for design and fashion houses or advertising companies. Students are encouraged to display their work throughout the year in the department's gallery.

Combined Cadet Force. The College has strong ties with the Military and has a very well supported Combined Cadet Force, with each wing of the armed forces well represented. Weekend exercises and training are a regular feature in the College calendar and include adventure training, canoeing, climbing, sailing and camping.

Admission. Entry at age 10, 11 and 13 is determined on cognitive ability testing and a trial day at the school. 13+ pupils will still be expected to take the Common Entrance Examination. Sixth Form entry is dependent upon GCSE results and interview. Pupils are required to have at least 45 points at GCSE (=9 C grades) and these should include English and Mathematics. Pupils may enter the school without one of these subjects on condition they retake. Overseas students are required to take an oral and written examination to determine level of comprehension in English.

Scholarships and Bursaries. (*see Scholarship Entries section*). Scholarships offered: Academic, Art, Design and Technology, Music (Choral and Orchestral) and Sport (13+ only). At 11+: Music/Choral only. Scholarship examinations are taken in February of the year of entry and are worth £500. Where a potential recipient of a scholarship is also in need of discounted fees, they must make an application through the bursary system and 'means testing'. Bursaries are offered to children of serving members of Her Majesty's Forces and siblings of existing pupils.

Fees per term (2008-2009). Senior School: £7,560 (Full/Weekly Boarding), £6,400 (4-day Boarding), £4,950 (Day). Junior School: £5,670 (Weekly Boarding), £4,975 (4-day Boarding), £4,000 (Day).

Extras. Drama, Clay Pigeon Shooting, Fencing, Fishing, Golf, Sailing, Museum & Theatre trips, Aikida, Archery, Debating Club, Astronomy etc.

Charitable status. Seaford College is a Registered Charity, number 277439. It exists to provide education for children.

Sedbergh School

Sedbergh Cumbria LA10 5HG
Tel: 015396 20535 (Headmaster)
015396 20303 (Bursar)
Fax: 015396 21301
e-mail: enquiries@sedberghschool.org
website: www.sedberghschool.org

Sedbergh School was founded in 1525 by Dr Roger Lupton, Provost of Eton, and endowed by him with lands connected with a chantry. Sedbergh School offers a blend of academic learning and all-round development of the individual through a strong and caring House system and a wide range of exciting and challenging extra-curricular activities. It is known for its excellence in sport, art and music, magnificent location and happy atmosphere. The £4.5 million Robertson Trust provides for Academic and Music Scholarships in addition to awards in other disciplines.

Motto: '*Dura Virum Nutrix*'

The Governing Body:
R S Napier, MA (*Chairman*)
The Most Revd and Rt Hon The Lord Archbishop of York, represented by The Bishop of Durham
Her Majesty's Lord-Lieutenant of Cumbria, J A Cropper, BA, FCA
The Master of St John's College, Cambridge, represented by Dr PT Wood, ScD
Mrs S E Bagot
Miss K Bruce-Lockhart
Mrs C Buchanan, LLB
M J Cutherbertson
R M Gourlay
J K MacAskill, BEd
The Hon Sir Richard McCombe, QC
S A M Rayner
W M Richardson
J S Rink
R G T Stenhouse
D M Strachan, MA

Clerk to the Governors and Bursar: P S Marshall, BSc, ACIB, AISMM
Foundation Director: R W Witt, BSc, CertEd, MIF

***Headmaster*: C H Hirst**, MA Cantab

Second Master: P M Wallace-Woodroffe, BA

Senior Mistress: Mrs S L Hirst, BEd

Director of Studies: J M Sykes, BSc, MSc

School Chaplain: The Revd P L Sweeting, BSc, BA

Assistant Staff:
Miss A P Astin, BA
*G Aveyard, DipAD, HDipDes, ATC
†G T Ayling, MA
Mrs H L Ayling, BA, MA (*Admissions*)
*M R Baggley, BSc
N H Brown, BSc
*P M Bush, MA
*L W Catlow, BA, DPhil
Mrs H J Christy, BEd (*Head of Girls' Games*)
G A Clarke, BA
*S J Cooling, BSc
H R Davies, BSc
Mrs S A Doherty, GRNCM
K A Downey, BA
S H Elmore, DipCeramicDes, SDC, SIAD
Miss K Farrand, BA
Miss C F Finn, BSc
*J E Fisher, BSc
B C Glover, BA
†*The Revd C D Griffin, BA
Mrs S A Griffin, BA, AdvDipEd SEN
†*C D Gunning, BEd
Mrs C S Hall, BSc
*S E Hall, BA, MA
D J Harrison, BA
*R C J Hartley, MA
C Hattam, BA
J-M Holliday, BA
P R Hoskin, BSc, DPhil
Mrs R C Hubbard, BSc
Miss K L Iliff, MA, MSc (*Archivist*)
T Jeffries, BSc
R Kellett, BA
A R Lewis, BPhil, NABBC, LTCL (*Bandmaster*)
†C P Mahon, BSc
S R D Milner, BEng, MSc
Mrs J M Mitchell, BA, ALA (*Librarian*)
Mrs C M Morgan, BSc
†C R I Morgan, BA
J R D Morgan, BA
*R G Northern, BA, MSc
S W Oliver, BA (*Head of Boys' Games*)
†Mrs G E Parry, BA
†Mrs P J F Prall, BA
Mrs J M Priestley, MA
M M Priestley, BA, MA
*M A F Raw, MA
J D W Richardson, BA
M P Ripley, MA, DPhil
*J H Seymour, BA, LTCL (*Director of Music*)
*S M Smith, MA
C W Swanson, BA, MFA
*H M Symonds, BA (*Careers Master*)
Mrs D K Thomas, MA
*M J O Valentine, BA
†Mrs S J Wallace-Woodroffe, BSc
†*C P Webster, BSc

Houses & Housemasters/mistresses:
Evans: C D Gunning
Hart: The Revd C D Griffin
Lupton: Mrs S J Wallace-Woodroffe
Powell: C P Webster
Robertson: Mrs P J F Prall
School: C R I Morgan
Sedgwick: G T Ayling
Winder: C P Mahon

Medical Officer: Dr P D Batty, MBChB, FP Cert, DRCOG, MRCGP, Dip FEM Bath, FFSEM UK

Headmaster's Secretary: Miss A J Bird, BA

There are 480 pupils in the Senior School, of whom 465 are boarders, distributed among eight boarding Houses where pupils live, eat all meals and have their studies/bedsitting rooms.

Pupils are looked after in their Houses by a Housemaster or Housemistress, the House Matron and a House Tutor, who keep in close touch with pupils' parents. If the pupils are ill, they are treated in the School Medical Centre, which is managed by fully qualified staff. The School has its own GP.

The Junior School (120) is situated 30 minutes' drive from Sedbergh and offers day, flexi, weekly and full boarding for pupils aged 4–13.

Both schools are fully co-educational.

The academic curriculum is designed to give pupils a thorough grounding in essential subjects and to delay as long as possible the need to specialise. In the Sixth Form, a flexible system makes possible a large number of combinations of A and AS Level subjects, while in addition all pupils study English, Religious Studies, Current Affairs and a number of options, ranging from Russian to Computing, Electronics to Music. There are also various academic societies (eg Art, History, Music and Science), and a programme of Civic Lectures throughout the year. The School has excellent computing facilities.

The School lays emphasis on introducing pupils to the Christian faith. Confirmation services for both the Church of England and the Church of Scotland are held each year. However, the School welcomes pupils of all denominations. It is usual for pupils to attend a service in Chapel on Sundays; each day begins with an assembly in Powell Hall and ends with prayers in the Boarding Houses.

Sedbergh tries to develop as many as possible of the pupils' individual skills and talents and to introduce them to a wide range of interests and activities.

Art and Design Centre. The Art School includes Studios for Painting, Pottery and Sculpture, Photographic Darkrooms and an Exhibition Gallery. The Design Centre provides multimedia workshops and Design Studios with CAD/CAM, and digital editing facilities. All pupils work in the studios and workshops as part of the curriculum, and have opportunities to do so in their spare time. Also in the Centre is a Lecture Theatre with facilities for video, films and drama.

Music. Music is encouraged at all levels and the School has strong Cathedral associations. There is a Chapel Choir and a Choral Society which performs two major works each year. Instrumentalists may join the Orchestra, String Orchestra, Junior or Senior Bands and Jazz Orchestra, and there is a considerable amount of music-making in small ensembles. There are two Music Schools, one dedicated to Brass. Music lessons, given by full-time music staff and visiting teachers, are offered for the usual orchestral and keyboard instruments. The School has two fine organs. Many pupils study Music at GCSE, AS and A Level. An annual Concert Series brings distinguished artists to the School and there are regular School concerts throughout the year. Music Scholarships are available.

Drama. As well as visits to theatres there are usually two major School plays a year and one Junior production; there are also House plays and year-group productions. Houses also organise entertainment for their own parents and pupils, usually plays, songs and revue sketches.

The Setting. The School capitalises on its beautiful situation in the Yorkshire Dales National Park and has a very active Natural History Society, which manages three conservation sites in the area; it also runs numerous expeditions on the fells and in the Lake District. The programme includes Geography and Biology Field Courses, Adventure Training, Duke of Edinburgh's Award and CCF camps, Climbing, Potholing, Canoeing and Sailing trips. It also includes major expeditions abroad; musical, geographical, historical, philanthropic, sporting and pure adventure. Pupils may enter for the Duke of Edinburgh's Award Scheme.

CCF. The School CCF has Army, Navy and Air Force Sections, and as well as undertaking Basic Training it gives boys and girls an experience of camping and preliminary instruction in Shooting in its indoor range. Rifle Shooting is encouraged and a high standard is achieved both on the indoor and open ranges. The School is a regular winner of major trophies at Bisley. There is a flourishing CCF Band and Corps of Drums which regularly tours the country and overseas.

Games. There is an extensive programme of games, almost all of which are open for boys and girls. The main games are Athletics, Cricket, Cross-Country Running, Fives, Hockey, Netball, Rugby Football, Shooting, Soccer, Squash, Swimming and Tennis. There is a fitness suite, sports hall, indoor swimming pool and all-weather surface.

There are opportunities for Sailing and Fishing, and School societies make provision for many other activities including Debating, Natural History, Archaeology, Geology, Photography and Art.

Fees per term (2008-2009). Senior: Tuition and Boarding £8,250; Day pupils £6,160. In addition there are voluntary fees (eg for Instrumental Music, CCF, EFL).

Scholarships and Bursaries. (*see Scholarship Entries section*). Scholarships and Exhibitions are awarded annually to those demonstrating Academic excellence, or talent in Music, Art, Drama, Design Technology and Sport, as well as all-round ability. All such awards can be supplemented by a further Bursary award, based upon the financial circumstances of the candidate's parents. All Scholarship examinations are held annually at the School in the Lent Term. Full details available from The Headmaster's Secretary.

Admission. A registration fee of £75 is payable at the time of registration.

Senior School: Application for admission at any age should be made to the Headmaster. At the age of 13 it is usual that a pupil would sit Common Entrance or Scholarship. Pupils are also accepted into the Sixth Form on the basis of GCSE results.

Junior School: Entry to the Junior School is either by Entrance examination, interview or assessment – according to age. Junior Bursaries are available to those parents who would encounter considerable hardship in the payment of fees.

The Old Sedberghian Club (c/o Malim Lodge, Sedbergh School, Sedbergh) flourishes and has branches all over the world.

Charitable status. Sedbergh School is a Registered Charity, number 1080672. It exists to provide boarding education and pastoral welfare to pupils from the ages of 4 to 18.

Sevenoaks School

Sevenoaks Kent TN13 1HU
Tel: 01732 455133
Fax: 01732 456143
e-mail: regist@sevenoaksschool.org (Admissions)
hm@sevenoaksschool.org (Head)
website: www.sevenoaksschool.org

Founded in 1432, Sevenoaks School is a co-educational, day and boarding school for pupils aged 11–18.

Motto: '*Servire Deo Regnari Est*'

Governing Body:
Chairman: A C V Evans, MA, MPhil, FIL
Vice-Chairman: Ms B Giles, MA, MSc

Governors:

Mrs F J Adler, BA
Ms D Casson, FCSD, FRCA
The Rt Revd Dr B Castle, PhD
P J Coates, FCA
A N Golding, MA
R N H Gould, BA
D Griffiths, MA, FCA
Ms E Johnson
Mrs A M Lonsdale, CBE, MA
Ms C Pimlott
Ms S Rausing
P Shirke
D R Walker, MA
J Warde
Prof M J Waring, ScD
M Whittow, PhD

Bursar and Clerk to the Governors: Air Vice-Marshal A J Burton, OBE, BSc Econ, FCIS, Chartered FCIPD

Academic Staff:

***Head*: Mrs C L Ricks**, MA

Undermaster: M J Bolton, BA
Deputy Head (*Pastoral*): Miss T M Homewood, MA, BSc
Deputy Head (*Academic*): T G Lacey, MA
Deputy Head (*Co-curriculum*): J Attwater, MA
Director of Teaching and Learning: C D Greenhalgh, BA, PhD
Director of International Baccalaureate: N S Alchin, MA

Director of Admissions and Communications: Mrs A M Stuart, BSc
Director of Information Systems: Mrs S J Williamson, BA, MSc
Director of Administration: Miss A A Franks, MA
Chaplain: The Revd N N Henshaw, BA
Sixth Form Registrar: A D Waldron, BA

Assistant Teachers:
* *Head of Department*
† *Housemaster/mistress*

P R Bassett, MA (*Mathematics*)
Miss J C Bevan, BA (*English*)
Miss E Boulton, BA (*History*)
M P Beverley, BA, MA, (*English*)
Miss M T Boyd, BSc, MA (*Mathematics*)
J N Burger, MA (*Mathematics*)
I C Campbell, BSc (**Psychology*)
T J Carden, BA, MA (**Instrumental and Vocal Studies*)
Miss T H Cardon, BA (*Biology*)
S Carr, MA (**Classics*)
†N K Connell, BEd (*French*)
Miss M T Connolly, BSc (*Physics*)
S A J Coquelin, MA (*French*) (*from January 2009*)
G Coupe, MA (*Art*)
J P Cox, BA (*Computing*)
S R Crook, BSc (*Chemistry*)
A G Day, MA (*Economics & Business Studies*)
Miss M-L Delvallée, MA (**Additional Languages, French*)
P G de May, BA (*Classics*)
G R Dinsdale, BA (**Physical Education*)
J Drury, MA (**Russian*)
A J Dunn, MA, DPhil (**History*)
Mrs C Duran-Oreiro (*Spanish*)
Miss A M Durnford, BA (*English, Drama*)
C H J Dyer, BA (**Music*)
Mrs H E Ellis, BA (*Biology*)
J C Emmitt, BA (*Physical Education*)
P L Eversfield, MA (**Economics & Business Studies*)
Miss N M Fayaud, MA (**French*)
P Ford, BSc (**Computing*)
Mrs G Frank-Gemmill, PhD (*German, *Careers*)
T B Fugard, PhD (*Mathematics*)
S J Gladstone, BA (*Music*)
M W Goff, BA (*English*)
J W Grant, BA (*Drama*)
Mrs R A Greenhalgh, BA (*Spanish, French*)
Mrs P O Hargreaves, BA (**Drama*)
P Harrison, MA (*English*)
†Mrs N J Haworth, MA (*Physics*)
N T Haworth, BA (*History*)
R B Hebbert, BA (*Economics & Business Studies, History*)
Mrs C J Henshaw, BA (**English*)
P T Hill, BEd (*Physical Education, Geography*)
Mrs B R Hobbs, BA (*Art*)
S Holden, BEd (*Physical Education*)
Mrs C A Hubbard, BSc (*Physics*)
P J Hulston, BSc (*Economics & Business Studies*)
Miss L N Jones, BA (*English*)
T R Jones, BA, MA (**Mathematics*)
Mrs E A Joseph, BA (*Physical Education*)
†L C Kiggell, MBA (*Economics & Business Studies*)
P I Kino, BA (*German*)
N Kunaratnam, BA (*French*)
P M La Rondie, BA (*Mathematics*)
G A Lawrie, BSc (**Design Technology*)
Miss R L Leeming, BA (*Design Technology*)
P G Leese, MSc (*Mathematics*)
†Mrs K Lewis, BSc
Miss V L Longhurst, MA (*Geography*)
Mrs S Lyth-Lawley, BA (*History*)
Mrs A J Maynard, BA (**Head of Learning Support, French*)
†Mrs E J McCoubrie, MA (*English*)
K J McLaughlin, BA (**Science, Physics*)
Miss R L McQuillin, MA (*History*)
A Merson-Davies, BSc (*Biology*)
D W Mott, BA (**Spanish*)
Mrs K A Mylod, BSc (*Biology*)
Miss A E Nairn, BHPE (*Physical Education*)
Miss J R Nowicki, MA (*English*)
Miss M Ochoa, MA (*Spanish*)
Mrs D Orme, BSc, MSc, PhD (*Mathematics*)
S M Owen, MA, PhD (**Chemistry*)
P X Pillet, BA, MA (**Modern Languages*)
Mrs K L Pitcher, BSc (*Biology*)
A J Presland, BSc (*Mathematics*)
D Proctor, BSc, MSc, PhD (*Chemistry*)
Miss S Rahman, BA (*English*)
Mrs A E Rochdi, BA (*French, Spanish*)
D J Rogers, BA (*Mathematics*)
R M Ruge, MA (*French, *German*)
S J Sharp, BSc, PhD (**Physics*)
A C Smith, BComm (*Economics & Business Studies*)
T D Stuart, BA (**Philosophy, Biology*)
J L Tate, BSc (*Physics*)
C J Tavaré, MA (*Biology, Physical Education*)
Miss H Tebay, MA (*Mathematics*)
C M Thomas, BA (**Art*)
P R Thompson, BA, MA (**Geography*)
R M Thompson, BSc (*Design Technology*)
Miss C Tostevin, MSc (*Chemistry*)
Miss A E Tully, BSc (*Biology*)
W R Vincent, BSc, MSc (*Biology*)
Miss H K Walker, BA (*Classics*)
Mrs B Walpole, BSc, MPhil, MIBiol (**Biology*)
Miss V K Walsh, BA (*History*)
Miss C S Watson, BA (*Classics*)
Ms C E Williams, BA, MA (*English*)
Mrs G P Williams, BSc, PhD (*Mathematics*)
S A Williams, BSc (*Mathematics*)
†G J Willis, BA (*Geography*)
A G Wilson, MA (*English*)
R C Woodward, BSc, MA, ARCS (*Chemistry*)
†J D Wyld, BA (*French*)

Part-time Staff:
Mrs K Agarwal (*Hindi*)
Mrs E J Alchin (*Theory of Knowledge*)
O C Barratt, BA (*Art*)
Mrs E M Bassett, BA (*Chemistry*)
Mrs M Bedford, BA, MA (*Classics*)
Mrs R Campbell, BA (*English*)
Mrs R Cargill Thompson, BSc, MSc, ACA (*Mathematics*)
Mrs R S Chard, BA (*Classics*)
Mrs E G Connell, BSc (*Mathematics*)
Mrs J Douglas (*Careers*)
Mrs C E Dyer, BA (*French, German*)
Ms S M Gale, BA (*Classics*)
Mrs C E Gilliat-Smith, BA (*Physical Education*)
Mrs M Gower (*Japanese*)
Miss L A Gray, BSc (*Geography*)
Mrs J Hendry (*Music*)
Mrs W J Heydorn, MA (*Religious Studies*)
Mrs W Y Huang (*Mandarin*)
Mrs L M von Kaufmann, MA (*Geography, Religious Studies*)
Mrs E Kelly (*Russian*)
Mrs J L Kiggell, MA, ARCM, AMus, TCL (*Music*)
Mrs Y Knott (*Japanese*)
Mrs S J MacLeay (*Geography*)
D Merewether (*Photography*)
A C Mitchell, BA (*Film, Video*)
Miss P A Morecroft (*Physical Education*)
Mrs J A Penney, BSc Ed (*Chemistry*)
B A Richards (*Drama*)

Mrs M Schofield, CertEd (*Italian*)
Mrs H Smith (*Learning Support*)
Mrs A Symons, MSc (*Italian*)
Mrs E E Taylor (*Swedish*)

Head of Library: Mrs P Kino, BA
Head's PA: Mrs M Thomas

Sevenoaks School is situated on an attractive 100-acre campus adjoining Knole Park and on the edge of the town. Sevenoaks is in Kent, just 30 minutes from central London, and is conveniently close to Gatwick and Heathrow airports, the Channel Tunnel and continental Europe. The school, while set firmly in its local community, has a strong international dimension – not only in its student body, but also in its ethos, its culture and its curriculum. Sevenoaks was named as *The Sunday Times* Independent School of the Year 2007–8.

There are seven boarding houses including a co-educational junior house (11–13), two boys' houses (13–18), two girls' houses (13–18) and two single-sex Sixth Form houses (16–18). All of these welcome students from the UK and from around the world. Accommodation ranges from a charming Queen Anne house to modern, purpose-built facilities. There are lessons and sport for all pupils on Saturdays and a full programme of activities for boarders on Sundays.

A wide range of subjects is offered at GCSE, with setting in core subjects. The IGCSE has recently been introduced for Maths and Science. In the Sixth Form all pupils study the International Baccalaureate – a rigorous two-year diploma designed to provide a broad and balanced education. It is a well respected qualification for UK, US and other leading universities worldwide. Academic results in the school are excellent – this year the school was at the top of *The Times* and *The Independent* school league tables – and over 35 pupils gained places at Oxford and Cambridge in 2007, in both the arts and sciences. An increasing number of students also choose to go to Ivy League and other top American universities.

There is also a strong emphasis on the co-curriculum, from sport to music, drama and art. Pupils regularly achieve representative honours at rugby, cricket, netball, hockey, sailing, basketball, shooting and tennis and there is a wide range of concerts, plays and exhibitions for pupils of all ages. A variety of clubs and societies provide opportunities for all pupils to find and develop their interests. The school has a voluntary Combined Cadet Force and is also proud of its strong tradition of community service and involvement in The Duke of Edinburgh's Award scheme.

Facilities are first class: a new dining hall, Sixth Form centre, language centre, theatre and athletics track have been built in recent years. The Sennocke Centre, a major new sports centre, was completed in 2005. A performing arts centre is in the final planning stages.

Admission. The main points of entry to the school are at 11, 13 and 16 years and a small number are admitted at other levels. At 11+, pupils are admitted on the basis of a competitive examination held in January, an interview and Head's report. At 13+, a pre-assessment day in October is followed by those in prep schools taking the ISEB Common Entrance Examination in June or, for others, the school's own Year 9 Entrance Examination in February. Alternatively, pupils can take the Year 9 Scholarship examinations in March. At 16+, pupils are admitted into the Sixth Form on the strength of entrance tests, school reports and academic grades. There are boarding and day places for boys and girls at all ages. All applications for entry should be addressed to the Director of Admissions (regist@sevenoaksschool.org).

Fees per term (2008-2009). Boarders £8,518; Day Pupils £5,312 (including lunch). Fees for pupils entering directly into the Sixth Form are £9,240 (boarding) and £6,034 (day).

Scholarships and Bursaries. (*see Scholarship Entries section*). Up to 50 scholarships are awarded annually at 11+, 13+ and 16+. A number of bursaries are available for pupils who could not otherwise afford the fees.

Charitable status. Sevenoaks School is a Registered Charity, number 1101358. Its aims and objectives are the education of school children.

Sherborne School

Sherborne Dorset DT9 3AP
Tel: 01935 812249
Fax: 01935 810422
e-mail: registrar@sherborne.org
website: www.sherborne.org

The origins of Sherborne School date back to the eighth century, when a tradition of education at Sherborne was begun by St Aldhelm. The School was linked with the Benedictine Abbey, the earliest known Master was Thomas Copeland in 1437. Edward VI refounded the School in 1550. The present School stands on land which once belonged to the Monastery. The Library, Chapel, and Headmaster's offices which adjoin the Abbey Church, are modifications of the original buildings of the Abbey.

Royal Arms of Edward VI: *Dieu et mon droit.*

Governors of the School:

Chairman: Professor R Hodder-Williams, MA, FRSA
Vice-Chairman: Major General P A J Cordingley, DSO

Ex officio:
The Representative of Her Majesty's Lord Lieutenant for the County of Dorset, Mrs Anthony Pitt-Rivers
The Representative of The Lord Bishop of Salisbury, The Rt Revd T M Thornton, MA
The Vicar of Sherborne, The Revd Canon E J Woods, MA, FRSA

Co-optative:
C R J Eglington, Esq
M R Beaumont, Esq
D R Burgess, Esq, ACA
Ms F H Maddocks
R M Morgan, Esq, MA
Mrs H Greenstock, MA
S H J Macdonald, Esq, BA
M L French, Esq, BSc, FCA
R S Fidgen, Esq, FRICS
Dr S Ball, BM, MRCPsych
R Robson, Esq
N Bowles, Esq, MA

Staff Representative: R A L Leach, MA

Bursar and Clerk to the Governors: Mrs M C McKenna, MA, MBA, FCMA

***Headmaster*: S F Eliot**, MA

Second Master: W A M Burn, MA
Deputy Head (*Pastoral*): M A Weston, MA
Deputy Head (*Academic*): M A Waldron, MA

Housemasters:	Tel:
Abbey House: M A Pryor, BSc	01935 812087
Abbeylands: S J Clayton, CertEd & Mrs VA Clayton, BA, MCILIP	01935 812082
The Digby: M J Brooke, MA	01935 812687
The Green: A M Hatch, BA	01935 810440
Harper House: S Tremewan, BA, PhD	01935 812128
Lyon House: G Brière-Edney, BSc	01935 812079
School House: P J Watts, BSc	01935 813248
Wallace House: G T W Robinson, BA	01935 813334

Staff:
R D Ambrose, MA, AFIMA (*Mathematics*)
Mrs E J Bonnell, BEd (*Learning Support*)
G Brière-Edney, BSc (*Geography*)
M J Brooke, MA (*Classics*)
D C Bryson, BA (*Modern Languages*)

W A M Burn, MA (*Modern Languages*)
D B Cameron, MA (*Modern Languages*)
D P K Carling, MA (*English and Theology*)
P R Chillingworth, BA (*Head of Design Technology*)
J R Q Clark, BA (*Theology & Assistant Chaplain*)
S J Clayton, CertEd (*Head of Physical Education*)
M J Cleaver, BA (*Classics*)
S Correia, BA (*Modern Languages*)
Miss J Coultas, Hon ARAM, GRSM, LGSM, LRAM (*Music*)
B J Davey, GRSM (*Music*)
A M Davis, DipEd (*Rugby, Mathematics*)
Mrs R de Pelet, MA (*Head of English*)
Miss S Drury, GRSM Hons, GRSM, ARCM (*Music*)
W M Duggan, BA, MA (*Head of Classics*)
D J Dunning, BA (*Head of Theology*)
Ms K M Fleming, BA (*Ceramics and Sculpture*)
Miss C Gomm, MA (*Art*)
Revd S J N Gray, MA (*Chaplain*)
Mrs C E Greenrod, BA (*English*)
S P H Haigh, MA (*English*)
C G B Hamon, PhD, CChem, MRSC (*Chemistry*)
R T B Harris, BA, MBA (*Economics & Business Studies*)
A M Hatch, BA (*Geography*)
D Hedison, BSc (*Head of Economics*)
J E C Henderson, MA (*Director of Music*)
R W Hill (*Hockey, Cricket*)
B J Holiday, MA (*English*)
R Hudson, BA (*History*)
J J Kimber, BSc (*Physics*)
Mrs C Le Sueur, BA, CertTEFL
M McGinty, BA (*Economics & Politics*)
P R Miles, BEd (*Physical Education & Director of Sport*)
Miss K L Millar, BA (*Geography*)
J S Mitchell, BSc (*Physics*)
G R Moffat, BA (*Modern Languages*)
A C Morgan, BSc, MSc, FRSA (*Mathematics*)
A D Nurton, BA (*Modern Languages*)
A R Oates, BA, MLitt (*Modern Languages*)
M P O'Connor, BA (*English*)
J-M Pascal, DEA, PhD (*Modern Languages & Theology*)
R G Patterson, BLitt, BA (*English*)
T W Payne, BA (*English*)
Miss C Pemberton, BSc, PhD (*Biology*)
J R Preston, BSc (*Head of Geography*)
Mrs G Pryor, BSc (*Head of Mathematics*)
M A Pryor, BSc (*Mathematics*)
G D Reynolds, MA (*History*)
H W Ridgeway, MA, DPhil (*Head of History*)
D J Ridgway, BSc (*Head of Biology*)
P Riley, BSc (*Physics*)
Mrs E L Robinson, (*Head of Performance Drama*)
G T W Robinson, BA (*English*)
P Rogerson, MA (*Classics, Head of Careers*)
P M Ryan, MA (*Mathematics*)
B A Ryder, BEng (*Head of Physics*)
J Salisbury, BEd (*Technology*)
Mrs S Salmon, MA (*Head of Business Studies*)
T Sampson, BSc (*Biology*)
N C Scorer, MChem (*Chemistry*)
Miss J M Skippen, BA (*Modern Languages*)
I C Smith, BA, MSci (*Head of Chemistry*)
A J Stooke, BA (*Head of Art*)
J R Storey, BA (*Classics*)
P T Such, MA, PhD (*Director of IB, Modern Languages*)
B P Sunderland, BEng (*Mathematics*)
J A Thompson, BA (*Mathematics*)
Mrs J R Thurman, BA (*Head of Modern Languages*)
M D Thurman, BSc (*Physics*)
S Tremewan, BA, PhD (*Classics*)
J J B Wadham, BSc, PhD (*Biology*)
R M Warren, BA (*History*)
D A Watson, BSc (*Chemistry*)
P J Watts, BSc (*Physics*)
M A Weston, MA (*Modern Languages*)
J G Willetts, BA, CPhys, MInstP (*Head of ICT, Physics*)
Miss P Wood, BSc (*Biology*)

Medical Officers:
S G F Cave, BSc, MBChB
G Miles, MA, MB Cantab, BChir, DA, DRCOG

Sister: Mrs S E Hancock, RSCN
Headmaster's Secretary: Mrs E Wills (Tel: 01935 812249)
Sports and Uniform Shop: A Willows (Tel: 01935 810506)
Registrar: M J Cleaver, BA (Tel: 01935 810402; Fax: 01935 810422; e-mail: registrar@sherborne.org)

Situation. The School lies in the attractive Abbey town of Sherborne. By train, Salisbury is forty minutes away, London and Heathrow two hours.

Organisation. There are about 525 boarders and 45 day boys accommodated in eight houses, all of which are within easy walking distance of the main school.

Admission. Entry is either at 13+ through the Common Entrance, Scholarship examinations, or special entrance papers or at 16+ after GCSE.

Parents, who would like to enter their sons for the School, or have any queries, should contact the Registrar.

Boys can be entered either for a particular House or placed on the general list.

Visits. Visits can be arranged at any time of the year by ringing the Headmaster's Secretary on 01935 812249.

Scholarships/Exhibitions. (*see Scholarship Entries section*). Sherborne offers a wide range of scholarships and exhibitions, Academic (March), Music (February), and Sport, Art, Design & Technology (March). Candidates should be under 14 on 1 September in the year of entry. Further details of all these awards are available from the Registrar.

Sixth Form Entry. Places are available for boys who wish to join the Sixth Form to study A Levels or the IB for two years. Both the entrance and scholarship examinations take place in November. There are up to two full fees worth of scholarships offered annually. Also available, for good A Level candidates, is the Arkwright Scholarship for Technology.

Curriculum. All pupils follow a broadly based curriculum for their first three years to GCSE. In the Sixth Form boys study at least three A Levels and one AS Level drawn from 27 A Level and 30 AS courses, as well as some non-specialist courses designed to broaden the scope of their studies. From 2007 the International Baccalaureate will be available as an alternative. Some of the courses for IB and A Level are run jointly with Sherborne School for Girls.

Careers and Universities. The Careers Department has an enviable reputation. Boys experience work shadowing programmes in the fifth and lower sixth forms – these are followed by careers conventions, university visits, parents' forums and lessons in interview techniques. There is an encyclopaedic, fully computerised Careers' Room with regularly updated contacts with those at university and at work. The department has visited all universities and places of higher education. Virtually all leavers go on to university.

Pastoral Care. The boys in each house are in the care of a Housemaster and his wife, resident tutors, and a resident matron. The School Chaplain also plays a major rôle and will talk with a boy whenever required. A School Counsellor is available.

Tutor. Each boy has a personal Tutor who not only monitors his academic progress but provides a useful contact point.

Religion. Theology courses are designed for each academic year. There is a wide variety of weekday and weekend services, which are held in the School Chapel or in Sherborne Abbey. Holy Communion is celebrated every Sunday and on some weekdays, including a Friday night candlelit Eucharist service. Boys are prepared for confirmation by the School Chaplain.

Community Service. Boys take part in a busy programme aimed at encouraging a sense of responsibility towards the local community. Entertainment, fund-raising and assistance are organised for the young, elderly and handicapped in and around Sherborne.

Art. The Art School is well known and highly regarded. The core disciplines are based around the study of fine art and architecture. Alongside these, there are extensive print-making facilities, photographic dark rooms and the opportunity for boys to work in computer-aided design, film and media studies, history of design and museum and heritage studies. The annual study tour to Europe or America allows all boys to appreciate culture in an international context.

Design and Technology. The Design and Technology Department has recently been completed refurbished. The subject is taught to advanced level and pupils go on to higher education courses in Product and Aeronautical Design, Architecture and Engineering. The department has developed links with local industries where pupils can see CAD/CAM production, commercial furniture design and precision casting in process. The department runs afternoon activities on all weekdays and at weekends.

Music. There is a strong music tradition in the School – over 400 music lessons take place every week. There are two full orchestras, various chamber music groups, many different types of jazz band, a brass group, a swing band, Chapel choir and a choral society, not to mention rock bands. Many of these groups tour both home and abroad. Numerous concerts, recitals and musical productions are held throughout the year. Lunch time concerts take place every Friday. Regular subscription concerts are given by visiting professional musicians.

Drama. Drama productions of all kinds are a major feature of school life, from large scale musicals to classical drama, substantial modern works and fringe performances, many staged with Sherborne Girls. The sophisticated technical resources of the Powell Theatre attract programmes from professional touring companies.

Information Technology. The main network links all academic departments, boarding houses, Library and the Careers Room. The School has a sophisticated Intranet system.

Sports. There are over fifty acres of sports fields, where, at any one time, seventeen various games or matches can take place. Other facilities include two astroturf pitches, twenty tennis courts, rugby fives courts and a shooting range. Within the School's sports centre there is a sports hall, a twenty-five metre swimming pool, a fitness suite and squash courts. A wide variety of sports and activities are offered including athletics, badminton, basketball, canoeing, cricket, cross-country, fencing, rugby fives, golf, hockey, polo, riding, rugby, sailing, shooting, soccer, sub-aqua, swimming and tennis.

Societies and Activities. Numerous academic societies meet regularly throughout the term. Other activities and clubs take place on Wednesday afternoons and whenever time allows. They include: bridge, chess, computing, debating, fishing, instrument making, modelling, model railways, photography, and woodland management.

The Duke of Edinburgh's Award Scheme is well supported. Expeditions are organised to Scotland, the Lake District, Wales, Exmoor and Dartmoor. Boys also take part in the annual 'Ten Tors Challenge'.

Membership of the Combined Cadet Force is voluntary – however the Army, Navy and Royal Marine sections usually attract about 150 boys each year. A large number of trips and camps are arranged during the term time and the holidays.

Old Shirburnian Society. Secretary: Old Shirburnian Office, Sherborne School, Dorset DT9 3AP. Tel: 01935 810557. Fax: 01935 810551. e-mail: OSS@sherborne.org

Girls' Schools. There is close liaison with the neighbouring girls' schools, which allows us to offer many of the real benefits of co-education with all the advantages of a single-sex secondary education. As well as the Joint Sixth Form academic courses with Sherborne Girls, drama, music and social activities are arranged throughout the year.

Fees per term (2008-2009). Boarders: £8,860; Day Boys: £7,175.

Charitable status. Sherborne School is a Registered Charity, number 1081228, and a Company Limited by Guarantee, registered in England and Wales, number 4002575. Its aim and objectives are to supply a liberal education in accordance with the principles of the Church of England.

Shiplake College

Henley-on-Thames Oxon RG9 4BW
Tel: 0118 940 2455
Fax: 0118 940 5204
e-mail: info@shiplake.org.uk
website: www.shiplake.org.uk

Founded by Alexander Everett in 1959, Shiplake College is an Independent boarding and day School for boys aged 13–18 with day and boarding girls joining the Sixth Form.

Motto: '*Exemplum docet*' (Example teaches)

Governing Body:
Chairman: B N Gilson, CA SA
S J A Cromack
D T Dalzell, BSc, PhD
The Rt Hon T J C Eggar, LLB
J S Gordon, LLB
J R B Hobbs, BA
J F Holmes
R C Lester
The Hon Sir William McAlpine, Bart
Lady Phillimore
S B Roberts, MA
Mrs S J Ryan, BSc
N Starmer-Smith, MA
D W Tanner, OBE, BA, FRSA
J P Turner, BSc, FCA
D S Williamson, BA

***Headmaster*: A G S Davies**, BSc St Andrews, Cert Mgmt

Bursar and Clerk to the Governors: J N Walne, BSc Loughborough, MBA Cranfield

* *Head of Department*

Senior Teaching Staff:
Deputy Headmaster: S J O'Brien, Dip Tchg Auckland NZ, BA Brunel, MBA Leicester
Senior Master: R T Mannix, BSc London, PGCE Bath
Senior Teacher: Mrs L G Cook, MEd Oxon, BA OU, CertEd Liverpool
Chaplain: The Revd Robert Prance, BTh Southampton
Assistant Chaplain: The Revd R C M Jarvis, MA Wales, MA St Andrews
Head of Pupil Development: P C J Gould, BEd Reading
Head of Teaching & Learning: *Dr T S Purser, MA Oxon, PhD Southampton, PGCE Bath

Housemasters:
C E Alcock, BA, PGCE Reading (*Orchard*)
N J Brown, BA, PGCE East Anglia (*Senior Housemaster and College*)
*T P J Caston, BA Exeter, PGCE Reading (*Orchard Assistant*)
A D Dix, BSc, PGCE Loughborough (*Skipwith*)
*Mrs A J Foakes, BSc, PGCE Sheffield (*Girls' Housemistress*)
A F J Hunt, BEd S Australia (*Welsh*)
C A M Lowndes, MA Oxon, BA, PGCE, MEd OU (*Burr*)

B D P Pavey, MA London, BSc Durham, PGCE London (*Everett*)

Teaching Staff:
Miss S G Andrew, BSc Heriot-Watt, PGCE St Martin's
*Miss E Arnold, Dip Design Farnham
*Mrs M A Baker, BA Oxon, PGCE
D J Brenton, BSc Aberdeen, PGCE Aberystwyth
S D Cane-Hardy, BA Cardiff, PGCE Sussex
T E Crisford, BSc Southampton, GTP Brunel
*R Curtis, BEd Brighton
*M Daniel, BA Essex, PGCE Worcester
*P M Davey, BEd London
S Dennis, MBE, BSc, MSc London, QTS
*K Dolan, BSc Brunel, PGCE Birmingham
D G Dovaston, BSc Aston, PGCE Bristol
M Edwards, MBA Reading, BA Southampton, PGCE E Anglia
Miss J C Erasmus, BSc Potchefstroom
B L Foakes, BA East Anglia, PGTC London
*Mrs H Gillings, BA Leeds, PGCE Liverpool John Moores
*Miss K A Harper, BMus Surrey, PGCE Cantab, LRSM (Teaching)
*G S Lawson, BSc Swansea, MSc, MPhil Southampton, PGCE OU
W H Mackworth-Praed, BSc Durham, PGCE Cantab
*S Le Paih, L-ès-Lettres Nantes, PGCE London
*Miss C Saker, BA London, AGSMD
K F Settle, BSc York, PGCE London
D D Seymour, BA South Africa, PGCE Natal
Mrs J A Smail, BA London, PGCE Oxon
C S Smith, Nat Dip Performing Arts
*R C Snellgrove, BSc, PhD CNAA
*Miss J E Stanley, BA Durham, PGCE Oxon
R P Starr, BA Bradford, PGCE Reading
D T Swan, BA Brunel
Miss A M Wanless, BMus London, MMus London, PGCE Roehampton

Part Time Teaching Staff:
Mrs L Bell, BA Liverpool, PGCE Leeds
Mrs E C Butt, BA Wales, PGCE Cantab
Mrs D J Clark, BA Cardiff, PGCE Exeter
Mrs S A Clark, BA Liverpool, PGCE Manchester
J A Cooksey, BEd Leeds, MEd Nottingham
Mrs N Cox, BSc Cardiff, PGCE Cambridge
Mrs A M E Davies, JP, BA Edinburgh, PGCE Leeds
Dr J E Hart, BSc, PhD Bristol, PGCE Oxford Brookes
Mrs C Forde-Halpin, BA Cork
*Mrs F Kowalczyk, MA Reading
Mrs S Krause, BA Buckinghamshire Chiltern
Mrs S Satch
P D Wisby, MA Reading
Mrs P Wallace, BA Dublin, PGCE London

SEN Administrator/TA: Mrs A C White, HLTA

Gap Tutors:
Z Cleaver
J Hall
H Wells

Medical Staff:
School Doctor: Dr Philip Unwin, MB BS, DRCOG
Sister: Mrs R Wyld, RGN, DN London
Sister: Mrs J Fitzgerald, RGN, RM
Matron: Ms D Gow

Administrative Staff:
Registrar: Mrs J Jarrett
School Accountant: Mrs K Burrell, MAAT
Bursary Assistant: Mrs J Sandal
Headmaster's PASchool Secretary: Ms S Bond
Office Administrator: Ms A Cooper
Administration/Finance Assistant: Mrs L Hatlee
Marketing Manager: Mrs S Kilgour, BA Hons Cardiff
Data Manager: Miss H Edimoh
Careers Assistant: Ms LE Rapple, BA Hons Reading
Estate Manager: D Greer, Dip SM, MIIRSM
Head Groundsman: R Evans
Examination Administrator: Mrs J Brenton, BA Open, Cert Teaching Cambs

Matrons:
Burr: Mrs J Hardy
Everett: Ms K Strickland
Orchard: Mrs J Burtt
Skipwith: Mrs J Miles-Thomas
Welsh & Senior Matron: Mrs J Knight
College: Mrs F Bensaad

Technical Support Staff:
Mrs M A Cousins
Mrs G M Findlay
Mr A Reford
Mrs F J Varnals, CertEd Bristol

Ethos. Shiplake College is a dynamic, purposeful, happy and caring place which produces tolerant young men and women who have a sense of humour yet are responsible and articulate and have the knowledge and skills to play an informed and useful part in their society.

Shiplake prides itself on bringing out the best in each and every individual.

The Shiplake College Promise.

- To help and encourage every pupil to achieve maximum potential according to individual abilities.
- To provide individual support for all abilities, so that academic development and progress is consistently achieved.
- To include all pupils in activities within the College, with everyone playing an active role whether it be on the river, on the sports field or in the cultural and spiritual life of the College.
- To educate and care for pupils in an open, inclusive and friendly atmosphere, whilst working hard and having fun.
- To produce self-confident, courteous and well-mannered young people ready to play a positive role in society.
- To promote a culture of tolerance and respect for others together with a "can-do" attitude.

Pastoral Care. At Shiplake pupils become a member of one of the four boarding houses: Burr, Skipwith, Welsh, and Everett or the day house, Orchard. Both day and boarding girls join Orchard House where they have separate study facilities. A dedicated girls' boarding house is due to open in September 2009. The Upper Sixth enjoys the separate facilities of College House which helps establish independence before the move to University or a career. There is a strong house spirit in evidence with competitions organised for arts, games and academic progress.

The houses provide excellent support for the pupils in addition to ensuring a comfortable, homely environment for pupils to study or relax.

Each house is run by a Housemaster who is supported by a strong team of staff including the House Matron, House Tutor, Visiting Tutors, the Medical Staff and the Chaplain. The Pastoral Committee meets regularly to ensure liaison between teaching and house staff in order that pupils' successes and challenges can be monitored closely.

As a Christian School there is an extensive programme of worship, very often provided in the neighbouring Parish Church. The Chaplain is always available to any member of the College community. Shiplake also welcomes pupils of other faiths.

Location. The College enjoys a riverside site of 45 acres including an island in the River Thames. Sitting high above the river, just over two miles upstream of Henley-on-Thames, Shiplake College is one of the most beautiful locations for a school.

Although pupils love the acres of sports pitches and the country trails, parents appreciate the fact that Shiplake is conveniently placed for access to the M4 and M40 and the railway stations at Henley and Reading. This idyllic countryside location is just an hour from London and within easy reach of Heathrow and Gatwick airports.

Facilities. Shiplake House, built in 1889 as a family home, is at the heart of the school. Pupils and staff take their main meals in the wood-panelled Great Hall beneath the Minstrels' Gallery. The College is fortunate to have the use of the twelfth-century Parish Church, where the poet Lord Tennyson was married, for assemblies and worship.

In addition to the main school buildings, Shiplake boasts a nineteenth century water tower which has been converted into an acoustically isolated recording studio, the Tithe Barn Theatre, Music Rooms, Sports Hall and Fitness Suite. A short walk from the main school building are the three boathouses, allowing direct access to the Thames; all boys are encouraged to try rowing in Year 9.

The College has state-of-the art computing facilities available to all pupils.

Developments. Over the last decade the College has invested heavily in building developments. Recently, new accommodation has been provided for English, Geography, History, Learning Support, Media Studies and Modern Languages with additional provision for Information Technology. A new girls' boarding house is due to open in September 2009.

Academic Structure. Pupils enjoy a broad and balanced curriculum in Year 9 to establish a strong foundation in a wide range of subjects and ensure that they are able to make an informed selection of subjects for GCSE.

In the Sixth Form, pupils select up to four subjects from a choice of seventeen.

Learning Development. Shiplake has a dedicated Learning Development Department to provide additional help for those pupils who need it. Up to 24 pupils each year with recognised learning support needs are admitted following assessment prior to joining the school. The 'Core' group receives five additional lessons each week in place of studying a Modern Foreign Language. The 'Extra' group has a double lesson each week in the Department. This arrangement provides opportunities for flexible learning and the following of individualised plans.

Gifted and mainstream pupils may benefit from the expertise of the LDD staff on an *ad hoc* basis as and when the need arises.

The aim of the Learning Development Department is to improve all pupils' confidence and self-esteem as well as equipping them with the skills they need to access the curriculum and demonstrate the knowledge they have acquired.

Sport. Almost all pupils take part in a sporting activity on most days. Shiplake has excellent on-site facilities including direct access to the river and boathouses, hockey, cricket and rugby pitches, tennis courts, squash courts and an outdoor swimming pool. The sports hall offers a variety of indoor sports, a weight-training gym and a fitness room.

Almost all boys play rugby football in the autumn term. In the spring term boys play hockey or row, and in the summer term there is the choice of cricket, tennis or rowing. The girls enjoy a mixed programme of sports and activities using almost all of the sporting facilities available.

Soccer, basketball, badminton, squash, judo, cross-country running and athletics provide additional activities to develop skills and fitness.

For a small school, Shiplake has a remarkable number of crews and teams taking part in events and competitions with national success. There have been a number of overseas tours involving the rugby, cricket, hockey and rowing clubs.

Music, Art and Drama. The College has a thriving mixture of Arts activities and performances and all pupils are encouraged to enjoy the Arts. The annual house music competition ensures that every pupil in the school is involved in preparing for a performance and every term there is at least one concert for pupils to demonstrate the progress they have made. The Headmaster's Hymn Practice furthers the growing reputation for community singing at the College.

Activities. Pupils choose from a wide range of activities including art, bridge, cookery, Film Club, football, golf, kart-building, Ecology and canoeing. The College has a thriving Combined Cadet Force with Air Force, Army and Navy sections. Pupils who are not members of the CCF take part in regular community service activities and the school has links to a Kenyan School for which fund-raising activities are regularly undertaken. The College also runs a Duke of Edinburgh's Award Scheme with a number of pupils each year collecting Gold Awards. In addition there are drama productions, debates and music recitals.

Careers. There is an experienced Careers Adviser and particular attention is paid to the choice of University and career from Year 11 onwards. The School is a member of ISCO.

Admission. The Registrar is the first point of contact for all admissions and admissions enquiries. Boys are admitted into Year 9 and there is an intake into the Sixth Form for boys and girls. Places are offered following an interview with the Headmaster. Occasional places arise in other years and there is a waiting list held by the Registrar.

Scholarships. Means-tested scholarships and bursaries are offered to outstanding sportsmen, artists or musicians at Year 9 level and in the Sixth Form for all academic subjects.

Fees per term (2008-2009). Boarders £7,666, Day Pupils £5,171. Fees are inclusive, covering all compulsory extras, such as laundry, books, visits and subscriptions to the Boat Club.

Alumni. The Old Viking Society has an annual programme of events including sports fixtures and a formal dinner. The Society produces an annual newsletter for Old Vikings.

Charitable status. Shiplake College is a Registered Charity, number 309651. It exists to provide education for children.

Shrewsbury School

Shrewsbury Shropshire SY3 7BA
Tel: 01743 280500 (Switchboard)
01743 280525 (Headmaster)
01743 280820 (Bursar)
01743 280550 (Registrar)
Fax: 01743 340048 (Headmaster)
01743 243107 (Reception)
01743 351009 (Registrar)
e-mail: headmaster@shrewsbury.org.uk
website: www.shrewsbury.org.uk

Shrewsbury School was founded by King Edward VI in 1552 and augmented by Queen Elizabeth in 1571. In 1882 it moved from the centre of the town to its present site overlooking the town and the River Severn.

Motto: '*Intus si recte, ne labora*'

Governing Body:

Chairman: R Burbidge, OBE, DL, BA
Lt Col S S Caney, MBE, BA
Prof C Dobson, FRS
A Haining, MA
Dr Fiona Hay, MA, BM, BCh, DRCOG, MRCGP, DFFP
A E H Heber-Percy
A G A Hillman, ACA
W R O Hunter, QC
Prof E W Jones, BSc Hons, PhD, FRAgS
Ms Lyndsey Pollard, LLB
Cllr M Owen
Professor D A Ritchie, CBE, FRSE

Cllr D W L Roberts
Dr Tiffany Stern, MA MPhil, PhD
The Hon Sir Stephen Tomlinson
H P Trevor-Jones, BSc

***Headmaster*: J W R Goulding**, MA

Bursar and Clerk to the Governors: S J Dowson, MBA
Director of Finance: M J Ware, ACA
Senior Master: P A Fanning, MA
Second Master: M J Tonks, BA
Director of Studies: M J Cropper, MA
Head of Careers and Staff Training: C W Conway, MA
Registrar: R E D Case, BA

Assistant Masters/Mistresses:
* *Head of Faculty*
† *Housemaster/Housemistress*

Mrs R W Adams, BEc, BEd
S F Adams, MA, MSc (**Physics*)
A J Allott, MA (**Biology*)
J C Armstrong, BA (**Mathematics*)
J Balcombe, BSc
A S Barnard, BA
G St J F Bell, BA (*†School House*)
A D Briggs, BSc, PhD
Miss J M M Burge, BSc
J R Burke, BSc
M D H Clark, BA
Mrs A J Clemson, BA
C E Cook, MA
S H Cowper, MA (*†Ingram's Hall*)
A Dalton, BA (**Religious Studies*)
N P David, BSc
S P Dearsley, MA, MMus
The Revd G W Dobbie, MA (*Chaplain*)
A L M Dunn, MA
M S Elliot, MA, PhD
B J Evans, BSc (**Chemistry*)
T R Foulger, BSc, PhD (**Geography*)
S A A Fox, BA (*†Moser's Hall*)
J Gabbitas, MA
J Godwin, MA, PhD (**Classics*)
P G Hamm, AB Harvard
Mrs S L Hankin, BA (*†Mary Sidney Hall – Sixth Form girls*)
D M Hann, MA
M H Hansen, BSc
M J Harding, BA
A W Hayes, BSc
S Hellier, BA (*†Port Hill – day boys*)
N D J Henderson, AB Harvard
R T Hudson, MA (*†Churchill's Hall*)
W A Hughes, BA (**Director of Sport*)
M A C Humphreys, MA (*†Ridgemount*)
R N R Jenkins, OBE, MA (*†Oldham's Hall*)
M D B Johnson, BSc, BA
D M Joyce, DipRCM, ARCM
P A Kaye, BEng (**Educational ICT*)
C W Kealy, BComm (**Business Studies*)
D Kirkby, BSc (*†Radbrook – day boys*)
P H Lapage, BA
Mrs E M A Lascelles, BSc
M J Lascelles, BA (*†The Grove*)
J W D Marshall, BA (**English*)
P A Merricks-Murgatroyd, BA (**Economics*)
P J Middleton, BA
C J Minns, MA, PhD (**German*)
J F Moore, BA, LRAM (**Music*)
T S Morgan, BSc, PhD
M M Morrogh, BA, PhD (**History*)
M A J Mostyn, BA, MA(*Ed*) (*†Rigg's Hall*)
D A G Nicholas, BA
D Nickolaus, CertEd (**CDT*)
Mrs D B Nightingale, MTD, LTCL
C W Oakley, MMath
P Pattenden, MA, DPhil, CPhys, MInstP
H R W Peach, BA
T P Percival, MA
A P Pridgeon
F O L Reid, MA
C M Samworth, BSc, PhD
M A Schutzer-Weissmann, MA
J A Sheppe, MPhil
Miss N J Thomson, BA
M Twells, MA (**IT*)
P R Vicars, MA (*†Severn Hill*)
T D J Warburg, MA
A S M Went, BA
Mrs K M Weston, MSc
T C Whitehead, BA (**French*)
Miss L J Whittle, BA
J M Williams, BSc
R M Wilson, MEng Hons
Miss G Y Y Woo, MSc
P N Woolley, BA, MFA (**Art*)
M P J Wright, BA (**Spanish*)
Mrs P A Wright, BA

Visiting American Master: M D Chalfin, AB Harvard

Visiting French Master: D Portier, BA, MA Université Michel de Montaigne – Bordeaux III

School Doctors:
The General Practitioner Team, Mytton Oak Surgery, Racecourse Lane, Shrewsbury

Dental Adviser: R J Gatenby, BDS, DGDP, RCS

Headmaster's Secretary: Mrs J Gibbs

Number in School. There are 700 boys in the School (574 boarders and 126 day boys).

Admission to the School. Most admissions are in September. Boys are admitted at 13 or (direct to the Sixth Form) at 16. Girls are admitted to the Sixth Form from 2008. Entrance forms and other information can be obtained from the Registrar. The registration fee, which is non-returnable, is £30.

Entry at 13. Boys usually take the Common Entrance Examination or the Scholarship Examination in the term preceding that in which they wish to come. The School has its own entrance test for boys who have not followed the Common Entrance syllabus. A Secured Places Scheme operates whereby boys aged 11 can take an examination set by the School and may receive an offer of a place, subject to a satisfactory school report the final year of preparatory school at 13.

Scholarships. (*see Scholarship Entries section*). The Scholarships are inflation-linked. In 2008 the Governors expect to offer 4 Scholarships up to the value of 50% of fees, 6 up to the value of 25% of fees and 7 worth at least £2,000 per annum.

In addition, they offer 10 House Foundation Awards worth up to the value of 50% of fees, 2 Music Scholarships up to the value of 50% of fees, 2 Music Scholarships up to the value of 20% of fees, 2 Art Scholarships up to the value of 20% of fees, 2 Sports Scholarships up to the value of 20% of fees and 2 All-Rounder Scholarships worth up to the value of 20% of fees.

Sixth Form Entry. Direct entry into the Sixth Form depends on an interview, examination at Shrewsbury and a favourable report from the applicant's present school. There are 2 Academic Scholarships up to the value of 25% of the fees and 6 up to the value of 15% of fees. In addition there are 6 Specialist Scholarships (for Art, Drama, Music or Sport), 2 worth up to 25% of fees, and 4 worth up to 15% of fees. There is also 1 Cassidy Sports Scholarship worth up to 100% of fees.

Buildings. The school operates a rolling programme of refurbishment for all boarding houses. This started again in 2004 and a brand new boarding house opened in 2006. Similarly, large-scale refurbishment of the teaching accommodation is currently being completed. All classrooms are professionally equipped to a very high standard. A new Music School, including an auditorium and a large ensemble room, was opened in February 2001, a cricket academy opened in 2006, and a new swimming pool opened in 2007. A new sixth form centre will be completed by autumn 2008.

The Moser Library houses The School Library, the Moser collection of water-colours, and the Ancient Library, which contains medieval manuscripts and early printed books.

Courses of Study. All boys follow a general course as far as the GCSE level Examinations. In the Sixth Form it is usual to study 4 subjects to AS level and 3 to A2 level. The number of combinations of subjects for which it is possible to opt is very large. Recent additions are PE and Theatre Studies AS and A2.

The School acts on the assumption that well-tried traditional methods of teaching work best. A full-time European Liaison Officer has been appointed to heighten awareness of Europe. There continues to be an increasing emphasis on Information Technology.

Games. Rowing, Cricket, Association Football, Swimming, Cross-country, Eton Fives and Rugby. The School has its own indoor Swimming Pool, Gymnasium, Multigym, Miniature Rifle Range, all-weather playing surface, Tennis Courts, Squash Courts and Fives Courts. The River Severn flows just below the Main Building and the Boat House is within the School grounds.

Activities. Boys offered a considerable range of outdoor activities via the Combined Cadet Force, leadership courses and the Duke of Edingburgh's Award Scheme. The programme of activities and opportunities continues to broaden as a boy moves up the School.

Art and Design. Art and Design are taught to all boys in their first year. For those not doing GCSE or A level courses they subsequently become activities followed mainly, but not exclusively, out of school hours. The Art and CDT centres are available 7 days a week. The CDT department offers the chance of advanced design work and of creative work in a variety of materials. AS and A2 and GCSE level design are also offered, as are AS and A2 ceramics and photography.

Societies. These range from Literary, Political, Debating, Drama and Language societies to those catering for practical skills like Printing or Electronics. Hill-walkers and Mountaineers make use of the unspoilt country on the doorstep and of the Welsh hills.

Music. Teaching is available in any orchestral instrument, as well as the Piano and Organ. The charge for this is £20.15 per lesson for all instruments. Regular Choral, Orchestral and Chamber Concerts both at the school and elsewhere (St John's, Smith Square; CBSO Birmingham) are given by the boys. In addition concerts are given during the winter months by distinguished visiting artists.

Drama. Although Drama is not taught as part of the curriculum, it is a major feature of school life, with two school plays and up to nine house plays per year, together with regular accolades at the Edinburgh Fringe.

Field Study Centre. Shrewsbury owns a farmhouse in Snowdonia used at weekends throughout the year as a base for expeditions.

Careers. There is a full time Careers Master. All boys are offered the Morrisby Aptitude Tests and the services of the Independent Schools Careers Organization.

Community Service. In association with other schools in the town, boys play an active part in caring for the old and needy in the Shrewsbury area.

Shrewsbury House. Founded in Liverpool as a Club for boys in 1903, it was re-built as a Community Centre in association with the Local Authority and the Diocese in 1974. There is residential accommodation in the Centre and groups of boys from the School have the opportunity to go there on study courses.

Shrewsbury International School. The school has close links with Shrewsbury International School in Bangkok, which opened in 2003. Teaching and pupil exchanges take place between the two schools, and Governors of Shrewsbury School serve on the board of management of the International School.

Fees per term (2008-2009). Boarders: £8,705, including tuition, board and ordinary School expenses. There are no other obligatory extras, apart from stationery. Day Boys: £6,110.

Application for reduced fees may be made to the Governors through the Headmaster.

Old Boys' Society. Most boys leaving the school join the Old Salopian Club. Secretary: A J Walters, c/o The Cottage, 17 Ashton Road, Shrewsbury SY3 7AP.

Charitable status. Shrewsbury School is a Registered Charity, number 528413. It exists to provide secondary education.

Silcoates School

Wrenthorpe Wakefield West Yorkshire WF2 0PD
Tel: 01924 291614
Fax: 01924 368693
e-mail: hmsilcoates@aol.com
website: www.silcoates.com

Silcoates was founded in 1820 on its present site, two miles north-west of Wakefield. While retaining its links with the United Reformed Church, the school aims to provide a broad, first-class education for boys and girls of all denominations and faiths. The Silcoates School Foundation comprises three schools: Silcoates School (Senior and Junior sections), Sunny Hill House School and St Hilda's School.

Motto: '*Clarior ex ignibus*'

Board of Governors:

Chairman: J H Bryan, LLB
Vice-Chairman: Mrs M C Chippendale, BSc

Revd J Arnold
Professor J C G Binfield, OBE, MA
G A Briggs, FCA
Dr P H Clarke
Revd A F T Evans
Dr M Gallagher, MBE
R S Hanson
Mrs J M Healey, ATCL
J D Hendry, BEng, CEng, MICE, MIGEM
Mrs V Jenkins, MEd, BPhil, ABD, ALAM, CertEd
Mrs A M Johnson, MA, ALA
J R Lane, LLB, AKC, TEP
Mrs G V Morrison
T J Mulryne, LLB, AKC, TEP
D W Owens, BSc, MD
D E Payling, MA, ACA
J E Payling, MA, ACA
E V Willings, BChD

Clerk to the Governors: D Dinmore, MBE, DL, MCIPD, MCMI

Staff:

***Headmaster*: D S Wideman**, MA

Deputy Heads:
D A Curran, BSc
S Fox, MA
Miss H M Wren, BA, MA

Head of Junior School: R C Lilley, BA

Chaplain: The Revd J A Campbell, DipREd

Assistant Staff:
R A Beecher, BA
Mrs S L Brindley, BA
Mrs L Burdekin, CertEd
R M Carey, BA
M Chester, BSc
Mrs A Clewarth
J C Clewarth, BEd, MEd
D Coll, BEd

Mrs S Coll, BEd
J Cooling, BSc, MMedSci, PhD
D B Coulson, BSc
G L Cox, GTCL, LTCL
Mrs H Crompton, BMus, MMus, LTCL
Mrs R L Dews, BEng
Miss H Drayson, CertEd
Mrs A Eckersley, MA, BSc
R Elliston, BA
R J Fenn, BEd
P Franks, BA
Miss A S Garbutt, BA
Mrs M Hayes, DipAD, SIAD
T W Hilling-Smith, BA, MA
Mrs E M Hornshaw, BA
G J Hughes BA
C Hugill, BSc
Mrs S Ingle, BA
N Jackson, BSc
M D Jeanes, BSc
W F Jepson, BSc, MSc
Mrs V Kinlin, CertEd, Cert SpLD (Dyslexia)
S Loren, BA
R Manser-Fiske, BA
Mrs K March, BEd
Ms C A Marsh, BEd
Miss L McLoughlin, BSc
Mrs J L McManus, BA
T J Mills, BEd
A Mistry, BA
J M Newell, BSc, CPhys, MInstP
Mrs J M Newell, BA
Miss E L Nuttall, BA
S Ogden, BSc
G E M Openshaw, BA
N Owen, BA
Miss H M Peach, BA
J R L Piggott, BSc
A Potter, BEd
B G Pye, BEd
D J Raggett, BSc
P A Richards, BSc
G Roberts, BEd
T J Roberts, BA
C Rowe, BA
S C Scholfield, BA
Mrs B W Shaw, BA
L J Shears, MA
Ms H Stalker, BA
Mrs L Sugden, BSc, MSc, PGCert
Mrs D J Townsend, BSc
T Verinder, BA
Miss G Walker, BSc
Mrs M Ward, CertEd, Cert Dyslexia & Literacy
Mrs O R K Wareham, BA
P V Watkin, BSc
Miss T Watson, BA
G Wetherop, BA
Miss N Widnall, BA
Ms B Witham, BA
Miss L E Wood, BA
P Wright, MSci, PhD

Bursar: J A J Dickson, MA, MA
Director of Marketing & Development: Mrs J Fikkert
Headmaster's PA: Mrs C Woodhead
Registrar: Mrs C Wade
School Secretary: Mrs L M Nutbrown
Junior School Secretary: Mrs A Dix
Bursar's PA: Mrs F Reed
Appeal Director: Dr D Heathcote, BSc, PhD, PGDip Music

Admission. There are 764 pupils at Silcoates. Boys and girls are admitted to the Junior School at the age of 7, and further entries take place between 7 and 14. Places are available for girls and boys wishing to study for A level in the Sixth Form.

Entrance Examinations take place in January for admission the following September.

The Foundation also provides a pre-preparatory education for boys and girls from 2 to 7 years at Sunny Hill House School and St Hilda's School, Horbury, offers education for girls from 0 to 11 and boys 0 to 7.

(*See also entry for Silcoates Junior School in IAPS section, and Sunny Hill House School entry in ISA section.*)

Curriculum. Recent inspection reports have been highly complimentary about the school's academic performance. Nearly all pupils sit a minimum of 9 GCSEs, 4 AS and 3 A2 levels, and the vast majority go on to degree courses. There is great flexibility of subject choice at GCSE and A level. A superbly-equipped new Sixth Form Study Centre was opened in June 2004.

Games and Activities. Drama, art, music and sport all flourish at Silcoates. The school has an excellent record of individual and collective achievement in all of its extra-curricular activities. The outstanding sports facilities include an indoor pool. A magnificent new £1.3 million Music School was opened in November 2004. Our very successful Duke of Edinburgh's Award programme makes extensive use of various venues in the north of England and abroad.

Pastoral Care and Careers Guidance. With a generous pupil:personal tutor ratio, the quality of pastoral care is of a very high order. We provide a full programme of careers advice and guidance.

Fees per term (2008-2009). Senior School: £3,656; Junior School: £2,164–£2,848.

Entrance Scholarships. (*see Scholarship Entries section*). Academic and Music Scholarships are offered at 11+ and above; Sixth Form entrants are eligible for these awards. Music Award holders enjoy free instrument tuition.

Substantial bursaries are available for the sons and daughters of Ministers and Missionaries of the United Reformed Church or of the Congregational Church, and of other recognised Christian denominations.

Charitable status. The Silcoates School Foundation is a Registered Charity, number 529281. It aims to provide a first-class education for boys and girls.

Solihull School

Warwick Road Solihull West Midlands B91 3DJ
Tel: 0121 705 0958 (Headmaster)
0121 705 4273 (Admissions)
0121 705 0883 (Bursar)
Fax: 0121 711 4439
e-mail: admin@solsch.org.uk
website: www.solsch.org.uk

Motto: '*Perseverantia*'

Chairman of the Governors: G M Hughes, FCA, FRSA

Bursar and Clerk to the Governors: C Warren

***Headmaster*: P J Griffiths**, MA

Deputy Headmasters:
S A Morgan, BA
R J Melling, BSc

Head of Sixth Form: Mrs L M Fair, BA
Master of the Middle School: M J Garner, BSc
Master of the Lower School: Mrs L D J Hughes, BA
Head of the Junior School: Mrs L J Brough, BA, LTCL
Director of Studies: D G Morgan, BA, MA Cantab

Assistant Staff:
* *Head of Department*

G Affleck, BA (**History*)
O Anderton, BSc
Mrs N J Atkins, BEd
Dr R A Atkinson, BA, DPhil
M P Babb, BSc
A C Barclay, BEd
Mrs R A Barralet, BA, LRAM, LTCL
Mrs M A Barrett, BA, MEd (**Modern Languages*)
O W H Bate, BSc
J H Belcher
L A Benge, BA, BEd
M R Bishop, MSc (**Mathematics*)
B Blessed, BSc (**IT*)
Miss N M Bouckley, BA
P D Brattle, BSc
M R Brough, BA, MPhil (**Sixth Form Enrichment*)
Mrs J S Brown, BA, MA
Miss T J Bryan, BA
Mrs D L Buckle, BSc
A Bussey, BA (**Economics & Business Studies*)
Miss E Campbell, BA
A Carter, BA
Mrs C Checketts, BA
Mrs N A Cheetham, BA
Revd Dr N Culey, BA, BSc
Dr D Coetzee, MA, PhD
N Corbett, BA
M J Covill, BSc
Miss S Crowther, BEd
G J Cureton, BSc
Mrs C D L Davies
Miss P J Davies, GBSM
Miss L Dickinson, BA
Ms H Dolby, AGSM, ATC
D A Farrington BSc
J Geldard, MA
Miss V Gill, MEd
J Grandrieux, Dip UEL

Miss C M Greswold, GLCM, AMus LCM, ALCM
P G Gunning, BA
Miss J Guy, BA, MPhil (**Classics*)
Mrs R R Hadley, BEd (*Director of Learning Support*)
S A Hart, BA (**English*)
S Hifle, QTS
P M Higley, BA, CertEd (**Design & Technology*)
P T Holt, MA
Mrs J Humphries, BEd
Revd A C Hutchinson, BA, MEd
P J Irving, BA, ARCM, FRCO
P R Jackson, BSc
D Jenkinson, MEd
A Jones (**Science*)
C H Jones, BEd
B J Keylock, BA (**Psychology*)
Mrs R Lancaster, BSc
N W S Leonard, BEd
P May, BSc
C I Mayer
Mrs H Middleton, BEng, BCom
S Mitchell, BSc
P Morgan, BA
Mrs U Mynette
J J Nickson, MA (**Art*)
Mrs A M Parker, BA
B Parkes, BA
M Penney, BA
S J Perrins, MA, FRCO (*Director of Music*)
Mrs S J Phillips, BSc
Mrs M J C Pierre, Angreg Ens Liège
Miss H E Pike, MA, BA
Dr K A Powell, PhD, MBA
Miss G J Powell, BA, MA
D Reardon, BSc (*Director of ICT*)
G P Reddington, BA
Mrs A C Roll, BA (**Geography*)
M K Smith (**Physics*)
Mrs C Steele, BEd
Mrs S Stout, BSc (**German*)
M K Swain, BA
Mrs V Taylor, CertEd
H J Thomas
Mrs S Thomas, BSc
S J Thompson, BSc (*Director of Sport*)
Miss C Townsend, BSc
Miss D L Trim, BA
J Troth, PhD, BSc (**Chemistry*)
Mrs D H Wild, BSc (**Biology*)
Mrs J Wilde, BA (*Director of Drama*)
Mrs S Wolffe, CAP, BA, MIL, MSc
M Worrall, MA
R C Wright (**Religious Studies, Philosophy*)

Careers: Revd Dr N A Cluley, BA

CCF: Capt N W S Leonard
SSI (*CCF*) WO2: P G Dean, MBE

Medical Officer: Dr S Kotecha, MB ChB, FRCGP, MSc
School Matron: Mrs E Haynes, RGN
Assistant to Matron: Mrs M M Thorne, RGN, RSCN

Headmaster's PA: Mrs L Johnson
Admissions Secretary: Mrs J Edwards
Bursar's PA: Ms S K Baldwin
Librarian: Mrs A M Vaughan

Solihull School was founded in 1560 with the income from the chantry chapels of the parish of Solihull. It now provides education for nearly 1,000 day pupils aged between 7 and 18. In 1973 girls were accepted into the Sixth Form and there are now over 100 girls in the School. From September 2005 the School became fully co-educational, with girls being admitted at 7+, 8+, 9+, 10+ and 11+. The School is particularly proud of the richness and diversity of the education that it provides. The School has always been closely involved with the community, making its sporting and theatrical facilities available, forming links with local schools, in particular Small Heath School in central Birmingham.

Organisation. In 2007/2008 there were 984 pupils in the School. The Junior School, which has its own separate building on the site, had 168 pupils aged from 7 to 11. The Junior School has its own Head. In the Senior School there are 520 pupils from Year 7 to Year 11. There are 296 pupils in the Sixth Form, of whom 89 are girls.

Site and Facilities. The School moved to its present site in 1882 and the original school building, School House, survives. The site now comprises over 50 acres of buildings and playing fields, which enable all teaching, games and activities to take place on the one site. In the last decade there has been a very substantial building programme. This programme originally involved the extension of the Science Department and Design and Technology Centre, the laying of an Astroturf pitch and three squash courts, the substantial redevelopment of School House. In 2002 a new hall/theatre, the Bushell Hall, was built. This hall can accommodate a theatre audience of 500 and an assembly for 800. At the same time the old hall was transformed into a library and IT rooms. In 2003, a new pavilion, the Alan Lee Pavilion, was completed. In September 2005 a new teaching area, the George Hill Building, was unveiled to provide 16 new classrooms and extensive social space, and the Junior School has been extended and entirely refurbished. Throughout the School there are excellent IT facilities for staff and pupils, including 51 interactive whiteboards.

Curriculum. In the Junior School particular emphasis is placed on establishing good standards in core subjects. The Junior School also has specialist areas for Art, Design and Technology and Music and benefits from the facilities of the Senior School.

At the beginning of the Senior School, all pupils have at least one year of Latin and in the second year Spanish and German are option subjects. English Language and Literature, Maths, French, Physics, Chemistry and Biology remain compulsory subjects to GCSE. Three other subjects are chosen from a wide range of options.

The size of the Sixth Form enables the school to offer a very wide range of subjects and combinations. These subjects are Art, 3D Art, Biology, Human Biology, Business Studies, Chemistry, Classical Civilisation, Design & Technology, English, Economics, French, Geography, German, History, ICT, Latin, Maths (and Further Maths), Music, PE, Philosophy, Photography, Psychology, Physics, Spanish, Theatre Studies. There is also a substantial programme of Enrichment for all pupils in the Sixth Form, ranging from Mandarin Chinese to Skiing.

Academic Success. In 2007 14 pupils received offers from Oxford and Cambridge, the average over the last 4 years being 14. In 2006 and 2007 more than 83% of A Levels were passed at A or B grade.

Games. Games are an integral part of the school curriculum and all pupils in the School are involved. PE is compulsory until Year 11 and all pupils in the School have a games afternoon. The School has a very strong tradition in the major team games for both boys and girls, but also offers a very wide range of other options. The principal team games are rugby, cricket, hockey (for both boys and girls), netball and rounders. Football is the main winter sport in the Junior School, but pupils are also able to play hockey and rugby. The School also has school teams in tennis, where the School has had national success, athletics, swimming, clay-pigeon shooting, cross-country, badminton, basketball and sailing. In recent years the School has organised very extensive tours for pupils of differing ages; in the Summer of 2006, a rugby tour of South Africa, a boys hockey tour of Australia, a girls hockey tour of Germany. Summer 2008 will witness our Senior rugby players in New Zealand, our boys' hockey teams in South Africa and our girls' netball and hockey teams in Barbados.

Music and Drama. The School has a very strong tradition in music and drama, which has been enhanced since the building of the Bushell Hall. Over one third of all pupils learn a musical instrument and there are over 20 different musical groups in the Senior School, ranging from a school orchestra to a samba band. Several of these groups are very successful in competition in local festivals. There are many opportunities for pupils to perform at concerts, both formal and informal, throughout the year. There is also an excellent chapel choir that performs during the school week but also at the voluntary chapel services which take place on each Sunday in term. A new Music School will be unveiled in September 2009.

There are two major dramatic performances each year, a school musical (*Les Misérables* 2005; *Barnum* 2006; *The*

Sound of Music 2007; *The Scarlet Pimpernel* 2008) and a school play (*A Streetcar Named Desire* 2004; *The Sea* 2005; *A Christmas Carol* 2006; *Romeo and Juliet* 2007). In addition, there are smaller productions in the course of the year.

Outdoor Pursuits. Outdoor pursuits play a major part in the School's life. In Year 7 pupils take part in an outdoor activities programme called Terriers. In Year 8 every pupil spends a week at the School's mountain cottage in Snowdonia. From Year 9 pupils are able to participate in the CCF, which has an Army and an RAF section, and/or the Duke of Edinburgh's Award Scheme. In 2007 there were approximately 150 pupils, including a number of girls in the CCF, and a similar number are involved at different stages of the Duke of Edinburgh's Award scheme. The School has a popular Mountain Club and organises biennial major expeditions: Peru in 2003, Tibet/Nepal in 2005 and Chile in 2007.

Admissions. Pupils are accepted into the Junior School through examination at 7+, 8+, 9+ and 10+, although the majority of pupils enter at 7+. Almost all Junior School pupils pass from the Junior School into the Senior School. The major point of entry is at 11+ (Year 7). Places and scholarships are awarded on the basis of written exams in English and Maths and, in many cases, an interview. Some pupils are also accepted to enter the School at 12+ and 13+. A substantial number of pupils, about 65 on average, enter the School at Sixth Form level. Admission to the Sixth Form, for both internal and external candidates, requires a minimum of 6 B grades at GCSE.

Fees per term (2008-2009). Tuition: £3,083 (£2,505 for pupils aged 7–10). Lunch charges per day: £2.45 Junior School, £2.70 Main School. There are few obligatory extras.

Scholarships and Assisted Places. (*see Scholarship Entries section*). The school is able to offer a substantial number of scholarships. About 15 pupils at 11+ and 20 at 16+ benefit from some form of scholarship. There are also music scholarships available at 11+ and 16+.

In addition to academic scholarships, means-tested Assisted Places are available to allow able children the opportunity of an education at Solihull School. Applicants for such awards are considered for entry at age 11+ and into the Sixth Form.

Old Silhillians Association. *Secretary*: A J Richardson, Memorial Clubhouse, Warwick Road, Knowle, Solihull. The aim of the Old Silhillians is to support and maintain links with the School. They also have their own clubhouse and extensive sports facilities.

Charitable status. Solihull School is a Registered Charity, number 529056. It exists to provide high-quality education for pupils between 7 and 18 years old.

Stamford School

Stamford Lincolnshire PE9 2BS
Tel: 01780 750300
Fax: 01780 750336
e-mail: headss@ses.lincs.sch.uk
website: www.ses.lincs.sch.uk

Founded by William Radcliffe, of Stamford, 1532.
Motto: '*Christe me spede*'

Chairman of the Governing Body: Air Vice-Marshal P Dodworth, CB, OBE, AFC, BSc, FRAeS, DL

***Principal of the Stamford Endowed Schools*: S C Roberts,** MA

Vice-Principal, Head: S A Burns, MA

Director of Staff & Student Development: W C Chadwick, MA
Director of Studies: J Crampin, MA, MBA
Senior Teacher: R D A Haynes, BEd
Head of Sixth Form: G P Brown, MA
Head of Middle School: J P Hodgson, BSc
Head of Lower School: K J Chapman, BEd
SES Chaplain: The Revd M Goodman, BA, BTh, MTh
Director of ICT: N A Faux, MA

Assistant Staff:
† *Boarding Housemaster*

Miss S Angove, MA
B D Bates, BSc
Mrs L Blissett, BA
M J Blissett, BA
C W Brace, BSc, MSc
P Braud, Baccalaureate
R A Brewster, BSc (*†Browne House*)
Miss E L Calvert, BSc
M C Caseley, MA
Mrs A Chauvaux, Staatsexamen
Ms H M Chew, BA, MPhil
Mrs S L Child, BA
Mrs N A Cliffe, BSc
D Colley, BEd
Ms A Davies, BA
J W Dawson, MA
R G A Dexter, BA
Dr R Fielden, MA, DPhil
C D Fox, BA
Mrs J C Fox, BA
G Froggett, BA
B Gantry, BSc
Dr R Gosling, BSc, PhD
Ms F Harrison, BA
Mrs F L Haunch, BSc
Miss K M Hawkswell, BSc
R J B Henry, BEd
H P Hewlett, BSc
D Hodder, BSc
M V Holdsworth, BA
Mrs A J M Holland, MA
Miss P Ingle, BSc
D N Jackson, BSc
T P Jones, Bed
S M Jordan, MBA, BEng
C V Killgren, BA
D J Laventure, BA
G S Lee, CertEd
Mrs K Leetch, MA
D Lennie, BA
J M Livingstone, BA
K J Mills, BA
M K Milner, BSc
G Mitchell, BSc
K G Nally, BEng, MBA
J A Peckett, BSc
A N Pike, BA (*†Byard House*)
Mrs C Pike, BA
N J Porteus, BSc
Mrs M Rigg, BSc
M G Sawyer, BSc
P J Scargill, MSc
M P Scriven, BA
Miss A L Spong, MA
D L A Stamp, BA
Miss R L Tomlinson, BA
Mrs C A Walklin, DipEd
L H Ware, BSc
G J Whitehouse, BEd
D F Williams, CertEd
Mrs C A Wray, BA

SES Music Department:
G E Turner, BA (*Director of Music*)
D McIlrae, BMus, HED (*Assistant Director of Music*)
S Chandley, CT ABRSM (*Head of Brass*)
Mrs N Ingrams, GRSM, RAM, LRAM
D Leetch, MA, GRSM, LRAM (*Head of Strings*)
Mrs J E Roberts, GRSM, LRM, ARCM
N S Taylor, BA

Visiting Music Staff:
S Andrews (*Kit Drum/Percussion*)
F Applewhite (*Violin, Viola*)
J Aughton (*Flute*)
S Barber (*Organ*)
C Bell, BSc, LRAM, ARCM (*Guitar*)
Mrs M Bennett, LRAM, LTCL (*Singing*)
Mrs S Bond, GLCM, LLCM (*TD*), FLCM (*Singing*)
Mrs K Bentley, GTCL, LTCL (*Cello, Double Bass*)
F Black (*Singing*)
G Brown, BMus (*Oboe, Piano*)
Mrs H Brown, BA (*Clarinet*)
P J Casson (*Saxophone, Clarinet*)
Miss A Chalmers, LRAM (*Cello, Double Bass*)
Revd Mrs J Dumat, ARCM (*Clarinet*)
M Duthie, BSc, ARCO (*Organ*)
N Gray (*Electric Guitar*)
Mrs E Hanlon, ARMCM (*Pianoforte*)
Mrs C Lee, LRAM (*Violin*)
Miss F Maclennan (*Pianoforte*)
Mrs M Maclennan, LRAM, ARCM (*Pianoforte*)
Mrs A McCrae (*Bassoon, Pianoforte*)

Mrs E Murphy, GTCL, LTLL, PGCE (*Violin, Pianoforte*)
D Price, LRAM (*Brass*)
Mrs G Spencer, CertEd, ACRM (*Pianoforte*)
Mrs A Sumner, CertEd, ARCM (*Pianoforte*)
Mrs E A Taylor, BA (*Violin, Viola*)
Mrs L Williamson, LTCC (*Pianoforte*)
Medical Officer: C S Mann, MBChB, BSc

Introduction. Stamford School is one of three schools within the overall Stamford Endowed Schools Educational Charity, along with Stamford High School (girls) and Stamford Junior School, the co-educational Junior School.

Buildings and Grounds. Stamford School dates its foundation to 1532. The grounds include the site of the Hall occupied by secessionists from Brasenose Hall, Oxford, in the early 14th century. The oldest surviving building is the School Chapel, which was formerly part of St Paul's Church, but which from 1548 until restoration in 1929 was used as a schoolroom. Extensive additions to the School continued to be made throughout the nineteenth and twentieth centuries. In 1956 the Old Stamfordians gave the School a swimming pool as a war memorial. The science school was built in 1957 and extended in 1973 when a new dining hall and kitchens also came into use and which have been completely redesigned and upgraded in 2003. A music school was built in 1977 and extended in 1984. A further extensive development programme was begun in 1980 and included the building of one new senior boarding house (Browne), opened in 1981, and extensive and comparable provision in the other (Byard). School House was converted principally into a teaching area is now used as a Sixth Form area. In the autumn of 1983 a mathematics and computer centre was completed, as were additional project rooms and laboratories in the science school. The library was refurbished in 1998 and a new Technology facility and refurbished Art Centre opened in 2005. Reorganisation in 2000 resulted in new classrooms and the development of an administration centre. A large number of classrooms are fitted with Interactive Whiteboards.

School Structure and Curriculum. The school consists of around 680 boys divided into Lower School (11–14), Middle School (14–16) and Sixth Form. The Heads of each section, with their assistants and Form Tutors monitor the academic progress of each boy and manage the pastoral arrangements.

The National Curriculum is broadly followed but much more is added to the curriculum to make it stimulating and rewarding. Information Technology, Art & Design and Design Technology form an integral part of the curriculum and from Year 8 boys may begin German, Spanish or Russian. All boys are prepared for a complete range of GCSE examination; the great majority of them continue into the Sixth Form and then onto higher education.

In the Sixth Form of about 180 boys (and 180 girls) the timetable is so arranged that a wide range of combinations of subjects is possible. In partnership with Stamford High School all Sixth Form students can choose from the full range of subjects available across the two schools, which allows a total of 28 subjects to be offered.

Activities. Art, Music, Drama, Games and Physical Education form part of the normal curriculum. There is a choral society, an orchestra, a band and a jazz band, and a chapel choir. The musical activities of the school are combined with those of the High School under the overall responsibility of the Director of Music for the Endowed Schools. The school maintains RN, Army and RAF sections of the CCF and there is a rifle club. A large number of boys are engaged at all levels of the Duke of Edinburgh's Award Scheme.

The school plays rugby football, hockey, cricket, tennis, golf. The athletics and swimming sports and matches are held in the summer term. In winter there is also badminton, cross-country running and basketball. Four squash courts were built in 1973. A full-sized astroturf hockey pitch suitable for most sports was opened in 1983 to which floodlights were added in 2006 and a new sports hall in 1985. There are many school clubs and societies and a thriving weekend activity programme.

Close links are maintained with the local community. The school welcomes performances in the hall by the music societies of the town and uses the excellent local theatre in Stamford Arts Centre for some of its plays.

Careers. The school is a member of ISCO and has a team of careers staff. There is an extensive new careers library, computer room and interview rooms.

House Structure. Boarding: Byard House (11–15) Mr A N Pike; Browne House (15–18) Mr R A Brewster.

Weekly and flexible boarding are available, as well as full boarding.

Competition in games, music and other activities are organised within a house system. Housemasters with their assistants monitor boys' commitments to the wider curriculum and act as counsellors when boys need to turn to someone outside the formal pastoral and disciplinary system.

Admission. Registration Fee £50; Acceptance Fee £250.

The main point of entry is at age 11, but boys are considered at any age. A number join at age 13 or directly into the sixth form. Application forms for admission may be obtained from the school office. The school's entrance examinations take place in late January, but arrangements may be made to test applicants at other times. Entry into the sixth form is considered at any time. Boys who enter through the Junior School progress automatically on to Stamford School at age 11 without having to take further entrance tests.

Fees per term (2008-2009). Day £3,616; Full Boarding £6,768; Weekly Boarding £6,732.

These fees include stationery, text books and games. School lunches for day boys are at additional charge.

Scholarships. (*see Scholarship Entries section*). Governors' Scholarships at 11+ and for the Sixth Form. Awards are given for musical ability and art. Bursaries up to full fees are available.

Charitable status. As part of the Stamford Endowed Schools, Stamford School is a Registered Charity, number 527618. It exists to provide education for boys.

Stewart's Melville College

Queensferry Road Edinburgh EH4 3EZ
Tel: 0131 311 1000
Fax: 0131 311 1099
e-mail: secretary@esmgc.com
website: www.esms.edin.sch.uk

Governing Council:
Chairman: Alan Robertson

Clerk to the Governors: Mr J Kerr

***Principal*: Mr J N D Gray**, BA

Bursar: Mr I McGregor, MA Hons

Deputy Headmaster: Mr N G Clark, MA
Director of Studies: Mr G Johnston, MPhys
Head of Upper School: Mr M R Kane, MA
Director of Sixth Form: Dr I Scott, MA, FRSA, PhD
Assistant Head Teacher, Regent: Mr H I McKerrow, BSc
Assistant Head Teacher, Guidance: Mr G J Brown, BEd
Operations Director: Mr G R S Wilson, MA
Director of Technology: Dr K Hussain
Registrar: Mr P G Waine, CertEd, BEd

* *Head of Department*
† *Head of House*

Art:
*Mr M Crichton, BA
Mr C A Nasmyth, BA

Biology:
*Mr D Lloyd, BSc, MEd
Mrs L A Lim, BSc
Mr R D Miller, BSc, CBiol, MIBiol
Mr S W Primrose, BSc (*†Ettrick*)

Chemistry:
*Mr P Johnson, BSc
Mr C P Kerr, BSc
Mr G Mitchell, BSc

Classics:
*Mr I Crosbie, MA
Mr M T Garden, BA

Computer Studies:
*Mr A Thomson, BA

Design & Technology:
*Mrs L Burt
Mr S Longair, BEd Des Tech
Mr A Scott, BEng

Drama:
*Miss A Marshall

Economics:
*Ms S Burns, MA
Mr C G Irvine

English:
*Mr David Higgins
Mr J C Allan, BA (*†Appin*)
Miss M Bowman, MA
Mr N G Clark, MA
Mrs S Frost, BA, MPhil
Mr I A Major, BA
Mr S Hart, MA
Mr M R Kane, MA
Ms G Reid

Geography:
*Mr D J Wood, MA, MEd
Mr K Turnbull, MA
Mr M S Kemp

History:
*Mr M Longmuir, BA, CAM
Mrs J D Bennett, MA
Mrs A J Ferguson, MA
Mr C D Currie, MA

Mathematics:
*Mr A J T Dunsmore, BEng, MSc
Mr G Johnston, MPhys
Mr R I Canter, BSc, HDE
Mr S Love, BA, MA, CEng, MBCS
Mr H I McKerrow, BSc
Mr J J Robertson, BSc (*†Galloway*)
Mr G Smith, BSc
Dr G Henderson, BA, BSc (*Maths*)

Media Studies:
*Mr D A Orem, MA, MPhil, Cert Media Ed, DipEd

Modern Languages:
*Mr M Z Hamid, MA
*Mrs C R Siljehag, MA
Mr J F Marsh, BA
Mrs V Chittleburgh, BA, MA
Mr N A C Connet, MA
Mr M Constable, BA
Mrs M Elswood, BA, Dip TESL (*†Kintyre*)
Mr A J Hyslop, MA
Mrs V Longbottom

Music:
*Mr J Orringe, BA Hons, MA
Mr Z Fazlic, BA
Mr A J Samson, Dip RSAMD

Physical Education:
*Mr C S Spence, BEd
Mr R G Allan, BEd
Mr G J Brown, BEd
Mr M R Burgess, BA(*Ed*)
Mr D G Ellis, BEd
Mr B G Lockie, BEd
Mr G A Mackenzie, BEd (*†Lochaber*)
Mr D A Roxburgh, BEd (*†Torridon*)
Mr P G M Waine, CertEd, BEd

Physics:
*Miss J Macdonald, BSc
Mr B W J Dunlop, BSc
Mr G Millar, BSc, FInstP, CPhys
Mr S D Jackson

Religious Studies:
*Mr G F W Park, BD
Mr G Innes, BD

Support for Learning:
*Mrs C G C Maxwell, BA
Mrs M Nimmo, BEd
Mrs R Meredith

Educational Psychologist:
*Mrs M Brown, MA, DipEdPsyc

Library:
Mr D Wright, BA

Junior School:
Head Master: Mr B D Lewis, MA
Assistant Head Teacher: Mr D McLeish, DCE
Deputy Head (*Primary 4–7*): Mrs G Lyon, DCE, DipRSA
Deputy Head (*Early Education*): Mrs M Rycroft, DipCE

'Daniel Stewart's Hospital' was founded (1855) by Daniel Stewart and has been administered since its inception by the Company of Merchants of the City of Edinburgh. Melville College, formerly The Edinburgh Institution, was founded in 1832 by the Reverend Robert Cunningham. The two schools combined in 1972 to form Daniel Stewart's and Melville College (now Stewart's Melville College). Since 1989 management of the School has been delegated by the Merchant Company Education Board to the Erskine Stewart's Melville Governing Council.

The School enjoys a commanding position on Queensferry Road, a mile from the City Centre. The original College building is occupied by the Senior School while the Junior School is in a modern building. There are a number of excellent facilities including a new state-of-the-art Performing Arts Centre, Games Hall, swimming pool and Sixth Form Centre.

Since 1978 the school has been twinned with The Mary Erskine School (*see entry in GSA section*). This includes a fully co-educational Junior School for children between the ages of 3 and 12, single-sex but very closely twinned secondary schools between the ages of 12 and 17 and a fully co-educational pre-university Sixth Form which provides the ideal bridge between school and university. Boys and Girls from Stewart's Melville College and The Mary Erskine School come together in the Combined Cadet Force, in orchestras, choirs, drama and musicals and in numerous outdoor education projects.

The Senior School (726 boys). S1 and S2 follow a broad curriculum, whereby boys are equipped to pursue all routes to Intermediate 2. In S3 boys commence eight courses, including English, mathematics, at least one modern language, at least one science, and a social or creative subject. In S5 boys are expected to take 5 subjects at Higher level. A majority will continue their studies for a Sixth Year, usually three Advanced Highers to provide a firm foundation for degree courses in Scotland and England. Most boys proceed to such courses.

The School has a sophisticated system of guidance. Boys in the first year are with a Form Tutor, under the overall direction of an Assistant Head Teacher. The next four years are spent in Houses of approximately 90 boys, each with its own Head of House and House Tutors. The Sixth Form is a co-educational year, as the girls from The Mary Erskine School join with the boys of Stewart's Melville College in a completely 'twinned' Sixth Form. There is a well-established Careers department. The Support for Learning Department helps boys with specific learning difficulties.

Games. Rugby and Cricket are played on the school playing fields at Inverleith, while Hockey and Tennis are played at Ravelston. There are also opportunities for Athletics, Curling, Golf, Swimming, Squash, Sailing and Shooting as well as the many sports played in the Games Hall. Boys from the school are frequently selected for national teams in many sports.

Music is much-valued and flourishes within the school. Approximately 500 instrumental lessons are given each week by an enthusiastic staff of 25 visiting teachers. Most orchestral activity is combined with The Mary Erskine School, including junior and senior orchestras, two concert bands, a jazz band and numerous chamber groups. Choral singing is also very strong, from large junior choirs to more specialised groups for madrigals and close harmony. A full programme of public performances includes two major musicals every year and large choral and orchestral concerts in which our musicians combine with an active parents' choir.

Activities. The School encourages boys to take part in The Combined Cadet Force which comprises Army and RAF sections or in The Duke of Edinburgh's Award Scheme. Each week the School offers approximately 70 clubs and societies to suit the appetites of all boys. In sport the school has particular strengths in rugby, swimming, sailing, basketball, hockey, athletics and skiing with representation at district or national level.

Boarding. Dean Park House, adjoining the school grounds, serves as the boarding house for up to 25 boys. They share dining and recreational facilities with The Mary Erskine boarders next door in Erskine House.

Fees per term (2008-2009). Day £2,830 (plus £143 for optional Lunches); Boarding £5,646.

Scholarships and Bursaries. Means-tested Bursaries worth up to 100% may be available to parents of children entering any year group in the Senior Schools. A number of awards are allocated for external candidates seeking to join the Sixth Form. Academic scholarships worth up to £1,000 annually are offered to boys applying to enter S1. Scholarships are payable to the pupil and are held in trust by the school for disbursement on recipients leaving school on completion of Sixth Form. Music Scholarships of £250 per annum are offered from S3.

Junior School. In The Mary Erskine and Stewart's Melville Junior School (1,226 pupils), girls and boys are educated together from age 3 to 12. Children in Primary Start to Primary 3 are based on the Mary Erskine School site at Ravelston, while boys and girls in Primary 4–7 are taught on the Stewart's Melville College site. Normal entry points are Primary Start (age 3 or 4), Primary 1, Primary 4, Primary 6 and Primary 7. The school is remarkable for the breadth of its educational programme and the quality of its sporting and cultural activities, in particular the professional standards attained in Music and Drama.

Daniel Stewart's & Melville College Former Pupils' Club. *Hon Sec*: Dr E J Wilkins, c/o Stewart's Melville College, Queensferry Road, Edinburgh EH4 3EZ.

Charitable status. The Merchant Company Education Board is a Registered Charity, number SC009747. It is a leading charitable School in the field of Junior and Secondary education.

Stockport Grammar School

Buxton Road Stockport Cheshire SK2 7AF
Tel: 0161 456 9000 Senior School
0161 419 2405 Junior School
Fax: 0161 419 2407
e-mail: sgs@stockportgrammar.co.uk
website: www.stockportgrammar.co.uk

Founded in 1487, Stockport Grammar School is one of England's oldest schools. The founder, Sir Edmond Shaa, was a goldsmith, 200th Lord Mayor of London and Court Jeweller to three Kings of England. The School's rich history and traditions are celebrated in the annual Founder's Day Service in Stockport.

A co-educational day school, Stockport Grammar School is non-denominational and welcomes pupils from all faiths and cultures. Almost all leavers go on into Higher Education, including many to Oxbridge. Although academic performance is formidable, it is not the be-all and end-all of life at Stockport Grammar School.

Motto: '*Vincit qui patitur*'

Patron: The Prime Warden of the Worshipful Company of Goldsmiths

Governing Body:

R L E Rimmington, BA, FCA (*Chairman*)
R H Astles (*Vice-Chairman*)
Lady Beatson, MA (*Vice-Chairman*)
A Bloxham
F A Booth, FCA
Miss S E Carroll, BA
Mrs C E Condliffe, GRSM, ARMCM (*Teaching Staff*)
P A Cuddy, BA, FCIPD, FCMI
P H Davies, LLB (*Ephraim Hallam Educational Foundation*)
E D Foulkes, LLB
K Lansdale, MRICS
P H Locke, BVSc, MRCVS
Mrs A Mack, BSc
Dr E M Morris, MBChB, DCH
J J Mott (*Old Stopfordians' Association*)
S Nuttall, BSc, PhD, FRSA
R P Yates, FIMI

Clerk to the Governors and Bursar: C J Watson, MA

***Headmaster*: A H Chicken**, BA, MEd, FRSA

Deputy Headmaster/Proctor: J P Ashcroft , BSc, MA
Deputy Headmistress/Director of Studies: Miss V L Barrett, MA
Head of Lower School: R W Wallington, BSc
Head of Middle School: Mrs H K Bridges, BSc, MIBiol
Head of Sixth Form: Mrs J White, BA
Senior Tutor: D W Howson, MA

Assistant Masters and Mistresses:
* *Head of Department*

Art:
Mrs C A Beckett, Dip AD
*R A Davies, BA, MA
Miss R J Upton, BA

Biology:
Mrs H K Bridges, BSc
Miss J Gilbert, BA, PhD
*P J Grant, BSc
J R Metivier, BSc, PhD
Miss L J Service, BSc
Mrs J White, BA
Mrs M Whitton, BSc
Mrs L J Withers, BA

Chemistry:
*Mrs L Earps, BSc, MSc, PhD
R Heyes, BSc
W Krywonos, BSc, MSc, PhD
T Pyeon, BSc
Mrs L Pitts, BSc, PhD

Classics:
J P Ashcroft, BSc, MA
A N Palmer, MA, PhD
*A C Thorley, BA
P A Urwin, BA
Mrs E Zanda, BA, PhD

Economics:
*R Parker, MA
R Young, BEd

English:
Miss V L Barrett, BA
*Mrs G A Cope, BA
Miss S L Ginty, BA
Miss S J Green, BA
D W Howson, MA
Mrs R G Johnson, BA, MA
Mrs H J Jones, BA
Ms H R Lawson, MA
B J Masters, BA, MA

French:
Mrs S L Belshaw, BA
Mrs B Garnier, MSc
*Miss S M Gibson, BA
D Lorentz, BA, MA, DEA
J D Wilson, BA

Geography:
Mrs A C Hicks, BA, FRGS
*R Howarth, BA
D S Martin, MA, FRGS
Mrs K Palfreyman, BA
D G Wright, BSc

German:
Mrs F S Forbes, BA
Mrs T Kampelmann, MA, PhD
*Mrs C S Muscutt, BA
Mrs J Turner, BA

History:
Mrs H R Ashton, BA
Miss K J Bamborough, BA, MA
S A Moore, BA
Mrs L S Pearson, BA
J P Russell, BA, MA
*S J D Smith, BA, PhD

Information Technology:
I H Bruce, BSc
*M J Flaherty, BSc
Mrs P W Hodkinson, BSc

Mathematics:
A B Cheslett, BSc, MSc
Miss R Darch, BSc
Mrs M Evans, BA
*Mrs D L Harris, BSc
Miss M E Higgins, BSc
Mrs L Lammas, BA
Mrs A S Larkin, BSc
Mrs C L Marshall, BSc, MSc
P T Moylan, BA
R W Wallington, BSc

Music:
*M G Dow, MA, ALCM
P F Robinson, BMus, LTCL
Mrs E N Short, MA, LLCM
Mrs E Taylor, BMus

Physics:
Mrs Z Dawson, MSc
M Ellis, BSc, DPhil
Mrs H M Fenton, BSc
*P L Giblin, MA, MEd
I Killey, BSc, BEng
Mrs K S Michael, BSc
Mrs G M Lockwood, MA

Physical Education:
R Bowden, BA
E H Corbett, BA
A Ehegartner
Mrs A Jones, BEd
A S Hanson, BEd
Mrs J Maskery, BEd
Miss L E Topping, BSc
Mrs K Wilkinson, BA

Miss S Withington, BEd
*C J Wright, BA

Psychology:
*Mrs S J Braude, BA
N I Browne, MA
Miss C E Pye, BSc

Life Studies/RS/Philosophy:
P P Elliott, BA
*Mrs K E Farrington, BA

Technology:
Mrs R E Groves, BA
Mrs T H Samways, BSc
Mrs H Tadman, BEng
Mrs Z A Vernon, BEd
G M Whitby
*N Young, MA

Learning Support:
Mrs A Sullivan, BSc

School Chaplain: Revd L E Leaver, MA, BTh
Director of Music: M G Dow, BA, MA
Director of External Relations: Mrs R M Horsford, BA
Systems Manager: P Roebuck, BSc
Librarian: Mrs D Sutton, BSc, MA
Headmaster's Secretary and Admissions: Mrs J E Baker
School Nurse: Mrs P Ward, RGN, DipHE

Junior School

Headmaster: L Fairclough, BA
Deputy Head: N Vernon, BSc, MA
Director of Studies: Mrs V L Hall, BSc

Assistant Masters and Mistresses:
Mrs H Carroll, BEd
Mrs R Cole, BA
Mrs S Coombes, BSc
Mrs C Hampson, BA
Mrs L Hardy, BEd
Miss J Haslam, BEd
Mrs K Horrocks, MA
Mr M Johnson, BSc
J Jones, BEd
D Makinson
Mrs P Martin, BEd
Mrs J Mercer, BA
Mrs C M Nichols, BEd
Miss R Penhale, BA
Mrs K Roberts, BEd, MA
Mrs R Scott, BA
Mrs H Shanks
Mrs C Smith, BA
Mrs A Sullivan, BEd
Mrs J Swales, BA
A Taylor, BSc
Mrs L Turner, BEd

Headmaster's Secretary: Mrs B Cheyne

Stockport Grammar School aims to provide the best all round education to enable pupils to fulfil their potential in a friendly and supportive atmosphere. The backbone of the school is academic excellence, with a clear framework of discipline within which every activity is pursued to the highest level. Entry is at 3, 4, 7, 11 and 16, but vacancies may occur at other stages. There are over 1,400 pupils aged 3–18 years, with 350+ in the Junior School and over 250 in the Sixth Form.

The Senior School. Admission at age 11 is by competitive entrance examination. This is held in late January or early February, for admission in the following September. There are several open events: see website for details. Occasional vacancies are considered on an individual basis and a few places are available in the Sixth Form each year. Visitors are always welcome to make an appointment to see the school.

Curriculum. The emphasis is on how to learn. The GCSE philosophies are introduced in the first three years as part of a broad general education. The sciences are taught as separate subjects and all pupils study Latin, French and German.

On entering the fourth year, at the age of 14, pupils retain a core of subjects but also make choices, so that individual aptitudes can be fully developed. GCSE examinations are taken in the fifth year; the percentage pass rate has not been less than 97%. In 2005, 64% of entries gained an A* or A. On entering the Sixth Form, pupils take four AS Level courses. The pass rate at Advanced Level was 100% in 2005, with 79% of all entries gaining the top two grades.

Art. A high standard is set and achieved. There are facilities for all aspects of two-dimensional work and textiles, plus a fully equipped ceramics area and a sculpture court. There are regular exhibitions in the School's Brooke Gallery.

Music. The curriculum provides a well-structured musical education for all pupils for the first three years. GCSE and Advanced Level are offered for those who aspire to a musical career as well as for proficient amateurs. Three main areas of musical ensemble – choirs, orchestras and wind bands – are at the centre of activities with opportunities open from First Year to Sixth Form. Emphasis is on determination, commitment and a sense of team work. All ensembles are encouraged to reach the highest standards.

Drama. A particularly strong tradition has been fostered over many years and regular productions involve all year groups. Drama is part of the English curriculum in the first three years and there are drama clubs, trips to local theatre groups and workshops in school.

Physical Education. The Physical Education curriculum is diverse, with activities including aerobics, ball skills, badminton, basketball, dance, gymnastics, health-related fitness, squash, swimming and volleyball. The main winter games for boys are rugby and football, and for the girls hockey and netball. In the summer, boys concentrate on cricket and athletics, whilst the girls focus their attention on tennis, athletics and rounders. Up to 350 pupils represent the school at Saturday fixtures and the teams have an excellent reputation, gaining success in regional and national competitions. Almost fifty pupils have represented their country, region or county in the last year.

Information Technology. Three dedicated Computer Suites accommodate full classes, each pupil having access to a Pentium PC on the school's site-wide network. All pupils have their own password and email address, and are able to use the Internet for research. The rooms are available to everyone as a computer resource at lunchtimes and after school. Information Technology skills are taught as part of the curriculum and academic departments incorporate the use of computers and interactive whiteboards into their everyday lessons. The subject is not currently studied for public examination.

Houses. Every pupil is a member of one of the four Houses, each led by two Heads of House staff assisted by a team of senior pupils. The Houses organise and compete in a wide range of sporting and non-sporting activities.

Clubs and Societies. The School has many active clubs and societies covering a wide variety of extra-curricular interests, for example, debating, where Fifth and Sixth Formers have the opportunity to participate in up to four Model United Nations Assemblies around the world each year.

Development. The new Library and Learning Resource Centre and Physics Department were completed in summer 2005. A Nursery for children aged 3+ will open in September 2006.

Visits. Well-established language exchange visits are made every year to France and Germany, in addition to hill walking, camping, mountaineering, skiing, sailing and cultural trips.

Assembly. Formal morning assemblies are held daily for all pupils; there are separate Jewish and Muslim assemblies. House assemblies, which include Junior School pupils, are on Wednesdays; the Sixth Form have an additional fortnightly assembly.

Pastoral Care. Form teachers get to know each pupil in the form individually, and are supported by Year Heads and by the Head of Lower School (years 1 to 3), the Head of Middle School (years 4 and 5) and the Head of Sixth Form.

Discipline. This is positive and enabling. Much importance is attached to appearance and to uniform, which is worn throughout the school.

Fees per term (2008-2009). Senior School £2,742; Junior School £2,112.

Bursary Scheme. The School's own Bursary Scheme aims to provide financial assistance on a means-tested basis to families who have chosen a Stockport Grammar School education for their children. Details available from the Bursar.

Stockport Grammar Junior School. (*See also entry in IAPS section.*) With its own Headmaster and Staff it has separate buildings and a playing field on the same site. The Junior School has boys and girls between the ages of 3 and 11 years.

Boys and girls join the Nursery when they are three. In its own building and with a designated play area, the Nursery is very well resourced. The children are looked after by qualified and experienced staff.

Entrance is by observed play at the age of 4 years into two Reception forms, and by assessment in February for an additional form at the age of 7. All pupils are prepared for the Entrance Examination to the Senior School at the age of 11.

The Junior School buildings provide special facilities for Art, Technology, Music and Computing. The winter games are soccer, hockey and netball, with cricket and rounders being played in the summer. There are swimming lessons every week; other activities include the gym club, life saving, athletics and chess. There are clubs running each lunchtime and after school for both infants and juniors. Matches are played every Saturday against other schools in the major sports. Many pupils have instrumental music lessons and there is an orchestra, band, recorder group and a choir. The musical, held in May each year, is a very popular event in which all pupils participate. Visits are made annually to Paris at Easter and to the Lake District in May. Short annual residential visits, are introduced from age 7.

Charitable status. Stockport Grammar School is a Registered Charity, number 1120199. It exists to advance education by the provision and conduct, in or near Stockport, of a school for boys and girls.

Stonyhurst College

Stonyhurst Clitheroe Lancashire BB7 9PZ
Tel: 01254 826345; 01254 827093 (Admissions)
Fax: 01254 827135 (Admissions)
e-mail: admissions@stonyhurst.ac.uk
website: www.stonyhurst.ac.uk

Stonyhurst College is a co-educational Catholic boarding and day school guided by the principles of the society of Jesus. This means that we attach particular importance to emotional and spiritual development as well as academic excellence. Founded in 1593, it stands in its own estate of 2,500 acres in the beautiful Ribble Valley on the slope of the Longridge Fells, ten miles from the M6 motorway, and just over 1 hour by car from Manchester International Airport.

The College houses a remarkable collection of items relating to the history of the Church in England. These are used as a learning resource. The College has a full-time curator.

Motto: '*Quant je puis*'

Governors:
President: Very Revd M Holman, SJ

Chairman: K M T Ryan
Deputy Chairman: M J Prior, JP, FCA

W P Boylan
Fr A Howell, SJ
Sr M Walmsley, CJ
A C F Verity
T O Mayhew
G J Lagerberg
Fr K McMillan, SJ
J Cowdall

***Headmaster*: A R Johnson**, BA

Father Superior: Fr A Howell, SJ

College Chaplain: Fr J Twist, SJ

Deputy Headmaster: A Gordon-Brown, MSc

Deputy Head Pastoral: J D Hopkins, BA

Deputy Head Learning : S P H Andrews, BSc, MA

Assistant Staff:
P R Ansell, BA (*Head of Modern Languages*)
Major A Barber (*Contingent Commander CCF*)
T A Bell, MA, DPhil (*Head of English*)
Miss C Brotherhood, BA (*Head of Girls' Games*)
A J Callinicos, BA, MA (*Poetry-Year 12- Playroom Master; Classics*)
D B Channing, BSc (*Mathematics*)
S J Charles, MSc, BA (*Head of Games & PE*)
J Cook, BA (*Design & Technology*)
L Crabtree, NDD (*Art*)
Mrs R Crossley, BA (*Geography*)
I Cunliffe, BSc, MBA (*Biology; Chemistry*)
Mrs H C Davies, Bed (*Head of Special Educational Needs*)
J Dixon, BA (*Head of ICT*)
D A Eachus, BTech (*Grammar-Year 10- Playroom Master; Head of Design & Technology*)
Miss J R Egar, BA (*Theatre Studies*)
Miss L. Fielding, BA (*Lower Line Girls' Housemistress; Fine Art*)
Mrs L Fisher, BSc (*Head of Physics*)
Mrs H L Flatley, BSc, MSc (*Biology*)
M Gibson, BA (*Director of ICT*)
Mrs C E S Gibson-Oxley, BA, MSt (*Head of Art; Lower Line Girls' Deputy Housemistress*)
Mrs J Graffius, MA (*Curator*)
D Hallam, BSc (*Biology; Chemistry*)
T Hardwick, BA (*English*)
Mrs H Harris, BSc (*Head of Geography*)
N Henshaw, BA (*History; Drama*)
P E Hodkinson, BSc, MSc (*Mathematics*)
G Hunter, BSc (*Physics*)
Dr H Hunter, BSc, PhD (*Head of Chemistry*)
H M Kaaber, BSc (*Physical Education; EAL*)
J.Ketchell, MA (*Mathematics*)
Mrs D J Kirkby, BSc (*Economics; Business Studies*)
D N Knight, BA (*Archivist*)
Mrs Y Luker, BEd (*Physical Education*)
D G Mann, BA (*Director of Music*)
Mrs C M Markarian, BSc, MSc (*Mathematics*)
Mrs P Massey, BA (*English Literature; Latin*)
Miss H Mercer, BA (*Hispanic Studies*)
Miss K Mitchell, BA (*English as an Additional Language*)
K Morgan, BA, FRCO, LRAM, LTCL (*College Organist & Head of Keyboard*)
B J P O'Connor, BSc (*Physics*)
S Oliver, BA, MLitt (*Lower Grammar-Year 9- Playroom Master; Classics*)
F J O'Reilly, MA, CertObsAst (*Head of Classics; Mathematics; Astronomy*)
Mrs G P Parkinson, BA (*Modern Languages*)
Miss J M Parkinson, MPhil, MA, BA (*Classics*)
R A Pearce, MA, BLitt (*Religious Studies; Professional Development*)
D N Rawkins, BSc (*Head of Mathematics; Prefect of Studies*)
D C Ridout, BA (*Head of Politics and General Studies*)
A Roberts, BA (*Modern Languages*)
Mrs J Robinson, BEd (*Art*)
D J Soars, BA (*Theology; Religious Studies*)
Ms J Shard, BSc (*Mathematics*)
J M B Sharples, BA (*Modern Languages*)
Mrs R Shipley (*Games; Higher Line Girls' Deputy Housemistress*)
J Smith, BA (*English*)
T Strain, BEd (*Rhetoric-Year 13-Playroom Master; Head of Economics & Business Studies*)
G Thomas (*Games; Head of Lights & Sound*)
Mrs L W Timmins, BA (*Economics & Business Studies*)
M J Turner, MA (*Head of History; Religious Studies*)
Miss H Vinnicombe, PhD, BSc (*Biology; Chemistry*)
Mrs M Wainwright, MusB (*Higher Line Girls' Housemistress; Music*)
T J Warner, BSc, PhD (*Head of Biology*)
P A Warrilow, BD (*Head of Religious Studies*)

Mrs V Watson, BEd (*Head of Girls' Games*)
Mrs E Whalley, BSc (*Syntax-Year 11- Playroom Mistress; Geography*)
Mrs I M Williams, BEd (*Geography*)
Mrs K Wright, BA (*Economics & Business Studies*)
Miss S. Young, BA, MA (*Lay Chaplain*)

Visiting Music Staff:
W Ashton (*Piano*)
G Banks, BA (*Brass*)
Mrs J Barlow (*Clarinet*)
D Baron (*Flute/Saxophone*)
Miss A Cooper (*Oboe, Bassoon*)
P Greenhalgh, BMus, ARCM, ALCM (*Piano*)
Mrs J Howarth (*Singing*)
Mrs E Hudson (*Harp*)
D Lewis (*Percussion*)
G Lister (*Drum Kit*)
Mrs C Lorriman (*Flute*)
C Marks (*Guitar*)
Mrs J Moon, BA, ALCM (*Singing*)
K Parry (*Guitar*)
Mrs M Rigby, GRSM, ARMCM (*Violin*)
Ms L Shaw, BEd (*Violin/Viola*)
Miss S Wagner (*Singing*)
R Waldock, GMus (*Double Bass*)
Mrs S White (*Head of Strings*)
L Wood, GNSM (*Cello*)

Bursar: J Ridley
Development Director: M Leslie
Director of Marketing & Admissions: J P C Hewat
Registrar: Mrs L Carr
Careers Coordinator: Mrs C Anderton
Domestic Bursar: Miss F V Ahearne
Headmaster's PA: Mrs L Holden

College Doctors:
Dr J Saunders, MBChB, MRCGP, DRCOG, DSM SA
Dr S Owen, MBChB, BA Hons, MRCGP, DRCOG, DFFP

Senior Nurse: Mrs N Fogden, RGN
Assistant Nurses:
Mrs A Bell, RGN, RSCN, DipFN, DN
N Riley, RGN
Mrs J Warburton, RGN

Stonyhurst St Mary's Hall
Stonyhurst Preparatory School (Boys and Girls 3–13)
(*see entry in IAPS section*)

Headmaster: L A Crouch, BA, MA, PGCE
Chaplain: Revd Fr A Howell, SJ

Aims. The School curriculum is intended to reflect the ideals of the founder of the Jesuits, St Ignatius Loyola: the importance of trying to find God in all things; the development to the full of each individual's talents whatever his or her gifts; the need for thoroughness and breadth in learning, helping pupils to think for themselves and to communicate well; above all an awareness of the needs of others. We aspire for our pupils to be men and women of competence, conscience and compassion.

Religion. The College is Roman Catholic and strives to educate its pupils in the principles and practice of their Faith. Christians of other denominations are welcomed and encouraged to be active in the school's worship and spiritual life.

Organisation. There are 470 pupils in the College, with 280 in the adjacent preparatory school, Stonyhurst St Mary's Hall, which admits boys and girls from 3 to 13 (*see Stonyhurst St Mary's Hall entry in IAPS section*). There are 170 day pupils. The school is fully co-educational from 13 to 18. The pastoral care is based on 5 year groups called 'Playrooms' each of which is in the care of married Playroom staff assisted by others including a Jesuit priest acting as Chaplain to the year. The younger girls are in the care of resident married House-parents and occupy their own designated area of the College. A resident Housemistress takes particular responsibility for the boarding and day girls in the Sixth Form. The Health Centre is self contained but within the main building; medical care is available on a 24 hour basis.

Academic organisation. A broad curriculum is offered up to GCSE in an attempt to avoid undue specialisation at an early age. There are 26 AS/A2 Level subjects available and all Sixth Formers must follow a course in Morals and Ethics. Academic progress at all ages is monitored on a regular basis by tutors, and progress reports are sent to parents throughout the term. There are five central ICT resource centres with Video Conferencing facilities. Sixth Formers have their own ICT resource centre and networked computers in their rooms with e-mail and controlled internet facilities. Recent developments have created the highest quality teaching areas across the whole curriculum, with a particularly impressive Science Department and provision for the Performing Arts. A splendid Library/ Learning and Resource Centre has also opened recently. Staff from the Special Needs Department are available to give help and support where required and EAL classes are held on either an individual or group basis without extra charge.

Music, Art, Design and Technology. These subjects form an integral part of the curriculum. All pupils entering the School at Year 9 must learn an orchestral instrument at the College's expense in their first year and the opportunities for both formal and informal music are extensive: there are several orchestras, a Concert Band, small string ensembles, several Choirs and other groups. Design and Technology is taught to all first year pupils along with Art, prior to the choice of GCSE subjects; the facilities for both these subjects are outstanding thanks to recent developments. Drama is strong and there are opportunities for taking part in a wide range of dramatic productions throughout the year either in our own Theatre or in the nearby Centenaries Theatre at Stonyhurst St Mary's Hall.

Games. The main games are Rugby Football, Cricket, Hockey, Netball and Athletics, but it is our aim to offer the widest possible range of sporting and recreational opportunity to all pupils. In addition to playing on our own golf course, pupils can take part in Soccer, Tennis, Badminton, Squash, Fencing, Basketball, Netball, Clay Pigeon Shooting, Sub Aqua and Cross Country. Our indoor six lane swimming pool offers first class opportunities for both competitive and recreational swimming, and the Sports Hall provides the usual range of indoor activities. An aqueous-based all weather pitch is available for Hockey and other sports.

Cadet Corps and Other Extra Curricular Activities. In their second year all pupils are members of the Cadet Corps, which introduces pupils to a number of activities such as canoeing, orienteering, climbing, trekking and shooting, in addition to an extensive programme of Army-based training. After the second year, membership of the Cadet Corps is by selection; it is invariably over-subscribed. An active Outdoor Pursuits Department offers opportunities for climbing, sailing, fell-walking and caving; the Duke of Edinburgh's Award Scheme is very popular with boys and girls at all ages.

Voluntary Service. Active work in the Community is a hallmark of Stonyhurst's commitment to others. Weekly programmes of community work are arranged and thousands of pounds a year are raised for charitable causes, in particular the College's own annual holiday for children with disabilities.

Higher Education and Careers. On average over 98% of our leavers go on to higher education either in the UK or abroad with an average of 10% to Oxbridge. No fewer than 9% of leavers entered Medical School last year. An average of 50% of our leavers have entered The Russell Group of Universities in the last few years. Our Careers department, based in a well-stocked Careers library with enviable research facilities, enables pupils to be fully informed about university choices and tutors are actively involved at all stages in the decision making. Careers conferences are regularly organised.

Fees per term (2008-2009). Boarding £8,064, Weekly Boarding £6,900, Day £4,714.

Bursaries and Scholarships. (*see Scholarship Entries section*). A large number of bursaries and scholarships are awarded each year at all age levels including the Sixth Form and 13+. Bursaries are intended for pupils likely to benefit from a Stonyhurst education and to contribute to it, and whose parents are unable to pay the full fees. Scholarships are awarded on the basis of academic achievement or potential after competitive examinations in May. Scholarships are also available each year for Music and Art. Details of all these awards can be gained by application to the Headmaster.

Admission. Enquiries about admission should be addressed to the Director of Admissions, Tel: 01254 827073 or 827093. Candidates entering at 13+ are normally required to pass the Common Entrance Examination, but alternative Tests are available for candidates from maintained schools or from abroad. Applications for Sixth Form boarding and day places for girls and boys are particularly encouraged.

Charitable status. Stonyhurst College is a Registered Charity, number 230165. The Charity for RC Purposes exists to provide a quality boarding and day education for boys and girls.

Stowe School

Stowe Buckingham Bucks MK18 5EH
Tel: 01280 818000
Fax: 01280 818181
e-mail: enquiries@stowe.co.uk
website: www.stowe.co.uk

Stowe aims to provide an all-round education of the highest standard, supporting Stoics in their passage to adulthood by developing individual talents, intellectual curiosity and a lasting sense of moral, social and spiritual responsibility. Confidence and tolerance of others flourish in a close community. The School provides a caring environment which promotes academic excellence, sporting prowess and artistic and musical creativity. Through teaching of the highest calibre, Stoics are encouraged to think for themselves, challenge conventional orthodoxies and pursue their own enthusiasms. Stoics acquire skills that enable them to live happily, work successfully and thrive in their future lives.

Motto: '*Persto et Praesto*'

Visitor: The Rt Revd The Lord Bishop of Oxford

Governing Body:
C Honeyman Brown, FCA (*Chairman*)
J R C Arkwright (*Chairman of the Old Stoic Committee*)
N W Berry
J M A Bewes, BA, ACA
Admiral Sir James Burnell-Nugent, KCB, CBE, ADC
J G (Algy) Cluff
S C Creedy Smith, BA, ACA
The Revd J M Fletcher, MA
Professor Sarah Gurr, BSc, ARCS, DIC, PhD, MA
R A Lankester, MA
R D Lord, QC, MA
G M Magan
Mrs S J Murray, MRICS
C J Tate, BA, MIMC
R P Taylor, MA
P J Thorogood (*Deputy Chairman*)
Air Vice-Marshal M van der Veen, MA, RAF Retd (*Vice Chairman*)
Sir Edmund Verney, BA, FRICS
C P J Wightman, BA, ACA
Mrs H E W Williams, MA

Secretary to the Governors: N Coulson, MA, MBA

***Headmaster*: A K Wallersteiner**, MA, PhD

Deputy Head (*Pastoral*): Mrs R E Masters, BA, PhD
Deputy Head (*Academic*): C C Robinson, MA, MPhil
Registrar: D Fletcher, BEd

Assistant Staff:
* *Head of Department*

Art:
*B L Johnson, MA
Ms L R Campbell, MA
G A Irvine, BA

Biology:
*R R Akam, MEd
Miss L M Carter, BSc
Ms E Chare, BA, DPhil
Mrs J Gracie, BSc
M A Righton, MA

Business Studies:
*P John, BA
M Pitteway, BCom

Careers:
*Ms S Naish, BSc, PhD

Chemistry:
*D S Jeffreys, BSc
Mrs K M McMahon, BSc
R G Johnson, BSc, MA
Miss L Ogilvie, BSc

Classics:
M J Bevington, MA
D J Critchley, MA, DipTheol
C J Townsend, BA

Design & Technology:
*D I Ardley, BEd
A G Eve, MA
S Grimble, CertEd
C Peratopoullos, BEd
M D G Wellington, BSc

Drama & Theatre Studies:
*N D Bayley, Dip Acting & Theatre
C D Walters, BEd

EAL:
*A P Longworth, BA
Ms D J Arscott, MA
Mrs J Y Johnson, MA

Economics and Politics:
*K Ryce, BA, MSc
Mrs J L Hamblett-Jahn, LLB
H J L Swayne, BA
C Barker, BA

English:
*P S Miller, MA, PhD
T K J Chan, BA, LLB
S G A Hirst, MA
R N M Rendall, BA
D A Roberts, MA
E S Thompson, MPhil
Miss V Edwards, BA

Games Coaching:
*L E Weston, DipPE, DipSpLD
S A Cowie (*Swimming*)
A Hughes (*Rugby*)
J A Knott (*Cricket*)
D S Orr (*Lacrosse*)
M J Walsh-Woolcott (*Hockey*)

Geography:
*P A Last, BA
Mrs S L Akam, BA
Ms Z Branford White, BSc
B G Durrant, BA
A K Murray, BSc

History:
*D M Smith, MPhil, PhD
J W Hayden, BA
A Lewis, MA
P Platts-Martin, BA
A K Wallersteiner, MA, PhD
M Way, BSc

History of Art:
*I O Young, MA
C C Robinson, MA, MPhil
M C Wilson, MA

ICT:
*J M Tearle, BA
S Gabbatiss, BSc
P S Edell, BA

Library:
*Mrs C M Miller, BA

Mathematics:
*D P C Blewitt, BSc
Mrs P A Bennett, MS
M P Dawson, BA
R D Knight, BSc
A McDaid, BEd
P A Rowan, BSc
E R Surrey, BSc
Mrs R E Trace, BA, DipSpLD

Modern Languages:
*Miss T L Hooker, BA
Mrs H Browne, BA
S G Dobson, MA
G D Jones, BA
Mrs C A Lawrance-Thorne, BA
Mrs R E Masters, BA, PhD
I Michael, BEd
Mrs A R G Tearle, MA
K P Staples, BA

Music:
H Jones, BA (*Acting Director of Music*)
Ms D J Arscott, MA
Miss H L Ford, BA
Mrs J L Nelson, LRAM

PE & Sports Science:
*R C Sutton, BA
P R Arnold, BSc
Mrs J M Duckett, BEd
R S Pickersgill, BA
Mrs S E Sutton, BA

Physics:
*S H Malling, MSc, CPhys, MInstP
J L Ing, MSc
R J W Tait, BSc
T O'Toole, BSc

PSHE:
*P A Last, BA

Skills Development:
*L E Weston, DipPE, DipSpLD
Mrs F E Atherton, BA, AMBDA
J A Cassidy, BA, RSA DipSpLD
Mrs S Rawlins
A A V Rudolf, MA

Ms E Sheard, BA, CertSpLD
Mrs R E Trace, BA, Dip SEN
Mrs M A Weston, DipEd, CertEd SEN
Mrs H Milne, BSocSci

Theology:
*D C C Mochan, MA
Miss S K Ross, MA
The Revd R B Jackson, MA (*Chaplain*)
Miss V Hunter Smart, BA

Houses and Housemasters/mistresses:

Boys' Houses:
Bruce House: R C Sutton
Temple House: A Lewis
Grenville House: R D Knight
Chandos House: B G Durrant
Cobham House: M J Way
Chatham House: J L Ing
Grafton House: C J Townsend
Walpole House: P Platts-Martin

Girls' Houses:
Nugent House: Mrs J M Duckett
Lyttelton House: Mrs J M Gracie
Queen's House: Mrs J L Hamblett-Jahn
New House: Mrs J L Nelson

Medical Officer: Dr R D Pryse, MB BS, DCH, DRCOG, DFFP

Bursar: R Litherland, MA

Assistant Bursar: Mrs J L Hill, MA, FCA

Stowe is a country boarding school with boys and girls from 13 to 18. The number of pupils in the School is 740, comprising 630 boarders and 110 day pupils. Pupils are also accepted each year for 2 year A Level courses.

Houses. There are 8 Boys' and 4 Girls' Houses, 6 of which are within the main building or attached to it and 6 at a short distance from it.

The Curriculum allows pupils to enjoy a wide variety of subjects before they settle down to work for their GCSEs (nine or ten) taken in the Fifth Form. A flexible Options system operates at this stage. Most boys and girls will go on to take 4 AS and 3 A Levels. Throughout the School, boys and girls have a Tutor to look after their academic welfare and advise them on higher education. A course in Visual Education was introduced in 1996 for boys and girls in their first year at Stowe. It promotes an understanding of Stowe's architecture and landscape gardens in particular and the built environment in general.

Art, Design and Information Technology. All pupils are introduced to these in their first year at Stowe. Art and Design are popular both for those pursuing hobbies and for those studying for formal examinations. Traditional skills are covered alongside more modern techniques such as computer-aided design and desktop publishing.

Music and Drama flourish as important and integral parts of the School's activities both within and outside the formal curriculum. There is plenty of scope in the School Orchestras, Jazz Band, Clarinet Quartet, Choirs, School plays, House plays and House entertainments. The timetable is sufficiently flexible to allow special arrangements to be made for outstanding musicians to study outside school. Drama Clubs and Theatre Studies groups have two fully-equipped theatres at their disposal.

Careers Guidance. Pupils are provided with a variety of opportunities which allows them to make sound career decisions. Seminars, Gap advice and an interview training programme are all offered. The Careers Centre is extremely well resourced, with a suite of computers and appropriate software, video facilities and a wealth of literature. Every encouragement is given to pupils to make regular visits to the Centre at Stowe and parents are always welcome to attend Careers events and to spend time using the available resources.

Religion. The School's foundation is Anglican and this is reflected in its chapel services on Sundays. Pupils of other faiths and other Christian Churches are welcomed and in some cases separate arrangements are made for them on Sundays. Every pupil attends the chapel services on weekdays.

Games. The major sports for boys are rugby, hockey and cricket, and for girls, hockey, lacrosse, netball and tennis. The other sports range from badminton, basketball, cross country, football, Eton fives and fencing in the winter to athletics, swimming, tennis, polo, rowing, sailing and golf in the summer; there are inter-school fixtures in most of these sports.

The School enters national competitions in many sports and encourages pupils to challenge for representative honours. The School has a heated 6-lane 25m indoor swimming pool, a sports hall, squash courts, Eton Fives courts, a weight training/fitness room and two floodlit Astroturf pitches which also provide tennis courts in the summer. There are also 11 hard tennis courts available all the year round, plus netball courts, 4 outdoor basketball courts, an athletics track, an indoor shooting range, a clay-pigeon shooting tower, a nine-hole golf course, where the National Prep Schools (IAPS) annual tournament is played, and extensive playing fields for rugby, hockey, football, cricket and lacrosse. Sculling, canoeing, sailing and fishing take place on a lake within the Landscape Gardens as well as at Northampton Rowing Club and Glebe Lake, Calvert.

Other Activities. Pupils complement their games programme with a large variety of extra-curricular activities, including clubs and societies. Stowe's grounds lend themselves to outdoor pursuits such as fishing and clay pigeon shooting, and the School has its own pack of Beagles. On Mondays a special activities programme is based on Outdoor Pursuits (Combined Cadet Force with all three service arms and the Duke of Edinburgh's Award Scheme), Community Service (in the neighbourhood) and Leadership skills.

Fees per term (2008-2009). Boarders £8,950, Day Pupils £6,620 payable termly in advance.

Nine months before the term of entry parents are asked to pay an advance deposit; this deposit is credited to the final term's fees. A full term's notice is required before the removal of a pupil.

Scholarships and Allowances. (*see Scholarship Entries section*). A range of Scholarships and Exhibitions, up to the value of 25% of the School fees is awarded annually. Academic, Music, Art and Sports Scholarships are available and are offered to candidates entering at 13+ and 16+ who demonstrate outstanding potential in the relevant examinations. Roxburgh Scholarships are awarded to any boy or girl of outstanding all-round ability and leadership potential, and Stephan Scholarships are awarded to academically bright day pupils who would not otherwise be able to come to Stowe. Scholarships may be supplemented by means tested bursaries, with a limited number of fully funded places, where there is proven financial need.

Admission. Boys and girls can be registered at any age. Full details can be obtained from the Admissions Department, who will supply entry forms. The School is always prepared to consider applications from pupils to enter the School at 14 if they have been educated overseas or in the maintained sector. The date of birth should be stated and it should be noted that boys and girls are normally admitted between their 13th and 14th birthdays.

The Old Stoic Society. The OS Society Manager is Tim Scarff, The Old Stoic Society, Stowe, Buckingham MK18 5EH

Charitable status. Stowe School Limited is a Registered Charity, number 310639. Its aims and objectives are the education of children at an independent boarding school.

Strathallan School

Forgandenny Perth Perthshire PH2 9EG
Tel: 01738 812546
Fax: 01738 812549
e-mail: secretary@strathallan.co.uk
website: www.strathallan.co.uk

Strathallan School was founded by Harry Riley in 1913 and moved to its present site in Forgandenny, Perthshire in 1920. The School is fully co-educational and numbers 502 pupils, of whom 173 are day pupils and 329 are boarders.
Motto: '*Labor Omnia Vincit*'

Governors:

Chairman: J B Gray, CA
A M Bisset, BSc, CA
Reverend Dr I C Bradley, BA, MA, DPhil
Mrs J S Cachia, BSc, MBChB, MD, MRCGP, DRCoG
S J Cannon, MA
J A R Coleman, MRICS
K C Dinsmore, BA, LLB, Dip LP
Mrs K J Dunn, LLB Hons
R G A Hall BArch Hons, DipArch, RIAS, RIBA
N Houston, MA, DipMusEd, PGDipEdTech CNAA, PGDipCouns
Professor Lady B Lane, BSc, PhD, FRSE, FMedSci
Professor R E Leake, MA, DPhil
R K Linton, LLB, NP
P J McKee, MA Cantab, BL, PGCE
B Raine, BA, PGCE
Sheriff D O Sutherland, MA, LLB, MSI, NP
A M D Wilkinson, MBA, MA Hons, FSI
Mrs G M Wilson, MA, PGCE
D L Young, BArch Hons, DipArch

***Headmaster*: B K Thompson**, MA Oxon

Assistant Staff:
Mrs E M Adam, MA, MEd
Mrs T Ailinger, Staatsexamen, Cert TESOL
D J Barnes, BSc, PGCE, PGCG, FRGS (*Second Master*)
G J Batterham, BSc, PGCE (*Simpson House*)
G A Bolton, BA, MSc
J S Burgess, BSc
P W W Bush, Dip IAPS (*Riley House*)
Miss E de Celis Lucas, BA, CAP
Dr A Collins, BSc, BA, PhD
Dr B Cooper, BSc, PhD, PGCE
S Cowper, BA, PGCE
Mrs M-L Crane, BA, PGCE
Dr S B Downhill, BA, MSc, PhD, PGCE, FRGS
N T H Du Boulay, BA
Mrs C A C Duncan, MA, DipEd, ALCM
Mrs E C Duncan, MA, PGCE
Dr S Ferguson, MA, PhD, MSc, PGCE
R H Fitzsimmons, MA
Dr C Flanagan, MA, PhD, PGCE
J R Fleming, BEd (*Thornbank House*)
Mrs S E Fleming, BEd (*Thornbank House*)
G Gardiner, BSc, PGCE
Dr M Gibson, BSc, PhD, PGCSE
D R Giles, BA, QTS, CertPP (*Nicol House*)
J Goddard, BSc, PGCE
A R Gordon, BEng, PGCE
Mrs E W Hamilton, MA, PGCE
N Hamilton, BMus
B A Heaney, BSc, DipEd (*Freeland House*)
A Henderson, UKCC
D M Higginbottom, MA, PGCE
Mrs J Higginbottom, MA, PGCE
Mrs C G Howett, BA, DipEd
Mrs D S Hunter, DA, DipEd
Miss J S R Hutcheon, DipPhysEd
Mrs A Ingram-Forde, BA
P J S Keir, BEd, CertSpLD
E G Kennedy, BA, PGCE
G Kitson, BSc, PGCE
Miss C Laurie, BSc, PGCE
Mrs F MacBain, BA, MA
Mrs I I M McFarlane, MA, CertSpLD, LLAM
Miss V S M McKay, BEd, DipLibInf, CertSpLD
A E C McMorrine, DA
Mrs C Menzies, BSc, PGCE
Miss J L Morrison, BTechEd
V Popescu, BA, MA
R J W Proctor, MA
Revd R A M T Quick, BA, PGCE
Mrs D L Raeside, BSc, HDE PG
G Roberson, BA, DMS
Mrs M C Robertson-Barnett, MA, PGCE
G R M Ross, BSc, MSc
Dr J D Salisbury, MA, PhD, PGCE
Mrs C Sim Sayce, BMus, PGCE
Miss A Sime, BEd (*Director of Sport*)
N Smith, BSc, BA, PGCE
A C W Streatfeild-James, MA, PGCE (*Director of Studies*)
Mrs K Streatfeild-James, BA, PGCE, Dip SpLD
Mrs J A Summersgill, BSc, PGCE
P R Summersgill, MA, PGCE
A Thomson, BA, MPhil, ACP
Mrs A J Tod, MA, PGCE (*Woodlands House*)
M R A B Tod, BSc (*Woodlands House*)
P M Vallot, BSc
R C A Walmsley, BA, MA (*Director of Music*)
A Watt, BComm, HDE (*Ruthven House*)
Mrs J C E White, MA, PGCE
Miss K E Wilkinson, BSc, PGCE

Bursar and Clerk to the Governors: A C Glasgow, MBE, BEng, MSc, CEng

Director of Marketing & Development: Mrs T C Howard-Vyse

Medical Officers:
Mrs J I Sinclair, MBChB, DCH, DRCOG
L D Burnett, MBChB, BSc, DRCOG, MRCGP

Situation. Strathallan School is located 6 miles south of Perth in the village of Forgandenny. It occupies a glorious rural location, situated in 150 acres of richly wooded estate on the northern slopes of the Ochils and overlooks the Earn valley. At the same time, Strathallan is within easy reach of the international airports – Edinburgh (45 minutes) and Glasgow (1 hour) – and Perth (10 minutes) with its mainline railway station and shopping facilities.

At the centre of the School is the main building which dates from the 18th century and was formerly a country house and home of the Ruthven family. The School continues to invest in its outstanding facilities. Recent additions include modern laboratories, a Theatre, Computer Centre, Library, Design Technology Centre, Sports Hall, Fitness and Weight Training Room, 2 Floodlit Astroturf pitches, Medical Centre and Art School. All boarding houses provide modern accommodation, with a single study bedroom for every boarder after the first senior year.

Aims. At the heart of the School's philosophy is the commitment to provide opportunities for all to excel, to help pupils to make the most of their abilities within the framework of a caring environment.

Organisation. The School is primarily a boarding school yet also takes day pupils who are integrated into the boarding houses. There are four Senior Boys' houses (Ruthven, Nicol,

Freeland and Simpson). There are two Girls' houses (Woodlands and Thornbank); a third will open in 2009. All boarding houses have their own resident Housemaster or Housemistress, assisted by House Tutors and a Matron. Boys have single study-bedrooms from the Fourth Form and Girls have single study-bedrooms from theThird Form.

The Junior House, Riley, is designed to cater for boys and girls wishing to enter the School at 9+. Riley is run by a resident Housemaster and his wife, assisted by tutors, one of whom is resident, and a resident Matron. After Riley, pupils move directly to one of the Senior houses.

Riley is situated within its own campus, yet also enjoys the facilities of the main School. It has its own Common Room, Library, dormitories and music practice rooms.

The whole School dines centrally and there is a wide choice of hot and cold meals as well as vegetarian options. All boarding houses have "brew rooms" for the preparation of light snacks.

Religion. Strathallan has a Chapel and a resident Chaplain who is responsible for religion throughout the School.

Curriculum. Pupils entering the School before the age of 13 are placed in Forms IJJ, 1J, I, or II, while those who join at 13 are placed in the Third Form where they are setted by ability for their core subjects. Up until the Fourth Form, all follow the same broad curriculum which comprises English, Mathematics, French, German/Spanish, Latin, Physics, Chemistry and Biology, History, Geography, Computing, Art, Design Technology, together with Divinity, Personal and Social Education, Music and Physical Education. Instruction in French and Latin begins in Form 1.

In the Fourth and Fifth Forms, pupils take nine subjects for GCSE and Computing at Standard Grade. All the above subjects (plus Business Studies) are available at this level.

A satisfactory performance at GCSE (a minimum of five passes or equivalent) qualifies a boy or girl for entry to the Sixth Form where he or she prepares for AS and A2 examinations or Scottish Higher. Scottish Higher examinations are generally taken at the end of the Upper Sixth year. AS and A2 examinations are taken in the Lower and Upper Sixth.

In the Sixth Form, there is greater flexibility in the range of courses available and full details of these are issued to parents in advance. Potential Oxbridge candidates are identified in the Lower Sixth Form and additional tuition is provided. On average, more than 95% of senior pupils go on to University.

Each pupil is allocated a tutor who is a member of the academic staff and one of the duty staff of the boarding house. The tutor monitors the academic progress of the boy or girl and is responsible for discussing their three-weekly reports with them. Teacher : Pupil ratio 1 : 7.

Games. The main School games are rugby, cricket, hockey, netball, athletics and tennis, and standards are high. Other sports include skiing, squash, rounders, football, fencing, judo, badminton, basketball, swimming, golf, horse riding and cross-country running.

Strathallan has two squash courts, 8 hard tennis courts, 2 netball courts, 2 floodlit synthetic pitches, a heated indoor swimming pool, sports hall, gymnasium and a fitness and weight training room. The sports hall comprises a basketball court, three badminton courts, a rock climbing wall as well as facilities for six-a-side hockey and indoor cricket coaching. Sailing, canoeing and skiing are recognised pastimes, and a large number of pupils participate in School ski days in the Spring term. Strathallan also has its own nine-hole golf course.

Activities. All pupils are encouraged to take part in a range of activities for which time is set aside each day. Among the activities available are dance, drama, pottery, chess, photography, first aid, lifeguarding, judo, horse riding, shooting (both clay pigeon and small bore) and fishing. There are also many societies and a full programme of external speakers who visit the School. Pupils also work towards awards under The Duke of Edinburgh's Award. They are also encouraged to take part in Community Service.

Music. The Music department has its own concert room, keyboard room and classrooms, together with a number of individual practice rooms. Music may be taken at GCSE, Higher and AS/A2 Level. There is a choir, choral society, traditional music groups, a jazz band, wind band, an orchestra, folk bands and rock bands. A house music competition takes place annually and there are regular concerts throughout the term. Individual tuition is available for virtually all instruments. Recitals and visits to concerts in Edinburgh, Perth and the environs are arranged. The School has a Pipe Band and a full time Piping Instructor.

Art. Art is recognised as an important part of the School's activities and there are opportunities to study the subject at GCSE and AS/A2 Level. Pupils benefit from regular art trips abroad and have the opportunity to exhibit their work both locally and further afield. A purpose-built Art School features facilities for ceramics, sculpture and print-making. National awards reflect pupils' achievements in this area.

Drama. Drama thrives throughout the School and the department makes full use of the theatre. There are junior and senior performances each year and pupils are encouraged to become involved in all aspects of production. The School also provides tuition in public and verse speaking and pupils regularly win trophies at the local festivals. There is also an annual Musical and pupils enter musical theatre exams.

Combined Cadet Force. There is a large voluntary contingent of the Combined Cadet Force with Navy, Army and Marines Sections.

Careers. Careers guidance begins in the Third Form. The Careers Adviser maintains close links with universities and colleges and regularly visits industrial firms. We have exchange programmes with schools in Australia and New Zealand. There is a dedicated Careers Library, well-stocked with prospectuses, reference books and in-house magazines. Strathallan is a member of the Independent Schools Careers Organisation, a representative of which visits regularly and of the Scottish Council for Development and Industry.

All pupils have the opportunities to gain work experience in the Fifth Form, after their GCSEs. There is also a GAP year programme which provides placements for pupils to work overseas prior to going to university, either with other schools with whom Strathallan has links, or with organisations such as Operation Raleigh or Project Trust.

Pastoral Care. There is a strong emphasis on pastoral care. The School has drawn up its own welfare guidelines in consultation with parents, governors and Perth and Kinross Social Work Department.

Medical Centre. Strathallan has its own purpose-built Medical Centre with consulting and treatment rooms. There are nursing staff at the Centre and the School's Medical Officers visit four times a week, and physiotherapy and chiropody also take place in the Centre during term time.

Entrance. Junior Entrance – Boys and girls are admitted to the Junior School (Riley House) at either age 9, 10, 11 or 12. An Entrance Day (including those sitting scholarship examinations) is held in early Spring each year. Entry is based on a a satisfactory school report.

Entry to the Senior School – Candidates for entry into the Senior School at 13 may enter via either the Open Scholarship examination (March) or Common Entrance (June) or a satisfactory school report.

Sixth Form – Boys and girls may also enter at Sixth Form level, either via the Sixth Form scholarship examination (which takes place in November) or on the basis of a satisfactory school report and GCSE/Standard Grade results.

Scholarships. (*see Scholarship Entries section*). Awards of between 5% and 50% are made on the basis of competitive examination/assessment. Bursary help is available to supplement awards for outstanding candidates on a financial need basis.

Awards are available in the following categories to candidates entering the school at three levels:

Junior School: Academic and Music/Choral/Piping/Drumming. Candidates should be under 13 on 1 September in the year of entry. Scholarship Examination: January.

Third Form: Academic, Music/Choral/Piping/Drumming, Art, Design Technology, Sports, and All-Rounder. Candidates should be under 14 on 1 September in the year of entry. Scholarship Examination: March.

Sixth Form: Academic, Music/Choral/Piping/Drumming, Art, Design Technology, Sports, and All-Rounder. Candidates should be under 17 on 1 September in the year of entry. Scholarship Examination: November.

Further information is available on the school's website: www.strathallan.co.uk. All enquiries about scholarships to: The Admissions Office, Strathallan School, Forgandenny, Perthshire PH2 9EG. Tel: 01738 815003, email admissions@strathallan.co.uk.

Fees per term (2008-2009). Junior School (Riley House): £5,590 (boarding), £3,490 (day). Senior School: £7840 (boarding), £5,320 (day).

Prospectus. Up to date information is included in the prospectus which can be obtained by contacting the Admissions Office or via the school's website.

Charitable status. Strathallan School is a Registered Scottish Charity, number SC008903, dedicated to Education.

Surbiton High School (UCST)

Surbiton Crescent Kingston-upon-Thames KT1 2JT
Tel: 020 8546 5245
Fax: 020 8547 0026
e-mail: surbiton.high@church-schools.com
website: www.surbitonhigh.com

Surbiton Preparatory School:
3 Avenue Elmers Kingston-upon-Thames KT6 4SP
Tel: 020 8390 6640
Fax: 020 8255 3049
e-mail: surbiton.prep@church-schools.com

Surbiton High Junior Girls' School:
95–97 Surbiton Road Kingston-upon-Thames KT1 2HW
Tel: 020 8546 9756
Fax: 020 8974 6293
e-mail: surbiton.juniorgirls@church-schools.com

Governing Body: The Council of the United Church Schools Trust

Local Governing Body:
Mrs Eileen Carroll
Revd Val Cory
The Rt Revd and Rt Hon the Lord Carey of Clifton (*Chairman*)
Mr David Cunningham
Mr Martin Donnelly
Sir Ewan Harper, CBE
Ms Ann Haydon
Mr Ruairidh Hogg
Ms Christina McComb
Mrs Gillian Norton
Mr Gordan Faultless
Mr Nick Pickles
Rt Hon Dame Angela Rumbold (*Chair*)
Mr Stuart White

Staff:

***Principal*: Ms E A Haydon**, BSc Hons London

Deputy Heads:
Mr S Edmonds
Mrs M C Anderton, BSc Wales
Mrs H Morgan, BA Wales

Head of Junior Girls' School: Miss C Bufton, BA Wales
Head of Surbiton Preparatory: Mr S Pryce, CertEd London, BA OU, MA Surrey

Assistant Staff:
Mrs J Aldous, CertEd Bedford
Mr S Bachelor, BA Oxford
Mrs N Banerjee, BA Delhi
Mrs J Bennett, BA Sheffield
Miss H Brennan, BSc Manchester Metropolitan
Mrs E Brickman, BA Keele
Miss C Broadway, BSc Surrey
Mr P Bywaters, BA Hertfordshire
Mrs E Carr, CertEd London
Mrs C Catlin, BEd Bristol
Mrs E Clark, BA City of London Poly
Ms J Clarkson, BA OU
Mrs I Coyle, CertEd London
Ms A Crump, BA Camberwell
Mrs A Dara, BSc Kingston
Mr G Davidson, BA Leics, MPhil St Andrews
Miss J Day, BSc Newcastle
Mrs H De Sarandy, BA Kent
Mrs A Deighton, BEd Brighton
Miss C Demetz, BA Exeter
Mr Z Dif, BSc Algiers
Mrs S Ditchfield, BA Nottingham
Mrs B Doe, BA Warwick
Ms S Egan, MSc Oxford
Mr T Ferguson, BSc Staffordshire
Mr M Ferrabee, BA London
Miss S Forrester, BA Dunelm
Mrs V Foster, BA Exeter
Mrs M Garrard, BA London
Mrs M Gates-Sumner, BSc Surrey
Mrs C Geard, BA CNAA
Mrs A George, BA OU
Mr M Gibbons, BA Oxford
Mrs A Godbold, BA Manchester
Ms A Gomez, BA Spain
Mrs S Green, BA Oxford Brookes
Mrs J Hall, BSc London
Mrs A Hamilton, MA Warwick
Mrs A Hammill, BSc Leeds
Mr L Hardie, BA York
Mrs E Harris, BSc Durham
Mrs H Hart, BSc Birmingham
Mrs R Harty, BA Waikato, NZ
Mrs H Hay, MA St Andrews
Mrs E-K Henry, BA Kent
Mrs E Hewitt, BEd Oxford Brookes
Mrs T Holden, BSc QTS St Martin's College
Mrs P Holman, BA Kingston, MA Surrey
Mrs C Holmes, BA Bangor
Miss S Hopper, BSc Surrey
Mr J Humphries, BA, MA Oxford
Ms B Huntley, BA Lancaster
Mrs A Jackson, BA London
Miss C Jeater, BA East Anglia
Mrs J Jones, BSc London
Mrs N Jones, BA, Dip Central School of Art & Design
Mrs A Keeling, BSc London
Miss L Keers, BA Wales
Mrs S Kendall, BA Canterbury, NZ
Mrs A King, BSc Manchester
Ms M Leturia, BA Granada, Spain
Ms A Lewis, BEd Perth
Dr R Lloyd, BMus, MMus, PhD London
Mrs E Magennis, BA Queen's Belfast
Miss J Mamelok, BSc Southampton
Dr R McDermott, BSc Leeds, PhD London
Miss A Millar, BA South Africa, DipRSA

Mrs R Mills, BEd London
Mr D Morgan, BSc Wales
Mrs D Morito, BA Kingston
Mr A Naden, BA Imperial College, London
Mrs A Nayler, CertEd, DipMaths Roehampton
Mrs G Newton, BSc CNAA
Mrs M North, CertEd Dartford College
Mrs M O'Connor, BA London
Mrs A Orlovac, BSc Birmingham
Miss J Palmer, MA Edinburgh
Mrs J Partridge, MA Cambridge, MA Surrey
Miss H Patel, BSc Sussex
Mr S Paxton, MA Glasgow
Mrs J Paynter, BSc Leeds
Miss R Peddler-Smith, MA, BA
Mme V Pegnall, CertEd Greenwich
Mrs J Pickles, BSc Dunelm
Miss A Pirie, BSc, MA Edinburgh
Mrs S Rawlinson, BSc Bristol, ACA
Miss A Reckermann, MA Dortmund
Mrs S Regal, BSc Aberystwyth
Miss T Rockall, BA Kingston
Mrs K Ross, BA Kingston, Diploma RA
Mrs J Rosser, BA Sheffield
Ms A Rusholme, BSc Dunelm
Mrs G Russ, BA St Mary's College
Mr T Ryan, BEd St Mark's & St John
Miss B Sacher, BA Roehampton
Mr K Salisbury, BSc, Bangor
Mr R Skinner, BA Bournemouth
Mrs M Spooner, BA Bristol
Mrs D Stanley, BA Warwick
Mrs S Stead, BA Surrey
Mr J Stephenson, BA Durham
Miss E Tanga, DEUG, Paris
Mrs P L Thomas, BEng Liverpool, MEd Unit Wolverhampton
Mrs A Vaughan, BA
Miss M Vazquez, BA Portsmouth
Mrs G Walker, BA Wales
Mrs R Ward, BEd Surrey
Mrs F Wells, BA Kingston
Mrs J Wilkey, CertEd Dartford College
Miss L Williams, BSc Birmingham

Extra Subject Staff:

Flute:
Mrs H Taggart, ARMCM
Mrs P Thompson, LTCL, FTCL
Oboe: Miss S Belchamber, ARCM, DipRCM
Saxophone: Mr S Gledhill, LTCL
Bassoon: Mr G J Twigg
Bass: Miss A Cammish
Violin:
Miss E Harling
Mrs D Hume, DSCM
Cello: Ms N Samuel, BMus, LRAM
Percussion: Mr C Terian, BA
Piano:
Mrs P Speed-Andrews, LTCL, MusEd, ATCL
Mrs M Turner, GRSM, LRAM
Guitar: Mr G Klippell, ARCM
Singing:
Miss J Arthur, LTCL BA, LRAM
Miss M Hayes
Mrs R Logan
Clarinet: Mr S Gledhill, LTCL

Speech and Drama:
Miss H Blair
Miss C De Brett
Mrs C Jones, FTCL, LGSM, LNEA
Mr N Ware, ATCL

Skiing: Mr M Erskine; Mr M Telling
Aerobics: Ms L Fleming-Gale
Tennis: Mr C Lamprecht
Rowing: Mr C Fox Molesey Boat Club
Hockey: Mrs F Benzies; Mr H Wilder
Netball: Ms E Neilson
Trampoline: Mr D Douglas
Gynmastics: Miss N Watson

Medical Officer: Dr J Setchell, MA, BS London
School Nurse: Mrs A McCool
School Registrar: Mrs M Try
School Librarian: Mrs A Ferrabee, BA Leeds, DipLib CNAA

A Day School, founded in 1884 and accommodating 1,227 pupils between the ages of 4 and 18. There are 192 pupils in the Sixth Form. Entry to the Boys' Preparatory School and Junior Girls' School is at age 4 and 7, and to the Senior School for girls at 11 by the School's own examination. Entry to the Sixth Form is by interview and qualifications.

The School is situated in the Kingston upon Thames postal area near the river and close to Surbiton Station. It is well served by public transport and draws its pupils both from the immediate neighbourhood and further adjacent districts. A school bus system operates over ten different routes.

The extensive school site consists of a Sixth Form College, two junior schools, Surbiton Assembly Rooms, a Science and Technology block, as well as the recently redeveloped main school site, including modern classrooms, an open-plan Art School and a landscaped recreation area. There are specialist facilities for Information Technology, Modern Languages, Music, Drama and Sport, as well as spacious dining facilities and a well-equipped stage and performing area.

The School's sports ground includes an astroturf multi-purpose pitch with floodlighting, tennis courts and grassed areas. All three schools are generously resourced with interactive whiteboards, linked to the School's computer network.

The School Curriculum includes English Language, English Literature, History, Geography, Religious Studies, French, German, Spanish, Latin, Mathematics, Biology, Chemistry, Physics, Design Technology, Theatre Studies, Information Technology, Economics, Business Studies, Government & Politics, Music, Art, Ceramics, Photography, Psychology, Critical Thinking, Physical Education and Sports Studies.

Extra Subjects: Piano, Cello, Flute, Violin, Voice, Dance, Percussion, Clarinet, Saxophone, Oboe, Bass, Bassoon, Guitar, Speech and Drama, Ballet.

Sixth Form. A wide variety of courses is offered in the Sixth Form so that the girls may choose a suitable group of AS and A2 level subjects to prepare them for University courses, Schools of Medicine, Art School, Colleges of Education and other professional training. Information and Communications Technology is an integral part of Sixth Form study with a dedicated ICT room in the Sixth Form College. There is also a Library and Resources room for individual study. A £1.9 million development was completed in 2003.

Games. Hockey, tennis, rounders, netball, rowing and athletics. Seniors, from Year 10 upwards, have a choice of activities on their games afternoons including aerobics, basketball, football, netball, squash, trampolining, youth leadership, martial arts, self-defence and weight-training. The School has skiing teams in all age groups and regularly holds several national titles. Girls have also won national competitions and represented Great Britain in rowing.

Religious Services. There is a daily assembly and all pupils are expected to attend.

Fees per term (2008-2009). Junior Girls: £2,216 (Reception, Years 1 and 2); £3,021 (Years 3–6). Boys' Preparatory: £2,174 (Reception, Years 1 and 2); £2,963 (Years 3–6). Senior School: £3,703.

When two or more children of the same family attend the School, a reduction in fees will be given. Reductions are also made for daughters of members of the Clergy.

Scholarships and Bursaries. (*see Scholarship Entries section*). Bursaries are available in the Sixth Form, along with Academic and Creative Arts Scholarships. Academic, Art, Music and Sport Scholarships are available at 11+.

For further particulars apply to the Admissions Registrar.

Assisted Places. The United Church Schools Trust offers a limited number of Assisted Places at 11+.

Surbiton Preparatory School. Day school for boys aged 4–11.

Entry is at 4 and 7 by assessment and examination, with occasional places in other year groups.

Surbiton Preparatory School follows an enhanced National Curriculum combining traditional values with the best of modern methods. French, music and physical education are taught by specialist teachers throughout the school and information technology is a particular strength. The School has contact with some 20 senior schools in south-west London and north Surrey. Regularly the children's success in entrance examinations allows the opportunity to choose between three or more senior schools and many pupils gain scholarship awards.

(*For further details, see entry in IAPS section.*)

Surbiton High Junior Girls' School. The Junior Girls' School opened in January 1994 and provides a caring, happy and secure education for girls aged 4 to 11. Entry is at 4 and 7 by assessment and examination, with occasional places in other year groups.

The School is housed in its own purpose-built, modern accommodation with bright modern classrooms, extensive computer facilities, a well-stocked library and performance areas. Specialist teaching is offered in French, music, physical education and a wealth of extra-curricular activities broaden and enliven the pupils' learning experience. At 11 almost all girls continue their education in the Senior School.

(*For further details, see entry in IAPS section.*)

Charitable status. The United Church Schools Trust is a Registered Charity, number 1016538. It exists to provide high quality education in keeping with the teaching of the Church of England.

Sutton Valence School

Sutton Valence Maidstone Kent ME17 3HL
Tel: 01622 845200
Fax: 01622 844103
e-mail: enquiries@svs.org.uk
website: www.svs.org.uk

Sutton Valence School has over 425 years of proud history, founded in 1576 by William Lambe under Charter of Queen Elizabeth I. Today the school is co-educational with 520 boys and girls on roll. The School occupies an area of about 100 acres on the slopes of a high ridge with unequalled views over the Weald of Kent, and in the historic, beautiful and safe village of Sutton Valence; an environment in which it is easy to learn and grow.

To succeed at Sutton Valence School pupils should be prepared to tackle their academic goals with enthusiasm and commitment and to involve themselves in the wider life of the school through sport, music, drama, and the extra-curricular and community service programmes. Flexible boarding arrangements allow pupils to stay at school in support of their school commitments or family life.

Education at Sutton Valence School is in the broadest sense, equipping our pupils to be self-reliant, resourceful and comfortable with the many challenges that adult life will throw at them. With the benefits of small classes and tutor groups and an all embracing philosophy of care and respect for others and ourselves, the way is paved for our pupils to mature into well-grounded, compassionate adults with a zest for life.

Motto: '*My Trust is in God alone.*'

Visitor: The Lord Archbishop of Canterbury

Foundation: United Westminster Schools
Director/Clerk: R W Blackwell, MA

Governing Body:
B F W Baughan (*Chairman*)
Major General David Burden, CB, CBE
Venerable Philip Down, MTh, MA
M S Hall, BSc
M Hatcher, MA, FRSA
H Hughes, FCA
The Revd Canon D H Hutt, MA, AKC
T D Page
Mrs D Perry, MA, DMS, FRSA
Mrs Z Reader
C J Saunders, MA
M J R Sealey, BA, MSc
D W Taylor, MA
C H Tongue, MA
Lady Vallance, JP, MA, MSc, PhD, FRSA, FCGI
E Watts, OBE, BA, FRSA

***Headmaster*: J S Davies**, MA St John's College, Cambridge

Deputy Head: R J Maloney, MTheol St Andrews, MA King's College, London
Bursar: A J Hutchinson, MA Churchill College, Cambridge, FCA
Director of Studies: D E Clarke, BSc Bristol, CBiol, MIBiol
Director of Extra-Curricular Activities: Mrs M T Hall, BEd Southampton

Academic Staff:
† *Boarding Housemaster/Housemistress*

†G N Alderman, BEd Avery Hill College (*Director of Sport*)
Mrs K L Andersen, CertEd Elizabeth Gaskell College (*Head of Home Economics, Head of Sixth Form Section, Director of Professional Development*)
Mrs S W Anstey, CELTA (*EFL, Head of Careers*)
Miss J M Beaton, BEng Nottingham (*Mathematics*)
A R Bee, BSc Manchester (*Head of Geography*)
F-Y Belver (*Modern Languages*)
A Brook (*Head of Drama*)
M Brown (*Physics*)
W D Buck, CertEd St Luke's, Exeter (*Modern Languages, RS, Games*)
Mrs J Burborough, BA Reading (*SEN teacher*)
†R H Carr, BA St John's College, Durham (*History, Games*)
D E Clarke, BSc Bristol, CBiol, MIBiol (*Biology*)
Miss F M Davidson, BA Rhodes (*Head of First Year, English*)
Ms A Derricott (*Head of History*)
Mrs L Dolan, BA St John's College, Oxford (*English*)
Miss T Draude, BA Stirling (*Head of Media Studies*)
Ms S V Easter, BA Exeter (*Art, Editor of 'The Suttonian' magazine*)
Mrs G Firmston, CertEd Cheltenham (*Head of SEN, English, Drama*)
Mrs J P A Fletcher, BSc Greenwich (*Head of Third Year, Chemistry*)
Ms V A Green, BSc OU (*Mathematics*)
†P N Gorman, BA Edinburgh (*Head of Art*)
Mrs M T Hall, BEd Southampton (*Geography*)
Mrs N S Hall, BMus Manchester (*Assistant Director of Music*)
Miss P L Hallett, BA Brighton (*Head of Academic PE and Girls' Games*)
A P Hammersley, BSc York (*Head of Year Five, Head of Biology*)

G Harris, BA King's College (*Head of Year Three, Mathematics*)
Ms M E Harrison, Dip Int Des Glasgow College of Building (*Design and Technology*)
Ms S E Herold, BA New York University, Hornsby Dip (*SEN teacher*)
S P Hiscocks, BSc Essex, PhD, CChem, MRSC (*Head of Science*)
†D W Holmes, LRAM (*Head of Strings*)
†Miss K E Horgan, BA Coventry (*Head of Economics and Business Studies*)
P J Horley, BA, ARCO, ALCM, College of Ripon and York St John (*Director of Music*)
Mrs L J Howard, BA Anglia, BSc Open (*Head of Second Year, Psychology, Community Service*)
D J J Keep, MA Greenwich, BEd Avery Hill College (*Head of Design and Technology, Gifted and Talented Coordinator*)
D R Kennedy, BSc Leeds, CBiol, MIBiol (*Biology, Games*)
Rev P A Kish, BD London, AKC, MA, DipSpPsych, MTh (*Chaplain*)
Mrs C J Kitchen, BEng Bradford, MSc Birmingham, BSc Open (*Head of Sixth Form Section, Head of Mathematics*)
R J Lindley, BEng Leeds and De Montfort, PhD Leicester (*Physics*)
Mrs K W J Luxford, BA Hull (*English*)
C Lynch, BEd Central Queensland (*ICT*)
Mrs M L Lynch, BExSc Griffith University (*Biology, PE*)
R J Maloney, MTheol St Andrews, MA King's College, London (*RS*)
G J Millbery, BA Lampeter (*Director of ICT*)
A D Mingay, BA Strathclyde (*Psychology, English*)
P Nunes-Carvalho (*Business Studies and Economics*)
A Penfold (*Head of Religious Studies*)
†J D Peverley, BSc Birmingham (*Sports Studies*)
Mrs R B Peverley, BA Rhodes (*Psychology, English, Games*)
R W J E Plowden, MA Wales, BA Newcastle (*History*)
Mrs F H Porter, BA Leeds (*Head of English*)
D R L Sansom, BSc Swansea (*Geography*)
†Mrs J Stanford, CertEd Lady Mabel College (*Science*)
Mrs E Taylor, CertEd St Mary's College (*SEN*)
J Walsh (*Biology*)
Mrs S Watson, BA Heriot-Watt (*DT Textiles*)
†K R Webster, MEd Crewe & Alsager College (*Head of Fifth Year, Mathematics*)
P Webster (*Modern Languages*)
C D Wesselink, BA South Africa (*Mathematics*)
Mrs A F F Wilkinson, Cert Ed Calder College, Liverpool (*Home Economics, CCF*)
A Wyles (*Geography, Director of Sixth Form*)

Headmaster's PA: Mrs S O'Connell
Admissions Officer: Mrs K Webster

Curriculum Organisation. The academic curriculum is innovative and aims to achieve a balance between the needs of the individual and demands of society, industry, the universities and the professions. Classes are small and the ratio of graduate teaching staff is 1:9.

In Forms 1 and 2 (Years 7 and 8) the National Curriculum is broadly followed, covering English, Mathematics, Chemistry, Physics, Biology, French, Spanish, History, Geography, Religious Studies, Design Technology, Home Economics, ICT, Art, Music, Physical Education and Drama.

The National Curriculum is again broadly followed in Form 3 (Year 9) where subjects offered are the same as Forms 1 and 2. However, the syllabi are designed to cater for not only those who enter Form 3 via Forms 1 and 2, but also the large number of pupils who join the school at 13+.

In Forms 4 and 5 (Years 10 and 11) pupils usually study nine or ten subjects to GCSE level. These are divided between the core – English and English Literature, Mathematics, a Modern Language (French/Spanish/German), Science, Religious Studies, PSHE and ICT – and option groups. Each group contains a number of subjects, offering a choice which allows every pupil to achieve a balanced education whilst, at the same time, providing the opportunity to concentrate on his or her strengths. Subjects on offer are History, Geography, Drama, Business Studies, a second Language, DT, Home Economics, Art, Music, i-media and PE.

In the two years covered by the Lower and Upper Sixth (Years 12 and 13) pupils usually study four subjects at AS Level. Pupils continue with three, or occasionally, four subjects in their final year to A Level and are well positioned to meet the entrance requirements of the universities and professions. Psychology, Media Studies and Theatre Studies are included in this programme.

Potential Oxbridge candidates are identified in the Lower Sixth year and suitable tuition is arranged.

Choice of Subjects: Separate booklets on GCSE and A Level options are available.

Setting, Promotion, Reporting. In Forms 1–5 Mathematics and French are setted. In Forms 1–3 a top group is selected.

The minimum qualification for entry into the Sixth Form is normally considered to be five B grade passes at GCSE Level. Academic progress is monitored by tutors and at regular intervals throughout the term every pupil is graded for achievement and effort in every subject. Every term full subject reports are written on all pupils. Promotion between sets is always possible.

ICT. In addition to well-equipped Computer Suites the School has developed a sophisticated campus-wide network with its own intranet and on-line systems of communication with parents.

The school network serves the academic departments, the library, the staff common room and Heads of Department. It provides open access for pupils in the computer rooms and various 'clusters' around the school via a Microsoft Windows-based system working on industry-standard software. The library stocks many CD ROMs and there is a CAD system in Design and Technology. Access to the network is available to pupils in their own rooms in boarding houses.

Higher Education and Careers. Sutton Valence has a fine modern and well-equipped Sixth Form Centre which incorporates a Careers Library and the latest technologies to help in degree and career selection.

Every pupil sits a series of aptitude and ability tests during the two years prior to GCSE. This is followed by a thorough interview with trained members of staff in conjunction with the Kent Careers Service, when suggestions are made for Sixth Form academic courses and possible degrees/careers to be explored.

In the Sixth Form further interviews are conducted, advice is given on university and college applications and a range of career lectures and visits are laid on.

Music. Music plays a very important part in the life of the school, and we have a deservedly fine reputation for the quality and range of our music-making. There is a fine modern music school which contains a concert hall, five teaching rooms, ten practice rooms and an ensemble room.

One quarter of the pupils learn a musical instrument; there are three choirs, an orchestra, wind band, string group, jazz band, and a very full programme of concerts. Music tours to Europe have been arranged, and the Music Society organises a programme of distinguished visiting performers every year.

Drama. As with Music, Drama is central to the life of the school and the creative expression of our students. Every year there will be a number of productions. In addition, there are theatre workshops and reviews. Drama scholars and others also receive one-to-one drama coaching lessons in preparation for LAMDA exams. Early in the academic year 2007–2008 a £1.6 million renovation of our theatre will be opened giving our students stunning drama facilities.

Sport and Physical Education. Sutton Valence has a deserved reputation as a strong sporting school, competing in seventeen sports. Forty pupils currently have representative honours at County, Regional and National levels.

Our 100-acre site has one of the best cricket squares in Kent, two floodlit Astroturf pitches for hockey, a new indoor heated swimming pool, tennis, netball and squash courts, a marvellous new sports hall with fitness suite and six golf practice holes. In all, there is a tremendous range of choice for both boys and girls, all of whom will be involved in sport on at least two afternoons of every week. A floodlit, all-weather running track is scheduled to come on stream in 2009.

Additional sports, such as football, judo, dance, horse-riding, badminton, basketball and fencing are offered through our activities programme.

Pastoral System. The School is arranged in Year Groups – from First to Upper Sixth. Each year group has a Head of Year and within each year group, pupils are divided into Tutor Groups. The Sixth Form is led by the Director of Sixth Form, supported by two Heads of Section. Sixth Formers are placed in 'vertical' tutor groups whereby ten or so Lower and Upper Sixth students are tutored together. Pupils meet with their Tutor twice a day and this allows their progress to be monitored as well as giving pupils an opportunity to seek guidance. In addition to monitoring academic progress, tutors help pupils develop their potential through the Personal, Social and Health Education (PSHE) programme.

The School is a Christian foundation, however, our values are very much based on openness, tolerance and inclusivity. As such, we welcome students from all faith backgrounds, as well as those families who have no faith commitment.

Community Service, CCF and Duke of Edinburgh's Award Scheme. All pupils are expected to join one or more of the service schemes offered by the School. The CCF with Army, RAF and Royal Navy sections, is popular and successful and offers a wide variety of activities through regular camps, adventure training, field weekends and range days. The Duke of Edinburgh's Award Scheme is, similarly, well supported. Others participate in Community Service activities whereby pupils visit local primary schools, old people's homes, hospitals, undertake charity work and help out with local conservation projects.

Clubs and Activities. Time is specifically set aside each week for clubs and activities. Every pupil spends time pursuing his or her own special interests, and with up to forty clubs or activities from which to choose, the range and scope is very wide. In addition, various school societies and some other activities take place out of school hours.

Entrance Scholarships. (*see Scholarship Entries section*). Scholarships and Exhibitions are available in Drama, Music, Art, Design Technology and Sports. Junior and Senior Academic Scholarships are available.

Fees per term (2008-2009). Boarders £6,320–£8,320; Day pupils £4,020–£5,260.

Instrumental Music: £205 per term (10 lessons).

Extras: Books, stationery and clothing are charged for as supplied. A small charge is also made for entry at each stage to The Duke of Edinburgh's Award Scheme. Any other extras are those expenses personal to the individual. We have a series of bus routes available to families from areas across Kent costing up to £300 per term. Further details of routes can be obtained on request.

Charitable status. United Westminster Schools Foundation is a Registered Charity, number 309267. Its aims are to promote education.

Taunton School

Taunton Somerset TA2 6AD
Tel: 01823 349200
01823 349224 Headmaster
01823 349223 Admissions
Fax: 01823 349201
e-mail: enquiries@tauntonschool.co.uk
website: www.tauntonschool.co.uk

Motto: '*Ora et Labora*'

Taunton School is a friendly, purposeful co-educational boarding and day community with high academic standards and a full extra-curricular programme. Pupils are expected to develop their talents to the full, and to learn habits of self-discipline that will stand them in good stead in Higher Education and professional training. The School is exceptionally well-equipped and attractively situated with extensive grounds. It has four parts: the Senior School (13–18) of about 480 pupils (with a Sixth Form of around 200), the Preparatory School (7–13) of about 330, the Pre-Preparatory and Nursery (2–7) of about 140, and an International Study Centre with about 70 pupils. Each section has a distinct persona within the whole family, but the School has the advantage of offering a coordinated curriculum and identical terms and holidays.

Governors:

President & Chairman: Mrs Jane E Barrie, OBE, BSc, ARCS, FSI

Deputy Chairman: Air Vice-Marshal Peter Harding, CB, CVO, CBE, AFC, FRAeS

Treasurer: David T Watson, MA, FCA

Charles N C Abram, CertEd
Clive N G Arding, FRICS (*Governor Elect*)
Michael H N Button, FCA
Revd David Grosch-Miller BA
Major General Jonathan Hall, CB, OBE, FCMI (*Governor Elect*)
John Hine, LLB
Mark Hobbs, MA
Miss Alannah E Hunt
Mrs Gillian Hylson-Smith, BA Hons
Alan M Large, LLB
Geoffrey A Matthews, BA
Simon Milsted, FCA, BSc
David A Sizer, FRICS
General Sir Roger Wheeler, GCB, CBE, MA
Mrs Elaine Waymouth (*Governor Elect*)
Michael J O Willacy, CBE, FCIPS

Honorary Life Vice-Presidents:
Nigel Fox Bassett, MA
Brian P Bissell, MBE, MA, BD (*HLVP Elect*)
Major General Barry M Lane, CB, OBE
William R G Pearse, FCA
Mrs Joan M R Williams, LLB, AKC

Bursar & Clerk to the Governors: David J A Taylor, GradICSA

***Headmaster*: Dr John H Newton**, MA, FCollP, DipMS(Ed)

Deputy Head: Jimmy M H Beale, BSc
Deputy Head: Mrs Claire Chalcraft, BA
Director of Studies: Neil Mason, BSc
Director of Recreation: Hugh K C Todd, CertEd (*†Wills East*)
Head of Sixth Form: Mrs Mary P Mason, GRSC
Head of Middle School: Mrs Carol Manley (*†Jenkin*)
Head of Boarding: Alistair J Hallows, BSc (*†Weirfield*)

Chaplain: The Revd David R Owen, BA, HDE (PG), BA Hons, MTh

Assistant Staff:
* *Head of Department*
† *House Staff*

Rob Abell, BSc (**Business Studies; †Evans*)
Mrs Christabel Ager, BA, ALA (*Librarian*)
Jonathan Baker, BA (**Design & Technology*)
David Bearman, BSc
Mrs Joan Bird, BA, CertEd, Dip French
Martin Bluemel, MA, CChem, MRSC (**Chemistry; IB Coordinator*)
Mrs Louise Bolland, BA
David Bridges, GRSM, ARCM, ARCO (*Chapel Organist*)
A John Brown, MA (*Examinations Officer*)
Miss Alexandra Carter, BA
Peter Cartwright, CertEd (**Learning Support*)
Chris Chalcraft, BA
T Mark Chatterton, BA (**History*)
Mrs Tracey Coleman, MSc
Mike Cook, BSc (*†Marshall*)
Mrs Ruth Coomber, BSc, MTeg
Mark Cracknell, BA (*Director of Music*)
Philip Cutts, MA
Chris Davenport, BA
Mrs Loreto Diaz, BA, Lic en Derecho
Richard Dolphin, MBA, ACIB, FInstD
Miss Audrey Dubois (**Modern Languages*)
Greg R Fabre, Maitrise, LLCE
Mrs Susan Falkingham, MA, BEd (**Spanish, *Psychology*)
Jonathon O Fernyhough, BSc
Mrs Gill Foster, BA
Dr Alison S Franklin, BSc
Miss Lin Gao, MA, BEd
Paul Gibson, BSc
Robert Goodhand, BSc
Thomas E Grant, BA
Neil Gush, BA
Mrs Tracy Hallows, BSc (*†Weirfield*)
Dr Lotte Hammer, BA (**Art*)
Mrs Claire Harvie, BSc (**Physical Education; i/c Girls' Hockey*)
David R O Hawkins, BA
Mrs Sarah J Hearn, BA (**Classics*)
Simon Hogg (*i/c Cricket*)
Mrs Fiona Holford, BA (**EFL*)
Miss Judy Iredale, BA, Dip St Couns (**German, *General Studies*)
Stuart H Jackson, BSc, CEng, MBA
Miss Tina Jones, BSc (*i/c Athletics*)
Cyril Kelly, BA (*†Goodland; i/c Rugby*)
Mrs Stephanie Knight, MA
Clive Large, BA, MA, MBA
Mrs Jeanne Leader, BSc (**Geography*)
Miss Pauline McKay, MSc
Neil McPherson, BA (**English*)
Miss Fiona Morris, BMus
Christopher Moule, MA
Mrs Patricia Owen, DipEd
Dr James H J Penny, BSc (**Biology*)
Ian Piper, BSc
Roger Priest, BA
Stephen Pugh, BSc (*†Wills West*)
Jonathan S F Riches, BA
Declan Rogers, MA (*†Fairwater*)
David Rookes, BSc, BEd (**ICT*)
Miss Meryl Smart, BEd (**Theatre Studies and Drama*)
Simon Smith, BEng (**Science; *Physics*)
Miss Joanna Southcott, BCom (*†Bevan*)
Mrs Kate M Stent, BA
David Tarr, BSc (*i/c Hockey and Tennis*)
Mrs Susan Treseder, MEd
Mrs Janette Turner, BSc
Mrs Lucy Turner, BA (**Leisure and Recreation*)
Luke Waller, BSc

Headmaster's Secretary: Mrs Carol Cotton, BA
Admissions Secretary: (*to be appointed*)
Bursar's Secretary: Mrs Jean Eales
School Secretary: Mrs Sue Goodall
Medical Officers:
Dr Tim Howes
Dr Hilda Gormley
Foundation Director: Neil Longstreet, BA

Situation. The School stands in its own grounds of over 50 acres on the Northern outskirts of Taunton, within easy reach of some of the most attractive countryside in England. Taunton is exceptionally well placed on the M5 and the Paddington to Penzance main line with easy access to all parts of the British Isles and Bristol and Heathrow airports.

Facilities. The School moved to its present site in 1870 to a fine range of buildings purpose built in the Gothic style. The original house, Fairwater, dating from 18th century is a boys' boarding house. The Wills family, notably Lord Winterstoke, made a series of munificent gifts including the Chapel (completed in 1907), a Library, and two boys' boarding houses, Wills East and Wills West.

A separate Science Building was added as a War Memorial after the Great War, and subsequently extended. Building has proceeded continually as a result of good housekeeping and appeals, adding specialist teaching facilities, including a Drama Studio, and a purpose-built girls' boarding house. A policy of continuous modernisation has seen additions to the Houses, and in 1998 further accommodation for boarding girls. There have also been improvements to the Science laboratories and other teaching facilities. The Preparatory School (*see separate entry in IAPS section*) was rebuilt in 1994/95. A new Arts Centre was built in 1995. A new Astroturf was opened in 2007 and an extension to the Music School will open in Sept 2008.

Worship. The Chapel plays a central role in the life of the community. The School is no longer denominational and welcomes members of all Christian beliefs, or other faiths. There is a daily service and a service on Sundays for all boarders in residence. The Chapel Choir plays a major role in the enhancement of worship on special occasions. There are also instrumental music items, as part of chapel services, each week. The present Chaplain prepares candidates for confirmation and membership of all Protestant denominations and celebrates Holy Communion for all who are in good standing with their church. Preparation for Roman Catholic First Communion and Confirmation can be arranged.

Curriculum. In the first year of the Senior School the timetable sets out to give a wide experience of subjects, including the separate sciences.

Nine GCSE subjects are offered with English (Language and Literature), Mathematics, a Modern Foreign Language and Science as a core, and a choice from Art, Business Studies, Classical Civilisation, Design & Technology, Drama, Geography, German, History, Latin, Music, PE, Religious Studies and Spanish. All Year 10 pupils take a Religious Studies short course.

Twenty-three subjects are offered at AS & A2 level, the latest additions being Theatre Studies, Physical Education and Psychology, with the majority of Sixth Formers aiming at university or college entry.

The School has recently added the International Baccalaureate to the courses available to Sixth Form students. Subjects available include English, German, French, Spanish, Mandarin, History, Geography, Economics, Philosophy, Biology, Chemistry, Physics, Maths, Further Maths and Visual Arts.

Careers. Careers advice is an important part of school life with work experience for all in the Lower Sixth. The Head of Careers and Director of Studies advise on applications for Higher Education.

Music. Music plays a vital part in the life of the School: about one third of the pupils take lessons in a great variety of instruments, and there are choral groups, orchestra, windband, ensembles, and a jazz band.

School Societies. Everyone is encouraged to participate in extra-curricular activities and a wide range is offered including debating, drama, the Duke of Edinburgh's Award Scheme, Combined Cadet Forces, community service and astronomy. The School has a distinguished international debating record.

Games. The School has an outstanding record in games and has strong fixture lists. The principal games are rugby, hockey, netball, cricket and tennis, with excellent facilities also for squash, badminton and basketball. The School has a shale and an artificial turf hockey pitch which was replaced in Summer 2007. The latter provides twelve tennis courts in the Summer. There are outdoor and indoor heated swimming pools. The Sports Hall is equipped with an up-to-date Fitness Suite, climbing wall and a wide range of indoor games. Pupils also take part in athletics, cross-country, canoeing, sailing, riding and golf. There is also a miniature rifle range. The School's philosophy is to encourage athletic excellence whilst remembering that these activities are essentially for recreation.

Medical. The School Medical Centre provides the medical service for the whole School community, and is staffed by qualified nurses under the supervision of the School Medical Officer who visits daily.

Admission. The main ages of admission are 13 and 16, but entry at intermediate ages is also possible. Prospectuses and registration forms are available from the Admissions Secretary, who will also be pleased to arrange visits (01823 349223).

The Admissions Secretary at the Preparatory School (01823 349209) will be pleased to assist with enquiries for children up to the age of 13 .

Entry at 13. The Taunton School Scholarship Examination is held annually in February or March, and is open to all candidates under the age of 14 in the following September.

Candidates attending Preparatory Schools would be expected to take the Common Entrance Examination in June. Candidates who have not been prepared for Common Entrance would be required to attend for interview and are asked to sit an assessment.

Members of Taunton Preparatory School proceed to the Senior School on the basis of a Record of Progress.

Entry to the Sixth Form. Entry to the Advanced Level course will normally be conditional on a minimum of 5 GCSE passes at grade A to C, but again, interview and report play an important part in determining the offer of places.

Scholarships and Bursaries. *13+ Open Scholarship.* A number of Scholarships of up to half fees and Exhibitions are awarded at the age of 13.

The examinations are held at Taunton School in the Spring, as announced in the Independent Schools Yearbook for Examination Group B. Papers may be sent to candidates' Preparatory Schools if it is wished to sit the examinations there. The compulsory subjects are English, Mathematics, a Modern Language (French, German or Spanish), Science, History, Geography, Religious Studies and a General Paper, with optional papers in Latin, Greek, French, Spanish, German and Design & Technology.

Sixth Form Scholarships. These are awarded annually in November preceding the year of entry to the Sixth Form to outstanding boys or girls who will be taking GCSE examinations in the current year and who are regarded as strong University candidates.

11+ Scholarships and Exhibitions. A number of Scholarships and Exhibitions are awarded to boys and girls under the age of 12 on 1st September of the year of entry. The examinations are held at Taunton Preparatory School in January and awards continue into the Senior School. Call 01823 349209 for more information.

Music and Art. A number of Scholarships and Exhibitions, including an Organ Scholarship, are offered in both Music and Art each year at 13+ and Sixth Form. These do not form part of the Open Scholarship Examination. Details may be obtained from the Admissions Secretary (01823 349223).

Sport and All-Rounder. Sport Scholarships are offered to candidates at 13+ and Sixth Form. All-Rounder Scholarships are available at 13+.

Details of all 13+ and Sixth Form Scholarships may be obtained from the Admissions Secretary (01823 349223).

Bursaries. Ministerial Bursaries may be offered to the sons and daughters of Ministers of all recognised denominations, from the age of 11, on condition that the candidates satisfy the academic requirements of the School.

Service Bursaries are available for the children of Service families.

Fees per term (2008-2009). Senior School: Boarders £7,530; Day £4,700.

Taunton Preparatory School: Boarders £3,275–£5,930; Day £2,030–£3,820. Pre-Preparatory & Nursery (full-time) £1,745.

There are rebates for families with more than one child in the school.

Charitable status. Taunton School is a Registered Charity, number 1081420. It exists to provide education for boys and girls.

Tettenhall College

Wood Road Wolverhampton West Midlands WV6 8QX
Tel: 01902 751119
Fax: 01902 741940
e-mail: head@tettcoll.co.uk
website: www.tettenhallcollege.co.uk

Tettenhall College was founded in 1863 by a group of Wolverhampton businessmen to provide a school for sons of nonconformists. Tettenhall is now co-educational and an interdenominational school, providing a quality education from nursery to university entrance.

There are about 500 pupils, of whom 85 are Boarders.

Motto: '*Timor Domini Initium Sapientiae*'

Governors:

Chairman: J F Woolridge, CBE, BSc

Vice-Chairman: Revd Prebendary G Wynne, MTh, BSc Soc, BD, AKC

Mrs C Baugh
P G Brough, BA
P H Creed
Mrs C Hammond, BA
Mrs V A Jones
Mrs D Margetts
Mrs J Parker, SRP, MCSP, JP
J H Rice
Professor R E Smallman, CBE, BSc, PhD, DSc, FEng, FRS
G D H Sower, BA
Mrs V Vaughan-Hughes
Miss M Whild, BA, DipArch, RIBA

***Headmaster*: P C Bodkin**, BSc, PhD

Deputy Head: H R J Trump, BA

Teaching Staff:
Mrs S Blake, BA, MA
J Bullock, BA
P J Bullough, BA
Mrs H Compain-Holt, MA
Mrs C Cooper, BSc
A J T Dyer, BEd
R J Ellmore, BSc
C J Evans, BSc, MIBiol, MCollP
P G Evans, BSc
A T Foster, BA
Mrs E J Gwilt, BSc
J D Higgs, BA
Ms C Hope, BEd

Miss A Y J Jarman, BA
Miss M Jones, CinE
Mrs P Jones, CertEd, DipRSA SpLD
Mrs J Kibble, BEd
S L Lawrence, BSc
R M Leighton, BA
Mrs M Lofting, BA, MA
A R Mottershead, BEd, PhD
Miss K E Murphy, BA
Mrs A Nash, ACIB
The Revd G J Parry, BA
J M Petfield, BSc
G J Raine, BA
Mrs A A Ridyard, BA
Mrs R Samra, BA
Mrs B Smith, BA
Mrs D E Spencer, BEd
Mrs C A Squire, BA
Mrs D Stone, BA, DipTEFL, MEd
Mrs K Stone, BA
Mrs S M Symons, BA
Mrs J L Taylor, C in E
Miss M D Uttley, BA
I F Wass, BEd
Mrs C E Whiting, BSc, BEd
Mrs G O Whitmore, BSc
C Woodward, BA, SpLD

Head of Lower School: P Meadows, MA
Deputy Head: P J Kay, BA

Visiting Teachers:
11 staff provide Music tuition, 3 take pupils for individual learning support and 2 provide additional sports coaching.

Clerk to the Governors: M J Kilvert
Bursar: S Howard, FCMI, FIH
Personal Assistants to the Headmaster:
Marketing & Admissions: Miss A Addison
Administration: Mrs N Phelps

Medical Officers:
Dr J Bright
Dr A Williams

School Nurses:
Mrs C Wagstaff
Mrs S Philpott

Situation and Buildings. Three miles west of the centre of Wolverhampton in the old village of Tettenhall, the school stands in 33 acres of extensive gardens, woods and playing fields.

The original building contains the Boys' Boarding House, the Dining Hall, the Chapel and also Big School which is now the School Library. A new Girls' Boarding House was built in 1989.

The Towers, acquired from the Thorneycroft Estate in 1942, houses the Music Department and a fine theatre built in the nineteenth century. The Drive and Lower School buildings are new and purpose-designed.

The Maurice Jacks Building incorporates new Science laboratories, administrative offices, a staff common room and form rooms for Upper School.

Other amenities include a Sixth Form Centre, an Information Technology Network, a Home Economics Centre, a separate Art Department, a Resources Room, a covered, heated Swimming Pool, a Sports Hall and courts for Netball, Tennis and Squash. There are two Cricket squares and playing fields for Rugby, Soccer, Hockey and Athletics.

Religion. Services in the College Chapel are interdenominational.

Entry. (*see Scholarship Entries section*). The school accepts girls and boys. Entrance to the Upper School (age 11–18) is normally by way of assessment in Mathematics, English and Verbal Reasoning. Pupils at independent preparatory schools take the Common Entrance Examination. By arrangement with the Headmaster, pupils may be interviewed and tested according to their individual needs. Assessments are set by the Head of Lower School for pupils between the ages of 7 and 11. These can be taken in any term by appointment.

Organisation. Upper School (Years 7 to 11 and the Sixth Form) and Lower School (Years 3 to 6) are each divided into 4 Houses which compete in activities, work and games. The Drive School comprises a Nursery, Kindergarten, Reception and Years 1 and 2.

Upper School Curriculum. GCSE may be taken in the following subjects: Art, Biology, Business Studies, Chemistry, Economics, Electronics, English, French, Geography, German, History, Information Technology, Mathematics, Music, Physics, Physical Education, Religious Studies and Statistics.

In the Sixth Form various combinations of subjects are possible, and AS and A level courses offered include Art, Biology, Business Studies, Chemistry, Drama and Theatre Studies, Economics, Electronics, English, French, Geography, German, History, Law, Mathematics, Music, Physics, Physical Education and Psychology.

Careers. Extensive advice is given by the Careers Teachers and the local Careers Service.

Societies and Activities. All pupils are encouraged to become fully involved in the life of the community and to play a part in the social and cultural organisations.

Pupils take part in the Duke of Edinburgh's Award Scheme, working for Bronze, Silver and Gold Awards.

Full facilities are provided for Badminton, Basketball, Chess, Computer Studies, Drama, Karate, Dance, Pottery, Snooker and Table Tennis. There are numerous clubs and societies that meet regularly. Excursions are frequently arranged to places of special interest for those doing Business Studies, Geography, History, Science and Technology, and foreign journeys have, in recent years, regularly included visits abroad, sports tours and exchanges with a school in Bensheim. School plays are produced each year; there is a house festival of Performing Arts and the Music Department is strong.

Lower School. Lower School is housed separately in a new, purposed-designed building opened in 2002. It shares a number of the facilities with Upper School and Upper School Staff help with games and specialist teaching.

Years 3 to 5 are taught mainly by their Form Teachers. Particular attention is paid to standards in Literacy and Numeracy. French is taught from the age of seven and German from Year 6.

Athletics, Cricket, Netball, Hockey, Rounders, Rugby, Soccer, Swimming and Tennis are the main sports and all pupils have PE and two afternoons of games each week. Extra-curricular activities include Badminton, Bridge, Chess, Computing, Dance, Drama, Squash and Table Tennis. Music and the playing of musical instruments are strongly encouraged.

The Drive School. The Drive, the pre-preparatory department for pupils aged 2 to 7 years, is accommodated within a new purposely designed building adjacent to The Towers. The emphasis is on the three Rs. The Humanities are approached through topic work; Science and Technology is experienced "hands on". Activities include Art and Craft, Music, PE, Dance and Swimming.

Fees per term (2008-2009). Year 7 and above: Boarders £6,513, Weekly Boarders £5,420, Day Boarders £4,102, Day Pupils £3,712. Below Year 7: Boarders £5,348, Weekly Boarders £4,340, Day Boarders £3,434, Day Pupils £3,025. The Drive School: £1,798–£2,379.

The Old Tettenhallians' Club. Correspondence should be addressed to Mr L N Chown at the College.

Charitable status. Tettenhall College Incorporated is a Registered Charity, number 528617. It exists to provide a quality education for boys and girls.

Tonbridge School

Tonbridge Kent TN9 1JP
Tel: 01732 365555
Fax: 01732 363424
e-mail: hmsec@tonbridge-school.org
website: www.tonbridge-school.co.uk

Tonbridge School was founded in 1553 by Sir Andrew Judde, under Letters Patent of King Edward VI. The Charter ordained that the Governors of the School after the death of the Founder were to be the Worshipful Company of Skinners, one of the oldest City Livery Companies. Sir Andrew, himself a distinguished member of this Company, left property in the City of London and in the Parish of St Pancras as an endowment for the school.

Motto: '*Deus dat incrementum*'

Governors:
J L Cohen, QC (*Chairman*)

J Aisher
J L Bazalgette
C Brodie
Mrs A Buggé
H C K Carson
J Coldman
R J Elliott
C J D Emms
D J Flint
J C F Hitchins
A B E Hudson, MBE
A Mayer
E Price
C Rudge
C A Stuart-Clark
Mrs S Tozzi

Clerk to the Governors: B Plummer, CBE

***Headmaster*: T H P Haynes**, BA

Second Master: D R Walsh, MA
Director of Studies: J C Pearson, MA
Director of Teaching and Learning: P S D Carpenter, MA

Assistant Staff:
* *Head of Department/Subject*

Classics:
*J S Taylor, MA, DPhil
J S Hodgson, BA
T W H Murgatroyd, MA, PhD
P W G Parker, MA
A P Schweitzer, MA

Mathematics:
*I R H Jackson, MA, PhD
S Burns, BSc
H B Evans, MSc, PhD
R J Freeman, MA
J D King, MA, PhD
M J Lawson, BA
N J Lord, MA
S T Seldon, BA, MEng
A R Whittall, MA
Miss A L Caldecott, BSc

Science:
*R Brookes, MChem, DPhil

J A Fisher, BSc (**Chemistry*)
M J Clugston, MA, DPhil
D A Cruse, MA, PhD, CChem, MRSC, MRI
J C Pearson, MA
Ms K E Wood, MChem
R D Woodling, MChem

R L Fleming, MA (**Physics*)
G M Barnes, BSc
S Chalk, BSc, PhD
N C Waite, BSc
D S Knox, MPhys
M Ogretme, BSc, MSc
G R Piper, BSc

P M Ridd, MA (**Biology*)
P J Belbin, BSc, MEd
C J C Swainson, MA
Miss E Lambert, BSc, PhD

English:
*R H Evans, MA
J P Arscott, MA
J R Bleakley, BA
P S D Carpenter, MA
A J Edwards, MA
Mrs D M Hulse, MA, DipModDrama
J Johnson, BA, MPhil
N J Waywell, BA

Modern Languages:
*L S McDonald, MA (**French*)
A E Bissill, MA (**Spanish*)
C E Wright, BA (**German*)
J X Wu, MA (**Mandarin*)
A L Austin, BA
R Burnett, MA
Mrs T Coomber, L-ès-L
Mrs C Cordero, Lda en Fil
R D Hoare, MA
Miss D M McDermot, BA, MA
J A Nicholls, MA
T W Richards, BA
S M Wainde, MA

History:
*D Cooper, MA
Mrs F C Dix Perkin, MA
J C Harber, MA
C W Jones, MA
R W G Oliver, MA
L W B Ramsden, BA, MSt
Miss M L Robinson, MA
D R Walsh, MA

Geography:
*C M Battarbee, BA
C M Henshall, BA
G P Gales, BEd
J E Perriss, BA (*Lower Master*)
M G Rowan, MA, FRGS
D H Tennant, BSc

Social Science:
*J D W Richards, BA, PhD (**Economics*)
A R Bird, MA, MSc (**Politics*)
J Blake, BA, MSc (**Business Studies*)
J D Gibbs, MA, LLB
Ms H M Harris, BA, MSc
A J Leale, BA
J H Maynard, BA
Miss K E Moxon, MA
N R V Rendall, BA

Art and Technology:
*Mrs C H Chisholm, BA (**Art*)
T W Duncan, BA
Mrs B Waugh, BA
R J Bradley, BSc (**Computing*)
K D Sammons, BSc
D Dixon, BA (**Design Technology*)
W D F Biddle, BSc
J M Woodrow, BA
D L Faithfull, BTech, MSc, CEng, MIEE (**Electronics*)

Divinity:
*J C F Dobson, MA
The Revd S M Beaumont, BD, AKC (*Chaplain*)
The Revd D A Peters, BA (*Assistant Chaplain*)

Drama:
*G E Henry, MA
M I Morrison, BA, MEd
L Thornbury, DipDrama

Music:
*M A Forkgen, MA, ARCO (*Director of Music*)
D J Clack, ARCM (**Brass*)
J N Holmes, MA, LRAM (**Woodwind and Academic Music*)
Miss M S Laing, GGSM, ARCM, LRAM (*Strings*)
A E L Pearson, BMus, LRAM, ARCM (**Strings*)

J R P Thomas, MA, FRCO (*Choirmaster*)
D L Williams, GRSM, ARCM, LRAM (**Piano and Organist*)

Physical Education:
*A R Whittall, MA (*Director of Sport*)
C D Morgan, BSc (**Physical Education*)

Director of ICT Services:
I N Lucas BSc

University Entrance and Careers:
Mrs A Rogers, BA

Learning Support:
Mrs P Brandling-Harris, BA, DipSpLD, AMBDA
Mrs C Clugston, MA
Mrs G T Featherstone, MA

Houses & Housemasters:

Boarding:
School House: R Burnett
Judde House: G P Gales
Park House: A J Leale
Hill Side: P W G Parker
Parkside: A P Schweitzer
Ferox Hall: C W Jones
Manor House: J S Hodgson

Day:
Welldon House: N C Waite
Smythe House: C M Henshall
Whitworth House: W D F Biddle
Cowdrey House: R W G Oliver
Oakeshott House: J R Bleakley

Administration:
Bursar: R E E Hart, OBE, JP
Librarian: Mrs B Matthews, MCLIP
Headmaster's PA: Mrs L R O'Neill
Director of Admissions: J S Hodgson, BA
Assistant Admissions Registrar: A R Bird, BA, MSc
Admissions Secretary: Miss R Hearnden
Secretary, including pre-selection testing: Mrs S Maynard
Secretary, including LoVIth Admissions: Miss I C Beeson
School Administrator: Miss E J Day

The School occupies an extensive site of 150 acres on the northern edge of the town of Tonbridge, and is largely self-contained within that site. The central buildings of the present school date from the second half of the nineteenth century.

The last two decades have been a period of extraordinary growth and development at Tonbridge – in numbers, in academic, cultural, and sporting standards, and in the facilities and amenity of the physical school. The latest development is the new Sports and Media Centre which opened in June 2008, and is a landmark in national indoor sporting provision.

There are 760 boys in the School, aged between 13 and 18, of whom 435 are boarders and 325 are day boys. There are 7 boarding houses, each with a complement of about 60 boys, and 5 day boy houses. Each boarding house has its own dining room, kitchen and domestic staff, and boys take their meals in their own houses.

Tonbridge is a Christian foundation, and the services in the splendidly restored Chapel are an important and regular part of school life. The whole school gathers for a short service or assembly on most weekday mornings. Boarders attend a full choral service each Sunday.

Admissions and Scholarships. (*see Scholarship Entries section*). The great majority of boys join the school at the age of 13, having gained admission through the Common Entrance Examination or the school's own Scholarship Examination (held in early May). About 140 boys are admitted at the age of 13 each year. There are also places available for entry to the Sixth Form at the age of 16. Except in special cases, entry is in September only.

About 50 scholarships are offered for award each year. In a typical year there are awarded 23 academic scholarships, 10 or more Music scholarships, up to 10 Art, Drama or Technology scholarships, 4 Cowdrey scholarships for sport, and 3 or 4 Sixth Form scholarships (academic/music). A number of Choral Boarding Exhibitions, with a value of 10% of the fees, are also offered each year for award to Choristers of Cathedral or other Choir Schools. The value of any scholarship may be increased, by any amount up to the full school fee, if assessment of the parents' means indicates a need.

Registration of a boy as a potential candidate for admission to the school at the age of 13 should be made as early as possible, and preferably not later than three years before the date of intended entry. Applications for Sixth Form entry are best made by September a year before entry, but may be considered later.

Each year all candidates for 13-year old entry in September are invited to spend two days at the school in March, just after the end of the Tonbridge Lent Term, and those who will be boarders spend the night in the boarding House they intend to join. The boys greatly enjoy this visit, and it contributes to the ease with which they settle in September.

Academic Life. All boys entering the school at the age of 13 join one of the six First Year sets of about 23 boys each. They are taught most subjects in these groups which are broadly streamed, but they are separately setted for Mathematics, French and Latin. In the Second Year and above, all subjects are taught in subject-specific sets; the average set size in the Second and Third Years is 17, and in the Sixth Form 9.

In the **First Year**, in addition to the usual range of academic subjects, all boys take courses in Art, Music, Drama and Technology (including Design & Technology and Electronics). Boys study two modern foreign languages, one of which must be continuation study, from a menu of French, German, Spanish and Mandarin Chinese.

The curriculum in the **Second and Third Years** is designed to offer flexibility both of choice and pace, so that boys can choose a programme which suits their own inclinations and needs. Many boys take some GCSE examinations at the end of the Second Year, and the remainder of their examinations in the Third Year; others take all of their GCSEs at the end of the Third Year. For most boys, then, the Third Year is a mixed economy – in some subjects continued work towards GCSE, in others more advanced work as a preparation for Sixth Form study.

A course in Information Systems is followed by all boys in the First and Second Years, leading to the industry-recognised European Computer Driving Licence (ECDL).

In the **Sixth Form** all boys study four subjects to AS Level in the Lower Sixth, and then either three or four subjects to A Level in the Upper Sixth. The choice of subjects is wide, and the timetabling allows virtually any combination to be taken.

The school believes strongly in the importance of general education; in the Sixth Form all boys attend a Seminar programme to extend their intellectual horizons and attitudes. In the Lower Sixth in small groups, each led by a member of staff, boys experience group exercises, lectures and discussions whose object is the enlargement of their ethical, cultural, scientific and political awareness. Special arrangements are made for the preparation of candidates for admission to Oxford or Cambridge.

All boys in the Lower Sixth Form are encouraged to spend a week of work experience during the holidays. There is a full-time Universities and Careers Adviser on the school staff.

Sport. The school offers expert coaching in some 20 sports, and has extensive indoor and outdoor facilities. These include 100 acres of playing fields, an all-weather athletics track of county standard, three Astroturf playing areas for hockey and tennis (one of them water-based), squash courts, fives courts, a rackets court, and a climbing wall. Sailing takes place at Bough Beech reservoir. Tonbridge has recently completed a £10.5m indoor sports centre which has a 6-lane 25m pool, a 6-court sports hall, a fitness centre, 2 sports studios, and an indoor climbing wall.

A distinctive feature of Tonbridge sport is that a very large number of boys have the opportunity to represent the school – not only the top sportsmen but also the average players. It is not uncommon for nearly half the school to be involved in representative matches on one afternoon: in the Michaelmas Term, for example, the school fields up to 23 XVs. There are also House Leagues in the main sports, which offer a particular opportunity to those who do not play in the major school teams.

Activities and Trips. Both Music and Drama play a major part in the life of the school.

There is a strong tradition of musical excellence: over half of the boys in the school learn a musical instrument and there are two string orchestras, a full symphony orchestra, a swing band and two symphonic bands. An afternoon each week is devoted to Chamber Music. The Chapel's four-manual Marcussen organ is internationally renowned; the Chapel choir sings weekly services and a smaller consort performs secular music. There is an informal weekly concert and many other performance opportunities for boys – the school has three fine Bösendorfer pianos and three good concert rooms of different sizes. A large-scale choral/orchestral concert is given termly in collaboration with several local girls' schools. There is a specialist early music teacher and boys have access to harpsichords, fortepianos and chamber organs. Composition flourishes: the Sibelius 3 programme has made this activity popular with a large number of boys. A fully-equipped recording studio is much used by Jazz and Rock groups. The professionally-equipped E M Forster Theatre is intensively used. There are performances on an almost weekly basis which include those by boys of all year groups, and by local, national and international amateur and professional companies. Up to date computerised lighting and sound equipment allows boys to develop significant skills in the technical areas as part of Stage Crew. The new Media Centre contains a TV studio control room and edit suites with state-of-the-art technology. Boys throughout the school are taught a variety of skills here, and can produce professional standard videos, as well as live webcasts, sports analysis material and support for school productions and events.

One afternoon each week is devoted by all boys to activities mainly separate from their academic and sporting programmes. The choice of activities is wide, and includes participation in the Community Service Group, the Duke of Edinburgh's Award Scheme, and the three sections of the CCF. The School has enhanced its community action programme with the appointment of a Community Action Director to coordinate community and charity work.

There are about 30 school societies and clubs which hold regular meetings. A Societies Fair is held at the beginning of each school year.

A large number of expeditions and trips is organised each year, with full staff supervision. There are bi-annual study trips to Germany, Spain and France, to Greece or Italy, to Sweden, China and America; Sixth Form reading parties; and a wide range of other academic, cultural, musical, and sporting tours. In the holidays between 10 and 20 such trips are regularly organised by the school in this country and abroad. In total the School takes up to 200 extra-curricular trips a year

Each year Easter and Summer holiday courses for children and adults are offered at the school in some 40 sports, crafts, and educational activities.

Fees per term (2008-2009). Boarders £9,380; Day Boys £6,970.

Charitable status. Tonbridge School is a Registered Charity, number 1097977. It exists solely to provide education for boys.

Trent College

Derby Road Long Eaton Nottingham NG10 4AD
Tel: Head: 0115 849 4949
General enquiries: 0115 849 4949
Bursar: 0115 849 4920
Registrar: 0115 849 4950
Fax: 0115 849 4997
e-mail: enquiry@trentcollege.net
website: www.trentcollege.net

The Foundation Stone of Trent College was laid by the seventh Duke of Devonshire in 1866 and the School opened two years later. The School was founded by Francis Wright.

Motto: '*Sapientia Fons Vitae*'

Governing Body:
President: His Grace The Duke of Devonshire, PC, MC
Chairman: Mr C M McDowell, FCIB
Professor A J Avery, DM, MBChB, BMed Sci Hons, FRCGP, DCH, DGM
Mr I F Bowness, BA, FCA
Mrs C Boddington, BA Hons
Professor M L Clarke, MSc, PhD, PGCAP, FGS, FRGS, MRSC, ILTM
Professor C W Day, CertEd, LRAM, MA, DPhil, PhD, FRSA
Mr A Ellis, BSc Hons
Mr P Giles, FRICS
Mrs E A Gregory, BSc, ACIS
Mr P M T Macildowie, ACA
Mr I R McNair, BSc Hons, MBA, DipProjMan RICS, MAPM
Mr R W Nelson, LLB Hons, FRSA
Mr K A Pickering, FCA
Mrs R E Rowley, BA Hons
Mrs P Spaven, BSc, DipSpLD
The Revd A F Walters, ACP, CertEd

Senior Management Team:

***Head*: Mrs G Dixon**, BSc Warwick, MBA Leicester

Bursar: Mr D M J Clark, MA London
Deputy Head, Academic: Mr A McGrath, BA Durham
Deputy Head, Pastoral: Mr M A Cowie, BSc Glasgow, MEd Manchester
Assistant Head, Head of Sixth Form: Ms L Matthews, BA Hull
Assistant Head, Head of Main School: Mr A D Stevens, BA Queens, Belfast, MA Man
Assistant Head, Head of Lower School: Mr W A Webster, BA Rhodes, SA
Director of Curriculum: Mr P D Kelly, BSc, PhD Loughborough
Director of Marketing & Development: Mrs C McNiven Young, BA Nottingham

Registrar: Mrs S Christie

Chaplain: Revd T R Haggis, MA Oxon

Boarding Houses & Housemasters/mistresses:
Bates: Mrs D B Webster
Martin: Mrs C Rayfield
Blake: Mr K P Taylor
Shuker: Mr P J Millward

Staff:
* *Head of Department*
† *Housemaster/mistress*

Art:
*Mr D Sprakes, Dip AD Newcastle Polytechnic, ATD Liverpool
Mr A S Northeast, MA Oxon

Mrs K O'Hare, BA Chester
Mrs V M Prince, BA Derby (*Team Manager Kemp*)

Biology:
*Miss E L Matthews, BSc London
Mrs E B L Stevens, BSc Manchester
Dr B T Chatha, BSc Nottingham, PhD Oxford
Mrs R Connick, BSc Leeds
Mrs M Daykin, BSc Nottingham Trent

Business Information Systems:
*Mr D J Tidy, BEd Nottingham Trent, MA Loughborough
Mr M A Cowie, BSc Glasgow, MEd Manchester
Mrs C Dimilta-Jones, BA Hull
Mr C J Hansen, MBA Hull, BA City of London Polytechnic
Mr I R Sanderson, MA Cantab (*Head of Academic Development*)
Mr M Stevens, MSc Nottingham Trent, BSc Salford
Mrs C E Welsby, BA Bradford
Mr M H Westhead, LLB Nottingham Trent, MSc Loughborough (*Coordinator of Initial Teacher Training and Newly Qualified Teaching*)

Chemistry:
*Mr N A Lambert, BSc Nottingham
Dr P D Kelly, BSc, PhD Loughborough
Dr S K Kelly, BSc, PhD Loughborough
†Mr K P Taylor, BSc Liverpool
Dr C Wakerley, BSc Nottingham Trent, PHD Loughborough

Classical Studies:
*Mr F W B Leadbetter, BD, AKC London, MA Nott, FRSA (*Director of Whole School Programme*)
Mr D Mitchell, MA Cantab (*Head of Year 11*)

Design & Technology:
*Mr J Prince, BSc Loughborough
Mr P Saville, BA Loughborough (*Educational Visits Coordinator*)
Mr G W Thompson, BSc Brunel
Mr B J Ward, BSc Brunel

English:
*Mrs E D Dunford, BA York
Mr D A Dunford, MA Cantab
Mrs K J Fletcher, BA Loughborough
Miss J Hunter, BA Edge Hill (*Martin House Resident Tutor*)
Ms L Matthews, BA Hull
Miss E J U Stableforth, BA Durham (*Team Manager Hanbury*)
Miss S Stuart, BA Durham
Mr W A Webster, BA Rhodes, SA

Geography:
*Mrs J E Hayward, MA Cambridge
Miss V G Bletsoe-Brown, BSc Reading (*Assistant Housemistress Bates*)
Mr J Marriott, BA Hons Leeds
Mr P A Shuttleworth, BSc Dunelm (*Coordinator of DofE Award and Expeditions*)

History:
*Mr P S Mayfield, BA Nottingham
Mr M R Field, BA Oxford Brookes (*Head of Careers*)
Miss E A McKenzie, BAEd Wilts
Mr A D Stevens, BA Queen's Belfast, MA Man

Learning Support:
*Mrs J Bowe, BSc London, DipSpLD
Mrs G Mann, BEd Ripon & St John, DipSpLD

Mathematics:
*Mr J W Bratton, BA York, MEd Nottingham, MBA Nottingham
Miss A C Berry, BSc Birmingham (*Head of Year 8*)
Mrs F A Brimblecombe, BSc Sheffield, CPhys, MInstP (*Head of Entry to Higher Education*)
Mrs J A Gale, BEng Leeds (*Head of Year 10*)
Mr D W Mitchell, MA Cantab
Miss M L Smith, BA Ripon & York St. John
Mr A Tarry, BEng Loughborough
Mr J Veazey, BSc Nottingham Trent
†Mrs D B Webster, BA Rhodes SA

Modern Languages:
*Mr A R Bradshaw, BA Hull
Miss G Green, BA Swansea (*Head of Year 12*)
Mrs L M L Leadbetter, BA Leicester (*Head of French*)
Mrs M Mills, BEd Wolverhampton
Mr K D Price, BA Cardiff (*Head of Spanish, German and Leadership*)
Mr I R Sanderson, MA Cantab (*Head of Academic Development*)
Miss A G Wright, BA Keele (*Assistant Director of Curriculum*)

Music:
*†Mrs C Rayfield, BMus Birmingham (*Head of Strings*)
Mr D A Curtiss (*Head of Brass*)
†Mr P J Millward, BA Oxon, FRCO

Physical Education/Games:
*Mr A M Benstead, BA QTS, MA Warwick
Mr O Clayson, BA Central Lancashire
Miss G L Gunter, BSc Gloucestershire
Mr G Hope, BA York St Johns College (*Head of Boys' Games*)
Mr A F Rolt, CertEd Doncaster, MA Loughborough Head of Year13)
Miss M L Smith, BA Ripon & York St John
Mrs S Taylor, BEd Leeds Polytechnic (*Head of Year 7*)
Mr W A Webster, BA Rhodes, SA
Ms L J Yates, BEd Bedford (*Head of Year 9*)

Politics:
*Mr F W B Leadbetter, BD, AKC London, MA Nott, FRSA (*Director of Whole School Programme*)
Mr M Stevens, MSc Nottingham Trent, BSc Salford

Physics:
*Dr J E Morley, BSc, PhD Leicester (*Director of ICT*)
Mr A Jackson, MEng Birmingham
Dr L J McKenna, BSc Liverpool John Moores

Religious Studies:
*Mrs K Sunderland, BRelSc Dublin (*Coordinator of PSHE*)
Revd T R Haggis, MA Oxon, DipTh Nottingham

Theatre Studies:
*Miss N J Duguay, MA Lancaster
Mr D Brown, BA Glamorgan (*Director of Drama*)
Miss H Statts, BA Royal Welsh College of Music & Drama Cardiff (*Stage Manager*)

School Sports Coaches:
Mr A Afford (*Cricket*)
Mr M Allen (*Tennis*)
Mr D Barnes (*Tennis*)
Mr C Gray (*Rugby*)
Mr C Keegan (*Hockey*)

School Doctor: Dr Gregory and the Overdale Medical Practice
School Sister: J van Craeyenest, SRN, MSSCh, MBchA
School Counsellor: Mrs M Braine, BA Hull
School Matron: Mrs M Douglas
SSI and Health & Safety Advisor: Mr A J McIntyre, WO1 CCF

Junior School Staff:

Headteacher: Mr K B Morrow, BA Hons, NPQH

Deputy Head: Mr J D Hall, BEd Hons

Assistant Teachers:

Mrs S Berryman, BMus	Mrs A Kent, BSc, PGCE
Miss E Buckley, BEd	Mrs C Lampon, BEd
Miss S Child, BA	Mrs S Limbert, BA, PGCE
Miss L Cook, BA	Mrs A Marshall, MA
Mrs L Davies, BA	Miss L Pattison, GRSM (*Music Coordinator*)
Miss L Draper, BA	Miss C Regan, BA
Mr D Fulton BA	Miss L Rigley, BA
Mrs C Green, BEd	Miss K Silveston, BA
Mrs J Hancock, BEd	Mr S Young, BSc
Mr J Harper, BA	
Mrs H Honarmand, BSc	

Part-time teachers:

Mrs K Benstead, BA	Mrs P McConnell, BSc
Mrs S Bratton, BA	Mrs S Throssell, BSc, PGCE (*Science*)
Mrs C Chivers, BEd (*Dance*)	

Nursery Nurses:

Mrs L Astle-Burgoyne	Miss R King
Mrs V Condon	Mr W Pearson
Mrs M Cox	Mrs S Shakespeare
Mrs R Davis	Mrs K Timms
Ms B Farr	Mrs A Winson
Mr M Hankinson	Miss A Woodward

Situation. Trent College is situated in 45 acres of attractive grounds, approximately midway between Nottingham and Derby, on the edge of the town of Long Eaton which has a population of approximately 35,000.

Pupils. In September 1999 the School opened its own Junior School, The Elms, which caters for 350 children from the age of 3 to 11. (*See IAPS entry.*)

The Senior School is divided into three key sections; firstly, the Lower School (11–13) with around 200 pupils. Pupils then move on to the Main School (13–16) with about 350 pupils. Finally the pupils move up to the Sixth Form of around 220 pupils where there are two Boarding Houses, one for boys and one for girls, housing 75 students.

Ethos. Trent is a selective and academic school, with considerable competition for places. It has a boarding school ethos, which means that the day pupils may stay in school until 6.00 pm on each weekday, three lessons are taught on Saturday mornings (except for those in the Lower School) and there are games for the vast majority on Saturday afternoon. We appreciate the changing needs of parents and we offer flexible boarding, where pupils can go home after their commitment on Saturday or stay and join in the weekend activities.

Buildings. Trent makes very good use of the original School building which contains the Chapel, the Dining Hall, the Teachers' Common Room and the School Administration. There has been an impressive development programme over the last 15 years with the addition of an Art, Design & Technology Centre, a Sixth Form Boarding House, a new Biology Centre, a Pavilion, new teaching facilities for Modern Languages and History, a new Business Centre and a refurbished Sixth Form Centre.

Academic. Whilst taking full note of the implications of the National Curriculum, Trent has its own curriculum to GCSE. All pupils take Maths, English (Language) and English Literature at GCSE. On top of this, six additional GCSEs are taken from a wide range of options. In the Sixth Form every student takes four Advanced GCE AS subjects; the more able may take further courses selecting from a wide range of options. The vast majority of the pupils leaving the school proceed to degree courses at university, including places at Oxford or Cambridge.

Games. The major sports, played on three afternoons a week, are rugby, hockey and cricket (for boys); hockey, netball and tennis (for girls). There are facilities for swimming, athletics, squash, fencing, tennis, badminton, basketball, cross-country, soccer and shooting. There is great emphasis on all pupils being given the chance to develop their sporting talent, whatever their level, and the School, with its large number of teams, tries to provide as many as possible with the opportunity of representing the School.

Music and Drama. Many pupils learn musical instruments and a large number play to a very high standard. With a First, an Intermediate and a Junior Orchestra, together with several other bands and ensembles, all musicians, no matter what their standard or age, are given every opportunity to perform with others in a group. An early experience of public performance helps maintain the overall high standard of musicianship.

There is a whole range of dramatic productions each year, performing in either the May Hall Stage or the Melton Studio Theatre, so that as many as possible are given the chance of developing their dramatic talent. For the past six years the students have performed at the Edinburgh Festival.

Societies. Tutors encourage their tutees to make good use of the many and varied societies and activities which are on offer either at lunchtime, late afternoon or early evening. This area of the school is flourishing and helps pupils develop broad interests.

Service Activities. On one afternoon each week, every pupil in Year 10 and above must opt for one 'Service' activity. These choices include: CCF (Army or RAF section), Community Service, Duke of Edinburgh's Award, Adventure Training and Life Saving. Many of the Service Activities, particularly CCF, Duke of Edinburgh's Award and Scouts, organise exciting holiday activities.

Expeditions. Trent over the last few years has established an impressive record of organising overseas mountaineering/trekking expeditions: Iceland (1998, 1991, 1994 and 2001), Siberia (1990), Pyrenees (1991), Belize (1992), Canadian Rockies (1992 and 1995), Canoeing in Canada (1994), Greenland (1997 and 1999), Norway (1998), Alaska (2002), Peru (2003) and India (2005).

Art, Design, Technology and Computing. Art, Design, Technology and Computing flourish at Trent, both as academic subjects and interests. Out-of-class involvement is strongly encouraged and, in recent years, Trent has established a most successful record in regional, national and international competitions.

Fees per term (2008-2009). Junior School: £2,080 (Foundation Stage), £2,167 (KS1), £2,253 (KS2). Lower School (Years 7 and 8): £3,395 (day). Main School: Year 9: £3,772 (day), £4,795 (boarding); Years 10–Sixth Form: £4,159 (day), £5,194 (boarding).

As far as possible we aim to make fees all-inclusive and only charge for genuine extras.

Admission. Entry to the Junior School is either at Nursery, Reception or Year 3. All pupils are assessed, and entry can be assured at any time during the year. Most pupils enter the Senior School in September, although it is possible for entry to take place at other times in the year.

Lower School (11+ entry): c 110 day places are available each year. Entry is decided as a result of a competitive examination held in late January.

Main School (13+ entry): 14 places, predominantly boarding entry. Entry is decided as a result of a competitive examination held in late January.

Sixth Form Entry (16+): there are approximately 20 places (split equally between boarding and day) available each year for girls and boys. Places are awarded following an interview and the receipt of a confidential report from the applicant's present school, but are ultimately conditional on a satisfactory performance at GCSE.

Scholarships. (*see Scholarship Entries section*). A large range of Scholarships is available.

Awards are made for excellence in Music, Drama, Art, Sport and Academic ability at 11+, 13+ and 16+.

Bursaries are also available to those in need of extra financial support.

The value of an Award depends on the age of the child, their ability and whether they are a day pupil or a boarder.

Full details on all scholarships, examinations and entrance procedures are available from the Registrar: Tel 0115 849 4950.

School Prospectus. A prospectus and registration details may be obtained from the Registrar, Mrs Christie (Tel: 0115 849 4950). Parents are encouraged to visit the School and appointments may be made by contacting Mrs Christie.

Old Tridents' Society. Most pupils who leave the School join this active Society. The Society's Administrator may be contacted at the School's address.

Charitable status. Trent College Limited is a Registered Charity, number 527180. Its aims are to provide education for boys and girls between the ages of 3 and 18.

Trinity School
Croydon

Shirley Park Croydon CR9 7AT
Tel: 020 8656 9541
Fax: 020 8655 0522
e-mail: admissions@trinity.croydon.sch.uk
website: www.trinity-school.org

The School was founded by Archbishop John Whitgift in 1596. The full title of the school is Trinity School of John Whitgift.

Motto: '*Vincit qui Patitur*'

Visitor: His Grace The Archbishop of Canterbury

Governing Body:

Chairman: I Harley, MA, FCA, FCIB

The Right Revd Nicholas Baines, The Bishop of Croydon
His Honour Judge William Barnett, QC, MA Oxon
The Revd Canon C J L Boswell, The Vicar of Croydon
Dr B Cross, BSc, PhD
C J Houlding
Mrs R A Jones, MA
D W North, BSc Eng, ACGI, MICE
Clr T Letts, OBE
P Squire, MA
G H Wright, TD, DL, FCIOB
Cllr G Barwell, BA
Cllr D Mead, FCCA, FCMA, FCIS
Ms N Clarke, MA
D C Hudson, MA

Clerk to the Governors: R J Smith

***Headmaster*: M J Bishop**, MA Oxford, MBA

Deputy Headmaster: J P McKee, BA Cambridge
Second Deputy and Tutor for Admissions: J G Timm, BA Cambridge
Director of Studies: N H Denman, MA Oxford
Head of Sixth Form: M J Case, BA Oxford
Head of Middle School and Senior Mistress: Mrs K A Goldsmith, BEd Warwick
Head of Junior School: R Brookman, BSc London

Assistant Staff:
* *Head of Department*
§ *part-time*

Miss A M Abad, BA Murcia, MA London (*Spanish**)
P G Abbott, BSc Cardiff (*Economics & Business Studies*)
M I Aldridge, BEd Lon (*Design Technology, Deputy Head of Sixth Form*)
E M Alexander, BEd St Luke's, Exeter (*Geography, General Studies**)
M Asbury, BSc Bath (*Mathematics, Internal Exams**)
M S Asquith, BA, MA, PhD London (*English*)
Mrs J L Barton, BSc Kent (*Biology, Deputy Head of Middle School*)
Ms N M Beaumont, BSc Oxford (*Mathematics*)
Mrs M Beard, BA London (*Artist in Residence*)
Miss H A Benzinski, BSc London (*Mathematics*)
J Bird, BSc Kent (*Biology*)
Mrs N Blamire-Marin, BA Granada (*Lektora*)
C R Burke Port Elizabeth (*Physical Education, English*)
J P Carter, BA Liverpool (*History, English*)
T W Chesters, BSc Strathclyde (*Design Technology*)
S W Christian, BA Liverpool (*French, Spanish, Language Awareness*)
R G Clarke, BSc Loughborough (*Physical Education*)
A J Codling, BA Portsmouth (*Director of Sport**)
A Cornick, BA Southampton Institute (*Physical Education*)
§Miss E Couling, BMus RAM, LRAM (*Music*)
G A Crouch, CertEd St Paul's (*Physical Education, Academic PE**)
D J de Warrenne, ARCM, LGSM (*Music*)
S J Dickens, BA Oxford (*English*)
Miss K A Dierckx, BA London (*Religious Studies*)
A B Doyle, MA, MA Glasgow, Open (*English**)
G du Toit, BA, BEd Pretoria (*Religious Studies*)
R G Evans, BSc Aston (*Electronics, Design Technology*)
§Mrs J E Farnfield, BA Swansea (*Economics and Business Studies, Marketing Manager*)
L M Flanagan, BSc Cambridge (*Physics*)
Mrs M Fletcher-Hale, BA Wales, DipLib, ALA (*Librarian*)
Mrs S L Flynn, BSc London (*ICT*)
Mrs A A Fulker, BA Oxford Brookes (*Art, French, Deputy Head of Junior School*)
T D Garrard, MA, BA Cambridge (*Assistant Director of Music, Academic Music**)
M P Geoghegan, CertEd St Mary's (*Design Technology**)
T M Glynn, BA West Surrey College (*Art**)
§Mrs D M Harbour, BA Southampton (*French*)
C Hoffmann, MA, PhD Göttingen, Berlin (*German*, Latin*)
J Janda, BA, ATC London (*Art, Photography**)
§Mrs C S Jennings, BSc London (*Biology, ICT*)
M V Johnson, BSc London (*Biology, Careers*)
Ms R Kanji, BSc, MEd Auckland (*Chemistry*)
D G Klempner, MA Cambridge (*Physics*)
Miss A M Larman, BA Cambridge (*Classics*)
D A Lawson, BEd Exeter (*Geography, Physical Education*)
Mrs J M Layden, MA Edinburgh (*English*)
R E Lee, MA Oxford (*Religious Studies*, CCF**)
J V Lucas, LLB Manchester (*Mathematics*)
P March, BA Oxford (*French*, Latin*)
Mrs D R M March, L-ès-L Strasbourg (*Lectrice, Language Awareness*)
M Mariani, BSc Kent, PhD UCL (*Physics*)
Miss A Marshall, BA Hull (*History, French*)
§Mrs A E Martin, BA Leeds (*Chinese*)
C Marvin, BSc London (*Electronics*, Director of ICT**)
P Mazur, BA Wales, MA London (*Classroom Drama*, English, PSE Coordinator*)
Mrs S J McDonald, MA St Andrews (*English*)
§Mrs R E McKee, BA Oxford (*French*)
Mrs S Million, MIL, CertEd, DipRSA (*German, Latin*)
R H Moralee, BSc Johannesburg (*Biology*)
D Moran, BSc, MA Dublin (*Chemistry, Biology*)
Mrs C Morgan, BA Exeter (*Economics and Business Studies*)
Miss N C Nightingale, BA Nottingham (*English*)
R J Paler, BA Kent (*History*)
C P Persinaru, DipRAM, LRAM London (*Music*)
N H Peters, BA Brunel, MA London (*Spanish, French*)
Mrs R J Petty, MA Oxford (*English*)
D K Price, 3D Design Wimbledon College of Art (*Design Technology*)
§Mrs B Quinn, DipSpLD, AMBDA (*English Assistant*)
P J Radford, BSc Manchester (*Mathematics, ICT*)
N W Rivers, BSc Leicester (*Science*, Chemistry**)

K R Rogers, BSc Cardiff, PhD London (*Chemistry*)
P H Rule, BSc Leicester CBiol, MIBiol (*Biology**)
Mrs M Sanders, BEd London (*Drama, English*)
G Sarwar, BSc Birmingham (*Mathematics*)
C T Shanks, BSc, PhD Heriot-Watt (*Chemistry, Careers**)
J A Short, BA UCL (*History*)
A E Smith, BA York, MA London (*Religious Studies*)
J J Snelling, BSc Swansea (*Geography**)
G Spreng, MA Glasgow (*History*)
J E Stone, BA Cambridge (*Classics**)
Ms T Stevens-Lewis, BA Goldsmiths (*Art*)
D J Swinson, MA, FRCO, ARCM, LRAM Cambridge (*Music**)
W S Tucker, BSc Exeter (*Physics**)
D G Urmston, BA Wales, MSc Surrey (*Economics and Business Studies**)
J K Waller, BA Sheffield, BA, MSc Open (*Mathematics*)
Mrs J J Walsh, BA Durham (*French*)
I M Wallwork, MA, PhD Birmingham (*Mathematics*)
R J Wickes, BSc Warwick (*Mathematics**)
S H Wilberforce, MA Oxford (*Physics*)
Ms J C Wiskow, MA Berlin (*German*)
Miss J K Woolley, BSc Cambridge (*Geography*)

The School, one of the three governed by the Whitgift Foundation, is an Independent Day School with 890 boys, of whom 220 are in the Sixth Form. The School aims to give a wide education to boys of academic promise, irrespective of their parents' income.

Buildings and Grounds. Trinity School has been in its present position since 1965, when it moved out from the middle of Croydon (its old site is now the Whitgift Centre) to a completely new complex of buildings and playing fields on the site of the Shirley Park Hotel. The grounds are some 27 acres in extent, and a feeling of openness is increased by the surrounding Shirley Park Golf Club and the extensive views to the south up to the Addington Hills. There are additional playing fields in Sandilands, ten minutes' walk from the school.

The resources of the Whitgift Foundation enable the School to provide outstanding facilities. All departments have excellent and fully equipped teaching areas.

Admission. The main ages of admission are at 10, 11 and 13. Entry is by competitive examination and interview. A reference from the feeder school will also be required. The School attracts applications from over 150 schools, with approximately 60% entering from state primaries. Entries into the Sixth Form are also welcomed.

Fees per term (2008-2009). £3,758 covering tuition, books, stationery and games.

Bursaries. From September 2008 the revised Bursary Scheme will substantially increase the level of support to families on low incomes, and a raised income threshold will benefit a wider range of middle income families.

Scholarships. (*see Scholarship Entries section*). Academic, music (instrumental), sports, art and technology scholarships are awarded to boys who show outstanding promise. They are awarded without regard to parental income, and are worth a percentage (maximum one-half) of the school fee throughout a boy's career.

Organisation and Counselling. The school is divided into the Junior School (National Curriculum years 6 to 9), the Middle School (10 to 11), and the Sixth Form. The Pastoral Leader in charge of each section works with the team of Form Tutors to encourage the academic and personal development of each boy. There is frequent formal and informal contact with parents.

There is a structured and thorough Careers service, which advises boys at all levels of the school and arranges work experience and work shadowing.

While the academic curriculum is taught from Monday to Friday, there is a very active programme of sports fixtures and other activities at the weekend, and all boys are expected to put their commitment to the school before other activities.

Curriculum and Staffing. The school is generously staffed with well qualified specialists. The organisation of the teaching programme is traditionally departmental based. The syllabus is designed to reflect the general spirit of the National Curriculum while allowing a suitable degree of specialisation in the Middle School.

The normal pattern is for boys to take 9 or 10 GCSE subjects, and to proceed to the Sixth Form to study an appropriate mixture of AS and A2 level subjects, complemented by a wide-ranging General Studies programme, before proceeding to university.

Games and Activities. Rugby, Football, Hockey, Cricket and Athletics are the main school games. Many other sports become options as a boy progresses up the school. Games are timetabled, each boy having one games afternoon a week.

At the appropriate stage, most boys take part in one or more of the following activities: Community Service, CCF, Duke of Edinburgh's Award Scheme, Outdoor Activities. There are many organised expeditions during the holidays.

Music. Music at Trinity has an international reputation, and every year Trinity Boys' Choir is involved in a varied programme of demanding professional work. The Choir has performed at the BBC Proms for the past five years and sings at the Royal Opera House 3–4 times each year. Recently the choristers have travelled to Vienna, Brussels, Venice and Hiroshima where they were invited to sing at the anniversary commemoration of the bombing. They also appear regularly on radio and television. Trinity Choristers, who specialise in religious music, hold an annual residential Easter Course at a British cathedral. Choral Scholarships are awarded annually and enable boys to receive additional professional voice training without charge.

Many boys learn at least one musical instrument, and a large visiting music staff teach all orchestral instruments, piano, organ and classical guitar. There are several orchestras, bands and other instrumental groups for which boys are selected according to their ability. There are currently fourteen pupils who are members of National orchestras and choirs.

Drama. There are two excellently equipped stages in the school and a lively and developing programme of formal and informal productions directed by boys, staff and members of the Old Boys Theatre Company. Drama forms part of the formal curriculum in Years 6 to 9.

Art and Design Technology. As well as the formal curriculum, which has led to 70% of the School taking a GCSE in art or design technology, boys are encouraged to make use of the excellent facilities to develop their own interests.

Charitable status. The Whitgift Foundation is a Registered Charity, number 312612. The Foundation now comprises the Whitgift Almshouse Charity for the care of the elderly and the Education Charity which administers three schools.

Truro School

Trennick Lane Truro Cornwall TR1 1TH
Tel: 01872 272763
Fax: 01872 223431
e-mail: enquiries@truroschool.com
website: www.truroschool.com

Truro School was founded in 1880 by Cornish Methodists. In 1904 it came under the control of the Board of Management for Methodist Residential Schools and is now administered by a Board of Governors appointed by the Methodist Conference. Although pupils come from all parts of the country and abroad, the roots of the school are firmly in Cornwall and it is the only HMC school in the county.

The religious instruction and worship are undenominational though the school is conscious of its Methodist origins.

There are over 820 pupils in the senior school (11+ and above), of whom 50 are boarders. There are another 220 pupils in the Preparatory School, where boys and girls may start in the pre-prep section at the age of 3.

The school is fully co-educational throughout and there is a strong Sixth Form of some 250 pupils.

Motto: '*Esse quam videri*'

Visitor: The President of the Methodist Conference

Administrative Governors:
Chairman: Revd F R Crewes, JP, MA, BD
Vice-Chairman: G Rumbles

R R Cowie, FCA
Revd M Dunn-Wilson
R S Funnell, MA
C N Harding, BSc
J Hay
Mrs C Hogg, BSc, MBA
P Kerkin, BSc, FCIB
Mrs I Livingstone, BA, MA
R Oliver, FCIB
M Pearse, BA, LLM
G Russell, MA
C S F Smith, DipArch, RIBA, FFB
Mrs S Stokes

***Headmaster*: P K Smith**, MA, MEd

Deputy Heads:
S Price, MA
Mrs A LFirth, BA

Director of Studies: N J Baker, BSc Econ

Chaplain: A de Gruchy, MTheol

Boarding House Staff:
Mrs R A Collenette, BA (*Pentreve/Malvern*)
J K Austin, BA (*Trennick*)

Heads of Year:
Dr C J Blake, BSc, PhD (*Sixth Form*)
J L Worthington, BA (*Assistant, Upper Sixth*)
J C Cornish (*Assistant, Lower Sixth*)
P H J Collenette, MSc (*Fifth Form*)
A N Sampson (*Fourth Form*)
Miss C A Gillam, MA(*Third Form*)
D J Hunt (*Second Form*)
S A Collinge, BSc (*First Form*)

Heads of Department:
D Meads, BA (*Art*)
G Baines, BA (*Biology*)
C Shaw (*Chemistry*)
I C MacDonald, MA, DipEd (*Drama*)
T R Tall, BEd (*Design and Technology*)
J C Cornish, BA (*Economics, Business Studies and Politics*)
Mrs S Spence, MA (*English*)
P H J Collenette, MSc (*Geography and Geology*)
Dr P J Flood, BA, PhD (*History*)
S J McCabe, MA (*Mathematics*)
M Homer, BA (*Modern Languages*)
M D Palmer, BMus, FRCO, LRAM (*Music*)
G C Whitmore, BEd (*PE and Games*)
M Huckle, BA, MA, CertRE (*Religious Education*)
Dr P D Allen, BSc, MSc, PhD (*Science and Physics*)

Truro School Preparatory School
(*see entry in IAPS section*)

Headmaster: M Lovett, BA Ed
Deputy Headmistress: Mrs J P Grassby, MEd, CertEd, CAP
Senior Master: R Lear, BPhil Ed, CertEd, DipMathsEd
Head of Pre-Prep Unit: Mrs A Allen, CertEd

Bursar and Clerk to the Governors: R G Burdell

Number in School. Main School: 837 pupils (532 boys, 305 girls; 787 day, 50 boarders). Preparatory School: 151 pupils (86 boys, 66 girls). Pre-Prep: 76 pupils (45 boys, 34 girls).

Boarding. At the Main School girl boarders live in Pentreve/Malvern supervised by married couples. Boy boarders live in the Main School (Trennick House), again supervised by resident married couples. Pupils eat in the central dining room with a cafeteria system. There is a School Medical Centre on site. Junior Boarding (Years 1–5) is currently being phased out.

Campus and Buildings. The Prep School's campus is built around a country house acquired by the school in the 30s. It has an indoor heated swimming pool, a large assembly hall and extensive areas for science, modern languages, computing, art and crafts, as well as a modern sports hall. The purpose-built Pre-Prep unit opened in September 1991.

The Main School occupies an outstanding site overlooking the Cathedral city and the Fal Estuary; it is only five minutes from the centre of the city but the playing fields reach into the open countryside. The school is excellently equipped. There is a first class Library, extensive science laboratories, excellent Technology and Art facilities, a computer centre, music school, upper and lower Sixth Form centres, a Sixth Form cafeteria and a range of classroom blocks. Sports are well served by a covered swimming pool, two large sports halls, a new astroturf, squash and tennis courts and 30 acres of playing fields. September 2001 saw the opening of a fine new block, containing six classrooms, a drama centre and the Burrell theatre, which has been extended to provide a Modern Languages Centre in The Wilkes Building (opened September 2004). An attractive and newly refurbished chapel provides a focus for the life of the school.

Organisation and Curriculum. Pupils are unstreamed in the first three years except for Mathematics (from Year 1) and French and German (from Form 2). The academic programme is conventional and the school follows the National Curriculum. All pupils take the basic subjects including the three sciences, design and technology and two foreign languages until the end of the third year when the students adopt their own balanced GCSE programme. All pupils take IT GCSE at the end of the 3rd year and a half GCSE in RE at the end of the 4th year. GCSE subjects taken include English Language, English Literature, French, German, Spanish, Geography, Drama, Geology, History, Religious Education, Music, Art, Design and Technology, PE, Physics, Chemistry, Biology and Mathematics. All pupils take Music, Religious Education and Physical Education at most stages and games appear in the timetable for the first five years.

Sixth Formers are encouraged to use their study periods to participate in Physical Recreation. They are usually studying for four AS levels in the Lower Sixth and these include English, History, Geography, Geology, Mathematics, Further Mathematics, Design and Technology, Art, Music, Religious Education, Physics, Chemistry, Biology, Economics, French, German, Spanish, Business Studies, PE and Theatre Studies. General Studies include modules on Careers, Religious Education, ECDL (European Community Driving Licence), Critical Thinking and Creative Studies. It is likely three subjects will be most commonly continued into the Upper Sixth at A2 level. The vast majority of Sixth Formers go on to further education when they leave.

Out-of-School Activities. Extra-curricular life is rich and varied. There is a choir, school orchestra, a jazz group, a brass band and many other ensembles. Facilities such as the ceramics room, the art room and the technical block are available to pupils in their spare time. A huge variety of activities includes fencing, climbing (2 indoor walls), squash, sailing, golf, basketball, debating, surfing, photography and many others. Many boys and girls take part in the Ten Tors Expedition, an exceptional number are engaged in the Duke of Edinburgh's Award Scheme, as well as local Community Service, and the Young Enterprise Scheme. Computing and electronics are very well catered for. Chess has traditionally been strong and the School has recently been very successful in national competitions. The School has an outdoor activities centre on Bodmin Moor and pupils have a chance to spend time there during the course of their education at the school.

Games. All the major team games are played. Badminton, cross-country, hockey, netball, squash and tennis are available throughout most of the year. Rugby and Girls Hockey are played in the Winter Term and Soccer and Netball in the Spring Term. In the summer, cricket, athletics and swimming are the major sports. The covered pool is heated. An astroturf opened in September 2004.

Scholarships. Truro School was once a Direct Grant Grammar School and most pupils join at the age of 11. There are vacancies for entry at other ages, particularly at 13 and 16. Scholarships are available and also a limited number of places under the School's own successor scheme to Government Assisted Places.

Fees per term (2008-2009). Main School: Boarders £6,460, Day Pupils £3,360. Prep: Day Pupils £3,045. Pre-Prep: £2,150.

Academic results. A number of pupils proceed to Oxbridge every year – 5 received offers for September 2008 – and well over 100 to other degree courses. The 2007 A level pass rate was 99.6%, with 74% at A or B grades. At GCSE the 2007 pass rate was 98% with over 57% at grades A* and A.

Former Pupils' Association. There is a strong Former Pupils' Association with centres locally and in London and it has its own webalumnus. The Truro Schools Society involves parents, staff, old pupils and friends of the school in social events and fund-raising.

Charitable status. Truro School is a Registered Charity, number 306576. It is a charitable foundation established for the purpose of education.

University College School

Frognal, Hampstead, London NW3 6XH
Tel: 020 7435 2215
Fax: 020 7433 2110
e-mail: seniorschool@ucs.org.uk
website: www.ucs.org.uk

University College School is a day school providing places for 500 boys aged 11–16, with a co-educational Sixth Form of 300 places. UCS admitted its first cohort of girls into the Sixth Form in September 2008.

Established in 1830 as part of University College, London, the School moved to its present site in Hampstead in 1907. Though now independently governed, UCS has sustained by continuous reinterpretation many of the ideals of its founders. Its basis remains the provision of the widest opportunities for learning and development without the imposition of tests of doctrinal conformity but within a balanced and coherent view of educational needs and obligations. This in turn rests on the recognition that care for a pupil's social, moral and spiritual upbringing is a shared responsibility between home and school, an understanding fostered by mutual trust and regular communication. Thirdly, the distinctive ethos of the School stems from the conviction that a positive, lively and humane community, both within and beyond the School, can only be created by the liberal encouragement and disciplined fulfilment of the diversity of gifts among its individual members.

It is in this spirit that the School day begins with a short Assembly.

Council:

Chairman: Sir Victor Blank, MA, FRCOG

Honorary Treasurer: L D Bard, MA, FCA, CTA

Professor P Bayvel, PhD, FREng, FIEE, FInstP, SMIEE
C W Eccleshare, MA, FIPA
E Fordham, BA
W H Frankel, Esq, OBE, BA
Sir Alan Greengross, MA
A Halls, MA
R I Harrington, MA
A G Hillier, Esq, BA, MBA
C Holloway, Esq, MA, FRSA
A S Jacobs, MA
Sir Brian Leveson, MA
S D Lewis, MA
D Maclean-Watt, MA, FRICS, FNAEA
Professor P Sands, QC

***Headmaster*: K J Durham**, MA, Brasenose College, Oxford

Vice-Master: C M Reynolds, BSc, MSc, FSS

Deputy Head (*Curriculum*): S R J Marshall, MA, MA, MPhil
Deputy Head (*Pastoral*): D J Colwell, BA, PhD

T J Allen, BA
Mrs K J Anthony, BA
E A Barnish, MA
I A Barr, MA
B J Bateman, BEd
O Bienias, BA
S M Bloomfield, BA
C Bowes-Jones, BEd
J M Bradbury, MA, GBSM, ABSM, FRSA
Miss P J Bradford, BA
S J Button, BA
R H Chapman, BSc
Miss L R Cheng, BA
P J Clarke, BA, MSc
J A Clifford, BSc
M P Collins, BA
J Cooke, BA
A Davis, BSc
P Dawson, PhD
Miss L A Dolata, BSc, MSc
P R Eggleton, BEd
P Ellis, BA, MA, PhD
J O Enemuwe, BSc
R J Finch, BA
[2]S A P FitzGerald, BA
I C Gibson, MA
A J Gowlett, BSc
A H Gray, BA
D Hall, BA
S J Hann, HND
R A K Hawkins, BTech
[2]S Hawley, BSc
Ms J L Heaton, MA
Miss R Hemming, BA, BMus, MSc
M J Hind, BA
M J Hitchcock, BA
A Hon, MA
Miss M Hudson, BSc
R Hyde, MA, MA
Mrs A H Isaac, BA, MA
[2]Mrs L M Jenkins, MA
T Jenkin, BA
[2]Ms J Kung, BA, BA
T Kyan, BA, PGCE
M J Matuszak, BSc
A McAra, MA
Mrs R McCann, BA
C C McCormack, BA
M A McElroy, BSc, MA, ARCS
N W McNaughton, BA, MSc
M McSherry, MSc, PhD
A M Mee, MA
P S Miller, BSc
M B Murphy, BA
Miss K E Murray, BA
D S Nelder, BA
J R L Orchard, BA
G Parker-Jones, BA
N R Peace, BSc, MA
T D Peck, BA
[2]G A Plow, MA, MA, PhD
Miss T B Postalian, MA, BA
D P Rance, CertEd
Ms S Reddy, BSc
D A Robb, BSc, PhD
E Roberts, MSci
S Rynkowski, CertEd
Miss A Sánchez-Blanco
E P Sawtell, BA
Mrs S L Slater, BA
M V Smith, DipAD, ATC
Mrs P R Spencer, BA
P S J Stancliffe, BA
A J Steven, BA
R F J Tear, BSc
Miss E M Thompson, MA
J Thomson, MA, DipLaw
[2]T P Underwood, BA
A G Vaughan, BA
S C Walton, MusB
A R Welch, BEd, MSc, PhD
S T Wells, BSc, ARCS
[2]A R Wilkes, BA
D J Woodhead, BA
Mrs G J Woodhead, L-ès-L
T F Youlden, BA, MSc

[2] *Deme Warden*

Bursar: J Witts, DSO, FRAeS
Headmaster's Secretary: Mrs J A Scott
Consulting Physician: Dr A Stuart

Junior Branch
11 Holly Hill, NW3 6QN. Tel: 020 7435 3068;

Fax: 020 7435 7332; E-mail: juniorbranch@ucs.org.uk

Headmaster: K J Douglas, BA

Deputy Head (*Pastoral*): Mrs S E Martin, BSc
Deputy Head (*Curriculum*): M A Albini, BSc, MA

A Arnold, BA
Miss N Banihashem
Mrs M Carnegie, BEd
Miss E Couture, BA, MA
M Cassell, BSc
D Edwards, BA
Mrs J M Eggleton-Rance, BEd
Mrs Y P Gregory, BEd
A P Haggar, BEng
S D B Hall, BA
W G Jones
M Lall-Chopra, BA
S Lanigan-O'Keefe, BMus, DipEd
Mrs S Miller, BEd, RSA Cert
Mrs P R Spencer, MA
Miss K Stanclova, BA
Mrs T Thomas, BA
Miss L Trinnaman, BSc
A G Walliker, BHum, BA
Mrs E Waterhouse, BA

Headmaster's Secretary: Miss D Campbell
Consulting Physician: Dr M McCollum

Entry. Entry is in September only.

Admission. Boys are normally admitted to the Senior School at either 11+ or 13+. Admission at 11+ is either by promotion from the Junior Branch or by examination held in January of the year of entry. Admission at 13+ is by the Common Entrance following the UCS Preliminary Assessment, and interviews. These are held two years prior to entry. A substantial deposit is required when a place is accepted which will be credited against the first term's account. Bursaries and Grants are available where financial need can be shown. Applicants of sufficient academic standing who lack financial resources are encouraged to apply to the Foundation's generous bursary programme.

Applications for entry should be made to the School Admissions Secretary at any time up to mid-September two years prior to admission (13+), or by the end of November preceding the proposed year of entry (11+). There is a registration fee of £50. Applications for 16+ entry should be made to the School Administrator by October one year prior to admission.

The Lower and Middle Schools. The Curriculum is designed to provide a broad range of knowledge and experience for all boys over the 5 years from 11 to 16. In the first 2 years boys take English, French, Geography, History, Mathematics, Biology, Physics, Chemistry, Latin, Art, Design Technology, Drama, Music, Information Technology and Personal and Social Education. At 13+ they add a further subject choosing two from Latin, Greek, German and Spanish. Some modifications are made one year later according to aptitude and ability and most boys offer 10 subjects at GCSE.

The Sixth Form. All boys and girls take 4 subjects to AS Level in the Lower Sixth, with the option of narrowing to 3 in the following year. In 2008 girls will be able to join UCS to study for their A Levels; 30 girls will join UCS each year.

AS Level subjects may be chosen from: Art, Biology, Chemistry, Design & Technology, Economics, English, French, Further Mathematics, Geography, German, Greek History (Early Modern or Late Modern), Information Technology, Latin, Mathematics, Music, Philosophy, Physics, Politics, Spanish, Theatre Arts, and History of Art.

Boys and Girls in the Sixth Form have their own spacious study and social areas in the Sixth Form Centre, opened in 1974, and have the major responsibility for its use and upkeep. Senior Tutors, in collaboration with the Careers Master, provide detailed advice for each pupil about the selection of courses at Universities and other further education opportunities as well as ensuring that a student's course in the Sixth Form meets the entrance requirements of his intended future course and professional career. The enormous majority of leavers go on to degree courses.

Students are prepared for entrance to Oxford and Cambridge. Tuition is on a seminar basis.

Pastoral Care. In the Lower School (11+–12) boys are cared for by form teachers, Heads of Year and the Warden of the Lower School. The Middle and Senior Schools are divided into 6 Demes, each under the supervision of a Deme Warden. Many activities outside the classroom are organised by Demes, but the primary responsibility of the Deme Warden is to maintain a personal relationship with each member of his Deme, constant throughout a student's school career. Consequently, in all important pastoral and disciplinary matters he/she deals directly with the student in consultation with parents and other teachers and is answerable to the Headmaster for the general welfare of his/her Deme.

In addition to parents' evenings, parents are encouraged to consult informally with teachers about any issues that arise with their child. A Parents' Guild exists to promote the general welfare of the School.

Careers. Boys and Girls are guided by means of interviews and tests towards careers appropriate to their gifts and personalities. Pupils are given opportunities to attend holiday courses directed towards specific careers. To this end also, visiting speakers are invited to the School and there are frequent Careers Conventions. There is a full Careers Library and a comprehensive programme of Work Experience. The Parents' Guild and Old Gower's also provide advice and support.

Physical Education and Games. The State-of-the-Art Sir Roger Bannister sports complex opened in December 2006. The boys have periods of Physical Education within their normal timetable in the sports complex.

The School playing fields cover 27 acres and are situated a mile away in West Hampstead. In addition to grass surfaces, there is a large all-weather pitch and two fully refurbished pavilions. The major sports are Rugby Football in the Autumn Term and Cricket and Tennis in the Summer. In the Spring there is an open choice between Soccer, Hockey and Cross-Country Running. The School has its own Tennis and Fives courts at Frognal, together with an indoor heated Swimming Pool. Other sports include Fencing, Athletics, Squash, Badminton, Basketball, Fives and outdoor pursuits.

Music and Drama. There is a strong musical tradition at UCS and many boys play in the Orchestras, Wind Band and a great variety of groups and ensembles. Choral music is equally strong and Jazz is a particular feature. Instrumental tuition is given in the Music School, opened in 1995, and this and Ensemble Groups are arranged by the Director of Music.

The School Lund Theatre, opened in 1974, is the venue for a range of Drama from major productions to experimental plays, mime and revue. An open-air theatre was completed in 1994. A regular programme of evening events is arranged for the Autumn and Spring terms.

In both Music and Drama, there are many opportunities for collaboration with South Hampstead High School.

Other School Societies. These cover a wide range of academic interests and leisure pursuits, including the Duke of Edinburgh's Award Scheme. There is a very active Community Action Programme, which works in the local community and there are regular fund-raising initiatives for both local and national charities.

Development Programme. The Foundation is now well-advanced upon an ambitious programme of redevelopment. A State-of-the-Art Indoor Sports Centre opened in late 2006, comprising Sports Hall, Swmming Pool, Fitness Centre and Health Club. The new Centres for Modern Languages and for Art & Technology opened in October 2008. A fund-raising Appeal is helping to achieve these improvements, and will enable us to double provision for bursary funding by 2011.

At the same time, three educational initiatives are underway: a learning strategy initiative is focusing on the learning experience of the pupils and the teaching styles that best promote good learning and work habits; an intellectual enrichment programme to complement the academic curriculum; and the development of an extranet site to enable efficient communication and e-learning opportunities.

Fees per term (2008-2009). Senior School: £4,850; Junior Branch: £4,480. Excludes fees payable in respect of music and other private lessons, and books.

Entrance Scholarships. (*see Scholarship Entries section*). A number of Scholarships may be awarded at 11+ to boys whose performance in the UCS Entrance Examination is outstanding. Scholarships and Exhibitions are also awarded for Music.

The Junior Branch. (*See entry in IAPS section.*) The Junior Branch is housed in separate buildings at Holly Hill, a few minutes' walk from Frognal. Like the Senior School, its main purpose is to provide full scope for the steady maturing of a boy's personality and capacity and for the preparation of boys for the Senior School in order to ensure a continuity of care, stimulation and reasoned discipline. It has its own Library, Computer Room and Laboratory and shares with the main School the playing fields and sports complex. A specialist building accommodates Art, Craft and Technology.

Boys are admitted at the ages of 7+ and 8+. Admission is by preliminary examination and interview. Applications should be made to the Headmaster's Secretary, The Junior Branch, 11 Holly Hill, Hampstead, at least a year in advance. There is a registration fee of £50.

History. A new History of the School was published in June 2007.

Old Pupils' Society (Old Gowers). The School maintains an active register of former pupils, accessible to members of the School community.

Charitable status. University College School, Hampstead is a Registered Charity, number 312748. Its aims and objectives are the provision of the widest opportunities for learning and development of students without the imposition of tests and doctrinal conformity but within a balanced and coherent view of educational needs and obligations.

Uppingham School

Uppingham Rutland LE15 9QE
Tel: 01572 822216
Fax: 01572 822332 (Headmaster)
01572 821872 (Bursar)
e-mail: admissions@uppingham.co.uk
website: www.uppingham.co.uk

Uppingham School was founded in 1584 by Robert Johnson who obtained a grant by Letters Patent from Queen Elizabeth I. For 300 years Uppingham remained an unremarkable local Grammar School until the arrival of Edward Thring in 1853, during whose Headmastership it was transformed into one of the foremost public schools of the time. His pioneering beliefs in the values of an all-round education still mark the School strongly today.

The Governing Body:

Chairman: ¶C C Williams
Vice-Chairmen:
¶The Rt Hon Stephen Dorrell, MP
Mrs J Richardson, MA

Chairman: C C Williams, Esq
Vice-Chairmen:
The Rt Hon Stephen Dorrell, MP
Mrs J Richardson, MA

The Rt Revd The Lord Bishop of Peterborough
The Very Revd the Dean of Peterborough
The Lord Lieutenant of Rutland
W F B Johnson, Esq
¶L J Wigglesworth, Esq
Lady Goldring, DL, JP
¶A J Trace, MA ,QC
W J A Timpson, Esq, CBE
Professor J Holloway, OBE
¶M C Allen, Esq
¶M L Glatman, Esq
Group Captain A R Thompson, MBE, MA, MPhil
¶Mrs F Walter
J C Hanson-Smith, Esq
A G Hancock, Esq, MA
Professor J A Pickett, CBE, DSc, FRS
R Peel, Esq

Bursar/Finance Director, Clerk to the Trustees: S C Taylor, MA, ACA

***Headmaster*: Mr Richard Harman**, MA

Deputy Head: Mrs P J Rowell, BA, MSc
Director of Studies: M R J Burton, MA
Senior Mistress: Mrs W F McLachlan, BSc, CBiol
Registrar: J P Rudman, BEd, MA
Chaplain: The Revd R K Harrison, BA, MA

Assistant Staff:

Art, Design & Technology:
*S A Sharp, BA
*A Wilson, BA, FRPS
J A Davison, BA, MEd
Miss L J Drake-Lee, BA
T A Ellis, BA
S T Hudson, BA
Miss O Karamenova, BA
Mrs J D Miller, BA
C Simmons, BSc

Biology:
*N K de Wet, BSc, CBiol
P L Bodily, BSc, MEd, CBiol, MIBiol, AIB
B P Fell, MA
Mrs W F McLachlan, BSc, CBiol
Dr J S Müller, MSc, PhD
Miss A S Roebuck, BSc

Chemistry:
*L G Bartlett, BA
Mrs S J Bialacki, BSc
§Dr S A Cotton, BSc, ARCS, PhD, DIC, CChem, FRSC
C L Howe, HDE
A Kowhan, BSc
Dr C Owens, BSc, PhD

Classics:
*G A Moodie, MA, PhD
P J Canning, BA
W A M Chuter, BA
S G Dewhurst, BA
†Mrs K J Gaine, MA
G S Tetlow, MA

Economics & Business Studies:
*†A C Hunting, DMS
Miss L R Hunter, BA
D Lovering, BSc
T G MacCarthy, BA
§T J Montagnon, BA

Electronics:
Dr M E Sewter, BSc, PhD, MInstP, CPhys

English:
*Mrs C A Miller, BA
D E Billing, BA
Mrs J S Broughton, MA
R S Harman, MA
Mrs M N L Hunting, MA
D A McLachlan, MA
C R O'Hanrahan, BA
Mrs N L Reihill, MA
I M Rolison, BA
Dr J N Waddell, BA, PhD

Geography:
*J Barker, BA
Miss A M Bagshaw, MA
Miss J K Bentley, BEd
T P Davies, BA
†Mrs N L Hunter, BA
†T L Jefferis, BSc
Mrs S J Kowhan, BA
†N S Merrett, BEd, FRGS

History:
*T P Prior, BA, MA
Mrs D Billing, MA
J S Birch, MA
M R J Burton, MA
Miss G A Dore, BA
Miss K A Frederick, BA
Revd R K Harrison, BA, MA
T Makhzangi, BA
J P Murrin, BA
Mrs P J Rowell, BA, MSc

History of Art:
*†D S R Kirk, BA
Miss O Karamenova, BA
†Dr C C Stevens, MA, DPhil

Information Technology:
*Miss S E L Webster, BSc
Mrs L J Allen, BSc, MBCS
W C Avallone, BIT

Learning Support:
*Mrs N C Halliday-Pegg, BEd, NDT
§Mrs J S Broughton, MA, DipRSA SpLD
§Mrs M Cuccio, DipSLD
Mrs L Howe, BA
†Mrs A M Merrett, BA
Mrs K L Tetlow, BA

Library:
H H S Spry-Leverton, BLib

Life Skills:
†Mrs M N L Hunting, MA

Mathematics:
*J Lickess, BTech
Mrs L J Allen, BSc, MBCS
§A R W Dawe, BSc
§Mrs M A Eales, BSc
§R Giles, MEng
†P Gomm, BSc
J C E Lee, MA
P G Logan, BSc
Dr A A Neville, MMath, PhD
Q H Sayed, MPhys

Modern Languages:
*P Stocker, BEd, FIL
*Miss M A Barefoot, BA
M R Broughton, MA
Ms F C Buckley, MA
†Mrs H M Draper, BA
M R Fries, MA (**French*)
†D J Jackson, BA (**Italian*)
Mrs J E A Newcombe, BEd
Mrs E M A Nicholls, BA
Mrs K Padolsky, BA
Miss S A Schneider, BA
†Dr C C Stevens, MA, DPhil
Mrs C L Webster, BA
†R M B Wilkinson, MA
T R Worthington, BA

Music:
*S J Williams, BA
*A Tester, MA
P M Clements, BA, FRCO
S K Drummond, DRSAM, ARCM
A A Ffrench, MA, AGSM, PGDipGSMD
S A Smith, BA, PPRNCM
C A C White, ARCM, DipARCM

Physical Education:
*Mrs S M Singlehurst, BEd, MSc
Miss J K Bentley, BEd
K G Johnstone, BEd

Physics:
*J D Hoult, BSc
†W S Allen, BEd
B J Fell, MA
C L Howe, HDE
G S Wright, BSc

Political Studies:
*T Makhzangi, BA
Miss G A Dore, BA
Mrs P J Rowell, BA, MSc
†K M Seecharan, BSocSci

Religious Studies:
*B Cooper, MA
Miss N H H Bishop, BA
Revd R K Harrison, BA, MA
R C Hegarty, BA
Miss C A Ruane, BA

Theatre Studies:
*A K Chessell, BA
§Ms R Higdon, BA
D A McLachlan, MA

Visiting Music Staff:
Miss I Adams, GRSM (*Viola*)
S Andrews (*Drums*)
Mrs E M Atkins, BA, MPhil (*Double Bass*)
Mrs J Burgess, BMus, LGSM (*Oboe*)
N Burt, BA, MMus, LRAM, ARCO (*Jazz, Piano, Organ & Composition*)
J T Byron, MA, PhD (*Piano*)
Mrs L Clements, BA (*Flute*)
A W Coleman (*Bass Guitar*)
S J Collisson, MusB, MMus, PhD, MIoL (*Cello*)
Miss R A Cullis (*Singing*)
Mrs J A Dawson, GRSM, LRAM (*Piano*)
Ms A Douglas, ARCM (*Harp*)
Miss S C Ellis, BMus, ARCM, LGSM (*Clarinet & Saxophone*)
M Fatichenti, MMus, DipRAM (*Piano*)
Mrs L H Ffrench, GRSM, LRAM (*Piano*)
Miss V F Fielding, LRAM, AGSM (*Clarinet & Saxophone*)
N France, GMus (*Drums*)
Mrs N J Gibbons, MMus, MPhil, LRAM, LRSM (*Piano*)
I Hildreth (*Bagpipes*)
C I'Anson, BMus, LLCM, LTCL (*Percussion*)
T M Kennedy, BMus (*Saxophone*)
K Learmouth, ALCM, FRSA (*Guitar*)
Ms C Li, BMus, LRAM, PGDip (*Flute*)
T Locke, (*French Horn*)
Miss S L Mayo, MMus, BA (*Violin*)
Miss C Millar, BMus (*Violin*)
Miss J A Moffat, DipRCM (*Singing*)
S P Morris (*Clarinet, Saxophone*)
L Novacek, BMus, MMus, PPGSMD, PGDip (*Piano*)
Mrs J Odriozola, FTCL, LRAM (*Cello*)
O N Parker, MMus, FGMS, FASC (*Singing*)
D N Price, LRAM (*Trumpet*)
Ms M Reinhard, ARCT, LPRCM (*Piano*)
Mrs A M Reynolds, MusB, GRNCM (*Piano*)
K E Rubach, ARCM (*Bassoon*)
Mrs Y S Sandison, PPRNCM (*Singing*)
K Slade, BMus (*Clarinet*)
N G Todd, BA (*Singing*)
J Turville, MA, MMus, ALCM, LLCM (*Piano*)
Ms P Waterfield, ARCM, MSTAT (*Alexander Technique*)
T J Williams, MA (*Singing*)
Mrs V D Williamson, GMus, RNCM, PPRNCM, LRAM (*Singing*)

Houses and Housemasters/mistresses:
Brooklands: Chris Stevens
Constables (*Girls*): Nic and Anna Merrett
Fairfield (*Girls*): Nicola Hunter
Farleigh: David Jackson
Fircroft: David Kirk
Highfield: Richard Wilkinson
Johnson's (*Girls*): Meriel Hunting
The Lodge (*Girls*): Katharine Gaine
Lorne House: Kurt Seecharan
Meadhurst: Sam Dewhurst
New House (*Girls*): Fiona Buckley
Samworths' (*Girls*): Helen Draper
School House: Philip Gomm
West Bank: Steve Allen
West Deyne: Tim Jefferis

Situation. Uppingham is a small market town set in beautiful countryside in Rutland. It is about 100 miles north of London and midway between Leicester and Peterborough on the A47 road. It is roughly equidistant from the M1 and A1/M11, and the A14 link road makes connections with the Midlands and East Anglia easier and faster. It is served by Kettering, Oakham, Peterborough and Leicester train stations, and by Stansted, Luton, Birmingham and East Midlands airports.

General Information. Uppingham School is a fully boarding school for boys and girls aged 13–18.

Many of the distinguishing characteristics of Uppingham School today were determined under the Headmastership of the great educationalist Edward Thring: that Houses should be small and family-like; that boys (and now girls) should have privacy; that an all-round education should be offered to a broad range of pupils and that children are happier and learn better in inspiring surroundings.

At the heart of the School is a traditional campus with innovative and award-winning recent additions. The developments of a third music school (state-of-the-art facilities, a 120-seat recital room, recording studios), drama studio and workshops, sports pavilion and two Astro-turf pitches reflect the importance in the all-round education on offer.

The facilities within the central area of the School include the Victorian School Room and Chapel (designed by George Edmund Street, who designed the Law Courts in the Strand), the Memorial Hall, a well-stocked Library (housed in a building dating back to 1592), Music Schools, Language Centre and classrooms. The western campus comprises the Science School, Sports Hall, Leonardo Centre (purpose built for ADT), Theatre, Drama Studios and Workshops, and Maths and IT Centre. Ranged around these facilities, like a university campus, are the fifteen boarding houses each with its own garden, recreational facilities and dining room.

Around 40 clubs and societies flourish within the School with a further 30 areas of activity on offer. After the first year girls and boys choose between CCF and Community Service, and The Duke of Edinburgh's Award Scheme is very popular. There is a dedicated sixth form social centre, which also houses the Higher Education, Careers and Gap Year Departments.

Uppingham is a Christian Foundation. That was the intention of the School's Founder, Archdeacon Robert Johnson in

1584, and it remains the policy of the School today. Some Uppinghamians are members of other faiths and every consideration is given to their needs. The whole School meets in the Chapel four days a week and on a Sunday there is a morning service usually with a visiting speaker.

There are around 770 pupils in the School, of which some 365 are in the Sixth Form. More than 97% of the School's pupils are full boarders. Girls have been accepted into the Sixth Form since 1975 and make up 46% of the Sixth Form numbers. Girls were first admitted at 13+ in September 2001. Around 5% of the School's pupils are foreign nationals, mainly from the European Union, Eastern Europe and South East Asia.

Academic Matters. Whilst the School is noted for its strong commitment to all-round education, its superb pastoral care and magnificent facilities, the pupils' academic studies are the priority. In 2007, 51.7% of all A Levels were A grades; 83.7% A or B. More than a quarter of our A Level candidates achieved straight A grades. At GCSE (A–C) pass rate was 99.4% and 24% of all entries gained A*; 61% A* or A.

The average UCAS score for 2007 was 367.9. With a staff: pupil ratio of almost 1 : 7.2 all subjects enjoy the benefits of small class sizes and a wide range may be taught. 28 different A Level subjects and 22 GCSE subjects are offered.

Until GCSE, specialisation is minimal and pupils normally take a minimum of 9 subjects. Pupils are in sets for most subjects. All members of the Sixth Form study four or five AS Levels in the Lower Sixth and three or four A Levels in the Upper Sixth which are complemented by a lecture programme and a wide variety of extra-curricular activities.

The progress of all pupils is monitored by an assigned Tutor and their Housemaster or Housemistress, as well as by a system of regular reviews and reports from subject teachers. Parents and pupils may also call on the School's Higher Education and Careers advisers. At all stages of a pupil's career, the Housemaster/Housemistress keeps in touch with parents regularly.

Nearly all students go on to further education although a few choose to go directly into careers. The School offers advice on planning GAP years to many leavers each year. A sizeable number of students are prepared for and accepted at Oxbridge.

Pupils have access to a beautiful, well-stocked central Library, as well as extensive, more specialist libraries for most subject departments.

For those with learning difficulties the School has trained staff to help with special education needs and any pupil may use the services of a professional psychologist or the School's trained counsellor.

Boarding. There are fifteen boarding houses, which are dotted around the town and school estate: nine for boys, two for Sixth Form girls and four for 13–18 year old girls. Houses are kept small and are usually home to around 50–60 children, 45 in the case of Sixth Form girls' houses. All students eat their meals in their own house dining room and are joined at lunch by teaching and non-teaching staff.

Almost all boys have their own private study upon arrival and by the time they reach the Sixth Form, they can choose to share or have their own study bedroom. All girls entering at 13 share a room with up to 3 other girls and also have their own study area. This arrangement changes in the Lower Fifth and Upper Fifth when girls have bed-sit rooms, usually shared with one other. The Sixth Form provision varies from sharing to single accommodation.

Much of the non-teaching life of the School is organised around the houses and they engender strong loyalties. In addition to excursions and social events, there exists a long-standing tradition of house drama productions, music concerts, artistic displays, as well as inter-house debating and sports competitions.

The resident Housemasters and Housemistresses are helped by a team of at least five tutors who are assigned to particular pupils. They assist with monitoring academic progress and social development.

Music. Uppingham has always had a very distinguished reputation for music since being the first school to put music on its curriculum for all pupils. In 2006 Uppingham opened its third music school. This inspirational music facility offers a unique environment in which to rehearse, cutting-edge music technology, and a 120-seat recital room. The School has an outstanding Chapel Choir, numerous orchestras and chamber groups, wind bands, a professional concert series as well as many thriving musical societies and rock groups. A busy programme of weekly recitals, house and year-group concerts, and larger public performances in the UK and abroad offer pupils of all abilities regular chances to perform. Around two-thirds of pupils learn an instrument. 43 visiting staff and 10 full-time staff enable pupils to receive conservatoire-style tuition at the school.

The School has recently been very successful at Oxbridge Organ and Choral trials and has produced several organ scholars and numerous choral scholars in recent years. Our distinguished results also extend to Conservatoires.

Further enquiries may be made directly to the Director of Music (01572 820696).

Sports and Games. Uppingham has a strong tradition of sporting excellence and often has pupils gaining international honours in a variety of sports. All students participate in sports or games three times a week. The major sports are Rugby, Hockey, Cricket, Tennis and Athletics for boys, and Hockey, Netball, Tennis and Athletics for girls. Many other sports are available from Cross-Country through to Sailing, Aerobics and Squash.

There is a full programme of formal House matches across all sports, providing an opportunity for all pupils to contribute within a team environment. The able are stretched and the very able are offered a high level of coaching from experienced coaches/professionals in all major sports, often going on to represent club, academy, county, regional or national teams. Success at first team level against rival schools is an expectation.

There are over 60 acres of playing fields including the Upper, dedicated to First XI Cricket. There are also 3 Astroturf surfaces (one is floodlit), Tennis, Netball, Squash and Fives Courts, and a Shooting Range. In addition to the Sports Hall and Gymnasium, there are indoor swimming pools and a well-equipped fitness and weights room.

All these facilities are open 7 days a week under the guidance of the Sports Centre manager and his appointed staff.

Further enquiries may be made directly to the Director of Sport on 01572 820835.

The Leonardo Centre. This award-winning Art, Design and Technology Centre was designed by Old Uppinghamian, Piers Gough, CBE. The glass-fronted structure allows a broad range of creative activities to take place in a single uncompartmentalised space and thereby stimulate each other. The Leonardo Centre houses a Fine Art and Printing space, studios for Design, Electronics, Ceramics, Sculpture, Photography, Sound Engineering, workshops primarily for wood, metal and plastic, and teaching rooms dedicated to History of Art. The Sunley Gallery is used to display the work of pupils, staff and other artists. The Centre is manned and open seven days a week, and is open to all pupils, whatever their public examination options.

Technological Environment. Uppingham is proud of the breadth and depth of its ICT provision. Over 1800 outlets exist around the school through which pupils can access an enormous variety of networked educational resources. Every single pupil is provided with a computer in his or her study or bedsit, and is also provided with an individual email account.

There is a School-wide intranet that assists in the delivery of the teaching and learning process, and there is a 10Mb high-speed broadband connection to the internet, suitably filtered by the School's IT Department. Dedicated ICT suites have been established throughout the School, offering rich access to resources across all curriculum areas. In addition, a high proportion of classrooms are fitted with data projectors and digital smartboards.

The School recognises that proficiency in ICT is important in the market place of the 21st century, so ICT GCSE (Short Course) is studied by all pupils to develop their skills. As technology continues to move forward, every endeavour is made to ensure that all pupils get to use the latest tools and software, thus keeping them at the leading edge of the ICT Revolution.

Admission. A prospective pupil may be registered for admission at any time after birth.

For 13+ entry, most prospective pupils and their parents visit the School at least three years before the final stages of the Admissions process. If it is decided that they would like their son/daughter to come to Uppingham then he or she should be registered at this time, if not already.

Two years before entry, at 11+, all registered pupils are invited to tests and interview. The Headmaster offers places to the successful candidates after this process has concluded. All applications must be supported by a satisfactory reference from the candidate's present School. At this stage parents are requested to complete an Acceptance Form and return an entrance deposit. Receipt of the entrance deposit guarantees a place in the School subject to the prospective pupil qualifying for admission. In completing the Acceptance Form parents also confirm that Uppingham is their first choice of school.

An offer of a place in the School is conditional upon the pupil qualifying academically (see below), and on his or her record of conduct. The latter is deemed satisfactory if the Headmaster or Headmistress of the current school says it is at the time when the qualifying examination is taken.

Most pupils are admitted in the September following their thirteenth birthday. If places are available, a few pupils may be admitted into the second year (Year 10).

There are three possible ways of qualifying academically:

(i) via the Common Entrance Examination (for which the qualifying standard is an average of 55% in the compulsory papers).
(ii) via the School's own Entrance Scholarship Examination.
(iii) in the case of pupils who have not been prepared for the Common Entrance Examination, by means of a report from the Head Teacher of their present school and tests and interviews at Uppingham.

To continue into the Sixth Form all Uppingham pupils are required to achieve six passes of grade B or above in academic subjects at GCSE, excluding short course GCSEs.

Places for girls, and a very limited number of places for boys, are available in the Sixth Form. Girls may register an interest in Sixth Form entry to Uppingham at any time, but the final interview, testing and offer procedures take place in November in the year prior to admission. Admission at this level is dependent on tests and interviews at Uppingham, and achieving six passes of grade B or above in academic subjects at GCSE (or equivalent), excluding short course GCSEs.

Enquiries and requests for information about admissions should be addressed to The Registrar (01572 820611).

Scholarships. (*see Scholarship Entries section*). A large number of scholarships are awarded annually. At 13, boys and girls may apply for Academic (ISEB Common Scholarship), Thring (All-Rounder), Art/Design & Technology and Music Scholarships. At 16 Academic, Art/Design & Technology, and Music Scholarships are awarded. All scholarships are worth up to 50% of the School fees. Means-Tested Bursaries are available up to 95% of the full fee in cases of real financial need, to assist children whose parents might not otherwise be able to afford an Uppingham education to take up such an opportunity.

For details of scholarships please contact the Admissions Secretary (01572 820611).

Fees per term (2008-2009). Boarding £8,780; Day £6,146. There is a scheme for paying fees in advance; further details may be obtained from the Finance Manager (01572 820627).

Former Pupils. The Uppingham Association was founded in 1911 to maintain the link between OUs and the School. All pupils may become life members when they leave and a database of their names, addresses, school and career details is maintained at the School by the OU Administrator. In addition to a range of OU events that are organised each year for members, a magazine is published annually, which contains news about OUs and activities at the School, and all members are encouraged to make full use of the OU Website. Enquiries may be made directly to the Secretary to the Uppingham Association (01572 820616).

Charitable status. The Trustees of Uppingham School is a Registered Charity, number 527951. It exists to provide education for boys and girls.

Victoria College
Jersey

Jersey Channel Islands JE1 4HT
Tel: 01534 638200
Fax: 01534 727448
e-mail: admin@vcj.sch.je
website: www.vcj.sch.je

The College was founded in commemoration of a visit of Queen Victoria to the Island and opened in 1852. It bears the Arms of Jersey.

Motto: '*Amat Victoria Curam*'

Visitor: Her Majesty The Queen

Governing Body:

Chairman: C Barton

J Giles
P Le Brocq
P Germain
J Billington
Mrs K Hay
Mrs P Ellyatt
S Stride
Mrs J Powell
C Scholefield

***Head Master*: Robert Cook**, BEd Hons, FRSA

Assistant Staff:

A Adkin, BEd Hons
K Baddeley, BSc Hons
Ms H Blake, BA
G Bloor, BD, AKC
Miss J Bryan, BA Hons
L Burns, BEd Hons
G Burton, BSc Hons
B F Carolan, BA Hons
J P Clark, MSc
S Cooke, PhD, BEng
J Craik, BA Hons
P Davis, GWCMD, CertEd
M Evans, BEd Hons
P T Germain, CertEd
A Gilson, BA Hons, MPhil
Miss N Good, BA Hons
W Gorman, BA Hons
M Gosling, BA Hons
P J Gray, BSc Hons
J Hale, MPharm
A R Hamel, MA
I A Hickling, BSc, MSc
R A Hopkin, BSc, CertEd
Mrs G Johnson, BA Hons Oxon
Miss H Medhurst, BA Hons
Ms D B Montgomery, BA
Ms M A Morrison, BA
A Murfin, BSc Hons
S Nye, MA
Miss A Perestrelo, BA Hons
A G Pickup, BSc, MIBiol
R Picot, BSc
Mrs P Ramsden, BSc Hons
J Randles, BA Hons
G D Reakes, BA, DipEd
S Roberts, PhD
C Rondel, BA Hons
D J Rotherham, BEd, FRGS
Mrs J Roussell, BA Hons
D Russell, MChem Oxon
I Simpson, BSc Hons
R L Stockton, BA Hons
Mrs A C C Swindell, BA Hons
M Taylor, MEd, CertEd
Mrs M Taylor, BSc Hons
Ms V Videt, BA Hons, MA
M Widdop, MSc Oxon
L Winn, BA Hons

Preparatory School
Headmaster: P Stevenson, BSc, CertEd

There are currently 706 boys in College, 276 in the Preparatory School and 90 in the Pre-Prep.

The fine building of 1852 with its Great Hall, libraries and administrative areas is set at the centre of new teaching accommodation including classrooms, music centre, extensive Science suite that was opened by Her Royal Highness The Princess Anne, a Sixth Form centre, Art and Design Technology Suite, and five computer suites. The Howard Davis Theatre opened in 1996. The College is situated in extensive grounds above St Helier and looks south over the sea.

College Field is adjacent to the main buildings and includes an all-weather hockey pitch. In the grounds are located a 25-metre shooting range, Squash courts and CCF Headquarters. A multi-million pound sports complex with swimming pool opened in 2003.

Education. There is an emphasis on academic success; nearly all boys go on to Universities in the UK. The curriculum conforms to the requirements of the National Curriculum. In the Junior School boys study Religious Education, English, Mathematics, French, Spanish, History, Drama, Geography, Biology, Chemistry, Physics, Music, Art and ICT.

Thereafter the basic curriculum includes Religious Education, English, Mathematics, a language, Sciences and ICT. In addition, boys select from optional subjects those which best suit their natural talents, the choice being guided by teaching staff in consultation with students and parents.

Boys may study four or five A level subjects suited to their objectives and abilities. Enrichment skills are developed through the CCF, Duke of Edinburgh's Award and wide-ranging extra-curricular programmes.

At all ages there is opportunity for voluntary work, Music and the Arts, and these, with other subjects, are also encouraged by numerous School Societies.

Prizes. The Queen gives three Gold Medals annually for Science, Modern Languages and Mathematics as well as two Prizes for English History. The States of Jersey offers a Gold Medal and a Silver Medal annually for French. There is an award given to the boy achieving the top score in Year 7 Entrance Examination called the St Mannelier et St Anastase Gold Medal.

Preparatory School. The College has its own Preparatory School which stands in the College grounds. Boys, on passing the Entrance procedure, progress to the College at the age of 11. (*For further details see entry in IAPS section.*)

Admission. The age of admission is 11 years though boys are considered for entry at all ages. Entrants must pass the College Entrance Examination.

Fees per term (2008-2009). £1,320. A grant is payable by the States of Jersey to supplement fees.

Physical Education and Games. The College places strong emphasis on sport and each year there are sports tours to different countries, and to the United Kingdom.

The principal games in the winter are Association Football, Rugby, Hockey, Squash; and in the summer Cricket, Swimming, Shooting, Tennis and Athletics.

Matches are played with Elizabeth College, Guernsey and College sides visit the mainland for matches against English Independent Senior Schools.

The College has an excellent CCF Contingent with an authorised establishment of 100 in the Army Section, 105 in the RAF Section and 40 in the RN Section. It is commanded by Squadron Leader David Rotherham.

Leaving Scholarships. There are a number of Scholarships (of varying amount). The Queen's Exhibition is tenable for three years at University; the Wimble Scholarship, the Sayers Scholarships and the Baron Dr Ver Heyden de Lancey Scholarship each of up to £750 a year, tenable at British Universities and the Rayner Exhibitions are recent additions to the rich endowment of Scholarships enjoyed by the College for its students.

Warwick School

Myton Road Warwick CV34 6PP
Tel: 01926 776400
Fax: 01926 401259
e-mail: enquiries@warwickschool.org
website: www.warwickschool.org

Warwick School is the oldest boys' school in the country and can produce documentary evidence that suggests its existence in the days of King Edward the Confessor, and it probably dates from 914. In 1123 the School was granted to the Church of St Mary of Warwick. In 1545 King Henry VIII increased and re-organised the endowments. The School subsequently moved to the Lord Leycester Hospital. In 1571 it moved to another site within the boundaries of Warwick, and in 1879 to its present site south of the town on the banks of the Avon.

Motto: '*Altiora Peto*'

Governing Body:

Chairman of the Warwick School Committee: Brigadier M J F Stephens, MA, CEng, MICE

R M Dancey, MA
C C L Davis, Esq
A C Firth, BSc, MBA
Mrs P Goddard
D Hanson, Esq
T P Jackson, Esq
Mrs J Marshall
Mrs V Phillips
Mrs S Rhodes
D B Stevens, Esq
Capt I Thorpe
Professor R H Trigg, MA, DPhil
R J Wyatt, Esq

Foundation Secretary: A Bligh, BSc, FCA

***Headmaster*: E B Halse**, BSc

Deputy Headmaster: W M Phelan, BA

Senior Master, Academic Administration: P J O'Grady, MA
Senior Master, Pastoral: T Hoyle, BA
Senior Master, Staff: C G McNee, BA

Head of Sixth Form: R A Chapman, BSc
Head of Upper School: J N Jefferies, MA
Head of Middle School: Mrs M Yates, BSc
Head of Lower School: Miss K Hutchings, BA

Senior Tutor: S R Chapman, BA

* *Head of Department*
† *Housemaster*

Art:
*R Flintoff, BA
D J Snatt, BA
G Ward, MA (†*School House*)

Classics:
*J E P Morris, MA
R Hudson, MA
C A Letchford, BA

Design and Technology:
*R A Bradley, BEd
C Riman, BA
B V N Schalch, BA
J D Stone, BSc

Drama:
*M C Perry
L Colgan, BA

Economics:
*D A Williams, MA
P J Shipley, MA

English:
*G S Wilson, MA, PhD
C M Bond, MA
Mrs L M Haines, BA
G I R Ogdon, MA
Mrs L Hodge, BA
Mrs A S Quinn, BA
Mrs S J Park

Geography:
*Dr A Hodskinson
S R Chapman, BA
M J Albrighton, BA

Mrs E Thornton, BA

History and Politics:
C G J Gibbs, BA (**History*)
J N Jefferies, MA (**Politics*)
C L Hammel, AB Princeton
Mrs A M Albrighton, BA
B Jeffreys, MA Hons
S Falk, BA

Computing:
*M Colliver, BSc
P Nield, MBA, BSc

Mathematics:
*Miss K Haynes, MEd
J W Clift, MA, MPhil
B L Davies, BSc
K Davenport
G Giudici
P J O'Grady, MA
D Seal BSc
D J Shield
M W Shield, BA
A Kemp, BSc

Modern Languages:
*E J Hadley, MA
Mrs C Morel-Bedford, BA
C G McNee, BA
Miss J A Wiltsher, BA (**Spanish*)
Mrs B Rossay-Gilson, BA (**French*)
R A Surr, BA (**Careers*)
Mrs A C Hadley, BA
Miss K Hutchings, BA
A Fromont
F Monier
Mrs A E Paley
Miss M Kato, BA
Mrs O P Thomas

Music:
*T G Barr, BA
R G Appleyard, GBSM
Mrs R Jefferies, MMus
M Cadman
S Hogg, GRSM

Physical Education:
*G A Tedstone, BEd
T Hoyle, BA
J W F Klopper
R Lane, BSc
M Nasey (*Director of Rugby*)
T D Pierce, BSc
N M K Smith

Religious Education:
*Revd A W Gough, BA
Revd M D Hewitt, BSc, BA (*School Professional Mentor*)
J Barker, BA

Science:
Dr Mo Afzal (**Science*)
I S Dee, BSc (**Biology*)
A D Millington (**Physics*)
Mrs C L Dowding, BSc (**Chemistry*)
P J Duckworth, MA
J A Cooper, MA
G Field, MA
G N Frykman, MA
T C O'Toole, BSc
Mrs S Rose, BSc
P A Snell, BSc
Mrs M Yates, BSc
Miss A R Drake
Dr E McDermott, BSc

Curriculum Support:
Mrs C McNee, MA
Mrs J Halse, BSc
Mrs A Finlay, BA
Mrs R Hawley, BA
Mrs J Lloyd, BA
Mrs C Oates, BA

Junior School

Headmaster: G Canning, BA

Deputy Head: J L Elston, BEd

Miss G E Beck
Mrs A J Appleyard, MA
Mrs D Caswell, BEd
Mrs E Crawford-Wallace, BEd
Mrs J Downes, BA
M Haynes, CertEd
Miss J Hirons, BA
Mrs L James, BSc
M Johnston, BSc
K Marshall, BEd
T C Lewis, CertEd
Mrs A C A Williams, BMus
T W Hancock, BSc
Mrs H J Jackson, BEd
Mrs K Bull, BA Ed Hons
Mrs E J Gemmell, BEd Hons
Dr S Marshall, BSc PhD

Bursar: N G R Stock, BSc, MRICS
Librarian: Mrs L Lucas, ALA
Medical Officer: Dr H Mulder
Headmaster's PA: Mrs C Dixon
Admissions Registrar: Mrs P Norton
Marketing Manager: Mrs A Hartin

Warwick School is an independent day and boarding school for boys. There is a Senior School (approx 800 boys) age range 11 to 18 years and a Junior School (approx 200 boys) age range 7 to 11. There is boarding accommodation for about 60 boys (Junior and Senior).

The School Buildings and Grounds. The school is situated on the outskirts of Warwick town with fine views over the River Avon and Warwick Castle. In 1879 the school moved into its present buildings designed in a rococo Tudor style with 50 acres of playing fields attached to the school. Many buildings have been built over the years. There is a programme of continuous development. In the last few years this has improved and extended the boarding, indoor sports facilities, music, drama and teaching facilities, an ICT and Library Building, a Performing Arts Centre, Music Department and a state-of-the-art Science Centre. A new classroom block will be completed in September 2008.

Admission is by entrance examination set by the School. Entry to Junior School is at the ages of 7, 8, 9 and 10. Entry to Senior School is at 11, 12, 13 and 16. The assessment at 11+ includes Non-Verbal Reasoning, English and Mathematics. The assessment at 13+ is based on the syllabus for the ISEB Common Entrance and includes English, Maths, MFL, Science and NVR. Sixth Form entry requires a minimum of 5 B grades at GCSE.

Curriculum. The aim of the school is to provide a broadly based education which allows pupils to achieve academic excellence. All pupils are encouraged to develop their individual talents to the full and to accept responsibility for themselves and others.

In the Junior School the curriculum aims to give a firm grounding in the National Curriculum foundation subjects English, Mathematics and Science. A range of other subjects including History, Geography, Technology, French, IT and Religious Education are taught throughout the school by specialist subject teachers. French is taught throughout as is Art, Music and Physical Education. In the Senior School the curriculum offers a range of options but there is a core curriculum of English, Mathematics, French and Science (including Physics, Chemistry and Biology as separate subjects) up to GCSE which all boys take in their fifth year. Virtually all boys continue into the sixth form where AS levels are taken after one year and full A levels after a further year. There is a wide range and programme of General Studies. The curriculum is designed to give all boys a broad general education and to postpone any specialisation for as long as possible.

Games and other activities. Active interest in out of school activities is much encouraged. Winter games are rugby, hockey and cross-country running. These are played in the Michaelmas and Lent Terms and our national reputation is strong throughout. Summer games are cricket, tennis, athletics and swimming. Archery, badminton, basketball, clay pigeon shooting, golf, rifle shooting, squash and volleyball are played throughout the year. There are fine sporting facilities in the indoor Sports Complex, including a 25m 6-lane Pool, squash courts, state-of-the-art rock climbing wall, fitness suite and Sports Hall.

There are usually some 80 different clubs and societies active in school life. There is a CCF contingent (with Army and RAF sections) an outdoor activities group and a Voluntary Service Group linked with the local community. Other activities include drama, music, poetry, sailing.

Religious teaching. The Chapel Services and teaching are according to the Church of England, but there are always pupils of other denominations and race and for these other arrangements may be made. Pupils attend services during the week and boarders and some day pupils the service on Sunday. The Chaplain prepares members of the school for Confirmation each year, the Confirmation Service taking place in the Lent Term.

Boarding. There is boarding for both Junior and Senior School boys. Boys may be weekly or full boarders. Boarding can sometimes be arranged for day boys to accommodate short term parental requirements. There is also an opportunity for an extended day facility.

Fees per term (2008-2009). Tuition: £3,230 (Senior School); £2,512–£3,195 (Junior School). Boarding: £3,662 (full), £3,212 (weekly).

Scholarships. (*see Scholarship Entries section*). *Governors Scholarships (11+, 12+, 13+, 16+)*. Scholarship are available to reward academic excellence and talent. Scholarships are awarded up to the value of 25% of fees based on the results of the entrance examination and interview. For existing Sixth Formers, the scholarships are awarded based on GCSE results and school reports.

Warwick Town Foundation Scholarship at 11+. This scholarship is available to boys from state schools and living within the town of Warwick (CV34 postcode). This is awarded up to the value of 25% of fees based on the results of the entrance examination.

Governors Music Scholarships at 11+ and 13+. Awarded up to the value of 25% of fees based on musical ability and potential with a satisfactory level of achievement in the entrance examination.

Sixth Form Science Scholarship. The Ogden Trust sponsors pupils of outstanding scientific ability to attend Warwick School in the Sixth Form. Awarded up to 100% fees, funded jointly by Ogden Trust and Warwick School. For pupils educated entirely in state sector achieving a minimum of 5 GCSEs at Grade A, including Mathematics. The successful candidate must study Mathematics and Physics at A Level and intend to read a science-related degree at university.

Old Warwickian Association. There is a flourishing Old Warwickian Association with a club, The Portcullis Club, in the centre of Warwick and a thriving Rugby Club with its own ground. There are regular OW events at the school. Membership Secretary: Mr P H E Bailey, 1 Church Street, Warwick CV34 4AB.

Charitable status. Warwick Independent Schools Foundation is a Registered Charity, number 1088057. It exists to provide quality education for boys.

Wellingborough School

Wellingborough Northamptonshire NN8 2BX
Tel: 01933 222427
Fax: 01933 271986
e-mail: headmaster@wellingboroughschool.org
website: www.wellingboroughschool.org

The endowment of this School was first set aside for charitable purposes in the year 1478. Further land, purchased from the Crown, was granted by Letters Patent in the reigns of Edward VI and Elizabeth I. The endowment was confirmed as being for educational purposes by an Order of the Lord Keeper of the Great Seal in 1595. The School moved to its present site in 1881 upon which new and improved buildings have from time to time been added.

The School offers day co-education for boys and girls from the age of 3 to 18. The School is firmly wedded to Christian principles, to equality of opportunity and the enrichment of individuals in the community. The School is divided into a Pre-Preparatory School (age 3–8: 169 pupils), the Preparatory School (age 8–13: 300 pupils) (*see also entry in IAPS section*), and the Senior School (age 13–18: 420 pupils).

Motto: '*Salus in Arduis*'

Governors:
J J H Higgins (*Chairman*)
C A Odell (*Vice-Chairman*)
A W Bailey
Mrs A Coles
Dr Jonathan Cox
D K Exham, MA
Mrs E Higgins
B Huckle
S Marriott
J Morris
Mrs P Perkins, OBE
P S Phillips
A H Robbs
C Westley
Mrs Clare Colacicchi (*School Solicitor*)
T Baldry (*School Accountant*)
M P Skidmore (*Bursar & Clerk to the Governors*)

***Headmaster*: G R Bowe**, BA Kent

Deputy Headmaster (*Pastoral*): I M Hunt, BA, University College London

Deputy Headmistress (*Academic*): Mrs E S Clark, BA Newnham College, Cambridge

Head of Sixth Form: Mrs S M Barnhurst, BSc Salford, MA Northampton

Assistant Staff:
S M Adams, BEd Exeter (*Director of Sport*)
J A Bialacki, PhD Loughborough (*Head of Chemistry*)
Mrs F J Burgess, BEd Exeter
Mrs R E Cowley, BA Manchester Metropolitan
R Dempster, BEd Middlesex
J A Dutfield, DipAD, CertEd UCW (*Head of Art*)
S L Egan, BEng Leicester (*Head of Design Technology*)
Mrs C Y Elwyn, Dip LIC
P J Farley, MA Liverpool
Mrs S E Fellows, BA Birmingham
A R Gamble, BA St Edmund Hall, Oxford (*Head of English*)
Miss C L Gavin, BSc Loughborough
Mrs S E Gibson-Foy, BA Sheffield
Mrs A J Gillam, BA Exeter
J R Gray BSc Bangor
R W Greenbank, BSc Sussex
S G Hawksworth, BSc Northampton
Dr A Higginson, PhD UMIST (*Head of Science & Physics*)
Mrs A S Holley, BA Birmingham (*Head of Classics*)
Miss C E M Horry, BA Kent
G E Houghton, BA Durham
Mrs H K Hunt, BA Bournemouth
P A Knox, BEd Durham
P J Lowe, BA Southampton (*Head of Geography*)
P R Marshall, BA Wales, LRAM (*Director of Music*)
C Martin-Sims, BSc Sussex, MSc Reading, BA Open (*Head of Drama/Psychology*)
Ms J A Mason, BA Teesside
Mrs L J McAuley, BSc Glasgow
A P McGinnes, BSc Exeter (*Head of Mathematics*)
M A Nugent, BA Leicester (*Head of Modern Languages*)
N W Papworth, BSc Loughborough
Mrs S Pyke, BSc Bradford
D A Ramsden, BA Fitzwilliam College, Cambridge (*Head of History and Politics*)
Mrs G M Rodgers, MA Newnham College, Cambridge
I Runnells, BA Northampton
C Scott, BSc Durham; MA Christ's College, Cambridge
Mrs K A Shutt, BSc LSE (*Head of Business Studies and Economics*)
Mrs R A Shuttlewood, BSc, MSc Sheffield (*Coordinator of Professional Development*)
Mrs B Strange, MA Open (*Special Needs Coordinator*)
M E Thompson, MA The Queen's College, Oxford
Revd M J Walker, BA Lincoln College, Oxford, DipES St John's College, Durham (*Chaplain*)
P B Waugh, BEd Manchester Metropolitan (*IT Manager*)
Mrs C L Woodward, BA Surrey Inst of A&D

Housemasters/Housemistresses:
M H Askham, BEd Loughborough (*Garne's House*)
T J Fourie, MSc Port Elizabeth SA (*Platt's House*)
R Campbell, BA Auckland NZ (*Fryer's House*)
T H J Hurdman, BSc Southampton (*Parker Steyne's*)
Miss C S Irvin, BSc Loughborough (*Marsh House*)

Miss J M Livingstone, BA Queen's Belfast (*Nevill House*)
R B McGuirk, BSc Nottingham Trent, MSc Warwick (*Cripps' House*)
Mrs H M Pattison, BSc King's College London (*Weymouth House*) (*Head of Biology*)

Registrar: Mrs Yvonne Pullen

Officer Commanding CCF: Major S Garfirth
School Nurses: Mrs L Bate RN, Mrs L R Wood, RGN Cert DN

Director of Music: P R Marshall, BA Hons, PGCE, LRAM
Assistant Director of Music: I Runnells, BA Hons, PGCE, ARCO
Pre-Prep Music Coordinator: S Garfirth, DipRCM, ALCM
Music Department Administrator: Mrs S M Miller, Lic CIPD

Instrumental Music Teachers
Peter F Baxter JP FRSA FA StC (*Flute, Recorder*)
Mark Chivers BMus Hons, PG DIP RNCH (*Violin, Viola*)
Peter Collins BA Hons, PGDipRCM (*Brass*)
Joel Garthwaite MMus GSMD, BMus RWCMD, Dip ABRSM (*Saxophone, Clarinet*)
Martin Gill LTCL, GTCL (*Violin*)
Mrs Karen Goss BLIB, LTCL, FTCL (*Clarinet, Bassoon*)
Steve Hamper (*Percussion*)
Mrs Susan Healey MA, GRSM Hons, CertEd, ATCL, ARCM, LTCL, LRSM (*Piano, Keyboard, Aural, Theory*)
Miss Janice Hooper-Roe ARCM, GBSM, ABSM (*Singing*)
Tim Jones (*Percussion*)
Wyn Jones BMus Hons II2, PGCE (*Cello, Bass*)
Keith Learmouth CertEd, ALCM, FRSA (*Guitar*)
Ms Bridget Marshall BA Hons, FLCM, ARCM, LRAM, PGCE (*Piano, Organ, Theory*)
Mark Pescott FTCL, LRAM, ARCM (*Piano, Organ, Theory*)
Ian Riley GLCM (*Piano*)
Philip Slane AGSM, DipEd ARCM (*Singing*)
Edward Swindell BMus Hons, MMus
Mrs Karen A Whitelaw BA Hons, LRAM, LGSM, ALCM (*Piano*)

Preparatory School:
Headmaster: R J Mitchell, BEd College of St Paul's & St Mary's

Deputy Headmaster: R W H Smith, BEd De Montfort
Assistant Head – Pastoral Care: Mrs L Leakey
Assistant Head – Curriculum: J R Chatburn, MA Cambridge
Assistant Head – Pupils' Academic Development: Mrs K Owen, BSc Exeter
Assistant Head – Extra-Curricular Activities: Mr G Arkley

Teaching Staff:
Miss S C Allan MA Cardiff
Mrs C Allen SpLD Cert
R Batley, CertEd Borough Road College, London
Mrs P Butler, BEd Westminster College, Oxford
Mrs J Burns, BSc of Greenwich
D A Coombes, BA Liverpool John Moores
Mrs F J Drye, BA Wales
M P Fursse, BEd North East Wales Institute, Wrexham
N R Grove, MA Liverpool
Mrs C Handford, CertEd Trent Park College of Education, London
S G Hawksworth, BSc Northampton
Mrs C J Hughes, BA Durham, SpLD Cert
Miss A S Kingstone, BA Northampton
J Knight, MTeach Kingston
M R Lower, BA Queensland
Mrs J Piercy-Hughes, CertEd Warwick, SpLD Cert
P P Ricca, MFLE LSL LA Montpellier & Toulouse
Miss R J Sanders, MA Durham
Mrs C Shuker, CertEd
Mrs A M Simmons, BA Stirling
Mrs C J Smith, BA Durham
P M Studd, BEd Chester College
Miss K E Ward, BA Hull
Mrs C L Whitaker, BA Brighton
L Williams, MSc Brunel

Librarian: Mrs K Cooper BA Aberystwyth
Registrar: Mrs Jayne Wilson

Pre-Preparatory School:
Headmistress: Mrs J D Jones, CPDE Open, Cert Mont Ed St Nicholas College, London

Assistant Head (*Curriculum*) D C Popplewell, BA Warwick
Assistant Head (*Pastoral*): Mrs S J Johnson, BA St Martin College

Assistant Staff:
Mrs J C Bradford, BEd York St John
Mrs J E M Espin, BA New Hall, Cambridge
S Garfirth, DipRCM, ALCM
Mrs R M Girling, BEd Cambridge
Mrs S A Jamieson, BA Northampton
Mrs L C Potter, BA Leeds
Miss C M Sullivan, BSc Nottingham
Mrs C H Waite, BEd Ripon and York St John
Miss L Woolhead, BA QTS Northampton
Mrs E Jakeman, BEd Worcester College

Nursery:
Mrs S M Sandall Dip Early Years Ed & NNEB Solihull Technical College
Mrs M Gutteridge, NNEB Southfields College
Mrs H Cockbill, NNEB West Bridgford College of FE
Miss S Ives, NNEB Triangle Training

Teaching Assistants:
Mrs S Cameron, BA Open, CSTA Firdale College
Mrs M E Campbell, BTEC, Art Dip Tresham College
Mrs K Harris, NNEB Tresham Institute
Mrs A Martin, NNEB Stoke on Trent College
Mrs C Ward, NNEB Northampton College
Miss A M Ystenes, NNEB Nene College
Miss B Gosling, NNEB Northampton College

Wellingborough is situated 63 miles from London, 10 miles east of Northampton. Close to the main railway line from St Pancras to Leicester and Sheffield, it is served by an excellent network of motorways and dual carriageways connecting the A1, A14 and the M1.

Buildings and Organisation. The School occupies a fine site on the south of the town, and stands in its own grounds of 45 acres. In the Senior School there are five boys' houses and three girls' houses, organised on boarding house lines. Each house has about 45 pupils. The Sixth Form numbers around 130 pupils, 90% of whom go directly to higher education.

Admission at 13+ for boys and girls is by means of entry tests and interview or the Common Entrance Examination from preparatory schools. Direct entry into the Sixth Form is on the basis of an interview, school report and likely GCSE results confirmed before entry. Please note that A Level courses begin in June after GCSE examinations.

The Preparatory School, while sharing some of the facilities of the Senior School, has its own buildings and classrooms on the east side of the campus. In 2006 a large new library, incorporating a computer research, fiction and non-fiction working areas, classroom and science laboratory was completed. The Pre-Preparatory School occupies its own modern purpose-built buildings which have been substantially refurbished and extended.

The main school buildings include an ICT study centre, a library, assembly hall, careers room, chapel, and three classroom blocks including seven newly refurbished science laboratories and the information technology department. There is a design technology centre, music school, modern languages centre, sports hall and central dining hall.

Religion. Religious teaching is according to the Church of England. Pupils attend a mixture of morning prayers and longer services on weekdays, and a morning service on some Sundays during term. The Chaplain prepares members of the School for confirmation each year, the confirmation service taking place in the Lent Term.

Curriculum. In the Pre-Preparatory School and the Preparatory School the curriculum is an enriched version of the National Curriculum. French, Latin and Spanish are also taught in the Preparatory School.

In the first year of the Senior School (Shell form) pupils follow a core curriculum in English, Mathematics, French, Physics, Chemistry, Biology, History, Geography, Design Technology, Art, Music, RE, Information Technology and PE. German and Latin are both options in this year. GCSE courses are offered in English, English Literature, French, Mathematics and dual award sciences. Options include separate Sciences, Latin, German, History, Geography, Art, Design Technology, Music, Drama, PE and Religious Studies.

The following subjects are offered for A Level examination: Art and Design, Biology, Business Studies, Chemistry, Design Technology, Economics, English Literature, French, German, Geography, History, Mathematics and Further Mathematics, Music, PE, Physics, Politics and Psychology. Information Technology, Drama, English Language and Religious Studies are offered as freestanding AS Levels.

Music, Drama, Art, Design. The Music School contains a new central teaching hall, a second newly refurbished teaching room and several practice rooms. Professional tuition is given on all instruments and there are chapel and concert choirs, junior and senior bands and a school orchestra.

Concerts, school and house drama productions and lectures are held in the School Hall, which has well-equipped stage facilities. The Richard Gent Design Centre offers workshops and studies for design technology and ceramics. The highly successful Two-Dimensional Art Department has its own dedicated building. Pupils are encouraged to make full use of these facilities in their spare time.

Sport. The playing fields, over 40 acres in extent, are used for the main boys' sports of rugby, soccer and cricket and hockey and netball for girls; cross country, athletics, and tennis are also highly popular. The school site also boasts a nine-hole golf course, astroturf pitch, five all-weather tennis courts, two squash courts, shooting range, gymnasium and sports hall. The latter has four badminton courts, indoor cricket nets and facilities for fencing, table tennis, basketball and dedicated fitness suite.

Other Activities. After their first term in the Senior School pupils join the Combined Cadet Force (RN, Army, Commando or RAF Section) until the end of Year 10 at least. Training is given in first aid, map reading and orienteering, and camping expeditions take place at weekends. There is an annual CCF camp and there are opportunities for band training, open range shooting, REME work, canoeing and sailing. The Duke of Edinburgh's Award Scheme is also a very popular option for older pupils.

A wide range of extra-curricular interests is available through various societies and clubs. Pupils may also take part in local community service work.

Careers. Guidance is available to all pupils on further education and careers prospects through the Head of Careers and other members of staff. The School is a member of the Independent Schools Careers Organisation.

Scholarships. (*see Scholarship Entries section*). Foundation scholarships are offered to external candidates for entry to the Preparatory School at 11+. At 13+ entrance scholarships are offered to pupils entering the Senior School. At 16+ up to two Sixth Form scholarships are offered. Performing Arts (Music and Drama) scholarships and awards are available at 13+ and 16+ for candidates of outstanding ability and potential. Art scholarships and awards are offered at 13+ and at 16+. Sports scholarships and awards are awarded at 13+ and at 16+.

Bursaries. Some bursaries are available for candidates who can make an outstanding/special contribution to the School where there is a proven case of financial need. All awards are means-tested and subject to satisfactory performance both academically and in other respects.

Further details and application forms for all the above awards may be obtained from the Headmaster.

Fees per term (2008-2009). Senior School: £3,772 (Years 9–11), £3,668 (Years 12–13); Preparatory School £3,521, Pre-Preparatory School £2,174–£2,274. Fees include most extras apart from instrumental lessons (termly payment), public examination fees and books.

Admission. Applications should be made to the Registrar for entry of boys and girls at 13+ and for direct entry into the Sixth Form. Enquiries concerning entries between the ages of 3 and 7 should be addressed to the Headmistress of the Pre-Preparatory School and entries between the ages of 8 and 12 to the Registrar of the Preparatory School.

Term of Entry. New pupils are accepted at the beginning of any term. The largest entry is in September each year.

Old Wellingburian Club. All former pupils who have spent at least one year in the School are eligible for membership. Correspondence should be addressed to the OW Club Secretary at the School.

Charitable status. Wellingborough School is a Registered Charity, number 1101485. It exists to provide education for boys and girls from the age of 3 to 18.

Wellington College

Duke's Ride Crowthorne Berkshire RG45 7PU

Tel: The Master: 01344 444101
Director of Admissions: 01344 444013
Bursar: 01344 444020
Reception: 01344 444000
Fax: 01344 444002
e-mail: info@wellingtoncollege.org.uk
website: www.wellingtoncollege.org.uk

Incorporated by Royal Charter, dated 13 December 1853.

Visitor: Her Majesty The Queen

President: HRH The Duke of Kent, KG, GCMG, GCVO, ADC, DL

Vice-President & Chairman of Governors: Sir Anthony Goodenough, KCMG

Ex officio Governors:
The Archbishop of Canterbury, FBA, DD, DPhil, MA
The Duke of Wellington, KG, LVO, OBE, MC, DL

Governors:
General Sir Redmond Watt
The Rt Hon The Baroness Symons of Vernham Dean
A G Bruce, BSc
Mrs V Mitchell
Dr A Borges
Brigadier (retd) M T A Lord, BSc, CEng, FIMechE
J G Sanger, MA, MBA, FCA
D Christie, BA, BSc
N R Kenyon, CBE, BA
P G C Mallinson, BA, MBA
Dr C M Marr, BA, DPhil
Mrs O Deighton
Rear Admiral H A H G Edleston, RN
The Rt Revd D D J Rossdale, MA, MSc, Bishop of Grimsby
Dr R Groves, BA, PhD
Dr P J A Frankopan, MA, DPhil, FRSA

Sir Michael Rake
Ms A E T Dean, BSc
Dr E M Sidwell, BSc, PhD, FRSA, FRGS
T B Bunting

Clerk to the Governors: M C Gowar, MA, FTII

***Master*: A F Seldon**, MA, PhD, MBA, FRSA, FRHistS

Second Master: R I H B Dyer, BA
Deputy Head: Miss L C Pearson, BA
Director of Admissions: R J W Walker, MA
Director of Studies: Dr J A Garrick, BA, MEd, PhD
Senior Mistress: Mrs E A Worthington, MA
Senior Master: R C Auger, MA

Assistant Staff:
* *Head of Department*
† *Housemaster/mistress*

C M St G Potter, BSc
†G Waugh, BEd
J D Oakes, ARCM
R A Peter, BA
D A Burns, BSc, MSc
J J Breen, MA, BA
*I C E Mitchell, BSc
†T J Head, BA
A R Dewes, MA
M Farrington, BSc, MSc, PhD
M N Halpin, MSc
D G Grainge, BSc
J L Price, BA
*Mrs L P Walker, MA
P Hucklesby, MA
R R Foskett, MA
*Mrs E M Hood, BSc, PhD
*M G Fowler, BA
†J C Rawlinson, BSc
G C Nurser, BEd, MA
†C M Oliphant-Callum, MA
†I M Henderson, BA
*Mrs C J Henderson, BA
B N Roth, BSc, BA, AFIMA
†N C Lunnon, BSc
†M T Boobbyer, BA
*E J Heddon, MBA, FICPD, MCT
†P G S Boscher, BA, PhD
*S R J Williamson, MA, FRCO
Ms S A Lang, BA
*J A F Jeffrey, BA
S D Laverack, BSc, PhD
*Mrs C J Blunden-Lee, BA
*M J Oakman, BA
Mrs D E Cook, BA
†S W Lockyer, BSc
*M J D Ellwood, BEd
Mrs B F Boscher, BA
*J S White, BA
B A Bayman, BA
†N D Gallop, BA
C C Morris, BA
I Frayne, BSc
I S Hendry, MA
G I Woodrow, BEd, MEd
†Mrs L Raabe-Marjot, BA
J M Gale, BA
†B Wielenga, BCom
*S C D Gutteridge
Mrs C Aguillon-Williams, MA
†G Owton, BA
C B Ewart, MA
R W Lancastle, BA
*D Wilson, MA
*M P Ford, BSc
*I R Morris, BA
A P Seldis, BA
Mrs K J Hamilton, BA
*Miss S L Spencer, BA
S J Allcock, BA
Miss B M Kaja, BA
Miss C O'Neill, BA
O Q King, BMus
Miss B C Thomas, BA
Miss M Churchill, BFA
Miss H E Lewis, BA
*D Walker, BSc
Miss R R Ross, BSc
Miss N R Pendle, BA
Mrs Y Tang, MA
†Mrs D A Draper, BSc
†Miss E J Gillan, BA
*L W Hedges, MA
*T Seth, BA
*P A Fairclough, BA
*N J Amy, MA
M E Schramm, BSc
W Heathcote, MPhys
*Dr D A James, MA, PhD
G J Williams, MA
*N J Maloney, BA
T J Elton, MMath
Mrs K E Granville-Chapman, BA
Miss E-J Huddart, BA
Mrs S J Henwood, GRSM Hons
Miss A E R Morse, BA
Ms K Jack, MA
S A S Owen, BA
*Mrs J M Grillo, BEd
†Mrs J M Waugh, BEd
Dr A B Hill, BSc, PhD
*M J Albrighton, MA
*Dr R S Bunce, MA, PhD
Dr J L Chapman, PhD, BSc
†Ms M J Chodak, BA
†G D Pearson, BEng
*Mrs S Y N Jobson
*Dr M J Milner, MA, DPhil
*J A Thomas, BA
*S Shortland, BEd, MSc
M Goves, BA
Mrs R E Crosby, BSc
Dr R J Cromarty, MA, PhD
E B R Venables, BA
J Giannikas, BA
B P Lewsley, BA
Miss L C Edwards, BA
K J Brennan, BA
G Franklin, BA
T C Hawes
X Iles, BA
Ms R G Shawe-Taylor, MA
Miss F Smith

plus 40 visiting instrumental teachers

Senior Chaplain: The Revd T W G Novis, BA, MDiv

Houses and Housemasters/mistresses:
Anglesey: B Wielenga
Benson: I M Henderson
Beresford: T J Head
Blücher: M T Boobbyer
Hardinge: C M Oliphant-Callum
Hill: S W Lockyer
Hopetoun: G Waugh and Mrs J M Waugh
Lynedoch: G D Pearson
Murray: J C Rawlinson
Picton: N D Gallop
Stanley: N C Lunnon
Talbot: Dr P G S Boscher
Apsley: Ms M J Chodak
Combermer: Mrs D Draper
Orange: Mrs L Raabe-Marjot
Wellesley: Miss E Gillan
White Cairn: G Owton

Commanding Officer CCF: Lt Col E J Heddon, MBA, FCIPD, MCT
Librarian: Ms J L Shepherd, BA, ALA
Bursar: Mrs S Meikle, BA Hons
Accountant: S Headdey, FCA
Works Bursar: G Burbidge, FCIOB, MCIOSH
Assistant Bursar: S J Blosse
Estate Manager: M F Brandom, BA, BSc
Medical Officer: A P McG Greig, MB BS, DCh, DRCGP
Medical Centre Sister: Mrs J L Whalley, BSc Hons
Registrar: Mrs L Peate, BSc
Master's PA: Mrs A Reed
College Secretary: Mrs E L Browne
Bursar's Secretary: Mrs S L Ball

Wellington College was founded by public subscription as a memorial to the Great Duke. It was granted a Charter in 1853 and took its first pupils in 1859. In the early days of the school there were strong connections with the Army. Today, places continue to be reserved for the children of deceased military servicemen and servicewomen and of others who have died in acts of selfless bravery, who apply to be Foundationers, but its intake has expanded to reflect a more modern world.

The school is set in a woodland estate of 400 acres. From September 2008 there will be approximately 890 pupils with (260) girls spread across all age groups. Pupils belong to one of the 17 Houses (seven in the main College buildings and ten in the grounds). Boarders (and some day pupils) at 13+ join one of ten Houses taking boys and four Houses taking girls. There are two (16+) Sixth Form Houses, one each for girl and for boy boarders (and a small number of day pupils), and two day Houses, one each for girls and for boys.

13+ boarders will share rooms in their first year, and may do so in a second or third year, but then move on to their own room. Some day pupils, with day rooms, a longer school day and some facility for very occasional stay overnight, are spread amongst the boarding Houses. Day pupils share common rooms.

There is a central dining hall with modern kitchens and serveries. Meals are taken here on a cafeteria basis by most of the pupils although 4 Houses outside the main buildings have their own dining facilities. The school has its own Medical Officer and an 8-bed Medical Centre constantly staffed by fully qualified nurses. All Houses have their own House Matrons and domestic staff.

Academic Work. Academic standards are very high; GCSE and A Level pass rates are in the 98–100% range, and nearly all pupils go on to university. There is a good rate of entry to Oxford, Cambridge, Durham, Edinburgh and many other good universities. Most work takes place in modern specialist blocks near to the main buildings. The Queen's Court building also contains a theatre. The Science laboratories have all been recently refurbished and the Kent Building houses well equipped Design and Technology Centre and Information Technology Centres. A new Art School and Physics laboratories have been built. A new Modern languages block is due to open. The old Art School in the main buildings has been converted into a new lecture room and conference room. New IT suites have been built in Queen's Court and near the Science laboratories.

The school is divided for teaching purposes into the Lower School (Third and Fourth Forms), the Middle School (Fifth Form) and the Sixth Form (Lower Sixth and Upper Sixth). The GCSE examination is taken in the Middle School. All the usual subjects are taught in the Middle and Lower Schools, including three separate sciences. In the Third Form the following subjects are taught: Religious Studies, Drama, English, History, Geography, French, Mathematics, Physics, Chemistry, Biology, Art, Music, IT, Textiles, Design & Technology. Not all pupils are required to study Latin, but most do. Greek, German and Spanish are taught, too. In the Fourth Form there are three "columns" of options which allow pupils some choice outside the main subjects.

In the Sixth Form, the IB programme and a wide range of AS and A2 Level choices are available. These include all the usual combinations but at least one-third of our pupils do a combined Arts/Science grouping.

Extra-Curricular Activities. All pupils on arrival join the Junior Society which introduces them to a wide variety of activities. Art, Music and Drama are outstanding. A Creative Writing Group meets regularly, and a literary magazine, The Wellingtonian, is edited by pupils.

Other societies include: Art, Astronomy, Chess, Bridge, Classics, Debating, Film, Golf, Mathematics, Music, Natural History, Opera, Photography, Pottery, Sailing and Science. There are two scholarly societies called The Academy and Food for Thought and a wine-tasting society called The Noble Rot. There are regular visiting lecturers on a variety of topics, an Artist in Residence, and master-classes in Art, Music/Drama and Literature.

Throughout the College, a conscious effort is made to provide all pupils with a programme of personal development based upon the eight aptitudes of each individual as codified by the Master. Experience of management, team-building and leadership training is included. Wellington introduced pioneering well-being classes in September 2006.

Wellington has been a Round Square school since 1995; the Round Square is made up of schools from around the world which are all pledged to foster international standing and to educate through service at home and overseas.

Games. The school has a national reputation for prowess in games, at the moment particularly in rugby, hockey, cricket, netball, lacrosse, shooting, swimming, athletics, rackets, golf and polo.

There are great opportunities for pupils to represent the school in teams across a wide range of sports, all of which are supported by the school's outstanding facilities. These include over 80 acres of playing fields, two all-weather pitches for hockey and all-weather tennis courts. There is a sports complex which incorporates a rackets court, five squash courts, an indoor pool and a large sports hall. This has a main hall 37m × 32m in size in which a wide variety of indoor games may be played as well as specialist weight training and rock climbing areas. A spectacular nine-hole golf course was opened in September 2001. The normal pattern of boys' games is rugby (we regularly field up to 18 XVs) in the Michaelmas Term, hockey, football and cross country in the Lent Term and cricket, athletics and swimming in the Summer. For the girls, hockey is the main sport in the Michaelmas Term, with netball in the Lent and cricket, rounders, athletics and swimming in the Summer. There is also the opportunity for girls to play lacrosse competitively. Other games for all pupils include squash, basketball, tennis, sailing, football, fencing, karate, badminton, canoeing, sub-aqua and volleyball.

Admission to the School. Most pupils enter the school in September when they are between 13 and 14 years of age. There are occasionally places available for pupils at 14+. Two Sixth Form Houses (one for girls and one for boys) mean that there are places for entry at 16+. Applications for registration should be addressed to the Director of Admissions, or in the case of Foundationers, to the Bursar. On registration, a fee of £100 is charged which entitles a child's name to remain on the register until two years or so before entry is due. Those registered for 13+ entry are invited for Pre-testing (usually in the first term of Year 7). Those successful in Pre-testing are either invited onto the 'Places List' and asked to confirm their intention to take up a place (with payment of a Confirmation of Entry fee), or invited to accept a 'Waiting List' place. Confirmed places are guaranteed, subject to satisfactory results in the Scholarship, Common Entrance or other entry exams. The Confirmation of Entry fee (at all levels) is £1,000, of which £500 is returned on the pupil's second term's account and a further £375 is returned on the final account.

Scholarships. (*see Scholarship Entries section*). There are thirty-six 13+ Scholarships and Exhibitions offered. In the academic field, the top four Scholarships are for 30% of the fees, there are up to seven of 20% of the fees, and ten Exhibitions of 10% of the fees. There are two Music Scholarships of 30% of the fees, one of 20% and two Exhibitions of 10%. There are also four Scholarships available for Art, Drama, Dance, Design & Technology and Sport worth 20% of the fees and six Exhibitions worth 10% of the fees. Candidates for non-academic awards must satisfy our general entry requirements. Scholarships of all values may be augmented by a bursary where the financial situation of the parents makes this necessary. Candidates must be under 14 on 1st September in the calendar year in which they sit the examination.

For pupils entering at 16+ there are four academic awards (two of 30% and two of 20% fees), four music awards (two of 30% and two of 20% fees) and seven awards in Art, Drama, Dance, Design & Technology and Sport (one of 30% and six of 20% fees).

Fees per term (2008-2009). Boarders £8,975, Day Boarding £7,625, Day £6,725. For pupils in the Sixth Form, there is an additional charge of £82.50 per term. Separate charges totalling £218 per instrument are made for musical tuition (10 lessons). The school runs an attractive fees in advance scheme for parents with capital sums available.

Old Wellingtonian Society. The OW Society has branches in ten countries, clubs representing ten different sports, around 7,000 members (including 500 girls) and a Secretary based at College (Tel: 01344 444069; Fax: 01344 444007).

Charitable status. Wellington College is a Registered Charity, number 309093. It exists to provide education for boys and girls aged 13–18.

Wellington School

Wellington Somerset TA21 8NT
Tel: 01823 668800
Fax: 01823 668844
e-mail: admin@wellington-school.org.uk
website: www.wellington-school.org.uk

Founded in 1837, Wellington School is a co-educational, academically selective school providing a friendly, disciplined environment and a wide range of co-curricular opportunities.

Motto: '*Nisi dominus frustra*'

Governing Body:

Chairman: D R Wheeler, BSc, FCA
Vice-Chairman: P H Nunnerley, BA, FCIB
Miss S Adams
A Bailey, BSc
J H Bradnock, MA, BA
J Clark
J P Elder
S P Meredith
K B Phillips, BSc
H Richards
Mrs C J Seymour
T M Taylor, MA Oxon, FRSA
Prof A M Tettenborn, Barrister, MA, LLB Cantab
Mrs S E Watts, ACIS, MBIM, JP
Mrs A Weekes, BA
E G Whall, BSc

Clerk to the Governors: T Pangraz

***Headmaster*: M S Reader**, MA Oxon, MPhil, MBA

Senior Deputy Head: R S Page, MA
Deputy Head (*Staff*): Mrs C A Christie, BSc, MSc
Deputy Head (*Academic*): Dr P M Owen, MA, PhD
Head of Lower School: P M Pearce, BA

Assistant Academic Staff:

A Anderson, BA
G J W Arnold, BSc
B Ashe, BA, LRAM
C F Barratt, BSc
C H Barrow, BA
Mrs A E Bazley, BEd
Ms A J Beaumont, MA
Mrs J C Bernard, BA
J F Bird, BA
P J Buckingham, BA, MA
Mrs L Burton, BA
J R Card, BSc
A R Carson, BSc
T S Clements, BA, MA
D A Colclough, BSc
Miss M Collins, BA, MA
Mrs L Davey, BSc
Mrs S A Dean, BA
A N Denham, BA, ATC
M E Downes, BSc
H D H Elkington, BA, MA
Dr I J Everton, MA, PhD
G Felletar, DipEd
Dr P T Galley, BSc, PhD
A Garcia, CertEd
Miss A Gluch
Mrs H C Hawkins, MBioCh
J F Helliar, BSc
The Revd J P Hellier, BD, AKC, DipRE, CF
T J Hill, BA
Miss F E Hobday, MA
Dr K A Hodson, BA, MA
Miss R S Isdell-Carpenter, BA
S W James, BA
Dr A R Jolliffe, BA, MA, DPhil
C G D Jones, BSc, CChem, MRCS
P Jones, BA, FRGS
Mrs J F Kingston, BSc
J Leonard, BA
Mrs L E Leonard, BA
Miss R L Marsden, BA
R Marsh, BA
R A Matthews, BSc, MSc
Miss S Middleton, BA
N McGuff, BSc
D Millington, BA, MSc
P F Norman, BA
Mrs S Page, MA
G Paterson, MA
I W Payne, BSc, MA
A Phillips, BSc
Miss J Renfrew, MA
M H Richards, BEd
Mrs V K Richardson, BSc
Mrs L A Rowe, BSc
Mrs H J Salter, BA
A C Shaw, BA, MSc
J P W Shepherd, MA
Mrs K Simon, MA
R E Stevens, BSocSci
A W Stevenson, MA
P J Swan, MSc
Mrs L Tabb, BSc
Miss S F L Toase, BSc, MIBiol
Miss C L Tomsett, BA
A J Trewhella, BA, ARCO
Mrs R Turner, BA
Dr W Vacani, BA, PhD
N H Vyse, MA
Mrs F Vyse, BSc
I G Webb-Taylor, MA
Mrs F N Wreford, BA

Assistant Music Staff:
Miss M Armitstead, BA
Mrs C Barrington, ATCL, CGSM, LRAM (*Piano*)
J F Campbell, GRSM, ARCO (*Piano*)
D Cottam, AGSM (*Classical Guitar*)
Mrs R Cox (*Cello*)
P Craig, BA (*Percussion*)
A Gillett, ARCM (*Violin*)
Mrs A Gullick, ARCM (*Double Bass, Cello*)
J H Hammonds (*Trumpet*)
Mrs K Jasper, ARCM (*Piano*)
Mrs D Jerrold, ARCM (*Woodwind*)
Miss A Kimber, BA, FTCL, ARCM (*Flute*)
J Loysen (*Trombone*)
Mrs J Morris, BA (*Voice*)
S Phippen, BA, LTCL (*Piano*)
Miss C D Rose, BA (*Clarinet*)
J Small, BA (*Guitars*)
T Waller, MA, BMus (*Piano*)
J A D White, BMus (*Violin, Viola*)
N C White, BA, PPGSM (*Saxophone, Clarinet*)
Mrs S E White, ARCM, DipRCM (*Saxophone, Clarinet*)
Mrs V Williams, ARCM (*Brass*)
J Young, BA (*Piano/Organ*)

Bursar: Cdr R D Coupe, OBE, RN
Curriculum Manager: P J Swan, MSc, FIMA, CMath
Registrar: Mrs C Loftus Owen, BA
Medical Officer: Dr J G Scott, MB BS, DRCOG
OC CCF: Revd J P Hellier, BD, AKC, CF
CCF SSI: RSM G T Farrar

Situation. Located on the southern edge of Wellington, at the foot of the Blackdown Hills, this fully co-educational School is equidistant from Tiverton Parkway and Taunton Railway Stations. The M5 approach road (Junction 26) is within a mile. Currently there are 750 pupils in the Lower and Senior Schools (10–18 years), of whom 20% board.

Buildings. The School has witnessed an extensive building programme over the last twenty years, the new buildings having been carefully and tastefully blended in with existing architecture.

Most recent buildings include the John Kendall-Carpenter Science Centre with its state-of-the-art laboratories and lecture theatre, a multi-million pound sports complex which opened in 2002 and a purpose-built Junior School. A new classroom block and examination hall completes in 2008 following which work starts on major improvements to Performing Arts facilities.

Grounds. There are 12 hectares of playing fields as well as a floodlit all-weather hockey pitch, squash courts, an indoor swimming pool and a climbing wall.

Houses. There are separate Houses for boys and girls, and for Seniors and Lowers. All Houses have their own changing, work and recreational facilities.

There is a central Dining Hall and all meals are served on a cafeteria basis. The School also has its own well equipped laundry.

There is a fully equipped Medical Centre, with a trained staff under the direction of the School Medical Officer.

Academic Organisation. The School is divided into the Upper School (Year 9–Sixth Form) and the Lower School (Years 6, 7 and 8). The Junior School (Nursery–Year 5) is on a separate, adjoining campus.

Most pupils enter the School at Year 6, 7 or 9. The Year 6 curriculum focuses on English and Mathematics but also includes an unusually wide range of subjects to take full advantage of subject specialist teaching and facilities. The curriculum in Years 7, 8 and 9 is designed to allow pupils to develop the skills needed to succeed at GCSE and features a good range of practical and more academic subjects including Latin. At GCSE all pupils study English, English Literature,

Mathematics and a Short Course in Religious Education as well as a Modern Foreign Language and a further five or six subjects. Pupils have a free choice of studying three sciences separately or as Dual Award Science. The Mathematics and Science courses lead to IGCSE qualifications. The most able mathematicians take IGCSE at the end of Year 10 before taking Additional Mathematics in Year 11. Students have a free choice from a wide range of subjects in the Sixth Form: most start on 4 AS Levels before reducing to 3 A2 courses. A system of grades every four weeks and tutor groups ensure that academic monitoring of pupils is supportive and effective.

Religious Education is part of the curriculum throughout the School. The School is Christian in tradition and there is a short Act of Worship in the School Chapel on each weekday with a longer Sunday service. The content and form of these services are based on contemporary Anglican procedures. Attendance is expected although sensitivity is shown towards pupils of other faiths for whom alternative provision can be made.

Music. Tuition is available on all orchestral instruments, as well as piano, organ, drum kit and percussion, classical and electric guitars and voice. The department consists of 3 full-time, 2 part-time and 25 specialist instrumental staff. Facilities include a fine Steinway model D Concert Grand Piano and there is a large Rodgers Digital Organ in the Chapel. Some 30 ensembles rehearse each week, giving plentiful opportunities to performers of all ages and all instruments. The department currently runs 7 choirs of various kinds and styles from the renowned Chapel Choir to the lighter sounds of Girlforce9. Concerts of all kinds take place throughout each term and the Wellington Professional Concerts Series bring world class musicians to the School to give recitals and masterclasses. The 'Full Circle' series invites former pupils who have pursued Music to return and perform at the School. Pupils are entered for ABRSM, Trinity Guildhall and Rockschool exams each term.

Physical Education and Games. All pupils play games regularly, unless exempt for medical reasons. Physical Education, which is also part of the curriculum for Years 6 to 11, takes place in the Sports Complex. All pupils learn to swim and are given the opportunity to take part in as many sports as possible. In the winter term, rugby and hockey are the main sports; in the spring term hockey, netball and cross-country running; in the summer term athletics, cricket, tennis, swimming and rounders. Team practices take place throughout the week with matches on Saturday afternoons. The school has a specialist fencing teacher and the Sports Complex houses a purpose-built fencing salle.

Out of School and CCF Activities. All pupils from the Year 10 upwards either join the large CCF contingent, with army, naval and RAF sections, or are engaged in other activities on a weekly basis, ranging from community services and conservation, to gardening and stage crew. Outward Bound Activities, both within the CCF and as part of the flourishing Duke of Edinburgh's Award Scheme, are very popular, with many trips organised. The CCF also has a highly respected Corps of Drums, which frequently features in local ceremonial events. Societies, in addition to the above, include art, chess and drama at various levels, cookery, computing and others.

Careers. A complete careers guidance service is offered in a well-equipped suite of Careers Rooms.

Admission. Entrance exam for Years 6 and 7. Interviews for Year 8 and above. There is a registration fee of £50 for all pupils.

Scholarships and Bursaries. A significant number of academic and all-rounder scholarships are offered each year for entrants to Years 6, 7 and 9. Music scholarships are awarded for entry into Year 7 and Year 9 and above.

The School also awards Academic Grants for entry into Years 6 and 7 – these are income-based awards and can provide remission of up to two-thirds of fees. A further bursary is available on entry to the Sixth Form.

Academic Grants. A number of reduced-fee places are given annually to those academically able pupils whose parents would not otherwise be able to meet the fees.

Fees per term (2008-2009). Boarders £5,983 which includes tuition, board, laundry, medical attention and Medical Centre, stationery and games. Day pupils: £3,365.

Extras. Apart from purely personal expenses, the termly extras are private music lessons from £160 to £205; Activities and CCF £4 and £8 respectively; Boarding House subscription £10; EFL lessons at various rates depending on need.

Charitable status. Wellington School is a Registered Charity, number 310268. It aims to provide a happy, caring co-educational day and boarding community, where pupils are provided with the opportunity of making best use of their academic experience and the School enrichment activities, in order to enhance their overall preparation for life after the age of eighteen.

Wells Cathedral School

Wells Somerset BA5 2ST
Tel: 01749 834200
Fax: 01749 834201
e-mail: admissions@wells-cathedral-school.com
website: www.wells-cathedral-school.com

In 909AD there was a Cathedral School in Wells providing education for choir boys. Today, Wells Cathedral School is fully co-educational. Its spirit is a passion for learning and life; its dream an inspiring education set in a musically alive and beautiful environment as a brilliant foundation for life; and its focus, inspiring success.

Patron: HRH The Prince of Wales

Governors:
Chairman: The Very Revd John Clarke, MA (*Dean of Wells*)
The Revd Canon A Featherstone
Stella Clarke, CBE, DL, JP, LLB
M Willey, FRTPI, FCIS
P McIlwraith, FCA
Rodney Drew, BSc
Prebendary Helen Ball, OBE
Robert Sommers, MA
Prebendary Elsa Van Der Zee
Martin Smout, BSc, CEng, MICE
Mrs Jo Ballan-Whitfield, BSc, ACA

Consultant to the Governing Body:
Prof David Strange, FRAM

Music Consultant:
Christopher Adey, FRCM, FRAM

***Head*: Elizabeth Cairncross**, BA

Deputy Head: C Cain, BA
Deputy Head (*Curriculum*): N D Walkey, MSc, FSS
Director of Music: Mrs D Nancekievill, BA, BMus

Senior School

Teaching Staff:
Mrs A M Armstrong, BMus, LRAM
M J Ashton, BA
Ms C Barker, BSc
Ms V Baron
Mrs H Bennett, BA
Prof J Berry, BSc, PhD, FIMA, CMath
N Bowen, BA
J Boot, BA
J Byrne, Dip Moscow Cons, PPRNCM, DipRAM
Mrs N Cage, BA
Mrs E Cheetham, BA
Mrs N A M Connock, BSc
C S Day, BA
P Denegri, FTCL, LTCL
Mrs S Evans, ALA (*Librarian*)
Mrs M C Fielding, BSc

Mrs P J Garty, BSc
Ms J Gearon, BA, MA
D Gowen, BA
M Grogan, MA, DipTEFL
D C Hansom, BMus, LRSM, ARCM
R Henson, GRLC, PhD
K H Humphreys, BSc
Mrs M Humphreys, BA
Miss S Jameson, BSc
D Jones, BSc
A M Laing, MA
Miss C Lord, ARCM, Juillard Diploma
J C C Machling, BMus, Grad RNCM
B McGee, BA
Dr H Murphy, MA, BMus, LRAM, PhD
Dr K Murphy, BA, MMus, PhD
Miss B Murray, GRSM, ARCM
Mrs J Obradovic, LTCL
K Orchard, BSc
K Padgett, BSc
Mrs E Paul, BA
L Plum, BA
W C R Robbetts, BA, MEd, MIBiol
D Rowley, BSc
Mrs S G Rowley, BA
B Salisbury, BA, PGCE
P Silverwood, ICA
M Souter
Mrs L J Stockdale-Bridson, BA
M Sully, BSc
M Swarfield, BA
Mrs J S Tapner, BA, ADT
S Tapner, BSc
Miss K Trego, BA
Mrs L E Walkey, CertEd
J Williams, BA

Junior School

The Head of Junior School: N M Wilson, BA

Deputy Head: Mrs J Barrow, BEd

Mrs J Bennett, BA
Ms D Bucknall, BSc
Mrs J Burns, TDip CSSD, LUD Drama
Miss A Clark, BEd
Miss V Clarke, BEd
Mrs E Drabble, CertEd
Mrs J Edmonds, BSc, ALCM
Mrs P Evans, BEd
Miss A Maidment, BEd
M Miller, BA
Mrs A Sparshott-Thompson, BEd
Miss K Summers, BEd
Mrs J Tucker, DipEd
Ms R Warner, BA

Bursar and Clerk to the Governors: S Webber, MA, FCMA, FCIS
Assistant Clerk to the Governors: D Shortland-Ball
Deputy Bursar: Ms P Smart
Registrar: A Deacon, BSc, ACIB, FRSA
Head's PA: Mrs C Edwards
Development Director: Revd A Bretherton
Marketing Manager: Mrs A Page
School Doctor: Dr C Bridson, MB BS, MRCGP, DipOCC, MED
School Sister: Mrs L Wiscombe, RGN

There is a Senior and Junior School with 696 boys and girls aged from 3 to 18. Boarders number 195, whilst the remainder are day pupils. Once accepted, a child normally remains in the School without further Entrance Examination until the age of 18+. There are 351 girls of whom 104 are boarders. They join in all activities but there are also opportunities for separate interests.

Fees per term (2008-2009). Senior School (Years 10–13): Boarders £7,457, Day £4,461. Lower School (Years 7–9): Boarders £7,177, Day £4,310. Junior School (Years 3–6): Boarders £6,116, Day £3,528. Pre-Prep (Reception–Year 2): Day £1,895. Nursery: £17.45 per 2 hour, 35 minute session.

Scholarships and Entrance. (*see Scholarship Entries section*). Scholarships are awarded as a result of Entrance and Scholarship Tests taken in January at the School. These consist of tests and interviews, whilst also considering any specialist gifts or aptitudes.

Sixth Form Scholarships are awarded on the basis of rigorous interview, predicted GCSE results and a confidential reference from the applicant's current school.

Cathedral Choristerships are awarded as the result of a Choral Trial. Applicants should be between 8½ and 10½ at the time of the Trial. Entrance Tests can be arranged in any term and special arrangements can be made for children overseas.

Situations and Buildings. The mediaeval city of Wells, with its famous Cathedral and a population of only 10,500, is the smallest city in England. It is just over 20 miles from Bath and Bristol where there is a good rail service, and easily accessed from the M4 and M5 motorways. Bristol International Airport is a 40-minute drive away. The School occupies all but one of the canonical houses in The Liberty. This fine group is planned to keep its mediaeval and 18th Century atmosphere while providing for the needs of modern boarding education. There are modern classrooms and science laboratories built amongst walled gardens. A Sports Hall provides indoor facilities for Tennis, Badminton, Cricket, Basketball, Volleyball, Hockey, Five-a-Side Football, Climbing and Multi-Gym. There are Theatrical and Concert facilities, a Music Technology Centre, a Computer Studies Centre, Art, Design and Technology Department, Drama Studio, Library, Sixth Form Centre, 25-metre covered Swimming Pool, Tennis and Netball courts, three sports fields and an all-weather hard play area.

There are two Boarding Houses in the Junior and Lower School and a further six in the Senior School, three for boys and three for girls, the most senior pupils having study-bedrooms. The aim is to give security to the younger and to develop a sense of responsibility in the older.

Organisation and Curriculum. Despite its national and international reputation, the School has retained close links with the local community, and its fundamental aim is to provide all its pupils with an education consistent with the broad principles of Christianity. More specifically, the School aims to be a well-regulated community in which pupils may learn to live in harmony and mutual respect with each other and with the adults who care for them. The curriculum has been designed to enable all children who gain entry to the School to develop fully all their abilities, and to take their place in due course in tertiary education and the adult community of work and leisure. There are four Forms before the Sixth Form. Forms are limited to a maximum of 25; average class sizes are typically less than this. Two years before GCSE a tutorial system is introduced whereby some ten boys and girls are the responsibility of one member of Staff for academic progress to GCSE. Pupils then choose a subject faculty for sixth form tutoring in similar groups.

The emphasis is on setting by ability in particular subjects rather than streaming. There is every attempt to avoid early specialisation. All take Mathematics, English, double Science, and a foreign language to GCSE. There is a Sixth Form of some 161 taking A Level courses in all major academic subjects.

Many places have been gained at Oxford and Cambridge in recent years and most Sixth Formers leave for some form of higher education.

Societies. There is a wide range of indoor and outdoor activities in which pupils must participate, although the choice is theirs. Outdoor education is an important part of the curriculum. Besides a Combined Cadet Force with Army and RAF sections and a Duke of Edinburgh's Award scheme, activities as diverse as chess and kite making, photography, sailing and golf are also on offer. Ballet and riding lessons are also arranged.

Music. The School is one of five in the UK designated and grant-aided by the Department for Children, Schools and Families (DCSF) to provide special education for gifted young musicians, who are given substantial financial assistance. Wells is unique in that both specialist and non-specialist musicians are able to develop their aptitudes within a normal school environment. These talents are widely acknowledged by audiences at concerts given by pupils from Wells throughout the world.

There are over 140 talented pupils following specially devised timetables which combine advanced instrumental tuition and ensemble work with academic opportunity. More than half of the School learns at least one musical instrument. Violin is taught to all children in the Pre-Prep as part of the curriculum. Pupils receive the highest quality teaching, often leading to music conservatoires and a career in Music. Central to specialist music training are the opportunities to perform in public and there is a full concert diary. There are also regular concerts by the many ensembles in the School.

For further details contact: The Registrar, Wells Cathedral School, Wells, Somerset BA5 2ST. Tel: 01749 834200, e-mail: admissions@wells-cathedral-school.com.

The Wellensian Association. Chris Neave, Chairman, Old Wellensians, Wells Cathedral School, Wells, Somerset BA5 2ST.

Charitable status. Wells Cathedral School Limited is a Registered Charity, number 310212. It is a charitable trust for the purpose of promoting the cause of education in accordance with the doctrine of the Church of England.

West Buckland School

Barnstaple Devon EX32 0SX
Tel: 01598 760281
Fax: 01598 760546
e-mail: headmaster@westbuckland.devon.sch.uk
website: www.westbuckland.devon.sch.uk

West Buckland School was founded in 1858 "to provide a first class education at reasonable cost". It has always stressed the importance of all-round character development alongside good academic achievement. Our size allows pupils to receive plenty of individual care and attention to their needs and talents.

West Buckland Preparatory School educates children between the ages of three and eleven. There is strong cooperation and support between the schools which share the same grounds, so making the transition as easy as possible.

West Buckland is fully co-educational.

Motto: '*Read and Reap*'

President: Mr Paul Orchard-Lisle, CBE, TD, LLD(hc), DSc(hc), MA, FRICS

The Governing Body:

Chairman: W H G Geen

Vice-Chairmen:
The Countess of Arran, DL
S D Fox, BA

Governors:
Prof L M la Velle, MSc, PhD
Mrs M E Collyer, BA
C Fletcher-Wood, OBE, BA
Lady Gass, JP, MA
The Venerable David Gunn-Johnson
G G Harrison, BSc, FRICS
J Nichols, MA, FRSA, FCollP
C D Phillips, BSc, FRICS, ACI, Arb, MEWI
M Popplewell, BSc Hons
J K Singh, JP
Mrs R Thomas, CBE, DSc(hc), DL
D Walker
Mrs C M Williams, BA

***Headmaster*: J F Vick**, MA St John's College, Cambridge

Deputy Head: D M Hymer, BSc University College, London

Director of Studies: C J Burrows, MA Exeter College, Oxford

Second Deputy Head: Mrs R C Tibble, BA Open University

Headmaster, Preparatory School: A D Moore, BEd

Chaplain: The Revd A M Kettle, MA

Houses & Housemasters/mistresses:
Brereton House: Mrs R H Berry, MA Bristol
Courtenay House: A J Calder, BSc Brunel
Fortescue House: Miss E Rushe, BSc University College Dublin
Grenville House: J A Ralph, BA University of Wales Aberystwyth

Teaching Staff:
C J Allin, BA
C Block, BA
Mme M LeBarth
Mrs J Beech
C J Block, BA
M T Brimson, BA
Mrs J E Brock, MEd
Mrs J F Bunclark, MA
Dr I Buschmann, PhD
Miss A Callow, BSc
Mrs J M Carter, BSc
R D Clarke, BA, BEd
Mrs H Clements, BA
B M Coates, MA
Mrs A Cope, BA Hons
P H Davies, BSc
C H Dawson, BSc
Mrs N M de Marco, BA
J W R Dougall, BSc Hons
R A Durrant, BSc
A D Evans, BEd
Mrs S G Fowles, BSc
M J Greer, BA
Miss A Griffiths, BA Hons
Mrs S P Hartnoll, BEd
Mrs Y Helicon, BA
Mrs K Hoey, BA
A P Hooper, BSc
R M C Horn, BSc
Mrs E M Kent, BMus
Revd A M Kettle, MA
Mrs A Klemz
Mme M LeBarth, L-ès-L
Miss E MacKay, CertEd
Miss K P MacBride, MA
N Minard, BA
W D Minns, BEng
J R Moor, MA
Mrs L Napier, BEd
T O'Brien, BSc
Miss A Pascaud
P J C Ponder, BEd
Miss A-S Prian
D Price, Ed Ord
S J Prior, BSc
Mrs A L Pugsley, BA
S Robinson, BSc
Miss D J Sharman, BSc
N T Shawcross, BSc
M G Stuart, BA
M J Tucker, CertEd
T Wilks, BSc Hons
Mrs J Whittal-Williams
L Whittal-Williams, CertEd
L K Woodward, BEd
Mrs A V Wyatt, BEd

Visiting Music Staff:
Mrs P Adie (*Singing*)
C Block (*Saxophone, Jazz Piano*)
M Bosworth (*Organ and Piano*)
Ms J Buckingham (*Clarinet*)
K Chetwin (*Guitar*)
T Collinson (*Double Bass*)
Mrs L Cooper (*Piano*)
Mrs A Hammond (*Violin and Piano*)
Mrs E Hewetson (*Violin*)
Ms H Kerry (*Cello and Piano*)
Mrs J Norris (*Violin, Viola, Oboe*)
A Parton (*Trumpet and Bass*)
Mrs A Prior (*Piano*)
Ms R Priscott (*Piano and Theory*)
Mrs S Steele (*Flute, Piano*)
B Waring (*Percussion*)

Bursar: Cdr A R Jackson, MILT, MInstAM
Finance Officer: Mrs K Powell
Domestic Bursar: Mrs T Widlake
Bursar's Secretary: Mrs J Harris
Fees Secretary: D Foster
Headmaster's Secretary: Mrs S Hughes
Registrar: Mrs L A Millar
Receptionist/Admin Assistant: Mrs L Lancaster
Registration Secretary/Admin Assistant: Mrs C Smalley
Medical Officer: Dr C A Gibb, BMed, BM, DA, MRCGP, DRCOG, DPD
School Sisters: Mrs C E Pouncey, RGN; Mrs G M Rowland, RGN

Houseparents:
Dr I M Buschmann
Mrs J E Moor
Mrs A Seager

Mrs N Stuart
Mrs J Hemus
Mrs A Davey

Development Office:
Mrs S Pollard (*Director*)
J Mason

Librarian: Mrs J A Thayre, ALA
Uniform Shop: Mrs T Stewart
School Staff Instructor: D J Morgan

Situation. The School stands in its own grounds of 100 acres on the southern edge of Exmoor. Barnstaple is 10 miles away and the M5 motorway can be reached in 40 minutes. Boarders arriving by train at Exeter station are met by coaches.

Buildings and Grounds. The central range of buildings, dating from 1861, still forms the focus of the school, and now includes a performing arts centre. Other recent developments include a Sixth Form Centre, Mathematics and Physics Centre, new boarding houses for boys and girls, a new Preparatory School classroom block and the IT Centre. The campus offers extensive sports facilities, including a 9 hole golf course, an indoor heated 25 metre swimming pool, and an Astroturf hockey pitch. The Jonathan Edwards Sports Centre is now completed and open.

Admission. Boys and girls are admitted as boarders or day pupils. The present number of pupils is: 92 boarding, 696 day.

Entrance to the Preparatory School is by interview and assessment. Entry to the Senior School is by examination at 11 and 13, or to the Sixth Form upon interview and school report. Entry at other ages is usually possible, and arrangements are made to suit individual circumstances.

Fees per term (2008-2009). Senior: Boarding £5,575–£6,225; Day £3,600 Preparatory: Boarding £4,625; Day £1,970–£2,960. Nursery £15.40 (mornings), £8.20 (lunch times), £15.40 (afternoons).

Scholarships and Bursaries. (*see Scholarship Entries section*). Several scholarships are offered at 11, 13 and 16 (value at the discretion of the Headmaster). Candidates must be under 12, under 14, or under 17 years of age on 1st September.

With the support of the West Buckland School Foundation, means-tested bursaries are available for boarders and day students at all ages.

Curriculum. In the Preparatory School the main emphasis is upon well-founded confidence in English and Mathematics, within a broad balance of subjects that adds modern languages to the national curriculum. Particular attention is given to the development of sporting, artistic and musical talents.

In the Senior School breadth is complemented by specialisation. All students study the three separate sciences from Year 7, while French and Spanish are the principal languages offered. Our flexible options arrangements at GCSE respond to students' individual strengths and preferences. A wide range of A Level subjects is offered to sixth formers whose results uphold the high academic standards of the School.

Careers. The Careers Staff advise all pupils upon the openings and requirements for different careers. They make full use of the facilities offered by Connexions.

Games, The Performing Arts and other activities. One of the most impressive features of life at West Buckland is the quality and range of extra curricular activities. The level of involvement by pupils and staff is very high indeed.

The school has a strong sporting tradition. Rugby, hockey, cricket, netball, tennis, athletics, swimming, cross-country, squash, golf, shooting and many other sports offer opportunities for inter-school and inter-house competition and for recreation.

About a third of all pupils receive instrumental and singing tuition from specialist teachers. The wide range of choirs and instrumental groups give concerts at least once a week throughout the year. Drama is a strength of the school with productions of many kinds throughout the year.

Music. Over 120 members of the school receive instrumental tuition on all instruments. They are encouraged to perform in concerts, in choirs and instrumental groups. Music Technology is a strong feature of the department's work.

Outdoor Education. Much use is made of the proximity of Exmoor and the coast for climbing, kayaking, mountain biking, surfing and other adventurous activities. All pupils receive instruction in camp craft, first aid and map reading. The Combined Cadet Force has Army and Royal Air Force sections, and offers a range of challenging pursuits. Our students succeed at all levels in the Duke of Edinburgh's Award Scheme each year, and there is a regular programme of expeditions in this country and overseas.

Religion. The tradition is Anglican but all denominations and religions are welcome. Services of worship are held throughout the week including many Sundays. A number of services are held at East Buckland Church. The Chaplain prepares boys and girls for confirmation every year.

Attitudes and values. The School sets out to be a friendly and purposeful community in which happiness and a sense of security are the foundation on which young lives are built. At all levels members of the school are asked to lead a disciplined way of life, to show consideration for others, to be willing to be challenged and to recognise that the success of the individual and the success of the group are inextricably linked.

Charitable status. West Buckland School is a Registered Charity, number 306710. Its purpose is the education of boys and girls from 3 to 18.

Westminster School

17 Dean's Yard Westminster London SW1P 3PB
Tel: 020 7963 1042 (Head Master)
020 7963 1003 (Registrar)
020 7963 1000 (Other enquiries)
020 7821 5788 (Westminster Under School)
Fax: 020 7963 1043
e-mail: registrar@westminster.org.uk
website: www.westminster.org.uk

Westminster School is a Boarding and Day School which is co-educational in the Sixth Form. The present number of boys and girls is about 740.

The School traces its origins to the grammar school that was attached to the Benedictine Abbey at Westminster. Queen Elizabeth I re-founded the School in 1560 as part of the College of St Peter at Westminster.

Motto: '*Dat Deus Incrementum*'

Visitor: Her Majesty The Queen

Governing Body:
Chairman: The Very Revd J R Hall, The Dean of Westminster
The Dean of Christ Church, The Very Revd Dr C A Lewis
The Master of Trinity, Lord Rees of Ludlow, OM, PRS
The Revd Canon Dr N Sagovsky
The Revd Canon R P Reiss
D H Rice, Esq, BPhil, MA
Dr J A Marenbon (*OW*)
The Lord Hunt of Chesterton, CB, FRS (*OW*)
M C Baughan, Esq (*OW*)
C N Foster, Esq, FCA (*OW*)
Dr P Chadwick, MA, FRSA
Professor C R W Edwards, MD, FRCP, FRCPEd, FRSE, FMedSci, HonDSc
Dr A C N Borg, CBE, FSA (*OW*)
B A Segal, Esq
A J T Willoughby, Esq (*OW*)
Sir Peter Ogden
T M S Young Esq MA

E R Neville-Rolfe Esq MA (*OW*)
I W Harrison Esq

Secretary to the Governing Body and Bursar: C A J Silcock

***Head Master*: M S Spurr**, MA, DPhil

Under Master: G J Savage, MA, PhD

Master of The Queen's Scholars: Mrs F M R Ramsey, MA, DPhil

Director of Studies: C R L Low, MA

Senior Master: Mrs D J Harris, MA

Registrar: J M Curtis, MA

Assistant Staff:
E A Smith, MSc
C Clarke, FRSA (*Senior Tutor*)
D L Edwards, MA
G Griffiths, BA
J E C Arthur, MA
Mrs J L Cockburn, MA, PhD
M C Davies, MA
P D Hargreaves, MA
A E A Mylne, MA
R J Pyatt, MA
C D Riches, BEd, MSc
S C Savaskan, BA, MMus, DPhil
J B Katz, MA, DPhil
R Dudley-Smith, BSc, MA
M N Robinson, BA
H A Aplin, BA, PhD
Miss G M French, MSc, MRSC, LTCL, FRSA
R R Harris, MA
G P A Brown, MA, DPhil
G K Jones, MA
J J Kemball, BSc
J R G Beavon, PhD
S Craft, MA
S N Curran, BA
R J Hindley, MA, CMath
Mrs A J Jørgensen, MA
A R Morris, BA, MSc, PhD
K D Tompkins, BA
G StJ Hopkins, BA
Mrs J A Lambert, BSc, MBA
D R Hemsley-Brown, BSc, MIEE
J N Hooper, BA
J D Kershen, BA, MA
Mrs L D MacMahon, BA
M H Feltham, MA
Mrs S M Barry, ARCM, LRAM
N G Kalivas, BSc, DPhil
Miss T E L Morris, MA
J M Barot, MA, MSc
Mrs F G Sharp, MA
Miss G D Ward-Smith, MA, PhD
J C Witney, MA, MIL
K A P Walsh, BSc, PhD
Mrs E Brown, BA, MPhil
R M Huscroft, MA, PhD
A Johnson, BA
M J Milner, MA, DPhil
R P Allnatt, BA, MLitt
M A Boulton, BEng, PhD
A M L Crole, BA, MA
P A Hartley, BSc, PhD
J A Ireland, MA
S D Wurr, BA
C J R Ullathorne, MA, MSci
C J Barton, BA
A J Law, BA
Revd G J Williams, MA
G J A Simpson, BSc
Mrs S Thomas, BA, DipLib
P A Botton, BSc
S C Hawken, MA
Mrs C Stevens, BSc
R Agyare-Kwabi, BEng, MPhil, PhD
S Baldock, BA
Mrs A E Cave-Bigley, MA
P J Chequer, DipPA
G A D Hayter, MMath
U Hennig, BA
T D Page, MA
A J Sproat, BA
Miss K E Radice, BA
B J Smith, MA
Miss E Veninata, BA
J B Baughan, MA, MLitt, PhD
J R Goodall, BA
Miss S E Leonard, BSc
A R P Perkins, BA
Miss H J Prentice, MSci, MA, PhD
N J Simons, MMath

Houses and Housemasters:

Boarding only House for Queen's Scholars:
College: Mrs F M R Ramsey, MA, DPhil

Boarding and Day Houses:
Boys:
Grant's, 2 Little Dean's Yard: P D Hargreaves
Rigaud's, 1 Little Dean's Yard: K D Tompkins
Liddell's, 19 Dean's Yard: T D Page
Mixed:
Busby's, 26 Great College Street: A E A Mylne

Girls' Boarding only House:
Purcell's, 5 Barton Street: R R Harris

Day only Houses:
Ashburnham, 6 Dean's Yard: G K Jones
Dryden's, 4 Little Dean's Yard: Dr M A Boulton
Hakluyt's, 19 Deans' Yard: J J Kemball
Milne's, 5A Dean's Yard: K P Walsh
Wren's, 4 Little Dean's Yard: M H Feltham

Chaplain: Revd G J Williams
Director of Music: G StJ Hopkins, BA
Librarian: Mrs S Thomas, BA, DipLib
Archivist: E A Smith, MSc
Head of Girls: Mrs D J Harris, MA

Westminster Under School

Master: J P Edwards, BA, MA
Deputy Head: D S C Bratt, BA

Assistant Staff:
Mrs G Howarth, MA
Miss S E K Corps, BSc
A J Downey, BA, MA
S R H James, BA
J S Walker, BEd, LRAM (*Director of Music*)
P Russell, BA
Mrs H M Arthur, CertEd
Mrs P McLean, BEd, MA
Ms F Illingworth, BA
Mrs C Stevens, BSc
E Jolliffe, BA, MMus
Miss M Ellis, BEd
Mrs M Barley, BSc
A J P Busk, Dip Fine Art
P J E V Evans, MA
Miss N C Evans, BSc
Mrs M Cade, BA, MA
I D Hepburn, BA
P L West, BA, BD, PhD
D Kendall, BA
Miss E Hart, BEd
D Swana, PPRNCM
P Cheetham, BA
Mrs F J Schwarz, BEd
I R Goodman, MA
S Thebaud, BSc

The Queen's Scholars, who normally number 40, board in College, one of our 6 boarding houses. 8 Queen's Scholarships worth 50% of the boarding fee are awarded annually following a competitive examination called The Challenge. Boys, who must be under 14 on 1 September of their year of entry, sit The Challenge at Westminster School in early May. Application forms and past papers may be obtained from The Registrar's Secretary (tel: 020 7963 1026, email: registrar@westminster.org.uk). The Challenge consists of papers in Mathematics, English, French, Science, Latin, History and Geography. There is also an optional Greek paper. A scholarship, which is not means-tested, is normally tenable for 5 years. Small awards (normally 6 a year) of between £510 and £1050 a year are made to candidates who perform well in the examination but who are not awarded Queen's Scholarships.

Music Scholarships. Up to 6 Music Scholarships worth 25% of the boarding or day fee and free tuition for 3 instruments are awarded annually. There are also several Music Exhibitions which provide for free music tuition on two instruments. Candidates must be under 14 on the 1 September of their year of entry. Applications close in early January and the auditions take place in early February. It is recommended that parents contact the Director of Music, Guy Hopkins, to arrange an informal audition before submitting an application. (Please telephone the Music Secretary on 020 7963 1017) Music Scholarships are also available at Westminster Under School at 11+.

Bursaries. Westminster School has, since its first foundation, made it possible for academically able pupils to attend the School who would not otherwise have been able to do so without financial support. Bursaries (remission of fees) up to a maximum of 100% are available and are awarded to pupils who gain a place on academic merit and according to individual need following a full financial assessment, which may include a home visit. Bursaries are awarded at 13 + and 16+ entry to Westminster School and at 11+ entry to Westminster Under School. All bursaries continue until a pupil leaves the

School at 18, although they may be adjusted up or down if financial circumstances change. Parents who wish to apply for financial assistance should request a Bursary Application Form from the Registrar at Westminster School (tel: 020 7963 1003) or Westminster Under School (tel: 020 7821 5788) as appropriate.

Admission. The two main points of admission are 13+ (boys only) and 16+ (girls and boys). Parents are advised to register their sons for 13+ entry by the start of Year 6 – the academic year of a child's 11th birthday – although registration does not close until the end of Year 6. While he is in Year 6 the boy will come to Westminster School to sit tests in Mathematics, English and Verbal Reasoning and he will also be invited for interview on a separate day. On the basis of the candidate's test results, the interview and a report from his present school a decision will be made whether to offer a conditional place. Boys with conditional places must still qualify for entry to the School by sitting the Common Entrance examinations or The Challenge (scholarship examinations) when they are 13, but failure at this stage is rare. Candidates who are not offered a conditional place may be invited to sit further tests at the start of Year 8. Registration for 16+ entry opens in the summer a year before entry. Entry is by competitive examination and interview at the School in November. Candidates choose four entry examination subjects, usually the four subjects they plan to take for A Level. For further information about entry at 13+ or 16+ or to arrange a visit to the School please telephone 020 7963 1003.

Fees per term (2008-2009). Boarding: £9,172, £4,586 (Queen's Scholars). Day Pupils (inclusive of lunch): £6,352, £6,888 (entry at Sixth Form). Under School: £4,412.

Preparatory Department (Day Boys only). The Under School has 260 pupils; entry is at 7, 8 and 11. All enquiries should be addressed to the Master (Mr J P Edwards), Westminster Under School, Adrian House, 27 Vincent Square, London SW1P 2NN (tel: 020 7821 5788).

(*For further details, see entry in IAPS section.*)

Charitable status. St Peter's College (otherwise known as Westminster School) is a Registered Charity, number 312728. The school was established under Royal Charter for the provision of education.

Whitgift School

Haling Park South Croydon CR2 6YT
Tel: 020 8688 9222
Fax: School Office: 020 8760 0682
Headmaster: 020 8649 7594
e-mail: office@whitgift.co.uk
website: www.whitgift.co.uk

Foundation: The Whitgift Foundation originated in 1596 and the School was opened by Archbishop Whitgift in 1600. It is an Independent Day School.

Motto: '*Vincit qui patitur*'

The Whitgift Foundation:
Visitor: His Grace The Lord Archbishop of Canterbury

Five members are appointed by the Archbishop of Canterbury, 2 by the London Borough of Croydon and 4 by co-optation. The Bishop of Croydon and the Vicar of Croydon are appointed ex officio.

Chairman of the Court of The Whitgift Foundation: I Harley, MA, FCA, FCIB

Whitgift School:
Patron: HRH The Duke of York, KCVO, ADC
Chairman of the Whitgift School Governors: G H Wright, TD, DL, FCIOB

Whitgift School Governors:
C A Barnett, MA, DPhil
M J Irwin
The Revd Canon C J Luke Boswell, Vicar of Croydon
P J Squire, MA
Sir David Hancock, KCB
Lord Palumbo
His Honour Judge W Barnett, QC
D C Hudson, MA Oxon
Cllr D S Mead, FCCA, FCMA, FCIS
R J A I Catto, MA, DPhil
Chair of the Whitgift School Association
The Second Master
The Deputy Headmaster
The President of the Common Room
The Bursar
The Clerk to the Foundation

***Headmaster*: C A Barnett**, MA, DPhil, Oriel College, Oxford

Second Master: J D C Pitt, MA
Deputy Headmaster: P J Yeo, BA
Assistant Head (Proctor): D E C Elvin, BSc, MSc
Assistant Head (Pastoral) & Head of IB: S D Cook, BA, MPhil
Assistant Head (Academic): D M Munks, MA, MSc, LRAM, ARCO
Head of Upper School & Head of Sixth Form: M J Brown, BA
Head of Lower School: A C Kingsbury, BA
Head of Academic & Project Development & Head of Third Form: J A Reddy, MA

Assistant Teaching Staff:
K Allenby, BSc
D W Attfield, BSc (*Examinations Officer*)
D Bailey, BA
J T Barber, BA
J Barfield, BA
S A Beck, BEd (*Deputy Head of Lower School & Registrar*)
H K Bedford, BA
L S Beecham, BA
M J Bradley, BA
J M Brown, BSc (*Head of Geography*)
J P D Cannon, BA, MPhil, PhD (*Head of English*)
C Carolan, HDE (*Head of Learning Development*)
J Carroll, BSc
D Chan, BSc
KJ Coffin, BA
W E Collinson, BA
B R d'Arcy, MA
L G d'Arcy, MChem (*Head of First Form*)
P J Dibsdall, BSc
R J Dinnage, BA
P Dinnen, MA
R Earl, BSc
D J Edwards, BA (*Housemaster, Mason's*)
P W Elliott, BSc (*Head of Science*)
P J Ellis, BSc (*Head of Mathematics*)
V R Ellwood, BA (*Housemaster, Smith's*)
C A Evans, BSc
F L Exley, BSc
L Faux-Newman, BSc, PhD
V Fifield, BSc
V Fitzgerald, BSc, PhD
P C Fladgate, BEd
E D Fountain, B Econ, LLB, MPhil, DPhil (*Head of History*)
E A Gell, MA
B Gouttenoire, BA
B Graoui, BSc
J B Green, BSc (*Housemaster, Brodie's*)
C B Griffin, BA (*Director of Art*)

K Gross, MA (*Head of Bilingual Studies*)
I P Hanley, BSc
D F Hares, BSc (*Head of Biology*)
D R Harkin, BA
C J Harwood, BSc (*Head of ICT*)
T Hibberd, BA (*Head of Theology & Philosophy*)
S M Hill, MA
S M Hooker, MA (*Head of Careers & Guidance*)
F E Holden, BA
J Humphrey, UEFA
A J Hunt, MPhil (*Head of Oriental Languages*)
G F Hunter, MA (*Head of Physics*)
M J Ibáñez, MA
L Jackson, BA
R B Johnstone, BEd (*Head of Design Technology*)
N M Kendrick (*Sports Liaison Officer & Cricket Coach*)
C J Kibble, BEd (*Director of Sports Facilities & Development*)
E G Lance, BSc (*Head of Fifth Form*)
S E Lane, BA
B Lewis, BA (*Head of ICT Coordination*)
P Liberti, U de Studi di Udine (*Head of Italian*)
R M Ling, BA
S W Litchfield, BEd (*Head of PE*)
L Ma, BA
A G Margerison, MA, DPhil (*Housemaster, Cross's*)
R F Martin, MA (*Senior Housemaster; Housemaster, Tate's*)
R M C McGrath, BA (*Head of Classics*)
C M McKay, BA,
I A McGregor, BA (*Head of Academic Music*)
S A McIntosh, BA (*Coordinator of Modern Languages, Head of German*)
W A Mehra, MA
S Merlin, BA
D J Milner, BSc, PhD
K Mitchell, BA
A G Moncrieff, BSc (*Housemaster, Andrew's*)
N P Morgan, BA
P J Morrison, BSc
C B Mulholland, BSc
C A Mulley, BSc
R I Munro, BSc
A Norris, BA (*Director of Sport*)
M Ofner, PhD, DipTEFL, DELE (*Head of Spanish*)
A G Osborne, BA (*Director of Sport*)
J O'Shea, MMath
J A Owen, BSc, PhD
C Pates (*Soccer Coach*)
A J Pearson, BSc
K D Pinnock, BA
E A Poole, MA
H M Poullain, MA
B Prestney, BA
C Range, Diploma, Speech & Drama
R D Ravenscroft, HDE (*Head of Hockey*)
D J Richards, BA
A-M C Rigard-Asquith, L-ès-L, M-ès-L
J M Rinder, BA (*Head of French*)
A D Seal, BEng
C D Shaw, BA
M L Shepherd, BSc
K A Smith, BA (*Contingent Commander, CCF*)
A H Starmer, BSc
N J R Stebbings, BEng
F M Stedman, MA
L F Temple, LRAM, ARCM
J Thevabalan, MChem
T A Thompson, BSc (*Head of Chemistry*)
V A Tidswell, BSc
D Tredger, BSc (*Head of Economics & Business Studies*)
P M Trewin, BA (*Head of Learning Support*)
S E Wall, MA
H L Wallis, BSc, PhD
D Ward (*Head of Cricket*)
A E Weakley, MA
D M White, MA
R C Whitfield, DipRCM
C J Wilkins (*Director of Sport*)
D R Williams, BTech (*Director of Resources*)
G I Williams, BA
K L Williams, MA
P S Wilson, MA (*Director of Music & Drama*)
J D Wilton, BA
P Winter, GBSM, DipNCOS (*Head of Strings*)
S J Woodward, BSc

Bursar: J T Stremes, BA
School Medical Officer: Dr C J Wilcock, MBBS
Headmaster's PA & Marketing Manager: Mrs C McCormack, DipM, ACIM

Numbers. There are 1,210 boys on roll, 646 in the Upper School and 564 in the Lower School.

Buildings and Grounds. The School has buildings of great character, opened in 1931 and situated in some 45 acres of attractive parkland with extensive playing fields. The original park, sited around a fine quadrangle, includes Big School, classrooms for most Arts subjects and Mathematics. 1990 saw the completion of a very substantial and superbly equipped extension which links Science, Computing, Design Technology and Art and also incorporates a large Library. In February 2005, a major new Sports and Conference Centre was opened, comprising state-of-the-art facilities, such as squash courts, fitness centre, swimming pool, classrooms and a conference suite.

Other separate buildings include the Lower School and the Music School. Sports facilities include courts for fives, squash and tennis and an all-weather hockey pitch.

Aims. The School offers a challenging and balanced education which will prepare its pupils for adult responsibility in the modern world. It aims to combine high academic achievement with the all-round development of the individual through games and co-curricular activities, and a strong encouragement of the pursuit of excellence.

Admission. Entry for boys aged 10, 11, 12 or 13 is by competitive examination and interview. Admission is on the basis of performance in the School's entrance tests and on an assessment of a boy's potential to contribute to, and benefit from, the extra-curricular programme and the wider life of the School. The majority of boys enter at 10 or 11. Application forms may be obtained from the School Office.

Fees per term (2008-2009). £4,272 covering tuition, books, stationery, and games. A substantial number of Bursaries is awarded each year according to need.

Scholarships. (*see Scholarship Entries section*). For entry at the age of 10 or 11, approximately 60 awards carrying partial remission of fees are offered to candidates of outstanding merit in the Selection Tests. At all ages, boys may be considered for all-rounder awards or for scholarships in particular subject areas as well as for academic scholarships. For music awards and scholarships, see **Music** below.

Curriculum. In the first three year groups a general preparation is given. With a few exceptions, boys take all of their GCSE examinations in the Upper Fifth Form. There is no early specialisation but various options are available, with a particularly wide range of languages, including Japanese and Chinese, available. There are bilingual sections in French, German and Spanish. PSHE is taught to all boys throughout the School. A Learning Support department assists boys with specific learning difficulties.

In the Sixth Form, A and AS level subjects can be taken in a wide range of combinations. The International Baccalaureate is also offered in the Sixth Form; in additon there are vocational BTec courses for Sports Science, Music Technology and

Business Studies. Pupils are also prepared for the Oxford and Cambridge entrance process.

Organisation. The academic progress of boys in the First and Third forms is under the supervision of the Head of the Lower School and that of the Fifth and Sixth Forms under the supervision of the Head of the Upper School. Pastoral matters are dealt with by the respective Heads of Year and their assistants. Boys are allocated to eight Houses, which have Upper and Lower School sections, and Housemasters have general responsibility for supervising pupils' development in co-curricular activities. Boys in the Upper Fifth and Sixth Forms have a personal tutor to whom they can turn for help and advice if required.

Religious Education. Every attempt is made to stress the relevance of religious thought to modern living. Although the School has a close link with the Anglican Church, teaching is given in an ecumenical spirit.

Physical Education. All boys, unless excused on medical grounds, take Physical Education, swimming and organised games: rugby, hockey, football, cricket, athletics and many options are available. Facilities are provided for badminton, basketball, fencing, fives, soccer, squash, tennis, shooting and a range of other sports.

Music. All 10 and 11 year old entrants learn a musical instrument for the first term free of charge and, thereafter, private tuition is available in school time. Boys perform in various choral and instrumental ensembles. Concerts are regularly held and opera and musicals are performed each year. Awards carrying free instrumental tuition are available to musically talented pupils, either on admission or subsequently. Music scholarships are also awarded.

Other activities. There are a Combined Cadet Force, with specialist Royal Navy, Army and RAF sections and a Duke of Edinburgh's Award group. There is a large number of play productions (more than ten a year) and boys are encouraged to join some of the many School societies. Field courses and foreign exchange visits are regularly arranged in the holidays, and there is a very large number of link schools in many parts of the world.

Careers Advice. There is a well-equipped Careers Room and a very full service of guidance is offered over choice of career and courses in higher education. The vast majority of pupils go on to universities and colleges after leaving school.

Charitable status. The Whitgift Foundation is a Registered Charity, number 312612. It exists to provide education for boys and girls.

Winchester College

College Street Winchester Hampshire SO23 9NA
Tel: 01962 621100 (Headmaster and Office)
01962 621200 (Bursar)
01962 621247 (Admissions)
Fax: 01962 621106
e-mail: admissions@wincoll.ac.uk
website: www.winchestercollege.org

Winchester College – 'the College of the Blessed Virgin Mary of Winchester near Winchester' – was founded in 1382 by William of Wykeham, Bishop of Winchester. Wykeham planned and created a double foundation consisting of two Colleges, one at Winchester and the other (New College) at Oxford. The two Colleges are still closely associated.

Motto: *'Manners Makyth Man'*

Visitor: The Lord Bishop of Winchester

Warden: Sir David Clementi, MA, MBA

Sub-Warden: R T Fox, CBE, MA, FCIB

Fellows:
Professor A J Ryan, MA, DLitt, FBA
Professor D C Hanna, BA, PhD, FRS
J B W Nightingale, MA, DPhil
R H Sutton, MA
Revd Canon J Shaw, MA, PhD
The Rt Hon Sir Andrew Longmore, PC, MA
M St John Parker, MA
R B Woods, CBE, MA

Honorary Fellow: A H Gordon, OBE, BA, MBA, Hon LLB

Bursar and Secretary: J E Hynam, BEd, MPhil, ACP

***Headmaster*: R D Townsend**, MA, DPhil

Second Master: R J Wyke, MA

Director of Studies: K M Pusey, MusB, GRSM, ARMCM
Deputy Director of Studies: J McManus, MChem, PhD

Undermaster: J G Webster, BA, DPhil (*Head of History*)

Registrar: A P Wolters, BSc, PhD, CChem, MRSC
Deputy Registrar: Mrs K A Richards

Assistant Masters:
P J Krakenberger, MA
M R S Nevin, BA
N Fennell, MA, PhD
G Eyre, MA
J D Falconer, MA, ARCM
T P J Cawse, BSc, PG Dip Dyslexia (*Learning Support Coordinator*)
C J Tolley, MA, DPhil, FRCO
S P Anderson, MA (*Head of Classics*)
S J Bailey, BEd, PhD, FRSA
R S Shorter, BSc, ARCS, DIC, PhD, MInstP, CPhys (*Head of Science*)
L Mackinnon, MA, MLitt (*Moberly Librarian*)
L C Wolff, MA, FRSA (*Head of History of Art*)
C H J Hill, MA (*Head of Mathematics*)
P A Nash, BA, ARCM, LTCL
M D Wallis, MA
P J Metcalfe, BSc Econ, MSc Econ
A S Leigh, MA
Dr B L H MacKinnon, BA, PhD (*Head of Modern Languages*)
N I P MacKinnon, BA
Mrs C A Cooper, BA
C F Upton, BSc
W E Billington, MA, MICE
P G Cornish, BA, MMus, FTCL, ARCM, PhD
J M Cooper, BSc, PhD
D J Ceiriog-Hughes, MA, PhD, FRSA
W G Day, MA, PhD (*Fellows' Librarian; Eccles Librarian*)
Miss C J Ovenden, MA
A P McMaster, BSc
P S A Taylor, BA (*Director of Drama*)
I E Fraser, BSc (*Head of Biology*)
L N Taylor, BA Ed
S K Woolley, MA
N R Chippington, MA, FRCO
M D Hebron, BA, DPhil
P J M Cramer, MA, PhD
C Cai, BA, MA, PhD
C J Good, BEd (*Director of PE and Sport*)
J E Hodgins, BSc, PhD
G J Watson, BA (*Head of Economics*)
C G Yates, BA
J P Cullerne, BSc, DPhil
C S McCaw, BSc, DPhil, DES, CChem, MRSC
T N M Lawson, MA
A D Adlam, Dip Mus
A P Dakin, BA
M Romans, BA, MA, PhD

Mrs L J Quinault, BA (*Head of English*)
Mrs K A Mendelsohn, MA
N A Salway, MA, MSc, DPhil, ARCM, LGSM (*Deputy Master of Music*)
R W Chee-A-Tow, MA
P M Herring, MA
J R Hunt, MA
D E Pounds, BSc (*Head of Geography*)
J E G L Bracey, BA, MA
Mrs R A Hodgins, BA (*Head of Community Service*)
Dr E E Coleman-Jones, BA, DPhil
W M A Land, MA (*Master in College*)
R Price, BA, PhD (*Head of French*)
P M Thomas, BSc
Mrs A M Lombardo, MA, BA
J J L Douglas, BA, MSc (*Head of Physics*)
Mrs G Dowell, MA, BA (*Director of Art*)
D I Follows, MChem, MSc
N P Wilks, MA, ARAM (*Master of Music*)
D E Yeomans, BA
M G Crossland, MPhys
M A Thompson, BSc, PhD, MRSC (*Head of Chemistry*)
M J Winter, MA (*Head of Religious Studies, PSHE Coordinator*)
Revd P A Burt, BA, MA, PhD (*Senior Chaplain*)
G E Munn, MSci
Revd J M White, MEng, MA, BA
R D Wilkinson, CVO, MA (*Head of Spanish*)
M D Archer, MA, FRCO, FGCM, FNMSM, ARCM
Miss M S Copin, BA
S E Hart, MEng
S A Tarrant, MEng (*Head of Design Technology*)
Mrs E Stone, LLB, MLitt, AMusA

In Junior Part (Year 9) boys study Art, Biology, Chemistry, Design Technology, English, French, Geography, History, ICT, Latin, Mathematics, Music, Physics, PE and Religious Studies. One subject is chosen from German, Greek, Chinese, Japanese and Spanish. In the final term of the academic year a choice must be made from Art, DT, ICT, Music or Russian. The core curriculum and the two option blocks continue throughout Middle Part (Year 10) and Vth Book (Year 11). Geography becomes an option against Dual Award Science for one set. The majority of boys continue to study three separate sciences. Geography is also available as an option against a second foreign language. Economics, History of Art, Geography and Religious Studies occur as transition courses in Vth Book. Some modern foreign languages can be studied ab initio at this stage. In VIth Book (Years 12 and 13), almost any combination of arts and sciences can be studied. From September 2008 almost all subjects will adopt the Cambridge Pre-U examinations. There are also post A Level courses. Division – a daily lesson encompassing many aspects of culture and civilisation – plays a central role throughout the curriculum.

Scholarships and Exhibitions. (*see Scholarship Entries section*). The election of scholars and exhibitioners takes place in May each year. Full particulars of the examination can be obtained from the Registrar.

About 14 scholarships and 6 exhibitions are awarded each year. There are 70 scholars, who live together in College. For 2008/09 Scholars are entitled to 25% remission of fees. Applications for bursaries are welcome. Exhibitions ensure a place in a Commoner House but carry no remission of fees.

Music Awards. For information about Music Awards please see entry in Music Scholarships section.

Sixth Form entry. Up to four awards are offered each year to boys joining the Sixth Form from other schools. Examinations and interviews for both awards and places take place in Winchester in late January each year. Enquiries should be sent to the Registrar.

Fees per term (2008-2009). Boarders £9,290 (£27,870 pa), Day Boys £8,825 (£26,475 pa). There is an entrance fee of £500.

Commoners. There are about 60 Commoners in each House and the present Housemasters are:

Chernocke House (A): T N M Lawson
Moberly's (B): P M Herring
Du Boulay's (C): L N Taylor
Fearon's (D): D J Ceiriog-Hughes
Morshead's (E): S J Bailey
Hawkins' (F): N I P MacKinnon*
**From Sept 2011*: J E Hodgins
Sergeant's (G): D E Yeomans
Bramston's (H): J P Cullerne
Turner's (I): N R Chippington
Kingsgate House (K): W E Billington*
**From Sept 2010*: M Romans

A boy's name cannot be entered before he reaches the age of 8; application should be made direct to a Housemaster or to the Registrar as soon as conveniently possible after the boy's eighth birthday. Housemasters do not normally allot firm vacancies until boys are 10½/11 and it is wise to make alternative arrangements until a promise of a vacancy has been given. The Headmaster has from time to time a Nomination for a House at his disposal, and the Registrar keeps a Reserve List; parents wishing to enter the name of a boy aged 10½ or more should write to him. Candidates for Nomination are usually expected to take the scholarship examination in the summer term.

Day boy Commoners are also admitted; details can be obtained from the Registrar.

The usual age of entry to the school is between 13 and 14, but exceptions may be considered in special circumstances.

The entrance examination covers the normal subjects; particulars and copies of recent papers may be obtained from the Registrar.

Term of entry. Usually September.

Old Boys' Society, Wykehamist Society. *Secretary*: D L Fellowes, 17 College Street, Winchester SO23 9LX.

Charitable status. The Warden and Scholars of Winchester College is a Charity. It is exempt from registration, being named as an exempt charity in Schedule 2 of the Charities Act 1960, and therefore has no registration number. The objects of the charity are the advancement of education and activities connected therewith.

Wisbech Grammar School

North Brink Wisbech Cambs PE13 1JX
Tel: 01945 583631 Senior School
01945 586780 Magdalene House
Fax: 01945 476746 Senior School
01945 586781 Magdalene House
e-mail: hmsecretary@wisbechgs.demon.co.uk
website: www.wgs.cambs.sch.uk

The School was founded in 1379 above the South Porch of the Church of St Peter and St Paul, Wisbech. Co-education is well established and this is reflected in the equal numbers of boys and girls who make up the School population. There are now 534 boys and girls in the Senior School, aged from 11 to 18, including about 130 in the Sixth Form. Magdalene House Preparatory Department has 170+ boys and girls aged from Reception to age 11.

The School was substantially rebuilt in 1991 when 19 new classrooms were added, together with specialist rooms for computers and electronics, an assembly hall and a sports hall. More recently the design technology facilities have been extended and upgraded, a second sports pavilion added and a business centre completed (September 2000). The ongoing development programme includes a performing arts centre and a second Astroturf pitch, both of which were opened in September 2003. The most recent development project, a new hall and two new classrooms for the rapidly expanding Magdalene House Preparatory Department, was completed in April 2008.

Governing Body:

Chairman: J A Hazel, FRICS, FNAEA
Dr D Barter, MB BS, FRCP, FRCPCH, DCH
Mrs J Easter, FCCA
F A N Grounds, MA Cantab, ARICS, MRAC
The Venerable Hugh McCurdy, Archdeacon of Huntingdon and Wisbech
Mrs E Morris, LLB
M Rayner
Dr F Sconce, MBChB
Dr F P Treasure, MA, MSc, PhD, CStat
J E Warren (*Junior Vice Chairman*)

Nominated by the Master of Magdalene College, Cambridge:
Dr C F Kolbert, MA, PhD Cantab, DPhil Oxon, FCIArb (*Vice-Chairman*)
R L Skelton, MA, CEng, FIChemE, MIMechE, FINucE

Bursar and Clerk to the Governors: Miss E P Thuburn

Teaching Staff:
* *Head of Department*
† *Head of House*
§ *Part-time*
¶ *Old Pupil*

***Headmaster*: N J G Hammond**, MA Cantab

Deputy Headmaster: J Aguilar, BA
Deputy Headmistress: Miss C M Noxon, BA (*Head of Sixth Form*)
Senior Tutor: A W Ayres, BA (**Chemistry, Higher Education Adviser*)
Director of Studies: M L Forrest, MA (*Chemistry, *General Studies*)

P B Bannister, ACP, CertEd (**Design Technology*)
Miss M P Barrington, BSc, CertEd (*Girls' PE & Games, DofE*)
R J Baty, BA (**Economics, Business Studies*)
§Mrs A L Beck, BA (*History, RS, Games*)
Mrs Z R Booth, BSc (*Mathematics, IT, Head of Lower Sixth Form*)
Mrs J Braybrook, BA (**Spanish*)
Miss A Braithwaite, MA, BSc, ACMI (**Information Technology*)
§Mrs M Calton, BSc (*Biology*)
Mrs J Challinger, BA (**German*)
T D Chapman, MA (*History, †Peckover*)
§A P Clarke, MA, MEd (*French, German*)
§T W Claydon, BSc (*PE & Games*)
Miss A M Clayton, BA (*English*)
Mrs S D Cooper, BA (**Textiles, Art & Design, Deputy Head of Lower School*)
K S Doman, MA (**German*)
§Mrs J Emsley, BA (*IT*)
J G Fitzsimmons, BMus (*Director of Music*)
Mrs S C Fox, BA (**Lower School Science*)
R D Frost, BEd (*Design Technology*)
¶D S Garfoot, BSc (*PE & Games, Geography, †Sparks*)
Mrs A George, BSc (*Geography*)
Miss S E Harris, BEd (**Girls' PE & Games, Science*)
P J Harrison, BA (*Art, †Clarkson*)
G E Howes, BSc (**Mathematics*)
Mrs J Hutchison, BSc (*Mathematics, IT*)
A P Jarvis, BA, MA (**English*)
K J Isaac, BSc, MSc, PhD (*Biology*)
R D Killick, BSc (**Geography*)
P J King, MA (*English, Marketing Director*)
K J Mann, BA, PhD (**History; Head of Lower School*)
Miss F C Meldrum, BA (*Art & Design, Textiles*)
S J Miller, BSc, PhD (**Science, *Biology*)
R P D Munns, BA (*English*)
G H Nunnerley, BSc (**Careers, Geography*)
Mrs S A Ramsay, MA (*English, Head of Middle School*)
§Mrs J T Reavell, BEd (*Games*)
I Ross, MA, BSc, CPhys, MInstP (**Physics*)
§K Rudd, MA (*Design Technology*)
Miss A Shaw (*Girls' PE & Games*)
§Mrs M Skinner, BA (*German*)
¶Mrs A L Sloan, BSc, MA (**Home Economics*)
M P Stump, BA (**Art & Design, Deputy Head of Middle School*)
C Thursby, BA, MA (*Mathematics*)
A Tomlins, BSc (*Boys' PE & Games*)
M J Wager, BA (**French, German, Acting Head of RS*)
P J A Webb, BA (**Boys' PE & Games, History*)
B P Wiles, BSc, MInstP, CPhys (*Physics, Learning Skills Coordinator*)
O Williams, BSc (*Geography, Games*)
K L Wood-Smith, BSc (*Mathematics*)

Headmaster's Secretary: Mrs K Massen
Admissions Secretary: Mrs S Davies

Magdalene House Preparatory Department
(Reception to Year 6)

Head: Mrs C H Cranwell, CertEd
Deputy Head: Mrs G D Reinbold, MA

§Mrs R E Brown, CertEd
Mrs T Crawley, BEd
§Mrs E Fenn, BA
Mrs A Fuller, CertEd
Mrs A Kelly, BA
Mrs C C R Mayer, MA
§Mrs J McAdam, BA
Mr M I McChlery , BA, GTTP Dip
Mrs J Page, BEd
¶Mrs C Sandall, BA
¶Mrs J Stonham, CertEd
Mrs J Whiteman, CertEd

Classroom Assistants:
Mrs V Andrews
Mrs J Baines
¶Mrs R Bingham
Mrs S Boughen
§Mrs L Gray
Mrs H Hawes
Mrs S Kennaway
Mrs A Kerridge
§Mrs V Norris
Mrs S Peck
§Mrs K Rust
N Waters
Mrs S J Webb

Secretary: Mrs Y Tilt
Receptionist: Mrs A Notley

Situation. The School occupies a position in the centre of Wisbech on a 26 acre site giving generous playing field accommodation.

Whilst strong links have been maintained with Wisbech and District other boys and girls travel from as far away as Hunstanton, King's Lynn, Whittlesey, Ely, Long Sutton and Peterborough. There are school buses from a number of these destinations and villages en route. For the large number of pupils who continue with activities after school there are late buses to most destinations.

Senior School (Years 7 to 13): Entry. The main intake is at 11+ by competitive examination. Places can also become available at other stages. Sixth Form entry is on the basis of GCSE results and interview.

There are a number of Governors' Assisted Places at 11+, 12+, 13+ and for entry into the Sixth Form. Boys and girls are prepared for the GCSE, A Level and entry to Universities.

Academic Organisation. There is a sound academic curriculum. All pupils receive a thorough grounding in mathematics, English, French, German, science, information technology, history, geography, music, technology (resistant materials, graphics, textiles and home economics), art and religious studies. For GCSE boys and girls study English, mathematics, and then choose six more subjects from a list of fifteen. This selection must include at least one science, although many take the three separate sciences, one language and one humanities subject. There are 22 different subjects available at A Level, including business studies, economics, music technology, further mathematics and Spanish.

Physical Education and Games. The main games for boys are rugby and hockey in the Christmas and Easter terms respectively, together with cricket and athletics in the Summer. Girls play hockey and some netball in the first two terms, tennis and athletics in the Summer. For boys and girls above Year 9, who are not involved in a major team game, there is a large range of options including basketball, volleyball, squash, aerobics, swimming, self defence and badminton. Facilities include several playing fields, a full-size sports hall and a new Astroturf pitch. Additionally, pupils use the sports centre next door, which provides a covered swimming pool, sports hall, fitness centre, as well as a second Astroturf pitch.

There are many opportunities for pupils to represent the School at sport via the extensive fixture programme with other schools in Cambridgeshire, Norfolk and Lincolnshire.

Activities. All pupils are encouraged to take part in one, or more, of the many activities, clubs or societies which form an essential part of the School's programme. As well as the usual games practices and music and drama rehearsals there are information technology, electronics, photography, public speaking, Duke of Edinburgh's Award, Young Enterprise, debating, skiing (dry slope), chess, scrabble and the School magazines. The art and the technology facilities and maths help club are also available throughout the lunchtimes.

Information Technology. The School has three dedicated computer rooms with network computers running industry standard products. In addition there is a suite of personal computers connected to the same network, for careers and sixth form use, in the Business Centre as well as other groups of machines around the school which connect every academic department to the network. Staff and pupils are therefore able to use a vast range of programs and information from almost any point in the school. There are 150 computers for use by pupils and these facilities are available each day until 5.30 pm.

All pupils have IT lessons throughout their 7 years at the school. They aim to complete courses in CLAIT at various levels as well as IBT (Information & Business Technology) levels I, II and III in the Fourth, Fifth and Sixth Forms.

Technology. All pupils receive a broad introduction in their first year. A whole afternoon (2 hours) per week is set aside and the year is divided into four 8 week blocks of work in resistant materials, graphics, home economics and textiles. These courses continue throughout the School and each subject is available at GCSE and A Level. There has been considerable investment in equipment in the recently extended technology block. This has allowed further development of the work in electronics. Due to a generous donation from the Stationers' Company, the School is also able to offer further advanced work in textiles using the automatic photo-silkscreen printing equipment.

Music and Drama. Lessons on a wide range of instruments are available to all boys and girls. There are various group musical activities including a school orchestra, woodwind ensembles, chamber choir, and junior and senior choruses. Each year two major stage performances are given, one of which is a musical. Past productions include The Glass Menagerie, An Inspector Calls, Grease, Fame and Smike.

Trips Abroad. These are popular; in recent years parties of pupils and staff have visited Austria (skiing), USA, China and Iceland. A cricket tour to the West Indies took place in July 2002. There are strong exchange links with Willibrord Gymnasium, Emmerich in Northern Germany and Institution Ste Ursule in France, with many pupils participating each year. Year 8 boys and girls visit a chateau in Normandy each year and lower sixth students studying French may undertake work experience placements, during their Easter break, in Brittany. Pupils studying Spanish in the fifth and lower sixth forms have the opportunity to spend a week attending classes at a language school in Salamanca during the Easter holidays.

Magdalene House Preparatory Department (Reception to Year 6). The refounding of this section of the School, after a break of more than 50 years, took place on 3 September 1997, and has grown from 83 to 180+ pupils with boys and girls from Reception to Year 6. In September 2005, the Junior and Infant Department was renamed 'Magdalene House' in recognition of the school's three century old connection with Magdalene College, Cambridge.

Great emphasis is placed on the acquisition of the basic skills in reading, writing and number. A high standard of work is expected from the children in all areas of the curriculum which includes Mathematics, English, Science, RE, Art, Music, Drama, Geography, History, IT, French, PE, Swimming and Games.

The Magdalene House pupils benefit from being part of an established senior school and so have access to many of the excellent facilities that already exist there. A science laboratory, sports hall and theatre are available to the Preparatory Department, as well as their own library and dedicated computer room. Specialist teaching is offered in Music, Design Technology, PE and Games, Information Technology and Drama. Many girls and boys are involved in peripatetic music lessons. Opportunities for performance in Drama and Music are regular features of the school year.

Completed in 2008, the School's latest building project provides a new hall and two new classrooms for the rapidly expanding Magdalene House Preparatory Department. The development also includes the complete refurbishment of the existing sports hall.

There are many sporting opportunities with a full timetable of fixtures each term, when pupils are involved in games against other schools. The main sports played are netball, hockey, rugby, tennis and athletics.

There is a very varied after school programme giving children the opportunity to develop sports and leisure skills, artistic and musical talents. A supervised homework club is also available each day.

School field trips, activity days at the local museum and visits by theatre groups and speakers from outside all form an important part of the curriculum. Years 5 and 6 enjoy a week at an activity centre during May.

Entry. Generally children can be admitted to the Reception class in September, at the beginning of the school year in which they reach the age of five. All children registering are invited to spend part of a day with the School during which time they are assessed in a manner appropriate to their age. Candidates for entry are also welcomed at all other stages of the Junior School age range.

All enquiries for Magdalene House Preparatory Department should be addressed to the Secretary, Magdalene House Preparatory Department, Wisbech Grammar School, North Brink, Wisbech, Cambs PE13 1JX. Tel: 01945 586780, Fax: 01945 586781.

Fees per term (2008-2009). Senior School £3,200, Magdalene House Preparatory Department £2,200.

Old Wisbechians Society. This is a thriving organisation which has several hundred members. Further information about the Society can be obtained from the Admissions' Secretary at the School, to whom requests for the School magazine, Riverline, should be sent.

Charitable status. The Wisbech Grammar School Foundation is a Registered Charity, number 1087799. It exists to promote the education of boys and girls.

Wolverhampton Grammar School

Compton Road Wolverhampton WV3 9RB
Tel: 01902 421326
Fax: 01902 421819
e-mail: wgs@wgs.org.uk
website: www.wgs.org.uk

Wolverhampton Grammar School was founded in 1512 by Sir Stephen Jenyns – a Wolverhampton man who achieved success as a wool merchant, became a member of The Merchant Taylors' Company then Lord Mayor of London. He decided to benefit his home town by founding a school "for the instruction of youth in good manners and learning". The school retains close links with the Company.

Wolverhampton Grammar School is now an independent, selective day school for girls and boys aged 10–18 from a wide catchment area throughout the West Midlands, Staffordshire and Shropshire.

Its philosophy places scholarship at the heart of a challenging education which promotes achievement through active involvement. It seeks to develop self-awareness and a sense of responsibility, values both individuality and altruism, and fosters the spirit of community traditional to the school.

The school was inspected in January 2007. The report can be read on the ISI website: www.isinspect.org.uk.

Governing Body:
Chairman: Dr S Walford, MA, MD, FRCP
Vice-Chairman: E A Sergeant, BSc, BTh (*OW*)
The Mayor of Wolverhampton (*ex officio*)
M Anderson, BA, ACA
Mrs T Crisp
B Gilmore, CB, MA (*OW*)
R D Hill, MA (*OW*)
D J Hughes, MA (*OW*)
Professor K Madelin, OBE, MSc, CEng, FICE, FIHT
Mrs J Mills, BA
Dr M Nicholls, MA, PhD
Dr J Orledge, MB BS, DRCOG, MRCGP
R Purshouse, LLB (*OW*)
Mrs J Riley, BA (*OW*)
S Sanghera, MA (*OW*)
A J Smith, FCIS, FCT, FCMI, FRSA
His Honour Malcolm Ward, MA, LLM (*OW*)
Dr E Westlake
P E J White, FInstMgt (*OW*)
Mrs C Wood, JP, LLB, SRCh, MChs

***Head*: J V Darby**, BA, NPQH

Deputy Heads:
A J Pattison, BA, MA, PhD, FRSA (Universities of Bristol & New Brunswick)
P A Hills, BA (University of Nottingham)

Assistant Staff:
N J C Anderson, BSc
Dr J Anketell, BSc, PhD
Mrs K E Baker, BA
T Baker, BSc
Mrs J Baxter, BA
B M Benfield, BA, GCD
A J Bennett, BSc, MA
P A Blackwell, LLAM, LALAM, ALAM, LSC Dip
N J Bradley, BSc, PhD
R J Brandon, MA
Mrs S F Brentnall, BA
T J Browning, BSc
J-P Camm, BSc, PhD
A P Carey, BSc
R B Charlesworth, BA
N H Crust, BA
Mrs H S Dalzell, BA
J G David, BA
Mrs J R Dovey, BA
J D Edlin, BSc, PhD
Miss L E Fallows, BSc
Mrs K L Finn, BA
Mrs K J Flavell, BSc, PhD
Mrs V E Fogarty, BSc
Mrs V N Gilchrist, BA, ARIAM, ARCM
Mrs P D Grigat-Bradley, Erstes und Zweites Staatsexamen
Ms N T Guidotti, BA
Mrs S K Hannah, BA
Mrs E S N Harris, BA
Mrs H Hills, BSc
S Hinchliffe, BA, PhD
A M Hopkins, BA
Mrs M I Howard, BA
Miss A L Humphrey, BA
J M Johnson, BSc
P Johnstone, BA
Miss C Jones, BA
D Jones, BA, MA, DMS
L J Judson, BSc
T King, Esq
Mrs R M Laurino-Ryan, CertEd
Mrs R L Lockyer, BA
Mrs J M Lloyd, BSc
Ms A J Maddox, BA, MA
Mrs P K Mahey, BA
Mrs P Manzai, BA
C W Martin, MA, PhD
Miss A M McAllister, BSc, MA
J J Millichamp, BA
R Morris, BEd
Mrs M J Moss, BA
Mrs K J Muir, BA
Miss K A Munden, BA
N P Munson, BSc
Mrs R E Munson, BA
C O'Brien, BSc, PhD
S L J O'Malley, BA
T D Page, BA
R A Pawluk, GRAM, LRAM, LTCL, ALCM
J W Perkins, BA
Mrs C A Preston, BSc
A A Proverbs, BA
Mrs I C Raymond-Barker, BEd
V P Raymond-Barker, BA
J P Ryan, BEd
D S Sanderson, BA, MSc
Ms A E Shorrick, BA
K Stott, BSc
Mrs O Trafford, ATD
I H M Tyler, BA, Dip DA, RADA
K Uppal, BA
Mrs D M Ward, BA, MA
Miss K I Ward, BA, MSc
Miss H V Whittaker, BSc
J R Wood, BA
Miss J S Zafar, BA

Visiting Teachers:
Mrs B Arnold, ABSM (*Singing*)
Mrs L Bausor, ALCM (*Oboe and Bassoon*)
R J F Cracknell, MA, LRAM (*Cello*)
Mrs N Loveridge, BMus (*Clarinet and Saxophone*)
Mrs J M Lowe, GRSM, ARCM, LRAM (*Piano*)
B Markland, MA, BMus (*Bass Guitar/Double Bass*)
Miss K Moran, BMus, MMus (*Violin/Viola*)
B Perkins, ABSM (*Guitar*)
Miss R Perry, BA (*Flute*)
Miss L Warren, ABRSM (*Singing*)
K Waterman, GBSM (*Percussion*)

Bursar: Mrs M Wilmot

Head's Secretary: Mrs J E Boss

Buildings. The school has a new, purpose-built music block, a magnificent Sixth Form Centre and a new £3.5 million Arts Centre to accommodate Art and Drama opened in April 2007. A Sports Centre and floodlit Astroturf pitch provide some of the best facilities in the area while the early 20th century Merridale and Caldicott buildings house laboratories that have been refurbished to the highest modern standards. State-of-the-art ICT facilities provide broadband internet access to all parts of the school.

Admission. Boys and girls usually enter the school in September. The school's own entrance tests are held in the preceding January. The main intake is at age 11 with small numbers admitted at age 12 and 13. A significant number of boys and girls join the school in the Sixth Form: offers of places are made subject to GCSE results and interview. Transfers at other ages can be made by arrangement.

Since September 2004 the school has taken approximately 35 children per year at 10+ into its 'Big Six' year.

Fees per term (2008-2009). Big Six £2,555, Year 7 upwards £3,425.

Entrance Scholarships. (*see Scholarship Entries section*). Following the January entrance tests, six Governors' Academic Scholarships (two 50% fees and four 25% fees) are awarded to the highest-placed candidates at 11+ and one Scholarship (33% of fees) is offered at 13+. Music Scholarships are available remitting 25% of fees, one at 11+ or 13+

and one at 16+, with free music tuition within the school on the instrument of the student's choice. Two Governors' Academic Scholarships are awarded at 16 to students transferring from other schools. Applicants are expected to achieve high academic standards and be able to make a significant contribution to extra-curricular activities.

Assistance with Fees. The Governors offer a small number of means-tested Bursaries to children from less affluent families who can demonstrate academically and personally that they will benefit from the opportunity of a WGS education.

Curriculum. In the first three years students study a broad curriculum of English, Mathematics, three Sciences, History, Geography, Art, Information Communication Technology, Design Technology, Theology & Philosophy, PE & Games and Music, in addition to French, German and Latin. In the fourth form students pursue a core of English Language and Literature, three separate Sciences, Mathematics, at least one Modern Language, and an IAM (Institute of Administrative Management) qualification. There is a wide range of additional optional subjects, and most students take ten GCSEs. 90% of students proceed to the Sixth Form to take three or four subjects at AS/A2 Level and some 98% continue in Higher Education, including a number of students who go to Oxford or Cambridge.

Games and Outdoor Activities. A 'sport for all' attitude exists in games and PE, where the staff endeavour to match the student to a sport or activity in which they can succeed. There is a commitment to the highest standards of skill and sportsmanship but the emphasis is also placed on enjoyment. The 4th Wolverhampton (Grammar School) Scout Troop, which celebrated its 75th birthday in 2005, is open to all students and the school participates in The Duke of Edinburgh's Award Scheme. Students find that there are opportunities to undertake field trips and foreign exchanges. There is a vigorous outdoor education programme.

Special Needs (Dyslexia). The WGS OpAL (Opportunities through Assisted Learning) programme, which started in September 1998, is designed to allow bright children with Specific Learning Difficulties (Dyslexia) to enjoy the challenge of a first-rate academic education. In the last five years OpAL students have consistently achieved 100% A*–C grades at GCSE, and all A Level students have been offered university places.

Arts and Other Activities. The Music Department runs several choirs, bands and orchestras which practise and perform regularly to popular acclaim. Theatre is an integral part of the vibrant arts policy at the school which mounts three full-scale drama productions yearly involving students of all ages as actors, technicians, set and costume makers, stage managers and directors. The Art Department exhibits regularly and has an artist-in-residence. There is a wide variety of extra-curricular clubs and activities giving students the opportunity to discover and cultivate new interests, both inside and outside the classroom. A Community Service programme and an active student Charity Fund-raising Committee ensure that all students are involved in working for the good of others.

Pastoral Care. The school is proud of the pastoral care and support it offers to its students. In the Lower and Middle Schools care is provided by a form tutor under the overall responsibility of the appropriate Heads of Schools. Regular consultations are held with parents supported by full and frequent reports. An important forum is the Student Council which consists of elected representatives from all year groups who are encouraged to voice concerns and suggest improvements to the running and organisation of the school. The weekly meetings, with the Head plus one other member of staff in attendance, are run by an elected Chair and Secretary.

Charitable status. Wolverhampton Grammar School is a Registered Charity, number 529006.

Woodbridge School

Woodbridge Suffolk IP12 4JH
Tel: 01394 615000
Fax: 01394 380944
e-mail: admissions@woodbridge.suffolk.sch.uk
website: www.woodbridge.suffolk.sch.uk

Motto: '*Pro Deo Rege Patria*'

Governing Body: The Trustees of The Seckford Foundation

Chairman: Air Vice-Marshal P J Goddard, CB, AFC, FRAeS, RAF Retd

***Headmaster*: S H Cole**, MA Oxon, MA Ed Mgt, CPhys, MInstP, PGCE

Deputy Head: M R Streat, MA, PGCE
Director of Studies: G B Bruce, MA, CertEd
Senior Master: R F Broaderwick, BA, PhD
Senior Mistress: Miss H V Richardson, BA, PGCE
Chaplain: The Revd I A Wilson, BTh

Assistant Staff:
J R Penny, MA, CertEd
I T Saunders, BTech
S J Ashworth, BSc, PGCE
Miss S Theasby, BA, PGCE
M R Ringer, BEd, CertEd
S E Cottrell, BEd, CSci, CPhys, MInstP
R E Fernley, BA, PGCE
Mrs V Jones, BA, ATD
A P Jackson, BSc, PGCE
R A Rabjohn, BSc
Miss J A Gill, MA Ed, BEd
Mrs E A M Davidson, DipMusEd
Mrs N Ingold, CertEd
J A Hillman, BSc, PGCE
J H Stafford, ARCM
Mrs A McGlennon, BA, PGCE
Mrs A P Willett, CertEd, AdDipEd SEN
R A Carr, BA, ATC
B T Edwards, BA
P A Trett, BSc, PGCE
Mrs C V E Johnson, BA, PGCE
N E Smith, BA, PGCE
Miss L R King, MA, PGCE
L V Rickard, BSc, PhD, PGCE
M Davis, MA, BA
Mrs W McNally, BSc, PGCE
Mrs E Mitchels, BA, PGCE
J Wharam, BSc, PhD, PGCE
Mrs M Wellings, BA, PGCE
J Percival BA
Mrs T H Knowles, BEd
A G Lubbock, BSc, PGCE
Mrs S E Carberry, BA, PGCE
Mrs A Hillman, BSc, PGCE
R J H Thorley, BA, PGCE
Mrs C E Brown, CSci, CPhys, MInstP
C Eager, BA, PGCE
B T Greatorex, BA, PGCE
P M Lawrence, MA, PGCE
D J Neuhoff, BA, UED
Mrs J Hill, BSc, CertEd
A Hunt, BSc
Mrs Schumann-Vaes, BEd
Mrs C F Neuhoff, BA, UED
Mrs M M Barclay, CertEd, TEFL
D A Brous, BSc, PGCE
S D Richardson, BA, TEFL, PGCE
Mrs E Green, BA, PGCE
Miss A Martin, BA, PGCE
C Roberts, BEng, PGCE
M Troughton, BSc
J M C Allen, BSc, MSt, PGCE
J P Chandler, MA
Miss S Crossland, BA, PGCE
Miss J N Middleditch, BSc
Miss C Parker, BSc, PGCE
M Rattray, MA, BA, PGCE
Mrs Hong Guan, BA Shandong, China, CertEd Qingdao, China
Mrs M Pilkington, BA, PGCE
Mrs E Bambridge, BSc, PGCE
Mrs R Doble, BEd
Ms N McDonald, BA Hons, PGCE
Dr A Renshaw BA Hons, MA, PhD
Ms I Brown, MA, MSc
I W Elder, MA, PGCE
H Tebbutt, BA

Bursar: G E Watson, ACIS
School Medical Officer: Dr John Lynch
Admissions Officer: Mrs N Clouter
Headmaster's Secretary: Mrs M Cookson

The Abbey (Woodbridge Junior School)
Tel: 01394 382673

Master: N J Garrett, BA, PGCE
Second Master: Mrs C M T Clubb, BEd
Director of Studies: Mrs S M Whymark, CertEd

Assistant Staff:

A H A Clarke, GRSM, ARCM, PGCE	Mrs E V Hamilton, BEd
C J French, BA, PGCE	Mrs J Williams, BEd
Mrs J King, BEd (*Head of Pre-Prep*)	C Smith, BSc, PGCE
M D Staziker, BEd	Mrs H Norman, BEd
Mrs P Salmond, CertEd	Mrs J Chamberlain, BA, PGCE
Mrs L Graham, BSc, PGCE	Mrs M Shipman, CertEd
R D O Earl, BA, PGCE	Mrs S J Howse, CertEd
Mrs L Ford, DipEd	Mrs J Lawrence, BSc, PGCE
D A Graham, BEd	Mrs R M Copestake, CertEd
Mrs S J E Woolstencroft, BA, PGCE	Mrs V R Porter, BEd, PGCE
Miss S K Olliff, BA	Mrs G R Baylis, BEd
Mrs R Walker, BEd	Mr R M Heazlewood, BEd, BSc
Mrs C R Hayhow, MSc, CBiol, MIBiol	Miss K Theobald, BEd
Mrs M Burgess-Simpson, CertEd, DipSEN	N A Tiley-Nunn, BA
	Ms S Campbell, BA
	Miss A J Kininmonth, BA, PGCE

Situation. Woodbridge is an attractive market town on the River Deben, opposite the site of the famous royal Saxon ship burial at Sutton Hoo. Timber-framed buildings dating from the Middle Ages, and Georgian facades draw many visitors to the town throughout the year as do the Aldeburgh Festival at the nearby international Snape Maltings Concert Hall. Excellent sailing facilities are available on the River Deben. Woodbridge is seven miles from the Suffolk coast and close to the continental ports of Felixstowe and Harwich. The rail journey to London takes a little over an hour.

History and Buildings. Woodbridge School was originally founded in 1577. The scholars were to be taught "both Latin and Greek until thereby they be made fit for the University (if it be desired), but in case of any of them be unapt to learn those languages . . . they should be taught only Arithmetic, and to Write, to be fitted for Trades or to go to Sea". They were also to be "instructed in the principles of the Christian Religion according to the Doctrine of the Church of England".

For 200 years, the School existed in cramped quarters in the town until its incorporation with the Seckford Trust. Endowment income then enabled it to move to its present undulating site overlooking the town and the River Deben and to begin the steady expansion and development which have accelerated over the last 25 years. The latest additions are the new state-of-the-art 350-seat Seckford Theatre and refurbished Briten-Pears Music School.

Woodbridge has had close links with the local community and, through its outstanding Music and Science, with Finland, France, Spain, The Netherlands, Hungary, India and Germany. Woodbridge has a British Council International School award and a BT Lifelong Learning Award for its international and community links. The School has been fully co-educational for nearly four decades.

The Abbey prep school is centred in a beautiful house dating from the 16th Century in the town, adjacent to which two large new buildings have been added. Taking pupils from 7–11, it has full use of the Senior School swimming pool, sports hall, tennis courts, etc. (*For further details, see entry in IAPS section.*)

Queen's House, the pre-prep department for 150 pupils aged 4–6, opened in 1993 in its own building on the Woodbridge School site.

Organisation. There are over 900 pupils. The Senior School (11–18) numbers 310 boys and 290 girls, with a Sixth Form of 200. There is a co-educational Sixth Form Hall of Residence for Boarders aged 16–18. A Day House system exists with a Junior House for 11 year old entrants and four other Day Houses for those aged 12–16. All Sixth Form day pupils are based in the Sixth Form Centre.

Music, Games and Activities. Music is at the heart of much of the life of the School. Over 50 concerts every year, large and small, offer pupils opportunities to perform at all levels. Some 45% of pupils study at least one instrument. In recent years Woodbridge School has had more members of the National Youth Choirs of Great Britain than any other school in the UK.

Woodbridge is a chess centre of excellence, representing England at the world chess championships.

Sailing, shooting and hockey are real strengths. Other main games are rugby and netball in the winter; cricket, also tennis, athletics, swimming and rounders in the summer. The Sports Hall has facilities for most indoor sports.

The first-class Combined Cadet Force embraces Army, RAF, and Royal Navy Sections. The large variety of clubs and societies includes the Duke of Edinburgh's Award Scheme. All 11 and 12 year olds follow the Seckford Scheme which paves the way for these, and many other, activities.

Careers. The School is a member of the Independent Schools Careers Organisation, the regional secretary of which visits regularly and there are close links with county and university careers departments.

Chapel and Religious Education. The School has a strong Christian ethos and pupils attend Chapel every week. There is an annual Confirmation Service.

Admission. The majority enter the Senior School at 11 through the School's own examination, interview and report. At age 13, entry is through the School's own or the Common Entrance examination. Entry to the Sixth Form is based on interview and GCSE results. Admission to The Abbey is at any stage from the age of four.

Registration Fee £50. Acceptance Fee £300 (Overseas Boarders £500).

Fees per term (2008-2009). Day: Pre-Prep (Queen's House) £2,200; Prep (The Abbey) £3,300; Senior School: Years 7–9 £3,794; Years 10–13 £3,998. Boarding: £7,064.

Remission of Fees. Due to its generous endowment, the School is able to offer remission of part of the fees to pupils whose parents have incomes in the lower and middle ranges. These awards are termed "Marryott Bursaries", after an early benefactor.

Scholarships. (*see Scholarship Entries section*). These are awarded on the results of the annual entrance examinations at 11+ and 13+. At 16+, Scholarships are awarded on the basis of interview. There are many Music scholarships, Drama, Art, All-Rounder and Sports scholarships and one Chess scholarship each year.

Charitable status. The Seckford Foundation is a Registered Charity, number 1110964. Its aims are to give education for "poor children" by the provision of scholarships and fee remissions out of charity funds, and to maintain "the elderly poor" by providing a subsidy out of the charity for the Almshouses and Jubilee House.

Woodhouse Grove School

Apperley Bridge West Yorkshire BD10 0NR
Tel: 0113 250 2477
Fax: 0113 250 5290
e-mail: enquiries@woodhousegrove.co.uk
website: www.woodhousegrove.co.uk

Woodhouse Grove is situated in spacious, well-kept grounds on the slopes of the Aire Valley and within easy reach of Bradford and Leeds. The moors are within view and the Dales National Park is not far away.

The School was founded in 1812 for the education of the sons of Wesleyan ministers but now welcomes members of all denominations and none, both as pupils and as staff. It is fully co-educational, taking pupils from the age of 2½–18.

Motto: '*Bone et fidelis*'

Visitor: The President of the Methodist Conference

Administrative Governors of the School:

G B Greenwood, JP (*Chairman*)

Mrs P Burton, CertEd
Mrs E E Cleland
R Davy, JP
A Ekoku, BA
His Honour Judge Stephen Gullick, LLB
Dr G H Haslam, MBChB
A S P Kassapian
MD Leigh, Ba, MA, DipEd
P Robertshaw
J H Robinson, FREng, BSc, CEng, FIChemE
G Russell, BA
I M Small, BA, DipEd
District Judge Mrs Helen Town, BEd, MA
Dr J N Tunnicliffe, BA, DPhil
J Weaving, BA, ACA
Revd P Whittaker, BA
A Wintersgill, FCA

Secretary, Methodist Residential Schools: G Russell, BA

Staff:

***Headmaster*: D C Humphreys**, BA

Deputy Headmaster: D N Wood, BA
Second Master: J K Jones, CertEd
Deputy Second Master: J C Cockshott, CertEd
Director of Studies: Dr J A Wilson, BSc, PhD
Head of Lower School: Mrs F L Hughes, BEd
Head of Upper School: D N Wood, BA
Assistant Head & Head of Sixth Form: Mrs E Enthoven, BSc
Chaplain: Revd R Atkinson, BA
Clerk to the Governors: R Hemsley, MA, FCA
Operations Manager: R G Morton, BA
Finance Manager: D Ainsworth, BA, ACA

* *Head of Department*
† *Head of House*

Mrs E Ainscoe, MA (**Biology*)
J A Baker, CertEd (**Design Technology*)
Miss A Barron, BA (*German, †Southerns*)
Mrs G Bruce, BA (*Spanish*)
A Cadman, BA (*PE*)
Mrs S C Candlish, MA (*Art*)
Mrs P N Charlton, MA (*Art & Design*)
Mrs A J Clack, BA (*Psychology*)
A J Copping, MA (*Director of Performing Arts*)
Mrs C J Couzens, BA (*PE and Games*)
A N Crawford, BA, ARCO (*Music*)
S Dillon, BA (*Mathematics*)
K Eaglestone, BSc (*Mathematics, †Findlay*)
Mrs J L Edger, BSc (**Physics*)
Mrs E Farley, BA (*English & Media Studies*)
Mrs H R Fennell, BA (*English & Media Studies*)
J Fothergill, BSc, DipEd (*Information Technology*)
R I Frost, BEd (*PE and Games*)
Miss L Gale, MA (*English, †Vinter*)
Mrs K L Goodwin, MA (*English & Media Studies*)
J Gowon, BA (*PE, Sports Development Officer*)
C K Henderson, BSc (*Chemistry, Biology*)
J P Heyes, MA, MSc (**Mathematics*)
D Hole, BSc (**Chemistry*)
Mrs A Howard, BA (*Physics*)
E R Howard, BA, BEd (**PE & History*)
Mrs F L Hughes, BEd (*French*)
A Jarvis, BA (*Modern Languages*)
Miss C D Jemmett, BA (*English*)
A Jennings, BA (**Religious Studies*)
Mrs K Jennings, BEd (*PE*)
R Johnson, BA (*English*)
Miss E Landy, BSc (*Chemistry, Biology*)
Mrs M Legg, MSc (*Chemistry*)
P W Lodge, BA (**Modern Languages*)
P Maud, BA (*English & Theatre Studies, Learning Support, Geography*)
J M McCabe, BSc (*Chemistry*)
C Mencattelli, BA (**Business Studies, *Careers, IT*)
P J Moffat, BA (*Geography, †Atkinson*)
Mrs E M Mollard (*PE, Mathematics, PSE*)
M F Munday, BA (**Geography*)
Miss L Oakley, BA (**English, Theatre Studies*)
J B Robb, BA (*Religious Studies, †Stephenson*)
I Rowe, BMus (**Music*)
Miss J Russell, BA (*IT*)
C J Shepherd, BSc (*Mathematics, Physics*)
Mrs D L Shoesmith-Evans, BA (**History & Politics*)
J Stephenson, BA (*Art, DT*)
Mrs E Stokes, BA (*Drama, English*)
D Sugden, BSc (*Mathematics*)
Miss R V Thompson, BA (*Geography, †Towlson*)
Mrs P L Watson, BA (*Business Studies, IT*)
Miss R Wilkinson, BA (*Politics*)
G Williams, BSc (**Science*)
R Wincer, BA (*Mathematics*)

Headmaster's Secretary & Registrar: Miss A Peebles

Brontë House
Headmaster: S Dunn, BEd

Ashdown Lodge
Headteacher: Mrs A Hinchliffe, BA, QTS

Numbers. There are 712 pupils in the Senior School including 105 boarders and 150 students in the Sixth Form. Brontë House (7–11) has 160 pupils including 8 boarders. Ashdown Lodge (2½–7) has 100 day pupils.

Buildings. Our buildings include a new sports centre with a multi-functional sports hall, two gymnasiums, a swimming pool, squash courts, floodlit outdoor courts and a state-of-the-art Performing Arts Centre. We have good science laboratories, well-equipped DT and Art centres, a spacious music block, language suite, fully-equipped IT rooms. Our facilities have been enhanced with the refurbishment of the Sixth Form Centre and the completion of a new Senior Boys Boarding house which has en-suite rooms, recreational areas and staff quarters. Developments continue, with work on a new Music and ADT centre.

Sport and Music. Playing fields adjoining the School cover about 40 acres. Cricket, Hockey, Netball, Rugby, Squash, Basketball, Athletics, Swimming, Tennis and Rounders are the main games, and there are several all-weather Tennis Courts and a floodlit outdoor court for netball and tennis. The Sports Centre includes a large multi-functional hall, two fitness gyms and aerobics studio.

There are 3 Orchestras, many ensembles, several Choirs and a Concert Band. Many pupils take extra instrumental lessons.

Curriculum. Boys and girls enter the Senior School at the age of 11, 13 or 16 and the curriculum is arranged to provide a continuous course from Ashdown Lodge, through Brontë House and upwards through the Sixth Form to University entrance. Special support is available for dyslexic pupils. For GCSE, all pupils take the following core subjects, (English, French, Maths, Science–Dual Award, IT), together with three others chosen from German, Geography, RS, History, Art, CDT, PE, Spanish, Drama, Music. In the Sixth Form each pupil selects 4 subjects from 23 possible options for study at AS and A2 level. In addition, all Sixth formers can take a two-year course in General Studies or other broadening options, such as Italian.

A school-wide IT network, full-time IT Manager and IT Technician, state of the art PCs ensure that all pupils enjoy access to excellent IT facilities.

Sixth Form Entry. Places are available for students who want to come into the School at the Sixth Form stage.

Entrance Awards. (*see Scholarship Entries section*). Academic scholarships are available at 11+ and 13+ and several Music and Art awards are made each year. Means-tested bursaries are available and special allowances for children of Methodist Ministers and Service Personnel. Sports scholarships are awarded in the Sixth Form.

Term of Entry. Pupils are normally accepted in September, though special arrangements may be made for entry in other terms. This applies to Woodhouse Grove and Brontë House, but admission to Ashdown Lodge can take place throughout the year.

Brontë House (named after Charlotte Brontë who was a governess at a house on the same site, and after her parents who were married from the Main School) is a Preparatory School and takes boys and girls, both boarding and day, from the age of 7. (*See entry in IAPS section.*)

Ashdown Lodge opened in September 1993 to extend the family of Woodhouse Grove to the pre-preparatory age range of 2½ to 7, and takes boys and girls on a day or part-day basis, all year round.

Fees per term (2008-2009). Main School: £6,180–£6,255 (boarders), £5,670–£5,755 (weekly boarders), £3,140–£3,220 (day). Brontë House: £5,500 (boarders), £4,940 (weekly boarders), £2,490–£2,830 (day). Ashdown Lodge: Nursery and Reception £2,030 (full day), £1,265 (half day), Years 1 & 2 £2,280. Fees include meals, books, stationery, examination fees and careers tests.

Extra Subjects. Piano, Violin, Viola, Violoncello, Organ, Flute, Clarinet, Oboe, Trumpet, Trombone, Horn, Saxophone, Bassoon, Guitar, Percussion, Singing, Speech and Drama Training, Dancing, Judo, extra sports coaching.

Old Grovians Association. *Secretary*: Mrs Heather Garner.

Charitable status. Woodhouse Grove School is a Registered Charity, number 529205. It exists to provide education for children.

Worksop College
A Woodard School

Worksop Nottinghamshire S8O 3AP
Tel: 01909 537100
Headmaster: 01909 537127
Fax: 01909 537102
e-mail: headmaster@worksopcollege.notts.sch.uk
website: www.worksopcollege.notts.sch.uk

Foundation. Worksop College is the last of the Woodard (Church of England) Schools to be founded personally by the 19th Century educationist Canon Nathaniel Woodard, who died between the School's foundation in 1890 and its opening in 1895.

Motto: '*Semper ad Coelestia*'

Governing Body:
The Board of Woodard Schools (Nottinghamshire) Limited

Visitor: The Rt Revd The Bishop of Chichester

Board Members:
The Revd Canon B Clover, MA, LT, LL (*Provost*)
T D Fremantle, MBA, DL (*Custos*)
R P H McFerran, FRICS, CAAV (*Vice-Custos*)
D B Moody, MA
His Honour Judge J V Machin, LLB
Prof D E Luscombe, LittD, FBA
Mrs J C Richardson, BA, JP
M A Chapman, MLIA Dip
Sir David Naish, DL
The Ven R F Blackburn, MA, BA
M E Hartley, BSc, FCA
Mrs P A Rouse
Mrs M F T Critchley, BA
C J D Anderson, MA
K S Jones, BSc, FRICS, FAAV
Ms J H Smith
Ms E Wilks, BA
R R Steel
G A R Cormack, BA

***Headmaster*: R A Collard**, MA, Sidney Sussex College, Cambridge

Deputy Head: S H C Reid, BA (*English*)
Director of Studies: D F Parker, BSc (*Chemistry*)
Assistant Deputy Head: Mrs E A Warner, CertEd (*Physical Education*)
Chaplain: Revd P Finlinson, MA, BA (*Head of Spiritual and Moral Studies*)
Registrar: Mrs C E Tilley, BEd (*Physical Education*)

Teaching Staff:
Mrs W H Bain, BA (*English, Head of Drama and Theatre Studies*)
Miss C Bainbridge, BA (*Business Studies & Economics*)
Mrs C M Beckett, BA (*Learning Support*)
Miss R Bellamy, BA (*English, Head of Physical Education*)
M P Boler, BSc (*Head of Physics*)
Mrs G Burton, CertEd (*Food & Nutrition*)
Miss A E Carter, BSc (*Head of Biology*)
Mrs M J Christodoulou, BEd (*Head of Food and Nutrition*)
C D Cook, BA (*Design Technology*)
J A S Driver, BSc (*Biology*)
G R Duckering, BEd (*Head of Design Technology*)
M Fagan, BEd (*Mathematics*)
T J Franse, BA (*Chemistry*)
M J Gibson, BA (*Head of Classics*)
M K Gillard, BSc (*Head of Chemistry, Head of Science*)
Mrs S J Gillard, BA (*Head of English*)
Mrs A A Gray, BEd (*Learning Support*)
Miss K J Grice, BA (*Modern Languages*)
Mrs S A Halsall, BA (*Art*)
T J Halsall, MEd, BA (*English and Theatre Studies*)
C J Hamlet, BSc (*Physical Education and Games*)
D A Hunter, BEd (*Learning Support*)
Miss K M Ingleby, BA (*History*)
Mrs J E Ireland, BSc (*Head of Business Studies and Economics*)
J R Johnson, BA (*English*)
Miss G J Johnston, BSc (*Head of Geography*)
A B B Kenrick, MA, BA (*Head of Art and Design*)
N A K Kitchen, MA (*Head of History, Head of Sixth Form*)
T P Larkman, BSc (*Geography*)
R J M Leach, BA, ARCO (*Assistant Director of Music*)
R J Marks, BEd, BPhil (*Learning Support*)
I C Parkin, BSc (*Director of Games*)
Mrs P S Parkinson, BA (*Head of Modern Languages*)
C G Paton, BA (*Modern Languages*)
Mrs H Platt-Hawkins, MA (*Art*)
Mrs S Powell, BSc (*Games*)
Mrs M C Reid, BA (*Modern Languages*)
P N Richardson, BA (*English, History*)
W G Robinson, BSc (*Mathematics*)
Mrs G J Robson-Bayley, BA (*English*)

J W Sampson, BA (*Business Studies & Economics, Head of Careers & Industrial Liaison*)
Mrs D L Sawoscianik-Murray, BA (*Art and Design*)
Dr L J Stannard, PhD, MA, BA (*English*)
Mrs E Sutton, L-ès-L (*Modern Languages*)
G R Tattersall, BSc (*Mathematics*)
K D Topham, MSc, BSc (*Biology*)
J D Turner, BSc (*Head of Mathematics*)
T Uglow, MA, ARCO (*Director of Music*)
Mrs S R White, BA (*Geography, Head of General Studies*)

Houses and Housemasters/mistresses:

Boys:
Mason: W G Robinson
Pelham: T P Larkman
Portland: T J Halsall
Shirley: C J Hamlet
Talbot: C G Paton

Girls:
Derry: Mrs S Powell
Gibbs: Mrs C E Tilley
School House: Mrs P S Parkinson

School Doctors:
Dr J Edbrooke
Dr J Fulton

Bursar: J K Wheeler, OBE, BA

Old Worksopian Society Secretary: Mrs W Marks

Ranby House Preparatory School
Headmaster: A C Morris, BEd

There are 420 pupils in the College of whom about 38% are girls.

Situation. The College is situated in its own estate of 300 acres with extensive playing fields and an 18-hole golf course. It is on the edge of Sherwood Forest, a mile or so south of Worksop in North Nottinghamshire, overlooking the Clumber and Welbeck Estates. Lying close to the M1 and A1 and only 7 miles from Retford on the main East Coast Inter-City route from London to the North, the College is easily accessible by road, rail and air from most parts of the country. It is also well placed for contact with the universities, museums, theatres and cultural life of Nottingham, Sheffield, Leeds, York and other cities in the region.

Buildings. Earlier buildings include the Chapel and the Great Hall, a swimming pool, the Churchill Hall, the main quadrangle of classrooms and boarding houses, a well-equipped Theatre and an Art School. Recent modernisation has taken place of all facilities, most particularly the boarding houses and classrooms, including extensive ICT and electronic whiteboard provision. In recent years a Computer Centre, a Music School, a Drama Studio and a Learning Support Unit have been added. A Sports Hall was opened in January 2003, a new girls' Boarding House and a new girls' Day House opened in 2007, and a new Modern Languages Department language laboratory will open in September 2008.

Houses. There are 8 Houses. The 4 boys' Boarding Houses, the boys' Day House and a girls' House are all in the main College. The girls' Boarding House and Day House are in separate buildings. The housemaster or housemistress, assisted by the house tutors, associate tutors and academic tutors, has the principal responsibility for the individual welfare and programme of the boys or girls in the house, with whom they are in constant contact. At the same time the compactness of the buildings makes it easy for boys or girls to seek advice from other members of staff, in particular the Chaplain, and to make friendships with boys or girls in other houses as well as their own.

Religion. The Anglican religion is at the centre of the School's life, in Chapel services and throughout the school routine. A genuine effort is made to show that Christianity remains a vital response to the challenges of the 21st Century. While the great majority of pupils are Anglican, pupils of other creeds and faiths are also welcome, not least for the distinctive vision of God which they contribute to the School's experience.

Curriculum. Because the College enjoys the ratio of 1 teacher to fewer than 10 pupils, close attention can be given to individual needs at every level. The Curriculum is designed to give pupils as wide an education as possible in the first three years, leading to the GCSE examinations. In the Sixth Form, a broad range of A and AS Level examinations is available including English, History, Geography, French, Spanish, Latin, Classical Civilisation, Mathematics, Physics, Chemistry, Biology, Further Mathematics, Economics & Business Studies, Music, Art, Design Technology, Theatre Studies, Physical Education and General Studies. Additionally, Applied Business and BTEC International Cuisine are offered.

About 97% of Sixth Form leavers go on to Higher Education.

Music. A large Music School containing a recital and rehearsal room with a capacity of 150, 10 teaching and practice rooms with pianos and a Music Library is the focal point for the Director of Music and a large visiting staff.

Art. The Director of Art has at his disposal 2 large studios for painting and drawing, a room for graphics and digital photography, textiles and sculpture areas and a library and teaching room.

Design and Technology. A purpose-built Technology Centre has facilities for design, the use of computers and areas for work in metal, wood and plastic, as well as CAD-CAM facilities.

Drama. There is a fully-equipped theatre as well as a Drama Studio, and plays involving boys and girls are put on 3 or 4 times a year. Theatre Studies is offered as a Sixth Form option.

Physical Education and Games. Physical Education is an integral part of the curriculum for a pupil's 5 years. The major games for boys are Rugby (Michaelmas Term), Hockey and Cross-Country (Lent Term), and Cricket, Athletics, and Swimming (Summer Term). For girls, they are Hockey (Michaelmas Term), Netball (Lent Term) and Tennis, Athletics and Swimming (Summer Term). Pupils are also encouraged to play other sports (Badminton, Basketball, Golf, Sailing, Soccer, Squash, Sub-Aqua, Tennis, Trampolining, Volleyball, Water Polo, Weight Lifting) and, as they become more senior, are permitted to specialise in them rather than in the main games if they choose. The Sports Hall has facilities for many sports and additional features for cricket as well as a fully-equipped fitness suite.

Activities. In their first year all pupils are taught life-saving, first-aid and other basic skills. There is then the choice of joining the CCF or voluntary community service. There is training in camping, orienteering, climbing, canoeing, motor engineering, shooting (the school has its own 25-yard range), signalling, and survival swimming. Boys and girls have all these options as well as the chance to take part in the Duke of Edinburgh's Award Scheme.

One afternoon a week is also set apart for Societies and Hobbies. These have included Archery, Art, Board Games, Boat Maintenance, Bookshop, Car Maintenance, Chess, CDT, Computers, Creative Fabrics/Dressmaking, Dance, Drama, Duke of Edinburgh's Award, Athletics, Conservation Work, Golf Coaching, Mountain Bikes, Model-kit Making, Photography, Theatre Technical Staff, Horse Riding, Fishing, Shooting, Music, Lacrosse and Kick-Boxing.

Ranby House. Over a third of the boys and girls in the School come from Ranby House, the preparatory school for Worksop, which is about 4 miles from the College and offers boarding and day education to boys and girls from 7–13. It also has a Pre-Prep Department.

See Ranby House entry in IAPS section.

Fees per term (2008-2009). Boarders £7,185; Day Pupils £4,870.

Scholarships. (*see Scholarship Entries section*). Scholarships and Exhibitions may be awarded annually, examination in February. (Candidates must be over 12 and under 14 on 1 May in the year of entry.) Sixth Form Scholarships are held in February each year.

Music Scholarships, Art Scholarships, Sports Awards and Golf Awards are also available.

The value of an award may, in special cases, be increased if the financial circumstances of the parents make this necessary.

A number of Bursaries are awarded to the children of Clergy and to children of members of Her Majesty's Armed Services (up to 15%) on the basis of financial need.

Admission. The main intake is in September each year, but pupils do join at other times. Pupils for September from preparatory schools will join through either the Entrance Scholarship or the Common Entrance Examination. Other Entry Tests are held at the College in February and May for 13+ applicants from the maintained sector. Increasingly boys and girls are joining the College after GCSE to study in the Sixth Form.

Charitable status. Woodard Schools (Nottinghamshire) Limited is a Registered Charity, number 1103326. It exists for the purpose of educating children.

Worth School

Turners Hill West Sussex RH10 4SD
Tel: 01342 710200
Fax: 01342 710230
e-mail: registry@worth.org.uk
website: www.worthschool.co.uk

Worth is a Benedictine 11–18 boarding and day school, valuing the individual and fostering a community life of learning, worship, friendship and service. The school offers pupils a high level of pastoral care and combines traditional values with modern approaches to teaching and learning.

Worth School is situated in the midst of the beautiful Worth Abbey estate, less than 15 minutes from Gatwick Airport and with convenient road and rail links to London and the South coast. The monastery was founded in 1933, using a country house and 500 acres of Sussex parkland. In 1957, the monastery became independent and Worth admitted the first boys to its own Senior School in 1959.

From September 2008, girls as well as boys will be able to benefit from the distinctive education and unique atmosphere at Worth. The school now welcomes girls into the Sixth Form and from 2010 girls will also be able to join other Years. Over the coming years, Worth will expand in size, so that the right co-educational ratio can be created without a marked reduction in the number of boys, while still remaining a relatively small-sized school.

The Abbot's Board of Governors, comprising both monks and laity.

President: Abbot Christopher Jamison, BA, MA

Chairman: Mr K Smyth

Mrs A Andreotti
Dom Mark Barrett, MA
Mr J Guyatt
Mr M Haan, FCA
Dom Luke Jolly, BA
Mrs R Lewis, BSc
Mr P Matthews, BSc, FIA
Mr G Moore, BA Econ, CA
Mr J Scherer, MA
Dom Kevin Taggart, MA
Dr R Townsend, MA, DPhil

***Head Master*: Mr Gino Carminati**, BA, MA

Deputy Headmaster: Dr James Whitehead, MA, MPhil, PhD
Director of Studies: Mrs Anne Lynch, BA
Director of Pastoral Care: Mr Alan Mitchell, BSc
Director of Academic Administration: Mr Simon Smith, BA

Teaching Staff:
* *Head of Department*

Mr Paul Ambridge, BA (*Physics*)
Mr Anthony Arratoon, Dip AD, ATC (*Art, Technology*)
Mrs Lyndsay Ashley, BA (*History*)
Dr Sheena Bartlett, BSc, PhD (*Sciences*)
Mr Jonathan Bindloss, BA (*Religious Studies*, Theory of Knowledge*)
Mr Stuart Blackhurst, HND (*Network Manager, IT*)
Mr Matthew Boughton, BA (*Drama & Theatre Studies**)
Mrs Judith Bridge, BSc (*Learning Support*)
Mrs Caroline Brown, PDLS (*More House Housemistress*)
Mr Nathan Brown, BA, Dip EFL (*English, St Bede's Housemaster*)
Mrs Anne Carminati, BA (*Learning Support*)
Mrs Louise Chamberlain, BSc (*Biology**)
Mrs Minakshi Chaudhuri, BA (*Learning Support*)
Mrs Arlette Childs, L-ès-L, MA (*Modern Languages*)
Mr Philip Chorley, MA (*English**)
Mrs Julia Cook, BEd, OCR Dip SpLD (*Learning Support**)
Mr Jonathan Cuff, BA (*Religious Studies, Physical Education, Rutherford Housemaster*)
Mrs Kate Cuff, BA, Dip TESL (*Drama & Theatre Studies*)
Mr Paul Curtis, BSc (*ICT**)
Miss Louise Daniels, BA (*English*)
Mrs Jayne Dempster, BSc (*Maths*)
Dr Brian Doggett, BSc, PhD (*Sciences**)
Mr Jeremy Dowling, BEd (*Mathematics*)
Ms Joanne Geraghty, BA, MA (*Spanish*)
Mr Kevan Goddard, BA (*Mathematics*)
Ms Sheila Gupta, BA (*Learning Support, EAL*)
Mrs Janny Harris, BA (*Librarian*)
Dom Thomas Haynes (*Chaplaincy Team*)
Mr Vincent Holden, BSc (*Physical Education**)
Fr Stephen Huggins (*Anglican Chaplain*)
Mrs Kate Huxley, MA (*Mathematics*)
Mr Paul Jones, BA, MA (*Religious Studies*)
Dom Roderick Jones (*Chaplaincy Team*)
Mr Richard Knowles, BA (*Modern Languages*)
Mr Andrew Lavis, BA (*Geography*)
Mr Terence Leggo, BA (*Art**)
Mrs Daniele Lloyd, L-ès-L, TEFL (*Modern Languages*)
Mr Robin Longworth, BSc (*Geography*)
Mr Simon Lucas, BA (*History**)
Ms Joanna Mattock, BA (*Assistant Director of Music*)
Dom Martin McGee, BA, MA (*School Chaplain*)
Mr Al Matthews, BA, MA (*Media Studies*, English*)
Mr Mike Matthews, BA (*Music*)
Mr Bruce Morrison, BEd (*Physical Education*)
Miss Eimear Neeson, BSc (*Mathematics*)
Mr Michael Oakley, BA, MMus (*Director of Music*)
Mr Andrew Oxley, BSc (*Sciences*)
Ms Rebecca Paterson, BA (*Religious Studies*)
Mrs Joanna Philippo Nevill, BA (*Girls' Physical Education**)
Mr Martin Pimentel, BSc (*Chemistry, Physics*)
Dr Duncan Pring, MA, PhD (*Economics and Business Studies, Farwell Housemaster*)
Mr Daniel Roberts, BA (*Economics and Business Studies*)
Mr Philip Robinson, MA, CertEd (*Classics**)
Mr David Smith, BSc, MSc (*Mathematics*)
Miss Bina Solomon, BSc, MSc (*Sciences*)
Miss Sherrie-Anne Spinks, BA (*Modern Languages*)
Mr Stefan Steinebach, Staatsexamen (*Modern Languages, Latin*)

Dom Kevin Taggart (*Chaplaincy Team*)
Mr Andrew Taylor, MA (*History, Gervase Housemaster*)
Mrs Tricia Taylor, BA (*French*)
Mr Guy Teasdale, BEd (*Economics and Business Studies**)
Ms Sarah Watson-Saunders, BA (*English*)
Mrs Susan Wilkinson, BA (*Learning Support Assistant*)
Mr James Williams, BSc (*Sciences, Physics, Chapman Housemaster*)
Mr Julian Williams, BSc (*Butler Housemaster*)
Mrs Naomi Williams, BA (*Psychology*)
Dom Peter Williams (*Chaplaincy Team*)

Bursar: Mrs Angela Higgs, BSc, ACA
Registrar: Ms Yvonne Lorraine
Headmaster's Secretary: Mrs Diane Coulson

Medical Officer: Dr Royds-Jones
Senior Nursing Sister: Cheryl Cheeseman, SRN, Paediatric Dipl
Nursing Sisters:
L Lindo, SRN
N Whiting, SRN
G Yacoubi, SRN

Continuous investment. The past decade has seen significant development at Worth. In September 2002 Gervase House was opened. Designed especially to meet the needs of Upper Sixth Form boys, the accommodation has 77 rooms with en-suite facilities. Boarders have a private room and day boys share rooms. Other developments include the introduction of electronic Smart Boards in all departments, refurbished sports pitches and upgraded boarding accommodation. A new Performing Arts Centre and Music School and two new Day Houses were opened in 1999. Perhaps the most striking and important 'new' building in size and significance since 1933 is the modern Abbey Church.

To achieve its co-educational aims, the school has invested in a new girls' boarding and day house, along with new facilities and staff. The school's extensive range of sports and extra-curricular activities will be expanded and the outstanding music and drama departments will be further enhanced by the inclusion of girls. A larger Sixth Form will also enable the school to offer a greater variety of subject options within the International Baccalaureate and at A Level.

Welcoming all Christians. About two-thirds of the 450 students at Worth are from Roman Catholic families, but there are a significant number of Christians from other denominations. Equal members of the community in every way, non-Catholic pupils have no difficulty integrating in the school and bring a different perspective which is most welcome. The School Chaplaincy team includes an Anglican Chaplain, as well as Catholic Chaplains and lay members.

Admissions Policy. Entry at 11+. Entrance tests in English, Maths and Non-Verbal Reasoning are held in January each year. Offers are based on test results, a report from the student's current school and an interview with the Head Master.

Entry at 13+. Entrance tests in English, Maths and Non-Verbal Reasoning are held in January each year. Offers are based on test results, a report from the student's current school and an interview with the Head Master. Common Entrance examination results will be used for setting purposes only.

Entry at 16+. Entrance into the Sixth Form will be dependent on the student's GCSE results or equivalent, an interview with the Head Master and a satisfactory reference from their current school. The normal requirement for students entering the Sixth Form at Worth is six GCSE passes at grades A to C, with at least three at grade B or above.

For further information on Admissions please contact the Registrar on 01342 710231.

Scholarships. (*see Scholarship Entries section*). Scholarships are awarded annually, varying in value up to 40% of the annual fees. The examination for Year 9 entrants is held in the Summer Term and candidates must be under 14 years of age on 1 September of the year in which they take the examination. Scholarships are also available for entry at 11+ through the entrance examination. Sixth Form Scholarships are awarded to students aged 16, based on scholarship examinations in November, good GCSE results and an interview. Music and All-Rounder Scholarships are available for entry at 11+, 13+ and 16+.

Fees per term (2008-2009). Senior: Boarding £8,012, Day £5,935; Junior: Boarding £6,999, Day £5,186.

Education. Worth offers students an education based on five key features:

Work: In the Senior School, students usually take nine or ten subjects at GCSE. The compulsory core is: English, French or Spanish, ICT, Mathematics, Religious Studies and Sciences. The options include: Art, Drama, Economics & Business Studies, Electronics, Geography, History, Latin, Music and Physical Education. Tuition is available (for an additional fee) in German, Greek, Italian and Chinese to GCSE and A Level.

There is a choice of a wide range of subjects at A Level; Art, Biology, Business Studies, Chemistry, Economics, Electronics, English, French, Geography, History, ICT, Maths and Further Maths, Film Studies, Music, Music Technology, Physics, Physical Education, Psychology, Spanish, Theatre Studies and Theology.

Alternatively, Sixth Form students may study the International Baccalaureate. This involves the study of six subjects, three at higher level and three at standard level. Students study one subject from each of the following groups:

Group 1: English, German

Group 2: English, French, German, Greek, Italian ab initio, Latin, Spanish ab initio

Group 3: Economics, Geography, History

Group 4: Biology, Physics

Group 5: Mathematics (HL), Mathematics (SL), Mathematical Studies (SL)

Group 6: Music, Theatre Arts, Visual Arts, Chemistry, French, History

Virtually all students go on to university. Sixth Form students may also choose to study for Oxbridge entrance and a significant number gain places at either Oxford or Cambridge.

Play: Sport is an important part of Worth life, with opportunities to pursue all major team sports, in some cases to county and national levels. The main sports are: rugby, soccer, hockey, netball, cricket, tennis and athletics. Other sports played at competitive level include fencing, squash and basketball. Minor sports are also available through school clubs. There is an eight-hole golf course, squash courts, tennis courts, fencing salle, dance studio and fitness suite and in their free time students can take advantage of the hard play area and the sports hall. The school also makes use of the excellent athletics facility and 50m swimming pool at the new multi-sports centre nearby.

Music is an important activity. There is a flourishing choir that is involved in tours and recordings as well as regular appearances in the Abbey Church. Parents, local friends and students join the Choral Society for at least two concerts each year (performing such works as Requiems by Faure and Durufle). The School orchestra performs regularly during the year within the school and beyond as does the Jazz Band. The annual House Music competition provides all pupils with an opportunity to perform competitively, celebrating the abilities of others.

Drama also flourishes with regular productions at all levels and overseas tours. The school joins forces with a local girls' school and the standard of performance is exceptional. The schools' annual joint Arts Festival in March included the musical "Les Misérables" and Ibsen's "An Enemy of the People" in 2008, in addition to concerts, art exhibitions and a debate. The school's purpose-built Performing Arts Centre was opened in 1999 comprising a theatre, drama office and workshop, dressing rooms, recording studio, a sound-proofed 'rock room', rehearsal rooms, a recital room and music classrooms.

One afternoon a week every pupil participates in an activity, ranging from cookery to conservation, clay pigeon shooting to polo. Worth is also a centre for The Duke of Edinburgh's Award Scheme. Almost a third of students are currently working towards their Bronze, Silver or Gold award.

Care: Care of the students is a central concern throughout the School. Each pupil is a member of a House and has a personal tutor who monitors work progress and assists the Housemaster and his team with overall care. The Benedictine tradition of community life underpins all this. Many staff families live on-site and parents are welcomed as integral to the school. There are regular points of contact, with parent-teacher consultations, meetings, social events and active support from the Friends of Worth (a parents' association).

The school has a long tradition of community involvement, reaching out to others through an extensive voluntary service programme taking place on a weekly basis, involving a large number of students.

Morality: The monastic community at Worth is committed to the Rule of St Benedict and it is this moral and spiritual ethos on which the school community was founded, providing stability in the moral confusion of our rapidly changing world. This sense of stability and a high level of pastoral care provides an enriching and secure environment in which students can live, as boarders and day pupils. The curriculum also provides opportunities for open discussion of moral issues, following a personal and social education syllabus.

Faith: Worth believes that each person is on a spiritual journey through life and that the school should support them wherever they are on that journey. There are prayers each day in Houses and Mass every Sunday for those boarding over the weekend and for local families. Religious Studies is a core GCSE, but is also a popular option in the Sixth Form. Beyond this simple framework, the Chaplaincy Team of monks, a Church of England Chaplain and lay people provide a variety of opportunities for students, staff and parents to meditate and to worship, to retreat and to travel.

Worth's special quality is that all five of the above features are first equal in importance. Some people excel in one area more than another but, as a community, we promote each feature equally, identifying and developing each student's potential. If Worth had a motto it would be: 'The glory of God is a person fully alive'.

Charitable status. Worth School is a Registered Charity, number 1093914. Its aims and objectives are to promote religion and education.

Wrekin College

Wellington Shropshire TF1 3BH
Tel: 01952 265600
Headmaster: 01952 265602
Fax: 01952 415068
e-mail: info@wrekincollege.ac.uk
website: www.wrekincollege.com

Wrekin College was founded in 1880 by Sir John Bayley and in 1923 became one of the Allied Schools, a group of six independent schools including Canford, Harrogate, Stowe and Westonbirt.

Motto: *'Aut vincere aut mori'*

Visitor: The Rt Revd The Lord Bishop of Lichfield

Governors:
¶ *Old Wrekinian*

¶C Reynolds-Jones, TD (*Chairman*)
Rt Hon The Viscount Boyne, MRICS
¶H W Campion, ACA, ATII
J Ellison, FCA
¶A C U Evans
Mrs M T Gwynne, BVSc, MRCVS
Mrs J Haggett
Mrs E Moore, LLB
A Stilton, MA
M P Willcock, FRICS
N Coulson, MA, MBA (*Secretary*)

***Headmaster*: Stephen Drew**, MA (St Catherine's College Oxford), MEd (Bristol)

Deputy Head (*Academic*): H P Griffiths, BSc, PhD

Deputy Head (*Pastoral*): Mrs S E Clarke, BA, FRGS

Assistant Head: I Williamson, BA

Chaplain: Revd M Horton, MA, MA CertTh, DipTh

Assistant Staff:
J Ballard, BSc
Miss A Beddall, BSc
†P J Berry, BA
†A J I Brennan, BA
H S R Brown, BA
S Cale, BSc
Mrs J Cliffe, BSc
Mrs F Coffey, BSc
J M Coffin, BEng
Mrs G Cordingly, BSc
Mrs M Crone, BA
Mrs L J Drew, BA
A Francis-Jones, BSc
J C Frodsham, CertEd, AdvDipEd
†H R Gray, BSc
Miss J Harris, BA
S J Hield, BSc
†A R Hurd, BSc
Mrs A John, BA
E John, CertEd, MEd
D A Johnson, BA, FRGS
Miss R R Jones, BA
Mrs J D Kotas, BA
K B Livingstone, BA
D McLagan, BA
F Murton, BMus, LRAM, LTCL, ARCO
Mrs M Pattinson, MA
Mrs E Perry, BSc
J G Phillips, BA
E Roberts, BA
G N Roberts, BSc, PhD
T A Southall, BSc
Mrs C Thust, BSc
C J Tolley, BSc
A J Ware, BSc
Mrs M N J Warner, BSc
M de Weymarn, BA
Ms G T Whitehead, BA
†D J Winterton, BA

Learning Support:
Mrs B Harbron, BA, CFPS
Mrs C Blacklaws, BA
Mrs H M King, BSc
Mrs A H Livingstone, MA, RSA CELTA

Visiting Music Staff:
C C Booth-Jones, ARAM (*Singing*)
D Bradley, BA (*Cello*)
Mrs R Clarke (*Piano & Oboe*)
M I W Hall, BMus, MMus
D Heywood, ABSM (*Trombone*)
Mrs J Horton, ARCM (*Piano*)
C J Jones, BMus (*Piano*)
A Kennedy, BA, BMus (*Violin*)
G Lamplough, BMus (*Trumpet*)
Miss S A Lane, ARCM (*Flute*)
P Parker (*Guitar*)
Mrs P Pickford, DDME, MEd (*Piano*)
G Santry (*Drums*)
Mrs F Stubbs, MA, GCLM (*Bassoon*)
J M Wynn (*Jazz Piano*)

Games:
J M L Mostyn (*Head of Games*)
Mrs C A Ritchie-Morgan (*Head of Girls Games*)

Sports Coaches:
S Aston (*Cricket*)
Mrs K Bennett (*Girls Games*)
D Clarke (*Swimming*)
J P Dawson (*Cricket*)
J Field (*Basketball, Cricket & Squash*)

S Floyd (*Hockey*)
K Holding (*Fencing*)
K F Hughes (*Cricket – Umpire*)
Mrs M Jenkins (*Girls' Games*)
R J Pinder (*Rugby*)
Mrs R Reilly (*Swimming*)
A K Reynolds (*Rugby*)
A C Sammons (*Rugby*)
Mrs C Still (*Gymnastics*)

Medical Officer: Dr G Wood

CCF:
SSI & Outward Bound Instructor: RQMS, E J Fanneran, late RA
Secretary OWA: M Joyner, BSc

Bursar: Mrs Y K Thomas, MBA, FCA

Deputy Bursars:
Enterprise: B C Crone
Operations: D N Broomfield

Development Director: C J McCulloch
Marketing Manager: Mrs A Nicoll
Admissions Registrar: Mrs C Williams
Headmaster's Personal Assistant: Mrs C L Barefoot

The College, known locally as 'the School in the Garden', is situated in an estate of 100 acres on the outskirts of the market town of Wellington. We pride ourselves on the excellent quality of our people, as well as the excellent quality of our facilities, and we measure our achievements not only by our outstanding examination results, but also by the whole development of individuals within the school. Being a relatively small school, about 470 pupils, the quality of relationships is good and enables a purposeful atmosphere to prevail in which students can achieve their potential, both in academic and extra-curricular activities. We are splendidly equipped with many modern facilities including a purpose-built Theatre, a double Sports Hall, Astroturf and swimming pool, together with all the expected classrooms, ICT facilities and a new Sixth Form Centre. Teaching is expert and disciplined. Co-educational since 1975, there are 7 Houses, which cater for both Day and Boarding pupils, and these include dedicated Junior Houses for the 11 to 13 intake. Everyone eats together in a central Dining Room and there is a Medical Centre available to all pupils. The Chapel is central to the school both geographically and in the impact it makes on the ethos of the College.

Admission. Boarders and day pupils are admitted at 11+ or 13+ after passing the Entry Examination or Common Entrance. There is also a Sixth Form entry based on GCSE achievement.

Term of entry. The normal term of entry is the Autumn Term but pupils may be accepted at other times of the academic year in special circumstances.

Fees per term (2008-2009). Full Boarding: £6,609 (Years 7–8); £7,645 (Years 9–Sixth Form). Weekly Boarding: £5,400 (Years 7–8), £6,300 (Years 9–Sixth Form). Day: £3,836 (Years 7–8); £4,630 (Years 9–Sixth Form). Private tuition may be arranged at an extra charge.

Music Fees are £17.75 per lesson. Registration Fee £100.

The School Curriculum is framed to meet the needs of the GCSE Examination, AS and A levels. In the Upper School boys and girls are prepared for entrance to Oxbridge and other Universities. Every pupil has an academic tutor. Expert careers advice is given and all members of the Fifth Form take an aptitude and assessment test before selecting their A levels. The school's careers staff organise work experience for Sixth Form pupils. Regular careers lectures take place in the two winter terms and there is an annual Careers Fair in the Summer Term. Links with businesses in the Telford Enterprise Zone are strong. Special courses in study skills and interview techniques are conducted in the Sixth Form. All pupils undergo a counselling course on important moral and social issues and Sixth Form pupils take part in a Leadership Course.

Games and Activities. We are particularly strong in Netball and Cricket, and the main games for girls are hockey, netball, tennis, athletics and rounders; for boys, rugby, soccer, hockey, cricket, tennis and athletics. Many other sports are available, including squash, basket-ball, volley-ball, cross country, fencing, shooting, climbing, badminton, sailing, canoeing and swimming for both boys and girls. On Tuesdays or Fridays, pupils select from a large range of other activities. Over one hundred pupils are involved with the Duke of Edinburgh's Award Scheme and there is a growing tradition of Community Service. There is also a Combined Cadet Force.

Art, Crafts, Music and Drama. There is a flourishing tradition of all these at Wrekin. Art, Pottery, Multimedia Design Technology and Music are all taught in the junior forms and it is hoped that everyone will continue with one of these creative activities throughout his or her time at the school. All can be taken at GCSE and A level. There is a large Choir and Orchestra and other instrumental and Jazz Bands. Many plays are performed by Houses, year groups and at school level.

Scholarships, Exhibitions and Prizes. (*see Scholarship Entries section*). Academic Scholarships and Exhibitions, open to boys and girls, are offered annually. Sixth Form scholarships are awarded to candidates entering Wrekin after GCSE. These are awarded in advance, based on GCSE predictions of at least six A grades and following an interview at the school. Valuable Music Scholarships, and Exhibitions are awarded annually. Bursaries are awarded to candidates who offer outstanding ability in games. Music and Art examinations and assessments take place in the Lent Term and are open to pupils for entry at all levels of the school. There is an important link with the Services and bursaries are available to support the sons and daughters of service personnel. Particulars of all scholarships and awards may be obtained from the Headmaster.

Old Wrekinian Association. A flourishing Wrekinian Association of over 3,500 members exists to make possible continuous contact between the School and its Old Pupils, for the benefit of both and to support the ideals and aims of the school. It is expected that boys and girls will become members of the Old Wrekinian Association when they leave Wrekin.

Charitable status. Wrekin Old Hall Trust Limited is a Registered Charity, number 528417. It exists to provide independent boarding and day co-education in accordance with the Articles of Association of Wrekin College.

Wycliffe College

Stonehouse Gloucestershire GL10 2JQ
Tel: 01453 822432
Fax: 01453 827634
e-mail: senior@wycliffe.co.uk
website: www.wycliffe.co.uk

Founded in 1882 by Mr G W Sibly, Wycliffe was placed on a permanent foundation under a Council of Governors in 1931.

President: S P Etheridge, MBE, TD, JP, MBA, FIFP, CFP, FCII, FLIA, ALIA Dip, ACIArb

Chairman of Governors: Major General G B Fawcus, CB, MA

Vice-Presidents:
Capt N B M Clack, MA, MSc, CEng, MIEE, FBIM RN Retd
M L Blinkhorn, FRICS

Vice-Chairman: Air Chief Marshal Sir Michael Graydon, GCB, CBE, FRAeS

Brigadier R Bacon, MBA, FCIPD, FCMI, CMILT
Mrs K R Fife, BSc, MRPharms
S J Fisher, LLB
A R Kirby, LLB
Mrs S J Lacey, MEng, BA Hons
J H Powell-Tuck, FRICS
J C H Pritchard, DipM, MIMC, MCIM, MIMgt
Group Captain G Reid, MB, ChB, FRCPsych, RAF
J Slater, FRICS
J R E Williams, FCA

Secretary to the Council: S J A Flanagan, MC

***Head*: Mrs M E Burnet Ward**, MA St Andrews

Deputy Head: P Woolley, BA Kent (*Politics*)
Director of Studies: S V Dunne, BA Glamorgan (*RE*)
Director of Pastoral Care: Mrs E A Buckley, BSc UCW, Aberystwyth (*Physical Education*)
Head of Sixth Form/Head of Higher Education and Careers: A M Laing, BA Swansea (*Economics & Business Studies*)
Head of Lower School: M Scott-Baumann, MA Cambridge, MA London (*History*)
Chaplain: Mrs C Welham, MA Durham (*RE*)

House Staff:
Haywardsfield: Mrs P J Mills, BA Sheffield (*French & Spanish*)
Ward's House: P D A Paine, BA Birmingham (*Head of German*)
Ivy Grove: Mrs L M Morris, CertEd, PG DipSpLD Cambridge/Kingston (*SEN*)
Haywardsend: Mrs J A White, BSc Surrey, RSADipTEFLA (*ESOL*)
Loosley Halls: G P Buckley, BA OU, MinstSRMDip, MILAM (*Head of Physical Education*)
Robinson House: R J Pavis, BA Durham (*Head of MFL*)
Lampeter House: P Hale, BSc Warwick (*Head of Mathematics*)
Collingwood House: Miss L A Hellewell, BA Birmingham (*Geography and Travel and Tourism*)

Teaching Staff:
G J Wheeler, BEd London (*Head of Design & Technology*)
Major P N Rothwell (*OC CCF; Physical Education*)
Mrs J M Macgregor, BSc Bath (*Mathematics, Examinations Officer*)
Mrs C V Collins, MA Oxon, DIDipSpLD (*Head of SEN*)
D Morrish, SRA Level IV Advanced (*Squash Coach*)
J M Hardaker, BA Manchester Metropolitan (*Head of Business Studies, Economics and Accounting*)
J Williams, BA Wales, Cardiff (*Business Studies and Economics*)
Mrs A M Creed, BSc Sheffield, CertEd (*Head of Biology*)
Mrs E A Dancer, BSc London, DASS (*Head of Psychology*)
W H Helsby, BA Newcastle, RSADipTEFL (*ESOL*)
M J Kimber, New Zealand Coaching Cert, ECB Level 1, RFU Levels I & II (*Sports Coach*)
D J Amies, BSc, MSc Nottingham (*Head of Science*)
Miss N Borovac, BEng Northumbria (*Mathematics*)
B D Cadenhead, BSc Surrey (*Physics, Careers Advisor*)
Miss K F Elliott, BA London (*ESOL*)
Miss C Dickinson, BA Leicester (*PHSE*)
Mrs N J H Scott, BA Exeter (*Head of History*)
M J Archer, BSc Oxon (*Head of Chemistry*)
W H Day-Lewis, BA DiELTA Central Lancs (*ESOL*)
N J Lowson, BA Central St Martin's (*Design & Technology*)
M D Milne, BA UWE, Bristol (*Business Studies and Accounting*)
Mrs L C Paine, BSc Birmingham (*Head of Physics*)
Miss A C Wells, BSc Reading (*Physics*)
Mrs L E Partridge, PGCert Central School of Speech & Language (*Head of Drama*)
J R Welham, BSc Durham (*Mathematics*)
S M Fisher BA Exeter (*Director of ICT*)
M P J Johnson, BA Oxon (*Head of Media and Film Studies*)
Mrs L Longthorn, BA Central Lancs (*Economics & Business Studies*)
Miss R Weaver, BSc Exeter (*Geography and Travel and Tourism*)
T R Brown, BA Gloucestershire (*Media Studies*)
Miss G L Eeley, BSc Wales (*Biology*)
Miss V S Hughes, BSc Surrey (*Chemistry*)
V Keat, BSc Malaya (*Chemistry*)
Miss S M Pearce, BSc (*Head of Girls' Games*)
Miss J Wilson, BA Lancaster (*English*)
E O Jenkins, BA Exeter (*Director of Music*)
P D Scott, MBioChem University College, Oxford (*Mathematics*)
Mrs B Cooke, BA Reading (*ICT*)
R Bristow, BA Oxon (*Assistant Director of Music*)
A C Naish, BSc Surrey (*Director of Sport*)
Miss P Tardio-Baeza, BA Valencia
I Russell, BSc Durham (*Mathematics*)
Miss A Dibbs, BA Birmingham (*Mathematics*)
J Garrow (*Rowing Coach*)
J Pyle, BA Cambridge (*English*)

Part -time Teaching Staff:
S J Hubbard, BA Gloucester College of Art (*Art*)
Mrs L A Wong Warwick, PGCE, RSADipTEFLA (*ESOL*)
Mrs H P Williams, BA Leicester (*Head of English*)
Mrs R Tranter (*Drama*)
Mrs S J Blythe, CertEd Redland College, Bristol (*English*)
Mrs R M Potter, BA UCW (*English*)
Mrs J Cottrell, BA Thames Valley (*SEN and English*)
Mrs J Smith, BA Liverpool (*French & Spanish*)
Mrs S Matthews, BSc OU (*Psychology*)
Mrs R Wordsworth, BA (*Artist in Residence, Ceramics and Photography*)

Teaching Support Staff:
Dr J E Hudson, MA Oxon, PhD (*Careers Librarian*)
C Dainton, BA OU, CertEd (*Design & Technology Technician*)
T Dyer, BSc Eng Bath (*Engineering Projects*)
S R Garley, BAF (*Fencing Coach*)
M A Williams, HNC (*Network Manager*)
Mrs A C Banyard, HNC (*Senior Laboratory Technician*)
N Dixon (*Health & Safety Officer*)
Mrs S A Hodgkins (*Librarian*)
Miss A J L Britton (*Laboratory Technician*)
B Whetter (*IT Technician*)
M Carslake (*Laboratory Technician*)
C Davis (*IT Technician*)

Visiting Music Staff:
Mrs J Baldwin (*Oboe*)
Mrs H Barry, ATRNCM, LTCL, CertEd (*Bassoon*)
M Boucher, DipPerc (*Percussion*)
J Carter, DipRAM (*Piano*)
I Dollins, BMus, ARCM (*Voice and Piano*)
S Ellsmore, ARCM (*Trumpet*)
Mrs C Gibbons (*Clarinet*)
Mrs V Green, GRSM, ARCM, LRAM (*Piano and Double Bass*)
J Lambert, MA Oxon, BMus (*Piano*)
Miss E May, GRSM, ARCM (*Flute*)
N Nash (*Saxophone*)
Miss J Orsman, GBSM (*Violin*)
P Reynolds (*Guitar*)
Mrs T Skitt, GRNCM (*Voice*)
Col W P Thomas, MIM (*Brass*)
Miss J Tomlinson, GRSM, LRAM (*Violoncello*)

Medical Officers and Staff:
Dr S Anslow, MBChB, MCCGP, DRCOG
Dr J Sivyer, MBChB, DRCOG

Dr I D Lake, MB, MRCGP, FPCert
Dr L A Lake, MB, FPCert, DRCOG, DPD

Administration:
Registrar: Mrs P Davis
Head's Secretary: Mrs R Whitworth
Staff Common Room Secretary: Mrs A Schranz
School Secretary: Mrs C Glynn
Financial Director: A C Golding, FCA
Development Director: S J A Flanagan, MC
Alumni Relations Manager: Mrs C Roberts
Director of Marketing: Mrs M Gray
Domestic Bursar: Mrs D Tetley
Caterer: Mrs J Johnson, Aramark Catering

Preparatory School
(*see also entry in IAPS section*)

Headmaster: A Palmer, MA, BEd

Deputy Head and Director of Studies: Mrs V Jackson, BA Liverpool
Director of Pastoral Care: Mrs L Askew, LAMDA

Boarding House Staff:
Mrs C Williams
Mrs L Field

Teaching Staff:
Miss S Ainge, BA, PGCE, QTS
S J Arman, BEd
D K Fisher, CertEd
Mrs C Brown, BA
Miss A Drew, BA
P Duffy, BMus, GBSM, ABSM, PGCE
Miss L Fyfe, BSc
R Gaunt, BA QTS
Mrs C Graham, BSc, CertSpLD
C Guest, BSc, PGCE
Ms R White, BEd
W A Humphreys, BEd
Mrs J Lyons, BA
A Milner, BA
J D Newns, CertEd
Miss A O'Sullivan, BEd
R E Rennicks, CertEd, BA
A Sinclair, BA
Mrs C Stanley, BA
M Stopforth, BA
G Stotesbury, BA
Miss E Upadhyay, BEd QTS
Mrs N C Warden, BEd
Mrs S Warren, BEd

Head of Pre-Prep: Mrs A Oliver, BA
Nursery: Mrs C Marsh, NNEB, C&G Child Care 0–7
Registrar: Mrs W Robertson
Headmaster's Secretary: Mrs S Rogers
Catering Manager: Mrs J Johnson, Aramark Catering

Location. 2 miles from M5 (J.13): Stonehouse Railway Station 200 metres; London Paddington under 2 hours; London Heathrow 90 minutes; Bristol Airport 50 minutes; Birmingham International 60 minutes. The Preparatory School (under its own Headmaster) is on a separate adjacent campus with its own extensive facilities, including a new Performing Arts Centre and Dining Hall.

Organisation. Senior School 13–18: 282 Boys, 139 Girls, two-thirds Boarding. Sixth Form number some 183. Class sizes vary from 3–17 pupils. Preparatory School 2–13: 200 Boys, 150 Girls.

Admission. At any age following interview and assessment, via numerous Scholarships and Awards; via Common Entrance or Scholarship examinations at 13+; via GCSE or Scholarship examinations into the Sixth Form. Application to the Head who is personally concerned about each student and available to meet any parent.

Religion. Interdenominational, all faiths welcome. Confirmation classes; Christian Fellowship group and daily worship in keeping with this generation are an integral part of College life.

Houses. Boarders reside in eight boarding Houses. There are three Sixth Form Halls of Residence each with Study Bedroom with en-suite facilities. A flexi-boarding Day House opened in January 2003, a new Sports Centre in January 2004, and an Advanced Learning Centre in September 2004. All boarding houses are being refurbished on a rolling programme to be completed by 2009.

Tutors. Each student has a House based tutor in the Lower School and a subject based tutor in the Sixth Form. Thus supported by Housemaster/Housemistress, Tutor, Chaplain and Head of Year each student may gain maximum advantage towards personal fulfilment in a community noted for its friendly and caring support.

Medical Centre. 24 hour attendance by qualified staff in a well-equipped separate Sanatorium. The Health Centre is in the same street. Healthy food is of prime consideration. Special dietary requirements for health or faith satisfied through a new Kitchen and Dining Hall.

Development Year. A unique English Language Course is provided for those in need of an additional year prior to the full two-year A Level course. It may also be used as an alternative to the A Level course leading directly to qualifications accepted by industry, commerce and most institutions of Higher/Further Education. Parts of the course may also be continued with A Levels. Options include English for Business; Mathematical Problem-solving; Business Studies; Media Studies; Science.

A Levels. As a general rule students choose four, or occasionally five, AS subjects to study in the Lower Sixth. Most students then continue to study three subjects in the second year to A2 Level. Apart from the traditional subjects, the following are also on offer to A2 Level: Art and Design, Design and Technology, Japanese, Psychology, Business Studies, Media Studies, Political Studies, Theatre Studies, Film Studies, Music Technology and Physical Education. Additional subjects to AS Level are Italian, Computing, Critical Thinking and Travel & Tourism.

GCSEs are usually taken three years after 13+ entry. Traditional subjects, including four Modern Languages – French, German, Spanish and Japanese – may be studied. Design and Technology, Computing, Physical Education and Drama are also available as GCSE options. Textiles, Italian and Philosophy are also available at GCSE to members of the Lower Sixth.

Scholarships and Awards. (*see Scholarship Entries section*). Thanks to the generosity of Governors and Old Wycliffians, a large number are available offering up to 50% of the fees. These may be supplemented in cases of financial need.

For 13+ entry a candidate must be under 14 on 1st September of year of entry and sit the examination in the Spring Term.

For 16+ entry, examinations are held in the Autumn or Spring prior to arrival or by arrangement.

At other ages, applications to be made to the Head.

Awards are made to candidates with academic talent or potential and also specifically in Music, Art, Design Technology, IT, Drama, Sport including Squash, Rowing and Fencing.

Special awards are also available to (a) those with all round merit, (b) children of serving members of the Services (up to 20% Forces Bursaries), (c) good Common Entrance candidates highly recommended, (d) children of teachers/clergy, (e) vegetarians.

Physical Education. Classes are part of the curriculum. Facilities are available for Rowing, Rugby, Hockey, Fencing, Soccer, Netball, Squash, Badminton, Basketball, Swimming, Cricket, Tennis, Athletics, Health and Fitness, Shooting, Adventure Training, Cross Country.

Training for Service is available via the Combined Cadet Force, Venture Scouts, Duke of Edinburgh's Award Scheme, Leadership Courses, and the Wycliffe Charitable Organisation.

International Travel is regularly organised for varied groups, whether musicians, scouts or cadets, and arduous training is available in the UK and overseas. Pupil trips and exchanges are arranged for those studying foreign languages.

School Societies. Among 90 available are: Drama Workshops; Stage Management; Philosophy; Language; Debating; Archaeology; Pottery; Craft; Computing; Electronics; Astronomy; Shooting; Choral, Instrumental Music; First Aid; Cookery; Dance and a Sixth Form Club.

Sunday Specials. A variety of activities, both at the College and locally, are organised for Boarders.

Music. A purpose-built music school with enthusiastic staff enables high standards to be achieved. Music is taken at GCSE and A Level and several pupils each year continue their music studies at the Conservatoires and Universities. There are several choirs, orchestras and three Bands, and Associated Board Examinations are taken every term. The College hosts professional concerts and dramatic productions annually.

Careers Guidance. A vital department which is recognised as a centre of excellence. The College is a member of the Independent Schools' Careers Organisation and the Careers Library is well-equipped with information on careers and entrance to Higher Education.

Teacher Training. Wycliffe has been selected as a training centre for teachers, reflecting the high esteem in which the College is held.

Fees per term (2008-2009). Boarders £7,745–£7,840 (£8,350 New Sixth Form entrants, £9,335 Development Year); Day pupils £4,715–£5,155 (£7,215 Development Year). Preparatory School: Boarders £4,410–£6,345; Day pupils £1,720–£4,520.

Extras are kept to a minimum but may include expeditions, certain Society subscriptions and ESOL (which is included in the Development Year's fees).

Alumni. The Old Wycliffian Society is based within the College campus and supports all OWs through its website and mailings. The OWS Office organises regular reunions, including the highly popular OW Carol Service, and publishes an annual issue of The Star and a termly issue of the Wycliffe Times. For further details, visit the OWS website at www.wycliffe.co.uk or contact Mrs Ginny Young, OW Registrar, Tel: 01453 820439, e-mail: ow@wycliffe.co.uk.

Charitable status. Wycliffe College Incorporated is a Registered Charity, number 311714. It exists to provide education for boys and girls.

Yarm School

The Friarage Yarm Stockton-on-Tees TS15 9EJ
Tel: 01642 786023
Fax: 01642 789216
e-mail: dmd@yarmschool.org
website: www.yarmschool.org

Yarm School, a co-educational day school, was established in its present form in 1978. It has its own co-educational Preparatory School for pupils from 4 to 11 years of age and a nursery for 3 year olds.

Governing Body:
Chair: Dr A Bonavia, MBChB, MRCGP
Vice-Chairman: A W Wright, BSc

Mrs S Anderson, FCA, BSc
M M Bisset, BA, MA
Mrs S E Cardew, MSc
His Honour Judge J de Guise Walford
Ms C Evans, MA, MBA, ARCM
J M James, BA, FCA, CTA
J D McDougall, CEng, FIMechE
W R Pickersgill, MCIBSE
Dr R S Sagoo, MBChB
Mrs C S Scholes, RGN
M Thompson, BA, ACMA

***Headmaster*: D M Dunn**, BA

Deputy Headmaster: D G Woodward, BSc, CBiol, MIBiol

Director of Studies: Dr P M Chapman, MA, PhD
Head of Sixth Form: Dr A M Goodall, MA, PhD
Head of Middle School: Mrs K A Gratton, BEd
Director of Learning: T F Spence, BA, MEd

Senior Masters:
R A Brown, BSc
J J Logan, BA, MA, FRGS

Headmaster's PA: Mrs J L Herbert, BSc, MIL

* *Head of Department*
† *Housemaster/mistress*
§ *Part-time*

Mrs J C Ankers, BA
J E Armitage, BSc
D Boddy, BA, MCollT (*Head of First Year*)
G C Booth, MA
*K R Brown, BMus, ALCM, FGMS
*I H Burns, BSc
*I T Chamberlain, MA, MA
§Mrs P Clarke, BSc
*P J Connery, MA, BA
*G B Cooper, BSc
S H A Crabtree, BSc (*Head of Careers*)
*E M Craig, BA
*P E Crookes, MA
§Mrs R M Crookes, BA
T J Day, CertEd
§Mrs F C Dunn, BEd (*Deputy Head of Sixth Form*)
*D V G Dunn, MA, BA (*Head of Fifth Year*)
S Edwards, BA, MPhil
G Emerson, BA (*Head of Fourth Year*)
*§Mrs L Findlay, BA
T L Foggett, MSc, BA, BSc
*A I Guest, BEd
§Mrs J L Guest, BEd (*Head of Third Year*)
S P Hardy, BEd
§Mrs S Heavers, BA
*Frau J Heinen, MA
Miss C T Holloway, BA ITT
J G Hulme, BSc
§Mrs A Jackson, BSc
§Mrs L Jackson, BA
D A Jardine, BSc
Miss G A Jolly, BA (*†Oswald*)
*H A Killick, BA, MPhil, ARCM
Mrs L Kneale, BA
*A D Law, MA
§Miss G Lumley, CertEd
C P Mulligan, BSc
*A O Newman, BA
Mrs J H Nickson, BA, CPE Law (†Cuthbert*)
*Mrs J Nixon, BA
*T D J Pender, BA
*Dr K W Perry, BSc, PhD
Dr P D Prideaux, BSc, PhD (*†Bede*)
§Mrs S J Pyke, MA
*S R Ravenhall, BA, MPhil
Mrs S M Rea, BA, MEd
Miss N E Redhead, BEd
Miss C E Rhodes, BSc
Miss E C Robinson, BA
M C Rye, BA (*†Aidan*)
§Miss K F Serdecka, BA, BSc, CertSocSci
§Mrs S Snape, BA, PGDip
§Ms E Stebbings, BA
I Stewart, BSc
P N Telfer, BA
C Thomas, BEd
S M Thompson, BSc
C A C Webb, BA (*Head of Second Year*)
§Mrs J Wilson, BSc

School Manager: Mrs N L Brown, LLM

Preparatory School

Head: Mrs G R Taylor, BEd

Deputy and Head of Early School: P Hardy, BA, PGCE
Director of Studies: S G Pearce, BA, BEd, ADEE
Head of Yarm at Raventhorpe: Mrs W J Young, MA Ed

§Mrs A Arrol, BA, PGCE
Miss C Brown, BA, QTS
§Mrs S Burke (*Learning Support*)
Mrs J J Catterall, CertEd
Miss R Clarke, BTEC Nat Dip (*Teaching Assistant*)
Mrs P Covell, BEd
C R Davis, BEd
§Mrs B Desmond, BEd
Miss E Frost, BA
Mrs A J Gray, BEd
J Grundmann, BSc
Miss R Hall, BEd
Mrs K Hampton, BA, MA
K Harandon, MA
Dr R G Harrison, BMus, PhD
Mrs V Harrison, BPhil, PGCE
§Mrs S Heavers, BA
Mrs E M Hodgson, CertEd
Miss J Horton, BA (*Teaching Assistant*)
§Mrs S Johnson, BEd
§Mrs D Jones, ALCM
E Jones, BA

Mrs J Jones, NNEB (*Teaching Assistant*)
Mrs K Mavin, BSc, QTS
Mrs H J McCormack, BA, PGCE
Mrs K Millne, BEd
§Mrs C A Pearce, BA, Cert TESOL
Miss L H Rowlands, BMus
Mrs G Selby, PPA Cert (*Teaching Assistant*)
M Sellers, BSc
§Mrs S Snape, BA, PGDip
§Mrs S Thomas, NCFE St2 (*Teaching Assistant*)
Mrs A White, BEd
Mrs C Williams, BEd, MA

There are about 1,000 pupils in the School including 350 pupils aged 3 to 11 years who are in a separate Preparatory School. There are about 180 in the Sixth Form. The school is fully co-educational. The School also owns and runs a satellite Preparatory School in Darlington for pupils aged 3–11. Known as Yarm at Raventhorpe, it can accommodate 100 pupils.

Situations and Buildings. Yarm is an attractive market town on the edge of the Teesside conurbation giving easy access to both town and countryside. The North York Moors National Park is only 15 minutes away.

The School occupies two adjacent sites on the outskirts of Yarm: the buildings of the original Yarm Grammar School (founded 1590, oldest building dated 1884) and The Friarage, comprising an eighteenth century mansion and several other buildings, set in attractive grounds bordering the River Tees. A classroom block to house the English, History and Geography departments was completed in 1988 and September 1992 saw the completion of a sports hall and squash court, a 600-seat theatre with adjacent music facilities and purpose built accommodation for modern languages. A new science block containing facilities for computing and geology in addition to the normal provision for physics, chemistry and biology was completed in May 1996. An exciting new electronics and technology centre opened in April 1997. There is a self-contained sixth form centre and a new sixth form library was opened in 2000. The School possesses about 26 acres of playing fields, an astroturf all-weather pitch for hockey and tennis, and a fitness suite.

The Preparatory School has its own accommodation which includes a gym, a school hall and specialist facilities for art and technology. A new computing room and library were added in 2002. (*For further details, see Preparatory School entry in IAPS section.*)

Admission. Pupils are admitted at 11 and 16 by means of the School's own Entrance Examination. The Preparatory School has its own entrance procedures.

Curriculum. The School's academic reputation in the Cleveland area is high and virtually all leavers go on to take university degrees. In 2007 over 10% of the Sixth Form achieved an Oxbridge place. In the Preparatory School the curriculum is both wide ranging and demanding. Whilst the basics in English and Maths are given great emphasis, the Sciences, Technology and Modern Languages also form an important part of the timetable. In the First Year all pupils study the following subjects: English, Maths, Physics, Chemistry, Biology, Technology, French, Latin, History, Geography, Information Technology, Art, RS and Music. Setting by ability takes place in Mathematics, English and in Modern Languages. In the Second Year many pupils begin a second Modern Language and setting in the Sciences is also arranged. GCSE is taken as a two year course comprising seven compulsory 'core' subjects (English, English Literature, Maths, German or French, Physics, Chemistry and Biology) and 3 or more 'options'. Options can usually be selected from French, German, Spanish, Latin, Classical Studies, Greek, History, Geography, Information Technology, Technology, Design and Realisation, Art, PE, Music and Religious Studies. The more able pupils (perhaps a third or more of a 'year group') will take Maths and a foreign language a year or more early enabling them to take these subjects to levels beyond GCSE whilst still in the Fifth Form.

In the Sixth Form A Levels are selected from about twenty options. All Lower Sixth students take 4 AS Levels and 3 or 4 A2s in the Upper Sixth. General Studies is also taught in the Upper Sixth.

Modern languages are enhanced by means of regular exchanges with 'twin' schools in France, Germany and Spain. Teams entered for nationwide Mathematics and Science/Technology competitions have won several awards in the last three or four years.

Organisation. Pastoral care is based on both a year group and a House system. Every pupil belongs to one of four Houses for his/her whole school career. Houses exist to promote competitions, sports events, charity fund-raising etc. Each pupil also has a personal Tutor and Head of Year whose task it is to look after all the pupils within a given year group. Sixth-formers have the opportunity to serve as House Monitors and School Prefects.

Games and Activities. Rugby, hockey, rowing, football and netball are the School's main winter games and there are representative teams in these sports for all age levels. In the summer, rowing, cricket, tennis and athletics become the major sports. In addition canoeing, squash, orienteering and cross-country are also pursued at inter-school level throughout the year. Several other games are available as options.

There are many school societies. A great deal of extra-curricular activity is centred on the Duke of Edinburgh's Award Scheme. Rock climbing, canoeing and other aspects of outdoor education are given some prominence and residential weekends at an outdoor pursuits centre are a fixed part of the curriculum. There is a flourishing CCF contingent (membership, though popular, is entirely voluntary). School excursions are frequent and very varied. Expeditions in recent years have travelled as far as India, America and Guyana. Drama (at least three major productions a year) and Music (several choir and orchestral concerts are given each year) are given every encouragement and have a strong following. Activities which are an extension of Art or Technology or Biology also flourish particularly well.

Religion. The School is an inter-denominational community comprising pupils of both Christian and non-Christian backgrounds. There are regular assemblies and occasional services held in the local Parish Church.

Fees per term (2008-2009). Senior School £3,167; Preparatory School £2,389–£2,643; Early School (Pre-Prep) £1,877–£1,946; Nursery £1,389 (full-time). Lunches are extra.

Scholarships. (*see Scholarship Entries section*).

Former Pupils. Past members of the School are eligible to join the Former Pupils' Society whose Hon Secretary may be contacted via the School Office.

Charitable status. Yarm School is a Registered Charity, number 1093434. It exists to provide quality education for boys and girls.

Entrance Scholarships

Abingdon School (see p 7)
The majority of awards are made at 13+ entry and are open to external and internal candidates. Some additional awards are available on entry to Sixth Form and to the Lower School. All Scholarships and bursaries are means-tested. They carry an entitlement to a nominal fee remission of £300 per year plus remission of up to 100% of the tuition fee on a means-tested bursary basis. Music Scholarships also carry an entitlement to remission on instrument tuition fees.

Academic Awards:

Up to six awards available at 11+.

Between 15 and 18 Scholarships available at 13+.

Up to three Scholarships to Sixth Form.

The Mercers' Company Scholarship offers remission of the entire tuition fee. The Duxbury Scholarship offers up to half of the total tuition and boarding fee. The Duxbury Scholarship is reserved for boarding candidates and may be awarded for music.

Ackworth School (see p 8)
Academic Scholarships are awarded annually. At ages 11+, 12+ and 13+ the awards are made on the basis of performance at the Entrance Tests and a subsequent interview.

At Sixth Form level an offer of a Scholarship is made following a scholarship examination in March.

Bursaries are also available for Members or Attenders of the Society of Friends and in other cases where need can be shown.

Aldenham School (see p 10)
Available at each point of entry, Scholarships and Exhibitions are awarded to boys and girls who have demonstrated outstanding achievement and who have the potential to make a special contribution to the School. In addition to Academic there are also opportunities for Music, Art, Sport and Design Technology scholarships and exhibitions. A Scholarship automatically carries a minimum 10% discount of fees and an Exhibition a discount of 5%.

The parents of Scholars and Exhibitioners may be eligible for a Bursary which is subject to a simple means test and to the availability of funds. They will normally have first call on Bursary funds. Bursaries are available up to 50% of fees.

Bursaries are also available to help boys and girls who will benefit from education at Aldenham but whose parents would not otherwise be able to afford the full fees or to help in cases where parents' financial circumstances have changed during their son's or daughter's time at the School. These Bursaries include the Lloyd's Cuthbert Heath awards, generous awards made available by the Brewers' Company and awards made by the OA War Memorial Fund.

Alleyn's School (see p 11)
(1) At 11+ up to 18 Academic scholarships of up to 1/3 of the full fee, plus 1 Art, 2 Music and 2 Sports scholarships. Bursaries available equivalent to 5 free places per annum.
(2) At 13+: 4 Academic scholarships and 2 Music scholarships.
(3) At 16+: 6 Academic scholarships, plus 2 Sports scholarships and 1 Music scholarship. Bursaries available equivalent to 2 free places per annum.

Ampleforth College (see p 13)
Scholarships are awarded annually on the results of examinations held at Ampleforth.

Academic Scholarships at 13+. ISEB Common Academic Scholarships are sat in February. The maximum scholarship awarded is 20% of the fees.

Sixth Form Entry. Academic Scholarship exams are held in November with the maximum of 20% fee remission.

Further details can be obtained from The Admissions Office, Ampleforth College, York, YO62 4ER. Tel: 01439 766863; e-mail: admissions@ampleforth.org.uk.

Arnold School (see p 17)
Several scholarships (including those for Music, Art & Design, and Sport) are available for entry at 11+. Music, Sport, Art, Design & Technology, and Drama scholarships are available in the Sixth Form. United Church Schools Foundation Assisted Places are also available. Further particulars from the Marketing and Admissions Secretary (01253 346391).

Bancroft's School (see p 22)
The School awards up to 15 Scholarships worth up to 50% of the fees, and up to five Francis Bancroft Scholarships, which are means tested, at age 11 as a result of its Entrance Examination in January. Two of the Scholarships may be Music Scholarships. There are five Scholarships worth 50% of the fees for Sixth Form entrants which may include Music awards.

Barnard Castle School (see p 24)
Scholarships are awarded to entrants to the Senior School at any level including the Sixth Form, on the basis of the School's own examinations held in February. As well as academic scholarships, awards may be made for Music, Art, Sport or all-round ability. The School also has a small number of means-tested Assisted Places. Particulars from the *Headmaster's Secretary*.

Bedales School (see p 27)
Academic scholarships are available for entry at 13+ and 16+; Music scholarships (usually up to 25% of the fees) for entry to Dunhurst (10+ and older; exceptionally, 8+) and to Bedales (13+ and 16+); Art scholarships for entry at 16+.

The basic award for scholarships (except Music) is £750, which can be increased through means-testing to a maximum of 85% of fees.

Means-tested bursaries are also available to those of proven need.

For full details of the scholarships and timing of assessment, please apply to the Registrar.

Bedford Modern School (see p 29)
The School has identified three explicit areas where we wish particularly to help gifted and talented students – academic, sport and performing arts. The Modern Scholarships enable these students to access specific mentoring and facilities in order to assist them achieve their dream. Further details may be obtained from the School.

Bedford School (see p 31)
Awards are available for boys entering the School at 11,13 or 16 years.

For more information about Bedford's new Access Award & Scholarship Scheme, please call our freephone helpline 0800 432 0084 or visit our website www.bedfordschool.org.uk.

Berkhamsted Collegiate School (see p 35)
Academic Scholarships are awarded on the basis of academic merit alone. Students qualify from their performance in the entrance examination and sit an additional Scholarship examination. The value of awards is up to 10% of the tuition fee. Further means-tested bursaries are available.

The **Art Scholarship** is determined by merit on the basis of the presentation of a folio of work, a practical test, an interview and an acceptable level at entrance examination. The award is renewable annually dependent on continued commitment to the subject.

The **Music Scholarship** is assessed by audition, which consists of a performance of two contrasting pieces on two instruments: there are also aural tests, sight-reading (instrumental and singing) and an interview. It is expected that the award holders will study music to at least GCSE and make a full contribution to the musical life of the School.

The **Sports Scholarship** is awarded on entry to the Sixth Form only. The award is determined by merit on the basis of the presentation of a folio of achievements in any one sporting area. The candidate is expected to have representative experience at county level or above and provide evidence of commitment to sport.

The **Incent Scholarship** is awarded on academic merit to a state school pupil at 11+, 13+ or 16+. Value up to 100% of tuition fee depending on parental income.

Bursaries are awarded for academic or other merit, taking into account parental income and pupils' needs.

More information about Scholarships and Bursaries may be obtained on application to *The Deputy Principal's PA*.

Birkdale School (see p 37)
11+ Scholarships: One Open Scholarship is offered, and up to three Foundation Awards are available only to candidates attending maintained junior Schools. The value of each Scholarship is up to 25% of tuition fees, but bursaries are available to increase the award to 100% of fees in case of proven financial need. Candidates should be under the age of twelve on 1 September and must excel in the School's 11+ Entrance Tests and subsequent Scholarship Examinations. Assessments take place early in the Easter Term.

16+ Scholarships: One Open Scholarship is offered, and up to four Foundation Scholarships are available only to new entrants to the co-educational Sixth Form. The value of each Scholarship is up to 25% of tuition fees, but bursaries are available to increase the awards to 100% in case of proven financial need. Additionally an Odgen Science Scholarship is available to a candidate from a maintained school. Assessments take place early in the Easter Term.

16+ Bursaries: A limited amount of Bursary funding is available for allocation to Sixth Form candidates for whom a Birkdale education would be beneficial but for whom there is a proven case of financial need. Assessments normally take place early in the Easter Term, but may be arranged at other times at the discretion of the Head Master.

Music Scholarships: Candidates must satisfy the school's general admission standards. One award is available at 11+ and one at 16+ of up to 25% of tuition fees plus free tuition by Birkdale staff on one instrument. Candidates should be of good Grade 3 (11+) or Grade 5/6 (16+) standard in their first instrument and show general musicianship commensurate with technical skill. A Music Scholar is expected to enter fully into the school's musical life. Assessments take place during the Easter Term.

Further details of the above awards are available from The Registrar.

Bishop's Stortford College (see p 40)
Scholarships are awarded at three levels: Sixth Form and under 14 in the Senior School, under 12 in the Junior School. There are Academic, Music and Art Awards available.

Bloxham School (see p 42)
Scholarships and Exhibitions are awarded on the basis of a competitive examination. The value of these awards is up to 50% of fees according to academic merit.

Among the awards offered are Roger Raymond Scholarships and John Schuster Scholarships (reserved in the first instance for Sons of Clergy or of members of the teaching profession). Boarding exhibitions may be awarded to sons of members of the HM Forces on the grounds of academic and/or all-round merit and promise.

Awards are made for all-round academic performance but subject Scholarships may be awarded for promising performances in a particular subject area. There are Art and Design Awards and Music Awards with free instrumental tuition. The auditions for the latter are held in February/March each year.

Chapel Centenary Awards of up to 10% of the fees per year may be awarded to good candidates of less than Exhibition standard on the basis of academic, musical or artistic performance or all-round merit and promise.

Day-boarders are eligible for all awards at equivalent value related to day-boarder fees. Candidates should preferably be under 14 on 1st September. An age allowance is made to young candidates.

Sir Lawrence Robson Scholarships or Exhibitions are awarded each year to Sixth Form entrants. The value of these will be up to 50% of fees. Candidates must be under 17 on 1st September. The examination is held in October.

Further details may be obtained from the Headmaster, Bloxham School, Banbury, Oxon OX15 4PE.

Blundell's School (see p 44)

- Open Scholarships and Exhibitions. Up to half of the chosen designation fee (ie boarding, weekly, flexi, day) are offered on the basis of our own examinations held during January (11+), March (13+) or November (Sixth Form). Awards for Art, Music, Sport and All-round ability are also made.
- Foundation awards. Up to full day fees based on completion of a Statement of Financial Means. Candidates should be resident in the County of Devon and preference will be given to those living in the Borough of Tiverton.
- Services Package available to the sons and daughters of serving members of the Armed Forces and Diplomatic Corps.
- Awards may occasionally be supplemented by bursaries at the discretion of the Head Master.

Full details may be obtained from *The Registrars, Blundell's School, Tiverton, Devon EX16 4DN. Tel: 01884 252543.*

Bootham School (see p 48)
John Bright Boarding Scholarships: up to four awards can be made of value up to 50% of full fees. Two scholarships are available at 11+, two at 13+ for boys and girls.

Major and Minor Scholarships of up to half fees are available at 11, 13 and for Sixth Form entry.

Music Scholarships of up to 50% fees are awarded at 11+, 13+, 16+.

Other awards can be made for entrance candidates at the Headmaster's discretion.

All awards are based on an evaluation of achievement and potential in candidates and are open equally to boys and girls.

Scholarship examinations and interviews are held in February (11+), March (16+) and May (13+).

All scholarships are means tested beyond the first 5%.

A number of bursary awards is also made annually.

Full details of all the above from the Headmaster.

Bradfield College (see p 49)
At 13+ awards are made annually on the results of a competitive examination held at the College in the Lent Term on the following basis: up to five Scholarships, three of which will be Major. Candidates must be under the age of 14 on 1 September. Further Honorary Awards conferring the status and privileges of a scholar are awarded at the end of Year 11 (post GCSE).

At 16+ Scholarships are awarded annually after competitive examinations in the Michaelmas Term.

All awards are augmentable according to financial need. Further information and entrance forms can be obtained on application to the Headmaster's PA, Bradfield College, Reading, Berkshire RG7 6AU.

Brentwood School (see p 53)
At 11+ and for entry to the Sixth Form Music, Drama, Art, Sport and Choral scholarships are awarded in addition to Academic scholarships. These may be supplemented by means-tested Bursaries.

The school offers a considerable number of Bursaries in addition to the awards described above.

Further details are available from the Headmaster.

Brighton College (see p 55)
The following awards are offered annually:

Academic scholarships to pupils entering the College at age 13 (candidates should be under 14 on June 1st of the year of entry). Entries must be in by 1st April.

One or two *Gill Memorial Scholarships* for the children of Regular Army Officers (serving or retired) up to a maximum of £1,000 pa.

A number of *Art, Music, Drama, Dance and All-Rounder Scholarships* are available.

Lloyd's Cuthbert Heath Memorial Bursary worth up to £1,000 pa awarded to a pupil wishing to enter the College at 13 who has a positive contribution to make to the life of the College, and whose parents would otherwise be unable to afford the fees.

A *Cooper Rawson Bursary* for children of Clergy. An award of up to £500 pa can be considered by the Committee which meets in June each year.

Sixth Form entry Scholarships: Candidates take papers in two A Level subjects plus general paper, or three A Level subjects. Entries by November 1st.

Further particulars can be obtained from the *Director of Admissions, Brighton College, Brighton BN2 0AL.*

Bristol Grammar School (see p 57)
The School runs a Scholars' Programme designed to meet the educational needs of its most gifted students. This programme offers extended individual learning opportunities, group activities and mentoring in and out of School by the Director of Scholars. At 16+ students may apply to become Subject Scholars and work more closely with Heads of Subject.

Bromsgrove School (see p 59)
Awards are made on the results of open examinations held at the school in January: a significant number of scholarships and bursaries for pupils of academic, artistic, musical, sporting and all-round ability are awarded at 11+, 13+ and 16+. Any award may be augmented by means-tested bursaries in case of financial need. Further details are available from the Admissions Department.

Bryanston School (see p 62)
(a) Academic, Art, ICT, DT, Music, Sport and Richard Hunter All-Rounder Scholarships are available annually for entry at 13+.
(b) Academic and Music Scholarships and Udall Awards for Sport are available annually for entry to the Sixth Form.

Scholarships range in value and may be supplemented by means-tested bursaries.

Further details may be obtained from the Admissions Registrar.

Canford School (see p 68)
Scholarships. It is Canford's policy to encourage excellence and to enable pupils to come to the school who, without the assistance of a scholarship, would not be able to do so. In accordance with the agreement of the majority of HMC schools, Canford limits the value of any one scholarship to 50% of the fees. All Canford's scholarships are indexed as a percentage of the fees so that their relative value remains constant throughout the scholar's school career.

13+ Scholarships: Scholarship examinations are held in February/March and awards are made as follows: a number of Academic scholarships ranging from 50% to 10% of the fees; a number of Music and Sports scholarships ranging from 50% to 10% of the fees; one Royal Naval scholarship of 20% to the son/daughter of a serving Naval Officer; one or two Art scholarships; one or two Design Technology scholarships and one or two Drama scholarships worth in total 20% for each discipline; one Canning Memorial Bursary of £100 pa for sons/daughters of Old Canfordians. Candidates must be in Year 8 at the time of the examination. All 13+ scholarships are tenable with effect from the September of the year in which they are awarded.

16+ Scholarships: The School offers a number of Academic, Music and Assyrian scholarships each year to entrants at Sixth Form level. Each Academic or Music scholarship may be worth up to 50% of the fees. Assyrian awards are offered for an extra-curricular contribution of excellent quality to school life and are worth from 10% to 40% of the fees. The examination is held in the November prior to entry.

Bursaries: Means-tested bursaries are also sometimes available from the School where the financial need of the parents has been established.

Further details about any awards can be obtained from The Registrar.

Caterham School (see p 70)
Academic scholarships are available at 11+, 13+ and 16+. They are awarded on the basis of an examination and interview. At 11+ and 13+ the awards are made on the basis of the entrance examinations and interviews; there is no separate scholarship examination and all candidates are automatically considered.

All-Rounder scholarships (for pupils entering at the age of 13), Music, Art and Sport scholarships at 11+, 13+ and 16+, Boarding scholarships and Sixth Form Science scholarships are also available.

Charterhouse (see p 72)
For entry at 13+. Up to 10 Foundation Scholarships and 5 Exhibitions are offered annually. The examination is held in May.

In addition a Benn Scholarship is offered for proficiency in Classics.

Five Peter Attenborough Awards are made annually to candidates who demonstrate all-round distinction.

The Park House Award is made annually to an exceptional sportsman.

The Sir William Blackstone Award is offered to sons of lawyers – for details see Educational Awards section.

For entry into the Sixth Form. The following awards are offered annually:

Four Sir Robert Birley Academic Scholarships and 7 Academic Exhibitions. In addition Music and Art Scholarships are offered (see relevant sections).

The Surrey Scholarship, sponsored by the University of Surrey, is awarded each year to a pupil entering the Sixth Form from a maintained school within the county.

All Awards (except Exhibitions) may be increased to the value of the full school fee in cases of proven financial need.

For full details apply to the Admissions Secretary, Charterhouse, Godalming, Surrey GU7 2DX.

Cheltenham College (see p 76)
The College offers academic awards to boys and girls entering at 13+ and into the Sixth Form: awards may reach 50% of the current fees. Awards are similarly offered to boys and girls demonstrating excellence in Sport and All-round potential. Awards are also made for Music, Art, and Design Technology.

Chigwell School (see p 79)
Sixth Form entrance interviews are held throughout the year, principally in November and January and there are generous Academic, Art, Drama and Music Scholarships available. Music Scholarships are also offered from age 11. A competitive examination for Academic Scholarships is held each year during the Lent term for pupils aged 11+ and 16+. Further details from the Headmaster, Chigwell School, High Road, Chigwell, Essex IG7 6QF.

Christ College (see p 80)
Up to 10 Academic scholarships and exhibitions, tenable at 11+, 13+ and 16+ and ranging in value from 10 to 50% of the fees, are offered annually. Also available at 11+, 13+ and 16+ are Sports and Music scholarships and are of similar value. Available at 13+ and 16+ are Science scholarships also ranging from 10 to 50% of the fees. In addition three scholarships are awarded each year to those entering the Sixth Form each worth £1500 a year: a Lord Brecon, Roydon Griffths and a G John Herdman Scholarship. W G Fryer All-Rounder Scholarships are available at 13+ and 16+ each year.

10% bursaries are available for sons and daughters of personnel serving in the Armed Forces. There is a remission of

25% of the fees for the sons and daughters of Clergy. The value of any award may be augmented in case of need.

Scholarship examinations are held at Christ College in early February (11+ and 13+). Age limits: seniors under 14 and juniors under 12 on 1st September in the year of examination.

Further details from The Head, Christ College, Brecon, Powys LD3 8AG.

City of London Freemen's School (see p 84)
City of London Scholarships are offered as follows:

At 13+: up to ten awards annually, valued at up to half tuition fees, on the basis of 13+ Scholarship examinations for entry to the Senior School.

For Sixth Form entry: up to 15 awards annually to the value of half tuition fees, or more awards of lesser value pro rata on the basis of Sixth Form Entrance Scholarship papers. These may be awarded to internal or external candidates for Sixth Form entry.

City of London School (see p 87)
The School offers approximately 30 Academic Scholarships each year to the value of up to half the cost of school fees. These Scholarships are available at any of the normal entry points. For ages 10+, 11+ and 13+ a Scholarship interview is awarded on the strength of a candidate's performance in the School's normal entrance examinations, which take place in January. At 16+ an Academic Scholarship may be awarded on the strength of a candidate's GCSE results.

The School offers a number of means-tested Sponsored Awards at 11+ and 16+ entry to bright candidates whose parents could not otherwise contemplate private education.

Clifton College (see p 90)
Entrance Scholarships: Candidates must be under 14 on 1 September. Boys and girls who are already in the School may compete. At least ten awards are made. The maximum value of scholarships will not exceed 25% of the fees, although awards will be augmented by a Bursary if need is shown.

There are special awards available for the sons and daughters of Old Cliftonians.

Scholarships are also awarded to boys and girls for entry to the Sixth Form.

Particulars of the conditions of examination from The Director of Admissions, Clifton College, Bristol BS8 3JH.

Cranleigh School (see p 96)
At age thirteen. Academic, Music and Art Awards are available, along with Eric Abbott Awards (for candidates of good academic ability with at least one other clearly established area of excellence). Music Awards include free musical tuition. In certain circumstances, additional consideration may be given to sons or daughters of public servants, members of the armed forces and the clergy of the Church of England. All Awards are fees-linked and may be augmented in cases of proven financial need.

At Sixth Form level. Academic, Music, Art and Eric Abbott Awards (for candidates of good academic ability with at least one other clearly established area of excellence) are offered. All Awards are fees-linked and may be augmented in cases of proven financial need. Awards can be made to boys and girls already at the school if their progress merits it.

Full details of awards can be obtained by telephoning 01483 276377.

Culford School (see p 99)
Scholarships and Exhibitions are awarded according to merit in the following categories:

At 7+: Academic

At 11+: Academic, Music and Sport

At 13+: Academic, Art, Drama, Music, Sport and Design Technology

At 16+: Academic, Art, Drama, Music and Sport

At 11+ and 13+: Jubilee Scholarships for all-rounders who board are worth 25% of boarding fees.

At 16+: The William Miller Scholarship for a pupil studying sciences is worth up to 25% of tuition fees. The Arkwright Scholarship for a pupil studying design technology allows an amount over two years to be shared between the pupil and the School.

Bursaries are available to those in genuine financial need and for children from a Methodist background.

A generous Forces Allowance is available to parents who are serving members of the Armed Forces and are in receipt of the MOD CEA.

For further details apply to The Registrar, Culford School, Bury St. Edmunds, Suffolk IP28 6TX. Tel: 01284 729308, Fax: 01284 729146 e-mail: admissions@culford.co.uk.

Dauntsey's School (see p 101)
Scholarships and Exhibitions are awarded on examinations held in November (Year 12), January (Year 7) and February (Year 9) for the following September.

Academic, Science, Art, Music, Design & Technology, Sports, Drama and All-Rounder scholarships are available to boarders entering Year 9.

Full particulars are available from the Registrar at the School.

Dean Close School (see p 103)
A competitive examination is held annually at the school in February/March. All awards are open to both boys and girls. Candidates must be under 14 on 1 September in the year of the examination. The following Scholarships are on offer:

Governors' Open Scholarships.

Fergus McNeile Scholarships for children of Clergy and Missionaries.

Daisy Cross Arts Scholarships for Sixth Formers to read Arts subjects.

All-rounder award.

Scholarships and Bursaries for the children of those serving in HM Forces.

Awards are also offered at 11.

Denstone College (see p 105)
Scholarships and Exhibitions are available in the following categories – All-Rounder, Academic, Choral, Design and Technology, Art, Music, Drama, and Sport – and are at the discretion of the Headmaster. They are mainly awarded at the ages of 11, 13 and for Sixth Form entry. Scholarships carry a remission of up to 40% of the fees.

For further details please contact the Admissions Secretary, Denstone College, Uttoxeter, Staffordshire ST14 5HN.

Dulwich College (see p 108)
Academic Scholarships

For entry to the Junior School (Year 3), Lower School (Year 7) and Middle School (Year 9).

Awards will be made to boys entering the College in September 2009. Scholarships range in value from 10% to one-third of tuition fees. Scholarships may be held by day boys and boarders.

Entry Bursaries

A number of Bursaries are awarded annually to new boys entering Year 3, Year 7 or Year 9 where parents are unable to pay the full tuition fee.

Applicants will be considered on the basis of their performance in the entrance examination and interview.

Bursaries are means-tested and reviewed annually.

Specialist Scholarships

Applicants for Music, Art and Sports Scholarships are required to meet the academic requirements of the College at all points of entry.

Music Scholarships: for entry to the Lower School (Year 7) and Middle School (Year 9).

Up to five instrumental music scholarships of up to one-third of the tuition fee may be offered.

Up to four music exhibitions may also be awarded enabling the holders to receive free tuition on two instruments, one of which must be an orchestral instrument.

Choral Scholarships: for candidates of all ages from 8 to 16+.

Vacancies occur annually in the College Chapel Choir which sings choral services in the chapel of the Foundation. Auditions are held in June.

Art Scholarships: for entry to the Lower School (Year 7) and Middle School (Year 9).

At least one scholarship of up to 10% of the tuition fee for excellence in art will be offered.

Sports Scholarships: for entry to the Middle School (Year 9) and Upper School (Year 12).

At least two Scholarships of up to one-third of the tuition fee for excellence in Sport will be offered.

Scholarships can be enhanced by means-tested Bursaries.

Durham School (see p 112)
A generous range of Academic, Music, Art, Design and Technology and Sports Scholarships (worth up to 50% of fees) is available. These can be supplemented by bursaries in case of financial need.

Eastbourne College (see p 113)
Academic, Art, Design & Technology, Drama, Music and Sports Scholarships are offered up to 50% of the fees if candidates of sufficient merit present themselves. Candidates must be under 14 on 1st September.

Academic, Science and Music Scholarships are offered up to 50% of fees at 16 to pupils entering the College at Sixth Form level.

Entry forms for scholarships can be obtained from: The Registrar, Eastbourne College, Eastbourne, East Sussex BN21 4JX.

The Edinburgh Academy (see p 115)
A number of Scholarships are offered for award to candidates of very high ability either academically or for Art, Music or Sport. Scholarships have a maximum value of 25% of the tuition fee, but means-tested Bursaries are also available which can increase the award as required. The Examination is held in early February. Further details from *The Rector's PA, The Edinburgh Academy, Edinburgh EH3 5BL.*

Ellesmere College (see p 120)
A wide range of Scholarships and Exhibitions recognising a range of talents is available. In cases of need, all these awards may be supplemented further. Regional and Foundation Awards are also available. Application forms are obtainable from the Headmaster.

Eltham College (see p 121)
Up to 20 Academic scholarships awarded on the entrance examination for boys of 11, annual value not less than one quarter of tuition fee, tenable for 7 years.

A number of Academic scholarships awarded on the entrance examination for boys of 13, to the value of half tuition fees, tenable for 5 years.

A number of Sixth Form Academic scholarships, usually 15, tenable for 2 years to the value of half tuition fees.

Further details from the Admissions Secretary.

Emanuel School (see p 123)
Scholarships, Exhibitions and Bursaries

There are two types of scholarship at Emanuel: Major Scholarships, known as "Dacre Scholarships", reduction of 25% (occasionally 50%) of the school fee and Normal Scholarships, reduction of 10% of the school fee.

Both types of scholarship can be "topped up" using school bursaries to a maximum of 100% of the school fee, depending on financial need. It is also possible for a pupil to apply for, and be awarded, a scholarship in more than one category. Categories can be added together.

Academic scholarships are awarded at 11+ and 13+ on the basis of outstanding performance in the school entrance examinations held in January. At 16+ Academic scholarships are awarded to internal candidates on the basis of their Mock GCSE results and overall academic record in Year 11, and to external candidates on the basis their performance in the assessment tests.

Candidates applying for Music, Art, Drama and Sports scholarships must meet the general criteria for admission to Emanuel (eg reach the required standard in the academic entrance examinations) before a scholarship can be awarded. Thereafter each department has specific criteria for their scholarship requirements.

Exhibitions are awards of £500 on the basis of a pupil's high attainment in the entrance exams.

Bursaries are intended to help parents of pupils who can demonstrate financial need. Most bursaries are used to "top up" scholarships.

Full details of Scholarships, Exhibitions and Bursaries can be found on the School Website or by contacting the Admissions Secretary.

Epsom College (see p 125)
Candidates may compete for one or more of the following types of Award: Academic, Music, Drama, Art, Design Technology, Sports, and All-Rounder.

Eton College (see p 127)
The Examination for King's Scholarships is held at Eton in May in the year of entry. Candidates need to be registered by 1st March. Candidates must be under 14 (and over 12) on 1st September.

Subjects of Examination: All candidates take the following four papers: English, Mathematics A, General I (general questions requiring thought rather than knowledge) and Science. Each must also offer *THREE or more* of the following: French (written, aural, oral), Latin, Greek, Mathematics B, General II (Literature, the Arts, moral and religious issues, etc) and a paper combining History, Geography and Divinity.

A King's Scholarship is normally tenable for five years.

Full particulars and entry forms may be obtained from *The College Examination Secretary, Admissions Office, Eton College, Windsor SL4 6DB.*

Exeter School (see p 129)
Academic Scholarships which offer a nominal discount off school fees are offered annually to pupils who excel in the School's entrance tests. Music and Art Scholarships are awarded annually following audition/ assessment and are conditional on applicants achieving the School's academic requirements for entry. A number of means-tested Governors' Awards may be available to external candidates whose parents could not afford to send them to Exeter School without financial assistance.

At age 7 – up to four Academic Scholarships offering a discount of £450 per annum off tuition fees throughout the Junior School. Up to two Academic Exhibitions offering a discount of up to £300 per annum off tuition fees.

At age 11 – up to five Academic Scholarships offering a discount of £600 per annum off tuition fees. Up to five Academic Exhibitions offering a discount of up to £300 per annum off tuition fees.

At age 13 – one Academic Scholarship offering a discount of £600 per annum off tuition fees.

At age 16 – one Ogden Science Scholarship, means-tested, offering up to 100% discount off tuition fees.

Felsted School (see p 132)
Academic, Music, Drama, Art, and Design & Technology Scholarships are awarded annually up to the value of 20% of the fees for entry at 13+ and to the Sixth Form. Bursaries are available to increase the awards in case of need up to 100% of the fees in certain cases. The examinations for the 13+ Scholarships take place in May and for the Sixth Form Scholarships in November and February.

Scholarships are also awarded at 11+ at Felsted Preparatory School and these may be carried through to the Senior School.

Arkwright Foundation Scholarships are also available to talented students in Design at 16+.

All-rounder Scholarships and Foundation Awards which recognise all-round ability or specific ability in one area are available on entry at 11, 13 and 16 years old.

Full particulars from the *Headmaster, Felsted School, Dunmow, Essex CM6 3LL.*

Fettes College (see p 133)
Scholarships to a maximum value of 33% of the fees are available for candidates aged 11+, 13+ and 16+. Any scholarship award can be supplemented by means-tested bursaries that can cover the full cost of the fees.

General Scholarships as well as Music scholarships, Piping Scholarships, Art Scholarships and All-Rounder awards are available.

Children of members of HM Forces qualify for a 12.5% reduction in fees and Special Bursaries (Todd) are available for descendents of Old Fettesians.

Full details of all awards are available from The Headmaster, Fettes College, Edinburgh EH4 1QX (Telephone: 0131 311 6701).

Forest School (see p 135)
A Scholarship examination is held at the School in January for the awarding of up to 12 Scholarships or Bursaries to cover full fees. Candidates must be under 12 on 1st September each year. There is further provision for Sixth Form, Music, Art, Sports, Drama and Old Forester Scholarships. Full details are available from the *Warden*.

Framlingham College (see p 138)
Scholarships are available at the following points of entry:

13+ and 16+: Open Academic, Art, Design & Technology, Music, Drama, and All-Rounder.

The Pembroke Scholarship worth 100% of full tuition fees may be awarded at 13+ and 16+. This scholarship is only available to students whose families would not otherwise be able to access independent education.

In cases of financial need scholarship awards can be increased by means-tested bursary.

Frensham Heights (see p 138)
Scholarships and Exhibitions, limited to £750 and £400 respectively, are awarded for Academic distinction or exceptional promise in Music or the other Performing and Creative Arts at 11+, 13+ and for Sixth Form entry.

Candidates for the Music or the other Performing and Creative Arts awards need to satisfy the school's entrance requirements.

Candidates for Music awards are expected to have reached at least Grade 5 in one or more instruments or voice.

Bursaries are awarded on the basis of a means-tested assessment.

Giggleswick School (see p 144)
Generous academic scholarships and exhibitions are offered for boys and girls as boarding or day pupils. The examinations are held in February and may be taken at age 10/11 or at age 12/13 and for Sixth Form entry to Senior School. The following categories are available: Academic, All-Rounder, Music, Sports, Art (13+ and Sixth Form only), Drama and Design and Technology (Sixth Form entrants only). A leaflet containing full details of the awards and examinations can be obtained from the Registrar.

Glenalmond College (see p 148)
Up to 10 Scholarships and Exhibitions ranging in value from 10% to 25% of the fees are offered for competition each year. Also available annually are about 5 Music Scholarships worth up to 50% of the fees. Awards are also made for Art.

The Entrance Scholarship Examinations are usually held in March for younger pupils and in November for entrants to the Sixth Form. Candidates may be considered for an All-Rounder Award.

Junior Scholarship candidates must be under 14 on 31 May of the year of entry. A short statement showing the scope of the examination will be forwarded on application, and copies of last year's papers may be obtained. Scholarship candidates will be examined at Glenalmond.

For further particulars application should be made to the *Warden, Glenalmond College, Perth PH1 3RY.*

Gresham's School (see p 152)
The School is extremely grateful to benefactors, in particular the Fishmongers' Company, for financing many of the awards below.

An Open Scholarship examination is held each year at Gresham's in late February or early March. Candidates are usually under 14 on 1st September in the year of entry.

As many as 15 Academic Scholarships are available to entrants each year and, though these generally represent a reduction of fees of between 25% and 50%, in certain cases such scholarships may be increased, by way of a bursary, up to 100%.

Some awards are restricted to pupils who are from state schools or pupils resident in Africa.

In addition to the above, up to 8 awards a year may be made in Art, Drama, Music and Sport to promote these areas and to recognise excellence in them. These Scholarships generally represent a fee reduction of between 25% and 33%, but for exceptional candidates can be increased to 50%.

Sixth Form Scholarships: Deserving candidates are assessed in November each year for acceptance into the Sixth Form in the following September and Academic Scholarships, as well as scholarships for those who are exceptional in Music, Art, Drama or Sport may be awarded. These generally represent a fee reduction of 25% to 50%, though, in rare cases, such scholarships may be increased, by way of a bursary to 100%.

Guildford High School (see p 154)
Academic Scholarships are offered at 7+, 11+ and 16+.

Haileybury (see p 159)
Many scholarships are available upon entrance to Haileybury. Academic and Music awards are available for 11, 13 and 16 year old entrants, All-Rounder Awards at 11 and 13, Art at 13 and 16, and Technology at 13. In addition, there are some specially founded Sixth Form Scholarships which are awarded as they fall vacant.

Scholarships and All-Rounder Awards can be awarded up to the value of 10% of school fees and are tenable for the whole of the pupil's career at Haileybury. No fee remission is awarded for Art or Technology Scholarships. Successful candidates will be awarded a book token to the value of £100.

Bursaries are available to increase awards, in cases of financial need, and can supplement up to 100% of the fees in some cases.

An Additional Information brochure is issued annually in September and this provides all appropriate information regarding dates and application procedure. This can be obtained from The Registrar, Haileybury, Hertford SG13 7NU or e-mail: registrar@haileybury.com. The Registry team will be pleased to discuss with parents any aspects of the scholarship procedure.

Hampton School (see p 161)
Scholarships normally remitting 25% and Exhibitions remitting 15% to 10% are awarded for academic, musical, artistic and all-round merit on entry at 11+ and 13+. At 11+ Choral awards are available in conjunction with the Chapel Royal, Hampton Court Palace.

Harrow School (see p 164)
The examination takes place annually in March at Harrow. About 12 Academic Scholarships range in value from 5% to 10% of the fees. Up to 6 Scholarships each year can be supplemented to the full amount of the school fees in cases of proved

financial need. These supplementable Scholarships are awarded only to boys of good academic ability. In addition fifteen awards are made for excellence in Music, Sport, Design Technology or Art, some of which can be supplemented with means-tested bursaries. Full particulars and forms of application can be obtained from *The Admissions Secretary, Harrow School, 1 High Street, Harrow on the Hill, Middx HA1 3HT.*

Headington School (see p 166)
Awards for girls with exceptional Academic potential. All awards judged on merit with nominal financial benefit of £300 pa (with a few higher awards up to 100% of fees, depending on financial need).

Scholarships may be supported by means-tested bursaries, which may significantly increase the size of the award.

Hereford Cathedral School (see p 170)
Up to 8 Dean's Scholarships are awarded as a result of the Junior Entrance and 11+ Scholarship Examination. Up to 3 Dean's Scholarships are also awarded at 13+. Up to 8 Dean's Scholarships are competed for entry to the Sixth Form. Dean's Scholars are admitted to the Foundation by the Dean of Hereford.

Highgate School (see p 171)
Up to twelve Foundation Scholarships and other Academic Awards are offered annually; the maximum award is half-fees, but any scholarship may be increased in case of need. For those joining the School at age 11+ or 13+ the examination is part of the entry procedure in January/February. Those transferring from Highgate Junior School are also eligible for scholarships and are considered separately. Hopkins and Venn Awards are available for those joining at 11+.

At least two Music Awards are offered each year at each age group and the holders also receive free tuition in one instrument in school.

Full details of Scholarships and Bursaries may be obtained from the Admissions Office.

Hurstpierpoint College (see p 174)
Scholarship examinations are held annually in May for candidates aged under 14 on 1st June of the year of entry and awards of value up to one-half of day fees are offered for Academic Scholarships. All-Rounder, Art, Drama, IT, Design & Technology, and Sports Scholarships are held in March. Awards of value up to one-half of day fees for Music Scholarships are offered in February for entrance into the Prep School or Senior School the following September.

Sixth Form awards are offered to external candidates for Academic, All-Rounder, Art, Drama, IT, Design & Technology, Music and Sports.

For 13+ entry contact Mrs Sally Lloyd, Senior School Admissions Officer. For 16+ entry contact Miss Claire Hockley, Sixth Form Admissions Officer.

Ipswich School (see p 178)
Queen's and Foundation Scholarships are awarded at 11 and 13, carrying up to half remission of tuition fees. Scholarships may be awarded for Music or Art as well as for academic excellence and a Sports Scholarship is offered at 13+. Academic, Music and All-rounder Scholarships are available for external entrants to the Sixth Form. Outstanding students intending to study Maths or a Physics related degree at University and currently at a state school may apply for an Ogden Trust Science Scholarship in the Sixth Form; awards are up to 100% of fees. Students intending to study Design Technology and Maths in the Sixth Form may apply for an Arkwright Scholarship. Scholarships may be supplemented by bursaries in case of proven need.

The John Lyon School (see p 179)
Scholarships normally provide for between 5% and 20% of tuition fees but may exceptionally provide for up to 50%.

All boys who sit the 11+ and 13+ entrance examination in January will be considered for Academic and All-Rounder Scholarships: their performance in the examination, current school report and interview will all be taken into consideration.

Consideration is given to candidates at 11+, 13+ and 16+ of outstanding potential and ability in Art & Design, Drama, Music and Sport. Separate applications need to be made and potential candidates are called for selection interviews and tests as appropriate.

Kelly College (see p 181)
Entrance Scholarships are available ranging from 10% to 50%. Our Entrance Scholarships are awarded annually in February (via our own 11+ entrance examination), and in March for candidates at under 14 on 1st September. Entries must be received by end-December for 11+ and end-January for 13+ candidates. All scholarships and exhibitions are competitive on entry to the school. Awards may be made at 11+, 13+ and 16+ in the following areas: Academic, All-rounder Awards, Art, Speech and Drama, Design and Technology, ICT (13+ only), Music, Sport (Swimming, Triathlon, Rugby, Hockey etc).

Sons and daughters of Old Kelleians are eligible for 10% reduction in fees.

Further particulars can be obtained from The Registrar, Kelly College, Tavistock, Devon PL19 0HZ.

Kent College (see p 184)
The school awards academic, music, sport and art scholarships to pupils for entry into Years 7, 9 and 12. Year 7 and 9 academic scholarships are awarded as a result of performance in our Entrance Test, usually held in the Spring Term, for entry the following September. Sixth Form academic scholarships are awarded on the basis of existing performance, a detailed report from the Head of Year or current school, and confirmation of high levels of performance in the final GCSEs. Music, sport and art scholarships are awarded in conjunction with the Entrance Test and appropriate separate performance assessments at Kent College.

Scholarships normally carry a value equivalent to a percentage remission of the fees which would vary according to circumstances but would not exceed a maximum of 50% of fees and would be at the discretion of the Head Master. Full particulars may be obtained from the Registrar.

Kimbolton School (see p 186)
A number of Scholarships are awarded at 11+ to those candidates who perform with distinction in the Entrance Examination.

Further Scholarships, known as William Ingram Awards, may be awarded at 13+ to those who perform well in the Kimbolton School Entrance Examination or in Common Entrance. A number of awards at 13+ are reserved for external candidates with strengths in music, art, games and leadership.

Sixth Form Scholarships and Exhibitions are awarded to those who achieve outstanding results in GCSE.

King Edward's School, Birmingham (see p 193)
Scholarships at 11+ and 13+: Up to twelve major scholarships of between half fees and one-fifth fees are offered. These scholarships may be increased to full fees in cases of financial need.

Music Scholarships are also available.

All scholarships are indexed to increase with increases in fees.

At 16+: 'Betts Scholarships' of value up to half fees for boys studying the Sciences at A Level and one Finnemore Scholarship for boys studying Arts subjects at A Level of up to half fees.

King William's College (see p 198)
Year 7 Academic Scholarships are offered up to the value of 50% of the current tuition fee and examinations take place in late January. There are papers in English, Mathematics and Reasoning and an interview.

Sixth Form Academic Scholarships are offered up to the value of 50% of the current tuition fee and examinations are normally held in November of the year prior to entry. There are papers in Mathematics, English, one other subject chosen by the candidate and an interview.

Music Scholarships, Performing Arts and Sports Awards to the value of 50% of the tuition fee are available to candidates in all age groups prior to entry to the College who demonstrate exceptional talent or potential. Examinations and auditions take place by arrangement.

There is also a Bursary fund to support students if the financial circumstances of parents make this necessary.

There is a separate bursary scheme for pupils in their last year in Manx Primary Schools run in conjunction with the Isle of Man Department of Education.

Further details of all scholarships may be obtained from the Principal's office and on the website.

King's College School, London (see p 200)
Academic Scholarship examination in early May, Art & Design Scholarship and Music Scholarship in February. Candidates must be under 14 years of age on 1st September of the year of entry. 12–15 academic awards, up to 2 art and design awards and up to 6 music awards are made, of varying values between 10% and 20% of school tuition fees, except in the case of Sixth Form entry. The maximum fee remission tenable by any award-winner is 25% but *in the case of proven financial need an award may be supplemented by a bursary.* Sixth Form Entrance Endowment awards of 10–50% remission are available. Notice of intention of applying for bursarial assistance must be given at the time of application but, if financial need occurs later, the School will always consider cases on their merits. Full details of all awards are available from the Registration Secretary.

King's College, Taunton (see p 202)
Scholarships are available to boys and girls who are under 14 and for entry into the Sixth Form. Major Academic scholarships are awarded, as well as scholarships for Music, Drama, Art and DT and Sport.

King's School, Bruton (see p 204)
The maximum financial value of any award or combination of awards is 20% of fees. The number and value of awards are at the Headmaster's discretion. Further details of specific entry requirements can be obtained from the Registrar on 01749 814220.

13+ Entry:

All applications require the support of the candidate's current school. Candidates for awards other than Open Academic Scholarships should be of good Common Entrance standard. All candidates for all awards sit a Verbal Reasoning Test and have one or more interviews.

Academic Scholarship examinations take place in May. The closing date is March. Candidates must be under 14 on 1 September the year they join King's. Candidates take papers in English, Mathematics, French (including an aural examination), History, Geography and Science. They may also offer optional papers in Greek, German, Latin and RS.

An Old Brutonian Scholarship, worth not less than £3,000 per annum may be awarded on the basis of performance in the Open Scholarship.

All-Rounder Awards: March. Candidates must demonstrate ability or potential in two areas outside the classroom. If sport is offered, 1st team experience is expected.

Sports Scholarships: March. Candidates must demonstrate ability in two team games to at least 1st team level. Reports are required from county/representative coaches.

Art and/or Technology Scholarships: March. Candidates undertake a practical test and provide a portfolio of recent work.

Sixth Form Entry:

All applications require the support of the candidate's current school in the form of a report. Candidates for awards other than Academic Scholarships need to reach the school's minimum requirement for entry to Sixth Form in order to take up their place at King's. All candidates for all awards take a Verbal Reasoning Test and have one or more interviews. All Sixth Form scholarships and awards are held in November.

Academic Scholarships: Candidates sit an English paper, a General paper and an academic paper in a subject of their choice (which is offered by King's at AS level, other than English).

Art Scholarships: Candidates undertake a practical assessment on the day of examination and provide a portfolio of recent work.

Sports Scholarships: Candidates must show exceptional ability in one or more major team sports. Candidates must demonstrate their ability on the assessment day. Reports will be expected from candidates' county/representative coaches.

The King's School, Canterbury (see p 207)
Up to 20 King's Scholarships and Exhibitions are offered annually for competition in March to pupils under 14 on 1 September in year of entry. The awards will be up to 25% of the annual fee in every year and will be 'inflation proof'. Further assistance above 25% is available but would depend on parental income.

For details of Music Scholarships see that section.

A scholarship leaflet is issued annually in the Autumn, and may be obtained from the Admissions Secretary.

The King's School, Ely (see p 211)
Entrance Scholarships and Exhibitions (i.e. scholarships of lesser value) recognise exceptional promise in academic work, Art, Design & Technology, Drama, Music or Sports.

The total value of scholarships will not exceed 25% of day fees (up to 15% in King's Junior School at Year 7).

King's Junior School Academic Awards are for the two final years (Years 7 and 8). A competitive examination is held in January each year and successful candidates enter Year 7 the following Michaelmas term. These Scholarships will be continued until the end of Year 11, subject to satisfactory progress, after which an application for a Sixth Form Scholarship may be made.

King's Senior School Academic Scholarships are for the three years leading to the GCSE examinations and are made on the basis of a competitive examination set by the school in February. Candidates may also sit the Common Entrance Scholarship paper, should they prefer. Successful candidates enter Year 9 the following September.

Sixth Form Scholarships are for the two years of the AS/A2 course and are made following an examination in November and an interview. Candidates should be on course for at least six A* or A passes at GCSE.

Music Scholarships are available for choral and/or instrumental excellence, including organ-playing and may include free weekly tuition on two musical instruments. Candidates for entry into Year 7 and Year 9 are invited to the school for auditions in February and in November for entry into Year 12 the following September.

All boy Choristers of Ely Cathedral are full boarders of King's Junior School and receive a choristership worth 50% of fees while they remain in the choir and a bursary worth 33% of fees on transfer to King's Senior School. Members of the Cathedral Girls' Choir are all boarders in King's Senior School and receive a bursary worth 33% of boarding fees.

Sports Awards, for entry into Years 7, 9 and 12, are open to boys and girls with potential for major county, regional or national representation or with all-round sporting excellence. Reports will be sought from the candidates' coach(es) and practical tests, if required, will be held at the school in February.

Art and Drama Exhibitions are also available for Years 7 and 9 and a Design and Technology Exhibition is available for Year 9. Interviews are held in late January or early February.

Full particulars of all awards are available from The Admissions Secretary, The King's School, Ely, Cambridgeshire CB7 4DB. Tel: 01353 660702; e-mail: admissions@kingsely.cambs.sch.uk.

The King's School, Gloucester (see p 213)
Academic Scholarships at this Cathedral School may be awarded to outstanding boys and girls at age 11, 13 and 16. A number of lesser Exhibitions are also available at this age. Scholarship examinations are held annually in November. Awards will also be considered to candidates on the results of the Common Entrance Examination at age 13. Music Exhibitions and Awards in Art, Drama and Sport are available at age 11, 13 and in the Sixth Form.

Choral Scholarships for Cathedral Choristers are available for boys aged between 7 and 9½.

Full particulars from the Headmaster.

King's School, Rochester (see p 216)
Up to five Major King's Scholarships of 30% of tuition fees, means-tested up to 75% reduction in tuition fees, and five Minor King's Scholarships of 15% of tuition fees, means-tested up to 60% reduction in tuition fees, may be awarded annually – at least five will be for pupils from the maintained sector. King's Scholars become members of the Cathedral Foundation.

Candidates are normally expected to be under 14 years old on the 1st September of the year in which they sit the examination. Allowance is made for age.

Candidates will be expected to sit the Common Entrance Scholarship Examination in June or, if not prepared for this, may take the King's Senior School Entrance Examination.

Governors' Exhibitions, all means-tested, are available up to 100% of tuition fees.

Up to five King's Exhibitions of 30% tuition fees, means-tested up to 75% reduction in tuition fees, are available for pupils aged 11+. Two are reserved for pupils from a maintained school.

Details of Music Scholarships are given elsewhere. A scholarship brochure, and further information, may be obtained from The Registrar, King's School, Satis House, Boley Hill, Rochester, Kent ME1 1TE. Tel: 01634 888555. Fax: 01634 888505.

The King's School, Worcester (see p 220)
Scholarships are available at 11+, 13+ and 16+ in the Senior School, value up to one third of tuition fees. At 11+ awards are made on the basis of the Entrance Test; at 13 + on the Entrance Test and an interview; at 16+ on the basis of an aptitude test and interview, a report from the candidate's school. Full details are available from the Registrar. Scholarships are available at 7+ and 8+, value up to one third of tuition fees (tenable only while in the Junior Schools) and are awarded to candidates of outstanding academic or musical ability.

Kingston Grammar School (see p 222)
At age 11 there are up to 10 half fee Academic Scholarships, including a Hans Woyda Memorial Mathematics Scholarship, awarded on the results of the Entrance Examination in mid January.

Two half fee Academic scholarships are available for entry at age 13+.

Scholarships are also awarded to entrants to the Sixth Form, following a written examination, interview and successful GCSE results.

Two half fee Music scholarships, including free tuition in one instrument, may be awarded at 11+, 13+, or 16+.

Similarly two Art scholarships may be awarded at 11+, 13+, or 16+ following interview and submission of a portfolio.

Further particulars may be obtained from the Registrar.

Kingswood School (see p 224)
Academic and Special Talent Scholarships (maximum value of 50% off the full fees) are available annually to pupils entering Year 7 and Year 9 (new boarders only), as well as some John Wesley All-Rounder awards at Year 9 and Sixth Form (only).

Lancing College (see p 227)
Candidates for the following awards must be under 14 years of age on 1st September in the year of the examination. The age of the candidate is taken into account in making awards. A candidate may enter for more than one type of award, and account may be taken of musical or artistic proficiency in a candidate for a non-musical award; but no one may hold more than one type of award, except in an honorary capacity.

(1) A number of Open Scholarships ranging in value from £1,000 per year to half of the annual boarding fee.

(2) Three or four Music Scholarships ranging in value up to half the annual boarding fee. Scholarships may be offered to pupils from schools where the time for Music is less than in some others, and where a candidate may have less musical experience but greater potential.
One Professor W K Stanton Music Scholarship of up to half the boarding fee for a Chorister from Salisbury Cathedral School, or failing that any Cathedral School. A Stanton Exhibition may also be awarded.

(3) A number of scholarships in Art, Drama and Sport, ranging in value up to a quarter of the annual boarding fee.

(4) A number of Ken Shearwood Awards, ranging in value up to a fifth of the annual boarding fee, are made to pupils of all-round ability and potential who have made outstanding contributions to their present schools.

Entry Forms for Academic, Art, Music, Drama, Sport and All-Rounder (Ken Shearwood) awards are obtainable from the Admissions Officer, Lancing College, Lancing, West Sussex BN15 0RW. These forms must be returned to her with a photocopy of the candidate's birth certificate.

Sixth Form Awards (Boys and Girls). Scholarships are available for new entrants to the Sixth Form with special proficiency in Academic Subjects or Music. There is also one Organ Scholarship. The candidate's general ability to contribute to the life of a boarding school community will also be taken into account. A small number of Scholarships is also available internally on the strength of GCSE results.

The value of all Entrance Scholarships may be augmented by bursaries up to a maximum of two-thirds of the annual fee, according to parental circumstances.

Latymer Upper School (see p 229)
A number of means-tested bursaries are awarded every year. These range from 25% of fees to full fees and are available at 11+ and 16+.

Academic Scholarships and awards can be offered as a result of performance in the 11+ entrance examinations and at interview. The examinations are held every year in January followed by interviews in late January/early February.

A small number of pupils are admitted at 13+, following entrance examinations in the February of the year of entry. Academic Scholarships and awards can also be offered to pupils who excel in the qualifying examinations at 13+.

At 11+ and 13+ Entry: Scholarships of up to half fees and Entrance Exhibitions are available for Music. Entrance Exhibitions are offered for Art, Drama and Sport.

At 16+ Entry: Scholarships and awards are available for Art, Drama, Music, Sport. Candidates who have satisfied the academic requirements will be invited to an interview and assessment in January.

Further details are available from the Registrar (0845 638 5978; registrar@latymer-upper.org).

Leicester Grammar School (see p 233)
Academic scholarships (maximum 25%) are available at all ages from 11+ upwards and are given on the results of the Entrance Examination (or, at Sixth Form entrance, GCSE results). Music scholarships are also available, awarded following audition, as are a small number of art scholarships, awarded on examination and portfolio.

Leighton Park School (see p 235)
Several Major Awards (up to 25% of fees) and Minor Awards (15% or 10% of fees) are made each year for academic work, music, art and sport. Bursaries may be available on a means-tested basis.

The Leys School (see p 237)
Scholarships are available for entry at 11+, 13+ and for the Sixth Form. The value is expressed as a percentage of the fees, the maximum value being 30%.

At 11+ two scholarships are available with the emphasis being on academic performance.

At 13+ and at Sixth Form the categories are Academic, Art, Music, Sport, Drama and Design Technology (Arkwright Award Scheme at Sixth Form level). There is also an All-Rounder Award at 13+. The number and value of awards is dependent on the calibre of the candidates in a particular year.

Full particulars are available by application to the Admissions Office for a prospectus.

Llandovery College (see p 240)
Thomas Philips Scholarships are for academically-able pupils from Wales or Welsh families. This means-tested scholarship is for a child's entire education whether boarding or day and may be as much as 100% of fees. Up to three Thomas Phillips Scholarships are awarded each year for entry at 11 (Year 7) on the basis of candidates' performance in the School's Entrance Examination and in a separate, demanding test of English, Maths and Non-Verbal Reasoning skills.

Lord Wandsworth College (see p 244)
Scholarships and Awards:

First Form (Year 7): Academic, Music and Sport;

Third Form (Year 9): Academic, Drama, Music, Art, Sport and All-Rounder;

Sixth Form: Academic, Drama, Music, Art, Sport and All-Rounder.

Further details may be obtained from the Admissions Office.

Loretto School (see p 245)
Loretto is pleased to announce a number of major Scholarships:

Junior School

A limited number of Junior School scholarships are available. Academic scholarships awarded in the Junior School are for the duration of the Junior and Senior School.

Senior School (Second, Third and Lower Sixth Form)

Academic Scholarships: Forbes Mackintosh Award and Hector Laing Scholarship for Third Form applicants. Academic awards to Sixth Form pupils including Langhorne Scholarships for applicants coming from a State School. Sixth Form applicants select three potential A Level subjects from Loretto's Sixth Form Curriculum and sit scholarship papers in those subjects.

Almond All-Rounder Award
Art Scholarships
Music and Drama Scholarships
Golf Scholarships
Sports Scholarships

Please contact Admissions on 0131 653 4455 for further details.

Loughborough Grammar School (see p 247)
A number of Scholarships are offered at 10+, 11+ and 13+/Common Entrance, based on performance in the Entrance Examination. Sixth Form scholarships are based on GCSE results. Choral and instrumental scholarships are also awarded at 10+, 11+, 13+/Common Entrance and Sixth Form. There are also a number of bursaries, dependent on parental income. The Governors have introduced Foundation Bursaries (formerly known as School Assisted Places) to replace the Government Assisted Places Scheme.

Magdalen College School (see p 249)
A limited number of bursaries is available to boys of 7, 9, 11 and 13, awarded on a combination of academic merit and financial need. Ogden Trust Sixth Form Scholarships are available to candidates of sufficient merit from state schools.

At age 13, up to 16 Scholarships of up to £300, but capable of increase up to half fees in case of need, are awarded each year on the results of a two-day scholarship examination in March. Candidates should be under 14 on the subsequent 1 September. Closing date for entries: 1 February.

Music, Art and Sports Scholarships are awarded each year on the results of assessments held in February (Music) or March (Art and Sports). Music award holders also receive free tuition in one instrument.

Further information can be obtained from the *Registrar, Magdalen College School, Oxford OX4 1DZ.*

For details of Choristerships (for boys aged 7–9) application should be made to the *Informator Choristarum, Magdalen College, Oxford OX1 4AU.*

Malvern College (see p 251)
Scholarships and Exhibitions are offered for competition in our Scholarship Examination which is held at the school. Candidates for all Scholarships must be under 14 years of age on 1st September in the year of the examination but there is no age limit for Exhibitions. Entries must be received three weeks before the examination. Entry forms are available from Preparatory Schools or the Registrar at Malvern College.

Up to twenty Academic awards are offered. They range from Scholarships of up to 50% of the fees to Exhibitions of a lesser value. Scholarships and Exhibitions are also offered for Art, Drama, Music, Choral singing, Sport and Technology, as well as the The Malvernian Society All-Rounder Award.

Further particulars may be obtained from The Registrar, Tel: 01684 581500, or e-mail srj@malcol.org.

Marlborough College (see p 254)
The College offers Open, Foundation (Clergy) and Armed Services closed scholarships. All are index-linked to the fees. Candidates must be under 14 on 1st September.

At least 12 academic scholarships and exhibitions altogether will be available, the value of any award depending on merit and need. One College Organ Scholarship/bursary is offered, which may be worth 100% of school fees. The merit component will range up to 25% of the fees. Awards will be eligible for augmentation above 25%, dependent on family financial circumstances, by means of bursaries.

Sports Awards and All Rounder Awards are also available.

In addition to Open Scholarships there are Foundation Scholarships for children of Clergy, and these may be supplemented by grants from the College's Children of Clergy Fund. (The minimum grant from this fund is 15% of the fee.)

There are also closed awards for children of Officers in HM Forces. Details of those available each year are available from the Senior Admissions Tutor.

The closing date for entries is February.

For Art and Music Scholarships, see separate entries.

There are also scholarships available for Sixth Form Entry.

A Scholarship Prospectus and copies of past papers may be obtained from The Senior Admissions Tutor, Marlborough College, Marlborough, Wiltshire SN8 1PA (01672 892300; e-mail: admissions@marlboroughcollege.org).

Merchant Taylors' School, Northwood (see p 257)
Entrance scholarships are awarded at 11, 13 and 16 on the results of examinations held in January and March. Their maximum value is 30% of the fee, but if there is financial need this can be increased. For Music Scholarships, see separate list. Details from the Admissions Secretary, Merchant Taylors' School, Sandy Lodge, Northwood, Middlesex HA6 2HT. Tel: 01923 845514.

Merchiston Castle School (see p 260)
Scholarships are offered for competition at 11+, 12+, 13+ and Sixth Form level. Junior examinations (Academic and All-Rounder) for boys aged between 10½ and 12 are held in January/February, when scholarships may be awarded. Main School examinations (Academic and All-Rounder) are held in February/March when scholarships may be awarded. NB for Main School awards, candidates must be under 14 on 1st February. All-Rounder scholarships assess academic ability

and two specialisms, eg Music, Sport, Drama etc. One Sixth Form scholarship or All-Rounder award may be awarded to a boy not already at Merchiston who wishes to follow a 2-year programme leading to A Level.

Further particulars may be obtained from the Director of Admissions.

Mill Hill School (see p 263)
Academic, Music, Drama, Art and Design, and Sports Awards are available at 13+.

Sixth Form Academic Scholarships and Exhibitions are available.

For further information please visit the school's website www.millhill.org.uk.

Monkton Senior (see p 269)
Four Anniversary Awards are offered at the age of 11 for open competition each year. They range in value from 25% to 10% of the appropriate fee.

At least ten Open Scholarships are offered at age 13 (including at least two for Music, at least one for Drama, at least one for Art and at least two for Sport) of value ranging from 35% to 10% of the appropriate fee.

Additional bursaries are available to supplement Scholarships in case of need. Candidates must be under 14 years of age on 1st September. Further particulars and copies of specimen papers can be obtained from the Registrar.

At least four Sixth Form Scholarships are also offered each year, ranging in value from 25% to 10% of the appropriate fee.

Details of all awards can be obtained from the Registrar.

Monmouth School (see p 272)
A generous number of Entrance Scholarships are awarded on the School's Year 7 Entry Assessments (held in February) for boys entering at the age of eleven, on the Foundation Scholarship Examination (held in February/March) for boys entering at the age of thirteen, and the Sixth Form Scholarship Examination (in February). In cases of need, Scholarships may be augmented by a Bursary.

At eleven: 1. Open Scholarships for dayboys or boarders.

2. Further Scholarships and Bursaries, including those from the Old Monmothian Scholarship Fund, will be awarded, their value being determined and annually adjusted according to parental need.

At thirteen: Foundation Scholarships are for day boys or boarders who are not currently pupils of Monmouth School. Candidates must be between the ages of 12 and 14 on the first day of September following the examination.

Sixth Form Scholarship awards for day boys or boarders. Candidates to be under the age of 17 on the first day of September following the Scholarship Examinations. The E F Bulmer Award is available to suitable Sixth Form candidates living in Herefordshire; awards range in value from 50% to 100% of the fees.

Morrison's Academy (see p 274)
Sixth Form Scholarships: A number of Scholarships are awarded after examination and interview in June. The awards, which do not carry a high financial value, recognise both achievement and potential. Full details from The Rector, Morrison's Academy, Crieff PH7 3AN.

Newcastle-under-Lyme School (see p 277)
The following Scholarships and Bursaries are available:

Governors' Scholarships: One Scholarship of value up to £2,000 per annum for up to 7 years and Scholarships of up to £1,500 per annum for up to 7 years to be awarded on the results of the 11+ and 13+ Entrance Examinations. Two Scholarships, of value up to £500 per annum, to be awarded to boys and girls on the basis of their performance at 7+.

Sports Scholarships: A number of Sports Scholarships may be awarded to candidates at 13+ entry offering particular sporting prowess. These will be of value up to £1,500 per annum for up to 5 years.

The Ogden Trust Sixth Form Science Scholarship: Two Scholarships equal in value to full school fees per annum for two years. Details on application.

The Robert S Woodward Scholarships: One or Two Scholarships, of value up to £1,250 per annum, to be awarded annually to pupils entering or in the Sixth Form, for outstanding performance in the field of Mathematical Sciences.

The JCB Sixth Form Scholarship: One Scholarship, of value up to £300 per annum, to be awarded annually to pupils entering, or in the Sixth Form, for outstanding performance in Physics.

Music Scholarships: To cover the cost of music tuition throughout the student's school career.

Bursaries: The Governors have established a Bursary Scheme to assist parents with school fees.

Further details may be obtained from the *Principal, Newcastle-under-Lyme School, Mount Pleasant, Newcastle, Staffordshire ST5 1DB.*

Norwich School (see p 279)
Scholarships are awarded to pupils with outstanding ability and flair, which the school assesses by examination, interview or audition. The financial value of a scholarship will typically be 20% of the annual tuition fee – irrespective of parental means. Scholarships are awarded in four categories: Academic; Music; Sport; and Art, Design or Drama.

Academic and Music scholarships are awarded at 11+, 13+ and Sixth Form entry. Sport and Art, Design or Drama scholarships are awarded only at Sixth Form entry. Pupils may apply for more than one scholarship, although the maximum financial benefit that can be cumulated is 40% of the school fees.

Nottingham High School (see p 281)
Part-Scholarships of a fixed sum may be awarded. They are not linked to parental finances and will normally continue throughout a boy's school career. Application does not have to be made for part-scholarships as these are awarded at the discretion of the Headmaster, subject to entrance examination performance and interview. Following the ending of the Government Assisted Places Scheme, Nottingham High School has introduced its own Bursaries to be awarded to boys entering the Senior School at either age eleven or sixteen. Odgen Trust Bursaries are available for Sixth Form entry for students studying Science and Mathematics. All Bursaries will be awarded at the Headmaster's discretion and will normally continue until a pupil leaves the School.

Oakham School (see p 282)
Academic and Music scholarships are available for 11+ entrants. Academic, Art and Design, Design and Technology, ICT and Computing, Music, and Sport scholarships are offered for boys and girls entering aged 13+. Additionally, Drama scholarships are available for 16+ entrants. Additional awards are made at the Headmaster's discretion. Bursary support is also available. A Scholarships and Bursaries information booklet is available from the Registrar, Tel: 01572 758758.

The Oratory School (see p 286)
A number of Scholarships and Exhibitions of varying values, not exceeding half fees. Academic, Music, Art and Sports Awards. Particulars from The Head Master.

Oundle School (see p 288)
11+ Academic Scholarships: 9–10 January
13+ Academic Scholarships: 6–9 May
16+ Academic Scholarships: 7–9 November 2008

11+: Four Junior Academic Scholarships for entry to The Berrystead or Laxton, to the value of up to 25% of the fees. Pupils transfer directly into the senior school at 13+ with the opportunity to increase their awards. Closing date: 1 December 2008.

13+: Fifteen Academic Scholarships to the value of up to 25% of the fees. Candidates must be below the age of 14 on 1 September 2009. A qualifying examination will take place during w/c Monday 9 February. *The Grocer's Scholar* is elected annually after completion of one year in the School.

13+: Eight General Scholarships, including the *Conradi* and *Stainforth* awards, to the value of up to 20% of the fees (1–2 March).

16+: Four Sixth Form Academic Scholarships to the value of up to 50% of the fees.

These Scholarships are tenable during the whole of the pupil's time at the School, provided progress is satisfactory. Successful candidates are assured of a place in the School regardless of whether their names are previously registered for a place or not.

Further details may be obtained from Rachael Wood, The Undermaster's Assistant, Oundle School, Oundle, Peterborough, PE8 4GH. Tel: 01832 277116. Fax: 01832 277119. E-mail: rcwood@oundleschool.org.uk.

Pangbourne College (see p 291)
Scholarships and Awards of up to 50% of fees are mainly offered at 13, when entering Form III, and at 16, when entering the Sixth Form, but some are occasionally offered at the age of 11, when entering Form I.

Academic Scholarship papers for entry at 13+ are set and held at the College over 3 days beginning on the first Monday in May.

The College is an Arkwright Technology Scholarship Centre and also offers one Design Technology scholarship every year.

Music, Art, Drama and Sport Scholarships, All-rounder Awards and Sixth Form Scholarships are available. Please see the relevant section for details or contact our Registrar for more information.

Plymouth College (see p 293)
For pupils entering at 11 there are 2 Major Scholarships (50% of fees pa) and 3 Ordinary Scholarships (one-third of the fees pa). Two of these awards are restricted to pupils coming from Plymouth College Junior School. There are also smaller awards for Art, Music, Drama and Sport (3 per category) and on occasion All-Round awards are given. Awards are made on the basis of the Entrance Examination.

At 13+ there is one Major and one Ordinary Scholarship and these are awarded on a Scholarship Examination.

For those entering the Sixth Form two further awards are made based on GCSE results.

There are 6 Scholarships and Awards for Art, Music and Sport. Three of these are awarded at 13 and three to Sixth Form entrants. The value of these are up to one-third of the fees.

Further information from the Headmaster's Secretary.

Pocklington School (see p 294)
Five academic scholarships up to the value of £2,500 and five exhibitions up to the value of £1,250 are offered to entrants to the First Year, Third Year and Sixth Form. Awards are available to internal and external candidates. Tenure of all awards is for the duration of the pupil's time at Pocklington School subject to satisfactory performance and behaviour.

Portsmouth Grammar School (see p 297)
A small number of Scholarships, each amounting to no more than 10% of full fees, are awarded to outstanding candidates in the 11+ Entrance Assessments. All candidates are automatically considered for Scholarships. No application is required.

Peter Ogden Scholarships, worth up to full fees, are offered at 11+ to outstanding candidates with parents of limited income from state primary schools. Additional assistance up to 100% of fees is available through the award of means-tested Foundation Bursaries.

Scholarships from the A D Nock Trust are offered at 13+ to both Common Entrance candidates and existing pupils.

Academic Scholarships and Bursaries are awarded for entry to the Sixth Form. Full details of all scholarships and bursaries are available on the School's website.

Prior Park College (see p 300)
An entrance examination is held in January each year and is linked to Scholarships at 11+. Scholarships are awarded annually to external candidates for 13+ entry and the examination is held during March. Sixth Form Scholarships are held in November.

All Scholarships are up to a maximum of 50% of fees.

Candidates must be under 14 years of age on September 1st following for the March Scholarship and under 12 years of age on September 1st following for the January Scholarship.

Queen's College, Taunton (see p 307)
Queen's College Scholarships: 10+, 11+ and 12+ scholarships are awarded in January, 13+ in March and Sixth Form in November.

Academic Scholarships by examination: up to 50% of fees for students of proven academic ability in one or more subjects. Up to 8 day and 5 boarding academic scholarships for students aged 8+, 11+ and 13+ on 1 September in year of entry. Eight Sixth Form scholarships are also on offer.

Music, Drama, Art and Sports Scholarships are also available (*see relevant section*).

For further information apply to the Headmaster.

Radley College (see p 309)
Up to 12 Academic Scholarships and Exhibitions are awarded annually. Awards may be supplemented by a means-tested bursary where necessary. Further details from our website or the Registrar.

Ratcliffe College (see p 311)
Academic scholarships are offered on entry to Year 7, Year 9 and the Sixth Form. A limited number of Bursaries are available on entry to Year 7.

At 11+, all candidates take the normal entrance examination papers in Mathematics, English and Verbal Reasoning and those obtaining the best results will be recommended to the Headmaster for a scholarship.

At 13+, candidates take papers in English, Mathematics, Science, History, French and Verbal Reasoning; those obtaining the best results will be recommended to the Headmaster for a scholarship. Pupils already at the College may enter for the awards as internal candidates.

Scholarships into the Sixth Form are awarded for academic excellence and are based on GCSE results. Pupils already at the College are also eligible for these awards.

There are two Music Choral awards and a limited number of additional awards are available at the Headmaster's discretion.

Scholarships are reviewed annually and, provided good scholastic and discipline standards are maintained, remain with the pupil throughout his or her school career.

Further details can be obtained from The Registrar, Ratcliffe College, Fosse Way, Ratcliffe-on-the-Wreake, Leicester LE7 4SG.

Reed's School (see p 314)
Academic Scholarships are offered each year at age 11, 13 and 16. The maximum value of any award is half fees per annum. All enquiries should be addressed to the Registrar.

Rendcomb College (see p 317)
A number of Scholarships (Academic, Art, Music, Performing Arts and Sport) and a small number of Forces Scholarships are awarded each year at 11, 13 and 16 years of age. They are based on an assessment of a pupil's potential and the value that we believe they will add to the life of the school. All awards are reassessed annually and are subject to satisfactory academic progress and behaviour. All cases are judged on their own merits and parents are invited to discuss their eligibility for a financial award with the Headmaster.

Repton School (see p 319)
A number of scholarships are offered annually at 13+ and 16+. Exhibitions may also be awarded. The value of any award may be increased where need is shown.

Entrance Scholarships at 13+: the examination is held at Repton in May for entry in September. Candidates must be under 14 on 1 September in the year of the examination.

16+ Scholarships: are offered for both boarding and day places. The examination takes place in November for entry the following September.

Further information on all awards, including the closing date for entries, can be obtained from The Registrar, Repton School, Repton, Derby DE65 6FH. Tel: 01283 559223. Fax: 01283 559228. e-mail: registrar@repton.org.uk.

Rossall School (see p 323)
The following are offered for competition every year in January/February: Trapnell Scholarship (value full boarding fee plus certain extras including school uniform clothing and replacement) intended principally for promise and ability in Mathematics or Science; One Jackson Scholarship (value full boarding fee plus allowance for extras, clothing and travel), based on character, personality and range of interests as much as on academic ability; Ten Open Scholarships, up to eight awards of 50% of basic fee; up to four Music Scholarships of value up to 50% basic fee according to ability of those selected. Music Scholars also receive free tuition in 2 instruments. Two sporting scholarships up to 85% of basic fee. Scholarships may be awarded on the results of the 11 year-old Entrance Examination.

Bursaries are awarded each year either on the Scholarship or on the Common Entrance Examination to children of Clergy, where need is shown. Service Bursaries are awarded for the children of members of HM Armed Forces and may be up to 20% of the basic fee. One Newell Scholarship of £1,740 pa is awarded on record and interview to a boy or girl of good character and wide-ranging interests educated in UK or Kenya; two Watson-Smith Scholarships of £750 pa for pupils who are worthy of encouragement.

Apply to *The Headmaster, Rossall School, Fleetwood FY7 8JW.*

Royal Grammar School, Guildford (see p 327)
King's Scholarships and Scholarships are awarded in recognition of outstanding academic merit, and vary in value from 50% to 10% fee remission. For boys entering the First Form at 11 there is a competitive examination in English and Mathematics, held in mid-February. For boys entering the Third Form at 13 there is a two-day examination covering all Common Entrance subjects, held in February or March.

For full details of these and of arrangements for boys entering the School at 11, 13 and 16, write to the Registrar.

The Royal Hospital School (see p 332)
Scholarships are awarded annually, at the Headmaster discretion, for academic excellence, musical or artistic talent, sport and for sailing to pupils entering the school at any age but normally Year 7 (11+), Year 9 (13+) and Year 12 (16+). All scholarship candidates are required to sit the school entrance examination (unless taking Common Entrance or GCSE examinations), have an interview with the Headmaster and take the scholarship examination in the case of academic scholarships or undergo an assessment in their relevant field for art, music, sport and sailing scholarships. Full details from the Admissions Office, Tel: 01473 326210 or email: admissions@royalhospitalschool.org.

Rugby School (see p 335)
Approximately 10% of the School's annual income is currently expended in Scholarships, Foundationerships, Bursaries and other awards. Scholarships are intended to open access to talented boys and girls irrespective of parental means. All scholarships therefore carry a nominal reduction of 10% of the fee; all may be augmented to 100% of the fees subject to means testing.

Academic Scholarships at 13+: Boys and girls who are 12 or over and under 14 at midnight on August 31st in the year the examination is taken may sit. Candidates who were previously registered for entry and who do not obtain awards are normally admitted to the school on the result of the Scholarship examination. The examination is held at Rugby in early May for entry in September of the same year. A generous number of scholarships are usually awarded.

Academic Scholarships at 16+: Boys and girls aiming to enter the School after GCSE may compete for a number of 16+ Scholarships. The Scholarship interviews are held at Rugby in mid-November in the year preceding the pupil's entry to the School. Candidates must first take the Sixth Form Entrance Examination and those showing scholarship potential will be called for Scholarship interviews with the relevant Heads of Department.

Music Scholarships: Several Scholarships are awarded each year at 11+, 13+ and 16+. At 16+ the examination audition is held at Rugby in November, at 11+ in early January, and at 13+ in late January or early February of the year of entry.

Art Scholarships: At 16+ potential Art Scholarship candidates are interviewed and present their portfolios as part of the 16+ Academic Scholarship in November and at 13+ in the May of the year of entry.

Design and Technology Bursary/Scholarship: Awards are offered at 13+ and 16+. The examinations are held in conjunction with the Academic Scholarships. At 13+, candidates can, but need not, take the Academic Scholarship as well.

Sports Scholarships: A number of Scholarships are awarded each year at 13+ and 16+ to candidates with outstanding ability in games. At 13+ applicants should be nominated by their Head Teacher to attend an initial assessment at Rugby. Short-listed candidates will then be observed in match conditions. At 16+ candidates will be interviewed as part of the sixth form entrance examination in November and will be observed in match conditions or be invited to participate in a training session at Rugby. Short-listed candidates will subsequently be observed in match conditions.

The Arnold Foundation: The Arnold Foundation aims to raise funds through charitable donations to support the education of talented boys and girls whose families would not be able to fund boarding school fees. Funds are available for several awards for entry to the sixth form and at 13+. Pupils offered a place through this scheme may be awarded up to 100% of the full boarding fee plus extras. The final selection is through interviews. Candidates are expected to pass the School's normal entrance requirements. Initial enquiries should be made via the Registry.

Foundationerships: In 1567 Lawrence Sheriff in his Will bequeathed money to establish a school in perpetuity in Rugby 'to serve chiefly for the children of Rugby and Brownsover'. It is in the execution of the terms of this Will that Foundation Scholarships are offered. Several awards are made each year to day boy and day girl candidates of 11+ and 13+. Awards are 10% of the fees but may be augmented up to 100% (subject to means testing) of the day pupil fee. All candidates for Foundation Scholarships must reside within a radius of 10 miles from the Rugby Clock Tower.

For further information and details of all scholarships please contact the Registrar, School House, Rugby School, Rugby, Warwickshire CV22 5EH; e-mail: registry@rugbyschool.net.

Ryde School with Upper Chine (see p 339)
Some Scholarships worth 10% of fees may be awarded on merit to external or internal candidates for entry at 11+ and 13+. Scholarships are also awarded to our best GCSE candidates. Scholarships may be supplemented by bursaries, which are means tested. Further details from the Headmaster.

St Albans School (see p 341)
There are numerous scholarships worth up to 50% of fees awarded on merit at each age of entry.

St Bede's School (see p 345)
A number of scholarships and bursaries are awarded each year. They are awarded both to boys and girls entering the School in

Year 9 and to those entering at Sixth Form level (Year 12). Candidates for a scholarship in Year 9 should be over 12½ years and under 14 years on 1st September of the year in which they sit the Scholarship Examination. This examination is suitable for boys and girls from any educational background.

Scholarships are awarded to those showing outstanding potential in the following categories: Academic, Art, Drama, Sport, Music and Dance. In addition a number of awards are made each year to boys and girls who are above average academically or particularly strong in individual subjects and, in addition, show real potential in Art or Music, or Drama, or Sport. Bursaries can be made available in exceptional deserving cases.

Scholarship auditions for music and drama, sports trials, examinations and interviews take place at the School in late January and early February each year. Interview and recommendation from the Head of a boy's or girl's present school play an important part in deciding to whom awards should be made. Further details regarding the procedure for entry are available from the Admissions Officer, e-mail: admissions@stbedesschool.org.

St Bees School (see p 346)
Scholarships and Exhibitions up to 40% of the fees are awarded to candidates under the age of 12 on 1 September. All candidates must take papers in English, Mathematics and Verbal Reasoning.

The School offers a limited number of means-tested bursaries.

St Edmund's College (see p 355)
Academic Scholarships, which vary between one-third and one-half of the basic College fee for boarders or day pupils, fall into 3 classes: (1) for pupils entering the College from St Hugh's, (2) for pupils entering the College from other schools at the age of 11, (3) Sixth Form scholarships. Further details may be obtained from the Headmaster.

Sixth Form Scholarships: At 16+, the Cardinal Allen Academic Scholarships are awarded by open competition using the results of specially set scholarship examinations. Music, Sport and Art scholarships may also be offered through competitive test.

St Edmund's School (see p 357)
Various scholarships and exhibitions of up to one half of the fees (which may be supplemented by bursaries at the Headmaster's discretion) are awarded on entry at the following ages:

Academic: 11 (Junior School), 13 (Senior School), 16 (Sixth Form).

Music: 11 (Junior School), 13 (Senior School), 16 (Sixth Form).

Art: 13 (Senior School), 16 (Sixth Form).

Drama: 16 (Sixth Form).

Sport: 13 (Senior School), 16 (Sixth Form). Also at 11 (Junior School) to candidates who show exceptional talent and achievement.

All-Rounder: At the discretion of the Headmaster and the Master, an All-Rounder scholarship may be made to a candidate whose combination of talents merits an award. Such a candidate will have sat the academic scholarship paper and been assessed for a scholarship in at least one other discipline.

St Edward's, Oxford (see p 360)
All scholarships carry a maximum value of 10% of current boarding fees with the opportunity of a means-tested supplement up to a value of 100% fee reduction.

Up to fifteen Academic scholarships and exhibitions are available each year. 16+ academic scholarships take place in the November prior to entry in the September, 13+ academic scholarships take place in the May prior to entry.

St George's College (see p 362)
Up to three *Major Scholarships* (25%–50% of the basic school fee) will be awarded at 11+, one of which must be awarded to a boy or girl at St George's College Junior School and at least one should be awarded to an applicant not at the Junior School.

Up to two *Minor Scholarships* (10%–24% of the basic school fee) at 11+.

Up to three *Major Scholarships* of will be awarded at 13+ for entry to the Third Form of St George's College.

Up to two *Minor Scholarships* of will be awarded at 13+ for entry to the Third Form of St George's College.

Up to 10 *Major* and 10 *Minor* Scholarships may be awarded for internal and external entry into Sixth Form.

Details may be obtained from the Headmaster's Secretary.

St Lawrence College (see p 366)
Academic and Sports Scholarships are offered to candidates at 8+.

Academic, Music, Sport, Art and All-Rounder Scholarships are offered to candidates at 11+, 13+ and 16+ for entry into Years 7, 9, and 12.

St Paul's School (see p 368)
A few Foundation Scholarships may be awarded to 11 year old boys at Colet Court on the basis of examinations. The Scholarship Examination for St Paul's is held in May. Candidates must be under 14 on 1 September. There are 153 Scholars at any given time and about 30 vacancies arise each year. All new Academic Scholarships are honorary, and carry an award of £60 per annum. Bursary assistance is available for families whose circumstances do not allow them to meet the cost of fees, subject to interview and means-testing. Those gaining scholarships will receive preferential treatment in the event of a change in family circumstances and any subsequent need to apply for Bursary assistance.

Further particulars from the Finance Director, St Paul's School, Barnes, London SW13 9JT.

St Peter's School (see p 370)
Means-tested Bursaries for those who qualify for more than 50% of the fees are available.

Honorary Academic Scholarships at 13/16 are available for those doing very well in the entrance tests, who are then invited to compete for honorary subject scholarships.

Seaford College (see p 372)
Academic, Choral Music, Instrumental Music, Art, Design Technology and Sports scholarships may be awarded to boys and girls entering the senior school at 13+. Music/Choral scholarships may be awarded to boys and girls entering Wilberforce House at ten or eleven. These scholarships are worth a fixed value of £500 per annum.

Special consideration will be given to pupils entering from maintained schools who have not studied the Common entrance syllabus.

Bursaries are available to pupils whose parents are in the Forces and siblings.

For further information please apply to the *Admissions Secretary, Seaford College, Petworth, Sussex GU28 0NB.*

Sedbergh School (see p 374)
Major and Minor Scholarships and Exhibitions may be awarded annually as a result of examinations held in February.

Scholarships are usually offered for entry to the Senior School at 13+ and 16+ (Sixth Form). Scholarships are offered for entry to the Junior School at 11+. In exceptional circumstances other years of entry may be considered.

In addition to Scholarships for Academic excellence, Art, Drama, Design Technology, Music and Sport awards are also available for all-round potential.

All awards may be supplemented by means of a Bursary according to parental need.

Further particulars and specimen papers are available from *The Headmaster, Sedbergh School, Sedbergh, Cumbria LA10 5HG.*

Sevenoaks School (see p 375)
Up to 50 awards available at: 11+ (Junior School), 13+ (Middle School), 16+ (Sixth Form), for:

- outstanding academic ability or promise;
- outstanding ability in music;
- outstanding ability in sport (at 13+ and 16+ only);
- outstanding ability in art (at 13+ and 16+ only);
- all-round ability: a Pipemakers' Scholarship, at 13+, is awarded specifically for this.

Scholarships are awarded to the value of a minimum of 10% of the day fee, and may be augmented by bursaries in cases of financial need.

The Sixth Form scholarship examinations (for those short-listed for the entrance tests) are held in November each year, all others during the Lent Term.

Applications should be made to the Director of Admissions, Sevenoaks School, Sevenoaks, Kent TN13 1HU by 30 September for all 11+ awards and by 31 January for 13+. Applications for 16+ awards for 2009 should be made to the Sixth Form Registrar by 24 September.

Sherborne School (see p 377)
The following awards are offered:

Open Scholarships: up to six Scholarships of up to 25% of fees (the top scholarship being the Alexander Ross Wallace Scholarship) and up to eight Exhibitions of up to 15% of fees may be awarded. In awarding one of these Exhibitions regard will be paid to special proficiency in a particular subject.

In addition Awards are available to those who are able to demonstrate outstanding ability in one of the following areas: Art, Design & Technology, Sport.

Closed Awards: Raban Exhibition of 10% of fees for the sons of serving or ex-service officers, a Nutting Exhibition of 10% of fees for sons of RN Officers.

All candidates should be under 14 on 1st September.

Music Awards: A number of Awards are available at 13+. In addition one Marion Packer Scholarship of £600 pa for an outstanding performance on the piano may be offered. Those given Awards receive free instrumental tuition.

Sixth Form Scholarships and Exhibitions are offered annually.

In common with most other HMC Schools the maximum value of any award is 25% of the fees but this may be supplemented in cases of financial need.

Further particulars and copies of specimen papers can be obtained from the *Registrar, Sherborne School, Dorset DT9 3AP. Tel: 01935 810402. Fax: 01935 810422.*

Shrewsbury School (see p 381)
The examination is held during the Summer term. Seventeen Scholarships are open to competition. Four are to the maximum value 50% of fees, six up to the value of 25% of fees and seven worth at least £2,000 per annum.

There are also two Music Scholarships up to the value of 50% of fees, two Music Scholarships up to the value of 20% of fees, two Art Scholarships up to the value of 20% of fees. Candidates must be under 14 on 1 September, following the examination.

In addition, there are two Sports Scholarships up to the value of 20% of fees, two All-Rounder Scholarships worth a maximum value of 20% of fees and ten House Foundation Awards, worth up to the value of 50% of fees, which are available for exceptional all-rounders and tied to particular day and boarding houses.

There are two Sixth Form Scholarships up to the value of 25% of the fees and 6 up to the value of 15% of fees.

For details of all Scholarships, please contact The Registrar, Shrewsbury School, Tel: 01743 280550.

Silcoates School (see p 383)
Academic and Music Scholarships are offered at 11+ and above; Sixth Form entrants are eligible for these awards. Music Award holders enjoy free instrument tuition.

Solihull School (see p 384)
At 11+ the School offers on average 15 academic scholarships, usually between 10% and 25% of the fees.

Scholarships are also awarded for entry into the Sixth Form, usually at 25% of the fees, and are available to internal and external candidates.

Stamford School (see p 386)
There are Governors' Scholarships and Bursaries available on entry. These are predominantly for Academic work, but also include Music and Art.

For further particulars apply to the Head, Stamford School, Lincolnshire PE9 2BS.

Stonyhurst College (see p 391)
Open Major and Minor Scholarships are awarded annually at 13+ on the result of an examination held at Stonyhurst in May. These vary in value up to a maximum of half fees. Open Major and Minor Music scholarships are also awarded in February. Sixth-form academic scholarships, scholarships for Art and Design and Technology and All-rounder awards are also made.

For further details please apply to the Headmaster.

Stowe School (see p 393)
Academic scholarships up to the value of 25% of the School fees are available for pupils entering Stowe's Third Form, at aged 13+, and are awarded to gifted children who will already be following the ISEB Common Academic Scholarship syllabus at their Preparatory School. Academic Scholarships are also available to pupils wishing to join the School in the Lower Sixth Form after GCSE. Competitive Entry Examinations are held in the November of the candidate's GCSE year. Successful Scholarship candidates would normally be expected to gain A* and A grades in all their subjects at GCSE. Full details may be obtained from: The Registrar, Stowe School, Buckingham MK18 5EH.

Strathallan School (see p 395)
Awards of between 5% and 50% are made on the basis of competitive examination/assessment. Bursary help is available to supplement awards for outstanding candidates on a financial need basis.

Awards are available in the following categories to candidates entering the school at three levels:

Junior School: Academic and Music/Choral/Piping/Drumming. Candidates should be under 13 on 1 September in the year of entry. Scholarship Examination: January.

Third Form: Academic, Music/Choral/Piping/Drumming, Art, Design Technology, Sports, and All-Rounder. Candidates should be under 14 on 1 September in the year of entry. Scholarship Examination: March.

Sixth Form: Academic, Music/Choral/Piping/Drumming, Art, Design Technology, Sports, and All-Rounder. Candidates should be under 17 on 1 September in the year of entry. Scholarship Examination: November.

Further information is available on the school's website: www.strathallan.co.uk. All enquiries about scholarships to: The Admissions Office, Strathallan School, Forgandenny, Perthshire PH2 9EG. Tel: 01738 815003, email admissions@strathallan.co.uk.

Surbiton High School (see p 397)
Scholarships are offered at 11+ and 16+. There are several Academic Scholarships offering a 50% or 25% reduction in the standard fees. The School also offers Scholarships in Music, Art and Sport of 33% reduction on standard fees.

Sutton Valence School (see p 399)
Academic Scholarships and Exhibitions are awarded at 11+, 13+ and for Sixth Form entry and can be in addition to scholarships in other disciplines.

The Westminster Scholarship supports well-motivated and able pupils who enter Sutton Valence School at Sixth Form level and who are expected to achieve 5 A grade passes at GCSE.

Further details may be obtained from the Admissions Officer.

Tettenhall College (see p 403)
Lower School Awards and Upper School Scholarships may be offered to outstanding boys and girls from either state or independent schools. Sixth Form Scholarships are available for boys and girls joining the Sixth Form from Year 11 or after taking GCSE elsewhere.

Tonbridge School (see p 404)
Up to 23 Academic Scholarships (awarded by examination in May); 10 or more Music Scholarships (examination in early February); up to 10 Art, Drama or Technology Scholarships (examination in early February); up to 4 Cowdrey Scholarships, for sporting ability and sportsmanship (assessment in early February). 3 or 4 Sixth Form Academic or Music Scholarships may be awarded.

The value of any Scholarship awarded may be increased, by any amount up to the full school fee, if assessment of the parents' means indicates a need. Resources are available from a variety of sources including the Tonbridge School Foundation and HSBC, for scholarships worth up to 100% of fees. These may be awarded to boys of exceptional academic ability or outstanding talent in any other field whose parents could not otherwise afford to consider a Tonbridge education for their son.

Choral Boarding Exhibitions, with a value of 10% of the school fee, are offered each year for award to Choristers of Cathedral or other Choir Schools.

Candidates for all awards must be under 14 on 1st June of the year in which they sit the examination. Entries for awards may be made at any time until three weeks before the examinations.

For boys over 10 and under 11 on 1st September, two Foundation Awards are awarded, tenable at a preparatory school. Candidates must be attending a County or Voluntary Primary School. Junior academic and music awards may be made to 10 or 11 year old sons of needy parents in fee-paying Prep Schools. They are awarded as 'Advance' Foundation Scholarships by competitive examination in November 2¾ years before entry to Tonbridge.

Entry forms and full particulars of all Scholarships and Foundation Awards may be obtained from the Admissions Secretary, Tonbridge School, Tonbridge, Kent TN9 1JP. Tel: 01732 304297; email: admissions@tonbridge-school.org.

Trent College (see p 407)
Awards are made for excellence in Music, Art, Sport, Drama and Academic ability at 11+, 13+ and 16+.

There are also boarding awards for those who could make an all-round contribution, and special consideration is given to those with a parent in the Services.

Bursaries are also available to those in need of extra financial support.

The value of an Award depends on the age of the child, their ability and whether they are a day pupil or a boarder.

Full details on all scholarships, examinations and entrance procedures are available from the Registrar, Tel: 0115 849 4950.

Trinity School (see p 410)
Up to thirty Entrance Scholarships are awarded annually to boys applying at 10+, 11+ or 13+. Boys must be of the relevant age on 1 September of year of entry. Awards are based on the results of an entrance examination and interview. Scholarships are also available for entry to the Sixth Form, based on GCSE results. The value of the Scholarship is up to half of the school fee and this may be supplemented up to the value of the full fee if there is financial need. Academic, Art, Design & Technology, Music and Sport Scholarships are offered.

University College School (see p 413)
A number of Scholarships will be awarded to boys whose performance in the UCS Senior School Entrance Examination is outstanding. These awards are largely Honorary though they will cover all textbook charges incurred by Scholars throughout their careers at the School. Similar awards will be made to boys in the Sixth Form at the Junior Branch on the basis of their performance in the special end of year examinations. Scholarships are held subject to a boy's satisfactory progress and behaviour.

Uppingham School (see p 415)
Approximately 30–40 scholarships worth between one-tenth and one-half of the fees are awarded annually, if suitable candidates present themselves, including academic, Thring (all-rounder), music and art/design and technology. A number of music exhibitions (granting free tuition on all instruments) are also awarded. Scholarship exams for 13+ entry are held in the February/March prior to the September pupils hope to enter the school. Academic, music and art/design and technology scholarships for Sixth Form entry are awarded in November in the year preceding entry to the school. Means-Tested Bursaries are available up to 95% of the full fee in cases of real financial need, to assist children whose parents might not otherwise be able to afford an Uppingham education to take up such an opportunity.

Details of all scholarships, examinations and procedures may be obtained from the Admissions Office (01572 820611).

Warwick School (see p 419)
Governors Scholarships (11+, 12+, 13+, 16+) are available to reward academic excellence and talent. Scholarships are awarded up to the value of 25% of fees based on the results of the entrance examination and interview. For existing Sixth Formers, the scholarships are awarded based on GCSE results and school reports.

The Warwick Town Foundation Scholarship at 11+ is available to boys from state schools and living within the town of Warwick (CV34 postcode). This is awarded up to the value of 25% of fees based on the results of the entrance examination.

Governors Music Scholarships at 11+ and 13+ are awarded up to the value of 25% of fees based on musical ability and potential with a satisfactory level of achievement in the entrance examination.

Sixth Form Science Scholarship: The Ogden Trust sponsors pupils of outstanding scientific ability to attend Warwick School in the Sixth Form. Awarded up to 100% fees, funded jointly by Ogden Trust and Warwick School. For pupils educated entirely in state sector achieving a minimum of 5 GCSEs at Grade A, including Mathematics. The successful candidate must study Mathematics and Physics at A Level and intend to read a science-related degree at university. Joint parental income should be less than £40K.

Further details from the Admissions Registrar, Warwick School, Warwick, CV34 6PP. Tel: 01926 776400; e-mail: enquiries@warwickschool.org.

Wellingborough School (see p 421)
Scholarships and Exhibitions are offered annually. Awards are based on the Common Entrance Examination held in June for candidates under 14 on 1 September following. Candidates who have not been prepared for the Common Entrance examination may be allowed to sit a restricted range of papers. Entries are required by the end of April. Foundation Scholarships are offered annually. The examination is held in January for candidates over 10 on 1 March. Entries are required by the end of December.

Music, Drama, Art and Sports Scholarships are also available at 13+ and 16+.

Further details and application forms may be obtained from the Headmaster, Wellingborough School, Wellingborough, Northants NN8 2BX.

Wellington College (see p 423)
There are thirty-six 13+ Scholarships and Exhibitions offered. In the academic field, the top four Scholarships are for 30% of the fees; there are up to seven of 20% of the fees, and ten Exhibitions of 10% of the fees. Two academic awards are reserved for boys entering Eagle House Preparatory School from the

maintained sector and remain tenable at Wellington. There are two Music Scholarships of 30% of the fees, one of 20% and two Exhibitions of 10%. There are also four Scholarships available for Art, Drama, Design & Technology and Sport worth 20% of the fees and six Exhibitions worth 10% of the fees. Candidates for non-academic awards must satisfy our general entry requirements. Scholarships of all values may be augmented by a bursary where the financial situation of the parents makes this necessary. Candidates must be under 14 on 1st September in the calendar year in which they sit the examination.

For pupils entering at 16+ there are four academic awards (two of 30% and two of 20% fees), four music awards (two of 30% and two of 20% fees) and seven awards in Art, Drama, Dance, Design & Technology and Sport (one of 30% and six of 20% fees).

For further information apply to The Director of Admissions, Wellington College, Crowthorne, Berkshire RG45 7PU.

Wells Cathedral School (see p 427)
Scholarships and Exhibitions are offered to those who show outstanding ability on the Entrance Scholarship Tests held in late January/early February at the School. At least three full Scholarships are offered annually between the ages of 11 and 13. The value of the awards will depend on individual financial circumstances. Auditions are held over the same weekend for those seeking places as specialist musicians.

Further details may be obtained from The Registrar, Wells Cathedral School, Wells, Somerset BA5 2ST. Tel: 01749 834200, Fax: 01749 834201, e-mail: admissions@wells-cathedral-school.com.

West Buckland School (see p 429)
A number of scholarships are awarded for entry at 11, 13 or 16 (value at the discretion of the Headmaster). Candidates must be under 12, under 14, or under 17 years of age on 1st September following the examination, which will take place in late January or early February.

Westminster School (see p 430)
An examination (The Challenge) will be held in May to elect The Queen's Scholars. There are 40 Queen's Scholars in College and the average number of Scholarships awarded annually is 8. The value of a Scholarship is 50% of the current boarding fee. All Queen's Scholars board in College. Boys who do not wish to board may be candidates for an Honorary Scholarship which carries a small award (worth £1,050 for 2008). Up to 5 exhibitions (valued at £510 a year) may be awarded each year to those who narrowly miss being offered a scholarship. The Challenge consists of papers in Mathematics, English, French, Science, Latin, History, Geography and an optional Greek paper.

The value of a scholarship may be supplemented by a bursary (remission of the fees) up to a maximum of 100% if there is proven financial need. Parents who wish to apply for financial assistance should request a Bursary Application Form from the Registrar (tel: 020 7963 1003; email: registrar@westminster.org.uk).

Whitgift School (see p 432)
Up to 25 Whitgift Foundation scholarships are awarded at age 10 with up to 41 being available at age 11. Further scholarships are also available at age 13 and at Lower Sixth level. Awards for sport, music, drama, art and design, design technology and all-round ability are also available.

Winchester College (see p 434)
The Scholarship examination (Election) is held in May each year, and an average of 14 scholarships are awarded. For 2008/09 Scholars are entitled to 25% remission of fees. Bursaries are available. Scholars live together in College and must board.

As a result of the Scholarship Examination about six Exhibitions will also be awarded which ensure a place in a Commoner House, but with no remission of fees. Applications for bursaries are welcome. There are also Music Scholarships, which for 2008/09 offer up to 25% remission of fees, and Music Exhibitions, which have no remission of fees but offer free tuition in one or more specified instruments. Enquiries about these awards should be directed to the Master of Music. Candidates for these who are not taking the Scholarship Examination will be required to take the Entrance Examination.

Candidates must be over 12 and under 14 on 1st September following the examination.

Further particulars and copies of specimen papers can be obtained from *The Master in College, Winchester College, College Street, Winchester, Hampshire SO23 9NA*.

Up to four Sixth Form Scholarships may be awarded each year to external candidates. Further particulars from the Registrar (address as above).

Wolverhampton Grammar School (see p 438)
Up to six Governors' Academic Scholarships (two 50% fees, four 25% fees) will be awarded to the highest placed candidates in the January 11+ entrance examination and subsequent interview. One scholarship will be offered at 13+ (33% fees), also awarded on the basis of the January examination and interview. Two Music Scholarships (25% of fees) will be offered to outstanding performers, one at 11+ or 13+ and another at 16+.

Sixth Form Scholarships: Two Governors' Academic Scholarships will be offered to candidates transferring to the Sixth Form from other schools.

For further particulars apply to the Head.

Woodbridge School (see p 439)
Academic Scholarships are available for entry at 11, 13 and 16. Art, Music, Chess, Sports and All-Rounder awards are also available.

Woodhouse Grove School (see p 440)
Academic scholarships are available at 11 and 13 on the basis of examination performance, interview and school report. In addition, parents may apply for financial assistance via our Bursary Scheme for which a means test is applied. Further details can be obtained from the Headmaster.

Worksop College (see p 442)
Scholarships (up to 33% of fees pa) and Exhibitions may be awarded annually by Examination in February.

Bursaries may be given in addition to Awards if the financial circumstances of the parents make this necessary. Application for such an increase in the event of an award being made should be sent to the Headmaster at the time of entry.

Sixth Form Scholarships: Several Sixth Form Scholarships are available each year, for which there is an examination for external candidates in February.

For further information, please contact the Assistant Registrar.

Worth School (see p 444)
At 11+: Awards of up to 40% of annual fees, based on tests in English, Maths and Non-Verbal Reasoning, held at Worth in the Lent Term.

At 13+: Awards of up to 40% of annual fees. Worth is part of the Common Scholarship Scheme and exams take place at Worth in May.

At 16+: Sixth Form scholarships of a value up to 40% of annual fees. These awards are based on examinations in the Autumn Term, a good school report, good GCSE grades and an interview.

Wrekin College (see p 446)
Examinations for Entrance Scholarships are held annually in March. All candidates must be under 12 or under 14 on 1st September in the year in which the examinations are held. There are a minimum of two Music Scholarships a year worth a maximum of half of the school fees. Music scholars and exhibitioners receive free tuition in music.

Art Scholarships worth a maximum of half fees are available, as are bursaries for sons and daughters of serving members of the armed forces. Wrekin Scholarships of up to three quarter fees for children from maintained schools are awarded annually. Bursaries may be given for outstanding ability in games.

Full particulars may be obtained from the Headmaster.

Wycliffe College (see p 447)
At least five Scholarships and Exhibitions being up to a maximum of 50% of school fees. These include a WA Sibly Scholarship (for vegetarians), and an F A Wilson Scholarship for Art or Music (preference being given to vegetarians or pupils with a food reform background). Additionally, a number of Exhibitions are offered for Music. Candidates must be under 14 years of age on 1 September in the year in which they sit the Examination. Pearson Bursaries may be awarded to pupils of all-round merit whose parents cannot afford full fees. They may also be supplemented where there is a clear case of financial need.

The Ward's Leaving Scholarship to a Cambridge college may be awarded twice in every three years.

The income from the Edwards Bequest provides Scholarships for pupils, who would not otherwise be able to do so, to extend their Sixth Form courses.

For particulars apply to the *Head, Wycliffe College, Stonehouse, Glos GL10 2JQ*.

Yarm School (see p 450)
Several (usually six each year) Academic Scholarships, up to the value of one-third of the full fee, are awarded as a result of performance in the 11+ Entrance Examination (held late January).

Academic Scholarships for Sixth Form entrants are available, awarded in open competition in a scholarship examination held in January. Ogden Trust Sixth Form Science Scholarships are available and awarded on academic merit (subject to other criteria being met) based on the January scholarship examination.

The school also offers Music Scholarships which provide for a reduction of up to 33%. Candidates for major awards are normally expected to offer a minimum of two instruments or one instrument plus voice. Music Scholarships can be awarded at any stage in the pupil's school career and modest awards can be upgraded in the light of further outstanding progress.

Music and/or Drama Scholarships

Abingdon School (see p 7)
Music Awards:

Up to two Music Exhibitions at 11+.

A flexible number of Scholarships and exhibitions are available at 13+ and to the Sixth Form.

The Scholarships include free tuition on up to three instruments, and when appropriate the Duxbury Scholarship. Exhibitions are also available which offer free tuition on one or two instruments.

Drama:

A drama award can be given on entry at 13+ or to the Sixth Form.

Ackworth School (see p 8)
Up to four Musical Scholarships are usually awarded at 11, 13 or 16+. The awards are made on the strength of an half-hour audition and recognise achievement and potential, preferably in two instruments. Free tuition in one or two instruments is also offered to promising musicians who do not gain an award.

Aldenham School (see p 10)
Scholarships and Exhibitions are available at 11+, 13+ and 16+ for Music under the same terms as for academic awards. Free Tuition is given to Music Scholars. The Forsyth Grant Organ Scholarship is associated with the fine organ in the School Chapel and is designed to encourage young organists. Any combination of choral and instrumental ability may be offered for the audition.

Alleyn's School (see p 11)
2 Music scholarships worth up to 1/3 fees are available to either 11+ or 13+ candidates. At 16+ a further scholarship is available up to a 1/4 of the current fee value per annum. One W J Smith Memorial Bursary will be awarded to a promising sixth form musician in need of financial aid.

Ampleforth College (see p 13)
Music Scholarships are available for entry to the College at ages 13 and 16 to a maximum of 20% fee remission. All scholarships carry free music tuition.

Further details can be obtained from The Admissions Office, Ampleforth College, York, YO62 4ER. Tel: 01439 766863; e-mail: admissions@ampleforth.org.uk.

Bancroft's School (see p 22)
Two Music Scholarships at 11+ which cover half fees and extra music tuition, plus up to two awards at Sixth Form level.

Bedales School (see p 27)
Music scholarships (usually up to 25% of the fees) are awarded each year to outstanding musicians for entry to Dunhurst (10+ and older; exceptionally, 8+) and to Bedales (13+ and 16+).

Full details from the Registrar.

Berkhamsted Collegiate School (see p 35)
The **Music Scholarship** is assessed by audition, which consists of a performance of two contrasting pieces on two instruments: there are also aural tests, sight-reading (instrumental and singing) and an interview. It is expected that the award holders will study music to at least GCSE and make a full contribution to the musical life of the School.

More information about Scholarships and Bursaries may be obtained on application to *The Deputy Principal's PA*.

Birkdale School (see p 37)
Candidates must satisfy the school's general admission standards. One award is available at 11+ and one at 16+ of up to 25% of tuition fees plus free tuition by Birkdale staff on one instrument. Candidates should be of good Grade 3 (11+) or Grade 5/6 (16+) standard in their first instrument and show general musicianship commensurate with technical skill. A Music Scholar is expected to enter fully into the school's musical life. Assessments take place during the Easter Term.

Bishop's Stortford College (see p 40)
Music candidates can compete for all major awards at Sixth Form level, under 14 and under 12.

Bloxham School (see p 42)
Up to 50% of fees with free tuition and music. Scholarships, Exhibitions and Chapel Centenary Awards. Musical ability taken into account in Open Scholarship and Common Entrance Examinations.

Further details may be obtained from the Headmaster, Bloxham School, Banbury, Oxon OX15 4PE.

Bootham School (see p 48)
Up to four Music Scholarships of up to half fees are awarded at 11 and 13. The scholarships are given in recognition of achievement and potential in musical ability, and are then confirmed by a competent result in the Bootham Entrance Exam.

Musical ability is also noted in connection with other Entrance Scholarships.

Muscial awards of other value can be made.

All scholarships are means tested beyond the first 5%.

Bradfield College (see p 49)
Up to 4 Music Scholarships of between 10% and 50% of full fees plus free tuition on up to three instruments.

One Drama Award of 10% of full fees is awarded each year.

Brighton College (see p 55)
A number of scholarships and exhibitions will be offered each year to candidates showing outstanding ability in Music. Examinations and interviews will be held at the College in February for candidates intending to enter at 13+ in the following September. The value and number of the awards will depend on the calibre of the candidates.

Bromsgrove School (see p 59)
A number of Music scholarships and exhibitions are awarded each year at ages 11, 13 and 16, offering fee remission of up to 50% and free tuition on up to two instruments. Means-tested bursaries may be used to supplement scholarships. Full details are available from the Admissions Department.

Bryanston School (see p 62)
Junior and Sixth Form Music Scholarships, which carry free music tuition and may be supplemented by means-tested bursaries.

Further details may be obtained from the Admissions Registrar.

Canford School (see p 68)
A number of Music scholarships ranging from 50% to 10% of the fees, with free tuition on two instruments, are awarded at 13+ and 16+. One or two Drama scholarships worth a total of 20% of the fees are offered annually at 13+.

Caterham School (see p 70)
Music scholarships are available to pupils joining the school at 11+, 13+ and 16+ who have exceptional musical promise on at least one instrument. In addition to a music audition, a candidate must have achieved the required standard in the entrance examination.

Charterhouse (see p 72)
At 13+ entry. Up to 5 Major Music Scholarships and 2 Exhibitions are offered. The examinations are held at the school in February.

Sixth Form entry. Three Music Scholarships are offered annually. These are normally awarded in December. In addition, there is the John Pilling Organ Scholarship.

Music tuition on two instruments is free for Music Scholars and Exhibitioners.

All Awards (except Exhibitions) may be increased to the value of the full school fee in cases of proven financial need.

For details write to the Admissions Secretary, Charterhouse, Godalming, Surrey GU7 2DX.

Cheltenham College (see p 76)
Music Scholarships and Exhibitions up to a maximum individual value of 50% of the fees may be awarded annually at 13+ and for entry into the Sixth Form.

Chetham's School of Music (see p 77)
Entry is by audition only; all who are selected (at any age between 8 and 16) qualify for grants from the DCFS under the "Aided Pupil (Music and Dance) Scheme". Parental contributions are calculated according to means, and parents on low incomes qualify automatically for full fee remission. The Bursar will be glad to advise about the scales.

Chigwell School (see p 79)
Generous Music Scholarships are available at all ages.

Christ College, Brecon (see p 80)
Up to 8 Music scholarships in total are available each year, for award at 11+, 13+ or 16+ ranging in value from 10 to 50% of the fees, together with free tuition on one instrument. The value of any award may be augmented in case of need.

City of London Freemen's School (see p 84)
The following music awards may be made for pupils of up to 13+, either from outside or within the existing pupil body:

- One Music Scholarship to the value of half tuition fees with free instrumental tuition.
- One Music Exhibition to the value of one-third fees with free instrumental tuition.

Various minor awards are available covering instrumental tuition at all age groups.

Details may be obtained from the Director of Music, and applications should be made to the School by 1st February.

City of London School (see p 87)
Several Music Scholarships, up to half fees, are available each year to candidates at any of the normal entry points. They are awarded after audition and interview, and candidates must also satisfy the School's academic entrance criteria.

In addition, choristers of the Temple Church and the Chapel Royal are members of the School and receive substantial bursaries from the Choirs while they remain choristers.

Clifton College (see p 90)
Awards for Music of up to 25% of fees, with free tuition in two instruments. Music awards are also available for entry to the Sixth Form.

Dauntsey's School (see p 101)
Musical ability or potential is considered for Awards at all ages. Music and Drama Scholarships are awarded at 13+. Details from the Registrar.

Dean Close School (see p 103)
Major Scholarships in Music (including Choral and Organ). Tenable for whole school career. Music tuition is free to all Music Scholars and Exhibitioners on a number of instruments.

Denstone College (see p 105)
Instrumental and Choral Scholarships of up to not more than 40% of the fees are available. In cases of need these Awards may be supplemented with Bursaries.

Dulwich College (see p 108)
Music Scholarships

Applicants for Music Scholarships are required to meet the academic requirements of the College at all points of entry.

For entry to the Lower School (Year 7) and Middle School (Year 9).

Up to five instrumental music scholarships of up to one-third of the tuition fee may be offered. In addition successful candidates will receive free instrumental tuition on two instruments, one of which must be an orchestral instrument.

Up to four music exhibitions may also be awarded enabling the holders to receive free tuition on two instruments, one of which must be an orchestral instrument.

Choral Scholarships
For candidates of all ages from 8 to 16+.

Vacancies occur annually in the College Chapel Choir which sings fifteen choral services in the chapel of the Foundation, Christ's Chapel of God's Gift in Dulwich Village. Auditions are held in June.

Choral Scholarships, which provide free instrumental and vocal tuition, are awarded on the basis of auditions held annually in June.

Choral Scholarships are available for boys with treble voices at ages 11, 12 or 13 and with alto, tenor or bass voices at age 16+.

Choral Probationerships (providing free vocal tuition only) are available for boys aged 8, 9 or 10.

For further information please contact the Music Department on 020 8299 9258, e-mail: music@dulwich.org.uk.

Durham School (see p 112)
Music Scholarships (worth up to 50% of fees) are available at 11, 13 and 16. At least one scholarship is available at each age group in each of the following categories: strings, brass, woodwind, piano. A Sixth Form organ scholarship is available annually. All holders of Music Awards receive some free music tuition.

Eastbourne College (see p 113)
Instrumental or Choral Scholarships and Drama Scholarships are offered.

The Edinburgh Academy (see p 115)
One or more Music Scholarships annually to the value of 25% (with means-tested Bursary assistance as required). Free tuition in two instruments.

Ellesmere College (see p 120)
Music Scholarships of not more than 50% fees, several choral Exhibitions of up to 25% of fees. In cases of need, all these awards may be supplemented further. Tenable while candidate remains at school, subject to progress.

Eltham College (see p 121)
Music scholarships of not more than 50% of fees at 11+, 13+ and 16+.

Drama scholarships of not more than 50% of fees at 16+.

Candidates are auditioned and also need to sit the entrance papers.

Emanuel School (see p 123)
Music scholarships may be awarded at 11+, 13+ and 16+. Free tuition in two instruments is included as part of a music scholarship, whether a Normal or a Major Scholarship is awarded.

Drama scholarships are also available at 11+, 13+ and 16+.

Full details can be found on the School Website or by contacting the Admissions Secretary.

Epsom College (see p 125)
Music candidates compete for all Open Scholarships. Music can be offered at a lower level as part of a candidature for an All-Rounder Award.

Drama awards are based upon a performance audition, interview and authorised record of achievement.

Candidates must be under 14 on 1st September of the year of entry or entering the Sixth Form.

Eton College (see p 127)
Up to eight Music scholarships may be awarded annually, each to the value of 10% of the full fee, and all of them supplemented up to the value of full fees (subject to means-testing).

In addition there are several Music Exhibitions carrying remission of the fees for instrumental lessons. Last year 17 awards in all were made.

Special consideration will be given to cathedral choristers who would still be able to sing treble in the College Chapel choir.

Further particulars and entry forms from *The Tutor for Admissions, Eton College, Windsor SL4 6DB.*

Exeter School (see p 129)
Music Scholarships are offered annually following auditions early in the spring term and are conditional on applicants achieving the School's academic requirements for entry.

The *Sammy Sargent Music Scholarship*, the top scholarship award made to an outstanding Music scholar, may be awarded at age 11, 12, 13 or 16 and has a value from 25–50% and means-tested off tuition fees, according to ability.

At ages 11, 12, 13 and 16 – One Music Scholarship offering a discount of £720 per annum off tuition fees. At 16, there are two additional music scholarships each offering a discount of £720 per annum off tuition fees. Music Exhibitions offering smaller discounts and/or a contribution to music lessons may also be awarded. Contributions to music lessons may be offered in addition to a Music Scholarship, Music Exhibition or other award.

Felsted School (see p 132)
Music and Drama Scholarships of up to 20% of fees are available at 13+ and for entry into the Sixth Form.

Fettes College (see p 133)
Music Scholarships of up to the value of 33% of the fees are available to instrumentalists at any age between 10 and 16; high musical potential is sought. The standard required at age 13 is normally at least Grade 5 in the main instrument. Preference will be given to orchestra players and singers. Ex-choristers and brass players are particularly welcome.

These awards can be supplemented by bursaries in the case of financial need.

Forest School (see p 135)
Up to the equivalent of 4 Music Scholarships to cover half tuition fees may be offered annually to candidates aged 11, 12, 13 or 16 on 1st September of the year concerned.

One Drama Award to cover up to 50% of the fees is offered annually.

Framlingham College (see p 138)
Music and Drama Scholarships are available of value up to 30% and 15% respectively of full fees.

Giggleswick School (see p 144)
A number of Music awards are available at 11+, 13+ and Sixth Form. Award holders receive free musical tuition.

Drama Scholarships are available at Sixth Form level.

Glenalmond College (see p 148)
About five Music scholarships worth up to half fees per annum (which may be increased in the case of need) may be available to boys or girls at 12+, 13+ or Sixth Form. Candidates will usually offer two instruments at least to Grade V. Promising string players and singers will be considered with great interest. Award holders receive free musical tuition.

Guildford High School (see p 154)
Music Scholarships are offered at 11+ and 16+.

Haileybury (see p 159)
Music Scholarships are available on entry at 11, 13 and 16.

Hampton School (see p 161)
Instrumental Scholarships normally remitting 25%. One Choral Scholarship in conjunction with the Chapel Royal, Hampton Court Palace.

Headington School (see p 166)
Awards for girls who demonstrate outstanding ability and further potential in Drama or Music.

Drama awards judged on merit with nominal financial benefit of £300 pa. Music awards cover tuition on up to two musical instruments. All awards may be supported by means-tested bursaries, which may significantly increase the size of the award.

Hereford Cathedral School (see p 170)
Two-thirds reductions in tuition fees are available for Cathedral Choristers (*see Scholarships section in main entry*). Up to four Music Exhibitions are awarded each year as a result of auditions held in the first half of the Spring Term. 11+, 13+ and Sixth Form Music Scholarships are also available. Details are available from the Director of Music.

Highgate School (see p 171)
At least two Music Awards ranging in value up to 50% of fees with free tuition in school on one instrument. Awards are made to candidates of outstanding ability or potential.

Hurstpierpoint College (see p 174)
Awards are offered of value up to one-half of fees with free musical tuition in two instruments. Informal auditions are encouraged and may be held at any time by arrangement with the Director of Music. The Awards are given subject to satisfactory Scholarship or Common Entrance results or the College's own entry tests.

Drama Awards are available at 13+ and 16+.

Ipswich School (see p 178)
Music auditions for promising instrumentalists to Years 7 and 9 are held in January/February. For 11+ entrants these are held the week before the entrance examination. Music awards to those under 14 on the 1st September wishing to enter Year 9 are made conditional on a satisfactory showing in either Common Entrance or the school's Entrance and Scholarship Examination in March. The highest awards carry one-half tuition fees but may be supplemented by bursaries in cases of proven need. Sixth Form Music Scholarships are also available and auditions are held in October.

Kent College (see p 184)
Music scholarships of up to half the tuition fee are offered in conjunction with the Entrance Examination to candidates for entry into Years 7, 9 and 12. Free tuition on two instruments is offered to Music Scholars. Full particulars may be obtained from the Registrar.

King's College School, London (see p 200)
Up to 6 Music Scholarships or Exhibitions, of varying values up to 20% of the full tuition fee, may be awarded to boys of high musical ability. Candidates must be under 14 years of age on 1 September of the year in which they sit the examination.

A Music Scholar/Exhibitioner will be expected to play an active part in the musical life of the School throughout his career at KCS.

One Music Scholarship is available in the Sixth Form, with a preference for Organ.

Further information is available from the Music Secretary or the Registration Secretary.

King's College, Taunton (see p 202)
Auditions for Music and Drama Scholarships and Exhibitions are held in February, and in November for Sixth Form.

King's School, Bruton (see p 204)
All Music Scholarships offer free tuition in two instruments in addition to any other financial benefit.

Candidates should offer two instruments, one at Grade 5 or above (for 13+ entry) or at Grade 6 or above (for Sixth Form entry). They will be tested on both instruments at the assessment which is in February. The closing date is in January.

Fitzjames (Drama) Scholarships are available at Sixth Form entry only. Candidates need to show extraordinary aptitude in either acting or theatre production skills. They will undertake a practical assessment in their field of choice.

The King's School, Canterbury (see p 207)
Up to 12 Music Scholarships are offered annually for competition in January or February to pupils under 14 on 1 September in year of entry. They vary in value, but all carry free tuition in 2 instruments. Further awards are available, sometimes tenable in conjunction with the Regular Music Scholarships: the system is flexible, and enquiries should be addressed to the Director of Music.

Those with exceptional ability in Drama may apply for a special Award two years after entry.

A Scholarship leaflet is issued annually in the Autumn, and may be obtained from the Admissions Secretary.

The King's School, Ely (see p 211)
The boy Choristers of Ely Cathedral are all full boarders in the Junior School. Choristers receive a 50% choristership while they remain in the choir. Bursaries worth 33% of the appropriate fees are available if a boy continues into the Senior School. A bursary of 33% of boarding fees is available to all members of Ely Cathedral Girls' Choir, aged 13–18, who are King's Senior School pupils in Years 9-13. Additional means-tested additional funding may be available. Chorister auditions are held in February for boys who will be aged 8 and for girls who will be 13 by the following September.

In addition, a very limited number of Music Scholarships are available by competitive audition to a maximum value of 25% of the tuition fee.

Music Scholarships and Exhibitions (ie scholarships of lesser value) are awarded during the Lent Term to candidates showing exceptional promise in music. Awards are available for choral and/or instrumental excellence, including organ-playing and may represent up to 25% of fees and may include free weekly tuition on two musical instruments. Candidates for entry into Year 7 and Year 9 are invited to the school for auditions in February and in November for entry the following September into Year 12.

Drama Exhibitions of up to 10% of fees are awarded for entry into Years 7 and 9. Auditions are held in January.

Full details are available from The Admissions Secretary, The King's School, Ely, Cambridgeshire CB7 4DB. Tel: 01353 660702; e-mail: admissions@kings-ely.cambs.sch.uk.

The King's School, Macclesfield (see p 215)
Two Senior School and three Sixth Form Music Scholarships are available for instrument or singing.

King's School, Rochester (see p 216)
Up to five Music Scholarships and an Organ Scholarship may be awarded annually with a value of up to 30% of tuition fees and means-tested up to 75% reduction.

Free tuition on all instruments studied in School is given to holders of major and minor awards.

The Scholarships, available from 11+, will be awarded after an examination, usually in February, consisting of aural, sight reading and practical tests, and a viva voce. In addition, candidates at 13+ will be expected to be of Grade 5–6 standard and capable of passing Common Entrance, or a genuine A Level candidate if 15+. 11+ candidates should be at about Grade 4 level.

The Peter Rogers Scholarship of £3,000 per annum is awarded from time to time to assist an exceptionally talented musician, and a Dame Susan Morden Choral Scholarship of £2,500 is occasionally available to a Cathedral Chorister.

Boy Choristerships to Rochester Cathedral (8+/9+) from Cathedral and School.

Details of Academic Scholarships are given elsewhere. A scholarship brochure, and further information, may be obtained from The Registrar, King's School, Satis House, Boley Hill, Rochester, Kent, ME1 1TE. Tel: 01634 888555. Fax: 01634 888505.

The King's School, Worcester (see p 220)
Music Scholarships and awards are available at 11+, 13+ and 16+.

Kingston Grammar School (see p 222)
Two half fee instrumental Scholarships plus free tuition on one instrument. Auditions are in early February for candidates who are applying for entry at either 11+, 13+, or 16+.

Kingswood School (see p 224)
Music Scholarships (maximum value of 50% off the full fees) are available annually to pupils entering Year 7 and Year 9 (new boarders only) and Sixth Form.

Drama Scholarships are also available for day and boarding pupils at Year 7, new boarding pupils only at Year 9 and both day and boarding pupils at Sixth Form.

Lancing College (see p 227)
Three or four Music Scholarships ranging in value up to half the annual boarding fee. Scholarships may be offered to pupils from schools where the time for Music is less than in some others, and where a candidate may have less musical experience but greater potential.

One Professor W K Stanton Music Scholarship of up to half the boarding fee for a Chorister from Salisbury Cathedral School, or failing that any Cathedral School. A Stanton Exhibition may also be awarded.

Drama Scholarships, ranging in value up to a quarter of the annual boarding fee, are available at 13+ entry.

Leicester Grammar School (see p 233)
Up to four scholarships are offered at any age. The scholarships are given on audition in recognition of achievement and potential in musical ability and are confirmed by a pass in the Entrance Examination. All awards can be supplemented by bursaries when appropriate.

Leighton Park School (see p 235)
Major awards of up to 25% of day fees, and minor awards of 15% or 10% of day fees, are available for Music.

Llandovery College (see p 240)
Music Scholarships are awarded from Year 7 upwards. Candidates must achieve satisfactory academic results. They will be auditioned and interviewed by the Director of Music.

Lord Wandsworth College (see p 244)
Music Awards are made annually at all stages of entry to the College. Further details may be obtained from the Admissions Office.

Malvern College (see p 251)
Music and Choral: Awards are made by audition and interview.

Drama: The award will be decided by an audition and interview.

Marlborough College (see p 254)
Up to six instrumental/choral scholarships/exhibitions are offered for competition each year in February to boys and girls at 13+. Up to four instrumental/choral equivalent awards are available for pupils entering the Sixth Form each September. The awards will be worth up to 25% of full fees depending on merit, augmented by bursarial assistance in cases of need. Scholars will receive free tuition on up to three instruments. At least grade 5 Merit or Distinction will be expected on the principal instrument of 13+ candidates: grade 7 to 8 Merit or Distinction for Sixth Form candidates; ability on a second instrument will be helpful but not essential. The examination will include two contrasting pieces on the main instrument and supporting skills will be tested. There will be a viva voce but no written test. Special consideration is always given to cathedral choristers and their potential for the Chapel Choir, even if their instrumental attainment has not reached the appropriate grade level.

Award winners must pass Common Entrance in June, unless they qualify for entry in the academic scholarship examination. They must be under 14 on 1st September.

Boys and girls should apply direct to the Director of Music for a preliminary audition (01672 892481). General information and registration forms are obtainable from the Senior Admissions Tutor, Marlborough College, Marlborough, Wiltshire SN8 1PA (01672 892300).

Merchant Taylors' School, Northwood (see p 257)
The awards in Music offered annually to boys at 11, 13 and 16 include one Scholarship of up to 25% of the fees, one Scholarship of up to 15%, and two exhibitions of up to 10% of the fees. All award holders receive free instrumental and/or singing tuition. Additional awards of free tuition may be made if there are more candidates of sufficient merit. Details from

the Admissions Secretary, Merchant Taylors' School, Sandy Lodge, Northwood, Middlesex HA6 2HT. Tel: 01923 845514.

Merchiston Castle School (see p 260)
Music scholarships, including free tuition on up to two instruments, may be awarded to suitably qualified candidates. Music Bursaries are available covering free tuition on up to two instruments. A Pipe Band Exhibition is also available to a suitably qualified candidate. (Applications by mid-January.)

Mill Hill School (see p 263)
Music Scholarships and Exhibitions are available at 13+.

For further information please visit the school's website www.millhill.org.uk.

Monkton Senior (see p 269)
Of the ten Open Scholarships offered at age 13 at least one may be for Drama and at least two may be instrumental Scholarships (see details under Entrance Scholarships). Free tuition in one or two instruments.

Monmouth School (see p 272)
Music Scholarships and Exhibitions may be awarded at 11, 13 and 16 up to the value of half of the fees and carrying free instrumental tuition. Sixth Form organ or instrumental scholarships also available.

Norwich School (see p 279)
Music Scholarships are awarded at 11+, 13+ and Sixth Form entry to pupils with outstanding ability and flair, which the school assesses by examination, interview or audition. The financial value of a scholarship will be typically 20% of the annual tuition fee – irrespective of parental means. Assistance is also given for instrumental tuition.

Drama Scholarships are awarded at Sixth Form entry only.

Cathedral Choristers hold Chorister Bursaries to the value of 50% of fees. Further assistance in cases of need is possible.

Oakham School (see p 282)
Music Scholarships may be awarded to candidates for 11+, 13+ or Sixth Form entry. Music Scholars also receive free music tuition.

A number of Drama Scholarships are available to Sixth Form entrants wishing to follow either an AS/A2 level or IB course in Theatre Studies.

The normal academic entry requirements must be satisfied. A scholarships and bursaries information booklet is available from the Registrar, Tel: 01572 758758.

The Oratory School (see p 286)
All annual scholarships are open to music candidates. Awards include free music tuition in two disciplines.

Oundle School (see p 288)
Music.

11+: Two Junior Music Scholarships to the value of up to 25% of the fees (Saturday 10 January; closing date 1 December).

13+: Ten Music Scholarships to the value of up to 50% of the fees, including One Junior Organ Scholarship (w/c Monday 2 February; closing date 5 January).

16+: One Sixth Form Music Scholarship and One Sixth Form Organ Scholarship, each to the value of up to 33% of the fees (7 November; closing date 25 October).

Drama.

13+: The Donaldson Drama Scholarship to the value of up to 20% of the fees (1 March).

Further details may be obtained from Rachael Wood, The Undermaster's Assistant, Oundle School, Oundle, Peterborough, PE8 4GH. Tel: 01832 277116. Fax 01832 277119. E-mail: rcwood@oundleschool.org.uk.

Pangbourne College (see p 291)
Several Music Scholarships of up to the value of 50% of College fees are offered annually. All awards carry free tuition on two instruments.

Candidates should be approximately Grade V standard or above on their main instrument. A second instrument, or experience as a chorister is an advantage. String players will be given special consideration for an award even if the standard is below Grade V provided that sufficient potential is shown.

Candidates should be under fourteen on September 1 in the year of entry. The exact date of the Scholarship Examination, which is in early March, may be obtained on application. Music Scholarships are also available for entrance to the Junior School at the age of eleven.

Drama awards are available at 11+, 13+ and 16+. Candidates are invited to attend an audition in the Lent term with the Director of Drama.

Plymouth College (see p 293)
One Open Music Scholarship (age 13+) of up to one-third of the fees.

One Open Music Scholarship (age 16+) of up to one-third of the fees.

Pocklington School (see p 294)
Four music scholarships up to the value of £2,000 and four exhibitions up to the value of £1,000 are offered to internal and external candidates at any level of entrance. Awards are subject to audition, school report and interview, under arrangements made by the Director of Music.

Portsmouth Grammar School (see p 297)
A variable number of Music Scholarships are available up to 10% of fees at 13+ and 16+, depending upon the quality of applicants. A Sixth Form Choral Scholarship is available up to 50% of fees. Candidates are obliged to attend for tests, interview and audition on two musical instruments.

Prior Park College (see p 300)
Music awards are available at three levels of entry: a Junior Scholarship (for entry at age 11), a Scholarship (for entry at age of 13), and Sixth Form Scholarships. Drama scholarships are available at 13+ and 16+. All awards are worth up to 50% of fees.

Queen's College, Taunton (see p 307)
Music Scholarships: up to 50% of fees for the most gifted scholars including free tuition in one or two instruments. Up to 8 scholarships for talented musicians aged 10+, 11+, 12+ and 13+ at the projected time of entry to the college. Three Sixth Form entry scholarships are also available plus an Organ award.

Drama Scholarships: Worth up to 50% of fees for the students of best ability. Queen's College offers up to 6 scholarships for talented students with proven drama ability aged 11+ and 13+ at the projected time of entry to the college. Sixth Form scholarships included.

Radley College (see p 309)
Music: On average five Instrumental Scholarships and several Exhibitions are offered annually. Free tuition.

Drama: A maximum of two Awards will be offered annually.

Awards may be supplemented by a means-tested bursary. Further details from our website or the Registrar.

Reed's School (see p 314)
Scholarships may be awarded for Music or Drama at age 11, 13 or 16.

Rendcomb College (see p 317)
Scholarships are available at 11, 13 and 16 for outstanding musicians or gifted singers. Applicants audition and are interviewed in January (at 11 and 16 years) and February (at 13 years). Further details from the Admissions Registrar on 01285 831213.

Repton School (see p 319)
A number of Music awards are made, usually at 13+ and 16+. Examinations take place in November (16+) and January

(13+). A Music Open Day for potential scholars is held in October.

A number of Drama Scholarships are also offered, usually at 13+ with auditions and interviews taking place in February.

Rossall School (see p 323)
Up to four Instrumental Music Scholarships value of which varies from 50% to 15% of the Basic Fee according to the merits of the candidate. Awards include free tuition in two instruments.

Royal Grammar School, Guildford (see p 327)
Available at 11 and 13. One King's Scholarship for music, and a number of music Scholarships. Values vary from 50% to 10% fee remission. It is hoped that at least one major award can be made each year to a boy of outstanding musical potential entering the First Form at 11.

St Albans School (see p 341)
A variable number of Music awards of not less than 12½% of fees is offered for internal candidates or for pupils entering at 13+.

Internally awarded bursaries of up to a value equivalent to free musical tuition are offered to pupils from each year in the school. These awards are re-assessed at 13+ and 16+.

St Bees School (see p 346)
Music Scholarships up to 40% of the fees are awarded to candidates under 12 or under 14 on 1st September or to candidates for entry into the Sixth Form.

St Edmund's College (see p 355)
Music Scholarships are available at 11+ and 16+ and are decided by audition and include the provision of free tuition in two instruments. Scholars will normally be required to play two instruments with at least one to a high standard (voice can be counted as one instrument). Music Exhibitions may also be awarded which give free tuition in either one or two instruments.

St Edmund's School (see p 357)
Music scholarships and exhibitions of up to one half of the boarding or day fees (which may be supplemented by bursaries at the Headmaster's discretion) are available for applicants aged 11–16. The Scholarship also covers the cost of occasional lessons with London teachers for pupils reaching a sufficiently high standard. Music Scholars are expected to take a full part in the School's instrumental and choral ensembles, and attend concerts specified by the Director of Music, either locally or in London (the cost being covered by the Scholarship).

Examination requirements: Candidates should be at least Grade 5 standard at age 13. Two contrasting pieces on first instrument, one on second. Scales, sight-reading, aural tests. Melody repetition, clapping rhythms, viva voce and musical tests covering basic rudiments and their application.

Drama scholarships and exhibitions of up to one half of the boarding or day fees are available for applicants aged 16+.

St Edward's, Oxford (see p 360)
Music scholarships are available at 13+ and 16+ entry. Normally candidates will be expected to perform on two instruments and all are encouraged to offer singing. Candidates are also encouraged to offer original compositions.

Dance and Drama scholarships are available at 13+ only. Candidates for both these awards will be expected to demonstrate considerable natural ability and also confirm that they have begun to reach high standards on the stage.

13+ scholarships take place in the January/February prior to entry, 16+ in the November prior to entry.

St Paul's School (see p 368)
Several Foundation Scholarships and other scholarships and exhibitions are offered for Music. The value depends on parental circumstances and may, in the case of Foundation awards, amount to full fee remission. One Sharp Scholarship is awarded at 16+. One Dennis Brain Scholarship is available on an irregular basis. Up to three South Square Scholarships may be awarded annually, in conjunction with Colet Court, for boys aged 8, 9 or 10 to sing in the Chapel and elsewhere with St Paul's Chamber Choir. Instrumental awards at Colet Court for boys aged 10 or 11 may be converted to Foundation awards at St Paul's after a further audition. Free tuition for Foundation Scholars in two instruments.

Candidates for Scholarship entry at age 13+ must be aged under 14 on 1st September.

Full particulars available from the Director of Music, St Paul's School, Barnes, London SW13 9JT.

St Peter's School (see p 370)
Various music awards up to half tuition fees are available for entrants at 13+ or Sixth Form. Additionally, up to five pupils in each Senior School year may hold an award which carries with it free tuition in a musical instrument. Interviews and auditions for these awards are held in February or early March.

Full particulars from the Head Master's Secretary, Mrs Jean Green, Tel: 01904 527408.

Sedbergh School (see p 374)
Music and Drama Scholarships are offered for competition. Music Scholars are usually offered free tuition in two instruments, and Scholarships to the value of half fees may be awarded.

The Director of Music will be happy to meet prospective candidates at any time.

Further details may be obtained from The Headmaster.

Sherborne School (see p 377)
A number of Awards are available for entry at 13+. In addition one Marion Packer Scholarship of £600 pa for an outstanding performance on the piano may be offered. Those given Awards receive free instrumental tuition. The examination takes place in February.

Shrewsbury School (see p 381)
Two Music Scholarships up to the value of 50% of fees and two Music Scholarships up to the value of 20% of fees.

Sixth Form Music and Drama Scholarships are available up to the value of 25% of fees.

For details of all Scholarships, please contact The Registrar, Shrewsbury School, Tel: 01743 280550.

Silcoates School (see p 383)
Music Scholarships are offered at 11+ and above. Award holders enjoy free instrument tuition.

Solihull School (see p 384)
There are several Music Scholarships which are awarded at 11+, 12+, 13+ and 16+.

Stonyhurst College (see p 391)
Music Scholarships are offered annually on a generous scale related to parents' income and pupils' talent.

Stowe School (see p 393)
As an approximate guide, in order to win a Major Scholarship of 25% fees remission at age 13, the candidate should be at least Grade Six standard on at least one instrument and preferably be near Grade Seven. A candidate gaining a Minor Scholarship of 10% may be around Grade Five standard. An Exhibitioner may be around Grade Four or Five standard. A good Pass standard for those sitting Common Entrance or Stowe's own Entry Papers will also be expected.

In order to win a Major Scholarship of 25% fees remission at age 16, candidates should be at least approaching Grade Eight Distinction on one instrument and be of an advanced standard on a second or voice. A candidate gaining a Minor Scholarship of up to 10% may be around Grade Seven standard. An Exhibitioner may be around Grade Six or Seven standard but offering only one instrument.

Full details may be obtained from: The Registrar, Stowe School, Buckingham MK18 5EH.

Strathallan School (see p 395)
Music/Choral/Piping/Drumming Awards of between 5% and 50% of fees are available for entry to the Junior School (at age 9, 10, 11 and 12) and to the Senior School at 13+ and 16+.

Sutton Valence School (see p 399)
Awards are available at 11+, 13+ and Sixth Form entry. Free tuition in two instruments given.

Tettenhall College (see p 403)
Two Music Scholarships may be awarded with free tuition.

Tonbridge School (see p 404)
10 or more Music Scholarships (which include free instrumental tuition) are awarded each year. The value of any Scholarship awarded may be increased, by any amount up to the full school fee, if assessment of the parents' means indicates a need.

In addition, a number of Music Exhibitions, giving free instrumental tuition, can be awarded each year.

Choral Boarding Exhibitions, with a value of 10% of the school fee, are offered each year for award to Choristers of Cathedral or other Choir Schools. Candidates for music awards must also satisfy the academic entrance requirements of the School through the Common Entrance Examination or Scholarship Examination.

Up to 3 Drama Scholarships may be awarded annually. Candidates will be asked to perform two contrasting monologues from published plays. There will also be an interview with the Head of Drama, and a written paper.

Full particulars of all Scholarships may be obtained from the Admissions Secretary, Tonbridge School, Tonbridge, Kent TN9 1JP. Tel. 01732 304297; email: admissions@tonbridge-school.org.

Trent College (see p 407)
There are several awards for Music and Drama available at 11+, 13+ and 16+.

The value of an Award depends on the age of the child, their ability and whether they are a day pupil or boarder.

We also offer free tuition to a number of deserving musicians each year.

Full details on all scholarships, examinations and entrance procedures are available from the Registrar, Tel: 0115 849 4950.

Trinity School (see p 410)
Music Scholarships are available of up to 50% of full fee, with free tuition in one or two instruments. Boys are required to play two pieces on principal instrument and show academic potential in the Entrance Examination. Awards are available for all instruments and singing ability can be taken into consideration. Further details from the *Director of Music*.

University College School (see p 413)
One Scholarship or a number of Exhibitions will be awarded for Music after auditions in the Spring Term. Details of these special awards and their values are available from the Director of Music. In cases of need, Music Scholarships may be supplemented from the Bursary Fund.

Requirements: Two contrasting pieces on main instrument and, if possible, a demonstration of some ability on a second. Ear tests, sight-reading and viva. Singing is welcome as an additional accomplishment. Successful candidates will be required to play full part in the musical life of the school. The Director of Music is pleased to answer queries at any time. Candidates must not be over 13 or under 11 on 1st September of the year in which they take the examination. All Music Scholars/Exhibiters will be required to qualify academically for the Senior School.

Uppingham School (see p 415)
A number of Music scholarships worth between one-tenth and one-half of the fees are awarded annually, if suitable candidates present themselves. An indefinite number of music exhibitions may be awarded, granting free tuition on instruments. Music scholarships and exhibitions for 13+ entry are awarded in February/March of the year of entry and for Sixth Form entry in November in the year preceding entry to the School. Means-Tested Bursaries are available up to 95% of the full fee in cases of real financial need, to assist children whose parents might not otherwise be able to afford an Uppingham education to take up such an opportunity.

Details may be obtained from the Admissions Office (01572 820611).

Warwick School (see p 419)
Senior School: Governors Music Scholarships at 11+ and 13+ are awarded up to the value of 25% of fees based on musical ability and potential with a satisfactory level of achievement in the entrance examination.

Junior School: Two J M A Marshall Music Scholarships are available to be awarded to boys entering Year 5 in the Junior School – 50% of the music tuition fees for two years for one instrument.

Two Choral Scholarships, each to the value of £1200 per annum, may be awarded each year to boys aged between 7 and 11 years on 1st September, who are either entering or who are in attendance at Warwick Junior School and the Choir of St Mary's Church, Warwick.

Further details from the Admissions Registrar, Warwick School, Warwick, CV34 6PP. Tel: 01926 776400; e-mail: enquiries@warwickschool.org.

Wellingborough School (see p 421)
Performing Arts (Music and Drama) Scholarships are available at 13+ and Sixth Form.

Wellington College (see p 423)
There are a total of five 13+ Music Scholarships or Exhibitions, two of 30% fees, one of 20% and two of 10% and four 16+ Music Scholarships or Exhibitions, 2 of 30% and 2 of 20% of the fees. Successful candidates are given free music tuition on up to two instruments; in addition Instrumental Awards for free tuition on up to two instruments may be given to candidates who display promise but do not achieve the standard for a Scholarship or Exhibition.

Drama Scholarships or Exhibitions may be awarded at 20% and 10% of the fees at 13+ and at 30%, 20% and 10% of the fees at 16+.

Wells Cathedral School (see p 427)
A number of Music Awards are available depending upon the standard and quality of applicants and individual financial circumstances.

In addition, the School is one of only four in England designated by the DCFS providing specialist musical education. The DCFS therefore provides generous assistance with tuition, boarding and music fees for up to 70 gifted musicians, grants being linked to parental income, under the DCFS Music & Dance Scheme.

Cathedral Choristerships are awarded annually for boys between the ages of 8½ and 10½, which can provide up to 45% of boarding and tuition fees. School bursaries of up to 10% are available for girl choristers.

Ex Chorister Bursaries. On ceasing to be a Chorister, boys and girls are eligible for an ex-Chorister Bursary giving up to 8% of tuition or boarding fees.

Further details may be obtained from The Registrar, Wells Cathedral School, Wells, Somerset BA5 2ST. Tel: 01749 834200, Fax: 01749 834201, e-mail: admissions@wells-cathedral-school.com.

West Buckland School (see p 429)
One Music scholarship for entry at the age of thirteen.

Westminster School (see p 430)
Up to six Music Scholarships up to the value of 25% of the boarding or day fee, including free music tuition for 3 instruments, are offered annually. These may be supplemented by additional means-tested bursaries to a maximum of the full fees. In addition, several Exhibitions may be awarded covering music tuition for two instruments. The closing date for entries

is early January. Candidates, who must be under 14 years of age on the following 1st September, must subsequently take either the Common Entrance or gain admission through the Scholarship Examination, The Challenge.

The Director of Music, Guy Hopkins, is happy to give informal advice to possible applicants (Tel: 020 7963 1017).

For further information on all Scholarships, write to the Registrar, Westminster School, Little Dean's Yard, London SW1P 3PF (tel: 020 7963 1003; email: registrar@westminster.org.uk).

Whitgift School (see p 432)
A number of Music scholarships and awards (for free instrumental tuition) is available up to the value of half the school fees to young musicians with outstanding potential. The closing date is mid-January with auditions shortly after that date. Further details are available from the Music Administrator.

Winchester College (see p 434)
Music scholarships are available annually; for 2008/09 they offer up to 25% remission of fees together with free instrumental tuition on two instruments and singing. In cases of financial need additional bursary grants can be considered. One or more awards may be reserved for Winchester College Quiristers and for Sixth Form entrants. Successful candidates are generally at the level of Grade VI-VIII distinction. Music award tests take place in late January/early February each year. Music can also be offered as an option in the academic scholarship examinations in May.

The award of all music scholarships is conditional upon candidates satisfying the academic requirements for entry into the school. For 13+ entry, candidates must be under 14 on lst September of the year they come into the school.

The Master of Music is pleased to answer queries and to see prospective candidates at any time. Full details available from *The Secretary, Winchester College Music School, Culver Road, Winchester, Hampshire SO23 9JF.*

Wolverhampton Grammar School (see p 438)
Two Music Scholarships (25% of fees) will be offered to outstanding performers, one at 11+ or 13+ and another at 16+. For further particulars apply to the Head.

Woodbridge School (see p 439)
Music Scholarships and Bursaries are available, ranging from 50% of fees plus free music tuition to free music tuition.

Drama Scholarships are available to the value of 25% of fees.

Woodhouse Grove School (see p 440)
Music scholarships are awarded to promising musicians. Awards generally contribute to or cover tuition fees on one or two instruments.

Worksop College (see p 442)
Music Scholarships and Exhibitions up to 25% fees. Entry forms and further details about the Scholarships are available from the Assistant Registrar.

Worth School (see p 444)
At 11+, 13+ and 16+: Awards of up to 40% of annual fees. Exhibitions are also offered giving free instrumental/vocal tuition. Auditions are held in the Lent Term.

Wrekin College (see p 446)
At least two Instrumental or Choral Scholarships worth a half and a third of the school fees. Free tuition in music.

Wycliffe College (see p 447)
Instrumental Scholarships and Exhibitions up to a total value of 50% of fees plus free tuition in music.

Yarm School (see p 450)
Several music scholarships are awarded each year up to a maximum value of a one-third fee reduction. Free instrumental tuition is usually included. Music scholarships can be applied for at any age.

Art and/or Design & Technology Scholarships

Abingdon School (see p 7)
Up to two Art and Design Scholarships at 13+.
Scholarships also available at Sixth Form.

Ackworth School (see p 8)
Up to two Art Scholarships are awarded at 11 or 12. The awards are made on the strength of a 3-hour Art Scholarship examination and the submission and discussion of a portfolio of work, all of which must be supported by competent performance in the Entrance Tests.

Aldenham School (see p 10)
A small number of awards at 11+, 13+ and 16+ is available each year. These are based on the candidate's portfolio and a short exercise at the school on a mutually convenient date.

Alleyn's School (see p 11)
11+ Art scholarship, up to the value of $^1/_3$ of fees.

Bedales School (see p 27)
Art scholarships are awarded for entry at 16+. These scholarships attract an automatic award of £750, which can be increased through means-testing.
Full details from the Registrar.

Berkhamsted Collegiate School (see p 35)
The **Art Scholarship** is determined by merit on the basis of the presentation of a folio of work, a practical test, an interview and an acceptable level at entrance examination. The award is renewable annually dependent on continued commitment to the subject.
More information about Scholarships and Bursaries may be obtained on application to *The Deputy Principal's PA*.

Bishop's Stortford College (see p 40)
Art candidates can compete for all major awards at Sixth Form level, under 14 and under 12.

Bloxham School (see p 42)
Art and Design Scholarships up to 50% of fees. Scholarships, Exhibitions, Chapel Centenary Awards. Artistic ability taken into account in Open Scholarship and Common Entrance Examinations.
Further details may be obtained from the Headmaster, Bloxham School, Banbury, Oxon OX15 4PE.

Bradfield College (see p 49)
Up to 5 Art and 2 Design Awards of up to 20% of full fees.

Brighton College (see p 55)
A number of scholarships and exhibitions will be offered each year to candidates showing outstanding ability in either Art or Design & Technology. Examinations and interviews will be held at the College in January (Art), May (DT) for candidates intending to enter at 13+ in the following September. The value and number of the awards will depend on the calibre of the candidates.

Bryanston School (see p 62)
Art, ICT and DT Scholarships, for 13+ entry, which may be supplemented by means-tested bursaries.
Further details may be obtained from the Admissions Registrar.

Canford School (see p 68)
One Art scholarship worth 20%, or two of 10%, of the fees is offered annually and one Design Technology scholarship worth 20%, or two of 10%, of the fees is offered annually at 13+.

Caterham School (see p 70)
Art scholarships are available at 11+, 13+ and 16+.

Charterhouse (see p 72)
Two Art Scholarships are offered for entry at 13+ as a result of an examination held at the school in February. In addition two Art Scholarships are offered for Sixth Form entry; the examinations for these awards will normally be held in November. All Awards (except Exhibitions) may be increased to the value of the full school fee in cases of financial need. For details write to the Admissions Secretary, Charterhouse, Godalming, Surrey GU7 2DX.

Cheltenham College (see p 76)
Art Scholarships may be awarded annually. Candidates should demonstrate ability in as many fields as possible, but particularly in drawing. Scholarships are also available in Design Technology. Awards may reach 50% of the current fees and are available at 13+ and for entry to the Sixth Form.

Christ College (see p 80)
One Art scholarship may be awarded each year at 13+, up to the value of 20% of the fees.

Clifton College (see p 90)
A number of Art awards are made annually, including the Roger Fry Scholarship. Candidates must by under 14 on 1st September.

Dean Close School (see p 103)
An Art Exhibition or Bursary may be awarded. This is based on the candidate's portfolio, an interview with the Director of Art and a drawing test at the School.
A Design Technology award is also available.

Dulwich College (see p 108)
Art Scholarships
Applicants for Art Scholarships are required to meet the academic requirements of the College at all points of entry.
For entry to the Lower School (Year 7) and Middle School (Year 9).
At least one scholarship of up to 10% of the tuition fee for excellence in art will be offered. All external candidates are required to sit the College Entrance and Scholarship Examination.
The Head of Art, Mrs Maria Jenkins (020 8299 9206), email: jenkinsgm@dulwich.org.uk is pleased to make an appointment to see the parents of prospective scholars and to give advice on the presentation of portfolios.

Durham School (see p 112)
Art Scholarships are available at 13 and 16; DT scholarships are available at 13.

Eastbourne College (see p 113)
Art and Design & Technology Scholarships are offered.

Ellesmere College (see p 120)
One or two Art Exhibitions awarded each year in May on the basis of an exam and a portfolio of pupil's work.

Eltham College (see p 121)
Art scholarships of not more than 50% of fees at 16+.

Emanuel School (see p 123)
Art scholarships may be awarded at 11+, 13+ and 16+.
Full details can be found on the School Website or by contacting the Admissions Secretary.

Epsom College (see p 125)
Art candidates compete for all Open Scholarships. They should submit a varied portfolio of about 15 pieces of work and they will then be invited to Epsom to discuss their work at interview and, at 13+, to do a timed drawing test.
Design Technology awards are based upon a portfolio presentation composing several contrasting items and, at 13+, a timed design test.
Candidates must be under 14 on 1st September of the year of entry or entering the Sixth Form.

Exeter School (see p 129)
One Art Scholarship is offered annually to a sixth form pupil following an assessment and interview. This scholarship offers a discount of £720 per annum off tuition fees. Art Exhibitions offering up to £600 per annum discount may also be awarded.

Felsted School (see p 132)
Art and Design & Technology Scholarships of up to 20% of the fees are available at 13+ and for entry into the Sixth Form. The School is a participant in the Arkwright Foundation Scholarship Scheme for Talented Students in Design at 16+.

Forest School (see p 135)
One Art Award to cover up to 50% of the fees is offered annually.

Framlingham College (see p 138)
Art and Design & Technology Scholarships of value up to 15% of full fees are offered at 13+ and 16+.

Giggleswick School (see p 144)
Art Scholarships and Exhibitions are available at either 13+ or Sixth Form level. Design Scholarships are available at Sixth Form level.

Glenalmond College (see p 148)
Candidates are invited to apply at 12+, 13+ or Sixth Form for Art Awards of up to 50% of fees.

Haileybury (see p 159)
Art Scholarships are available at entry to those joining at 13 and 16.

Technology Scholarships are available on entry at 13.

No fee remission is awarded for Art or Technology scholarships. Successful candidates will be awarded a book token to the value of £100.

Hampton School (see p 161)
Art Scholarships normally remitting 25% and Exhibitions remitting 15% to 10% may be awarded on entry at 11+ and 13+.

Headington School (see p 166)
Awards for girls who demonstrate outstanding ability and further potential in Art.

All awards judged on merit with nominal financial benefit of £300 pa. Scholarships may be supported by means-tested bursaries, which may significantly increase the size of the award.

Hurstpierpoint College (see p 174)
Awards are available for Art and Design & Technology Scholarships at 13+ and 16+ for external candidates. A folio of work is presented and there is an objective test as well as an interview. Academic assessment will be on the basis of a sound pass at Common Entrance or by the College's own entry tests.

Ipswich School (see p 178)
Art: Pupils submit a portfolio of their work prior to their entrance examination. The highest awards carry one-half tuition fees and may be supplemented by bursaries in case of proven need.

King's College School, London (see p 200)
One or two Art and Design Scholarships or Exhibitions, worth up to 20% of the full tuition fee, may be awarded annually to boys of high artistic ability and potential. Candidates must be under 14 years of age on 1 September of the year in which they sit the examination.

Selection will be by folio inspection, and by invitation to a half-day of practical work in an informal and friendly atmosphere in the KCS studios. Candidates will be offered a number of objects or groups of objects from which to work in their chosen medium.

An Art Scholar will be expected to take Art as an examined subject throughout his career in the School.

Further information is available from the Director of Art or the Registration Secretary.

King's College, Taunton (see p 202)
Applicants for Art and Design & Technology Scholarships are invited to visit the school during the Lent term with a portfolio of work.

King's School, Bruton (see p 204)
Art and/or Technology Scholarships are available at 13+ entry.

Art Scholarships are available at Sixth Form entry.

The King's School, Canterbury (see p 207)
Art Scholarships are available to candidates of outstanding ability. Candidates must be under 14 on 1 September in year of entry. Further details from the Admissions Secretary.

The King's School, Ely (see p 211)
Art Exhibitions of up to 10% of tuition fees are awarded during the Lent term to candidates showing exceptional promise for entry into Years 7 and 9.

A Design and Technology Exhibition of up to 10% of tuition fees is available for entry into Year 9.

Candidates will be invited to the school in February for interview with the appropriate Head of Department.

Full details are available from The Admissions Secretary, The King's School, Ely, Cambridgeshire CB7 4DB. Tel: 01353 660702; e-mail: admissions@kings-ely.cambs.sch.uk.

Kingston Grammar School (see p 222)
Two Art Scholarships of half fees may be awarded at 11+, 13+, or 16+ following interview and submission of portfolio.

Kingswood School (see p 224)
Art Scholarships (maximum value of 50% off the full fees) are available for day and boarding pupils entering Year 7, boarding at Year 9, and both boarding and day at Sixth Form.

Design Technology Scholarships are available at Sixth Form only.

Lancing College (see p 227)
Art Scholarships, ranging in value up to a quarter of the annual boarding fee, are available.

Leighton Park School (see p 235)
Major awards of up to 25% of day fees, and minor awards of 15% or 10% of day fees, are available for Art.

Additional awards may be made by the David Lean Foundation.

Llandovery College (see p 240)
Art Scholarships are awarded from Year 7 upwards. Candidates must achieve satisfactory academic results. They will be interviewed and references requested.

Lord Wandsworth College (see p 244)
Art Scholarships are offered to entrants to the Third Form and Sixth Form. Further details may be obtained from the Admissions Office.

Malvern College (see p 251)
Art: A special examination is set and candidates will be required to bring a portfolio of their work.

Technology: The award will be decided by work carried out prior to the examination, a practical examination and an interview.

Marlborough College (see p 254)
One Art Scholarship is offered annually at 13+. The merit component will range up to 25% of the fees. An Award will be eligible for augmentation above 25%, dependent on family financial circumstances, by means of bursaries.

Candidates will be required to submit their portfolio for short listing. It should contain a range of studies, colour work, objective drawing, imaginative work and indeed anything found to be visually interesting. Promise as well as achievement will be taken into account.

Award winners must pass Common Entrance in June, unless they qualify for entry in the Academic Scholarship Examination. However, they will be judged for the art scholarship entirely on the strength of their promise as artists. They must be under 14 on 1st September.

Details of the Art Scholarships can be obtained from The Senior Admissions Tutor, Marlborough College, Marlborough, Wiltshire SN8 1PA (01672 892300).

Merchiston Castle School (see p 260)
One Art and Design scholarship may be awarded. (Applications by mid January.) Candidates are required to submit a portfolio of work though promise, as well as achievement, is taken into account. Candidates will also be expected to achieve a sound academic standard. The Colin Paton Technology Award is open to boys aged 13+, 14+, and 16+ who can demonstrate a technological aptitude, particularly in Electronics. (Interview flexible.) The Arkwright Scholarship for Sixth Formers is awarded for Engineering, Design and Technology.

Mill Hill School (see p 263)
Art and Design Awards are available at 13+.

For further information please visit the school's website www.millhill.org.uk.

Monkton Senior (see p 269)
Of the ten Open Scholarships offered at age 13 at least one may be for Art.

Norwich School (see p 279)
Art and Design Scholarships are awarded at Sixth Form entry only.

Oakham School (see p 282)
Art and Design, and Design and Technology Scholarships and Exhibitions may be awarded to candidates for 13+ and Sixth Form entry. The normal academic entry requirements must be satisfied. Awards made to Sixth Form candidates are intended for those who wish to follow an A Level course in Art or Design and Technology, with the aim of taking up a career in these fields.

A scholarships and bursaries information booklet is available from the Registrar, Tel: 01572 758758.

The Oratory School (see p 286)
Any of the existing Scholarships and Exhibitions may be awarded for Art.

Oundle School (see p 288)
13+: Two Art Scholarships to the value of up to 20% of the fees (6 May).

13+: Two Technology Scholarships to the value of up to 20% of the fees (6 May).

16+: One Art Scholarship to the value of up to 33% of the fees (7 November; closing date 25 October).

16+: One DT Scholarship to the value of up to 33% of the fees (7 November; closing date 25 October).

Further details may be obtained from Rachael Wood, The Undermaster's Assistant, Oundle School, Oundle, Peterborough, PE8 4GH. Tel: 01832 277116. Fax: 01832 277119. E-mail: rcwood@oundleschool.org.uk.

Pangbourne College (see p 291)
Art scholarships of up to 50% of fees are available at 13+ and 16+. Candidates must present a folio of work completed over the previous two years and attend an interview in the Lent term. Successful candidates are likely to be those who have worked in a variety of media and can show depth of thought on individual pieces.

One scholarship of up to 50% of fees will be awarded to an applicant who shows particular strength in Design Technology. Candidates must present a folio of work, discuss design-related ideas at an interview and sit a short exam paper.

As an Arkwright Technology Scholarship centre, Pangbourne may nominate outstanding students at 16+ for this prestigious award. Further details of the application procedure are available from the College Registrar.

Plymouth College (see p 293)
One Open Art Scholarship (age 13+) of up to one-third of the fees.

One Open Art Scholarship (age 16+) of up to one-third of the fees.

Portsmouth Grammar School (see p 297)
Art Scholarships are available at Sixth Form level.

Prior Park College (see p 300)
Art Scholarships are available to exceptionally able applicants at ages 13+ and 16+. An Art Exhibition (minor Scholarship) is available to exceptionally able applicants at age 11+, who may then become eligible for the 13+ Scholarship when they reach the appropriate age.

Queen's College, Taunton (see p 307)
Art Scholarships: Worth up to 50% of fees for the most talented scholars. Scholarships are for talented students with an existing standard and potential for considerable development. Candidates to be aged 11+ or 13+ at projected time of entry to the college. Sixth Form scholarships included. Art scholarships are awarded as part of the Academic scholarship and are based on portfolio and interview.

Radley College (see p 309)
Up to two Art Scholarships and an Exhibition will be offered annually. Awards may be supplemented by a means-tested bursary. Further details from our website or the Registrar.

Reed's School (see p 314)
Scholarships may be awarded for Art at age 11, 13 or 16. Design & Technology scholarships are available at age 13 or 16.

Rendcomb College (see p 317)
Scholarships are available at 11, 13 and 16 for outstanding artists. Applicants audition and/or bring their portfolio and are interviewed in January (at 11 and 16 years) and February (at 13 years). Further details from the Admissions Registrar on 01285 831213.

Repton School (see p 319)
A number of Art Scholarships and Exhibitions are offered, usually at 13+ and 16+. Examinations take place in November (16+) and January (13+). Candidates will be invited for examination, interview and an assessment of their portfolio.

A number of Design and Technology Scholarships and Exhibitions are offered, usually at 13+. Examinations take place in January. Candidates will be asked to complete a practical session and interview and to provide a folder of work for assessment.

A number of Information and Communication Technology (ICT) Scholarships and Exhibitions are offered, usually at 13+. Examinations take place in January. Candidates will be asked to complete a practical session and interview and to provide a folder of work for assessment.

Royal Grammar School, Guildford (see p 327)
One Art Scholarship is available annually.

St Albans School (see p 341)
At least one Art Scholarship worth not less than 12½% of fees is offered for internal candidates or for pupils entering at 13+.

St Edmund's College (see p 355)
Art Scholarships are available at 11+ and 16+ and are decided by examination of a portfolio and a test. Scholars are required to make a significant contribution to the artistic life of the College and to contribute work to an annual Art Scholars' Exhibition.

St Edmund's School (see p 357)
Art Awards of up to one half of the boarding or day fees (which may be supplemented by bursaries at the Headmaster's discretion) are available for pupils entering at 13 or into the Sixth Form. The departments teach drawing, painting, sculpture, ceramics, photography, printmaking, textiles, and design and technology. Art may also be taken as part of the academic scholarship examination. A candidate offering Art will be expected to produce a folio of recent work.

St Edward's, Oxford (see p 360)
Art scholarships are available at 13+ and 16+ entry. Candidates must submit a portfolio of work prior to the assessment. On the

day of the award they will be asked to draw from observation and take a simple test to assess colour sense. 13+ scholarships take place in the January/February prior to entry, 16+ in the November prior to entry.

Sedbergh School (see p 374)
Art and Design Technology Scholarships are offered for competition.

Sherborne School (see p 377)
Art and Design & Technology Awards are available.

Shrewsbury School (see p 381)
Two Art Scholarships up to the value of 20% of fees.

Sixth Form Art Scholarships are available up to the value of 25% of fees.

For details of all Scholarships, please contact The Registrar, Shrewsbury School, Tel: 01743 280550.

Stonyhurst College (see p 391)
Stonyhurst offers Scholarships in Art. Applicants are invited to submit portfolios of their work, personal as well as set pieces, which demonstrate a lively interest in and enthusiasm for the subject(s). There should also be evidence of proven ability through a variety of media and approaches. Portfolios should be sent or brought by the applicant early in May.

Stowe School (see p 393)
Art Scholarships are available for pupils entering Stowe at age 13 or 16, and are offered to candidates who submit evidence of outstanding ability and a strong interest in Art.

Candidates at 13+ will be required to sit an examination in Art in the course of one day. They should bring a portfolio of recent work. This portfolio should contain a broad selection of work in whichever field of Art the candidate has studied. Two-dimensional work need not be mounted. Photographs or slides of three-dimensional work are acceptable. In general, particular attention will be paid to good objective drawing. A good Pass standard for those sitting Common Entrance or taking Stowe's own Entry Papers will also be expected.

Candidates at 16+ will be required to provide a portfolio of recent work for assessment. This should contain a broad selection of work in whichever field of Art has been studied. Two-dimensional work need not be mounted. Photographs or slides of three-dimensional work are acceptable. Particular attention will be paid to good objective drawing. Candidates are also required to pass Stowe's Entry Examinations, held in the November of their GCSE year, in two subject papers (related to their AS Level choices), a Verbal Reasoning paper and an interview.

Full details may be obtained from: The Registrar, Stowe School, Buckingham MK18 5EH.

Strathallan School (see p 395)
Art and Design Technology scholarships of between 5% and 50% of fees are available for entry to the Senior School at 13+ and 16+.

Arkwright Design Technology scholarships are also available for entry to the Sixth Form.

Sutton Valence School (see p 399)
Available at 11+, 13+ and 16+ entry.

Tonbridge School (see p 404)
Up to 8 Art or Technology Scholarships may be awarded annually. The value of any award may be increased by any amount up to the full school fee if assessment of the parents' means indicates a need.

Candidates for Art Scholarships will be assessed by interview and practical assessment in early February. A representative portfolio of previous work will be requested together with two pieces of work done in advance of the examination.

Candidates for Technology Scholarships will be assessed by interview and written examination in early February. A portfolio may be requested as evidence of design and/or manufacturing skills.

Candidates for these awards must also satisfy the academic entrance requirements of the school through Common Entrance or the academic Scholarship examinations.

Full particulars of all Scholarships may be obtained from the Admissions Secretary, Tonbridge School, Tonbridge, Kent TN9 1JP. Tel: 01732 304297; email: admissions@tonbridge-school.org.

Trent College (see p 407)
Awards are available in Art at 11+, 13+ and 16+. The value of an Award depends on the age of the child, their ability and whether they are a day pupil or a boarder. The school is also a member of the National Arkwright Scholarship Scheme.

Full details on all scholarships, examinations and entrance procedures are available from the Registrar, Tel: 0115 849 4950.

Uppingham School (see p 415)
Scholarships between one-tenth and one-half of the fees may be awarded for Art/Design and Technology annually. Means-Tested Bursaries are available up to 95% of the full fee in cases of real financial need, to assist children whose parents might not otherwise be able to afford an Uppingham education to take up such an opportunity.

Details may be obtained from the Admissions Office (01572 820611).

Wellingborough School (see p 421)
Art Scholarships are available at 13+ and 16+.

Wellington College (see p 423)
Scholarships or Exhibitions in Art or Design & Technology may be awarded at 20% and 10% of the fees at 13+ and at 30%, 20% and 10% of the fees at 16+.

Wells Cathedral School (see p 427)
Discretionary Art Scholarships may be awarded. Art candidates compete for all open awards.

Further details may be obtained from The Registrar, Wells Cathedral School, Wells, Somerset BA5 2ST. Tel: 01749 834200, Fax: 01749 834201, e-mail: admissions@wells-cathedral-school.com.

Whitgift School (see p 432)
A small number of Art and Design Technology awards is available to promising pupils. Please apply to the Registrar for further information.

Woodbridge School (see p 439)
An Art Scholarship to the value of 25% fees is available annually.

Woodhouse Grove School (see p 440)
Art scholarships are available each year.

Worksop College (see p 442)
Art Scholarships up to 25% of fees. Folios should be sent to the Director of Art by mid-April. Candidates will be called to the school in May. They will be required to take a practical examination and, in some cases, a written examination in English comprehension and composition.

Entry forms, available from the Assistant Registrar, should reach the school by mid-April.

Wrekin College (see p 446)
Wrekin College Scholarships of a maximum of half of the fees may be awarded annually to pupils entering at any level in the school.

Sports and/or All-Rounder Scholarships

Abingdon School (see p 7)
Up to two sports Awards at 13+.

Sports scholarships also available at Sixth Form.

Alleyn's School (see p 11)
Two 11+ Sports scholarships up to the value of 1/3 fees. At 16+ 2 Sports scholarships, up to the value of 1/6 fees, also available.

Ampleforth College (see p 13)
All-Rounder Scholarships at 13+ – The Basil Hume Scholarships. For candidates who have a strong commitment to extra-curricular activities. The maximum scholarship will be worth 20% of school fees.

Further details can be obtained from The Admissions Office, Ampleforth College, York, YO62 4ER. Tel: 01439 766863; e-mail: admissions@ampleforth.org.uk.

Berkhamsted Collegiate School (see p 35)
The **Sports Scholarship** is awarded on entry to the Sixth Form only. The award is determined by merit on the basis of the presentation of a folio of achievements in any one sporting area. The candidate is expected to have representative experience at county level or above and provide evidence of commitment to sport.

More information about Scholarships and Bursaries may be obtained on application to *The Deputy Principal's PA.*

Bradfield College (see p 49)
Up to 8 Bradfield Exhibitions of between 10% and 30% of fees for boarders or day pupils. The Awards are made for a combination of academic merit and distinction in music, drama or sport (or any combination of these).

Up to 3 Sports Exhibitions of 10% of fees are awarded to pupils who are outstanding in one or more sports and who would make a significant contribution to this area of College life.

Bryanston School (see p 62)
Sport and Richard Hunter All-Rounder scholarships are available annually for 13+ entry and Udall Awards for Sport for entry to the Sixth Form, which may be supplemented by means-tested bursaries.

Further details may be obtained from the Admissions Registrar.

Canford School (see p 68)
A number of Sports scholarships ranging from 50% to 10% of the fees are offered annually at 13+. A number of Assyrian scholarships for excellence in non-academic areas ranging from 40% to 10% of the fees are offered annually at 16+.

Caterham School (see p 70)
Sport scholarships are available at 11+, 13+ and 16+. All-Rounder scholarships are available for pupils entering at age 13.

Christ College (see p 80)
Sports scholarships are available annually at 11+, 13+ and 16+ to candidates showing outstanding talent ranging in value from 10% to 50% of the fees.

One or more All-Rounder awards are available at 13+ and 16+.

Clifton College (see p 90)
Sport scholarships are available at 13+ entry.

Dulwich College (see p 108)
Sports Scholarships

Applicants for Sports Scholarships are required to meet the academic requirements of the College at all points of entry.

For entry to the Middle School (Year 9) and Upper School (Year 12).

At Year 9 successful candidates should be able to perform to a high level in one of the following sports: rugby, cricket, soccer, hockey. Candidates must offer at least two other sports.

At Year 12 successful candidates should be able to perform to Regional or International level in one of the following sports: rugby, cricket, soccer and hockey. Candidates must be able to offer at least one other sport.

Candidates will be expected to attend an interview with the Director of Sport and the Head of Physical Education and provide evidence of the level of their performance.

All recipients of a Sports Scholarship are expected to contribute fully to the sporting life of the College in all three terms of the academic year.

The Director of Sport (020 8299 9266), e-mail: info@dulwich.org.uk, is pleased to make appointments to see prospective sports scholars to offer advice about the requirements for the scholarship and information about the sporting life of the College.

Durham School (see p 112)
Sports Scholarships are available at 13 and 16 for suitably talented pupils.

Eastbourne College (see p 113)
Sports Awards are offered.

Eltham College (see p 121)
Sport scholarships of not more than 50% of fees at 11+ and 16+.

Emanuel School (see p 123)
Sports scholarships may be awarded at 11+, 13+ and 16+.

Full details can be found on the School Website or by contacting the Admissions Secretary.

Epsom College (see p 125)
Sport awards are based upon a combination of skills' tests and authorised records of achievement.

All-Rounder awards require applicants to offer an academic element plus one or more elements to be selected from Art, Design Technology, Drama, Music and Sport. The latter are assessed through tests and interviews.

Candidates must be under 14 on 1st September of the year of entry or entering the Sixth Form.

Felsted School (see p 132)
All-rounder Scholarships and Foundation Awards which recognise all-round ability or specific ability in one area are available on entry at 11, 13 and 16 years old.

Forest School (see p 135)
One Sports Award to cover up to 50% of the fees is offered annually.

Haileybury (see p 159)
All-Rounder Awards, up to the value of 10% of the fees, are available to those entering at 11 and 13.

Hampton School (see p 161)
All-Rounder Scholarships normally remitting 25% and Exhibitions remitting 15% to 10% may be awarded on entry at 11+ and 13+.

Headington School (see p 166)
Awards for girls who demonstrate outstanding ability and further potential in Sport.

All awards judged on merit with nominal financial benefit of £300 pa. Scholarships may be supported by means-tested bursaries, which may significantly increase the size of the award.

Hurstpierpoint College (see p 174)
Sport and All-Rounder Scholarships are available at 13+ and 16+.

Kent College (see p 184)
Kent College awards Sports Scholarships of up to half the tuition fee to pupils for entry into Years 7, 9 and 12. For Years 7 and 9 these will be awarded in the Spring Term in conjunction with the Entrance Test and on the basis of assessment at

Kent College. For Year 12, Sports Scholarships will be based on current performance and other assessment methods during the year. Full particulars may be obtained from the Registrar.

King's College, Taunton (see p 202)
Haywood Scholarships (for Sport) and Barrow Scholarships (for all-round contribution to the life of the school) are available for competition each January. Sports scholarships are also available in November for entry into the Sixth Form. The Somerset Scholarship, for academic achievers from the maintained sector, is a new scholarship available for entry into the Sixth Form.

King's School, Bruton (see p 204)
Sport Scholarships and All-Rounder Awards are available at 13+ entry.

Sports Scholarships are available at Sixth Form entry.

The King's School, Canterbury (see p 207)
Gower Sports Scholarships (up to 20% of fees) and Awards (a set annual financial award) are available for boys and girls of character and integrity who display both excellent sporting ability and sportsmanship in at least one of the main school team games.

The awards will be determined by recommendation and assessment. Candidates must be proposed and recommended by the Head of their current school, though this may be accompanied by references/testimonials from other sources (club/ county/national coaches etc). Selected candidates will then be invited to the school for an Assessment Day, where they will be examined in their chosen sports and in generic sports aptitude and teamwork exercises.

The King's School, Ely (see p 211)
Sports Awards, for entry into Years 7, 9 and 12, are open to boys and girls with potential for major county, regional or national representation or with all-round sporting excellence. Reports will be sought from the candidates' coach(es) and practical tests, if required, will be held at the school in February.

Full details are available from The Admissions Secretary, The King's School, Ely, Cambridgeshire CB7 4DB. Tel: 01353 660702; e-mail: admissions@kings-ely.cambs.sch.uk.

Kingston Grammar School (see p 222)
Awards for candidates demonstrating outstanding sporting potential in the school's main games are available at 11+, 13+ and 16+. Further details are available from the Registrar.

Kingswood School (see p 224)
Sport scholarships (maximum value of 50% off the full fees) are available annually to pupils entering Year 7 and Year 9 (new boarders only) and the Sixth Form.

John Wesley All-Rounder Award: A special All-Rounder Scholarship is available for those pupils who can demonstrate a high level of academic ability in addition to extra talents in either Art, Music, Drama or Sport (DT at Sixth Form level). This award is available at entry to Year 9 (new boarders only) and to the Sixth Form (boarders only). A report from the pupil's current school outlining contribution to school life will also be required.

Lancing College (see p 227)
Sports Scholarships, ranging in value up to a quarter of the annual boarding fee, are available annually at 13+ entry.

Ken Shearwood Awards, ranging in value up to a fifth of the annual boarding fee, may be made at 13+ entry to pupils of all-round ability and potential who have made outstanding contributions to their present schools.

Leighton Park School (see p 235)
Major awards of up to 25% of day fees, and minor awards of 15% or 10% of day fees, are available for Sport.

Llandovery College (see p 240)
Carwyn James and Ian Gollop Scholarships are offered for pupils having superior sporting skills in Rugby. Scholarships are also offered in Hockey, Athletics and Cricket. Assessment days are normally held in the Lent Term. Candidates may also sit the academic scholarship examinations.

Lord Wandsworth College (see p 244)
Sports and All-Rounder Awards are offered to entrants to the First Form, Third Form and Sixth Form. Further details may be obtained from the Admissions Office.

Malvern College (see p 251)
Sport: Proven record of performance, or evidence of potential, at County, Regional or National level.

The Malvernian Society All-Rounder Award: This award is for candidates who meet the following criteria:

- Satisfactory marks in the Common Entrance or Scholarship Examination.
- Strong interests outside the classroom and a proven record of performance in them.
- An exceptional report from the Head of his/her present school.
- Good performance at interview.

Merchiston Castle School (see p 260)
Laidlaw Awards are for anyone who is 'academically strong' or shows talent in one or more of the following areas: art, drama, leadership, music or technology, and with good academic ability.

Scholarship can start for S1, S2, S3 or S5 and will continue until end of School Career.

Mill Hill School (see p 263)
Sports Awards are available at 13+.

For further information please visit the school's website www.millhill.org.uk.

Monkton Senior (see p 269)
Of the ten Open Scholarships offered at age 13 at least two may be for Sport.

Monmouth School (see p 272)
Sports Awards are available to suitable candidates at 11, 13 and Sixth Form entry.

Old Monmothian and Mountjoy Award: Good all-round candidates are encouraged to apply for awards that are made at the Headmaster's discretion.

Norwich School (see p 279)
Sports Scholarships are awarded at Sixth Form entry only.

The Oratory School (see p 286)
Awards are made to sportsmen of outstanding ability. All-round boys are recommended by the Head of their Prep School.

Oundle School (see p 288)
11+: The John Adams Scholarship, to the value of up to 50% of the day fees. This is a means-tested scholarship for both day and boarding pupils. Assessment date: Thursday 13 November.

13+: Eight General Scholarships, including the Conradi and Stainforth awards, to the value of up to 20% of the school fees (1–2 March).

Further details may be obtained from Rachael Wood, The Undermaster's Assistant, Oundle School, Oundle, Peterborough, PE8 4GH. Tel: 01832 277116. Fax 01832 277119. E-mail: rcwood@oundleschool.org.uk.

Pangbourne College (see p 291)
All-Rounder Awards are given to pupils of outstanding all-round talent, in academic work and a number of other areas of College life, such as sport, music and drama.

Candidates come to Pangbourne on the first Monday of the scholarship week in May and undertake a variety of academic and practical tasks relevant to their talents. Their current Head-teacher's report carries considerable weight.

The College offers a small number of Sports Scholarships to candidates who are gifted in one or more sports. Candidates will be asked to demonstrate academic potential to achieve at least B grades at GCSE or C grade at A Level and sporting potential to be a significant member of our first teams in one or more major games, and the ability to compete at county or higher representative level.

Plymouth College (see p 293)
One Open Sport Award (age 13+) of up to one-third of the fees.

One Open Sport Award (age 16+) of up to one-third of the fees.

Prior Park College (see p 300)
Sporting exhibitions are available at 11+. These can be converted to full scholarships at 13+ following further assessments. Sporting Excellence scholarships are available at 13+ and 16+.

Queen's College, Taunton (see p 307)
Sport Scholarships: Worth up to 50% of fees for the students of best ability. Queen's College offers up to 6 scholarships for talented students with proven sports ability aged 11+ and 13+ at the projected time of entry to the college. Sixth Form scholarships included.

Radley College (see p 309)
On average 6–8 All-Rounder Scholarships will be awarded annually. Awards may be supplemented by a means-tested bursary. Further details from our website or the Registrar.

Reed's School (see p 314)
Scholarships may be awarded for Sport at age 11, 13 or 16. All-Rounder Scholarships are available to applicants who offer a high performance in more than one area.

Repton School (see p 319)
A number of Sports Scholarships are offered, usually at 13+ and 16+, to pupils of exceptional talent. Assessments are held by arrangement with the Director of Sport, prior to the end of the Lent Term.

C B Fry All Rounder Award: a number of awards worth up to 20% of the Repton boarding fee may be offered at 13+ to candidates exhibiting outstanding all round leadership potential. Assessments take place in April when candidates are in Year 7.

Royal Grammar School, Guildford (see p 327)
Sports scholarships are available for boys joining at 11 and 13.

St Edmund's College (see p 355)
Sports Scholarships are available at 11+ and 16+. They are decided by open competition and references from sport clubs or teachers where the child is already involved in sport at a very high level.

All-Rounder Scholarships are available at 11+ and are decided by interview, school report, confidential report and mark in the entrance exam. For this award, the child will be competent academically and also be able to make a substantial contribution to other areas of life at St Edmund's such as drama, technology, the Catholic life of the College, specialised sports or outdoor pursuits.

St Edmund's School (see p 357)
Sport scholarship awards of up to one half of the boarding or day fees are available for applicants aged 11–16. It is expected that candidates will be playing sport outside school and have the potential to play at county or national level in at least one of the principal sports played at St Edmund's.

St Edward's, Oxford (see p 360)
Sport scholarships are available at 13+ and 16+ entry. Candidates will show considerable natural ability in at least one sport. We are particularly looking for players of rugby, cricket, hockey, netball, tennis and rowing.

All-Rounder scholarships are available at 13+ only. Candidates must be academically sound, expecting to obtain over 65% at Common Entrance, show strong leadership qualities and be able to demonstrate considerable talent in two of the following areas: art, music, dance, sport and drama.

13+ scholarships take place in the January/February prior to entry, 16+ in the November prior to entry.

Shrewsbury School (see p 381)
Two Sports Scholarships up to the value of 20% of fees, two All-Rounder Scholarships worth a maximum value of 20% of fees and ten House Foundation Awards, worth up to the value of 50% of fees, which are available for exceptional all-rounders and tied to particular day and boarding houses.

Sixth Form Sports Scholarships are available up to the value of 25% of fees.

Additionally, one Sixth Form Cassidy Sports Scholarship worth up to 100% of fees.

For details of all Scholarships, please contact The Registrar, Shrewsbury School, Tel: 01743 280550.

Stowe School (see p 393)
Sports Scholarships may be awarded for exceptional candidates showing outstanding potential in at least one of Stowe's key sports: hockey, lacrosse or tennis for girls and rugby, hockey or cricket for boys.

Candidates at 13+ must be able to demonstrate significant potential for sporting achievements at a high level. Assessment will take the form of a full day at Stowe. Candidates will sit Stowe's own Entry Examinations of Maths, English, Headmaster's Essay paper and a Verbal Reasoning paper, followed by a fitness test and a sports assessment. A good Pass standard for those sitting Common Entrance will also be expected. Candidates must also submit a portfolio for assessment which should show clear evidence of their sporting achievements and two references from people who have coached them.

Candidates at 16+ must be playing at County or Divisional level in their chosen sport. Assessment will take the form of a full day at Stowe, sitting Entry Examinations followed by a fitness test and a sports assessment. The Entry Examinations are held in the November of the candidate's GCSE year and will be two subject papers, related to their AS Level choices, a Verbal Reasoning paper and an interview. Candidates must also submit a portfolio for assessment which should show clear evidence of their sporting achievements and two references from people who have coached them.

Roxburgh Scholarships are intended to enable any boy or girl of outstanding all-round ability and leadership potential to benefit from Stowe's unrivalled environment to develop fully his or her talents. In addition to strong academic potential, which will be demonstrated in Stowe's Entry Examinations and by tests taken during the assessment day, candidates will be asked to submit a portfolio which should include the candidate's interests and achievements. Nominations for this Scholarship will normally be made by the candidate's Headmaster or Headmistress, supported by a full school report.

Full details may be obtained from: The Registrar, Stowe School, Buckingham MK18 5EH.

Strathallan School (see p 395)
Sports and All-Rounder scholarships of between 5% and 50% of fees are available for entry to the Senior School at 13+ and 16+.

Tonbridge School (see p 404)
Up to 4 Cowdrey Scholarships may be awarded annually on the basis of sporting excellence in one or more of the main team games: rugby, hockey and cricket, and sportsmanship. Candidates will be assessed in early February during a day of sports and athletic activity, together with an interview with the Director of Sport.

The value of any award may be increased by any amount up to the full school fee if assessment of the parents' means indicates a need.

Candidates for these awards must also satisfy the academic entrance requirements of the school through Common Entrance or the academic Scholarship examinations.

Full particulars of all Scholarships may be obtained from the Admissions Secretary, Tonbridge School, Tonbridge, Kent

TN9 1JP. Tel: 01732 304297; email: admissions@tonbridge-school.org.

Trent College (see p 407)
Sports Awards are available at 11+, 13+ and 16+.

The value of an Award depends on the age of the child, their ability and whether they are a day pupil or a boarder.

Full details on all scholarships, examinations and entrance procedures are available from the Registrar, Tel: 0115 849 4950.

Uppingham School (see p 415)
A number of All-Rounder, known as Thring, scholarships worth between one-tenth and one-half of the fees are awarded annually. Means-Tested Bursaries are available up to 95% of the full fee in cases of real financial need, to assist children whose parents might not otherwise be able to afford an Uppingham education to take up such an opportunity.

Details may be obtained from the Admissions Office (01572 820611).

Wellingborough School (see p 421)
Sports Scholarships and awards are available at 13+ and at 16+.

Wellington College (see p 423)
Sport or All-Round Scholarships or Exhibitions may be awarded at 20% and 10% of the fees at 13+ and at 30%, 20% and 10% of the fees at 16+.

Whitgift School (see p 432)
A number of awards for Sport and All-Round ability is available.

Woodbridge School (see p 439)
Sports and All-Rounder awards are available for entry at 11, 13 and 16.

Woodhouse Grove School (see p 440)
Sports scholarships are awarded in the Sixth Form.

Worksop College (see p 442)
Sports Awards, to the value of up to 25% fees pa, available for entrants at 13+ and at Sixth Form. Examinations in March and May. For further details contact the Assistant Registrar.

Educational Awards/Bursaries

Alleyn's School (see p 11)
Bursaries are available equivalent to 7 free places (5 at 11+ and 2 at 16+) per annum to academically able candidates whose parents could not afford full fees.

Bishop's Stortford College (see p 40)
Means-tested bursaries are awarded based on individual need. This may be up to 100% in some cases.

Bloxham School (see p 42)
Generous support is available to children of Armed Forces parents, Clergy and Teachers.

The Roger Raymond Trust Fund sponsors the boarding education of outstanding pupils who would not otherwise be able to attend the school.

Further details may be obtained from the Headmaster, Bloxham School, Banbury, Oxon OX15 4PE.

Bootham School (see p 48)
Bursary help may be available to sons and daughters of Quakers. Further details from the Headmaster.

Brighton College (see p 55)
One or two Gill Memorial Scholarships offered in the Senior School and one in the Junior School for children of regular Army officers (serving or retired). Fee concessions may also be made to children of clergy of the Church of England where there is financial hardship. Cuthbert Heath Memorial Bursary available 3 years out of 5 for pupils who have a positive contribution to make to the life of the College.

Canford School (see p 68)
One Royal Naval Scholarship worth 20% of fees pa for the son/daughter of a serving Naval Officer is offered annually at 13+.

Caterham School (see p 70)
Bursaries for the sons and daughters of URC Clergy, Old Caterhamians and Forces Personnel are available.

There are also a number of Caterham Assisted Places for those joining the school at the age of 11.

Charterhouse (see p 72)
For sons of lawyers a Sir William Blackstone Award is offered annually to boys when aged 11 for entry to Charterhouse at the age of 13.

A limited number of Bursaries is available for boys who would benefit from a Charterhouse education, but whose parents are unable to afford the fees. These may be awarded at age 13.

For details write to the Admissions Secretary, Charterhouse, Godalming, Surrey GU7 2DX.

Cheadle Hulme School (see p 74)
Bursaries are offered at 11+ based on academic merit and financial eligibility. A number of other Bursaries are available for entry to the Sixth Form on the same basis.

Cheltenham College (see p 76)
Dill Memorial Scholarship awarded every 3 years – open in the first instance to descendants of the Prince of Wales Leinster Regiment (Royal Canadian) and the East Lancs Regiment and to pupils from Northern Ireland.

The Boyes' Scholarship is awarded in the first instance to sons and daughters of serving members of Her Majesty's Forces.

Christ College (see p 80)
There is a 25% fee remission for sons and daughters of the Clergy, and 10% bursaries are available each year for the children of serving members of the Armed Forces.

City of London Freemen's School (see p 84)
A significant number of Bursaries from Livery Companies are also available.

City of London School (see p 87)
The School offers a number of means-tested Sponsored Awards at 11+ and 16+ entry to bright candidates whose parents could not otherwise contemplate private education.

Clifton College, Bristol (see p 90)
Special awards are available for the sons and daughters of old Cliftonians.

The Birdwood Award, for sons and daughters of serving members of HM Forces, is awarded on the results of the Entrance Scholarship exam.

Dean Close School (see p 103)
Means-tested bursaries for sons and daughters of Clergy. Automatic discounts, known as Thierry Awards, are offered to parents serving in HM Armed Forces on a scale according to rank.

Denstone College (see p 105)
Bursaries are available for the sons and daughters of the Armed Forces and Clergy.

Durham School (see p 112)
Bursaries are available at all ages in cases of financial need and these can be held alongside academic and non-academic awards. Additionally, each year the School awards up to three Foundation Bursaries at 11+. There are generous concessions for brothers and sisters, children of clergy and the Armed Forces.

Eastbourne College (see p 113)
Bursaries are awarded in appropriate circumstances. All are means tested.

Ellesmere College (see p 120)
Reduction in fees for children of the clergy. Foundation and Regional awards for children of parents of limited means.

Eltham College (see p 121)
Bursaries are available up to 100% of fees subject to ISBA confidential means test. Please contact the Admissions Secretary for further details.

Epsom College (see p 125)
Scholarships and bursaries for children of the medical profession.

Eton College (see p 127)
Apart from the King's Scholarships, Music Scholarships, Sixth Form and Junior Scholarships described in the main entry, Eton offers a number of Bursaries. Application should be initiated immediately after a Conditional Place is offered at age 11. Further particulars and application forms from *The School Bursar, Eton College, Windsor SL4 6DJ.*

Felsted School (see p 132)
Special Bursaries for children of Clergy in the County of Essex and Diocese of Chelmsford, and children of those in the Armed Services.

Forest School (see p 135)
Reductions for children of the Clergy.

Framlingham College (see p 138)
Special bursaries are available for the sons and daughters of serving members of HM Forces.

Giggleswick School (see p 144)
Discount available for children of HM Forces.

Glenalmond College (see p 148)
A number of means tested bursaries are available each year. Applications should reach the Treasurer no later than 15th March in the year of entry. Bursaries are also available for the sons and daughters of Clergy and the children of serving Armed Forces families.

Guildford High School (see p 154)
An External Competitive Scholarship and a number of Internal Bursaries are available at Sixth Form level. Bursaries are available throughout the School for daughters of Clergy.

Haberdashers' Aske's Boys' School (see p 156)
A significant number of Governors' Bursaries are awarded at age 11+, valued from a few hundred pounds to full fees, depending upon financial need. Open equally to boys already in the School and to those applying from other Schools. One Bursary is reserved for Music.

Haileybury (see p 159)
Bursaries are available to increase awards, in cases of financial need, and can supplement up to 100% of the fees in some cases.

Harrow School (see p 164)
A number of means-tested Bursaries up to full fees are available for boys who do very well in the Academic, Outstanding Talent and Music Scholarship examinations.

Highgate School (see p 171)
A limited number of sons and daughters of Anglican clergy are admitted at half the Tuition Fee.

Kelly College (see p 181)
A generous reduction in fees for sons and daughters of Forces families is available (10% in Year 7 and 8, 20% in Years 9 to 13).

Kent College (see p 184)
Bursaries will be awarded in accordance with, and after consideration of, the financial circumstances of parents. Parents will be invited to complete a financial assessment form and the scale of bursary awarded will be based on the information provided and the financial criteria which the school applies to all bursary awards. All bursaries are reviewed annually.

In addition, the school operates an awards system for the children of HM Forces, NATO and War Graves Commission personnel, whereby the parents pay a set figure, normally 10% of the inclusive fee, plus the amount of Boarding School Allowance which they receive. The balance is treated as a Bursary Award. Full particulars may be obtained from the Registrar.

King's School, Bruton (see p 204)
The School offers a 20% remission of fees to all boarding students with one or both parents serving in the Armed Forces. The maximum combined value of Forces remission plus other awards is 25%. Other awards may be subsumed within the Forces remission. Both Forces remission and other awards may be augmented by means-tested bursaries.

The King's School, Ely (see p 211)
A 10% discount in fees is available from age 4 upwards for children of clergy serving the Christian faith and boarders who are children of service personnel in receipt of BSA. Bursaries may be awarded in cases of financial need. Parents should contact the Bursar for details of these and any sibling discounts that may be available.

King's School, Rochester (see p 216)
Children over the age of 8 of Church of England ministers are given a 10% reduction in tuition fees, means-tested beyond.

Children over the age of 8 of Service Personnel are allowed a 20% reduction in tuition fees for the first 2 years and 10% for the next 2 years.

Parents with three or more children at the School are allowed a reduction after the second child of 10% of the third child's fees, 20% for the fourth child and 40% for the fifth child.

King's School Governors' Exhibitions is a means-tested scheme for the purpose of assisting financially the parents of academically gifted children who, in the opinion of the Governors, qualify to take up a place at the School.

The King's School, Worcester (see p 220)
Bursaries of up to one third the cost of tuition may be granted to candidates who face financial hardship.

Those in receipt of a combination of scholarships/bursary will only receive a maximum of one half of tuition fees.

Kingswood School (see p 224)
Very special provisions are made for the children of Methodist Ministers (up to 100% bursary assistance) and consideration may also be given to assist the sons and daughters of clergymen of other denominations, with a reduction in fees according to circumstances.

HM Forces families receive a reduction in boarding fees of up to 20% for each child, although the scheme is limited depending on demand for places within any particular year group at this rate.

The Leys School (see p 237)
Certain awards for sons of Methodist Ministers and of Methodist families are available. Special consideration is given to the sons and daughters of Old Leysians and members of HM Forces.

Llandovery College (see p 240)
Forces bursaries are available for the children of serving members of the armed forces. Service families guaranteed to pay no more than 10% of fees.

Sons or Daughters of the Clergy from the Province of Wales are eligible for a reduction of up to one third of the fee.

Means-tested bursaries are available in some cases.

Lord Wandsworth College (see p 244)
Foundation places are available to pupils who have lost one or both parents through death, divorce or separation. Apply to the Foundation Registrar for full details.

Loretto School (see p 245)
Loretto Bursaries are available for parents who need help with fees. Bursaries are means-tested and are available for prospective pupils as well as existing pupils who experience unforeseen financial difficulty. Bursary funds are limited. A number of Bursaries are available to sons and daughters of the Clergy and the Armed Forces. In circumstances of special need contact the Bursary.

Loughborough Grammar School (see p 247)
The School offers a 25% boarding fee remission to sons of HM Forces and sons of Clergy.

Marlborough College (see p 254)
The College offers a range of Academic and Music Scholarships at both 13+ and 16+, and Art and Sports awards at 13+, all of which are awarded as a result of competitive assessment. In addition, scholarships are available each year for children of Clergy, for whom there is an automatic remission of 15% of fees, with additional assistance as necessary. Other endowed scholarships and bursaries, and closed awards for children of Armed Forces personnel, are available from time to time when vacant.

Merchiston Castle School (see p 260)
Community Award: One means-tested scholarship, providing financial support to a boy who would otherwise not be able to attend Merchiston, is available to candidates aged 8–18 years living in Edinburgh and surrounding area (EH postcode). Assessed by interview in conjunction with Entrance or Scholarship examination. (Application by early January.)

Trust Applications: The School can apply to charities on behalf of prospective pupils.

Forces: 10% fees remission is given to sons of serving members of HM Forces.

Hong Kong/Europe/Kenya/India: One All-Rounder scholarship award for each country given either to a scholar or a boy who would otherwise not be able to attend Merchiston.

A number of other bursaries are available on application in cases of special need.

Mill Hill School (see p 263)
Means-tested Bursaries may be awarded to pupils entering at 13+.

Up to three full Bursary places (100% fee remission) may be awarded in the Sixth Form.

There are also a number of special scholarships and bursaries for the children of Old Millhillians, Christian Ministers, members of the Armed Forces and the Diplomatic Services.

For further information please visit the school's website www.millhill.org.uk.

Monkton Senior (see p 269)
Some Bursaries to supplement Scholarships on proof of need. Remission of up to one-third of the composite fee to a limited number of children of Clergy and Missionaries on proof of need.

Monmouth School (see p 272)
Service Bursaries are available for the sons of serving members of HM Armed Forces, thus guaranteeing no more than the minimum 10% of fees is payable by parents.

Boarding Bursaries are available, depending on parental circumstances.

Morrison's Academy (see p 274)
A number of bursaries are available to pupils in the secondary school. The bursaries are income-related and are restricted to those who live within daily travelling distance of the School. Further details from The Rector, Morrison's Academy, Crieff PH7 3AN.

In special circumstances consideration will be given to pupils at other stages.

Norwich School (see p 279)
In addition to the School's bursary provision:

The Worshipful Company of Dyers, through its charitable trust, is able to give financial support to a pupil with all-round talent in both L4 and L6.

The school has an association with the Ogden Trust which is able to give financial support to selected Sixth Form pupils who join us from the state sector with primary academic strengths in mathematics or the applied sciences. The Trust's financial criteria are similar to our own.

Oundle School (see p 288)
Schools and parents should be aware that Oundle will offer financial help towards the payment of fees in cases of proven need. This assistance is available in the form of Bursaries, which will vary in size according to the circumstances and which may be as high as 100%. These Bursaries are awarded solely according to need and are not dependent on scholastic merit, except insofar as the pupil in question must satisfy the School's entry requirements and must continue to work to capacity during his or her progress through the School. It may be that parents of a Scholarship winner will need to apply for a Bursary in addition. We will, of course, look sympathetically on such requests. We encourage parents who feel that they may need the support of a Bursary to discuss the matter with their child's present Head Teacher, and with us, well in advance of the due date of entry to the School. This could be as long as two years or more before entry.

Further details may be obtained from Rachael Wood, The Undermaster's Assistant, Oundle School, Oundle, Peterborough, PE8 4GH. Tel: 01832 277116. Fax: 01832 277119. E-mail: rcwood@oundleschool.org.uk.

Plymouth College (see p 293)
Bursaries of up to half fees, together with various similar Scholarships.

Prior Park College (see p 300)
Bursaries are available, including HM Forces Bursaries of up to 20% of fees. The Bursar is pleased to discuss individual cases. Sibling discounts apply.

Reed's School (see p 314)
A large number of Foundation awards are made each year to boys and girls who have lost one or both parents, or whose parents are divorced or separated or whose home life is for some special reason either unhappy or unsatisfactory. The awards, which are means tested, vary according to circumstances. Enquiries should be addressed to the Registrar.

Rendcomb College (see p 317)
Scholarships are available for Forces personnel by application to the Headmaster, Rendcomb College, Near Cirencester, Gloucestershire GL7 7HA.

Repton School (see p 319)
Bursaries may be available to those who, on grounds of hardship, would not otherwise be able to attend an independent school. These may, in appropriate circumstances, be added to Academic awards. Means-tested bursaries are also available to Forces families.

Rossall School (see p 323)
A number of clerical bursaries, awarded on a means test to sons of Clergy who can sustain a proportion of the Fees themselves but who need extra help. Bursaries are also available to families from the British military forces.

The bursaries rise to meet increases in the Fees.

Rydal Penrhos (see p 338)
Up to 12 bursaries or awards ranging up to 50% of school fees are offered by examination in February each year for Year 7 entry. There are also 2 Free Day Places reserved for candidates residing in our County for Year 7 entry. There are 4 Sixth Form Bursaries for candidates seeking entry at this point, of which 2 are reserved for music and sport.

Reductions are available for children of Ministers of the Methodist and Anglican Churches and bursaries for children of serving members of the Armed Forces.

For full details of all these awards, please apply to *The Admissions Office, Rydal Penrhos School, Colwyn Bay, Conwy LL29 7BT*.

Ryde School with Upper Chine (see p 339)
Bursaries are awarded to suitably qualified candidates who are already attending the school or pupils who apply from outside. Bursaries are means tested. Further details from the Headmaster.

St Bees School (see p 346)
The School offers a limited number of means-tested bursaries.

St Edmund's College (see p 355)
Reductions are offered for sons and daughters of serving members of the Armed Forces. Means-tested Bursaries are available at 11+, of up to 100% of fees.

St Edmund's School (see p 357)
Bursaries and fee concessions are granted to the children of former pupils, clergy, members of the armed forces, diplomatic personnel and to the third and subsequent children of the same family in the school at the same time. The School was originally founded to provide a free education for the fatherless sons of the clergy of the Church of England and the Church in Wales and still accepts applications from boys and girls for Foundationer status.

Applications should be made to the Headmaster.

St Edward's, Oxford (see p 360)
There are three Widening Access bursaries available each year: two at 13+ and one at 16+. There is also one bursary for the children of serving RAF personnel and the school may offer bursaries of up to 30% of current boarding fees for children of clergy and university dons at the Warden's discretion.

St Lawrence College (see p 366)
Bursaries are awarded annually to pupils in need of financial assistance and who are likely to make a positive contribution to the life of the school. Sibling discounts are also available in the Senior School.

Sedbergh School (see p 374)
Grants are made from the Sedbergh School Education Fund to sons and daughters of Old Sedberghians. The Headmaster has at his disposal other funds to help with the expenses of educating pupils at Sedbergh.

Sherborne School (see p 377)
Exhibitions are available for the sons of serving or ex-service officers, for the sons of RN officers and bursaries for the sons of Church of England clergy.

Silcoates School (see p 383)
Substantial bursaries are available for the sons and daughters of Ministers and Missionaries of the United Reformed Church or of the Congregational Church, and of other recognised Christian denominations.

Solihull School (see p 384)
The school runs its own means-tested Assisted Places Scheme to offer opportunities to able pupils with financial needs.

Sons and daughters of the clergy are offered a 50% fee remission.

Stonyhurst College (see p 391)
A number of Bursaries up to half fees are awarded annually to pupils in need of financial assistance and who are likely to make a positive contribution to the life of the school.

Stowe School (see p 393)
A range of Scholarships and Exhibitions, up to the value of 25% of the School fees is awarded annually. Academic, Music, Art and Sports Scholarships are available and are offered to candidates entering at 13+ and 16+ who demonstrate outstanding potential in the relevant examinations. Roxburgh Scholarships are awarded to any boy or girl of outstanding all-round ability and leadership potential, and Stephan Scholarships are awarded to academically bright day pupils who would not otherwise be able to come to Stowe. Scholarships may be supplemented by means tested bursaries, with a limited number of fully funded places, where there is proven financial need. Full details may be obtained from: The Registrar, Stowe School, Buckingham MK18 5EH.

Strathallan School (see p 395)
Bursary help is available to supplement awards for outstanding candidates on a financial need basis.

Tettenhall College (see p 403)
Reduction in fees for the children of clergymen and members of HM Forces.

Trent College (see p 407)
Boarding Awards for children of clergy and children of retired, deceased or active members of the armed services. On evidence of need Bursaries might be available to increase the grant.

Two Albert Ball Scholarships for sons of RAF officers of £250 pa. The Kenneth May Award (value £250) is awarded on evidence of qualities of leadership together with games ability.

Wellington College (see p 423)
Foundation places for sons and daughters of deceased military servicemen and servicewomen and of others who have died in acts of selfless bravery. Also Scholarships and Exhibitions.

Whitgift School (see p 432)
A significant number of bursaries is available each year courtesy of the Whitgift Foundation.

Winchester College (see p 434)
Particulars of bursaries may be obtained from the Bursar. Bursaries are available to support boys entering the school, and where financial assistance is required for existing pupils. All bursaries are awarded on a means-tested basis.

Wisbech Grammar School (see p 435)
About 25 means-tested bursaries are awarded each year with fee remission of up to 75% according to circumstances.

Woodhouse Grove School (see p 440)
Means-tested bursaries are available.

Special assistance is given to the children of Methodist ministers (to boarders and day pupils) and to boarders who are sons and daughters of serving members of HM Forces.

Worksop College (see p 442)
A wide range of bursaries is offered to enable talented pupils to attend the school who would not otherwise be able to do so.

Wrekin College (see p 446)
Special bursaries are available for sons and daughters of serving members of the armed forces.

Yarm School (see p 450)
Means-tested bursaries are available to allow children who satisfy the entry criteria to be educated at Yarm School.

Headmasters' and Headmistresses' Conference International Members

* co-educational schools

Schools in Europe

The British School of Brussels

Leuvensesteenweg 19, 3080 Tervuren, Belgium
Tel: 00 32 2 766 04 30
Fax: 00 32 2 767 80 70
e-mail: principal@britishschool.be
admissions@britishschool.be
website: www.britishschool.be

Patron:
Her Excellency the British Ambassador to the King of the Belgians

Chairman of the Board: Mr Andrew Mafeld

***Principal*: Dr Brenda Despontin,** BA Hons, MA, PhD, PGCE, MBA

Creation. The British School of Brussels (BSB) was founded in 1969 as a non-profit making organisation in Belgium and was opened in 1970 by HRH The Duke of Edinburgh. It is run by a Board of Governors, comprising distinguished British and Belgian citizens from both the professions and the world of business, together with parent and staff representatives.

Site. The School occupies a beautiful site of 13 acres, surrounded by woodlands and lakes near the Royal Museum of Central Africa in Tervuren, which is 25–30 minutes by car from the centre of Brussels. The site belongs to the Donation Royale, the foundation which manages the estates left to the Belgian people at the beginning of the 20th century by King Leopold II.

Buildings. The School has excellent facilities and almost all buildings have been fully refurbished within the past ten years. The modern buildings include a science and maths centre, networked IT suites all with internet access, a modern languages department, dance and drama studios as well as an art and technology block and a self-service cafeteria. "Kindercrib", BSB's own childcare facility for children aged 1–3, is situated in a separate villa next to the School.

Organisation. The British School of Brussels is an independent, fee-paying, non profit-making international school. English is the language of tuition. The school is a co-educational non-selective day school for students from 3 to 18 years of age, with 1,245 currently on roll of which 205 are in the Sixth Form. 53% of the students are British and there are 71 other nationalities represented in the school. Our curriculum, both in the Primary and Secondary Schools, is based on the English (UK) National Curriculum, adapted to suit the needs of our international students. In the Secondary School, students sit GCSE/IGCSE examinations at the end of Year 11 (aged 16). Senior students then study either the International Baccalaureate Diploma or the GCE A Level course prior to moving on to Higher Education in the UK, Belgium or beyond. Provision is also made for Oxbridge tuition. Our examination results are impressive.

We introduce the teaching of French to Year 1 students and Spanish, German or Dutch as optional additional languages in the Secondary School. We have developed programmes to help students with learning difficulties and to help students who join us with little or no English skills. There is an Educational Psychologist and a Learning Support Department as well as two counsellors.

Sports and Extra Curricular Activities. Use of the extensive sports facilities (2 gymnasia, state-of-the-art all weather artificial pitches, grass pitches, floodlit training area, 4 outdoor tennis courts, squash courts, and indoor sports hall), the 240-seat Theatre and Arts Centre, together with the very popular children's summer holiday courses, make the School a focal point for the local and international community. In addition to curricular sport, a wide range of competitive sports is offered: athletics, cricket, cross-country, gymnastics, hockey, rugby, soccer, swimming and tennis, as well as recreational activities such as basketball and golf. The School participates very successfully in the International Schools Sports Tournaments.

Music and Drama. The Music Department houses a well-equipped music technology studio, a recording studio and a rehearsal studio for the School's orchestras, concert bands and instrumental ensembles. Individual instrument lessons are available from visiting specialist teachers. The School is the largest Associated Board centre in Europe.

Each year up to fifteen drama productions – including student-directed performances – are presented across the full student age-range and the Theatre has its own workshop and Green Room.

Careers. The School has the highest expectations of its student population and advice on careers, as well as higher and further education opportunities, is of vital importance to the further development of the students. The School takes part in many careers conventions as well as hosting its own annual Careers Week each spring.

Fees per annum (2008-2009). From €12,100 (Reception class) to €25,200. Some assistance with tuition fees may be available.

Past Students' Association. The School is developing this area of activity. Visit the website: www.webalumnus@britishschool.be.

The British School in The Netherlands

website: www.britishschool.nl
e-mail: admissions@britishschool.nl

BSN Foundation School (3–5 years)
Tarwekamp 3, 2592 XG, The Hague
Tel: 00 31 (0)70 315 4040
Fax: 00 31 (0)70 315 4054

BSN Junior School Diamanthorst (3–11 years)
Diamanthorst 16, 2592 GH, The Hague
Tel: 00 31 (0)70 315 7620
Fax: 00 31 (0)70 315 7621

BSN Junior School Vlaskamp (5–11 years)
Vlaskamp 19, 2592 AA, The Hague
Tel: 00 31 (0)70 333 8111
Fax: 00 31 (0)70 333 8100

BSN Senior School (11–18 years)
Jan van Hooflaan 3, 2252 BG, Voorschoten
Tel: 00 31 (0)71 560 2222
Fax: 00 31 (0)71 560 2200

BSN Junior School Assen
(The Helen Sharman School) (3–11 years)
Lottingstraat 17, 9406 LX, Assen
Tel: 00 31 (0)592 344 590
Fax: 00 31 (0)592 370 998

Principal: **Mr Martin Coles**
Principal's Office: **Boerderij Rosenburgh, Rosenburgherlaan 2, 2252 BA, Voorschoten**
Tel: 00 31 (0)71 560 2251
Fax: 00 31 (0)71 560 2290

The British School in The Netherlands (BSN) was founded in 1931 as an independent, non-denominational school. Since then, it has grown into a school of over 2,000 pupils from Foundation 1 (age 3) to Year 13 (age 18). Although around half the pupils are of British origin, the school truly serves the international community, with children on roll from over 80 nations.

The BSN has four sites in The Hague and one in Assen in the north of Holland.

Aims. The School aims to develop the potential of its pupils by providing a caring environment, in which they are offered the greatest possible educational opportunities. Pupils are helped to develop their powers of reasoning, increase their knowledge and become aware of the importance of their individual contribution and responsibility to society. All are encouraged to aim for excellence and to respect one another. These aims are achieved in a happy school whose pupils join with high expectations and where they are encouraged in the belief of their fulfilment.

Junior School Diamanthorst. Opened in September 2003, this school was totally refurbished to provide top-class facilities for children aged 3–11 years. The smaller of the two Hague-based junior schools, BSN Diamanthorst prides itself on its close community.

Junior School Vlaskamp. Purpose-built in 1997 for children aged 5–11 years, this award-winning building stands on a greenfield site close to the centre of The Hague.

Foundation School. This school caters for Foundation 1 (Nursery) and Foundation 2 (Reception) classes (ages 3–5). Its beautifully refurbished building is situated very close to both junior schools.

Senior School. The Senior School is located in Voorschoten (a small town just north of The Hague). A huge building project was completed in 2003 offering enviable state-of-the-art facilities, including new science laboratories, information technology stations, library resources, gymnasium and much more. This investment represents a commitment to providing a modern and stimulating learning environment, to support the comprehensive educational programme.

Staff. Each school has a Headteacher, supported by Deputies. The Principal has overall responsibility for all schools in the BSN group. All teachers (156 full-time, 63 part-time) are fully qualified and are mostly recruited from the United Kingdom.

Transport. An independent school bus service links the schools and covers most of The Hague, Voorburg, Leidschendam, Wassenaar, Voorschoten, as well as parts of Rotterdam, Rijswijk, Leiden, Amsterdam and Zoetermeer.

Curriculum. Pupils follow challenging programmes of study based on the National Curriculum for England and Wales but with an added international dimension. All pupils study English, mathematics, science, technology, history, geography, music, art and physical education from the age of five years. Dutch is taught from the age of five and French from the age of ten. In the Senior School, Spanish, German, French and Dutch are taught from Year 7. Pupils prepare for the GCSE (at 16+) and IB Diploma Programme or AS/A2 Level examinations at 17/18 years. The School has a long and proud record of success with the majority of pupils entering universities and other higher education establishments all over the world.

The School was inspected by HMI in November 2003 using the inspection criteria for Independent Schools. The report stated that GCSE results were "well above those of comparable schools [. . .] close to that of selective (grammar) schools" and that "overall performance at A Level is very good".

Sport. Facilities are available for indoor and outdoor games, including rugby, hockey, aerobics, tennis, athletics, judo, football, basketball, volleyball and gymnastics. At Senior School level, fixtures are arranged with local clubs and other schools, including annual tours and tournaments in the United Kingdom and elsewhere in Europe.

Activities and Trips. The School takes pride in its regular participation in the annual Model United Nations Conference in The Hague. It also operates a full programme of field and activity trips in The Netherlands, the United Kingdom, France, Switzerland, Spain and Germany, capitalising on its central location in Europe.

Pastoral System. To ensure that each pupil is known individually, and cared for, there is a pastoral system which begins with the form teacher, who is responsible to a year group leader. Together they work to care, support and guide the individual in all aspects of school life. Success is achieved only through close cooperation between home and school, a positive learning environment and high standards of discipline.

Special Needs. Special provision is made for pupils with learning difficulties. Any child with Special Needs will be considered according to the School's policy on Special Needs Provision, which is available on request. Specialist help is provided throughout the School for pupils requiring individual tuition in English as an Additional Language.

Admission. Admission is granted at any time in the school year, depending on availability and the School's ability to meet the academic needs of the child. Great care is taken to ensure the academic and social integration of each child.

Fees per term (2008-2009). Foundation 1 (Nursery): €1,940 (part-time), €3,900 (full-time); Foundation 2 (Reception) – Year 6: €3,850; Years 7–13: €5,250.

Charitable status. Vereniging The British School in The Netherlands is a Registered Charity, number V409055. It aims to offer a British education to international children living temporarily or permanently in The Netherlands.

King's College

The British School of Madrid

Paseo de los Andes 35, 28761 Soto de Viñuelas, Madrid, Spain
Tel: 00 34 91 803 48 00
Fax: 00 34 91 803 65 57
e-mail: info@kingscollege.es
website: www.kingscollege.es

King's College is a British co-educational day and boarding school founded in 1969. It is the largest British curriculum school in Spain and the first school to have had full UK accreditation through the Independent Schools Inspectorate. The Headmaster is an international member of HMC, while the school is a member of COBIS and NABSS.

The school is governed by the Board of Directors and School Council which is composed of distinguished members from the business and academic communities.

***Headmaster*: David Johnson**, BEd Hons Leeds, MSc Oxon

Deputy Headmaster: Paul Fear, BA Hons, PGCE Wolverhampton
Head of Primary: Angela Gasca, CertEd London
Head of Spanish Studies: Fernando Lage, Lic Filosofía UAM
Head of Residence: Matthew Raggett, BSc Newcastle, PGCE Worcester, MBA Charles Sturt, NSW
Director of Admissions: Helen Williams, BA Hons Sheffield

The school caters for children of approximately 40 nationalities between the ages of 2 and 18 years. Pupil enrolment is

1,760 (890 boys and 870 girls), including 20 boarders. There are over 135 fully qualified staff, most of whom are British.

The aim of King's College, under the key phrase of its Charter "A British Education in Spain for Europe and the World", is to provide students with an excellent all-round education while fostering tolerance and understanding between young people of different nationalities and backgrounds.

Location. There are three school sites in Madrid:

King's College, Soto de Viñuelas. The main school, for pupils between the ages of 2 and 18 years, stands on a 12-acre site in a residential area about 25 km to the north of Madrid near the Guadarrama mountains and surrounded by open countryside. It is well connected to the city centre by motorway and rail. There is an optional comprehensive bus service to the city of Madrid and its outlying residential areas and all routes are supervised by a bus monitor.

Facilities. The main school has extensive, purpose-built facilities which include 7 science laboratories, 2 libraries, art studio, 3 computer centres with multimedia stations, and 2 music rooms. From Reception to Year 13, all classrooms are fitted with interactive whiteboards and there are computers in all Primary classrooms. Recent additions include a purpose-built Early Learning Centre, an Auditorium with seating for over 350 people and a Music School with 6 rooms for individual or small group tuition. The sports facilities include a 25-metre indoor heated swimming pool, a floodlit multi-purpose sports area, football pitches, basketball and tennis courts, a gymnasium with fitness centre and a horse riding school. Future development includes plans for a covered sports hall.

The Residence (boarding) is currently located on two floors of the school's west wing and has a capacity for approximately 40 Secondary age pupils. During the period 2008–2010 a new Residence will be built in the school grounds.

King's Infant School, Chamartín. Conveniently located in the Chamartín area of central Madrid, the school offers purpose-built facilities for boys and girls between the ages of 3 and 6 (Nursery to Year 2) and has a capacity of 200 pupils. There are spacious, well-equipped classrooms, complete with independent bathrooms for the Nursery pupils, a library and computer room and a playground area. At the age of seven, at the end of National Curriculum Year 2, pupils from King's Infant School automatically transfer to the Junior schools at the main site in Soto de Viñuelas or La Moraleja.

King's College School, La Moraleja. This brand new, purpose-built school is located on 10,000 sqm of land in La Moraleja, one of the most highly regarded residential areas in Madrid, 15 kilometres from the centre of the city. With a current roll of over 250 pupils, the school will eventually house 450 pupils from the age of 3 to 14 years (Nursery to Year 9). The modern on-site facilities include a library, ICT centre, laboratory, music room, multi-purpose sports surface and gymnasium.

At the age of fourteen, at the end of National Curriculum Year 9, pupils transfer to the main school site in Soto de Viñuelas to complete their final four years of study.

Curriculum. Pupils at all three King's College sites follow the English National Curriculum leading to (I)GCSE, GCE AS and A Level examinations. There are Induction English Classes for children over the age of 7 who need to improve their English while gradually integrating into the mainstream of the school. There is also a Spanish section at the main site for pupils wishing to follow the Spanish Baccalaureate from the age of 16 (Y12). All pupils learn Spanish. The school has a reputation for high academic standards and excellent examination results with students going on to top universities in Britain, USA and Spain amongst others. An Oxbridge preparatory group works with the most able students to prepare university applications. There is a very experienced Careers and University Entrance Advisory Department for all students.

Activities. King's College has choirs, musical ensembles and drama groups, which participate in numerous events throughout the year. Pupils are encouraged to explore their capabilities in the areas of music and the arts from a very early age.

Sports play an important role at the school and pupils are encouraged to take part in tournaments and local competitive events, in addition to their normal PE classes. King's College currently has football, basketball and swimming teams participating in local leagues, and also takes part in inter-school championships in athletics and cross-country.

There is a programme of optional classes which includes horse riding, ballet, judo, Spanish dancing, swimming, tennis, tuition in various musical instruments, performing arts and craft workshops.

Admission. Pupils entering the school at the age of 7 or above are required to sit entrance tests in English and Mathematics and possibly other subjects, while younger candidates are screened by our Educational Psychologist. For those applying to the Sixth Form, admission depends on the results of the (I)GCSE examinations, or equivalent.

Fees per term (from January 2008). €1,727–€3,335 excluding lunch and transport. Boarding fees are an additional €2,509.

Scholarships. The school offers a small number of scholarships to Sixth Formers selected on academic merit.

Further information may be obtained from The Director of Admissions at the School.

St George's British International School

Senior & Junior Schools:
Via Cassia, La Storta, 00123 Rome, Italy
Tel: 00 39 06 3086001
Fax: 00 39 06 30892490
e-mail: secretary@stgeorge.school.it
website: www.stgeorge.school.it

Junior School:
Via Spallanzani 12–14, Via Nomentana, 00161 Rome
Tel: 00 39 06 44230486
Fax: 00 39 06 4402609
e-mail: sarah.mattei@stgeorge.school.it
website: www.stgeorge.school.it

Visitor: HBM Ambassador to Italy

***Principal*: Martin J Hales**, BSc

Assistant Staff. 62 full-time and 4 part-time teachers, all fully qualified (95% British with degrees from British universities, including Oxford or Cambridge).

Enrolment. Around 650 pupils, ages 3 to 18, evenly balanced boys and girls; approximately 40 in each Primary and 50 in each Secondary year-group, 90 in the Sixth Form.

Founded in 1958, St George's is a fully independent school owned by a non-profit-making Association and run as a limited company. Its purpose is to provide the international community of Rome with a British-system education, with a full academic programme, enriched by extra-curricular activities, good pastoral care and encouragement of self-discipline and independence. Children come from over 60 nationalities, the majority having had all their education in English, and a large number would expect to stay at St George's until completion of their school years.

The school owns a 14 acre site on the north-west side of Rome, with 19 school buses serving all principal residential areas of the city. Facilities include a full range of standard and specialised classrooms, gymnasium, a library with first-class internet facilities, 7 science laboratories, 4 ICT/technology rooms and 3 art/design studios. The music and drama departments are very active and sports facilities are considerable, with an athletics track, rugby, cricket and football pitches and all-weather courts for tennis, volleyball and basketball.

It has also leased a large villa off the Via Nomentana, set in its own garden and with additional facilities in the Villa Torlonia Park immediately opposite, to provide an additional city-centre Junior School for children aged 3 to 11.

The 15 years of schooling provided at the St George's schools incorporate the work of British primary and secondary schools, leading to GCSE and International Baccalaureate in all standard subjects. Maximum class size is 25, with key subjects divided into smaller 'sets' in the secondary age-group, according to ability. Special care is taken over the teaching of English, whether mother-tongue or English-as-an-Additional-Language. The school organises many educational trips, to take advantage of its splendid location, as well as many activities in breaks and after school.

Most children go on to university or other further education, the majority to the UK with an average of 8% to Oxbridge.

2007 GCSE results. 93% pass rate grades A, B or C with 46% grade A or A*.

2007 International Baccalaureate. 95% awarded diploma. 34% gained 36 points or more (pass 24 points). Average diploma score: 32 points.

Admission is dependent on interview, reports from previous school and a screening test. Entrance is possible at any time of the year. The school year runs from early September to late June, Mondays to Fridays. Fees are set in Euros and adjusted each year in the light of inflation.

Fees per annum (2008-2009). Junior Schools: €10,890–€14,630. Senior School: €15,650–€17,250.

Other International Schools

Africa

South Africa

Bishops Diocesan College

Bishops Camp Ground Road, Rondebosch, Cape Town 7700, South Africa
e-mail: principal@bishops.org.za
website: www.bishops.org.za

***Principal*: Grant R B Nupen**

Hilton College

Private Bag 6001, Hilton 3245, Kwazulu-Natal, South Africa
e-mail: hc@hiltoncollege.com
website: www.hiltoncollege.com

***Head*: David Lovatt**

Michaelhouse

Balgowan 3275, Kwazulu-Natal, South Africa
e-mail: guypea@michaelhouse.org
website: www.michaelhouse.org

***Rector*: Guy N Pearson**

St Andrew's College

PO Box 182, Grahamstown 6140, South Africa
e-mail: d.wylde@sacschool.com
website: www.sacschool.com

***Head*: David Wylde**

St Stithian's College

Private Bag 2, Randburg 2125, Gauteng, South Africa
e-mail: rector@stithian.com
website: www.stithian.com

***Rector*: Stephen B Lowry**

Zimbabwe

Peterhouse

Private Bag 3741, Marondera, Zimbabwe
e-mail: PeterRec@mweb.co.zw
website: www.peterhouse.org

***Rector*: Jon B Calderwood**

St George's College

Private Bag 7727, Causeway, Harare, Zimbabwe
e-mail: btiernan@stgeorges.co.zw
website: www.stgeorges.co.zw

***Head*: Brendan T Tiernan**

Asia

Brunei Darussalam

Jerudong International School

PO Box 1408, BSB BS8672, Bandar Seri Begwan, Brunei Darussalam
e-mail: john.price@jis.edu.bn
website: www.jis.edu.bn

***Principal and CEO*: John S Price**

Hong Kong

Island School

20 Borrett Road, Hong Kong
e-mail: mjh@mail.island.edu.hk
website: www.island.edu.hk

***Principal*: Mrs Michelle Hughes**

India

Bishop Cotton School

Shimla 171 002, Himachal Pradesh, India
e-mail: headmaster@bishopcotton.com
website: www.bishopcottonshimla.com

***Head Master*: Roy C Robinson**

The Cathedral & John Connon School

6 Purshottamdas Thakurdas Marg, Fort Mumbai 400 001, India
e-mail: cajcs@bol.net.in
website: www.cathedral-school.com

***Principal*: Mrs Meera Isaacs**

The International School Bangalore

NAFL Valley, Whitefield-Sarajapur Road, Near Dommasandra Circle, Bangalore – 562 125, Karnataka State, India
e-mail: hbindu@tisb.ac.in
website: www.tisb.org

***Principal*: Dr Bindu Hari**

Kodaikanal International School

PO Box 25, Kodaikanal 624101, Tamil Nadu, India
e-mail: principal@kis.in
website: www.kis.in

***Principal*: Geoffrey Fisher**

Indonesia

The British International School
Bintaro Jaya Sector 9, Jl Raya Jombang – Cileduk, Pondok Aren, Tangerang 15227, Indonesia
e-mail: principal@bis.or.id
website: www.bis.or.id

***CEO and Principal*: Peter J Derby-Crook**

Malaysia

The International School of Penang
Jalan Sungai satu, Batu Feringgai, 11100 Penang, Malaysia
e-mail: info@uplands.org
website: www.uplands.org

***Principal*: Gary D Benfield**

Malaysia

Kolej Tuanku Ja'afar
Mantin, 71700 Negeri Sembilan, West Malaysia
e-mail: waj@ktj.edu.my
website: www.ktj.edu.my

***Principal*: Walter A Jones**

Pakistan

Aitchison College
The Mall, Lahore 54000, Pakistan
e-mail: aitchison@aitchison.edu.pk
website: www.aitchison.edu.pk

***Principal*: Shamim S Khan**

Australia and New Zealand

Australia

All Saints' College
PO Box 165, Ewing Avenue, Bull Creek, Willetton, WA 6149, Australia
e-mail: info@allsaints.wa.edu.au
website: www.allsaints.wa.edu.au

***Principal*: Dr Geoffrey Shaw**

Barker College
91 Pacific Highway, Hornsby, NSW 2077, Australia
e-mail: hm@barker.nsw.edu.au
website: www.barker.nsw.edu.au

***Headmaster*: Dr Roderic E Kefford**

Brighton Grammar School
90 Outer Crescent, Brighton, VIC 3186, Australia
e-mail: msurwin@brightongrammar.vic.edu.au
website: www.brightongrammar.vic.edu.au

***Head*: Michael S Urwin**

Camberwell Grammar School
PO Box 151, Balwyn, VIC 3103, Australia
e-mail: pgh@cgs.vic.edu.au
website: www.cgs.vic.edu.au

***Headmaster*: Dr Paul Hicks**

Canberra Grammar School
Monaro Crescent, Red Hill, ACT 2603, Australia
e-mail: simon.murray@cgs.act.edu.au
website: www.cgs.act.edu.au

***Headmaster*: Simon Murray**

Caulfield Grammar School
PO Box 610, 217 Glen Eira Road, East St Kilda, Melbourne, VIC 3185, Australia
e-mail: cgs@caulfieldgs.vic.edu.au
website: www.caulfieldgs.vic.edu.au

***Principal*: Stephen H Newton**

Christ Church Grammar School
Queenslea Drive, Claremont, WA 6010, Australia
e-mail: gwynne@ccgs.wa.edu.au
website: www.ccgs.wa.edu.au

***Headmaster*: Garth E Wynne**

Cranbrook School
5 Victoria Road, Bellevue Hill, NSW 2023, Australia
e-mail: head@cranbrook.nsw.edu.au
website: www.cranbrook.nsw.edu.au

***Headmaster*: Jeremy J S Madin**

The Geelong College
PO Box 5, Talbot Street, Newtown, VIC 3220, Australia
e-mail: turner@geelongcollege.vic.edu.au
website: www.geelongcollege.vic.edu.au

***Principal*: Dr Pauline C Turner**

Geelong Grammar School
50 Biddlecombe Avenue, Corio, VIC 3214, Australia
e-mail: principal@ggscorio.vic.edu.au
website: www.ggscorio.vic.edu.au

***Principal*: Stephen Meek**

Guildford Grammar School
11 Terrace Road, Guildford, WA 6935, Australia
e-mail: rzordan@ggs.wa.edu.au
website: www.ggs.wa.edu.au

***Headmaster*: Robert A Zordan**

Haileybury College
855 Springvale Road, Keysborough, VIC 3173, Australia
e-mail: registrar@haileybury.vic.edu.au
website: www.haileybury.vic.edu.au

***Principal*: Derek Scott**

The King's School
PO Box 1, Parramatta, NSW 2124, Australia
e-mail: headmaster@kings.edu.au
website: www.kings.edu.au

***Headmaster*: Dr Timothy F Hawkes**

Knox Grammar School
7 Woodville Avenue, Wahroonga, NSW 2076, Australia
e-mail: weeksj@knox.nsw.edu.au
website: www.knox.nsw.edu.au

***Headmaster*: John Weeks**

Melbourne Grammar School
Domain Road, South Yarra, Melbourne, VIC 3004, Australia
e-mail: mgs@mgs.vic.edu.au
website: www.mgs.vic.edu.au

***Headmaster*: A Paul Sheahan**

Pembroke School
342 The Parade, Kensington Park, SA 5068, Australia
e-mail: admissions@pembroke.sa.edu.au
website: www.pembroke.sa.edu.au

***Principal*: Malcolm L Lamb**

Scotch College
1 Morrison Street, Hawthorn, VIC 3122, Australia
e-mail: scotch@scotch.vic.edu.au
website: www.scotch.vic.edu.au

***Principal*: Tom Batty**

The Scots College
Victoria Road, Bellevue Hill, NSW 2023, Australia
e-mail: reception@tsc.nsw.edu.au
website: www.tsc.nsw.edu.au

***Principal*: Dr Ian P M Lambert**

Shore School
PO Box 1221, Blue Street, North Sydney, NSW 2059, Australia
e-mail: twright@shore.nsw.edu.au
website: www.shore.nsw.edu.au

***Head*: Dr Timothy Wright**

Sydney Grammar School
College Street, Darlinghurst, NSW 2010, Australia
e-mail: vmc@sydgram.nsw.edu.au
website: www.sydgram.nsw.edu.au

***Head*: Dr John T Vallance**

Trinity Grammar School
PO Box 174, 119 Prospect Road, Summer Hill, NSW 2130, Australia
e-mail: mcujes@trinity.nsw.edu.au
website: www.trinity.nsw.edu.au

***Head*: G Milton Cujes**

Wesley College
577 St Kilda Road, Melbourne VIC 3004, Australia
e-mail: principal@wesleycollege.net
website: www.wesleycollege.net

***Principal*: Dr Helen Drennan**

Westbourne Grammar School
300 Sayers Road, Truganina, VIC 3029, Australia
e-mail: information@westbourne.vic.edu.au
website: www.westbournegrammar.com

***Principal*: Geoffrey G Ryan**

New Zealand

Christ's College
Rolleston Avenue, Private Bag 4900, Christchurch, New Zealand
e-mail: headmaster@christscollege.com
website: www.christscollege.com

***Headmaster*: Simon Leese**

King's College
PO Box 22–012, Otahuhu, Auckland 1133, New Zealand
e-mail: r.kelley@kingscollege.school.nz
website: www.kingscollege.school.nz

***Headmaster*: Roy Kelley**

Wanganui Collegiate School
Private Bag 3002, Wanganui 5020, New Zealand
e-mail: wcs@collegiate.school.nz
website: www.collegiate.school.nz

***Headmaster*: T J Wilbur**, BA, PGCE

Central and South America

Argentina

St Andrew's Scots School
Roque Saenz Peña 654, 1636 Olivos, Buenos Aires, Argentina
e-mail: gabriel.rshaid@sanandres.esc.edu.ar
website: www.sanandres.esc.edu.ar

***Head*: Gabriel Rshaid**

St George's College North
C Rivadavia y Don Bosco, Los Polvorines 1613, Buenos Aires, Argentina
e-mail: iant@stgeorge.com.ar
website: www.stgeorge.com.ar

***Headmaster*: Ian D Tate**

St George's College Quilmes
Guido 800, CC2 (1878), Quilmes, Buenos Aires, Argentina
e-mail: info@stgeorge.com.ar
website: www.stgeorge.com.ar

***Headmaster*: R S Dillow**

Brazil

St Paul's School
Rua Juquiá 166, Jardim Paulistano, CEP 01440–903, São Paulo, Brazil
e-mail: spshead@stpauls.br
website: www.stpauls.br

***Headmaster*: Crispin Rowe**

Chile

The Grange School
Av Principe de Gales 6154, La Reina, 687067, Santiago, Chile
e-mail: rectoria@grange.cl
website: www.grange.cl

***Rector*: Rachid R Benammar**

El Salvador

Academia Británica Cuscatleca
Apartado Postal 121, Santa Tecla, El Salvador
e-mail: headmaster@abc.edu.sv
website: www.abc.edu.sv

***Head*: J George Hobson**

Peru

Markham College
Apartado 18–1048, Miraflores, Lima, Peru
e-mail: headmaster@markham.edu.pe
website: www.markham.edu.pe

***Headmaster*: David Dowdles**

Europe

Cyprus

The English School
PO Box 23575, 1684 Nicosia, Cyprus
e-mail: head@englishschool.ac.cy
website: www.englishschool.ac.cy

***Head*: Stuart J Haggett**

Czech Republic

The English College in Prague
Sokolovska 320, 190-00 Praha 9, Czech Republic
e-mail: headmaster@englishcollege.cz
website: www.englishcollege.cz

***Headmaster*: Peter M de Voil**

France

The British School of Paris
38 Quai de l'Ecluse, 78290 Croissy sur Seine, France
e-mail: headmaster@britishschool.fr
website: www.britishschool.fr

***Headmaster*: Richard Woodall**

Greece

Campion School
PO Box 67484, Pallini, Athens 153 02, Greece
e-mail: satherton@campion.edu.gr
website: www.campion.edu.gr

***Headmaster*: Stephen W Atherton**

Portugal

St Julian's School
Quinta Nova, 2776–601 Carcavelos Codex, Portugal
e-mail: mail@stjulians.com
website: www.stjulians.com

***Headmaster*: David Smith**

Switzerland

Aiglon College
CH-1885 Chesières-Villars Switzerland
e-mail: info@aiglon.ch
website: www.aiglon.ch

***Principal*: Peter Armstrong,** MA

Middle East

Sultanate of Oman

The Indian School, Al Ghubra

PO Box 1887, CPO Seeb, Code 111, Muscat, Sultanate of Oman (Arabian Gulf)
e-mail: principal@indianschool.com
website: www.indianschool.com

***Principal*: G Thanga Durai**

United Arab Emirates

The British School – Al Khubairat

P O Box 4001, Abu Dhabi, United Arab Emirates
e-mail: principal@britishschool.sch.ae
website: www.britishschool.sch.ae

***Principal*: Paul Coackley**

North America

Bermuda

Saltus Grammar School

PO Box HM 2224, Hamilton HMJX, Bermuda
e-mail: head@saltus.bm
website: www.saltus.bm

***Head*: Nigel J G Kermode**

Canada

Ridley College

PO Box 3013, St Catharine's, Ontario L2R 7C3, Canada
e-mail: jonathan_leigh@ridleycollege.com
website: www.ridley.on.ca

***Headmaster*: Jonathan Leigh**

St Andrew's College

15800 Yonge Street, Aurora, Ontario L4G 3H7, Canada
e-mail: ted.staunton@sac.on.ca
website: www.sac.on.ca

***Head*: Edmund G Staunton**

Shawnigan Lake School

1975 Renfrew Road, Postal Bag 2000, Shawnigan Lake, BC V0R 2W1 Canada
e-mail: dbr@sls.bc.ca
website: www.sls.bc.ca

***Head*: David Robertson**

Headmasters' and Headmistresses' Conference

Additional Members

The Constitution of the Headmasters' and Headmistresses' Conference provides that the membership shall consist mainly of Headmasters and Headmistresses of Independent Schools. At the same time, it is held to be a strength of the Conference that its membership should include also a limited number of Headmasters and Headmistresses of schools of Voluntary or Maintained status. There is therefore provision for the election of Headmasters and Headmistresses of schools other than Independent when it is felt that their contribution to education makes their membership appropriate.

Headmasters and Headmistresses elected in this category are in every way full and equal members of the Headmasters' and Headmistresses' Conference, but their schools are not included in the section of the Independent Schools Yearbook which gives detailed particulars of the Independent Schools.

The following is a list of Headmasters and Headmistresses in this special category of the membership:

DR STUART D SMALLWOOD
Bishop Wordsworth's Grammar School, Salisbury, Wilts
Tel: 01722 333851
website: www.bws.wilts.sch.uk

JOHN GRANGER
Bournemouth School, Bournemouth, Dorset
Tel: 01202 512609
website: www.bournemouth-school.bournemouth.sch.uk

ANNE WELSH
George Stephenson High School, Newcastle-upon-Tyne
Tel: 0191 200 8347
website: http://gshs.org.uk

DENIS MULKERRIN
Gordon's School, Woking, Surrey
Tel: 01276 858084
website: www.gordons.surrey.sch.uk

KATE GRIFFIN
Greenford High School, Greenford, Middx
Tel: 020 8578 9152
website: www.greenford.ealing.sch.uk

DR ELIZABETH M SIDWELL
Haberdashers' Aske's Federation, London SE14
Tel: 020 7652 9500
website: www.haaf.org.uk

ROBERT J MASTERS
The Judd School, Tonbridge, Kent
Tel: 01732 770880
website: www.judd.kent.sch.uk

ANDREW M JARMAN
Lancaster Royal Grammar School, Lancaster
Tel: 01524 580600
website: www.lrgs.org.uk

RT REVD PETER HULLAH
Northampton Academy, Northampton
Tel: 01604 402811
website: www.northampton-academy.org

SHAUN FENTON
Pate's Grammar School, Cheltenham, Glos
Tel: 01242 523169
website: www.pates.gloucs.sch.uk

MICHAEL THOMPSON
St Ambrose College, Altrincham, Cheshire
Tel: 0161 980 2711
website: www.st-ambrosecollege.trafford.sch.uk

SIMON DUGGAN
St Anselm's College, Birkenhead, Merseyside
Tel: 0151 652 1408
website: www.st-anselms.com

JOHN E WASZEK
St Edward's College, Liverpool
Tel: 0151 281 1999
website: www.st-edwards.liverpool.sch.uk

TONY JARVIS
St Olave's Grammar School, Orpington, Kent
Tel: 01689 820101
website: www.saintolaves.net

DR ALAN MCMURDO
Thomas Deacon Academy, Peterborough, Cambs
Tel: 01733 426051
website: www.thomasdeaconacademy.com

TONY HALLIWELL
Welbeck College, Loughborough, Leics
Tel: 01509 891700
website: www.dsfc.ac.uk

MARIE GETHRIDGE
Writhlington School, Radstock, Bath and NE Somerset
Tel: 01761 433581
website: www.wsbe.org.uk

PART II

Schools whose Heads are members of the Girls' Schools Association

ALPHABETICAL LIST OF SCHOOLS

GEOGRAPHICAL LIST OF GSA SCHOOLS

Individual School Entries

The Abbey School

Kendrick Road Reading RG1 5DZ
Tel: 0118 987 2256
Fax: 0118 987 1478
e-mail: schooloffice@theabbey.co.uk
website: www.theabbey.co.uk

Founded 1887. Incorporated 1914. Church of England Foundation.

Board of Governors:
Chairman: Mr P Smith, MA
Mrs M Blackburn, OBE
Mrs J Burrell, London, MBS Part 1 Open, AMA
Mrs J Cornell, BA
Mrs M Cottingham, BA
Mr P Doctor, BSc Hons
Mrs M Edwards
Mr R G Griffiths
Professor A Jones, BA Hons, PGCE, DipSoc, FRSA, FCP, FCMI, FInstCPD, FQMW
Dr I Kemp, MB, MRCP, MRCGP, DCH, DOBST, RCOG
Mrs B McDiarmid, CertEd, DipSEN, DipSpLD
Mr G O'Brien, BBS, FCCA, CTA
Revd Béatrice Pearson, BTh, PGCE, MA France, BA France
Dr C F Print, DBA, ACMA, ADipC
Mr R Rand, JP, FCA
Mrs H Rennie, ACA
Mrs F M Rutland, MA
Mr S Smith, BSc Est Man, FRICS, FCIArb, FBEng
Dr B J Snell, BSc Hons, MB BS, MCopth, DO, MRCS, LRCP

***Head*: Mrs Barbara Stanley**, BA QUB, PGCE, FRGS

Deputy Head: Mrs S Jones, NPQH, MA Ed Open, BSc Reading, PGCE Oxon

Assistant Heads:
Mrs S Colebrook, BSc Sheffield, PGCE
Mrs A Lovett, JP, BA, PGCE Durham

Director of Sixth Form Centre: Mrs R Dent, BA Southampton, QTS

Head of Junior School: Mrs J Tuckett, MA Cambridge

Assistant Heads of Junior School:
Mrs Y Goldthorpe, BA Huddersfield, PGCE
Mrs L Glithro, BSc St Andrews, MA Ed Open, PGCE

Early Years Coordinator: Miss R Parsons, BA Lancaster, QTS

Heads of Department:
Art: Mr M Singer, BA Nottingham, PGCE
Biology: Mrs R Johnson, BSc, ARCS London
Business Studies: Mrs S Watt, FCA
Chemistry: Mrs J Harrison, BSc Warwick, PGCE (*also Head of Science*)
Classics: Mrs L Lyle, BA QUB, MLitt Newcastle PGCE
Drama: Ms P Flannery, BA, MA, PGCE, PGDip London
Economics: Mrs V Whistance, BScEcon Aberystwyth, PGCE
English: Mrs J Turkington, BA Lancs, BA Open, MA Lancaster
Food Technology: Mrs S Parsons, CertEd Bath
French: Mrs B Downes, BA Durham, PGCE
Geography: Mrs J Gray, BSc, PGCE Reading
German: Mr C Hammond, BA Reading, PGCE
History: Mrs P Kemp, BA London MA Ed Reading, PGCE
ICT: Ms G Reilly, BSc Dublin, HDipEd, MEd Cambridge
Mathematics: Miss E Cook, BA, MA Oxford, PGCE
Music: Mr S Willis, BA, MA Cambridge, PGCE
Instrumental Music: Mrs B Salisbury, ARCM, LRAM (*also Director of Pastoral Support*)
Physics: Mrs M Robinson, BSc Liverpool, PGCE
Physical Education: Miss R Floyd, BEd Bedford
Psychology: Miss A Davies, BA Sussex, PGCE
Religious Studies: Mr M Giles, BA Wales, PGCE
Science: Mrs R Johnson, BSc, ARCS London (*also Head of Biology*)
Spanish: Mrs M Giblin, LFL Salamanca
Textiles: Mrs J Lesbirel, BEd Cardiff

Junior School:
Science: Mrs L Glithro, BSc St Andrews, MA Ed Open, PGCE
IT: Mrs S Scrace, CertEd Reading, MA Reading
Music: Mrs R Adams, BA Ed Music Exeter
PE: Mrs N Orr, BA Birmingham

There are 20 Visiting Music Staff, 1 Teacher of Speech & Drama, and a School Nurse.

Bursar: Mr G P Kerruish, FRGS

Registrar: Mrs J Miles

Number of Girls. 1,020.

School Ethos. A Church of England School that warmly welcomes girls of all persuasions. The Abbey School has a reputation for academic excellence that is achieved through strong pastoral care and encouragement to participate and achieve each individual's full potential in the particularly broad curricular and extra-curricular programme.

Facilities. Many improvements and extensions to the buildings have been added: a state of the art science block, a separate sixth form suite, six computer rooms, an extensive modern library, a music centre with rooms for class teaching and individual instrumental teaching, and two large assembly halls. In addition, the current major redevelopment of the school will provide additional state-of-the-art classrooms by January 2009. There is a Modern Language Centre with language laboratories. The school has an indoor heated swimming pool. The Junior School has its own buildings, including science laboratories, music facilities, computer room and a fine assembly hall. September 2006 saw the opening of a superb new building for Years 5 and 6 and an expanded library. The Early Years Centre (Nursery and Reception) is housed in a self-contained house with a secluded garden, so that outdoor education is incorporated into the curriculum.

Education. The Abbey School provides a balanced academic education from Nursery to University and Oxbridge levels. Younger girls thrive in the happy, stimulating environment of the Nursery and Junior Schools, where academic, physical and social skills are developed. They easily make the transition to the Senior School, where girls enjoy a similar stimulating academic education. A very broad range of subjects covers all academic subjects, including, Latin, Greek, Psychology, Sociology, Theatre Studies, the Technologies and PE to A level. Standards of Music and Art are outstanding, and the school has achieved Sportsmark Gold (Seniors) and Activemark Gold (Juniors) level in recognition of the range of quality of the Physical Education programme.

Optional Extra Subjects. Music and Speech and Drama lessons are available to children from the age of 7. Tuition is available in a variety of musical instruments: Pianoforte, Violin, Violoncello, Double Bass, Flute, Clarinet, Oboe, Cornet, Trumpet, Horn, Trombone, Euphonium, Tuba, Saxophone, Percussion.

Admission is by assessment for the youngest girls and examination and interviews from Key Stage 1 upwards.

Fees per term (2008-2009). Early Years Centre: Nursery (3+ years) £2,330, Reception (4+ years) £2,700. Junior School: £2,850 (Year 1), £3,250 (Years 2–6). Senior School: £3,660 (Years 7–13).

Scholarships and Bursaries. (*see Scholarship Entries section*). Academic Scholarships are available at ages 11 and 16, including a Wolfson Bursary offering an award of one third fees. Music Awards are also offered at ages 11, 14 and 16. The School has its own Assisted Places Scheme.

Charitable status. The Abbey School is a Registered Charity, number 309115. The School exists to educate academically able girls.

Abbots Bromley School for Girls

A Woodard School

Abbots Bromley Staffordshire WS15 3BW
Tel: 01283 840232 (24 hrs)
Fax: 01283 840988
e-mail: head@abbotsbromley.net
website: www.abbotsbromley.staffs.sch.uk

Founded in 1874, the school is part of the Woodard Schools Corporation (Midland Division).

Visitor: The Rt Revd The Bishop of Lichfield

Council:

Chairman: Mrs B Marlow
Vice-Chairman: Mr R Mansell, ACIB
Prebendary Mrs H Ball, OBE
Mr M Copestake
Mr D J Skipper, MA (*co-opted*)
Mr J Bridgeland, MA
The Revd Canon W Weaver
Mrs S Fisher
Mrs P Norvall
Revd P North, MA
Mrs J Morgan
Captain R Wilson
Revd Canon B Clover (*ex officio*)

Clerk to the Council and Bursar: Mr B I Jones, BSc, FCA

***Head*: Mrs P J Woodhouse**, BMus Hons

Deputy Head: Mr M A Fisher, BEd Hons
Assistant Head, Senior School: Mrs D Crispin, CertEd
Assistant Head, Roch House Preparatory Department: Mrs A Johnson, CertEd
Head of Sixth Form: Mrs A Copley, BA Hons
Head of Boarding: Mrs S May, CertEd
Chaplain: The Revd P Green, MA, PGCE, PGDip
Medical Sister: Sister B Lambert, RGN, NEBSM
Housemistresses:
Meynell Lowe: Mrs B Coulthard, BA Hons, PGCE
Heywood Rice: Mrs M Steer, BA Hons, DipSEN, PGCE
Talbot (*Crofts*): Mrs K Rowlands, BA Hons, PGCE
Coleridge: Mrs E Rigby, BA Hons, PGCE
Keble S Benet's: Mrs S Slater
Selwyn: Mrs V Hawley, BA Hons
Boarding Housemistress: Miss R Francis, BA Hons
Relief Housemistress: Mrs A Anderson

Senior School Academic Staff:

Art:
*Mr D Gleeson, BA Hons, MA Fine Arts, PGCE
Mrs D Crispin, CertEd
Mrs A Moore, BA Hons, PGCE

Business Studies:
Mr M A Fisher, BEd Hons

Careers Officer: Mrs E Rigby, BA Hons, PGCE

Sociology & Politics:
Mrs V Hawley, BA Hons

English:
*Mrs M Steer, BA Hons, PGCE, DipSEN
Mrs E Rigby, BA Hons, PGCE
EFL: Mrs E Lampard, BA Hons, PGCE, CELTA
Drama: Miss J Brandrick, BA Hons

Geography:
*Mrs A Copley, BA Hons, PGCE
Mr C Machell, BA Hons

History:
*Mrs S Towell, BA Hons, PGCE

Home Economics (Cookery & Needlework):
*Mrs S May, CertEd

Information Technology:
*Miss J Hill, BEd Hons
Mr R Ellis (*Technician*)

Learning Enrichment & Support/Gifted & Talented Coordinator:
Mrs U Griffiths, BA Hons, DipT SpLD
Mrs B Bell
Mrs S Walker

Mathematics:
*(*to be appointed*)
Mrs S Booth, BSc Hons, PGCE
Mrs M A Clapham, BSc Hons, PGCE

Modern Languages:
*Mrs K Rowlands, BA Hons (*German/French*)
Mrs B Coulthard, BA Hons, PGCE (*Spanish/French*)
Mrs E Lampard, BA Hons, PGCE, CELTA (*French*)

Music:
Director of Music: Mr C Walker, MMus, ARCM, AMusTCL, LTCL, LRAM
Assistant Director of Music: Miss E Barter, MA Cantab, PGCE, ARCO

PHSE Coordinator: Mrs S May, CertEd

Physical Education:
*Mrs Y Menneer, BEd Hons
Miss J D Hill, BEd Hons
Miss N Lewis, BSc, PGCE

Visiting Specialist Coaches:
Swimming, Tennis, Netball, Fencing, Akido

Religious Studies:
The Revd P Green, MA, PGCE, PGDip
Miss R Francis, BA Hons
Mrs P J Woodhouse, BMus Hons

Sciences:
*Mrs S Adams, BSc Hons, PGCE (*Biology*)
Miss C Tipper, BSc Hons, PGCE (*Chemistry*)
Mrs M Whitehouse, BA, PGCE (*Physics*)
(*to be appointed*)
Mrs K McLoughlin, BA Hons (*Laboratory Technician*)

Junior Department Academic Staff:

Head of Department: Mrs A Johnson, CertEd, Cert Prof St Ed

Mrs S Crout, DipEd
Mrs J Jackson, CertEd
Mrs L S Pickering, CertEd
Mrs C A Spratt, BA Hons, PGCE
Mrs W Gordon, BEd Hons
Mrs L Evans, CertEd
Mrs M Swinnerton, BA Hons, PGCE

Kindergarten:
Mrs A Dunmore, NVQ3

Learning Enrichment & Support:
Mrs M Swinnerton, BA Hons, PGCE
Miss C Hilton
Mr S Woodhouse

Pastoral Assistants:
Mrs E Morton
Mrs J Elkington

GAP Assistants:
Senior GAP Assistant: Miss R Carberry
Miss K Hewitt
Miss R Langtree
Miss E Parker

Ballet:
Artistic Directors:
Mr Russell Alkins, RAD Cert
Mrs Marianne Alkins, RAD Cert

Modern and Tap Dance:
Guest Choreographers and Specialist Teachers

Riding (Abbots Bromley Equestrian Centre):
Director of Equitation: Miss S Vickers, BHSI, CertEd
Instructors:
Mrs S Hemingfield, BHSAI, BHS Stage 4 HK & C, BHS Assessor, NVQ2
Yard Manager:
Miss D Whalley, NVQ3, BHS Stage 2, BHS PTT
Trainee: Miss R Fone, BHS 1 & II

Duke of Edinburgh's Award Scheme:
Mrs S Slater
Mr P Gardner

Administration:

Bursary:
Bursar: Mr B I Jones, BSc, FCA
Assistant Bursar: Mrs M Cochrane
Bursar's Office: Mrs A Heywood
Domestic Bursar: Mrs S Slater
Assistant Domestic Bursar: Mrs S Humphries

Operations Manager: Mr G Stockle

Clerk of Works: Mr A Strudwick

Headmistress's Office:
PA: Mrs H J Meadows
Registrar: Mrs J Dale
Reception: Mrs K Addy

Marketing & Publicity: Mr R Alkins

Visiting Staff:

Speech & Drama:
Mrs M Palmer, LAMDA, LLAM, FRSA
Mrs A-M Morrell, LLAM, FRSA, HND Theatre Design, Dip Fashion & Design

Instrumental Music Staff:

Piano:
Mr C Walker, MMus, ARCM, AMusTCL, LTCL, LRAM
Miss E Barter, MA Cantab ARCO
Mrs J Merriman, MA, PGCE, CTABRSM
Miss H Coupe, GRSM, ARMCM
Mr R Dingle, MA Cantab
Organ: Miss E Barter, MA Cantab, ARCO
Violin & Viola: Mrs M Lloyd, MA
'Cello: Mrs J Merriman, MA, PGCE, CTABRSM
Flute & Piccolo: Miss A Chadwick, GBSM, ABSM, Dip Orchestral Studies Goldsmiths
Clarinet & Saxophone:
Mr I Otley, BA
Bassoon & Oboe: Mr I Otley, BA
Brass:
Mr I Otley, BA
Mr C Walker, MMus, ARCM, AMusTCL, LTCL, LRAM
Percussion: Mr B Griffiths
Guitar: Mr M Dale
Singing:
Miss D Bilodeau, BMus, MMus
Mr R Dingle, MA

Located in a beautiful Staffordshire village, Abbots Bromley School for Girls provides a high-quality all-round education for over 300 girls aged 3–18. This flourishing boarding and day school offers an exceptionally enriching experience for girls of all ages, enjoying and taking advantage of first-class resources and excellent opportunities. These include the unique chance to pursue Dance studies at all levels; Riding in the indoor and outdoor schools and the cross-country course; a dedicated Music School and Performing Arts Theatre; Sports Hall, indoor Swimming pool, astroturf Hockey pitch and Athletics track providing unrivalled Sporting opportunities for girls. Unashamedly non-selective, the school provides an effective and supportive environment where each and every girl is valued for herself and encouraged to give and achieve of her very best. The school boasts an impressive academic record and equally fine standards in Music, Dance, Sport, Riding and Speech and Drama. 'AB' is also an exceptionally friendly community. The Christian ethos, natural surroundings, and Boarding tradition help make for a secure and happy atmosphere where girls can expect to leave the Sixth Form independent and ready and able to take their place in society, confident of their own worth.

"*I am proud to lead such a successful and exciting school, a school with unique gifts and whose value is truly immeasurable*", Trish Woodhouse.

Fees per term (2008-2009). Boarding: £4,140–£7,000; Day: £2,370–£4,200.

Charitable status. Abbots Bromley School for Girls is a Registered Charity, number 1103321. It exists to provide education for girls.

Abbot's Hill School

Bunkers Lane Hemel Hempstead Herts HP3 8RP
Tel: 01442 240333 (both Junior & Senior Depts)
Fax: 01442 269981
e-mail: registrar@abbotshill.herts.sch.uk
website: www.abbotshill.herts.sch.uk

Founded 1912.
Motto: *Vi et Virtute*

Chairman of the Governing Body: Mr C Morgan, MBA, BSc

***Headmistress*: Mrs K Lewis**, MA, BSc, PGCE

Head of Junior Department: Miss K Twinn, BA Hons QTS

Head of Senior Department: Mrs A Stevens, BA Hons, PGCE, NPQH

Bursar: Mr Mark Stephens, BA Hons, FCMA

Registrar: Ms A Cooper

Abbot's Hill School is an Independent Day School for girls aged 3–16 years and boys in the Nursery only. There is a total of 480 pupils in the School from Nursery through to Year 11.

A great emphasis is placed on providing a complete and balanced education. Class sizes are deliberately kept small, which helps to ensure that pupils are well motivated and eager to learn, and allows individual attention from staff members. Each pupil is actively encouraged to achieve his or her potential, and parent-teacher relationships are excellent in this warm and enabling environment. Excellent results are achieved that are at least commensurate with pupil ability, and the outstanding Key Stage results in particular can be seen as a reflection of the School's success.

With small classes and a high teacher-pupil ratio, the school aims to develop the academic and creative talents, social skills and confidence of each pupil. Every girl benefits from being known personally by the Headmistress and teaching staff who seek to create a happy and caring environment.

Premises. The School is situated in 76 acres of parkland on the edge of Hemel Hempstead. The main building is a spacious and comfortable 19th Century house, which, combined with purpose built teaching blocks, Science, Technology and ICT suites, provides our pupils with first class facilities.

Curriculum. During the first three years, a broad programme based on the National Curriculum is followed, encompassing both academic and creative subjects. Each girl's potential and progress is carefully monitored by both teaching staff and a personal tutor. Subjects studied include English, Maths, Science, French, Spanish, Geography, History, Information and Communication Technology, Religious Studies, Music, Personal, Social and Health Education, Art and Design, Food Studies and Home Economics, Physical Education and Child Development.

In Years 10 and 11 a core GCSE curriculum of 6 subjects is followed with girls choosing up to three further subjects.

Music. The School has a very strong Music Department with excellent facilities. The new Performing Arts building includes studios for dance, drama and music. The School Choirs and Orchestra perform regularly in concerts, recitals, plays, musicals and various functions throughout the year.

Sports. The School has a strong sporting tradition. There is a new well-equipped Sports Hall, lacrosse pitches, grass and hard tennis courts, and a heated outdoor swimming pool. The main sports played are Lacrosse, Netball, Athletics, Tennis, Rounders and Swimming. All girls are encouraged to participate in the sporting opportunities at Abbot's Hill and currently there are a number of girls who have reached County and National standard in selected sports.

Extra-Curricular Activities. Many activities and clubs are held outside of School and these vary in range from Dance, Art, Duke of Edinburgh's Award Scheme, Music, Speech and Drama and all sports.

Sixth Form and Beyond. Baird House girls are encouraged to consider their future prospects and are very well prepared to choose from a wide range of A level and GNVQ courses offered to them when they leave. There is a comprehensive careers programme available to further enhance their decisions including an annual Sixth Form Forum where many schools exhibit their Sixth Form Courses.

Religion. Abbot's Hill is a Church of England foundation. Children of all faiths are welcome at the School and all religious observations are respected.

Admission. (*see Scholarship Entries section*). Admission to Abbot's Hill is by Entrance Examination, interview, and a report from the previous school. Girls are admitted to the Senior Department at 11. There may be occasional vacancies at 12 and 13. Bursaries and scholarships are available.

Fees per term (2008-2009). Baird House: £4,330 (Years 7–11); St Nicholas House: £2,445–£3,040 (Reception to Year 6); Nursery: £240 (per morning session), £160 (per afternoon session).

Junior Department. The Junior Department of Abbot's Hill, St Nicholas House, is situated in the same grounds as Baird House. St Nicholas House provides nursery, pre-prep and preparatory education for girls aged 3–11 and boys in the nursery only.

Further information. Abbot's Hill welcomes visits from prospective parents and pupils. If you would like to visit the School. please contact the Registrar for an appointment on 01442 240333 or e-mail registrar@abbotshill.herts.sch.uk.

Charitable status. Abbot's Hill Charitable Trust is a Registered Charity, number 311053, which exists to provide high quality education for children.

Alderley Edge School for Girls

Wilmslow Road Alderley Edge Cheshire SK9 7QE
Tel: 01625 583028
Fax: 01625 590271
e-mail: admissions@aesg.co.uk
website: www.aesg.info

Chairman of Governors: Mr George Hutchison

***Headmistress*: Mrs Kathy Mills**, BA Hons, DipEdMan Wales

Deputy Headmistress: Mrs T Pollard, BEd Hons Secondary

Head of Junior School: Mrs C Hulme-McKibbin
Head of Lower School (*Years 7–9*): Mrs A Baker
Head of Upper School (*Years 10–11*): Mrs J Waterhouse
Head of Sixth Form: Mrs C Sarsfield
Curriculum Development Officer: Mrs E Duthie
Bursar: Mrs P McGill
Registrar: Mrs J Bedigan

Heads of Department:

Art: Mrs J Jamieson
Biology: Mrs A Williamson
Business Studies: Mrs J Waterhouse
Chemistry: Mrs C Broady
Classics: Mrs C Walster
Design Technology: Mrs B Milner
Drama: Miss C Bonham
English: Ms L Telford
Geography: Mrs C Wood
History: Mrs J Nicholson
ICT: Mr G Allcock
Mathematics: Dr G Gladman
Modern Foreign Languages: Mr C Randall
Music: (*to be appointed*)
Physical Education: Mrs S Waite
Physics: Mrs K Torr
Psychology: Mrs A Raval
Religious Education: Mr A Mason
Science: Mrs A Williamson

Age Range. 3–18.

Number in School. Nursery 26; Junior School 183; Senior School 406.

Fees per term (2008-2009). Nursery £1,521; Key Stage 1 £1,829; Key Stage 2 £2,197; Senior £2,759.

Background. For many years the village of Alderley Edge was the location for two of the finest Independent Girls' Schools in the North West of England. In September 1999 the two schools became one. An independent, all girls, ecumenical school is unique in England and the merger of the two schools was welcomed and supported by the Anglican and Roman Catholic clergy and the founders of both schools.

The Sisters of St Joseph, a Roman Catholic Order, founded Mount Carmel School in 1945. St Hilary's was founded in

1817 and became part of the Woodard Corporation, a Church of England foundation, in 1955. Alderley Edge School for Girls is linked to the Woodard Corporation, the largest group of schools in England. Among them are independent and maintained schools in England, the United States and Australia.

General. This forward-looking girls' school offers a high level of personal attention. Respect for hard work, the development of the whole person and good discipline are the traditional principles on which our creative and innovative educational philosophy is based. We aim to provide a well-balanced education which celebrates achievement in all aspects of school life from Nursery to Sixth Form.

Location. The school is situated in a semi-rural area of Alderley Edge, 15 miles south of Manchester with easy access to the motorway network and only minutes from Manchester Airport and two Intercity main line stations. Transport is readily available throughout the area.

Admissions. The Nursery School caters for girls and boys from 3 years. Admission for girls to the Junior School is at 4/5 years old. Admission to the Senior School is at 11 years by Entrance Examination and interview.

Curriculum. *Senior School*: Students follow a broad and balanced curriculum based on the National Curriculum but with many additions. Subjects include: Mathematics, English Language, English Literature, IT, Biology, Chemistry, Physics, French, German, Spanish, Latin, History, Geography, Music, Drama, Religious Studies, Food Technology, Design & Technology, Art, Design Technology, Business Studies, PPE (Philosophy, Politics,Economics), PSHE (Personal, Social, Health Education) and Physical Education. At A Level the following subjects are offered in addition those listed above: Further Mathematics, Classical Civilisation, Philosophy & Ethics, Psychology, Performance Studies and General Studies. Academic excellence is the school's main aim and attention is paid to meeting the individual needs and abilities of the students. Small classes and continuous assessment ensure high levels of pupil achievement.

Junior School: Creative learning is at the heart of the Junior School. The work is based on the National Curriculum with English, Mathematics and Science providing the foundations for learning with History, Geography, RE, Art, Design, ICT, Music, PE and French completing the curriculum. Latin is also taught from Year 5.

Examination Results 2007. *Key Stage 2 SATs*: 100% of pupils achieved Level 4 in English, Science and Mathematics. 75% achieved Level 5 in English, 54% in Mathematics and 70% in Science.

GCSE results: Overall pass rate (A*–C) 95%; Average passes per candidate (A*–C) 9.7.

A Level results: Pass rate 100%.

The Arts. *Music*: A very large percentage of pupils learn a musical instrument and examinations may be taken. The school runs 4 choirs, 2 orchestras, a jazz band and numerous smaller instrumental ensembles including 3 string groups, a brass group and 5 different woodwind groups. Many cups have been won in local festivals and pupils perform in local youth orchestras.

Drama and Dance: Both are offered. ESB examinations may be taken. The majority of pupils are involved in school productions and all pupils participate in House and other productions.

Sports and Clubs. *Sports*: tennis, rounders, hockey, athletics, netball, gymnastics, football, swimming, dance, cross-country, badminton, volleyball, squash, fitness, self-defence. Sixth Form only: aerobics, Break-away skills for women.

Senior Clubs: language club, Bio/Chem workshop, Physics workshop, French club, book club, DT club, magazine committee, dance, drama, poetry, public speaking, hockey, netball, tennis, rounders, athletics, Duke of Edinburgh's Award, Games, Comenius European Educational Project, Young Enterprise (Sixth Form only).

Junior Clubs: Contemporary Dance, Drama, Judo, Short Tennis, Brownies, Fencing, Gardening, Fit 'n' Funky, French, Netball, Spanish, Library, Beacon Prayer Group, Cycling Proficiency.

Facilities. In building a new school we have achieved our objective to remain small enough to care for every child's needs and yet the school enjoys all the benefits and resources of a much larger school. A multi-million pound investment programme has provided a new Senior School, and a completely refurbished Junior School. Facilities include six superbly equipped science laboratories, two ICT suites with on-line facilities throughout the school, Language Suite with language laboratory, Humanities block with Business Studies centre, competition-size Sports Hall, Gymnasium, Performing Arts Centre, Chapel and a Library with breathtaking views over the Cheshire Plain.

Scholarships/Bursaries/Financial Support. Several Academic scholarships and scholarships for Music, Art and Sport are awarded at 11+. Some Bursaries are available (income linked).

Charitable status. Alderley Edge School for Girls is a Registered Charity, number 1006726. It exists to provide education for children.

Amberfield School
Ipswich

Nacton Ipswich Suffolk IP10 0HL
Tel: 01473 659265
Fax: 01473 659843
e-mail: registrar@amberfield.suffolk.sch.uk
website: www.amberfield.suffolk.sch.uk

Chairman: Mr A Lang, MA, MBA, MCIBS

Governors:
Revd Canon G Grant
Mr G Hall
Mrs J Hall
Mr G Thomas
Mrs C Whight
Mr M T Williams
Mrs S Marsh

***Acting Headmistress*: Mrs L Ingram**

Head of Junior School: Mrs C Dungey

Bursar: Mr T Llewellyn

Management Team:
Mrs L Ingram
Mrs H Leeder
Mr T Llewellyn

Registrar: Mrs C Charles

Amberfield School is an independent day school for girls aged 3–16 and boys aged 3–7 years that nestles in pleasant woodland on the edge of Nacton village, near Ipswich. Benefiting from its peaceful, out-of-town location it is nonetheless well placed for major routes including the A12 and A14. In addition to the original buildings there are modern, purpose-built classrooms, laboratories, ICT suites and a Drama Studio: all rooms are light, airy and well equipped. Within the grounds there are plenty of opportunities for outdoor learning including a full range of outdoor sports facilities.

We have a wonderfully supportive and friendly environment with talented, enthusiastic and expert teachers who will really get to know your child. Our small classes mean that we can nurture our pupils' individual talents. Personalised education is not a new concept at Amberfield. We create an environment that is safe and happy in which we all have fun learning together.

We are justly proud of the achievements of our pupils; our value added scores are high. A full set of GCSE A grades, outstanding musical and sporting achievements and highly-developed leadership skills are not unusual. In our care, all our pupils grow in confidence.

Our ethos is to 'have a go and believe in yourself'. There is a wealth of opportunity for involvement in a wide range of sporting and cultural activities. Our robot team has been national champions for two consecutive years, won the World Championship in Germany in 2006 and this year two teams have qualified for the International Finals. Teamwork and leadership skills are important; these are developed as the girls go through the senior school. In Year 9 they can opt for the Duke of Edinburgh's Award Scheme and by Year 11 the girls are at the top of the school so they have lots of opportunities to gain posts of responsibility.

The School Day. For all children the school day begins at 8.40 am and ends at 3.45 pm. We have provision for supervised care beyond the school day from 8.00 am to 5.30 pm. Nursery children attend on a full-time or session basis.

Entry to the School. Juniors are tested informally in a classroom situation. Nursery children must be 3 years of age before entry and qualify for the Early Years Grant. We encourage prospective pupils to spend a day with us to experience the unique Amberfield atmosphere for themselves. There is an 11+ test in January for girls entering the Senior school.

Curriculum. A broad range of subjects is offered at GCSE (including Astronomy) and girls in Year 10 can opt for the Sports Leadership Award.

ICT plays an important part in delivering the curriculum throughout the school from a basic introduction in Reception to GCSE in the senior school. The school is fully networked and well equipped with computers and interactive whiteboards.

The careers staff are supported by Suffolk Connexions and advice is provided to help pupils select the most appropriate subjects for their planned career path. Amberfield students continue their studies in a variety of local sixth forms, both in the independent and maintained sector.

There is a dedicated member of staff who gives learning support and is fully qualified to assess and deliver help in the areas where it is required.

Pastoral Care. Maintaining the highest standards of pastoral care is at the heart of Amberfield School's philosophy. This is crucial to each pupil's self-confidence and success. Every effort is made to ensure pupils are happy and at ease with school life.

Form teachers are the mainstay of the pastoral care system. By developing an open and trusting relationship with their pupils, form teachers can provide a receptive ear and the essential support that may be required. There is excellent communication with parents so that school and family can work in partnership.

Creative Life. Artistic talent and practical skills are encouraged at all ages. Original and exciting work is produced in art, textiles and home economics. There are junior and senior choirs, specialist singing and ensemble groups and orchestras. The Drama Studio with its sound and lighting box provides many opportunities for dance and theatre studies.

Sport. Sport is an integral part of life at Amberfield. Physical fitness is essential to our well-being and pupils benefit greatly from the experience of working as a team. There are regular matches against other schools in netball, hockey, cross-country, athletics and tennis. Amberfield pupils have played at county and national level in all these sports and also in skiing and gymnastics. Tennis is particularly strong with LTA coaching and we have huge success in tournaments across the full age range. The wide range of sports on offer, from aerobics and trampolining to volleyball, enables every pupil to find their forte.

Fees per term (2008-2009). Senior School: £3,075; Junior School: £2,395; Nursery (full time) and Reception: £1,955.

Scholarships. Academic, Art, Music, Sport and Tennis Scholarships are awarded annually to pupils at 11+.

Bursaries. Five Junior Bursaries are available annually.

Badminton School

Westbury-on-Trym Bristol BS9 3BA
Tel: 0117 905 5271
Fax: 0117 962 8963
e-mail: admissions@badminton.bristol.sch.uk
website: www.badminton.bristol.sch.uk

Motto: *Nurture. Inspire. Empower*
Founded 1858. Non denominational.

Board of Governors:

Vice-Presidents:
Professor Sir Mark Richmond, BA, PhD, ScD, MRCPath, FRS
Mrs P Stone, MA
Mr A M Urquhart, OBE, BA

Chairman: Mrs Alison Bernays

Vice-Chairman: Mr R Hodder Williams

Clerk to the Governors, Secretary and Bursar: Mr T Synge

***Headmistress*: Mrs J A Scarrow**, BA Manchester

Deputy Head: Mrs V Drew, BA Wales
Head of Sixth Form: Mrs K Dodd, MA Essex
Head of Junior School: Mrs A Lloyd, MA Ed Open, CertEd Oxon, LGSM

Heads of Department:

English: Miss L Griffith, BA Oxon
Theatre Studies: Mr S Gentry, BA Leicester

Mathematics: Dr D Cook, BA Oxon

Science:
Chemistry: Dr C Enos, BSc, PhD Swansea
Physics: Mr P Foster, BSc London
Biology: Mrs N Warden, BSc Exeter, BA Oxon
Home Economics: Mrs J E Jones, DipHEc Cardiff
ICT: Mr D Williams, MSc Warwick

French: Mrs N Walton, BA Durham
German: Miss S J Whyatt, BA London
Spanish: Mrs K Dunn, BA Hull

Classics: Mrs C Hamlett BA Classics Bristol

Humanities:
History: Ms M Stimpson, MA Edinburgh
Geography: Mrs F Annear, BA Durham
Economics: Mrs D Betterton, BA Exeter
Religious Education: Mrs J Kearey, MA Oxon

Music: Mr M Bale, GRSM, LRAM, LGSM

Creative Arts: Miss F Creber, BA Wales

Physical Education: Miss G Richards, CertEd Bedford

Houses and Housemistresses:
Head of Boarding: Mrs J Dowling, MA Cantab
Housemistresses:
Mrs S Callister, DipDomSc, PGCE
Miss L Van Os
Mrs S Holdaway, BSc Open

School Doctor: Dr D Kershaw, MBChB, MRCGP

Marketing Director: Mrs H Lightwood, BA Leicester, PG Dip Marketing
Admissions Officer: Miss K Balmforth
Headmistress's PA: Mrs P Thompson

Badminton is an independent girls' boarding, weekly boarding and day school situated in a 20 acre site on the edge of Durdham Downs on the outskirts of the university city of Bristol.

Age Range of Pupils. 4 to 18.

Number of Pupils. 434: Boarding 197; Day: Senior 127, Junior 110.

Number of Staff. Full-time teaching 45, Part-time teaching 12. Teacher Pupil ratio is currently 1:7.

Educational Philosophy. At Badminton a broad curriculum, the study of national and international affairs, adequate leisure and self-disciplined freedom give opportunity for the fullest development of personality and individual talent. Girls at Badminton regularly achieve outstanding academic results. However the School is certainly not a production line for bright girls destined for top university honours. Girls leave Badminton not only having gained first-rate results but having developed into thinking and independent young women. Constant encouragement is the key to the success of girls in a relaxed yet purposeful environment, in which they are well taught, challenged and enabled to achieve.

Staff/pupil relations are mature and friendly, based on the principles of courtesy and mutual respect; high standards are expected for both work and behaviour, and an honest and open response is particularly valued. The ethos of the School has traditionally encouraged caring moral attitudes, individuality and challenge.

Boarding. Boarders need security, affection and lots to do at weekends, and life is geared towards keeping them busy and fully occupied. Full-time, weekly or flexi boarding are offered, allowing girls to easily combine their academic schedules with the many activities that are on offer after school and at weekends. Junior boarders have their own house adjacent to gardens and play area and within easy access of the swimming pool and other facilities. Northcote and School House accommodate boarders in Years 9, 10 and 11 and the Sixth Form are accommodated in the Sixth Form Centre where they have single or double study bedrooms. A new middle school boarding house with state-of-the-art facilities is being constructed for Years 9–11, ready for September 2008. In each House boarders have the support of a resident Housemistress, an Assistant Housemistress and House Tutor.

Curriculum. The School Curriculum reflects the career-minded aspirations of both parents and pupils and there is an outstanding record of academic achievement and entry to higher education. The emphasis at Badminton is on all-round education, not narrowly academic, and both the curriculum and the timetable are constructed to create a balance between academic achievement, personal development, life skills and other enterprising activity.

The school currently offers 18 subjects at GCSE and A Level: most of the girls take 9 GCSE Levels and go on to take 4 or 5 AS and 3 or 4 A Levels in the Sixth Form. Mathematics and Science are particularly strong. Class size averages 16 in the main school, and about 12 in the Sixth Form.

There is a full general studies course in the Sixth Form which includes Health Education, Politics, Model United Nations, European Youth Parliament, First Aid, Computing, Information Technology and additional languages. The Careers section is particularly strong.

Academic Record. Badminton has a fine academic record at GCSE, AS and A Levels and believes in the pursuit of academic excellence without cramming. The school is currently No 4 in the national league tables. Girls are expected to produce results according to their ability and to develop their individual talents. The GCSE and A Level pass rate is 100% and 100% of the Sixth Form go on to degree courses, including Oxford and Cambridge (20%).

Facilities. The School is well equipped with classrooms, including a large modern block containing 8 science laboratories, a Creative Arts Centre, several re-equipped computer rooms, a languages' listening room, theatre, gymnasium, 7 tennis courts, playing fields, heated indoor swimming pool, a new all-weather sports facility, Casson Library, fiction library, numerous satellite libraries, eight common rooms, an extended and refurbished Sixth Form Centre and 2 Music Schools.

Music and Creative Arts. It is the policy that all girls are involved in the Creative Arts, both within the curriculum and as extra-curricular activities, and the School attaches great importance to the development of musical and artistic talent.

Music is extremely popular at Badminton with over 85% of all pupils studying at least one musical instrument. There is a wide range of choral and instrumental groups available to choose from at the school including Junior and Senior Choir, Schola (choral group), Barbarella (female barber shop), orchestra, swing band, rock groups, string ensembles, woodwind ensembles and other mixed musical groups. With nearly 30 visiting peripatetic teachers, all of whom are professional musicians, the students can study any instrument of their choice. There are a wide variety of performance opportunities including informal concerts, concerts for the local community, music festivals, two major concerts a year plus a rock concert. Badminton musicians have also toured internationally to Ireland, Hungary and Italy.

There is a wide choice of Creative Arts – Art, Drama, Pottery, Light Crafts, Textiles, Printmaking, Design, Jewellery-making and Photography. There are seven dramatic productions every year where the girls have the chance to produce, direct and stage-manage house plays: there are also joint music and drama productions with boys' schools.

Clubs and Societies. Science, Politics, Young Enterprise, Languages Vivantes, Geographical, Mathematical, Debating, Public Speaking, Social Service, Drama, Art, Librarians, Historical, Young Engineers, Model United Nations, European Youth Parliament, Christian Union, Chess.

Games and Activities. The School offers hockey, tennis, netball, swimming, athletics, rounders, squash, gymnastics, badminton, volleyball, trampolining and enters girls for county trials where appropriate. There are international sports tours every year.

Optional extras include self-defence, fencing, riding, driving, golf, judo and skating. All girls participate in activities which include the full choice of games and creative arts as above and boarders have the opportunity of additional activities at the weekend. The Duke of Edinburgh's Award is taken by over half the pupils with many gaining bronze, silver and gold awards. There are regular trips abroad to European countries, especially for art, history, music, geography, skiing and exchanges with trusted schools in France, Germany and Spain.

Badminton is fortunate in being in a university city; regular visits are arranged to concerts, lectures and theatres, including municipal and civic activities, and there is considerable contact with the University and outside visits to industry and universities; girls attend short courses on Industry. There is a flourishing Social Services Group, where girls help in primary schools, day nurseries, and with elderly people, gardening and cooking.

Admission. Entry to the Junior School is by personal interview, English, Mathematics and non-verbal reasoning tests; to the Senior School it is by a Badminton entrance examination for girls aged 11–13. The Headmistress likes to see all girls and their parents before entry where possible. Entry to the Sixth Form requires girls to sit entrance exams in two subjects they would like to study for A Level plus a general paper.

Prospective parents are encouraged to visit the school individually. To obtain a prospectus and arrange a visit, please contact the Marketing and Admissions Department.

Scholarships and Bursaries. (*see Scholarship Entries section*). Scholarships and Bursaries of up to half fees are offered both for entrance to the Senior School and the Sixth Form for academic excellence, music, art and all-round ability.

Bursaries are means-tested and awarded on the basis of parents' financial circumstances.

Fees per term (2008-2009). Day: Seniors £4,790, Juniors £2,230–£3,270. Boarders: Seniors £8,510, Juniors £5,640.

Charitable status. Badminton School Limited is a Registered Charity, number 311738. It exists for the purpose of educating children.

Bedford High School for Girls

Bromham Road Bedford MK40 2BS
Tel: 01234 360221
Fax: 01234 353552
e-mail: head@bedfordhigh.co.uk
website: www.bedfordhigh.co.uk

The School is part of the same foundation as Bedford School for Boys endowed by Sir William Harpur in 1566.

Governors
Chairman: Mrs R Wallace, FRCS
Deputy Chairman: Mr W M B Steele, MSc, BSc, MBA
Staff Representative: Mrs J Abbott
Parent Representative: Mrs D Stewart, BSc, MBA
Ms J Anderson, LLB
Mr F Cattley
Cllr D Lawrence
Dr D Livesey, PhD, BSc, ACGI
Ms T Winter

‡ *Post-graduate Certificate in Education/QTS or equivalent*

***Headmistress*: Mrs J A Eldridge**, BSc Bristol, MBA EdMan ‡

Deputy Head: Mrs J Pan, BSc London ‡
Assistant Head (*Performance Management*): Mrs S Mason Patel, BA Dunelm ‡
Assistant Head (*Pastoral*): Mrs G Surtees, BA Manchester, CertEd ‡
Head of Sixth Form: Mr C Canning, BA, BD NUI ‡
Head of Key Stage 4: Mr G Burden, BSc London
Head of Key Stage 3: Mrs G Sayce, CertEd Manchester

Art, Design & Technology:
Mr M Bean , MA UCE, BA ‡ (*Head of Art*)
Mrs J Wilkins, BA Leicester Polytechnic
Mrs K Nelson, BA Duncan of Jordanstone College of Art ‡
Mrs P M Villé, Art TCert, Durham, PGD SpLD (*Art*)
Mrs G Sayce, CertEd, Manchester (*Tech*)
Mrs G Surtees, BA Manchester, CertEd ‡ (*Tech*)

Business Studies & Economics:
Mr J Lawrence, BA Leicester, MA London, Trinity TESOL Cert ‡
Mrs L Birch, BA Open University, CertEd

Careers:
Mrs A Samuel, BA Leeds, ACCEG ‡

Classics:
Mrs J Morris, MA Cantab (Girton) (*Head of Classics*)
Mrs L Parker, BMus Manchester, GRNCM, ARMCM ‡

Dance & Drama:
Mrs F Kemp, MA Leeds (*Head of Drama*)
Miss L Bream, Dip LCD, AISTD
Mrs C McCormack
Mrs L Parker, BA De Montfort
Mrs H Redish, LRAD
Mrs C Riddington-Smith, Acting Diploma Bristol Old Vic
Mrs E Sancto, BA Middlesex, AISTD
Miss S Wilkins, FISTD
Mrs S Winter, BEd De Montfort

English:
Mrs C-L Oldfield, BA Manchester ‡ (*Head of English*)
Mrs D Clifton, BA Bristol ‡
Mrs J Marriott, BA Manchester ‡
Mr J Owen, BA Cantab (St Catharine's College) ‡
Mrs S Mason Patel, BA Dunelm ‡
Mrs A Wilson, MA Northampton, Higher Dip Education UCD, BA UCD

Geography & Geology:
Mrs D Whiteley, BSc London ‡ (*Head of Geography*)
Mr B Purser, BSc Sheffield ‡
Mrs C Rogers, BA Liverpool, PG Dip Occupational Health & Safety ‡

History:
Mrs K Cruse, BA Sheffield ‡
Mr D Griffiths, BA Manchester ‡
Mrs L O'Cleirigh, MA, BA Sheffield

ICT:
Mr M Bean, MA UCE, BA ‡ (*Head of Department*)
Mr D Leitner, MSc Hertfordshire, Professional Cert RAM

International Baccalaureate Coordinator:
Mr P Herrick, MA OU, BTech Bradford ‡

International Support:
Mrs A Laing, BA Newcastle ‡

Learning Support:
Mrs M Long, GRSM

Mathematics:
Dr I C H Pullen, BEd Cantab (Churchill College), BA, MSc, PhD Open, MIMA, CertEd HCHE (*Head of Department*)
Mrs C Bawden, BSc Loughborough, CertEd ‡
Mrs A Dorber, BSc London ‡
Dr K Dwamena, MSc, PhD Minsk Belarus ‡
Mrs C Gribben, BSc Leeds ‡
Mrs M Hardman, BSc Salford ‡
Mr D McFarlane, BSc Exeter ‡
Mrs G Malik, BSc Hertfordshire ‡

Modern Languages:
Mrs M Gomez, Licenciàda en Filologia Inglesa, Madrid ‡ (*Head of Spanish and MFL*)
Mrs D Arrowsmith, MA Nottingham ‡ (*Head of French*)
(*to be appointed*) (*Head of German*)
Mrs J Chadwick, BA Oxon (St Hugh's) ‡
Mrs L Cebula, BA Reading ‡
Mrs R Collier, BA Birmingham, CFPS TESL Primary ‡
Mr O Hertout, DEUG Beauvais, Licence Amiens ‡
Mrs A Samuel, BA Leeds, ACCEG ‡

Language Assistants:
Mrs S Bell (*French*)
Ms Nina Gottschlich (*German*)

Music:
Dr S J Weston, MPhil, PhD Leicester, GRSM London, LTCL, Professional Cert RAM ‡ (*Director of Music*)
Mr D Leitner, MSc Hertfordshire, Professional Cert RAM (*Music Technology*)
Mrs L Parker, BMus Manchester, GRNCM, ARMCM ‡ (*Class Teaching, Piano*)
Mrs J Leitner, GRSM London, LRAM (*Music Technology*)
Mr L Arnold (*Percussion*)
Miss E Attwood, BA Open, LRAM, ARCM, FTCL, FLCM, Professional Cert RAM (*Cello, Piano*)
Mr S Barber, MA Cantab, FRCO ‡ (*Organ, Piano*)
Miss J Benham, BMus London, LRAM Teacher's & Performer's, CT ABRSM (*Piano*)

Mr P J Bond, GRSM Manchester, ARMCM, DipEd Reading ‡ (*Senior Piano Teacher*)
Mr A Boynton, BA Reading, FRCO, ARCM, LRAM, FTCL, CHM, ADCM ‡ (*Piano*)
Mr P Davies, ALCM (*Guitar*)
Mrs H Goldsmith, BMus London, MA Lit Open, LGSM ‡ (*Flute, Recorder & Flute Ensemble*)
Mr P Gyles, GTCL, LTCL (*Violin, Viola, Ensembles*)
Mrs C Harrison, LRAM, LCST (*Piano*)
Mr A Haughton, LRAM ‡ (*Keyboard, Jazz Piano*)
Ms K Hills, GRSM London, ARCM (*Bassoon, Flute*)
Miss R Hoskins, BA Newcastle, ARCM, MSTAT (*Piano*)
Mrs C John, GRSM London, Cert AdvStudies RCM, ARCM, LRAM, MTC ‡ (*Clarinet, Piano*)
Mrs L Lavery, BA Liverpool ‡ (*Oboe, Recorder, Piano*)
Miss E Scorah, LRAM (*Harp*)
Mr M Wells, BMus RCM, ARCM (*Brass and Wind Band*)
Miss H Western, LRAM, ARCM (*Voice*)
Mrs D Williams, BA Southampton, ATCL (*Violin, Viola and Ensembles*)

Political Studies:
Mr D Griffiths, BA Manchester ‡

Physical Education:
Mrs J Axford, BA Ed Exeter (*Head of PE*)
Mr M Deards, BSc De Montfort
Miss Z Gray, BSc Chichester ‡
Miss D Harris, BEd De Montfort
Mrs F Stedman

Psychology:
Mr R Mavenga, MSc, BEd Zimbabwe

Religious Education:
Mrs S Crisp, MA Oxon (Regent's Park) ‡
Mrs T Monks, MA, BA Cantab (Girton)

Science:
Mrs A Jackson, BSc Sussex (*Head of Science & Head of Chemistry*)
Mr G Burden, BSc London ‡ (*Head of Physics*)
(*to be appointed*) (*Head of Biology*)
Mrs L M Davies, BSc Wales
Mr P Herrick, MA OU, BTech Bradford ‡
Mrs G Hopton, BSc London (King's College) ‡
Mrs M Samuels, BEd Cantab
Mrs S Sellars, BSc Nottingham ‡
Mr A Stuart, BEd Nottingham ‡
Mrs M Wathen, BSc Leeds ‡
Mrs M Nayar

Librarians:
Mrs S Coleman, BA Manchester Polytechnic, MCILIP
Mrs S Figg, City & Guilds Library and Information Assistants Certificate

Housemistresses:
The Quantocks: Mrs S Nicholson, BA Newcastle ‡
Wimborne Grange: (*to be appointed*)
Westlands: Mrs J Leitner, GRSM, LRAM

Junior School:

Headmistress: Mrs C Royden, MA
Deputy Headmistress; Mrs D Parkman, BSc Loughborough ‡

Junior School Staff:
* *Head of Year*
Mrs H Brimble, BEd Birmingham
*Mrs P Burgess, CertEd London
Mrs T Copp, BA Surrey ‡
*Mrs C Ibbotson, BA Birmingham ‡
Mrs K Nicholls, BSc UCW Aberystwyth
*Mrs K Potter, BA Durham ‡
Mrs A Pettifar, BEd De Montfort
Mrs B Weltz, BA London ‡
Mr D Williams, BA Southampton, LRAM, ARCO, CertEd
*Miss S Wormald, BEd Manchester Metropolitan

School Nurses:
Mrs L Ensor-Clinch, BA Luton, RGN
Mrs M Lenehan, RGN, UKCC

School Doctor:
Dr J Butlin, MBChB, MRCGP, DRCOG

Administrative Staff:
Bursar: P Tyldesley
Registrar: Mrs D Banham

Bedford High School for Girls, founded in 1882, has a long tradition of academic excellence. As a day and boarding school taking girls from 7 to 18 years (average number 800), we provide outstanding opportunities and the highest standards in pastoral care to create a positive environment where all are inspired to achieve their potential.

The on-site Junior School provides an ideal foundation, fostering an enquiring mind and establishing good study skills, within a caring atmosphere. Juniors have the benefit of specialist teachers and use main school facilities whilst enjoying their own purpose built accommodation.

Following a broad, general education a choice may be made from 15 GCSE subjects, 30 A Levels and the International Baccalaureate. Academic results are consistently high. 11 fully equipped laboratories accommodate the large numbers taking Sciences for A Level. Modern Foreign Languages and the Creative Arts are particular strengths. The recent installation of superb ICT facilities, fully networked enabling fast access to the Internet, illustrates a commitment to the future. With 23 acres of playing fields, 11 grass and two hard tennis courts, a new Sports Hall and Swimming Pool and the river nearby, the provision in sports is outstanding. Teams excel in lacrosse, hockey and tennis. The school has an enviable reputation for swimming and rowing. The theatre also enables all to experience the fun and excitement involved in performance.

There is an emphasis on the importance of realising individual potential. Careers guidance and preparation for Higher Education begin at the age of 13 years. A programme of personal development and health awareness is conducted by form tutors. Almost all in the Sixth Form continue their education at university with a number of Oxbridge entrants each year.

Extra-curricular activities are diverse: examples include chess, cricket, dance, harp, internet club, rock band, Duke of Edinburgh's Award, Combined Cadet Force, and Young Enterprise. Many activities take place with our brother school, Bedford School.

Boarding. There is a vibrant community of 134 girls from 32 countries living in a family atmosphere under the care and guidance of housemistresses. A full range of weekend activities is provided and included within the fees, with transport supplied at the beginning and end of terms. Centrally sited in Bedford, the school is convenient for all London airports.

Entrance Examination. Assessments and entrance examinations are held in January for entry the following September. Entrance to the Sixth Form is by GCSE results, school report and interview.

Scholarships and Bursaries. (*see Scholarship Entries section*). Scholarships are awarded for academic, artistic and sporting excellence at 11+, 12+ and 13+ and also on entry to the Sixth Form. Bursary assistance is available from 11+ to support tuition fees.

Fees per term (2008-2009). Tuition: Junior School £2,508; Senior School £3,537. Boarding: £3,091.

Charitable status. The Bedford Charity (The Harpur Trust) is a Registered Charity, number 204817. It exists to provide a high quality education for girls.

Benenden School

Cranbrook Kent TN17 4AA
Tel: 01580 240592
Fax: 01580 240280
e-mail: registry@benenden.kent.sch.uk
website: www.benenden.kent.sch.uk

Council:
Mr C A A Covell, MA (*Chairman*)
Mrs R J Johnston (*Vice Chairman*)
Mr G S Cherry (*Chairman of the Building Committee*)
Mrs F H Crewdson, BSc Hons
Mr O R Darbishire, MA, MSc, PhD
Mr M C C Goolden, MA (*Chairman of the Finance Committee*)
Mrs S J Hayes, BA
Mr T H P Haynes, BA
Miss D M Lavin, MA, DipEd
Mr C H Moore, BA
Mr H Salmon, BA (*GBGSA Representative*)
Mr S Smart, BSc, FCA
Mr B V R Thomas, MA
Mr M K H Leung, BA, Dip Soc (*Honorary Representative for the Hong Kong Trust*)
Mr N Allen (*Secretary to the Council and School Bursar*)

***Headmistress*: Mrs C M Oulton**, MA Oxon (*History*)

Deputy Head: Dr H M D Petzsch, MA Edinburgh, BD, PhD Edinburgh FSA Scot (*History*)

Assistant Head/Director of Studies: Dr P Silverwood, MA Cantab, MSc, PhD Manchester, QTS, CChem, MRSC (*Chemistry*)

Assistant Head/Head of Boarding: Miss A Steven, BA Bristol (*English*)

Housemistresses/masters:
Echyngham: Mrs R van der Vliet, BA UCW Aberstwyth (*Modern Languages*)
Guldeford: Mrs N Hart, Licence Caen (*Physical Education*)
Hemsted: Mrs M Cass, CertEd (*Information Technology*)
Marshall: C W Humphery, MA St Andrews (*English*)
Medway: Miss E Stone, BA Aberystwyth (*History*)
Norris: Mr S Mansfield, BA Staffs (*History of Art*)
Founders:
Beeches: Mrs F Breeze, MA Oxon (*Classics*)
Elms: Mrs P Wileman, BA Nottingham (*Classics*)
Limes: Mrs S J Perry, BSc Liverpool (*Biology*)
Oaks: Mrs B Scopes, BA Kent (*History*)

School Chaplain: Mrs J Ashton, MA London

Administrative Staff:
Bursar: N J Allen
Deputy Bursar: N Scott-Kilvert
Estates Bursar: A Cawley
Domestic Bursar: Mrs S E Franklin, HCIMA

Development Office:
Mrs D Price (*Development Director*)
G E Smith (*Deputy Development Director*)
Mrs E A Ward (*Admissions Secretary*)
Mrs S K Davies (*Admissions Assistant*)
Miss K H Urquart (*Seniors' Officer*)
S Thorneycroft (*Marketing Assistant – Publications*)
Mrs D Bradford (*Marketing Assistant – Events*)
Mrs S B Leathart (*Web Assistant*)

Secretariat:
Mrs J A Sullivan (*Headmistress's Personal Assistant*)
Mrs D M Benson, LTCL, FTCL (*Music Administrator*)
Mrs S Birchall (*Development Director's Personal Assistant*)
Miss E Carrington (*Head of Boarding's Secretary*)
Miss A Chittenden (*Deputy Head's Personal Assistant*)
Mrs A G Pissarro (*School Secretary – termtime*)
Mrs G D B Trott (*Bursar's Personal Assistant*)
Mrs N K Wood, BA Cornell (*Director of Studies's Secretary*)
§Mrs C Andrews (*Common Room*)
§Mrs S Cramp (*PE Administrator*)
§Mrs M E Murphy (*Careers Administrator*)

Accounts:
N Scott-Kilvert (*Financial Controller*)

Medical:
Dr A M Wood, MBChB, MRC Psych (*Medical Officer*)
Sister J L Mallion, RGN
Mrs E O'Dell, BSc Manchester, RSCN, RGN
Mrs K Perry, RGN

Academic Staff:
§ *Part-time/Visiting*

English:
N van der Vliet, BA UCW Aberystwyth
Dr D Barsham, BA, PhD Hull
Mrs S Carroll, BA Oxford
Miss S J Hatt, BA, MA Kent
C W Humphery, MA St Andrews
Miss L V Mason, BA Dunelm
Mrs R Smith, BA, MPhil Oxon
Miss A Steven, BA Bristol

Mathematics:
Mrs D G Swaine, BSc Wales
M Albertyn, BSc South Africa
Mrs V A Burgess, BSc Dunelm
S Campbell, BSc Cantab
Mrs E Peacock, BSc Oxford Brookes
Mrs G Thomson, BA Cape Town Technical
Mrs J Tremble, BA Open
§Mrs J Mills, BSc Reading

Science:
Dr N J Dowrick, BA Oxon, DPhil Oxon
Mrs J Hall, BSc London
S C Heron, BSc London
O N Hunter, BSc Durham, MA Open
N Moxham, BSc London
Mrs S J Perry, BSc Liverpool
Miss A J Pullman, MA, MSc
Dr P R Silverwood, MA Cantab, MSc, PhD Manchester, QTS, CChem, MRSC
§Mrs A Linney, BSc Birmingham
§Dr D H Scarisbrick, BSc Bangor, MA Cantab, PhD Nottingham
§Ms S Stevens, BSc Birmingham
§Mrs W Grosvenor
§Mrs F Hadfield
§Mrs S Harris

Modern Languages:
Miss C L Lesieur, BA, MA Amiens
J D Crouzet, L-ès-L, M-ès-L St Étienne
Mrs M S Curran, BA Oxon
Miss V Fleitas Diaz, DTAS BA Madrid
Mrs M S Griffith, BA Brighton
Mrs A Jarman, MA Oxon
Dr C L J Tsai, MA, PhD Kent
Mrs R van der Vliet, BA UCW Aberystwyth
Mrs D Wyles, BA Bath, MCIL
§Mrs A Fuentes-Mansfield, MA Caen
§Mrs C Rennick (*French Conversation*)
§Miss M Pol
§Miss A Garcia

Classics:
A D Matthews, BA, MLitt Newcastle

Miss L Boyce, MA Oxon
Mrs F Breeze, MA Oxon
Mrs J Chapman, BA Bristol, TESOL
Mrs P Wileman, BA Nottingham

Drama:
J McCarthy, BA, MA Cantab, PGCE Bristol
Ms D Caron, BA Loughborough, LGSM, AIMENTS
M S Kemp, HND Stage Mgt/Tech Theatre Bristol Old Vic Theatre School
Miss L Porter, BA York
§Mrs R J Clements, BA Open, BEd
§G R Lee, CertEd Roehampton
§Ms N Thorndike, Dip LAMDA
§Mrs E Vernon, Dip Drama Studio Acting
§Miss A L Wickens, LLAM, LAMDA

Economics:
Mrs S J Northridge, BHum London, MBA Reading
C E Williams, BSc Southampton

Geography:
C E Williams, BSc Southampton
Mrs S J Northridge, BHum London, MBA Reading
Mrs S Bosher, BHum London
§Miss P A Hubbard, BSc Leicester

History and Politics:
J Watts, MA Oxon, BPhil York
Miss K M Dobson, BA Newcastle
Mrs C M Oulton, MA Oxon
Dr H M D Petzsch, MA Edinburgh, BD, PhD Edinburgh, FSA Scot
Mrs B Scopes, BA Kent
Miss E C Stone, BA Abertystwyth

Religious Studies:
A Nicol, BA Christchurch Uni College Canterbury, PGCE St Mary's Twickenham
Mrs J Ashton, MA London
P Sage, BA Leeds, PGCE

Art & Design:
R S Leighton, BA Stourbridge
Mrs P J Futrell, BA Middlesex Polytechnic
Mrs J L King, BA Nottingham Trent (*Textiles*)
S H Mansfield, BA Staffs (*History of Art*)

Design and Technology:
A Vincent, BA Manchester
Mrs L F Palmer, BA Camberwell
Miss S Silliborne, BA KIAD
C Fahy

Information Technology:
A D Sanderson, BSc Warwick, MSc Bath
Mrs M E Cass, CertEd
P Eagling, BSc Open

Music:
E S Beer, MA Oxon, LRAM
J Fitzgerald, BA Bristol
Mrs S Lamberton, BA Wales
Mrs V Lewis, ARCM, DipRCM (*Piano/Cello*)
§Mr S Chapman, ALCM, LLCMTO (*Guitar*)
§Mrs J M Colman, LTCL (*Piano*) (*Double Bass*)
§Ms E A Clarke, LRAM, LTCL (*Singing*)
§Mr A Ellingworth, Military School of Music, Knellerhall (*Clarinet/Saxophone*)
§Mrs K Fish, LTCL, Dip TCL (*Clarinet/Saxophone*)
§Mr T Foster, BMus, PGDip RAM, LRAM (*Percussion*)
§Ms S Graham, GRSM, LRAM, DipRAM (*Singing*)
§Mr A W Haigh, ARCM, LRAM (*Piano*)
§Miss R J Hanson, BMus BMUS (*Hons*)
§Ms N Harling, BMus RCM (*Harp*)
§Mr M D Hines, AGSM (*Bassoon*)
§Ms M Lowbury, BA Bristol, ARCM (*Cello*)
§Mr D M Manente, BMus, PGDip (*Strings*)
§Mrs H Manente, BMus, MMus RCM (*Flute*)
§Miss G A Mendes, GDipM Huddersfield, LTCL (*Recorder*)
§Miss J M Miller, AGSM (*Solo Singing*)
§Mrs S Purton, LRAM (*Oboe/Piano*)
§Ms H Ramsay, BMus Glasgow (*Piano*)
§Mr M Riley, BA, MA Cantab (*Organ*)
§Miss E J Roberts, GRNCM, PPRNCM, PDOTGSMD (*Horn*)
§Ms J Rowan, BA Reading LTCL (*Flute*)
§Mrs I Sellschop, LRAM (*HFYO Strings Tutor*)
§Miss L F Temple, ARCM, LRAM (*Brass*)
§Mrs J M Tilt, GGSM LRAM (*Singing*)
§Ms A Wynne, BA Birmingham, MMus Leeds (*Harp*)
§M Williams, BMus Dunelm, FRCO. MTC, FLCM, GRSM, ARCM, HonLCM

Physical Education:
Miss V A Sawyer, MBA Keele, LLB Hons Open, BEd Hons Reading
Mrs J E Fahy (*Sports Centre Supervisor*)
Miss S Kenny (*Fitness Instructor*)
Miss J Marlowe, BEd Leeds
Mr J Mitchell, BA Hons Bedford
Mrs Y Reynolds, CertEd Dartford College
Miss H Tipples (*Fitness Instructor*)
Mr D Weighton, DipPhysEd Strathclyde
Mr C Bowles (*Judo & Self Defence Coach*)
§Mr J Chorley (*Fencing*)
§Mrs R M Elliott, RAD, ISTD, LAMDA (*Modern & Tap Dance*)
§Mr M D Geer (*Swimming Coach*)
§Mrs V Mitchell, BEd Hons Bedford
§Mr J Morris (*Lifeguard*)
§Mrs J Morris (*Lifeguard*)
§Mr M Morris (*Lifeguard*)
§Mr T Sayer (*Squash Coach*)
§Mrs K M Steel, BEd Hons Bedford
§Miss J Wilson, ISTD, Dip LCDD (*Ballet*)

Careers & College Guidance:
Miss K M Dobson, BA Newcastle
§Mrs M Murphy

Special Needs:
§Mrs J H Edwards, BEd London, MEd UCNW, TCert, DipPsych
Mrs A Barker, BA Open, MSc MMU, PGCE Dyslexia and Literacy, TCert

Librarian:
Miss A Morley, BA Brighton, MA Sussex, MCLIP, DipTEFL, DipPub

Assistant Librarians:
Ms A Rae, BA Sussex
§Mrs L J G Traill
§Mrs A M Taylor

Benenden School aims to give each pupil the chance to develop her potential to the full within a happy and caring environment. We want her to feel ready to take on whatever challenges lie ahead and able to make a positive difference to the world, whether that is at work or at home or both. Whilst we aim to help each girl to achieve her best possible results in public exams, we also emphasise the importance of spiritual growth and of developing as a person, most particularly in confidence, compassion and courage. We want to encourage each pupil to develop as an individual as well as a responsible and caring member of a community.

We aim to do this by providing

– a full and balanced curriculum and a very wide range of extra-curricular and co-curricular activities, designed to

promote academic, cultural, creative, physical, spiritual and social development;
- well-taught lessons within facilities designed to encourage the best teaching and the best learning;
- supportive individual academic and pastoral care;
- group and individual higher education and careers guidance designed to help every student to make wise personal choices;
- a wide range of opportunities for leadership within the school;
- a culture of praise, encouragement and support within a framework designed to develop self-reliance and self-esteem;
- the experience of learning to understand other people which a full boarding school can provide;
- opportunities for a close partnership with parents so that school and home can work together to help every pupil.

General Information. The School is an independent girls' boarding school standing in its own parkland of 240 acres. In the heart of the Kentish Weald, it is easily reached by road, or by rail to the neighbouring main line station at Staplehurst, and is well placed for the air terminals of Gatwick and Heathrow, the continental ferry ports of the South East coast and the Channel Tunnel (Ashford International).

The School provides education for girls between the ages of 11 and 18 years. There are 520 students at Benenden; all are boarders and they come from a wide range of backgrounds.

Girls are taught by highly qualified full-time staff of over 70 men and women, together with some 40 part-time specialists, many of whom are leaders in their particular fields.

Each student belongs to a House in which she sleeps and spends much of her private study and leisure time: it is, in effect, her home from home. There are six Houses for 11 to 16 year olds, while Sixth Form students live in the Founders' Sixth Form Centre in one of four Sixth Form Houses.

Each House has a resident Housemistress or Housemaster, who is also a member of the teaching staff and responsible for the academic and pastoral well-being of each student in the House. Much of the day-to-day work is shared with Assistants and Day Matrons, while other non-resident members of the teaching staff are Personal Academic Tutors.

The School's facilities have been greatly improved in recent years. The new Benenden School Theatre and Drama teaching complex was officially opened in October 2007. The Clarke Centre, a £3.5 million Study Centre, providing state-of-the-art classrooms equipped with the latest computer technology, library and IT Centre. Since 2001, a programme of extensive refurbishment has taken place in boarding houses, including a new suite of classrooms and floor of study bedrooms which opened in 2003. Extensions to the Sixth Form centre have taken place in 2006 and 2007. For physical recreation there are nine lacrosse pitches, 13 all-weather tennis courts, sports hall containing a further full-sized tennis court, an indoor heated swimming pool, a second sports hall (also used for badminton, volleyball, netball and fencing), a fitness centre and gym, two squash courts and a grass running track.

The School is a Christian community, based on Anglican practice, and the ethos of the School reflects Christian principles. Members of other communions and beliefs are welcomed to the School and every effort is made to help them in the practice of their own faith, in an atmosphere of respect and toleration for the views of others.

Entrance to the School is after internal assessment at Preview Weekend, but dependent upon candidates meeting the School's standard at 11+ and 13+ Common Entrance or in entrance papers. There is also a small intake at Sixth Form level, with competitive entry by the School's own examination. All of the School's students are expected to qualify for degree courses, leaving School with at least three A Levels and at least eight subjects at GCSE. A full careers programme is a key component of the Personal Development Programme, aimed to foster the widest range of skills.

The core subjects up to GCSE are English, mathematics, science and modern languages. The compulsory balanced science course ensures that all three sciences are studied (either for single sciences at GCSE or for Dual Award), and every student studies in Key Stage 3 at least two of the three modern languages offered in addition to Latin. Cross-curricular skills and the balancing of theoretical concepts with practical applications are actively encouraged. The ability to work independently is critical to enjoyment and success, and students are given every opportunity to acquire appropriate study habits. The curriculum is under constant review and development, reflecting national initiatives and the aspirations of staff and students.

Benenden believes in close cooperation between School and parents and there is regular contact with them. Formal reports are sent at the end of every term. Parents are encouraged to visit the School for concerts, plays and other events, as well as to take their daughters out for meals or weekend exeats. There is a flourishing programme of social events for parents.

Curriculum. *Lower School*: English, mathematics, biology, chemistry, physics, French, German or Spanish or Classical Greek, Latin, geography, history, religious studies, art & design including textiles, design technology, information technology, drama, music, physical education.

GCSE Core: English, mathematics, biology, chemistry, physics, a modern foreign language.

GCSE Options: German, Spanish, Classical Greek, Latin, geography, history, religious studies, art, textiles, design & technology, music, drama & theatre arts.

A Level Options: English language and literature, English literature, mathematics, further mathematics, biology, chemistry, physics, French, German, Spanish, Greek, Latin, classical civilisation, economics, geography, history, politics, religious studies, art & design, history of art, music, theatre studies, design and technology. All Sixth Form students take Critical Thinking.

(All students' programmes also include careers education, information technology, physical education, religious education, personal, social and health education.)

Sport. Lacrosse, tennis, swimming, netball, rounders, badminton, athletics, volleyball, squash, basketball, gym, dance, fencing, trampolining, aerobics, hockey, riding.

Opportunities in Music. Tuition is available in all orchestral and keyboard instruments as well as singing. Numerous opportunities exist for instrumental and choral performance. The School is home to a full youth symphony orchestra, and in which students from other schools also play. Benenden also enjoys a strong choral tradition and hosts recitals by musicians of international calibre.

Opportunities in Speech and Drama. Students are able to pursue drama as an extra-curricular activity throughout their School career by participating in drama workshops, House and Lower and Upper School plays. Speech and drama lessons are available and students are prepared for both English Speaking Board and LAMDA examinations. There are several debating societies and students compete at the Oxford and Cambridge Union debating competitions. Sixth Formers are encouraged to run drama and debating clubs.

Optional Extras. Speech and drama, ballet, tap, modern dance, brass, guitar, percussion, piano, string, voice, woodwind, squash, tennis, fencing, judo, self-defence, yoga, riding, clay pigeon shooting, Duke of Edinburgh's Award Scheme, foreign languages.

Fees per term (2008-2009). £9,180 payable before the start of term, or by the School's Advance Payment of Fees Scheme.

Scholarships. (*see Scholarship Entries section*).

Admission. Prospective parents are encouraged to visit the School, either individually or with others at a Prospective Parents Morning. Prospectuses and full details of entry and scholarship requirements may be obtained from the Admissions Secretary.

Charitable status. Benenden School (Kent) Limited is a Registered Charity, number 307854. It is a charitable foundation for the education of girls.

Berkhamsted Collegiate School

Kings Road Berkhamsted Hertfordshire HP4 3BG

(See entry in HMC section)

Birkenhead High School (GDST)

86 Devonshire Place Prenton CH43 1TY
Tel: 0151 652 5777
Fax: 0151 670 0639
e-mail: admissionssec@birkhs.gdst.net
website: www.gdst.net/birkenheadhigh

Founded 1901.

This is one of the 29 schools of The Girls' Day School Trust. For further information about the Trust, see p. xxiv. A more detailed prospectus may be obtained from the school.

Local Governors:
Chairman: Mrs J Greensmith, DL, BCom

Dr M Azurdia, OBSTJ, MB ChB, MRCGP, DObst, RCOG
Mr B J Cummings
Mr B Gibson, BSc
Prof R S Jones, MVSc, DrMedVet, JP, FRCVS, DVA, MIBiol
Mr I Matthews, JP
Mr G Nissen, CBE, MA
Mr J Rae
Mrs M Read, BSc, DipEd, JP
Dr J Sneddon, MSc, PhD

***Headmistress*: Mrs C H Evans**, BA Wales (*Economics*)

Deputy Head: Mrs N I Matthews, BSc Sheffield (*Mathematics*)

Senior Mistress: Mrs J Milligan, BSc Manchester (*Geography*)

Head of Junior Department: Mrs R O'Connell, BEd Matlock

Deputy Head of Junior Department: Miss J Parry, CertEd London

Number of Pupils. Senior School: 415, age range 11–18 years, including 93 Sixth Form. Junior Department: 205, age range 3+–11 years. The normal ages of entry are at 3, 4+, 7+, 11+ and Sixth Form. Admission is by the school's own entrance examination.

The School was opened in September 1901. It is situated at 86 Devonshire Place, Birkenhead in a residential area. The catchment area includes Birkenhead, Wallasey, Wirral, Liverpool, Chester and the school is easily accessible from all districts. The Junior Department and Nursery have separate buildings in the School grounds.

The school is well equipped with a hall, library, computer suite, design and technology workshops, drama studio, art facilities, 8 science laboratories, specialist music facilities and Sixth Form Centre. The Sports Building has a large Sports Hall and a 25m swimming pool.

There are 9 tennis courts, some are floodlit and an all-weather pitch.

Physical activities include lacrosse, hockey, netball, tennis, rounders, gymnastics, dance, volleyball and many others.

A large number of girls participate in the Duke of Edinburgh's Award Scheme at Bronze, Silver and Gold levels. In the Sixth Form many girls are involved in the Young Enterprise Scheme.

Curriculum. The curriculum is planned to provide a wide general education which includes Music, Drama, Art and Physical Education and defers specialisation as long as possible. All academic subjects are included. Girls are prepared for the GCSE and AS/A2 level examinations and for university entrance. A wide choice of course is offered in the Sixth Form and all girls are expected to proceed to university, college or some other form of higher education.

Visits to theatres, concerts, art galleries, museums, lectures and conferences are arranged frequently for a wide age range.

School uniform, black and white, is worn up to the end of Year 11.

The Head Girl is elected to office. Each girl is encouraged to exercise responsibility for herself, and for others if she so wishes.

The Sixth Form girls have their own accommodation and are not required to wear uniform. It is hoped that the Sixth Form will be a bridge between school and the next stage of education or training and that it will foster independence and self-reliance. Sixth Form girls have many opportunities to run clubs and societies, organise concerts and produce plays.

A flourishing Parents' Association provides opportunities for parents to meet informally, and many social and cultural activities take place each year. The Association has recently provided a new minibus and a new Arts/Technology Centre in the Junior Department.

Meetings of Old Girls are held annually in Birkenhead and London.

Fees per term (2008-2009). Senior School £2,966, Junior Department £2,150, Nursery £1,776.

The fees cover the regular curriculum, school books, stationery and other materials, choral music, games and swimming, but not optional extra subjects or school meals.

Fees for extra subjects, piano, strings and woodwind instruments, speech and drama, are shown in the prospectus.

Following the ending of the Government Assisted Places Scheme, The Girls' Day School Trust has made available to the school a substantial number of scholarships and bursaries.

Bursaries. The bursaries are means tested and are intended to ensure that the school remains accessible to bright girls who would profit from our education but who would be unable to enter the school without financial assistance.

Bursaries post-entry are available in cases of financial need. Application should be made to the Headmistress.

Scholarships. These are at present available to internal or external candidates scholarships for entry at 11+ or to the Sixth Form.

Charitable status. Birkenhead High School is part of The Girls' Day School Trust, which is a Registered Charity, number 306983. The aim of the Trust is to provide a fine academic education for girls at a comparatively modest cost.

Blackheath High School (GDST)

Vanbrugh Park London SE3 7AG
Tel: 020 8853 2929
Fax: 020 8853 3663
e-mail: info@bla.gdst.net
website: www.blackheathhighschool.gdst.net

Junior Department: Wemyss Road London SE3 0TF
Tel: 020 8852 1537
Fax: 020 8463 0040
e-mail: info@blj.gdst.net

Founded 1880.

This is one of the 29 schools of The Girls' Day School Trust. For further information about the Trust, see p. xxiv. Additional information may be found on the school website and a detailed prospectus is available from the school.

Chairman of Local Governors: Mr C Young, MB BS, FRCOG, MSc

***Headteacher*: Mrs E A Laws**, BA Liverpool, PGCE

Deputy Head: Mrs S Clements, BSc Southampton, PGCE

Assistant Head: Ms M Wolloshin, GTCL London, PGCE

Head of Junior Department: Miss A Cordingley, Licentiate, Trinity, PGCE

Head of Sixth Form: Mrs J Tricks, BA Cardiff, PGCE

Admissions Secretary: Mrs F Nichols, BA London

School Administrator: Mr A W L Sutherland, MBE

Blackheath High School is a good-sized school – small enough for all girls to be valued as individuals but large enough to offer stimulating competition. With support from well-qualified and enthusiastic teachers, our girls work hard and attain excellent results. The vast majority of our sixth formers go on to Higher Education, gaining places at top universities.

Academic success is at the heart of what we offer, but good exam results are only part of the package. The school's happy, caring environment and impressive range of extra-curricular activities help girls to develop well rounded personalities and the skills and understanding they will need to be happy and successful in their adult lives.

Good communication skills are encouraged through activities such as Drama, debating, event management and public speaking, plus an emphasis on modern languages. Pupils study French throughout the school from Nursery and Year 7 students are also offered Spanish, German, Mandarin and Latin. As computer technology is an increasingly important form of communication, the school's two multimedia resource centres help girls develop the necessary ICT skills and qualifications needed for the modern workplace.

We aim to ensure that every girl achieves the very best that she can through a holistic approach to learning. We try to enhance the learning environment and give attention to the needs of our students as whole human beings. In recognition that the teenage years can be a stressful time for young people, activities such as yoga and pilates are on offer to Senior students, as well as advice on relaxation techniques.

The key to success for girls is confidence, and the confidence developed through taking on challenges spills over into all areas of their life, including the academic. All students are encouraged to participate in activities that challenge them physically, emotionally and socially, such as sport, performing arts, debating, outward bound courses and the Duke of Edinburgh Award Scheme.

The Junior site is housed in the original 19th Century premises in Blackheath Village and includes a new purpose-built nursery with its own entrance and playground. The Senior Department is just across the Heath, near to Greenwich Park, and combines historic buildings with modern purpose-built facilities, including a new performing arts centre. The school's five-acre sports field includes a newly-built sports pavilion, an all-weather pitch and 13 tennis courts.

Many of our students live in the local area whilst others travel from further a field. The area is well served by public transport but we also provide school transport to east London, Docklands & Surrey Quays areas.

Admission to the school is by examination and interview; scholarships and bursaries are available. Regular Open Days are held in the autumn but visitors are always welcome and the Headteacher likes to discuss each girl's particular needs individually with pupils and parents. Please telephone our Admissions Secretary on 020 8557 8409 for a prospectus and to arrange a visit.

Curriculum. We offer a broad choice of subjects at GCSE and an even wider choice at AS and A Level. We offer all the traditional A Level subjects plus other newer but popular ones, such as Psychology, Business Studies, Photography, Music Technology, Theatre Studies and Sports Studies.

Fees per term (2008-2009). Senior School £3,700, Junior Department £2,879, Nursery £2,221.

The fees cover the regular curriculum, school books, stationery and other materials, choral music, games and swimming, but not optional extra subjects or school meals.

Bursaries. The GDST makes available to the school a number of scholarships and bursaries. The bursaries are means tested and are intended to ensure that the school remains accessible to bright girls who would profit from our education but who would be unable to enter the school without financial assistance.

Scholarships. (*see Scholarship Entries section*). A number of Scholarships are available to internal or external candidates for entry at 11+ or to the Sixth Form.

Charitable status. Blackheath High School is part of The Girls' Day School Trust, which is a Registered Charity, number 306983. The aim of the Trust is to provide a fine academic education for girls, which is distinguished by breadth.

Bolton School Girls' Division

Chorley New Road Bolton Lancs BL1 4PB
Tel: 01204 840201
Fax: 01204 434710
e-mail: seniorgirls@boltonschool.org
website: www.boltonschool.org/seniorgirls

Bolton School Girls' Division seeks to realise the potential of each pupil. We provide challenge, encourage initiative, promote teamwork and develop leadership capabilities. It is our aim that students leave the School as self-confident young people equipped with the knowledge, skills and attributes that will allow them to lead happy and fulfilled lives and to make a difference for good in the wider community.

We do this through offering a rich and stimulating educational experience which encompasses academic, extra-curricular and social activities. We provide a supportive and industrious learning environment for pupils selected on academic potential, irrespective of means and background.

Governors:
Chairman: M T Griffiths, BA, FCA
D H V Brookes
R J Byrom, JP, BA Arch, MPhil, RIBA, FSVA, FCIArb
Professor C L Cooper, CBE
C Cowling, BSc, FIA, CMath, FIMA
E Fairweather, FCIB, CeMAP, CeRGI
Mrs S E Fisher, MSc, MBChB, BDS, PDSRCS, FRCS
The Hon Mrs M J Heber-Percy
Mrs L Henthorn, ACMI
N Hirst, MA, CEng, FIChemE
Mrs L A Hopkinson, BEd
Mrs M Kenyon, DL, MA
B H Leigh-Bramwell, MA
Mrs W P Morris, OBE
A D Oldershaw
Mrs G E Sidebottom
Mrs S R Tonge, JP, DipHarb
Mrs F Windsor, BSc, MA, FCMA, FCIS, FRSA, MIBA, CBM

Clerk and Treasurer: S P Marsden, BA, MCMI

***Headmistress*: Mrs G Richards**, BA, MEd

Deputy Heads:
Mrs P M Fairweather, BA
A J Green-Howard, BSc

Senior Mistress: Mrs C A Brown, BA, PhD
Head of Sixth Form: Mrs C E McLellan, BA
Head of Upper School: Mrs P B Keenan, BA
Head of Middle School: Mrs C A Greenhalgh, BEd

Senior School:
* *Head of Department*

Art:
*Miss J A Fazackerley, BA
Mrs T J Fisher, BA
Mrs R A Kidd, BA
Mrs R E Langley-West, BA

Careers and Higher Education:
*Mrs E Lowe, BA
Mrs K L Bell
Mrs C Sutcliffe

Classics:
*Miss V C Coyle, BA
Mrs J D Partington, BA

Design Technology:
*P J Linfitt, BSc, MEng
Mrs R E Langley-West, BA

Economics & Business Studies:
*Mrs A L Robinson, MA
Mrs L C Rixon, BSc

English:
*Mrs J T M Sowerby, BA
Miss Y Ariff, BA
Miss R Bendelow, BA
Mrs R E Hadjigeorgiou, BA
Mrs C J Jones, BA
Mrs M J Kingsford, BA
Mrs E A Lowe, BA
Mrs P Sargeant, BA (*Learning Support – Dyslexia*)
Ms R E Worthington, BA

Food Technology:
*Mrs I M H Smalley, BSc
Mrs C S Haslam, BEd

Geography:
*Ms S Noot, BA
Mrs J R Watson, BSc
Mrs P B Keenan, BA
Mrs C E McLellan, BA
Mrs S Waters, BSc
Mrs J Watson, BSc

History:
*Mrs S A Heap, BA
Mrs J M Birch, BA
A B Davies, BA
Mrs J M Head, BA
Mrs S L Pritchard, MA
Miss A Ross-Nichol, BA

ICT:
*Ms S Jones, BSc
Mrs M E Brown, BSc
Mrs J A Drinkwater, BA

Mathematics:
*Mrs L D Kyle, BSc
Mrs K A Baldwin, BSc
Mrs J A Derbyshire, BSc, MSc (*Learning Support Coordinator*)
Mrs V Hanrahan, BSc
Mrs E M Hayes, BSc
Miss C McCarthy, BSc

Modern Languages:
*Mrs A Shafiq, BA
French:
*Mrs A J Kolot, MA
Mrs R O Artley, BA
Mrs D Ganley, DEUG
Mrs K Humphreys, BA
Mrs B A Lowe, BA
Mrs J Patterson, BA
Mrs A Shafiq, BA
Miss C A Slatter, BA
Mrs P Sheaff, BA, MA
Miss C A Slatter, BA
German:
*Mrs R O Artley, BA
Mrs A J Kolot, MA
Mrs B A Lowe, BA
Mrs P Sheaff, BA, MA
Spanish:
*Mrs A Shafiq, BA
Mrs K Humphreys, BA
Mrs J Patterson, BA
Miss C A Slatter, BA

Music:
*A MacKenzie, GRNCM
Mrs V Carter, BA, MSc
Miss P Simpson, BMus
Miss N Swan, BMus

Physical Education:
*Mrs K A Heatherington, BA
Miss A Donaghy, BEd
Miss J Hall, BA
Mrs P M Hall, CertEd
Mrs M M McCulloch, CertEd

Religion and Philosophy:
*Mrs K E Porter, BA
Mrs N Bradley, BA
Mrs C A Brown, BA, PhD
Mrs C A Greenhalgh, BEd
Miss T Rigby, BA

Science:
*Mrs S M O'Kelly, BSc
Biology:
*Mrs A D Furey, BSc
Miss H J Beresford, BSc
Mrs S A Berne, BSc
Mrs A R Reid, BSc
Mrs M Walsh, BSc
Chemistry:
*Mrs J M Appleyard, BA
Mrs K B Blagden, BSc
Mrs P M Fairweather, BA
Mrs S M O'Kelly, BSc
Physics:
*R J West, BEng
A J Green-Howard, BSc
M Jones, MPhys
Mrs C E McCann, BSc
Psychology:
*Mrs C Bell, BA
Mrs J H Sanders, BSc

Textile Technology:
*Miss R Stafford, BEd
Mrs H McCumiskey, BA

Instrumental Music Staff:
Ms A Barry, BMus (*Singing*)
Miss F Berry, BMus, LRSM, LTCL, LLCM (*Clarinet, Saxophone*)
G Curtin, BMus, MA (*Brass*)
S Death, BSc Mus, PPRNCM (*Piano*)
Mrs K P Dewhurst, BA (*Piano*)
I Forgrieve, GMus, RNCM, PPRNCM (*Percussion*)
P Fowles, BA, LLCM, AMusTCL (*Guitar*)
Miss J Gleeson, GRNCM (*Violin*)
Miss B James, BMus (*Violin*)
Mrs E Jordan, GRNCM, PPRNCM (*Clarinet, Saxophone*)
Mrs S Middleton, GMus, RNCM, PGDip, RNCM (*Piano*)
Mrs R Moore, FRNCM (*Cello*)
P Morrison, MA, GRNCM, FRCO (*Piano, Organ*)
Miss L Nielsen-Racz, GRNCM (*Clarinet*)
Miss C Swain, GRNCM, PPRNCM (*Oboe*)
Mrs A C Swinford, LRAM, GRSM (*Piano*)
Miss R M Thompson, GRNCM (*Violin*)
Mrs E C Tristram, GRNCM (*Flute*)
Mrs S L Walker, GRNCM, PPRNCM (*Flute*)
M Wildgust, GMus, ARCM, LTCL (*Brass*)

Lower Schools:

Junior Department (Age 7–11)
Head of Junior Department: Miss S Sergeant, BSc
Deputy Head of Junior Department: Mrs K M Critchley, BE

Mrs J Dunne, BEd
Mrs A J Forshaw, BA
Mrs G A Hilton, BA
Mrs H R Holt, BEd
Miss B A Howard, BEd
Miss A Howarth, BEd
Mrs B J Tatlock, TCert
Mrs M G Worsley, BSc, MA

Teaching Assistants:
Mrs M S Drinkwater, BA
Mrs A Williamson

Beech House (Age 4–7)
Head of Beech House: Mrs H J Crawforth, BEd
Deputy to Head of Beech House: Miss M C Briggs, BA

Mrs K L Aldred, BEd
Miss K J Bevon, BSc
Miss N Brierley, BA
Mrs P Clarke, BA
Mrs C J Glaister, CertEd
Mrs S Gliddon, BEd
Mrs J Marshall, BA
Mrs A V Ryder, BEd
Mrs K Shaw, BA

Nursery Nurses:
Miss R Davis, NVQ Early Years Care & Education
Mrs G Donaldson, NNEB
Mrs K Milne, CACHE Dip Childhood and Education
Mrs C Naughton, NNEB

Teaching Assistant:
Mrs A L Scattergood, NVQ Early Years Care & Education
Miss J Strange, BA

Librarian: Mrs L M Frew, BA, ALA
Assistant Librarian: Mrs J Groves

Secretarial Staff:
Headmistress's Secretary: Mrs L Graham
Secretary to the Deputy Heads: Mrs J Holland
Secretaries for Senior School: Mrs N Asquith, Mrs S Wright
Secretaries for Lower Schools: Mrs A Bradbury, Mrs K Gore

Curriculum Support Staff:
Mrs J Stone, BSc (*Academic & Technical Support Manager*)
Mrs V Birkenhead (*Assistant Academic Support Manager*)

P Baker (*Science & Technology Technician*)
Mrs A Grundy-Nugent (*Biology Technician*)
Mrs E Jones (*Textiles Assistant*)
Mrs C Kelly (*Food Technology Assistant*)
D Kyle (*Performing Arts Technician*)
V Marsden (*ICT Support Assistant*)
L Marsh (*Design Technology Assistant*)
F Mohamed, BSc (*ICT Support Assistant*)
E Morgan (*Science Technician*)
Mrs P Rushton (*Art Assistant*)
J K Speakman, BSc (*Physics Technician*)
P Stulock (*Chemistry Technician*)
Mrs J Whitehead (*Assistant to Examinations Officer*)

Medical Staff:
Mrs G Grundy, SEN
Mrs H Hodgkins, RSCN
Mrs J Grice (*School Counsellor*)

Bolton School Girls' Division was founded in 1877 as the High School for Girls and quickly gained a reputation for excellence. In 1913 the first Viscount Leverhulme gave a generous endowment to the High School for Girls and the Bolton Grammar School for Boys on condition that the two schools should be equal partners known as Bolton School (Girls' and Boys' Divisions).

Bolton School occupies a superb 32-acre site and the Girls' Division contains almost 1,300 day pupils. The co-educational infants' school, Beech House, offers an education for 200 pupils aged 4–7 and a further 200 girls are educated in the Junior Girls' School (age 7–11). In the Senior School of 840 girls, 240 are in the Sixth Form. The School also has its own nursery.

Facilities. The Girls' Division has a Great Hall to seat 900 people, two fully computerised libraries, with a full-time and a part-time librarian, a theatre, seven laboratories, three Information Technology rooms, a Design Technology Suite and many well-appointed specialist teaching rooms. Our computer network extends across more than 200 PCs. These allow pupils access to basic software, CD-ROMS and the Internet in the Libraries, Careers Room, the Computer Suite and several departmental areas. The Sixth Form Suite includes a kitchen and study area with networked computers. The Careers Department has a resource centre giving access to all the latest information. This, too, is fully staffed by two experienced assistants. Besides having its own gym, the Girls' Division shares the modern sports hall, swimming pool and sports pavilion with the Boys' Division. In addition to these excellent facilities for Physical Education, the school has an outdoor pursuits centre at Patterdale in the Lake District which is used regularly by girls from the Junior and Senior schools.

Beech House (Preparatory Department). The curriculum, though based on the National Curriculum, extends far beyond it. Specialist teaching is provided for older pupils in Physical Education and Music and all children are taught French. There is a PC in every classroom and, in addition to its own resources, Beech House benefits from the use of Senior School facilities such as the swimming pool, computer room and Arts Centre.

The Girls' Junior Department. There are 2 classes in each of Years 3–6. Most of the department is housed within the main building and has its own computer suite and well-resourced library whilst enjoying the magnificent facilities available to the Senior School. Besides following the National Curriculum with Senior School specialists teaching PE, Music and French, pupils have additional opportunities. The many clubs and wide range of extra-curricular activities ensure a full and well-balanced programme.

The Senior School. The curriculum encompasses all the National Curriculum but also offers the study of two modern languages, the classics and a wide range of modules in Technology. At age 11 all girls follow a similar weekly timetable. The twelve subjects offered are: Art, English, French, Geography, History, Classical Studies, Mathematics, Music, PE, Religious Studies, Science and Technology. This list, however, does not fully show the great variety of opportunities available which also include: Athletics, Biology, Chemistry, Computer Graphics, Dance, Drama, Earth Science, Electronics, Food Technology, Gymnastics, Information Technology, Lacrosse, Netball, Physics, PSE, Resistant Materials Technology, Rounders, Swimming, Tennis and Textiles Technology. This breadth is maintained to GCSE with a second language, German, Latin or Spanish, being offered in Year 8. In Years 10 and 11 we also offer Badminton, Basketball, Football, Unihoc and Volleyball.

GCSE. There is extensive choice at GCSE. All follow a common curriculum of English, English Literature, Mathematics, and either Dual Award or separate Sciences together with non-examined courses in Information Technology, PE, and Religion and Philosophy. Students take 10 subjects at GCSE: the core subjects plus options chosen from Art , Biology, Business and Communication Systems, Chemistry, Food Technology, French, Geography, German, Greek, History, Latin, Music, Physics, Religious Studies, Resistant Materials Technology, Spanish and Textile Technology. Essential balance is maintained by requiring all to include one Humanity and one Modern Language, but the choice is otherwise entirely free.

The Sixth Form. Flexibility has always been a key feature of the Sixth Form. Students choose from a list of approximately 30 AS courses. Breadth is promoted further by our complementary Curriculum Enrichment Programme. All students have the opportunity to follow a range of non-examined courses as well as Physical Education (sports include golf, football, life-saving, rugby, self-defence, tennis and yoga). Links beyond school include the Community Action Programme and Young Enterprise scheme, as well as opportunities with Business Awareness and Work Experience.

Teaching in the Sixth Form is in smaller groups. Students have greater freedom which includes wearing their own clothes, exeat periods and having a common room and private study facilities. Joint social events are organised with the Boys' Division and girls and boys have access to each other's common room facilities. There are opportunities for students to assume a variety of responsibilities both within the school and in the wider community. Increasing personal freedom within a highly supportive environment helps students to make the transition to the independence of the adult world.

Almost all students (95%) go on to Higher Education (10% to Oxford and Cambridge).

Music and Drama are popular and students achieve the highest standards in informal and public performances. The wide variety of concerts and productions may take place in the Arts Centre, the Great Hall or the fully-equipped Theatre all of which make excellent venues for joint and Girls' Division performances.

Personal and Social Education, and Citizenship. PSE and Citizenship are targeted in a variety of ways and coordinated centrally. Some issues may be covered within departmental schemes of work while others will be discussed in the informal atmosphere of form groups led by the form tutor. Those areas which require specialist input are fitted into longer sessions run by experts from outside school.

Careers. The Careers Department helps prepare students for adult life. The extensive programme starts at age 11 and includes communication skills, work sampling, and support in making choices at all stages of schooling. In addition, girls prepare their CVs and applications to Higher Education with the individual help of a trained tutor.

Extra-Curricular Activities. Patterdale Hall, our outdoor pursuits centre in the Lake District, offers many activities including abseiling, gorge walking, orienteering and sailing. Awards are regularly made to enable individuals to undertake a variety of challenging activities both at home and abroad while every year over 50 pupils embark on the Duke of Edinburgh's Award Scheme. In addition to the annual exchanges for Modern Languages students, we also offer a wide range of educational and recreational trips both at home and abroad. All have the opportunity to follow a wide range of non-examined courses of their choice, including Physical Education.

Admission. Entrance to the school is by Headteacher's report, written examination and interview in the Spring term for girls aged 7 and 11. New girls are also welcomed into the Sixth Form.

A significant number of Governors' Foundation Grants have been created in response to the loss of the Assisted Places Scheme.

Fees per term (2008-2009). Senior School £2,930; Junior and Infant Departments £2,198. Fees include lunches.

Charitable status. The Bolton School is a Registered Charity, number 1110703. Its aims and objectives are to maintain in or near the County Borough of Bolton a public secondary school for boys and girls as a day school. Under the terms of the Charity it is administered as two separate Divisions providing for boys and girls under a separate Headmaster and Headmistress.

The Girls' Grammar School
Bradford

Squire Lane Bradford Yorkshire BD9 6RB
Tel: 01274 545395
Fax: 01274 482595
e-mail: headsec@bggs.com
website: www.bggs.com

Established under a Scheme of the Endowed Schools' Commissioners on 5 August 1875, now administered under a Scheme of the Charity Commission of 13 April 1983. Incorporated 4 November 1879, under the Charitable Trusts Act, 1872. The Charter of Incorporation was granted by Charles II to the Bradford Grammar School in 1662.

Governors:
J M Holmes, Esq (*Chairman*)
N J Shaw, Esq, LLB (*Vice-Chairman*)
Miss N. Bashir, MBA, Dip MS
P Clough, Esq, FCIS
D Trevor Lewis, Esq, LLB
E Marshall, Esq, MInstM
Ms L-D Morris
Miss S Pattison
Mrs S Sedgwick, FCA

***Headmistress*: Mrs L J Warrington**, MEd

Senior Manager Curriculum: Mrs A Ashton, BSc UMIST, CChem, MRSC (*Chemistry*)
Senior Manager Pastoral: Mrs M Muirhead, BA Hull (*Head of Russian*)

Heads of Department:
Mr P Groves, BA Newcastle, LTCL (*Music*)
Mr D Ham, BA Manchester (*Three D Design*)
Mr C Hannam, BScTech Sheffield (*Physics*)
Mrs J M Harland, TCert Ilkley College of Education (*Food Technology*)
Mrs J Hemsley, BA Liverpool (*Director of Physical Education & Sport*)
Mrs A Kerry, BSc UMIST (*German*)
Mrs C Morrel, BA Leeds (*Art*)
Mrs M Muirhead, BA Hull (*Russian*)
Mrs N Murphy, BA Sheffield, MA London (*History*)
Mr G M Nicholas, BA London (*Classics*)
Mrs D Plunkett, BA Lancaster (*Religious Studies*)
Mrs B Raby, BSc Bradford (*Psychology*)
Mrs C Rowe, BSc Bradford (*IT*)
Mr J Ryan, BSc Leeds, MEd Leeds (*Science and Biology*)
Mrs L Stead, BSc Manchester (*Geography*)
Mrs J C Warham, BA Reading, MA Leeds (*English*)
Mr W Steel, BSc Leeds, DipEd University of the West Indies, MEd Open University (*Mathematics*)
Mrs A Wicks, BA Bristol (*Modern Languages, French*)
Mrs J Wilton, BSc Newcastle, MPhil Leeds (*Chemistry*)

Preparatory School:
Acting Head: Mrs J Jenkinson

School Business Manager: Mrs M Taylor
Headmistress's Secretary & Clerk to the Governors: Mrs J Newman
Admissions Secretary: Mrs M Mackenzie

The School, founded in 1875, stands in an estate of 17 acres on the outskirts of the City.

The number of pupils in the School is approximately 600, including over 200 in the Preparatory School.

There is a programme of constant renewal and extension of buildings and facilities. In recent years a Sixth Form College was opened in a new building adjacent to the main school, and a Sports Centre with a large and small hall was completed. A building housing eight additional teaching spaces and a glass covered atrium was completed during 1996. A new kitchen and dining room was added in 1999.

The facilities in the school include Art Rooms, 11 Science Laboratories, Language Laboratories, Craft, Design and Technology Centre, Information Technology Centre, libraries and heated swimming pool.

The Preparatory School moved into brand new purpose-built accommodation in 2008, and is well situated so that the pupils can take full advantage of the specialist facilities. The accommodation includes new areas for the nursery and kindergarten children as well as outdoor play areas.

Physical Education is well established and facilities include gymnasium, nine tennis/netball courts, two hockey pitches, an athletics area and an artificial pitch. The school has been awarded national Sportsmark Gold in recognition of our outstanding commitment to physical education and sports provision.

Music and Drama are well established and there is a Senior Dramatic Society and Orchestra, together with instrumental groups and choirs. Debating is a popular activity.

Hours of attendance: Monday to Thursday (inclusive) 8.35 am–12.30 pm, and 1.45 pm–3.50 pm. Friday 8.35 am–12.30 pm, and 1.20 pm–3.30 pm.

Examinations. Public examinations are taken in the Upper Fifth and Sixth Forms at GCSE, Advanced, and Scholarship standards, according to the requirements of individual pupils.

Fees per term (2008-2009). Senior School £3,511; Preparatory School (age 3–11) £2,544; Kindergarten (age 3) and Nursery (age 2) £2,147 (full-time).

The fees include all subjects of tuition and stationery. Music fees, according to instruments.

Bursaries have been given by the Governors in the Senior School each year since September 1976. These are of varying amounts and include 1 entirely free place per year and an additional free place in the Sixth Form.

Charitable status. Bradford Girls' Grammar School is a Registered Charity, number 528674. It exists to provide high quality education for girls.

Brighton and Hove High School (GDST)

The Temple Montpelier Road Brighton East Sussex BN1 3AT
Tel: 01273 734112

Fax: 01273 737120
e-mail: enquiries@bhhs.gdst.net
website: www.gdst.net/bhhs

Junior Department:
Radinden Manor Road Hove East Sussex BN3 6NH
Tel: 01273 505004

Founded 1876.

One of the 29 schools of The Girls' Day School Trust. For general information about the Trust and the composition of its Council, see p. xxiv. Additional information may be found on the school's website and a more detailed prospectus may be obtained from the school.

Chair of Local Governors: Mrs P Stiles

***Acting Head & Deputy Head*: Mr Keith Roberts**, BEd, PGDipEd, MA

Head of Junior Department: Miss C Vickers, BEd Bristol

Head of Sixth Form: Mrs S Mashford, BSc Manchester

(*Full staff list available in prospectus.*)

Number of Pupils. 417 Girls in the Senior Department (age 11–18), including 73 in the Sixth Form; 245 in the Junior Department (age 3–11).

Location. The school stands in its own grounds in the centre of the city of Brighton and Hove. It is about half-a-mile from Brighton Railway Station and pupils come in from Lewes, Haywards Heath and Lancing by train. It is easily reached by bus from all parts of Brighton and Hove.

The Junior Department is housed in premises in Radinden Manor Road. The Senior School is in the Temple, a gentleman's residence built by Thomas Kemp in 1819 which has been considerably altered and enlarged to offer all modern amenities, most recent of which is a Sports Hall. There is a self contained Sixth Form Centre and the school owns a Field Centre on the River Wye in mid-Wales.

Curriculum. The school course is planned to provide a wide general education. Girls are prepared for the General Certificate of Secondary Education and in the Sixth Form a wide choice of subjects is offered in preparation for universities and other forms of professional training. In addition to their Advanced Level subjects girls take Key Skills courses and can choose work experience as an option.

The school has an all-weather hockey pitch at the Junior Department site with facilities for hockey, rounders, netball and tennis. Gymnastics and dance are also taught with swimming for junior forms, and senior forms choose from activities including badminton, squash, swimming, aerobics and self-defence.

Fees per term (2008-2009). Senior School £2,966, Junior Department £2,150, Nursery £1,776.

The tuition fees cover the regular curriculum, school books, stationery and other materials, choral music, games and swimming, but not optional subjects or school meals.

The fees for extra subjects (instrumental music and speech and drama) are shown in the prospectus.

Admission at all ages is by interview and test/entrance examination, except at 16+ where GCSE qualifications are essential. The main entry points are 3+, 4+, 11+ and 16+, though occasional vacancies occur at all ages.

Scholarships and Bursaries. The GDST has made available to the school a number of scholarships and bursaries. The bursaries are means tested and are intended to ensure that the school remains accessible to bright girls who would profit from our education but who would be unable to enter the school without financial assistance.

A few Trust Scholarships are available on merit, irrespective of income, to internal or external candidates for entry at 11+ or to the Sixth Form.

Charitable status. Brighton and Hove High School is part of The Girls' Day School Trust, which is a Registered Charity, number 306983. The aim of the Trust is to provide a fine academic education for girls, which is distinguished by breadth.

Brigidine School Windsor

Queensmead King's Road Windsor Berkshire SL4 2AX
Tel: 01753 863779
Fax: 01753 850278
e-mail: mail@brigidine.org.uk
website: www.brigidine.org.uk

Governors:
Chairman: M Wyld, Esq
Mrs A Bradberry
G Clarke, Esq
Miss L Cordeiro
Miss F E Doonan
P Lock, Esq
Sister Patricia Mulhall
H Salter, Esq
Mrs E Bell (*Clerk*)

***Headmistress*: Mrs Elizabeth Robinson**, MA, BSc, PGCE

Deputy Headmistress, Senior Dept: Miss L F Morrison, MA, BA Hons, PGCE

Senior Department Staff:
Mrs O Alade-Akinyemi, BSc, PGCE
Mrs A Bersier, BEd, CertEd
Dr B Billingsley, PhD Science Ed
Mrs C J Cahillane, BA Hons, PGCE
Mr P Chidzey, MA
Mrs E Coleman, BEd, CertEd
Mrs S Davies, TCert
Mrs M Davy, BA Hons, PGCE
Mr J W Fitzpatrick, BSc, PGCE
Mrs S Goddard, BA Hons
Mrs E Hawkes, CertEd, AdvDipEd, GradDipEd
Mrs K Holloway, BSc
Miss B Horvath, DipEd
Miss R Humby, BA Hons, PGCE
Mrs J Johnson, BSc Hons, PGCE
Mrs G Lilley, BSc, PGCE
Mrs M Llewellyn, MEd, CertEd, AMBDA (Teaching)
Mr A Mackay, MA, PGCE
Mrs D Mallinson, MA, TCert, BEd
Mrs M Morris, BA Hons
Mrs L Pearson-Hall, LGSM, LLAM, LTA, AISTD
Mrs F Pelly, BA Hons, PGCE
Mrs J Pratt, BSc Hons, PGCE
Mrs S Pullman, BSc, PGCE, MA Ed
Mrs E Quick, CertEd
Miss T Robertson, BA, Grad DipEd
Miss A Rougeot, PGCE
Mrs S Rossell, BSc
Mrs N Simmonds, MA, PGCE
Mrs G Slater, BSc, PGCE
Mr P Thompson, BA, BEd
Mr A Warren, MBA, LTCL, GTCL
Mrs L Williams, BA, PGCE, DipM, MInstM, ACBSI

Junior School:
Assistant Head (*Head of Juniors*): Mrs T Milton, CertEd Cambs

Mrs B Baguley, DipEd (Distinction)
Mrs Z Gallagher, DipEd
Mrs C Jones, DipEd
Mrs T Lega, CertEd

Mrs C Lever, BA Hons, PGCE
Mrs R O'Hara, BSc, PGCE
Mrs J Perrett, BA, QTS
Mrs S Whittaker, BEd

Classroom Assistants:
Mrs J Coutts
Mrs S Furby
Mrs B Guise
Mrs H Rouse
Mrs J Surman

After School Assistant: Miss W Stevens

Administration Staff:
Bursar: Mrs E Bell, BA, ACA, IAM
Bursar's Assistant: Mrs K Daniels
Accountant: Mr M Studd, FCA
Marketing Manager: Mrs J Tomalin
Marketing & Communications: Mrs N Walsh
Head's PA/Admissions: Mrs S Jackson
Faculty Administrator: Mrs D Bates
Reception: Mrs K Grewal
Librarian: Miss R Molloy
Lab Technicians:
Mrs A Hunjan, MSc
Mrs M Bose, MSc
ICT Technician: Mrs J Jafri

Age Range. Girls: rising 3–18 years; Boys: rising 3–5 years.

Number of Pupils. 275 day pupils.

School Hours. 3–11 years: 8.30 am – 3.30 pm. 11+–18 years: 8.30 am – 4.05 pm.

Brigidine School Windsor was established in Windsor in 1948 by the Congregation of the Sisters of St Brigid. Today, it continues its Roman Catholic foundation whilst welcoming children of all other denominations and faiths.

It offers a broad education in a friendly, caring atmosphere and caters for children with a wide range of abilities and talents. It provides support and opportunities for each girl to develop her full potential as a unique individual so enabling her to become a confident, compassionate and accomplished young adult.

The full curriculum is available to all pupils with girls studying, on average, ten GCSE subjects in Years 10 and 11. Our Sixth Form offers a very good range of subjects at Advanced Level.

There is a wide range of co-curricular activities with tuition in ballet, modern dance, speech and drama and musical instruments being available. Sporting extras on offer include tennis coaching, trampolining, short tennis, rowing, yoga, self defence, aerobics, fitness training, Duke of Edinburgh's Award, golf, swimming, fencing and life saving. All pupils are encouraged to participate.

Admission. The usual ages for entry are rising 3, 8, 11 and 16, but entry can be at any stage. From 8 years old, the pupils are interviewed and assessed prior to entry.

Registration fee (non-returnable): £75.

Fees per term (2008-2009). Senior School: £4,075–£4,155, Sixth Form £3,905. Junior School: £2,900–£3,440. Nursery: £2,680 (full-time), £1,350 (part-time).

Charitable status. Brigidine School Windsor is a Registered Charity, number 1104042. It exists to provide quality education for girls.

Bromley High School (GDST)

Blackbrook Lane Bickley Bromley Kent BR1 2TW
Tel: 020 8468 7981
Fax: 020 8295 1062
e-mail: bhs@bro.gdst.net
website: www.bromleyhigh.gdst.net

Founded 1883.

This is one of the 29 schools of The Girls' Day School Trust. For further information about the Trust, see p. xxiv.

Additional information about the school may be found on the school's website. A more detailed prospectus may be obtained from the school.

Chairman of the Local Governors: Mr A Michael, BA, MBA, JP

***Headmistress*: Mrs L Duggleby**, BA York, MSc Leeds M, PGCE

Deputy Head: Miss J A Butler, BEd Sussex

Head of Junior Department: Mrs M Trask, BEd Southampton, MA Lancaster

Assistant Head (*Senior*): Mrs P Anderson, BSc Manchester, PGCE

School Business Manager: Mrs A Shepherd

Director of Studies: Mrs J M Smith, BSc Bristol, PGCE

Head of Sixth Form: Mrs J Dick, BSc London, PGCE

Admissions Secretary: Mrs D Woodfield

Founded in 1883 by the Girls' Day School Trust, Bromley High School was originally situated in the centre of Bromley. In 1981 it moved to Bickley to occupy new buildings set in 24 acres of beautiful grounds.

Pupil Numbers. Senior School (ages 11–18): 600 (including the Sixth Form).

Junior School (ages 4–11): 312.

Sharing the same site, the buildings of both departments provide excellent facilities.

The Junior School. Our two-form entry Junior School is housed in separate purpose-built accommodation on the same site as the Senior School. We provide a stimulating and happy environment in which our pupils are encouraged to strive for excellence in all they do and to derive satisfaction from their achievements both great and small. From the earliest years we offer a broad curriculum which encourages, challenges and excites the young mind. Our aim is to foster a love of learning, develop independent thinking and promote a spirit of enquiry. In our approach to teaching and learning we blend the traditional with progressive insights into learning styles and the particular needs of young girls as learners in a modern world. We teach the full range of the National Curriculum, including French, Spanish, German, and Mandarin, and accord sports and the creative arts a significant place in the timetable whilst ensuring that the foundations of the core subjects are well established. Class lessons are differentiated and we offer extension and support where appropriate and specialist teaching, sometimes from Senior School staff, in a number of subjects. Our girls achieve high standards and we are proud of our excellent results in public examinations. We have an extensive extra-curricular programme.

In the delivery of our curriculum we are well served by outstanding facilities which, in addition to comprehensively equipped classrooms, include a music wing, a library, and ICT suite, a science room, and an art and technology room. We share many other facilities with the Senior School including a swimming pool, gymnasium, sports hall, tennis courts and an all weather pitch. Our pupils have their lunch in the main school dining room where a wide variety of hot dishes or sandwiches are served.

The Senior School. The school provides an environment in which girls of all ages work hard to develop their abilities. Academic studies are of paramount importance and standards are high with a curriculum making equal provisions for arts, sciences, practical and creative subjects.

The Senior School houses eight laboratories, some refurbished in August 2005, a new large well-stocked library/resource centre and Sixth Form Block opened in March 2003, a careers room and specialist library as well as specialist teaching rooms for Art, Technology and Ceramics and Geography. A new Drama Building is scheduled for completion in 2009. Full use is made of audio-visual equipment for the teaching of Modern Languages, including satellite. The Music department includes an octagonal Recital Room, nine practice rooms and a music technology room with recording facilities. Music Technology is taught at Key Stages 3 and 4. The main ICT suite consists of four teaching rooms fully equipped with networked PCs and refurbished within the last two years. Other networked machines are distributed throughout the school and clusters can be found in the Art/Design Technology wing, modern languages and the recent new Library, as well as some non-specialist teaching rooms. All PCs have permanent access to the Internet through a high-speed leased line. The school's website can be found on the Internet at www.gdst.net/bromleyhigh.

Sport. Sports facilities include a large, well-equipped Sports Hall, a gymnasium, a 400-metre athletics track, two grass hockey pitches, netball and tennis courts, a fine indoor heated swimming pool, and an Astroturf pitch, which was opened in 2000.

Sixth Form. The large Sixth Form enjoys a wide GCE Advanced Level and AS Level curriculum, a broad provision for minority studies, opportunities for taking responsibility and for travel to Europe and beyond; video conferencing facilities are available to support distance learning. In addition to the many sports available in the Senior School, Sixth Formers are able to participate in a range of sports including rowing. Almost all students go on to higher education and each year girls maintain the school's "Oxbridge" tradition. Applications for Sixth Form entry are welcome. Careers education has a high profile throughout all key stages and the school is a member of ISCO and has strong links with Connexions.

Extra-Curricular Activities. A great emphasis is put on an enthusiastic involvement in music, art, sport, drama and community activities. The school has a high local reputation for its annual dance production and holds several sports championships. Major school concerts are organised at venues such as Westminster Abbey and Southwark Cathedral.

All extra-curricular activities flourish in this lively community where Young Enterprise, work experience, work shadowing, Neighbourhood Engineer and Challenge to Industry schemes have considerable support. The Bromley High Parents' Association supports the school most generously. Girls enjoy contributing to local, national and international charities and to community service. They are prepared for the Bronze standard of the Duke of Edinburgh's Award Scheme and there is a keen interest in environmental issues. There are many clubs in which girls of all ages take a share of responsibility. There are regular exchanges to France, Germany and Spain as well as annual Geography and Biology field trips. World challenge expeditions have visited Malaysia, Ecuador, Thailand, Guyana, Namibia and Vietnam and Zambia. The Annual Music Tours have travelled to Australia, Venice, Malta, South Africa, Malawi, Slovenia, Catalonia, the United States, China and Estonia. The Year 6 and 7 Music Tours have visited Paris, Brussels, Normandy and Bruges.

Fees per term (2008-2009). Senior School £3,700, Junior Department £2,879.

Fees cover tuition, stationery, textbooks and scientific and games materials as well as entry fees for GCSE and GCE Advanced Level examinations. Extra tuition in Music and Speech and Drama is available at recognised rates.

Bursaries. Following the ending of the Government Assisted Places Scheme, the GDST has made available to the school a substantial number of scholarships and bursaries. The bursaries are means tested and are intended to ensure that the school remains accessible to bright girls who would profit from our education but who would be unable to enter the school without financial assistance.

Scholarships. There are Academic scholarships for the most successful candidates in the 11+ examinations and for entry into the Sixth Form. There are also Music and Sports scholarships at 11+ and Music, Science, Arts, Sports and Drama scholarships are awarded in the Sixth Form.

Admission and Entrance Examination. Admission into the school is at 4+ (Reception) and 7+ (Year 3) by assessment and testing. The 11+ (Year 7) entrance examination will include papers in English and Mathematics and a General Paper with a section including science data, which will give candidates the opportunity to show their ideas, and some non-verbal reasoning. Entry into the Sixth Form is dependent on at least six GCSE subjects at A/B grade.

Charitable status. Bromley High School is part of The Girls' Day School Trust, which is a Registered Charity, number 306983. The aim of the Trust is to provide a fine academic education for girls, which is distinguished by its breadth, as well as its depth.

Bruton School for Girls

Sunny Hill Bruton Somerset BA10 0NT
Tel: 01749 814400
Fax: 01749 812537
e-mail: info@brutonschool.co.uk
website: www.brutonschool.co.uk

Boarding, weekly boarding and day.
Founded in 1900.

Governors:
Chairman: Mr T Wood
Vice-Chairman: Mr J Bingham

***Headmaster*: Mr John Burrough**, BA, CertEd

Deputy Heads:
Mrs Rachel Robbins, BA Hons
Mrs Linda Smallwood, BSc, PGCE

Head of Preparatory School: Mr David Marsden, JP, BSc, CertEd, DipIT

Bursar: Mr A H D Harvey-Kelly

Registrar: Miss Louise Ross-Kellaway

A preparatory, senior school and sixth form of approx 400 pupils, of whom roughly 100 board, with recent significant developments to buildings, facilities and curriculum. Set on a 40 acre campus in an outstanding location in beautiful countryside, the School is easily accessible by nearby road and rail links to London, Bristol, Bath, Salisbury, Exeter and Taunton together with the network of daily buses serving the local area. The teaching week is Monday–Friday with no Saturday lessons and staff contribute towards the extra-curricular and boarding programme.

Structure. There are 3 elements of the School.

Sunny Hill Preparatory School, for girls aged 3 to 11 years and boys aged 3–7 years, has its own specialist accommodation and a pupil : teacher ratio of 11:1. There is a nursery and pre-prep department. Small orderly classes develop strong learning habits and make the most of the inquisitive childhood years. Girls explore the exciting world of science, information technology, French, music (including Suzuki) and creative arts. Mathematics and English programmes build firm foundations for purposeful learning.

Bruton Senior School is a very successful 11 to 16 school with a pupil : teacher ratio of 13:1. At GCSE, 20 subjects are offered with a 99% A to C pass rate in up to 10 GCSE subjects. Information Technology is seen as an important 'transferable skill' developed across the curriculum. Mathematics, English, Modern Languages and Sciences are 'setted' individually to maximise pupil potential. Pupils with academic potential but specific learning difficulties benefit from support specialists.

The Sixth Form is an innovative approach to pre-university study, with tutorial support and individual study programmes. The School has a considerable reputation for academic achievement, "Oxbridge", and university entrance. Cultural and social skills are developed to enhance independence and career ambitions. An extensive range of A Levels is enhanced by cultural activities, extension studies, and extra-curricular programmes which include driving tuition, public speaking and the Leiths Certificate in Food and Wine. Career and Higher Education advice feature prominently at this stage and are reinforced by our association with various professional bodies, and a well-equipped careers resource centre.

Boarding accommodation is provided within two houses on site offering a close family atmosphere of warmth and security to girls from 8 to 18 years reflecting the changing expectations of girls according to age and affording the flexibility to meet the needs of busy families. Accommodation is provided in shared and individual rooms and girls are cared for by Housemistresses and assistant house staff. Sixth formers occupy a separate wing of individual study-bedrooms with washbasin, telephone and computer point, and enjoy a degree of freedom that reflects our aim to bridge between 'school' and 'university'. Full, weekly and casual boarding is available, and with no compulsory Saturday schooling, parents can choose the frequency of visits and exeats. A varied and stimulating programme of activities is offered each weekend.

A Medical Centre is staffed by well qualified Sisters who provide 24 hour care and are supported by Bruton Surgery.

A high standard of catering is provided and specific dietary needs are provided for.

Extra-Curricular Activities. Art, Drama, Music and Sport feature strongly. The success of the Art Department is reflected not only in work displayed around the school but also further afield in public competitions and exhibitions. Drama, Public Speaking and Theatre Studies are offered to all girls from the age of 11, and the school has several productions each year. Sports-women frequently represent the county and attend national competitions; tennis coaching, horse-riding, judo and fencing are offered year-round, in addition to a full fixture list of competitive matches. However an important philosophy of the school is respect for sport as healthy recreation, therefore a choice of non-competitive activities including modern and classical dance, fencing, martial arts, yoga and individual exercise regimes are available in the Fitness Suite and Dance Studio. There is also a popular Duke of Edinburgh's Award programme.

Fees per term (2008-2009). Day: £3,857 (Senior School), £2,927 (Preparatory School), £2,104 (Prep-Preparatory School), £18.25 per session (Nursery).

Boarding (in addition to Tuition): £2,620 (full), £2,066 (weekly boarding), £44.50 per day (casual boarding).

Entry. There is open entry into the pre-prep and preparatory schools from which pupils normally progress seamlessly into the Senior School. Entry into the Senior School is by our own examinations and interviews. Entry into the Sixth Form is by interview and subject-specific testing.

Scholarships. (*see Scholarship Entries section*). Bruton School for Girls has a range of scholarships and awards at 11+, 13+ and Sixth Form entry which are awarded on the basis of aptitude or particular areas, e.g. Music, Art, Sport, Drama etc. Further details are available from the Registrar.

Location. The School is 4 miles from Wincanton and the M3/A303 corridor between London and the South West. It lies 25 miles south of Bristol and Bath and within 40 miles of Salisbury and the south coast. The Paddington London railway to Exeter and Plymouth is 1 mile away and the line to London Waterloo is 12 miles – the School offers minibus connections. Students can also be collected from Heathrow and other airports. A network of daily buses also serves the school.

Charitable status. Bruton School for Girls is a Registered Charity, number 1085577, and a Company Limited by Guarantee. It exists to provide education for girls.

Burgess Hill School for Girls

Keymer Road Burgess Hill West Sussex RH15 0EG
Tel: 01444 241050
Fax: 01444 870314
e-mail: registrar@burgesshill-school.com
website: www.burgesshill-school.com

This independent day and boarding School was founded in 1906.

***Headmistress*: Mrs A Aughwane**, BSc Hons, PGCE, NPQH

Deputy Headmistress: Mrs E Laybourn, BEd Hons

Senior Teacher: Mr R Tapping, BSc Hons, PGCE, NPQH, CGeog FRGS

Head of Sixth Form: Mr T Butterworth, BA Hons

Head of Junior School: Miss F Fulleylove, BA Hons, DipEd

Deputy Head of Junior School: Mrs M Brown, CertEd

Head of Upper School: Mr T Clarke, BA Hons, PGCE

Head of Lower School: Miss M Bramley, BSc Hons, PGCE

Heads of Faculty:
English: Ms S Trivière, BA Hons, MA, PGCE
French: Mrs I Martin, Licence Maîtrise, DDT
German: Mrs A Corcut, BA Hons
Spanish: Mrs S West, BA Hons, PGCSE
Classics & Latin: Mrs B Johns, BA Hons, PGCE
Mathematics: Mrs L Woroniecki, MA, BSc, Adv DipEd
Biology: Miss C Brooks, BSc Hons, PGCE
Chemistry: Mrs S Lympany, BSc Hons, MSc, PGCE
Physics: Mrs S Marsh
Business Studies & Economics: Mrs J King, BEd
Information Technology: Mrs N Williams, BSc Hons, MBA, PGCE
Geography: Mr T Lucas, MA, PGCE
History: Mr D Tuck, MA, PGCE
Psychology: Mrs C Humprey, BSc Hons, PGCE, GMBPS
Art: Mrs M Carruthers, Dip AD, ATC, PGCPD
Music: Nr R Haslam, BEd Hons, ARCM
Drama: Miss E Tarratt, BA Hons, PGCE
Physical Education: Miss S Clapp, BA Hons QTS
Technology: Mrs S Bradley, BEd City & Guilds Embroidery & Fashion, C & G
Religious Studies: Mr T Lucas, MA, PGCE

Bursar: Mr S Fowle
Registrar/Marketing Executive: Miss Y Lowe, DipM ACIM
Senior Housemistress: Mrs L Bussell, Cert PPB
Housemistresses: Miss M Peskett, BEd and Miss M Buckley
School Nurse: Sheila Ramanan, RGN
Careers Advisor: Mrs J Edey, MA Hons, PGCE

General. The ethos of the School is to provide a happy, challenging and supportive atmosphere which encourages young people to use their initiative, be inquisitive and creative and develop responsibility and independence. Boys are welcome in the Nursery. Ours is a school in which girls flourish; from age 4 the focus is firmly on girls and the way they learn. They develop self-esteem and confidence and go on to make a positive contribution in their chosen professions. We have small classes with fully qualified, professional staff dedicated to catering for the needs of the individual child. The School has established a reputation for excellence in Music, Sport, Art, Textiles and Drama and achieves impressive academic results. We are consistently highly ranked nationally and regularly lead the field in Sussex. We believe that education for life involves much more than academic success alone. Girls can, and do, strive for excellence wherever their talents lie.

School Facilities. In September 2006 the School completed the extension to the Sixth Form Centre providing a spacious new Upper Sixth Common Room, new teaching rooms and an exciting, large and flexible space for lectures, events and activities. Also opened in September 2006, enhanced outdoor PE facilities provide new tennis courts and an Astroturf training area. The Senior School also benefits from an excellent Learning Resource Centre, a Design and Technology laboratory and specialist Textiles room. The Sports Pavilion houses a well resourced Drama studio. In the Junior School, an enlarged computer suite and upgraded music room add to the excellent facilities available to support the curriculum. In September 2007 the next phase of developments began with the building of a new Nursery and Infant block. There are 3 boarding houses, two adjoining the school grounds. The rooms and common rooms are spacious, light and pleasantly furnished and the atmosphere is informal and friendly.

Curriculum. The curriculum is broad and challenging and relevant to the needs of young people. There is a wide choice of subjects both at GCSE and A level with many extra-curricular activities.

ISC Inspection January 2003. The report clearly confirms that the School has a great many strengths in nearly all aspects of its provision. The inspectors praised the strong system of pastoral care, which enables the pupils to make the most of their strengths, the high standard of teaching and learning and the extensive activities programme, which does much to enrich the pupils' curriculum. They state that the Junior School, including the under 5s, provides an excellent foundation.

The inspectors noted that the pupils are well motivated, competent learners, the staff are committed, experienced and set a high value on the quality of their relationships with pupils, and that the School is ably governed and well managed by the Headmistress.

Entrance Procedures. Entrance to either the Junior or Senior school is by examination and school reference. Senior girls are also interviewed by the Headmistress. Scholarships are awarded each year for academic and/or musical excellence into Years 3, 4, 7, 8, 9 and the Lower Sixth. Creative scholarships are available for students entering Year 9 and the Lower Sixth.

Fees per term (2008-2009). Senior School: £4,000 (day girls); £6,950 (boarding). Junior School: £1,910–£3,350 (day girls).

Old Girls' Association. The Old Girls' Association is an association run by Girls. It helps to keep them in touch with each other and what is happening at the School. Chairman: Mrs S Arnold. Secretary: Mrs K Ruff (katharineruff@yahoo.com).

Charitable status. Burgess Hill School for Girls is a Registered Charity, number 307001. It exists to promote the education of any age.

Bury Grammar School Girls

Bridge Road Bury Lancs BL9 0HH
Tel: 0161 797 2808
Fax: 0161 763 4658
e-mail: info@bgsg.bury.sch.uk
website: www.bgsg.bury.sch.uk

Motto: *Sanctas Clavis Fores Aperit*

Chairman of Governors: Revd Dr J C Findon

Bursar and Clerk to the Governors: Mr D A Harrison, BSc Econ, FCA

***Headmistress*: Mrs R Georghiou**, BA Manchester, MEd Liverpool

Deputy Headmistresses:
Mrs L D Billinge, BSc Leicester
Mrs J A Buttery, BA Lancaster

Senior Teacher: Mrs E J Schofield, MA Manchester

Heads of Departments:
Mlle A Brenot, BA Manchester (*Extra-Curricular Activities*)
Miss R Britton, BMus Manchester (*Music*)
Miss J D Cebertowicz, BA Bath (*Art and Design*)
Mrs S Cheyne, BSc Bradford (*Psychology*)
Mrs J E Coulthard, BA Cambridge (*Classics*)
Mrs S Fielden, BSc London (*Science and Biology*)
Mrs H Hammond, BA Liverpool (*Theatre Studies*)
Mrs Y G Hanham, BSc Salford (*Mathematics*)
(*to be appointed*) (*Design and Technology*)
Mr M Joyce, MA Oxon (*Modern Languages*)
Mrs L C A Kerr, BA Manchester (*RS*)
Mrs V Leaver, BSc Hull (*Geography*)
Mrs V Livsey, BA Liverpool (*German*)
Mr D Ashworth, BA Manchester Metropolitan (*ICT*)
Mrs J Slade, BSc Loughborough (*PE*)
Mrs S Taylor, BSc Manchester (*Careers*)
Mrs S Thorpe, BA Salford (*Politics*)
Mrs A Vyce, BA Edinburgh (*English*)
Mrs H Ward, BA Leicester (*History*)
Mrs M Whitlow, BA York (*Economics and Business Studies*)
Dr J Yates, BSc Durham, PhD Bristol (*Chemistry*)

Head of Sixth Form: Mrs H Ward, BA Leicester
Head of Upper School: Mrs I Petela, BA Nottingham
Head of Middle School: Mrs J Haworth, BA Keele
Head of Year 7: Mrs S C Banfield, BA Bangor

Kindergarten and Junior School:
Mrs D E Robinson, CertEd Didsbury (*Kindergarten*)
Mrs B Bottoms, BSc Liverpool (*Junior School*)

The Girls' School was founded in 1884 as the Bury High School for Girls and amalgamated, a few years later, with the Bury Grammar School (Boys). The school maintains high academic standards and traditional grammar school values whilst encouraging each girl to develop her individual talents and abilities as far as she can in a lively environment which responds to the challenge of change.

The **Senior School** is housed in a distinctive Edwardian building which dates from 1906. The school is conveniently situated near the centre of the town and the bus-tram interchange. Facilities are regularly improved and updated; significant additions and modifications to our buildings have been made in recent years including the Dorothy Lester Library with an attached Resource Centre, Sports Hall, Humanities block, ICT Centre and additional specialist teaching rooms for Science, Design and Technology, Textiles, Food Technology, English and Music. The Swimming Pool has been completely refurbished.

The curriculum is broad and balanced in the first five years of the Senior School. At Key Stage Three all girls follow courses in Art, ICT, Design Technology, Latin, Classical Civilisation, Business Studies and two Modern Languages from a choice of French, German and Spanish, in addition to the core curriculum of Mathematics, English, the three Sciences, PE, RS, History and Geography. Traditional teaching methods are combined with pupil-centred learning work, group work, investigative work and a problem-solving approach. In a variety of cross curricular projects, pupils seek solutions to problems and take an ever-increasing responsibility for their own learning.

PE and Music are well established; in recent years the School has been represented in National Netball, Tennis and Swimming Championships and on County Netball, Hockey, Cross-Country, Swimming, Tennis, Athletics and Badminton teams. Each year the Festival Choir gives concerts internationally and in the UK. They regularly sing for the BBC Radio 4 Daily Service. There are also two orchestras, string quartets, a flute choir and a jazz band.

The School works closely with Bury Grammar School (Boys) for dramatic and musical productions, and other extra-curricular activities. The Sixth Form common rooms are open to both boys and girls.

Public examinations are taken in Years 11, 12 and 13, according to the requirements of individual pupils. There is a wide choice of subjects in the Sixth Form and each year all or virtually all students proceed to degree courses at prestigious universities, including Oxford and Cambridge. The School achieves high pass rates in public examinations.

These successes and initiatives, along with PSE, careers advice and extra-curricular activities, clubs, visits, holidays in England and abroad, charity work and school productions, offer wide educational opportunities and encourage links to be forged with industry and commerce and with the community in Bury and beyond.

The **Junior School** has its own purpose-built premises on the Senior School site, has shared use of the Roger Kay Hall, Gymnasium, Sports Hall, and Swimming Pool. The eight large and attractive classrooms, Music Room and large Library/Computer suite provide a comfortable and very pleasant environment in which the girls aged 7–11 learn and work.

The Junior School follows the National Curriculum. The curriculum includes the three core subjects and Design/Technology, ICT, History, Geography, Religious Education, Art and Craft, Music and Physical Education. Particular emphasis is placed on the teaching of skills in reading, writing and mathematics. The aim is to provide a broad and balanced education and to give each girl the opportunity to develop her full potential. The combination of a dedicated staff and excellent facilities allows girls to maintain the high academic standard enriched by many extra-curricular activities with particular strengths in music and sport.

The School has a **Pre-School and Kindergarten** for boys and girls from the age of 3–7 situated within the main building. In lively and stimulating surroundings the children progress rapidly in all six areas of learning. They also make use of the Senior School pool and sports facilities and have specialist tuition in music. There is an After School Club.

The numbers at present are 30 in the Pre-School, 167 in the Kindergarten Department, 162 in the Junior School and 673 in the Senior School.

Scholarships. At 11+ the Governors offer one Kay Scholarship and a number of means-tested bursaries.

Fees per term (2008-2009). Pre-School, Kindergarten and Junior School £1,905; Senior School £2,566.

Charitable status. Bury Grammar Schools Charity is a Registered Charity, number 526622.

Casterton School

Kirkby Lonsdale Carnforth Lancashire LA6 2SG
Tel: 015242 79200
Fax: 015242 79208
e-mail: admissions@castertonschool.co.uk
website: www.castertonschool.co.uk

The School was founded at Cowan Bridge in 1823 by the Reverend W Carus Wilson for the education of daughters of the clergy and was moved to Casterton in 1833. Famous alumni include the Bronte sisters.

Casterton is now a boarding and day school for girls aged 11–18. A separate Preparatory Department caters for day boys and girls aged 3–11 and for boarders (girls only) between the ages of 8 and 11.

Governing Body:
Chairman: Mrs G M Hunter, JP
Vice-Chairman: Mr G R Ward, MA Cantab, FCA
Mrs J Cawley
Dr P A L Faux, MBChB, DMRD
Mr R Gregg
Mr P V Hoyle, FCIS, ATII
Miss J Laycock
His Honour Judge A J Proctor, MA, LLM Cantab
Mrs E Raitt, BA Hons, PGCE, AdvDipEd Mgt
Mr M C B Spens, MA Cantab
Mr P Thurnham, MA, FInstMechEng
Mr C Tomlinson

Visitor: The Right Revd The Lord Bishop of Carlisle

Staff:

***Headmaster*: P McLaughlin**, BA, PhD

Deputy Head: Mrs P A Gee, MA Oxon, BA Open, PGCE Cheltenham (*History*)
Deputy Head: Mrs G A Sykes, BSc Hons Exeter, PGCE Sheffield (*Mathematics*)
Senior House Mistress: Miss H Whitfield, CertPhysEd Anstey College
Bursar: Mrs J Thistlethwaite, BA Hons UCL, MAAT
Development Director: Miss E Clarke, BA Hons, PGDL Birmingham
Medical Officer: Dr P J I Hall, MBChB, MRCGP

Senior School

* *Head of Department*

Art:
*Mrs J A Blackmore, MA Central England, BA Hons Leeds, PGCE Liverpool
Mrs J Aveyard, BA Hons Wimbledon, PGCE Leeds
Mrs V Eden, CertEd, Dip Ceramics
Ms A Ashton, BA Hons Loughborough Coll of Art & Design, MA Chelsea Coll of Art & Design

Drama:
*Mrs N Marriott, BA Hons Birmingham, PGCE Leeds
Mrs L Blackwell, BEd Coll of Ripon & York St John

English:
*Mrs J Chandor, BA Hons Cantab, PGCE Cantab
Mrs V Bray, CertEd Matlock
Mrs F Norman, BA Hons Manchester
Miss T King, MA Cantab, PGCE Oxon

Economics & Business Studies:
*Miss C E Jones, BA Hons Leeds Met, PGCE Manchester

Geography:
*Miss H L Rowland, BA Hons Nottingham, PGCE Nottingham
Mr D Elphick, BSc Hons East Anglia, PGCE St Martin's, Lancaster

History:
*Mrs P A Gee, MA Oxon, BA Open, PGCE Cheltenham
Mrs K Ellis, BA Hons UCW, PGCE Hull
Miss S E Tamplin, BA Hons Cardiff, PGCE

Home Economics:
*Miss A C Rigby, CertEd Gloucester College

Information & Communication Technology:
*Mrs P J Symonds, BSc Hons Durham, PGCE Oxford

Mrs C E Birtwistle, BA Open, BSc Edinburgh, PSC, RMCS
The Revd P S Atkinson, BD, AKC London, MA Durham, DipRE London
Mr Robin Bailey

Languages:
*Mrs C A Cochrane, MA Hons St Andrews, AIL
Mrs C Peek, BA Hons Bangor, CertEd Liverpool
Mrs J Wheeler, MA Aberdeen
Mr J Watts, BA Hons Oxon PCGE Edge Hill
Mrs C A Ortega, MA University of Valencia, MSc Lancaster
Miss P A Hayward, BA Hons Durham

Learning Support:
Miss D Vernon, MAEd Open, BA Hons Open

Mathematics:
*Mr J Cochrane, BSc Salford, PGCE Manchester Met
Mrs A Cox, BEd Liverpool, CertEd Chester
Mrs G A Sykes, BSc Hons Exeter, PGCE Sheffield
Mrs J Fielden, BSc Hons Nottingham, PGCE Bristol

Music:
*Mr D C Chapman, MA Oxon, LRAM Accompaniment, LRAM TDip
Mr R Fudge, BMus Hons Birmingham
Mrs K Guidici, GMus, RNCM Hons, PPRNCM

Physical Education:
*Miss A De Miranda, BEd Leeds Polytechnic
Mrs K J Culshaw, BEd Hons I M Marsh
Mrs G Barton, BEd Hons Sussex
Mrs P Sneddon, BEd Neville's Cross, RYASI
Mrs H Wallace, BPhEd, BCom Otago
Mr M Harris, Nat Dip of Sports Science, BTec
Miss H Ripp, BSc Mariot College, New York (*Lacrosse*)
Miss S B Nelson, BHSII
Mrs J Howarth, ASA
Miss K Fisher, LTAReg

Religious Studies:
*The Revd P S Atkinson, BD, AKC London, MA Durham, DipRE London
Miss C L Summerhayes, BEd Hons Leeds

Science:
*Mr R J Sanders, BSc Liverpool, PGCE Chester
Mr A Bell, BSc Hons St Andrews
Miss S L Haddrill, BA Open, CertEd Durham FIST
Dr M Martin, MSc UMIST, PhD, CertEd Manchester
Dr J L Howard, CChem MRIC, PhD Salford, CertEd Lancaster

Sociology:
*Mrs J Clarke, BSocSci Birmingham, PGCE Avery Hill

Ballet:
Miss H Burns, LISTD DIP ND, AISTD OB, MBBO, RAD and ISTD Reg

Careers:
*Miss D Vernon, MAEd Open, BA Hons Open
Mrs A Cox, BEd Liverpool, CertEd Chester
Miss H L Rowland, BA Hons Nottingham, PGCE Nottingham

Outdoor Pursuits:
Mrs A Cox, BEd Liverpool, CertEd Chester

Housemistresses:
Dobson House: Miss J Howe, BA British Columbia
Harben House: Miss H Whitfield, CertPhysEd Anstey College
Vincent House: Mrs B Leahy
Williams House: Mrs P Sneddon, BEd Neville's Cross, RYASI (*and PE*)
Crookenden House: Mrs H Wallace, BPhEd, BCom Otago (*and PE*)
Garner House: Mrs S Cox, CertEd I M Marsh (*and PE*)
Old Hall House: Mrs A Atkinson, RGN (*and Senior Sister*)
Bronte House: Mrs C Y Cookson, CertEd Lancaster (*and French*)

Administration:
Bursar: Mrs J Thistlethwaite, BA Hons UCL MAAT
Head's PA: Mrs M Holden
Bursar's Assistant and Lettings Manager: Ms E Clark, BA UCLan
Bursar's Secretary: Ms S Booth
Finance Assistant: Ms J Brown
Travel Secretary: Ms C Coggins
Registrar's Assistant: Mrs A Clowes

Preparatory School

Head of Preparatory School: Mrs G M Hoyle, BEd Hons Southampton, CertEd King Alfred's College
Head of Pre-Prep: Mrs S Tatham, BEd Chester, MA

Ms V May, CertEd Madeley College of Education
Mrs J M Slater, BA Hons St Martin's, Lancaster
Mrs A Procter, CertEd Credit Coventry Coll of Education
Mrs T Christie, Nursing Dip, Outdoor Leaders Cert Humber Coll, Toronto, BA Hons York Univ, Toronto, PGCE
Mr R Christie, BSc Hons Loughborough
Mrs C Y Cookson, CertEd Lancaster
Mrs A Mason, BEd Lancaster
Mrs H Woodward, BEd Hons Manchester Polytechnic
Mrs D Baines, BTech Lancaster (*Nursery Nurse in Charge*)

Number of Pupils. There are 250 girls in the Senior School and 70 girls and boys in the Preparatory Department.

Situation. The School is situated where three counties meet: North Yorkshire, Cumbria and Lancashire. Casterton is one mile from the town of Kirkby Lonsdale and only 7 miles from the M6. Harrogate and Ilkley are only an hour a way, on good road links. International links are via Manchester and Leeds Bradford Airports.

Facilities and Development. Casterton is a boarding school and a strong vertical House system prevails. There is a Junior House, mixed-aged Houses and Sixth Form Houses. All current boarding Houses are light and airy. Day girls are fully integrated in to the House system. In early 2006, the Governors and Dr McLaughlin, decided to master plan the entire campus using a specialist firm of architects. The master plan will form the backbone of the school's strategic development for the twenty-first century. The plan will focus on the provision of first-class facilities to match the first-class academic profile. Facilities for boarding will feature heavily in the plans ensuring that girls have superb provision for work and recreation. Casterton has an outstanding purpose-built Art and Design Centre as well as a very spacious purpose-built Science and Maths Centre, large Gymnasium/Hall, Libraries, Classrooms, Home Economics Centre, Music Wing, ICT Centre, Language Laboratory, Theatre and Sixth Form study area. A new Sports Pavilion with full changing facilities and a full-size, all-weather pitch for hockey and tennis is also supplemented by lacrosse pitches, athletics track and indoor pool.

Education. The education includes; RE, English, History, French, Geography, Economics, German, Spanish, Latin, Mathematics, Physics, Chemistry, Biology, Computer studies, Business Studies, Music, Art, Physical Education, Home Economics and Drama.

Examinations. Pupils are prepared for GCSE and A level examinations, the Universities (Entrance and Scholarships) and the examinations of the Associated Board of the Royal Schools of Music, LAMDA, Royal Academy of Dance, Duke of Edinburgh's Award and equestrian examinations.

PE and Games. These form part of the normal curriculum and include Hockey, Netball, Lacrosse, Tennis, Rounders, Athletics, Cross-Country and Swimming. Riding is available at the school's own stables. Sailing and training for the Duke of Edinburgh's Award scheme are also offered.

Age of Admission. Entrance can be considered at any age – there is an Entrance Examination for applicants from the age of 8 upwards.

Fees per term (from January 2008). Boarding: £7,211 (Year 9 and above), £6,868 (Year 8), £5,884 (Years 6 & 7), £5,736 (Years 6 & 7 weekly), £5,489 (Years 3–5), £5,345 (Years 3–5 weekly).

Day: £4,315 (Year 8 and above), £3,747 (Years 5–7), £2,940 (Years 3 & 4), £2,231 (Years 1 & 2), £2,009 (Reception).

Extras, which are optional, include instruction in a wide range of musical instruments, singing, speech and drama, riding, tennis coaching, ballet. Termly rates for these are available from The Headmaster on request.

Scholarships and Bursaries. (*see Scholarship Entries section*). There are Bursaries available for the daughters of Clergy. The number is now limited and grants can be offered only as vacancies occur.

Casterton School Old Girls Association. *Secretary*: Miss J Laycock, Hillcrest Cottage, Cherry Clough, Denshaw, Saddlesworth, OL3 5UE or via the School.

Charitable status. Casterton School is a Registered Charity, number 1076380.

Central Newcastle High School (GDST)

Eskdale Terrace Newcastle-upon-Tyne NE2 4DS
Tel: 0191 281 1768
Fax: 0191 281 6192
e-mail: cnhs@cnw.gdst.net
website: www.newcastlehigh.gdst.net

Junior Department:
West Avenue Gosforth Newcastle-upon-Tyne NE3 4ES
Chapman House Sandyford Newcastle-upon-Tyne NE2 1NN
Tel: 0191 285 1956
Fax: 0191 213 2598
e-mail: cnhsjuniors@cnn.gdst.net

Founded 1895.

This is one of the 29 schools of The Girls' Day School Trust. For further information about the Trust, see p. xxiv. Additional information may be found on the school's website. A detailed prospectus may be obtained from the School.

Pupil Numbers: 930: Senior Department 605 (aged 11–18 years) of whom 160 are in the Sixth Form; Junior Department 325 (aged 3–10 years).

Chair of Local Governors: Mrs M Martin, BA Hons

***Headmistress*: Mrs H J French**, MA Oxon, MEd, PGCE Durham, NPQH

Deputy Head: Mr M Tippett, MA Oxon, PGCE Cantab

Head of Sixth Form: Mrs A Hutchinson, MA Oxon, PGCE Bristol

Situated in the heart of Newcastle upon Tyne, Central Newcastle High School is one of the country's leading day schools for girls. Central High is committed to using its strong traditions of academic excellence and sound moral values to offer the girls of today the opportunity to grow into the strong and independent women of tomorrow.

The School's ethos encourages curiosity, independence and enthusiasm as well as a lifelong love of learning. It offers girls aged 3–18 the opportunity to develop and mature in an environment that focuses on their individual needs. The academic standards are high and there is a vibrant and happy atmosphere that permeates the whole School. Pastoral care is a priority as the School helps to guide girls through all their stages of development. Sport, Music, Art, Dance and Drama are all encouraged. The School achieved Sportsmark Gold Extension Award in 2005 for its outstanding provision of Sport both within and outside the curriculum. The girls are also involved in a wide variety of other activities ranging from Gospel Choir to Poetry Society, Greek Drama to Community Service. The School has one of the largest Duke of Edinburgh's Award Schemes in the area.

The facilities across the whole School are excellent and all girls are able to take full advantage of them. The Junior Department includes Nursery and Infants based at West Avenue, Gosforth. During Key Stage Two girls move to Chapman House, Sandyford. Both locations offer spacious surroundings in which to grow and develop. The Senior Department is based at Eskdale Terrace, Jesmond, where girls benefit from the exciting and stimulating environment provided. There is a purpose built Music School with outstanding facilities as well as an excellent Sports Hall and Sixth Form Centre. A Drama Studio with teaching rooms was completed in Spring 2003. Extensive redevelopment of the Senior Department was completed in October 2006 and includes a new library and ICT suites, additional laboratory, multi-purpose hall, the creation of an Art School and an English Centre. Classrooms and the Reception area have all been refurbished. The Sixth Form facilities have also been extended.

The School's GCSE and A Level results are excellent and Central High was placed in the top 100 independent schools for its 2007 GCSE results.

Curriculum. The curriculum throughout the Junior Department is rich and varied and whilst the Foundation Stage and National Curriculum are closely followed, it offers much more including French, Dance, Classics and instrumental music lessons.

The Senior Department's curriculum provides a broad and balanced education. During the first three years girls study a wide range of subjects. In Year 9 discussion of career opportunities begins and girls make their subject choices. Mandarin has been introduced as an optional subject both in the Junior and Senior School. Most girls take ten GCSE subjects. In the Sixth Form 30 subjects are offered at AS Level. Most can be continued to A Level. There is a high take-up of all three Sciences and Mathematics.

Admissions. Junior Department: by assessment and interview.

Senior Department: by entrance examination, interview and school report.

Sixth Form: by GCSE results, interview and school report.

Fees per term (2008-2009). Senior School £2,966, Junior Department £2,150, Nursery £1,776.

The fees cover the regular curriculum, school books, stationery and other materials, choral music, games and swimming but not optional extra subjects or school meals. The fees for extra subjects, including instrumental music, speech and drama and, in the Junior Department, dancing, are shown in the prospectus.

Bursaries. The GDST Bursaries Fund provides financial assistance in the Senior Department to suitably qualified girls whose parents could not otherwise afford the fees to enter or remain in the school.

Scholarships. The GDST makes available a number of scholarships for entry at 11+ or directly into the Sixth Form. Scholarships are awarded on the basis of academic merit.

Charitable status. Central Newcastle High School is part of The Girls' Day School Trust, which is a Registered Charity, number 306983. The aim of the Trust is to provide a fine academic education for girls, which is distinguished by breadth as well as depth.

Channing School

Highgate London N6 5HF
Tel: 020 8340 2328 (School Office)
020 8340 2719 (Bursar)
Fax: 020 8341 5698
e-mail: info@channing.co.uk
website: www.channing.co.uk

Governors:
Mr M Steiner, MA Oxon (*Chairman*)
Mrs M R Banks, MBE, MEd
Mr S Barber, BSc, FCA (*Vice-Chair*)
Ms C E A Budgett-Meakin, BA Kent
Mr J M Burns, MA Oxon
Baroness C Coussins, MA Cantab
Miss J A M Davidson, BSc London
Mr R Katz
Mrs V A Schilling, MCSP
Mrs C Stephenson, CertEd
Dr A G White, MBChB, FRCP, DPhysMed
Dr D J Williams, MB, BCh

Bursar & Clerk to the Governors: Mr R Hill

***Headmistress*: Mrs B M Elliott**, MA Cantab (*Modern & Medieval Languages*)

Deputy Head: Mrs C Mawston, BA Kent (*History*)

Assistants (Senior School):
* *Head of Department*
§ *part-time*

Miss S Ablewhite, BA Bath (*French*)
Ms J Addley, MA Cantab (**Mathematics*)
Mr A Atkinson, MA Dundee (**Geography, Assistant Head of Middle School*)
Ms G Best, MA Cambridge (**History*)
Mrs G Bhamra-Burgess, BA, MSc London (*Economics*)
Ms J Bramhall, BA Oxon (*Geography*)
Mrs J Brown, BA Oxon (**English*)
Mr P Boxall, GRSM, ARCO (*Director of Music*)
§Dr M Bremser, DPhil Oxon (*English, *Critical Thinking*)
Ms A Gill-Carey, BA Kent (**Drama & Theatre Studies*)
Mr D Coram, BA Durham, MA London (*Classics*)
Ms A Cornacchia, BA Hamilton, Canada, BEd London (*Mathematics, PE*)
Mr R Crawford, MA London (**Art*)
Ms A Derbyshire, BA Central School of Art & Design (*Art*)
Mrs W Devine, BA Reading (*History, *Politics*)
§Dr N Devlin, DPhil Oxon (*Classics*)
§Ms L Feilden, BA Brighton (*Art*)
Mr S Frank, BSc Birmingham (**Biology*)
Miss S-L Fung, BSc Coventry (*Physics*)
Ms E Gale, BA, Leeds Met (**PE*)
Mr P Gittins, BA Wolverhampton (*Art, *PSHE*)
Mrs J Glasser, BA UEA (**Additional Learning*)
Mrs R Harper, BA Kent, ALAM (*English, Head of Middle School*)
Mr M Holmes, BSc City of London Polytechnic (**ICT*)
Ms S Ikram, MSc, BEd Alberta (*Chemistry*)
Ms S Ikram, BSc Alberta (*Chemistry*)
Mr R Jacobs, BA Oxon (**Science*)
Miss E Johnson, BSc Birmingham (*PE*)
Mrs H Kanmwaa, BA Oxon (*English*)
§Mrs T MacCarthy, BSc Edinburgh (*Mathematics*)
Ms M Mort, BSc Sydney (*PE*)
Mrs E Morton, BA Sheffield (**Modern Languages*)
Ms J Newman, BA Leicester (**Economics, Head of Sixth Form*)
§Ms H Nissinen-Lee, MA London (*Geography*)
Mrs J Ogidan, BSc Liverpool (*Biology, Careers Coordinator*)
Mr H Rees, BMus Wales (*Music*)
§Mrs R Roots, MA Sussex (*English*)
Mr H Ross, BA Hull (*French & Spanish*)
Ms S Saig, BA Ontario, Canada (*French, Spanish*)
Mrs M Sharma-Yun, BSc London (*Mathematics*)
Ms D Shoham, MSc London (*Biology*)
§Mrs C Soto, BA London (*Spanish*)
Ms A Stöckmann, MA Westfaelische Wilhelms (**German*)
§Mrs L Thomas, BA Hons Exeter (*PE*)
§Mr P Thompson, MA Oxon (*History*)
Mrs K Thonemann, MA Oxon (*Director of Studies*)
Mrs V Thorpe, MA Cantab (**Classics, Head of Upper School*)
§Revd S M Tinker, BA Birmingham (**RE*)
§Mrs R Williams, BSc London (*Mathematics*)
Miss M Wharmby, BA Loughborough, ALA (*Librarian*)

Junior School:
Head Teacher: Ms L Tarr, BA Port Elizabeth, SA (*Primary Education*)
Deputy Head: Mrs H Reznek, BEd Herts (*Form Teacher, Year 6*)

Miss J Cameron, MA Edinburgh
Miss B Gayton, BEd Reading
Miss D Green, BA Manchester (*ICT Curriculum Coordinator – Both Schools*)
§Mrs I Hawkins, BEd London
Ms K McGovern, BEd New Zealand
Mrs N Morgan, BA Sheffield
Mrs H Oberg-Brown, MA New Zealand
§Miss M Pepper, LTCL
Ms A Phipps, BEd Middx Polytechnic
Mrs L Robson, MA Cambridge
Miss S Snowdowne, BEd Plymouth
Miss J Tunnicliffe, BEd New Zealand
Ms K Vanstone, BEd New Zealand

Learning Support Assistants:
Ms S Ahmed
Mrs C Brierley
Ms S Ibrekic
Ms B Tadros

Visiting Staff:
Mr S Allen, ARCM (*Clarinet*)
Miss Y Behar, BA, LRAM, ARCM (*Piano*)
Miss S Bircumshaw, GRSM (*Violin*)
Mr A Brown, DpTCL (*Percussion*)
Mrs P Capone, AGSM (*Piano*)
Ms V Curran, GSMD, RAM PG Dip (*Trumpet*)
Miss L Forbes, LRAM, LTCL, DipNCOS (*Cello*)
Ms J Herbert, BA York (*Double Bass*)
Miss R Kerr, BA Hons (*Voice*)
Mr A Khan, LTCL (*Guitar*)
Mr R Martyn, AGSM, LRAM (*Brass*)
Mrs C H Mendelssohn, LRAM (*Violin*)
Miss N Myerscough, ARAM (*Violin*)
Miss C Philpot, LRAM (*Oboe*)
Ms S Riches, BMus RAM (*Double Bass*)
Miss H Shimizu, BMus (*Piano*)
Ms A Szreter, BA Oxon (*Voice*)
Mr T Travis, BMus (*Saxophone*)
Miss S Vivian, LTCL (*Voice*)
Miss J Watts, FRCO, GRSM, LRAM (*Piano*)
Ms H Webster, GRSM (*Flute*)

Bursar's Secretary: Mrs L Davies
Headmistress's Secretary: Ms L Carreras, BA London
Registrar: Mrs M McHarg
Senior School Secretary: Mrs E Ingram
Assistant Senior School Secretary: Ms S Glazier
Junior School Secretary: Mrs L Mc Inerney

Development Secretary: Miss N Thorn
Nurses: Mrs S Golding & Mrs T Franklin

Founded in 1885, Channing is a day school for girls aged 4 to 18, approximately 400 in the Senior School (Sixth Form 100 girls) and 180 in Fairseat, the Junior School. It is situated in Highgate Village, in attractive grounds, and offers a balanced education combining a traditional academic curriculum with modern educational developments. The complex of old and new buildings has been constantly adapted to provide up-to-date facilities, and there are strong links with the local community and local schools.

Teaching groups are small in size, which allows a friendly relationship between girls and staff. Girls usually take nine or ten subjects to GCSE and there is a wide range of A and AS Level choices, including Ancient Greek, Further Maths and Theatre Studies. Option blocks are re-drawn each year to suit the needs of the current year groups. The Junior School has its own building – the elegant and gracious family home of Sir Sydney Waterlow, one-time Lord Mayor of London – set in spacious gardens, and is notable for its happy and secure atmosphere.

Art, Drama, Music and Sport are all strong. Most girls learn at least one instrument and there are frequent concerts and theatrical productions. The school is fortunate in its gardens and open space (there are seven tennis courts on site) and in its facilities. There is a new Sixth Form Centre and fully-equipped performing arts studio.

Entry is by test and interview at 4, 11 and 16, and is subject to a satisfactory report from the entrant's current school. There are occasional chance vacancies.

Further information can be obtained from the School Prospectus and the Sixth Form Handbook, available from the School Office.

Scholarships and Bursaries. (*see Scholarship Entries section*).

Fees per term (2008-2009). Junior School (Reception to Year 6): £3,810; Senior School (Years 7–13): £4,130.

Charitable status. Channing House Incorporated is a Registered Charity, number 312766. It aims to provide full-time education for girls aged between 4 and 18 years.

The Cheltenham Ladies' College

Bayshill Road Cheltenham Glos GL50 3EP
Tel: 01242 520691; Bursary 01242 253233
Fax: 01242 227882
e-mail: enquiries@cheltladiescollege.org
website: www.cheltladiescollege.org

The Cheltenham Ladies' College has been at the forefront of girls' education for over 150 years. It has a reputation for academic excellence, for encouraging a real love of learning and for nurturing the personal development of every girl and member of staff. We seek to develop the talents of each girl and provide an environment in which girls can achieve the very highest standards in whatever they choose to do. There is a friendly openness about College which makes it a very happy place to live and learn.

The Council:
Chairman: Mrs C Kirby, LLB

***Principal*: Mrs Vicky Tuck**, BA, MA, MIL

Director of Finance & Resources: Mr Jeffrey Speke, BSc, MPhil, ACA

Vice-Principal (*Academic*): Miss J R Adams, BSc

Vice-Principal (*Pastoral*): Mrs S Roberts, MA

Admissions Tutor: Mrs F J Weldin, MA

Heads of Division:
Sixth Form College: Mr J Hole, MA
Upper College: Mrs D J Vass, BA
Lower College: Mrs C M Pellereau, BSc

Director of Extra-Curricular Studies: Dr Joanna Bratten, BA, MLitt, PhD

Director of Development: Miss J S Tudge, BA

Marketing and Communications Director: Mrs A Naylor, BSc

Chaplain: The Revd T Merry, BA, AKC

The pattern of day-to-day life revolves around two centres which complement each other – the College teaching buildings and the Boarding and Day Girl Houses. College is divided into three divisions – Lower College for girls in years 7–9, Upper College for girls in years 10 and 11, and Sixth Form College. The latter normally contains about 300 girls and nearly all proceed to degree courses. From September 2008 College will be offering the International Baccalaureate Diploma, alongside its existing successful A Level provision.

Numbers. Day 220, Boarding 630.

Fees per term (2008-2009). Day £5,710, Boarding £8,503. Some extras, eg music, riding are charged.

Admission. Entry at 11+, 12+ and 13+ via Common Entrance or the College's own examinations. Sixth Form entry is via the College's own entrance papers.

Pastoral Care. The systems of pastoral care are exceptionally good. Each girl is looked after by her Housemistress, the House Staff and a Tutor. All Tutors are full-time academic members of staff and advise girls on matters relating to their academic work and progress, including university advice and applications.

Buildings. The main building is built in a Gothic revival style, and its interior decorations owe a great deal to the Arts and Crafts Movement. With three Libraries, 17 laboratories, 5 networked computer rooms, an Electronics workshop, state of the art language laboratories, an Art and Technology Wing (including etching studio) and a fully-equipped careers and university advice library, the resources available to pupils are constantly kept up to date.

Houses. There are six Junior Boarding Houses and three Day Houses, all girls move House at Sixth Form which is an excellent stepping stone to university life. Day girls are fully integrated into all College activities, often joining boarders on weekend trips and expeditions.

Music, Drama and Dance. Over 800 individual music lessons take place each week, and there are generally five choirs and five orchestras running at any time. 450 girls have individual drama lessons in addition to the large number of productions put on each year. Dance and gymnastics are also available and very popular.

Sport. College's aim is to encourage all girls to enjoy physical exercise and take up an interest which will last throughout their lives. The main sports are hockey, lacrosse, netball, swimming, athletics but the College provides what girls enjoy and about 40 sports are offered, including rowing, cricket, soccer, squash, tennis and golf. There is a large and superbly equipped sports centre, including a fitness suite and indoor swimming pool. There are 2 synthetic astroturf pitches (one floodlit).

Scholarships and Bursaries. (*see Scholarship Entries section*). Over twenty Academic, Music, Art or Sport Scholarships and other awards are made annually. Applications for bursaries are welcome from applicants whose parents genuinely require some form of financial assistance in order to help their daughter join College.

Former Pupils, known as The Guild. There are 9,000 former pupils throughout the world, and they are a valued source of help to present girls, particularly in providing work-shadowing and careers advice.

Charitable status. The Cheltenham Ladies' College is a Registered Charity, number 311722. It exists to provide a high standard of education for girls.

City of London School for Girls

St Giles' Terrace Barbican London EC2Y 8BB
Tel: 020 7847 5500
Fax: 020 7638 3212
e-mail: info@clsg.org.uk
website: www.clsg.org.uk

Motto: *Domine Dirige Nos*

Staff:
***Headmistress*: Miss D Vernon**, BA Hons Dunelm

Deputy Head: Mr W A Douglas, BA Hons Oxon
Second Deputy: Ms J Gandee, MA Cantab
Head of Sixth Form Years 12 & 13: Ms J Henderson, BA Hons Durham
Assistant Head of Sixth Form: Dr S Schoenfield, PhD Kiel, Germany, MA
Head of Senior School Years 9, 10, 11: Mrs P R Restan, BA Hons Nottingham
Assistant Head of Senior School: Mme N Signeux, English-University of Orléans, Modern Foreign Languages-Lancaster, FLE
Heads of Lower School Years 7 & 8: Mrs K N Brice, MA Cantab and Mrs F M Angel, BA Hons Bournemouth

Heads of Department:

Art:
Miss J Curtis, BA Hons London, St Martin's School of Art, ATC London

Classics:
Miss P A Perkins, BA Hons Dunelm, DipEd

Design Technology:
Miss S McCarthy, BSc Hons Brunel

Drama:
Mr S Morley, DipCCSD Acting, Full Equity Member

Economics/Politics:
Mr A C Genillard, BSc Hons Brighton

English:
Mrs G Guest, BA Otago, New Zealand, BA Hons London

Geography:
Ms E A Moore, BA Hons Liverpool, FRGS

History:
Mrs K N Brice, MA Cantab

History of Art:
Mrs D M B B Southern, MA Edinburgh

ICT:
Mr D Libby, BSc Hons Bristol

Mathematics:
Mr K Latham, BSc

Modern Languages:
Miss C Macko, BA Orléans, MA
French: Mr G Tyrrell, BA Oxford Brookes, MA
Spanish: Miss C Macko, BA Orléans, MA
German: Mrs V W Potter, Mag Phil Innsbruck
Italian: Ms J Henderson, BA Hons Dunelm
Mandarin: Ms J-C Lee, MBA Leicester, MSc London

Music:
Mrs M Donnelly, BEd Hons London

Physical Education:
Mrs E A McLean, CertEd Dartford

Psychology:
Mrs K Winterbottom, BA Hons Durham

Religious Education:
Mrs K Bullard, MA Cantab

Science:
Mrs D S Barry, BSc Hons London, MA, CBiol, MIBiol
Biology: Ms N Brown, BSc Hons Edinburgh, MRes Edinburgh
Chemistry: Miss S Clements, BSc Hons Southampton
Physics: Mr M Wilkinson, BSc Nottingham

Careers:
Mrs C E Lipman, BA Hons Manchester

Preparatory Department:
Mr J Brough, BEd Hons Cantab, NPQH

Bursar: Colonel E L Yorke
Assistant Bursar: Mrs C Bright, MIMgt
Bursar's Secretary: Miss L Coldwell
Admissions Secretary: Mrs V S Sampson
PA to Headmistress: Mrs R Smith
Marketing & Development Officer: Mrs C Stephenson, B BehSc Griffith

Health and Support Network:
School Doctor: Dr D Soldi, MBChB, DCH
School Sister: Mrs D Patel, RSCN
School Counsellor: Ms D Marcus, BA Hons (UK CP Registered)
Learning Support Teacher & Special Needs Coordinator: Mrs A Shilsler, CertEd, RSA DipSpLD, CAPS (Communication Difficulties)

There is a buzz about life at City of London School for Girls, a lively, purposeful and happy atmosphere. City of London School for Girls is a unique day school for girls aged 7 to 18. Our location helps to make it so, nestled in the Barbican centre yet surrounded by one of the most dynamic and diverse cities in the world. We have galleries, museums, libraries and theatres on our doorstep, along with all the other resources of an international centre of commerce. Our pupils have access to the very best London has to offer.

The School Course includes English Language and Literature, History, Geography, Religious Studies, Latin, Greek, French, German, Spanish, Mathematics, Biology, Chemistry, Physics, Economics and Politics, Art, Music, Singing, Technology, Physical Education, Classical Civilisation, Design and Technology, History of Art, Theatre Studies, and Psychology.

Pupils are prepared for the General Certificate of Secondary Education and for Advanced Supplementary and A2 Level Examinations offered by EDEXCEL, OCR and AQA. They are also prepared for Entrance to Oxford, Cambridge and other Universities. The Sixth Form courses are designed to meet the needs of girls wishing to proceed to other forms of specialised training.

Facilities are provided for outdoor and indoor games and the School has its own indoor Swimming Pool and an all-weather sports pitch. Extra-curricular activities in the lunch hour or at the end of afternoon school include Debating, Football, Drama, Science, Technology, Fencing, Netball, Gymnastics, Swimming, Tennis, Climbing and classes in Japanese and Mandarin. Guest speakers are frequently invited to meetings of Societies. There are also Junior and Senior Choirs, a Madrigal group, a Barbershop group, Junior and Senior Orchestras, a Wind Ensemble, a Chamber Orchestra and a Swing Band. Lunch hour music recitals, with visiting professional players, are encouraged. Many girls take the Duke of Edinburgh's Award Scheme at bronze, silver and gold level.

Admission. Girls are admitted at 7 and 11 years of age, and to the Sixth Form: for girls over 11 years old, vacancies are only occasional. The entrance examination for age 7 and 11 admission in September will usually be held in the Spring Term. Admission to the Sixth Form is also by written examination and interview.

Applications for 11+ should reach the Admissions Secretary by the end of the previous November and for 16+ by the end of October.

Scholarships. The School has a variety of generous academic, art and music scholarships for entry at 11+ and is fortunate in receiving generous support from many Livery Companies and The City of London in this regard. Academic, music and art scholarships are also awarded at 16+ for entry to the Sixth Form, including a joint scholarship with the Guildhall School of Music and Drama Junior Department.

Further details of the awards available may be obtained from the Admissions Secretary. Bursaries can be awarded on entry at 11 and 16 to those in financial need.

Tuition Fees per term (2008-2009). Preparatory Department: £4,125 (including lunch); Main School: £4,125 (excluding lunch).

Senior School lunches are paid for with a cashless system based on credited payment cards. Pupils in the Preparatory Department are expected to take school lunch for which there is no extra charge. After-school supervision is also available at £150 per term.

Extra Subjects: Pianoforte, Violin, Cello, Flute, Clarinet, Organ, Guitar and a wide variety of other instruments, including Singing: £204 per term; group instruction £96 per term (fees are all payable in advance).

Clifton High School

College Road Clifton Bristol BS8 3JD
Tel: 0117 973 0201 (Upper School)
0117 973 8096 (Lower School)
0117 973 3853 (Bursar)
Fax: 0117 923 8962
e-mail: admissions@cliftonhigh.bristol.sch.uk
website: www.cliftonhigh.bristol.sch.uk

Clifton High School, founded in 1877, is an independent school offering a first-class education to 238 girls and boys in the Lower School (age 3–11) and 274 in the Upper School – girls only aged 11–16 with the Sixth Form (age 16–18) becoming co-educational from September 2008. Family boarders are accepted in the Sixth Form from the age of 16 years.

Governing Body (School Council):

President: Mr H Stebbing, BSc, FRICS, FBIFM, FRSA, FICPD
Vice-President: Miss L A Seager, MBA, BA

Mr A Antonius, BSc, FCA
Dr M S Cook
Mr J Curran, OBE, FCA
Dr R Gliddon, BSc, PhD
Mr S C Hegarty, LLB
Mrs J M Huckman, MCSP, SRP
The Revd Canon P F J Johnson
Dr S E Lloyd, BEd, PhD
Mr A D Marvel, BArch, DipArch, RIBA
Mr C Nash, FCIB

***Headmistress*: Mrs Colette Culligan**, MEd Bristol, BA Hons Lancaster, PGCE

Head of Upper School and Sixth Form: Dr A M Neill, PhD UCW Aberystwyth, PGCE

Head of Lower School: Mr A J Richards, MBE, BSocSc Hons Birmingham, PGCE

Upper School Staff:
Deputy Head of Upper School: Mrs E A Anderson, BSc Hons Nottingham, PGCE
Senior Teacher: Dr G Hallett, PhD Durham, MRSC, CChem

Heads of Year:
Y7 – Dr Dand
Y8 – Mrs Hosty
Y9 – Mr Taylor
Y10 – Mrs Aberdeen
Y11 – Revd Pemberton

* *Head of Department*

Art & Design:
*Miss S Duncan, BA Hons Bristol, PGCE, DipExtStudies (*also Enrichment Coordinator*)
Mr P Ayers MA Falmouth, BA Hons Cornwall, CertEd

Business Studies:
Mr P G Jackson, BA Westminster, PGCE (*also Mathematics and Enrichment*)

Careers:
*Mrs L M Broomsgrove, BSc Exeter (*also Science, Mathematics, Enrichment*)

Classics:
*Mr M Psarros, BA Hons Wales, MA Bristol, C&G Teacher Training
Mrs B Bell, BA Hons London, PGCE

Design & Technology:
Miss W Fowler, BSc Hons Bath, PGCE
Miss E Warwood, BSc Hons Bolton, PGCE

Drama:
*Mrs G Malpass, BA Hons London, Labon Dance Cert, PGCE (*also Theatre Studies*)
Mrs S Johnson-Martin, BA Hons Royal Holloway Colege, London, PGCE

English:
*Mr T C Beddow, MA London, PGCE
Mrs M C Culligan, MEd, BA Hons Lancaster, PGCE
Mrs S P Hosty, MA Kingston, DipTEFL (*also SENCO*)
Mrs J P Pritchard, BA Hons Exeter, PGCE (*also Drama*)
Mrs S Swallow, MA Hons Edinburgh, PGCE

Geography:
*Mrs S Leafe, BSc Hons Bristol, PGCE
Miss H Coates, BSc Manchester, PGCE

History:
*Mrs R Pullen, BSc Cardiff, PGCE

Information Technology:
*Mr G A Taylor, BA Hons York, PGCE (*also Mathematics*)
Mr R Hardie, BA Hons, QTS UWE

Mathematics:
*Mrs S Hargroves, BSc King's College, London, PGCE, DipInfEng
Mrs E A Anderson, BSc Hons Nottingham, PGCE
Mrs D Jones, BSc Liverpool, PGCE
Mr S Fawcus, BSc Hons, PGCE

Modern Languages:
Dr E M Dand, PhDBristol, PGCE (**Modern Languages, French*)
Mrs H Aberdeen, BA Hons Bristol, PGCE (*German and French*)
Mrs B Charlton, Licenciatura Filologia Barcelona (*Spanish*)
Mrs P M Winter, BA Durham, PGCE (*French*)

Assistants:
Mrs A Mebarki (*French*)

Miss M Frias (*Spanish*)
Mrs K Pestell (*German*)

Music:
*Miss S Richards, BA Hons Bristol, MA, PGCE (*Director of Upper School Music*)
Mrs M Johnson, BA Hons, MEd Cambridge, PGCE

Physical Education:
*Miss K Price, BEd Hons Sussex Chelsea College of PE
Mrs D J Kingston, BEd Hons Cambridge Bedford College of PE
Mrs V Williams, CertEd, DipPE Bristol
Mrs J Winn, CertEd Cambridge Bedford College of PE

Personal & Social Education:
*Mrs A Crossley, BEd Hons, MA London (*also Government & Politics, Classical Civilisation, History, Enrichment*)

Psychology:
Mrs V Papanikolaou, BARTS South Africa, Edud Dip GTP To QTS

Religious Studies:
*Revd C Pemberton, MTheol St Andrews, PGCE
Mrs J Awolola-Hill, BEd, CertEd Birmingham (*also SENCO*)

Science:
Mrs S Archer, BSc Hons Brunel, PGCE (**Science, *Biology*)
Dr G Hallett, PhD Durham, MRSC, CChem (**Chemistry*)
Mr T Hilton, BSc Loughborough, DipIS (*Chemistry*)
Dr A M Neill, PhD UCW Aberystwyth, PGCE (*Biology*)
Mrs L M Broomsgrove, BSc Hons Exeter, PGCE (*Chemistry*)
Dr A Camacho, PhD Cardiff, PGCE

Lower School Staff:
Deputy Head of Lower School: Mrs S Barker, BEd Hons UWE
KS1 Coordinator: Mrs A Roberts, BSc Hons Southampton, PGCE
Foundation Stage Coordinator: Mrs E A Osborne, BEd Bath College of HE
Director of Studies: Mrs K Harrold, BA Hons Southampton, PGCE
Director of Lower School Music: Mr A Cleaver, BA QTS Hull
SENCO: Mrs S Lloyd, BEd UWE, PGDip York, CertCouns

Junior Department KS2:
Mrs F Barnard, BSc Hons Birmingham, PGCE
Mrs J Knott, BEd Bristol
Mr C Lowe, BA Ed Joint Hons Goldsmiths College, London
Miss H Phillips, BEd Hons Winchester
Mr D J E Pye, BA Hons West London Inst of HE, PGCE
Miss H Sims, BA Hons QTS Surrey

Preparatory Department KS1:
Miss R S Clay, CertEd Crewe & Alsager College
Mrs S J Jones, BA Bristol, PGCE
Mrs J Lee, BA Hons Plymouth, PGCE
Mrs Manning, BEd Hons Kingston
Mrs L Mitchell, BSc Hons Edinburgh, PGCE UWE

Foundation Stage:
Mrs D Andrews, BSc Hons QTS Bath College
Mrs P Cook, GIBiol Bristol Polytechnic, PGCE
Mrs J Sutcliffe, BA Hons Warwick, PGCE

Classroom Assistants:

Learning Support: Mrs B Williams, NNEB

Junior Department KS2:
Mrs V Owen, CertEd Bristol
Mrs S Owen, NNEB

Preparatory Department KS1:
Miss D Clark, HNC
Mrs L Ottley, BA Hons Canterbury, Kent, PGCE UWE
Mrs V Stanley, CertEd Bulmershe, Reading

Foundation Stage:
Mrs A Clancy, NNEB
Mrs N Dunne, NNEB
Mrs A Godshaw, NNEB
Miss A Heath, BTEC Nat Dip
Mrs J Treasure, NNEB
Mrs H Price, NNEB

Visiting Staff:

Music:
Miss M Baker, GTCL, LRAM, ALCM (*Clarinet*)
Mrs R Carpenter, BMus (*Piano*)
Mr A Chetland (*Electric Guitar*)
Ms E J Cormack, BA Hons (*Singing/Piano*)
Mrs J George, BA Hons LLCM, (*Classical Guitar*)
Mr P Gittings, ARM, DipRCM (*Oboe, Piano*)
Miss S Grundy, BA, LRSM (*Flute*)
Miss C Johnstone, BA, DipNCOS (*Cello*)
Mr M Jones, BA Hons (*Percussion*)
Mr S Jones, BMus (*Upper Brass*)
Mr S Lewins, BA Hons (*Drum Kit*)
Miss S Richards BA Hons, MA, PGCE (*Harp*)
Mrs K Skeet, BA Hons (*Violin & Viola*)
Mr A Stewart, BMus (*Lower Brass*)
Mrs Tucker, AGSM (*Singing*)
Mrs H Vale, LRAM, ARCM (*Piano*)
Mrs R Whitworth, BSc Hons (*Violin*)

Speech & Drama:
Mrs J Owens Powell, BA Hons UWE
Mrs S Johnson Martin, BA Hons Royal Holloway College, PGCE

Tennis: Mr R Conway
Dance: Mrs S Miller
Tae Kwon Do: Mr D Chance

Marketing & Business Development:
Mrs N Koniakhina, BA Hons Moscow, MBA Bath
Mrs N Prince, BA Hons Bournemouth

Bursarial Office:
Bursar: Mr R Smith
Bursary Administrative Assistant: Mrs H Warr
Fee Administrator: Mrs T Gajewski, BA Hons OU
Purchase Ledger Administrator: Mr A Willford

Headmistress's Office:
PA to Headmistress: Mrs D Kent
Admissions Registrar: Mrs H Thomas

Upper School:
Secretary to the Head of Upper School & Sixth Form: Mrs T J Scales

School Office:
Office Manager: Mrs N L Cross

Lower School Office:
Secretary to Head of Lower School: Mrs E J Hill
Lower School Secretarial Assistant: Mrs S Furlong

IT Systems & Support:
Mr J Fulop
Mr M McKelvaney
Mr J Geake

School Librarians:
Mrs A Dobson, BA, MCILIP (*Head Librarian*)
Mrs L Parnell (*Assistant Librarian*)
Mrs J Plum, BSc Hons Bristol, PG Dip (*Assistant Librarian*)

Child Protection Officers:
Dr A Neill (*Upper School*)
Mrs T Richards (*Lower School*)

Examinations Officer: Mrs J Rosser

Matrons:
Mrs S Clifton, RGN
Mrs E Shaw, RGN

School Counsellors:
Mrs S Malting
Mrs P Telling

Family Boarding Coordinator: Mrs E Young

Science Technicians:
Mr M Johnson
Mrs H Power

Catering Manager: Mr R Kellaway

Maintenance Staff:
Mr C Everett (*Site Manager*)
Mr G Hooper
Mr C Lear
Miss J Ledger
Mrs Z Curran

Aims. The school aims to provide each pupil with an excellent education in a wide range of subjects in a happy, secure and stimulating environment. Individual talents and interests are fostered and a broad spectrum of extra-curricular pursuits offered, with particular focus on sporting and practical activities. Emphasis is placed on self-discipline, courtesy and consideration for others, good moral values and attitudes and the development of self-confidence, self-reliance and initiative.

Facilities. The school occupies a splendid site in Clifton, near the Downs and Suspension Bridge. The Lower School shares many Upper School facilities but maintains its own identity, with each of the three individual departments housed in its own spacious Regency building. The facilities and accommodation are first class including recently refurbished Science Centre with seven laboratories, well stocked libraries and network of 250 workstations using modern hardware, a multimedia language laboratory, Sixth Form Centre and a complex for the creative arts. Sports facilities include a heated 25m indoor swimming pool, gymnasium and floodlit netball courts on site, together with a new partnership with Bristol University including an indoor tennis centre (4 courts) and 2 artificial turf hockey pitches.

Curriculum. Class sizes average 15 in the Lower School and 18 in the Upper School.

The **Lower School** offers an excellent academic, social and moral foundation. (*See also Lower School entry in IAPS section.*)

The **Nursery and Reception** Years follow the Foundation Stage curriculum, focusing upon: personal, social and emotional development; communication; language and literacy; mathematical development; knowledge and understanding of the world; physical development and creative development. The children enjoy a myriad of experiences embracing art, craft, cookery, music, information technology, PE and the development of reading, writing and mathematics in a safe, stimulating and secure environment. High praise both by Ofsted and ISI Inspectors during 2004, achieving the Bristol Standard and accreditation by an Investors in Children quality assurance scheme, have all endorsed the splendid reputation of our Foundation Stage.

Years 1 and 2, working in an informal atmosphere within a structured framework, focus on high standards of literacy and numeracy, stimulating the children's minds through creative work and challenging projects. The curriculum also includes ICT, Science, History, Geography, Drama, Art, Music, PE, Swimming and Games.

The **Junior Department** gives children a strong grounding in English, Mathematics, Science, ICT, History, Geography, Music, Art, Drama, Design Technology, Religious Studies, Gymnastics, Athletics and Games (Netball, Hockey, Rugby, Football, Tennis and Cricket).

French, Latin and Swimming are taught in the Junior Department by specialist teachers from the Upper School. A wide range of extra curricular activities are on offer including Choirs, Orchestra, ICT, Speech and Drama, TaeKwonDo, Art and Craft and an array of sports clubs.

Visiting speakers and regular trips to the local area and further afield enhance the curriculum in all departments. Children in the Junior Department also have the opportunity to enjoy overnight visits each year and there is a biennial ski trip.

Throughout the **Upper School**, girls have a personal tutor who monitors their academic and social welfare. In Years 7 to 9 all girls study a broad and balanced curriculum. Subjects include English, Mathematics, Physics, Chemistry, Biology, ICT, History, Geography, Religious Studies, one or two modern languages (French, German, Spanish), Latin/Classical Studies (with opportunity to study Greek from Year 9), Drama, Music, Art & Design, Technology (Textiles and Food), PE and Personal and Social Education (PSE). There is also a programme for Critical Thinking at Year 7. In Years 10 and 11, Physical Education and PSE form part of the general programme. For study at GCSE there is a common and balanced core of English, Mathematics, Science (Double Award or three separate sciences), a modern foreign language and ICT (Short Course), in addition to which girls may select subjects based on their interests and career plans.

The school has an excellent academic record at GCSE, AS and A Levels.

The **Sixth Form**, which will become co-educational from September 2008, is a thriving centre of excellence within the school, the students playing an important part in the whole school community, developing their leadership skills with the younger pupils. Students have a free choice from 24 A Level subjects including all those offered at GCSE level as well as Theatre Studies, Business Studies, Sport Studies and Further Mathematics and Psychology. Almost all go on to university, the most able being encouraged to apply for Oxbridge entrance. All Sixth Form students take part in an Enrichment Programme designed to offer breadth and a range of experiences. Key Skills evidence can be accessed through this programme in addition to A Level studies.

Family Boarding. Clifton High School offers a unique opportunity for Sixth Form students (especially those from overseas) to board, full-time or weekly, with families known to the school. Our Family Boarding Coordinator acts as liaison officer and oversees the welfare of both the students and the host family.

Physical Education. Pupils are encouraged to challenge themselves physically. In addition to the school's traditional activities of hockey, netball, swimming, athletics, rounders, tennis and gymnastics (BAGA), specialist staff teach a wide variety of other activities including volleyball, basketball, soccer, cricket, aerobics and trampolining. Fencing and self-defence are optional. Pupils regularly gain county and national honours.

Music and Drama. Virtually any instrument, including voice, may be studied, with over 50 per cent of pupils having individual lessons. Associated Board examinations are taken. There are opportunities to belong to orchestras, wind bands and choirs, performing in a variety of concerts and choir tours. In Speech and Drama, a large number of pupils enter LAMDA examinations. Each year there is both a Lower and Upper School major production, as well as numerous smaller ventures such as a House Drama Competition.

Charitable and Extra-Curricular Activities. Pupils have a strong sense of social responsibility and are actively involved, often in their House groups, in various local and national charity fund-raising events. Annual collections amount to several thousand pounds. There is a lively extra-curricular activities programme both in the Lower and Upper sections of the school, responding to pupils' interests. There are over 20 clubs currently running including Pottery, Science, Debating and Public Speaking, Christian Union, and Mathematics. Girls regularly take part in the Duke of Edinburgh's

Award. Regular trips overseas and exchange with trusted schools in Europe are organised.

Admission and Scholarships. Entry to the Lower School is by in-class assessment. Entry to the Upper School is dependent on the results of an entrance examination. This year the entrance examination (entry to Year 7) has been abolished for internal candidates (Year 6 pupils from Clifton High Lower School). Academic Scholarships are awarded each year at Year 7, Year 9 and at Sixth Form level, some school assisted places and John James scholarships (means tested) are available for girls entering at Year 7. Music scholarships are also available. Registration forms and further details are available from the Admissions Registrar.

Fees per term (2008-2009). Tuition: Lower School £905–£2,380, Upper School £3,200. Family boarding (in addition) £2,020. Full details are available from the school. Discounts are given for siblings currently in the school.

Charitable status. Clifton High School is a Registered Charity, number 311736. It exists to provide first-class education for pupils aged 3 to 18 years.

Cobham Hall

Cobham Kent DA12 3BL
Tel: 01474 823371 (School)
Fax: 01474 825902/825904/825906
e-mail: enquiries@cobhamhall.com
website: www.cobhamhall.com

Founded 1962.

Governing Body:
Mr C Sykes (*Chairman*)

The Earl of Darnley
Mr R P Mountford
Mr A Tuckwell
Mrs T Balch
Mr C Balch
Ms P Cook
Mrs L Ellis
Dr M Griffin
Mrs A Travis, DipSpLD
Mr W Trelawny-Vernon
Mr J Dick

Staff:

***Headmaster*: Mr P Mitchell**, BSc Newcastle

Deputy Headmistress: Dr S Coates-Smith, BSc, PhD London

Bursar: Mr N Powell, DipEng, MCIM

Director of Studies: Mr S Dearnaley, BA Leeds

Head of Sixth Form: Mr A Pinchin, MA Cantab

Middle School Senior Tutor: Mrs W Barrett, BSc London
Lower School Senior Tutor: Miss K Lee, BSocSc Cape Town, CELTA

Coordinator of Boarding and International Students: Dr E Smalova, MSc

* *Head of Department*

English:
*Miss J Stevens, BA Hull
Mr R Allen, BA Christ Church College, Canterbury
Miss K Driscoll, BA Liverpool, OCR CertSpLD

Mathematics:
*Mrs W Barrett, BSc London
Mr P Gilchrist, BSc Leeds
Mrs M Martin, BSc Loughborough

Science:
*Mr J Fryer, BSc Leicester (*Biology*)
Dr S Coates-Smith, BSc, PhD London (*Physics*)
Mr B Mallon, BSc London (*Physics/Biology*)
Mrs A Story, BSc/DipEd Newcastle upon Tyne (*Chemistry*)
Mr I Geldard, BSc Durham (*Chemistry*)

Art:
*Mrs K Walsh, BA Kent Inst Art & Design (*Art*)
Ms T Shield, BA, MVA Australian National University (*Photo Media*)
Mr A Arevalo, BA, MA Ravensbourne College

Classics:
*Mr S Dearnaley, BA Leeds
Mrs S-A Edmonds, BA Kent, MA Bristol

Drama:
*Ms K Martin, BEd Queensland
Miss A McKay, CertEd Brighton

Economics:
*Mr A Pinchin, MA Cantab

Geography:
*Mrs L Shawyer, BSc Greenwich, MA Christ Church College, Canterbury

History:
*Miss M Parsons, BA East Anglia

Information and Communications Technology:
*Mr A Owen, BA Wales

Modern Foreign Languages:
*Miss K Fortin, MA Lille (*French*)
Mrs E Barry, MA London (*German*)
Mrs A Smart, BA Belfast (*French/Spanish*)
Mrs M Cook, BA Seville (*Spanish*)
Mrs M Haynes (*French Assistant*)

Music:
*Mrs D Wallace, BMus London, LRAM, LTCL Perf, LTCL MusEd
Mr S Wallace, MSc, BMus London

Physical Education:
Miss K Paterson, BA Greenwich
Mrs M Martin, BSc Loughborough

Religious Studies:
Mrs H Davy, MA Oxon
Dr J Payne, BA Sheffield, PhD Pennsylvania, USA

EFL:
*Mrs E Gourlay, BA Nottingham, CELTA
Miss K Lee, BSocSc Cape Town, CELTA
Dr E Smalova, MSc B Bystrica, PaedDr Nitra, CELTA

Susan Hampshire Centre:
*Miss K Driscoll, BA Liverpool, OCR CertSpLD
Mrs D Rabot, BA Lancaster, OCR Cert SpLD
Mrs J Balson (*Teaching Assistant*)

Careers:
Sixth Form: Mr A Pinchin, MA Cantab
Middle School: Mrs W Barrett, BSc London
Lower School: Miss K Lee, BSocSc Cape Town, CELTA

PSHE: Miss A McKay

Librarian: Mrs K Smith

Laboratory Technicians:
Mrs B Reed
Mrs D Weaver

Computer Support:
Mr D Suman
Mr C Randhawa, BSc University of East London

Pastoral Staff:
Dr E Smalova, MSc Bariska Bystrica, CELTA (*Coordinator of Boarding*)

Miss M Aird, BA Fredericton, CELTA, TESL (*Middle School Housemistress*)
Mrs M Gardner, RGN/RSCN (*Resident Nurse/Housemistress*)
Nurse G Powell, RGN (*Resident Nurse/Housemistress*)
Mrs E Fong (*Housemistress*)
Miss P Toorenburg (*Housemistress*)

Visiting Staff:
There are visiting staff for Cello, Clarinet, Double Bass, Drums, Flute, French Horn, Guitar, Keyboard, Oboe, Percussion, Piano, Recorder, Saxophone, Trombone, Trumpet, Tuba, Viola, Violin, Speech & Drama, Ballet, Self Defence, Life Saving and Tennis.

Administration:
Registrar: Mrs S Ferrers
Receptionist/Assistant Registrar: Mrs J Booth/Mrs S Hammock
School PR & Events Coordinator: Mrs D Usher
Headmistress's PA: Mrs C Blackwell
School Secretary: Mrs W Friend
Bursar's Secretary: Mrs B Taylor
Accountant: Mr B Jelley, CPFA
Accounts Administrator: Mrs K Pinder, MAAT
Accounts Assistant: Mrs M Vinall, ACIS
Estates Manager: Mr T Curran, ARICS
Household & Functions Manager: Miss S Windiate

Cobham Hall is an international boarding and day school for over 200 girls aged between 11 and 18.

Situation. The School is set in 150 acres of parkland. Situated in North Kent close to the M25, adjacent to the M2/A2. Forty minutes from London, 60 minutes Heathrow, 40 minutes Gatwick and Stansted, 60 minutes Dover and Channel Tunnel, 40 minutes Ashford International. Escorted travel to and from airports can be arranged.

School Buildings. This beautiful 16th century historic house was the former home of the Earls of Darnley. There are many modern buildings providing comfortable accommodation for study and relaxation. Brooke and Bligh Houses are separate buildings, within the School grounds, offering Sixth Form accommodation in single or twin study-bedrooms, some with en-suite facilities. Both Houses have common rooms with Satellite TV and DVD, a kitchen and computer room.

Curriculum. The School is a centre for the GCSE, AS and A Level examinations. It has well-equipped science laboratories. Physics, Chemistry and Biology can be studied to university entrance. Languages, Mathematics and a wide range of Arts subjects are also offered. The average number of GCSE passes is 9.

Reports are issued twice a year and parents are always welcome to come and discuss their daughter's progress.

Sixth Form. The Sixth Form numbers approximately 60 girls across the two years. The range of subjects and specialist teaching is exceptional for a small school. Critical Thinking is taught to AS in addition to the main A Level subjects offered. In 2006/7 five students secured Oxbridge offers. There are many leadership opportunities open to students, including election by the whole school to the offices of Guardian (Head Girl), Deputy and House Captain.

Sporting and other activities. The School's main sports are Tennis, Swimming, Hockey, Athletics and Netball. There are seven hard tennis courts, 6 netball courts, a large, indoor multi-sports complex, including fitness centre, dance studio and a heated indoor swimming pool, which is in use throughout the year. Horse-riding and golf may be taken as 'extras'. A wide variety of extra-curricular activities is available.

Careers. Careers Advisers for Sixth Form, Middle and Lower School provide Careers and Higher Education guidance within a comprehensive careers programme. Over many years, all students wishing to continue to university have successfully achieved their goal.

Round Square. The School is a member of this international group of schools, which subscribes to the philosophy of educationalist, Dr Kurt Hahn. Annual conferences are attended by a school delegation including sixth formers; in recent years these have been in Australia, America, India, South Africa and Germany. Students have the opportunity to visit other member schools on an exchange programme as well as visit other countries by taking part in service projects and relief work organised by the Round Square International Service.

Health. There are resident trained nurses giving 24-hour medical care.

All Terms. Girls have two Exeat Weekends and a Half Term holiday. There is escorted travel to and from London Victoria and the airports for younger girls.

Admission. Admission is by the School's own entrance examination which can be taken at the annual Newcomers' Day in January or at a girl's own school. Girls normally enter the School between the ages of 11+ and 13+ and follow a course leading to GCSE level at the end of the fifth year and A Levels at the end of the seventh. Girls wishing to enter the Sixth Form should achieve at least five GCSE or equivalent examination passes at Grade C or above.

Scholarships. (*see Scholarship Entries section*). Scholarships are available for 11+, 13+ and Sixth Form entry.

Bursaries. Special Bursaries are available for boarders from British Services families, diplomats and those families working for UK Charitable Trusts overseas. (For further information, contact The Registrar.)

Fees per term (2008-2009). Day girls: £4,400–£5,500. Boarders: £6,600–£8,300.

Old Girls' Association. Known as Elders. There is a representative committee which meets regularly in London or at the School. The Chairman is Mrs Tracey Balch, e-mail: tracey.balch@virgin.net.

Charitable status. Cobham Hall is a Registered Charity, number 313650. It exists to provide high quality education for girls aged 11–18 years.

Combe Bank School

Sundridge Sevenoaks Kent TN14 6AE
Tel: 01959 563720; 01959 564320; 01959 562918
Fax: 01959 561997
e-mail: enquiries@combebank.kent.sch.uk
website: www.combebank.kent.sch.uk

Council of Management:
Chairman: R I Lynam, Esq

Mrs J Branson
A Cowan, Esq
P Dickinson, Esq
Father R Harvey
Mrs C Hopkins
Mrs P Maynard
Mrs D Mills
D Nichols, Esq
Mrs K Surgison
T Theaker, Esq

Bursar: Mr D Rossi, MAAT

***Headmistress*: Mrs R Martin**, MEd, NPQH, FRSA

Senior School Staff:

Assistant Head (*Academic*): M Broderick, Esq, BSc Hons, MSc, PGCE (*Head of Science*)

Assistant Head (*Pastoral*): Mrs E Bird, BSc Hons, CertEd (*Head of Geography*)

Heads of Departments:
Mrs A Abt-Stein, 1st Staatsexamen Frankfurt, TCert (*English*)
Mrs L Baker, BEd Hons (*PE*)
Miss M Carter, CertEd (*History*)
Miss A R Chapman, MA Cantab (*Modern Languages*)
Mrs F Dunn, BA Hons, PGCE (*Theatre Studies/Drama*)
Mrs C Graham, BSc Hons, PGCE (*Mathematics*)
Miss S Hughes, BSc Hons, PGCE (*ICT*)
Dr H Isom, PhD, BA Hons, DipRSA, HonGCM (*Director of Music*)
Mrs A Jagelman, CertEd (*Home Economics*)
Mrs H Lorigan, BA Hons, PGCE (*Art*)
Mrs M Southgate, BA Hons, PGCE (*Religious Studies*)
Mrs J Dixon, BEd, MA (*Business Studies*)

Head of the Preparatory School: Mrs S Walker, BA Hons, CertEd

Deputy Head: Mrs E Dale, CertEd

School Chaplain: Father Duncan Lourenz

Combe Bank is an independent day school for girls. Founded in 1868 by the Society of the Holy Child Jesus, in 1972 the Combe Bank Educational Trust was established to administer the School. As a Roman Catholic Foundation the School aims to provide a Christian education for girls of all denominations and to encourage each girl to develop her individual talents to the full.

The School occupies beautiful buildings including some designed by Roger Morris in 1720 and a Library decorated by Walter Crane. It is set in 27 acres of parkland. There is a school chapel in which voluntary Mass and Holy Communion are celebrated. There are 420 girls, 220 in the Senior School. A new Sixth Form centre opened in September 2003.

Entrance is by interview and assessment to Preparatory School from 3–11, to Senior School at 11+ by School's examination, and at 16+ by interview and a minimum of 6 GCSE grades A–C for 4 AS Levels.

Scholarships. (*see Scholarship Entries section*).

Fees per term (2008-2009). Senior School £4,450, Prep School £2,485–£3,420.

Curriculum. Girls are prepared for GCSE Examination Groups and A Levels, and in the Sixth Form for University Entrance. The Examinations of the Associated Board are taken in Music and of the Guildhall in Speech and Drama. As well as the usual subjects girls study Home Economics, Information Systems, Business Studies, Music, Drama, German and Spanish. In the Sixth Form they may study Psychology and History of Art as well as the usual A Levels.

Games. Winter games are hockey, netball, cross-country running and uni-hoc, and summer games are tennis, rounders and athletics. Swimming all year round (25 metre indoor pool). Girls also take part in gymnastics, badminton, volleyball, table tennis, trampolining, judo and dancing. A new sports complex has just opened including a large fitness suite.

Pastoral Care is mainly in the hands of Form Tutors. They are assisted by the Assistant Head (Pastoral), Careers Mistress and School Chaplain.

Charitable status. Combe Bank School Educational Trust Limited is a Registered Charity, number 1007871. It exists to provide a good education for girls aged 3 to 18.

Cranford House School

Moulsford Wallingford Oxfordshire OX10 9HT
Tel: 01491 651218
Fax: 01491 652557
e-mail: office@cranfordhouse.oxon.sch.uk
website: www.cranfordhouse.oxon.sch.uk

Members of the Board of Governors:
R Bray, Esq (*Chairman*)
S J W McArthur, Esq, BSc, MA
Miss E A Scoates, BSc, MPhil
B Howell Pryce, Esq
G Cole, Esq
A Harper, Esq
Mrs G Walsh

***Headmistress*: Mrs Claire Hamilton**, MA Cantab

Head of Senior School: Mrs P Hawson, CertEd Bristol
Head of Junior School: Mrs H Osborn, CertEd Hull
Head of Lower School: Mrs G Smeeton, BSc, QTS Ripon & York St John

Senior School Teaching Staff:
Mrs M Bradley, BA Reading, PGCE
Mrs N Butler, BA, CAPES
Miss C Chaplin, BEd Hons Bedford College of HE
Miss M Clark , BSc Hons London, PGCE Open
Mr C Cooper, BSc Hons London, PGCE East Anglia, MA Warwick
Mrs S Eccles, BA UNISA
Mr P Ellis, BSc, MPhil, CChem, MRSC
Mrs S Elston, BSc Manchester
Mr P Evans, MPhil, PGCE, BA
Mrs E Gardner, BSc Manchester, PGCE Southampton
Mrs K George, BA, PGCE
Mrs P Hawson, CertEd Bristol
Mrs C Hills, BA Open, CertEd Ulster
Miss M Johnstone, CertEd London
Mrs S Kirkwood, Higher DipEd South Africa
Mrs J McCallum, MA Hons Edinburgh, PGCE Cambridge
Mrs J Powell, BA Hons, Dip Adv Studies RAM
Mrs M Powell, CertEd Bath
Mme C Robichez, BA Sorbonne
Mrs M Sardeson , BSc Hons Nottingham, PGCE Reading
Mrs C Shaikh, CertEd Oxford
Mrs Y Spittles, CertEd London
Mrs P Wallace, BSc, PGCE

Junior School Teaching Staff:
Mrs A J Cheeseman, BEd London
Mrs E Gardner, BSc Manchester, PGCE Southampton
Mrs J Hill, BEd Manchester
Miss M Johnstone, CertEd London
Mrs H Osborn, CertEd Hull
Mrs J Powell, BA Hons, Dip Adv Studies RCM
Mrs F Weikert, CertEd London

Lower School Teaching Staff:
Mrs E Day, BSc Hons, PGCE
Mrs E Drury, BEd Herts
Mrs A Greedy, BEd, TEFL
Mrs J Lake, BA Hons London, PGCE Oxford
Mrs S McNaught, BEd Hons Southampton
Mrs G Smeeton, BSc, QTS Ripon & York St John
Mrs A Howell, BEd

Nursery Staff:
Mrs N J Pearce, NNEB North Tyneside (*Head of Nursery*)
Mrs A Bateman, NVQ Level III in Child Care
Mrs K Knight, BTEC Child Studies
Mrs J Ireland
Mrs J Sangan, NNEB
Mrs C Frank, NVQ Level III in Child Care

Centre for Individual Development:
Mrs G Mabbett, BEd, RSADipSpLD (*Head of Learning Support, Senior School*)
Mrs S McNaught, BEd, RSADipSpLD (*Head of Learning Support, Junior and Lower School*)
Miss J Carter, NNEB, Montessori DipSpLD
Mrs V Little, BEd, RSADipSpLD

Visiting Music Staff:
Mr C Bache (*Clarinet/Saxophone*)
Mr J Boughton, BA Hons Bath, ALCM (*Piano & Recorder*)
Mrs C Bromley (*Violin*)
Miss L Gifford-Guy, BMus Hons (*Singing*)
Mrs S Murrell (*Piano*)
Miss A Pickering, LLCM TD, ALCM (*Flute*)
Mrs R Powell (*Brass*)
Mrs M Thorns, BMus Hons, CertEd, LRAM (*Cello and Piano*)

Other Visiting Staff:
Mr H Batten, MSc, 5th Dan, Renshi (*Judo*)
Mrs H Murphy, BA Hons (*Dance*)
Mrs N Lawson (*Self-Defence*)
Mr P Meakin (*Football/Rugby*)
Mr P Worroll, LTA Level 1 Licence

Support Staff:
Mrs S Andresen-Guimarães
Mrs A Bryan
Mrs E Davies
Miss R Fox
Mrs J Goddard
Mr M Howard
Mrs S Kirkwood
Miss J Livesey
Mrs K McKenzie
Mrs J Plant
Miss S Powell
Mrs W Rant
Mrs J Sangan
Miss H Stanley
Mrs S Steggeman
Mrs M Stoker
Mrs V Stretch
Miss S Treadwell

Administrative Staff:
Mrs S Crowe (*Matron*)
Mrs J Cuffe (*Receptionist/Administrator*)
Mr D Gillespie (*ICT Manager*)
Mrs E Hayward (*Bursar's Assistant, Staff Development Officer*)
Mrs R J Huntington (*Bursar*)
Mrs S Jubb (*Bursar's Assistant*)
Miss K Spence (*PA to the Headmistress*)
Mrs J Simmons (*Registrar*)
Mrs J White-Zamler (*Business Manager*)
Mrs J Ecapo (*School Secretary*)
Mrs S Coulton (*School Secretary*)

Cranford House is an independent day school for around 330 pupils, girls aged 3–16 years and boys 3–7 years.

The Lower School (pre-preparatory) caters for boys and girls aged 3–7 years and includes a purpose built Nursery. Pupils work towards the Foundation stage in Nursery and Reception and on to Key Stage 1 in Forms 1 and 2.

The Junior School (preparatory) comprises Forms 3 to 6 where a balance is struck between the traditional reading, writing and numeracy skills and the enquiry based approach of modern science, design technology and information and communication technology. The Juniors benefit from Senior School facilities. Specialist subject teachers are increasingly used in French, Mathematics, Science, Religious Studies and Physical Education. Lesson content is based on the National Curriculum Key Stage 2 programmes of study, and results are consistently very good.

For the first three years in the Senior School girls follow a common core curriculum of English, Mathematics, Science, History, Geography, French, Spanish, German, Art, Music, Drama, ICT, Textiles and Food Technology. In Forms 10 and 11 they study their chosen GCSE subjects, with the majority of girls sitting nine or ten subjects. Physical Education, Religious Studies and Personal, Health and Social Education are studied throughout the Senior School. Girls belong to a House system and, on reaching Form 11, enjoy positions of responsibility and privilege.The school has extensive recreational and games fields. In winter, hockey and netball are played, and in summer, tennis and athletics. Swimming takes place in the school's heated outdoor swimming pool. Dramatic, musical and dance productions are an important aspect of school life.

In addition to the many clubs and activities offered throughout the school, all pupils have the opportunity to join educational trips and excursions. For Senior pupils, the Duke of Edinburgh's Award Scheme and the Fox Award can be undertaken. There are opportunities for travel with the Senior Choir and the Modern Languages department who have visited France, Germany, Holland, Italy and Belgium. Ski trips are offered bi-annually. School transport operates over a wide area.

Scholarships offered are the Laurence Scholarship, an internal scholarship available to a Form 6 pupil moving into the Senior School, a Music Scholarship and a scholarship for a good 'All-rounder'.

Our aim is to encourage pupils not only to achieve the best possible academic results, but to become responsible and useful citizens; happy, and with a high degree of self esteem – adaptable and equipped for life.

Fees per term (2008-2009). £861–£3,950.

Charitable status. Cranford House School Trust Limited is a Registered Charity, number 280883.

Croydon High School (GDST)

Old Farleigh Road Selsdon South Croydon CR2 8YB
Tel: 020 8651 5020
Fax: 020 8657 5413
e-mail: info2@cry.gdst.net
website: www.gdst.net/croydonhigh

One of the 29 schools of The Girls' Day School Trust. For further information about the Trust, see p. xxiv.

Additional information about the school may be found on the school's website and a more detailed prospectus may be obtained from the school.

Founded 1874.

Chairman of Local Governors: Mr R Crail

***Headmistress*: Mrs Z M Braganza**, BSc London, MSc Durham, CBiol, MIBiol

Deputy Headmistress: Mrs P Clark, BEd Birmingham, MA London

Director of Studies: Mrs J E Evans, BSc Nottingham

Head of Junior School: Mrs V H Sergeant, BEd Exeter

Deputy Head of Junior Department: Miss N Carter, BEd Surrey University

School Administrator: Mr D Gibson, BA Heriot Watt

For more than a century, Croydon High School has provided a superb all-round education for girls, around the Croydon area and further afield. The school was founded in 1874 and combines tradition with a forward-looking, supportive and nurturing atmosphere where every girl is encouraged and supported to achieve her personal best. The school welcomes girls from a wide range of backgrounds; excellent pastoral care ensures that each girl is known as an individual.

Croydon High offers girls a wide range of extra-curricular opportunities ensuring that each can find something she enjoys. The school regularly achieves local, regional and national success in Sport; its Arts are also outstanding, with a vibrant Music department offering opportunities to musicians at varying ability levels to develop their talents in all musical genres. Termly productions involve students across all year groups and young artists are motivated and inspired to develop their creative talents in different media.

The school aims to develop confident young women with wide ranging interests and abilities who have also achieved excellent academic results. Emphasis is placed on ensuring that girls are happy and fulfilled in whatever career path they choose for the future, be this as a business high flyer or a contented homemaker.

Number of Pupils. Senior School (aged 11–18): 472 girls (including 142 in the Sixth Form). Junior Department (aged 3–11): Junior School 263 girls, Nursery 20 girls.

Facilities. The purpose-built school has outstanding facilities; including specialist music rooms, a drama studio, a language laboratory, 5 computer suites, 10 science laboratories, design technology room and a recently refurbished sports block incorporating sports hall, gym, indoor swimming pool, fitness room and dance studio. The school is surrounded by spacious playing fields with netball/tennis courts, athletics track and an all-weather hockey pitch.

The Junior School, which has its own Nursery, is in an adjacent building on the same site.

The Sixth Form have their own suite of rooms, including a common room and quiet study area, adjacent to the school library.

Curriculum. Most girls take 10 GCSE subjects with the aim of providing a broad and balanced core curriculum which keeps career choices open. Over 23 subjects are offered at AS and A Level including Government & Politics, Economics, Latin and Physical Education. Most girls take four AS Levels and then three A Levels. Almost all girls proceed to University, and, each year, a number are offered places at Oxbridge.

Admission. A whole school Open Day is held annually in October. An Open Evening is held in the Summer Term.

The school admits girls to the Junior School on the basis of either individual assessment (younger girls) or written tests (girls of 7+ and above). Selection procedures are held early in January for Juniors and assessments for Infants are held during the Autumn and Spring Terms for entry in the following September.

For entrance to the Senior School in Year 7, the school holds Entrance Tests early in January for entry in the following September. All applicants are interviewed by the Headmistress and references are taken up.

For the Sixth Form, the school interviews applicants and requests reports from the present school. A Sixth Form Open Evening is held in October.

Fees per term (2008-2009). Senior School £3,700, Junior Department £2,879, Nursery £2,221.

Scholarships and Bursaries. Following the ending of the Government Assisted Places Scheme, the GDST has made available to the school a number of scholarships and bursaries.

Academic scholarships are available for entry at 11+ or to the Sixth Form. Music, art & design and sports scholarships are available at 11+. A music scholarship is offered at 16+.

Bursaries are means tested and are intended to ensure that the school remains accessible to bright girls who could not otherwise benefit from the education we offer. These are available to Senior School girls.

Charitable status. Croydon High School is part of The Girls' Day School Trust, which is a Registered Charity, number 306983. The aim of the Trust is to provide a fine academic education for girls, which is distinguished by breadth.

Mrs J Beard
Mrs C Beddoes
Mr D Brownridge
Mr D Evans
Mrs R Gutteridge
Mr C Hiatt
Miss J Lawley
Mr R Levene
Mrs J McCardle
Mr J Mingay
Dr H Sismey-Durrant
Prof W Stephens

Clerk to the Governors and School Bursar: Mr J-M Hodgkin, BSc, FCA, FSI, ACIS

***Headmistress*: Mrs J Berry**, BA, MEd

Head of the Junior School: Mrs S Braud, BA, NPQH

Deputy Headmistress: Mrs F McGill, BEd

Assistant Headmistresses:
Mrs N Keeler BSc
Mrs S Willis BLib

Teaching staff:
Mr P Allison, BSc
Mrs B Ansell, CertEd
Mrs J Armitage, BSc
Mrs S Aylen, MA, BMus, ALCM, ARCM, PGTC
Mrs E Baker, DipEd, LUDDA
Mrs A Baxter, BSc, PGCE
Miss C Benfield, BA, PGCE
Mrs V Bistram, BSc
Mrs G Bland, BSc
Mrs C Bollington, BA, AdvDipEd
Mr O Bowden, BEng Hons, PGCE, AM IMechE
Mrs J Brearley, BEd, BA
Miss C Brice, BA, PGCE
Mrs S Bryan, BA, PGCE
Mrs V Bryant, BA, MA
Ms A Calder, FIST, AISC
Miss E Calvert, BA
Mrs C Chapman, BEd, DipSpLD
Mrs J Chubb, BSc, MEd, CChem, MRSC
Mrs F Clements, BSc Hons, PGCE
Mrs J Davies, BA Hons, PGCE
Mrs D Day, BA, PGCE
Mrs J Dewar, BA
Mrs M Ellwood, BSc, PGCE
Mrs C Everitt, BA, PGCE
Mrs C Fourey-Jones, L-ès-L, PGCE
Mrs A Goodman, BA Hons
Mrs A Grafton, CertEd
Mrs S Gurteen, BSc
Mr J F Handscombe, BSc
Mrs S Hardy, BA, PGCE
Mrs E Harling, BSc
Mrs P Harrold, BA, MA, PGCE
Mr P Hindess, MMath, PGCE
Mrs J L Holmes, CertEd
Dr N Holmes, PhD, MRCS
Mr L Howard, BMus
Mrs C Hopkins, BEd
Mrs R E Houghton, BA, MA, PGCE
Mrs G Hubbard, BSc, PGCE
Mrs A Huddart, BA Hons, PGCE
Mr D Jackson, CertEd
Mrs S Johnson, CertEd
Mrs C Jones, BSc, PGCE
Mrs A B Lambert, BSc
Mrs H Lascelles, BSc, PGCE
Mrs T Lennie, BA Hons, MPhil, PGCE
Mr J Lewes, BA, MA
Mrs M Lincoln, BCom Hons, PGCE
Mrs A Lippett, L-ès-L
Mrs C Lugsden, MA(Ed), PGCE
Mrs F Marquand, BA
Mrs C Matthews, BEd
Mrs P Milton, BEd Hons
Mrs A Myers, CertEd
Mrs S Noble-Layng
Miss R Page, BA Hons, PGCE
Mrs E Pagliaro, BEd
Mrs J Paradiso, BSc
Mrs Y Pemberton, BA Hons
Dr L Penney, BSc, PhD, PGCE
Mrs S Perren, CertEd
Mrs C Randall, BEd
Miss L Raper, BA Hons, PGCE
Mrs V Redford, LLAM
Mrs R Reed, BA, PGCE
Miss K Rix, BA Hons, MA, PGCE
Mrs L Sadler, BA Hons, PGCE
Mrs C Salusbury, CertEd
Ms V Sanders, MA
Mrs K Scorer, BEd
Mr J Sedeño, Lic en Derecho
Miss D Smith, BSc
Mrs M Smith, BA
Miss J Smith, BMus, PGCE, ABRSM Dip
Mr D Solomons, BA, MA, PGCE
Miss G Stuart, BA, PGCE, Maîtrise FLE
Dr S Sullivan, MA, PhD
Mr H Taylor, BSc, PGCE
Mrs N Tekell-Mellor, BSc Hons, PGCE
Mrs J Thomas, BEd

Dame Alice Harpur School

Cardington Road Bedford MK42 0BX
Tel: 01234 340871
Fax: 01234 344125
e-mail: admissions@dahs.co.uk
website: www.dahs.co.uk

Foundation – The Harpur Trust.

School Committee of Governors:
Chairman: Mrs D Danes

Mrs L Whapples, BSc, PGCE
Mrs C Williams, BEd
Mrs E Williams, CertEd
Mrs J Williams, CertEd
Mrs P Woodhouse, BEd
Mrs S Wright, BEd

Admissions Manager: Ms V Hicks

Number of Girls. 950.

The School is attractively situated on the banks of the Great River Ouse. The Senior School offers excellent facilities for all curriculum areas, together with a spacious and well-stocked library, Sixth Form Centre, Sports Hall, indoor swimming pool, and floodlit all-weather sports pitch. The Junior School occupies Howard House, which is set in attractive gardens opposite the Senior School campus, and offers its own wide range of accommodation including a magnificent Hall, Library, Science Laboratory, Computer Room, tennis/netball courts and Coach House suite which serves as a Year 3 base.

The School provides a broad education for able girls aged 7–18. Subjects offered at the different stages include English, French, German, Spanish, Latin, Greek, Economics, Business Studies, History, Politics, Geography, Religious Studies, Mathematics, Further Mathematics, Physics, Chemistry, Biology, Psychology, Art, Information Technology, Creative Textiles, Food Technology, Design Technology, Music, Drama, Dance, Theatre Studies and Physical Education. Every pupil follows a programme of Personal and Social Education appropriate to her age. An extensive range of extra-curricular activities is available. Senior pupils have the opportunity to participate with students from the other Harpur Trust schools in a range of activities, including the joint Combined Cadet Force, French Society, Science Forum and the Harpur Trust Debating Society.

Bursaries. A candidate for entry to the Senior School may apply for a Bursary Award, which takes into account not only her academic ability but also her family's financial circumstances.

Holidays. About 3 weeks at Christmas, 3 weeks at Easter, and 7/8 weeks in the summer.

Fees per term (2008-2009). Junior School (7–10 years) £2,358; Senior School (11–18 years) £3,293. Registration and Entrance Examination Fee: £50.

The Dame Alice Harpur School Association. Hon Assistant Secretary, c/o the School.

Charitable status. The Bedford Charity (The Harpur Trust) is a Registered Charity, number 204817. It exists to promote the highest standards in education.

Dame Allan's Girls' School

Fenham Newcastle-upon-Tyne NE4 9YJ
Tel: 0191 275 0708 (School); 0191 274 5910 (Bursar)
Fax: 0191 275 1502 (School); 0191 275 1501 (Bursar)
e-mail: enquiries@dameallans.co.uk
website: www.dameallans.co.uk

The School was founded in 1705 by Dame Eleanor Allan and in 1935 was moved to Fenham on a site of 13 acres.

Governors:
Chairman: Mr E Ward
Vice-Chairman: Mr B W Adcock
Mrs K Bruce
Mrs G Coffey
Miss M Foster, BA, FRGS
Mrs O Grant, OBE
Dr J A Hellen, MA, PhD
Prof P D Manning
Mrs M E Slater, MBE, JP
Mrs J Slesenger
Mr A M Stanley
Mr D Tait Walker
Mr T St A Warde-Aldam
Miss J Weatherall
Revd N Wilson
Mr G I Wanless

Ex officio:
The Lord Mayor of Newcastle upon Tyne
The Dean of Newcastle
The Vicar of the Parish of St John

Clerk to the Governors and Bursar: J Fleck, ACMA

***Principal*: J R Hind**, MA Downing College, Cambridge, MEd Newcastle, PhD Durham

Vice-Principal: M J Middlebrook, BA Leeds
Assistant Head: A M Fairbairn, BA, MA, MEd Newcastle
Director of Studies: A Hopper, BA Merton College, Oxford
Head of Sixth Form: D C Henry, BSc Heriot-Watt, FIMLS
Assistant Head of Sixth Form: J C Downie, BSc Lancaster, MA Newcastle, CBiol, MIBiol
Chaplain: Revd Canon J M Dotchin

J Bolton, BSc Newcastle
L M Boulton, BSc Keele
A Brown, BA Newcastle
J Buckler, CertEd St John's College, York
M C Carson, BA, PhD Newcastle
L Clough, CertEd IM Marsh College of PEd
V Cooke, BA Durham, MA Durham
J Donald, BEd Durham CNNA
S Dutton, CertEd Leeds
E C Fiddaman, BA Hertford College, Oxford
K Fraser, BSc, PhD Newcastle
A H Gillis, BSc, MSc, PhD Durham
D Gillott, BSc Hull
J Golding, BA Northumbria
K F Heatherington, BA Newcastle
K Henderson, BA Glasgow
M Hill, BSc Leicester
K P Jones, CertEd Newcastle
A Lill, BSc Northumbria
P Lincoln, BA Newcastle
C McFall, BSc Hull
G M Maughan, BEd Homerton College, Cambridge
G S Mundy, MA Newnham College, Cambridge
I Le Moallic-Bell, DEUG Nantes, BAEd Sunderland
E Palmer, BSc Salford
C Parker, MBA Sunderland
M Pyburn, BSc Manchester
S Rickaby, CertEd Lady Mabel College of PE
L Robson, BA Northumbria
C J Scorer, BA Sheffield
S Stewart, CertEd Northern Counties College of Ed.
J Strong, MA Queens' College, Cambridge
C Turnbull, BA Goldsmiths College, London
S Whewell, MSc Sunderland
A Wiegand BA Sunderland
S A Winton de Lezcano, BSc Nottingham, MSc Imperial College, London

Junior Department:
Head: A J Edge, MA St Andrews

A Brown, BSc Northumbria
L P Cruickshank, BA Newcastle
D M Farren, BA Warwick
M Hallowell, BA Newcastle
K Carruthers, BSc Loughborough
K Ellis, BA Liverpool

There are approximately 400 girls in the School which has a three-form entry at 11+. With the Boys' School, which is in the same building, it shares a mixed Sixth Form and a mixed Junior Department (8+ to 10+).

The Main School follows the normal range of subjects, leading to examination at GCSE. German is introduced in Year 8 and Spanish is offered in Year 9.

Most girls stay on into the Sixth Form and from there normally go on to Higher Education.

Buildings. In recent years, developments have included additional classrooms, a new Library, Computer Resource Centre, Technology Centre, ICT network, a new Sixth Form Centre, and a Drama and Dance Studio.

School Societies. The current list includes: outdoor pursuits (including Duke of Edinburgh's Award scheme), choirs, orchestra, drama, computing, art, Christian Fellowship, Amnesty International, history, science, electronics, mathematics, dance, public speaking and debating.

Pastoral. Each girl is placed in the care of a Form teacher who oversees her progress and development. In the Sixth Form she has a Tutor who is responsible for both academic and pastoral care.

Careers. There is a structured programme, beginning in Year 9, with a significant contribution from Connexions.

Sixth Form. In 1989 the Sixth Form was merged with that of our brother School, giving both Schools the rare constitution of single-sex education (11–16) with a co-educational Sixth Form. The Head of Sixth Form is Mr D C Henry who will welcome enquiries concerning admission.

Physical Education. Hockey, Netball, Tennis, Gymnastics, Athletics, Fencing, Badminton, Squash, Swimming. The playing fields adjoin the school. Instruction in swimming is given at a local pool. Dance is particularly popular.

Admission. Governors' Entrance Scholarships are awarded on the results of the Entrance Examinations held annually in the Spring Term at all ages from 8+ to 13+. A limited number of Bursaries are available to pupils aged 11+ and over on entry.

Fees per term (2008-2009). Senior School £2,894; Junior Department £2,277.

Dame Allan's Old Allanians Association. Joint President: Mrs C Straker, 13 Glendale Avenue, Whitley Bay, NE26 1RX.

Charitable status. Dame Allan's Schools is a Registered Charity, number 1084965. It exists to provide education for children.

Derby High School

Hillsway Littleover Derby DE23 3DT
Tel: 01332 514267
Fax: 01332 516085
e-mail: headsecretary@derbyhigh.derby.sch.uk
website: www.derbyhigh.derby.sch.uk

Founded in January 1892; taken over from the Church Schools Company in 1910 by a local Governing Body. In 1959 the school became associated with the Woodard Corporation.

Governors and Foundation Governors:

Chairman: [1]Mr J G R Rudd, DL, FCA, FCMI
Mr M R Beardsley, FCA
Revd Canon B Clover, MA, FRSA, LTCL
Mr D Eade
Dr R Faleiro
[1]Mr M R Hall, DL, Hon D Univ, FCA, FCMA, FCT
Mrs R Hughes, BA, ACIB
[1]Mr H M L Jenkins, DM, FRCOG
[1]Mrs M Moore
Mrs C Owen, BDS
[1]Revd P M Taylor, DipEVA, DipC
Mrs C M Taylor, RGN, ITU, CertRM, DANS RCNT, MSc
Mrs R Williams

[1] *Foundation Governor*

***Headmaster*: C T Callaghan**, BA Comb Hons Exeter, MA OU

Deputy Head: Mrs A K Penny, BA Comb Hons Birmingham, PGCE Loughborough, MEd Nottingham

Director of Studies: Mrs J Sample, BSc Hons Durham, PGCE Cambridge

Head of Sixth Form: Dr N Brown, BSc Leeds, PhD Leeds, PGCE Leicester

Chaplain: Revd R Barrett, MA Exeter, BA Hons Exeter, PGCE Exeter (*PSHE, Religious Education*)

Bursar: Mrs S Marson

* *Head of Department*

Mrs A Arthey, BA Comb Hons Birmingham, PGCE Nottingham (**French and Careers*)
Mrs M Aspinall, BA Hons Durham, PGCE Durham (**Modern Languages*)
Mrs L Baxter, MA Hons Oxon, PGCE Leeds (*Modern Languages*)
Mrs T Bullas, BEd Hons London (*Physical Education*)
Mrs S Bussey, BSc Econ Hons Aberystwyth (*Information Resources*)
Mrs C M Cleave, BSc Hons Exeter, PGCE Cambridge (**Physics*)
Mrs S Collingwood, BA Hons York, CBiol, MIBiol (**Biology*)
Mr D Connell, MBA Derby, PGCE Staffordshire, ACIB (**Business Studies, ICT*)
Mrs N Driver, BEd Hons Lancaster (**Religious Education, PSHE, Head of Years 7-9*)
Mrs C Eales, PGCE Birmingham (*Mathematics*)
Mrs J Fraser, BSc Hons Derby, PGCE Nottingham Trent (*Psychology*)
Miss D Fry, HND, BA Hons Derby, PGCE Nottingham (*Art*)
Miss A Jordan, BA Hons Wolverhampton, PGCE Newcastle (**History*)
Mr P Gould, GRSM, FRCO, ARAM, LRAM, ARCM, DipEd (*Music*)
Mrs L Hamblett, BSc London, PGCE Derby (*Mathematics and DofE Award*)
Mrs J Hancock, BEd Hons Manchester Metropolitan (**Physical Education*)
Mrs K Hewitt, BA Hons Birmingham (*Biology*)
Mrs L Hough, BSc Hons Brunel CertEd (**Design Technology, Young Enterprise*)
Miss S Kelliher, BA Hons Dublin, PGCE Birmingham (*German*)
Mrs V L Lucas, BA Hons OU, TCert Southampton Dip PDE Derby, MEd Derby (**Mathematics, Records of Achievement*)
Mrs A Mansfield, BA Hons Derby, PGCE Nottingham (*History, Geography*)
Mrs S Martin-Smith, HND Swansea, BA Hons Swansea, PGCE Swansea (**Art*)
Mrs C McDonald, BSc Hons Manchester, PGCE Manchester (**Home Economics*)
Dr J A Nelmes, BSc Hons London, PGCE Nottingham (*Physics and Chemistry*)
Mrs J A Priestnall, BSc Hons Hatfield, PGCE Leicester (*Biology*)
Mrs C E Read, BA Hons Reading, PGCE London (*English, Young Enterprise*)
Miss M Render, BA Hons Hull, PGCE Hull (*English*)
Miss C V Riley, BSc Hons Leeds , PGCE Leeds (**Chemistry, Head of Years 10 & 11*)
Mr N Robinson, BA Hons (*Director of Music*)
Mrs M Roe, BA Hons Nottingham (*Geography*)

Mrs D G Stringer, BEd Hons Cardiff, DipEdMan Nottingham (*Home Economics*)
Miss F Supran, BA Hons Manchester, PGCE Oxford, Cert TEFLA Oxford Brookes (*English and Drama*)
Dr C Wakerley, BSc Hons Nottingham Trent, PhD Loughborough, PGCE Nottingham Trent (*Chemistry, General Studies*)
Miss S Walton, BSc Hons Sheffield, PGCE Sheffield (*Physical Education*)
Mrs J Webster, MA Hons Cambridge (**English & Psychology*)

Music:
Mrs C A Barker, TCert Manchester, CT ABRSM (*Flute and Fife*)
Mrs V Cunningham, BA Hons (*Oboe and Clarinet*)
Mr E Garrard, LRAM, LGSM (*Singing, Piano and Choirs*)
Mrs D Gould, CertEd (*Violin, Viola*)
Mrs M Marubbi, MA, BA Hons, ALCMTD (*Flute and Piano*)
Mr M Smith, ARMCM, GRSM, DipEd London (*Brass and Piano*)
Mr C R Susans, TCert Birmingham (*Classical Guitar*)
Miss S Watts, BMus Hons, LRAM (*Clarinet and Saxophone*)

Junior School:
Head: Mrs K M E Carey, BEd Liverpool Chester College
Deputy Head: Mr S Bullas, BEd Exeter
Mrs C A Alvis, BEd Nottingham
Miss L Baker, BA Hons Derby, PGCE Derby
Mrs D Hinds, BEd Hons Derby
Mrs K Hopkinson, BEd Hons Derby
Mrs L Soutar, BA Hons Nottingham, PGCE Leeds
Mrs J Swainston, BEd Hons Sheffield
Mrs J Golding, BEd Doncaster Coll of HE
Mrs A Trindell, BSc Hons London, QTS

Kindergarten:
Head: Mrs M Hannaford, BEd Hons Derby, MA Ed OU
Mrs L Brebner, DipEd Jordan Hill College, Glasgow, ITC Notre Dame College, Glasgow
Mrs M Blount, BEd Hons Derby
Mrs P R Charge, CertEd Poulton-le-Fylde
Mrs A Dowell, BSc Hons, QTS Newman Coll of HE
Miss S Doyle, BA Hons Derby, PGCE Nottingham Trent
Mrs J Needham, BA Leeds, PGCE Nottingham Trent
Mrs E Sanderson, BEd Hons Derby

Headmaster's PA: Miss S Callaghan, BA Hons Warwick

There are 580 pupils in school of whom 300 are in the Senior School, which is for girls only and 280 are in the Junior and Kindergarten which are both co-educational.

The Junior School and Kindergarten follow an enhanced national curriculum course. KS1and KS2 SATs are taken. However, there is considerable enrichment in the curriculum with a wide variety of sports, music, drama and other activities available both within the curriculum and at club time.

The Senior School offers courses in Art and Design, Biology, Business Studies, Chemistry, Design Technology, Drama, English Language and Literature, French, General Studies, Geography, German, History, Home Economics, Mathematics, Music, Physical Education, Psychology, Physics, Religious Studies. The curriculum is enhanced by activities such as Young Enterprise, The Duke of Edinburgh's Award Scheme and the charitable work undertaken in Ethiopia and Thailand. Sports, drama and music are also strengths.

The main points of entrance are at 11+ and 16+ where Scholarships and Assisted Places are available. Entrance is by examination and interview. Entrance at other ages is by assessment and takes place by arrangement.

The school has an active Christian ethos and broadly follows the teaching of the Church of England, but pupils of all faiths are welcomed and valued.

Examinations. Pupils are entered for KS1 and KS2 SATs, GCSE and GCE AS and A level examinations. The school takes part in PIPS, MIDYIS and YELLIS. CLAIT and short course GCSE IT are taken by all pupils, Music through the Associated Board of the RCM and the Young Enterprise examination may be taken by Company members.

Games. Hockey, Netball, Rounders, Tennis, Swimming, Athletics, Short Tennis, Tag Rugby, Football and Trampolining are major sports.

Fees per term (2008-2009). £2,180–£2,910.

Charitable status. Derby High School Trust Limited is a Registered Charity, number 1007348. It exists to provide education for children.

Dodderhill School

Droitwich Spa Worcestershire WR9 0BE
Tel: 01905 778290
Fax: 01905 790623
e-mail: enquiries@dodderhill.co.uk
website: www.dodderhill.co.uk

Founded in 1945, Dodderhill School is an independent day school for girls from 3–16 years and boys from 3–9 years.

Governors:
Revd D Chaplin
Mr N Goodman
Mrs F Grimer
Mrs K Hill
Judge M D Mott
Mr P D H Richards
Mrs R J Shearburn
Mr D Street
Mrs G E Warman
Mr D Watson
Mr J Wheatley (*Chairman*)

***Headmistress*: Mrs J M Mumby**, BA Hons, DipEd

Deputy Headmistresses:
Miss G Betteridge, CertEd
Mrs A Clancy, BEd Hons, DipRSA

Director of Studies: Mrs A Benigno-Thomas, BA Hons

Academic Staff:
Mrs J Allen Griffiths, BA Hons
Mrs S J Amos, BA Hons
Mrs E R Barnett, BA Hons
Miss S Berwick, BA Hons
Dr K Blackmore, BSc Hons
Mrs R Bradley, BA Hons
Mrs A Cartwright, BSc Hons
Mrs G Cook, CertEd
Mr P D Cross, BSc
Mrs J Feltham, CertEd
Mrs H R Forecast, BEd Hons
Mrs C German, BA Hons
Mrs M Grey, DUELI
Mrs R Hatfield, BA Hons
Mrs S G R Loveday-Fuller, BEd Hons
Mrs J E Lowe, BSc Hons
Mrs S Maciej, CertEd
Mrs T Palmeri, BEd Hons
Mrs V Plant, BA Hons
Mr R J Porter, BA Hons
Mrs C E Radcliffe, BSc Hons
Mrs F Turberville, BA Hons
Mrs S Young, BEd Hons

Administrative Staff:
Bursar: Mrs P A Lewis
Domestic Bursar: Mrs A Beaven
Headmistress's PA: Mrs Y Wood
School Secretary: Mrs A Lane
Matron: Mrs J Cameron-Price
Administrative Assistant: Mrs M Paget
Marketing Consultant: Ms R Key, BA Hons

Introduction. Dodderhill School is a non-denominational day school administered by a Board of Governors. The school provides a seamless education for girls aged 3 to 16 years and welcomes boys from 3 to 9 years. Small classes and experienced, motivated staff mean that pupils can achieve their academic and personal potential. Good pastoral care and a friendly, family atmosphere help pupils to build the confidence, self-esteem and maturity that will help them to continue to achieve in the world of post-16 and higher education.

Location. The school is set in its own grounds on the outskirts of Droitwich Spa and only minutes from the M5/M42 interchange. It serves families from Droitwich Spa, Bromsgrove and a wide area of North Worcestershire. Minibus transport is provided between school and Droitwich Spa station and many pupils take advantage of the excellent local rail network.

Facilities. A superbly designed new foundation stage and junior block incorporating a spacious multi-purpose school hall complements the newly refurbished original Georgian buildings. As part of the continuing development programme instituted by the governors in 1998 the ICT suite, first opened in 2001, was upgraded in 2006 and the buildings networked to provide pupils throughout the school with access to the latest technology. Two new classrooms were established 2002 and the teaching rooms in all practical areas have been completely refurbished since 2003. In March 2004 an exciting new Nursery was opened in the Early Years area. It provides babies and toddlers (6 weeks to 3 years) with the same warm, happy, caring and family friendly atmosphere enjoyed throughout the school. In 2008 a new building was opened providing further classroom accommodation and a new food technology room.

Curriculum and Teaching. In the Foundation Stage and Key Stage 1 emphasis is on literacy and numeracy and children are class taught with specialist input in ICT, French and Music. In Year 3 specialists also teach Science, Design and Technology and PE. From Year 4 all subjects are specialist taught and in Years 5 and 6 increasing use is made of senior facilities to ease transition and enhance learning opportunities. In Key Stage 3, in addition to the core subjects of English, Mathematics, Science and PE, all girls learn Art, French, German, Geography, History, Catering, ICT, Music, RE and Textiles. For GCSE all girls take English, Mathematics, Science, a modern foreign language, History or Geography and two additional subjects from a choice of a second foreign language, a second humanity and the creative subjects. Class sizes are small, expectations are high, teachers are well qualified and experienced and the individual is paramount. Results are excellent. Since 2006 Dodderhill has been at or near the top of the Government GCSE performance tables for Worcestershire.

Extra-Curricular Activities. The school offers a stimulating and diverse range of extra-curricular opportunities. Creative Arts, music, outdoor activities, including the Duke of Edinburgh's Award and sport are all catered for. Pre-school care is available from 8.00 am. There is an after-school club until 6 pm and a Holiday Club in the long holidays – a charge is made for these services.

Admissions and Scholarships. Formal entrance examinations are held in January each year for entry at 9+, 11+ and 13+. Two 11+ academic scholarships and an 11+ music scholarship are available at this time. Children may transfer from other schools at any time during the year and admission is then by taster day, examination and school reference. Entrance for younger children is by taster day and individual assessment.

Fees per term (2008-2009). Tuition fees are from £1,680 in Kindergarten to £2,900 in the senior school, inclusive of lunches and text books. There is a 5% reduction for siblings.

Charitable status. Dodderhill School is a Registered Charity, number 527599. It exists to provide education for girls and boys.

Downe House

Cold Ash Thatcham Berks RG18 9JJ
Tel: 01635 200286
Fax: 01635 202026
e-mail: correspondence@downehouse.net
website: www.downehouse.net

Founded 1907.

Governors:
Chairman: Mr R Parry, BA
Dr C Alsop, MA, MB BS, MRCGP
Mr R C Farquhar
Mrs D R Flint, BA
Mr D S Jenkins, FCA
Mr C D Keogh
Mr R D Marsh, BA
Mr S Robinson, BA, FRSA
Mrs J Scott, BSc, PGCE
Mr J Stephen, BSc, FRICS
Mrs B Wheeler

***Headmistress*: Mrs E McKendrick**, BA Liverpool

Deputy Head: Mrs N Huggett, MA Oxon
Senior Mistress: Mrs J Wood, BSc Leicester
Director of Studies: Mr A N Hutchings, BSc Surrey, MA Leeds, MBA Leicester
Senior Resident: Mrs T MacColl, MA Hons Aberdeen
Bursar: Mr J Frere, MBE, BA Bristol

Housemistresses/Housemaster:
Hermitage House: Mrs A Nash, B Teaching and Learning Canterbury NZ
Hill House: Mrs F V Capps, CertEd Bedford College
Darwin: Mme F Chartrain, MA Nantes
Veyrines (France): Mrs A Gwatkin, MA London
Aisholt: Mrs A Carter, BA Portsmouth
Ancren Gate North: Ms Virginia Woods, MA Oxon
Ancren Gate South: Mrs G Ford, BA Bristol
Holcombe: Mrs L Lennard, BSc London
Tedworth: Mrs W D Nurser, BA Birmingham
Willis House East: Mr J Long, BA Natal
Willis House West: Mrs V Ryan, BA Bangor
York House North: Mrs J Fletcher-Dyer, BA, BEd Queensland
York House South: Mrs K Simpson, MA Oxon

Heads of Department:
English: Miss J Doyle, BA Portsmouth, MA Reading
History: Mr A J Hobbs, MA Cantab
Classics: Mr C Letchford, MA Cantab
Religious Studies: Mrs P Toogood, BA Leeds
Modern Languages: Mrs J Bassnett, BA Westminster
Geography: Mr R Barnes, BSc Bristol
Social Sciences: Dr A R Mickleburgh, BA ANU, MPhil Sussex, PhD Cantab
Science: Mrs Y J Charlesworth, BSc Reading
Biology: Mrs B Gordon, BSc Reading
Chemistry: Mr A Reynolds, BSc Loughborough
Physics: Mr J Morris, BSc Sussex
Mathematics: Mr R S Barnes, BSc East Anglia
ICT Coordinator: Mr R Heysmond, BA Lampeter, MA Leicester
Technology: Mr D Savage, BA Humberside
Music: Mr A B Cain, ARAM, FTCL, FLCM, LRAM, ARCM
Art: Mrs S J Scott, BA Central England
Drama & Theatre Studies: Mrs M Scott, BEd Brisbane
Physical Education: Mrs L J M Rayne, BEd Brighton

Photography: Mr G Roberts, LMPA, MFEP
Personal & Social Education: Mrs N Riddle, B PhysEd Dunedin NZ
Learning Support:
Mrs G Moorcroft, BEd Liverpool, MA Kent
Mrs J Caiger-Smith, BA Melbourne, RSA Dip SpLD
Careers: Ms M Akhtar, BA, MA Lucknow, India
Chaplain: Revd G Rainey, BA Dunelm, Cert Theol Cambridge, MA Reading
Medical Department: Mrs R Nicklin, RN
Registrar: Mrs C Long

Numbers on roll. 556 Boarding girls, 12 Day girls.

Age Range. 11–18.

Downe House is situated in 110 acres of wooded grounds, five miles from Newbury and within easy reach of Heathrow Airport. The school's proximity to the Universities of Oxford and Reading allows the girls to take part in a rich variety of activities outside the school.

Buildings. There are Junior Houses for girls aged 11+ and 12+, and five recently refurbished mixed-age Houses for those between 13 and 16. When girls enter the Sixth Form they move into one of two Lower Sixth Houses where they have twin-shared study-bedrooms and facilities appropriate to their needs. Upon entering the Upper Sixth, the girls all have single study-bedrooms. All the Housemistresses are members of the teaching staff and are responsible for the coordination of the academic, pastoral, social and moral development of the girls in their care.

The school buildings include Science Laboratories built in 1990, Art School, Music School, indoor Swimming Pool and Squash Courts and Library. The games facilities are excellent; a new Sports Centre opened in September 2001 and an all-weather pitch is under construction. The school has a new Performing Arts Centre opened in September 2004 and a Concert Hall which are used for lectures, concerts and plays.

Religion. Downe House is a Church of England school having its own chapel, which girls attend for daily prayers and for a service of either Matins or Evensong on Sunday. Holy Communion is celebrated once a week and girls are prepared for confirmation if they wish. Other denominations are welcome. Arrangements are made for Roman Catholics to attend Mass and prepare for confirmation.

Curriculum and Activities. The curriculum includes the study of English, History, Geography, Religious Studies, French, German, Spanish, Italian, Latin, Greek, Mathematics, Physics, Chemistry, Biology, Design and Technology, Information & Communication Technology, Music, Art, Drama and Theatre Studies, Food and Nutrition and Textiles. In addition, Classical Civilisation, Business Studies, Sports Science, Politics, Economics, Photography and History of Art are offered at A Level as well as General Studies and Critical Thinking. Leiths Food & Wine Certificate is also offered to girls in the Sixth Form. Girls are prepared for GCSE, AS and A Level examinations, with all girls going on to University or some other form of Higher Education.

ICT skills are developed across the years with all girls following the ICDL course. All girls have an e-mail address.

All girls in the Lower Fourth, aged 12, spend a term at the School's House in France in the Dordogne, to study French and increase European awareness.

A Careers Specialist gives help to the girls in selecting their careers and a Careers Room is available to all ages.

There are many extra-curricular activities, including a variety of musical instruments, Fencing, Drama, Sub Aqua, Pottery, Woodwork, Photography, Art, Craft, Singing, Speech & Drama Training, Cookery, Clay Pigeon Shooting, Rowing, Model Making and Self-defence. There is a regular programme of varied Weekend Activities, including the Duke of Edinburgh's Award Scheme. Expeditions abroad such as World Challenge, which develops leadership qualities, are offered alongside Young Enterprise which offers an insight into business practice in the UK.

Fees per term (2008-2009). £9,075 for Boarders and £6,570 for Day Girls.

Admissions. Girls may enter the school at 11+, 12+ or 13+ after assessment, interview and Common Entrance. A few girls annually are given places, on interview and entrance test, to follow the A Level Course in the Sixth Form.

Application for entry should be made well in advance. Prospective parents are asked to make an appointment to see the Headmistress, at which time they are offered a comprehensive tour of the school.

Scholarships. (*see Scholarship Entries section*). The School offers a number of Academic Scholarships at 11+, 12+, 13+ and for entry into the Sixth Form. Scholarships are also awarded in Music, Art and Drama (13+ and 16+ only) and there are Head's Discretionary Scholarships awarded to outstanding all-round performers.

Seniors' Bursaries are available for the daughters of 'Old Seniors' if their parents are in need of financial assistance.

Charitable status. Downe House School is a Registered Charity, number 1015059. Its aim is the provision of a sound and broadly based education for girls, which will fit them for University Entrance and subsequently for a successful career in whatever field they choose.

Dunottar School

High Trees Road Reigate Surrey RH2 7EL
Tel: 01737 761945
Fax: 01737 779450
e-mail: info@dunottar.surrey.sch.uk
website: www.dunottar.surrey.sch.uk

Day School for Girls.

***Headmistress*: Mrs J Hellier**, BA Hons Durham, PGCE Bristol, MA London

Senior Management:
Deputy Head: Mrs T McKee, BSc Hons London, ARCS
Head of Junior School: Mrs A Cooper, BEd Hons Exeter
Director of Sixth Form: Mrs M Gannon, BEd Hons London
Director of Academic Support: Mrs M Kennedy, BA Hons Newcastle, PGCE, CFPS Bristol, ACCEG Kent
Bursar: Mr S Heald

* *Head of Department*

English Department:
*Mr A Simmons, MA Greenwich, BA Hons London, PGCE
Miss T Katesmark, BA Hons Surrey, PGCE (**Theatre Studies*)
Ms K Lewis, MBA De Montfort, BEd Hons Sunderland
Mrs T Munro, BEd Hons Leeds, PGCE
Mrs C Turner, BA Hons London, PGCE

Mathematics Department:
*Mrs L Smith, BSc Hons Oxford, PGCE
Mrs M Gannon, BEd Hons London
Miss S Gough, BA Rhodes, S Africa, GRSM Hons, MMus Performance, LRSM, ARCM, FTCL, HDE Cape Town QTS
Mrs T McKee, BSc Hons London, ARCS
Mrs J Pardoe, MA Cantab, PGCE

Science Department:
*Mr H Loughlin, BSc Hons Durham, PGCE, CChem, MRSC, MCoT (*Senior Chemist*)
Miss P Wood, MIBiol, CBiol, CertEd (*Senior Biologist*)

Mr G Michaud, MA Sherbrooke, Canada, BSc Montreal, Canada (*Senior Physicist*)
Mr C Dew, BSc Hons Reading, PGCE
Mrs J O'Dwyer, BSc Hons Durham, PGCE
Mrs J Prothero, BSc Hons Leeds, PGCE (*PSE Coordinator, Biology*)
Mrs P Williams, BSc Hons Southampton, PGCE

Foreign Languages Department:
*Mrs B Collett, Maîtrise-ès-Lettres Aix-en-Provence
Mrs T Biffen, Profesorado de Inglés Buenos Aires, AIL
Mrs C Cleaver-Smith, BA Hons Aberystwyth, PGCE
Miss S Gough, BA Rhodes, S Africa, GRSM Hons, MMus Perf, LRSM, ARCM, FTCL, HDE Cape Town (*Latin*)
Mrs B Jackson, BA Hons Loughborough, DipIL, PGCE
Mrs M Sales, CAPES Lic d'Enseignement d'Anglais Nantes

Information and Communications Technology Department:
Mr J Lyne, HND Surrey, PGCE

Design and Technology Department:
*Mr P Anspach, MCSD, CertEd

Geography Department:
*Mr D Lock, BA Hons London, PGCE
Mrs S Thorne, BA Hons Leicester, PGCE

Economics and Business Studies Department:
Mrs N Wintle, MA Oxon, PGCE

History Department:
*Mrs J Boden, MA St Andrews, PGCE
Mrs J Hellier, BA Hons Durham, PGCE Bristol, MA London
Mrs M Kennedy, BA Hons Newcastle, PGCE, CFPS Bristol, ACCEG Kent

Sociology Department:
*Mrs J Boden, MA St Andrews, PGCE
Mrs N Wintle, MA, BA Hons Oxon, PGCE

Art and Design Department:
*Mrs A Sillifant, CertEd
Mrs M Baker, BA Hons Bath Academy, PGCE

Music Department:
*Mr W T Lamont, BMus Wales, PGCE (*Director of Music*)

Peripatetic Staff:
Miss N André, MMus Hons RNCM (*Piano*)
Mr B Bryant, BMus Hons RAM, LRAM (*Percussion*)
Miss R Calaminus, BA Hons Cantab, LRAM, DipPG Perf RAM (*Violin*)
Mr S Chapman, ALCM, LLCM TD (*Guitar*)
Miss K Eves, MMus, MusB Hons Manchester, GRNCM, PPRNCM (*Piano*)
Mr R LeServe, ALCM, LLCM (*Clarinet, Saxophone*)
Mr E Maxwell, BA Hons, DipRCM, TCL
Mr G Morrison, GGSM, Dip Adv Studies Perf (*Flute*)
Mrs A Morse-Glover (*Recorder*)
Miss L Nagioff, DipNCOS (*Violoncello*)
Mr C Thompson, BA Hons East Anglia, MTC (*Voice, Piano*)
Miss C Walford, AISTD Dip (*Dance*)

Physical Education Department:
*Miss T Miller, BEd Hons De Montfort
Mrs E Pieters, BA Hons Brighton, QTS
Miss L Upchurch, BEd Hons Brighton, QTS

Religious Studies Department:
*Mrs A Runcorn, BA Hons Southampton, PGCE

Home Economics Department – Food Technology:
Mrs J Prothero, BSc Hons Leeds, PGCE (*PSE Coordinator*)

Careers:
Mrs M Gannon, BEd Hons London, CertEd (*Sixth Form*)
Mrs B Jackson, BA Hons Loughborough, DIPIL, PGCE (*Years 7 to 11*)

Work Experience Coordinators:
Mrs M Gannon, BEd Hons London, CertEd
Mrs B Jackson, BA Hons Loughborough, DIPIL, PGCE

Junior Department:
*Mrs A Cooper, BEd Hons Exeter
Mrs G Christodoulou (*Teaching Assistant*)
Mrs S Coles, BA Hons Roehampton
Mrs A Dempster (*Teaching Assistant*)
Mrs E Denny, BA Hons Leicester (*Music*)
Miss K Dolman, BA Hons King Alfred's, Winchester
Mrs L Doughty (*Teaching Assistant*)
Miss N Dryburgh (*Teaching Assistant*)
Mrs J Emburey, BEd Hons West Sussex Inst HE, CNAA
Mrs L James, NAMCW Diploma
Miss A Lawrence (*Teaching Assistant*)
Mrs M McIntyre, BEd Hons Cheltenham, CNAA
Mrs L Nicholson, BEd Hons Avery Hill, CertEd London
Mrs D Read, BScHons Reading, PGCE
Miss J Stokes, BA Hons Bristol, PGCE

Support Staff:
Headmistress's PA, Admissions Secretary: Mrs S Edwards
Special Needs Coordinator: Mrs A Aylwin
Marketing Manager: Mrs K Kelsey, MBA Bradford, BA Hons Leeds
Assistant Bursar: Mr S Carey
Bursar's Secretary: Mrs C Aris
School Secretary: Mrs J Jones
School Matron: Mrs L Kelly
Laboratory Technician: Mrs S Evans
Laboratory/Art & DT Technician: Mrs S Machacek
After-School Care Supervisor: Miss A Lawrence
IT Systems Manager: Mrs S Ameen, BSc Hons Southampton, AIEE

Dunottar is a day school for some 360 girls, between the ages of 2½ and 18. The School was founded in 1926 and became an Educational Trust in 1961. It is situated in 15 acres of gardens and playing fields on the outskirts of Reigate, convenient to mainline stations and bus routes. Development over the years has provided additional classrooms, art and design & technology studios, careers room, Assembly hall, music rooms, Sixth Form common room and 25-metre heated indoor swimming pool. The school is fully networked and has three dedicated computer suites. A new Science Block opened in the early 1990s, followed by a new block of eight classrooms in 1997. A major development programme has provided a new sports hall, sixth form facilities, library and art studios.

Aim. The School's aim is to ensure that we provide an inspiring, happy and fulfilling place of learning for every girl. She will be taught and encouraged to work hard, to discipline herself, to make the most of her opportunities, while recognising and responding to the needs of others. High standards of behaviour are maintained. Parents receive detailed reports twice yearly and have regular opportunities to discuss progress with teachers. Appointments can be made at any time to see the Head. There is a flourishing Friends' organisation.

Religion. The School holds the Christian ethos paramount and welcomes children from any denomination or none.

Curriculum. Eighteen GCSE and twenty A Level subjects are on the curriculum, which is planned to provide a broad education and to preserve a balance between arts and science subjects. Early specialisation is avoided, though some subject options become necessary from the beginning of the GCSE year. Subjects include Religious Studies, English Language and Literature, French, German, Spanish, Latin (Years 7 to 9), History, Geography, Mathematics, Biology, Physics and Chemistry taught for the OCR 21st Century Science and Additional Science examinations, Business and Economics, Design & Technology, Information and Communications Technology, Physical Education, Theatre Studies, Home Economics, Music, Art & Design and Sociology. The School has strong sporting and music traditions. Teaching is given in a wide range of musical instruments and girls are encouraged to join the School orchestras and music groups. There are a number of School choirs. Instruction is available in Speech & Drama, in Dance, and in a wide variety of musical instruments. Drama and music performances are given frequently. There are excellent on-site games facilities including a large indoor heated swimming pool and playing fields. A great number of extra-curricular activities are provided and the School participates most successfully in The Duke of Edinburgh's Award Scheme at Bronze, Silver and Gold levels.

Careers. Advice is provided at each key stage of education. Girls are encouraged to research and discuss career plans and opportunities with staff and work experience is offered in a variety of careers.

Physical Education. Sports and games are an important part of School life, and there are excellent facilities for tennis, badminton, rounders, lacrosse, netball, volleyball, croquet, gymnastics, athletics and swimming.

Examinations taken. GCSE and A Levels, Associated Board of the Royal School of Music, London Academy of Music and Dramatic Art, Imperial School of Dancing, Royal Society of Arts.

Admissions. 11+ entrance examinations are held in January prior to entry the following September. Early application is advised. Girls are accepted directly into the Sixth Form.

Fees per term (2008-2009). Range from £2,415 (Reception) to £3,750 (Year 7 to Upper Sixth).

Scholarships. Academic Scholarships are awarded annually at 11+ and 13+ to those girls who reach the highest standard in the entrance tests, effective for five and three years respectively.

16+ scholarships will be awarded to those girls who reach a high standard in the scholarship papers. The 16+ scholarship examinations take place in November.

Music Scholarships at 11+, 13+ and 16+ are offered to pupils who show exceptional promise and talent in Music, effective for seven, five and two years respectively to the end of the Upper Sixth.

The School offers Sports Scholarships to girls who show exceptional talent and promise in at least two sports. The awards are offered at 11+ and at 16+, effective for seven and two years respectively to the end of the Upper Sixth.

Art and Design Scholarships are offered at 13+ and 16+ to pupils who show exceptional talent and promise in either Art, or Design & Technology, or both, effective for five and two years respectively to the end of the Upper Sixth. Assessments take place in November.

All scholarships are offered to both new and current pupils except for the prestigious John Zinn Scholarship, which is awarded annually to a current prospective Sixth Form student on the basis of academic performance and contribution to the life of the school.

Further particulars may be obtained from the Headmistress's PA who will also arrange an appointment to visit the school and meet the Head.

Charitable status. Dunottar School Foundation Limited is a Registered Charity, number 312068. It exists to provide high quality education for girls.

Durham High School for Girls

Farewell Hall Durham DH1 3TB
Tel: 0191 384 3226
Fax: 0191 386 7381
e-mail: enquiries@dhsfg.org.uk
website: www.dhsfg.org.uk

Governors:
Mr W Hurworth (*Chairman*)
Professor G Blake, MA, PhD
The Rt Revd Mark Bryant, The Bishop of Jarrow
The Revd Canon Rosalind Brown, MDiv, BA, Dip TP, MRTPI retd
Mr S Cheffings
Mrs A M Chapman, BA
Mrs M Cummings, BA
Mr K Delanoy, FCCA
Mrs V Hamilton, MA, MEd
Mrs D Hedley, MB BS, MRCP, MRCGP, DCH
Captain M Hill
Miss J L Hobbs, MBE, MA, FRSA
Mrs G Prescott, BVM&S, MRCVS
Professor L Stuckenbruck, BA, MDiv Phd

***Headmistress*: Mrs A J Templeman**, MA, Dip Th Oxon (*Classics*)

Senior Deputy Head (*Teaching and Learning*): Miss L Clark, BEd Hons, MA

Assistant Heads:
Mrs N Freeman, BA Exeter (*Theological Studies*) (*Pastoral*)
Mrs L Ibbott, BA Cardiff (*English*)
Mr R May, BA Exeter (*History*)
Mrs I Woodland, MA Cantab (*Geography*)

Head of Junior House: Mrs G Settle, BEd Leeds

Bursar: Mrs S Ruskin, FCA

Publicity & Development: Mrs K Anderson, BEd Nevilles Cross

Senior House:
Mrs C Ackerley, BA Dunelm (*Psychology*)
Dr N Alvey
Mrs Sian Baker
Mrs T S Bickerdike, BSc Dunelm (*Mathematics*)
Dr R A Brinham, BSc Hons Dundee, PhD Bristol (*Chemistry*)
Mrs M I Brown, BA Hull, MSc LSE (*History*)
Mrs R Bruce, BA Oxon (*French, German*)
Mrs P G Clarke, BSc Cork (*Physics, PSHE, Citizenship*)
Mrs J Coxon, BEd Liverpool (*Physical Education*)
Mrs C I Creasey, BA Dunelm (*Geography*)
Mrs V M Dyson, BA Dunelm (*LTCL, Music*)
Mrs S A Egglestone, BEd Dunelm (*ICT*)
Mrs D L Elliott, BSc Dunelm (*Biology*)
Miss C Fox, BA Dunelm (*Classical Civilisation*)
Mrs E Gentry, BSc St Andrews (*Science*)
Dr S Grant, BSc Newcastle (*Chemistry*)
Mrs S Harrison, BA London (*English*)
Mrs A Hawkins, BA London (*English, Sociology*)
Mrs J M Hush, BSc Open University (*Mathematics*)
Miss C Iveson
Mrs K Jacklin, BA Dunelm (*Religious Education*)
Miss K Jackson, BA Manchester (*History & Economics*)
Mr T Lonsdale, BA Leicester (*French, German*)
Mrs S May, BEd Cheltenham and Gloucester (*Physical Education*)
Mrs L Middleton
Mr J Neeson, MA Manchester (*Art*)
Mr J Priest, MSc Bath (*Mathematics*)
Mrs D Rabot, MA Ed Sunderland (*ICT*)
Mrs K M Roberts, BA Newcastle (*English, Drama, Learning Support*)
Mrs K Rochester
Mrs J V Slane, BSc Surrey (*Physical Education*)
Mr C Spick
Mr D Stone
Mrs M M Thomas, MA St Andrews (*French, German*)
Ms D Todd
Mrs J Tomlinson, BSc Newcastle (*Biology*)
Mrs S Waite, BSc Worcester, (*Sports Science, Biology*)
Miss C Weingaertner

Mrs D Woodman, BA Newcastle (*Classics*)

Junior House:
Mrs E Brothers, BSc Sheffield (*Deputy Head*)
Mrs K A Anderson, BEd Nevilles Cross
Mr R Dellar, MSc Birmingham
Mrs J Dilley, CertEd Sussex
Miss S Edwards, BA Dunelm, MA Sunderland
Mrs K A Hall, BA Central Lancashire
Mrs C M Hopper, BA Nottingham
Mrs G H Hudson, BEd Bristol
Mrs K M Jackson, CertEd Dunelm
Mrs L Mock, BA Dunelm
Miss L Pickering, BA Dunelm
Mrs C Slee, BEd Dunelm
Mrs L C Tallentire, CertEd Nottingham
Mr G Wright, BA Hons Sunderland

Junior House Support Staff:
Miss A Gowland, NNEB Durham
Mrs C Gorman

Visiting Staff:
Miss V Bojkova, Diplomas in Conducting & Piano Performance (*Singing and Piano*)
Miss S Innes, BMus, LRAM (*Violin & Viola*)
Mr P Judson (*Bassoon*)
Mrs R Barton-Gray (*Cello*)
Mrs J Rousseau (*Oboe*)
Mr G Ritson, GRNCM, PPRNCM (*Brass*)
Miss R J Shuttler, BA, MMus, LTCL (*Piano*)
Miss C Smith, BA, FRSA (*Clarinet & Saxophone*)
Miss R Thodey, BD, LGSM (*Classical Guitar & Lute*)
Mrs J D Wakefield, Gold Medal LAM (*Speech & Drama*)

Administrative Staff:
Head's PA/Office Manager: Mrs C Scutt
Junior House Secretary: Mrs A Thompson
Marketing/Publicity Secretary: Mrs A Wright
Librarian: Mrs J Durcan, ALA
Assistant Bursar: Mr B Craig
Financial Assistant: Mrs K A Halliday
ICT Systems Manager: Mr J Kerton
ICT Technician: Mr P Cass
Receptionist: Mrs J Lathan
Catering Manager: Mrs A Hibbart
Laboratory Manager: Mrs M A Bartley, BSc Open University
Laboratory Technician: Mr T Beck, BSc Hons Hull
Laboratory Assistants: Miss J Cummings, Mrs L Deveaux-Robinson
Reprographics Technician: Mrs C Gillham
Caretaker: Mr K Riding
Assistant Caretakers: Mr D Wilson, Mr P Tennant, Mr P Davis

Durham High School for Girls aims to create, within the context of a Christian ethos, a secure, happy and friendly environment within which pupils can develop personal and social skills, strive for excellence in academic work and achieve their full potential in all aspects of school life.

- Highly qualified, specialist staff.
- Excellent examination results.
- Continuity of education from 3 to 18 years.
- Entry at 3, 4, 7, 10, 11 and 16.
- Superb modern facilities include state-of-the-art Science/ICT/Library Block.
- Performing Arts Suite opened 2007.
- Academic, Music, Performing Arts, Art and Sports Scholarships.
- Academy for Girls' Sport.
- Financial assistance available at all stages.

Number on roll. 627 day pupils.

Age range. Seniors 11–18; Juniors 7–11; Infants 4–7; Nursery from age 3.

Entry requirements. Assessment, formal testing and interview if age is applicable. Sixth form entry is dependent on the level of achievement at GCSE.

Junior House (age range 3–11). A purpose-built Nursery provides a stimulating environment for children aged 3–4 years. Children may start the day after their 3rd birthday.

Junior House follows a topic-based curriculum linked to the National Curriculum which enables girls to enjoy every aspect of learning and discovery. Form teachers encourage and support a high standard of achievement in all areas of the curriculum and promote a feeling of warmth and security.

Extra-curricular activities include: Choirs, Instrumental Tuition, Young Textiles Group, Drama, Gymnastics, Hockey, Rounders, Netball, Tennis, Ballet, Chess, Karate, Dance and Drama. A range of sports fixtures are made with other schools.

The immediate environment plays an important role in stimulating learning and regular visits are made to the theatre, museums and places of educational interest.

Senior House Curriculum. The curriculum is designed to be enjoyable, stimulating and exciting, providing breadth and depth in learning.

- Wide choice of options at GCSE and Advanced Levels.
- Languages: French, German, Italian, Latin and Classical Greek.
- Separate Sciences.
- Personal and Social Awareness programme.
- Careers Education and Guidance.

Extra-curricular activities include regular visits abroad, foreign exchanges, visits to the theatre, art galleries, museums and concerts. There is also a thriving programme of Music, Drama and Sport, as well as a flourishing Duke of Edinburgh's Award scheme. Sixth Form students have the opportunity to spend one month's service in Lesotho.

The Sixth Form. The Sixth Form of 114 girls takes a full and responsible part in the life and organisation of the school. A wide range of A and AS Level subjects is available. Girls take 4 or 5 subjects in L6, 3 or 4 in U6.

Fees per term (2008-2009). Nursery £1,880, Infants (Reception–Year 2) £2,015, Juniors (Years 3–6) £2,225, Seniors (Years 7–13) £2,980.

Extra subjects. Elocution and Music (piano, strings, brass, woodwind, singing).

Scholarships and Bursaries. Means-tested Scholarships are available at 7–9+.

At 11+ a number of academic Open Scholarships are offered and bursaries are available in cases of financial need. There is also the Barbara Priestman award of £600 per annum for daughters of practising Christians. Scholarships (Academic, Performing Arts, Sport and Music) are awarded at 11+ and financial help is available at all stages from age 11.

At 12–14+ Academic, Music, Performing Arts and Sport Scholarships are available.

At 16 there are a number of academic scholarships available to external and internal candidates. Music scholarships are also available at 16+, as well as Performing Arts, Sports and an Art Scholarship.

Means-tested Bursaries are available to daughters of Old Girls.

Transport. Transport is available from most local areas and the school is also accessible by public transport.

After School Care. After School Care is available and is free of charge until 5.30 pm.

Further information. The Headmistress is always pleased to welcome parents who wish to visit the school. For further information and a full prospectus please contact the School Secretary: tel: 0191 384 3226; fax: 0191 386 7381; website: www.dhsfg.org.uk; e-mail: enquiries@dhsfg.org.uk.

Charitable status. Durham High School for Girls is a Registered Charity, number 1119995. Its aim is to provide a high standard of education.

Edgbaston High School

Westbourne Road Birmingham B15 3TS
Tel: 0121 454 5831
Fax: 0121 454 2363
e-mail: admissions@edgbastonhigh.co.uk
website: www.edgbastonhigh.co.uk

President: The Rt Hon Sir Stephen Brown, GBE, Hon LLD

Vice-Presidents:
Sir Dominic Cadbury, BA, MBA

Council:
Chairman: Mr I Marshall, BA
Deputy Chairman: Mr G H Tonks, BSc, FCA
Lord Bhattacharyya, KB, MBE
Mr D J Cadbury, MSc, DSW, CQSW
Mrs S A England Kerr
Mrs C Fatah, RGN
Mrs V J Fuller
Mr S Hampton
Ms J C Howl, BA, MPhil
Dr J Leadbetter, PGCE, BSc Hons, MEd, AFBPsS
Mr A Moore, BA
Dr J F C Olliff, FRCR
Mr A D Owen, OBE, MA Cantab, HonDSc
Mr J D Payne
Mr P C Stone
Her Honour Judge S Thomas, LLB

Representing the Old Girls' Association:
Mrs A E Howarth, CertEd Anstey College, DipEd Birmingham

Representing the Friends of Edgbaston High School:
Mr P Glenn

Secretary to the Council: (*to be appointed*)

School Staff:

***Headmistress*: Dr Ruth A Weeks**, BSc, PhD Birmingham

Deputy Head: Mrs C L Jones, BSocSc Birmingham (*English*)

§ *Part-time*

Ms G Ajmal, BA Wolverhampton (*English*)
Mrs L Batchelor, BSc Birmingham (*PE*)
Mrs J D Blake, BSc Open University (*Geography*)
Miss A G Bosc, BSc Birmingham (*§Biology*)
Mr P M Brassington, BA Leeds, MSc Cranfield, MA Exeter (*Business Studies*)
Dr C Brown, BA London, MEd Birmingham, PhD (*Classics*)
Mrs J Chalmers, BA York (*Mathematics*)
Mrs A Cirillo-Campbell, BA UCE Birmingham (*§ICT*)
Mr M Cleland, BEd Goldsmiths College London (*Drama & Theatre Studies*)
Mrs J Coley, BA Reading (*History*)
Dr F Cook, MA Cambridge, PhD Warwick (*Physics*)
Mrs M-P Dalal, BA Open University (*French/German*)
Miss J K Dhaliwal, BSc Birmingham (*Chemistry*)
Mr M L Dukes, BA Wolverhampton Polytechnic (*Art*)
Miss S Easton, BA Oxford (*Classics*)
Mr J Ede, BMus Sydney (*Music*)
Mrs C A Evans, CertEd Birmingham Polytechnic (*§PE*)
Mr A Flox-Nievo, BA Castilla, Spain (*Spanish*)
Mr B Ford, BSc De Montfort (*§Mathematics*)
Mrs J Forrest, BSc Open University (*§Biology*)
Dr H Gay, BSc, PhD London (*Biology*)
Ms C Greenwood, BA Leicester (*German*)
Miss M Griffiths, BSc Newman College of HE, Birmingham (*PE*)
Miss H Grimmitt, BA Wales (*Drama & Theatre Studies*)
Miss M Harper, GRNCM, ARMCM (*Music*)
Miss J P Harrison, BA Southampton, MA Birmingham (*English*)
Mrs J Hayward, BSc Newcastle upon Tyne (*§Mathematics*)
Mrs G Hennesey, CertEd Bath College of FE (*HE, Textiles*)
Mrs H Howell, GBSM, ABSM (*§Music*)
Mrs R Jackson-Royal, BA King's College London, MA School of Oriental & African Studies, London (*§Religious Studies*)
Miss A L Joyce, BPhil Ed Sheffield Polytechnic (*HE*)
Miss N Khodabukus, BSc Oxford (*Chemistry/Physics*)
Mr M Khuttan, BSc Keele (*Mathematics*)
Mrs A Lacey, BSc University of East Anglia (*Biology*)
Mrs P M Lampard, CertEd Bath College of HE (*§HE, Textiles*)
Mrs A Lee, BSc Birmingham (*ICT*)
Mrs C Lund, BD Wales, MA Cheltenham & Gloucester College of HE (*Religious Studies*)
Mrs L Maile, BA Cambridgeshire College of Arts & Technology (*§History*)
Miss C Mellor, BA Surrey (*French, German*)
Ms S A Morris, BSc Leicester (*§Psychology*)
Miss S Mullett, BA Nottingham (*Art*)
Mrs K E Newling, Birmingham (*Mathematics*)
Miss E Newton, BA Oxford (*§Religious Studies*)
Mrs R Norman, BSc Liverpool (*Mathematics*)
Mrs S Park, BA Wales (*English*)
Mrs M S Petchey, BEd Leeds, MEd Birmingham (*§French, Spanish*)
Mr C J Proctor, BA Swansea (*English*)
Miss F Richards, BSc Bristol, BA Birmingham Polytechnic (*§Art*)
Miss R Richardson, BA Reading (*History*)
Mrs J Rodgers, BEd (*§ICT, Art*)
Mrs J Ruisi, BEd Sussex (*§PE, Psychology*)
Mrs D Snabel, BA Leicester (*English*)
Mrs K J Stocks, BMus Birmingham, ARCM (*§Music*)
Miss R Thomas, BSc Bristol (*Physics*)
Mr M Tomaszewicz, BSc Birmingham (*Chemistry*)
Miss S E Vann, BEd de Montfort (*PE*)
Mrs H Watts, BA London (*Geography*)

Librarian: Mrs S E Sansom, BA
Library Assistant/Examinations Officer: Mrs J Hall, BSc

Language Assistants:
French: Mrs J Wilkinson
German: Fraulein C Poradka
Spanish: Mrs A Gardner-Gomez

Technicians:
Mrs C Harris
Mrs A Jan Mughal, BTEC HND
Miss S Seville, BSc
Miss E Whitehouse
Miss V Gutzmore, HND
Mrs S Griffiths

Network Manager: Mrs S Srinivas, MSc

Lower School:
Head of Department: Mrs L Bartlett, MA Ed Warwick
Deputy Head of Department: Mrs T Norris, BA Open University, TCert Bordesley College of Education, ACP
Mrs V Alderson, CertEd City of Birmingham College of Education
Mrs A Aston, BSc, PGCE Birmingham
Miss R Brittain, BA University of Wales, PGCE Sheffield
Mrs A M Collins, BEd Birmingham, TCert Dudley College of Education
Miss R Deacon, BSc QTS Newman College, Birmingham
Mrs S Draper, BSc PGCE Swansea
§Mrs S Dudley, CertEd Northumberland College of Education

Mrs A L Gelderd, BSc Leeds
Miss A Hornsby, CertEd West London Institute
Mrs S Hurst, BA QTS Warwick
Mrs J Knott, BA, PGCE Birmingham
Ms K McKee, BA Sussex, PGCE Warwick
Miss L Paice, BSc Birmingham, PGCE Birmingham
Mrs C Paton, BA Exeter, PGCE UCE Birmingham
Miss C Robinson, BA Exeter
Mrs S Robinson, TCert Westhill College
Mrs S Smye, BA Birmingham, PGCE Birmingham
§Mrs L Spencer, BEd
Mrs K Waterworth, BSc Aston, PGCE Essex
Mrs F Watson, BA Leeds, PGCE Worcester

Classroom Assistants:
Mrs C Mills
Mrs J Russon
Mrs L Smith
Mrs H Coulson

Technician: Mrs S Lees
Secretary: Mrs L Barton

After-School Supervisors:
Mrs J Eyres
Mrs K Hancocks
Mrs M Henry
Mrs M Rees
Mrs P Murphy

Pre-Preparatory Department:
Head of Department: Mrs L Bartlett, MA Warwick
Miss H Ashworth, BA, PGCE University of Wales
Mrs S Grant, BEd University of Central England
Mrs A Hartland, BEd Birmingham, CertEd Dudley
Mrs D A Kennedy, BEd West Midlands College of HE
Miss H Palmer, BEd University of Wales

Classroom Assistants:
Mrs N Ash
Mrs R Aulak
Mrs E Barnsley
Mrs J Corbett
Mrs A de Salis
Miss E Smith

Visiting Staff:
Ballet: Miss D Todd

After School Supervisors:
Miss E Butler
Mrs D Cox
Miss C Johnson

Special Subjects:

Head of Music Department: Miss M Harper, GRNCM, ARMCM
Pianoforte:
Mrs J Gopsill, LRAM
Mrs H Howell, GBSM, ABSM
Mrs L Kitto, GBSM, ABSM, LTCL
Miss M Mugnaini, MA, LGSM, LRSM
Mrs C J Purkis, GBSM, ABSM, LRAM
Flute:
Mrs A Humphreys, ARCM
Miss H Jones, BA
Mrs S Wilson, BA
Oboe/Recorder: Mrs K J Stocks, BMus, ARCM
Clarinet/Saxophone: Miss C Pountney, LTCL
Bassoon: Mr P Brookes, GBSM, ARCM, DipOrchStudies
Violin/Viola:
Miss A Chippendale, BMus
Mrs S Gough, BA, ARCM
'Cello: Mrs R Storey, BA, ARCM
Double Bass: Mrs N Rolinson, GBSM
Harp: Miss K Thomas, BMus, LGSMD
Guitar:
Miss F Griffin, LGSM, LTCL
Mrs D Saxon Reeves, BMus
Singing: (*to be appointed*)
Brass: Mrs S Dyson, AGSM
Percussion: Mr S Palmer
Trombone: Mrs M Brookes, DRSAMD
Trumpet/Horn: Mrs S Dyson, AGSM

Fencing: Professor P Northam, BAF

Domestic Bursar: Mr S Watson, MHCIMA
Matron: Mrs G L Taylor, RGN, SCM
Headmistress's PA: Ms G Franchi
Director of Marketing & Admissions: Miss R Lowe, BA

This independent day school, founded in 1876, attracts girls both from the immediate neighbourhood and all over the West Midlands. They come for the academic curriculum, the lively programme of sporting, creative and cultural activities, and for the individual attention and flexibility of approach. There are some 940 day girls, aged two and a half to eighteen years.

Personal relationships at EHS are of paramount importance. Parents, both individually and through their association, give generously of their time to support our activities; while staff, through their hard work and good relationship with the girls, create an atmosphere at once orderly and friendly.

Organisation and Curriculum. There are three departments working together on one site which caters for over 900 girls aged two and a half to eighteen. One of the features of EHS is the continuity of education it offers. However girls can be admitted at most stages. Staff take special care to help girls settle quickly and easily. Pupils enjoy a broadly based programme which substantially fulfils the requirements of the National Curriculum and much more.

The Pre-Preparatory Department, known as Westbourne, offers facilities for about 100 girls aged two and a half to five in a spacious, purpose-built, detached house. The staff aim to create an environment in which they can promote every aspect of a girl's development. A brand new Nursery (part of the new £4 million Octagon building) was opened in February 2005.

The Preparatory Department accommodates over 350 girls from 5+ to 11 in up-to-date facilities, among them a new IT suite, Science Laboratory, Library and Design Technology Centre. A full curriculum, including English, Mathematics, Science and Technology, is taught throughout the department.

The Senior School caters for about 500 girls aged 11+ to 18. Girls follow a well-balanced curriculum which prepares them for a wide range of subjects at GCSE and Advanced Level.

Examination results are very good with high grades distributed across both Arts and Science subjects. Almost all the girls in the Sixth Form of over 100 proceed to Higher Education. Every year girls obtain places at Oxford and Cambridge.

Extra Curricular Activities. Girls can take part in a broad range of activities including art, ceramics, dance, drama, Duke of Edinburgh's Award, music, sport and Young Enterprise. There are clubs during the lunch hour and after school. Instrumental music lessons are available. There is a strong music tradition in the school. Girls go on visits, foreign exchanges and work experience in this country and abroad. We encourage girls to think of the needs of others.

Accommodation. There is a regular programme of improvements to the buildings. The Pre-Preparatory and Preparatory Departments have recently been refurbished and the Music Department doubled in size. In 2005 the Sixth Form Centre was completely refurbished. An exciting new multi-purpose hall, The Octagon, was opened in February 2005. A floodlit all-weather surface was opened in Summer 2006. The school has its own indoor swimming pool, 12 tennis courts and 8 acres of playing fields.

Location. The school is pleasantly situated next to the Botanical Gardens in a residential area, 1½ miles south-west of the city centre. It is easily accessible by public transport and also has its own privately run coaches.

Fees per term (2008-2009). Pre-Prep: £1,250 (mornings only), £1,826 (5 days); Prep £1,890–£2,654; Seniors £2,810.

Scholarships and Bursaries. (*see Scholarship Entries section*). Scholarships are available at 11+ and 16+, including two for Music (see relevant section). Sports and Arts Scholarships are also offered in the Sixth Form. A bursary fund exists to help girls enter the Sixth Form and to assist those whose financial circumstances have changed since they entered the Senior School.

Further information. Full details may be obtained from the school. Parents and girls are welcome to visit the school by appointment.

Charitable status. Edgbaston High School for Girls is a Registered Charity, number 504011. Founded in 1876, it exists to provide an education for girls.

Farlington School

Strood Park Broadbridge Heath Horsham West Sussex RH12 3PN
Tel: 01403 254967
Fax: 01403 272258
e-mail: office@farlingtonschool.net
website: www.farlingtonschool.net

Founded 1896.
Motto: *Vive ut Vivas*

Governing Body:
Council of twelve members
Chairman: J L McGuffog

***Headmistress*: Mrs J Goyer**, MA, PGCE

Deputy Head: Ms J Lodrick, BA, MA, PGCE

Senior Mistress: Mrs A Binns, BA, PGCE

Head of Upper School: Miss L Higson, BSc, PGCE

Head of Lower School: Mrs A Higgs, BEd

Head of Prep School: Mrs J Baggs, BEd, CertEd

Deputy Head of Prep School: Mrs S E Povey, BEd, CertEd

Bursar: Mr R Hills, MInstAM, MCMI

Registrar: Mrs E Healy

Boarding Staff:
Mrs D Mills, BA (*Housemistress*)
Mrs V Kelly, BA (*Assistant Housemistress*)

Nurses: Mrs C Parsons, RGN, Mrs A Woods RGN
Doctor: Dr E Fisher, MB BS, DRCOG, MRCGP, DFSP, DOccMed

The School. The official foundation of Farlington School (then Farlington House) was in 1896 at Haywards Heath. The School moved to its present site in 1955. It is situated in 33 acres of beautiful parkland on the Sussex-Surrey border. It has two lakes, sports and recreational facilities.

We have approximately 500 girls aged from 3 to 18. Girls can board from the age of 8, on a full, weekly and occasional basis, or attend as day girls. All are equally important members of the School community. In September 2008 our new Courtyard Building opened, designed to complement the existing Prep School building which opened in 1997. This offers facilities for our new co-educational Nursery Class for children aged 3–4 years. The new building also includes further classrooms, a dedicated Prep music room, a multi-purpose hall, a kitchen, a library and administration offices. Girls at Farlington also enjoy a purpose-built Science Building, new IT facilities, a Sports Hall with facilities for badminton, volleyball, netball and basketball, a floodlit all-weather hockey pitch, and a new Sixth Form Centre.

Curriculum. We aim to provide a broad and balanced curriculum for all age groups. Our academic standards are high, and we encourage girls to raise their own expectations of achievement. Our approach involves good teaching practice coupled with clearly set targets and positive encouragement throughout every girl's school life. The rewards are good examination results: a 100% pass rate at A Level with 69.3% at grades A and B, and 97.8% A* to C grades for GCSE in 2007 with 65.8% A* and A grades. Over 95% of our sixth formers go on to university or other degree courses.

Important though academic standards are, education is about more than examination results: we aim to educate the whole child. We are concerned to encourage spiritual, physical and personal development, as well as academic achievement.

Spiritual awareness, care for others, tolerance and compassion are the basis of our religious education. We are a Church of England foundation, but we welcome all faiths. There is an assembly most weekday mornings, and boarders are given the opportunity to attend a service at a church of their choice on Sundays. Work for charity and service to the community are part of the ethos at Farlington.

Farlington's emphasis on care and guidance in personal development is underlined in our tutorial system. Each girl is placed in a tutor group where she is given individual attention. Tutors liaise with other members of the teaching staff, boarding staff (where appropriate) and parents. They monitor academic progress and extra-curricular activities. Each week a tutor period is devoted to the discussion of a wide range of topics within our personal, social and health education programme (PSHE), including moral issues, personal relationships, health education and study skills.

Extra-Curricular Activities. Opportunities for pursuing activities of all sorts exist after school and during lunch hours. Some are physical activities, such as The Duke of Edinburgh's Award Scheme, step classes, fencing; others are more creative like Art or Drama club. Musical activities are popular, or then again, girls can become debators or join the Chess Club.

A wide range of sporting activities is available and the School enjoys considerable success at county and national level in many sports. There is a strong drama and music tradition within the School. All girls are encouraged to take at least one activity, and there is also supervised prep until 5.45 pm.

Admission. Admission is by the School's own entrance examination and interview.

Scholarships and Bursaries. (*see Scholarship Entries section*). A variety of Scholarships is available at 11+, 13+ and Sixth Form entry.

The School offers means-tested bursaries for all prospective and current pupils from Year 5 upwards.

Fees per term (2008-2009). Tuition: Prep School £1,971–£3,505, Senior School £4,196. Boarding (in addition to Tuition fees): £2,342 (weekly), £2,477 (full).

Charitable status. Farlington School is a Registered Charity, number 307048. It exists to provide education for girls.

Farnborough Hill

Farnborough Hampshire GU14 8AT
Tel: 01252 545197/529811
Fax: 01252 529812
e-mail: devdir@farnborough-hill.org.uk
website: www.farnborough-hill.org.uk

Founded 1889.

Motto: *In Domino Labor Vester Non Est Inanis*

Board of Governors:
M Maher, Esq (*Chairman*)
Sister E McCormack, RCE (*Deputy Chairman*)
Mrs S Bell
B H Brufal de Melgarejo, Marquesa de Lendinez
Mr M D Hoad, FRICS
Mr J Hull
Mrs E Lockett
Ms J Mackett
J D MacMahon, Esq
Mrs D O'Leary
Mrs J Phelps
Mrs C Siebert

***Headmistress*: Mrs S Buckle**, BSc Exeter, MA, PGCE Reading, NPQH

Deputy Head: Mrs A Griffiths, BEd Roehampton Inst, MA Surrey, NPQH

Assistant Head Teacher: Mr A Whelpdale, BA, PGCE Wales

Teaching Staff:
Miss D Andrews, BSc Cardiff, PGCE Homerton (*Biology, Chemistry*)
Mrs S Bond, BA Southampton, CertEd Sheffield Hallam (*Art and Design*)
Dr M Bright, BSc Sierra Leone, MSc PhD Birmingham (*Chemistry*)
Mrs G Brocklehurst, BSc UWIST, PGCE OU (*Mathematics*)
Mrs O Brophy, BSc LSE, PGCE Inst Ed (*English*)
Miss E Buck, BA Birmingham, PGCE St Mary's (*Classics*)
Mr F Budge, BA OU, CertEd London, Dip BusEd (*Information Technology*)
Mrs S Burtsell, CertEd Battersea (*Design and Technology*)
Mr P Butler, BA, PGCE Reading (*French, Classics*)
Mrs R Byrne, BA South Glamorgan Inst, Art TCert Goldsmiths College (*Art and Design*)
Mrs S Camprubi-Reches, BA Barcelona, MEd Cardiff, PGCE Barcelona (*Spanish*)
Mrs C Cantor, BA Bath, PGCE Oxon (*German*)
Mr N Cartledge, BMus, DipRCM London (*Music Technology*)
Miss E Casey, BA Exeter, PGCE Roehampton (*French, Spanish*)
Mrs G Chapman, BSc, DipEd Reading (*Physics*)
Mrs C Clarke, BSocSc Bristol, PGCE Bristol Polytechnic (*Psychology*)
Miss K Clarke, MA Cardiff, PGCE Bath Spa (*English*)
Mrs L Craven, BA Berkeley, MA Kent, PGCE Oxon (*English*)
Miss K Davis, BSc London, PGCE Surrey (*Mathematics*)
Mrs A de Winter, BA Liverpool, PGCE Lancaster (*Careers*)
Mrs J Downer, BA Leeds, MA London (*Drama, English*)
Miss R Fielder, BMus Surrey (*Music*)
Mr P Forrest-Biggs, MA London, OTS CFBT (*Classics*)
Miss K Gibson, BA QTS St Mary's (*Physical Education*)
Mrs L Glover, BEd, CertEd Manchester (*Religious Education, English*)
Miss E Goddard, BA Oxon, PGCE Oxon (*Geography*)
Mrs M Gosney, BA Hull (*French*)
Mrs S Gregory, MA Cantab, PGCE Moray House (*French, Spanish, Italian*)
Mrs S Hayes, BSc Leicester, PGCE Ripon and York St John (*Biology*)
Mrs S Haynes, BSc Imperial College, PGCE Reading (*Chemistry, Physics*)
Mr J Hoar, BA Hull, PGCE Southampton (*History*)
Mrs L Hooper, BSc Liverpool, GTP Reading (*Mathematics*)
Miss F Kelsey, BA QTS St Mary's (*Physical Education*)
Mrs S Macey, BSc UMIST, PGCE Cantab (*Chemistry*)
Mrs E Matthews, BA QTS Brunel (*Design and Technology*)
Mrs E Nelson, BSc St Andrews, CertEd Dundee (*Mathematics*)
Mrs J Nix, BEd Winchester (*Design & Technology, Information Technology*)
Mrs V Peters, BA, PGCE Leicester (*Economics, Business Studies, Geography*)
Mrs K Phillips, BA Reading, ALCM (*Music*)
Miss K Price, BA Bristol, PGCE Southampton (*History*)
Dr S Rawle, MA, DPhil Oxon (*Physics*)
Mrs H Rix, BATh Maynooth, HDipEd Trinity College Dublin (*Religious Education*)
Mrs D Robinson, BEd Central School of Speech & Drama (*Drama*)
Dr J Russell, MA PhD London, QTS Reading (*English*)
Mrs A Smith, MA Cantab, PGCE Cantab (*Mathematics and ICT*)
Mrs L Storrie, BSc Salford, PGCE Manchester (*Biology*)
Mrs R-M Thomson, CertEd Chelsea (*Physical Education*)
Mrs L Walker, MA UCCA, Art TCert Goldsmiths College, Cert HistArt Southampton (*Art and Design*)
Miss B Weeks, BA Birmingham, PGCE Southampton (*Geography*)
Mr R Wellington, BA Exeter, PGCE Birmingham (*Theology*)
Mrs M Williams, BSc LSE, PGCE Institute of Education (*Mathematics*)
Mrs L Winch-Johnson, BA Hertfordshire, MSc, PGCE Surrey, CCRS Dip Perf Coach Newcastle (*English, Drama, Learning Support Coordinator*)

Librarian and Website Manager: Mrs J Wood, MA Cantab, DipLIS London
Matron: Mrs K Catling, RGN
Bursar: Cmdr A Woolston, CDipAF
Development Director: Mrs C Duffin, BA Hons, FCIM Chartered Marketer
Chaplain: Miss S Farmer, BA Hons, DipCounselling UEA
ICT Coordinator: Mr A Labuschagné
Examinations Officer: Mrs S Cahalane, BSc Hons

Farnborough Hill is an independent day school for 500 girls aged 11 to 18. It is housed in the former home of the late Empress Eugenie of France to which a purpose built school has been added. Facilities include science laboratories, technology workshops, chapel, refectory, sports hall, indoor heated swimming pool, gymnasium, art rooms, information technology facilities and extensive playing fields.

Although within a few minutes' walk of both Farnborough Main and Farnborough North railway stations, the school is situated in 63 acres of parkland and woodland with magnificent views over the Hampshire countryside. Pupils come from Hampshire, Surrey and Berkshire with many travelling by train or by school coach.

The school was established in Farnborough in 1889 by The Religious of Christian Education and is now an educational trust. A Roman Catholic foundation, the school welcomes girls of other Christian denominations and religious faiths provided that they participate in the religious activities of the school and respect its Christian ideals.

Farnborough Hill is committed to the education of the whole person in an environment based upon Christian values. Each pupil is valued for herself and helped to develop all her talents, grow in confidence and learn leadership skills.

Academic standards are high with students usually taking ten GCSE subjects. In the Sixth Form most students take four AS subjects in the Lower Sixth and three A levels in the Upper Sixth. The vast majority then go on to Higher Education. The school is a member of ISCO and there is a well equipped Careers Department and a specialist Careers teacher.

The school offers a wide range of extra-curricular activities and is especially renowned for its reputation in sport and in the creative arts. Many girls take individual tuition for speech and drama or a musical instrument and perform in choirs, orchestras and drama productions.

Admission and Scholarships. (*see Scholarship Entries section*). Entry is by examination taken in January for the following September. The school offers academic, music and sports scholarships and also bursaries for parents who are in need of financial assistance.

Fees per term (2008-2009). Tuition: £3,280.

Further information. The prospectus is available from the Development Director. The Headmistress is pleased to meet prospective parents by appointment.

Charitable status. The Farnborough Hill Trust is a Registered Charity, number 1039443. Its aim is to educate the whole person through academic achievement, personal development and values based in Catholic Christian tradition.

Farringtons School

Perry Street Chislehurst Kent BR7 6LR
Tel: 020 8467 0256
Fax: 020 8467 5442
e-mail: admissions@farringtons.kent.sch.uk
website: www.farringtons.org.uk

Board of Management for Methodist Schools.

Governing Body:
Chairman: Miss M Faulkner, BSc
Vice-Chairman: Mrs R L Howard, BSc, BA

Members:
Mr W Allen, FCIB
Mr D G Cracknell, LLB
Revd J Impey, BSc, MA
Ms B Johnson, BA, MA
Mrs H S Richardson, BA
Mr G Russell, MA
Mr S J Frankham
Mr A R Turner-Smith, DPhil, CEng, CSsc, CS, FIPEY
Dr A G Williams
Mr T Harris, FRICS, FCIArb

Bursar and Clerk to the Governors: Mrs J Niggemann

***Headmistress*: Mrs C James**, MA (Liverpool and London)

Deputy: Mrs S Worth, BA Hons, PGCE
Chaplain: Revd C J Samuel
Registrar: Mrs F Vail (*Boarding*), Mrs J Grima (*Day*)

* *Head of Department*

English:
*Miss A Oliver, BA Hons, PGCE
Mrs J Ward, BA, PGCE
Mrs S Worth, BA Hons, PGCE
Mrs M Dunckley, CertEd
Miss S Bliss, BA Hons, PGCE
Mrs H Schofield, Dip/Cert TEFL

Mathematics:
*Mrs S Dolan, BA Hons
Ms R Quinney, CertEd
Mr J Dolan, BA Hons
Mrs I Haider, PGCE
Mr M Sansom, BTech, PGCE, AdvDipEd

Science:
Mr R H A Flack, BSc
Mrs P Drury, CertEd
Mr D Mahoney, BSc
Mrs M Raybould
Mrs A Roberts

Modern Languages:
*Mlle I Mosqueron, L-ès-L, PGCE
Mrs L Clarke, DipEd
Mrs M Baron

Humanities:
*Mrs A R T Springer, BA, PGCE
Mrs J W S Baillie, BEd
Mrs A Harris, ICA
Mrs J Pyle, CertEd
Mrs K Hodge, BSc Hons
Mrs D Halls, PGCE
Mr J Attridge

Technology:
*Mrs G Allen, BA Hons, MA, PGCE
Mrs S Magni, CertEd
Mrs K Matthews, CertEd
Miss S Thorne, BEd

ICT:
Mr J Gardner, BSc, MSc, PGCE

Performing Arts:
*Mr G James (*Director of Music*)
Miss S Bliss

Learning Support:
Mrs J Maynard, OCR Cert

Sport:
*Mrs G Ody, BEd Hons
Mrs J Wood, BEd Hons

Junior School:
Mrs L Knight, BEd, CertEd
Mrs W Reed, LTCL, CertEd
Mrs J Lloyd, BA, CNAA, ARCM
Miss V Bloomfield, CertEd
Mrs J M Hook, BEd Hons
Mrs J Lally, BA Hons, PGCE
Mrs N J Tetley, BA Hons
Ms V Coatz, BEd
Mr M Dutton, BEd, CertEd
Mrs J Munro, DipEd
Mrs P Brookman, BA, JPED, BEd
Mrs L Long, BEd
Ms J Ellis, BA Hons
Miss K Wiseman, BEd Hons
Mrs C Williams, CertEd
Mrs L Hayes, CertEd, DipSpLD

Boarding Staff:
Mrs M Dunkley
Miss K Wiseman
Mrs R Buchanan

Nursery:
Mrs S M Bainbridge, BA Hons, PGCE (*Teacher in charge*)
Mrs C Dolding-Smith
Mrs S Carter

Farringtons School is situated in 26 acres of green belt land in Chislehurst, which provide attractive surroundings while still being within easy reach of London (20 minutes to Charing Cross), the South Coast and Gatwick (45 minutes) and Heathrow airport via the M25 (1 hour).

The School is committed to providing a first-class education for pupils of all ages in a caring community which supports all its members and helps each pupil to achieve his or her full potential both academically and personally. After school care is available until 6 pm.

The curriculum offered is that of the National Curriculum, with a wide range of GCSE and A Level subjects available. Nearly 100% of Sixth Form leavers customarily go on to degree courses at Universities or Higher Education Colleges. Academic standards are high from a comprehensive intake of girls and in 2007 ran at 90% of all Year 11 girls securing 5 or more A*–C grades and a 100% pass rate at A Level.

The excellent facilities include a Technology building, a large Sports Hall with Dance Studio and Weights Room, splendidly-equipped Science and Modern Language departments, well-stocked libraries, CD-ROM computers, Careers Room, heated swimming pool and extensive playing fields, as well as a School Chapel, where the School regularly comes together.

The main sports are netball, tennis, swimming and athletics, but badminton, volleyball and table tennis are also undertaken and other extra-curricular activities available include the Duke of Edinburgh's Award Scheme, Young Enterprise, various choirs and instrumental ensembles, gymnastics, jazz-dance, ballet, drama club, fencing, etc.

To obtain a prospectus and further information or to arrange a visit, contact the Registrar.

Fees per term (2008-2009). Day £1,950–£3,610, Weekly Boarding £6,200, Full Boarding £6,600. In addition, we offer a special 4-night weekly boarding package for £5,110.

Charitable status. Farringtons School is a Registered Charity, number 307916. It exists solely to provide a high quality, caring education.

Francis Holland School
Regent's Park

Clarence Gate Ivor Place London NW1 6XR
Tel: 020 7723 0176
Fax: 020 7706 1522
e-mail: admin@fhs-nw1.org.uk
website: www.francisholland.org

Founded 1878.

Patron: The Right Revd and Right Hon The Lord Bishop of London

Council:
Chairman: Mrs C Longworth, BA
Vice-Chairman: Mrs S Singer, BA

The Revd J Cave Bergquist, BA
Dr C Carpenter, BA, MA, PhD
Mr C Clark, MA
Mr P Davis, BA, DArch, RIBA, ACArch (Pres)
Mrs C Elliott, MA, MBA
Mrs S Graham-Campbell
Mrs A Grainger, LLB
Mr K Hoggart, BSc, MSc, PhD
Mrs J Khayat, MA
Mr B Lenon, MA
Mr R Lewis, MA
Miss S Mahaffy, BA
Mrs B Mathews, BA, FCA
Mr I A N McIntosh, MA, FCA
Mr C Sheridan
Dr S Watkinson, MA, PhD
Dr G Young, MB BS, DCH

Bursar and Secretary to the Council: Mr C W Martinson, BSc, ARICS, The Bursary, Francis Holland Schools Trust, 35 Bourne Street, London SW1W 8JA.
Tel: 020 7730 8359, e-mail: bursary@fhst.org.uk

***Headmistress*: Mrs V M Durham**, MA Oxon

Deputy Headmistress: Miss J B Addinall, MA Cantab, PGCE

Senior Mistress: Mrs F J Forde, CertEd Dartford College

Director of Studies: Miss J Green, MA Cantab, MSc London

Head of Sixth Form: Mrs H L Forbes, BA Oxon, MA, PGCE

Head of Year 7: Mr M Chiverton, BA, MA, PGCE Oxon
Head of Year 8: Miss C Mahieu, BEd Sydney
Head of Year 9: Mr H Clayton, BA Liverpool, PGCE
Head of Year 10: Miss M Gustave, BA Montpellier, MA Montpellier, PGCE Nottingham
Head of Year 11: Mr P Price, BSc East Anglia, PGCE

Teaching Staff:

Art:
Miss B Conway, BA Edinburgh, PGCE Moray House College of Education
Miss H Gardner, BA Hons Nottingham, PGCE
Miss J Orr, BA NkU, MA Sussex
Dr R Chaplin, BA, MA, DPhil Sussex, CertEd NELP
Miss V Taylor (*Pottery*)

Careers/Librarian:
Mrs J M McGinlay

Classics:
Mr S F Jenkin, MA Oxon, PGCE
Miss J B Addinall, MA Cantab, PGCE
Mrs J Cohen, MA Oxon
Miss D O'Laoire, MA, PGCE

Economics:
Miss J Green, MA Cantab, MSc London

English:
Miss M Williamson, BA London, PGCE Cantab
Mrs N Foy, MA London, PGCE
Mrs K F Oakley, BA London, AKC
Mr A Smith, BA York

Geography:
Miss S Hack, BA Portsmouth, PGCE Southampton
Mrs F Forde, CertEd
Miss J Green, MA Cantab, MSc London
Miss A Sainty

History:
Mr M Chiverton, BA, MA, PGCE Oxon
Mr H Clayton, BA Liverpool, PGCE
Miss V Bacon

History of Art:
Dr R Chaplin, BA, MA, DPhil, Dip Painting, CertEd NELP

Information Technology:
Mr P Phillips, BSc, CertEd Leeds

Mathematics:
Mrs J Walker, BSc, PGCE
Miss R Francis, BSc, PGCE
Mrs J Merry, BA Reading, PGCE
Miss N Murugan, BSc, PGCE
Miss A C Williams, BSc Dunelm

Modern Languages:
Mrs B Edwards, BA, PGCE Hull (*French and German*)
Mme M Atwood, BA, PGCE (*French and Spanish*)
Mrs N Bullock, LFL Salamanca, MA Madrid (*Spanish*)
Dott M Cicora, Instituto Universitario Lingue Moderne, Milan (*Italian*)
Miss A Derguesse, Université de Picardie Jules Verne (*French and German*)
Miss M Dickens, MA Cantab, PGCE (*Italian and French*)
Herr R Diesel (*German*)
Miss M Gustave, BA Montpellier, MA Montpellier, PGCE Nottingham (*French and Spanish*)

Music:
Mrs E Rolfe Johnson, BMus, PGCE London
Mr P Thorne, BA Oxon, MMus UEA, PGCE Keswick Hall

Visiting:
Mr K Abbs, FTCL (*Clarinet/Saxophone*)
Ms J Cohn, BA Lon, ARAM (*Voice*)
Mr D Cotton, TCM PG Dip (*Trumpet*)
Miss R East, MA Oxon (*Violin*)
Ms F Firth, LTCL (*Voice*)
Ms L Friend, ARCM (*Flute*)
Mr C Glynn, MMus Oxon (*Pianoforte & Accompanist*)
Miss E Gourlay, MMus LCM (*Oboe*)
Mr E Hackett (*Percussion*)
Mrs C Hall, LRAM (*Voice*)
Miss K Hodges
Miss N Kennedy, BA Bristol (*Voice*)
Miss R Lindop, LLCM, ARCM (*Voice*)
Ms J Lewey, ARCM (*Music Theory*)
Mr R Morris
Mr D Parsons, ARCM (*Guitar*)
Mr M Radford, ARCM, LTCL (*Cello*)
Mr P Robinson, MMus Cambridge (*Voice*)
Miss E Rolfe Johnson
Ms J Schloss, BMus Qld (*Piano*)
Ms A Thwaite, BMus Guildhall (*Piano*)

Also visiting teachers for:
musical instruments, aerobics, kick boxing, ju jitsu, pottery, cookery, fencing, yoga and Alexander Technique, according to demand.

Physical Education:
Miss J Tucker, BEd
Mrs S Drummond, CertEd
Miss K Gallagher, BEd, TDip
Miss C Mahieu, BEd Sydney
Mr M Stepinac, AFA, BAF
Miss J Laytham, BEd

Psychology:
Mrs H Bowman

Religious Education:
Mrs C Elderkin, MA Oxon, PGCE
Mrs J Locke, BEd
Mrs S Bexon, BA, PGCE
The Revd J Bullock, BD London
Mrs Z Curtis, BA

Speech and Drama:
Mrs K Mount

Science:
Mr C Davis, BSc, MSc Sheffield, MEd (*Chemistry*)
Mrs A Adlam, BSc Southampton, MSc London, PGCE (*Physics*)
Mr A E Lowe, BSc London (*Physics*)
Mr P Price, BSc East Anglia, PGCE (*Biology*)
Dr G Jones, BSc, PhD Bristol, PGCE
Ms R Francis, BSc Sheffield (*Biology/Chemistry*)
Mrs S Drummond, CertEd (*Biology*)
Miss N Webb, BSc, PGCE

Art Technician: Ms C Overton, BA
ICT Technician: Mr S Andrews
Laboratory Technician: Mrs G Unwin, BSc Greenwich
Registrar & Head's PA: Mrs S Bailey
School Secretaries: Miss A Heining, Mrs D Fahy
School Keeper: Mr V Sheriffs
Catering Manager: Mr S King
Learning Support: Mrs F Forde, CertEd
School Counsellor: Mrs D Webb

There are about 424 day girls and entry by examination and interview is normally at 11+, with a small number joining at 16+ for the Sixth Form. The school was founded in 1878 and is affiliated to the Church of England, but girls of all Christian denominations and other faiths are accepted.

Curriculum. Girls are prepared for GCSE, A and AS Levels, and for admission to Universities, and Colleges of Art, Education and Music. Games are played in Regent's Park and full use is made of the museums, theatres and galleries in central London. Extra lessons are available in fencing, music, pottery, Speech and Drama, Alexander Technique, kick boxing, ju jitsu, and cookery. For the first five years, to GCSE, girls follow a broad curriculum and normally take 10 GCSE subjects. Careers advice is given from the third year, and all pupils receive individual guidance through to the Sixth Form. In the Sixth Form a wide choice of Advanced Level subjects is combined with a general course of study. All girls are expected to stay until the end of the Advanced Level course.

Scholarships and Bursaries. (*see Scholarship Entries section*). These competitive awards are given each year:

At 11+ entry: One Academic Scholarship and one Music Scholarship, each of value up to 25% of the current school fee for seven years.

Sixth Form: Two Academic Scholarships of value up to 50% of the current school fee for two years and one Music Scholarship of value up to 25% of the current school fee for two years.

The school is able to offer a limited number of bursaries at entry to the school at 11+, of value of up to 100% of the current school fee. These bursaries are means tested and reviewed annually. Further information is available from the Bursar.

Fees per term (2008-2009). £4,300.

Situation. The school is situated just outside Regent's Park and is three minutes from Baker Street and Marylebone stations. Victoria and Hampstead buses pass the school.

Charitable status. The Francis Holland (Church of England) Schools Trust Limited is a Registered Charity, number 312745. It exists to provide high quality education for girls and religious instruction in accordance with the principles of the Church of England.

Francis Holland School
Sloane Square

39 Graham Terrace London SW1W 8JF
Tel: 020 7730 2971
Fax: 020 7823 4066
e-mail: office@fhs-sw1.org.uk
website: www.fhs-sw1.org.uk

Founded 1881.

Patron: The Right Revd and Right Hon The Lord Bishop of London

Council:
Chairman: Mrs C Longworth, BA
Vice-Chairman: Mrs S Singer, BA

The Revd J Cave Bergquist, BA
Professor C Carpenter, BA, MA, PhD
Mr C Clark, MA
Mr P Davis, BA, DArch, RIBA, ACArch (Pres)
Mrs A Edelshain, MA, MCIPD
Mrs C Elliott, MA, MBA
Ms G Gourgey, BA
Mrs S Graham-Campbell
Mrs A Grainger, LLB
Mr K Hoggart, BSc, MSc, PhD
Mrs J Khayat, MA
Mr B Lenon, MA
Mr R Lewis, MA
Miss S Mahaffy, BA
Mrs B Mathews, BA, FCA
Mr I A N McIntosh, MA, FCA
Mr C Sheridan
Professor J Yeomans, MA, DPhil
Dr G Young, MB, BS, DCH, MRCPCH

Bursar and Secretary to the Council: Mr C W Martinson, BSc, ARICS, The Bursary, Francis Holland Schools Trust, 35 Bourne Street, London SW1W 8JA.
Tel: 020 7730 8359, e-mail: bursary@fhst.org.uk

***Headmistress*: Miss S J Pattenden**, BSc Durham

Deputy Headmistress: Mrs S Pepper, MA Oxon

Senior Mistress: Miss S Majury, BSc London

Senior School

Full-time Staff:
Mrs E Archer, BSc Brunel (*Physical Education*)
Mr C Bartram, BSc Portsmouth (*Biology/Science*)
Miss E Boon, BA Oxon (*History*)
Mr C Chisnall, BSc UCW Aberystwyth (*Computer Science*)
Mrs K Cronan, BA York (*English*)
Miss S Deadman, BEd Bedford (*Physical Education*)
Mr D Edes, BA Exeter (*Art*)
Miss S Ferro, BA Oxon MA London (*Classics*)
Miss H Ford, BA Cantab (*Mathematics*)
Miss W Grimshaw, BA Manchester (*History*)
Mr M Hill, BA Durham, MSc London (*Geography*)
Miss D Kaleja, I and II Staatsexamen (*German*)

Mr M Kenny, BA Leeds (*Religious Studies*)
Miss M McLaren, BSc Glasgow (*Chemistry/Science*)
Mrs A Margetson, PECert, Australian CPE (*Physical Education*)
Mrs E Nash, BA Durham (*French & Spanish*)
Mrs E Nesbitt, BA Oxon (*Classics*)
Mr C Palmer, BSc NY, USA (*Physics*)
Miss D Powell, BA York (*Biology*)
Mrs C Remy-Miller, BSc, MSc France (*French*)
Ms A Sidwell, BA Liverpool (*Geography*)
Miss A Stevenson, BA Durham (*French & Spanish*)
Miss L Sylvester, BA Leeds (*French & Spanish*)
Dr N Upcott, BSc, PhD Leeds (*Physics/Science*)
Miss H Vickery, MA Cantab, DipRAM, LRAM (*Music*)
Mrs K von Malaisé, MA Cantab (*English*)
Mr P Williams, BA Oxon (*Mathematics*)

Part-time Staff:
Dr G Allen, BA, DPhil Oxon (*Chemistry/Science*)
Mrs J Banks, BA Durham (*English*)
Miss S Bryant, BA, ATC (*Art*)
Ms S Carr-Gomm, BA UEA, MA London (*History of Art*)
Mr D Davies, BA Keele (*Music*)
Ms J de Rome, BEd London, CertEd Homerton (*Art*)
Mrs M Gepfert, BA Maths Essex, MSc (*Computing, Mathematics*)
Mrs P Homer-Norman, BA Exeter, MA (*English*)
Ms M Leaf, BA London (*Drama*)
Mme A Lenec'h, Licence Rouen, MA Connecticut, USA (*French*)
Mrs V Mrowiec, BEd Liverpool (*Physical Education*)
Ms D Ortega, MA London (*Spanish*)
Miss G Stevens, BA Sheffield (*Psychology*)
Ms M Tetzlaff, BA, MTheol London (*Religious Studies*)
Mr K Wadsworth, BSc London (*Economics*)

Junior School
Head of Junior School: Mrs M Bown, DipEd Bishop Otter, CertEd, SRN

Full-time Staff:
Mrs V Adamson, BA OU, CertEd
Mrs G Fall, CertEd Liverpool
Miss E Gallagher, BEd, CertEd London
Miss M Gallagher, CertEd London, BA London DipMathEd
Miss E Horn, NNEB, DBH
Ms J Jeevanjee, Montessori Dip
Mrs A Jones, BA London
Mrs M Law, CertEd Sheffield
Mrs N Mikac
Miss S Rideout, BA King Alfred's
Mrs S Roberts, CertEd London

Part-time:
Mr O-J Ruthven, MusB Manchester (*Music*)
Miss S Pope, BSc City

Visiting Staff:
Mr G Acosta (*Violin*)
Ms G Bailey-Smith (*Jazz Dance*)
Miss J Benson (*Singing*)
Mr Y Bouvy, CertAdvStudies, RAM, Diplôme d'État de Professeur de Musique Traversier (*Flute*)
Mr R Brunning, BSc (*Kick Boxing*)
Miss C Constable, MMus London, BMus, ABSM (*Cello, Piano*)
Miss B Corsi, FTCL (*Clarinet, Recorder, Piano*)
Miss A Cviic, BA, PGDipRCM (*Singing*)
Miss L Duggan, BMus, PG Dip (*Harp*)
Mr J Godfrey, BMus, PGDipRCM (*Percussion*)
Mr N Hawken, BMus (*Saxophone*)
Mrs V Hitchen, RBS, TTCDip, Children's Examiner, RAD (*Ballet*)
Miss M Leaf, BA London (*Speech & Drama*)
Mr S Mantas (*Chess*)
Mr M Mason (*Cricket*)
Mr P Moore, BMus, LRAM, LGSMD, DipRAM, PPRAM (*Piano*)
Mrs S Pratschke, MMus (*Singing*)
Mrs S Shaub, LRAM, GRSM (*Piano*)
Miss V Smith, BMus RCM (*Violin*)
Mr J Sparks, BA, MA, FCCM (*Guitar*)
Ms S Stewart, BMus, LRSM, PGDipRCM (*Singing*)
Miss V Taylor (*Pottery*)
Miss E Tingey, BMus (*Oboe*)
Mr R Turner, BMus (*Trumpet*)
Mr C Weale, BMus, PGDipRCM (*Piano*)
Mr W Whitehead, BA, MMus, FRCO, ARAM (*Organ*)

Librarian: Miss S Bassington, BA London, DipLib, MLS, ALA
Lab Technicians: Mrs C Bradshaw, Mr P Bannister, BSc New South Wales
Computer Technician: Mr P da Costa, BSc
Registrar: Mrs J Ruthven, BA
School Secretary: Miss V Phillips

Numbers and age of entry. There are 450 Day Girls in the School and entry by the School's own examination is at 4+ for the Junior School (ages 4–11), 11+ for the Senior School (ages 11–18) (member of London Schools consortium) and 16+ for Sixth Form.

Curriculum and Aims. The school aims to provide a strong academic education and girls are prepared for GCSE, AS and A Level and admission to Universities and Colleges of Art and Music. Full advantage is taken of the school's proximity to museums and art galleries.

Junior School. There is a Junior Department attached to the school.

Religious Education. The school's foundation is Anglican but girls of other faiths are welcomed.

Physical Education. Hockey, Netball, Volleyball, Gymnastics, Athletics, Tennis and Swimming are taken. Senior girls have a choice of other activities as well including Squash, Step Aerobics, Jazz and Rowing. Optional activities open to girls are Kick Boxing, Fencing, Rowing and Jazz.

Fees per term (2007-2008). £3,515–£4,145.

Scholarships and Bursaries. (*see Scholarship Entries section*). There are the following competitive awards each year:

At 11+: 1 Academic and 1 Music scholarship, both up to the value of 25% of fees.

Sixth Form: 4 Academic scholarships (3 internal, 1 external) up to the value of 50% of fees and 1 Music scholarship up to the value of 25% of fees for the two years leading to A Level.

3 up to full fees Bursaries are available at 11+ and one at 14+.

For daughters of Clergy there is a remission of one-third of the School Fee.

Charitable status. The Francis Holland (Church of England) Schools Trust Limited is a Registered Charity, number 312745. It exists to provide high quality education for girls.

Gateways School

Harewood Leeds LS17 9LE
Tel: 0113 288 6345
Fax: 0113 288 6148
e-mail: gateways@gatewayschool.co.uk
website: www.gatewayschool.co.uk

Governing Body:
Chairman: Mr M Shaw, Leeds

Revd Canon A F Bundock, Rector of Leeds
Mrs L Croston, BSc Hons, PGCE, ALCM
Mr J D Halliday, ACA, Ripon
Professor D Hogg, BSc Hons, MSc Hons, DPhil
Mrs P Hemming, DL, York
Dr S Lee, Northumberland
Mr R Marsh, BSc, FCA, Leeds
Mr K G Nussey, Wetherby
Professor D Shorrocks-Taylor, Leeds
Dr R H Taylor, BEd, MA, PhD, Harrogate
Mr V H Watson, CBE, LLD, DL, Leeds
Dr C Wilson, BSc Hons, MBBS, MD, FRCP
Mr R Webster, BSc, Leeds

Staff:

***Headmistress*: Mrs D Davidson**, BA Hons, MEd (*History*)

Deputy Headmistress: Mrs K T M Matthews, MA, BSc Hons, PGCE (*Mathematics*)
Head of Preparatory School: Mrs S A Wilcox, BEd Hons

Miss K Ashurst, BSc Hons, PGCE (*Physics*)
Mrs C Bartle, NNEB (*Head of Pre-Prep*)
Miss A Berntsen, BA Hons Pre-School Teaching (*Foundation Stage*)
Miss E Blackwell (*Foundation Stage*)
Mrs E A Bottomley, BEd (*Physical Education*)
Mr N Box, BEd Hons (*Physical Education*)
Mrs G A Brennan, BA Hons, PGCE (*French and Spanish*)
Mrs K Brown, BEd Hons (*Director of Studies – Prep*)
Mrs R Burton, BSc Hons, PGCE (*Assistant Head Pastoral, Chemistry*)
Mrs L Casper, CertEd, AdvDipSecEd (*Business Studies*)
Miss C Davidson, BTEC Level IV Nursery Nurse (*Nursery Nurse*)
Mrs A Davies, BMus, LTCL (*Music*)
Mr M Davison, BA Hons, PGCE (*Head of Sixth Form, English, Media Studies*)
Mrs S Derrig, BEd Hons
Mr P Dewhurst, BMus, MMus, PGCE (*Music*)
Mr P Dutton, MA, LTCL, PGCE (*Music*)
Miss S Ellison, BTEC, FdA in Early Years (*Foundation Stage*)
Mrs J Emerick, BA Hons, Dip Dramatic Art (*English and Drama*)
Miss F Feeney, BA Hons, PGCE (*Form Lower II*)
Mrs D L Fellerman, BA Hons, PGCE (*Art and Design*)
Mrs S M Finan, BEd Hons (*History*)
Miss C Fox, BA Hons, QTS (*Physical Education*)
Mrs M Gilliver, BA Hons, PGCE (*Form Lower II*)
Miss E M Green, CertEd, DPSE (*Learning Support*)
Mrs S Harrison, BS Hons, PGCE (*English*)
Mrs E Hayward, BSc Hons, PGCE (*Geography, Psychology*)
Mrs B Hetmanski, BEd Hons (*Religious Studies*)
Mrs A Hill, BEd, CertEd (*Art*)
Mrs G M Holloway, CertEd (*Reception*)
Mrs S Holmes, BA Hons, QTS (*Head of Lower School, Technology*)
Miss A Jeffords, BA Hons, QTS (*Form Upper II*)
Mrs J Johnson, MBA, BSBA, PGCE (*Mathematics, ICT*)
Mr C Keeton, BA Hons, PGCE (*Art and Design Technology*)
Mrs D Kennedy, BSc, PGCE (*Mathematics*)
Dr C Leachman, BA, MA, PhD, PGCE (*History, Classics*)
Mr S Llewellyn, BA Hons, PGCE (*Classics*)
Mrs C McDermott, MEd, BA, PGCE (*Assistant Head CPD, Head of Humanities Faculty, Geography*)
Dr S Newton, BSc, PhD, PGCE (*Physics, Biology*)
Mrs J Ralph, MA, BA Hons, PGCE (*German and French*)
Mrs T Richmond, BSc Hons, PGCE (*Mathematics and ICT*)
Mrs J Rooney, FdA in Early Years, NNEB (*Foundation Stage*)
Mrs B Ryatt, BSc Hons, PGCE (*Mathematics*)
Mr Q Sands, BEd Hons (*Drama and Theatre Studies*)
Mrs H Sharpe, BA Hons, PGCE (*Modern Languages*)
Miss H Shipton, BA Hons, QTS (*Reception*)
Mrs A Starkey-Smith, BEd Hons (*Form Upper II*)
Miss J Suggitt, BEd Hons (*Form Lower II*)
Mr W Swan, BA Hons, CertEd (*English*)
Mrs K Titman, BEng, PGCE (*ICT*)
Mrs A Tunley, MPhil, BA Hons, CertEd (*Religious Studies*)
Mrs H Wallis, BA Hons QTS (*Lower III*)
Miss R Walton, BSc Hons, PGCE
Mrs F Wilson, BA Hons, PGCE (*Spanish*)
Mrs D Wilson, BA Hons, PGCE (*French and German*)
Mrs L Wood, BSc Hons, PGCE (*Chemistry*)

Associate Staff:
Miss K Bland (*Teaching Assistant*)
Miss S Britton (*Assistant Chef*)
Mrs L Brydon (*Assistant Chef*)
Mrs A Chatto, CIMA (*Business Manager*)
Mrs J Chennells, BA Hons, MHSM, DipHS (*Extra-curricular Coordinator*)
Mr S Clark (*Laboratory Technician*)
Mrs D Dixon (*Registrar*)
Mrs E Donovan, CertEd, CertLib (*Development Coordinator*)
Mrs S Drake (*Learning Support Assistant*)
Mrs S Forbes (*Catering Assistant*)
Mrs J Foster, BA Hons (*Teaching Assistant*)
Mr L A Goodwin, MCSE, RICS, LIOB (*Network Manager*)
Mrs N Harris (*PA to the Headmistress*)
Mr J Hawkins, BMusTech (*Performing Arts Technician*)
Mrs L Holloran (*Catering Assistant*)
Mrs B Leeming (*Learning Support Assistant*)
Mr R Lumb (*Maintenance Supervisor*)
Mrs G MacHugh (*School Secretary*)
Mrs N Marathoo, LLB Hons (*Learning Support Assistant*)
Mr R Maxfield (*Maintenance Supervisor*)
Miss K O'Callaghan (*Development Administrator*)
Mrs C Purnell-Bower (*Learning Support Assistant*)
Mr T Smith (*Maintenance Supervisor*)
Mrs D Stevenson (*Facilities Coordinator*)
Miss G Suwali (*Nursery Nurse*)
Mr R Swain (*ICT Technician*)
Mrs C Thomas-Varcoe, BA Hons, MA (*Marketing and Communications Manager*)
Mr B Wallace (*Catering Manager*)
Mrs D White, RGN (*School Nurse*)
Mrs S Wood (*Finance Assistant*)
Mrs S Wright (*School Secretary*)

Visiting Teachers:
Miss W Crawford, LTCL (*Classical Guitar*)
Mr D Darling, BA Hons, QTC (*Voice and Piano*)
Mrs P Dunford, STCL (*Voice*)
Mrs H Fitton (*Oboe*)
Mrs E Green, ARMCM, ARNCM (*Violin*)
Mr G Kilroy (*Percussion*)
Mrs D Lee, CT ABRSM (*Woodwind*)
Mr D Longden, GCLCM (*Keyboard*)
Mr D Roberts (*Brass*)
Mrs S Robertson, DipMusEd, LTCL (*Piano*)
Mr C Shaw (*Guitar*)
Miss S Shelton (*Flute*)

Gateways is a forward-looking, friendly and successful school for girls aged 2 to 18 and boys aged 2 to 7. The school was founded in 1941.

The ethos and objectives of Gateways School are to provide, within a disciplined framework, the opportunities and encouragement for every pupil to achieve his or her personal best. The environment is safe and caring, and pupils develop self-confidence, self-discipline and a breadth of interests which prepares them for an enjoyable and successful life. Equipped with excellent academic qualifications all girls go on to further education.

Teaching and Learning. The curriculum at Gateways is broad and challenging and pupils are always encouraged to think for themselves, and to become inquiring and independent learners. French and Latin are taught in the Prep School and all girls entering the High School study three modern languages as well as Latin. The three sciences are taught separately and there is an opportunity to take up Greek. A wide range of subjects is offered at AS and A2 Level, including Critical Thinking and Psychology. The Stella programme ensures that the most able girls are challenged and support is available to help individuals with specific learning needs.

Pupils participate in a variety of extra-curricular activities including Drama, Music, Sport, the Duke of Edinburgh's Award Scheme, World Challenge, Young Enterprise and Community Link.

Facilities. The school has an ongoing programme of development to renew and enhance its facilities. Recent projects have included a purpose-built Junior School, Nursery School, Performing Arts Centre, Sports Hall and Fitness Suite, extensive ICT facilities, The Cox-Simpson Library, and specialist new facilities for Science, Languages, Mathematics and Business Studies.

The Gateways Community. The Friends of Gateways (PTA) and The Old Gatewegians Association both play an active role within the school community. The Development Coordinator is responsible for alumni and development matters and is always delighted to hear from Old Gatewegians.

Location and Transport. Gateways School is set in beautiful parkland in the village of Harewood, just north of Leeds. The former Dower House of the Harewood Estate forms the heart of the School. Gateways is within easy reach of Harrogate, Wetherby, Otley and the surrounding villages. A comprehensive school transport service is available.

Scholarships. (*see Scholarship Entries section*).

Fees per term (2008-2009). High School £3,093; Prep £2,412; Pre-Prep £1,971; Lower Reception: £2,169 full day, £1,704 school day, £1,266 mornings, £1,053 afternoons; Nursery: competitive rates for various daily sessions available on request.

Charitable status. Gateways Educational Trust Limited is a Registered Charity, number 529206. It exists to offer a broad education to girls aged 2–18 and boys aged 2–7, where they are encouraged to strive for excellence to the best of their ability.

The Godolphin and Latymer School

Iffley Road Hammersmith London W6 0PG
Tel: 020 8741 1936; 020 8563 7649 (Bursar)
Fax: 020 8735 9520
e-mail: office@godolphinandlatymer.com
website: www.godolphinandlatymer.com

Motto: *Francha Leale Toge*

Foundation: Godolphin and Latymer, originally a boys' school, became a girls' day school in 1905. It was aided by the London County Council from 1920 onwards and by the Inner London Education Authority when it received Voluntary Aided status after the 1944 Education Act. Rather than become part of a split-site Comprehensive school it reverted to Independent status in 1977.

Governors:
Chairman: Lady Patten, BA

Dr J S Axford, BSc, MD, FRCP
Miss J Barfield, MBE, AA, Dip RIBA
Mr J B Boyer, BA, MSc
Mrs L Bown, MA, MBA
Mrs C Davies, BA, ATD
Mr A Fry, BA
Mr J R Gabitass, MA
Mr C S H Hampton, BA, FCA
Ms S J D Illingworth
Mrs A J S Paines, BA
Professor Dame Jessica Rawson, DLitt, FBA
Mr R D Sidery, BSc Econ, FCA, FCMA, MIMC
Miss J M Taylor, BSc

Clerk to the Governors: Mr A F B Harvey, FCA, JDip MA, AGI Arb

Staff:

***Head Mistress*: Miss Margaret Rudland**, BSc London
from January 2009: Mrs R Mercer, BA Hons London, PGCE Oxford

Deputy Head Mistress: Mrs E Gleadhill, MA Oxon

Senior Mistresses:
Miss J A Hodgkins, BEd CNAA, MA Brunel
Mrs S Kinross, BA Exeter
Mrs C M Trimming, BA London, BA Open

Teaching Staff:
Miss S Adams, BEd Melbourne
Miss S Adey, BEd Brighton
Mrs S Andreyeva, BA Leningrad
Miss A J Arthurton, BSc Bristol
Mrs S Banks, L-ès-L Paris
Miss K Barac, BSc, BEd British Columbia
Mr J M Barot, MSc Open, MSc Durham, MA Cantab
Mr P Barnes, BSc London
Mr A Belfrage, CertEd Leeds, Dip Computer Ed WLIHE
Mr J F Bell, BA Cantab, MA Sussex
Mrs M A Beresford, BA Lancaster
Dr P Bickley, BA London, PhD London
Miss R L Biggins, BA Leeds College of Music
Mrs C L Blackman, BA Durham
Dr C R Bradstreet, PhD London, MA Constanta, BA Leicester
Dr A C Bunting, PhD Soton, MA Soton, BA Soton
Miss A M Clark, BA Oxon
Mrs M Cockbain, MA Oxon
Ms D Colf, MSc Bucharest
Miss L Cooper, MA Wimbledon School of Art, BA Staffordshire
Mrs N Cooper, BSc Leicester
Mr W Cooper, MPhil Cantab, BA Cantab
Mr P Cosgrove, BA Bristol College of Art & Design
Mr P M Culling, MA Cantab, LRSM
Mrs G Cuming, MA Sorbonne
Mr A Davies, BA Cardiff Institute
Mr Q J Davies, MA Keele
Mrs A Devadoss, BSc London
Mr G C de Villiers, BA RAM, LRAM
Miss C E Drennan, BA Oxon
Miss E C Elfick, BEd Exeter
Mrs U D Fenton, Diploma PH Freiburg
Mr W A G Ford, BA London
Miss E S Fox, MA Oxon, MSc LSE
Mr A J Francis, BSc Bristol
Miss S V R Fryer, BA Bristol
Mrs C E C Gatward, BA Oxon
Miss J Gibbon, BPhil Oxon, BA Oxon
Mrs R A Haddon, BA Oxon
Mrs V A Halls, BA Sorbonne
Mrs J H Hardie, BA Oxon
Ms R E Hart, BA Oxon
Miss K Healy, BA Leicester
Mrs E M Henley, BA Leeds, MPhil Leeds
Mrs I C Hill, BA Cantab, LPC Guildford College of Law
Mrs R J Hollis, BSc Portsmouth, PhD Birmingham
Miss G Hulme, BSc London

Dr C Jacobi, PhD London, MA Northumbria, MA London, BA Anglia
Miss I Jacobson, BA Bristol
Dr I W Jones, PhD CNAA, MSc Cardiff, BSc Liverpool
Miss A M Kersten, BA Otago
Miss S Kingston-Martin, MA Chelsea College of Art, BA London
Dr N Le Nezet, PhD Lyon3, BA Lyon
Mrs C Lee, MA London, BEd Exeter
Mr A Leithes, BSc London
Mr K Llewellyn, MA London, BSc London
Mr J H Lloyd, MA Leeds, BTech Brunel
Mrs J M Mackenzie, BA Southampton
Mr P D Martin, BA Cantab
Mrs H Mason, MA London, BA Durham
Miss H J Matthews, BA Cantab
Mr C J McCarthy, MSc Aberystwyth, BA Keele
Mr J McGrath, MSc Cranfield, BSc Wales
Mr P McGuigan, BA Open, CertEd St Mary's, Twickenham
Mrs L G Norrie, BSc Newcastle
Miss L Ockenden, MA RCA, BA Central St Martins
Mrs D O'Connor, MSc London, BSc Galway
Miss L R Padalino, BA Bologna
Miss A Prodhomme, BA Sorbonne
Mr S Raleigh, BA Cantab
Mrs S H Rendall, BA Manchester
Mr S J Ridgwell, MPhil Swansea
Miss K M Rixon, BEd Sydney
Mrs E A Rooke, BSc London
Miss K Routledge, BPE Ed Auckland College
Miss M Row, MSc Brunel, BSc Brunel
Miss A M Salmon, BA London
Mrs A R Sellars, BSc Cardiff
Mrs M Sergeant, MA Cantab
Miss L H Shackleton, BA Cantab
Miss P M Shadlock, MA Sheffield, BA London
Mr A Shah, MEd Sheffield, BA City
Dr L G Shaw, BA Cantab,
Dr J M Stevens, PhD London, MA London
Mrs S V Sutherland, BA Aberystwyth
Mr B Tait, BA Central School of Speech & Drama
Mrs M T Troya, BA Santa Cruz de Tenerife
Miss C E Vickers, BA Oxon
Miss S von Haniel, MA Edinburgh
Ms J A Waltham, BSc Manchester
Miss A Weldon, BSc Durham
Dr A R Werker, PhD Cantab, BSc Bangor
Mr D White, MEd Warwick, BSc Leeds
Mr N S White, BSc London
Dr K M Wolfe, PhD London, BD London, Dip Theology Geneva, DipEd London
Mrs J Wright, BEd Bath College

Visiting teachers in Music and Speech Training:
Miss R Andreiser, LLCM
Miss R Buxton, BMus RCM, LGSM Guildhall
Mrs J Clark-Maxwell, BMus London, LTCL
Mrs H Davey, BMus Guildhall
Miss E Doroszkowska, BMus Manchester, RNCM
Miss M Drower, ARCM
Miss C J Egan, BMus London, PgDip Birmingham
Mrs K Feltrin, MA Cracow, PGDip Guildhall
Miss V L Galer, BA York
Mrs J Garcia BMus Surrey
Mrs K Hempsall, BA Warwick
Miss G James, AGSM Guildhall
Miss R A Latham, BMus, ARCM
Mr M Lewington, DipRCM
Miss C-C Lim, MMus RCM, LRSM, FRCL, LTCL
Miss A J Lower, MMus, BMus, BA, Queensland
Mr A Mitchell, GMus RNCM, PPRNCM
Miss C Morphett, BMus Sydney
Ms V L Munday, BMus Sydney
Mr D Neville, BA RCM
Mrs R Richardson, MMus Guildhall
Ms C Riley MMus Auckland NZ, LRSM
Miss C Sampson, BA Cantab
Miss J A Staniforth, Virtuosité DipRAM, GRSM, DipALCM
Miss E Tingey, LWCMD, ACC WCMD, TCM
Miss L Tricker, BEd CSSD
Mrs P Whinnett, GMus, RNCM
Miss A Whittlesea, BMus RCM, LRAM
Mr R K J Williams, M Mus Guildhall, BMus Exeter
Miss E Zakrzewska, BMus RAM, RSAMD, DipRAM, LRAM

Bursar: Mrs D Lynch, BSc Kingston, FCCA
Registrar: Mrs F R Beckwith
Head Mistress's Secretary: Mrs V S Cox, BA
School Doctor: Dr L B Miller, MA Cantab, MB, BChir, DRCOG, MRCGP
School Nurse: Mrs C A Owen, SRN

Godolphin and Latymer is an independent day school for 700 girls, aged 11 to 18. The school stands in a four acre site in Hammersmith, near Hammersmith Broadway and excellent public transport. The original Victorian building has been extended to include a gymnasium, pottery room, computer studies room and language laboratory. Buildings opened in 1991 offer science and technology laboratories, art studios, a dark room and an ecology garden. This redevelopment enabled a refurbishment of the Library and Music and Drama facilities. In 1993 a grass playing field was converted to an all-weather surface for hockey and tennis. In Autumn 2000 we opened a new building to provide a Sixth Form Centre, specialist room for Technology and Pottery, four classrooms and a servery. From September 2006, the school is leasing St John's Church and its Vicarage, both adjacent to the existing site. The Vicarage, renamed the Margaret Gray Building, is providing additional classrooms. The new Rudland Music School will be opened in the Autumn Term 2008 and the renovated church, The Bishop Centre, for the performing arts is expected to be completed in early Spring 2009.

The Godolphin and Latymer School aims to provide a stimulating, enjoyable environment and to foster intellectual curiosity and independence. We strive for academic excellence, emphasising the development of the individual, within a happy, supportive community.

Girls are expected to show a strong commitment to study and are encouraged to participate in a range of extra-curricular activities. We aim to develop the girls' self-respect and self-confidence, together with consideration and care for others so that they feel a sense of responsibility within the school and the wider community.

Pastoral Care. The school has a close relationship with parents, and every member of the staff takes an interest in the girls' academic and social welfare. Each girl has a form teacher and a deputy form teacher and there is a Head of Lower School, Head of Middle School and a Head of Sixth Form, each with deputies.

Curriculum. We offer a broad, balanced curriculum including appropriate education concerning personal, health, ethical and social issues. During the first three years Philosophy and Religion, English, French, Latin, History, Geography, Mathematics, Physics, Chemistry, Biology, Food Technology, Design Technology, Art, Music, Technology, and Physical Education are studied. In Year 8 there is a choice between Spanish and German and in Year 10 Italian, Russian, Greek and Classical Civilisation become available. Girls take ten or eleven subjects to GCSE. Drama is studied in Years 7, 8 and 10.

In the Sixth Form there is a choice of curriculum between the Advanced Level (AS and A2) and the International Baccalaureate Diploma. All subjects offered to GCSE can be continued into the Sixth Form with the addition of Ancient History, Drama and Theatre Studies, Economics, Government and Politics and History of Art. Sixth Formers also follow a General Studies programme (AL) or Theory of Knowledge (IB), including lectures given by outside speakers.

The Sixth Form. The Sixth Form facilities include a Common Room, Work Room and Terrace. The 200 girls in the Sixth Form play an important role in the school, taking responsibility for many extra-curricular activities, producing form plays and organising clubs. They undertake voluntary work and lead our social service programme. Almost all proceed to Higher Education degree courses (including an average of 15 a year to Oxford and Cambridge).

Careers Advice. A strong careers team offers advice to girls and parents. Our specialist room is well stocked with up-to-date literature and course information, and lectures and work shadowing are arranged.

The Creative Arts. Music and Drama flourish throughout the school. The Rudland Music School will have outstanding facilities for music: 20 soundproofed rooms for individual or group work, a recording studio, ICT suite and two classrooms which will open out into a very large rehearsal space for choirs and orchestras. There are four choirs, two orchestras and several small ensembles, and a joint orchestra and choral society with Latymer Upper School. Individual music lessons are offered in many different instruments. Each year there is a pantomime, form play competition, and Year 10 and Sixth Form plays as well as the school productions. The refurbished church, to be known as The Bishop Centre, will offer a superb performing arts space for music drama and dance. Venues out of school have included the Cochrane Theatre, Lyric Theatre, Riverside Studios and the Edinburgh Festival.

Physical Education is a vital part of a girl's development as an individual and as a team member. Younger girls play netball, hockey, tennis and rounders and have gymnastic and dance lessons. In the senior years there is a wider range of activities offered, including rowing and squash off-site. There is a gymnasium and fitness room.

Extra-Curricular Activities. The many opportunities for extra-curricular activities include the British Association of Young Scientists, Computing, Chess, the Young Enterprise Scheme, Debating, Creative Writing, Classics Club and the Duke of Edinburgh's Award Scheme, as well as a wide range of sporting activities such as karate, fencing and triathlon.

Activities outside the School. We organise language exchanges to Hamburg, Nantes and Moscow, a musical exchange to Hamburg and Sixth Form work experience in Versailles and Berlin. There is also an exchange with a school in New York. Each year, Year 9 girls ski in the USA and there are study visits to Spain and History of Art visits to Paris, Bruges, Venice and Florence and, for the Upper Sixth, a visit to the Sinai Desert.

We take advantage of our London location by arranging visits to conferences, theatres, exhibitions and galleries. Field courses are an integral part of study in Biology and Geography.

Admission. Girls are normally admitted into Year 7 (First Year Entrance) or into our Sixth Form. Examinations for First Year entrance are held in January and for the Sixth Form in November. There are occasional vacancies in other years. Entry is on a competitive basis.

Fees per term (from January 2008). £4,490. Fees may be raised after a term's notice. Private tuition in music and speech and drama are extra. Most girls have school lunch, but it is an option from Year 8.

Scholarships. (*see Scholarship Entries section*). There are music scholarships available on entry to Year 7 and, in the Sixth Form, music and art scholarships. All scholarships are worth up to 30% of fees and may be topped up by means-tested bursaries in cases of need.

Bursaries. A number of school bursaries are available annually.

Uniform. Uniform is worn by girls up to and including Year 11.

Charitable status. The Godolphin and Latymer School is a Registered Charity, number 312699. It exists to provide education to girls aged 11 to 18.

The Godolphin School

Milford Hill Salisbury SP1 2RA
Tel: 01722 430500
Preparatory School: 01722 430652
Fax: 01722 430501
e-mail: admissions@godolphin.wilts.sch.uk
website: www.godolphin.org

Motto: *Franc Ha Leal Eto Ge* (Frankness and Loyalty be Yours)

Founded by Elizabeth Godolphin in 1707; date of the will of the Foundress, 24 June 1726; a new scheme made by the Charity Commissioners and approved by HM, 1886, and re-issued by the Charity Commissioners in February 1986. The Godolphin School is an independent boarding and day school for girls aged 11–18, with its own purpose-built preparatory day school for girls from the age of 3. Of the 435 girls in the senior school, over 130 are in the Sixth Form.

Governing Body:
G Fletcher, Esq (*Chairman*)
M R T Bryer Ash, Esq
Lady Ruth Hawley
Mrs S Herd
Mrs Susan Key, BSc
J S Lipa, Esq, LLB, MJur, FINZ, ICFM
S G Metcalf, Esq, MA
R E T Nicholl, Esq, BA
M J Nicholson, Esq
The Revd C Mitchell-Innes
Mrs Sarah Streatfeild
Mrs Susan Thomson
Mrs T Watkins, BA
Dr B Whitworth

Bursar and Clerk to the Governors: K G M Flynn, Esq, BSc, FCMA
Assistant Bursar: J Walsh, Esq

***Headmistress*: Miss M J Horsburgh**, MA Oxon

Deputy Head: R T W Dain, Esq, MA Oxon
Director of Studies: Mrs H Portas, BA Wales
Admissions Secretary: Mrs V Power, BSc Hons London

Staff:
* *Head of Department/Subject*

Religious Studies:
*F R Spencer, Esq, BA Essex, BTh Southampton
P Sharkey, Esq, BA London

English:
*Mrs J Carlisle, BA London
Mrs M Johns, BA Wales
Mrs L Hodgson, TCert Bromley, AMBDA
Mrs T Nicholls, MA Keele, BEd Cambridge
Mrs R Carville, BA Hons Birmingham
Ms S Jones, BA Hons Wales
R T W Dain, Esq, MA Oxon

History:
*Miss J Miller, BA Belfast, MEd Open
Dr A Dougall, Esq, LLB London, MA, PhD Southampton
Mrs S Eggleton, MA Aberdeen
Miss M J Horsburgh, MA Oxon

Mrs H Portas, BA Wales

Psychology:
Miss A Bowler, BA Manchester, BA Wimbledon

Business Studies and Economics:
*D J Miller, Esq, BA Nottingham
Mrs K Naylor, BSc Cardiff, PGCE

Geography:
*Miss S L Stone, BSc Swansea
Mrs C Morgan, BSc Wales
Mrs D Osborne, BEd Southampton
Mrs C Vaughn, BA Manchester

Classics:
*Miss A Codd, MA Oxon
P Farrier, Esq, BA Durham
Mrs S Radice, BA Reading
Mrs M Highcock, MA Cantab

Modern Languages:
*Miss F Bolton, MA Oxon, PGCE
Mrs S Smith, MA Cantab (*Deputy Head of Department*)
Ms M A Cibis, BA, MA Sheffield
Mrs C Dunning, L-ès-L Bordeaux
M Dunning, Esq, MSc Southampton, DSE Madrid
Dr L Rojas-Hindmarsh, DPhil Leeds
Miss M Reyes Avila Cabrera, Lda Alicante
Miss S Naranjo Uroz Almeria
Mrs S Dawson (*Assistentin*)
Mlle M Beillet (*Assistentin*)

Mathematics:
*K J Davis, Esq, BSc City University
(*to be appointed*)
Mrs K Healey, BSc Bristol
Mrs J L Robson, BSc Bristol
Mrs R C Stratton, BSc Exeter
Mrs N Owers, BA Hons Nottingham, PGCE
Mrs A Bacon, BSc Hons Southampton PGCE

Science:
A J Brown, Esq, BSc Dunelm (**Chemistry, *Science*)
Dr B Medany, BSc London, PhD Nottingham (**Biology*)
Mr J Eyre, BSc Hons, MSc Southampton (*responsibility for Physics*)
Miss H Broughton, BSc Edinburgh
P Hill, Esq, BSc London
Dr C Thrower, PhD, MSc, BSc Manchester
Miss R Gillingham, BSc Hons London
(*to be appointed*)

Technology:
*M Berry, Esq, BEd Leeds, MA Open
Mrs P Parry-Jones, BSc Bath College of Higher Education
Mrs C Complin, BSc Bath College of Higher Education

Information and Communication Technology:
*Miss J A Thomas, BEd Worcester
Mrs W Laptain, BEd Manchester
D J Miller, Esq, BA Nottingham
Mrs S Eggleton, MA Aberdeen

Art and Design:
*N Eggleton, Esq, BA London, ATC
Miss A Bowler, BA Manchester, BA Wimbledon
Mrs S Duggan, BA Winchester
Miss E Findley, BA Leeds Metropolitan
Mrs J Palmer, MA Northumbria
C Wright, Esq, BA Napier
Mrs J G Whiteley, BA Camberwell

History of Art:
*Mrs S Radice, BA Reading

Music:
*R A Highcock, Esq, BMus London
W P Ings, Esq, BA Cantab
Mrs O Sparkhall, BA Dunelm

Instrumental Staff and Ensemble Coaches:
Miss S Cox, BA
Mrs G Cullingford
N Ellis, Esq
Mrs A Felton
G Green, Esq, GMus, RNCM
C Hobkirk, Esq, BA MusEd, ARCO
D Kennell, Esq
R Leighton Boyce, Esq
Mrs J Littlemore, BMus, LRAM
Mrs C Long, GTCL, LTCL
Mrs L Margetts, GRNSM
M Marshall, Esq, MMus, BA Oxon, LGSM
Ms S McKenzie-Park
P Moore, Esq, BMus, LRAM, LGSMD
R Preston, Esq, RMBS Retd, MISM
J Sharp, Esq, RMBS Retd, MISM
Miss C Stevens
Miss S Stocks, LRAM, LGSM
Miss V Walton, ALCM, LLCM, GLCM
M Wilkinson, Esq, CertEd

Physical Education:
*Mrs S Pokai, BA Brighton
Mrs W Laptain, BEd Manchester
Mrs L Norris, BSc Hons Loughborough
Mrs S Ramsdale, BEd Liverpool
Miss A J Wells, BA Manchester, PGSC Physical Education
Miss S Trentham, BSc Hons Cardiff
D J Miller, Esq, BA Nottingham

Drama:
*D Hallen, Esq, BA Hons Middlesex, PGCE
Mrs L Hodgson, TCert Bromley, AMBDA
Miss N Strode, BA Cardiff

EFL Coach: Mrs M Dance
Speech and Drama Coach: Mrs M Ferris, LGSM, LTCL
Chaplain: The Revd J Ball, BEd Lancaster
Librarian: Mrs H Clarkson, BSc Bristol, ALA
Senior Tutor and Higher Education Adviser: Dr A Dougall, LLB London, MA, PhD Southampton
Careers Adviser: Mrs B Ferguson, BA Hons Newcastle upon Tyne
Upper School Tutor: Dr C Thrower, BSc Plymouth, MSc Exeter, PhD Manchester
Middle School Tutor: Mrs S Eggleton, MA Aberdeen
Lower School Tutor: Miss J Miller, BA Belfast

Further Learning:
Mrs D Bentley, BA Exeter, SpLD
Mrs J Priest, BA Open, DipCDT, DipSpLD

Housemistresses and Deputy Housemistresses:
School House & Sixth Form Centre Coordinators:
Mrs L Hodgson, TCert Bromley, AMBDA, Ms S Jones, BA Hons Wales
Douglas:
Mrs P Loxton, CertEd Sussex, Miss M Reyes Avila Cabrera, Lda Alicante
Hamilton:
Mrs W Laptain, BEd Manchester, Mrs G Wasley
Jerred:
Miss E Findley, BA Leeds Metropolitan, Mrs J Palmer, MA Northumbria
Methuen:
Mrs S Ramsdale, BEd Liverpool, Miss J Tatem, BEd Southampton

Head of Development: (*to be appointed*)

Sanatorium:
Mrs G Davey, RGN

Mrs V Block, RGN
Mrs R Nicholls, RGN
Mrs J Kennerson, RGN
Mrs J Palk

The Godolphin School stands in 16 acres of landscaped grounds on the edge of the historic cathedral city of Salisbury, overlooking open countryside.

A strong academic life combines with thriving art, drama, music and sport. A five-studio art centre provides excellent art and design facilities, while the Blackledge Theatre provides a professional environment for drama and music performance. Other notable developments include the Baxter Pool and Fitness Centre, a new boarding house and a dedicated Sixth Form Centre, the latter providing a focus for careers and higher education advice, and the Sixth Form social programme, as well as study-bedrooms, work space and recreational areas. Sciences are taught within the well-equipped laboratories and have a strong tradition of Oxbridge success. The whole site is served by a wireless network.

Religious Instruction. Godolphin has strong affiliations with the Church of England, but religious instruction covers all the major world faiths.

Curriculum. High academic standards (84.8% A and B grades at A level and 64.1% A and A* grades at GCSE in 2006) are combined with an exceptional range of clubs, societies and weekend activities; also an outstanding programme of trips and expeditions. Activities include: cookery, photography, Duke of Edinburgh's Award, Combined Cadet Force, community service, debating, creative writing, academic societies and wide ranging opportunities in art, drama, music and sport. 24 subjects are available at A Level, and virtually all students continue to higher education, most to universities, including Oxbridge; some to art colleges, drama schools and music conservatoires. There is considerable emphasis on Careers guidance, including an excellent work shadowing scheme.

Physical Education. Strong sporting record with pupils regularly selected for county and regional teams; a few at national level. 22 sporting options include lacrosse, hockey, netball, tennis, athletics, swimming, gymnastics, dance, rounders and cross-country. Each girl is encouraged to find at least one sport she really enjoys during her time at Godolphin.

Entrance Examination. Generally through Common Entrance Examination for Girls' Schools Ltd at 11+, 12+ and 13+. Godolphin's own examination and interview for Sixth Form candidates.

Scholarships and Bursaries. (*see Scholarship Entries section*).

(a) 11+, 12+ and 13+ Academic, Art (13+ only), Music and Sports Scholarships are awarded for outstanding merit and promise. It is likely that a music award would only be made to a candidate who has attained at least Grade 4 at 11+ (Grade 6 at 13+) on one instrument.
(b) Sixth Form Academic, Art, Drama, Music and Sports scholarships are also available.
(c) Six means-tested Foundation Bursaries, each worth 70% of the fees, are available from time to time to boarding candidates from single parent, divorced or separated families who have been brought up as members of the Church of England.
(d) The Old Godolphin Bursary, a means-tested bursary worth up to 50% of the boarding fees, is awarded from time to time by the Old Godolphin Association to the daughter of an Old Godolphin.

Fees per term (2008-2009). Boarders £7,397, Day Girls £5,093, Prep School £1,653–£3,210. Fees include tuition, textbooks, stationery, sanatorium, laundry, and most weekday and weekend clubs and activities.

Extra Subjects. Individual tuition in music, speech and drama, Italian, tennis, fencing, judo, EFL and learning support.

Old Godolphin Association. *Secretary*: Miss H Duder, Keith Cottage, Cold Ash, Thatcham, Berkshire RG18 9PT, or via Development Office, Tel: 01722 430570.

Charitable status. The Godolphin School is a Registered Charity, number 309488. Its object is to provide and conduct in or near Salisbury a boarding and day school for girls.

Greenacre School for Girls

Sutton Lane Banstead Surrey SM7 3RA
Tel: 01737 352114
Fax: 01737 373485
e-mail: admin@greenacre.surrey.sch.uk
website: www.greenacre.surrey.sch.uk

Motto: *Fides et opera*

Council:
Chair: Miss G Smith
Mr N Beesley
Mr P Owens
Dr R Prentis
Mr R Saunders
Mr D J Smith
Mr J P Staddon
Mr R J Steward
Mr P Watts
Mr G Wildig

Bursar and Clerk to the Council: Ms K A Scott, AInstAM Dip

***Headmistress*: Mrs P M Wood**, BA Hons Hull

Deputy Headmistress: Ms L Clancy, BEd Nottingham

Head of Junior School: Mrs J Hirst, BA Open, CertEd

Teaching Staff:
* *Head of Department*

Miss C Black, BA Hons QTS Manchester Metropolitan (*PE*)
Mrs B Bradley, BEd Avery Hill, CertEd (*Business Studies*)
Mrs K Bramley, BTEC Dip Eastbourne, BA Hons Wimbledon, QTS (*Art Textiles*)
Miss H Briggs, BSc Hons Southampton, PGCE, MA (*Teacher i/c Geography*)
Mrs S Burge, BSc London, PGCE (*Geography*)
Mrs C Carter (*Learning Support*)
Mrs A Chance, Cert Ed Wall Hall Cambridge Institute of Education (*Art*)
Mrs L Chessell, BSc Hons Durham, PGCE (*Mathematics*)
Mrs P Clarke, CertEd, DipT (*Juniors*)
Mr E Coetzer, BA Ed Pretoria (**ICT and Marketing*)
Mrs L Collins (*Learning Support*)
Mrs M Y Emery, BA Hons London, PGCE (**Spanish, Head of Sixth Form*)
Miss L Entwistle, BSc Hons Birmingham, PGCE (*Teacher i/c Biology*)
Mrs D Fewtrell, BA Swansea, M-ès-L (*French*)
Mr J Flanagan, BA Leeds (**Drama*)
Mrs C Garrod, C&G Catering (*Food Design*)
Mr J Gaudoin, BSc, BSc Hons, PGCE (*Chemistry*)
Mrs M George (*Learning Support*)
Mr P Griffiths, BA Hons Leicester, MA Classics Ontario (*Latin*)
Mrs P Hanham, BSc Hons Goldsmiths London, PGCE (*Psychology*)
Mr M Huxley, BSc Hons Westminster, PGCE (*Photography*)
Mrs M-J Jeanes, MA Oxon, PGCE (**Science, *Chemistry*)
Mrs J Karlsson, BTh Cambridge, PGCE (**Religious Studies*)
Mrs W King, BA Hons Surrey (*Juniors*)
Mr C Lester, BSc Hons, PGCE, PG Dip (*Teacher i/c Physics*)

Mrs J Long, BSc Hons Surrey (*Biology*)
Mrs S Maundrell, DEUG, PGCE (*French*)
Mrs H McMeechan, BSc Hons Sheffield, PGCE, TEFL Cert (*TEFL*)
Mrs T Milbourn, BA Hons, PGCE (*Junior PE*)
Mrs R Murphy, CertEd Furzedown College (*Juniors*)
Mrs E Nissan, BA Hons Sussex, PhD LSE, PGCE (*Juniors*)
Mrs C Paine, BEd Roehampton
Mrs S Parker, BEd Hons Surrey (*Juniors*)
Mrs R M Pedrick, BA Hons Durham, PGCE (**Modern Foreign Languages*)
Mrs C Peers-Noakes, BA Hons St Mary's College, PGCE (*English*)
Mrs D Perry, BA Hons King's College London, PGCE (*English*)
Mrs L Richards (*Early Birds*)
Mrs S Sevier (*Exams Officer, Duke of Edinburgh's Award Coordinator*)
Mrs S Sheehan BSc, HDipEd (*Mathematics*)
Mrs G Skidmore, BSc Hons Edinburgh, CertEd (**Mathematics*)
Mrs A Smith, BEd Hons Brighton (**Physical Education*)
Mrs D Smith (*Early Birds*)
Mrs H Smith, NNEB Foundation, BA Hons Kingston, EYPS
Mrs I Smith, BA Pretoria, MA Bloemfontein (**English*)
Miss M Smith, BA Australia (*English, Media Studies*)
Miss J Stamford, BSc Hons UCL, PGCE, MIBiol, CBiol (**Biology*)
Miss E Stuart, BA Hons Liverpool, PGCE (*Music*)
Mrs D Thomas, BEd Hons Roehampton, DipMathEd Southlands College (*Juniors*)
Mrs S Thomas, BA Hons Sussex, PGCE (*French and German*)
Mr J Tizzard, BMus Cardiff, PGCE (**Performing Arts, Director of Music*)
Dr R Waller, BA Oxford, MA Oxford, DPhil Oxford (**History & Politics*)
Mrs J Windett, BEd Hons Crewe and Alsager (*Juniors*)
Mrs M Wraith, HND Manchester, CertEd Manchester, Dip A&D (**Creative Arts*)

Head's PA: Miss C Berger
Assistant to the Bursar: Mrs S Ball
Admissions Registrar: Mrs L Armstrong
Careers and Sixth Form Secretary: Mrs J Rawlins

"A local school at the heart of the community"

Situated on the edge of the Banstead Downs, Greenacre School offers a clean, safe, bright and modern setting for children to learn. Children can join us at any stage.

The nursery offers an outstanding start to any child's education; with a "school" focus, our youngest children learn to make new friends easily and grow with confidence.

The junior school has a high standard of achievement in the classroom coupled with fantastic opportunities for Sport, Music, Art and Drama. Our children receive lessons from specialist teachers, using the best resources. At the end of the junior school all our students are prepared for the Senior School Entrance Examination, although they are guaranteed a place in the Greenacre Senior School.

In the senior school a balanced education is supported by a range of outstanding extra curricular activities, whether a child is on the field, in the concert hall or on the stage, Greenacre children have the confidence to shine. Pupils, staff and parents work cooperatively to support the girls in their aspirations. Learning, teaching, assessment and reporting methods are constantly under review.

The sixth form offers real opportunities for its students. Small classes, personal tutors, amazing resources and a wealth of subjects on offer we can cater for the budding medical student to the sound engineer. With specialist teaching staff our students receive excellent examination results.

Extra curricular activities are considered a vital part of each pupil's life. A wide range of clubs allow sporting, dramatic and musical involvement at all levels. The Duke of Edinburgh's Award attracts large numbers, whilst the Model United Nations broadens outlook and instills awareness of the wider world.

Extensive travel both at home and abroad allows for new and fun experiences and the school plays a major part in our local community, participating in community and parish events.

Why not come and visit the school – it may be the best thing you ever do!

Fees per term (2008-2009). £2,195 (Nursery full-time)–£3,775 (Year 11), including lunch. Sixth Form: £3,595, excluding lunch.

Scholarships. (*see Scholarship Entries section*).

Charitable status. Greenacre School for Girls Ltd is a Registered Charity, number 312034. It exists to provide education for girls.

Guernsey – The Ladies' College

Les Gravées St Peter Port Guernsey Channel Islands GY1 1RW
Tel: 01481 721602
Fax: 01481 724209
e-mail: office@ladiescollege.sch.gg
secretary@ladiescollege.sch.gg (Registrar)
website: www.ladiescollege.sch.gg

Motto: *Fais ce que dois, advienne que pourra*

Chairman of the Board of Governors: (*to be appointed*)

Senior School:

***Principal*: Ms J Riches**, MA Oxon, PGCE

Deputy Principal: Mrs J Pearson, BSc Hons Hull, MPQH
Director of Studies: Mr R S Harbour, BSc Hons Dunelm, FRAS

Art and Design:
Miss B Chmiel, BA Hons Exeter, PGCE
Miss L Kirby, BA Hons Plymouth, PGCE

Classics:
Miss J E M Geach, MA Oxon, PGCE

Design and Technology:
Mr D Turner, MEd Exeter, CertEd London

Drama:
Mr G Swann, BA Hons OU, BA Acting Royal Scottish Academy, CertEd
Miss S Thackeray, BEd Hons Bedford College

Economics and Business Studies:
Mrs A Niven, MAEcon Edinburgh, ACIB

English:
Miss Z Bougourd, BA Hons Southampton, PGCE
Mr E Campbell, BA Hons Southampton
Miss L Cooke, BSc Hons Durham, PGCE
Mrs J Massey, BA Hons OU, CertEd Oxford
Ms J Riches, MA Oxon, PGCE

Geography:
Mrs M Brogan, BSc Hons Exeter, PGCE
Miss H Watts, BSc Hons Cheltenham & Gloucester College for FE, PGCE

History:
Mrs C Montague, BA Hons Southampton, CertEd
Miss B Murie, BA Hons Canterbury, New Zealand, PGCE

Information Technology:
Mr A Wade, BSc Hons Cardiff, PGCE

Mathematics:
Mr R S Harbour, BSc Hons Dunelm, FRAS
Mrs C Gribbens, BSc Hons, QTS West of England, Bristol
Mrs J Haskins, BSc Hons Cardiff
Mr P Hill, BSc Hons University of Cape Town
Mrs C Rabey, MA Cantab, BA, PGCE

Modern Languages French, German, Spanish:
Mrs J Sproule, MA Edinburgh, PGCE
Mrs S Devine, BA Hons Manchester, AdvDipEdMan Open, Dip Spanish Open, PGCE
Mrs K Elward, BA Hons Hull, PGCE, TEFL
Mrs V Hanna, BA Hons Bedford College, London, Licensed Teacher
Mrs M Shepherd
Mr Y Thoz, L-ès-L Rennes, CAPES

Music:
Mr J M Henderson, BA Hons CT ABRSM Leeds, PGCE
Mrs R Wright, GTCL, PGCE

Physical Education:
Mrs R F Dovey, BEd West Sussex Inst of HE, Chichester
Miss H Watts, BSc Hons Cheltenham & Gloucester College for FE, PGCE
Miss S Thackeray, BEd Hons Bedford College

Religious Studies:
Mrs J Le Poidevin, CertEd Portsmouth College of Education
Mrs C Claxton, BMus Hons London, PGCE LRAM

Science:
Mr H Barnes, BSc Hons York, PGCE, MRSC
Mrs J Clare, B Home Economics, Socio Economics Potchefstroom SA, BSc, NARIC
Mr M Cooper, MSc Imperial College, London, Dip IC University College of Wales, Swansea, BSc Hons OU, PGCE
Miss I Ellen, BSc Hons St Andrews, PGCE
Mr C Grant, BSc Hons Liverpool, PGCE
Mr I Harding BA OU, MA York, CertEd
Mrs P Knight BSc Portsmouth Polytechnic, PGCE

Psychology:
Miss V Mitchell, BSc Hons University of Wales, PhD Glasgow

Careers Guidance:
(*to be appointed*)

Librarian: Mrs E Hutchinson
Assistant Librarian: Mrs H Hill

Laboratory Assistants:
Mrs D Coxon
Mrs R Wolfe

IT Technician/Reprographics Technician: Mrs J Le Cras
Design Technology Technician: Mrs J Dyer

Administrative Staff:
Bursar and Clerk to the Governors: Mrs K Fell
Assistant Bursar: Mrs M Adam
PA to the Principal: Mrs D Hillion
Registrar: Miss R McClean
Receptionist: Mrs J Pill

Junior School:
Head Mistress: Mrs P Cann, BA Hons King's College, London, BEd, MEd
Deputy Head: Mrs S Spurrier, BEd Hons Westminster College

Full-time Staff:
Mrs M Bailey, CertEd London
Mrs A Beebee, BEd Hons Northern College of Education, Dundee
Mrs C Cave, BEd Hons London Inst of Education
Mrs L Kreeve, BA Hons Witswatersrand, SA, PGCE
Mrs E Ozanne, BEd Hons Brighton, PGCE
Mrs S Spurrier, BEd Hons Westminster College
Mr G Walsh, CertEd Drama and English Bretton Hall, Leeds

Part-time Staff:
Mrs M Watts, CertEd Dorset Inst of HE, TEFL Canterbury University
Mrs R Wright, GTCL, PGCE

Classroom Assistants:
Mrs E Reynolds (*full-time*)
Mrs J Sebire (*full-time*)
Mrs J Le Ray (*part-time*)
Mrs A Reynolds (*part-time*)

Administrative Staff:
Secretary to Head Mistress: Miss K Anders

The College was founded in 1872 as an independent school with a non-denominational Christian ethos. It is now Direct Grant with approximately one third of the pupils in the Senior School holding State Scholarship places. The College aims to achieve high academic standards and at the same time maintain the traditional values of courtesy and consideration for others.

Number of Girls. Senior School: approximately 400, with 100 in Sixth Form. Junior School: approximately 140.

Curriculum. The Junior School (Melrose) offers a caring environment in which pupils from 4+ to 11 years are given a sound foundation in the traditional skills of reading, writing and number work. In addition they study Science, History, Geography, Music, IT and Art. French, Religious Knowledge, PE and Drama form part of the general curriculum. From September 2008, girls in Year 6 at Melrose will no longer be required to sit the Common Entrance test for a place in the Senior school. Further information can be obtained from the Registrar.

The Senior School has a selective entry and places are only given to those applicants who have achieved a satisfactory result in the College entrance tests. In the first three years, all girls follow a broad general curriculum, including Latin, and start German as a second modern language in addition to French. There is an option to start Spanish in Year 10. Eighteen subjects are offered at GCSE.

The Sixth Form curriculum is essentially an academic one. Twenty-four subjects are offered at A Level and it is expected that the majority of Sixth Formers will proceed to Higher Education.

The College operates a Sixth Form Partnership with the local HMC School, Elizabeth College. Students can choose their A Level subjects from the combined provision of both schools and may study one or more subjects at Elizabeth College. Boys from Elizabeth College may likewise study a subject offered at the Ladies' College. The Ladies' College provides tutorial guidance and pastoral care for all the girls regardless of where they are taught for A Level.

Music. There is a high standard of music at the College, which has a wide variety of instrumental groups and choirs. Instrumental lessons are available from the College staff and from peripatetic teachers.

Sport. The College has a large gymnasium and has its own outdoor heated swimming pool. In addition to the usual sports of hockey, netball, rounders, tennis, swimming and athletics, the school offers badminton, fencing, dance, football and cricket.

Drama. The College offers Drama at GCSE and at A Level in the Sixth Form. Extra-curricular Drama flourishes with school productions taking place two or three times a year.

Extra-Curricular Activities. The Duke of Edinburgh's Award Scheme is well supported as is the Young Enterprise and Management Shadowing schemes. Pupils are also involved in work in the community and in fund-raising for charity.

Entry Procedure. All applicants must initially contact the College Registrar (Registration Fee £100).

Fees per term (2008-2009). Senior School £1,795; Junior School £1,988 (£175 for cooked lunches).

Scholarships. (*see Scholarship Entries section*).

Haberdashers' Aske's School for Girls

Aldenham Road Elstree Herts WD6 3BT
Tel: 020 8266 2300
Fax: 020 8266 2303
e-mail: theschool@habsgirls.org.uk
website: www.habsgirls.org.uk

Motto: *Serve and Obey*

This School forms part of the ancient foundation of Robert Aske and is governed by members of the Worshipful Company of Haberdashers, together with certain representatives of other bodies.

Clerk to the School Governors: Mr C M Bremner

***Headmistress*: Mrs E Radice**, MA Oxon

Personal Assistant to the Headmistress: Mrs B Cohen

Deputy Head: Mr R James-Robbins, BA London
Deputy Head: Dr S Lindfield, BSc Reading
Deputy Head: Dr M Short, BA London

Bursar: Mr D Thompson, BA Manchester, ACIB

Teaching Staff:
* *Head of Department*

Art:
*Miss L A Powell, Dip Swansea Coll of Art, TCert Wales
Miss S Wiseman, MA London
Mrs P White, BA Sheffield School of Art & Design

Careers:
*Mrs J Crane, BSc Birmingham

Classics:
*Mr A Doe, BA Oxon
Miss C Jessop, MA Cantab
Miss C Nixey, BA Cantab
Miss D Spain, MA Oxon

Design and Technology:
*Mr M Squire, BSc South Bank
Mrs S Deamer, BA Manchester
Mr J Oliver, BA Warwick
Mr S Turner, BSc Brunel

Economics:
*Mr M Catley, BSc LSE
Mrs A Bennett, BA Oxon
Mrs S Kaur Hender, BA Leeds

English and Drama:
*Miss A M Harvey, MA Oxon
Miss C Leaver, BA York
Mr R James-Robbins, BA London
Miss A Manning, BA Birmingham
Ms A Puranik, BA Tennessee
Mr D Thakerar, BA London
Mrs L Winton, BA Manchester
Mrs A Yates, BA London, MA London

Geography:
*Mrs S Ashton, BSc Keele
Miss A McCrea, BSc Bristol
Mrs A Bowen, BSc Manchester, MSc London
Mrs M Candy, BA Melbourne

History:
*Mrs A Pearson, BA Dunelm
Mr P Harper, BA Oxon
Mr K Davies, MA London
Mrs R Davies, BA Cardiff (*Deputy Head of Sixth Form*)
Mrs E Devane, BA Cantab
Dr M Short, BA London
Mrs C Wilding, BA Bristol

Individual Educational Needs:
*(*to be appointed*)

Information Technology:
*Mr D Wade, BA Salford

Library:
Mrs A Fynes-Clinton, BA Canterbury, New Zealand, Dip Lib

Mathematics:
*Mrs C Godfrey, BSc Leicester
Mr A Bowyer, BSC Rhodes
Miss S Burke, BSc Manchester
Mrs M Hodgskin, BA Open (*Head of Middle School*)
Mr C Howlett, BSc Dunelm
Mr J Kinoulty, BSc Exeter
Miss L Marx, BSc Edinburgh
Miss S Pathakji, BA Cantab
Mrs K Roantree, BA York

Modern Languages:
*Mr J Carbonell, MA London
Miss J Bouchard, Lyon
Miss M Chambas, Blaise Pascal Univ
Mrs E Green, BA Oxon
Mrs T Johnson, BA Hertfordshire
Miss R Maldonado, BA Anglia Polytechnic University
Miss G Mellor, BA Exeter (*Head of Upper School*)
Miss A Millet, Tours
Mrs F Ray, L-ès-L Maîtrise, CAPES (*French*)
Miss Y Steinruck, Julius Maximilians Univ Würzburg
Mrs K Osmond, BA Bristol
and 5 visiting oral teachers

Music:
*Mr A Phillips, BMus London
Mrs R Bardou, BA Cardiff
Miss L Caperon, BA Oxon
Miss A Turnbull, LRAM
and 25 visiting teachers

Physical Education:
*Miss C Hill, BSc Birmingham
Miss C Baker, BA Brighton
Ms D Dawson-Evers, BA Brighton
Miss K Roberts, BSc Loughborough
Ms A Williams, BSc Crewe & Alsager

Religion and Philosophy:
*Mrs M Wax, MA Essex
Mr P Moriarty, MA Oxon (*Head of Sixth Form*)
Mrs V Porter, BA Oxon
Mrs A Saunders, BA Cantab

Science:
*Mrs V Leigh, BSc London (*Biology*)
Mrs L Brown, MA London
Mrs H Burgess, BSc Cantab
Dr R Catchpole, BSc London
Mrs J Dabby-Joory, BSc Southampton

Mrs N Ghinn, BSc Nottingham
Mr G Jervis, MA London
Miss R Lane, BA Cantab
Dr S Lindfield, BSc Reading
Mrs Z Makepeace-Welsh, MChem Oxon
Mrs J McNally, BSc Hatfield, CChem, MRSC
Miss N Percy, BSc Leeds (**Physics*)
Mr E Stock, MPhys Oxon
Mrs J Wilding, BSc Exeter (**Chemistry*)
Mrs K Little, BSc London, ARCS
Miss C Simms, BSc Edinburgh

Junior School:
Head: Mrs S Worthington, MA Oxon
Deputy Head: Mrs J Charlesworth, BSc Nottingham
Head of Infants: Miss S Hattaway, DipEd Auckland
Miss M Aylett, CertEd Leicester
Miss R Brant, BSc London
Miss E Burman, BA Surrey
Mrs P A Dear, BSc UCW
Miss E Galvin, BA Warwick
Miss C Heywood, BSc Coventry
Mr N Hobley, BSc Oxford Brookes
Miss E Hodgson, BEd Gloucester
Dr J Hogg, BSc Bangor, PhD Bangor (*Curriculum Coordinator*)
Mrs J Millman, BEd Leeds
Mrs J Moffatt, BSc Wales
Mrs J Nicholas, BA Newcastle
Miss E Galvin, BA Warwick
Mrs S Rose, BEd Cantab
Miss C Sawkins, BEd Surrey
Mr I Stroud, BSc North East London Polytechnic
Mr P Swinden, BA London
Mrs E-L Temple, LLB Bristol
Ms S Tersigni, BA Middlesex
Mrs T Wilkins, BSc Loughborough
Miss Y Yokozawa, BA Kyorin University

Haberdashers' Aske's Girls' School is situated on a site of over 50 acres, and has an excellent reputation for academic, sporting and musical achievements. Entry to the Junior Department at the Girls School is at 4+, 5+ or at 7+; the Senior School is at 11+ and Sixth Form. The academic results are outstanding, the reflection of able pupils who enjoy learning and thrive on a full and challenging curriculum.

Top-class facilities for a very wide range of extra-curricular activities are provided within the school. Sport, music, drama, art and debating thrive and there are many other opportunities for leadership within the school community including the Duke of Edinburgh's Award Scheme, the Community Sports Leadership Award and a very active community service team. Life at Habs' is busy and challenging, embracing new technology, for example, digital language labs, touch-screen interactive whiteboards and remote access to all electronic work areas via the intranet, alongside old traditions, which include the celebration of St Catherine's Day as patron of the Haberdashers' Company.

Over 110 coach routes, shared with the Boys' School next door, bring pupils to school from a thirty-mile radius covering north London, Hertfordshire and Middlesex. The provision of a late coach service ensures that pupils can take part safely in the wide range of the many clubs and societies organised after school.

The school follows its own wide-ranging academic curriculum tailored to the needs of its very able pupils. Much of what is taught draws upon the best practice of what is happening nationally and in other schools. The curriculum is balanced and broadly based, and promotes the spiritual, moral, cultural, mental and physical development of our pupils and of society and prepares our pupils for the opportunities, responsibilities and experiences of adult life. All pupils are expected to acquire skills in speaking and listening, literacy and numeracy skills.

The school provides full-time supervised education for pupils of between the ages of 4 and 18 which gives them experience in linguistic, mathematical, scientific, technological, human and social, physical and aesthetic and creative education, appropriate for their ages and aptitudes. At each level, it prepares them for the opportunities, responsibilities and experiences of the next stage of their education and their lives.

Junior School. The curriculum in the Junior School aims to enable pupils to develop lively, enquiring minds, the ability to question and discuss, and to apply themselves to a range of tasks. It aims to enable pupils to develop skills and to acquire knowledge; to use language and number effectively; to instil respect for moral values and tolerance of other races, religions and customs; to understand the world in which pupils live and the interdependence of individuals, groups and nations; and to help pupils to appreciate human achievements and aspirations. Subjects taught include English, Mathematics, Science, French (from Year 6), Japanese (from Year 1), Geography, History, Religious Studies, ICT, Art, Music, Design Technology, Physical Education and Personal, Social and Health Education. Pupils are not entered for the SATS tests but they are tested internally annually from Year 1 in order to track the progress of groups and individuals.

Senior School. *Key Stage 3*: The curriculum during the first three years of the Senior School is designed to give a broad and balanced education. Fifteen subjects are taught: English, Mathematics, French, Latin, Geography, History, ICT, Biology, Chemistry, Physics, Religion and Philosophy, Music, Art, Design Technology and Physical Education. Girls choose a second modern language, German or Spanish, in Year 8. Lessons are taught in form groups apart from, in Years 8 and 9, Mathematics, French and Spanish, which are set to allow for difference of pace. There is a weekly tutorial lesson for every form and each year group follows a specific programme of Personal, Social and Health Education.

Key Stage 4: A broad spread of subjects in Years 10 and 11 offers the best possible range both at GCSE and AS/A2 Level. Twenty subjects are taught. All pupils study a core of English, English Literature, Mathematics, a Modern Foreign Language, Biology, Chemistry and Physics or Double Certificate Science, and one of the Humanities. Girls opt to study additional subjects to a maximum of ten. In addition, each week, all pupils attend a tutorial lesson, follow a specific programme of Personal, Social and Health Education (covering religion and ethics, careers, health education, politics and economics, budgeting, European studies) and follow a compulsory programme of physical activities.

Sixth Form. In the Sixth Form, approximately twenty subjects are offered from which girls will choose four at AS Level in the Lower Sixth, continuing with three or four at A2 in the Upper Sixth. The Sixth Form provides a sound academic and social basis for progression to university and careers. In the Lower Sixth, pupils follow a programme of General Studies (including Personal, Social and Health Education and a course on Critical Thinking), part of which is run jointly with Haberdashers' Aske's School for Boys, and a programme of physical activities. In the Upper Sixth, guidance and advice with university applications (including Oxbridge), interviews and careers are available on individual basis from specialist staff as well as tutors and senior staff. An extension programme is available in a wide range of subjects. There is a weekly tutorial lesson for every tutor group.

Pastoral Care. In our big and busy school we aim to care deeply about each individual girl. The provision of pastoral care is designed to help girls make decisions about themselves and to care about others within the framework of a very diverse community. We provide an outstanding range of opportunities for the girls' personal development and to help them consolidate a system of spiritual beliefs and a moral code.

From the moment she becomes a Habs' girl we emphasise the partnership with parents; hand in hand we can support each girl, operating on a basis of trust and with the support of a face she knows from the start. Pupils are thoughtfully allocated to form groups depending on where they live, so that they will have school friends nearby. The form tutors and form prefects play a key role in the girls' welfare. Each form becomes a family unit consisting of the tutor, a deputy, two sixth form prefects and two elected form captains from within the form itself. Strong peer support comes from the girls in the year and from the older girls in the sixth form. Much emphasis is placed upon their responsibility for the ethos and happiness of the form.

We have a full-time nurse and a trained counsellor to meet the needs of individual girls. Our anti-bullying policy is displayed in all the form rooms and ensures that rare instances of bullying are dealt with swiftly according to widely known procedures. The premise is that everyone has the right to feel comfortable, at ease and happy both in school and travelling to and from school. The coach service provides additional support and reassurance and the sixth form stewards keep a watchful eye.

We have comprehensive pastoral, tutorial and guidance systems, which support the educational and personal development of the girls. Section Heads, form tutors and subject staff work closely together overseen by the Deputy Head (Pastoral), so that the needs of the pupils, whether academic, social or pastoral are speedily evaluated and appropriate measures taken.

Fees per term (2008-2009). Senior School £3,562; Junior School £2,934. A number of scholarships are awarded annually and means-tested bursaries (up to full fees) are also available.

Charitable status. The Haberdashers' Aske's Charity is a Registered Charity, number 313996. It exists to promote education.

Haberdashers' Monmouth School for Girls

Hereford Road Monmouth NP25 5XT
Tel: 01600 711100
Fax: 01600 711233
e-mail: admissions@hmsg.co.uk
website: www.habs-monmouth.org

Motto: *Serve and Obey*

Trustees: The Worshipful Company of Haberdashers

Governing Body:
Chairman: J B S Swallow, MA, FCA

The Master of the Worshipful Company of Haberdashers (*ex officio*)

J A Ackroyd
M Anderson
Dr M G Archer
Dr P E G Baird
Professor P Blood
Mrs H M Bosanquet
Cllr W A L Crump
E J S Hiscocks
D J Hitchcock
Miss H Hutton
Mrs L Kelway-Bamber
A M Kerr
Mrs G B Kerton-Johnson
A D Kirk
Mrs M A Molyneux
Mrs T Pike
J E G Prevett
Revd Dr J T Rigney
Mrs M Wetherell

Clerk to the Governors: Mrs F Creasey, BCom, ACMA

Bursar: Mrs Tessa Norgrove

***Headmistress*: Mrs Helen Davy**, MA Oxon

Deputy Headmistress: Mrs N Walker, BSc Hons Lancaster, PGCE Oxford, MBA Leicester

Assistant Deputy and Head of Sixth Form: Mrs K J MacDonald, BA Manchester, PGCE Wales, MSc Econ Wales

Assistant Deputy and Head of Upper School: Mrs O E Davis, BSc Joint Hons Salford, PGCE York, MA Ed

Head of Middle School: Mrs C A Griffiths, BA Hons London, PGCE Reading

Chaplain: Dr S G Barnden, BA Hons, MA, PhD, PGCE

Head of Year 7: Mrs A Poyner, BSc Hons, PGCE

* *Head of Department*

Art:
*Mrs V Reynolds, BA Hons, MS, PGCE
Mrs N Clayton, BA, PGCE
Miss L Porritt, BA Hons, PGCE

Biology:
*Miss L Woodburn, BSc Hons, PGCE
Mrs L Cartwright, CertEd
Mr J C Cheeseman, BSc Newcastle
Mrs M E Dummett, BSc Open
Mr L J Ison, BSc, PGCE
Miss L Wright, BA Hons, PGCE

Business Studies:
*Mr D R Evans, BA Hons Coventry, PGCE Wales
Ms M C Attrill, BTEC, Dip Bus Studies, CertEd
Mrs C Jones, BSc Hons, PGCE Wales

Careers:
Mrs A Jervis, BSc, MA, PGCE Wales

Chemistry:
*Mrs M M Newcomb, BSc Hons London, PGCE Bristol
Mrs D E Clarke, BSc Hons, PGCE
Mrs S P Marks, BSc Hons Open, PGCE Wales
Dr I Wallace, BSc Hons, PhD, PGCE

Classics:
*Mrs J Treasure, BA Hons Bristol, PGCE London
Mrs L Beech, BA Hons, PGCE
Mrs J Hards, BA Hons, PGCE

Design Technology:
*Mrs N Clayton, BA, PGCE
Mr S McClusky, BSc Hons, PGCE

Drama & Theatre Arts:
*Miss S Slingo, BEd Hons Wales, LRAM, LUD, DA
Mrs H Wragg, BA Hons Leeds

Economics:
*Mr D R Evans, BA Hons Coventry, PGCE Wales

English:
*Mrs Z Harvey, BA Hons, PGCE
Dr S G Barnden, BA Hons, MA, PhD, PGCE
Mr J Edwards, BA Hons, MA Warwick, PGCE Wales
Mrs C Gunter, BA Hons, MEd, DipEd
Mrs D M Hardman, BA Hons, PGCE
Miss R Lovell, BA Oxford
Mrs J Read, BA Hons, CertEd

Geography:
*Mr N Meek, BA Hons Middlesex, MA Leicester, PGCE Wales
Mr P M Jones, BA Hons, PGCE

History:
*Mr D Griffiths, BA Hons, PGCE
Mrs K A Callaghan, BA Hons Surrey
Mrs K MacDonald, BA, PGCE, MSc Econ
Miss R Miles, BA Hons, MA, PGCE

Home Economics:
*Mrs P Curtis, CertEd Leicester
Mrs J Vickers, CertEd
Mrs C M Ward, CertEd
Mrs P Ward, CertEd

ICT:
*Mrs J Jones, BComm, PGCE
Mrs C Jones, BSc Hons, PGCE Wales
Mrs E Martin, BA Hons, PGCE

Mathematics:
*Mrs C L McGladdery, BSc Hons, PGCE Manchester
Mrs D J Crawshaw, BSc Hons, PGCE
Mrs B N Keyton, BSc Hons, PGCE
Mrs J E Morris, BSc Hons, PGCE
Mrs V R Price, BSc
Mrs J A Poyner, BSc Hons, PGCE
Mrs N Walker, BSc Hons, PGCE

Modern Languages:
*Ms A Thiry, BA Hons Lille, PGCE Sheffield (*French*)
Mrs E M Adams, BA Hons, MA, PGCE (*French*)
Mrs E W Barlow, BA Hons, PGCE (*German*)
Mrs O E Davis, BSc Jt Hons (*Spanish*)
Mrs C A Griffiths, BA Hons (*German, French*)
Mrs A Hutchings, BA Hons, PGCE (*German*)
Mrs D C McClune, BTS Comm France (*French*)
Mrs D Mori, BA Hons Sussex, Dip TEFL, PGCE (*French*)
Mrs H K Smail, BA Hons Wolverhampton, MA Reading, PGCE (*French, German*)
Mrs L M Vincent, BA Hons, PGCE (*Welsh*)
Mrs J Ward, MA (*German*)

Music:
Head of Academic & Choral Music: Miss A Randles, BMus Hons London, LRAM, LTCL
Head of Instrumental Music and Music Technology: Mr M Conway, MusB Hons, MA, PGCE, LTCL, ARCM
Mrs A M Milledge, BA Hons, PGCE
Miss V Walker, BMus Hons, PGCE
Mrs R Friend, LRAM

PSE:
Miss V Walker, BMus Hons, PGCE

Physical Education:
*Ms R V Parry, BA Hons Bedford, PGCE Bedford
Mrs K Callaghan, BA Hons (*Senior Rowing Coach*)
Mr J C Cheesman, BSc Hons (*Assistant Rowing Coach*)
Mrs C E Jones, BSc Hons, MSc
Mrs A J Norris, BA Hons, PGCE
Mrs S J Rossiter, BSc Hons
Miss C W Tamplin, BSc Hons Wales, PGCE

Physics:
*Mrs A B Kavanagh, BEd Hons Cheltenham
Mrs D Davies, BSc Hons, PGCE
Mrs G Manning, BA, PGCE

Psychology:
*Mrs A Jervis, BSc, MA, PGCE
Mrs J McQuitty, BSc Hons

Religious Studies:
*Mr J M Lewis, BDiv MTh, PGCE Wales, MPhil
Mrs J Hards, BA Hons, PGCE

Special Needs & TEFL:
Mrs D Mori, BA Hons Sussex, DipTEFL, PGCE Wales, DipSEN Wales

Preparatory Department (Gilbert Inglefield House):
Head: Mrs R Vigrass, BA Hons, PGCE London
Mrs P M Champion, Dip Primary Education
Mrs M E Dummett, BSc
Mrs H D Edmunds, BEd Liverpool
Miss H Fanus, BA Hons, PGCE
Mrs A Griffiths, BA Hons
Mrs R J Hallett, BEd Hons
Mrs S C M Hartley, BEd Hons
Mrs J Jones, BA Hons, PGCE
Mrs L Reynolds, BA Hons, PGCE
Miss C Williams, BA Hons

Head of Boarding:
Mrs M Edwards

Librarian:
Mrs F Green, ALA, MSc Wales

Haberdashers' Monmouth School for Girls is one of the three schools of the Jones's Monmouth Foundation, arising from a bequest of William Jones, Merchant, in 1615, and administered by the Worshipful Company of Haberdashers. The School stands high on the outskirts of the town of Monmouth, in the beautiful countryside of the Wye Valley.

There are about 511 girls in the Main School with a Sixth Form of 146. Pupils from 7–11 have their own modern Preparatory Department of 112 girls on site. Thriving Boarding Community with accommodation on the school site, includes a Junior House and modern Senior House with study bedrooms.

A £2 million Science Building opened September 1994, updated Sixth Form block in 1998 and new Music rehearsal rooms in May 1999. Classrooms and laboratories are extensive, with special Sixth Form provision. Specialist workshops are provided for DT and Drama. Full use is made of the ample sports facilities; spacious playing fields, all-weather pitch, tennis courts, sports hall, indoor swimming pool and gymnasium. All are adjacent to the School. A new classroom extension, including 4 new ICT suites, opened in September 2006.

The School has its own Chaplain and is a Christian foundation. Girls are encouraged to attend the places of worship of their own denomination; the majority attend the parish church.

A large and fully qualified staff of graduates teaches a modern curriculum, which aims to achieve high academic results within a broader education, acknowledging our cultural inheritance and technological and social needs.

Classics is taught throughout the School. At examination level, Latin GCSE, Greek GCSE, Latin AS/A Level, and Classical Civilisation AS/A Level are offered. Ancient Greek is offered at Sixth Form level.

Almost all pupils progress to Higher Education. With excellent careers advice, girls are aware of the scope of degree subjects. A number annually enter Oxford and Cambridge.

Every encouragement is given to creative and practical work, especially Music and Drama. Girls frequently attend concerts, plays and exhibitions, and an active interest is taken in industry and management. Local businesses lend support to the School's Young Enterprise schemes.

Girls participate in the Duke of Edinburgh's Award scheme, CCF at Monmouth School, help in the community and many also belong to local voluntary organisations.

Main sporting activities include lacrosse, netball, tennis, rowing, fencing, hockey and dance, many played at County, National and International level.

Fees per term (2008-2009). (*see Scholarship Entries section*). Tuition £2,834–£3,676. Boarding element £2,829.

Entry is usually at 7, 11, 13 (Common Entrance) or post GCSE, although occasionally other vacancies occur. Entrance to the first year of the Senior School is by examination in January; scholarships and bursaries are awarded at this age, 13+ and for the Sixth Form.

Tests for entry to the Preparatory Department for girls of 7 years are held in the Spring Term.

Prospectus etc on application to the Admissions Secretary, e-mail: admissions@hmsg.co.uk.

Old Girls' Association. *Secretary*: Mrs S Rossiter, c/o Haberdashers' Monmouth School for Girls, Monmouth. The

OGA Annual General Meeting is held at the school on the second Saturday in November.

Charitable status. William Jones's Schools Foundation is a Registered Charity, number 525616. The object of the Foundation shall be the provision and conduct in or near Monmouth of a day and boarding school for boys and a day and boarding school for girls.

Harrogate Ladies' College

Clarence Drive Harrogate North Yorkshire HG1 2QG
Tel: 01423 504543
Fax: 01423 568893
e-mail: enquire@hlc.org.uk
website: www.hlc.org.uk

Board of Governors:
Mrs R Bradby
Mr S Brown
Mrs R Cunnicliffe
Mr C Davies
Mrs V Davies
Dr A Fahy
Mrs S Gosling
Ms S Hollingworth
Mr J Poskitt
Mrs S Pullan
Mr A Skidmore (*Chairman*)
Mr A Taylor

Secretary to the Governors and General Manager of Allied Schools: Mr N Coulson, MA, MBA

***Interim Headmaster*: Mr Geoffrey F Hazell**, MA Cantab, PGCE

Deputy Head: Mrs P D Harrison, BA Sheffield, PGCE
Head of Boarding: Mrs A Wood, BSc Bristol, MA Ed Surrey, PGCE
Director of Studies: Mrs S Bailey. BA Birmingham, PGCE
Bursar: Mr J I Gibson, MCIPD

Academic Staff:
Mrs C S Alp, GRSM, LRAM, LGSM (**Academic Music, Pianoforte, Flute*)
Mrs G A Andrews, BA Mus Reading (*Flute, Pianoforte*)
Mr D C Andrews, BA Mus (**Director of Music*)
Dr R Ashcroft, BA Huddersfield, PhD, PGCE (*History, Classics*)
Mrs S Bailey, BA Birmingham, PGCE (*Mathematics, German*)
Mrs B Beckett, BA Leicester, PGCE (*English*)
Mrs M Bovino, BA Mus Hons (*Singing*)
Mrs J Burnell, BA OU, Teaching Cert (*Mathematics*)
Mrs M Bushby, BA Leeds LTCL, PGCE (*Piano, Violin*)
Miss N Butters, BA Leeds, PGCE, MEd Sheffield (**Physical Education*)
Miss C Cave, BA (*Singing*)
Mrs J D Chapman, BSc Birmingham, PGCE (**Careers, Business, Accounting, ICT*)
Revd Dr J Cheeseman, BA King's College, PhD, PGCE (**Religious Studies*)
Mrs A Chestnutt, BSc Bristol, PGCE (*Biology*)
Miss H Clothier, BA Salford, PGCE (*Geography, DofE*)
Mr M Coghlan, Professional Photographer (*Photography*)
Mrs P M Coghlan, ALCM, LAM Gold Medal Speech and Drama (**Speech and Drama*)
Mr M Cook, Dip NCDT, MA King's College, PGCE (**Drama*)
Mrs J Coomber, BA Natal, UEDiploma (*Latin*)
Miss V C Cooper, BSc Manchester, MEd Leeds, PGCE (**Mathematics*)
Mrs J Davison, BA Leeds, PGCE (*German, French*)
Miss R Dent, BMus (*Harp*)
Miss D Easterbrook (*Physical Education, Support*)
Mrs C K E Faber, MA Cantab (*Spanish, French*)
Miss J Frampton, BA Glasgow SoA, PGCE (*Art*)
Mrs J Frazer, LRAM,ARCM (*Piano, Flute*)
Mr P C Gill, BA Leeds, MA Leeds, PGCE (*Assistant Head of Sixth Form, Religious Studies*)
Mrs J Grazier, BEd Warwick, ACA (*Business, Accounting*)
Mrs P D Harrison, BA Sheffield, PGCE (*Deputy Head, Head of Sixth Form, English*)
Mrs J Havas, BA Nottingham, PGCE (*TEFL*)
Mrs A V Hickling, BEd Worcester (*Head of Middle School, *Textiles*)
Mrs A Hodge, BA Stamford, MA Wisconsin, RSA TEFL (*TEFL*)
Mr R Horton, BSc Dunelm, PGCE (*Director of IT Systems*)
Mrs J Hudson, BA OU, PGCE (*Business, ICT*)
Mrs F Irvine, BEd Bedford (*Physical Education*)
Mrs J Jackson, BA Hons OU, LRAM, PGCE (*Piano*)
Mr D Johnson (*Bassoon*)
Mr S Langford, BSc Heriot-Watt, PGCE (*Mathematics, ICT*)
Miss S Laverick, BA (*Cello*)
Mr M Laycock, BEd Leeds Met (**Design and Technology*)
Mrs J List, BA York, PGCE (**Biology*)
Mrs E Livesey, BA Central Lancashire, PGCE (**Food & Nutrition, Textiles*)
Mrs B Lumber, BSc Manchester, PGCE (*Mathematics*)
Mrs C M Martin, BA Leeds Polytechnic, PGCE (*French*)
Mrs D Martoglio, Montessori Teaching Diploma, CELTAA, CELTYL (*TEFL*)
Mr S T Meacham, BA Leicester, PGCE (**Classics, *Languages*)
Miss A Mitchell, BA Kent, PGCE, CELTA (*English*)
Mr L Moya-Morallón, LLB Jaen, Spain, Diploma, PGCE (*Spanish, French*)
Mrs D M Murray, BA Cardiff, MA Bretton Hall, PGCE (**English*)
Mr I Peak, BEd, LGSM (*Clarinet, Saxophone*)
Mrs A Phelps, BA, ABRSM, PGCE (*Piano*)
Mrs J E Power, City & Guilds Teaching Cert (**ICT, Careers Advisor*)
Miss C Preece, BSc Manchester, MA OU, PGCE (**Physics, *Science*)
Mr P Pritchard, BSc Exeter, PGCE (**Chemistry*)
Mrs C Pygott, GRSM, ARMCM Ed (*Piano and Oboe*)
Mr S Rouse, BSc Imperial College, PGCE (*Physics*)
Mrs S Rouse, BA Sunderland, PGCE (*Geography*)
Mrs A J Saunders, BSc York, PGCE (*Chemistry, Examinations Officer*)
Mr A P Selway, FRCO, GRSM, ARMCM Perf, ARMCM Teach (*Organ, Pianoforte, Choir Accompanist*)
Miss F Shen, BA Fudan University (*Mandarin, Network Engineer*)
Mr M Sidwell, BA, LRSM (*Trombone*)
Mrs M C Smith, GRSM, LRAM Ed (*Pianoforte, Clarinet, Saxophone, Recorder*)
Mr A C Staniland, BA Leeds, PGCE (**History*)
Mrs H Stansfield, BEd Bedford (*Head of Lower School, Physical Education*)
Mrs L A Taylor-Parker, LRAM (*Speech and Drama*)
Mrs H Wakefield, BSc Aberystwyth, PGCE (*Biology, Mathematics*)
Mr D Webster, BA Mus (*Guitar, Brass, Percussion, Music Technology*)
Miss K Williams, BEd Hons Leeds (**Art*)
Mrs A Wood, BSc Bristol, MA Ed Surrey, PGCE (*Head of Boarding, Mathematics*)
Miss N Woods, BA (*Cello*)

Houses & Housemistresses/masters:
Oakdale: Mrs A Wood

York/Clarence: Mrs P Johnson, Mrs D Easterbrook (*Acting Assistant Housemistress*)
Lincoln East/Lincoln West: Mrs J Knibbs
Tower: Mrs V Hutton
Support Staff:
Medical Officer: Dr S O'Neill, MB, BChir, MA, DRCOG, MRCGP, FPCert
Health Centre Head Nurse: Mrs L Lenehan, RGN
Chaplain: Revd Dr Jan Cheeseman, BA King's College, PhD, PGCE
Assistant Bursar: Mrs J Horner
Registrar: Mrs W Hutchinson
Office Manager: Mrs M Laverack, BEd Reading
Head Secretary: Mrs L O'Neill
Librarian: Mrs F Brady, BSc Leeds Poly, MCLIP
Marketing Manager: Mrs P Robertson

Numbers and Location. Harrogate Ladies' College is a Boarding and Day school for 320 girls aged 11–18. Situated within the College campus, Highfield Prep School, which opened in 1999, is a Day prep school for over 230 boys and girls between the ages of 4–11. The College is situated in a quiet residential area on the Duchy Estate about 10 minutes walk from the town centre and is easily accessible by road and rail networks. Leeds/Bradford airport is 20 minutes' drive away. Harrogate itself is surrounded by areas of natural interest and beauty.

Accommodation. Over half of the pupils are full or weekly boarders. Pupils enter 'Oakdale', the boarding house for 8–13 year olds and then progress to one of the five main houses on site. Upper Sixth Formers enjoy a greater sense of freedom in their own accommodation called 'Tower House'. This contains a large, modern kitchen, comfortable lounges and relaxation areas and girls have individual study bedrooms. Each house has a Housemistress/Housemaster and Assistant Housemistress who are responsible for the well-being of the girls.

Curriculum and Examinations. The College aims to provide a broad-based curriculum for the first three years in line with National Curriculum requirements. This leads to a choice of over 20 subjects at GCSE, Applied, AS and A Level mainly using syllabuses of the Northern Examination and Assessment Board (AQA). Each girl has a form tutor who continuously monitors and assesses her development.

Facilities. The central building contains the principal classrooms, hall, library, and dining rooms, and a VI Form Centre with studies, seminar rooms, kitchens and leisure facilities. The College Chapel is nearby. An extension provides 8 laboratories for Physics, Chemistry, Biology and Computer Studies. Three dedicated computer suites, provision in the boarding houses and throughout the school, form a computer network of 208 computers running Windows XP. Additional facilities for specialised teaching include studies for Art, Pottery, Design and Technology, Drama and also for Home Economics and Textiles. The College has its own amateur radio station. There is a well-equipped Health Centre with qualified nurses.

Sport. The College has its own sports hall, a full size indoor swimming pool, gymnasium, fitness centre, playing field, 9 tennis courts and 2 squash courts. Girls are taught a wide range of sports and may participate in sporting activities outside the school day. Lacrosse and netball are played in winter, and tennis, swimming and athletics are the main summer physical activities. Extra-curricular sports include horse riding, golf, badminton, sub-aqua, windsurfing, skiing, self-defence, judo, sailing and canoeing.

Sixth Form. The College has a thriving Sixth Form Community of 120 pupils. Girls may follow their chosen courses of AS/A Levels or follow the Applied Business qualification for 2 years. They also follow a General Studies course covering a wide variety of subjects, and there is a broad range of general cultural study. In preparation for adult life, Sixth Formers are expected to make a mature contribution to the running of the school and many hold formal positions of responsibility. Personal guidance is given to each girl with regard to her future plans and most pupils choose to continue their education at University.

Religious Affiliation. The College has a Church of England foundation although pupils of other religious denominations are welcomed. Religious teaching is in accordance with the principles of the Church of England and all girls attend Chapel services. A school confirmation is held each year in the chapel and girls may be prepared for acceptance into membership of churches of other denominations.

Music. A special feature is the interest given to music and choral work both in concerts and in the College Chapel, and the girls attend frequent concerts and dramatic performances in Harrogate. There are Junior and Senior choirs, orchestra, string, wind and brass groups.

Scholarships. Open scholarships including music scholarships and exhibitions are awarded annually on the results of an examination held each Spring term and there are also several awards to girls already in the School. Church music scholarships are also awarded.

Fees per term (2008-2009). Full and Weekly Boarding £7,060; Day £4,150. There is a reduction for a girl joining her sister in the School. The fees cover most normal school charges. Individual tuition in a musical instrument, Dance (Ballet/Tap/Modern), Riding or Diction is an extra charge.

Entry. Entry is usually at age 11, 13 or at Sixth Form level. Entry is based on the College's own entrance examination and a school report. Sixth Form entry is conditional upon GCSE achievement and an interview with the Headmaster.

Charitable status. Registered Charity, number 529579. Harrogate Ladies' College exists to provide high quality education for girls.

Heathfield St Mary's
Ascot

London Road Ascot Berkshire SL5 8BQ
Tel: 01344 898343
Fax: 01344 890689
e-mail: registrar@heathfieldstmarys.net
website: www.heathfieldstmarys.com

Board of Governors:
Chairman: Tom Cross Brown, MA Oxon, MBA Insead
Vice-Chairman: Surgeon Vice-Admiral Sir Godfrey Milton-Thompson, KBE, MA, MB Cantab, FRCP, DCH
Anthony Deal
Robert Gregory
Sir John Montgomery-Cuninghame, Bt MA Oxon
Tessa Smith, BA, PGCE, DipM
Mrs Sally Tulk-Hart
Roland Wreford

***Headmistress*: Mrs M McSwiggan**, MA Surrey

Deputy Head, Pastoral: Mrs J Heywood, BSc Kingston
Bursar: Mr J Bueno, FAIA, MCMI
Chaplain: Revd D Duncanson, TD, BA Open, MA Ed London, AKC
Director of Studies: Miss C Fowler, MA London, BA Oxford, PGCE Cambridge

+ *Head of Faculty*
* *Subject Leader/Coordinator*

Science:
*Mr B Russell, BEng London
Mrs J Kemp, BSc London (*Physics, Biology*)
Mrs K Shaw, BEd Warwick (*Physics, Biology*)

Miss C Wells, BSc Hons Bath, PGCE Exeter (*Physics, Biology, Chemistry*)
+Mrs J Treloar, BSc Hons Birmingham, PGCE London (*Chemistry*)
Mr R Taylor, BSc Hons Edinburgh (*Chemistry*)
Mrs J Heywood, BSc Kingston (*Science*)
Mrs C Hobden, BSc Jnt Hons Birmingham (*Senior Lab Technician*)
Mrs A Milner, HND Ulster, BSc Ulster (*Lab Technician*)

Mathematics:
+*Mr J Prout, BSc Hons Oxford Brookes, PGCE Reading
Mrs S Diplock, BSc Exeter, PGCE Canterbury
Miss C Edwards, BA Hons Liverpool, PGCE Bristol
Mr A Mughal, BA Hons Kingston, PGCE Brunel
Mrs M Sherwood, BA Cambridge, PGCE Sussex

ICT:
*Mrs H Edge, BA Liverpool, PGCE Liverpool
*Mrs J Skinner, CertEd Worcester
+Mr J Prout, BSc Hons Oxford Brookes, PGCE Reading

Cookery:
*Mrs C Smith, Cert HE & Ed London
Mrs M Blackburn, BEd Cardiff

Creative Technology:
*Miss K White, BA Hons Oxford Brookes, ABIPP
Mrs V Squires, BA Hons Virginia, USA
Mrs M Blackburn, BEd Cardiff

English:
*Mr S Plummer, BA Hons Liverpool, PGCE Cambridge
Mrs C Kew, BA South Africa, PGCE South Africa
Ms C Leaver, BA York, MA York, PGCE London
Mrs A Andrew, MA Oxon, PGCE

History & Politics:
+*Mrs M Brown, BA Univ of Wales
Mrs G Moore, MA Open, BA London

History of Art:
Dr P Wickson, BA Hons Birmingham, MPhil Birmingham

Latin & Classical Civilisation:
*Mr A Pitman, BA Hons Reading, TESOL Barcelona, PGCE Cardiff
Mrs C Green, BA Bristol, PGCE Cambridge

Geography:
+*Mrs B Mason, BA Hons Nottingham, PGCE London, Cert SpLD
Mrs S Ingram, BEd Hons London

Business Studies:
*Mrs J Skinner, CertEd Worcester

Religious Studies:
*Miss K Slocock, BA Jnt Hons Durham, PGCE Oxford
Revd D Duncanson, TD, BA Open, MA Ed London, AKC
Miss C Fowler, MA London, BA Oxford, PGCE Cambridge

Modern Foreign Languages:
Miss F Rayner, MA Strasbourg, PGCE Oxford Brookes (*Spanish*)
Mrs R Lankshear, M-ès-L Pau, L-ès-L Pau (*French*)
Miss A Baude, M 2 FLE Boulogne, PGCE Canterbury
Mrs A Pullen, BA Hons Spain
Mrs C Clark-Maxwell, BA, MMus Manchester, PGCE Reading, Dip Inst of Linguists (*German*)
Mrs J Tovell, BA Bauru, Brazil (*Portuguese*)
Miss E Lee, BSc Brunel, PGCE Brunel Chinese
Mrs K Forester, BA Hons Spain
Mrs M Strain

Art:
Mr N Tomlinson, MA Oxford Brookes, PGCE London
Mr A Crucefix, BEd Hons London, MA Reading
Mr C Evans

Drama:
Mrs A Andrew, MA Oxon, PGCE
Mrs R Tudor-Barry, BA Hons Bradford, PGDPT
Mrs N Shaw, BA West Sussex, ALAM, RAD TC, AISTD
Mr C Evans

Dance:
Mrs N Shaw, BA West Sussex, ALAM, RAD TC, AISTD

Music:
Miss J Stevens, MA Leicester
Mr B Moles, MMus London, BMus Hons London
Mr M Hallas, BMus Hons London
plus Visiting Peripatetic Staff

Physical Education:
*Mrs N Edwards, BA Hons Liverpool (*Director of Sports and Wellbeing*)
Miss J Talbot, BPhysEd Otago, NZ
Mrs S Reed, BEd Hons Bedford
Miss L Westcott, BSc Hons Manchester, PGCE Birmingham
Miss L Mooney, BSc NC USA
Mrs S Bettison, DipEd London
plus Visiting Tennis and Fencing Coach

PSHE:
*Mrs N Edwards, BA Hons Liverpool
Miss C Fowler, MA London, BA Oxford, PGCE Cambridge

Librarian & Head of Careers:
Mrs K Bramley, MA Univ of Wales, Dip Lib

Spectrum Learning Development:
Mrs T Hynard, Cert SpLD East Berkshire
Mrs A Jones, Diplome de Langues Paris
Mrs B Mason, BA Hons Nottingham, PGCE London, Cert SpLD
Mrs S Butler, BA Hons Oxford
Mrs E O'Kelly, Cert TESOL Trinity
Mrs R Fotheringham, MA Natal, BA Hons Natal, BEd Natal
Mr S Lagden, MA Hons Aberdeen, PGCE Exeter

Pastoral:
Deputy Head, Pastoral: Mrs J Heywood, BSc Kingston
Senior Housemistress: Miss E Pointon
Head of Sixth Form: Mrs S Ingram, BEd Hons London
Residential Head of UVI: Dr P Wickson, BA Hons Birmingham, MPhil Birmingham
Head of House, Somerville: Mrs H Edge, BA Liverpool, PGCE Liverpool
Head of House, Austen: Mrs R Lankshear, M-ès-L Pau, L-ès-L Pau
Head of House, Seacole: Mrs C Kew, BA Hons South Africa, PGCE South Africa
Head of House, De Valois: Miss J Talbot, BPhysEd Otago, NZ
KS3 Coordinator: Mrs J Kemp, BSc London
KS4 Coordinator: Mrs J Skinner, CertEd Worcester
Housemistress, Form I: Mrs C Beresford
Housemistress, Form II: Ms S Crafer
Housemistress, Form III: Ms A Brooks
Housemistress, Form IV: Miss P Turner
Housemistress, Form V: Mrs P Kerley
Housemistress, UVI Form: Mrs A Diaz
Housemistress, LVI Form: Miss S Broomfield
Housemistress, Forms III & IV: Mrs V Leathart

Nursing Sisters:
Senior Nursing Sister: Sister E Hill, SRN, DNCert
Deputy Nursing Sister: Sister V Viljoen, RGN, OHC SA, CNS SA

Administration:
Director of Development : Mr P Geach

Director of IT: Mr M Taylor, BSc Eng London, PGCE Greenwich, FIDM, MBCS, MCIM
Headmistress's PA & Administrative Coordinator: Ms P Lavender, BA Hons Open
Registrar: Mrs R Farha
Deputy Bursar: Mrs L Farrin

Introduction. Heathfield St Mary's is a leading boarding school for girls aged between 11 and 18 years. The school is set in thirty-five acres of stunning grounds with outstanding facilities, just twenty-five miles from London and within easy reach of major airports, motorways and rail networks.

Heathfield St Mary's is unashamedly comfortable but also competitive and academically rigorous. The day does not finish at 4 pm, or the week on Friday! We offer unrivalled opportunities for personal growth and development, seven days a week.

Being part of our community is a real joy. We believe the time spent outside the classroom is just as important as the time spent in it. Evenings and weekends are filled with a diverse range of activities, from clubs and sports, to the Duke of Edinburgh's Award and foreign exchange trips.

Atmosphere and Ethos. At the heart of our school runs a guiding and enlightening Christian ethos. We also embrace technology and use contemporary teaching methods to achieve academic goals. Our aim is to help every student get the most out of life by providing the very best intellectual stimulation, physical challenges and pastoral care.

Pastoral Care. Heathfield St Mary's is a true home from home. Every girl is supported by a team of academic staff, Housemistress, Head of House and two Sixth Form prefects. They work together to provide the highest level of pastoral care, which is one of the school's hallmarks. We believe in individual attention for every girl and teachers will meet with your daughter regularly to discuss her particular needs and to ensure she is achieving her maximum potential.

Curriculum. While the more traditional subject combinations remain most popular, there is also excellence in art, drama and music. Twenty-four subjects are offered at AS and A Level, along with the Leith's basic Certificate of Food and Wine. Academic results are consistently impressive and all girls go on to higher education including Oxbridge.

Activities. The Sports Hall is always a hive of activity and there are many other extra-curricular activities: frequent museum and theatre trips, field trips, workshops and work experience abroad for linguists.

Sport. We have a large multi-purpose gym, two squash courts, dance studio, two lacrosse pitches, tennis courts and an indoor swimming pool. The school competes in lacrosse, netball, polo, skiing and swimming.

Boarding Accommodation. Our boarding accommodation is excellent. From Form IV onwards all girls have single rooms, offering all-important privacy. For more freedom and independence, the Upper Sixth live in a modern Sixth Form House with comfortable lounges and kitchen facilities.

Medical Welfare. We are not just focused on a healthy mind. Two full-time nursing sisters and the school doctor are in charge of the girls' medical welfare supported by heads of years and Housemistress. If you have any concerns please call your daughter's Year Head or Housemother who is available at all times.

New Facilities. The plan for the development of our new facilities including a fully-equipped Sixth Form accommodation block, a Performing Arts Centre and a well-equipped teaching block will take place over the next two years. The library has been extended and refurbished in 2007.

Admission. Entry for the majority of pupils is at eleven; a few girls join at twelve or thirteen or come into the Lower Sixth Form for A Level studies. Junior entrants take entrance papers set by the school or the appropriate Common Entrance examination.

Entry into the Lower Sixth Form is via predicted GCSE grades and tests in intended AS and A Level subjects.

Scholarships. A number of academic, music, art, drama and sports scholarships for entry to the Junior School and Sixth Form are awarded each year.

Fees per term (2008-2009). £8,100 (Years 7–8), £8,698 (Years 9–13).

Charitable status. Heathfield St Mary's School is a Registered Charity, number 309086. It exists to provide a caring boarding education leading to higher education for girls aged between 11 and 18.

Heathfield School (GDST)
Pinner

Beaulieu Drive Pinner Middlesex HA5 1NB
Tel: 020 8868 2346
Fax: 020 8868 4405
e-mail: enquiries@hea.gdst.net
website: www.heathfield.gdst.net

One of the 29 schools of The Girls' Day School Trust. For further information about the Trust, see p. xxiv.

Additional information about the school may be found on the school's website. A detailed prospectus may be obtained from the school.

Founded 1900.

Governing Body:
Sir Michael Partridge, KCB (*Chairman*)

***Headmistress*: Miss C M Juett**, BSc London

Deputy Headmistress: Ms K Hollingdale, BA East Anglia

Assistant Head & Head of Sixth Form: Mrs L Estruch, BSc Manchester

Assistant Head & Programme Director: Ms M Heryet, BA Anglia Ruskin

Head of Junior Department: Mrs C McCulloch, BA Leeds

Head of Careers: Mrs K Walley, BA Oxon

Examinations Officer: Mr R J Pimlott, BA Middlesex

Admissions Secretary: Mrs J Smith

Number of Pupils. 552 (Juniors 161; Seniors 391 including 95 in the Sixth Form).

Heathfield School was founded in Harrow and it moved to its present location in September 1982, and became a member of the Girls' Day School Trust in September 1987. The School is situated on a nine-acre site, including 6 tennis courts and playing fields, and is well served by trains and buses, the nearest stations being Eastcote and Rayners Lane.

We aim to provide a broad and balanced education which will enable girls to achieve their academic personal and social potential within an intellectually stimulating, caring and secure environment, and to prepare them to take responsibility for themselves and others.

The accommodation includes seven Science Laboratories, four Computer Rooms, Art Rooms, Textiles Room, and a large Learning Resources Centre. The Junior Department is housed in new purpose-built separate accommodation where there are 11 classrooms, a Hall, Library and specialist rooms for Music, Science and Technology. A new indoor Swimming Pool, Sports Hall and Senior Library were opened in January 2000. These have been followed by a new Music Suite, ICT Rooms, Careers Room and Science laboratories. A new dining room and Drama Studio followed in 2004. A new Sixth Form Centre is currently under construction and is due for completion in September 2008.

In the Nursery, children learn through the teaching of specific skills and structured play. All the National Curriculum subjects are then taught up to Year 6. ICT is an integral part of the curriculum for all girls and the Juniors have their own computer room and library.

The Senior School then provides a general education up to GCSE and AS/A2 Level, and also offers a wide range of trips, visits and extra-curricular activities. All Sixth Form leavers continue to Universities, including Oxford and Cambridge. All the National Curriculum subjects are offered, plus Textiles, Drama, Latin and Classics. Mandarin, Spanish, German and French are taught. A particular emphasis is placed on the use of ICT across the curriculum. The girls take 10 GCSEs and non-examined courses in PE and Personal, Social and Health Education. Twenty-nine subjects are taught at A Level including Government and Politics, Economics, Business Studies, Psychology, History of Art, Theatre Studies, PE, Law, Media Studies and Sociology. Sixth Form classes are small and the students are encouraged to take greater responsibility for their own learning. Careers education begins in Year 8 and continues right through the Sixth Form. Emphasis is placed on the development of enterprise and leadership skills at all ages.

A special feature of the school is its happy, caring and friendly ethos and its family atmosphere. Pastoral care is accorded a high priority throughout the School and we believe strongly in a triangular partnership between parents, girls and staff. Sport, Music and Drama have a high profile as does Public Speaking and The Duke of Edinburgh's Award. The National Sportsmark Award was given in 2003 and the Artsmark Silver in 2004. A wide range of clubs and societies are on offer covering activities as varied as Model United Nations, Speech and Drama, Chess and dance. Girls are also encouraged to take their share of responsibility for school affairs by serving as form captains and participating in the School Council, as well as serving the local community through social service work.

Admission. Girls enter the School in the Junior Department at 3+, 4+ and 7+, or the Senior School at 11+ and 16+.

An Entrance Examination is held each January for girls wishing to enter the Senior School at 11+ in the following September. Sixth Form places are available for girls who have reached a certain standard at GCSE.

A number of scholarships and bursaries are available. The bursaries are means-tested and are intended to ensure that the school remains accessible to bright girls who would profit from our education but who would be unable to enter the school without financial assistance.

Fees per term (2008-2009). Senior School £3,700; Junior Department (for age 4+ to 10) £2,879; Nursery (for age 3+) £2,221 (including lunches).

Prospectus and registration forms may be obtained from the Admissions Secretary at the school; e-mail: j.smith@hea.gdst.net.

Charitable status. Heathfield School, Pinner is part of The Girls' Day School Trust, which is a Registered Charity, number 306983. The aim of the Trust is to provide a fine academic education for girls, which is distinguished by its breadth, as well as its depth.

Hethersett Old Hall School

Hethersett Norwich NR9 3DW
Tel: 01603 810390
Fax: 01603 812094
e-mail: enquiries@hohs.co.uk
website: www.hohs.co.uk

Chairman of Governors: Revd Michael Yorke

***Head*: Mr S G Crump**, BA, MA, PGCE

Deputy Headmistress: Mrs J Davies, BA Oxford

Senior Housemistress: Ms A Holmes

Bursar: Mrs L Findlay

Head's Secretary: Mrs T O'Hara

Admissions and Marketing Manager: Mr J Harrison

Hethersett Old Hall School, founded in 1938, is conveniently situated between Norwich and Wymondham in 16 acres of attractive grounds.

The school is a charitable trust administered by a Board of Governors, which is in membership of AGBIS. The Head is a member of the GSA and SHA.

The school provides flexi-boarding and day education for 220 pupils aged between 4 and 18 years old. The Pre-Prep Department accepts boys and girls aged 4–7 and from September 2008, the Junior Department will become co-educational with boys accepted into Year 3.

Boarders live in the main house and in the Sixth Form house, in the care of resident house staff who organise an exciting programme of evening and weekend activities. Sixth Form boarders have single or double study-bedrooms.

Aims. Hethersett offers a friendly, supportive environment in which each girl is encouraged to develop her academic, creative and practical skills and to become self-reliant, adaptable, tolerant and concerned for others.

Curriculum. Classes are small, never exceeding 20 pupils for core subjects. Teaching staff are well qualified, well informed and enthusiastic.

The Junior Department provides a thorough grounding in the core curriculum and many opportunities for creative work and music. Girls have access to the main school's specialist facilities.

Pupils in the Senior School are offered a broad range of academic, technological and creative subjects including an independent research project in Year 9, not found in any other school in Britain. Support, advice and individual care throughout the senior school enables pupils to be confident in making the choices involved to plan their future education and careers.

'Value added' results show that pupils achieved up to a whole grade above prediction across the curriculum in the 2007 GCSE and A Level results.

Sixth Form. A wide range of AS and A2 Level subjects is offered. Most Sixth Formers go on to university. In 2007, 100% applicants gained entry into their first-choice university, while 100% applicants in 2008 have been offered places or interviews to study everything from medicine at Oxford to Art at Chelsea. Some choose vocationally-orientated careers in business or community care as an optional career path. Examination results at GCSE and A Level have been consistently good and our pupils are very successful in gaining entry to the course and university of their choice.

Buildings and Facilities. Excellent teaching facilities are the result of an extensive building programme which, in recent years, has included a purpose built Pre-Prep Department, new science laboratories, a sports hall, an indoor swimming pool as well as a new art and technology suite with photography dark room. A new Junior Department building opened in September 2004.

Recreational Activities. The school offers a wide range of recreational activities and optional extras which include music, sport, community service, The Duke of Edinburgh's Award scheme, Young Enterprise and Sports Leaders.

Entrance. Entry is by the school's own assessment or the Common Entrance and interview. Entry to the Sixth Form is by interview, school record and assessment. To obtain a prospectus please contact the Admissions and Marketing Manager.

Fees per term (2008-2009). Pre-Prep Department £2,250; Junior Department (age 7–11): £2,650 (day), £4,450 (boarding); Senior School: £3,525 (day), £6,595 (boarding).

Scholarships. (*see Scholarship Entries section*). Academic: two at 11+; one boarding scholarship from 11+ to 13+; up to 3 at Sixth Form. Two Jubilee Bursaries also available at 11+ (means tested). Non-Academic: Sport for Year 7 entry, Music in Year 9, significant contribution to a specific area or subject for Year 12 entry.

Charitable status. Hethersett Old Hall School is a Registered Charity, number 311273. It exists to provide a high quality education.

Highclare School

10 Sutton Road Erdington Birmingham B23 6QL
Tel: 0121 373 7400
Fax: 0121 373 7445
e-mail: abbey@highclareschool.co.uk
website: www.highclareschool.co.uk

Founded 1932.

Highclare School is an independent day school for girls from 18 months–18 years and for boys aged 18 months–11 years and a co-educational Sixth Form.

Governors:
Mr J A Barrett (*President*)
Mrs L Flowith (*Chairman*)
Mr I Hazel
Mrs P Mayall
Mr B Pattni
Mr R O Dauncey
Mrs S Watson
Mr K Brown
Mr D Travers
Mr G Comfort
Mr J Brain

***Headmistress*: Mrs M Viles**, BA Hons Nottingham, MEd, PGCE Cambridge

Academic Head: Mrs B J Brown, BSc Hons Nottingham, PGCE
Pastoral Head: Mrs E Bates, CertEd, BEd Hons Southampton
Head of Abbey Junior Department: Mrs H Jones, CertEd, BEd Manchester
Head of Highclare Woodfield: Mrs L Jude, CertEd Chester
Deputy Head of Highclare Woodfield: Mrs A Clarke, BEd Hons Leeds, CertEd Bingley
Head of Highclare St Paul's: Mrs J Booker, DipEd Edinburgh, MEd Birmingham
Deputy Head of Highclare St Paul's & Curriculum Manager KS1 & KS2: Mrs B Mandley, CertEd Keele
Head of Sixth Form: Mrs L J Embury, LLB Hons Wolverhampton, C&G CertEd
Head of Nursery: Mrs J Laker, NVQ3
Examinations Secretary: Mrs S Nash, CertEd Durham, Dip PrimScience UCE
Registrar: Mrs J Baden, AMDIS Diploma
Finance Manager: Mr N Hitchman, ACCA

* *Head of Department*

Careers Department:
Mrs S Howell-Jones, GMus Huddersfield, PGCE UCE

Art:
*Mrs H Suter, BA Hons Birmingham, PGCE
Mrs H Good, BEd Hons Worcester

Business Studies and Law:
*Mrs L J Embury, LLB Hons Wolverhampton, C&G CertEd
Mrs S L Ratledge, HND Business and Finance

English:
*Mrs S Riley, BA Hons Leicester, PGCE
Mrs E Bates, CertEd, BEd Hons Southampton
Mrs K M Quirke, BEd Hons Leeds
Mrs A Moore, BA Hons UCE, PGCE Birmingham
Mrs J Hobbs, BA Hons Bristol, PGCE, MA Birmingham

Geography:
*Mrs L Clarke, BA Hons Birmingham, PGCE
Mrs K Rivett, BEd Birmingham, CertEd

Health and Social Care: *Mrs A Sargent, SEN

History:
*Mrs L Edwards, BA Hons Swansea, PGCE
Miss M Watson, BA Hons Durham, MA Warwick

Home Economics: *Mrs A Cobbold, BEd Bath

ICT:
*Mrs M Morris, ANCM
*Mrs H Geddes, TCert C&G

Mathematics:
*Mrs A Toley, BSc Hons London, PGCE
Mrs S Cook, BSc Hons Nottingham, PGCE
Mrs A Healey, BA Hons Durham, PGCE Durham

Modern Languages:
*Mrs J Lightfoot, BA Hons Newcastle upon Tyne, PGCE Warwick
Mrs A Owen, BA Hons Leicester, PGCE
Mrs P K Litting, BA Hons London Ext, PGCE
Mrs J Unsworth, BA Bristol, PGCE

Music:
*Mrs S Howell-Jones, GMus Huddersfield, PGCE UCE

Physical Education:
*Mrs A de Sousa-Bartlett, BEd Hons St Mary's College
Miss K Harvey, BA, HDipEd Rhodes University

Psychology:
*Mr P Slobodian, BA Hons Hull, MPhil Psychol, PgD Clin Drim Birmingham, DASS, CQSW Southampton, PGCE Leeds

Religious Education: *Mrs A Murray, BA Theol, CertEd Manchester

Science:
*Dr M Smyth, BSc, PhD Belfast, PGCE QTS Wolverhampton
Mrs M Bellshaw, BSc Hons London, PGCE
Mrs B J Brown, BSc Hons Nottingham PGCE
Mrs J Baker, Goldsmiths London, CertEd
Miss M J Hopkins, BSc Hons, PGCE Bath

Sociology: *Dr D Edwards, BA Hons Liverpool, PhD, PGCE

Speech Training and Drama:
*Mrs J Thornton, BA Hons Birmingham, PGCE UCE

Junior Department Staff:
*Mrs H Jones, CertEd, BEd Manchester
*Mrs J Booker, DipEd Edinburgh, MEd Birmingham
Miss J Arnold, BEd Hons Newman College
Miss H Berry, BA Hons Durham, PGCE
Miss D Dunne, CertEd Rugby, BEd Walsall, MEd Birmingham
Miss J Elkington, BSc Hons, PGCE
Mrs S Nash, CertEd Durham, DipPrimScience UCE
Mrs A Olney, BA Hons Hull, PGCE Birmingham
Mrs S C J Pears, BSc Hons Leeds, PGCE Open
Mr D Read, BEd Hons Derby
Mr M Robinson, BEd Hons, CertEd ONC
Mrs S Spare, BA York
Mrs S Taylor, CertEd Wales

Mrs S Toseland, BA Hons Birmingham, PGCE

Preparatory Department Staff:
*Mrs L Jude, CertEd Chester
Mrs C Antcliffe, BA Hons Westhill, PGCE
Mrs B Barlow, CertEd Birmingham
Mrs L Bayliss, BA Hons Liverpool, MA RCA, PGCE, QTS Birmingham
Mrs K S Butts, BA Hons UCE, PGCE
Mrs A Clarke, BEd Hons Leeds, CertEd Bingley
Mrs J Colman-Clarke, BA Open, CertEd Oxford
Mrs M Craddock, BEd
Mrs D Dyal, BA Hons Open, CertEd, NNEB
Mrs S Gething, CertEd
Mrs J Harris, FdA Ey's Birmingham, NNEB
Mrs B Mandley, CertEd Keele
Mrs S McElveny, BA Hons
Mrs M Moore, Catholic TCert in RE Birmingham
Mrs M Smith, CertEd Birmingham
Mrs M Spooner, CertEd Bristol
Mrs D Read, BA Hons Sheffield, QTS
Mrs Y Wildig, CertEd Worcs
Miss S Wilkins, BA Hons, MSc Humberside, QTS
Mrs J Wilson, CertEd Birmingham
Mrs P Wright, CertEd Nottingham

Nursery and Care Scheme:
Mrs J Laker, NVQ3 (*Manager*)
Mrs B Cook, NNEB (*Deputy Manager*)
Mrs S Pointon, NNEB (*Deputy Manager*)

Location. The School is situated on three sites on the main road (A5127) between Four Oaks, Sutton Coldfield and Birmingham. The girls' Junior and Senior Department and co-educational Sixth Form, occupying a former Benedictine Abbey, is on direct train and bus routes from Birmingham City Centre, Tamworth, Lichfield and Walsall. There are school buses from Coleshill, Four Oaks, Aldridge, Streetly, Tamworth and Lichfield to all three sites. Wrap-around care operates from 8.00 am until 6.00 pm for the parents who require it, including holiday cover.

Number of pupils. Approximately 720 day pupils.

Organisation. The school is divided into four departments:

Nursery and Preparatory Department (age 18 months to 7 years, Girls and Boys).

The Nursery caters for children from 18 months to 3 years and although an independent unit it has the support of the facilities and resources of the Preparatory Department. The staged development programme stimulates and encourages children providing a natural progression of continuous educational care.

The Preparatory Department staffed by qualified teachers, teaching assistants and NNEB nursery nurses caters for children from 3 to 7+ years. Because of small classes staff are able to devote a great deal of attention to each child thus encouraging both confidence and independence. A wide variety of well balanced activities ensures that each child is given every opportunity to develop his/her physical, social and academic potential to the full. The Department is able to provide a secure and stimulating introduction to school life with much emphasis being placed on Maths, English, Science and IT at Key Stage 1.

Junior Departments (age 7+ to 11 years, Girls and Boys on two sites). (Entry by School's own assessment procedure).

The Junior Departments with classes of approximately 20 pupils follow National Curriculum guidelines. Pupils are taught as a whole class or within ability groups using a combination of traditional and modern methods. Much emphasis is placed on the teaching of English and Mathematics where work takes account of the National Numeracy and Literacy Strategies. Science and ICT are also taught as core subjects. Pupils have the benefit of specialist tuition in Science, French (from age 7), PE and Music and ICT in Year 6. Thus a solid foundation is established for an easy, natural transition to Senior School.

Other foundation subjects are taught by subject and by class teachers.

Many extra-curricular activities are open to pupils in the Junior School. These include instrumental tuition, choirs, orchestra, windband, recorder club, speech and drama, dance, ballet, art, computing, knitting, golf, judo, chess, table tennis, games and scrabble clubs. In addition a wide range of sporting activities are pursued, led by the school's PE staff, with the assistance of tennis, football, golf and cricket coaches.

Senior Department (age 11 to 16, Girls). (Entry by School's own examination).

Highclare prides itself on providing all the benefits of a small school constantly striving to attain individual excellence for all members of its community which embraces all aspects of 'Every Child Matters'. Alongside a pastoral system which embraces all the facets of pupil development, we offer a wide academic curriculum which offers flexibility and is tailored to pupil need. The PSHE programme includes careers guidance, industrial awareness, health education and citizenship and encompasses the school ethos.

Through a wide programme of enrichment activities every child has the opportunity to enjoy activities beyond the academic and develop areas of expertise helping them to develop into confident and multi-skilled adults.

The full curriculum is covered at KS3. At GCSE all students study English Language and Literature, Mathematics, Science and Additional Science, with the opportunity for some to study the separate sciences, and a modern foreign language, either French or German. Options choices include Geography, History, Religious Studies, Art & Design, Home Economics, Music, Drama, Design & Technology and Physical Education, and a second language (either French or German). There is also the opportunity for some to study Spanish in addition to their language. In addition to their examination subjects girls also study PSHE which includes careers guidance and citizenship. From Sept 2007, girls will take the ECDL qualification in Information Technology. Physical Education also forms an important part of the curriculum.

Co-educational Sixth Form (age 16+). The Sixth Form timetable is structured to meet the individual requirements of each student. The school has a strong academic tradition and students may select from a wide range of A and AS Level subjects. Those students seeking a vocational course may choose to combine A Levels with an applied A Level (single or double award) in Business or Health and Social Care. Opportunities for leadership and community service are an integral part of the Sixth Form life and enable the students to develop into mature and responsible citizens.

Examinations. *GCSE*: OCR including CLAIT I, EDEXCEL, AQA

GCE: EDEXCEL, AQA, OCR, Applied Business, Health & Social Care.

Music examinations: Associate Board of Royal School of Music.

Elocution and Drama: LAMDA.

Sport. The flourishing Sports Department has a gymnasium and sports fields. Activities include hockey, netball, swimming, rounders, tennis, athletics, football, cricket, cross-country, golf, trampolining, badminton, dance and gymnastics.

Extra-Curricular Activities include orchestra, windband, choirs, debating society and tuition is available in a variety of musical instruments and singing. Speech and drama are also available and community service is encouraged.

Entrance Scholarships. (*see Scholarship Entries section*). Entrance scholarships are available each year for the 11+ age group. These will be awarded to the best all-round candidates, consideration being given to girls exhibiting special academic qualities and having musical, artistic or sporting talents. There are also scholarships for the Sixth Form.

Bursaries. Some bursaries are available for candidates who can make an outstanding/special contribution to the School where there is a proven case of financial need. Awards are means-tested and subject to satisfactory performance both academically and in other respects.

Fees per term (2008-2009). £1,335–£3,050.

School Aims.

- To provide high quality teaching and to encourage independent learning within a secure and happy environment.
- To motivate each individual pupil to achieve her (his) full all round potential.
- To develop the values of self-respect and self-discipline, alongside tolerance and respect for others.

Charitable status. Highclare School is a Registered Charity, number 528940. It exists to provide education for children.

Hollygirt School

Elm Avenue Nottingham NG3 4GF
Tel: 0115 958 0596
Fax: 0115 989 7929
e-mail: info@hollygirt.co.uk
website: www.hollygirt.co.uk

***Headmistress*: Mrs P S Hutley**, BA Hons Worcester, PGCE Wales, MSc Huddersfield

Deputy Head: Mr J M W P Burslem, BEng Hons Brunel, PGCE Nottingham (*Physics*)

Senior School:

Heads of Pastoral Care:
Lower School: Mrs S W Atherton, MA Oxon, PGCE Oxford
Upper School: Miss J C Melia, BEd Hons Leeds

Assistant Staff:
Mrs S W Atherton, MA Oxon, PGCE Oxford (*Head of Science, Biology*)
Mr R A C Bill, BEng Hons Liverpool, PGCE Oxford, MIT (*Director of ICT*)
Mr D Briggs (*Head of Geography*)
Mrs S Brooksby, BA Hons Leeds, PGCE Bristol (*Head of History*)
Mrs R Brown, DipEd Bristol (*Head of Design & Technology*)
Mrs D Griffiths, BA Hons Leicester, PGCE Nottingham (*Head of Religious Studies*)
Miss G Harris, BA Hons Anglia (*English and Drama*)
Miss L Howd, BSc Hons East Anglia, PGCE Nottingham (*Head of Mathematics, Examinations Officer*)
Miss M Ifould, BEd Ilkley, Dip Careers Education (*Head of Physical Education & Outdoor Pursuits, Head of Careers*)
Mr C Kay, BA Hons Sheffield, PGCE Nottingham (*English and Drama*)
Mrs B McEwen, BA Hons CNAA, Cheltenham, PGCE Leeds (*Art & Design, Design & Technology*)
Dr D McKitterick, BSc Hons, PhD Nottingham (*Physics*)
Miss J C Melia, BEd Hons Leeds (*Head of English*)
Mrs J Miles, BEd Sussex (*Physical Education*)
Mrs S C Price, BSc Hons York (*Chemistry, Special Educational Needs*)
Mrs J Purchase, BA Hons, CertEd Keele (*Head of Music*)
Mrs C Searle, BEd Cardiff (*Design & Technology*)
Mrs A R Standing, BA Hons Newcastle, PGCE Leeds (*Head of Art & Design*)
Mrs J E Storey GRSM Music – ACCM – Saxophone (*Music*)
Mrs M A Turner, BSc Hons Durham, PGCE Oxford (*Science*)
Mrs F Twomey, BA Hons Nottingham, PGCE Leicester (*French and German*)
Mrs G Walsh, BSc Hons Durham, PGCE Oxford (*French*)
Mrs A M Whitaker, BA Hons Coventry, PGCE Huddersfield (*Head of Modern Languages*)
Mrs S Williams, BSc Hons, PGCE Sheffield (*Mathematics*)
Mrs C Wood, BEd Hons Nottingham

Junior Department:
Head: Mrs J Holberton, BSc Hons London, MSc Hull, PGCE Hull
Deputy Head: Mrs E Straw, BA Hons Hull, PGCE Nottingham, MEd Sheffield

Assistant Staff:
Mrs S Allen, BA Hons, PGCE Leicester
Miss V Carlin, BSc Hons Warwick, PGCE Kingston
Mrs J Fitzgerald, CertEd London, DipSpLD Nottingham (*Learning Support*)
Mrs C Keyworth, BA Hons NTU
Mrs Stephanie Payne, BA Hons Sheffield, PGCE Warwick
Mrs D Plumb, BA Hons, PGCE
Miss G Pykett, BEd Hons Plymouth
Mrs H Nicholson, NNEB Nottingham (*Nursery Nurse*)
Mrs C Gibson, CertEd Coventry (*325 Club Supervisor*)
Mrs P Upton (*325 Club Assistant*)
Mrs J Woodfield, ASA (*Swimming*)

Classroom Assistants:
Mrs L Swift, NNEB (*Healthcare Coordinator*)
Mrs S Mahl
Mrs P Mason, BTEC

Bursar: Mrs D M Zinsaz, BA London
Marketing Manager: Mrs W Nuttall, BSc Hons Coventry, Dip Mktg NTU
Registrar & Headmistress's Secretary: Miss L E Raybould, BA Hons NTU
School Secretary: Mrs D Wojtulewicz, BA Hons NTU
Receptionists: Mrs L Clark, Mrs B Marson
Science and Technology Technician: Mr R Arnold, BA Hons, BTEC Nat Science
ICT Technician: Mr M Blakemore

Visiting Staff:
Mr C Bowen (*Drums*)
Mr T Elliot, BMus Hons RCM (*Woodwind*)
Mr D Hollingsworth, BA Hons, MSc (*Guitar*)
Mrs J Ibbett, ALCM, LRAM, LLCM, DPSE (*Piano*)
Mr D Ives (*Flute*)
Mrs M A Land, Gold Medal LAM, Member of Society of Teachers of Speech and Drama (*Speech and Drama*)
Mrs J McDouall, ARCM London (*Singing*)
Mrs J Parsons-Wiles, BA Hons CNAA, PGCE Manchester (*Flute*)
Mr J Schofield (*Drums*)
Mrs C A Seedhouse, BMus Sheffield, CertEd Nottingham (*Violin*)
Mr A Wheat (*Oboe*)
Mrs M Wright, LRAM, LLCM (*Piano*)

Located in a tree-lined walkway, just North of the city centre, Hollygirt School occupies several large Victorian houses, which are designed to create a 'family feel'.

Founded in 1877, Hollygirt is a day school and administered as a non-profit making educational trust. There are about 300 girls in the School between the ages of 3 and 16 of whom 90 are in the Junior School. In 2003 the school added another building to provide facilities for Drama and Textiles, and additional classrooms. The school has the use of Nottingham University's sports facilities, including a swimming pool, as well as Harvey Haddon Athletics Stadium. Recently the school purchased a new garden to provide recreational facilities for the Senior School and extended facilities for 3–5 year olds.

The school aims to provide a well-balanced education in a caring environment with emphasis on the needs and abilities of individual girls. In addition to academic success, the school is concerned with the spiritual, moral, cultural and physical development of each girl as she is prepared for the opportunities, responsibilities and experience of adult life. All girls are encouraged to take a positive and enthusiastic approach to whatever they undertake, whether in form, games or leisure activities. Extra help in Mathematics and English is given on an individual or small group basis.

After leaving Hollygirt, girls proceed to A Level courses in the sixth forms of other independent day and boarding schools or local sixth form colleges and schools.

Curriculum. The curriculum includes English, Mathematics, Science, French, German, Design and Technology, Art, History, Geography, Religious Studies, ICT, Music, Drama, Vocational Studies and Physical Education. Statistics is also offered.

Games. Hockey, netball, athletics, cross-country running, tennis, basket and volleyball, unihoc, rounders, football, softball, badminton and swimming.

Careers. A programme of careers advice begins in Year 9. The School is a member of the Independent Schools Careers Organisation, which offers careers guidance to parents, staff and girls in member schools.

Extra-Curricular Activities. These include Orchestra, Choir, Duke of Edinburgh's Award, Netball Club, trips to the theatre, ice skating, a programme of sports matches, drama productions, and lunchtime clubs that include Art, French, Computing, Cookery and Table Tennis. School travel opportunities have included visits to France, Germany, Mexico and skiing in various parts of Europe.

Admission. Entry to the Preparatory Form (age 3 or 4 years) is dependent on readiness for school and availability of places; for Years 1 and 2 on availability of places. Girls entering Years 3, 4, 5, 6 spend a day in School during which informal testing takes place. Entry to the Senior School is at 11 (Year 7) although places occasionally become available in other years. Early in the Spring Term preceding entry, applicants are required to sit the School's entrance examination and have an interview.

Fees per term (2008-2009). £1,950 (Nursery Class to Year 2), £2,090 (Years 3–6), £2,760 (Years 7–11). Speech and Music tuition are extra at £155 per 10 lesson term.

Hollygirt Old Girls Association (HOGA). The Secretary, Mrs S Allan, can be contacted via the school.

Charitable status. The Rhoda Jessop Educational Charity is a Registered Charity, number 508617. The aim is to provide an all round education which will prepare a girl for today's competitive, uncertain and rapidly changing world.

Assistant Headteachers:
Mr M Dunnington, CertEd
Mrs V Vincent, BA, PGCE, AMIA

School Chaplain: The Revd D Lamb, BA

Senior School Staff:
Dr M Amin, BSc Hons, PhD, QTS
Mrs E Beverley, Lic d'Anglais, PGCE
Mr E Carwithen, MA Hons, CertEd
Mrs W Fryman, MA, BSc, PGCE
Dr M J Hinton, BSc Hons, PhD, PGCE
Mrs K Isherwood, BEd
Mrs K Johnston, BA Hons, PGCE
Mrs J Mackie-Smith, BA Hons
Mrs A Pioli, CertEd
Mr A Rex, MA, PGCE
Mrs H Tehan, BA Hons, QTS
Mrs J Thomas, BEd
Mrs K Townley, MA, BA Hons, CertEd
Mr C Walmsley, BA Hons, PGCE

Lower School Staff:
Mr P Booth, BEd
Mrs E Desmond, MA, BSc, PGCE
Mrs J Ferris, BA Hons, PGCE
Mrs C Kingett, CertEd
Mrs J Powell, BEd Hons (*Director of Music*)

Nursery School Staff:
Nursery Manager: Miss G Carter, BTEC Cert

Miss S Brown, BTEC Dip
Miss E Browning, BTEC Dip
Mrs B Buckby
Miss C Cartwright NVQ Early Years
Miss J Egginton
Mrs C Evans, BTEC Dip
Miss L Harris, BTEC
Miss S Hall
Miss J Gallagher, NNEB
Mrs M Laughton, NVQ Early Years
Miss K Moore, NVQ Early Years
Mrs J Owen, NNEB
Miss K Pandhal, BTEC Dip
Miss J Potter, NNEB
Miss A Smith, BTEC
Miss J Smith, BTEC Cert
Mrs S Smith, Cert Childminding Practice

Elocution/Ballet/Music:
Ms S Broder
Miss A Brown, LLAM, ABBO
Mrs J Fisher, CertEd
Mrs N Lane
Miss J Lau
Mrs A Lipman, LRAM
Mrs S Reading
Mrs C Vetch, GTCL, LTCL
Mrs M Willmot

Classroom Assistants:
Mrs J Farley, HND
Mrs P Naylor
Mrs M Polito, PPA Dip

Administrative Staff:
Finance Officer: Mrs T Irving
Headteacher's PA/Registrar: (*to be appointed*)
Office Manager: Miss S Hartland
School Secretary: Mrs M Guinan
Laboratory Technician: Mrs H Moore, BSc Hons

Holy Trinity School
Kidderminster

Birmingham Road Kidderminster Worcs DY10 2BY
Tel: 01562 822929
Fax: 01562 865137
e-mail: office@holytrinity.co.uk
website: www.holytrinity.co.uk

***Headteacher*: Mrs Y Wilkinson**, BA Hons, PGCE, NPQH

Deputy Headteacher: Ms P Wright, BEd Hons

Introduction. Holy Trinity School is a member of International Education Systems and welcomes all denominations and none. Catering for children in the Nursery from 3 months to 18 years of age in the Sixth Form, we provide a continuity of education which ensures a smooth transition through every Key Stage of development. In Nursery and Lower School, our classes are co-educational, progressing to a single-sex senior girls school and a co-educational Sixth Form from September 2008.

HTS is a caring, nurturing school and believes strongly in an environment which encourages and supports the individual and allows everyone to shine. Visitors to the school frequently comment on our friendliness and welcoming community – our pupils are happy! HTS continues to achieve very impressive examination results with significant value added and is ranked amongst the top 50 independent schools in the country. Opportunities abound, including overseas trips, clubs, societies and charitable work. Music, drama and sporting activities all contribute to pupils' development.

Inclusive pre-school and after-school care is available from 8.00 am (7.30 am by prior arrangement) until 6.00 pm.

Location. Located approximately ten minutes from Kidderminster train station and positioned on the A456 road to Birmingham, the school is easily accessible by all main services.

Buildings. The school is housed on one campus with connecting buildings. Facilities include spacious classrooms, specialist subject science laboratories, two computer suites, gymnasium and fitness suite, senior and lower school libraries and an impressive refurbished indoor swimming pool.

Organisation. The school is divided into five sections:
Nursery: boys and girls (3 months–3 years)
Little Trinity: boys and girls (3–4+ years)
Lower School: boys and girls (5–11 years)
Senior School: girls only (11–16 years)
Sixth Form: boys and girls (16–18 years)

Curriculum. With the emphasis on a broad, balanced education, the curriculum provides both stretch and support. There is a wide range of subjects available at GCSE. Most students sit eleven GCSE subjects. 18 subjects are offered at A Level. Throughout the senior school, girls are set for core subjects and, on entry, they are assigned to one of the four houses. Reports are sent to parents on a half-termly basis to help monitor progress, with one full report annually. Parents are always welcome to discuss their child's progress, but the school holds one official parents' evenings a year to allow discussion with subject staff.

Extra-Curricular Activities. Students' talents and interests are extended through an exciting programme of activities. Extra-curricular activities include 'Learning to Lead', international exchanges, fencing, self-defence, science club, drama, public speaking, choirs, orchestra, Duke of Edinburgh's Award Scheme, ballet, art, chess, cookery, dance, fitness, Latin, netball, gymnastics, speech and drama, ornithology and many more. The Lower Sixth participates in the Young Enterprise Business Scheme.

For all students, pre-school and after-school care and homework clubs are available on a daily basis.

Admissions. Students are invited to visit the school for two days and undertake the entrance examination appropriate for their age. The 11+ Transfer Assessment/Scholarship Examinations for entry to the Senior School are taken in the January preceding September entry. Admissions for all ages are accepted throughout the academic year. You are warmly invited to visit us.

Scholarships. Academic, music and sporting scholarships are available at 11+ and Sixth Form. A limited number of means-tested Bursaries are also available.

Fees per term (from January 2008). Nursery £1,490 (full-time); Transition £1,590 (full-time); Reception £1,725, Years 1–2 £1,895, Years 3–4 £2,100, Years 5–6 £2,340, Senior School £2,865.

Charitable status. Holy Trinity School is a Registered Charity, number 517893. It exists to provide quality education for girls and boys.

Howell's School
Denbigh

Denbigh North Wales LL16 3EN
Tel: 01745 813631
Fax: 01745 814443
e-mail: enquiries@howells.org
website: www.howells.org

***Principal*: Miss Rachael Hodgson**, BA London

Senior School Staff:
Miss Julie Anglesea (*Careers; Examinations Officer*)
Miss Sally Armond, BA, MSc, ScTech, PGCE (*ICT*)
Mrs Frances Bagnall, BSc, PGCE (*Physics*)
Mrs Caroline White, PGCE, BA (*Business Studies*)
Mrs Lorraine McCale, BA Ed (*Head of History*)
Mrs Clare Leavy, BEd (*RE, PE, Senior Mistress*)
Dr Paul Humberstone, BSc, PhD, PGCE (*Chemistry*)
Mrs Patricia Jones, MEd, BS Ed, BA (*English; Psychology*)
Miss Philippa Jones, BSc, PGCE (*Head of Mathematics*)
Mrs Liz Loughlin, BA, PGCE (*Head of Languages/Head of Sixth Form*)
Mrs Donna MacLennan, BEd (*Geography*)
Mme Benedicte Gillet, MEd, BA (*French*)
Dr Daniela Molinari, PhD
Mrs Chris Morris, BSc, PGCE (*Biology*)
Mrs Morwen Murray, BA, AGSM (*Music*)
Miss Helen Price, BA, PGCE (*PE*)
Mrs M Scott, BA, PGCE (*Mathematics*)
Mr Paul Vernon, BA, PGCE (*Art*)
Mrs Anne Wales, BA, PGCE (*Drama, English & German*)
Dr Michelle Wilton, BSc, PhD, PGCE (*Biology*)
Miss Anna Wright, MA, PGCE (*Head of English Language/Literature and Drama*)

Preparatory School Staff:
Mrs Gillian Platt, BA, PGCE (*KS2*)
Mrs B Glover, BPhil Ed
Miss Bethan Hughes, NNEB (*Nursery*)
Mrs Anne Lowe, BA, MA, PGCE (*Year 1 Teacher; PE Coordinator*)
Mrs Elaine Lewis, BEd
Miss S Roberts, BA Hons, PGCE (*Primary*)
Miss T Noakes, NQT
Mrs Diana Stafford, BEd (*Technology; Art*)
Mrs Valerie Sydenham, BSc, PGCE (*KS1*)
Mrs Sioned Terry, BMus, DipTech (*Music; Club & Music Productions*)
Miss Kellie Kibble-White, Childcare Dip Level 3 (*Nursery*)
Mrs Deborah Griffiths (*Nursery*)
Miss Rachael Jones (*Nursery*)

Principal's Assistant: Mrs Patricia Pearson
School Officer: Mrs Cathy Hughes
Bursar: Mrs Metta Smith
Prep School Secretaries: Mrs Sue Salt, Mrs Emily Collins

Peripatetic staff:
Music:
Mrs Rebekah Noot
Mr Geoff Coward
Mrs Lorna Todd
Mrs Nia Roberts
Mr Richard Shemilt
Mr David Hopkins
Mrs Mary Hopkins
Speech and Drama:
Mrs P Evers-Swindell, LAM, LSRB

Mrs Deborah Thomas (*Speech and Drama*)
Welsh: Mr Trevor Lewis

Nursing Staff:
Mrs Caroline Haydon

Technical Staff:
Mrs Christine Rendall (*Science*)
Mr Mark Hill (*IT*)

Boarding Staff:
Stanley House (5th and 6th): Mrs Caroline White, Mrs Jennie Weijburg
St George's (Prep, 1st–4th): Miss Jo Lea, Mrs A Van Heedan

Equine Staff:
Mrs S Hamlyn (*Yard Manager*)
Miss W Gerrard

Estates Staff:
Caretaker/Porter: Mr Paul Gibson
Catering Manager: Mr Phil Watson
On-site Catering Manager: Mrs Gwenfyl Wynne
Housekeeping Manager: Mrs Maureen Jones

Howell's is a flourishing Boarding and Day School for some 250 girls and boys. The Senior School is all girls, the Preparatory School and Nursery co-educational. Academic performance is strong and 95% of the Sixth Form go on to Higher Education at Universities. Pupils gain places at Oxford and Cambridge. The Nursery is open 52 weeks of the year and places are available from age 2.

The School is situated in delightful surroundings on the edge of the market-town of Denbigh and is easily accessible via the motorway network from the North and the Midlands. Chester is 40 minutes distant and Liverpool and Manchester one hour away. Centres in Shropshire are up to two hours driving time away. British Rail operates frequent services to Rhyl and to Chester.

The Principal will be happy to send a prospectus, DVD, fact sheet and examination results on request and to meet parents, sons and daughters at any time, to provide full information and to show them round the School.

Fees per term (2008-2009). Boarders: £3,500–£6,050 (age 7–18); Day Pupils: £1,650–£3,700 (age 2–18).

Entrance requirements. The main 11+ examinations take place in January. Assessments for other age groups (2 to 16) occur throughout the year and scholarships/awards are available. A limited number of Scholarship awards are also reserved for those who exhibit special talents such as in Art, Music, Speech and Drama or Sport. Service Bursaries and reductions for siblings are also offered.

Buildings. The original school was built in 1859, and has been enlarged and improved on numerous occasions since that time. The School contains all the normal facilities including six science laboratories, a large library, twenty-five individual music practice rooms, Art and Design complex, a drama studio, a theatre workshop area and recording studio, IT teaching floor consisting of a teaching classroom and 12 individual computer suites.

Grounds. There are completed laytex courts, 4 grass tennis courts and grounds of a quality to have been used for international matches, a heated swimming pool, a magnificent sports complex and aerobics suite. The equestrian centre provides riding as well as equine qualifications. The School also has lakeside facilities at Brenig Lake.

Curriculum. The School presently has an overall staff student ratio of 1:9. The school subjects include Religious Studies, English, English Literature, Media Studies, History, Geography, French, Performing Arts, German, Spanish, Welsh, Mathematics, Information Technology, Business Studies, Physics, Chemistry, Biology, Physical Education, Art, Music, Spoken English, Gymnastics and Games, Drama, Sports Leadership and Duke of Edinburgh's Award. Additionally, at Sixth Form level: Photography, Psychology, Equine Studies and Young Enterprise, CSLA.

Examinations. Girls are prepared for GCSE, AS and A Level examinations; University Entrance and Scholarship Examinations; Schools for Music and Speech and Drama, the Poetry Society and Guildhall School of Music and Drama and London Academy of Music and Dramatic Art examinations.

Charitable status. The Foundation of Howell's School, Denbigh is a Registered Charity, number 1061485. The income derived from the charity is to be awarded to pupils or former pupils in the form of prizes, scholarships, allowances or grants. The school functions within a framework of Christian beliefs and values.

Howell's School Llandaff (GDST)

Cardiff Road Llandaff Cardiff CF5 2YD
Tel: 029 2056 2019
Fax: 029 2057 8879
e-mail: mail@how.gdst.net
website: www.gdst.net/howells-llandaff

Howell's School, Llandaff was founded in 1860 as a school for girls. It was built by the Drapers' Company from the endowment left by Thomas Howell, son of a Welshman, merchant of London, Bristol and Seville and a Draper, in 1537. In 1980 the Council of the Girls' Public Day School Trust became the Trustee.

Howell's School is one of the 29 schools of The Girls' Day School Trust. For further information about the Trust, see p. xxiv. Additional information may be found on the school's website and a more detailed prospectus may be obtained from the school.

Chairman of Governors: Mrs A Campbell, JP, DL

***Principal*: Mrs S Davis**, BSc London

Deputy Principal: Mrs M Gosney, BSc Bristol, PGCE Cambridge, MA EdMgt London

Head of Sixth Form College: Mrs N Chyba, BA London

Head of Senior School: Dr S Southern, BSc PhD Durham

Head of Junior School: Mrs J Ashill, BEd Swansea

School Business Manager: Mr J S Williams, BSc Wales

Student numbers. 850: Nursery 40; Junior School 260; Senior School 550 (187 in Sixth Form College).

Howell's School is regarded as the leading academic school in Wales with consistently outstanding results. All students are encouraged to fulfil their considerable potential by becoming confident, independent learners, a process which begins in the Nursery and Junior School and continues throughout the Senior School and College. There is a strong commitment to pastoral care and a wide range of talents and essential life skills are fostered through the academic curriculum and the extensive extra-curricular programme. With its first-class facilities for music, sports, drama and art, the school provides an all-round education for girls between the ages of 3 and 16 and male and female students between the ages of 16 and 18.

The school is situated within easy reach of the Cardiff city centre and set in 18 acres of grounds. The splendid grey stone building, designed by Decimus Burton which has been expanded and modernised, is still the focal point of the school. In addition there are four large Victorian houses and new purpose-built accommodation which house the Junior School, the Nursery, Music School and the Sixth Form College.

A new style co-educational Sixth Form College opened in September 2005. The College is located in the newly refurbished Sixth Form houses and offers students a distinctive programme of education designed to prepare students for higher education and equip them with the necessary life skills for the workplace and their future careers.

There are six ICT suites and interactive whiteboards or projectors in all teaching rooms; all students achieve a recognised ICT qualification. Outstanding art work and subject displays enhance all areas of the school.

Curriculum. All National Curriculum subjects including Welsh are taught at Key Stages 1, 2 and 3. In addition, girls in the Junior School study French and in the Senior School, Latin. A broad range of AS and A2 subjects is available in the College. Examinations in all AS subjects are taken at the end of Year 12. Active learning styles are seen as an essential part of the classroom experience. The curriculum is made more diverse by:

- educational visits, locally and abroad;
- visiting authors, poets, musicians, artists and lecturers;
- Book Week;
- Science Week;
- Astronomy Week;
- Geography Action Week;
- Languages Week.

Extra-curricular activities. Howell's is proud of its aim to fulfil the potential of all the students, which it achieves through a rich extra-curricular programme of activities:

- four orchestras, six choirs;
- chamber, jazz, madrigal and pop groups;
- astronomy, reading, green, science and language clubs;
- concerts, plays, drama festival and eistedfoddau;
- tennis, hockey, rounders, lacrosse, swimming, athletics, cross country and netball teams;
- The Duke of Edinburgh's Award, First Challenge, World Challenge, Young Enterprise, Envision and Achievers International;
- quiz, public speaking and debating teams;
- community service and fund-raising for charities.

The academic and social inclusiveness of education at Howell's is further enhanced by such initiatives as peer-led drug education and an active CHIPS (Childline in Partnership with Schools) scheme. The school seeks to support the widest range of students' needs through specialist dyslexia teaching at our on-site Dyslexia Institute satellite, and through an extensive and comprehensive careers programme.

Admission. A selection process operates for all forms of entry. The examination for entry at 11+ is held in early February. A number of suitably qualified students is admitted each year to the large Sixth Form.

Fees per term (2008-2009). Senior School and College £2,985, Junior School £2,204, Nursery £1,854.

Scholarships and Bursaries. Bursaries, which are means tested, are available in the Senior School and in the Sixth Form College; these are intended to ensure that the school remains accessible to bright girls (and in the sixth form, to able students of both sexes) who would profit from our education, but who would be unable to enter the school without financial assistance.

Details of scholarships, bursaries and music exhibitions are available, on request, from the school.

Charitable status. Howell's School Llandaff is part of The Girls' Day School Trust, which is a Registered Charity, number 306983. The aim of the Trust is to ensure that the GDST remains at the forefront of education – extending excellence and innovation in dynamic educational settings and maintaining GDST leadership in the education of young women.

Ipswich High School (GDST)

Woolverstone Ipswich 1P9 1AZ
Tel: 01473 780201
Fax: 01473 780985
e-mail: admissions@ihs.gdst.net
website: www.ipswichhighschool.co.uk

Ipswich High School is one of the 29 schools of The Girls' Day School Trust. Founded in 1872, the GDST continues to be at the forefront of education and is the largest group of independent schools in the UK. For further information about the Trust, see p. xxiv.

Chairman of Local Governors: Dr Julia Howard-Griffin

***Headmistress*: Ms Elaine Purves**, BA Hons (Hull)

Head of Junior School: Mrs Jane Pomeroy, BA (Essex)

Admissions Officer: Mrs Bernadette Ross-Smith

A pioneering heritage

Founded in 1878, Ipswich High School's early pupils were among the first women to obtain university degrees and to enter professional work. Today, although the school has grown and changed immeasurably, the pioneering spirit and commitment to education for young women remain.

An inspiring choice

Our philosophy is to create an environment in which our girls – be they in our Nursery, Junior School, Senior School or Sixth Form – are inspired to reach new heights.

Outstanding results

We provide an extraordinary breadth of education and as a single-sex school there is no gender stereotyping in the choice and enjoyment of subjects. It is not considered unusual to excel in Maths, Science or Design & Technology any more than in Languages, Arts or Humanities. We have high standards and expectations of all our pupils in every subject and that is reflected in our outstanding exam results at all age ranges.

Developing the whole girl

We spend time with our pupils in extra-curricular activities such as sport, music and drama to enhance their personal development. This helps them develop not just academic skills, but social skills as well – preparing them for their life ahead.

An enriching environment

We are privileged to have the magnificent Woolverstone Hall as our home with 80 acres of beautiful parkland, splendid buildings and an incredible array of facilities – a huge sports hall, theatre, spacious labs, design technology workshop, language laboratory, IT suites, a 25m indoor swimming pool and most recently an all-weather pitch for hockey and tennis – providing us with a stimulating and inspiring environment in which our girls can learn, play and grow.

The support of the GDST

As part of the GDST, Ipswich High School has a strong and secure future. The GDST gives each of the schools autonomy to identify its own needs and determine its own development, but then gives guidance, helps planning and supports financially to realise projects.

Prepared for the future

Above all, at Ipswich High School no girl is silent. Even those who lack confidence when they join us soon find the space and encouragement to discover their voice. Our girls act as inspirational role models for each other. They are ambitious, enthusiastic and have a real zest for learning and life. When the time comes for them to leave us, all our girls go forward with the confidence and courage not to be held back by social stereotypes, but to take themselves to new levels of success.

Ipswich High School has a proven track record and a bright future ahead – we hope you will choose to be part of it.

Admissions. Admission to Nursery is on the basis of informal assessment in a play situation. Entry to the Junior School is on the basis of informal assessment or written test. Entry to the Senior School is on the basis of interviews, written tests and school report. Sixth Form entry is on the basis of interviews, GCSE results and school report.

Fees per term (2008-2009). Senior School £2,966, Junior School £2,150, Nursery £1,776.

Scholarships. Our Scholarships are highly sought after and are reserved for those candidates we believe to be of an exceptional standard. We look to our Scholars to continuously raise the standard in their chosen field and to provide inspiration to others. For entry at 11+ (Senior School) and 16+ (Sixth Form) we offer Academic, Art, Drama, Music and Sports Scholarships.

Bursaries. The GDST provides the school with a number of bursaries for entry at 11+ and Sixth Form. These are means tested and ensure that the school remains accessible to bright girls who would profit from the education provided but who would be unable to enter the school without financial assistance.

Charitable status. Ipswich High School is part of The Girls' Day School Trust, which is a Registered Charity, number 306983. The aim of the Trust is to provide access to the very best education to as many individuals as possible.

James Allen's Girls' School (JAGS)

East Dulwich Grove London SE22 8TE
Tel: 020 8693 1181
Fax: 020 8693 7842
e-mail: enquiries@jags.org.uk
website: www.jags.org.uk

Governing Body:
Dame Valerie Strachan, BA Hons, DCB (*Chair*)
Mr Michael Brooke, BA Hons
Miss Joanna Dodson, MA, QC
Mrs Nicola Meredith, BA Hons, FCCA
Mrs Alison Miles, BA Hons
Professor John Moxham, MD, FRCP
Miss Erica Pienaar, BA Hons, MBA
Mrs Frances Read, MA Cantab,FCA,MSI
Mr David Smellie, MA
Dr Geraldine Strathdee, OBE, MB, BCh, BAO, MRPsych London
Mr Thomas Van Oss, MA
Mr John Williams, CA
Mr Hugh Taylor, BA Hons, CB

Clerk to the Governors and Bursar: Mr John Reid, ACIB, MIMgt

***Headmistress*: Mrs Marion Gibbs**, BA Hons, MLitt Bristol, FRSA

Deputy Head: Mrs Deborah Bicknell, BSc Hons Durham (*Biology*)

Teaching Staff:
** Head of Department*

Miss Helen Adie, BA Hons London (*Drama and English*)
Miss Alice Allgrove, BA Hons Bristol (*Religious Studies*)
Mrs Vikki Askew, MA Hons Edinburgh (*History, Head of Sixth Form*)
Mr Arvind Arora, Staatsexamen Germany (*Head of German*)
Mrs Hélène Bardell, Licence-Maitrîse Poitiers (*French*)
Mrs Wendy Barratt, BSc Hons Kent (*Biology*)
Mrs Corrine Barton, BA Hons Sheffield (**History and Politics*)
Mrs Janet Bates, BSc Leicester (*Mathematics*)
Mrs Joanna Billington, BA Hons Middlesex (**Drama*)
Mr Timothy Billington, BA Hons London (*German, French, ICT*)
Mrs Beatrice Blake, Dotoressa Bocconi-Milan (**Italian*)
Ms Aude Boulanger, BA Sorbonne (**French*)
Miss Bryony Britten, BA Hons Sheffield (*History & Politics*)
Miss Antonia Buccheri, BSc Hons Manchester (*Mathematics*)
Mr Stuart Byfield, BSc Hons London (*Biology*)
Mrs Anita Carpenter, BEd Liverpool John Moores (**Physical Education*)
Mr Andrew Carter, BA Hons Central St Martin's (*Art*)
Miss Louise Cook, BA Hons Wolverhampton (**Technology*)
Miss Elinor Corp, BA Hons Bristol (*Music*)
Mrs Caroline Davis, ARCM (*Head of Strings*)
Mrs Margaret Davis, BA Hons Newcastle (**Geography*)
Mr Paul Davies, BSc Hons Newcastle (*Physics*)
Dr Paul Dawson, BA Hons, PhD London (*Philosophy*)
Ms Kay Dickson, GRSM, Dip RCM London
Ms Melanie Duignan, MA Manchester (*English*)
Dr Matthew Edwards, BA Hons, PhD Bristol (*English*)
Mrs Rachel Edwards, BA Hons Cambridge (*English*)
Miss Polly Everden, BA Hons Cambridge (*English*)
Mrs Katharine Firth, BA Hons CNAA (*Art*)
Mr Martial Fouilleul, BA Hons (*French*)
Mrs Sally George, BA Hons London, MA London (*Russian & French*)
Miss Chantal Gillingham, BA Hons Norwich School of Art (*Art*)
Ms Sara Glover, BSc London (**Mathematics*)
Mrs Clare Grant, BSc Hons Sussex (*Chemistry*)
Mr Thomas Hamilton-Jones, BA Hons Oxford (**Economics*)
Mrs Jennifer Hanner, BSc Hons London, DPSE (*Biology & Careers*)
Mrs Marilyn Harper, MA Cambridge, FRCO, GRSM, ARMCM (*Music*)
Ms Claudia Harrison, BA Hons Oxford (*Geography*)
Mrs Joyce Hawting, BA Hons London (*History*)
Mrs Elizabeth Head, BA Hons Brighton (*Physical Education*)
Mrs Catharine Henley, BA Hons Bristol, MA Canada (*Classics*)
Mr Andrew Hicklenton, BSc Hons Southampton (**Physics*)
Miss Wendy Johnson, BEd Hons London (*Physical Education*)
Mrs Anna Jones, BA Hons Nottingham (*English*)
Mrs Ruth Jones, BA Hons Durham, MA Southampton (*Classics*)
Dr Sarah Knight, BSc Hons, PhD London (**Chemistry*)
Mrs Jean Larkman, BA Hons Open, MCSP (*Mathematics, Head of Years 10-11*)
Mrs Ellie Latham, BSc Hons London (*Physics*)
Dr David Lazar, BSc Hons London, DPhil Oxford (*Economics*)
Ms Georgina Legg, BA Hons Susssex (*French*)
Mrs Deborah Lewis, BA Hons Sheffield (**Religious Studies*)
Miss Paula Limbert, BA Hons Bradford (*French, *Russian*)
Miss Alice Little, BA Hons, MA Oxon (*Chemistry*)
Dr Mary Lloyd, BSc Hons Birmingham, DPhil Oxford (*Biology*)
Ms Sarah Macpherson, MA Hons Edinburgh (*History & Politics*)
Mrs Giulia Marchini, Dottoressa Bari (*Italian*)
Miss Clare Martin, BA Hons Oxford (*Spanish*)
Mrs Ann Massey, BA Hons Oxford (*History*)
Mrs Emma Mayo, MA Cambridge (*History, Head of Years 7-9*)
Mrs Catherine McCleave, BD Hons KCL (*Religious Studies & Dance*)
Ms Paula McCormick, BA Hons London (*Design Technology*)
Mrs Lara Meeran, BEng Hons London (*Design Technology*)
Mrs Cherie Millsom, BA Hons Sheffield (*Classics*)
Mrs Greta Mountain, BSc Nottingham (*Chemistry*)
Miss Fiona Murray, BEd Hons London (*Physical Education*)
Mr Roger Nicholls, BSc London, MSc London (*Mathematics*)
Mrs Kathryn Norton-Smith, BA Hons Birmingham (*Drama*)
Mr Leigh O'Hara, BA Hons York, MMus London (*Director of Music*)
Mr Hiroshi Okura, BA Waseda, Tokyo (*Japanese*)

Mrs Gillian Oxbrow, BSc Hons Exeter (*Mathematics, Assistant Head*)
Mrs Janet Parkinson, BA Hons Belfast (*English*)
Mr John Pattison, BSc Hons Newcastle, MA Lancaster (*Mathematics*)
Miss Samantha Payne, BA Hons Central St Martins (**Art*)
Mr Howard Peacock, BA Hons Oxon, MPhil London (*Classics & Philosophy*)
Mrs Natalie Plant, BSc Hons Bristol (*Mathematics*)
Mr John Putley, BSc Hons Nottingham (**Science*)
Miss Jane Quarmby, BA Hons Bristol (*English*)
Ms Irene Riddell, BA Hons Glasgow (*Art*)
Miss Cristina Sanchez-Satoca, BA Hons Barcelona, MA London (**Spanish*)
Mr Peter Sanders, BSc, MSc London (*Computer Studies, Information Systems Coordinator*)
Mrs Frances Shaw, MA Oxford (**Classics & Philosophy*)
Miss Pauline Simpson, MA Cambridge (*Mathematics*)
Miss Gina Thomson, BA Hons Brighton (*Physical Education*)
Mrs Olivia Thompson, MA Hons Edinburgh (*Italian*)
Ms Karen Trinder, BSc Hons York (*Biology*)
Miss Stella Turner, BSc Hons Nottingham (*Mathematics*)
Ms Anne-Marie von Lieres, BA Hons Paris (*French*)
Mr Robert Wallace, MA Birmingham, MBA Nottingham (*Design Technology, Assistant Head*)
Miss Heather Webb, MA Oxford (*Chemistry*)
Mr Laurence Wesson, BSc Hons London (**Biology*)
Miss Alice Wynn-Jones, MA Hons Edinburgh (*Geography*)

Librarians:
Mrs Cynthia Pullin, BA Hons York, DipLib
Mrs Susan Stacey, BA Hons Manchester (*Library Assistant*)

Deputy Bursar: Mr Kevin Barry, ACA
Registrar: Mrs Julie Ellis
PA to Headmistress: Mrs Shirley Cottrill
Development Director: Miss Alison Evans, MA Oxford, MBA Manchester, ALCM
Communications Director: Mrs Alison Venn, BEd Hons Cambridge

School Nurses:
Mrs Karen Cattenach, RGN
Ms Jacqui Martin, RGN

The school was founded in 1741 as part of the Foundation of Alleyn's College of God's Gift and is the oldest independent girls' school in London.

JAGS is set in 22 acres of grounds in the heart of Dulwich, with extensive playing fields and long-established Botany gardens. The school buildings include a well-equipped modern library, 13 laboratories, a purpose-built suite of language laboratories, 6 art rooms, 4 computer rooms, design and technology workshops, new indoor swimming pool, floodlit artificial turf pitch, dance studio, sports hall with squash courts and fitness room, a professionally-managed theatre and a Music school. The Sixth Form Centre has its own tutorial rooms, common rooms and lecture theatre. A new dining hall and teaching block is opening in 2008.

There is a four-form entry at 11 and JAGS has about 770 pupils with 200 in the Sixth Form. About a third of girls come up from our junior department, James Allen's Preparatory School (qv) with about two-thirds entering from other preparatory and state primary schools.

Girls follow a broad curriculum with a wide choice of GCSE options, structured to ensure a balanced programme. Advanced Level courses are available in all the usual subjects as well as Classical Civilisation, Greek, Latin, Russian, Spanish, Italian, Economics, Philosophy, Physical Education, Politics, Music and Theatre Studies. Art is a particular strength throughout the school.

The extra-curricular programme is a key part of the JAGS education. The excellent Prissian Theatre enables first class, full scale drama productions, while the active music department plays a central role, offering some 30 ensembles including 6 choirs, 4 orchestras, brass ensembles, wind ensembles plus jazz and big bands. A great variety of other interests is encouraged, from The Duke of Edinburgh's Award, debating, photography, and the Literary Society, to Politics and Amnesty International. Exchange visits to Russia, France, Germany, Italy, and Spain are regularly organised. The choirs, orchestras and sports teams also visit overseas. Community Action plays an important part in school life, and there are extensive partnership activities with other local schools and organisations.

Sports: Hockey, netball, football, aerobics, basketball, gymnastics, dance, tennis, rounders, swimming, athletics and self-defence are taught in the curriculum, with opportunities for fencing, rugby, badminton, sailing, ice-skating and riding.

Individual lessons in Instrumental Music and Speech and Drama are available (fees on application).

Fees per term (2008-2009). £4,095.

Admission. Girls are admitted at 11+ and 13+ and also into the Sixth Form. Registration fee: £50.

Entrance Examination. Every candidate for admission will be required to pass an examination, graduated according to age. For details and method of admission apply to The Registrar, Mrs J Ellis.

Scholarships. (*see Scholarship Entries section*). Up to twenty Foundation Scholarships are awarded every year to girls of 11 years of age on entry to the School. Sixth Form scholarships are also available. Scholarships are awarded for academic ability and for Music and Art; there is also a Sports Exhibition.

All Scholarships are augmented by a means-tested element in cases of need.

Following the demise of the Government Assisted Places Scheme, the School has introduced James Allen's Scholarships to continue to enable talented girls from families of limited means to enter JAGS. Fee support up to 100% is available.

Charitable status. James Allen's Girls' School is a Registered Charity, number 312750 and exists for the purpose of educating girls.

Kent College Pembury

Old Church Road Pembury Tunbridge Wells Kent TN2 4AX

Tel: 01892 822006
Bursar: 01892 820220
Fax: 01892 820221
e-mail: admissions@kentcollege.kent.sch.uk
website: www.kent-college.co.uk

Kent College Pembury is a day and boarding school for girls aged 3 to 18. A happy thriving school with high academic standards and an ethos of providing opportunities to build confidence. The school provides for the educational and cultural needs of day students and boarders from all over the world. Set in beautiful countryside, just 35 miles from London, students benefit from high teaching standards in a superbly equipped environment, within a caring Christian community. All girls participate in the imaginative programme of music, drama, sports, clubs and other activities. The school has strong EAL and learning support provision and accepts girls with a wide academic background. ICT and drama are major strengths of the school and the provision of Design and Technology is wide. Art, Sport and Music have a growing profile in the school and local area.

Board of Governors:

Chairman: Mrs P J Darbyshire, MBE

Vice-Chairs:
Mrs V Knight
E Waterhouse, Esq

Mrs H Alleyne
R J Bamford, Esq
Mrs V Burch
J Harrison, Esq
Revd J Hellyer
J Ingram, Esq
Mrs G Langstaff
J Morgan, Esq
Mrs M Richards
G Russell, Esq
H Shaw, Esq
Mrs J Stevens
T Sturgess, Esq
Mrs C Veall

Bursar and Clerk to the Governors: Mrs L E Akerman

***Headmistress*: Mrs S A Huang**, MA Oxon, PGCE

Academic Deputy: Mrs D Hatcher, BEd Hons Chester College
Senior Deputy Head: Mr M Chanter, BSc Hons Brunel, PGCE North London

Senior School Staff:

** *Head of Faculty*
* *Head of Department*
§ *Part-time*

§Mr C Armour (*Drama*)
Mr N Ashton, BA Hons Worcester College, PGCE London (*Second in Dept Drama*)
Ms E A Benfield, BA Birmingham, MA London (*EAL*)
Miss L Bennett, BA Hons, PGCE Cambridge (**Religious Studies, Citizenship and History, Assistant Housemistress*)
Mr S Brown, BDes Dundee, MA Wales (**Art*)
Mr G G Bullough, BSc Hons, PGCE Swansea (***Science*)
Miss J Burisky, BSc Hons Staffordshire, PGCE Brighton (*Science*)
Mrs S Caird, BA Hons Stirling, PGCE Cambridge (**History*)
§Mrs R C Castle, BA Hons Loughborough, PGCE Leeds (*Textiles and Art*)
Mr A Chan, MEng Hons UCL, PGCE Greenwich (*Science/Physics*)
Miss A M C Church, BA Oxford, PGCE Birmingham (***English*)
Mrs D Cowley, PCET (***Curriculum ICT and Business*)
§Mrs M Dalyanci, Acting Dip Birmingham SSD (*Drama*)
Mrs C Davidson BA Hons, QTS Kent, AEP Dib Brighton (*PSHE/Citizenship Coordinator, *Outdoor Education, Charities Coordinator, Careers Assistant*)
§Ms N Davies (*PE, Gym & Aerobics Coach*)
§Mrs J Denman BA Hons, PGCE Durham, PG Dip Courtauld Inst (**German, French*)
Mrs N Denton, BSc Hons Loughborough, QTS (*Second in Dept, PE*)
§Mrs M Doe, BA Hons Christ Church, PGCE Greenwich (**Economics & Business Studies*)
Mrs J Dooley, BA Hons Kent, MA Nottingham, PGCE Chichester (**Media Studies, English*)
§Mr M Duff, BA, MA Cambridge, MA UCL, Dip Ed Newcastle (*Classics*)
§Mrs K Dunlop, BSc Hons Edinburgh, PGCE Queen's Belfast (*Mathematics*)
§Mr S Dutta, Phil Oxon, MA Oxon, MA Kings (*Classics*)
Miss E Evatt, BA Hons De Montfort, QTS (*PE*)
§Mr K Fitzell BEd Hons Reading (*English*)
Mrs V Fitzpatrick, BA Hons Liverpool, PGCE, MA King's College London (*French*)
Mme M-T Ford, MA Hons Sorbonne (***Modern Foreign Languages*)
Miss H Gibbs, BA ITT St Mary's College, Twickenham (*PE*)
§Mrs M Gower, BA Aichi, TCert Japan (*Japanese*)
Mrs L Hallam, BA Hons Southampton (**Spanish and French, Head of Year 7*)
Mrs M Hambleton, BA Hons Reading, PGCE London (**Geography*)
§Mrs M Haslett, CertEd London (*Technology*)
Mrs R A Havard, BSc Hons Roehampton (*Additional Support Tutor*)
Mrs F Hedgeland, BA, MA Cambridge, PGCE Cambridge, DipM CIM (*Head of Sixth Form, English*)
Mrs J Hill, BSc Hons, PGCE Hertfordshire (*Second in Dept, Mathematics*)
Mrs A Hobrow BScEcon Bristol, PGCE Sussex (***Mathematics*)
Mrs V Homewood, BA Hons, PGCE Southampton (**Religious Studies, Head of Years 10 & 11*)
§Mrs Helen Horseman, BSc Hons Liverpool, QTS (*Mathematics*)
Mrs L Jeal, BSc Hons Exeter, PGCE Reading (**Learning Support, Mathematics*)
§Mrs M Keech, BA Hons Bristol, ATC London (***Arts & Technology, *Art Critical & Contextual, HSBC Coordinator*)
Mr M Kent-Davies, BMus Hons Sheffield, PGCE Manchester Polytechnic (**Director of Music*)
Mrs H Kilgour, BMus Hons Edinburgh, MMus GSM, PGCE London (*Music*)
Mr A Kirk-Burgess BSc Bath, PGCE Oxford (**Physics*)
Mr D Lee, BSc London Guildhall, QTS (***Humanities and Social Sciences,*Psychology, Weekday Activities Coordinator*)
Miss C Mortlock (*IT, Acting Head of Years 10 & 11*)
Mr J Mossman, BA Hons, MA, PGCE King's College London (**Classics*)
Mr R F G Nash, MA Cantab, DipEd East Africa (**Chemistry*)
§Mrs A Nieto, BA Madrid, PGCE London (*Spanish*)
§Mrs K North, BSc Econ London, QTS (*Mathematics*)
Mrs L J Oliver, BEd Bedford College (*Weekend Boarders' Activities Director; PE; Housemistress Osborn*)
Mrs K Pusey, GGSM, PGCE Middx (*Second in Dept, Music*)
§Ms K Russell BA Hons Guildhall (*Geography*)
Mrs C Skinner BA Hons Kent, PGCE Lancaster (*Second in Dept, English*)
§Mrs C Snowball, BA Hons Leeds (*Drama*)
Mr O Snowball, BA Hons Nottingham, MA Goldsmiths, PGCE London (**Drama*)
Mrs A Stone, BEd I M Marsh (***PE*)
§Ms S Timson (*Trampoline Tutor*)
Miss G Thorpe BA Hons Lancaster (*Drama, Coordinator of Speech & Drama, Theatre Manager, Head of Years 8 & 9*)
Mrs H Tomlin Cert Ed Bristol (**Food Technology, Leith's Food and Wine*)
Miss J Vincent, BSc, PGCE Birmingham (*PE*)
Ms C Waller, Acting Dip Mountview Theatre School (*Drama*)
Mr B Wallis, BA Hons West Surrey, MA Hons Textile Institute, PGCE Exeter (*Art and Textiles Technology*)
Mr J Watson, BSc Canterbury, QTS (*Science*)
Mrs K Wintle, BA Hons, MA Brighton, LTI Textile Institute, ALCM (**Textiles, Technology and Coordinator of Design & Technology*)

plus 12 Visiting Instrumental Staff.

Chaplain:
Revd Dr J Quarmby, BSc Hons Bath, MTh Cardiff, PhD Bath (*Mathematics*)

Careers Coordinator:
§Mrs G E Shukla, BEd Bradford College, PGCE Reading

Library & ICT:
Mrs S Waller, ALA (***Learning & Life Skills, Librarian*)
Mrs J Manning (*Library & ICT Assistant*)
Mrs L Maule (*ICT Support Assistant*)
Mrs C Songhurst (*Library and IT Assistant*)

Duke of Edinburgh's Award Scheme:
Mrs Carol Davidson, BA Hons QTS Kent, AEP Dib Brighton

Housemistresses:
Mrs J Parker, BA South Africa, BSA Cert Prof Boarding Practice, Speech TDip Rose Bruford College (*Head of Boarding and Housemistress Hawkwell House*)
Miss S Timmerman, MA Kent, M-ès-L Moderne Lyon (*Housemistress, James House*)
Mrs L J Oliver, BEd Bedford College (*Housemistress, Osborn House*)
Mrs C Tarr (*Housemistress Hargreaves House*)
Ms M A Turnbull (*Deputy Housemistress, James and Osborn House*)
§Miss L Bennett, BA Hons, PGCE Cambridge (*Assistant Housemistress*)
§Mrs V Cowan (*Relief Housemistress*)
Miss P Thompson (*GAP student*)
Ms K Weber (*GAP student*)

Medical Staff:
Medical Officer: Dr P Lautch, MB BS, MA, MRCGP
Nursing Sister: Mrs J M Devine, RGN
School Nurse: §Mrs K Underdown, RGN

Administrative Staff:
Head of Administration and PA to the Headmistress: Mrs J Bearne
Registrar: Mrs D Sainsbury
School Secretary: Mrs A Masters
Assistant School Secretary: §Mrs V England
Marketing & Admissions Assistant: §Mrs N Sneddon, BEd Hons Cheltenham
Marketing Assistant: Mrs E Chandler, BA Hons Surrey Institute
Receptionist: §Mrs J Gowen-Smith
Afternoon Receptionist: §Mrs L Bone

Bursar's Office:
Assistant Bursar-Finance: Mrs I Scinteie, BA Bucharest
Bursar's PA: Mrs J Miles
Accounts Assistant: §Mrs V Carter

Technical Support Staff:
Mr W Burles, BA Hons, MCSE (*Director of ICT & Internet Safety Officer*)
Ms J Hinton (*Senior Laboratory Technician*)
Mr C Hayward (*Laboratory Technician*)
Mr G Hougham HND Northbrook College (*Theatre Technician*)
Mrs S Coggins (*Design & Technology Technician*)
Miss Emma Slora, BA Hons Kingston (*Art & Design Technology Technician*)
Mr W King (*IT Technician*)

Catering Manager: Mrs S Stone
Site Manager: Mr M Cooper

Kent College Preparatory School:

Headmistress: Mrs A Lawson, BEd Hons Exeter

Mrs S Beazleigh, BA Hons Brighton (*PE Coordinator & Games*)
§Miss L Budden, National Diploma in Counselling, NNEB Croydon College (*Play Therapist*)
Mrs H Chapman, BEd Brighton, London College of Music (*Head of Music, Year 6*)
Mrs C Corp, BEd Derbyshire (*Year 2*)
Mrs P Dabin, CertEd London, BSc Hons OU (*Reception Class*)
Miss R Dalby, BA Hons Wales, BA Hons OU, PGCE (*Senior Teacher, Year 6*)
Mrs J Dearlove, BEd Hons Montreal, CertEd Canterbury (*Year 4*)
Mrs C Goodrum, CertEd Nottingham (*Reception*)
Mrs C Gregory, CertEd Nottingham (*Year 3*)
Miss P Lamb, BA Hons Staffordshire, CertEd Keele (*Year 5*)
Mrs A Lees, CertEd London (*Year 1*)
§Mrs C Marnane BA(*Ed*) Goldsmiths (*Year 5*)
§Dr C Parr, MBChB, PGCE Leeds (*Year 2*)
Miss L Paul BSc Hons, PGCE Southampton (*Year 4*)
Mrs C Wilson, BEd Hons London (*French*)
Mrs G Wilson, BA Hons, MA Sussex (*Learning Support*)
Mrs T Youdale, CertEd Brighton, BA Hons Manchester (*Year 5*)
Mrs E Andrews (*Teaching Assistant*)
Mrs M Cuttill, ASA Cert (*Swimming*)
Mrs S Morris (*Classroom Assistant, Swimming, After School Care*)
Mrs J Rhoades, NVQ Level 3 (*Reception Classroom Assistant*)
§Mrs N Rose, BA Greenwich (*Nursery*)
Miss K Soutter, Dip Montessori (*Nursery*)
Mrs K Tyler (*Teaching Assistant*)
§Mrs S Vincent, BSc Hons Surrey, PGCE Roehampton (*Year 1*)
Mrs K Wicks (*Nursery Classroom Assistant*)
Mrs J Wolton (*After School Care, Teaching Assistant*)

Administrative Staff:
Headmistress's PA & Registrar: Mrs D Shepherd
Assistant School Secretary : §Mrs S Williams

Ethos and Aims. The Prep School (ages 3–11) and the Senior School (ages 11–18) are part of a group of Methodist Schools, which have an ethos of being caring, Christian environments, and welcoming pupils from all faiths or none. Kent College is a happy school with high academic standards and pupils achieve excellent results in public examinations. With 180 girls in the Prep School and 370 in the Senior School there is a real community feel and teaching staff know each girl as an individual. Building self-esteem is at the heart of our ethos. All girls get a chance to shine, try something different, feel good about themselves and develop new and existing talents. Exciting opportunities to develop confidence are an integral part of school life: overseas music, drama and sports tours, an Australian exchange, 65 extra-curricular activities, and Leith's Food & Wine Course to name a few. Our aim is to equip students with the confidence, skills and positive attitude to succeed in their examinations, at university, in their chosen career and in life ahead.

Location and Facilities. The Prep School and the Senior School share the site which is set in 75 acres of beautiful green countryside in Pembury, three miles from Royal Tunbridge Wells. It is just forty minutes to London by train and within easy reach of Gatwick, Heathrow and Luton airports, channel ports and the Channel Tunnel. The Senior School campus comprises an elegant Victorian manor house, used for offices and boarding, and purpose-built facilities include language laboratories, a music school, Sixth Form Centre, and new science laboratories for September 2008. The two schools benefit from an excellent range of shared facilities including a large sports hall, state-of-the-art theatre, an indoor heated swimming pool and dining hall; excellent ICT facilities include Apple Mac suite, wireless laptops and smartboards in the majority of the teaching rooms. There are three boarding houses, one of which is for girls aged 10–14. The other two boarding houses, recently refurbished to a superior standard, are for girls aged 14–18. The Prep School is based in its own modern, purpose-built building with spacious playgrounds. The Preparatory School has its own range of after school clubs and also offers supervised prep, late after prep care facility including supper and an early morning breakfast club.

(*See also Prep School entry in IAPS section.*)

Curriculum. In the first years of the Senior School all girls follow a wide curriculum which includes academic as well as creative and practical subjects. They learn keyboard skills and develop confidence in the use of computers and technology. At GCSE level, all girls take English language, English literature, mathematics, science, and select other GCSE option subjects. At 16+, girls take the two-year Advanced Level course in four subjects and all follow a structured Curriculum Enrichment programme. In addition to A Levels, students can take the prestigious Leith School's Basic Certificate in Food and Wine. All students are given extensive careers and higher education advice and academically able students are prepared for admission to Oxford and Cambridge. The majority of students proceed directly to universities and colleges of higher education.

Sport. Sporting activities include hockey, netball, rounders, basketball, athletics, cross-country, water sports, horse riding, swimming, tennis, trampolining, dance and self-defence. The school has a reputation for achievement in inter-school matches and talented athletes can enter county and national competitions. The superb facilities include an indoor heated swimming pool, sports hall and spacious grounds with a variety of courts and pitches.

Extra-Curricular Activities, Music and Drama. The school prides itself on offering an extensive programme of extra-curricular activities at lunchtimes, after school and at weekends which are open to day girls and boarders. Senior School pupils are expected to take part in at least two activities from a list which includes sports, pottery, horse riding, choirs, orchestra, first aid, Duke of Edinburgh's Award, TaeKwonDo and drama. There are frequent visits to London theatres and overseas trips in the holidays. The school has a reputation for high standards in music and drama. There are opportunities for girls of all ages to take part in drama productions.

Christian Community. Kent College was founded by the Wesleyan Methodist Schools' Association in 1886. The school continues to benefit from having its own resident Chaplain. There are Christian assemblies on some weekdays and a school service each Sunday.

Entrance. (*see Scholarship Entries section*). Main intakes to the Prep School are to the Nursery (aged 3) and Reception (aged 4) classes. The school will take girls into other year groups subject to places being available. Entrance is based on a place being available; however entrance into Years 3–6 pupils is based on the school's own entrance tests.

The main entries to the Senior School are at 11+, 13+ and 16+. Entrance is by the school's own Entrance Examinations, interview and a report from the previous school. Academic, Drama, Music, Art and Sport Scholarships are awarded to outstanding entrants at 11+, 13+ and 16+. Girls wishing to study A Levels are required to gain at least six GCSE passes at grade C or above. Boarders are welcomed from age 10.

Fees per term (2008-2009). Senior: Day £4,862, Boarders £7,838. Prep: Day £2,215–£3,334, Boarders £6,027. 20% discount for Forces' personnel. Discounts for sisters.

Charitable status. Kent College Pembury is a Registered Charity, number 307920. It exists for the education of children.

Kilgraston

Bridge of Earn Perthshire PH2 9BQ
Tel: 01738 812257
Fax: 01738 813410
e-mail: headoffice@kilgraston.pkc.sch.uk
website: www.kilgraston.com

Chairman of Board of Governors: Mr Timothy Hall

***Principal*: Mr Michael Farmer**, BA Hons, PGCE

Bursar and Secretary to the Board: Mr B Farrell, BCom, FIDE, ACIS

Deputy Head (*Academic*): Mrs C A Lund, BA Hons, MA, MA Ed Man, PGCE

Deputy Head (*Pastoral & Boarding*): Mrs V Sherwood, BEd

Head of the Preparatory School: Mrs A Kellaway, BEd, DipPD Ed Man

Chaplain: Father Andrew Clark

Academic & Pastoral Staff:
Miss D Anderson (*Nursery Manager*)
Miss S Barton (*Butterstone Asst Boarding Housemistress*)
Mrs A Bluett, BA Hons, PGCE (*French, Kinnoull Housemistress*)
Mr G Bryson BSc Hons (*Network Administrator*)
Mr B Campbell, DipEd (*Geography, PE & Outdoor Activities*)
Miss J Campbell, BDes Hons, MDes, PGCE (*Art, Artist in Residence*)
Mrs J Carmichael, LLB, PGCE (*Form Teacher*)
Mrs C Clarke, BSc (*Home Economics*)
Ms P Corral (*Nursery*)
Miss V Curry, MA Hons, PGCE (*Religious Studies*)
Mrs M Dallas, SVQ3 (*Nursery*)
Mr A Dempster, BSc Hons, PGCE (*Mathematics*)
Mrs H A Dempster, BA Hons, DipAdvEdSt (*Computing, Geography, Photography*)
Mlle I Depreux, BA Hons, Maîtrise, PGCE (*French*)
Mrs K Ebrahim, BSc Hons, PGCE Primary (*English*)
Mrs M-A Farmer (*Religious Studies, Boarding Mistress*)
Mrs P Ferguson, MA Hons, PGCE (*Form Teacher*)
Mrs J Gordon (*Barat/Swinton Assistant Boarding Mistress*)
Miss P Gourlay (*Mater Asst Boarding Mistress*)
Mrs K Greig, BHSAI (*Equestrian Manager*)
Mrs K Guthrie, MA Hons, PGCE (*ESOL*)
Mrs M Halmarack, BA Hons, MSc, PGCE (*Biology*)
Mrs E Harte (*Head of Sixth Form and Head of Geography*)
Miss E Herriot Maitland (*Boarding Mistress*)
Mr D Hewitt (*ICT Support*)
Mrs S Hewett, BSc, MSc (*Physics*)
Mr A Jenkins, BA, PGCE (*Music*)
Mrs L Jenkins, Reg Nurse, NATC/RCGP Dip Asthma (*Butterstone Boarding Housemistress*)
Mrs H Lawrenson, BA, PGCE (*English, Classics, Drama*)
Mrs T M Little, MA, PGCE (*English*)
Mrs S Lockett, MA Hons, PGCE (*Prep School Teacher*)
Miss A M Losty, BSc, PGCE (*Chemistry, Arran Housemistress*)
Mrs M Malloch (*Prep Classroom Assistant*)
Mrs M McCabe, MA, PGCE (*Spanish, RE*)
Mrs G McFadden (*Boarding Mistress, Physical Education*)
Mrs J McGregor, BA Hons LAMDA
Miss G McMaster, BA Hons, PGCE (*Art*)
Mrs L A Murray, RGN, SCM (*Matron*)
Mrs P Murray (*Infirmary Assistant*)
Ms A Neilson, DipArt, DipEd (*Art & Design*)
Mrs A Ness (*LAMDA*)
Mrs A O'Hear BSc Hons (*Biology, Form Teacher*)
Mrs L Oswald, BEd Hons (*English, History & Form Teacher*)
Mrs R Reid, MA, BEd (*Learning Support & ESOL*)
Mrs S E Rhodes, DipPE (*Physical Education*)
Mrs S Robertson, DipEd, DipSpLD (*Support For Learning*)
Mrs E Rodger, BEd Hons (*Physical Education, Form Teacher*)
Mrs M Rose, DipComm, PGCE (*Business Studies*)
Mrs M Saunders, BA Hons (*English*)
Mrs I Scott (*Barat/Swinton Assistant Boarding Mistress*)
Mrs L Scott, BA (*Drama*)
Miss B Spurgin, MA Hons (*Librarian*)
Mrs E Stewart, DipEd (*Form Teacher*)
Mrs N Strachan, HND (*Laboratory Technician*)
Mrs P Todrick, Montessori Dip (*Nursery*)
Mr G Vandermeulen (*Swimming Pool Manager*)
Mr G Watson (*Mathematics*)
Mrs C Wilson, BSc Hons (*Mathematics, ICT & Form Teacher*)

Director of Development & PR: Mr R Baird, MInstF Cert

Administrative Staff:
Principal's PA & Admissions Coordinator: Mrs L-A Drane

School Secretaries: Mrs S Harrison, Mrs T Stack
Reception: Mrs A Marnoch

The School was founded in 1920 by the Society of Sacred Heart and moved from its original site in Edinburgh to Kilgraston in 1930. Today Kilgraston is an independent Catholic charitable trust but is still a member of the International Network of Sacred Heart Schools which provides invaluable contacts for the school and pupils. Kilgraston warmly welcomes girls of all denominations and faiths who make up a large proportion of the pupil population.

Kilgraston is a Georgian mansion house and the campus is set in 54 acres of stunning parkland three miles from the centre of Perth close to the M90 with Edinburgh and Glasgow less than an hour's drive by car. An exciting long-term capital development programme is underway which in April 2008 saw the completion of the new state-of-the-art 25m Swimming Pool Complex which followed the opening of the new theatre, bistro-style dining room and tennis pavilion. Plans for future development will be announced shortly.

The Curriculum. Generally Kilgraston follows the Scottish educational system with all the girls following a broad curriculum before selecting subjects to continue at Standard Grade (GCSE equivalent). Over 18 subjects are offered at Higher/Advanced Higher (A Level equivalent). Kilgraston has a record of high academic achievement and the girls gain entrance to top universities including Oxford and Cambridge.

Classrooms are well equipped and modern IT facilities are spread throughout the school. Music, Art and Drama play an important part of life at Kilgraston. The Music Department alone has 14 individual teaching rooms, a recording studio and two large music rooms designed to suit all needs. There are also many opportunities for pupils to perform throughout the year by participating in, orchestra, string orchestra, string, woodwind and brass groups, samba band, rock group of one of several choirs. The Art Department is housed in the top of the mansion with superb views across the Ochil Hills and the school boasts an impressive number of past pupils who are practicing artists. In 2005 a new theatre was opened incorporating state of the art audio visual facilities.

Sports and recreation are catered for within a superb sports hall including a climbing wall and fitness gym. The extensive grounds incorporate nine floodlit all-weather courts, playing fields and athletics track. Whilst the main sports are hockey, netball, tennis, rounders, swimming and athletics other sports include football, rugby, skiing, cricket, badminton, yoga, karate, aerobics, ballet, modern dance and highland dancing. Fixtures and competitions are also arranged against other schools throughout the year. Kilgraston is the only school in Scotland to have riding facilities on campus and girls may bring their own horses and ponies. The school hosts a major equestrian event each year.

Kilgraston is divided into houses which compete against each other in games, music and debating. The girls can also take part in the Duke of Edinburgh's Award Scheme and are encouraged to use all the facilities not only for curriculum lessons but also for leisure activities.

Kilgraston Preparatory School and Nursery is co-educational up to the age of nine. The boarders live in the newly refurbished Butterstone House. Girls in the Prep School are prepared for Common Entrance to Kilgraston and other leading schools. Until the age of nine the girls are with class teachers at which stage they begin to be taught by specialist teachers in the Senior School. All of the pupils benefit from the many facilities of the Senior School. (*See separate entry in IAPS section.*)

Admission is normally interview and school report. Entry to the Prep School is by interview and assessment.

Scholarship Examinations are held in February. Substantial awards are offered each year as a result of outstanding performance in the Academic Scholarship Examinations. Scholarships are also offered in Art, Music, Tennis and Sport.

Fees per term (2008-2009). Senior: Day £4,275, Boarding £7,295. Prep: Day £2,475–£4,125, Full Boarding £5,995, Weekly Boarding £5,395.

Charitable status. Kilgraston School Trust is a Registered Charity, number SC029664.

King Edward VI High School for Girls

Birmingham

Edgbaston Park Road Birmingham B15 2UB
Tel: 0121 472 1834
Fax: 0121 471 3808
e-mail: admissions@kehs.co.uk
website: www.kehs.org.uk

Independent, formerly Direct Grant.

Governing Body: The Governors of the Schools of King Edward VI in Birmingham

***Headmistress*: Miss S H Evans**, BA Sussex, MA Leicester, PGCE

Deputy Headmistress: Miss A C Warne, BA Birmingham, PGCE

Assistant Staff:
Mr N J Argust, BMus Birmingham, FRCO, PGCE
Miss B Ashfield, BA Oxon, PGCE
Mrs M Atkins, BA Spain
Mrs J L Bagnall, BSc Sheffield, PGCE
Mr R P Barrett, BA Leeds, PGCE
Mrs L D Birchall, LLCE France, PGCE
Miss S A Blanks, BA Birmingham, GTP
Mrs M C Britton, BA London, PGCE
Miss C A Brown, BA Cambridge, PGCE
Miss A L Buckley, BA Oxon, GTP
Mrs L J Burnett, BA London QTS
Mrs G K Chapman, BEd Brighton
Mrs C E Coleman, BA Warwick QTS
Mr T O Cooper, BA Bristol, PGCE
Mrs E B Cummings, BA Nottingham, PGCE
Mrs R D'Aquila, BA Italy
Miss E M Edwards, BEd Bristol
Mr N Freeman-Powell, MA Oxon, PGCE
Dr C E Gruzelier, MA, PhD Oxon
Mrs F Hall, BA Oxon, PGCE
Dr S Hayton, BSc, PhD Newcastle, PGCE
Mrs J Herbert, ALAM, LLAM
Mr C Hope, BA Hull, PGCE
Mr R M Hopkinson, BSc Hull, MSc London, PGCE
Mrs C M Hosty, BA York, PGCE
Mrs L H Hutton, MSc Durham, PGCE
Mrs S A Huxley, BA Bradford
Mr H J Kavanagh, BA Cantab, PGCE
Miss V Krutin, BA Bath, PGCE
Miss R Laurent, DEUG Mulhouse, PGCE
Mr F Mackinnon, BA Strathclyde, PGCE
Mrs J K Mahon, BSc Royal Holloway, PGCE
Mrs A Marquette, BA, MA France, PGCE
Miss R Medlock, BA, MA Cantab, PGCE
Mrs J E Moule, BA Durham, PGCE
Miss J Oldfield, BSc Durham, PGCE
Ms S Pallister, MA Birmingham, PGCE
Mrs C M Pollard, BSc Nottingham, PGCE
Miss H Proops, BA Birmingham, GTP
Miss J L Rance, BSc Manchester, PGCE
Miss H D Rankin, BA Bristol, PGCE
Mrs P J Rutter, BSc Birmingham

Mrs K Sangha, BA Warwick, PGCE
Ms L C Seamark, BA Birmingham, PGCE
Mr R T Sheppard, BEng Manchester, PGCE
Mrs S K E Shore-Nye, BA Swansea, PGCE
Mrs J C Smith, CertEd Bedford College of PE
Miss A Stanley, BA, MA Cantab
Dr B L Tedd, BSc London, PhD Leicester, PGCE
Miss O N Terry, BA Cardiff, PGCE
Mrs B Thompson, BSc Sheffield Hallam, PGCE
Mrs A K Timms, BMus Birmingham, PGCE
Miss N C White, MA Warwick, PGCE
Mrs J Whitehead, BSc Birmingham, PGCE
Miss C E Woods, BA QTS Warwick
Mrs S M Wright, BA London
Mrs A Young, BA Birmingham, PGCE

Librarian: Mrs A Z Moloney, BA, MA, PGCE

Secretary: Mrs C L Tovey

Matron: Mrs E Mathers

Founded in 1883, the School moved in 1940 to its present buildings and extensive grounds adjacent to King Edward's School for Boys. There are 540 girls from 11 to 18 years of age, all day pupils.

Curriculum. The curriculum is distinctive in its strong academic emphasis and aims to inspire a love of learning. The purpose of the curriculum is to help girls realise their full potential. Excellence is sought in aesthetic, practical and physical activities as well as in academic study. Our aim is to achieve a balance of breadth and depth, with dropping of subjects postponed as long as possible so that girls may make informed choices and have access to a wide range of possible careers.

In **Year One** all girls take English, Mathematics, separate Sciences, Religious Studies, French, History, Geography, Music, Art and Design, Drama, Information Technology, Games, Swimming, Dance and Creative Skills.

In **Years Two and Three** all girls take English, Mathematics, separate Sciences, Religious Studies, French, Latin, History, Geography, Music, Art and Design, Information Technology, Physical Education, Creative Skills.

Core subjects in **Years Four and Five** are English Language, English Literature, Mathematics, Biology, Chemistry, Physics, Latin, French. Girls then choose from 3 option blocks their other GCSE subjects. Greek or another modern language can be taken as a two year GCSE course.

In the **Sixth Form** girls choose for AS and A2 from a wide range of subjects, all Arts, or all Sciences or a mixture of the two. Some subjects are taken jointly with King Edward's School. Stress is placed on breadth at this level. All girls take General Studies at A Level (normally as their fifth subject) with courses for all in Critical Thinking. Various philosophical, scientific and practical topics are explored in short courses.

All girls follow a course in personal decision-making in which they explore and discuss a wide range of issues which call for personal choice and which helps develop life skills.

Religious and moral education are considered important. Academic study of them is designed to enable girls to be informed and questioning. In the last two years, courses (apart from the choice of Religious Studies at A Level) are designed as part of the General Studies programme. There is no denominational teaching in the school in lessons or morning assembly. Girls of all faiths or of none are equally welcome.

Girls take part in Physical Education, until the Upper 6th Form where it is voluntary, with increasing choice from gymnastics, hockey, netball, tennis, rounders, dance, fencing, badminton, squash, swimming, athletics, basketball, volleyball, self-defence, aerobics, archery, health related fitness. We have our own swimming pool, sports hall and extensive pitches, including two artificial hockey areas.

In addition to the music in the curriculum, there are choirs and orchestras which reach a high standard. These are mostly joint with King Edward's School. Individual (or shared) instrumental lessons, at an extra fee, are arranged in school in a great variety of instruments. Some instruments can be hired. Individual singing lessons can also be arranged.

A large number of clubs (many joint with King Edward's School) are run by pupils themselves with help and encouragement from staff. Others (eg Drama, Music, Sport) are directed by staff. Help is given with activities relating to the Duke of Edinburgh's Award scheme. Some activities take place in lunch hours, others after school and at weekends.

As part of the school's commitment to developing an awareness of the needs of society and a sense of duty towards meeting those needs, girls are encouraged to plan and take part in various community service projects as well as organising activities in school to raise money to support causes of their choice.

A spacious careers room is well-stocked with up to date information. Individual advice and aptitude testing is given at stages where choices have to be made. One member of staff has overall responsibility but many others are involved with various aspects. Girls are encouraged to attend conferences, gain work experience, make personal visits and enquiries. Old Edwardians and others visit school to talk about their careers. There is good liaison with universities and colleges of all kinds. Virtually all girls go on to higher education. A wide range of courses is being taken by Old Edwardians.

Admission of Pupils. Entry is normally for girls of 11 into the first year of the school in September. Applications must be made by January for entry in September. Girls should have reached the age of 11 years by 31st August following the examination. Girls up to 1 year younger than this can be considered in some circumstances; parents of such girls should communicate with the headmistress in the previous autumn term. Girls are examined at the school in English, Mathematics and Reasoning. The syllabus is such as would be normally covered by girls of good ability and no special preparation is advised.

Girls from 12 to 15 are normally considered only if they move from another part of the country, or in some special circumstances. Applications should be made to the headmistress in writing as soon as the move is planned. Such girls can be admitted at any time if there is a vacancy.

There is an entry into the Sixth Form for girls wishing to study four main A Level subjects and General Studies. Application should be made to the Headmistress as early as possible in the preceding academic year.

Fees per term (2008-2009). £3,000.

Scholarships and Assisted places. (*see Scholarship Entries section*). The equivalent of up to a total of two free-place scholarships may be awarded on the results of the Governors' Admission Examination to girls entering the first year, with a maximum of 50% for any individual scholarship. These are independent of parental income and are normally tenable for 7 years.

Governors' Assisted Places are available for girls entering the first year and additional places are available for girls entering at 16+. These are means tested.

The Headmistress will be pleased to provide further information.

Charitable status. The Schools of King Edward VI in Birmingham is a Registered Charity, number 529051. The purpose of the Foundation is to educate children and young persons living in or around the city of Birmingham mainly by provision of, or assistance to its schools.

King's High School

Smith Street Warwick CV34 4HJ
Tel: 01926 494485
Fax: 01926 403089
e-mail: enquiries@kingshighwarwick.co.uk
website: www.kingshighwarwick.co.uk

Chairman of Governors of Warwick Independent Schools Foundation:
Prof M L Shattock, OBE, MA Oxon

Chairman of King's High School Committee:
Mrs J Marshall, BA

Ex-Officio:
The Lord Lieutenant of Warwickshire
The Mayor of Warwick

Members of the King's High School Committee:
Mr R V Cadbury, MA Cantab
Mr A J L Cockburn
Dr A D Cocker, MA, DPhil
Mrs J Edwards, BA, MBA
Professor D Grammatopoulos, PhD, FRCPath
Mr D E Hanson
Mrs S Lampitt
Mrs E Moloney
Mrs C Sawdon
Professor R H Trigg, MA, DPhil Oxon

Foundation Secretary: Mr R James

Staff:
***Head Mistress*: Mrs E Surber**, BA, MA Exeter

Deputy Head (*Academic*): Mr S Bethel, BSc Birmingham
Deputy Head (*Pastoral*): Mrs C Renton, BSc Leicester, MSc London

Head of Sixth Form: Mrs H M Cave, BA York
Head of Key Stage 4: Mrs K Hewitt, BA Bristol
Head of Key Stage 3: Dr R Cheetham, BSc London, PhD
Year 7 Coordinator: (*to be appointed*)
Head of Careers: Miss J A Dormer, BA Durham
Head of Science: Mrs R Chapman, MA Oxon
Examinations Secretary: Mrs L Y Sherren, BSc Sheffield

* *Head of Department*

Art, Design and Food Technology:
*Miss S J Lewis, MA Wales
§Mrs S Didlick, BEd, CNAA (*Teacher in Charge, Food Technology*)
Mrs E Ashby, BA Kent
Miss A L Beacon, BA Manchester Metropolitan
§Miss L Sinden, BA, MA Nottingham Trent
Mr N C Walker, BSc Brunel (*Teacher in Charge, Design Technology & DofE Award*)

Business Studies:
§Mrs E A Thornton, BA Nottingham (*Teacher in Charge*)
§Mrs A E Browning, BA London

Careers:
*Miss J A Dormer, BA Durham
§Mrs E Browning, BA London (*Work Experience Coordinator*)
Mr M Vale, BA Cantab (*Oxbridge Coordinator*)

Classics:
*Mrs J A Nicolson, BA Leeds
Miss J A Dormer, BA Durham

Drama:
*Mrs S Barker-Doherty, BA Northumbria
§Ms J Whitehouse, MA Sussex

English:
*Miss R Bradbury, BA York, MA Leeds
§Mrs C A Andrews, MA Edinburgh
Mrs H M Cave, BA York
§Mrs K Greaves, BA East Anglia
Mrs F Hill, BA Surrey
Mrs C Richards, BA Exeter

Economics:
§Mrs J Roberts, BA Leeds (*Teacher in Charge*)

Geography:
*Mr A Duncombe, MA Cantab
Miss K Biggs, MRes Glasgow, BSc Glasgow
§Mrs A E Browning, BA London
Mrs C Renton, BSc Leicester, MSc London

History:
*Mr M J Vale, MA Cantab
Dr R Lidgett, BA, PhD Birmingham
Mrs C Wellman, BA Warwick

Information Techology:
*Mrs P Prance, BSc Warwick
Miss L Blachford, BSc Exeter
§Mrs N Russell, BSc Loughborough
Mrs E Selley, BSc Anglia Ruskin

Mathematics:
*Mr A Wild, BSc Wales
Miss U Birbeck, BA Warwick
Miss R M Court, BSc London
Mrs P Davies, BSc Warwick
Mr R Sharpe, BEd Bristol Polytechnic
Mrs L Y Sherren, BSc Sheffield

Modern Languages:
*Mr E W MacFetridge, BA Coventry
Mrs M E Forde, BA Oxon, MA Birmingham
Mrs M Hedley, Dip Inst of Linguists, MBA Leicester (*Teacher i/c German*)
Miss L Hooper, BA Warwick
Ms N Lambert, BA Oxon
§Mrs A C Lochner (*German Assistant*)
Mrs J A Nicolson, BA Leeds
§Mrs M H Quinney, DEUG Nantes & Chartres (*French Assistant*)
§Mrs M Esteban-Stephenson (*Spanish Assistant*)

Music:
*Mr M Smallwood, BA Mus Anglia Polytechnic University
Mrs G Jones, BA Leeds, ARCM

Physical Education:
*Miss C E A Gilbert, BA Liverpool John Moores
Miss L McFarlane, BSc Sheffield Hallam
Miss E J Waite, CertEd Bedford, Cert PDE Open
§Mrs C Walker, BEd Chelsea School of Movement

Psychology:
§Mr N Orrock, BA Leicester (*Teacher in Charge*)

Religious Education:
*Mrs K Hewitt, BA Bristol
Ms N Lambert, BA Oxon
Dr R Lidgett, BA, PhD Birmingham

Science:
*Mrs R Chapman, MA Oxon

Biology:
*Mrs J M Grant, BSc Durham
Dr P M Boulton, BSc London, PhD Birmingham
Mrs S Burgham, BSc London
§Dr C M Pickup, BSc Manchester, DPhil Oxon
§Mrs K Pitchford, BSc Southampton

Chemistry:
Dr A Grist, BSc, PhD Leicester (*Teacher in Charge*)
Mrs S Burgham, BSc London
Mrs R Chapman, MA Oxon

Dr R Cheetham, BSc London, PhD London
§Mrs A Mather, BSc Dundee
Physics:
Dr A Chamberlain, BSc, PhD Warwick (*Teacher in Charge*)
§Mrs E Mottram, BA Oxon
Mrs B Stewart, BSc Manchester

Special Educational Needs Coordinator:
§Mrs P Cronin, BA Cardiff, OCR DipSpLD, AMBDA

Visiting Music Staff:
Mr M Adlington, BMus (*Brass*)
Miss K Bagshawe (*Singing*)
Mr C Druce, FRCO, GBSM, ARCM (*Piano*)
Miss A L Hill, LTCL, FTCL, GBSM, ABSM (*Clarinet*)
Mrs S M Irving, BEd Cantab, MMus (*Piano/Violin*)
Mrs S M Lucas, BA, LRAM, ARCM, LGSM (*Woodwind/Brass*)
Mr P Luckhurst, ATCL (*Teachers*) (*Guitar*)
Mrs J J Matthews, LRAM (*Flute*)
Mr R B Meteyard, AGSM (*Violin*)
Mrs S Meteyard, GBSM, ABSM (*Violin/Viola*)
Miss B Morley, BA Coll (*Bass/Singing*)
Mr R A Payne (*Drum Kit*)
Mrs M Todd, Diploma Lucerne Conservatoire (*'Cello*)

Visiting Coaches/Teachers for Activities:
Mrs E Barkans (*Yoga*)
Dr P Cormack (*Fencing*)
Ms C Cornwallis (*Real Tennis*)
Mrs L England (*Dance*)
Mr P Helps (*Clay Pigeon Shooting*)
Mrs H M Jeffery, BA TDipRAD, Ballet Fellow NATD (*Ballet & Contemporary Russian Classic Ballet*)
Mrs D Monnington (*Badminton & Gym*)
Mr T Perkins (*Dance*)
Mrs C Esposito Faraone (*Italian*)

Marketing/Communications Manager: Mrs M K Bray
Registrar: Mrs G Worrall
Head's Secretary: Mrs D Ralphs
Office Manager: Mrs A Lall
Staff Secretary: Mrs G Brown
Administrator: Mr A Sherren
Bursar: Mr J Musselwhite
Assistant Bursar: Mrs S Jasinska
Receptionist: Mrs M Coles
Matron: Mrs S Ward
Network Manager: Mr T Rushton
Assistant Network Manager: Mr J Wiltshire
Librarian: Mrs E Alkhalaf, ALA
Development Manager: Mrs C Musselwhite, BSc Leeds
Database and Administration Assistant: Mrs A Lima
Secretary of Old Girls' Association: Mrs P Beidas

King's High School is an independent day school for girls aged 11 to 18. From its beginning in 1879 it has been a forward looking, friendly school which is proud of its reputation for both academic success and the personal development of its girls. The school is part of the Warwick Independent Schools Foundation, alongside Warwick School and Warwick Preparatory School.

Located in the heart of Warwick, the school has remained on the same town site for 127 years. The 15th century Eastgate Tower and 18th century Landor House are complemented by modern additions such as the Sixth Form Centre and St Mary's Building opened by Dame Judi Dench in 2006. A new Creative Arts Centre will open in 2009.

The curriculum aims to give students as broad an education as possible. All students study two modern languages and Latin, and ICT is widely used across the curriculum. There is a wide choice of A level subjects.

Our winning formula of hard work and lots of fun has produced consistently good performances for King's High which has appeared within the top 100 schools for the past five years. In 2007 four pupils were in the top five marks in the country for GCSE ICT, two in Food Technology, one in French and one in Spanish. One pupil was in the top 10 for GCSE English.

The school also recognises the importance of the creative arts: it has numerous music and drama groups. Yoga, ballet and creative textiles are some of the activities on offer outside of the curriculum, most of which take place at lunchtimes. All girls are encouraged to enjoy some form of exercise or sport and some perform at the highest levels in individual events or school and county teams. There are strong links with our brother school in the Foundation, Warwick School.

The school organises many day, evening and residential trips to complement the curriculum. Recent visits abroad include trips to India, Iceland and the USA, with exchange trips to France, Germany and Spain.

Admission. Girls are required to take an entrance examination and attend an interview.

Fees per term (2008-2009). Tuition £3,042. Music: Brass, Pianoforte, Strings, Woodwind, Guitar, Drums, Singing £184 for 10 lessons.

Financial Assistance. Scholarships are available on entry at age 11 and for internal and external candidates to Sixth Form. Warwick Foundation Awards, up to the value of full fees, are also available on entry at 11+ and at Sixth Form.

Charitable status. King's High School is a part of the Warwick Independent Schools Foundation which is a Registered Charity, number 1088057. The aim of the charity is "to provide for children (3–18) of parents of all financial means – a high proportion of whom shall come from Warwick and its immediate surroundings, but subject to satisfying academic standards where required – education of academic, cultural and sporting standards which are the highest within their peer groups".

The Kingsley School

Beauchamp Hall Beauchamp Avenue Leamington Spa Warwickshire CV32 5RD
Tel: 01926 425127
Fax: 01926 831691
e-mail: admin@kingsley.warwickshire.sch.uk
website: www.thekingsleyschool.com

Independent Day School for Girls aged 3 to 18, and boys up to 7 years, founded in 1884 and ISC accredited.

Council:
President: Lady Butler

Joint Chairs:
Mrs A Darling
Mrs J White, BSc Eng, FCA

Vice-Chair: Mrs R Skilbeck, BDS

Governors:
Mrs L Bartlett
R N Button
A Bye
Mrs V C Davies
Mr N Evans, BSc, FRICS
Mrs M P Hicks, CertEd
Dr L Long, MA, PhD
Professor R Naguib
P S Sanghera, BA
Mrs P Watson, BSc

***Headmistress*: Mrs C A Mannion Watson**, BA, MSc Ed

Deputy Head: Mrs C Robbins, BA, MPhil, PGCE
Head of Junior Department: Mrs J Kay, GNSM, LRAM, CertEd

Curriculum and Administration Coordinator: Miss R Dyson, BA, PGCE, Dip in Counselling

Staff:

Art:
*Miss N Smethurst, BA, PGCE

Classics:
*Mr D Menashe, BA, PGCE

Economics and Business Studies:
*Mrs C Benn, BSc QTS

English:
*Mrs A Hamilton, BA, PGCE
Mrs D Morgan, BA, PGCE
Mrs C Robbins, BA, MPhil, PGCE
Mrs K Todman, BA, PGCE

Geography:
*Mrs J Bailey, BA
Mrs D Frydman, BSc, CertEd
Mrs S Watson, BA, PGCE

History:
*Mrs S Waterson, BA, PGCE
Miss R Dyson, BA, PGCE, Dip Counselling
Mrs A Warren, BA, PGCE

Information Technology:
*Mrs J Jones, BEd, CertEd, DipRSA
Mrs E Ronchetti, BA, PGCE

Mathematics:
*Mr K Stimson, BSc, PGCE
Miss K Davis, BSc, PGCE
Mrs L Laubscher, HE Dip SA, QTS
Mrs S Morris, BSc, CertEd

Modern Languages (French, German, Italian, Spanish):
*Mrs S E Jessett, BA, PGCE
Ms A Fretwell, BA
Mrs K Baker, BA, PGCE
Mrs F M Harris, BA, MA, PGCE
§Mrs E Horvath, BA, CertEd
Mrs C A Mannion-Watson, BA, MSc Ed

Performing Arts:
*Mrs J Walton, BEd (**Drama*)
Mr J Smith, BMus, PGCE
Mrs A Vallance, BA, IDTA (*Dance*)

Instrumental Staff:
Mr G Cooke, CertEd (*Double Bass*)
Miss J Dodd, BA, PGCE (*Vocal Studies*)
Mrs K Knott, BA, PGCE (*Flute/Guitar*)
§Mr C Langdown, MMus, GRSM, DipRCM, ARCM (*Piano & Music Theory*)
Miss B Morley, BA (*Head of Vocal Studies*)
Mrs E Murphy, BA, PGCE (*Piano*)
Mr R Payne (*Percussion*)
Miss C Robinson (*Clarinet/Saxophone*)
Mr J Smith, BMus, PGCE (*Brass, Electric Guitar*)
Mrs M Walton, BMus (*Violin*)
Mrs C Wimpenny, GBSM, ABSM (*'Cello/Double Bass*)

Speech & Drama:
§Mrs J Parkinson, ALAM (*LAMDA*)
Mrs J Leonard, LAMDA
Mrs V Comer, LAMDA

Dance:
Miss N Shurvinton (*Modern Dance*)

Physical Education:
*†Mrs S Bates, BA, CertEd
§Mrs P Rogers, BEd, CertEd
Miss S Windsor, BEd, PGCE

Psychology:
*Ms J McLoughlin, BSc, PGCE

Religious Studies:
§*Mrs E Mackenzie, BPhil, MEd, CertEd

Science:
*Mrs J Hilton, BSc, PGCE, CPhys, MInstP
*Mrs S Croft, BSc, PGCE
*Dr C Robertson, BSc, PhD, PGCE
Mrs G Hermitage, BSc, PGCE
Mrs C Duke, BSc, PGCE
Mr A Edwards, BA, PGCE

Technology:
*Mrs S Bresnen, CertEd
Mrs C Dempsey, BEd
Mrs K Hughes-O'Sullivan, MA, BEd
Miss L Pedley, BEd
§Mrs J Stephens, CertEd, BEd

Careers:
Ms A Fretwell, BA

Learning Support:
*Mrs L Stevenson, LLB
Mrs Y Raja

Learning Resources Centre:
Mrs F M Harris, BA, MA, PGCE
Mrs J Kelway

Duke of Edinburgh's Award Scheme:
Mrs S Palliser, CertEd
Mr T Palliser

Junior Department & Early Years:
Head of Junior Department: Mrs J Kay, GNSM, LRAM, CertEd
Mrs G Adair, BN, PGCE
Mrs C Close
Mrs V Comer, LAMDA
Mrs M James, CertEd
Ms J Marsh, BEd
Mrs R Parkes, MA, PGCE
Mrs J Pendred
Mrs K Liverton, BA, PGCE
Miss C Gray, BEd
Mrs Y Hargreaves, NNEB
Mrs S Jones, BEd
Mrs S Lilley
Mrs K Parker
Miss L Tilley, BA PGCE
Mrs H Turner, NNEB

Administration:
Senior Finance Manager: Mr B Cheney, ACMA
Finance Manager: Mrs A-M Reddin
Head's PA: Mrs J Bostock
Finance Assistant: Miss T Durbin
Finance Assistant: Mrs S Punj
Registrar: Mrs C Watson
School Secretary: Mrs A Griffiths
Reception/Secretary: Mrs M A Wright
School Nurse: Mrs T Ball, RGN, BSc
Administrative Assistant: Mrs K Parker, RGN

Technical Support:
Mr O B Shodeinde, BA Dip (*Network Manager*)
Mrs L Litchfield, BSc (*Chief Technician*)
Mrs D Jones, GRSC
Mrs J Kelway

The Kingsley School has a long history of success in every area of the curriculum and its traditions and ethos combine to make it a happy and secure environment for its pupils. The school is a Christian foundation but welcomes pupils of different faiths. Since 1884, Kingsley has upheld traditional values in a happy, purposeful and well-disciplined environment. It enjoys an enviable teacher : pupil ratio of 1 : 8 and the talents of each individual are recognised and nurtured in all fields.

The **Junior School** provides a secure and exciting environment within which a broad curriculum is followed that extends beyond the National Curriculum whilst stressing the importance of literacy and numeracy. There is a strong commitment to music and drama with regular opportunities for performance. Swimming, gymnastics and a range of games are actively pursued, being a particular strength of the school. The Foundation Stage is housed in its own Early Years Centre.

Throughout their junior years, children thrive in a caring, homely and stimulating setting that prepares them well for entry to the Senior School.

The **Senior School** provides a wide range of GCSE subjects including 3 separate sciences, 4 modern languages, Latin, Business and Communication Studies, Physical Education, Drama, Dance and Music. Academic standards are high with the 2007 results showing a 95% pass rate at grades A*–C with 38% of passes at grade A or A*.

In the **Sixth Form** a choice of 22 A Level subjects is offered including Psychology, ICT, Music, Theatre Studies and Sports Studies. Latest A Level results show a 100% pass rate, with nearly a third of these at grade A and two-thirds at A or B. Most girls go on to the university of their first choice, including Oxbridge.

Extra-Curricular Activities. Music, Drama, Dance and Public Speaking flourish throughout the school. Sport is well catered for and pupils regularly represent Warwickshire. Kingsley boasts highly successful competitive riding teams which have won both the National Schools' Cross Country and National Show Jumping Championships. There is a wide variety of clubs and societies including a thriving Duke of Edinburgh's Award scheme in which over 100 Gold Awards have been gained. An extensive range of field courses, visits and expeditions is organised in Britain and overseas, including popular World Challenge expeditions that have been to Rajasthan, Africa and South America in recent years. Every girl can find something in which to participate with enthusiasm and success.

Fees per term (2008-2009). Junior School: £2,520 (Reception–Year 2), £2,940 (Years 3–6). Senior School: £3,160.

Scholarships. Academic, Art, Music and Drama scholarships are available at 7+, 11+, 13+ and 16+.

Private transport serves a wide area and after school care is available.

Charitable status. The Kingsley School is a Registered Charity, number 528774. It exists to provide high quality education for girls aged 3 to 18 and boys up to 7 years.

The Lady Eleanor Holles School

Hanworth Road Hampton Middlesex TW12 3HF
Tel: 020 8979 1601
Fax: 020 8941 8291
e-mail: office@lehs.org.uk
website: www.lehs.org.uk

This Independent Girls' School derives its endowment from a Trust established in 1710 under the will of Lady Eleanor Holles. The Cripplegate Schools Foundation has administered the Trust since 1711 when the original school for girls was founded in Cripplegate in the City of London. It is governed under schemes of the Charity Commissioners (1868, 1875), and the Ministry of Education (1905, 1910, 1933). The present school in Hampton accommodates about 865 girls, aged from 7 to 18 years.

The Cripplegate Schools Foundation

Chairman of the Foundation: Mrs J Ross, BSc, CPFA

Governors:
Mr M Breckon
Mr G Cox, ACE, CA SA
Mrs M Lomax
Mrs P C G Longmore, MCSP, SRP
Ms A Meyric Hughes, BA, PGCE, MA
Mrs M I Nagli
Mr R Niven, BA
Dr L Sherski, MB, BCh, DCH, DObst, RCOG
Mr J Tomlinson, CC, BA, MSc, FCMA
Mr R Young, BSc Hons, DipArch Hons

Clerk to the Governors: Mr A Pitchers, BEd Hons, MCIPD

***Head Mistress*: Mrs G Low**, MA Somerville College Oxford

Deputy Head Mistress: Mrs L C Hazel, BA Hull

Assistant Head Mistress: Miss M E Beardwood, CertEd Dartford College of Physical Education, BA Open, MA Reading

Assistant Staff:

Senior School

Art and Craft:
Miss S Pauffley, BA Goldsmiths College London
Mrs M Barclay, DipAD Hons, ATC Hornsey College of Art
Mr L Curtis, BA Slade School of Art, MA Royal College of Art
Ms K Jeffery, BA Leicester (*History of Art*)
Miss H Peat, BA Loughborough College of Art and Design
Ms A E Seaborn, BA Winchester School of Art

Classics:
Mr D Piper, BA King's College London
Miss K C Eltis, BA Balliol College Oxford
Miss M Hart, BA Exeter
Mrs L C Hazel, BA Hull
Mrs S Welsh, BA Leicester

Design Technology including Home Economics:
Miss A M Travers, BEd Surrey
Mrs A M Angliss, BEd Trinity College Dublin
Mr S G Bicknell, BSc Brunel
Ms L Espinola, BEd Newcastle, Australia

Drama:
Miss P Flannery, BA London, MA King's College London, RADA (*Director of Drama*)

Economics:
Miss A J Matthews, BA Leicester
Miss D A Self, BSc Brunel

English:
Miss S Gamblin, BEd Newnham College Cambridge, MA London Institute of Education
Mrs C L Gilroy-Scott, BA Birmingham
Mr S Halse, BA London, MA London
Mrs J Morris, BA King's College London
Mrs H M Ndongong, BA St Edmund Hall Oxford
Mrs C Richardson, BA Reading
Ms V Smolen, BA Homerton College Cambridge
Mr M RD Wright, MA Birkbeck College London, MA Merton College Oxford

Geography:
Mrs S E Coggin, BA Swansea, FRGS
Mrs J C Ballard, BSc Loughborough
Mr G Budd, BA Durham
Mrs J M Mackay, BSc Southampton, MA London

History:
Mr M Christmas, MA Queen's College Oxford
Mrs A M Bradshaw, MA St Andrews

Miss S J Easton, BA Newcastle
Miss S E Stowe, BA Warwick

Information Technology:
Mrs F M Wimblett, BSc Royal Holloway College London
Miss M E Beardwood, CertEd Dartford College of Physical Education, BA Open, MA Reading
Mrs M Barclay, DipAD Hons, ATC Hornsey College of Art
Mr R Nicholson, BA Pembroke College Oxford

Mathematics:
Mr S J Waters, BSc Gonville and Caius College Cambridge
Mr A Ademola, BSc UMIST
Mrs N Banerjee, BA Delhi
Mrs N C Camilleri, BSc Manchester
Mrs J V Fairhurst, BSc Imperial College London, MA Lancaster
Mrs S Leigh, BSc Edinburgh
Mrs J B Painton, BSc Southampton
Mrs A C Patrick, BA Bristol
Mrs P A Sharp, BSc Sheffield
Miss C Swainston, BSc Surrey
Mr M J Williams, BA City of London Polytechnic
Mrs F M Wimblett, BSc Royal Holloway College London

Modern Languages:
Mr M Tompsett, MA Selwyn College Cambridge (*Head of Modern Languages and German*)
Mrs A Buck, Licenciada en Filología Anglogermanica Universidad de Valencia (*Spanish and German*)
Mrs I M Colclough, BA Royal Holloway College London (*German*)
Mrs R A M Johnson, BA Cologne (*German*)
Mrs V M Kean, BA Leeds (*French*)
Mr S Lauret, Licence d'Anglais Université Lumière, Lyon (*Head of French*)
Mrs K M Munday, BA Manchester (*German*)
Miss L Pla-Miro, BA Universidad de Alicante (*Head of Spanish*)
Dr P J Rand, BA, MPhil, PhD Pembroke College Oxford (*French*)
Mrs N J Rees, MA New Hall Cambridge (*Spanish*)
Miss D L Robbins, MA St Andrews (*French*)

Music:
Director of Music: Mrs M Ashe, MA St Catherine's College Oxford
Mrs N C Rook, BA Southampton, LTCL, PGCE (*Head of Curriculum Music*)
Mr B L Hughes, MA St Catherine's College Oxford, MMus Goldsmiths College London, QTS (*Composer-in-Residence*)
Mr R Millett, Dip RCM Performing (*Music Technology and Studio Music*)
Mr R Nicholson, BA Pembroke College Oxford, ARCO
Miss A Prowse, BA Girton College Cambridge
Mr J Akers, BMus TCM, MMus, PGADip RCM (*Classical Guitar*)
Mrs B Cassidy, MMus, DipTCL (*Voice*)
Miss F Chesterman, BMus, Dip Perf (*Violin*)
Ms A Cohen, DRASM, ARCM, LRAM (*Piano*)
Mr F D'Albert (*Electric Guitar, Rock Bands*)
Mr J Fichert, MMus RCM, PG Dip Adv RCM Dist, Dip-Musiklehrerprüfung Karlsruhe (*Piano*)
Ms N Garty, BMus, LRAM, LRSM, ATCL, LTCL (*Voice*)
Mr A J Gee, BMus Royal Holloway College London (*Double Bass, Electric Bass Guitar*)
Mr G Hobbs, BMus, PGDipMus (*Bassoon*)
Mrs K Hobbs, BMus Hons RNCM, PP RNCM, Dip PG RAM (*Clarinet*)
Miss E Hodgkinson, BMus, PGRNCM, LRAM (*Piano*)
Mrs D L Hume, DSCM (*Violin*)
Miss S James, BMus, LRAM, DipRAM (*Saxophone*)
Miss I Jones, BMus, Dip RCM, Advanced RCM (*Oboe*)
Ms D Kemp, BA, MA, ARCM PG, Dip RCM (*Viola*)
Mr R Kennedy, ARCM (*Brass*)
Mrs P A Kent, GRSM, LRAM (*Piano*)
Miss L Knight, BA, MA (*Voice, Music Theatre*)
Mr R Millett, Dip RCM (*Percussion, Percussion Group*)
Ms A Moore (*Harp*)
Miss S Morfee, ARCM, LTCL (*Flute*)
Mr I Mullin, BMus, LRAM (*Flute*)
Miss E O'Connor, BMus, Dip RCM (*Voice*)
Mrs H Roberts, MMus, GTCL, LTCL, FTCL (*Voice*)
Mr T Sharp BSc, MSc, LGSM (*Piano, Jazz Piano*)
Miss E Sheridan, BMus Hons RCM, PG Dip RCM (*Clarinet*)
Mr N Stringfellow, BA Mus, Grad RNCM, ARCMPG (*Cello*)

Natural Sciences:
Mrs H Beedham, BSc Hull, MSc Kingston (*Chemistry, Head of Science*)
Mrs L J Anstey, MA New Hall Cambridge (*Psychology and Biology*)
Mrs L Baker, BSc Sussex (*Biology*)
Mrs J Barwise, BSc Manchester, MA London (*Head of Physics*)
Mrs N C Camilleri, BSc Manchester (*Physics*)
Mr M J Crewe, BSc Birmingham (*Physics*)
Mrs K M Ellis, BSc Durham (*Physics*)
Mrs B L Flood, BA St Hugh's College Oxford (*Chemistry*)
Mr A Hayter, BSc Durham (*Head of Chemistry*)
Mrs A Lim, BSc Edinburgh, MSc Aberdeen (*Biology*)
Mrs S Jansz, BSc Bangor (*Chemistry*)
Mrs J Monteil, BSc Swansea, MSc London (*Head of Psychology, Biology*)
Mrs C R Nicholls, BSc Cardiff (*Head of Biology*)
Miss S S Ostrander, BSc Bristol (*Psychology and Biology*)
Miss R Parker, BSc Manchester (*Chemistry*)
Miss K Whitehouse, BSc Manchester (*Biology*)

Physical Education:
Miss M J Waters, BEd Bedford College of HE
Miss S Bowyer, BEd de Montfort
Miss G A Lindsay (*Rowing*)
Miss L Paulin, BA Sydney
Miss N Tilbury, BSc Brighton

Religious Education:
Mrs P Gibbons, BA Surrey, MA Surrey
Miss L Brown, BA St Mary's, University of Surrey

Careers Advice:
Miss A J Matthews, BA Leicester Polytechnic (*Economics*)
Mrs H Beedham, BSc Hull, MSc Kingston (*Chemistry*)
Mrs R A M Johnson, BA Cologne (*German*)
Mrs H M Ndongong, BA St Edmund Hall Oxford (*English*)
Mrs C R Nicholls, BSc Cardiff (*Biology*)
Miss S S Ostrander, BSc Bristol (*Psychology and Biology*)
Mrs J B Painton, BSc Southampton (*Mathematics*)
Miss R E Parker, BSc Manchester (*Chemistry*)
Miss K Whitehouse, BSc Manchester (*Biology*)

Manager LRC: Mrs L Payne, MA San Francisco

Junior Department

Head of Department: Mrs J M Adams, BA Newcastle

Assistant Staff:
Mrs J E Allden, BSc London, MSc
Miss V M Barnes, BA Kingston
Mrs M M Bass, BEd Natal
Miss E Brannon, BA Leeds Metropolitan
Mrs M Crowley, BA Exeter
Mrs J Deverson, BEd Oxford Brookes
Mrs J Dilworth, BSc UCL, MPhil Cambridge
Mrs J Gazetas, BSc Newcastle
Mrs S Grant-Sturgis, BA Exeter
Mrs A Jain, BCom Delhi
Mrs C Lyne, Dartford College of PE, BA OU

Mrs V M Moran, BA Durham
Mrs A E Sutherland, BA Southampton
Ms R Walsh, BEd De Montfort
Mr P J Ward, BEd London, MEd USA

Administration:
Bursar: Mr A Pitchers, BEd Hons, MCIPD
Facilities Manager: Mr D A Curtis-Donnelly
Marketing & Development Coordinator: Ms S Newton
Head Mistress's Personal Assistant: Mrs C E Grieveson
School Secretary: Mrs R Filby
Registrar: Mrs R D'Albert
Medical Adviser: Dr S J Bowskill, MB BS London
School Nurse: Mrs M J Court, SRN
School Secretary (*Junior Department*): Mrs J Rees

The school dates from 1711 and is named after its benefactress The Lady Eleanor Holles who directed that the surplus from her Will should be used to establish a school for young girls. Originally in the Cripplegate Ward of the City of London, it moved in the nineteenth century to Hackney and then in 1937 to Hampton. The present, purpose-built, school was opened by Princess Alice, Duchess of Gloucester and accommodated 350 pupils. Numerous additions to the building and the acquisition of more land have enabled the school to increase in size to some 720 girls who enjoy a wealth of specialist facilities and the use of 30 acres of playing fields and gardens. Nine science laboratories, new Learning Resources Centre and Sixth Library, an Art Block, a Design and Technology suite, a Music and Drama wing, extensive IT and multimedia language facilities and a dedicated Careers area are complemented by grass and hard tennis courts, netball courts, 5 lacrosse pitches, track and field areas and a full-sized, indoor heated swimming pool. A Boat House, shared with Hampton School, was opened in October 2000 and a large Sports Hall, adjacent to the swimming pool, in September 2001.

Both the Junior and Senior Departments are equipped with a lift for the disabled.

The School's Statement of Purpose embodies the original aim, to encourage every girl to develop her personality to the full so that she may become a woman of integrity and a responsible member of society. It also emphasises the value of a broad, balanced education which gives due importance to sport, music and the creative arts in general whilst providing the opportunities for girls to achieve high academic standards within a framework of disciplined, independent study.

The Curriculum. In DCSF Years 7–9 girls experience two modern, foreign languages, two years of Latin, the separate sciences, dedicated ICT lessons and a PSHE programme which continues throughout the school. Selection rather than specialisation for GCSE allows girls to respond to individual abilities and attributes whilst the School's scheme ensures that every girl continues to experience a broad education in which as few doors as possible are closed. A large sixth form of about 190–200 girls enables a wide choice of Advanced and Advanced Subsidiary subjects to be offered by the School. Most girls will study four or five subjects at Advanced Subsidiary level, proceeding to A level with three or four and most are entered for the A level General Studies examination. All sixth form students move on to further training, the majority to universities, and there is a sizeable Oxbridge contingent annually. The formal Careers programme which begins in Year 9, before GCSE choices are made, continues throughout the school and uses external specialists, parents and past pupils, ECCTIS and other computer programmes as well as the School's own, trained staff.

Extra-Curricular Activity. A key strength of the school is the range and diversity of its flourishing extra-curricular provision. Some 120 clubs run each week ranging from Music, Drama and PE to Outward Bound and subject clubs, all aiming to further stimulate and inculcate a love of learning outside the classroom: 'The Other Half'. Sixth Formers lead a number of groups which focus on various political, environmental and ethical issues, including 'Model United Nations', 'Amnesty' and 'Make Poverty History'. Girls are encouraged to take the initiative to form their own clubs with a Medic Group, Law Society and Book Club formed in the recent past. The school is very much at the heart of the educational community and has developed a wide range of activities to ensure that students are aware of their social responsibilities, including Service Volunteers which works with disadvantaged students and the elderly, and running numerous activities in local primary schools, including language and drama clubs. Pupils are strongly encouraged to participate in extra-curricular activities.

The Junior Department (188 pupils aged 7–11) is accommodated in a separate building in the grounds, which was very extensively renovated and refurbished in 2003. It is an integral part of the whole school community and uses some specialist facilities.

(*See entry in the IAPS section for more details.*)

Entrance. (*see Scholarship Entries section*). All applicants must sit the School's competitive entrance examinations, which are held in November (Sixth Form) and January (7+ and 11+) each year for admission in the following year. Pupils may enter the Junior Department from the age of 7, and the Senior School at 11 years. Girls with good academic ability may apply for direct entry to the Sixth Form.

Registration and Entrance Examination Fee: £75.

Some Academic and Music Scholarships are available for both internal and external candidates at 11+ and Sixth Form entry stages and the Governors of the Cripplegate Schools Foundation offer a small number of Foundation Entrance Bursaries which are available to girls of suitable academic standards. The amount of assistance is calculated on a sliding scale which is related to family income.

Fees per term (2008-2009). £3,150 in the Junior Department; £4,180 in the Senior School, inclusive of Books, Stationery, Games and Public Examination fees. Younger sisters of pupils already in the School are eligible for certain reductions.

Optional Subjects. Individual lessons in instrumental Music £207 per term, Rowing £210 per term, Speech and Drama from £96 per term, Chess £47 per term, and Fencing from £56 per term.

Former Pupils' Association. The Holly Club address for communications: Secretary of The Holly Club, c/o The School.

Charitable status. Cripplegate Schools Foundation is a Registered Charity, number 312493. The Foundation is now responsible only for The Lady Eleanor Holles School which exists to provide education of a high standard to girls between the ages of 7 and 18.

Lavant House

West Lavant Chichester West Sussex PO18 9AB
Tel: 01243 527211
Fax: 01243 530490
e-mail: office@lavanthouse.org.uk
website: www.lavanthouse.org.uk

Governors:
Mrs P E Senior (*Chair*)
J Bartlett
D M Green, MA Cantab, FRSA
Mrs A Hancock, BA, ACP, FRSA
R Hoare, OBE, MA Oxon
A MacFarlane, LLB Buckingham
R H Malcolm-Green, CEng, BSc London
Mrs R M Moriarty, MA Oxon, MTh London
Mrs P Mould, Dip Primary Science
M J Pressdee, FCA

Clerk to the Governors: Mrs M Lowe

***Headmistress*: Mrs M Scott**, MA Cantab

Senior Staff:

Deputy Head & Director of Studies: Dr N Sturt, BA Hons London, PhD London, PGCE London

Head of Junior Department: Mrs Z Woolley, BA Hons Birmingham

Senior Mistress: Mrs K Bartholomew, MA London, PGCE Cantab

Teaching Staff:

Sciences:
Biology: Mrs E J Marks, BSc Hons Warwick, SRN, RM, PGCE Leicester, MSc Open
Chemistry: (*to be appointed*)
Physics: Mrs J Dowle, BSc Hons Exeter, PGCE Southampton
Mathematics: Mrs D van Beek, BEd Exeter, DipEd Southampton
Mrs J Martin, BEd Hons Chichester
Computer Studies: D Ward, BSc Hons Leicester, MSc London, CPhys

Humanities:
English: Ms M Mack, BA Hons Durham, PGCE London
History: Mrs K Bartholomew, MA London, PGCE Cantab
Geography: Mrs E Blows, BA Hons Manchester, PGCE Sussex
French: Mrs B Harrison, BA Hons London, PGCE Cantab
Spanish: Mrs G Rosado, BA Cuidad Real, PGCE Granada University
Classics: Dr N Sturt, BA Hons London, PhD London, PGCE London
Drama: Miss C Boyd-Wallis, BA Hons Lancaster
Psychology: Mrs S Jones, BA Hons Open, CertEd Gloucester, DipSpLD Kingston
Art & History of Art: Mrs E Houghton-Connell, BA Hons West Surrey College of Art & Design, PGCE London
PE: Mrs H J Kyffin, CertEd Avery Hill College
Miss E Wiggs, BSc Hons UCC, GIBiol, PGCE UCC
Miss P Chambers, BEd Exeter
Business Studies: Ms P Furmidge, BEd Hons, MA Sussex, BA OU
Media Studies & RE: Mr D Musty, BA Hons Chichester
Economics: Mrs C Howard, MA, BA, CertEd, MInstM
Director of Music: Mrs S Howell Evans, GTCL Trinity College, London, ARCM, LTCL, PGCE London, ARSCM, FGMS
Learning Support: Mrs S Street, BSc Sydney, DipRSA SpLD
EFL: Mrs B Harrison, BA London, PGCE Cantab
Speech & Drama: Mrs J Pressdee, LGSM, ANEA Stage Technique
Tennis: Mrs E Ellicott, LTA registered

Junior Lavant House:
Mrs Z Woolley, BA Hons Birmingham
Mrs J Young, CertEd London
Miss E Steele, BA Hons Chichester, PGCE UCC
Mrs L Eldred, CertEd London
Mrs C Odell, BEd Chichester
Mrs L Taylor, CertEd Southampton
Mrs E Taws
Mrs J Waite

Boarding:
Mrs H J Kyffin, CertEd Avery Hill College (*Deputy Housemistress*)
Miss E Wiggs, BSc Hons UCC, GIBiol, PGCE UCC

School Nurse: Mrs F Campbell, RGN, SN
Matron: Mrs J MacGregor

Administration:
Bursar: Mrs M Lowe
Assistant Bursar: Mrs S Greenwood
Secretary & Head's PA: Mrs L Cranfield
Secretary: Mrs J Shrubb

Librarian: Ms J Thurston, BA Hons Reading

Housekeeper: Mrs R Platnauer

Catering:
Mr A Nelson
Mrs K Staples

Lavant House is a forward-looking independent school. It aims to provide girls with a challenging and positive academic education within a caring community, to enable each individual to develop her abilities to the full whilst acquiring a strong set of personal values. The school is small with about 160 pupils throughout the age range from 3 to 18. The intimate size of its classes creates an opportunity for real personalised learning within an atmosphere of trust and cooperation, bringing out the best in every pupil and resulting in confident, sociable and successful young women ready to meet the challenges of the future.

Boarding. The school has a mix of day and boarding pupils, with both full and flexible boarding arrangements. There is an informal family atmosphere in the House, and Sixth form boarders have a considerable degree of independence in their own adjacent accommodation, "The Cottage".

Situation and Facilities. The school is situated between the South Downs and the sea, just north of the historic cathedral city of Chichester, in the heart of glorious Sussex countryside. The lovely eighteenth century flint buildings and well tended gardens and grounds contribute to a secure and tranquil environment, which nevertheless has modern facilities for Science, ICT, Drama and Sport. A new Art Studio opened in September 2006. All main teaching rooms have computers with Internet access, in addition to the main Computer Suite which contains 20 networked PCs. The Junior Department is housed separately on site with its own safe play area.

Curriculum. A traditionally broad academic curriculum is taught through to GCSE and a full range of subjects is offered at AS and A Level in the small, lively Sixth Form. The school boasts strong Art and Drama departments which regularly run exhibitions and major productions, and there is an accomplished Senior Choir. Regular Chamber Concerts give young musicians a chance to perform.

Specialist help for dyslexic pupils is available, and English as an Additional Language for overseas students.

Sport. Games provision includes a large playing field, three superbly surfaced netball and tennis courts, and an outdoor heated swimming pool, as well as the gymnasium The main curriculum sports are netball and hockey in winter, and rounders, tennis, athletics and swimming in the summer, but girls also do badminton, volleyball, aerobics, dance, gymnastics and table tennis. Many matches are organised for girls of all age groups, and the teams are very successful in area competitions. The senior netball team has been West Sussex West Area and League Champions for the last four years.

Lavant House Stables are next to the school and many girls ride. There are two floodlit all-weather arenas in addition to fifty acres of pasture and woodland.

There is an active Duke of Edinburgh's Award scheme, with expeditions organised during the summer.

Transport. The school operates four minibus routes over a twenty mile radius for daygirls. From Chichester there are rail links along the South Coast and up to London; Heathrow and Gatwick airports are about one and a half hour's drive away.

Admission. Admission is by interview and informal testing. There is an assessment day in the Spring Term for entry at 11+. Academic scholarships are available for the Senior School and the Sixth Form.

Fees per term (2008-2009). Junior Day: £1,970 (Foundation), £2,540 (Years 1 and 2), £3,305 (Years 3–6). Senior Day: £3,995. Boarding: £5,240 (Junior), £6,285 (Senior). A returnable deposit of one term's boarding fees is charged for overseas pupils.

Charitable status. Lavant House School Educational Trust Limited is a Registered Charity, number 307372.

Leicester High School for Girls

454 London Road Leicester LE2 2PP
Tel: 0116 270 5338
Fax: 0116 244 8823
e-mail: enquiries@leicesterhigh.co.uk
website: www.leicesterhigh.co.uk

The school is a Trust with a Board of Governors in membership of AGBIS and the Headmistress belongs to the GSA.

Board of Governors:
Chairman: Mr P S Bonnett
Mrs M R Banks, MBE, MEd
Ms D Bolland, BA, MSc
Prof M M De Souza, BSc, BE, PhD Cantab, FInstP
Mr A Jarvis
Mr J Jethwa
Mr G Norris
Mr R W Pain, FCA
Mr M Russell
Mrs M Sheldon
The Revd Canon Peter Taylor, MEd, MA
Mr A Williams

Clerk to the Governors: Mrs A Morris, ACMA, BA Hons Manchester

***Headmistress*: Mrs J Burns**, BA Hons Southampton

Deputy Head: Miss D E J Wassell, BA Hons Leeds

Assistant Head: Mrs S M Dobson, BA London

Examinations Officer: Mr B D Holness, BSc Hons Southampton
Head of Sixth Form: Mrs J Alexander-Orr, BA Hons Essex

Senior Department:

Assistant Staff:
Miss R Amin, BSc Lancaster
Mrs V A Birch, LLM Exon
*Mr A Chappell, BSc Hons Leicester
*Mrs J Davison, BEd Hons Cheltenham & Gloucester Coll HE
Mrs P Formoy, BA Manchester
Mrs P Gascoigne, BA Hons Wolverhampton
§Mrs R Hall, BSc Hons Aberystwyth
Mrs R Hall, BSc Hons London
*Mrs E Heap, BA Hons Leicester
*Dr S Hills, BSc Hons York, PhD Nottingham
Mr P Hoyle, BSc Rhodes
§Mr M Joannou, BSc Salford, MEd Nottingham
Miss S Khachik, BA First Class Hons Durham
§Mrs B L Krokosz, BA Hons Coventry
§Mrs E Martin, BEd Hons Bedford
*Mrs L C Martin, BA Hons London, DipPsy
Mrs B Morell, Maîtrise d'Anglais Perpignan
*Mrs D A Morgan, BSc Hons Warwick
§Mrs W Noble, CertEd Keele
Mr S Norbury, BSc Liverpool
Miss A Paul, BA Hons Leicester
Ms L P Pearson, BA Hons Leicester
*Miss K Price, BA Hons Exeter
*§Mrs N Pulham, BA Hons Southampton
Mrs H Rai, MSc Bradford
Mrs H Rees, BA Hons Birmingham
*Mrs J M Robbins, Dip in Art Edinburgh
Dr N Singleton, BSc Hons Birmingham, PhD De Montfort
Miss E Stell, BA Liverpool
Mr A Stewart, BSc Leicester
Mrs A Sykes, CertEd Leicester
Mrs B Thompson, BA Hons Newcastle
*Mrs S Varnam, BA CSSD
*§Mrs J Whalley, BSc Hons Leicester
*Mr A Wilson, BA Hons Nottingham
Miss L-J Wood, BA Hons Warwick

Bursar: Mrs A Morris, ACMA, BA Hons Manchester
Headmistress's PA: Mrs V E Shortland
Registrar: Mrs A-M Neal
Secretary: Miss D Taylor
Librarian: Miss A Adams, MA Liverpool
Assistant Librarian: Mrs L M Humrich, BA Lancaster, DipLib
Accounts Assistant: Mrs E J Mackay, AAT
Payroll: §Mrs J T Greasley, FCCA
IT Systems Manager: Mr A Collins
IT Technician: Miss J Hayre
SIMS Coodinator: Mrs K Lock
Laboratory Technicians: Mrs L Hirst, Mrs M Cupac
School Nurse: Mrs A Olalobo

Visiting Staff:
Mr N Bott (*Drums*)
Mrs J Bound, GBSM (*Piano*)
Ms A Donnelly, BA Hons (*Piano*)
Mr T Gascoigne (*Tennis*)
Miss R Guillain, GSMD, LAMDA, EMPA, IDTA (*Speech and Drama*)
Mrs K Loomes, FIDTA (*Ballet*)
Mrs A Mitchell, LTCM (*Clarinet/Flute/Saxophone*)
Mrs W M Philpott, BA Hons, PGCE, LTCL (*'Cello/Piano*)
Miss S Stephens (*Singing*)
Mrs C Sullivan (*Speech & Drama*)

Junior Department:

Head of Department: Mrs C A Jolley, BEd Hons Sheffield
Assistant Head: Mrs S J Davies, BEd Hons Exeter
Foundation Stage Coordinator: Miss C Pow, BA Hons QTS Chichester

Miss Z Cottam, BA De Montfort Leicester
Mrs P Jackson, NNEB
Mrs K Jarvis, BA QTS Northampton
Miss J Palmer, BA Hons Canterbury
Mrs S Peake, NNEB
Miss V Roe, BEd Hons Exeter
Mrs J Vick, BA Hons Leicester
Mrs S Wayman, BEd Hons Manchester

Ancillary Staff:

Mrs A Blood	Mrs C Holyland
Mrs L Dunn	Mrs S Lonnergan
Mrs R Graham	Mrs M Singh
Mrs E M Hay, DipPrimEd Scotland	Mrs C Williams
	Mrs D Wood

Leicester High School is a well established day school for girls situated in pleasant grounds on the south side of the city. Founded in 1906 as Portland House School it now comprises a Junior Department of 100 girls (3–9 years) and a Senior School of 325 girls (10–18) sited on the same campus.

The school offers an academic education of a high standard, and the Sixth Formers almost invariably go on to Higher Education. It is a friendly community where an emphasis is placed on honesty, integrity and respect for the views of others. Class size is kept small so that there is every opportunity for each girl to achieve her full potential while developing the self confidence and self discipline to help in her future.

The Headmistress is responsible for both junior and senior departments. The staff are well qualified specialists and the school is renowned for both its academic excellence and extra-curricular programme. At present 19 subjects are offered at GCSE Level and 24 subjects at A Level.

Facilities. The premises are a combination of modern purpose built units and the original Victorian house, skilfully adapted to its present purpose. The facilities of the school have been systematically improved over the past ten years and more recently the school has undergone an exciting building programme. This includes a drama studio, music room, three fully equipped computer rooms, plus an extra science laboratory and subject teaching rooms. A purpose-built library and resource centre was opened, followed by a new sixth form centre in September 2001. The junior department has also benefited from new buildings which opened in January 2002. The extension and improvement includes a computer suite and new library, enlarged hall and dining facilities and new classrooms.

Religion. Religious instruction is based on that of the Church of England, but members of other denominations and faiths are welcome.

Admission. All candidates over the age of 7 are required to pass an entrance examination for admission into the Junior and Senior sections. Entry into the Senior School would normally be at 10+ or 11+ but entry at other ages is considered. There is also direct entry into the Sixth Form dependent on GCSE results. Entrance into the Foundation Unit is by assessment. A registration fee of £50 is payable for all applicants.

Fees per term (2008-2009). £1,975–£2,900.

Extras. Individual Music lessons, Speech and Drama, and Ballet are offered.

Scholarships. (*see Scholarship Entries section*). These are awarded annually to girls of 11+ on entry into the Senior School through the Entrance Examination. Music scholarships are also available, as are bursaries throughout the school, including the Sixth Form.

The Headmistress is always pleased to meet parents of prospective pupils and to show them the school. All communications should be addressed to the Registrar from whom prospectuses, application forms and up-to-date details of fees may be obtained.

The Headmistress is always pleased to meet parents of prospective pupils and to show them the school. All communications should be addressed to the Headmistress from whom prospectuses, application forms and up-to-date details of fees may be obtained.

Charitable status. Leicester High School Charitable Trust Limited is a Registered Charity, number 503982. The Trust exists to promote and provide for the advancement of education based on Christian principles according to the doctrines of the Church of England.

Leweston School

Sherborne Dorset DT9 6EN
Tel: 01963 210691
Fax: 01963 210786
e-mail: admin@leweston.dorset.sch.uk
website: www.leweston.co.uk

Independent Boarding (full, weekly and flexi) and Day School for Girls aged 11–18 with a separate, purpose-built, co-educational Prep School for boys aged 2½–7 and girls aged 2½–11 on the same campus. Roman Catholic foundation but all denominations welcome. Excellent academic reputation and strong Sixth Form.

Governing Body:
Mr A May (*Chairman*)
Mr E W Ludlow (*Deputy Chairman*)

Mr P Burns
Mr I Crowther
The Countess C de Salis
Mr N Evans
Mrs H Harper
Mrs M Head
Fr Peter Knott SJ
Mrs T Skepelhorn
Mrs J Townsend
Mrs A Wedge
Mrs B Williams
Mrs B Wingfield Digby

***Head*: Mr A J F Aylward**, MA Oxon

Deputy Head: Mrs J Miles, BA Hons Oxon, PGCE (*Modern Foreign Languages*)

Assistant Head, Head of Sixth Form: Mrs E J Carling, BA Hons Oxon, PGCE, DipTEFL (*English*)

Director of Studies: Mr G Smith, BSc Hons Open, PGCE (*Mathematics*)

Director of Boarding: Mrs S Ryan, BA Hons Oxford (*History, Religious Studies, English*)

Commercial Director: Mrs L Robins, BSc Hons Reading, MRICS

Chaplain: Revd R E Meyer, BA Durham

Teaching Staff:

Classics:
Dr R Chiappiniello, MA Naples, PhD Manchester, DEFL Naples/Paris French (*Classics*)
Mrs M Highcock, MA Cantab, PGCE (*Classics, French, Latin*)

English and Drama:
Miss S Evans, BA Hons Sheffield, PGCE London (*Head of English*)
Mrs L Evans, BA Hons Leeds, PGCE (*English*)
Mrs S Ryan, BA Hons Oxford (*Director of Boarding, History, Religious Studies, English*)
Mrs K A Meades, MA Ed Open, SEN, PGCE (*English, Drama, Individual Needs, Health & Social Care*)
Mr A Irvine, BA Hons Oxon, PGCE, DipTEFL (*Head of Drama, History*)
Mrs C Dempsey, Gold Medal Verse & Prose LAMDA, BA Hons Graphic Design (*Drama*)
Mrs S Nias, BA Hons Rose Bruford College, Gold Medal LAMDA (*Speech & Drama*)
Mrs J A Miller, MEd Bristol, BA Hons Southampton, PGCE Keele, DipSpLD (*Head of Individual Needs, Head of Year 7*)

Modern Languages:
Mrs L Bryson, BSc Hons Bournemouth, CertEd Exeter (*Head of Modern Languages, Spanish*)
Mrs S O'Connor, BEd Hons London (*German, French, Head of Years 10 and 11*)
Mrs L Maynard, MA University of Liberec (*French*)
Mrs M Highcock, MA Cantab, PGCE (*French, Latin*)
Mrs J Miles, BA Hons Oxon, PGCE (*Modern Foreign Languages, Deputy Head*)

Geography:
Mr D Barlow, BSc Hons Nottingham, MSc London, PGCE Birmingham (*Head of Geography, Physicial Education*)
Mrs J Hopkin, BA Hons Exeter, PGCE Leeds, FRGS (*Government & Politics, Geography*)

Mathematics:
Mr M Crozier, BSc Hons, PGCE Dunelm, CMath, MIMA, CSci (*Head of Mathamatics*)
Mr J Cross, BSc Hons London (*Mathematics*)
Mr G Smith, BSc Hons Open, PGCE (*Mathematics, Director of Studies*)
Mrs H Claxton, BSc Hons Napier (*Mathematics with Finance*)

Religious Studies:
Miss J Kelly, BEd Hons, MA Leeds, Catholic TCert Leeds (*Head of Religious Studies*)
Ms C O'Toole, BA Hons London PGCE, Catholic TCert Liverpool (*Religious Studies, , History, Head of Years 8 & 9*)

Psychology:
Mrs S Hunt, BA Hons Bournemouth, PGTC Exeter

Science:
Mrs F M Crossman, BSc Hons, MEd Manchester, PGCE (*Head of Science, Physics*)
Mrs J Marsh, BSc Hons Reading, PGCE Exeter (*Head of Biology, PHSE Coordinator*)
Mr J Ralph, BSc Liverpool, PGCE London (*Biology*)
Mr J Sherwood Taylor, BA Open University, MSc York, CertEd (*Science*)
Dr O Kemal, BSc Hons, PhD London PGCE (*Head of Chemistry*)
Mrs A Valentine, BSc Hons Swansea, PGCE London (*Physics*)

Economics and Business Studies:
Mrs S Antill, BA Hons Kingston-upon-Thames, PGCE (*Economics & Business Studies*)
Mrs L Rondeau-Robinson, MBA Rivier College, NH BA Cum Laude Lowell, MA, TCert Yeovil (*IT Coordinator*)

History:
Mr M Hayward, BA Hons Oxon (*Head of History, History of Art*)
Mrs G Gregory, BA Hons Worcester, MA Hons Exeter, PGCE

Art, Design and Technology:
Mrs E Williams, BA Hons London, PGCE Manchester (*Head of Art & Design*)
Miss J Turner, BA Hons Cardiff, PGCE UWE (*Head of Design*)
Mr F Bush, BTEC Nat Dip Plymouth, BA Hons St Martins (*Art, D&T*)

English as a Foreign Language:
Mrs A Kennedy, BEd Oxford Inst of Ed, MA TESOL, RSA DipTEFLA
Mrs K M Walker, MA Birmingham, BA Hons Bristol, Dip TEFSL

Physical Education:
Mrs K DuValle, BSc Hons Liverpool John Moores, PGCE St Mark & St John (*Head of Physical Education*)
Miss K Mullen, BEd Hons Sussex, CertEd Chelsea (*Head of Sports Studies*)
Miss G Phipps, CertEd Chelsea (*EAL Coordinator, Senior Housemistress*)
Mr T Pollard, USPTR (*Associate Instructor, Tennis*)
Mrs C Adams, LTA Part 1 (*Tennis*)
Miss D Laxton, TCRAD

Music:
Mr L Tubb, BA Hons Oxon (*Director of Music*)
Mr A M Nye, BA Hons Mus, QTS Colchester
Mr P Bray, BMus, DSCM, ARCO, LTCL (*Organist*)
Mr D Bednall, BA Hons, FRCO (*Piano, Organ*)
Mrs W Bednall, BA Hons Southampton, ALCM (*Piano*)
Miss C Bentley, GTCL, ARCM, LTCL (*Flute*)
Mr J Candor, LTCL, FTCL (*Clarinet, Saxophone*)
Miss K Evans, MA, BMus Hons Wales (*Flute*)
Mrs J Fenton, ARCM (*Singing*)
Mr M Hewitt (*French Horn*)
Mr P Huddleston, BTech (*Percussion*)
Miss E Marsden, ARCM (*Oboe*)
Mr D Miles (*Double Bass, Electric Guitar*)
Miss M Nightingale, LGSM (*Recorder*)
Mrs K Payne, BA Hons (*Cello*)
Mr D Price, LRAM (*Violin, Viola*)
Mrs N Price, RCM, GRSM Hons, ARCM, LRAM (*Piano, Bassoon*)
Miss M Verity (*Harp*)
Mrs S Whitfield (*Piano*)

Marketing & Admissions Manager: Miss L Cox, BA Hons
Registrar: Mrs L Lison
Librarian: Mrs A King
Headmaster's Secretary: Mrs S Chant
House Manager: Mrs J Wareham

Leweston School welcomes girls aged 11–18 as full, weekly and flexi boarders or as day pupils. Admission is usually by means of Common Entrance at eleven, but girls are also admitted at twelve, thirteen and sixteen.

Situated in 46 acres of beautiful Dorset parkland, 3 miles south of Sherborne, the school offers all the advantages of both the traditional and modern in education with excellent facilities, particularly in the Sciences, Design & Technology and Sport.

Founded by the Sisters of Christian Instruction in 1891, the school is a Catholic School but has a large percentage of pupils from other denominations. There are approximately 250 girls in the School of whom around 90 are boarders. The ethos of the school is based on a wide social mix with a spread of talents, firm but friendly discipline and a keen sense of Christian and moral values. The Head is forward looking with a strong sense of leadership and vision. The school has a resident Chaplain and girls are expected to attend Chapel once a week. Preparation for confirmation is available for both Catholic and Anglican pupils.

The academic standard of the school is high. At both GCSE and A Level pass rates are consistently over 95% and the school's reputation for excellence in Music and Drama runs parallel with academic achievement in Sciences and The Arts. The real success of the school, however, is achieved by realising the full potential of each individual girl, whether they are high fliers or not. Each year girls gain places at leading universities and go on to read a wide range of degrees.

Teachers are dedicated and imaginative, including specialist teachers for Dyslexia and EFL. The school's special quality is its ability to encourage in each pupil a sense of her own worth and ability. Girls are outgoing, well-mannered and unstuffy. While Leweston has a high proportion of day girls, the school is fully committed to boarding offering a wide programme of activities in the evenings and at the weekends. Riding is especially popular.

The school has close links with Sherborne School and there are many combined social, recreational, musical and cultural activities between the schools. Milton Abbey join in with many of our music activities and this year the Sixth Form visited Italy with Winchester School. Sherborne is an attractive historic abbey town with few of the distractions of a large city but at the same time is served by regular Network Express trains to and from London and good road links to Salisbury, Exeter and Bath. The school's facilities are among the best in the West Country. There is a fine floodlit all-weather sports pitch, Design and Technology Centre, modern Senior Science Centre, arts studio, health centre, heated swimming pool, sports hall, multi-gym, squash courts, tennis courts and extensive well-maintained grounds and playing fields. Recently opened are the new dining hall and library.

Leweston Preparatory School (IAPS) for girls aged 2½–11, with boarding provision from age 7, is situated on the same campus, thus offering continuity of education for girls to age 18. Boys are welcome from age 2½ to 7. Excellent early years provision including French from 3 years, beautifully situated Nursery and weekly Parent and Toddler Group. Head Teacher: Mrs M Allen, Tel: 01963 210790. (*For further details, see entry in IAPS section.*)

Scholarships. (*see Scholarship Entries section*). Scholarship provision for Academic, Music, Sport, Art, Drama and Science.

Further particulars may be obtained on application to the Head or Registrar.

Fees per term (2008-2009). Full Boarding £5,995–£7,345; Weekly Boarding £5,455–£6,295, Day £4,595–£4,765. Flexi Boarding (including supper) £38.50 per night.

Charitable status. St Antony's – Leweston School Trust is a Registered Charity, number 295175. It is a charitable foundation set up for educational purposes.

Lodge School

11 Woodcote Lane Purley Surrey CR8 3HB
Tel: 020 8660 3179
Fax: 020 8660 1385
e-mail: principal@lodgeschool.co.uk
website: www.lodgeschool.co.uk

Lodge School comprises West Dene Lodge (co-educational early years 2–5), Downside Lodge (co-educational prep) and Commonweal Lodge (senior girls only). Lodge School and West Dene Schools merged in January 2008 and West Dene has moved to the Woodcote Lane site.

Governors:
Chairman: Heather Starbuck, BA
Vice-Chairman: Elaine Warburton
Anthony Carter-Clout, FCA
Pauline Cardwell
Paul Cook
Elaine Cox, BA
Anne Horne, BA
John Jones
Janet May
Penny Norris
Andrew Pickering
Ann Stranack, BA Hons
Neville Thirtle
Jeremy Way

***Principal*: Miss P A Maynard**, BEd Hons, MA

Commonweal Lodge:
Deputy Head: Mrs E Suter, BSc Hons LSE, MBA, PGCE

Mr T Austin, MA Oxon
Mrs S Baldwin, BSc Hons London
Mrs E Baughan, CertEd London
Ms S Bort, BA Hons Bristol, PGCE
Mrs A Bottiglia, BA Hons St Martins School of Art & Design
Mrs J Coombe, BA Hons Manchester
Ms C Dalton, BSc Dundee
Mrs S Dixon, BSc Hons Nottingham
Ms C Fournès, BA Toulouse, PGCE Sussex
Mrs S Gleed-Smith, BEd Hons, MA
Mrs P Goodwin, CertEd Dartford College
Mrs A Griffiths, BSc Hons London
Mrs K Hammond, BEd Hons Brighton
Mrs B Hanson, BSc Hons London
Mrs C Hosker, BSc Hons Imperial College, PGCE
Mrs B Lee-Smith, BA Hons, PGCE Central School of Speech & Drama
Mrs C Lipscombe, BA Open, CertEd London
Mrs R Parker, BA Hons Leeds
Mrs P Vogel, BEd Hons London

Downside Lodge:
Head: Mr P Kelly, DipEd South Africa

Mrs A Allan, BEd Hons Chichester
Mrs E Barnett, CertEd Bristol
Miss E Bennett, BA Hons, QTS Roehampton
Mr K Bugden, BA Hons QTS Bournemouth
Mrs D Edmunds, BA Hons Exeter
Mrs J Edwards, BA, PGCE Bedford
Mrs C Halliday, BA Hons, PGCE Roehampton
Mrs A Harrington, BEd Hons Canterbury
Mrs N Horrocks, BSc Hons Loughborough, CertEd
Mrs E Leadbetter, CertEd Birmingham
Ms J Lewis, BSc Hons, PGCE Worcester
Mr J McArthur, Teaching Cert
Mrs S Stoby-Cater, BEd Hons Southampton
Miss M Woolley, BEd South Africa

West Dene Lodge:
Reception:
Miss J Clarke, BEd South Africa
Mrs A Lee, CertEd Bristol
Mrs D King
Mrs L Sussemilch
Mrs H Wiggins, CertEd Bristol
Kingergarten Manager: Mrs E Bruton, NNEB, Cert Early Years
Mrs D Brown
Miss S Catto, CACHE Diploma
Miss J Gowlett, CACHE Diploma
Mrs A Jay
Mrs A Lander
Mrs R Mayer, CACHE Diploma
Mrs M McGovern, DPP
Mrs L Okecha
Mrs M Rogers
Miss A Wharton

Inclusion Manager: Mrs S Gleed-Smith
EAL: Mrs J Vening
Technical: Mrs A Austin, ONC

Administration:
Office Manager, PA to Principal: Mrs F Lancaster
Registrar: Mrs P Miners-Jones
Finance Manager: Mr A Earl, ACMA

Lodge School is set in wonderful grounds in the heart of the exclusive Webb Estate, a protected conservation area free from road traffic and pollution, providing a peaceful and focused place of learning. Situated at three neighbouring sites, or 'Lodges', each closely linked with many shared facilities, the priority in each Lodge is to create a warm and secure environment in which young people can grow and develop, confident about their place in the world and their value as individuals. An exceptionally high teacher-pupil ratio ensures pupils receive the individual attention they need to thrive and reach their potential.

Admission. Pupils are admitted at any time if there are vacant places. An assessment is made during a day visit at most levels, though an examination is set at 7+ and 11+. Silverdene takes boys and girls from the age of 2. An extended day is available at West Dene and Downside from 8.00 am to 6.00 pm if required. Senior girls may stay after the end of the school day by prior arrangement.

Curriculum. An enhanced National Curriculum is offered and the Sixth Form offers a wide range of subjects and subject combinations. Boys and girls are prepared for senior school entrance examinations, although most girls transfer into the Lodge School senior department (Commonweal). Individual needs are met through tailoring the curriculum in a variety of ways ranging from acceleration through the public exam system to additional support for pupils for whom English is an additional language or who require support for dyslexia.

Aims. The school's primary purpose is to enhance children's quality of learning by the effective and efficient delivery of the curriculum and to strive to continually improve every aspect of the school. Lodge School is committed to honesty and responsibility in all relationships, respecting the rights of individuals and stressing the importance of social development and sensitivity to others.

Believing in the value of small classes and the development of the individual, the school places great importance on high standards of behaviour, self-discipline and mutual respect. Lodge School provides a happy, caring environment that enhances personal confidence. With a commitment to inclusion, team spirit is fostered and a sense of self-worth and pride in the school is encouraged. Acknowledging the importance of academic success, the school also provides for wider achievements in the Performing Arts and Sport and in extra-curricular activities, including the Duke of Edinburgh Award Scheme and Community Service. Working as a constructive partnership with parents and with consistently high expectations, pupils develop the skills and knowledge to obtain the best possible examination results and to participate in this rapidly-changing society.

Fees per term (2008-2009). £1,275–£3,725.

Scholarships. Scholarship examinations for boys and girls at 7+ and for girls at 11+ are held in January. Performing Arts Scholarship at 11+.

Commonweal Lodge Old Girls' Association is called Old Knots.

Charitable status. Lodge and West Dene Educational Trust Limited is a Registered Charity, number 312610. It exists to provide independent education for girls and boys to the age of 11 and girls to the age of 18.

Loughborough High School

Burton Walks Loughborough Leicestershire LE11 2DU
Tel: 01509 212348
Fax: 01509 215720
e-mail: admin@leshigh.org
website: www.leshigh.org

Loughborough High School is part of Loughborough Endowed Schools. Loughborough Grammar School (*see HMC entry*) is the brother school and the co-educational junior school is known as Fairfield (*see IAPS entry*). We enjoy a very old foundation, established in 1850 as one of the earliest girls' grammar schools in England. The High School is located on a delightful 46 acre site close to the town centre with many first rate facilities, which are being added to and improved continuously.

Loughborough High School is an 11 to 18 school of approximately 600 day girls with a large Sixth Form numbering above 170. At the High School we aim to provide an excellent academic education in a caring atmosphere. Since we are a comparatively small school, we are able to know our pupils as individuals and this leads to a strong community spirit. In providing a strong academic education in a disciplined atmosphere we hope to enable each girl ultimately to enter the career of her choice. The school offers a wide range of cultural, recreational and sporting activities and there are clubs and societies for virtually all tastes and interest (many in the senior school are run jointly with Loughborough Grammar School). We believe that our academic curriculum and extra-curricular activities nurture our pupils and encourage them to become active citizens of a modern world.

Further details about the school can be obtained by contacting the school's Registrar.

Governing Body:

Chairman: H M Pearson, BA Econ, LLB, ACIS
Vice-Chairman: A D Emson, BPharm, MRPharmS

Non-Executive Vice-Chairmen:
G P Fothergill, BA, FCIM
Dr J E Hammond, BDS
Dr P J B Hubner, MB, FRCP, DCH, FACC, FESC

Nominative Governors:
A J Bowen, MA University of Cambridge
Professor D Robertson, MA, PhD University of Oxford

Co-optative Governors:
Professor S F Brown, OBE, DSc, FREng
Dr A de Bono, MA, MB, BChir, MFOM
Professor J Feather, BLitt, MA, PhD, FLA
Mrs M Gershlick, RGN, DipNEd
D Godfrey, BSc, CEng, FIEE
The Lady Gretton, JP, Lord-Lieutenant of Leicestershire
I A Hawtin
P M Jackson
A M Kershaw
M Mulla, BSc, MSc, MIM
W M Moss
Mrs J G E Page, JP
Mrs C Wales

Foundation Secretary & Treasurer: K D Shaw, MBE, MSc, FCIS

***Headmistress*: Miss B A O'Connor**, MA Oxford (*Classics*)

Deputy Head: Mrs J Prescott, BSc Cardiff (*Geography*)
Assistant Head, Curriculum: Dr S Jackson, BSc, PhD UMIST (*Chemistry*)
Assistant Head, Staff: Mrs P J Kent, BA Bristol (*Classics*)

Assistant Staff:
Mrs L Beasley, BA Reading (*Economics*)
Mrs S Bell, BSc Nottingham, PGCE Nottingham (*Physics*)
Mr P W Blissett, CertEd Shoreditch College of Education (*Information & Technology*)
Ms S E Boon, BA Plymouth (*Head of Drama*)
Miss S Budzik, MA Surrey (*Art*)
Mrs R Burn, MA Cantab (*Head of Classics*)
Miss A E Chambers, MA Nottingham (*History*)
Mrs J Conway, MA Ulster (*English*)
Mr A Cooper, BSc Loughborough (*Head of Geography*)
Mrs I F E Dance, BA Wales (*Geography*)
Mrs A Denyer, BA Oxon (*Biology*)
Dr J Downing, BSc Bristol (*Head of Chemistry*)
Dr E C Eadie, BA Birmingham (*History*)
Miss O J Flanagan, BA Loughborough (*Physical Education*)
Mrs M Ghaly, BSc Teesside (*Chemistry*)
Mr D Gough, BA Sheffield (*Modern Languages*)
Mrs J Harlock, CertEd Wales (*SENCO*)
Mrs L Harrison, BA Leeds Metropolitan (*English*)
Mrs S R O Henson, BA Loughborough (*Head of Fine Art*)
Ms C Hitchen, MEng Newcastle-upon-Tyne (*Mathematics*)
Mrs K Kroon, BSc Nottingham (*Head of Physics*)
Mrs L Lambert, BA Durham (*Religious Studies*)
Mrs C F Leah, Dip Dance Chelsea School of Human Movement, DipEd Bedford (*Physical Education*)
Mrs J A Lewis, BA Nottingham (*Religious Studies*)
Ms R Lewis, BSc Leeds (*Mathematics*)
Mrs B Lott, BA Sussex (*Modern Languages*)
Mrs C Mackie, MA Cantab (*Modern Languages*)
Mrs J Mayfield, BSc Loughborough (*Head of Physical Education*)
Mr P Melanaphy, BEd Manchester Metropolitan, MA Loughborough (*English*)
Mr A J Mitchell, BA, LLCM (*Director of LES Music School*)
Mr R J L Needs, BA Nottingham, IMS Cert, ACCA, Dip EdMgt (*Head of Economics*)
Miss C E Nelson, BSc Manchester (*Chemistry*)
Miss S-J Nicholas, BSc Loughborough (*Physical Education*)
Mrs M Overlunde, BA York (*Biology, Science Team Leader*)

Miss H Parsons, BA, MA University College London (*English*)
Ms J M Partridge, BA UCE Birmingham (*Creative Textiles*)
Mrs M A Reilly, BSc Surrey (*Head of Home Economics*)
Mrs E Raouf, BA Salford (*French*)
Miss C Shawcross, BSc Loughborough (*Mathematics*)
Mr J Singh, BA Coventry (*Director of Academic ICT*)
Mr G Spalton, BSc Hull, PGCE Nottingham (*Chemistry*)
Mrs J Squire, CertEd Nottingham (*Home Economics*)
Miss V Standring, BSc Chester (*Physical Education*)
Mr M Starbuck, BA Kent, MSc Leicester and Oxford, DPhil Oxford (*Head of Psychology and Sociology*)
Mrs M Starkings, BSc Nottingham, BA Open (*Physics*)
Mr G C Stevens, BA Liverpool (*Classics & Religious Studies*)
Mr J R Stoeter, BSc Leicester (*Head of Mathematics*)
Dr R Strong, MPhys Bath, PhD Cambridge (*Mathematics*)
Mrs J E Stubbs, BSc Nottingham (*Head of Biology*)
Ms K Thompson, BA John Hopkins University Baltimore USA, MEd Boston College, USA (*English*)
Miss C E Todd, BSc Manchester (*Biology*)
Mr L Toone, BSc Edinburgh, PGCE Loughborough, MSc Warwick (*Biology*)
Mr R W Tomblin, MA Oxford (*Head of Modern Languages*)
Mrs C Urwin, BSc Warwick (*Mathematics*)
Ms L Wainwright, BA Leeds Metropolitan (*Physical Education*)
Mrs A White, BA Coventry, PGCE Warwick (*Modern Languages*)
Mrs A Woollard, BA Huddersfield (*History*)
Mrs N J Young, BA East Anglia (*Head of English*)

Accountant: Mr R Harker, BA Coventry, FCAA
Estates Manager: Mr T Allardice
Librarian: Mrs G Burton, BLS
Matrons:
Mrs S Sweeney, RGN, DN
Mrs L Wood, RGN
PA to the Headmistress: Ms L Shipman
School Secretary: Miss B McKay
Receptionist: Mrs R Westran
Data Manager & Registrar: Mrs A Brackstone, BSc Aston
ICT Support Assistant: Mrs R Richards
Laboratory Technicians:
Mrs J M Hines
Mrs J F Owens, BA Hons Keele, MPhil Loughborough
Mrs K M Tomkinson
Miss N Walker
Art/Food Technician: Mrs B Armstead
Modern Languages/Humanities Technician: Mrs T Hicks
Support Assistants:
Mrs L Townsend
Mrs J Calow
After School Care: Mrs J Jones
Doctor: Dr A M Bagley, MBChB

LES Music School:
Mr A J Mitchell (*Director*)
Mr T H Lax (*Head of Performance Studies*)
Dr P J Underwood (*Head of Senior Curriculum Music*)
Mrs E Foulds (*KS3 Music*)
Miss C E Revell (*KS3/4Music*)
Dr A P Bean (*KS4/5 Composition*)

A list of Visiting Music Teachers is available separately.

School Curriculum. Art and Creative Textiles, Biology, Chemistry, Classical Civilisation, Economics, English, French, Games (hockey, netball, tennis, rounders, swimming and athletics), Geography, German, Greek, Gymnastics, History, Latin, Mathematics, Modern Dance, Music, Physics, Politics, Religious Studies, Spanish, Food Technology, ICT, Sociology, Psychology and Theatre Studies. Careful note is taken of the National Curriculum with additional subjects included within the curriculum to provide breadth and depth.

Fees per term (2008-2009). £2,913. Additional Fees: Music (individual instrumental lessons) £190.

Entrance Awards and Music Scholarships. (*see Scholarship Entries section*). Foundation Bursaries replace the Government Assisted Places.

Charitable status. Loughborough Endowed Schools is a Registered Charity, number 1081765, and a Company Limited by Guarantee, registered in England, number 4038033. Registered Office: 3 Burton Walks, Loughborough, Leics LE11 2DU.

Luckley–Oakfield School

Wokingham Berks RG40 3EU
Tel: 0118 978 4175
Fax: 0118 977 0305
e-mail: registrar@luckley.wokingham.sch.uk
website: www.luckley.wokingham.sch.uk

Governing Body:
Mr S Richmond (*Chairman*)
Mr D Cook
Revd G Curry
Mrs J Farmer
Dr J Ledger, BSc Hons, MSc Eng, PhD, FIMgt
Ms L Moor
Dr J Orr, MBBS, DRCOG
Mrs E Percival
Mr G Sanderson
Mr M Walker, MA, BSc, FRES
Mr G Williams
Mrs S Wingfield Digby

***Head*: Miss V A Davis**, BSc Hons London, ARCS (*Chemistry*)

Deputy Head: Dr G Williams, MA Cambridge, PhD Cardiff
Assistant Head: Mrs D Mason, BEd Dual Hons Sheffield (*Biology, Chemistry*)
Head of Sixth Form: Mrs M E Matthews, BA Hons London (*History*)

Staff:
Mrs A Bell, BEng Hons Cardiff (*Mathematics*)
Mrs C Bennett, BEd Hons Plymouth (*Physical Education*)
Mrs E Bull, GRSM, ARCM (*Music*)
Miss A E Caldwell, BSc Hons Hull (*Geography*)
Mrs H Chaddock, BA Hons Swansea (*Physics*)
Mrs J Collett, BSc Hons Manchester (*Science*)
Mrs J Cordery, Dip Musical Theatre (*Drama*)
Mr G Cromb, BSc Hons London (*Geography*)
Mrs S Dixon, BA Hons Central Lancs (*Art, Senior Housemistress*)
Mr S Drury, BA Hons Kent, MA (*Psychology*)
Mrs J M Eastaugh, BSc Hons Leicester (*Mathematics*)
Mrs J Eifler, BSc Hons Leicester (*Mathematics*)
Mr R J Everatt, BSc Hons York (*Chemistry*)
Mrs B Gathercole, BA Theology Nottingham (*Religious Studies*)
Mrs S Gibson, BSc Bath College of HE (*Food & Textile Technology*)
Mrs J Goodall, BA Hons Liverpool (*French, German*)
Mrs D Gummery, BA Hons Southampton (*Classics*)
Mrs S Hills, BEd Hons Leeds Polytechnic, MSc City (*SENCO, Outdoor Education, Physical Education*)
Mrs M Kempton, BEd Hons London, BA Hons Reading, MA Reading (*English*)
Mrs L Keyte, BA Hons London (*History*)
Mrs E A Leary, BSc Hons Birmingham (*Mathematics*)

Mrs A Lee, BA California (*English*)
Mrs C McCafferty, BTec HND in Design (*Food & Textiles Technology*)
Mrs K McGonnell, BEd Hons Exeter (*French, History*)
Dr M B McLeod, BSc Hons Southampton, MSc, PhD Birmingham (*Biology*)
Mrs A O'Sullivan, BA Hons Central Lancs (*Food & Textiles Technology*)
Mrs M Pearce, BA Hons Reading (*English*)
Mrs E Samnee-O'Brien, BA Cologne (*Spanish*)
Miss J Simmonds, BA UCL (*Art & Design*)
Mrs A Spellman, BA Hons Reading (*English*)
Ms L Stephens, BA Hons York (*Business Studies*)
Mrs H Tooze, BSc Hons Nottingham (*Physical Education*)
Mrs M Vogel, BEd Hons East Anglia, LGSM (*Music*)
Mrs J Waugh, BEd Loughborough (*Physical Education*)

Bursar: Mr M Browning, ACIB, MIMgt, MIITT, MRIPHH
Registrar: Mrs M Cope
School Secretaries: Mrs J Leatherby, Mrs L Laing
Headmistress's PA: Mrs L McCarthy
School Nursing Sister: Mrs J Craven
Marketing Manager: Mrs C Clark, MEd Open, BA Hons Reading
ICT Manager: Mr B Clarke

Luckley-Oakfield has high expectations for all its students, achieves excellent academic results and is proud of its exceptional added-value record. Luckley-Oakfield was founded on its present site in 1918. In 1959 it amalgamated with Oakfield School, established in 1895 in the Lake District. Initially the school was administered by the Church Society but in 1969 it became an independent educational trust. A gracious Grade II listed Edwardian country house forms the centre of the school, which is on a 14-acre site with views of the countryside and woodlands. More recent buildings provide accommodation for classrooms, laboratories and the Sixth Form. There is also a sports hall, covered swimming pool and a superb new library and English faculty complex.

The school numbers approximately 300 girls aged 11 to 18. The majority are day pupils, but approximately 30–40 girls are either full or weekly boarders. Pupils are selected on the basis of an entrance examination and interview. The main age of entry is at 11, 13 and into the Sixth Form. A number of coach routes are available.

Curriculum. The curriculum is broad and challenging with girls taking 9.5 subjects for GCSE. A wide variety of AS and A2 courses is offered and almost every girl goes on to higher education as a preparation for careers in, for example, languages, medicine, engineering, law, business and design.

The school has a well deserved reputation for Art, Drama, Music and Sport and offers a range of other activities including computing, debating, riding, polo, The Duke of Edinburgh's Award Scheme, CCF and Young Enterprise. Boarders and Day girls are encouraged to join in this extensive programme of extra curricular activities during the extended day slot from 4–5.30 pm. Instrumental lessons, Singing, Speech and Drama, and Latin are offered as additional subjects.

Boarding. Weekly boarding offers the opportunity to experience the fun of boarding while keeping close links with home and avoiding long daily journeys. Full boarding, with an extensive weekend activity programme, can provide a stable and secure education for girls whose schooling would otherwise be interrupted. Year 7–11 boarders live in the Main House, while sixth form boarders have their own study-bedroom accommodation within the Sixth Form Centre.

Ethos. Luckley-Oakfield encourages high aspirations, independent thinking and community spirit. Each student experiences a truly holistic education developing her academic, cultural, creative, physical and ethical dimensions. At Luckley-Oakfield pastoral care is considered paramount because every girl is important. The school has an evangelical Church of England Foundation, but girls of all faiths and none are welcomed. Christian values shape the ethos of the school and there is a regular Sunday service for boarders.

Fees per term (2008-2009). Boarders £6,988; Weekly Boarders £6,476; Day Girls £4,101.

Scholarships and Bursaries. Scholarships are awarded at 11+ on the results of the Entrance Examination and on entry to the Sixth Form. A music scholarship is available at 11+.

Means-tested Bursaries of 100% and 50% of fees are offered at Year 7 and Sixth Form entry. Forces Bursaries are also available.

Charitable status. Luckley-Oakfield is a Registered Charity, number 309099. It offers day and boarding education for girls on the basis of Christian values.

Malvern St James

Avenue Road Great Malvern Worcestershire WR14 3BA
Tel: 01684 892288
Fax: 01684 566204
e-mail: registrar@malvernstjames.co.uk
website: www.malvernstjames.co.uk

Malvern St James, at the forefront of girls' education.

Governors:
Mrs S M E Adeney, BEd, BLit
Mrs E J Anson, JP
The Revd Prebendary Carl Attwood, BA, MA (*Vice-Chair*)
Mrs A Borrowdale, LLB (*Chair*)
Mr R Capper, LLB Hons, LLM
Mrs V J Dukes, BA
Mr C S Galliers, FCA
Mr P N Guy, FCA
Mrs H Kingham, BSc, PGCE
Mrs A Lloyd, MA Ed, CertEd Oxon, LGSM
Mrs G M Lumsdon, BPharm, MEd
Dr C E Morrison, MA, CEng, MIMechE
Miss E Mullenger, BA, CertEd, FRSA
Mrs G M Wagstaffe, MA

Secretary to the Governors and Bursar: Mr A J W Davis

Leadership Team 2008/2009:

***Headmistress*: Mrs R Hayes**, BA Hons Reading, MA Open, PGCE, FRGS

Deputy Headmistress: Mrs S Musgrave, BSc Hons Bristol, PGCE

Director of Teaching and Learning: Mrs A Hewitt, MA Oxon, PGCE

Assistant Head responsible for Boarding: Mrs E Drake, BA Hons Southampton, MA Sussex, PGCE, MA Ed, Man AIL

Acting Assistant Head responsible for Sixth Form: Miss R Webb, BSc Hons Newcastle, PGCE Oxford

Assistant Head responsible for Years 10 and 11: Mrs J Newby, BA Hons Worcester, PGCE

Assistant Head responsible for Years 7, 8 and 9: Miss G Owen, BA Hons Open, CertEd

Bursar: Mr A J W Davis

Director of Admissions and Marketing: Miss A O'Neil

Malvern St James is a boarding and day school for approximately 360 girls between the ages of 5 and 18. The school is located in the heart of Malvern, and has excellent transport links, with Great Malvern train station situated opposite the main school and a daily mini-bus service in operation.

Aim. As an all-girls' school, our strategies and curriculum content are geared to the learning styles of girls and our staff are sensitive to their intellectual and social development. We celebrate the female perspective and way of doing things. Our girls are accustomed to being heard and valued for who they are; they stop being the audience and become the players. Excellent teaching and learning provide each girl with the stimulus to develop her academic abilities to the full.

Curriculum. Our teaching and learning strategies develop the competence and confidence of all our girls by actively challenging and stretching them. We complement this individual emphasis with teamwork and a sense of collective responsibility. Experienced and inspirational staff have high expectations to ensure each girl makes maximum progress and realises her full potential. Recognition of individual learning styles enhances the classroom experience.

A full range of academic subjects is offered in the Arts and Humanities, Languages, Science and Technology up to Advanced Level.

Learning Support. Critical Thinking is offered throughout the School to provide a exciting challenge for the most able pupils whilst the Learning Support Department is recognised for the excellent level of support it provides for girls.

Boarding. MSJ offers a range of boarding options with excellent flexibility including full and weekly whilst flexi-boarding is available to day girls wishing to stay overnight. House staff work with the girls to organise a busy weekend programme of social and weekend activities, creating a happy atmosphere in each boarding house.

Extra-Curricular Activities. There is a busy and varied programme of activities to suit all interests.

Sport. The school offers a wide range of sporting options, including lacrosse, netball, hockey, tennis and athletics with excellent facilities including the new £4.5 million Sports Hall.

Admission. *Junior Department*: There are no formal examinations for the entrance into the Junior Department, girls are invited to enjoy a School Taster Day, during which they are assessed within the classroom environment.

Middle School Entry (aged 11+): Girls are invited to take Entrance Examinations at Malvern St James. The examinations take the form of Cognitive Ability Tests (CAT3) and a comprehension examination.

Alternatively, girls may apply via the Common Entrance Examination. We are also happy to send entrance papers to schools overseas to administer on our behalf for those girls applying from outside of the UK.

Sixth Form Entry: Girls will study four subjects during their time in the Sixth Form; four to AS Level and continue three to A Level.

As part of the application procedure UK girls are required to take a written paper in one of the subjects the student intends to study at Advanced Level and a general essay paper.

Girls applying from overseas are required to take a written paper in one of the subjects the student intends to study at Advanced Level and an English as a Second Language (EAL) paper.

For details please contact the Registrar, Mrs Jane Tuthill, e-mail: registrar@malvernstjames.co.uk.

Fees per term (2008-2009). Full Boarders £8,140–£8,710 (£9,620 New Sixth Form entrants), Junior Boarders £5,800; Weekly Boarders (Years 7-11) £7,840; Day £2,000–£4,405.

Scholarships and Bursaries. Academic, Music, Art, and Sport Scholarships are available for Middle School entry, Academic, Music, Art, Drama and Sport Scholarships for Sixth Form entry. A Scholarship is worth up to a maximum of 40% of annual fees and an Exhibition is worth up to a maximum of 20% of the current fees.

Charitable status. Malvern St James Limited is a Registered Charity, number 527513, which exists to support excellent education for girls.

Manchester High School for Girls

Grangethorpe Road Manchester M14 6HS
Tel: 0161 224 0447
Fax: 0161 224 6192
e-mail: administration@mhsg.manchester.sch.uk
website: www.manchesterhigh.co.uk

Board of Governors:
Chairman: Mrs C Walker, BA
Mr D Cash, BA, MA, DipArch
Mr A Clarke, FCA
Professor R Cooper, PhD
Mrs M Grant, CertEd
Mrs S Klass, MA Oxon
Mrs D Kloss, LLB, LLM, Hon FFOM
Her Honour Judge L Kushner, LLB, QC
Professor R W Munn, DSc
Mr A B Murray, CA, ACMA, FIMI
Mrs C V F Sargent, BSc
Mr C J Saunders, OBE, MA, FSI
Mr F R Shackleton, MA, LLM
Mrs S E Spence, BA
Professor A K Webb, FRCP
Mrs A M Wilkinson, NFF, CertEd
Mr K S Yeung, MBE

Hon Treasurer: Mr A B Murray, CA, ACMA, FIMI

***Head Mistress*: Mrs C Lee-Jones**, JP, DL, MA, MIMgt, FRSA

Head Mistress designate (*January 2009*): Mrs A C Hewitt, BSc, PGCE

Deputy Head Mistresses:
Ms H Huber, BA Manchester, Dip Management of Education Manchester Metropolitan (*Geography*)
Mrs S M Smith, BSc Leeds, MEd Bristol (*Mathematics*)

Senior Teachers:
Miss E A M Bridges, BA Glamorgan, PGCE (*Head of Preparatory Department*)

Staff:
* *Head of Department*
§ *Part-time*

Mrs R C Abson, BA Chester (*Drama*)
Mrs B M Alvarez Taylor, Lic en Filología Zaragoza, PGCE (*Modern Languages*)
Mrs D Austin, BSc Bolton Institute, MSc (*Psychology*)
Mrs J Bailey, BA York (*Mathematics*)
§Mrs P Bell, BA Leeds Polytechnic (*Art & Design Technology*)
Mrs C Bennett, BSc Staffordshire (*Physics*)
Miss P Catlow, BSc Manchester (*Chemistry*)
Mrs A G T Chambers, BA West Surrey College of Art & Design, ATC (**Art & Design Technology*)
Mr J Clarke, BA, MPhil Manchester (**History*)
Miss L Cooke, BSc Wales (**Careers*)
Mrs J H W Cox, BA North West University, China (*Mandarin*)
§Mrs D Crichton, BA London (*Modern Languages*)
Dr S Crook, BSc, PhD Dundee (**Biology*)
Miss S A L Davies, BA Cardiff (*Modern Languages*)
Mrs S de Courcy, BA York (*Mathematics*)
Mrs E A Diamond, BA Birmingham (*Religion & Philosophy*)
Mrs P J Flatman, CertEd, PE Bedford (*Physical Education*)
Mrs J L Fordham, CertEd Manchester (*Art & Design Technology*)
Ms S C Gaskell, BA, MA Oxon (*English*)
Miss M E Gibson, BSc Leeds, PGCE (*Physical Education*)
Mr K Gilkes, BSc Bolton, PGCE (*ICT*)

Dr D Haggerston, BSc, PhD Southampton, PGCE *(*Physics*)
Miss C Hannan, MA Cantab (*Classics*)
§Mrs J Haves, BA Leicester, PGCE (*Drama and English*)
Mrs J R Heydecker, BA Leicester (*History*)
Dr R E Hoban, BSc, PhD Newcastle (**Chemistry*)
Mrs M G Hobson, BSc, MA Salford (**Modern Languages*)
Mrs H F Jeys, BA Durham, PGCE (**Religion & Philosophy*)
Mr D L Jones, BSc Manchester (*Mathematics*)
Miss E S King, BA Leeds, MSc Birmingham, PGCE (*French, German*)
Ms H Keegan, BA Durham, MA Durham, PGCE *(*English*)
Miss K Large, BSc Leeds (*Chemistry*)
Miss D McCluskey, BMus Lancaster, PGCE (*Music*)
Dr F Menon, MSc Padova, PhD Manchester, PGCE (*Biology*)
Mrs J Miles, BA Liverpool (*History*)
§Dr L Moore, BSc Lebanon, MSc UMIST, PhD, PGCE (*Chemistry*)
Mrs S Newman, BEd Leeds Metropolitan (**Physical Education*)
Mr R Nisar, BSc King's College, London, PGCE (*Physics*)
§Mrs C J Ousey, BA Southampton (*English*)
Mrs C Pattison, BSc Newcastle (*Mathematics*)
Dr C M Poucher, BSc, PhD Leeds (*Biology*)
Mrs M Price, BA Manchester (*English*)
Ms A N Protheroe, BSc Swansea (**Mathematics*)
Mr M Randall, BA CNAA, MA Leicester (**Business Economics IT*)
§Mrs S Reynolds, BA UCL, MSc Kingston, PGCE (*Geography*)
Mrs P L Roberts, BA Durham (**French*)
Miss A Robinson, BA Leicester, PGCE (*English*)
Miss S C Rowley, BA Staffordshire, PGCE Physical Education
Mrs K Rundell, BMus Manchester (**Music*)
Mrs P Scott, BA Duncan of Jordanstone College of Art (*Art & Design Technology*)
Dr R Smither, BSc Bath, MPhil, PhD Cambridge (*Biology*)
Mrs T Slack, BA Manchester, PGCE (*Modern Languages*)
Mr N M Tattersall, MPhys Oxford (*Mathematics*)
Dr I K Tranter, BSc, PhD Birmingham (*Chemistry*)
§Mrs D E Troth, BA Exeter (*History*)
§Mrs C M Tynan, BA York (*Physics*)
Mr S R F Vance, BA Manchester (*Art & Design Technology*)
Miss C Verheecke, BA Sorbonne, MA Rennes (*Modern Languages*)
Mr P R Warburton, BA Portsmouth Polytechnic, MPhil Leicester (**Geography*)
§Mrs D M Watkins, BEd Liverpool (*Physical Education*)
§Mrs A T Wells, BA Essex, PGCE (*English*)
Miss J Welsby, BA Manchester (**Classics*)
Mrs K A Whelan, BSc Bradford (*Business Economics and IT*)

Preparatory Department Staff:
Mrs A Allman, Teacher's Dip Sedgely Park
Mrs C Callanan, BA MMU, PGCE
Mrs S M Callaghan, BA Bolton Institute
Miss S Diamond, BEd Cantab
Miss J H Floyd, BA Charlotte Mason College
Mrs M Foley, CertEd Phillipa Fawcett College
Miss I P Head, CertEd Caerleon
Mrs M R Heggie, BMus, BEd New South Wales
Miss J K Meek, BA Manchester, PGCE
Mrs J C Philip, BA Manchester
§Miss E Pope, BA Oxon
Mrs K Robinson, BA London
§Mrs A Taylor, CertEd Didsbury College
Mrs M A Watt, BEd Cheltenham
Miss V Wilson, BSc Lancaster, PGCE

Bursar: Mr J P Moran
Registrar: Mrs L Hughes
PA to Head Mistress: Mrs S Bowker
Librarian: Miss Z Hawker, BA Liverpool, MSc Northumbria
Archivist: Dr C Joy, BA, PhD Leeds
School Medical Officer: Dr J Herd, BM BS, DFFP, DRCOG, MRCGP

Manchester High School for Girls is a day school for students aged 4 to 18. The School provides an academic education which is both dynamic and forward-looking, and which produces students who distinguish themselves in many professions. There is a well-structured, supportive guidance system. A broad range of subjects offers challenging learning activities. An exceptional programme of lively extra-curricular activities and educational visits helps to develop personal strengths and communication skills. Students achieve impressive performances at GCSE and A Level. Almost all leavers go on to university.

The Preparatory Department forms an integral part of the School but has its own purpose-built accommodation comprising eleven classrooms, two assembly halls and resource areas including a computer suite and libraries. Admission is by means of an assessment for Infants and an entrance examination in Mathematics and English for Juniors. Girls may enter at ages 4 to 9. There are occasional vacancies at intermediate ages.

Many pupils join at the age of 11. The School sets its own entrance examination in January for vacancies the following September. School Bursaries are available for a limited number of pupils annually. Scholarships may be offered to candidates who show exceptional performance in academic work and/or music and/or sport. (*see Scholarship Entries section*) The Sixth Form welcomes applicants at age 16. Sixth Form assessment is by interview and GCSE qualifications.

The academic and personal development of each pupil is supported by an exciting learning environment. This includes IT suites, a specialist Music block, a new purpose-built Sports Hall and Fitness Centre, an indoor swimming pool, all-weather sports pitches, refurbished science and modern foreign language laboratories, a Sixth Form Centre and a multi-purpose auditorium. The School benefits from proximity to stimulating cultural and intellectual events in Manchester and its universities. Instrumental and Speech & Drama lessons are optional extras.

Further details and a prospectus are available from The Registrar.

The Report of the ISI Inspection in October 2004 is available on the School's website, www.manchesterhigh.co.uk.

Fees per term (2008-2009). Seniors £2,878, Juniors £2,093, Infants £2,050.

Charitable status. Manchester High School for Girls Foundation is a Registered Charity, number 532295. The aim of the charity is the provision and conduct in Manchester of a day school for girls.

Manor House School

Manor House Lane Little Bookham Surrey KT23 4EN
Tel: 01372 458538
Fax: 01372 450514
e-mail: admin@manorhouseschool.org
website: www.manorhouseschool.org

Motto: *To Love is to Live*

Governors:
Chairman: Mr P Barlow, FIA
Treasurer: Mr H von Bergen
Mr J Compton
Mrs F Culshaw (*Parent Governor*)
Dr L Lawrence
Mrs R Martin, MEd, NPQH, FRSA
Miss Z Axton, BSc Hons, PGCE

Mrs C Turnbull, BA Hons
Mrs A Vincent, CertEd, BEd Hons
Mr D Wright

***Headmistress:* Miss Z Axton**, BA Hons, PGCE

Deputy Headmistress: Mrs C Williamson, BA Hons, PGCE

Senior Department:
Mrs G Arnold, BSc Hons, PGCE (*Science*)
Mrs T Banfield, BEd Hons (*Physical Education*)
Miss A Berry, BA Hons (*English*)
Mrs W Boulton, BA Hons, BEd Hons (*English*)
Mrs S Buck, BSc Hons, PGCE (*Physical Education*)
Mr J Conway, BSc Hons, PGCE (*ICT*)
Mrs K Dabill, PGCE (*Mathematics*)
Mrs M Darke, BA Hons, PGCE (*German*)
Miss C Grindrod, BSc Hons, PGCE (*Geography*)
Mrs E Hunter, MA, BEd Hons (*History*)
Mrs S Hutton, MA Oxon, PGCE (*Religious Studies*)
Mrs H Jewell, CertEd OU Dip (*Spanish*)
Mrs G Kumar, MEd, PGCE (*Chemistry*)
Mrs E Landon, MA Oxon, PGCE (*French and Latin*)
Ms A Le Souchu, BEd Hons (*French*)
Mrs J Perkin, BSc Hons, PGCE (*Science*)
Miss C Poultney, BEd Hons (*Physical Education*)
Mrs S Parsons, BA Hons, PGCE
Mr T Pratt, BA Hons (*Music*)
Mrs S Roberts, LAMDA (*Drama*)
Mrs V Robinson, BA Hons, PGCE (*Science*)
Mrs J Sinnamon (*Drama*)
Mrs S Smith, BCom (*Mathematics*)
Mrs K Symons, BSc, MBA (*Mathematics*)
Mrs K Tercan, BEd Hons (*Home Economics*)
Mrs T Williams, BA Hons, PGCE (*Art and Drama*)
Mrs C Williamson, BA Hons, PGCE (*Mathematics*)

and 14 Peripatetic staff

Junior Department Staff:
Head: Mrs J Baker, BA Hons, PGCE
Mrs T Botting, BEd
Mrs J Cho, BEd Hons
Mrs A Coleman, CertEd
Mrs D Horrocks, HDip PrimEd
Mrs J Lelong, Dip Bilingual Studies
Mrs L Luke, BEd Hons
Mrs J Lurie, BA Hons, PGCE
Mrs I Rodwell, BEd Hons
Mrs K Turner, Dip ABRSM

Prep Department Staff:
Head: Mrs V Kyte, DipEd
Mrs V Burden, CertEd, NVQ3
Mrs V Cannon, BA Hons, PGCE
Mrs A Heath-Taylor, BA PrimEd

Nursery Department:
Head: Mrs J Roy, Montessori Dip (Dist)
Miss J Buchanan, Child Care & Education Dip
Mrs A Harvey, NNEB
Mrs A Matthews, CertEd
Mrs S Viscione, NNEB

Finance Manager: Mrs C Miller, MBA
Administration Manager: Mrs V Allcott
Admissions Secretary: Mrs J Clifford

Manor House is an independent day school for girls between the ages of 2 and 16 years. Founded in 1927, the school is a charitable trust situated in a Georgian building and set in seventeen acres of parkland within easy distance of London. Our own minibuses meet the trains at Effingham Junction station and collect pupils from other points before school each day. Manor House is a day school with a day boarding system (8 am to 6 pm).

A recently completed building programme has provided a new Early Years Department block, and new Art, Drama, Music and Home Economics rooms. The School has excellent sports facilities which include an open-air heated swimming pool, five tennis and netball courts, two of which are floodlit, with all-weather surfaces, hockey and rounders pitches, and an athletics track.

The girls follow a wide curriculum throughout their school career and generally take 9 GCSE subjects which must include English, Mathematics, Science and a modern language. Girls are expected to partake fully in the life of the school and develop their individual talents in Drama, Music and Sport. Tuition is available for a wide range of musical instruments including piano, flute, brass, saxophone, violin, cello, guitar, clarinet and harp. The school has flourishing choirs and instrumental groups.

The aim of the school is to create a happy, secure and disciplined environment where each girl can achieve her individual academic potential. Manor House is a Christian non-denominational school but has close links with the Church of England. A Manor House girl is confident and outgoing with a strong sense of values and the ability to succeed in her chosen career. Girls are encouraged to be independent and to take responsibility for themselves and others.

Admission. (*see Scholarship Entries section*). Admission is by entrance examination at 7+ to the Junior Department and at 11+ to the Senior Department. Junior and Senior Department Scholarships may be awarded as a result of these examinations. Entry at other ages is subject to availability of places and is determined by assessment and interview. Means-tested bursaries may also be applied for.

Fees per term (2008-2009). Tuition: £750–£3,970.

Charitable status. Manor House School is a Registered Charity, number 312063. It exists for the promotion of children's education according to their academic, social, sporting and musical abilities.

The Marist Senior School

Kings Road Sunninghill Ascot Berkshire SL5 7PS
Tel: 01344 624291
Fax: 01344 874963
e-mail: pa2head@marist.ascot.org.uk
website: www.themaristschools.com

Independent Catholic Day School for Girls aged 11–18 founded in 1870 by the Marist Sisters. The school has been at the current site since 1947 and is set in 60 acres of attractive grounds in the village of Sunninghill near Ascot.

Chair of Governors: Mrs M Cairns

***Headteacher:* Mr K McCloskey**, BA Hons, PGCE, MA

Deputy Headteacher: Mrs C Trelfa, BA Hons, PGCE, NPQH

Assistant Headteacher: Miss W Grantham, BA Hons, PGCE

Heads of Department:
Art: Mrs S Maynard, CertEd
Classics: Mrs A Osmond, BA Hons
Drama: Mrs J Harris, BA Hons
Economics/Business Studies: Mrs P Elstone / Mr S Paxton, MA, PGCE
English: Mrs J Cox BA Hons, PGCE
Food Science: Mrs G White, CertEd
Geography: Mrs F Montgomerie, BA Hons, PGCE
History: Mrs G Fisher, BA Hons, PGCE
ICT: Mrs J Shill, CertEd, CertSpLD, DipWp
Mathematics: Mrs S Heard, BSC Hons, PGCE
Modern Foreign Languages: Mrs M Halksworth, L-ès-L, PGCE

Music: Mrs J Dance, BA Hons, ARCM, PGCE
Psychology: Mrs J Cope, BA SA, Higher Education Diploma SA
Physical Education: Mrs J Bishopp, BA Ed
Religious Education: Miss L Vaughan Neil, BA, PGCE
Science: Mrs A Royston, BSc Hons, PGCE
Textiles: Ms M Tooman, BSc, PGCE

Number of Pupils. 320 girls.

Mission Statement. The Marist is a community where Christian values inspire all aspects of learning and where the potential of each individual is recognised, valued and affirmed.

Strengths.

- Strong reputation for academic excellence as well as sport, drama, music and creative arts.
- Able to offer a wide range of both academic and extra-curricular activities.
- Strong emphasis on pastoral care, spiritual and personal development; care and consideration for others.
- Small class sizes to enhance individual progression and recognition (max class size is 20).
- The school is renowned for its high standards regarding moral values, community spirit, respect and care. This is in line with the overall ethos of the Marist order which has a worldwide presence, providing a truly international dimension to a girl's education.

Facilities. Indoor swimming pool, dedicated Sixth Form suite, comprehensive ICT suite, new music and drama building, language laboratory and library.

Academic Curriculum. Art, Biology, Business Studies, Classical Civilisation, Chemistry, Drama/Theatre Studies, Economics, English, French, Geography, German, History, ICT, Italian, Latin, Mathematics (also Pure & Mechanics, Pure, Statistics, Pure & Statistics), Music, Personal, Social & Health Education, PE, RE, Religious Studies: Philosophy & Ethics, Science, Spanish, Sports Studies, Textiles, Food Science, Psychology.

Sixth Form. The school offers a total of 26 subjects at AS/A2 Level. Year 12 students will study 4 four subjects at AS Level in their first year (in certain circumstances some students can take 5). After AS Levels, girls will decide which 3/4 subjects they wish to continue on to A2 Level.

Extra-Curricular Activities. Art, Athletics, Craft, Choir, Clarinet & Saxophone Ensemble, Drama Club, Duke of Edinburgh's Award, Flute Group, French Films, Greek (Ancient), Guitar Group, History Films, Hockey, Human Rights, ICT, Latin, Library Club, Literacy, Netball, Orchestra, Prayer Group, Public Speaking/Debating, Recorder Club, Rock Band, Science, Strategy/Numeracy, Swimming, Swing Band, Textiles, Tennis, Young Enterprise.

Results. 2007: Ranked 1st in the Royal Borough of Windsor & Maidenhead DCSF Performance Tables. Ranked second highest performing Independent School in the UK.

Admission. Entrance examination tests in (1) English, (2) Mathematics and (3) cognitive abilities, (4) Portfolio, (5) Compulsory Interview with the Headteacher and (6) Reference from Primary/Preparatory Headteacher.

Sixth Form Entry. General requirements for 3 or 4 AS subjects: a minimum of 5 GCSEs at C grade or above, preferably B grade in subjects to be studied.

General requirements for 5 AS subjects: most grades at GCSE should be A*.

Note: there are recommended subjects and grades at GCSE for each AS subject available in the Sixth Form Prospectus and on the school's website.

Fees per term (2008-2009). £3,220. Extra benefits: Generous sibling discount scheme (4th and any subsequent children free), after school care provided.

Scholarships. Year 7 and Sixth Form Academic, Art, Drama, Music and Sport scholarships are available.

Preparatory School. We also have a Preparatory school on the same campus which is for girls aged 3–11. This allows girls to continue their education with their friends in the happy and secure environment they are used to. (*For further details, see the Marist Preparatory School entry in the IAPS section.*)

Affiliations. Girls' Schools Association (GSA), Catholic Independent Schools Conference (CISC).

Charitable status. The Marist Schools is a Registered Charity, number 225485. The principal aims and activities of the Marist Schools are religious and charitable and specifically to provide education by way of an independent day school for girls between the ages of 3 and 18.

The Mary Erskine School

Ravelston Edinburgh EH4 3NT
Tel: 0131 347 5700
Fax: 0131 347 5799
e-mail: principal@esmgc.com
schoolsecretary@esmgc.com
website: www.esms.edin.sch.uk

Governing Council:
Chairman: Alan Robertson

Clerk to the Governors: Mr J Kerr

***Principal*: Mr J N D Gray**, BA

Bursar: Mr I M McGregor, MA Hons

Deputy Head: Mrs L A Douglas, BEd, CMath, MIMA
Assistant Head Teacher: Mrs A Y Angus, BSc, PGCE
Assistant Deputy Head: Dr E A Murray, BSc Hons, MEd, PhD, PGCE
Assistant Head Teacher: Ms K S S Nicholson, MA Hons, PGCE
Assistant Head Teacher: Dr I R Scott, PhD, FRSA, CertEd
Assistant Head Teacher: Mrs L C Thomas, DPE

* *Head of Department*
† *Head of House*

Art:
*Mrs J M Read, DA, CertEd
Mrs C Burns, BA Hons, PGCE
Miss F J Lindsay, BDes Hons, PGCE

Biology:
*Miss J M Houston, BSc Hons, PGCE
Dr S Corbet, BSc Hons, MSc, PhD, PGCE
Mrs J D Fraser, BSc, CertEd
Dr C Turnbull, BSc, MSc, PhD

Business Studies:
*Mrs F K McCrudden, BA Hons, PGCE
Miss R A McBeath, DipC, CertEd (*†Appin*)

Careers:
Mrs C M Gray, MA

Chemistry:
*Mr P Wilson, MA Hons, PGCE
Miss S Clougher, BSc Hons, PGDE
Mrs C Murdie, BSc Hons, PGCE
Dr E A Murray, BSc Hons, MEd, PhD, PGCE (*Assistant Head Teacher*)

Classics:
*Miss A E Cowperthwaite, MA Hons, PGCE
Mrs C D'Arcy, BA, PGCE

Computing:
Dr T Hely, MSc, PhD, PGCE

Design Technology:
*Mr D K Bowen, BA Hons, ATC, DipSIAD
Mrs C A Hemmati, BSc Hons, PGCE, MSc

Drama:
*Mrs G Riddell, BA Hons, LLCM Hons, LAMDA
Mrs L Howarth, MA Hons, PGCE

English:
*Mr N Dawson, MA Hons, Med
Miss N Anderson, MA Hons, PGCE
Mrs R Connet, BA Hons, PGCE
Ms D Esland, BA Hons, PGCE
Mrs A Holt, BA Hons, PGCE, ALCM (*†Lochaber*)
Mrs C S Park, MA Hons, PGCE (*†Torridon*)
Mrs K A J Yip, BA Hons, MA, PGCE

Geography:
*Mrs J A Wright, MA Hons, DipEd
Ms K S S Nicholson, MA Hons, PGCE (*Assistant Head Teacher*)
Miss J F Pollitt, MA Hons, PGCE
Mrs C Wallace, MA Hons, PGCE
Mrs J Watson, MA Hons, PGCE

History:
*Mrs E P Trueland, MA Hons, DipEd
Mrs L J Allan, MA Hons, PGCE (*†Kintyre*)
Mrs G Bateman, BA Hons, PGCE
Mr R Robertson, MA Hons, PGCE

Home Economics:
*Mrs J Hetherington, Dip DomSc, LSSN
Mrs N L Murray, BA, PGCE, PGC

Mathematics:
*Mrs M Grant, MA Hons, PGCE
Mrs A Angus, BSc, PGCE (*Assistant Head Teacher*)
Dr B Cohen, MPhys, PhD, PGCE
Mr R Davies, MA Hons, PGCE
Mrs L A Douglas, BEd, CMath, MIMA (*Deputy Head*)
Mr J D Hamilton, MSc
Dr T Hely, MSc, PhD, PGCE
Mrs F J Houbert, BEd Hons
Miss C A Leslie, BSc, DipEd (*†Galloway*)

Modern Languages:
*Mr M G Chittleburgh, MA Hons, DipEd, PGCE
*Mrs S Old, MA Hons, DipEd
Dr S M Benn, MA, PhD, PGCE
Ms J H Bremner, MA Hons, PGCE
Mrs E R Hyslop, MA Hons, DipEd (*Deputy Head, Sixth Form*)
Miss L McGuinness, MA, PGCE (*†Ettrick*)
Mrs P McInally, BA Hons, PGCE
Mrs J Scott Fitzgerald, MA Hons, PGCE
Mrs M L Thornton, MA, DipEd

Modern Studies:
*Mrs J A Wright, MA Hons, DipEd

Music:
*Mrs M H Mitchell, LRAM, DipEdMus
Mrs S Headden, DRSAM, DipEd

Philosophy:
Dr I R Scott, MA Hons, PhD, FRSA, CertEd (*Director, Sixth Form*)

Physical Education:
*Mrs V G Thomson, BEd Hons, BSc
Miss G Bailey, BEd Hons
Miss M Cooper, BEd Hons
Miss K Mackay, BEd Hons
Mrs J L Miller, BEd Hons
Miss C Lampard, BEd Hons
Mrs K A Mundell, BEd Hons
Mrs L C Thomas, DPE (*Assistant Head Teacher*)

Physics:
*Mr J Herbison, BSc Hons, DipEd
Dr T Hely, MSc, PhD, PGCE
Mrs M Marshall, MSc, PGCE

Religious Studies:
*Mr D Kemp, MTheol, PGCE
Mrs J Watson, MA Hons, PGCE
Miss Olivia Williams, MA Hons, PGDE

Support for Learning:
*Mrs C Maxwell, BA, DipEd
Mrs M Brown, MA Hons, DipEd, DipEdPsych
Mr S Hollins, BA Hons, PGCE
Miss R Meredith, BSc, PGCE, PGDip

Junior School:
Head Master: Mr B D Lewis, BA
Assistant Head Teacher: Mr D McLeish, DCE
Deputy Head (*Primary 4–7*): Mrs G Lyon, DCE, DipRSA
Deputy Head (*Early Education*): Mrs M M Rycroft, DipCE

The Mary Erskine School was founded by Mary Erskine and the Company of Merchants of the City of Edinburgh in 1694. It is therefore one of the oldest schools in the UK endowed specifically for girls. Known in its early years as 'The Merchant Maiden Hospital', its aims were to educate and care for the daughters of City Burgesses who found themselves in reduced circumstances. Throughout its history, the school has been administered by the Edinburgh Merchant Company. In November 1989 this authority was devolved to the Erskine Stewart's Melville Governing Council.

The school, named The Mary Erskine School in 1944 to mark the 250th anniversary of its foundation, has been housed on various sites in the city – the Cowgate, Bristo, Lauriston and Queen Street – and the buildings are depicted on the engraved glass panels in the Sports Centre and on murals in the Assembly Hall. The current school buildings, at Ravelston, command splendid views of the nearby city and castle.

Since 1978 the school has been twinned with Stewart's Melville College (*see entry in HMC section*). This includes a fully co-educational Junior School for children between the ages of 3 and 12, single-sex but very closely twinned secondary schools between the ages of 12 and 17 and a fully co-educational pre-university Sixth Form which provides the ideal bridge between school and university. The girls and boys from The Mary Erskine School and Stewart's Melville College come together in the Combined Cadet Force, in orchestras, choirs, drama and musicals and in numerous outdoor education projects.

The Senior School (732 Girls). The school curriculum corresponds predominantly with practice in Scotland. Girls generally sit the public examinations prescribed by the Scottish Qualifications Authority.

SI and S2 follow a broad curriculum, whereby girls are equipped to pursue all routes to Standard Grade or Intermediate 2. In S3 girls commence eight courses, including English, Mathematics, at least one modern language, at least one science, and a "humanities" subject. In S5 the majority of girls take five subjects at Higher level. Girls are expected to achieve their full potential. The majority will continue their studies for a Sixth Year, usually for Advanced Higher level, to provide a firm foundation for degree courses in Scotland and England. Most girls proceed to such courses.

The playing fields at Ravelston underpin a fine tradition in hockey and tennis. Physical Education facilities include grass hockey pitches, an all-weather hockey pitch, a state-of-the-art floodlit astroturf hockey pitch, a running track and tennis courts. A Games Hall and Fitness Suite complement the other sporting facilities. The Pavilion, which provides the Sixth Form girls and boys with a Common Room and Study area during the week, is available to parents and friends as a coffee area on Saturday mornings and other times when sports events take place.

Staff from the well-equipped Technology Centre work closely with those in the bright, modern Home Economics Department. The attractive new Library is next to one of the computer rooms, forming a combined resource centre which is accessed by all departments.

In the Art Department the girls enjoy first class facilities which help them develop diverse artistic talents. There is a specially designated area for Sixth Form girls, many of whom proceed to Art colleges, as well as darkroom facilities for keen photographers.

The Music Department possesses fine facilities in Ravelston House and the school enjoys a notable reputation for the quality and range of its musical activities. The attractive School Hall and designated Studio offer good facilities for drama and there are frequent productions involving girls and boys of all ages.

The Combined Cadet Force comprises Army and RAF sections. The combined Pipe Band has an international reputation and girls in the Highland Dancing team also achieve frequent success in competition. Many girls participate in the Duke of Edinburgh's Award Scheme, as well as in hillwalking and other forms of outdoor recreation. Each week the school offers to girls a wide variety of extra-curricular clubs and societies ranging from curling to drama.

The school has a sophisticated system of Guidance. SI tutors, led by an Assistant Head, help girls to make the transition from Junior School to Senior School a smooth and happy experience. During the next four years girls belong to one of six houses. The Heads of House liaise closely with colleagues on each girl's academic progress, teach the personal and social education programme in house groups and encourage each girl to derive maximum benefit from the school's extra-curricular programme.

The Sixth Form is co-educational with the Sixth Formers of Stewart's Melville College. While girls sustain their loyalty and commitment to The Mary Erskine School, they are equally at home in the Sixth Form Centre of the boys' school. We see the Sixth Form as a preparation for university, when girls and boys assume greater responsibility for their academic programme and their career aspirations. All girls in the school receive guidance and help from the staff of a well-established careers department based in the Library Resource Centre.

Boarding. There is a boarding house (Erskine House) with accommodation for approximately 25 girls in brightly decorated study-bedrooms. The girls share dining and recreational facilities with the Stewart's Melville boarders in Dean Park House. Both Houses have a friendly, family atmosphere and provide an ideal "home from home" for brothers and sisters.

Fees per term (2008-2009). Day £2,830 (plus £143 for optional Lunches); Boarding £5,646.

Scholarships and Bursaries. Means-tested Bursaries worth up to 100% may be available to parents of children entering any year group in the Senior Schools. A number of awards are allocated for external candidates seeking to join the Sixth Form. Academic scholarships worth up to £1000 annually are offered to girls applying to enter S1. Scholarships are payable to the pupil and are held in trust by the school for disbursement on recipients leaving school on completion of the Sixth Form. Music Scholarships of £250 per annum are offered from S3.

Junior School. In The Mary Erskine and Stewart's Melville Junior School (1,206 pupils), girls and boys are educated together from age 3 to 12. Children in Primary Start to Primary 3 are based on the Mary Erskine School site at Ravelston, while boys and girls in Primary 4–7 are taught on the Stewart's Melville College site. Normal entry points are Primary Start (age 3 or 4), Primary 1, Primary 4, Primary 6 and Primary 7. The school is remarkable for the breadth of its educational programme and the quality of its sporting and cultural activities, in particular the professional standards attained in Music and Drama.

The Mary Erskine School Former Pupils' Guild. Contact: MES Guild Office, The Mary Erskine School, Ravelston, Edinburgh, EH4 3NT. Tel: 0131 347 5722.

Charitable status. The Merchant Company Education Board is a Registered Charity, number SC009747. It is a leading charitable school in the field of Junior and Secondary education.

Marymount International School

George Road Kingston-upon-Thames Surrey KT2 7PE
Tel: 020 8949 0571
Fax: 020 8336 2485
e-mail: admissions@marymountlondon.com
website: www.marymountlondon.com

An Independent boarding and day school for girls aged 11–18. A member of GSA, ECIS and MSA (USA).

***Principal*: Sister Kathleen Fagan**, RSHM

Number of Pupils. 245, including 100 boarders.

Established in 1955 by the Sisters of the Sacred Heart of Mary, Marymount International School is an independent day and boarding school for girls, aged 11–18 (grades 6–12), representing approximately forty different nationalities. The school is within a half-hour's drive of Heathrow Airport and conveniently located for M25/A3 road links.

The school aims to provide an intellectually stimulating and emotionally secure environment in which the academic, social and personal needs of each individual student may be met. Education is seen as a continuous process of growth in awareness and development towards maturity in preparation for participation in the world community. Small classes enable students to attain their full personal and academic potential. Each student's schedule is individually tailored to the subjects she wishes to follow. The overall student:teacher ratio is 12:1 and the average class size numbers 14 students.

Entry requirements and procedures. Previous reports, teachers' recommendations, placement testing and interview.

Facilities in the beautiful seven-acre campus include a £1 million block which comprises Library, Computer Centre and classrooms, as well as a Sports Hall, Auditorium, Art Studio, Language Laboratory, Science Centre, Music Centre, Design Technology Centre and tennis courts. A new boarding wing was completed in 1995 incorporating additional facilities for day and boarding students alike.

An integral part of the school programme each year is the option to visit a variety of foreign locations to learn about the history and culture of the area. For 2008 the choice was Switzerland and a China Tour.

Examinations. Students are prepared for the International Baccalaureate Diploma (ages 17/18, grades 11–12) by the IB Middle Years Programme (ages 11–16, grades 6–10). Marymount was the first British school to be accepted to teach the MYP, and now offers students an IB curriculum from ages 11–18 (grades 6–12).

The IB diploma syllabus leads to UK university admission and US college credit. On average, ninety-eight percent of graduates go on to third level education in the UK and abroad. Two students in 2007 received perfect scores of 45, the equivalent of 5 A grades for A level.

Fees per annum (2008-2009). Day Students: £14,895 (Grades 6–8); £16,945 (Grades 9–12). Boarding: Grades 6–8: £25,135 (5-day), £26,340 (7-day); Grades 9–12: £27,185 (5-day), £28,390 (7-day).

Charitable status. The Institution of the Religious Sisters of the Sacred Heart of Mary Immaculate Virgin is a Registered Charity, number 228365. It exists for the promotion of education.

The Maynard School
(Sir John Maynard's Foundation)

Denmark Road Exeter Devon EX1 1SJ
Tel: 01392 273417
Fax: 01392 355999
e-mail: office@maynard.co.uk
website: www.maynard.co.uk

Endowed 1658.

The Governors:
Appointed by the Governing Body of St John's Hospital:
Mrs L Kingdon
S Gregory, Esq
S Marsh, Esq
Mrs J P Regan

Co-opted by the Governors:
Mrs K Bickley
Mrs J Jones
Mrs T Murray (*Chairman*)
G Myers, Esq
G A F Owens, Esq
Mrs S Pritchard
N Shiel, Esq

Appointed by the Exeter City Council:
Mrs Y Henson

Appointed by the Devon County Council:
B C J Hughes, Esq

Appointed by the University of Exeter:
I C Powell, Esq

Parent Governors:
S Butcher, Esq
C Hoult, Esq

Staff Governors:
Mrs H Reynolds
Ms F Smart

The Right Worshipful, The Lord Mayor of Exeter (*ex officio*)

Secretary to the Governors: T A Hughes-Parry, Esq

***Headmistress*: Dr Daphne West**, BA, PhD, LTCL
from January 2009: Ms Bee Hughes

Deputy Head: Mrs A Boyce, BSc Exeter (*Biology*)

Senior Academic Administrator: Miss M Ellis, MA Cambridge (*Physics*)

Head of Junior Department: Mr S Smerdon, BEd Exeter (*History*)

Head of Sixth Form: Mrs P Wilks, MA Oxford (*History*)

Staff:
Miss H Bacon, BA Bristol (*Junior Department*)
Miss G Bailey, BSc Manchester (*Physics*)
Dr J Burgess, BA, PhD Reading (*Classics*)
Mrs E Burrow, BA Plymouth (*Art*)
Mrs J Elson, BSc, MPhil London (*Geography*)
Mrs S Fanous, BEd Keele (*Food & Nutrition, Textiles*)
Mr I Flower, BSc Sussex (*Chemistry, Physics*)
Miss K Gwynne, MTheol St Andrews, ThM Princeton (*Religious Studies*)
Mrs A J Horton, BSc Exeter (*Mathematics*)
Mr N V Horton, BA Bristol, ARCM (*Music*)
Mr S Janssens, BA Birmingham, DipTh (*Classics, Religious Studies*)
Mrs S Kerrane, BSc Swansea (*Biology*)
Dr P Le Gallez, BA Bristol, MA, PhD Exeter (*English*)
Mrs V Martin, BA Hull (*English*)
Mrs L Masson, BSc Pietermaritzberg (*Junior Department*)
Mrs L May, BEd De Montfort (*Physical Education*)
Mrs E McCormack, BSc Loughborough (*Physical Education*)
Mr J McGrath, BA Hons Wales (*History*)
Dr P Merisi, MPhil, PhD Exeter (*Mathematics*)
Miss L Millar, BEd Belfast (*Physical Education*)
Dr E Ouldridge, BSc Birmingham, PhD Leeds (*Biology, Physics, Chemistry*)
Mrs H Palmer, BA Hons Sheffield (*Junior Department*)
Mrs H Reynolds, BSc Open University (*Junior Department*)
Mrs C Roche, BSc Exeter (*Mathematics*)
Mrs C Rowe, DipEd, Edinburgh (*Junior Department*)
Mrs A Rowley, BA Liverpool (*English*)
Dr P Rudling, MA Cambridge, MSc, PhD Exeter (*Psychology*)
Mr S Ryder, BSc Hons Birmingham, MSc London (*Information & Communications Technology*)
Mrs O Saunders, BA Exeter (*French, German*)
Ms F Smart, BSc Exeter (*Mathematics*)
Mrs C Smith, MA Tours (*French, Spanish*)
Mrs S Thorne, BSc Nottingham (*Chemistry, Biology*)
Mrs S Woolley, MA Oxford (*Study Skills & Learning Support*)
Mrs Z Vingoe, BA Manchester Metropolitan (*Art*)

Part-time Staff:
Mrs C L Austin, GRSM, LRAM (*Music*)
Mrs I T Colley, BEd, MA, LRAM (*Drama*)
Mr I Crew, GMus RNCM, PPRNCM (*Music*)
Mrs J Dalton, BSc Open University, (*Maths*)
Mrs C Farrington, MA Columbia (*English, Classics, RS*)
Mrs K Fry, BEd Exeter (*Junior Department*)
Mrs C M Gabbitass, BSc Loughborough (*Physical Education*)
Mr A Ganley, BA Nottingham (*Drama*)
Mrs A Govier, BA Exeter (*French, Spanish*)
Mrs D Lewis, BA Cheltenham (*Geography*)
Mrs M McKenzie, MA Munich (*German*)
Mrs A Pearson, BEd Exeter (*Food & Nutrition, Textiles*)
Mr P Pienkowski, BSc London (*Economics, ICT*)
Mrs I Powell, BSc, MSc Rennes (*French*)

In addition there are 17 Visiting Music Staff and 4 Visiting Coaches for extra-curricular activities.

Headmistress's PA: Mrs T Taylor
Assistant Secretary: Mrs J Crowley
Estate Manager: Ms J Beever
Marketing & Admissions Officer: Mrs C McLaughlin
Marketing & Admissions Assistant: Mrs L Stuckey
School Nurse: Mrs S Ayres
School Counsellor: Mrs B Bragg

Ethos. A warm-hearted, challenging school for able girls, the Maynard provides a rich breadth of curriculum and encourages individual talent and confidence. It is non-denominational and values the contribution made by pupils of other faiths. Assembly is held 4 times per week and the spiritual and moral development of each pupil is furthered by a carefully-planned pastoral programme. Extra-curricular activities foster concern for others as well as the development of personal giftedness in Music, Art, Drama, Sport etc.

Numbers. There are approximately 500 day girls in the School, of whom 100 are in the Junior Department and 110 in the Sixth Form.

School Buildings. The School is situated in an attractive conservation area five minutes from the centre of the City. The extensive buildings include a separate Sixth Form Centre (extended and refurbished in 2004); a purpose-built block for Science (9 laboratories), Mathematics, and Information Technology; well-equipped Food & Nutrition and Textiles Rooms; refurbished Music and Art Rooms; two specialist Geography Rooms, a large Gymnasium, and an impressive Sports Hall which provides full-scale indoor facilities for sports. The Junior Department is situated in a detached building within the grounds, and is fully equipped for the education of girls aged 7–10 years.

Curriculum. The curriculum is academically strong, maintaining a good balance between Arts and Science subjects. Music, the Sciences and Sport are particular strengths; full scope is given to creative and practical activities, as well as IT skills. The School prepares all girls for the Universities, including Oxford and Cambridge. A carefully developed programme of careers advice, begun at 13+ and continuing through to the Sixth Form, ensures that all pupils are individually guided in subject options etc with their long-term career interests at heart.

Examinations. Candidates normally take 9 subjects at GCSE and 3 at Advanced Level. Pupils are fully prepared for Oxford and Cambridge University Entrance.

Physical Education. Hockey (outdoor and indoor), Netball, Badminton, Basketball, Volleyball, Fencing, Dance and Gymnastics are offered in the winter terms; Tennis and Rounders are played in the Summer Term. Training is given in Athletics and regular instruction in Swimming as part of the normal timetable for all girls during the Summer Term. Besides its excellent indoor facilities and the three hard courts in its own grounds, the School is close to three heated swimming pools and an Astroturf playing area. The school has an extensive fixture programme in Netball, Hockey, Indoor Hockey, Badminton, Basketball, Tennis, Swimming, Athletics and Rounders. Teams have regularly reached national standard.

Admission. All admissions are subject to an Entrance Examination graduated according to age and are held in January each year for entry in the following September.

Fees per term (2008-2009). Junior Department £2,522, Senior School £3,155.

Scholarships and Bursaries. (*see Scholarship Entries section*). A number of means-tested Governors' Bursaries are awarded annually. Music scholarships and exhibitions are available. Wolfson Foundation bursaries are awarded at Sixth Form level. Up to four Governors' Leaving Exhibitions are awarded in the Upper Sixth year. There are Sixth Form scholarships available in Art, Music, Science and Sport, plus the new 350th Anniversary Academic Awards.

Further Information. The Prospectus and Governors' Bursaries information are available from the Admissions Office. Visitors are very welcome by appointment, and tours and taster days can be arranged for girls considering the school.

Old Maynardians' Society. *Secretary*: Mrs Jane Jones, 5 Matford Avenue, Exeter, Devon.

Charitable status. The Maynard School is a Registered Charity, number 1099027. It exists to provide quality education for girls.

Merchant Taylors' Girls' School
Crosby

Liverpool Road Crosby Liverpool L23 5SP
Tel: 0151 924 3140
Fax: 0151 932 1461
e-mail: admissionsmtgs@merchanttaylors.com
website: www.merchanttaylors.com

Motto: *Concordia Parvae Res Crescunt*

Governors:
Chairman: L C Coligan, Esq, BA
Chairman of Finance: F C Mercer, Esq, JP, FCA
Prof P W J Batey, BSc, MCB, PhD, FRTPI, FRSA
P J R Evans, Esq, FCA
Mrs S M I Hetherington, JP
Dr M I Hughes, MBChB
D R Jacks, Esq, LLB
Mrs V A P Johnson, BEd
P G Magill, Esq, MSc, CFIPD
Mrs D F Shackleton, MA, FCIH, FRSA, MAPM
Dr R Thind, MB BS, DMRD, FRCR
R J Walker, Esq, CEng, MIMechE

Bursar & Clerk to the Governors: P S Gaunt, MA, FCA

***Headmistress*: Mrs L A Robinson**, BA Hons York, PGCE, NPQH, MEd Liverpool

First Deputy Headmistress: Miss J Tyndall, BD/AKC Hons London

Deputy Headmistress: Mrs M L Bush, MA Liverpool, BMus Hons Wales, FRSA, NPQH

School Staff:
§ *part-time*

Art & Craft:
Mr M Gill, BA Hons Newcastle upon Tyne
Miss L McWatt, BA Hons Bristol

Biology:
Mrs J Johnson, MA Oxon
Mrs N Houghton, BSc Hons Liverpool John Moores
§Mrs L Dickinson IM Marsh College of PE
Mr J S Jones, BSc Hons Liverpool
Dr M McWatt, PhD Birmingham, BSc Hons Birmingham
Mrs B Miller, BSc Hons Bristol
Mrs H M Peppin, BSc Hons Leeds

Business Studies:
Mrs A H Irwin, BA Hons Preston

Chemistry:
Mrs B Miller, BSc Hons Bristol
Mrs P Colvin, MA Oxon
Mrs H Heaton, BSc Hons Durham
Mr J S Jones, BSc Hons Liverpool
Dr M McWatt, PhD Birmingham, BSc Hons Birmingham
Mrs L Syms, BSc Hons Central Lancashire

Classics:
Mrs A Wadsworth, BA Hons Durham
Mrs J Doyle, BA Hons
Mr D Lamb, MA Liverpool, BA Hons Liverpool
Mr M Routledge, BA Joint Hons Nottingham

Drama & Theatre Studies:
Ms S Tickle, BA Manchester, MA
Mrs A O'Connor, BA Hons Lancaster

English:
Mrs J Cecil, BA Hons Aberystwyth
Miss N McCabe, BA Hons, MA Edge Hill College
Mr D Donnan, BA Hons Cantab
Mrs M Myring, MPhil Bangor, BA Hons UCNW, MA SDUC
Mrs E Neophytou, BA Birmingham
Mrs A O'Connor, BA Lancaster
Miss S Jackson, MA Oxon, BA Hons Oxon

Geography:
Mrs M Hart, BA Hons Liverpool, MA
Mrs C Mason, BSc Hons Manchester Polytechnic
Mrs H M Peppin, BSc Hons Leeds

History & Politics:
§Mrs C Grindley, BA Hons Leeds
Mr G Evans, BA Hons Hull
Miss S Hathaway, BA Hons Oxon

Home Economics:
Mrs B Jones, BEd Liverpool
Mrs S Phillips, CertEd Leeds

Information Technology:
Mr J Hood, BA Hons Humberside

Librarian:
Mrs A Barry, BLib Aberystwyth, ALA

Mathematics:
Dr S R Barge, DPhil Oxford, BA Hons Oxford
Mrs P M Carter, BSc Hons Liverpool
Mrs H F Hurst, BSc Hons Keele
Mrs A Stevens, BSc Nottingham
Mr M Wood, BSc Hons Aberystwyth, MSc Dundee

Modern Languages:
Mrs Y Whalley, BA Hons Leeds
Mrs J Doyle, BA Hons Nottingham
§Mrs J Garside, BA Hons Newcastle
§Mrs F Menzies, CLA d'Abidjan
Mrs P Mistry, Licence University of Metz
§Mr F Rubia
§Mrs C Southworth, BA Hons Bristol
Mrs S M Thompson, BEd Hons Liverpool

Music:
Director of Music: Mrs J Thompson, BMus Hons Wales, MA
Mrs M L Bush, MA Liverpool, BMus Hons Wales, FRSA

Visiting and Part-time Music Staff:
Mrs K L Adewale, ARMCM Dip (*Violin*)
Mr D Bridge (*Guitar*)
Mr D Byles (*Percussion*)
Mr C Jones (*Saxophone*)
Miss D O'Hara, GRNCM Hons, ARCM (*Piano*)
Mrs R Partington
Mrs J Richards, LWCMD (*'Cello/Double Bass*)
Miss D Wright, BA (*Flute*)

Physical Education:
Miss E Jones, BEd Hons Liverpool
Mrs L Dickinson IM Marsh College of PE
Mrs A P Stenson IM Marsh College of PE

Physics:
Mrs J E Custard, BSc Hons Coventry
Mrs H Heaton, BSc Hons Durham
Mr P Perry, BSc Leeds

Religious Studies:
Mrs M Dodds, BA Hons Newcastle
Mr E Wilson, MA Durham, BA Hons Durham, BSc OU

Marketing and Admissions:
Marketing & Development Director: Miss M J Riches, BA Hons
Admissions Officer: Mrs S Barrington

Administration:
PA to Headmistress: Mrs J Baccino
School Secretary: Mrs A Regan
Receptionists: §Mrs A Cave, §Mrs J Kirkwood
Examinations Secretary: Mrs G Hurst
Computer Network Manager: Mr S Coughlan, BA Hons
ICT Technician: Mr R Mackenzie
Print Services Manager: Mrs S Nield
Print Services Assistants:
§Mrs A Bramhall, §Mr S Dixon, §Mrs L Blair
Lab Technicians:
Mrs J Heckford, Mrs S Childs, Mrs S Cheetham, Mrs N Oakes, Mr D Forfar

Junior School 'Stanfield'
Head of Junior School: Miss J E Yardley, BA Hons, PGCE, NPQH
Deputy Head: Mrs J Roberts, BEd Hons Lancaster

Mrs J Birtwistle, BA Hons Loughborough
Mrs S Curwen, BEd Hons Lancaster
§Mrs C Darbyshire, BTech Child Ed (*Form Assistant*)
Mrs A Dunne (*Form Assistant*)
Mrs C Evans (*Netball Coach*)
Mrs S Garforth, BEd Hons Lancaster
Mrs L Gaskell, BA Hons Huddersfield
Mrs J Harman, CertEd C F Mott
§Mrs J Hill, BEd Hons Coventry
Mrs A-L Hodkinson (*Swimming Coach*)
Mrs J Howard (*Infant PE*)
Mrs A Hunter, CertEd Gloucester
Miss C Jeans, BA Ed Hons Durham
§Mrs R Loan, BA Hons Nottingham
Mrs L Lymath, NNEB (*Form Assistant*)
Mrs K MacKenzie, CertEd Bristol
Mrs S McEvoy, BA Hons Liverpool
§Mrs A Nagy, BEd Liverpool
Mrs C Oakes, BA Hons Manchester
Mrs J O'Mahony, BA, CertEd Lancaster
Mrs B Richardson, BEd London
§Mr T Roberts, BA Hons Durham, ATCL
Mrs L Rothwell, CertEd
§Mrs S Ryan, NNEB
Mrs A Saunders (*Form Assistant*)
Mrs M Silverman, BA Hons Liverpool
Mrs S Taylor, BEd Leeds
Miss K Wilson, BA Hons

PA to Head: Mrs M Langham

ICT Coordinator: Ms A Crichton

Visiting Music Staff:
Miss H Burgoyne (*Piano*)
Mrs J Richards (*'Cello and Double Bass*)
Mrs S Rookyard (*Singing*)
Mrs K White (*Violin*)

The Senior Girls' School was opened in 1888 on the site which had been occupied by the Boys' School for over 350 years; the original grey stone building, erected in 1620, is still in daily use. Extensions have been made from time to time including a Fitness Suite, Science Laboratories and Sixth Form Centre in 2007. The Centenary Hall provides exciting accommodation for concerts, plays and as a Sports Hall. The School is beautifully situated in its own grounds, about 8 miles from Liverpool and within 10 minutes' walk of the sea. There are Netball and Tennis Courts on the premises and a playing field a short distance away.

There is a separate Mixed Infants and Junior Girls' School situated in separate self-contained buildings near to the Main School with Girls aged 4–11, and Boys aged 4–7. The Senior Girls' School age range is 11–18. There are at present 890 pupils in the School.

The girls receive a broad academic education. Subjects included in the curriculum are English Language and Literature, Mathematics, Biology, Chemistry, Physics, Government and Politics, Information Technology, Latin, Classics, History, Geography, French, German, Spanish, Art, Psychology, Economics, Religious Studies, Home Economics, Music (Vocal and Instrumental), Drama, Theatre Studies, Physical Education and General Studies.

Fees per term (2008-2009). Senior School £2,727; Junior School £2,004.

Examinations. Pupils are prepared for the GCSE and A Level examinations.

The Music Examinations taken are those of the Associated Board of the Royal Schools of Music.

Parent Teachers' Association. *Hon Sec*: Mr D Yarwood, c/o The School.

Old Girls' Association. *Hon Secretary*: Mrs S Duncan, 'Fairhaven', The Serpentine South, Liverpool L23 6UQ.

Charitable status. Merchant Taylors' Schools is a Registered Charity, number 526681. The object of the Charity is the provision and conduct in or near Crosby of a day school for girls.

Moira House Girls School

Upper Carlisle Road Eastbourne East Sussex BN20 7TE
Tel: 01323 644144
Fax: 01323 649720
e-mail: info@moirahouse.co.uk
website: www.moirahouse.co.uk

Established 1875.
Motto: *Nemo A Me Alienus*

The Council:
Chairman: Ms J A Jackson-Hill (*Company Director and former pupil*)
Dr P Frost (*University lecturer, parent of pupil*)
Mr P Hawley (*Hotelier, parent of former pupil*)
Mr S Dodds (*Solicitor, parent of former pupil*)
Mr A H Price (*Solicitor, parent of former pupil*)
Mrs J Henshaw (*former pupil*)
Mrs J Herold (*Consultant Orthodontist, parent*)

The Common Room:

Senior Management Team:

***Principal*: Mrs Lesley Watson**, MA Ed, MInstD

Bursar: Mr David E Ingham, BSc, ACA
Head of Junior School: Mrs Linda Young, CertEd, NPQH
Deputy Principal: Mr Kevin D Ashby, MA, BA Hons, QTS
Head of Boarding, Pastoral Care and Sixth Form: Mrs Carol J Richards, BA, PGCE (*Business Studies and Economics*)
Director of Human Resources, CIPD: Mrs Patricia Gates
Senior Mistress: Miss Pamela S Merritt, MA, BA Hons, PGCE (**Geography, Examinations Officer*)
Director of Admissions: Mr Eric Reynolds, BA Hons, PGCE

Senior School Staff:
Miss Gillian Aitken, MA, PGCE, RSA DipTEFL, Dip Psych, AMBDA (**EAL, English, Special Needs*)
Mrs Barbara E Ashby, GGSM, PGCE (*Music, Music Coordinator KS4 & 5*)
Mr Howard Barlow, BA, TEFL Cert (*Careers Counsellor*)
Mrs Cheryl Burchett, BEd Hons (*Science Technician*)
Mr Peter Burge, BMus Hons, PGCE, ALCM (*Director of Music*)
Ms Gabriella Chowdhury, BA Hons, PGCE (**Religious Education*)
Miss Dawn Cook, BEd (*Physical Education*)
Mr Stephen D Crum, BA Hons, PGCE (*Mathematics, KS3 Pastoral Coordinator*)
Mrs Lucy A Dean, BA Hons (*Drama*)
Miss Katharine M Fermor, BA Hons, PGCE (**History*)
Mrs Alison Gamester, BA Hons, PGCE (*Religious Education, History*)
Mr Christopher G Harper, CertEd (*Design Technology*)
Mrs Ruth Harris-Moss, BAHons, PGCE (**German, Deputy Head of Sixth Form*)
Ms Carrie Harrison-Iddon (*Drama*)
Mr Alan Hodge, BSc Hons, PGCE (**Chemistry*)
Miss Katherine A James, BA Hons, QTS (**PE*)
Mrs Natasha Jordan, Dip Prof Acting Hons (*Director of Drama*)
Mrs Jane Lambert, BA Hons (*Mathematics*)
Mrs Jillian Lindley, FSRSB, AISTD (*Dance*))
Mrs Anne Lucarotti, BA Hons, PGCE (**Modern Languages and Classics*)
Ms Moira Lucas, BA Hons, PGCE (*Art*)
Dr Fiona Mansfield (*Subject Leader Biology*)
Mr Duncan Martin, BA Hons, PGCE, CELTA (*EAL*)
Mrs Michelle C Martin, MEd, BA Hons, PGCE Dip TEFLA (*English and EFL, KS4 Pastoral Coordinator*)
Mrs Bernardine M Mcnamara, BA Hons, PGCE (*French*)
Mr Christopher M O'Reilly, BA Hons, PGCE, TEFL (*Spanish*)
Mrs Barbara Power, PG Dip, CertEd (**ICT*)
Mrs Lesley A Pyle, BEd Hons (*Physical Education*)
Miss Katie Reid, BEd Hons (*Physical Education, Mathematics*)
Mrs Claire Richard (*Languages; School Fundraiser*)
Mr Patrick Richard, BSc Hons, PGCE, AM Inst P (**Science, Physics*)
Miss Aileen M Rickard, BSc, PGCE, NPQH (*KS5 Mathematics Coordinator, Staff Development Coordinator*)
Mrs Sylvia Robinson, MIScT (*Laboratory Technician*)
Ms Linda Rosson, BA Hons, PGCE, MA (*English*)
Miss Hannah Savage (*Subject Leader Psychology*)
Miss Elizabeth Scott, BSc Hons, MPhil Sc, PGCE (*Science*)
Mr Stephen M Simpson, BSc Hons, PGCE (*Science*)
Mrs Lindy Smart (*Assistant Librarian*)
Mrs Alison J Standen, BA Hons (*Senior Librarian*)
Mrs Pamela M Tait, BA Hons, PGCE (**English*)
Mrs Lucinda Westwood, BA Hons, PGCE, CTEFLA)
Mrs Nicola Whitefield-Smith, BA Hons, MA, PGCE, Adv Dip RSA C&G (*Literacy, EFL*)
Mrs Pamela J Wigmore, CertEd, CTEFLA (*Food Technology*)
Mrs Jacqueline Wood, BSc Hons, PGCE (*Geography, Science*)
Mr Stephen Wood, MA Ed, BA Hons, PGCE (**Business Studies & Economics*)

Administration:
Mr Damian J Baldry, BSc Hons (*IT Support Technician*)
Mrs Linda Burnett (*School Receptionist*)
Ms Caroline Francis (*School Office Administrator*)
Mrs Jayne Hollister-Sheppard (*School Accountant*)
Mrs Judith C Hussey (*Accountants Assistant*)
Mrs Anna Ingham (*Old Girls Liaison*)
Mr Kevin R Ives, BSc Hons (*IT Manager*)
Mr Graham James, MIH (*Operations Manager*)
Miss Rhiannon Jones (*School Office Administrator*)
Mrs Jane K Mole (*Database Administrator*)
Mrs Elizabeth Powell (*Bursar's Secretary*)

Junior School Staff:
Mrs Linda Young, CertEd, NPQH, (*Head of Junior School*)
Mrs Theresa Bees, BSc, QTS (*Year 2 Teacher*)
Mrs Jane Fisher, BEd (*Year 4 Teacher, Head of KS2*)
Mrs Lisa J Gough, BA Ed Hons (*Year 3 Teacher*)
Mr Christopher Kerswell, BA Hons (*Year 5 Teacher*)
Mrs Wendy Lambert, BA Hons, PGCE (*Physical Education*)
Mrs Fiona D Martirossian, BA Hons, PGCE (*Year 1 Teacher*)
Mr Martin Neill, Dip Mus, BMus Hons, PGCE (*Head of Junior School Music*)
Mrs Karon F Pont (*Teaching Assistant*)
Mrs Ruth M Sibson, BEd (*SEN, Year 6 Teacher and Deputy Head of Junior School*)
Mrs Joy Stephenson, BEd (*Reception Teacher, Head of Pre-Prep*)
Mrs Linda Whicker (*Lunchtime Supervision, After School Club Supervisor*)
Mrs Rosalind F Forbes (*After School Club Supervisor*)

Junior School Administration:
Mrs Jennifer Hafernik (*Junior School Secretary*)

Nursery:
Mrs Sarah Hughes, BTEC Nat Dip Childcare (*Head of Nursery*)
Miss Carly Brooks, Dip Childcare & Education (*Nursery Assistant*)
Mrs Rebekah Cochran, NNEB Childcare (*Nursery Assistant*)

Mrs Judith H Partridge, Dip Childcare & Education (*Nursery Assistant*)
Miss Helen Wallis, NVQ2 Childcare (*Nursery Assistant*)

House Staff:
Mrs Angela Clift (*Assistant Housemistress, School House; Activities Coordinator*)
Miss Patricia Hibbs, BEd Hons ((*Senior Housemistress, Boston; History*)
Mrs Marion I Knight (*Housemother, Boston*)
Mrs Caroline Madden (*Housemother, School House*)
Ms Anna Romnaki (*Assistant Housemother, School House*)
Miss Lucinda Stuart-Grant, BMus Hons (*Assistant Housemistress, School House; Activities Coordinator*)

Medical Centre:
Dr K Leeson, MBBS, DCH, DRCOG, FPA Cert (*School Doctor*)
Mrs Sarah Day, RGN, BA Hons, Cert HEd, Dip Asthma (*Senior Sister*)
Mrs Irene Hatton, RGN (*Sister*)
Mrs Lisa Lane, RGN, HV Cert (*Sister*)

Swimming Pool:
Mr Trevor Boswell (*Swimming Teacher*)
Mrs Claire L Bryant, IOS ISTC (*Pool Manager*)
Mrs Heather M Curry, BA Hons, MInst BRM, FIST (*Swimming Teacher*)
Mrs Renee Harris (*Swimming Teacher*)
MS Wendy Pritchard, ISTC (*Swimming Teacher*)
Mrs Patricia A Smith (*Swimming Teacher*)
Mrs Gwendoline C Taylor (*Swimming Teacher*)

Visiting Staff:
Miss Clare Adams, CertEd, LRSM Dip, ABRSM, ALCM, Dip LCM (*Brass*)
Mr Mark Ashworth (*Youth Worker, All Saints Church*)
Mr Jonathan Chappell (*Percussion*)
Mrs Zoe Clay, BMus (*Clarinet, Saxophone*)
Mrs Maeve Cooper, Dip RCM Perf, Dip RCM Ten (*Violin*)
Mr Eric Cornelisse (*Encounter*)
Miss Rachel Crowe (*Encounter*)
Mr James R Cruttenden, BA, ABRSM (*Double Bass*)
Miss Valerie Dent (*LAMDA*)
Miss Eileen Godier, GLSM, LLCM TD, ALCM, PGCE (*Piano, Wind*)
Ms Susan Gregg, BA, ABRSM (*Flute*)
Mrs Rebecca Kelly, BMus Hons,, PG Dip (*Singing*)
Mrs Franciska Laursen, DRS (*Piano*)
Ms Jane J Lister, MA Cantab, LRAM, PGCE, Premier Prix, Prix Speciale Brussels Royal Conservatoire (*Harp*)
Revd Robert Lovatt (*School Chaplain, All Saints Church*)
Mrs Elaine Patience, BA Dip, NCOS (*Violin, Viola*)
Mrs Philippa J Poulton-Smith (*Singing Teacher*)
Ms Angelika Schlussel, MA (*Languages Teacher*)
Mr Michael B Shirley, BA (*Guitar*)
Mrs Sally A Thorkildsen, BA Hons, PGCE (*Cello*)

Foundation. Moira House was founded in 1875 in Surrey. The School moved to its present site in 1887. The founders, Mr and Mrs Charles Ingham, were regarded in their time as gifted pioneers in the field of female education. In 1947 the School was converted into an educational trust. It is represented on the Girls' Schools Association, the Boarding Schools Association and SHMIS.

Situation and Facilities. Situated on high ground in Eastbourne with views over the sea, the grounds open directly onto the Downs which provide magnificent walking country and offer opportunities for expedition work and field studies. There are extensive playing fields with facilities for Tennis, Hockey, Netball and Athletics, a 25-metre indoor heated swimming pool and an excellent new all-weather sports hall. Each subject has its own resource base, double subject rooms being allocated to each academic area. Eastbourne is a thriving cultural centre containing 3 theatres, an art gallery and a concert hall.

Faith. The School is inter-denominational.

Organisation. *Junior School*: The Junior School has provision for 120 day girls starting at age 2 and junior boarders starting from the age of 9.

Senior School: The Senior School has provision for 110 boarders and 260 day girls.

Boarding Houses: There are two boarding houses, including two separate Sixth Form houses. Each house has a Senior Housemistress and Assistant Housemistresses most of whom are teachers in the school. Emphasis is placed upon a full range of organised activities, both in the evenings and at weekends.

Day Houses: There are 2 leisure areas for Day Girls including a separate house for fourth and fifth years.

Curriculum. *Junior School*: We offer a wide curriculum, whilst preparing for transfer to the Senior School.

Senior School: The formal academic course follows the normal curriculum in Arts and Sciences to GCSE, AS and A Level and University Entrance. At GCSE we offer English, English Literature, Mathematics, Biology, Chemistry, Physics, Science, French, German, Spanish, Latin, History, Geography, Religious Studies, Music, Drama, Art and Design, Design/Technology, Information Systems, Physical Education and Statistics.

Sixth Form: A Levels are offered in English Literature, IT, History, Geography, French, German, Spanish, Music, Theatre Studies, Art, Mathematics, Further Mathematics, Chemistry, Physics, Biology, Business Studies, Physical Education, Religious Studies, and Psychology. AS Levels are offered in all A Level subjects plus Economics.

Careers' Counselling. We have a strong programme of Careers' Counselling, developed by our Careers' Counsellor, Howard Barlow.

Drama and Music. Drama and Music have always been strengths of Moira House. We are aware of the part Speech and Drama play in the development of clear communication and creative expression. There are a number of School productions and concerts each year, and school choirs take part in performances throughout Sussex. We also enter the local festival of Music and Drama and proximity to Glyndebourne gives girls a chance to have their first taste of opera at an early age. As well as regular class music lessons, there is every opportunity to learn a musical instrument, and the exams of the various musical examining bodies are taken. Overseas tours to Europe, America and Australia have also taken place.

Physical Education and Sport. We provide excellent new facilities. The main sports are Swimming, Netball, Tennis, Athletics and Hockey, and teams represent the School in these and in cricket and football. In addition, coaching is given in Sailing, Riding, Squash, Dance, Golf and Badminton.

Activities. Activities are considered an essential part of the curriculum. Many activities are offered, including: Drama, Music, Trampolining, Needlework, Pottery, Bridge, Chess, Local History, Sailing, Down-walking, Environmental Studies, Poetry/Play Reading, Table Tennis, the Young Enterprise Scheme and Debating. Girls are also encouraged to be aware of the needs of others. Old people and disabled people are visited on a regular basis and senior girls work with local charities. There are annual expeditions both within this country and to Europe and the School has links with French and German schools of a similar nature to ours.

Health. The school doctor holds a weekly surgery at the School and there are Sisters in charge of the sickbay.

Entry. Entry is by interview and review of previous school reports. Admission to the Junior School at any age; to the Senior School usually at 11–13+ and 16+.

Scholarships and Bursaries. (*see Scholarship Entries section*).

Fees per term (2008-2009). Senior School: £3,795–£4,370 (Day Pupils); £5,785–£6,825 (Weekly Boarders); £6,500–£7,530 (Boarders)

Junior School: £3,035–£3,430 (Day Pupils); £5,460 (Weekly Boarders); £5,875 (Boarders).

Charitable status. Moira House Girls School is a Registered Charity, number 307072. It exists to provide quality education for young women.

More House School

22–24 Pont Street London SW1X 0AA
Tel: 020 7235 2855; Bursar: 020 7235 4162
Fax: 020 7259 6782
e-mail: office@morehouse.org.uk
website: www.morehouse.org.uk

Governing Body:
Chairman: Mr J Davidson, BA, OBE
Mr F M Broadbent, MI FHCIMA (*Vice-Chairman*)
Ms E M Buchanan, BA, Dip Radio Journalism
Mrs M M Burns, BA
Mr P I Ewings, BA
Mrs M S Shale, BA, ACA
Mr J W Wates, MA, BSc, FRICS

***Headmaster*: Mr R M Carlysle**, BA Hons, MBA, AKC, PGCE, Cert Dysl & Lit, MCollP

Deputy Head: Mr S Fletcher, MA Oxon, MMus London
Senior Teacher: Mrs A Leach, BSc Liverpool
Bursar: Mr A J Murray, MA Oxon, LLB London
Chaplain: Father Peter Burrows, PhD, MTh, BFS, Lic MFCC
PA to the Headmaster/Admissions: Ms A McCarthy

Staff:
* *Head of Department*

Mrs E Allen, MA Courtauld (*History of Art*)
Mrs H Anson, MA Cantab (*Classics*)
Ms A Baeza, LLB, MA London (*Spanish*)
Mr R Benson, BA London, PGCE London
Ms L Beatty, BA London (*Art*)
Ms H Beaumont, BSc NZ, BTch NZ (*Biology*)
Mrs A Blenkinsop, JP, BA Newcastle (*Mathematics, Latin*)
Ms G Collins, BA Birmingham (**History*)
Miss J PCrowe, BSc Aberdeen, MA London (*Chemistry, Physics*)
Miss G Doyle, BSc Reading (*Biology, Chemistry*)
Mr M C A Ginever, BSc Exeter (**Mathematics*)
Ms C Gremillet, BA Barcelona (*French, Spanish*)
Mrs M Haig, MA Glasgow (*History, Geography*)
Miss S Hill, BSc Brighton (*PE*)
Ms A Hope, RADA (*Drama*)
Ms C Hoult, MA Oxon (*Classics*)
Mr M R Keeley, BMus London (**Music*)
Mrs A Leach, BSc Liverpool (*Biology*)
Mr A Lloyd, BSc Hons Birmingham (**Physics*)
Mrs C Masefield, BA Bristol (*French*)
Mrs P A Maudsley, BA London (**German, French*)
Mrs J McCluskey, BA Southampton (**Drama, English*)
Ms J North, BA London (*English*)
Mrs V Parrott, BA London (*French*)
Ms S Reimer, BEd Canada (*Learning Support/Library*)
Ms P Revell, BA Wellington, NZ, TIC, DipT NZ (*Economics*)
Ms D Rigby, MA Chelsea (*Art*)
Mrs S Skinner, DA Aberdeen (**Art*)
Mr P Thompson, BA Manchester (**Religious Studies*)
Miss C Vardon, MMath Oxon (*Mathematics*)

Mr S Keeley (*Network Manager*)
Mr O David (*Laboratory Technician*)

Peripatetic staff:
Mrs T Henderson, ISTD (*Dancing*)
Professor J A Parkins, Diplomé de l'Académie (*Fencing*)
(*plus various instrumental teachers*)

More House is an Independent Day School of up to 220 girls between the ages of eleven and eighteen. It occupies two adjoining houses, conveniently situated in Knightsbridge, retaining many of the original architectural features, but modernised to include four laboratories, two computer rooms, common rooms, study room and computer room for the sixth form, a chapel, a library and a newly refurbished gymnasium. More House is a small and happy community in which a generous teacher : pupil ratio allows the talents of each girl to flourish with all the stimulus and encouragement that she needs. The maximum class size is normally twenty, streamed where necessary in mathematics, science and languages. All girls leaving the Sixth Form proceed to Higher Education, including Oxbridge, and then to careers in every field. Girls are given full advice about careers and Higher Education.

A Catholic Foundation, More House was opened in 1953 by the Canonesses of St Augustine; since 1969 it has been under lay management as a charitable trust and with a Board of Governors which has always included parents of present pupils. More House celebrated its Golden Jubilee in the academic year 2003–2004. The School attracts pupils from a wide area of London. More House warmly welcomes girls of all faiths.

Places at the school are usually awarded on the basis of an interview, a report from the candidate's previous school, and an examination held in January each year. Girls who join us in the Sixth Form are required to have achieved grades A–C in at least six subjects at GCSE Level, with a grade B or above in the subjects they wish to study to Advanced Level.

Our level of pastoral care is very high indeed, supporting the girls in all aspects of their lives.

Instrumental tuition is available in school and in recent years the School Choir has given performances in Portugal, Spain, Paris, Rome, Malta and the USA. The most recent school choral concert featured Messa di Gloria at Cadogan Hall. Full advantage is taken of the school's position in Central London and regular visits to lectures, galleries and exhibitions are organised.

Extra-curricular activities include Music, Drama, Sport, Dance, Art, Fencing, Photography and the Duke of Edinburgh's Award Scheme and World Challenge Expeditions. The latest school drama production was 'The Wizard of Oz' performed at a professional theatre.

The Curriculum. The school curriculum offers a wide range of subjects at all levels. In the first two years all girls study Mathematics, Science, English, French, German, Latin, History, Geography, Religious Studies, Information Technology, Drama, Art, Physical Education and Music. Spanish is added in the third year, giving the possibility of taking two modern languages at GCSE, where the core curriculum of Mathematics, Science, English Language and Literature, French and Religious Studies is supplemented by three further options.

The Advanced Level courses offered are structured around each girl's choice of subjects, new options available at this stage being History of Art, Classical Civilisation, Economics, Textiles and Theatre Studies; further breadth of study is achieved through a General Studies programme. Each subject has its own specialist rooms and for Physical Education the excellent sport and leisure facilities available in the neighbourhood are used in addition to the school's gymnasium.

Fees per term (from January 2008). £4,255 including lunch, textbooks, stationery and some educational visits. Academic and Music Scholarships are available on merit.

Charitable status. More House Trust is a Registered Charity, number 312737. It exists to provide an academic education for girls aged 11 to 18 within the framework of a Catholic Day School.

Moreton Hall

Weston Rhyn Oswestry Shropshire SY11 3EW
Tel: 01691 773671
Fax: 01691 778552
e-mail: forsterj@moretonhall.com
website: www.moretonhall.org

Moreton Hall was founded in 1913 by Ellen Lloyd-Williams (Aunt Lil) in Oswestry and moved to its present location in 1920. In 1964, the school became an educational trust. Although the school is predominantly boarding, a number of day pupils are admitted each year.

Member of GSA, AGBIS, ISCO.

Governing Body:

Chairman: M N Mitchell, MA, ACIS

L A C Ashby, BA
R Auger, MA
G J Beasley
N Bevan, MA
Christine, Lady Bibby
Dr L V Boon, MBBS, LLCPMRS
D Edwards
Mrs J France-Hayhurst, LLB Hons
R Graham-Wood, MA, FRICS
Mrs K Neilson
Mrs D Rylands

***Principal*: J Forster**, BA, FRSA

Deputy Head (*Academic*): A Wilkinson, BSc
Head of Moreton First: Mrs S Grace, BA

Teaching Staff:
* *Head of Department*
† *Housemaster/mistress*

Mrs J Barlow, BA (*Special Needs Coordinator*)
N Blake, BSc (**Physics*)
Mrs J Cantrill, BSc (*Biology*)
G Collier, BSc (**Physical Education; Geography; †Charlesworth House*)
Mrs H Collier, BA (*Spanish/French; Head of Sixth Form; †Charlesworth House*)
T Davidson, MA (**English*)
Mrs G Denham, BEd (**Religious Education; †Lloyd Williams House*)
I Edwards, MA (**Art*)
Mrs L Eyre, BA (**French*)
Miss C Farris (*Lacrosse Coach*)
Mrs J Field, BEd (**Food and Textiles Technology*)
Mrs A Greaney, BA, MA (*French*)
Miss K Groves, BCom (*Physical Education*)
Mrs C Hadfield, BEd (*Mathematics*)
P Hillier, BSc, PhD (*ICT Coordinator; Biology*)
Miss S Hughes (*Religious Education*)
Miss S James (*Moreton First*)
Mrs J Knight, CertEd (*Drama*)
Mrs E Langford, BA (*Art*)
Mrs V Lewis, BA (*English*)
Mrs R McKechnie, MA (*Careers Advisor*)
Mrs J Morton, MA (**Latin*)
J Nanson, BA, MA (**Geography*)
Miss A Naylor, BA (*Moreton First*)
Mrs E Nolan, BA (*Librarian, Admin*)
T Nolan, BEd (*ICT*)
Mrs S Peat, BSc (**Mathematics*)
Mrs A Rincon (*Assistant †Charlesworth House*)
Miss H Roberts, BMus (*Assistant Director of Music*)
Mrs A Simpson, BA, MA (**Modern Languages*)
R Singleton, BSc (**Science*)
Mrs C Tilley, GRNCM (*Director of Music*)
Miss A Walker, BA (*Drama*)
A Wilkinson, BSc (*Chemistry*)
M Withington, BA (*Mathematics*)

Part-time:
Mrs C Ashworth, BEd (*Business Studies*)
Mrs S Bayton, DipEd (*Food Technology*)
Mrs K Booth, HND (*Business Studies*)
Mrs A Brown, BA, BEd (*Geography*)
Mrs S Champion, MSc, BSc (*Science/ICT*)
Mrs P M Forster, BA, DipLib (*Assistant Librarian; EFL*)
M J Hartley, MA, MEd (*Chemistry*)
Mrs K Hatcher, BA (*EFL*)
Mrs H Ingoldby, BA (*German*)
Mrs C Lapage, MA, BMus, ARCO (*Music*)
Mrs K M Malin, BA (*English, Drama*)
Mrs A J Matthews, BSc, MSc (*Economics*)
Miss H Prescott, BA (*English*)
Mrs J Sanderson, BEd (**Games, *Lacrosse*)
Mrs S Thomas, BSc (*Mathematics*)

School Doctors:
Dr J Roberts, BA, MA, BMBCH, MRCP, DRCOG, MRCGP, DFFP
Dr E Thompson, MBChB
School Sister: Sister A Tomley, SRN

Admission. Moreton First takes girls from Reception to Year 6, boys from Reception to Year 4.

Girls are admitted to Moreton Hall, normally in September at the age of 11 and 13, either by Common Entrance or by the School's entrance examination which is held at the end of January each year. This examination requires no knowledge of foreign languages and is designed to test potential ability rather than factual recall. This examination can be taken by pupils at 10+, and with supplementary papers at 12 and 13. Candidates from preparatory schools may enter through Common Entrance if they so choose at 11, 12 and 13. Sixth Form entrance is by examination and interview, and numbers are limited. All applications should be addressed to the Principal.

Scholarships. (*see Scholarship Entries section*). A number of scholarships worth up to 10% of fees will be made to pupils at 11+, 12+ and 13+. Students may apply for more than one scholarship. Means-tested bursaries may be awarded up to the value of 100% of fees. Sixth Form Scholarships and bursaries, given in memory of Miss Bronwen Lloyd-Williams, are awarded to girls entering Lower VI or to assist a pupil in the school to complete her education. Awards for Music, Drama, Art and for outstanding sporting talent are made at 11+, 12+, 13+ and 16+.

Fees per term (2007-2008). Boarders: £5,100 (Moreton First), £7,500 (Years 7 and 8), £7,950 (Years 9–13). Day Girls: £2,300–£3,100 (Moreton First), £5,900 (Years 7 and 8), £6,400 (Years 9–13).

Curriculum. Going well beyond the National Curriculum, some 20 subjects are available at GCSE, varying from traditional academic subjects such as Latin and the Sciences, to practical subjects such as Drama, Dance and Physical Education. Modern Languages available include French, German, Spanish and Russian. A Levels in History of Art, Social Biology, Business Studies and Theatre Studies extend the range of the curriculum. Information Technology is a compulsory subject up to Sixth Form, optional thereafter.

Examinations offered. GCSE (MEG, SEG, NEAB, London), A level (Oxford, JMB, London). ABRSM (English Speaking Board). Over three quarters of second year Sixth Form go on to University.

Religious activities. Non-denominational. Weekday service, longer service on Sunday, visiting preacher.

Academic, Sporting and Extra-Curricular facilities. Moreton Hall is engaged in an ambitious development programme and has facilities of the highest quality designed to provide the right environment for the education of girls in the twenty-first century.

Younger girls are housed in the Norton-Roberts building under the supervision of resident houseparents, assistants and matrons. The building is designed to create a family atmosphere with dormitories split into smaller units, close to common rooms, washrooms and staff accommodation.

As pupils progress up the school, the dormitories are gradually replaced by double and finally single study bedrooms, as girls move from middle school houses to the new Sixth Form House which provides single and double ensuite facilities. Here, within the structure of a boarding school, senior girls are given the necessary freedom to prepare for the next stage in their career.

The laboratories, Information Technology rooms and Art and Design Centre are housed within a short distance of the central classroom, careers and library complex.

In 1999 a new ICT development plan was implemented to network classrooms, libraries and laboratories linked to a new ICT Centre. In 2000 all classrooms, libraries and boarding houses were networked. All Sixth Formers have internet access from their study bedrooms.

An exceptionally well-equipped Sports Centre comprising a sports hall and floodlit tennis courts along with a heated swimming pool, tennis courts, nine-hole golf course, a new all-weather surface, and playing fields are set in one hundred acres of beautiful parkland at the foot of the Berwyn hills. The school offers a wide range of sporting options, including Lacrosse, Netball, Hockey, Cricket, Tennis and Athletics. Sailing and Riding are also popular.

The Musgrave Theatre, Outdoor Theatre and Music School stimulate theatrical and musical activities ranging from house plays, lunchtime shows and jazz evenings through to ambitious school plays and orchestral concerts. A full digital sound studio was completed in 2000. Great emphasis is placed on girls taking part in as wide a range of extra-curricular interests as possible.

Moreton Enterprises offers the girls real business experience. Supervised by professional advisers, Moreton Enterprises runs the tuckshop, payphones, Barclays Bank recording studio and radio station.

Boarding houses at Moreton Hall are all linked informally with houses at Shrewsbury School, pupils meeting regularly for social and cultural occasions.

A limited number of day girls are admitted each year.

Old Moretonian Association. Celia Jenkins, c/o Moreton Hall.

Charitable status. Moreton Hall Educational Trust Limited is a Registered Charity, number 528409. It exists to provide a high quality education for girls.

The Mount School

Milespit Hill Mill Hill London NW7 2RX
Tel: 020 8959 3403
Fax: 020 8959 1503
e-mail: admin@mountschool.com
website: www.mountschool.com

***Headteacher*: Mrs J K Jackson**, BSc London, PGCE, MA, FRSA
from January 2009: Ms C Cozens, BSc Exeter

Assistant Headteachers:
Mrs E Smith , BA London, PGCE, MA
Mrs J Smith, BSc Edinburgh (*RE*)

Mrs C Adams, BA Nottingham, PGCE (*History*)
Mrs A Allen, BEd Nonington (*Physical Education, Juniors*)
Mrs M Amankwah (*Reception Teacher*)
Mrs H Baneth, BA Sussex, PGCE (*Juniors*)
Ms J Bausor, BMus Hons RCM, PGDip RAM (*Junior Music*)
Ms J Berens, BA Hons, PGCE Sydney (*Juniors*)
Mrs G Bhagwanani (*Private Study Supervisor*)
Mr B Broadhurst, MA Cantab, PGCE (*Maths*)
Ms E Bush, BSc Hons Bristol, PGCE
Miss N Cahn, BA Hons, PGCE (*Drama*)
Mrs Z Carlos, BEd Slovakia (*Juniors*)
Miss L Carrington, BSc London, PGCE, Dip Psych (*Maths*)
Mrs C Collins, BA North London, CertEd (*Business Studies, Economics*)
Mrs M Corcoran, BEd Hons Hertfordshire (*Juniors*)
Mr R Davies, MA Hons Oxon (*English & Classics*)
Ms L Earley, BA Hons N London, CertEd
Miss A Ellam, BSc Nottingham, PGCE (*Chemistry, Physics*)
Miss K Ferson, BA Sussex, Dip TEFLA, MA (*ESOL*)
Ms T Fuller (*Juniors*)
Mr J Gonzales, BA Spain, PGCE Spain, Dip Speech & Language Spain (*Modern Languages*)
Miss S Green, CertEd, Dip CDT Middlesex (*DT, Textiles*)
Mrs E Grilli (*Classroom Assistant, Juniors*)
Mr Havardi, BA, MA, MPhil, BA, PGCE (*History*)
Mrs N Hirsch, BMus RCM, ARCM, PGCE (*Director of Music*)
Mrs C Hughes, MA Newcastle upon Tyne, PGCE (*English*)
Mr G Jones, BSc Kent, PGCE (*Chemistry*)
Mr T Klidzia, GMUS, PGCE (*Music, Psychology*)
Mrs A Lalova, MA Blagoevgrad, Bulgaria (*Maths, ICT*)
Mrs N Leach, Dip Montessori (*ESOL*)
Miss K Lingwood, BEd Liverpool (*Physical Education, PSHE&C*)
Mrs C McBeath, BA Manchester, PGCE (*Geography*)
Mr T Messom, BA Exeter, PGCE (*English*)
Mrs S Mitchell, BA John Moores, PGCE (*Art*)
Mrs C Mrozek, HND (*ICT*)
Mrs L Owen, BEd Nonington, RSA Dip (*Physical Education, Careers*)
Miss R Owen, BA Ed
Mrs A Paintin, BA Ed Hons New Zealand, Dip Teaching (*Primary*) (*Pre-Prep*)
Ms A Perez, BA Oviedo, Spain, CAP (*PGCE equivalent*)
Mrs L Phote (*Teaching Assistant*)
Mrs E Short, BA North London, PGCE (*French, Spanish*)
Mrs S Smith, BA UCNW Bangor (*German, Latin, Junior French*)
Mr J Sumray, BA Brighton (*Art*)
Miss J Sweeney, BSc London, BA Open, LLAM (*Juniors*)
Ms H Taguchi, BA Ed, Dip Japanese as a second language (*Japanese*)
Mr A Ward, BA Canberra, PGCE (*Science*)
Mrs H Warnock, BA Surrey, PGCE (*English*)

Visiting Music Staff:
Miss J Bausor (*Oboe, Head of Junior Music*)
Mrs C Emmanuel (*Violin*)
Miss L Keller (*Brass, Woodwind*)
Mrs A Leyland (*Voice*)
Mr R Mack (*Piano*)
Mrs M Noakes (*Cello*)
Mr T Punn (*Percussion*)
Ms E Rossiter (*Piano*)
Mr J Sparks, BA (*Guitar*)
Mr B Sydor (*Clarinet/Sax*)
Mrs H Philippou (*Ballet*)

Ancillary Staff:
Ms L Asante
Ms K Roddis
Mrs M Hollis
Ms C Nimmons
Mr A Roddis
Ms V Burton
Mr S Choyce

Administrative Staff:
Bursar: Mrs J Sanders
Finance Assistant: Mrs Z Akhtar
Finance Assistant: Mrs J Noakes
Management Accountant: Mrs H Stammers
Registrar: Mrs P Lewis
PA to Headmistress, School Secretary: (*to be appointed*)
Reprographics, Stationery, Homework Club: Mrs S Flaherty
Nurse: Ms P Dulley
Laboratory Technician: Mr M Cassidy
Laboratory Technician: Ms L Fiorenzo
Librarian: Mrs N Ransley
Caretaker: Mr C Choyce
Traffic Control Personnel: Mrs M Hollis
Traffic Control Personnel: Mrs P Rider
Chartwells Catering Manager: Mrs R Ghatora

The Mount School was founded by Mary McGregor in 1925 in Highgate and moved to Mill Hill in 1935. Miss McGregor's aim was to found a school where the personalities of the children could develop along wide and individual lines and where a true love of learning for its own sake could be fostered. The school motto is 'Esse quam videre' – 'to be rather than to seem to be'. We are a community of 400 girls aged 4–18. There are 100 girls aged 4–11 and 300 aged 11–18. This wide age range helps foster the family atmosphere of the school. We have a reputation for being a caring and friendly school and we work hard to make sure that this reputation is well founded. We offer small classes, lots of support and a wide range of co-curricular activities. All faiths are represented at the school and we value this opportunity for spiritual growth as we worship together and learn to understand and respect one another's cultures as well as deepening our understanding of our own.

Curriculum. We offer a well rounded academic environment for girls to develop their full potential, balancing intellectual growth with physical, emotional, cultural, spiritual, creative and moral growth enabling them to be able to make positive contributions as good citizens in all realms of their future lives.

The Early Years aims to encourage the love of learning through a very caring, creative and stimulating environment. The form teacher plans a carefully structured scheme of work for the majority of subjects; however music, singing, physical education, dance and religious education are taught by specialist teachers. Our concern is for the individual child and helping the girls develop their talents and interests. Small classes of girls who work cooperatively ensure good progress and a smooth transition to the Senior School. Year 6 are prepared for SATs and the Senior School Entrance Examination. Parents are kept well informed about their daughter's progress and are encouraged to take an interest in school activities.

Senior School: In Year 7 we have three forms of 20 girls. Every girl has an academic tutor who sees her two or three times a term to help set targets and discuss her study skills. There is a Year Head for each year and each form has a Sixth Form Friend who can help with any difficulties. The Head has an open door policy for all girls. There is a wide academic curriculum throughout Key Stage 3. The girls have a free choice of optional GCSE choices and the timetable block are made on the basis of the girls choices, in Science girls may choose to do three separate Sciences or the double award.

Sixth Form: The Sixth Form have their own block with an Internet Café and a room for relaxation which includes an air hockey table! Good use is made of our proximity to Central London for lectures and other visits. There is an active extension programme to provide a good well-rounded educational experience. We currently offer over 20 subjects at A Level.

Extra Curricular Activities. Regular expeditions are made to museum, galleries and other places of interest to supplement the courses of study. We go on trips abroad to supplement our language and classics courses as well as Ski trips and Water sports weekends. Clubs include: Chess, Band, Orchestra, Choirs, Drama, various sports, dance, creative writing, art, Japanese calligraphy and language, Euroclub, debates etc.

Fees per term (2008-2009). £2,800–£3,375.

Method of Entry. Between December and January we interview the first 30 children on the list for entry into Reception and choose girls who are ready for school. Junior children are assessed in the form that they hope to join. They are assessed in English and Mathematics and have a chance to find out whether they will enjoy the school. Senior School entrance examination is held on the second Monday in January. It is a straightforward test in English, Mathematics and Science based on the Key Stage 2 syllabus so it is equally fair to those from State Primary and Prep school. All girls are interviewed. The Mount School does well by sensitive able girls and those who are willing to work hard and participate fully in all aspects of school life.

We are very proud of our added value. This means that statistically any girl coming to The Mount School will do better at GCSE for her ability than if she chose to go elsewhere.

We also have an overseas department and we welcome applications from all nationalities.

Scholarships and Bursaries. Scholarships are awarded on the basis of the entrance examination and as a result of our internal year 9 tests. Sixth Form Scholarships are available for those with 8 or more A grades at GCSE. Sixth Form Bursaries are available to girls who have spent at least five years in the school.

Music Scholarships are available to pay for music tuition for girls with musical ability.

Old Scholars. There is an active Old Girls' association, including a branch in Tokyo.

Charitable status. The Mount School is a Registered Charity, number 312593. It exists to provide a high standard of education for girls.

The Mount School

York

Dalton Terrace York YO24 4DD
Tel: 01904 667500
Headmistress's PA: 01904 667508
Bursar: 01904 667504
Fax: 01904 667524
e-mail: head@mount.n-yorks.sch.uk
website: www.mountschoolyork.co.uk

Motto: *Fidelis in Parvo*

The Mount, a Quaker Girls' School dating from 1785, is a thriving boarding and day community where girls of all faiths and none are welcomed. The school's distinctive Quaker ethos is a major strength, which allows each pupil to be valued as an individual. Public examination results are evidence that Mount School staff are experts at teaching girls, with Medicine, Law, Engineering, Mathematics, Sciences, Arts and Humanities all popular choices for degree courses. The Mount stands in extensive and beautiful grounds close to York's historic centre.

Committee of Management:
Clerk: Danielle Palmour
Secretary: Julie Davis

Jean Asher	Teresa Killeen
Alison Baldwin	Michael Phipps
Susan Dickinson	Philip Green
James Geoghegan-Breen	Adam Sinclair
Elizabeth Grierson	Elisabeth Wilson
Judith Holding	Roger Pierce

Staff:

***Headmistress*: Diana J Gant**, BD Hons King's College, London, PGCE London

Deputy Head: Amanda Barrie, BA Hons Ravensbourne Coll, PGCE Goldsmiths

Director of Studies: Michael Lingard, MA Oxon, PGCE Bristol

Heads of Departments/Subjects:
English: Louise Williams, BA Hons Lancaster, PGCE Eltham College
Mathematics: Helen Mumby, BSc London, PGCE Durham
Modern Languages: Cherry Bailey, BA Hons Cantab, PGCE Sheffield
Latin, Greek and Classical Studies: A Rosemary McEvoy, BA Hons Lancaster, PGCE Nottingham
Science: Anthony Welbrock, BSc Hons Edinburgh
Religious Education: Linda Moore, BEd Hons Sussex, MA College of Ripon & York St John
History: Helen Snelson, BA Hons Oxon, MSc Hull, PGCE York
Geography: Carol Cook, BA Hons London, PGCE Newcastle upon Tyne
Art & Design: Sian Gabraitis, BA Hons Bristol, PGCE Cardiff
Design Technology: Rachel Milton, BA Hons, PGCE Coll of Ripon & York St John, MSc Huddersfield
IT: Amanda Barrie, BA Hons Ravensbourne Coll, PGCE Goldsmiths
Music: Derek Chivers, BA Hons York, DPhil Keele, PGCE Open University
Economics: Gwynneth Lewis, BSc UCW Aberystwyth, PGCE Leeds
Special Needs Coordinator: Vivien Moon, BA Hons, PGDipEd Sheffield
Sociology: Gerry Hallom, BA Hons York, PGCE Huddersfield
Psychology: Geoffrey Brookes, BEd, CertEd Cheltenham
PSHE: Vivien Moon, BA Hons, PGDipEd Sheffield
Physical Education: Rachel Blatchford, BSc Hons, PGCE Loughborough
Careers: Wendy A Thompson, CertEd Edge Hill College, Lancaster
English as an Additional Language: Jo Soden, MA York, BA Hons Bristol, PGCE York
Learning Support (*Dyslexia*): Ian Donaghy, BEd LMU Leeds

Librarian: Eileen Gamble, ALA Birmingham

Tregelles (Junior Department)

Head of Tregelles: Mary Anderson, CertEd Hull College of Education
Rachel Capper, BEd Hons Bretton Hall Coll (*Deputy Head and Head of Foundation Stage and Key Stage 1*)
Cheryl Snowden, BA Hons Lancaster, PGCE St Martins (*Deputy Head and Head of Key Stage 2*)
Nursery: Jan Wilson, BEd Durham, MA York

Housemistresses:
School House: Eliza Mellor, BA Hons Northumbria
College House: Kirsty Brien, BA Sheffield Hallam, PGCE Manchester

Health Centre:
Angela Wardale, SRN, SCM
Alison Oliver, SRN, SCM

Medical Officer: Dr Hazel Brown, BM, DRCOG

Administrative Staff:
Bursar: Julie Davis
Finance Officer: Jayne Copeland
Headmistress's PA: Norma Wright

Numbers on roll. 40 Boarding, 13 Weekly boarding, 180 Day.

Age range. 11–18.

Normal age of entry. 11, 13 or 16.

Method of Entry. Interview, School's own examination and former Head's report.

Curriculum and Aims. Wide basic curriculum – Arts, Languages, all Sciences, Mathematics. The School aims to provide a friendly ordered community in which girls learn to work hard, to recognise a sound set of values and to make the best use of their individual gifts.

Statement of Values:

The Mount School and Tregelles encourages everyone to:

- think and live adventurously
- respect and value every individual
- grow in a calm and caring community
- strive for personal excellence

and

- make a difference in a changing world

Extra subjects (in addition to a wide curriculum). *Crafts*: eg ceramics, textiles, photography. *Dancing*: as required. *Languages*: eg Spanish. *Music*: piano, brass, strings, wind (Associated Board examinations). *Speech and Drama*: LAMDA examinations. *Sports*: eg fencing, riding and judo.

Facilities. The School has excellent facilities in all areas; subjects are taught in specialist rooms with full access to modern technology. Excellent computer facilities are accessible to pupils in and out of normal school hours. Set in 16 acres of gardens and games fields, with a 25m indoor swimming pool, multi-purpose sports hall and fitness suite, grass tennis courts.

Fees per term (2008-2009). Senior School (Years 7–13): Boarders £6,840; Weekly Boarders £6,450; Day £4,400.

Additional charges are made for private lessons, craft materials, external examination fees, outside lectures and concerts. Further details about registration, offers of places and Awards may be obtained from the Admissions Secretary.

Tregelles Junior Department: £2,650 Juniors (7 to 11 years); £1,995 Infants (4 to 7 years); £1,750 Nursery class. Government Nursery Vouchers are accepted in part payment.

Composition Fees Scheme. Parents are encouraged to consider paying School Fees by lump sum in advance. This can generate considerable reductions in the overall cost. The acceptance of a Composition Fee Payment is not a guarantee that a place can be offered at the appropriate time, but such payments are normally transferable between schools. Composition Fees may be accepted at any time prior to the probable date of entry and may be supplemented by additional payments either prior to or during the child's schooling. Further particulars are available from the Bursar.

Scholarships. (*see Scholarship Entries section*). Academic and Music Scholarships at 11, 13 and 16.

Means-tested bursaries are also available. Children of members of the Society of Friends are charged according to parental income.

Anniversary Scholarships, celebrating our 175th Anniversary, are available to maintained school pupils and are subject to a means-tested assessment.

Year 9 Scholarships are available in Science, Art and Design, Mathematics, Modern Languages, Music, English, Humanities and Drama.

Mount Old Scholars' Association. *Hon Secretary*: Elizabeth Morgan, via The Mount School, York.

Tregelles, which is the Co-educational Junior Department for day children aged 3 to 11 years, shares the ethos of the Senior School, to encourage and develop the potential of the individual. There is a creative and stimulating learning environment which promotes the exploration of skills and the development of confidence. Academic standards are high and progress is carefully observed.

Charitable status. The Mount School, York is a Registered Charity, number 513646. It exists to provide education for girls from 3 to 18 and junior boys.

New Hall School

Boreham Chelmsford Essex CM3 3HS
Tel: 01245 467588
Fax: 01245 464348
e-mail: registrar@newhallschool.co.uk
website: www.newhallschool.co.uk

***Principal*: Mrs K Jeffrey**, MA Oxon, PGCE Surrey, BA Div PUM, MA EdMg OU, NPQH

Head of Preparatory School:
Mrs S Conrad, BA, PGCE Dunelm

Vice-Principals:
Mrs J Hopkinson, BSc Hons London, QTS
Mrs L Moule, BA Hons Manchester, PGCE Liverpool
Mrs R Owens, MA Oxon, PGCE Open

Bursar: Mrs J Crame, BSc Leeds, ACA, PGCE Mid-Essex

Heads of Academic Departments:

Religious Studies:
Miss K Edwards, BA UEA, PGCE Liverpool

English:
Mrs A Harris, BA Hons Nott, MPhil Nott, PGCE Nott

Mathematics:
Mr C Tye, BSc Hons London, DipMathMan, MA

Information Technology:
Mrs L Fletcher, BSc Surrey

History:
Mrs C Wren, BA Hons Warwick, PGCE Cambridge, MHist Warwick

Geography:
Mr J Sidwell, BSc Hons Loughborough, PGCE London

Modern Languages:
Mrs N Smart, MA Glasgow, PGCE

Classical Studies:
Ms I Peace, BA Hons Durham, PGCE Cambridge

Sciences:
Mr J Rubery, BEd, CertEd Birmingham (*Head of Science*)
Dr A Wheadon, BSc Leicester, PhD Leicester, PGCE Aberystwyth, MRSC (*Head of Chemistry*)
Mr M Fradley, MPhys Southampton, PGCE Cambridge (*Head of Physics*)

Music:
Mr A Fardell, BA Kent, LRAM

Drama:
Mrs K Wimsett, BA Surrey, Dip Tchg Waikato, Dip LAMDA, AISTD

Art, Design & Technology:
Ms D Colchester, DipAD Kent, ATD Liverpool

Careers:
Mrs J Bignold, BA OU, CertLib Wales

Learning Development:
Mrs J Fawdry, BSc Hull, PGCE London, PGDip SpLD, AMBDA

Physical Education:
Mr S Winsor, BEd Hons Cheltenham & Gloucester (*Director of Sport*)
Miss M Gibney, BSc Hons, PGCE Loughborough (*Head of Girls' PE*)

Pastoral Care:

Housemasters/Housemistresses:
More House: Miss K Fox, MA Cantab, BA Hull, QTS
Priory House: Mr T Owens, BA Dunelm, PGCE Dunelm
Hawley House: Mrs C Mingham, CertEd Kent
Campion House: Miss L Kerbey, BA Lampeter
Earle House: Mr A Sweeney, BA Ulster, PGCE Liverpool

Heads of School:
Sixth Form: Miss H Kiernan, BA Oxon, PGCE Surrey
Upper School Girls: Mrs N Cooper, BA Oxon, BSc OU, PGCE London
Upper School Boys: Mr G Bickersteth, BA Hons Manchester, PGCE Reading
Middle School Girls: Mrs J McGlynn
Middle School Boys: Mr P Howson, BA Hons Plymouth, QTS Dartford, AST Westminster

Chaplaincy: Mrs J Hopkinson, BSc Hons London, QTS

Medical Department:
Medical Officer: Dr M Edelsten, MBChB
School Nurse: Mrs J Kavanagh

New Hall Voluntary Service:
Chairman: Mrs J Hopkinson, BSc Hons London, QTS

Pupil numbers. Senior School (11–18): 533 (Day 357, Boarding 176). Preparatory School (3–11): 314.

A Broad and Balanced Curriculum. Students benefit from a broad and rigorous curriculum and the opportunity to engage in a wide range of extra-curricular activities that enrich their learning. To prepare them for a fast-changing world we introduce students to a wide range of concepts, skills and knowledge.

New Technology. Changes in the world of work mean that it is important that every student is competent in the use of technology. The school has recognised this and has an ongoing programme of investment in state-of-the-art equipment. A new Technology Centre opened in November 2007 with a workshop, digital design suite (including 3D laser printer) and a separate purpose-built food room. The library is a multimedia resource centre and is open to students late into the evening and throughout the weekend. Here students can learn to use periodicals, to skim and scan books and to extract information from a variety of sources.

First-Class Facilities. These currently include: 8 laboratories for Science; 7 Information Technology suites as well as the provision of computers in departments; laptops for all teachers; a purpose-built Performing Arts centre, including Dance, Music and Drama facilities and a recording studio; Art & Design studios. Sports facilities include a 6-lane 25m indoor swimming pool; a well-equipped gymnasium; a sports hall; ten floodlit hard courts for tennis and netball; three pitches used for hockey and athletics; cricket and rugby pitches; a floodlit Astroturf; national standard running track; cricket wickets.

A Community of Faith. At the heart of our foundation lies the faith that is essential to the character of the school. The school is a Catholic community and welcomes all those who are in support and value its ethos.

The Performing Arts. Many students enjoy the creative arts and benefit from the talents they can develop in this area. Our modern purpose-built Performing Arts centre, Walkfares, allows students to participate in Music, Drama and Dance within the curriculum and also outside the classroom. Many leisure-time activities take place in Walkfares. Choirs, instrumental groups and ensembles meet regularly to perform all kinds of music from the Blues to Mozart. Students can film and record their performances in the school's own recording studio. New Hall runs drama workshops for all ages and many of these lead to public performances ranging from major productions to small studio plays. In addition to timetabled Dance lessons, students can enjoy lessons in Ballroom, Jazz, Contemporary, Tap and Ballet. The Performing Arts faculty works as an integrated unit and many activities will combine elements of all three areas: Dance, Drama and Music.

Clubs and Interest Groups. School societies and clubs abound at New Hall. The school caters for every interest from the historical to the scientific, and from public speaking to computer design. For students who enjoy Art, there is the opportunity to be creative with pottery, fabric work, sculpture and painting. The school's darkroom allows students to pursue an interest in photography. Students can improve their language skills by watching carefully selected foreign television and videos.

Activities. At weekends both Boarders and Day Students can enjoy the many activities organised within the Houses and use all of the facilities on the campus. They can also take part in visits run by the Entertainment Society. The school's location close to London (Chelmsford to Liverpool Street Station, London, is 32 minutes) and the motorway system make it possible for New Hall to arrange visits to historic, cultural and recreational sites. Many foreign students particularly appreciate the chance to see more of England.

Day Students. Day Students and Boarders are fully integrated as members of one of five Houses in the Senior School. We encourage them to stay for tea and to join in the wide range of activities on offer after lessons. The school provides a supervised study room where they can complete their homework. Many travel to school on the daily coaches.

Boarding. For Boarders, the school becomes their home away from home. New Hall provides an environment where friendships flourish and students enjoy companionship and security. The House staff recognise their special responsibility for those who do not have daily contact with their parents. They do their utmost to guide and direct those in their care. Boarding can provide a stable and secure education for students whose schooling would otherwise be interrupted. It is the logical answer for parents living overseas. Many students who live locally also opt for boarding as it can provide a valuable experience of living with others. Students gain confidence and maturity and build lifelong friendships. Boarders in all Year Groups may have their own modern study-bedrooms.

Flexi-boarding. By staying in the Boarding House for one, two or three nights a week, students can benefit from the school facilities, strengthen friendships and learn to be more independent and organised. Maximum contact is maintained with home. This can be a good introduction to boarding life and can lead to full boarding as the student matures.

An International Community. We welcome a number of students of other nationalities at New Hall. Students enjoy the diversity to be found within the community. Living alongside students from other countries offers all students the chance to learn from the richness of other cultures. The teaching of English as an Additional Language is available to support and encourage students from overseas. The extra assistance we provide helps these students to integrate quickly into mainstream classes and to enjoy their stay in the UK.

Service to others. The New Hall Voluntary Service (NHVS) responds to the needs of the local community. Sixth Form volunteers lead the action groups. Students come to appreciate the needs of a variety of people – the elderly, the handicapped, the lonely and the terminally ill. They become aware of the importance of commitment, dependability and service. NHVS has won a number of national awards for its charitable work over 26 years.

Visits, Expeditions and Events. Many older students join the Duke of Edinburgh's Award Scheme. The award aims to develop young people not only physically and mentally, but socially as well. Service to the local community is therefore a vital component of this scheme. Students attend courses such as those given by the Fire Service and the Police. They develop initiative and a spirit of adventure on the highly enjoyable expeditions to untamed areas of the country.

We foster many social and educational contacts with other schools. This leads to debates, workshops, competitions at regional and national levels and special occasions including the annual Ball. Social opportunities also include mixed choirs, discos, field trips and combined religious events.

Our staff arrange many overseas visits which take place during half-term and the holidays. These reflect the broad range of interests nourished at New Hall. Recent trips have included choir tours to Italy, the study of business in Prague, art in Paris, classical antiquities in Tunisia, history in Russia and skiing in the Alps. There are language exchanges with schools in France, Germany and Spain as well as European work experience for older students.

Careers and Higher Education. The school gives expert guidance to students preparing for university and the world of work. There is a programme for guidance led by the Head of Careers and the Tutors. Students benefit from comprehensive, up-to-date information on education, training and employment opportunities. The school recognises that students need a variety of knowledge, work experience and specialist support in order to make informed choices. The school is a member of the Independent Schools Careers Organisation (ISCO).

Fees per term (2008-2009). Senior School: Day £4,520–£4,820; Boarding £6,140–£7,270.

Preparatory School: Day £2,350–£3,500, Boarding (from age 8) £4,770–£5,270.

Entry requirements. Own entrance papers, plus reports, and if possible interview. Further information on the curriculum and a copy of the prospectus is available from the Registrar.

Scholarships. (*see Scholarship Entries section*). Details about Scholarships can also be obtained from the School.

Charitable status. New Hall School Trust is a Registered Charity, number 1110286. Its aim is the education of children within a Christian environment.

The Newcastle upon Tyne Church High School

Tankerville Terrace Jesmond Newcastle-upon-Tyne NE2 3BA
Tel: 0191 281 4306
Fax: 0191 281 0806
e-mail: info@churchhigh.com
website: www.churchhigh.com

Motto: *Vincit Omnia Veritas*
Founded in 1885.

Governing Body:
President: The Lord Bishop of Newcastle

Governors:
Chairman: Mr P Buchan
The Reverend D R J Holloway
Mrs S Jacques
Dr R Plummer
The Rt Revd Paul Richardson
Mrs S Stobart
Dr B Tasker
Mrs H Tavroges-Huner
Mr M Thompson

Executive Group:

***Headmistress*: Mrs J Gatenby**, BA Dunelm, PGCE

Deputy Headmistress: Mrs A Roe, BA Newcastle, PGCE

Headmistress of Junior School: Miss J A Cunningham, BPhil Newcastle

Bursar: Mr P J Keen, FCCA

Assistant Head (Sixth Form and Marketing): Mrs J Grundy, BEd Huddersfield, CIM Diploma

Teaching Staff:
Mrs K Aarvold, BSc Hons Edgehill, PGCE
Miss K Bailey, BA Hons Durham, PGCE
Mrs E Barnett, BEd Hons Northumbria
Mrs A Box, Bristol, PGCE
Mrs P A Breakey, BEd Roehampton Institute of FE
Mrs J Brown, BEd Hons Leeds Metropolitan
Miss S E Carolan, MA Glasgow, PGCE
Ms C Chambers, PGCE Nottingham
Miss C Chapman, MA Hons Aberdeen, PGCE, Telematics Cert NCFE
Mrs D Chipchase, PGD
Mrs D Colwell, BEd Hons Sheffield
Mrs L F Crawford, BSc Edinburgh, PGCE
Mrs K Cuthbertson, Reading PGCE
Mrs J Evans BA Hons Leicester PGCE
Ms R M A Everton, BA Hons, MA Newcastle
Mrs R Fairless, TCert
Mrs P Y Farrin, MSc Newcastle, PGCE
Mr J L Fleck, BA Oxon, PGCE
Miss K Fraser, BA Hons Northumbria, PGCE
Mr T Gaughan, BSc Manchester,PGCE
Miss R Gee, BA Hons London, CertEd
Mrs J Gordon, TCert
Miss H Hall, BSc Hons Leicester, PGCE
Mrs A Hardie, BA Hons Oxford, PGCE
Mrs S M Harris, BSc Hons Newcastle, PGCE
Mrs H Harrison, Newcastle, PGCE
Miss D Hefford, PGCE Northumbria
Mr D Hyde, Durham, PGCE
Mr K Jones, BSc Hons Newcastle
Mrs J Kirkham, BEd Bath
Mrs L Kitto, BA Hons Manchester
Mrs G Macdonald, BEd Hons Newcastle
Mrs B Mayhew, BA Newcastle, PGCE
Ms F Merrick, PGCE Durham
Mrs M Michie, BA Hons Leeds PGCE
Mrs A J Morgan, MA Newcastle, DipEd
Mrs C Oliver, MA Hons Institute of Linguists, PGCE
Miss J Ornsby, BA Hons London
Mrs C Packham, BSc Birmingham, PGCE
Mrs L Parry, BA Hons Birmingham, PGCE
Dr D P Raymond, BSc, PhD Cardiff, CChem, PGCE
Mrs J Rollings, TCert
Mr R Simpson, CertEd Durham
Mrs H Temperley, BA Hons Newcastle Polytechnic
Mrs J K Thew, BA Hons Durham, PGCE
Miss H Thomsen, BA Hons Durham
Mrs S Timney, BEd Hons Newcastle, FRSA
Mr J G Wells, BA Hons Trent Poly, Slade UCL, PGCE
Miss J Wrighton, BSc Hons London, PGCE

Administrative Staff:
School Secretary: Mrs M Cowell
Junior School Secretary: Mrs K Murdoch
Bursar's Assistant: Mrs B Cavanagh
Secretary: Mrs L Ferguson
Secretary: Mrs L Watson
IT Systems Manager: Mr S Farrell
IT Systems Administrator: Mr D Cocallis

Ancillary Staff:
School Nurse: Mrs S Leighton
Classroom Assistant: Mrs S Glover, BA Hons Durham
Nursery Nurse: Mrs J Goodwill
Reprographics Technician: Mrs J Kirkup
Senior Laboratory Technician: Mrs L Lant
Art Technician: Ms Z Robinson
Site Manager & Cleaning Manager: Mr G Qeku
Assistant Site Manager: Mr W Ewing
Nursery Nurse: Mrs K Salkeld

Joy Gatenby, Headmistress at Church High School in Newcastle says, "What always impresses me is that when visitors come to the school, without exception, they comment on the warm, welcoming atmosphere and the confidence shown by our girls."

Church High incorporates all stages of schooling for girls, from Nursery through to Sixth Form. Established in 1885, many of the values adopted by the school back then are still prevalent today. There has always been a great emphasis placed on developing the individual and ensuring that each child achieves their full potential in every sense. You only have to meet one of Church High's Sixth Formers to realise that the school continues to be very successful in producing its end product – articulate, mature young women who are quietly confident and understand how to achieve their personal objectives. The school remains true to its strong ethos of developing strong moral values and equipping girls to deal with the modern world.

The excellent pastoral care at Church High is widely recognised and girls know that they are going to get that individual support and the attention that they need to develop academically and personally. Parents, too, are secure in this knowledge.

The school is large enough to offer a really challenging learning environment and strong sense of community throughout each year group, but small enough to ensure every girl is known to staff as an individual. It means all their needs really can be met and that produces something quite special.

The success of this support and encouragement is reflected in the grades attained by the pupils, which surpass external benchmark predictions. The school has many strengths and in recent years has achieved top marks in the country at GCSE for Religious Studies, English Literature, and Home Economics. Art, Music, Drama and Sport are also highly valued here and the wide range of subjects available in the Sixth Form reflects changing demand. Subjects such as Theatre Studies, Psychology, Dance and Sports Studies are offered alongside the more traditional A Level subjects.

The school is very forward looking and is open to change. Our aim is to send out into the world young girls with the attributes that are necessary for them to lead successful lives.

A Church High education, then, is about more than just academic excellence. We care for, nurture and develop student's whole potential in a challenging and stimulating learning environment. A Church High girl is prepared for all aspects of life and supported to realise her personal ambitions.

Primary messages:

- Our academic results at all levels and abilities are outstanding – in a mixed ability community where the individual really does matter, the most able girls achieve the very best academic results and all our girls achieve grades well above those predicted by external benchmarking.
- Church High has one of the highest staff to pupil ratios in the region. We pride ourselves on being small enough to know and care for each child individually, yet large enough to offer girls a broad, stimulating and appropriate range of academic and extra-curricular activities and support.

Secondary messages:

- The Church High community is made up of a strong network of happy, confident, motivated students, enthusiastic, dedicated staff and a well informed body of parents and governors. We work together to create the best possible academic and personal opportunities for our students in a caring, family-orientated environment.
- A Church High girl is a happy, confident girl. She is nurtured and cared for in an accepting environment by dedicated staff, committed to student's wellbeing. We believe a happy child is more receptive to learning opportunities and able to fulfil and exceed their full potential, both academically and personally.

- Church High girls are taught and cared for in a single-sex environment. We support them to grow, develop and focus both personally and academically, at their own pace, without the natural distractions and pressures a mixed-sex educational environment can create.

Fees per term (2008-2009). Nursery £1,530 (full time), Kindergarten £1,816, Junior School £2,327, Senior School £3,073.

Reduced fees for daughters of Clergy. Registration fee £20.

Scholarships. (*see Scholarship Entries section*).

Charitable status. The Newcastle upon Tyne Church High School is a Registered Charity, number 528151.

North London Collegiate School

Canons, Canons Drive, Edgware, Middlesex HA8 7RJ
Tel: Senior School: 020 8952 0912
Junior School: 020 8952 1276
Fax: 020 8951 1391
e-mail: office@nlcs.org.uk
website: www.nlcs.org.uk

North London Collegiate School has provided an outstanding education for girls since its foundation in 1850 by Frances Mary Buss.

Named "Independent School of the Year" by *The Sunday Times* in 1999 and again in 2006, this unique school is distinctive in several ways: it is a large London day school set in 30 acres of beautiful country estate; it has a stunning academic record offering a choice of A Levels or the International Baccalaureate in the Sixth Form; and it runs a comprehensive extra-curricular programme, now enhanced by the opening of its state-of-the-art, 350-seat Performing Arts Centre.

The Governing Body:
Ms H Stone, OBE, BSc, CEng, FICE, FRSA (*Chairman*)

Mr J Allen, FRICS
Mr N Carrington
Professor J Drew, BA, MPLT, PLD, d.CIT, PGCE, DipEA, FRSA, FSRHE (*Imperial College London nominee*)
Mrs C Froomberg, MA, FCMA
Dr L Goldman, BA, MA, PhD (*University of Oxford nominee*)
Ms L Hill, BSc, MBA
Mrs S James, BA, JD
Mr S N Kamath, BCom, FCMA
Dr M Mays, BA, MA, PhD (*University of Cambridge nominee*)
Dr D Popplewell, MA, MB, BChir Cantab, MRCP
Mr L Rabinowitz, QC
Mrs E A Raperport, BA, FCT
Mr D Shah, BSc, ACA
Mr M V Sternberg, MA, LLM
The Hon Charles Wigoder, BA, ACA

Bursar and Clerk to the Governors: Mr Graham Partington

***Headmistress*: Mrs Bernice McCabe**, BA, MBA, FRSA

Deputy Headmistress:
Mrs B J Pomeroy, BSc Nottingham

Deputy Head:
Mr J J Morrow, MA Oxon, MA Wake Forest, North Carolina

Head of Sixth Form: Mrs H A Turner, MA Cantab

Director of Studies and Administration (IB Coordinator):
Mr M Burke, BA Newcastle, MA Durham

Marketing & Development Director:
Mr R M C Kitt, BA Durham, MA London

Head of Upper School:
Mrs M A Fotheringham, MA Oxon

Head of Middle School:
Mrs P S Tabraham, CertEd Liverpool

Head of Junior School:
Mrs J M Newman, BEd Cantab

Director of University Admissions:
Mrs K Hedges, MA Cantab

Careers Advisor: Miss E Duggan, BA Dublin

Heads of Academic Departments:

Religious Studies: Mrs A Wilson, MA London

English: Mr D James-Williams, MA London

Drama: Mr D Lewis, BA Monash, Australia

History and Government & Politics:
Miss C Thompson, BA Exeter

Geography: Miss M Wheatley, BSc London

Economics: Mrs G Hurl, BSc Liverpool, MSc London

Classics: Mr M Shoults, MA Oxon

Modern Languages and Spanish:
Mr M English, BA Oxon, MA Liverpool

German: Miss M Wenham, BA Oxon

French: Mrs J Seth, BA Manchester

Russian: Mrs T Kinsey, BA Tver

Mathematics: Mrs J F Huntly, BSc Leicester

Science: Mr E Nicol, BSc Strathclyde

Biology: Miss K Fleming, BSc Manchester

Chemistry: Mr J E Nicol, BSc London

Physics: Mr A P Wingfield, MA Oxon

Information Technology: Dr A P Cripps, PhD London

Art and Design: Mr T Hardy, BA Middlesex

Music: Mr L D Haigh, BMus Edin

Physical Education: Mrs G James, CertEd Liverpool

Assistant to the Headmistress: Miss N Carter, BA Surrey

The pupil teacher ratio is 11:1

North London Collegiate School combines the beauty and space of a rural setting with the convenience of being only a short distance from the heart of London. The school provides an ambitious education for girls from a wide range of social backgrounds. The very best of academic teaching is coupled with the widest range of extra-curricular activities to help the pupils fulfil their potential.

There are 1,057 girls at North London Collegiate School: approximately 120 in the First School, aged from 4+ to 7, 180 juniors, aged from 7–11, and 760 in the Senior School, 11–18, of whom 230 are in the Sixth Form.

North London Collegiate School draws on a rich tradition. It was founded by Miss Frances Mary Buss in 1850 to provide an education for girls that would equal that of boys and produced many of the first women graduates.

The school's academic record is outstanding. It has been named as *The Sunday Times* "Independent School of the Year 2006" and *The Daily Telegraph* has described it as the most consistently successful academic girls' school in the country. Results in 2007 were again consistent with the school's academic profile. 99.3% of A levels were A and B grades, placing the school first in national rankings in terms of A grades for the third time in 10 years.

For the second year the school has maintained it's top position as the leading International Baccalauriate school in the UK, with 100% of IB Diploma results graded 7,6 (equivalent to A grade) or 5 (equivalent to B grade), with an average score of 41. One student achieved a "perfect score" of 45 points – only achieved by approximately 50 students out of over 30,000 worldwide each year.

Over a third of the year group went to Oxbridge (44).

The GCSE results were equally outstanding, with the school ranked in the top 3 again in the national press league tables, with a "best ever" 97.4% of grades at A*/A.

The facilities at the school are first class, designed to offer the girls every opportunity to develop themselves both academically and socially. These facilities include lacrosse pitches, all-weather tennis courts and a Sports Centre with indoor swimming pool and fitness centre.

A new Performing Arts Centre opened in Spring 2007, with a 350-seat auditorium, orchestra pit, galleries and rehearsal rooms. Music and Drama are strong, with opportunity for all to take part in productions, choirs and orchestras. The music programme includes challenging pieces for the most able, with such events as the National Chamber Group competition where the school has won the Founder's Trophy as the most successful competing school on several occasions. On the campus are a Music School, Drawing School and Design Technology Block, all situated around the lake, where waterlilies in the summer make it the ideal place to relax during the long lunch interval. Alternatively, girls may visit the beautifully light and spacious four-floor library.

There is an extensive school coach scheme.

Full details of Open Days and "School in Action" Days are on the website, www.nlcs.org.uk. Midweek visits can be arranged by appointment. Please contact 020 8952 0912 to arrange a visit.

Bursaries. A number of bursaries are offered to girls who do well in the 11+ test and those entering the Sixth Form, whose parents can demonstrate financial need.

Scholarships. (*see Scholarship Entries section*).

Fees per term (2008-2009). Senior School: £3,975; Junior School: £3,372.

Charitable status. The North London Collegiate School is a Registered Charity, number 1115843. It exists to provide an academic education for girls.

Northampton High School (GDST)

Newport Pagnell Road Hardingstone Northampton NN4 6UU

Tel: 01604 765765
01604 667979 Junior School
Fax: 01604 709418
e-mail: nhsadmin@nhs.gdst.net
website: www.gdst.net/northamptonhigh

One of the 29 schools of The Girls' Day School Trust. For further information about the Trust, see p. xxiv.

Local Governing Body:
Mrs E Kelly (*Chairman*)
Lady S North (*Trust representative*)
Mrs M Adams
Mr M Brown
Mrs R Eden, MBE
Mr R M J Fountain (*Vice-Chairman*)
Dr S D Gregory
Mrs D Hodgkinson
Mrs J Howell Williams
Mrs S Moody
Mr C Oliver
Mrs C Pearce
Mr R Pinnock
Mrs A Rowe
Mrs D Runchman
Mrs A Tate

Staff:
‡ *Holder of Teacher's Certificate or Diploma*
§ *Part-Time*

***Head Mistress*: Mrs S A Dixon**, BA Hons Warwick (*English*)

Deputy Heads:
‡Miss S Casson, MA Edinburgh (*Latin*)
‡Mrs L Davies, BA Sheffield (*German/French*)

Miss J Ainsworth, MA Cambridge (*Classics*)
‡Mrs J Allen, BA Birmingham (*History*)
‡Mrs C Allison, BEd Cheltenham (*Physical Education*)
‡Mr W Asbury, BSc Sheffield (*Physics*)
‡Mrs K Attridge, BA Leicester (*Design Technology*)
Mr R Attwood, BSc Leeds (*Biology*)
§Mr D Balazik, CertEd Manchester (*Design Technology*)
§Mrs S Battams, BSc Nottingham (*Physics*)
‡Mrs M Beacroft, BA Northumbria (*Art*)
‡§Mrs E Bevan, BSc Loughborough (*Physical Education*)
‡Mrs R Boyce, BA Lancaster (*German/French*)
‡Miss G Brindley, BA Central England, MA (*Music*)
Miss A Buxton, BALib Wolverhampton/Cumbria (*Librarian*)
Dr N Carr, BSc (*Chemistry*)
‡Mr G Chamberlain, BSc Hull (*Geography*)
‡Mrs D Claridge, BEd Manchester (*Physical Education*)
‡Mrs J Coupland, MA Oxford (*French and German*)
Mrs C Courtheoux-Allison (*French*)
‡Mrs K Cowell, BEd Birmingham (*Mathematics*)
‡Mr R Cox, BA Open (*Biology*)
‡Miss L Cramp, BA Bangor (*English*)
‡Mrs J Davis, CertEd Ilkley College (*Food, Textiles & Design Technology*)
‡Mrs J Drew, BA Cardiff (*Music*)
‡Mrs G Drinkwater, BSc, BA, MSc Leeds (*Mathematics*)
‡Mrs J Edge, BA, DipEd Cardiff (*English*)
‡Mrs S Ellam, BSc London (*Mathematics*)
‡Mrs S Emmins, BA Leeds, MBA (*French, German and Russian*)
Mrs C Fieldhouse, BA, PGDip, CertEd Northampton College/Hertfordshire Theatre School (*Drama*)
‡Mr J Glover, BA London (*Religious Education*)
§Mrs G M Gray, BA, MA London (*English*)
‡Mrs A Halstead, BA London (*English*)
‡§Mrs K Harrison, BA Lancaster (*Mathematics*)
‡Mrs J Hennessy, BA Leicester (*Art*)
‡Mrs D Hill, BA Leeds (*French*)
‡Mrs H Hill, BA Kent (*History*)
‡Mr T Hoddle, BA London (*Computer Education*)
‡Mr T Holden, BA Birmingham (*Spanish*)
‡Mr J Holland, BA Leicester, MA Hertford, MSc Cambridge (*Classics*)
Mrs S L Holland, MA Oxon (*Latin, Greek, Classical Civilisation, History*)
Miss C Hurst, BA Brighton, QTS (*Physical Education*)
‡Mrs R Hymers, BSc Bradford (*Economics*)
Mrs J Jackson, CertEd Hull (*Physical Education*)
‡Mrs C Jacobs, BSc Birmingham (*Chemistry*)
Mrs G Jones, MA St Andrew's (*English*)
Mrs J Kingham, BSc Leicester (*ICT*)
‡Mrs S Lamb, MA (*Religious Education*)
‡Mrs M Langhorn, BSc Coventry (*Geography/Economics*)
Mr Laubscher, BA South Africa (*Art*)
Mrs Laubscher, BSc South Africa (*Mathematics*)
‡Mrs J Leech, BA, MA Oxford (*French*)
‡Mrs R Littlewood, BEd Liverpool (*Physical Education*)
‡Mrs K Loughney, BSc Portsmouth (*Mathematics*)
‡Mrs J M Lumb, BA Coventry (*French, Spanish*)

‡Ms S Margareto, BA, DipEd Macquarie, Sydney (*Special Needs*)
‡Mrs A Mayhew, BSc London (*Biology*)
Mrs S Moss, BEd Keele (*Home Economics*)
‡§Mrs E Pearson, MSc Birmingham (*Biology/Science*)
‡Mrs R Pointer, BSc York (*Chemistry*)
Miss L Roberts, MA Leicester (*English*)
‡Mrs J Rydon, BSc Newcastle-upon-Tyne (*Design Technology*)
Miss L Swift, BA Bishop Grosseteste Univ College (*Drama*)
‡§Mrs I Tansley, BA Hons Kingston (*Business Studies*)
Mrs C Turner, BSc Nottingham (*Physics*)
Mrs P Warford, BA, MA Northampton (*Art*)
Mrs C White, BSc Nottingham (*Mathematics*)
‡§Mr D Wright, BA (*English*)

Junior School:

Headmistress: ‡Mrs W Nugent, BSc Leicester

Deputy Headmistress: ‡Mrs K Allport, BA Kent

Assistant Deputy Head of Junior School: Mrs J Purvey-Tyrer, BEd Leeds

‡Mrs J Arrowsmith, BEd Sheffield
Mrs C Bleech, BSc Bristol
‡Mrs J Cooper, BA Nottingham
‡Mrs S Dadge, BA Warwick
§Mrs A Davis, OGCE University College Ripon and York
Mr M Francis-Scott, BA Hons College of St Mark & St John, MA Surrey
‡Mrs L Green, BA Manchester Polytechnic
Mrs H Greenbank, BEd Plymouth
Mrs A Love, BEd Southampton and Salisbury College of Education
Miss K Marson, BEd Nene College Northampton
Miss S Mayes, BA Surrey
Mrs C Meanwell, CertEd University College Northampton
‡Mrs C Miller, GTCL Trinity College of Music, London
‡Mrs S Norris, BEd Girton College, Cambridge
‡Mrs E Parry, CertEd Kirkby Fields College of Education, Liverpool
‡Mrs R Platt, CertEd Milton Keynes College of Education
‡Mrs H Russell, MA Aberdeen
‡Mrs O Schumskij, CertEd St Paul's College, Rugby
‡Mrs E Shaw, BEd Newman College, Birmingham
Mrs R Smith, BA North East London Polytechnic
‡Mrs J Stock, BEd Newland Park College
‡Mrs J Stone, BA Canterbury Christ Church College
Miss N Taylor, BSc Bristol

Headmistress's Secretary: Mrs D Brown

Peripatetic Instrumental Staff:
Miss K Bickerdike, BMus Hons, DPS, PGDip (*Viola*)
Miss F Brannon, BMus (*Flute, Recorder*)
Mrs A Cowley, BEd (*Clarinet, Flute*)
Mr P Cunningham, LLCM, GLCM, LTCL, AMUSLCM (*Piano, Jazz Piano, Theory*)
Mr B Duncan, LGSM (*Classical Guitar*)
Mrs J Evans, BA, LRSM, CTABRSM, ALCM (*Piano*)
Doctor B Gates, BA, LGSM (*Clarinet, Saxophone, Theory*)
Miss J Hooper-Roe, ARCM, GBSM, ABSM (*Singing*)
Mrs C Jones, BMus MTC (*Cello, Double bass*)
Miss C Leech, BMus, PGDip RCM, DPS (*Violin/Viola*)
Mr D Lloyd (*Oboe*)
Mrs N Roberts, Dip RCM (*Violin*)
Mr P Slane (*Singing*)
Ms A Sparks (*Singing*)
Ms K Tompkins (*Piano*)
Mr R Truman, ARCM, Dip RCM (*Brass*)
Mr M Wild (*Drum Kit*)
Mr J Winn, ARCM (*Piano*)

Our school, which opened in 1878, is an independent day school for girls. We encourage our pupils to develop values which will provide them with a constant base in an ever changing world and aim to respond to the individual needs of every girl. In 1992 we moved to a 27 acre site on the southern edge of town. Our extensive purpose-built accommodation includes 8 well-equipped laboratories, Art, Textiles, Information Technology, Music, Design Technology, Home Economics, Modern Languages and other specialist rooms for all curriculum areas. A large library with computer facilities for independent study is also provided.

The Junior School, which takes girls from the age of three, adjoins the main buildings and has its own hall, dining facilities, library, practical room and IT suite. At the age of 11 the majority of girls transfer to the Senior School.

There are splendid sports facilities on the site. These include a 25m swimming pool, all-weather pitch, badminton, squash, netball and tennis courts and hockey pitches.

Girls are prepared for GCSE and Advanced Level examinations and go on to universities and other institutions of higher education.

Scholarships are offered at 9+, 10+, 11+, 13+ and in the Sixth Form. Means-tested bursaries are available in the Senior School.

Fees per term (2008-2009). Senior School £3,169, Junior School £2,427, Nursery £2,137.

Old Girls and Associates. *Secretary*: Mrs C White, Northampton High School, Newport Pagnell Road, Hardingstone, Northampton NN4 6UU.

Charitable status. Northampton High School is part of The Girls' Day School Trust, which is a Registered Charity, number 306983.

Northwood College

Maxwell Road Northwood Middlesex HA6 2YE
Tel: 01923 825446
Fax: 01923 836526
e-mail: admissions@northwoodcollege.co.uk
website: www.northwoodcollege.co.uk

An independent day school for girls.
Motto: *Discover, Learn, Succeed*

Governing Council:
Chairman: Mr G Hudson

Mrs D Dalton	Mr A Patteson
Lady Dyson	Mr K Riley
Mr A Mansell	Mr J Soughton
Mrs S Marris	Mr D Tidmarsh
Mr K Patel	Mr K Wild

***Head Mistress*: Mrs R Mercer**, BA Hons London, PGCE Oxford
from January 2009: Ms Jacqualyn Pain, MA, MA, MBA, NPQH

Deputy Head Mistress: Miss J Jackman, BA Hons Manchester, PGCE Southampton, MBA Nottingham

Deputy Head Mistress: Mrs E Skelton, MA St Andrews, DipEd Edinburgh

Head Mistress Junior School: Mrs J Johnson, CertEd London

* *Head of Department/Faculty*
§ *Part-time*

Mrs J Adams, BA Hons Hull, PGCE City of Birmingham College of Ed (*Junior School*)
§Ms S Ahmed, BA Hons Essex, MA London, PGCE Cambridge (*English, Drama*)

Mrs N Asquith, BSc Hons Birmingham, PGCE Bristol (**Biology*)
§Miss J Bacon, BA Hons Oxon (*Music*)
Mr A Bailey, BMus Hons London College of Music & Media, PGCE Inst Ed London (*Music*)
Miss S Ballantyne, BA Hons Bristol Polytechnic, MA Chelsea College of Art (**Art*)
§Mrs J Barraclough, BEd Hons College of St Mary & St Paul, RSACertSpLD (*Junior School*)
Miss M Bennett-Goodman, AGSM, PGCE (*Assistant Director of Music*)
Mrs G Bhatia, BSc Hons Kingston, PGCE London (*Mathematics*)
Miss R Blaxill, BSc Hons Brunel, PGCE St Mary's Twickenham (*Vincent House*)
Mrs C Brant, BSc Hons Exeter, PGCE OU (*Science*)
Mr S Brant, MA Oxon, PGCE London, FCSM, FGMS, FFCM (*Director of Studies, Chemistry*)
Mr D Brown, BA Hons Hull (**English*)
Mrs L Brown, BSc Hons UCL, PGCE Inst Ed London (*Psychology, Head of Year 9*)
§Ms T Bush, BA Hons Kingston, MA Camberwell College of Arts, PGCE London (*Art*)
Mr L Casey, BA Hons Polytechnic of Wales, MA Middx Polytechnic, PGCE Sheffield Polytechnic (*Economics*)
§Mrs M Cooper, BEd Hons West London Inst (*Religious Studies*)
§Mrs M Coulson, AGSM (*Drama*)
Ms E D'Souza, BSc Hons Aston, PGCE Herts (*Junior School*)
Miss J Dabski-Nerlich, BA Hons, PGCE Inst Ed London (*Vincent House*)
Miss A Direkze, BSc Hons UMIST, MA London, PGCE Middlesex (*Vincent House*)
§Mrs P Douglas, BEd Hons Brighton Polytechnic (*Mathematics*)
§Mrs M Doyle, BEd Hons Homerton College Cambridge (*English*)
Miss B Eagles, BEd Hons Cheltenham (*Junior School*)
Mr R A Elliott, BA Hons Southampton (*Assistant Head, Head of Sixth Form, History and Politics*)
§Mrs C Evans, BA Hons London (*English*)
Mrs A S Evans-Evans, BSc Hons, PGCE Manchester (*Physics*)
Mrs C Ezekiel, BSc Hons Manchester Metropolitan, PGCE Cambridge (**Geography*)
Mr D A Ezekiel, BA Joint Hons Manchester, PGCE Cambridge, MA London (*French, German*)
Mrs K Fellas, BSc Hons London, PGCE Inst Ed London (*Mathematics*)
§Mr A Gerolemou, BMus Hons London College of Music (*Music Technology*)
Mrs E Greenley, BA Hons, PGCE Newcastle (**Modern Languages, *French*)
§Mrs M Hamilton, BSc Hons, PGCE Primary Swansea (*Vincent House*)
Ms A Harne, BA Hons Winchester School of Art, PGCE Brighton (*Art*)
Miss A Hollis, BA Hons QTS, Brunel (*Physical Education*)
Miss J Hurt, BA Hons QTS Brunel (**Creative & Expressive Arts, *Physical Education*)
Miss L Johannes, BSc Hons Southampton Inst, PGCE Inst Ed London (**Humanities & Social Sciences, *Psychology*)
Mrs C Jones, CertEd Twickenham (*Vincent House*)
Mrs S Kern, BA Hons Southampton, PGCE Roehampton (**History & Politics*)
Mrs E LeRoux-Baker, HDipEd Boland College of Education, SA (*Physical Education*)
Mrs H Levy, BSc Witwatersrand, PGCE London (*Chemistry*)
Mr P Lowe, BSc Aston, PGCE North London (**ICT*)
Miss Y Matsushita, BA Hons University of Surrey (*Vincent House*)
Mrs H McConnon, BA Hons Exeter, PGCE Hertfordshire (*English*)
Miss C McCoy, BA Hons, PGCE, MA Central School of Speech & Drama (**Drama*)
§Mrs J McDermott, BSc Hons, PGCE Birmingham (*Chemistry*)
Mrs C McMahon, CertEd College of St Mary & St John (*Junior School*)
§Mrs G Mead, BA Hons Kent, PGCE Canterbury (*Religious Studies*)
§Miss K Millen, BSc Hons, PGCE Newcastle (*Geography*)
Mrs D Miller-Smith, BSc Hons Thames Valley, PGCE OU (*Assistant Director of Studies, French, Spanish*)
Mrs C Morgan, BSc Hons OU, PGCE St Mary's College, Twickenham (**Mathematics, Head of Year 11*)
Miss S Morrish, BSc Hons, PGCE Roehampton Inst (*Technology*)
Mrs S Norris, BSc Hons London, PGCE London, MSc Cambridge (*Chemistry*)
Mrs J Onslow, BEd Bath, Cert Sec Maths Chelmer Inst (*Technology Coordinator, Textiles, Head of Year 10*)
Mrs K Opie, BA Hons, MA, PGCE London (**Religious Studies*)
Miss S Parnaby, BA Hons Dunelm, PGCE Dunelm (**Classics*)
Mrs A Pearson, BA Hons Reading, PGCE Southampton (*Junior School*)
Miss R Pink, BEd Hons W London Inst Ed, CertEd (*Junior School*)
Mrs C Pritchard, Dip Home Econ Queens College, CertEd Jordanhill Coll of Ed (*Food Technology*)
Miss C Quirk, MA Liverpool, PGCE Durham (**Spanish, French*)
Mrs E Rees, BA Hons W Sussex Inst HE, PGCE Brunel (*Physical Education*)
Miss J Richards, BEd Hons Cheltenham (*Nursery Teacher*)
Dr I Roche, BA OU, MMus, DMus London, CertEd London (**Director of Music*)
§Mrs S Roche, BA Hons OU, CertEd London (*History*)
§Mrs V Rowntree, BSc Hons Bristol, PhD London, PGCE Chelsea College (*Biology*)
Mr S Sandys-Winsch, BA Hons, PGCE Aberystwyth, MSc South Bank (*Senior Teacher Junior School*)
Miss S Schmiedel, BEd Univ of Wuppertal (**German, Head of Year 7*)
§Mrs H Sieff, BSc Hons Univ Coll S Wales, PGCE Wales (*Mathematics*)
Miss L Silverstone, BA Hons Middlesex, PGCE Inst Ed London (*Drama, English*)
Mrs J Simister, MA Hons Cambridge, PGCE Roehampton (*Director of The Advanced Cognitive Development Programme*)
Mr T Smith, BEd Massey Univ, NZ, Dip Sec Ed Massey Univ, NZ (*Mathematics*)
§Mrs A Spicer, BSc Hons LSE, PGCE London (*Geography*)
§Mrs L Spicer, BEd Hons Westminster College, Oxford (*English*)
Mrs P Spikings, BSc Hons Nottingham (*Mathematics*)
Mrs H Stewart, BA Hons Bath PGCE London, MAEd OU (*Junior School, KS2 Coordinator*)
§Mrs F Sykes, BSc Hons Leicester (*Coordinator of Pupil Learning Needs*)
Mrs E Taylor, BA Hons Nottingham, PGCE Cambridge (*Classics, Head of Year 8*)
Miss V Taylor, BA Hons, PGCE St Mary's College Twickenham (*Physical Education*)
Mrs H Thaker, BA Hons East London, PGCE North London (*Vincent House, Foundation/KS1 Coordinator*)
§Mrs M Thomas, CertEd Bristol, AdvDip Children's Language & Literature Cambridge, RSADipSpLD (*Junior School*)
Ms R Thompson, BA Hons, PGCE Sheffield (**Careers*)
Mrs C Weeks, MA Oxon, PGCE Oxon (*French, Spanish*)
Mrs M Wong, BSc Hons Edinburgh, PGCE Hertfordshire (*Biology, Chemistry*)

Mr G Wyber, BSc Univ of Queensland, Australia (*Biology, ICT*)
Mrs H Yarde-Martin, BSc Hons Southampton, PGCE Bath (*Physics*)

Miss M Edmonds, BA Hons London Poly, DipIS, MCLIP (*Librarian*)
§Mrs P Pandit (*Assistant to Librarian*)

Visiting Staff:
Mrs C Anderson (*French Conversation*)
Mrs C Gauci (*Spanish Conversation*)
Mrs C Shirmeister (*German Conversation*)

Miss J Mitchell, MA, BPhil Hons Durham, FRAD (*Ballet*)
Mr J Hodgson (*Chess*)

Mr J Bridge (*Brass*)
Mrs A Chancellor, MA, PGDip MusEd RCM, LRAM (*Violin/Viola*)
Mr R Cole (*Acoustic/Electric Guitar*)
Mrs R Ferguson, Grad CMRE, Grad Hons Brussels Conservatoire of Music (*Violin*)
Mrs H Frankland (*Piano*)
Mrs J Gallagher, BA Hons Reading, LRAM (*Violin/Viola/Piano*)
Mr T Godel, BMus Hons (*Electric Bass*)
Miss O Hinman, BA Hons, DipSinging Birkbeck College (*Voice/Piano*)
Mrs R Hinman, BA Hons, LRAM (*Voice/Piano*)
Mr J Holling, BA Hons (*Drumkit/Orchestral Percussion*)
Miss H Lambert, GRSM Hons (*Clarinet/Saxophone*)
Mrs J Maclean, BSc Hons, LTCL (*'Cello*)
Mr P Noble, BA Hons Kent (*Flute*)
Miss L Peacock, BMus Hons (*Drums*)
Mr E Puddick, BMus Hons Jazz Birmingham Conservatoire (*Drums*)
Mrs J Rippon, LRAM, ARCM (*Piano*)

Admin Staff:
Bursar and Clerk to the Governors: Mr C Siggs
PA to the Head Mistress: Mrs D Cittern
PA to the Bursar: Mrs K Forbes-Mitten
Admissions Secretary: Mrs J Davidson

Foundation. The College was founded in 1878 by Miss Catharine Buchan-Smith. There are now 815 girls in the School aged between 3 and 18 years.

Location. Northwood is 14 miles from Central London and is served by the Metropolitan Line and several good local bus services. A supervised school bus service brings girls from Edgware, Canons Corner, Stanmore, Hatch End, Queensbury, Kingsbury, Kenton, Harrow, Pinner, Borehamwood, Elstree, Radlett, Bushey, Chalfont St Peter, Chorleywood, Rickmansworth, Beaconsfield, Gerrards Cross, Denham, Uxbridge, Hillingdon, Ruislip, Ealing, Greenford and Ickenham (5 routes).

Organisation. The College is divided into: the Junior School (Nursery to Year 6), and Senior School (Years 7–13), both of which are located on the same site. The Junior School occupies its own self-contained buildings.

Facilities. All parts of the school are equipped with specialist subject facilities. In the Junior School, a new ICT suite opened in September 2004. In addition to standard classrooms, the Senior School is equipped with a well-stocked Library, three art rooms, eight laboratories, an assembly hall, and specialist centres for Technology, Modern Languages, four newly-equipped computer rooms and the Sixth Form Centre. A new Drama and Music Centre with state-of-the-art facilities opened in October 2004.

Considerable use is made of interactive classboards throughout the school.

The sporting facilities include a Sports Hall and adjoining indoor 25 metre six-lane swimming pool and a fitness suite. This facility is used by girls from all sections of the school.

The attractive grounds include gardens, three hard tennis/netball courts, a hockey/rounders field and a field for junior games.

Aims. The aims of the College are: to foster a love of learning through an excellent academic education, to develop creative and sporting talents, to encourage initiative, independence and self-confidence in a friendly and supportive community and to promote traditional values of social responsibility and concern for others. We want girls to 'Discover, Learn and Succeed'.

We hope each girl will develop her talents to the full within the framework of a disciplined community where courtesy, consideration and sensitivity to the needs of others are highly valued. Above all, it is hoped that a girl leaving Northwood College will have the confidence to succeed at whichever career she chooses, the ability to adapt to an ever-changing world and the strength of character to uphold values and standards. We offer a unique Thinking Skills Programme designed to enhance the critical and creative development of all our girls.

Examinations. Pupils are prepared for the General Certificate of Secondary Education, for AS and A2 levels and for University Entrance.

Curriculum. The College offers all National Curriculum subjects. In addition, French is taught from Year 3. Spanish and German are taught from Year 6, Latin from Year 4. Drama is taught throughout the school. A very wide range of A level subjects is available in the Sixth Form, including Psychology, Economics, Politics, and Music Technology.

Scholarships. A number of academic scholarships are available for girls joining Northwood College Senior School in Year 7 and the Sixth Form. At Year 7 (11+), the College uses the North London Independent Girls' School Consortium examination as part of its assessment. Interview and a school reference are also part of the assessment. At Sixth Form entry (16+), girls are required to sit an examination prior to entry into the Sixth Form. A number of scholarships in other subjects including Art and Design, Sport and Music are also available. Means-tested bursaries are offered to the value of full fees.

Music. The Music department offers a wide range of choral and instrumental opportunities within the many orchestras, bands and choirs. Concerts are held each term as well as music competitions and fully-staged Musical Productions. Instrumental tuition is extensive and girls are prepared for the Associated Board examinations.

Drama. There is one major dramatic production in both Junior and Senior schools each year, together with a number of smaller productions. Girls may take individual drama lessons with visiting teachers.

Physical Education. Trained Staff teach a wide variety of sports such as Hockey, Netball and Gymnastics during the winter months and Tennis, Rounders, and Athletics in the summer. Swimming is taken all year round and senior girls are able to explore other sports such as Golf, Self-Defence and Fitness Training.

Fees per term (2008-2009). Senior School and Sixth Form £3,791, Junior School £2,999–£3,198, Pre-Prep £2,602, Nursery £2,303.

Charitable status. Northwood College is a Registered Charity, number 312646. It exists to provide education for girls between the ages of 3 and 18 years.

Norwich High School (GDST)

95 Newmarket Road Norwich NR2 2HU
Tel: 01603 453265

Fax: 01603 259891
e-mail: admissions@nor.gdst.net
website: www.gdst.net/norwich/

Founded 1875.

One of the 29 schools of The Girls' Day School Trust. For further information about the Trust, see p. xxiv. Additional information may be found on the school's website. A detailed prospectus may be obtained from the school.

Local Governors:
Chairman: Mr S Thompson, BSc, MBA

***Headmistress*: Mrs V C Bidwell**, BA Newcastle-upon-Tyne

Deputy Head: Mr S D Kavanagh, BA Leicester

Deputy Head Academic: Mr A P Walker, MA Oxon

Head of Junior Department: Mrs J Marchant, BA London, MPhil London

Senior Master: Mr S Orton, MA Cantab

Head of Sixth Form: Miss J L Nimmo, BSc Worcester

School Business Manager: Mrs C Molineux

Registrar: Mrs L Mathie, BA Strathclyde

Number of pupils. Senior Department: about 650, aged 11–18 years, of whom about 160 are in the sixth form. Junior Department: about 250, aged 3–10 years.

Norwich High School draws its pupils in almost equal numbers from the city of Norwich and the county of Norfolk. It stands in 13 acres of grounds on the main Newmarket Road, a mile-and-a-half from the city centre. The main buildings are attached to a distinguished Regency house, built in 1820. In addition, there is a junior department with many specialist rooms, a sixth form centre, music school, spacious sports hall, 25m indoor heated pool and a state-of-the-art performing arts centre. All the playing fields are around the school and a wide range of indoor and outdoor physical activities is offered, including tennis, rounders, badminton, gymnastics, dance, netball, hockey, lacrosse and athletics. The school holds the International Schools' Award, the Sportsmark Gold Award for its sporting achievements, Artsmark for creative subjects and Investors in People.

The school is a caring community and parent-friendly. We are open early for breakfast and late for tea. Girls may use the ICT and library facilities after school in the senior department; the junior department has its own after-school club. There is a minibus service from Norwich Railway Station before and after school.

Admission. All girls are assessed prior to entry. The normal ages of admission are 3, 7, 11 and 16. Occasional vacancies may occur at other ages.

Curriculum. The curriculum is planned as a continuum and on the assumption that all girls remain at the school to take A Levels. The school has always been proud to provide a liberal education, preparing girls for admission to universities, professions, commerce and industry. A wide range of subjects is available, currently 23 at A Level and 21 at GCSE. All sixth form girls are encouraged to study widely in addition to their examination subjects.

Information systems. A computer network is shared by all departments, including the laboratories, library, all teaching rooms, two computerised language laboratories, the sixth form IT suite as well as the two senior and two junior IT suites. All girls take the Short Course ICT GCSE in Year 9 and work towards the European Computer Driving Licence qualification in the sixth form. Computers and interactive whiteboards are widely used for teaching, along with extensive digital and Intranet based learning resources. Satellite television is used in sixth form modern language teaching.

Careers education and advice. A carefully planned Careers Information Education and Guidance programme commences in Year 7. The majority of sixth formers enter higher education, having received comprehensive guidance and preparation from their tutors, the Head of Sixth Form, the careers department and those in higher education and the world of work. The well-stocked careers room keeps up-to-date information through a variety of resources. Girls attend regular careers talks and events, both in and out of school. They also undertake work experience and job shadowing.

Extra-curricular activities. These are extensive, for infants through to seniors. Music, sport and drama are all strong features of the school. Girls also participate in both the Duke of Edinburgh's Award and Young Enterprise schemes, rowing, equestrian, debating and chess clubs, Amnesty International, Christian Union, fencing and life saving.

Many excellent residential and day trips are arranged each year, by various departments. These are finely tuned to the curriculum and cover a full range of activities.

Fees per term (2008-2009). Senior School £2,966, Junior Department £2,150, Nursery £1,776.

The fees cover the regular curriculum, school books, stationery and other materials, games fixtures and swimming lessons, but not optional extra subjects or school meals. The fees for extra subjects, including individual music tuition, are shown in the prospectus.

Financial Assistance. The GDST has made available to the school a substantial number of scholarships and bursaries.

Bursaries are available on or after entry to the senior department and applications should be made to the Headmistress in cases of financial need. All requests are considered in confidence. Bursaries are means tested and are intended to ensure the school remains accessible to bright girls who would profit from a GDST education, but who would be unable to enter the school without financial assistance.

Various **Scholarships**, including music scholarships, are available to internal or external candidates for entry at 11+ or to the sixth form.

Charitable status. Norwich High School is part of The Girls' Day School Trust, which is a Registered Charity, number 306983. The aim of the Trust is to provide a fine academic education for girls, which is distinguished by its breadth, as well as its depth.

Notre Dame Senior School

Burwood House Cobham Surrey KT11 1HA
Tel: 01932 869990
Fax: 01932 589481
e-mail: headmistress@notredame.co.uk
website: www.notredame.co.uk

Notre Dame is a Catholic Day School for Girls established in Cobham in 1937 by the Sisters of the Company of Mary.

Governors:
Chairman: Mr Glen Travers
Deputy Chairman: Mrs Suzanne Ware, LLB

Mr Stephen Arthur
Sister Anne Gill, ODN
Mr John Hefferman
Sister Patricia Kelly, ODN
Sister Catherine McLenaghan, ODN
Mr Brian Mepham, FCA
Sister Maria Nieves, ODN
Mr Gerald Russell
Sr Ernestine Velarde, ODN
Father Mervyn Williams, SDB

Financial Controller: Mrs Tracy Jones, CA SA

***Headmistress*: Mrs Bridget Williams**, MA, NPQH, BEd

Deputy Headmistress – Curriculum: Mrs C Jackman, BSc Hons, PGCE
Pastoral Deputy: Mrs V Cochrane, BEd, Cert in Counselling
Head of Sixth Form: Mrs I Oettinger, CertEd
Chaplaincy: Sister Catherine McLenaghan, ODN
Staff:
Ms S Badger, BSc SpHons, PGCE (*Mathematics*)
Mrs S Barney, ASA FIST, TCert (*Swimming Coach*)
Mrs E Barton, MA Hons (*English*)
Mr P Beastall, BSc (*Physics*)
Mrs R Cassell, MSc, BSc Hons (*Geography*)
Mrs C Chislett, BA, HDE (*English*)
Mr M Coackley, BA Hons, PGCE (*History*)
Mrs V Cochrane, BEd, Cert Counselling (*English*)
Mrs A Cox, BA Hons, PGCE (*French, Spanish*)
Mr J Davies, BA Hons (*Latin*)
Miss C Davis, BA Hons, PGCE (*Art*)
Miss H Dean, BA Hons (*History*)
Mrs L Dixon, CertEd, BEd (*Design Technology*)
Mrs S Duckworth, BA Hons, TESOL, DipSpLD (*Learning Support*)
Miss S Dudgeon, BEd Hons (*Physical Education*)
Mrs J Farrell, BA, PGCE (*Science*)
Dr R Fenton, BMus, MMus Hons, PGCE, PhD (*Music*)
Sr Patricia Grady, ODN (*Theology*)
Miss C Graham, BA Hons, PGCE (*Drama*)
Mrs A Griffiths, BA Hons (*Geography*)
Miss M Grzesik, BA Hons, PGCE (*French and Spanish*)
Mme G Guibert, MA, PGCE (*French*)
Mrs P Hall, CertEd (*Design Technology*)
Mrs C Hearne, BA Hons, PGCE (*French and German*)
Mrs A Ingram, BSc (*Mathematics*)
Mrs I James, Odessa State University (*Science*)
Mr M John, MEd, BA Hons (*Information Technology*)
Mrs C Johnson, BA Hons (*English*)
Mrs M Lewis, BA Hons, PGCE (*English*)
Mrs H Marsh, BA Hons, PGCE (*Physical Education*)
Mrs S Morton, MA DipEd, CertEd (*Learning Support*)
Mrs C Mosley, BSc, PGCE (*Physics*)
Mrs I Oettinger, CertEd (*German*)
Ms C O'Keeffe, BSc (*Science*)
Mr S Owen, MSc, BA Hons (*Chemistry*)
Mrs L Plummer (*Information Technology*)
Mrs M Rowe, BA, PGCE (*Theology*)
Ms S Siddiq, BSc (*Biology*)
Mr S Seidler, BD Hons PGCE (*Theology*)
Mrs L Shore, BSc, MSc (*Mathematics*)
Mrs N Skerrit (*PE*)
Mrs M Smith, BA, PGCE (*English*)
Miss E Tinniswood, BA Hons (*Drama*)
Mrs J Tudor, BSc Hons, PGCE (*Science*)
Mrs M Turner, BA Hons, PGCE (*English, French*)

Associate Staff:
Headmistress's PA & Registrar: Mrs J Francis
Senior Administrator: Mrs L Harper
Administrator: Mrs J Russell
Assistant Registrar: Mrs J Clay
Librarian: Mrs P Thomas
Laboratory Technicians: Mrs V Catalano, Mrs J Matkin
Computer Technicians: Mr L Hepworth, Mr D Barnett
Art/Technology Technicians: Mrs C Nation, Mrs E Cranwell
School Nurses: Ms N DeVizia, DipRN, BSc, Mrs K Utchanah, RN, BA Hons

Foundation. Notre Dame School was established in 1937 by the Sisters of the Company of Mary, Our Lady who have a four hundred year old tradition of excellence in education worldwide. The Sisters of the Company of Mary continue to play a very important role in the pastoral life of the school ensuring that the ethos is maintained. Through the Company of Mary the school has well-established links with schools in France, Spain and the USA.

Notre Dame is a Catholic school which welcomes families from all religious denominations. Whilst helping our Catholic children to deepen their understanding of our faith we teach universal tolerance and understanding of all religious beliefs. The school provides a friendly and caring environment in which every girl is encouraged to fulfil her potential. There are approximately 383 girls aged from 11 to 18 in the Senior School. Notre Dame Preparatory School occupies the same site and has approximately 316 girls from 2½ to 11. (*See IAPS entry*)

General information. Located in tranquil rural surroundings, easily accessible by road and served by an extensive network of school coaches, Notre Dame boasts comprehensive facilities for the pursuit of academic work, drama, music, art, sports and other activities. Facilities include a heated indoor swimming pool, sports hall, brand new, well-equipped science laboratories (opening Autumn 2007) and extensive computer network suites. A beautiful Chapel is located in the heart of the school.

Curriculum. All pupils follow a broad curriculum leading to the achievement of up to 10 GCSEs. In addition to the core subjects of English (literature and language), Mathematics, Science and Religious Studies, girls may choose to take French, German, Spanish, Latin, History, IT, Geography, Drama, Music, Art, Food and Textiles Technology and Physical Education. In the Sixth Form most girls will take four AS level and three A level subjects chosen from a large range of options. All girls are prepared for university entrance (including Oxbridge).

Extra-Curricular Activities. Notre Dame excels in swimming and netball and offers a wide range of other sporting activities including tennis, athletics, gymnastics, badminton, lacrosse and rounders. The school boasts thriving Drama and Music Departments with all girls having the opportunity to participate in productions, various choirs and musical ensembles ranging from the chamber orchestra to jazz groups. All girls take part in a weekly activities programme. Other ongoing extra-curricular activities include The Duke of Edinburgh's Award Scheme, Young Enterprise and community service within the local parish.

Admission. Admission is normally at 11+, although girls may be admitted at other ages subject to an entrance examination and the availability of places. Academic scholarships are awarded at 11+ based on the entrance examination. Scholarships are also awarded to girls entering the Sixth Form. Short-term bursaries may be made available to assist parents in times of personal financial hardship. Approximately half our intake at 11+ comes from Notre Dame Preparatory School.

Fees per term (2008-2009). £3,710.

Charitable status. Notre Dame School Cobham is a Registered Charity, number 1081875. It exists to provide education for girls.

Notting Hill and Ealing High School (GDST)

2 Cleveland Road Ealing London W13 8AX
Tel: 020 8799 8400
Fax: 020 8810 6891
e-mail: enquiries@nhehs.gdst.net
website: www.nhehs.gdst.net

Founded 1873.

One of the 29 schools of The Girls' Day School Trust. For further information about the Trust, see p. xxiv. Additional information may be found on the school's website and a more detailed prospectus may be obtained from the school.

Chairman of Local Governors: Professor Susan Malcolm, MA, PhD, FRcPath

***Headmistress*: Ms L Hunt**, BSc London, ARCS

Deputy Head: Miss L Ashley, BSc London, PGCE, MSc Econ

Senior Teacher: Ms S Cohen, BEd London

Head of Junior and Preparatory Departments: Mrs G Solti, BA Hons Oxford, PGCE London

Number of Pupils. There are approximately 880 pupils, of whom 575 are in the Senior School (150 in the Sixth Form) and 305 in the Junior Department.

The school was opened at Notting Hill in 1873 and moved to Ealing in 1931. Ealing Broadway station is nearby, and buses pass the door. Girls come from Ealing and from outside the Borough. The Parents' Guild provides active support for the school in numerous ways.

The buildings have been added to over the years to give modern and attractive facilities. The Junior Department has its own computer suite, as well as computers in each classroom, and new science and art/technology rooms. The Senior School has five computer rooms and interactive whiteboards, or their tablet equivalent, are in use throughout the Junior and Senior schools. The entire system is networked and ICT is used across the curriculum as well as being taught as a distinct subject. Pupils are taught to use the Internet efficiently and wisely, and its use by individuals is monitored by modern regulatory software. ICT creativity is fostered in website design.

The West Wing provides a swimming pool, recital hall, recording studio, Sixth Form centre, and new Art, English and Music departments.

Curriculum. The curriculum includes a wide range of academic and practical subjects, with 22 offered at AS and A2 Level, including History of Art, Government & Politics, Economics, Psychology and Theatre Studies. Girls usually take ten subjects at GCSE, including a compulsory core of English Language and Literature, Mathematics, 3 Sciences (IGCSE) and a Modern Language. All girls study Latin and two or three Modern Languages up to Year 9, including Chinese, and may choose two modern languages at GCSE. Many girls come from families with a second language at home, and may take that language at GCSE and A Level outside school at some point. In the Sixth Form, we also have a General Studies programme which contains the choice of an option in Year 12. Students are well prepared for university entry, and for the use of critical thinking in their studies and interviews.

The school is proud of its standards in Art, Drama and Music, as well as in traditional academic fields. Many girls take private tuition leading to examinations at LAMDA and The Royal Academy of Music, and there are numerous extra-curricular activities including Chinese Club.

To complement the academic curriculum, all girls throughout the school also follow a programme of personal and social education, which includes health issues, study skills, relationships, careers advice, interview techniques and the GDST CareerStart programme for sixth formers.

Virtually all girls proceed to higher education. Most girls go straight to university (including Oxbridge and various medical schools); some attend Art College first. Many girls take a year off before going to university.

Sport. Sport is taken seriously with success in local fixtures and championships, but enjoyment at all standards is encouraged. There is specialist teaching throughout the school, and the Senior school makes use of the facilities at a local club. Netball and hockey are the main winter sports, with tennis, athletics and rounders in the summer. Gymnastics are very popular, and there is an excellent gym squad. Lifeguard training is available for sixth formers, as well as swimming throughout the school. Cricket and football are also played by some year groups.

Fees per term (2008-2009). Senior School £3,700, Junior Department £2,879.

The fees cover the regular curriculum, necessary school books, normal examination fees, the ISCO careers aptitude test, stationery and other materials, choral music and the Sixth Form CareerStart programme, but not optional extra subjects or school meals.

The fees for extra subjects including instrumental music, speech and drama, are shown in the prospectus. Certain off-site sports are charged for separately if taken, as are school trips.

Scholarships and Bursaries. The GDST offers a number of scholarships and bursaries to the school.

Scholarships are available to internal or external candidates for entry at 11+ or to the Sixth Form. They include academic scholarships, and for the Sixth Form, awards for Physical Education, Drama, Art, and an All-Rounder scholarship. At the age of 11 there is in addition a Music scholarship.

Bursaries are means tested and are intended to ensure that the school remains accessible to able girls who would profit from our education but who would be unable to enter the school without financial assistance. Application should be made via the school.

Charitable status. Notting Hill and Ealing High School is part of The Girls' Day School Trust, which is a Registered Charity, number 306983. The aim of the Trust is to provide a fine academic education for girls at a comparatively modest cost.

Nottingham Girls' High School (GDST)

9 Arboretum Street Nottingham NG1 4JB
Tel: 0115 941 7663
0115 950 0423 Junior School
Fax: 0115 924 0757
e-mail: enquiries@not.gdst.net
website: www.gdst.net/nottinghamgirlshigh

Founded 1875.

The largest of the 29 schools of The Girls' Day School Trust. For further information about the Trust, see p. xxiv. A detailed prospectus may be obtained from the school.

Chairman of Local Governors: Mrs J Munro, BSc, AKC

***Headmistress*: Mrs S Gorham**, BA, MA Ed Mgt

Joint Deputy Heads:
Mrs D A Leonard, BEd, MEd
Miss S C Peacock, BSc

Head of Junior School: Mrs M J Renshaw, BSc Bristol

School Business Manager: Mr J C Dunn, ACA

Director of Communications: Mrs P A Higgins, BEd

Admissions Secretaries:
Seniors: Mrs S Webb-Bowen
Juniors: Mrs S Eustace

Number of Pupils. Senior School 825 (including 218 in the Sixth Form); Junior School 256.

A selective day school situated just north of the City of Nottingham, Nottingham Girls' High School was originally housed in a group of Victorian mansions. Recent major works have ensured that our pupils have fully equipped and purpose built classrooms, laboratories and workshops, together with a well-stocked library, lecture theatre, drama studio and music house. The Junior School is separately housed in a spacious building, opened in 1990, which provides a light, pleasant environment with library, hall and specialist teaching rooms for science, technology and art. The Sixth Form have their own area and the school is fully networked for IT.

The school grounds include a large all-weather pitch, gymnasium, sports hall and fitness suite. There is also a sizeable sports field close to the school. The new dining hall has excellent facilities for providing a wide choice of snacks and meals throughout the day. The school is immediately adjacent to Nottingham High School and some extra-curricular activities are organised with their boys.

Although our examination results are among the best in the country, we believe that education for life involves much more. Leadership, confidence, teamwork, flexibility and reliability are among the qualities increasingly demanded in today's ever changing society. Everyone is encouraged to take the opportunity to participate fully in a wide range of extra-curricular activities to develop skills and qualities that will lead to a happy, successful and fulfilling life.

At all ages, we hope that the girls will enjoy their studies. We provide a lively, stimulating learning environment to encourage girls to discover the excitement and satisfaction of high academic achievement coupled with growing knowledge and understanding.

Curriculum. The curriculum is designed to give a broad academic education and full note is taken of the National Curriculum throughout the school. In the Junior School as well as following a pattern of work designed to help develop a confident grasp of core skills, the girls benefit from the highly praised "Explorations" scheme which stimulates creativity. Girls take government Key Stage SAT tests in Years 2 and 6 and results are consistently very high. There is liaison with the Senior School staff, helping to ensure continuity for pupils at 11+. In the Senior School girls are prepared for GCSE, AS and A2 Levels, with almost all girls proceeding to university.

To assist the personal and social development of the girls a programme of life skills is followed at all ages including aspects of careers, citizenship, health and sex education, current affairs and environmental issues.

Throughout the school girls are encouraged to develop their physical skills and the school has an excellent sports record; teams regularly win trophies at City and County level with many being selected to compete at regional or national level.

Admissions. At 4+ entry is by an informal test and assessment of group play activities. Entry at 7+ and 11+ is by interview and a written test which includes English and mathematics and is designed to determine potential and understanding. Most of the existing students stay on at 16+ and a number of students are admitted into the Sixth Form from other schools. The entry requirement is 8 GCSE subjects at an average of grade B, with grades A or B in any subject to be studied in the Sixth Form as specified by the department. This is supported by individual interviews and a report from the current school.

Fees per term (2008-2009). Seniors £2,966 excluding lunch, Juniors £2,150 plus £140 for lunch.

The fees cover the regular curriculum, school books, stationery and other materials, class music, games and swimming, but not optional extra subjects.

Scholarships and Bursaries. The Girls' Day School Trust makes available a number of scholarships each year for entry to the Senior School at both 11+ and direct into the Sixth Form. The maximum value of a Trust scholarship is normally half the current tuition fee. Scholarships are awarded solely on the basis of academic merit and no financial means test is involved.

The GDST has made available a substantial number of bursaries. These are means tested and intended to ensure that the school remains accessible to bright girls who would profit from our education but who would be unable to enter the school without financial assistance. These are available through the Senior School and confidential application should be made to the Headmistress in cases of financial need.

Charitable status. The Girls' Day School Trust, which is a Registered Charity, number 306983. The aim of the Trust is to provide excellent and innovative education.

Ockbrook School
Derby

The Settlement Ockbrook Derbyshire DE72 3RJ
Tel: 01332 673532
Fax: 01332 665184
e-mail: enquiries@ockbrook.derby.sch.uk
website: www.ockbrook.derby.sch.uk

Founded in 1799.

Independent Day and Boarding School for girls aged 3–18. Member of GSA and AGBIS.

Motto: *In Christo Omnia Possum*

Governing Body:
Chairman of Governors: Revd Robert Hopcroft, BSc
Dr G D Lamming, FRCOG, LRCP, MRCS, MB BS
Mr J Luke
Mrs V Poultney, MEd
Mrs M Ralph, MEd, MCollP
Mr J A Thompson, FCA
Revd K Woolford

Clerk to the Governors: Mrs J Buckley

Staff:

***Head Teacher*: Mrs A M Steele**, BSc Leeds

Deputy Head: Mrs J Gwatkin, BEd Birmingham (*Physical Education*)

Curriculum Manager: Ms V Lee, BA Leeds (*French*)

Assistant Teachers:
Dr S Allen, PhD, BSc Salford (*Chemistry*)
Mrs C Beckett, BA, MA Nottingham (*French/German*)
Mrs E S Berry, BEd Derby (*Primary*)
Miss J Biss, BA Warwick (*Mathematics*)
Mrs S Breedon, BEd Nottingham (*Primary*)
Miss K Cleland, BA Hull (*English & German*)
Mrs E Dennis, MSc Liverpool (*Chemistry/Biology*)
Mrs F Faulkner, BSc Newcastle, MA Nottingham (*Technology/ICT*)
Mr N Gupta, BSc, MAPSE Leicester (*Physics/Mathematics*)
Mr D Hannigan, MA London (*Drama*)
Ms S Humberston, BA Hull (*German, French, Spanish*)
Mrs L Ireland, BEd Derby (*Primary*)
Miss C Kendall, BA Hull (*English/Drama*)
Mrs H Killip, BEd Sheffield (*Food Tech/Technology*)
Miss S Kotschi, NA Karl-Mark Universitat (*German Assistant*)
Mrs M Lamell, BA Exeter (*Primary*)
Mrs G Lloyd, BEd Nottingham (*Primary*)
Mrs A Logie, BA Hull (*Geography*)
Mrs H Marsden, BA Derby (*Primary*)
Mrs E Marsh, BSc Leeds (*Physics/Sciences*)
Mr G Maskalick, MA Carnegie (*Music*)
Mrs C McBeth, MEd Loughborough (*Primary*)
Mrs S McCool, BEd Manchester (*Primary*)
Mrs J McGahey, BA Birmingham (*Art and Design*)
Mrs S Mitchell, BA Hull (*English*)
Mrs K Moorhouse, BSc Loughborough (*PE*)
Mrs J Mullineux, BEd Bedford College (*PE*)
Mrs A Newton, BSc (*Mathematics*)

Mrs R O'Reilly, BA Liverpool (*PE and Dance*)
Miss A Renow, BA, MEd Nottingham (*History*)
Mrs C Saunders, BA London (*Religious Studies*)
Mrs L Shaw, DipPE Dunfermline (*Primary*)
Mrs S Taylor, BA Scarborough (*Primary*)
Mrs B Thornton, BEd Derby (*Primary*)
Mr A Walsh, BA Hull (*Economics, Business Studies*)
Mrs P Ward, CertEd Esteven (*French/Assistant Head of Primary*)
Mrs M Watkins, BA Leeds (*French/Spanish*)
Mrs J Whitaker, MSc Leicester (*Biology*)
Mr D Williams, BEd Wales (*Primary*)
Mrs W Wilton, MEd, BPhil Nottingham (*Mathematics*)
Mrs S Worthington, BA Exeter (*Head of Primary*)

School Administration: Mrs J Fowkes, Mrs C Derbyshire

Bursarial Manager: Mrs J Buckley

Finance Manager: Mrs L Humphries

Boarding House Staff:
Mrs M Griffin (*Assistant Housemother*)
Mrs K Fisher (*Assistant Housemother*)
Mrs M Smith (*Housemother*)
Mrs G Hawksworth (*Assistant Housemother*)
Mrs P Parker (*Assistant Housemother*)
Mrs S Ritchie (*Assistant Housemother*)

Medical:
Dr D Disney, MBChB, MRCGP, DPCOG, DPD
Dr M Keeling, BSc, BMedSci, MB BS, DCH, MRCGP, DRCOG
Dr R James, MBChB, MRCGP, DPCOG
Mrs W Holmes, EN

Classroom Assistants:
Mrs J Harvey
Mrs L Holmes, NNEB
Mrs A Kenyon
Mrs J Leighton, CACHE Dip 3
Mrs M Oliver
Mrs K Morris, CACHE Dip 3
Mrs S Smithson

Technician: Mrs L Kendall, BSc Manchester

Visiting Music Teachers:
Mrs M Eades, BA Durham, DipEd, ARCO (*Piano/Violin*)
Mrs J Franklin (*Cello*)
Mrs J Fraser-Burton, GBSM, ABSM (*Voice*)
Mrs J Geary, GGSM, PGOS (*Strings*)
Mr M Johnson, HonVCM, AVCM, SVCM, TCert (*Guitar*)
Mrs J Millensted, GRSM, LRAM (*Voice*)
Mrs C Morgan, BMus Manchester, GRSM, ARMCM (*Oboe/Piano*)
Mrs A Negus, University of Performing Arts, Stuttgart (*Woodwind*)
Mr M Thorpe (*Woodwind*)
Mr G Truman, LRAM (*Brass*)

Situation. Situated in the heart of the Midlands, Ockbrook School lies between the historic towns of Derby and Nottingham and is easily accessible from motorway networks, rail and air transport. The School is set in a superb rural position overlooking the Trent Valley and it is surrounded by its own estate including landscaped gardens, grounds, playing fields and farmland. This setting and the high standard of facilities within it provides an excellent environment for learning . . . free from urban noise and distractions.

Pupils. There are c500 pupils – girls aged 3–18 and boys aged 3–11 – who are divided between the Primary (3–10) and Senior (11–18) Departments. Boarders are accepted from the age of 11 years.

Ethos. The pursuit of excellence is our central ethos. This is realised through a twin track pupil development strategy . . . educating each pupil to realise their capabilities and achieve their personal best, and providing the motivation to attain the highest grades in GCSE and AS/A2 level examinations.

Ockbrook combines tradition with a clear understanding of the demands of the world in which we live. We aim to engender a strong sense of self-worth, self-assurance and confidence and to guide each pupil towards developing into responsible, socially aware and mature young adults.

We believe that education should be a partnership between School, pupils and parents. To this end we provide comprehensive feedback on progress in the classroom and welcome family and friends at our extra-curricular drama productions, concerts, sports events and acts of worship.

We hope that you will join us and experience our sense of purpose, achievements and commitment to our ethos.

Curriculum. *Primary Department*:

Early Years (Ages 3–5). A dynamic programme of language, numeracy and scientific activities provide a secure foundation for later conceptual development.

Key Stage 1 (Years 1 & 2). The core subjects of Mathematics, Science and English are covered in addition to nine other subject areas including French and Information Communications Technology.

Key Stage 2 (Years 3–6). Study for the core of subjects continues with additional experience in nine other subjects including Dance, Drama and Gymnastics.

Teachers' assessments are carried out throughout both Key Stages and form the basis of internal assessment procedures for entrance to the Senior Department at 11+.

Senior Department:

Lower School (Years 7–9). Pupils study the core of subjects and a broad range of additional subjects including Information Communications Technology, Drama and PSE (Personal & Social Education). In Year 8 all pupils study German in addition to French.

Upper School (Years 10–11). At GCSE level all pupils study for Mathematics, English Language and English Literature, plus six or more additional subjects chosen from a wide range of options.

Sixth Form. Students usually study for 4 AS Levels in the Lower Sixth and proceed to 3 A2 subjects in the Upper Sixth. A wide range of subjects is available. Great emphasis is placed on the development of Life Skills which help to develop the competences so necessary for adult life, whilst adding to the breadth of study. The vast majority of pupils leaving the Sixth Form proceed to higher education, including Oxbridge.

The new purpose-built £1 million Science Complex opened in September 2004. The School is now planning for a new purpose-built Library and a new Sixth Form Centre will open in September 2008.

Sport. The Sports Complex opened in March 1998. Netball, hockey, and cross country are the main games of the School. In addition there is also a strong tradition in athletics, swimming and rounders. A rapidly expanding programme of outdoor pursuits is also available for pupils which includes sailing, waterskiing and golf. Teams of various ages, in most sports, have full fixture lists with neighbouring schools and the School is proud of its County and National representatives.

Activities. The Duke of Edinburgh's Award Scheme is available to pupils over the age of 14, together with a wide range of trips and outdoor holidays, walking, canoeing and skiing. Other activities include Young Enterprise, World Challenge Expeditions, Community service, Guides, Cycling Proficiency, chess, debating, and 50 other clubs or societies.

Music and Drama. Many pupils learn musical instruments and a large number play to a high standard. Opportunities are provided by the Primary and Senior choirs, orchestras, chamber choir, strings group, windband and madrigal group. Performance venues include Westminster Abbey, Manchester, Derby and Barcelona Cathedrals and Chatsworth. There is a wide range of dramatic productions each year providing as many pupils as possible with the chance of developing any dramatic talent.

Art and Design & Technology. Great emphasis is given to the development of creative talent both as academic subjects and interests. Out of class involvement is strongly encouraged.

Fees per term (2008-2009). Tuition: £1,065–£2,940. Boarding: £2,500 in addition to tuition fees.

Admission. Ockbrook is an academically selective School with considerable competition for places. Most pupils enter in September, although it is possible for entry to take place at other times in the year.

Primary Department. Entry is decided as a result of a combination of interview, assessment day and school report (if applicable).

Senior Department. Entry is decided as a result of a combination of interview, assessment, school report and entrance examination held throughout the Year and in January for Year 7.

Sixth Form. Entry is decided as a result of a combination of interview, school report, and ultimately a good performance in the GCSE examinations.

Scholarships and Bursaries. A range of scholarships is available for 11+ entry and Sixth Form entry. Bursary applications are considered by way of a full means test. Full details are available from the Admissions Secretary, Mrs Jo Fowkes.

School Prospectus. A prospectus and registration details may be obtained from the Admissions Secretary (Tel: 01332 673532; Fax: 01332 665184; e-mail: joanne.fowkes@admin.ockbrook.derby.sch.uk; website: www.ockbrook.derby.sch.uk). Parents are encouraged to visit the School and appointments may be made by contacting the Admissions Secretary.

Charitable status. Ockbrook School is a Registered Charity, number 251211. Its aims are to provide an education for girls between the ages of 3 and 18.

The Old Palace School of John Whitgift

Old Palace Road Croydon Surrey CR0 1AX
Tel: 020 8688 2027
Fax: 020 8680 5877
e-mail: info@oldpalace.croydon.sch.uk
website: www.oldpalace.croydon.sch.uk

Governing Body:
Chairman: Sir Douglas Lovelock, KCB

Cllr T Letts
Prof J W Dougill, PhD, FEng, FCGI
Mr A D Sexton, BA
Mr M A Fowler, FCA, FCIArb
Mr D W North, BSc Eng, ACGI, MICE
The Revd Canon Colin J Luke Boswell, Vicar of Croydon
Mr P J Squire, MA
Mr C J Houlding
Mr R Smith (*Clerk to the Foundation*)
Mr G H Wright, TD, DL, FCIOB
Mr I Harley, MA, FCA, FCIOB
Mr V F Long, FCIB (*Governor Emeritus*)
The Venerable Nicholas Baines, Bishop of Croydon
His Honour Judge William Barrett, QC, MA Oxon
Dr B Cross, BSc, PhD
Mrs R A Jones, MA
Cllr D Mead, FCCA, FCMA, FCIS
Cllr G Barwell, BA

***Head*: Ms J Harris**, BA Hons Birmingham, PGCE

Deputy Head: Mr N Balchin, BSc Bristol, BA Open, PGCE
Deputy Head: Mrs C Jewell, MA St Andrews, PGCE
Assistant Head: Miss K Stewart, BSc Stirling, PGCE
Assistant Head: Miss J Guppy, MA, BSc Southampton, PGCE
Bursar: Mr D Poole
Head of Junior Department: Mrs J Wermig, MEd Open, BA Hons Birmingham, PGCE
Deputy Head of Junior Department: Mrs M Moore, BA Hons Reading, PGCE
Staff Representative: Mr S Talleux, L-ès-L, M-ès-L Sorbonne Nouvelle, BA Hons London

Senior Department Staff:

* *Head of Department*

Art:
*Mrs G Crozier Meares, BA Hons Birmingham, MA Sussex, CertEd CDT
Mrs C Langley, MA Hons Edinburgh, Art TCert London
Mrs S Pressney, BA Hons Leeds, Art TCert (**Textiles*)

Business Studies and Economics:
Mr A Shah, BA Hons, MEd Sheffield, PGCE
Mr D J Wilkins, BSc Hons London, PGCE

Classics:
*Miss A Bertram, MA Cambridge, PGCE
Mrs S Crampton, BA Sydney
Miss S Funnell, MA Oxford, PGCE
Mrs C Jewell, MA St Andrews, PGCE
Mrs J Wermig, MEd Open, BA Hons Birmingham, PGCE

Drama:
*Mr A Campbell, BA Hons Bristol, PGCE
Miss H Cook, BA Hons Manchester; PGCE

English:
*Mrs A H Lister, BA Hons London MA
Miss H Cook, BA Hons Manchester; PGCE
Miss G Dryden, BA Hons Bristol, PGCE
Miss A Radelat, BA Hons Bristol, PGCE
Miss C Sodoma, Trinity College TCert TEFL
Miss K Wall, MA Oxford, PGCE

Geography:
*Mrs M Salter, BSc Hons Salford, PGCE
Ms K Norris, BSc Hons Edinburgh, PGCE
Mrs A Ford, BA Hons Durham, PGCE (**PSHE*)

History and Politics:
*Miss E Phillips, BA Hons Oxford, PGCE
Mrs J Barter, BA Hons Bristol, PGCE
Mrs S Freeman, BA Hons Birmingham, PGCE
Mrs L Jeffries, BA Hons London, PGCE (*Head of Upper School*)

Information and Communications Technology:
*Mr M Wilcock, BEd London, QTS
Mrs K Burdett, BSc Hons Lancaster, PGCE
Mr I Chin, BEng London, PGCE

Mathematics:
Dr D Robson, MA Cambs, PhD London
Miss J Doyle, BSc Queens, Belfast, PGCE
Mr H Evans, BSc Wales, PGCE
Mrs J S Greenfield, BSc Hons Southampton, PGCE
Mrs A McKinlay, BHum Joint Hons London, PGCE
Mrs S M O'Hanlon, BSc Joint Hons London, PGCE, ACCEG
Mr R Shelley, BSc Hons UCL, DipEd Oxon

Modern Languages:
*Mr S Talleux, L-ès-L, M-ès-L Sorbonne Nouvelle, BA Hons London
Mrs C Barnard, BA Comb Hons Dusseldorf, PGCE
Mrs J Hollingum, BA Hons London, PGCE
Mrs L Mazzeo, BA Hons Wales, PGCE
Miss C Pepin, BA Hons Bristol, PGCE

Miss C Periton, BA Hons London, PGCE
Miss C G C Poirier, Licence d'Anglais Angers, PGCE, Licence FLE French as a Foreign Language
Ms E Vazquez Rivera, Graduate Universidad Complutense, Madrid, Universidad de Santiago de Compostela, PGCE
Music:
Mr G Hemmings, MA Cantab; PGCE
Ms T Fitzgerald, BMus Hons London, PGCE
Mr J Hargraves, BMus Hons London, PGCE

Physical Education:
*Mrs L Coster, BA Hons Wales, Bangor, PGCE
Mrs A Eley, BSc Loughborough, PGCE
Miss J Hall, BEd Hons Greenwich
Mrs T Mills (*Swimming Instructor*)
Mrs J Sugarman, CertEd Chelsea
Mrs K Tamplin (*Swimming Support/Life Guard*)

Psychology:
Mr N Walker, BSc St Andrews, MA Manchester Met, PGCE

Religious Studies:
*Miss E Hayward, BSc Open, BEd
Mr T Finch, BA Hons Birmingham, CertEd Durham, MA London

Science:
Physics:
*Mr C Barwell, BSc Hons Southampton, PGCE (*Head of Science*)
Miss R Jackson, BSc Hons Durham, PGCE
Mr R Shirley, BSc Edinburgh, MSc London, PGCE
Biology:
*Mrs P Shaw, BSc Hons Leeds, PGCE
Dr J Bannister BSc Hons Sheffield, PhD Leeds, PGCE
Miss M Montagu, BMedSc, MSc London, PGCE
Mrs J Lloyd, BSc Hons Nottingham, PGCE
Chemistry:
*Dr L Nicolas, BSc Hons Sheffield, PhD London, PGCE
Mrs J Gradon, BA Hons Cambridge, PGCE
Dr A Gray, BA Cambridge, PhD, PGCE
Mrs C Marren, BSc Hons Swansea, PGCE

Technology:
Mr J Plater, MA RCA, BEd Hons Southampton, MSD-C
Mrs A Nariapara, BSc Hons QTS Loughborough (*Head of Sixth Form*)
Mrs G Solari, BA Teesside, PGCE

Junior Department Staff:

Head of Junior Department:
Mrs J Wermig, MEd Open, BA Hons Birmingham, PGCE

Deputy Head of Junior Department: Mrs M Moore, BA Hons Reading, PGCE

Class Teachers:
Reception: Mrs A Edwards, BEd Hons London, AdvCert Mgt Studies
Reception: Mrs C Munro, CertEd Sussex (*responsible for Reception to Year 2*)
Year 1: Mrs S Keanie, CertEd Froebel (*RS Coordinator*)
Year 1: Miss F Smith (*Literacy Coordinator*)
Year 2: Mrs C Blok, BEd London (*History Coordinator*)
Year 2: Mrs S Williams, CertEd Digby Stuart College (*Art Coordinator*)
Year 3: Miss F Clements, MA Oxon, MMus Sheffield, PGCE, ARCM (*Learning Support*)
Year 3: Mrs G Stone, BEd Hons Cambs (*Learning Support*)
Year 4: Ms S Lansdale, BMus Manchester PGCE (*Extra-Curricular Coordinator*)
Year 4: Mrs S Saito, BA Hons Newcastle PGCE
Year 5: Miss N James, BSc Hons Loughborough, PGCE (*Science Coordinator*)
Year 5: Mrs M Moore, BA Hons Reading, PGCE (*Deputy Head*)
Year 6: Mrs C Pedersen, BA Open, DipEd Edinburgh (*Geography Coordinator*)
Year 6: Ms T Skuse, BSc Manchester PGCE (*Mathematics Coordinator*)

Subject Coordinators:
Music: Miss T Fitzgerald, BMus Hons London, PGCE, LTCL, ALCM
ICT: Mrs A Frost, BSc Hons Birmingham, PGCE
PE: Mrs J Goatcher, BEd Sussex, AdvCert Early Years Ed Christ Church, Cantab
Drama: Mrs A Palmer, CertEd Roehampton
French: Mrs M Sarkis, BA Hons, Dip MRS, PGCE London
DT: Mrs T Wallis, BEd Hons Oxford

Teaching Assistants:
Lead Teaching Assistant: Miss H Ward, Foundation degree in Teaching and Learning Roehampton
Mrs E Marshall, NNEB
Mrs E Morrison, Dip Pre-School Practice
Mrs A Nissan, NNEB
Mrs S Stevens
Mrs J Russell, MA Edinburgh
Mrs J Tooze, Dip Fashion

Peripatetic Staff:

Music:
Miss N Beckley (*Voice*)
Mr D Black, MWS BMus (*Guitar*)
Miss Z Bolton, BMus, AdvCert Flute, Recital Cert Piano (*Piano and Theory*)
Miss J Bruce (*Piano & Bassoon*)
Mr C Craft (*Brass*)
Mrs P Craft, LGSM (*Violin*)
Mr S Dean, ARCM, LGSM (*Flute*)
Mrs S Eastick, ARCM (*Clarinet and Saxophone*)
Mrs M Gray (*Clarinet and Saxophone*)
Mr S Pachnine, HBC Dip (*Percussion*)
Miss E Parry, BA Cantab, PG Dip Perf, BA Hons Warwick, PGCE, ARSM
Mrs H Takayama, DipEd, MSTAT (*Cello*)
Mrs M Williams, GSM, Music TCert (*Violin and Viola*)
Miss J Williams, GRSM, ARCM, ARCO (*Piano*)
Mrs H Wilson, Division V, Division IV Performance Certificate, LRAM (*Oboe*)
Mrs A Winter, GCSM, ABSM, Diploma NCOS (*Violin and Viola*)

Speech & Drama:
Mr J Lemmon, BA Oxford, MA UCL
Mrs C Redgrove, Dip French Studies La Sorbonne, LAMDA
Mrs H Jerome, LLAM, TDip, BTEC Nat Dip Perf Arts

Administrative Staff:
Bursar: Mr D Poole
Head of Administration & Head's PA: Mrs F Evison
Office Manager: Mrs S Stark
Deputy Office Manager: Mrs K Rayner
Reception – KS3 Secretary: Mrs M Smith
Admissions Secretary: Mrs J Stevens
Reception & Office Secretary: Mrs D Hemmings
Reception Secretary: Mrs C Moar
Health & Welfare Coordinator: Nurse: Mrs M Grewe, SRN, RM, RHV
Librarian: Mrs K Stevenson
Assistant Librarian: Mrs B Bhatt
Network Manager: Mr S Bridges, TEC Diploma AICTT

Old Palace School of John Whitgift is a girls' independent day school for 850 girls aged 4–18, 550 in the Senior Department and 300 in the Junior Department. It is situated on the site of the Old Palace of the Archbishops of Canterbury in the heart of Croydon. It is well served by public transport being within walking distance of main line stations, bus routes and tram routes.

The School was founded in 1889 by the Community of the Sisters of the Church. It became a member of the Whitgift Foundation in 1993. The School aims to provide education to the highest academic standards and to develop the individual talents of each girl to the full within an environment of mutual respect and support.

Facilities. The original Grade 1 listed – English Heritage – buildings have been enhanced by a science block of eight well-equipped laboratories, an Arts and Technology block comprising very good facilities for art, music and design technology. Five computer rooms are fully networked with internet access. There are sports facilities on site for netball, gymnastics, tennis and a swimming pool. A further six new classrooms were opened in 2003, together with a Modern Languages Technology Suite, areas for Drama and dining facilities. There is a large designated area for Sixth Form accommodation which houses their own resources area in addition to the main Library and resources centre.

A purpose-built Junior Department opened in Summer 2001 giving good sized classrooms, facilities for music and computing and a library to complement the existing science and art rooms.

Curriculum. *The Junior Department* follows a wide curriculum in a friendly atmosphere. At four years old the girls are welcomed into Reception classes and are quickly introduced to the skills of reading and number. Girls are progressively introduced to specialised teaching in French, Science, ICT, Music and Design Technology.

The Senior Department curriculum for ages 11–16 is based upon traditional disciplines but keeps abreast of modern developments. All subjects are taught by well qualified specialist staff. Girls study French and Latin together with a third language from Italian, German or Spanish, Japanese (taster) courses are offered to pupils in Year 8. Information Technology is taught as a separate skill and is also integrated within subjects. Design Technology, Textiles and Art are studied by all girls and are available within the GCSE option choices. Extra-curricular activities thrive with three orchestras, four choirs, over 100 girls gaining Duke of Edinburgh's Awards each year, drama performances in each age group, debates, and support for charities through Caritas. Visits enhance the curriculum in many subjects and girls studying languages have the opportunity to stay in the relevant country. There is a wide programme of visits and musicians have recently travelled to Belgium, Venice and Hungary. There is a strong house system.

The Sixth Form. Most girls remain at Old Palace for their AS/A2 level studies. New students integrate quickly and become happy and committed members of the School community. A wide range of A and AS are offered with girls usually studying four subjects in the first year. An enrichment programme provides guidance in study skills, careers and opportunities for sport, community service and Critical Thinking. Russian is offered as an extra GCSE. Girls may take part in Young Enterprise and World Challenge. Almost all girls proceed to university, including Oxford and Cambridge, to read a diverse range of subjects.

Admissions. Girls are normally admitted at 4, 7, 11 and 16 with occasional vacancies at other ages. Admission is by examination and interview and at Sixth Form by interview and GCSE results.

Scholarships and Bursaries. Girls of outstanding merit in the 11+ entrance examination may be offered scholarships of up to 50% fee remission. Bursaries are also awarded on the 11+ entrance for families who need financial assistance. Up to a quarter of girls in the Senior Department are awarded a bursary place.

Fees per term (2008-2009). Senior Department £3,286; Junior Department £2,457.

Fees cover tuition, stationery, textbooks and examination entries. Extra tuition is available in music and speech and drama.

Charitable status. The Whitgift Foundation is a Registered Charity, number 312612, which administers three schools.

Oldham Hulme Grammar Schools

Chamber Road Oldham Lancs OL8 4BX

(See entry in HMC section)

Our Lady's Abingdon Senior School

Radley Road Abingdon Oxfordshire OX14 3PS
Tel: 01235 524658
Fax: 01235 535829
e-mail: office@olab.org.uk
website: www.olab.org.uk

Board of Governors:
Chairman: Mr P F J Tobin, MA, FRSA
Deputy Chairman: Mrs M Goodwin, BA Econ, ACA

Governors:
Mr T Ayling MA Oxon
Mr J Cunliffe, MA Oxon
Dr C Ferdinand, MA, DPhil
Dr T Hands, BA, AKC, DPhil
Mr D Heavens
Mr P Mason, ACCA
Mr E McCabe, MA Oxon, MBA
Mr M Moreton-Smith
Mgr J Nelson, STL, JCL, VG
Mrs M Shinkwin, BA, MA Ed, NPQH
Sr K Staunton
Mr I Yorston, MA
Institute Representative: Sr M Sheehy, RSM, BEd

Bursar & Clerk to the Governors: Mr S Hughes, BA Hons

***Head*: Mrs Lynne Renwick**, BEd, NPQH

Deputy Head: Miss B Habayeb, MSc, PGCE

Senior Mistresses:
Mrs P Huntzinger, BA Hons, PGCE
Mrs S Wales, BA Oxon, PGCE

Sixth Form Tutor: Miss F Gunn, LIB Hons, PGCE, MA
Year 11 Tutor: Mr P Hudson, BSc Hons, PGCE
Year 10 Tutor: Mrs J Jones, BA, PGCE
Year 9 Tutor: Mr L Irving, BA Hons, PGCE
Year 8 Tutor: Mrs P Huntzinger, BA Hons, PGCE
Year 7 Tutor: Mr H Shallard-Brown, MSc Oxon, PGCE

Heads of Departments:
Art: Mrs H Holden, BA Hons, MSt, PGCE
Business Studies: Mrs J Acutt, BA Hons, PGCE
Careers: Mrs A Varney, BEd, CertEd
Classics: Miss P Smith, BA Hons Oxon
English: Miss M Hemingway, BA Hons, PGCE
Geography: Mrs S Wales, BA Hons Oxon, PGCE
History: Mrs J Mead, BA Hons, PGCE, MA
Home Economics: Mrs H Black, BA Hons, PGCE
Information Technology: Miss B Habayeb, MSc, PGCE
Mathematics: Mrs H Matheson, BA, PGCE
Modern Languages: Mrs C Friend, MA Hons Oxon, MA, PGCE
Music: Mr O Kraftl, BMus Hons, LRAM, LTCL

Physical Education: Ms M Jezzard, BA Hons, QTS
Psychology: Mrs A Beasley, MA Hons, PGCE
Religious Studies: Mrs A Curran, BA Hons, PGCE, MA
Science: Mr P Hudson, BSc Hons, PGCE
Special Educational Needs: Mrs L Gamlin, BSc, TCert, DipSEN, DipSpLD
Technology: Mrs A Okeke, BSc Hons, MSc, PGCE
Textiles: Mrs K Rowe, CertEd

General. Our Lady's Abingdon has a reputation for academic achievement coupled with strong support for the development of every pupil as an individual. The school was founded in 1860 by the Sisters of Mercy and retains their ethos of care and dedication to the teaching of Christian values. It provides for "each according to her needs" whether those needs be support for outstanding talents in music, sport, art, drama or academic subjects. The school encourages independence of thought and responsibility for one's own learning and behaviour. Our Lady's Abingdon, a Christian school in the Catholic tradition, welcomes girls of all beliefs who wish to share its ideals and expectations.

The 2003 inspection report was most complimentary, noting in particular that pupils are 'pleasant, courteous, well-behaved and very good academic learners; the quality of teaching is always sound; the provision for pupils' spiritual, moral, social and cultural development is very good; very effective provision is made for all the girls' well-being; and the school is excellently led'.

Numbers, facilities and buildings. There are 397 girls in the Senior school aged 11 to 18 and 160 girls and boys aged 3–11 in the Junior section which is on the same site under its own headmaster, Brendan O'Neill. Bright, spacious classrooms and an excellent library provide a pleasant ambience conducive to study and learning. The grounds surround both buildings, an attractive setting of lawns, flowerbeds and trees in which the girls can relax during breaks. Sports facilities include a number of tennis courts, a sports hall with squash court, hockey and athletics provision and a newly refurbished indoor swimming pool. It has benefited recently from the creation of a new auditorium and library, the latest in ICT equipment, and an extended Art department. Music also has newly acquired facilities for music technology to aid composition and to support the wide variety of instruments taught in the school.

Curriculum. The school teaches a balanced range of subjects both academic and practical during the first three years. Latin is a core subject. Pupils take 9 or 10 subjects at GCSE, including English, Mathematics, Science, Religious Studies and two modern languages. Options are chosen from the Humanities to Classics and Physical Education. Four subjects are studied in the Lower Sixth at AS, continuing with three at A2. 98% of the Sixth Form go on to Higher Education. There is also support for Special Educational Needs, and for girls for whom English is not their mother tongue.

Extra-curricular activities. The school provides a wide programme of extra-curricular activities including drama, music, art, debating and many forms of sport. Rowing and sailing are particularly popular. Buses run later on three evenings of the week to accommodate these activities and to allow for supervised homework.

Fees per term (2008-2009). £3,185.

Admission. Through the school's own Entrance Examination at 11; and at Sixth Form level. Girls interested in entering the Sixth Form for whom English is a second language must in addition have achieved a minimum level of 6.5 in IELTS for each category.

Girls may apply for Scholarships for entry to Year 7 and the Sixth Form. Candidates may also apply for Bursaries which are awarded at the discretion of the Governors.

Charitable status. Our Lady's Abingdon Trustees Limited is a Registered Charity, number 1120372, and a Company Limited by Guarantee, registered in England and Wales, number 6269288.

Oxford High School (GDST)

Belbroughton Road Oxford OX2 6XA
Tel: 01865 559888
Fax: 01865 552343
e-mail: oxfordhigh@oxf.gdst.net
website: www.gdst.net/oxfordhigh

Founded 1875.

One of the 29 schools of The Girls' Day School Trust. For further information about the Trust, see p. xxiv.

Chairman of Local Governors: Mr J H Smith, JP, FRICS, FCIArb

***Headmistress*: Miss O F S Lusk**

Deputy Headmistress: Mrs O B Curry

Deputy Head – Academic: Dr P Secker

Head of Junior Department: Mrs J Scotcher

Business Manager: Mrs C Charlton

Head of Sixth Form: Miss R Pallas-Brown

Pupil numbers. 932: Junior Department 351, Senior Department 581.

The school is on three sites in North Oxford, juniors (boys 3–6, girls 3–10) are at The Squirrel and Greycotes.

The Senior Department has a sports hall, indoor swimming pool, The Mary Warnock School of Music, and separate purpose-built centres for all other subjects and the Sixth Form. The school is networked with well-equipped ICT areas.

Oxford High School will open two schools in Shanghai, China and one in India over the next three years.

Curriculum. The broad curriculum offers a full range of subjects, using ICT throughout the curriculum. Girls are prepared for GCSE and AS/A Level. Sixth-formers choose from 27 subjects. Mandarin was introduced as a compulsory language for Year 7 in 2006. About 30% proceed to Oxbridge annually. Boys are prepared for entrance to their prep school at 7 years. Many girls take examinations in Music, and Speech and Drama, as well as belonging to the Duke of Edinburgh's Award Scheme, Young Enterprise and the Combined Cadet Force.

A strong extra-curricular programme offers about 100 clubs at any one time, with everything from rock band to gardening.

Admission. The main points of entry are at Nursery, Reception, Years 3, 7, 10 and 12 by assessment and interview throughout, except Reception and the Nursery. The school is over-subscribed. From September 2009 boys will no longer be admitted to the Nursery.

Nursery: There are no specific assessment criteria governing admission to the Nursery. Applications can be made at any time and offers of places will be confirmed approximately a year in advance of the proposed term of entry. Priority goes to siblings.

Reception: Entry procedures are straightforward. Children attend a taster day. There is no formal assessment.

Years 2–10: We test English, Mathematics and Reasoning, with a language likely in Years 8–10.

Sixth Form places are offered provisionally following assessment and interview. Candidates will sit short papers in the subjects that they intend to study at AS level. Offers are confirmed when the results of the GCSE examinations are known. As a minimum requirement, we expect five B grades to include English, Mathematics and Science, and A grades in the subjects which the candidate wishes to follow in the Sixth Form.

Fees per term (2008-2009). Senior School £2,966, Junior Department £2,150, Nursery (mornings only) £888.

The fees cover the regular curriculum textbooks, stationery and other materials, choral music, games and swimming, but not optional extra subjects or school meals. Lunch (currently £175 per term) is compulsory for girls from Year 2 to Year 11. Children at The Squirrel bring a packed lunch.

Bursaries. The GDST provides the school with a number of bursaries. These are means tested and ensure that the school remains accessible to bright girls who would profit from the education provided but who would be unable to enter the school without financial assistance. Bursaries are available before or after entry throughout the Senior Department and confidential application can be made to the Headmistress.

Scholarships. Academic and music scholarships are available for Year 7 and in the Sixth Form, with art and sport scholarships available in the Sixth Form.

Charitable status. Oxford High School is part of The Girls' Day School Trust, which is a Registered Charity, number 306983. The aim of the Trust is to provide a fine all-round education for girls at a comparatively modest cost.

Palmers Green High School

Hoppers Road London N21 3LJ
Tel: 020 8886 1135
Fax: 020 8882 9473
e-mail: office@palmersgreen.enfield.sch.uk
website: www.pghs.co.uk

Founded 1905.
Motto: *By Love Serve One Another*

School Council
Chairman: Mr D Lewis, ACIB
Mrs S Campion
Mrs M Curtis
Mrs C Janko
Mrs J Mayhew, CertEd
Mr D Orfeur, JP, FRICS, FSVA retd
Mr B D Smith, FRIBA
Mr M Richman
Mr J Zinkin, FCA

***Head Mistress*: Mrs Christine Edmundson**, BMus London, MBA Exeter, PGCE, LRAM, ARCM

Deputy Headmistress: Mrs D Hammersley, BSc Loughborough, PGCE East Anglia (*Examinations Officer*)
Head of Lower School: Mrs A Robinson, BA Middlesex (*Form Teacher Junior 3*)

Staff:
Mrs A Atkinson, BEd (*Nursery Teacher*)
Mrs S Banks, NNEB (*Nursery Assistant*)
Mrs A Beaven, DipAD Hornsey, CertEd Middlesex (*Head of Art; Form Tutor S11*)
Mrs H Bhundia (*Lower School Auxiliary Assistant*)
Mrs J Billingham, BA Nottingham (*Art*)
Mrs B Broad, BEd Leeds (*Head of Physical Education*)
Mrs E Christodoulou BA Middlesex, PGCE (*Form Teacher Prep 2*)
Mrs K Conlon BSc London (*Librarian*)
Miss A Davey, BA Leeds, PGCE (*English*)
Mrs C Doe, BA East Anglia, MA Open, PGCE (*Head of English; Form Tutor S10*)
Mrs L Dufton, BA Middlesex (*Form Teacher Junior 6*)
Ms H Eve, BA, PGCE Bristol (*English, Drama, History; Form Tutor 97C*)
Mrs G Gabzdyl, BA London (*Head of History; Form Tutor S7B*)
Mrs S Hagi-Savva (*Nursery Assistant*)
Miss S Harding, BSc Kingston, PGCE (*Head of Science, Form Tutor S10*)
Mrs E Hassan (*Lower School Auxiliary Assistant*)
Mr D Healey, MA London, CertEd, DipAD, DipCDT London (*Design and Technology*)
Mrs J Kobylanski, BSc London (*Head of Mathematics; Form tutor S11*)
Miss M Laratonda, MA London, BEd Spain, PGCE (*SS Relief Teacher*)
Mrs A Lee, BEd Birmingham (*Form Teacher Junior 4*)
Miss H Lucas, BSc Sussex, MSc London, PGCE (*Form Teacher Reception*)
Miss E Marshall, BMus London, ARCM (*Music, Flute, Recorder*)
Mr J Matthews, BMus Cardiff, LTCL (*Head of Music*)
Miss E McNally, BSc Gloucester, PGCE Exeter (*Physical Education; Form tutor S9B*)
Miss S Mandal, BSc, MSc Visva Bharati, India, PGCE Exeter (*Science; Form tutor S7B*)
Miss L Martin, BA Manchester, MSc London, PGCE (*SEN*)
Mrs M Mehran, BSc North London (*Science Technician*)
Miss J Newman, BA London, PGCE (*French, Spanish; Form Tutor S10C*)
Mrs K Parry-Garnaud, Lic d'Anglais, BA Sunderland (*Head of Modern Foreign Languages; French, Spanish; Form Tutor S7C*)
Mrs J Pauk, BA Aberystwyth, PGCE (*Form Teacher Junior 5*)
Mrs P Ryland, Dip Special Education (*PE Teacher*)
Mr I Saxton, BA Hons Cheltenham, PGCE (*Head of Geography; Form Tutor S7C*)
Mrs C Shaw, BSc Warwick, PGCE (*Mathematics; Form Tutor S8*)
Mrs M Suleyman, NVQ3 Childcare (*Lower School Auxiliary Assistant*)
Mrs K Thompson, BA Denver, Colorado (*Head of ICT; Form Tutor S8*)
Mr C Vincent, BSc Swansea, PGCE, DipCEG (*Head of Careers Education & Guidance; Life Skills & Work Experience; Geography; Form Tutor S11*)
Mr K White, BA Brunel, PGCE Reading (*Drama*)
Mrs S Worringham (*ICT Systems Manager*)
Mrs L Young, BEd Bath (*KS1 Coordinator; Form Teacher Prep 1*)

Visiting Staff – Instrumental Tuition:
Cello: Miss F Nisbett
Flute: Miss S Pylkkönen
Musicianship: Miss C Banwell
Piano: Mrs S O'Connor, LRAM
Saxophone/Clarinet: Mr J Matthews
Singing: Miss M Armstrong
Violin: Miss V David, Miss H Bartlett

Bursar: Mrs L Ranson, BA Open, DipEurHum, MBIFM
Bursar's Assistant: Mrs A Monty
Headmistress's PA & Office Manager: Mrs M Harding

Assistant School Secretaries:
Miss V Bennett
Mrs A Dudley

School Caretaker: Mr D Spurling, MMA, HVCA, ASME
Caretaker Assistant: Mr G Stevens

Palmers Green High School is a girls' independent day school for up to 310 girls aged 3–16 in Winchmore Hill, North London. It is well served by a number of bus routes and close to British Rail Stations in Winchmore Hill and Palmers Green. Southgate, on the Piccadilly Line is the nearest Tube Station.

The School was founded by the late Alice N Hum in buildings in Green Lanes, Palmers Green and transferred to Avondale Hall on its present site in Hoppers Road, Winchmore Hill in 1918.

The School's motto 'By Love Serve One Another' was carefully selected by Miss Hum to reflect her deep Christian convictions derived from her membership of the Society of Friends (Quakers).

The ideals of integrity and care implicit in that philosophy have been maintained by succeeding generations of teachers in the face of changing standards and are still a vital part of the School's ethos.

Palmers Green High School continues to provide the warm and sympathetic environment of a small school in which both sound academic and personal development go hand in hand. The School aims to foster and maximise the individual talents of each girl while encouraging her to think independently, act in a responsible way and acquire self-discipline.

The compact site has been developed in recent years to extend the school's facilities.

The games facilities used are among the best in the area, covering a wide range of sport. Outward bound courses are organised on a regular basis and this wide range of sporting activities forms the basis for the study of a GCSE in Physical Education at the age of 14 and the Bronze Award of the Duke of Edinburgh's Award Scheme.

The Alice Nursery is situated approximately 10 minutes' drive from the main school. From September 2008 the Nursery will be open from 8.45 am until 3.45 pm. The day will be divided into morning and afternoon sessions with a break in the middle of the day for lunch. Girls may attend Nursery for the whole day, morning only or afternoons only. Pupils follow a stimulating but demanding curriculum in preparation for the main school.

The curriculum, embracing the National Curriculum, is designed to give a broad education in which the active acquisition of skills, as well as knowledge is encouraged. Children are familiarised with computers from the Preparatory Department upwards with all pupils taking the RSA Computer Literacy and Information Technology Certificate by the age of 14.

Educational visits to take advantage of the facilities of London in particular are considered important and are often arranged.

The performing arts are encouraged in the school and each term sees a large number of pupils taking part in plays, musicals and concerts.

Careers education is an integral part of the timetabled curriculum from 11–16 and all pupils participate in careers lectures, exhibitions and work experience placements.

Pupils are prepared for up to 10 GCSE subjects, with a view to continuing their studies to A level and beyond.

Fees per term (2008-2009). Nursery: £32 per full day; Prep £2,250; Junior £2,660; Senior £3,400.

Scholarships. Academic scholarships and exhibitions of up to 50% of fees and Music awards are available to candidates aged 11+ for entry in September.

Entrance. Admission to all forms is by test and interview, the main intakes being at 3+, 4+ and 11+.

Charitable status. Palmers Green High School Limited is a Registered Charity, number 312629. It exists for the education of girls.

The Perse School for Girls and the Stephen Perse Sixth Form College

Union Road Cambridge CB2 1HF
Tel: 01223 454700; 01223 454701 (Bursar)
Fax: 01223 467420
e-mail: office@perse.cambs.sch.uk
website: www.perse.cambs.sch.uk

Founded 1881.

Governors:
Dr G Sutherland (*Chairman*)

Lady Adrian
Dr H D Allen
Mr C H W Birch
Mr R F Blanchard
Dr M T Caleresu
Professor C Carpenter
Mrs P Cleobury
Dr A Crowden
Mr J Dix
Dr E Powell
Councillor S Reid
Mrs J Rigby
Mr A Ross
Professor B Sahakian
Dr F Salmon
Ms N M Silverleaf
Mrs R Wenham

Clerk to the Governors: Mrs S Wall

***Principal*: Miss P M Kelleher**, MA Oxon, MA Sussex

Vice-Principal, Curriculum: Dr C E Mullen, BA Hons, PhD London (*French & Latin*)

Head of Senior School, Pastoral: Dr H Stringer, BA Hons, MA, DPhil (*History*)

Director of Sixth Form: Mr S D Armitage, BA Hons Oxon, MPhil Cantab

Director of Teaching and Learning: Miss B Pankhurst, BA Cantab, MA Cantab

Senior School Staff (Full-Time):
* *Head of Department*

Ms E Anderson (**Art*)
Miss R Appleton, BA Hons Cantab, MPhil Oxon (**English*)
Ms H Barrell, CYGNET (*Drama*)
Mrs C M Beadle, BA York (*Chemistry, Year Head*)
Mr R Bett, BA Hons Loughborough, LTCL (**Design Technology*)
Mrs L Booth, BA Warwick (*Physical Education*)
Mr P Bullen-Smith, BSc Bristol (*Economics*)
Miss H Chambers, BA Hons Cantab (*Classics*)
Mrs T Churilina, BA St Petersburg (*Russian*)
Mrs E Currie, BEd Cantab (*Religious Studies*)
Mrs G Dambaza, BA Cantab (**Physics*)
Miss C Freeman, MA Cantab (*German*)
Ms D Gillanders, BA Hons Leicester (**Mathematics*)
Mrs N Goldup, BA Hons Ulster (*Textiles*)
Mrs J Handcock, BSc Hons Exeter (**Information Technology*)
Mrs B Horley, BA Hons Birmingham, MA OU (**Religious Studies*)
Mr S Jack, BA Hons Cantab, MA Cantab (**History*)
Mrs D Jimenez, BA Hons Manchester (**Spanish*)
Miss R Johnson, BSc Hons Lancaster (**Careers, *PSHE*)
Miss S Juggins, BSc Loughborough, MSc Leicester (**Physical Education*)
Miss A Kilby, MA Cantab (*Classics, Year Head*)
Mlle J M Lambert, MA Cantab (*French*)
Mrs L Lloyd, MA Oxon (*Biology, Sixth Form Senior Tutor*)
Mrs S Lynn, BSc Hons Bristol (*Chemistry, *Science*)
Mrs E Mack, BA Hons York (*English*)
Mrs C Mahey, Agrégée, M-ès-L Bordeaux, CAPES (**French*)
Miss F Mason, BEd Hons London (**Drama*)
Ms S McPhoenix, BA Cape Town, Dip RSA King's College London (*English*)
Mrs T McMahon, BEd Canberra (*Physical Education*)
Mr V Minei, BSc Hons OU (**Italian*)
Miss K Murray, BA Canberra (*Physical Education*)
Mrs L Norman, BA Hons Cantab, MA Cantab (*Mathematics*)
Miss S Parente, MA Lyon (*French*)
Mrs J Paris, BSc Hons Leeds (**Chemistry*)
Mrs J Payne, BA Cantab (*General Studies Coordinator, History*)
Mrs E Pyle, BA Oxon, MSc Aberdeen (**Geography*)
Mrs K Roberts, BMus King's College London (*Music*)

Mr M Rudd, MA Oxon (*Music*)
Mr A Reid, BA Hons Chelsea School of Art, MA Oxford Brookes (*DT*)
Mrs J Reilly, BA Hons Sheffield, MA OU (*Spanish*)
Mrs C Ryan, DUEL Orleans, License Orleans (*French*)
Mr P Ryan, BSc Hons Manchester, MSc Manchester (*ICT*)
Dr S Sangster, BA Hons Oxon, PhD Cantab (*Biology*)
Mrs A Smith, BSc Hons York (*Mathematics*)
Mrs A Thompson, BA Liverpool, MPhil Oxon (**Classics*)
Dr H Timo, BA Hons Nottingham, PhD Nottingham (*English*)
Mr A Williams, BSc Hons Exeter (*Geography*)
Mrs S Williams, BSc Hons Manchester (**Biology*)
Mrs E Wilshaw, BA Sheffield (*Art*)
Miss E Wood, GRSM, ARMCM (*Music, Projects Manager*)

PA to the Principal: Mrs V Farbon

Bursar: Mrs J Neale

The Senior School comprises over 600 girls between the ages of eleven and eighteen. There are 54 full-time and 17 part-time teaching staff and 30 peripatetic music staff. The Junior School has over 170 girls between the ages of seven and ten with 11 full-time staff. Some Senior School staff also teach in the Junior School. The School's own entrance tests and interviews are held annually for applicants at 7+, 8+, 9+, 10+, 11+ and 13+. There is also regular entry at the Sixth Form stage, on the results of interviews and GCSE examinations. Entry to other year groups is by testing and interview if places are available.

Fees per term (2008-2009). Junior School £3,600; Senior School £4,230, Sixth Form £4,035.

Extras: Individual music lessons in most instruments, speech and drama.

Scholarships, Exhibitions and Bursaries. One Exhibition is offered by Trinity College, Cambridge, to a student going up to Oxford or Cambridge. Sixth Form Scholarships and Exhibitions are awarded on academic merit based on an essay and interviews. A Sixth Form Music Scholarship is also offered. Scholarships for KS3 are based on performance in the entrance tests. Bursaries are available for pupils in the Senior School. Information about these may be obtained from the Principal.

Senior School Curriculum. The School celebrates achievement in all aspects of school life. It offers a first-class, broad, well-balanced curriculum in a supportive and structured environment and provides opportunities and challenges for pupils to discover their talents and to reach their full potential. At Key Stage 3 there is a three-form entry; forms are unstreamed with setting in certain subjects. Pupils acquire knowledge and skills in a very wide range of subjects which retain the finest traditions and promote newer technologies. A second Modern Language (German, Italian, Russian or Spanish) and Latin are introduced in Year 8. At GCSE the compulsory core consists of English, English Literature, Mathematics, French, Biology, Chemistry, and Physics (double or triple award). The options, of which girls choose three or four, include the second Modern Language, History, Geography, Religious Studies, Latin, Greek, Design and Technology, Information Technology, Art, Drama, Music, and Textiles. Pupils who sit French GCSE in Year 10 may take a certificate in Japanese in Year 11. Courses in Physical Education and General Religious Education continue throughout the Middle School, together with PSHE and Careers Guidance. Class excursions, fieldwork, foreign exchanges, clubs, activities, and theme days enrich the curriculum. International links are strong, with six modern languages taught, partner schools in Portugal, Finland and Hungary for a Year 9 Creative Arts project, and several cross-curricular ventures with an international dimension. Drama, Music and Sport thrive both within and beyond the curriculum.

Stephen Perse Sixth Form College. The School has established a sixth form college on a separate site offering both traditional A Level courses alongside the IB Diploma Programme.

AS/A2 courses are offered in the following subjects: English, English Language and Literature, Mathematics, Further Mathematics, Computing, Biology, Human Biology, Chemistry, Physics, Psychology, Economics, Geography, History, Religious Studies, Classical Civilisation, Latin, Greek, French, German, Italian, Japanese (AS only), Russian, Spanish, Design and Technology, Art, Music, Theatre Studies, and Textiles. Students have traditionally chosen to broaden their Sixth Form studies and can choose up to five subjects at AS in the first year, reducing to three or four A Levels in the second year. In addition, ICT is delivered through a compulsory General Studies programme which leads to AS Level. Students may also choose certificated courses from a Complementary Studies programme: Foreign Languages at Work (FLAW) in French, German, Italian, Russian and Spanish, further GCSE subjects in the Creative Arts and Technology, Classical Greek, languages ab initio including Japanese, and ICT. All students participate in Creative Activities which offers sporting and leisure activities as well as cultural pursuits. European Work Experience is available for linguists and overseas visits extend the experience of other subjects.

IB Diploma Programme subjects include a compulsory CAS module, Theory of Knowledge, and a selection from the following courses at Higher and Standard Level: English, Latin, German, French, Italian, Spanish, Russian, Economics, Environmental Systems and Societies, Geography, History, Philosophy, Psychology, Biology, Chemistry, Physics, Mathematics, Theatre, Visual Arts.

The School is a member of ISCO and has links with Cambridgeshire Connexions. An extensive careers programme, including individual counselling, enables students to make informed choices about Higher Education and Careers.

Results. The results are consistently outstanding. In 2007, 79% of A Level results were graded A, 96% A–B and 100% A–C. At GCSE 63% of results were graded A*, 93% A*–A, and 99.5% A*–B.

Junior School Curriculum. The Junior School aims to nurture enthusiasm for knowledge and skills and to encourage imagination in a happy and secure environment. The curriculum includes English, Mathematics, Science, French, History, Geography, Religious Studies, Information Technology, Design and Technology, Art, Music, Drama, Physical Education and PSHE. Recorder, violin, cello and speech and drama classes are available in addition to individual music and speech tuition. Staff develop cross-curricular projects and arrange outings both locally and further afield, including residential visits. The interests of pupils are also catered for in the range of clubs and societies.

Pastoral Care. Great emphasis is placed on pastoral care and the well-being of all pupils. Established pastoral structures support the pupils and foster personal development, responsibility and informed choice. Subject teachers and year staff care for the academic progress and individual welfare of each student.

Buildings and Facilities. The School is situated in the centre of Cambridge. Facilities include well-equipped laboratories, language laboratories, computer rooms, a drama studio, a DT workshop, netball and tennis courts and hockey pitches, including an all-weather surface pitch. The Bedson Music Wing provides 18 individual teaching rooms. The Junior School building has been re-built and refurbished and was re-opened in January 2001. The Senior School has just completed a major redevelopment of its hall and dining facilities, to include a two-storey building on the site of the previous School Hall. The Senior School opened a new library and learning resource centre in March 2008.

Opening in September 2008, a brand new Sixth Form College has been built purposefully for pupils. This is a co-educational facility on Shaftesbury Road and includes disabled access to all areas.

Old Persean Guild. *Secretary*: Miss Claire Gould, c/o The Perse School for Girls, Union Road, Cambridge CB2 1HF.

Charitable status. The Perse School for Girls and the Stephen Perse Sixth Form College is a Registered Charity, number 1120608, and a Company Limited by Guarantee, number 6113565.

Peterborough High School

A Woodard School

Thorpe Road Peterborough PE3 6JF
Tel: 01733 343357 Bursar: 01733 355720
Fax: 01733 355710
e-mail: phs@peterboroughhigh.co.uk
website: www.peterboroughhigh.co.uk

Peterborough High School provides care and education for girls aged 6 weeks–18 years and boys aged 6 weeks–11 years. It was founded in 1895 and welcomes pupils from a variety of faiths and cultures. The school, which has its own chapel and promotes the teaching of Christian principles, prides itself on excellent examination results and outstanding pastoral care.

School Council:
Chairman: Miss L Ayres, LLB
Mr C Beard
Dr D L Chinn
Mrs L Frisby
Canon R Hemingray, LLB
Prof C J Howe, MA, DPhil, FLS
Mrs E Payne
The Revd Canon B Ruddock
Mr D Sandbach, FCA
Mr P Southern
Mrs D J Ward
Air Commodore MCG Wilson RAF Retd
The Senior Provost, The Woodard Corporation

***Head*: Mr A Meadows**, BSc Hons Manchester

Deputy Headmistress: Miss P M Facy, BEd Hons Keele (*Home Economics*)
Director of Studies: Mrs L Chambers, MA Oxford
Head of the Preparatory Department: Mrs A M Elding, MEd OU, BEd Hons Derby

Staff:
Mr S Awcock, BSc Hons De Montfort (*Head of Science, Physics*)
Mrs A M Axe, BA Hons Birmingham (*Physical Education*)
Mr P Batterbury, BSc Hons Durham (*Biology*)
Mr K D Bingham, BA Hons Hull (*Preparatory Department*)
Mrs L Boyle Cert EYP (*Preparatory Department*)
Mrs K A Brown, BA Hons Oxford (*Mathematics*)
Miss S M Clarkson, BA Hons Cantab (*History*)
Mr G Cloke, BSc Reading (*Preparatory Department*)
Mrs P Cooper, BEd Cantab, DipEd Bedford (*PE*)
Mrs C Coulson, MSc OU (*Business Studies and ICT*)
Mrs K Davis, BSc Newcastle upon Tyne (*Chemistry*)
Mrs S Davis, BEd Hons Anglia (*Preparatory Department*)
Mrs R Ditcher, BSc Hons Greenwich (*Preparatory Department*)
Ms T Doyle, MNATD (*Director of Creative Arts*)
Mrs J Evans, Licence Limoges (*French*)
Mrs S Fiddy, BEd Oxon (*Preparatory Department*)
Mrs E Foster, MA Oxon (*Mathematics*)
Mrs L Grinyer, BEd Hons Warwick (*English*)
Mrs O Guillet, BA Hons Loughborough (*English*)
Mrs R Hampson, BA Hons Derby (*Art, Textiles*)
Mr A Harwin, BA Hons Norwich (*Art*)
Mr D Hodges, BA Hons London (*Geography and History*)
Mr A Jackson, BA Hons Warwick (*German*)
Mr C King, BSc Hons, CMath, MIMA Keele (*Mathematics*)
Mrs B A Laing, BA, DipRSA Drama Edinburgh (*Drama*)
Revd C Mason, BA Hons Leicester (*Chaplain, Religious Studies*)
Mrs G Mason, OND Hotel & Catering (*Food Technology & Preparatory Classroom Assistant*)
Miss R J Mayle, BA Hons Reading (*Geography*)
Mrs I McGregor, BA Hons Munich (*German*)
Mr C H McManus, BA Hons Ulster (*Director of Sixth Form, History*)
Ms L Nicol, BA Hons Exeter (*French*)
Mr M Ratchford, BA Hons York (*Preparatory Department*)
Mrs P Samuels, LGSM (*Speech & Drama*)
Mrs M Sharp, CertEd, NFF Assoc Member of Early Years Glasgow (*Preparatory Department*)
Miss K Smith, BSc Hons Birmingham (*Physical Education*)
Miss L Smith, BEd Hons Wales (*Preparatory Department*)
Mrs A Taylor, BA Hons Oxon (*Preparatory Department*)
Mrs S Ward, BSc Hons Leeds, PGCE (*Science*)

Music Department:
Mr M Vessey, CertEd London (*Director of Music*)
Mr I Stafford, BEd (*Choir Master*)
Mrs H Bell, DipMus OU, ATCL, MusEd (*Flute*)
Mrs N Gibbons, MMus RCM, MPhil Cantab (*Piano*)
Mrs E Hamilton-Box, BA Hons, LTCL (*Violin*)
Mr J Radford, BA Hons Music (*Brass*)
Mrs Y Sandison, PPRNCM (*Singing*)

Boarding House:
Mr & Mrs N Kirkwood (*House Parents*)
Mrs A Heard, BA Hons Durham (*Matron*)

Administrative Officers:
Bursar: Mr C Charlton, BA Hons
Head's Secretary: Mrs A Field
Marketing Manager/Registrar: Ms L Hodgkinson
Administration Assistant: Mrs J Percival
Accounts: Mrs P Chapman
Domestic Bursar: Mrs Z Clark
Estate Manager: Mr D Thornton
Laboratory Technician: Mrs P Reid
ICT Technician: Mr D Helstrip
Reprographics: Mrs V Tobin
Bursar's Secretary: Mrs K Ross
LRC Manager: Mrs C Thomson
Development Manager: Mrs J Hart

Situation and Buildings. The School is located in beautiful secluded grounds, near the centre of Peterborough, 50 minutes by fast train from King's Cross and easily accessible by road from the A1 and A47. The elegant Victorian house which formed the original School is now the centre of a modern purpose-built complex of classrooms, well-equipped laboratories, Music School, Gymnasium, Art Block, Sixth Form Centre, Library and a modern ICT Suite. A new Refectory Gallery was completed in September 2006.

Boarding. Peterborough High is mainly a day school, but there is a boarding house which offers termly and weekly facilities for girls from 7–18 and flexi-boarding for both girls and boys, from the age of 7.

The Preparatory Department. Boys and girls are admitted into the Reception Class from the age of 3+. The National Tests are taken at Key Stage One and Two. The whole range of Key Stage subjects is covered in addition to a variety of other subjects and activities. Some subjects are taught by specialist staff from the Senior School. There is emphasis on academic standards, Physical Education, Music and Drama, with concerts or productions several times a year.

The Senior School. The curriculum of the main school is characterised by small classes and an emphasis on individual guidance and target-setting. A balanced programme leads to high achievement at GCSE in up to ten subjects. English, Mathematics, Science, Religious Education, Games and PE, remain compulsory throughout; Languages, History and Geography, Art (including Textiles), Music, Drama and Physical Education form the matrix of options. Unusually, both German and French are studied from Year 7.

Pupils are selected from the entrance examination and thereafter are in unstreamed tutor groups, although there is setting in Mathematics and Science.

The school has a large, modern ICT suite with state-of-the-art equipment. All classrooms are networked. ICT skills are central to the work of every department, and coordinated to allow the girls to build up CLAIT certification in several modules by the end of Year 11.

There are specialist laboratories for all sciences.

The Sixth Form offers AS and A2 courses in English Literature, Mathematics, Further Mathematics, Biology, Chemistry, Physics, Psychology, Media Studies, Theatre Studies, Travel & Tourism, Physical Education, Geography, History, French, German, Art, Music, Religious Studies and Business Studies. General Studies and Critical Thinking are available at AS Level.

All Sixth Form students follow an intensive tutorial programme in the skills and techniques of study, and build up a portfolio. The destination of most Sixth Formers is university.

As a school with pupils from Reception and children in the Nursery from 6 weeks and above, older girls have many opportunities to develop a sense of involvement and responsibility, and carry out valuable service in the wider community of the city during the Sixth Form. Business sense is developed through the Young Enterprise scheme, in which the school has reached the national final.

A thoughtful and balanced programme of personal and social education operates throughout the school, and includes careers advice and guidance.

The Nursery. Peterborough High School Nursery offers daycare for children aged from 6 weeks to 4 years. Optional lessons include French, Ballet and Little Kickers football.

Religion. Weekly Communion Services are held in the School Chapel. Arrangements are also made for termly boarders to attend local churches, including Peterborough Cathedral, or to worship in the School Chapel on Sundays.

Music and Drama. The music of the school, in particular its choral tradition, is renowned and the school is benefiting from its new Centre for Creative Arts. Tuition in piano and all orchestral instruments is available. Major theatrical and musical productions take place several times a year, and the school enjoys its links with theatres in the city. Standards are extremely high.

Games and Physical Education. The pupils achieve outstanding success in team and individual sports and athletics. Many girls have represented the county, the region, and even England. The school estate is spacious with several pitches and all-weather courts. The Olympic standard sporting facilities of the city are within easy reach for swimming and major athletic events.

Extra-curricular Activities. Many clubs and societies operate in extra-curricular time, and field visits and excursions illuminate classroom work. Exchange schemes for French and German operate on an annual basis to Paris and Augsburg. Many pupils undertake the Duke of Edinburgh's Award Scheme at both Bronze and Gold levels, with outstanding success.

Fees per term (2008-2009). Senior School: £3,497 (day), £5,573 (weekly boarding), £6,457 (termly boarding).

Preparatory Department: Day: £2,476 (Reception/Infants), £3,004 (Yrs 3–6); Boarding (Yrs 3–6): £5,252 (weekly), £5,969 (termly).

Scholarships. Academic, Art and Music are the main scholarships available. Please apply to the Head for more information.

Westwoodians' Association. Hon Chairman: Miss L Wilcox, 14 Martins Way, Orton Waterville, Peterborough, PE2 5DY.

Charitable status. Peterborough High School Limited is a Registered Charity, number 269667. It is an independent school which exists to promote the education of children.

Pipers Corner School
High Wycombe

Great Kingshill High Wycombe Bucks HP15 6LP
Tel: 01494 718255
Fax: 01494 719806
e-mail: theschool@piperscorner.co.uk
website: www.piperscorner.co.uk

Visitor: The Rt Revd The Lord Bishop of Buckingham

Board of Governors:
Chairman of Governors: R Corner, Esq, LLB Hons
Lady Allison (*Vice-Chairman*)
M F T Harborne, Esq (*Vice-Chairman*)
Mrs B Y Boyton-Corbett, CertEd, DipEd
The Countess of Buckinghamshire
B Callaghan, Esq, FCA
D B Jones, Esq
Professor P B Mogford
J H Phimester, Esq
H Roberts, Esq

***Headmistress*: Mrs H J Ness-Gifford**, BA Hons Exeter, PGCE

Deputy Head: Mrs H Murphy, MA Oxon, PGCE

Bursar and Clerk to the Governors: Mr P R Forrester, MA, FCA

Pipers Corner is an independent boarding and day school for girls aged 3–18. Set in 36 acres of beautiful Chiltern countryside, the school is 4 miles north of High Wycombe and 2 miles from Great Missenden.

From Pre-Prep through to Sixth Form there a focus on academic excellence which is reflected in the quality of teaching we provide and our outstanding examination results. In addition, all girls benefit from involvement in the wider life of the school community. There is an extensive programme of extra-curricular activities on offer – from choir, dance and drama, to lacrosse, swimming and photography – all interests are catered for. Our girls also benefit from the use of our excellent facilities including the swimming pool, sports hall, ICT suite and dance and drama studios.

The boarding community at Pipers offers flexibility, freedom and peace of mind to both girls and their parents. We offer boarding on a full, weekly and flexible basis which means that we can provide practical solutions to the often demanding needs of modern family life. All girls can also take advantage of an extended school day where they are welcome in school from as early as 7.30 am and can remain with us well after the lessons end.

The Pipers Corner environment allows girls to thrive. Whatever their strengths, the girls are challenged and supported as they pursue their own unique learning journeys. This approach enables them to fulfil their academic and personal potential and emerge as mature, confident and independent young women.

Fees per term (2008-2009). (*see Scholarship Entries section*). Day Girls £1,925–£3,975; Weekly Boarders £5,320–£6,470; Full Boarders £5,400–£6,550.

Charitable status. Pipers Corner School is a Registered Charity, number 310635. It exists to provide high quality education for girls.

Polam Hall School

Grange Road Darlington Co Durham DL1 5PA
Tel: 01325 463383
Fax: 01325 383539
e-mail: information@polamhall.com
website: www.polamhall.com

Motto: '*Concordia Crescimus*' – *We Grow in Harmony*

***Headmistress*: Miss M Green**, BA Hons Lancaster

Deputy Headmistress: Mrs S Davison, TDip Darlington Col of Education

Bursar and Clerk to the Governors: Mr M N Carr, ACIB

Polam Hall School was founded in 1848 and is now a day and boarding school for girls aged 3 to 18 of all religious denominations. The school admits boys to the Nursery Department and has a co-educational Sixth Form. The school stands in 20 acres of parkland within 5 minutes' walking distance of Darlington town centre. The school is ideally placed, being close to the main east coast rail line, the A1(M) and Durham Tees Valley Airport, providing excellent access for both local and overseas students.

Numbers on roll. There are over 420 pupils, including 50 boarders, 75 Sixth Form students and 170 Juniors.

Age and method of entry. 3 to 16. Assessment/examination and interview with Headmistress where applicable.

Scholarships and Awards. (*see Scholarship Entries section*). Scholarships and Bursaries available at 7+, 11+, 14+ and 16+, Music Awards at 11+, 14+ and 16+, Sports Scholarship at 16+. One 11+ Scholarship is known as The Simon Bailes Scholarship.

Fees per term (2008-2009). Early Steps: £725 (afternoons only), £1,100 (mornings only), £1,925 (full day with lunch). Junior School: £1,925–£2,730 (Day), £5,325 (Boarding). Senior School: £3,520 (Day), £6,570 (Boarding). Fees for weekly boarders are reduced by £200 per term.

Academic. From Early Steps Nursery to Sixth Form students are encouraged and supported so that they achieve to their full potential. Small classes and dedicated teachers provide students with an excellent education – both in and out of the classroom.

Early Steps Nursery provides Foundation Stage education for girls and boys aged two and a half upwards. The children join with the main school for various activities, joining the Junior School for lunch, but the Nursery is run as its own unit.

Polam Hall Junior School starts at Reception where the girls have a dedicated teacher for all subjects. Once the girls reach Year 3 they embark on a more varied curriculum with a more structured timetabled day and are taught the different subjects by specialist staff.

Girls entering the Senior School take a diagnostic examination, which helps to identify their educational needs. A broad curriculum in Years 7 to 9 leads to girls taking a wide range of GCSE subjects. A choice of 23 subjects is currently available, including the three separate sciences, allowing for individual needs to be addressed.

The Sixth Form is co-educational and is divided into small tutorial groups with over 22 subjects available. Educational visits are arranged to various points of interest around the area and further afield. The students are allocated a Personal Tutor to help guide them through Career and University choices. A Careers room is available to them and a UCAS advisor and an Annual Careers Convention assist in making choices. Almost all pupils go on to higher education.

Extra-Curricular Activities. An outstanding range of activities are available throughout the school. There are regular sports fixtures in lacrosse, hockey, netball, tennis, rounders and athletics. Girls also do gymnastics, modern dance, self-defence, riding, volleyball, trampolining and swimming. There is a Brownie Pack for the Juniors and the Duke of Edinburgh's Award is widely taken up by the Seniors.

Our Learning Support Unit has specialist teachers fully trained in helping girls with learning difficulties, such as dyslexia or dyspraxia. There is also specialist teaching for those for whom English is not their first language.

Boarding. Boarding is available from age 8. There are 3 boarding houses – South View, Grange House and New House. The girls are arranged in small groups and are looked after by 7 Housemistresses who take a sensitive interest in each girl's personal welfare. A full programme of evening and weekend activities is arranged.

Facilities. The school boasts a fully-equipped Science block containing 5 laboratories, a Domestic Science lab, 3 Computer Suites, a school Library containing fully-networked flat-screen computers, and a fully-equipped Theatre seating over 200 people. The Sixth Form has its own Centre for both study and leisure.

A Resource Centre complements teaching in the Junior School and is equipped with 10 computers, interactive whiteboard and library.

PHOSA Polam Hall Old Scholars' Association. *Secretary*: Mrs C Maxey, c/o Polam Hall School, Grange Road, Darlington, DL1 5PA.

Charitable status. Polam Hall School is a Registered Charity, number 527369. Its aim is to provide, maintain, and carry on a school for the education of children.

Portsmouth High School (GDST)

25 Kent Road Southsea Hampshire PO5 3EQ
Tel: 023 9282 6714
Fax: 023 9281 4814
e-mail: headsec@por.gdst.net
website: www.gdst.net/portsmouthhigh

Founded 1882.

This is one of the 29 schools of The Girls' Day School Trust. For general information about the Trust and the composition of its Council, see p. xxiv. Additional information may be found on the school's website and a prospectus pack is available from the Admissions Secretary at the school.

Chairman of the Local Governors: Mr J R Bannell, FRICS

***Head*: Mrs J Clough**, MA Cantab

Deputy Head: Mr C J Campbell, BSc Aston, MSc Surrey

Head of the Junior Department: Mrs C Hadfield, CertEd Kingston, DipMgtSt Leeds Polytechnic, ALCM

Admissions Secretary: Mrs C Baczynski

Number of Pupils. 600. 425 are in the Senior School, including 91 in the Sixth Form.

Portsmouth High School provides a happy, vibrant and safe educational environment in which girls of intellectual promise can achieve the success they deserve. Each girl is nurtured so that she feels valued and is able to develop into a confident, caring and socially responsible adult. A broad based education encourages each girl's talents and potential to the full in an atmosphere of achievement and excellence. Characteristic of the GDST philosophy, Portsmouth High School has a profile of sustained academic achievement and strong relationships with the local community. Situated close to the sea the school draws pupils from an extensive area of Hampshire, West Sussex and the Isle of Wight. All major transport providers serve the area.

The Senior School is accommodated in the original building, and an ongoing capital investment programme has seen the development of a Sport, Design Technology and Geography building on the senior school site.

A partnership with the University of Portsmouth means the school has joint use of the Langstone sports ground facilities, including a floodlit synthetic turf pitch and a new multi-use games area; the site is just 2 miles from the school. In addition, the school site facilities include a Sport England standard sports hall, 4 hard tennis courts and 6 netball courts, with a recently re-laid senior school netball court.

The Junior School is located 2 minutes' walk away in a wonderful period house with extensive gardens and a range of indoor and outdoor facilities. Major investment in the Junior School saw the completion of an award-winning Early Years building. With the addition of a nursery class, the school is able to offer continuity of education throughout the Foundation Stage.

Curriculum. The aim at Portsmouth High School is to foster in each girl an appreciation of aesthetic, cultural, spiritual and moral values and to meet the needs of all girls, be they educational or pastoral, by providing appropriate teaching, advice and support. A balanced programme of study delays the need to make subject choices as long as possible and in this way, the widest career options are maintained. There is the highest level of achievement in a wide variety of academic subjects, sport, music and drama. In addition to the GCSE and Sixth Form subjects there is an extensive programme of extra-curricular activities ranging from aerobics to public speaking. Girls have the opportunity to become involved in World Challenge and the Duke of Edinburgh's Award Scheme. There are regular exchange trips, music tours and opportunities for pupils to undertake work experience. Sixth Form students do not wear uniform and have a modernised separate Sixth Form Centre with a large common room, kitchen, study rooms and IT room.

Admission procedures/entrance exams. At 11+ entry the examinations in Mathematics and English are designed to test potential rather than knowledge. Prior to the test all girls take part in a series of team activities in an informal setting. Specimen papers are available following registration. Sixth Form entry is based on having 7 or more GCSEs with grades A to C with A or B in the subjects that students wish to study at AS and A2 Level. Entry into the Junior School is based on assessments dependent on age.

Fees per term (2008-2009). Senior School £2,966, Junior Department £2,150, Nursery £1,776.

The fees cover the regular curriculum, school books, stationery and other materials, public examinations, choral music, games and swimming, but not optional extra subjects or school meals.

The fees for extra subjects, including individual lessons in instrumental music and speech training, are shown in the Admissions Handbook.

Scholarships and Bursaries. The GDST makes available to the school a number of scholarships and bursaries. Bursaries are means tested and are intended to ensure that the school remains accessible to bright girls who would be unable to enter the school without financial assistance. A number of scholarships are available to internal or external candidates for entry at 11+. In addition to Sixth Form Academic Scholarships, we are also able to offer 16+ scholarships / exhibitions for Art, Drama and PE. There are also music scholarships for 11+, 13+ and 16+ entry.

Charitable status. Portsmouth High School is part of The Girls' Day School Trust, which is a Registered Charity, number 306983. The aim of the Trust is to provide a fine academic education for girls, which is distinguished by breadth.

The Princess Helena College

Preston Hitchin Hertfordshire SG4 7RT
Tel: 01462 432100
Fax: 01462 443871
e-mail: head@phc.herts.sch.uk
website: www.phc.herts.sch.uk

Motto: *Fortis qui se vincit*

Patron: Her Majesty the Queen

President: HRH The Duchess of Gloucester

Vice-President: Miss Mary Beattie, MBE, JP, DL

Governing Body:
Chairman: Dr Mary Buchanan, MA, MIMMM, CEng, PhD
Vice-Chairman: Mr Tim J R Wood
Treasurer: Mr George McNaught

Clerk to the Governors and Bursar: Mr Christopher Marley

***Headmistress*: Mrs Jo-Anne Duncan**, MA St Andrews

Deputy Head: Mrs Camilla Wilson, BEd Liverpool

Director of Studies: Mr Keith Miller, MA Herts, BEd

Head of Sixth Form: Ms Rachel Poston, BSc, PGCE

Head's PA & Registrar: Mrs Heather Baim

Old Girls' Association Secretary: Mrs Susannah Goodbody

The Princess Helena College (PHC) is a dynamic school, where you will find happy, successful and confident day girls and boarders aged 11–18. We provide a vibrant, modern and challenging education whilst respecting and encouraging traditional values.

History. Founded in 1820 we are one of England's oldest academic girls' schools. We are extremely proud of our heritage and aim to maintain high academic standards and respect for traditional values. The school was founded for daughters of officers who had served in the Napoleonic Wars and daughters of Anglican priests. We now encourage this tradition by offering bursaries to daughters from families that are in the forces and the clergy.

Ethos. Your daughter is an individual and at PHC we aim to inspire her to achieve in both her academic and personal goals. We choose to remain a small school because we strongly believe this unique approach provides many benefits in academic, extra-curricular and pastoral areas. The educational benefits include a flexible curriculum and small classes. Both result in individual attention and excellent value-added attainment. A smaller school allows teachers to understand girls' individual learning styles, to recognise their particular strengths and weaknesses and to set individual learning targets. In a small school pastoral care is strengthened by excellent relations between pupils and staff, which result in a strong family atmosphere. Knowing our girls well allows us to encourage them to take risks safe in the knowledge that we will support them. This allows every girl to be challenged, to take risks, to achieve and to grow. Within a small school your daughter's chances of being selected for a team, a place in the orchestra, a part in a play or a position of responsibility are far higher. Having the opportunity to take part or perform in these activities will increase her confidence and self-belief. The value of this should not be underestimated.

Facilities. As well as an idyllic and safe learning environment, PHC has excellent educational facilities. The main building is a beautiful Queen Anne mansion that lies in fine Gertrude Jekyll gardens and 183 acres of parkland. Over the past 5 years the school has invested heavily in developing the facilities for all girls. In the last year a new fitness suite has been added, the Sixth Form boarding facilities have been improved and the school dining room has been refurbished. Other developments include a new science centre, art and design studios, a Sixth Form study and recreational area in the main school, and the refurbished learning resources centre.

Curriculum. We offer each girl the opportunity to excel within a varied and stimulating curriculum. Taught in small classes by highly qualified and enthusiastic teachers who are dedicated to supporting each girl's talents and interests, our girls attain high levels of academic excellence and confidence. Girls are taught in sets that rarely exceed 18 and their potential and progress is carefully monitored.

The lower school curriculum (Years 7–9) consists of English, French, Spanish, Latin, German, Mathematics, Information Communications Technology, Biology, Physics, Chemistry, History, Geography, Religious Education, Music, Drama, Physical Education, Art, Design and Technology. There are also programmes in PCC (PSHE, Citizenship and Careers), touch typing and information resource skills.

Prior to the Sixth Form, girls choose their GCSE subjects, following much consultation with staff and parents. On average, girls study between 8 and 10 GCSE subjects. The pass rate A*–C is 98% with over 50% of the GCSEs being passed at A* or A grade.

In the Sixth Form, A Level courses are available in all the traditional academic subjects, as well as Business Studies, Dance, Government & Politics, Health & Social Care, Media Studies, Psychology and Theatre Studies. Extensive career and Higher Education support and advice is provided.

A flexible approach to boarding. PHC is a vibrant community made up of day girls and boarders. We offer a very flexible approach to boarding and full, weekly, and flexible boarding are well established. Day girls can choose to stay into the early evening to make full use of the optional extended school day, participating in supervised prep or one of the numerous after school activities.

The Arts. PHC is particularly strong in Art & Design, Dance, Drama, Music and Speech & Drama. Girls may enter examinations in all these areas. Dance is a hugely popular activity, with girls learning jazz, modern, ballet, Irish and tap. Most of the College is involved in some form of musical activity, with many girls choosing to take part in one of the many different music groups or ensembles. Plays are staged throughout the year and there are regular joint productions with neighbouring boys' and co-educational schools.

Sport. In addition to timetabled lessons, there are sports activities on weekdays after school and on some Saturdays. Girls participate in a wide range of sports including lacrosse, netball, tennis, athletics, badminton, cross-country, rounders and swimming. Girls at PHC are given the opportunity to participate in competitive sport, recreational sport and fitness – we aim to encourage all girls to find an activity they will enjoy at school and in the future.

Extra-curricular activities. Life is busy at PHC – there is an exciting array of extra-curricular activities and clubs. Girls can choose to join in with these activities either during their extended lunch break or in the early evening. From photography to public speaking, from language club to life saving and from touch typing to trampolining, there is an activity for everyone. The Duke of Edinburgh's Award Scheme is also a popular activity, with girls attaining Gold, Silver and Bronze awards each year. CCF, with St Columba's College, is an increasingly popular activity.

Lifeskills Programme. We recognise the importance of developing young women who demonstrate a range of abilities above and beyond their academic achievements. Our LINKS lifeskills programme provides all girls with the enrichment experiences required to prepare them for life beyond PHC. These include independence of thought, self-confidence, teamwork, effective communication and problem-solving. LINKS has been designed to specifically provide activities, lectures and experiences that will allow all students to cultivate these valuable skills.

Religion. Girls attend the nearby village church of St Martin's in Preston, which is also used for the school's Confirmation Services. Although the school's affiliation is to the Church of England, girls of other denominations and religions are welcomed.

Location. Set in 183 acres of rural parkland the College offers an easily accessible location within a safe and beautiful environment. The College is situated 30 minutes north of London between the A1 and the M1, just 5 minutes from the market town of Hitchin. Our excellent transport links include a network of school minibus routes, rail access (35 minutes to King's Cross) and proximity to several airports (Luton 15 minutes, Stansted 45 and Heathrow 60). Current school bus routes extend to Brookmans Park, Buntingford, Cuffley, Digswell, Enfield, Gustard Wood, Hadley Wood, Harpenden, Hertford, Kimpton, Luton, Potters Bar, Stevenage, Wheathampstead and Welwyn. Possible future routes may include Ashwell, Radlett, Elstree and St Albans.

Admission. We welcome girls aged 11–18. Most girls join the school at age 11 (Year 7), but there are also entrants at age 13 (Year 9) and the Sixth Form (Year 12). Please contact Heather Baim, Registrar (01462 443888) for a prospectus or to find out the date of our next Open Day. All girls must sit either the College's own Entrance Exam or the Common Entrance Exam. Sixth Form places are conditional on GCSE results.

Fees per term (2008-2009). Day Girls: Years 7 and 8 £4,020; Years 9–Sixth Form £5,080. Weekly Boarding or Full Boarding: Years 7 and 8 £5,745; Years 9–Sixth Form £7,335. Fees include lunch and supervised prep but exclude some books. Flexible boarding costs between £39 and £47 per night.

Scholarships and Bursaries. Some scholarships (worth up to 15% of annual fees) are available for academically able pupils. Art, Drama, Music and Sport scholarships are also available. Bursaries of 10% of fees are available for daughters of the clergy and of members of the armed forces. Sibling bursaries of 5% of fees.

Charitable status. The Princess Helena College is a Registered Charity, number 311064. It was founded in 1820 for the purposes of education.

Prior's Field

Godalming Surrey GU7 2RH
Tel: 01483 810551
Fax: 01483 810180
e-mail: office@priorsfieldschool.com
website: www.priorsfieldschool.com

Founded in 1902.

Motto: *We live by admiration, hope and love.*

Board of Governors:
Chairman: Mr R Green, FCA
Mr N A Andrews, LLB
Mr B G Burton-Brown, BSc
Mrs D C C Colvin
Nr I N H Davis, BA, BArch, RIBA
Dr L Elghali, MSc, EngD, AIEMA
Mrs C W J Formstone, HDCR
Mrs M Huxley, BSc, ARICS, PGCE
Mrs D H Jerwood, MA
Mr R W J Long, FRICS
Mr J R MacLeod
Mrs A Morris, BA
Mrs E A S Prescott-Decie, MA
Mr C J D Robinson, TD, BA
Mr A R Taylor, BA, PGCE

***Headmistress*: Mrs Julie A Roseblade**, MA (*English, Drama*)

Deputy Head (*Pastoral*): Mrs Jane Lunnon, BA (*English*)
Deputy Head (*Curriculum*): Mrs Ruth Saunders, BSc (*ICT*)
Bursar and Clerk to the Governors: Mrs Leonie Ranson, BA

Academic Staff:
Miss Ana Alvarez Monferrer (*Spanish Assistant*)
Mrs Ann Barnes, BA (*Textiles*)
Mrs Rachel Bartlett, BSc (*Mathematics*)
Mr Parvesh Behal (*Mathematics*)
Mrs Penny Boisset, MA (*Psychology*)
Mrs Wendy Braithwaite, BA (*Spanish, French*)
Mrs Isobel Broadbent-Trower, BA (*Sociology*)
Mrs Jillian Buckley, MEd, DMS, MIMgt (*Head of Careers*)
Mr Nigel Cassidy, BMus Hons, PGCert, GSMD, LTCL (*Music*)
Mrs Nicola Castle, LLB, DipEd, AMBDA (*Head of Learning Support*)
Mrs Mary Claire Cook, BEd, CertEd (*Geography, Charities, Head of Lower School*)
Miss Cendrine Conchon, Maîtrise LCE (*French and Spanish*)
Mrs Catherine Cundy, BA (*Director of Music*)
Mr Bruno Di Mario, MA (*Photography*)
Mrs Pamela Edworthy, BSc, DipSpLD (*Head of Mathematics*)
Mrs Yakuri Elliott (*Japanese*)
Dr Celia Ellis, BSc, PhD (*Biology*)
Ms Andrea Fairbairn, MA (*Mathematics*)
Mrs Cherry Gay, LTCL, DipTESOL (*English as an Additional Language*)
Miss Joanne Gellard, BA (*Art*)
Mrs Charlotte Gomez, BA (*Spanish, French*)
Miss Louise Gordon (*Physical Education*)
Mr Jeremy Hepworth (*Head of ICT Curriculum*)
Mrs Susan Holmes, BA, CertEd (*Economics, Business Studies, History of Art*)
Mrs Catherine Humphreys, BSc (*Science*)
Mr Geoffrey Jones, BSc, MSc (*Head of Science*)
Miss Katie Kennon, BA, BSc (*Physical Education*)
Mr Stephen Kinder, BA (*Head of Creative Arts*)
Ms Valerie Klein, BA (*Head of Modern Foreign Languages*)
Miss Jaclyn Leach, BSc (*Physical Education*)
Mr Stuart Lodge, BA (*Head of Drama*)
Mrs Desi Lyon, MA (*Head of English*)
Mrs Natasha Macdonald (*Biology*)
Mrs Emma MacMillan, BMus, LRAM, ARCM (*Head of Religious Studies*)
Mrs Paula Miller, BA, DipEd (*History, Sixth Form Day Matron*)
Mrs Georgina Morris, BA (*Drama*)
Mrs Amanda Morwood, MA (*Head of History, Head of Lower Sixth Form*)
Mrs Sarah Onions, MA (*Media Studies*)
Mrs Valerie Page, BA (*English*)
Miss Hester Pretorius, BSc, MEd (*Design Technology, Science*)
Mrs Joanna Prudence, BA, TESOL (*English, Religious Studies, Critical Thinking, Scholars' Tutor*)
Mrs Jose Purkiss, BA, (*Head of Boarding, PSHCE*)
Mrs Kerry Sapseid, BA, DipEd (*English*)
Mr Peter Sapseid, BA, HDE (*English, History, Debating*)
Mr Michael Slocombe, CertEd (*Music Technology*)
Dr McDonald Smith, BSc, PhD (*Chemistry*)
Miss Tiffany Teasdale (*Food Technology*)
Mrs Angie Tipping, BSc, BTeach (*Head of Biology*)
Ms Catrin Treanor, BSc (*Head of Geography, Gifted and Talented Tutor*)
Ms Rachel Troup, BSc (*Mathematics*)
Miss Michelle Trudgeon, BSc (*Head of Physical Education*)
Mrs Karen Wilcock, BSc (*Mathematics, Director of Studies*)

Visiting Staff:
Mrs Barbara Awbery (*Tennis Coaching*)
Mrs Rachel Bowen-Perkins, BMus Hons (*Classical Singing Vocal Tutor*)
Mrs Linda Bomford (*Oboe*)
Mr Mike Briggs, BA Hons (*Violin, Viola*)
Miss Amie Jane Brown (*Rock Singing Vocal Tutor*)
Mr Vic Cox, BA Hons, PGCE (*Bass Guitar*)
Miss Anne Marie Curran, BMus, LRAM (*Violin*)
The Revd John Fellows, MA (*Chaplain*)
Mrs Nicola Fournel, BAMus Hons (*Piano, Theory*)
Mrs Elizabeth Freeston, TCL, Cert TESOL (*English as an Additional Language*)
Mr Nicholas Higgins, BMus, PGCE (*Flute, Clarinet*)
Miss Rachel Howells (*Classical Singing Vocal Tutor*)
Ms Jan Kobzik, ISTD, LLAM (*Speech and Drama*)
Mr Darren Lucas (*Guitar*)
Mr Paul Munro (*Saxophone*)
Ms Emilia O'Connor, GRSM, BMus (*Singing*)
Mrs Karen Porter, BSc (*Mathematics*)
Mr Bob Price (*Trumpet, Trombone*)
Miss Jayne Spencer, AGSM, LGSM, ALCM (*Cello, Theory*)
Mrs Jean Stevens, ATCL, MISM (*Piano, Theory, Associated Board Accompanist*)
Mr Adam Turner (*Tennis Coaching*)
Mrs Karen Van Lokven, BA Hons (*Clarinet*)
Mr Jonathan Wills (*Drums*)

Administration:
PA to Head: Mrs Deborah Roberts-Barter
School Secretary and Office Manager: Mrs Sophie Irving, BA
School Receptionist/Secretary: Mrs Caroline Cook, Miss Judy Sinning
Registrar: Miss Penelope Harris, BSc Hons, MSc
Admissions: Miss Anne French
Old Girls' and Development Office Coordinator: Mrs Margaret Elliott, BA
Management Information Coordinator: Mrs Christine Milton
School Accountant: Mrs Juanita Percival, FCCA
Assistant Accountant: Mrs Diane Cant
Facilities Manager: Mr Gordon Duncan
PA to Bursar: Mrs Liz Harker
Examinations Officer: Mrs Anne Sheldrake, CertEd
Medical Centre:
Mrs Miin Worsdell, RGN, BSc
Mrs Helen Whiffen, SRN, DN
Head of Boarding: Mrs Jose Purkiss, BA
Boarding Housemistresses (1st–5th Forms):
Miss Katie Kennon, BA, BSc
Miss Jacyln Leach, BSc
Mrs Sarah Naylor
Miss Tiffany Teasdale
Sixth Form Housemistrees: Mrs Emma Picken
Assistant Sixth Form Housemistress: Miss Hester Pretorius, MEd, BSc
Sixth Form Day Matron: Mrs Paula Miller, BA, DipEd

Boarding, Marketing and Resources Assistant: Miss Stephanie Bramley
Librarian: Mrs Wendy Hilliam
Laboratory Technician: Mrs Joanne Slaytor
ICT Systems Manager: Mrs Julia Allmark
Network Support Technician: Mr Lincoln Burton
Digital Media Coordinator: Mr Simon Carnell

Age Range. 11–18.

Numbers. Boarders 40, Weekly Boarders 91, Day Girls 219.

The School was founded by Julia Huxley, mother of Aldous and Julian, to provide a progressive and exciting education that also broadened the girls' outlook. This legacy lives on today as PF provides an excellent all-round education which recognises achievement in all its forms.

Visitors to PF frequently tell us that the school has a unique and distinctive 'feel'. We are fortunate in our size – small enough to provide tailored, individual care and large enough to offer a wide and exciting curriculum. Girls choose from over 20 subjects at A Level and from a range of 46 clubs and activities.

Relationships are key to our success and pupils of all abilities do exceptionally well in an environment that builds confidence and encourages everyone to aim high. At Prior's Field each individual can find something at which to shine and we are proud of our track record of "adding value" (top 6% nationally). This is achieved without unnecessary stress and pressure, through small classes, excellent teaching and a careful balance of challenge and support. We know our girls well and encourage them to be themselves, think independently and engage fully in the life of the school and wider community. Opportunities for leadership, initiative and responsibility mean that girls are well equipped for the world ahead. The Sixth Form leave, for the Universities of their choice, as self-assured, well-qualified and interesting young women of integrity.

The Good Schools Guide recently quoted a parent saying that Prior's Field is "one of Surrey's best kept secrets".

Buildings. The original buildings were designed by Charles Voysey and the garden by Gertrude Jekyll. Additions in recent years have been two new ICT rooms, a new Sports Hall, an extension to the Sixth Form House, a new Hall/Theatre, dining room, superb Science Centre and a brand new Library. In addition to the classrooms, the main building includes a Drama studio, technology area and new multimedia digital language laboratory.

Boarding. Weekly boarding is a very popular option for many of our girls and boarders are placed in the care of the Housemistress. Bedrooms are generally shared between one and four girls, the younger girls being in the larger rooms with many senior girls (Year 10 and above) having single study-bedrooms. First form boarders have a dedicated area within the house, including study, kitchen and sitting area. Sixth Form boarders reside in a separate sixth form house, which incorporates 20 en-suite study-bedrooms. Here they lead more independent lives under the supervision of the resident Sixth Form Housemistress. Throughout the boarding houses the emphasis is on working together and the creation of a warm, supportive, environment which enables the girls to achieve highly and mature into young women who think for themselves.

Curriculum. Girls at KS3 follow a general curriculum including Japanese, Spanish, ICT, Design and Technology (including digital photography), Art and Drama as well as all the 'core' subjects. Girls in the First and Second Form follow a course in Thinking and Learning which involves philosophy, touch-typing, debating, library/research and study skills.

GCSE and A Level courses are offered at KS4 and in the Sixth Form. Girls are prepared for Oxbridge and other competitive universities by a dedicated tutor. Others typically go on to study at a wide range of universities and art colleges. Careers is taught across the school as part of the PSHE programme. In addition, visits are arranged to university open days and the school also arranges talks by visitors from a wide range of professions. Fifth formers are encouraged to join a work experience scheme. Those studying languages at A Level are encouraged to take up work placements in Europe. The school has excellent IT provision to support teaching and learning; a well-established programme for its most able students and a programme specifically for scholarship girls.

Music. Music flourishes throughout the school. A wide range of instruments is taught and 70% of the girls take individual lessons. Extra-curricular activities include 3 main choirs, orchestra, jazz group, rock groups and many instrumental and vocal ensembles. Professional engagements include the RPO at Wembley, local festivals, the Royal Albert Hall and churches in London. Music Technology is taught in Years 9 to 11 and offered alongside Music at A Level.

Extra-Curricular Activities. Girls may join over 46 clubs ranging from Drama and Young Engineers to Photography, Rifle Shooting, Salsa and Chess. Older girls can join the Duke of Edinburgh's Award Scheme, Young Enterprise and Model United Nations. Outings and social events with a range of boys' schools, including Eton , Harrow and Charterhouse, are arranged for boarders at the weekends, whilst throughout the year there are numerous educational visits to theatres, adventure and field centres and venues for debating and public-speaking competitions. Each year trips go off to Europe and beyond. In 2006 a group of Fifth and Sixth Form girls went to Peru for a charity venture as part of the school's Outreach programme. In 2009 a group will go to South Africa.

Sport. Hockey, netball, tennis, athletics and rounders are the main games, but opportunities exist for many other sports and dance through the after-school clubs and activities. Games take place in the 23-acre site. Tennis coaching is available throughout the year. Coaching in golf, fencing, self-defence and aerobic training is also available. Ice skating, bowling and swimming take place at the Guildford Spectrum for all pupils who are interested and the equestrian team practises locally and competes in 'eventing'. A number of girls are regular horse-riders at local stables and the school has an eventing team.

Access. The school is situated between Godalming and Guildford and is less than a mile from the A3. Godalming and Guildford are the nearest railway stations, and we are conveniently placed (via the A3 and M25) for both Heathrow and Gatwick Airports. At the start and finish of term, girls may be escorted to, or met from, either airport or railway station. There is a weekly minibus to and from London and girls are collected from and returned to Godalming station each day.

Admission. Admission is by the School's entrance examination. Open days are held every term and individual visits are arranged at parents' convenience by the Registrar.

Scholarships and Bursaries. (*see Scholarship Entries section*). Academic Scholarships of up to 50% of school fees and Exhibitions for Academic promise are offered at 11+ along with scholarships for Art, Music, Drama and PE worth up to 25% fees. There is also a 10% reduction in fees for the daughters of old girls and for siblings. The fee for pupils who have a parent serving in the Armed Forces is 10% of the total boarding fee plus the MOD's CEA. Scholarships are also available at 13+ and again in the Upper School for 3 years, including the Sixth Form. Scholarships are also offered for entry into the Sixth Form and a number of 95% Academic Bursaries are available for Sixth Form day places, for those who would not otherwise be able to access an independent school education.

Fees per term (2008-2009). Boarders £7,150; Day Girls £4,420.

Charitable status. The Prior's Field School Trust Limited is a Registered Charity, number 312038. It exists to promote education and to offer and provide Scholarships, Exhibitions, Prizes and Awards at any school carried on by the Trust.

Putney High School (GDST)

35 Putney Hill London SW15 6BH
Tel: 020 8788 4886
Fax: 020 8789 8068
e-mail: putneyhigh@put.gdst.net
website: www.gdst.net/putneyhigh

Founded 1893.

This is one of the 29 schools of The Girls' Day School Trust. For further information about the Trust, see p. xxiv. A more detailed prospectus may be obtained from the school.

There are about 860 pupils, of whom 550, including a Sixth Form of 140, are in the Senior School (ages 11–18) and 305 in the Junior Department (ages 4–11).

Local Governing Body:
Mr P Dixon, MA, MBA, CEng, MIEF
Mrs L Bond MA
Prof C Kinnon, BSc, PhD
Lady North, OBE, DL, JP, MA (*Council Representative*)
Prof P O'Prey, PhD
Mrs J Railton, BA
Mrs P Sherratt, BSc (*Chairman*)
Mr P Wake, MSc

***Headmistress*: Dr Denise V Lodge**, BSc, MSc, PhD London, PGCE

Senior Leadership Team:
Deputy Head (*Academic*): Dr J Moore, BA Leeds, MA, EdD Open
Deputy Head (*Pastoral*): Ms O Carlin, BSc Imperial
Head of Junior Department: Mrs J Stevens, BA Manchester
Head of Sixth Form: Mr G Casley, BA Bristol
Head of Years 10 & 11: Mrs M Kazi-Fornari, MA Oxon
Head of Middle School: Ms A Simmons, BA Bristol
Assessment Coordinator: Mrs G John, BSc Exeter, MSc London, MSc Sheffield Hallam
School Business Manager: Mrs L Kelleher
Sims.net Coordinator: Mrs R Wells, BA Kingston

Senior Department:

Art:
Mr A Haworth, BA Gloucestershire, MA Royal College of Art
Mr N Murray, BA Camberwell

Business Studies and Economics:
Ms N Bassam, BSc, MA London
Ms J Krey, BSc Limerick
Mr A Ross, BCom Edinburgh

Classics:
Ms A Noble, MA Cambridge
Mrs C Christie, BA London, MPhil Cambridge
Mrs G Witty, BA Liverpool

Design Technology:
Ms M Mescall, BEd Surrey
Ms D Burton, BA Goldsmiths
Miss S Norman, BA Brunel

Drama:
Mr C Haddock, MA Lancaster

English:
Miss J Sharp, BA, MLitt Newcastle
Mr E Artro-Morris, BA Oxford
Mrs C Child, BA Birmingham
Miss S Cockburn, BA Cambridge
Miss J Dampier, BA Exeter

Geography:
Miss E Close, BSc Liverpool
Mrs M Beaumont, BA Newcastle

History:
Miss A Simmons, BA Bristol
Ms S Knowles, BA London
Mrs S Meakins, MA Cambridge
Dr J Moore, BA Leeds, MA, EdD Open

History of Art:
Ms C Osborne, MA Sussex

ICT:
Mr N Walia, BTech Brunel

Learning Support:
Mrs S Meakins, MA Cambridge
Mrs A Barrett, BA London

Mathematics:
Mr D Licudi, BSc Salford
Dr K Baskerville, BSc Melbourne, PhD Cantab
Mrs S Fairlamb, BSc Birmingham
Mrs B Hawkins, BSc Hull
Mrs I Heycock, BSc Leicester
Mrs G John, BSc Exeter, MSc London, MSc Sheffield Hallam
Mrs M Kazi-Fornari, MA Oxon

Modern Languages:
Mrs M Matley, MA Oxford
Mrs E Cleary, BA London
Ms J Holl, BA Reading
Miss P Coate, MA Oxford
Mlle C Pamart, Maîtrise Degree Orleans
Mrs J Patton, MA Oxford
Miss H Zhang, MA Brunel

Music:
Mr D Hansell, MA Durham, ARCO, CHM
Ms J Nicholls, BA Bristol

Physical Education:
Mrs E Fraser, BA Brighton
Mrs M Hayes, CertEd Anstey College
Miss J Phillips, BSc Birmingham

Psychology:
Miss A Meyer, BA Stellenbosch

Religious Studies:
Miss J Heap, BEd Cambridge
Mr G Casley, BA Bristol

Science:
Mr H Gunasekara, BSc Sussex (*Head of Science*)
Ms O Carlin, BSc Imperial
Biology:
Mr M O'Brien, BA Cambridge
Mr J Bright, MA Cambridge
Mr H Gunasekara, BSc Sussex
Chemistry:
Mr A Stylianou, BSc London
Ms V Filsell, BSc London
Mr J Walia, BSc London
Physics:
Dr M Guy, BSc, MSc, PhD London
Mr S Farrow, BSc London
Mrs M Baines, MSc London

Junior Department:
Head of Junior Department: Mrs J Stevens, BA Manchester, PGCE, NPQH
Deputy Head of Junior Department: Mrs G Al-Samerai, CertEd Cambridge
Mrs W Archibald, BA OU, LTCM
Mrs A Barrett, BA London

Miss L Cunneen, BA Dublin
Mrs A Davies, MA Oxford
Miss A Dimmer, BA Durham
Miss A Grimwood, BA University of the West of England
Miss S Hathaway, BSc Wales
Mrs J Leaning, BEd West Sussex
Mrs R McNamara, BA Sussex
Mrs P Proctor, CertEd London
Ms A Sanders, BA Leeds
Mrs N Smart, BA Exeter
Miss A Williams, BEd Cheltenham & Gloucester
Mrs R Wyatt, BSc London

Visiting Staff – Instrumental Music:
Ms J Edwards, ARCM, RCM (*Violin*)
Miss A Gledhill, BMus (*Clarinet, Saxophone*)
Ms K Halsall, Dip RCM, ARCM (*Performer*)
Ms J Holland, LRAM (*Clarinet*)
Ms E Hosker, ARCM, GRSM (*Violin*)
Ms G James, AGSM (*Double Bass, Flute*)
Mrs M Johnston, ARCM, GRSM, LTCL (*Piano*)
Ms A Kendall, BMus London (*Voice*)
Mr S Keogh, GGSM, ARCM (*Trumpet*)
Ms V Longhurst, BA Durham, BMus London (*Harp*)
Mrs M McGhee, BEd Cambridge, ABRSM (*Flute*)
Mrs R Melvin, BEd, LRAM Piano, LGSM (*Recorder*)
Miss A Morrison, BMus Manchester (*Cello*)
Ms R Munro, BA London (*Voice*)
Mr T Murray, MMus (*Piano*)
Ms C Philpot, ARCM (*Oboe*)
Mrs J Raeburn, BA Durham, ARCM (*Flute*)
Ms G Spragg, BMus London, LRAM (*Piano*)
Mr P Taggart, ARCM (*Flute*)
Mr M Wheeler, ACM (*Percussion*)
Mr G Williams, RCM (*Saxophone*)
Ms J Withers, BMus Guildhall, GSMD (*Horn*)

Secretary to the Headmistress: Mrs R Wells, BA Kingston

School Doctor: Dr G Provost

Putney High School is an independent selective girls' day school located on a green and leafy site close to the heart of Putney in London. Spacious lawns surrounded by flowerbeds, shrubs and trees create a tranquil and secluded environment.

We are a school with a family ethos where each girl encounters stimulating personal and intellectual challenges, whilst receiving care and guidance. This ensures that all girls are successful in this happy, enriched environment. The girls here take pleasure in discovery and gain an understanding of the ways of life – they work together to engage in discussion, to challenge the opinions of each other and those from outside.

We anticipate that each girl will contribute in her own individual way to our school, through her studies and many other activities including art and design, drama, music, sport and through charity and working with the local community.

Students leave here conscious of their own worth, prepared for an independent life and capable of making a positive contribution to society. It is from this basis that they go on to pursue a variety of fulfilling careers.

Established in 1893, we are well known for providing the challenge of a rich and broad education to bright girls from 4–18. When a girl joins the school she is supported and encouraged to make the most of her own gifts. At Putney the girls are able to develop the self-confidence they need to take intellectual risks and thinking skills which allow them to make sound judgements about the world around them.

We have excellent facilities throughout the school – in the Senior Department these include purpose-built classroom blocks, a spacious Sixth Form centre, an impressive Music Centre, seven well-equipped Science laboratories, excellent Art studios, a Design and Technology centre, a superb Sports Hall, and extensive ICT provision. Our on-site Junior Department, Lytton House, houses a well-equipped Hall, specialist Science facilities, an Art Studio, a large ICT suite and a well-stocked, comfortable Library.

Putney High has earned a reputation for excellence in sport across the school. Each term has a full extra-curricular fixture list and squads regularly compete and achieve success in regional and national level competitions. The school also promotes a 'sport for all' policy which encourages participation of all pupils in a variety for enjoyment and fun.

The school's facilities plus use of additional off site grounds enables a wide range of sports to be played and has allowed further extension of both the curricular and extra-curricular activities on offer.

All girls have lessons in netball, lacrosse, gymnastics, tennis, rounders and athletics. Additional extra-curricular clubs are activities which include dance, badminton, trampolining, cross-country, fencing and rowing. The girls compete in netball, lacrosse, cross-country and gymnastics during the winter terms and tennis and athletics during the summer.

Well-qualified, specialist staff, provide continuity of education from Reception through to A levels at 18 and deliver our curriculum. Girls are welcome to enter the school at 4+, 11+ and 16+ or if an occasional vacancy arises.

In the Senior Department, the girls follow a broad and balanced curriculum, which includes Latin, French, Mandarin, German or Spanish, Design Technology and ICT. On entering the GCSE years girls may study Triple Science, Statistics, Textiles, ICT, Design Technology, Art, Drama, Latin, Classics, PE and Music in addition to a choice of Modern Languages, Humanities and the core curriculum subjects. At AS and A Level these subjects may be supplemented by Business Studies, Greek, Economics, Government & Politics, History of Art, Further Mathematics and Psychology. A carefully structured Life Skills programme broadens their interests and skills and helps prepare them for life beyond school.

Sixth Formers play an very important part in school life, acting as role models for younger children. The Head Girl, Deputies, House Officials and Prefects are essential to the smooth running of the school and there is ample scope for all to become involved in School Council, the organisation of House events, debating, charity work, lunchtime clubs, drama, music and sport.

The Junior Department, Lytton House, provides a secure and encouraging environment where the girls grow in skills and confidence. A warm relationship is established with each family so that parents and staff work together throughout the girls' years at Lytton House.

A cross-curricular approach to learning is adopted and many visits to places of interest, concerts, museums, art galleries and theatres are included in the timetable. Wide opportunities capture the girls' unlimited enthusiasm and enable them to explore and extend their natural talents.

The Junior Department has earned a reputation for success in music, netball, tennis, gymnastics, chess, and writing skills in local, county and national events in recent years. The Lytton House choirs have been invited to perform for the BBC – and at the Royal Festival Hall and the Royal Albert Hall several times – and those performances have provided memorable occasions for all those taking part.

Putney is renowned for its musical excellence throughout both Junior and Senior departments. Homefield, the Music suite, provides spacious and well-equipped facilities for class teaching, private tuition and practice rooms. Private tuition is available in all instruments and voice. Girls have many opportunities to participate in music – three orchestras; Chamber, Saxophone, Jazz, Guitar and Recorder groups; four Senior choirs and a Junior choir; annual inter-House Music Festival in Senior Department; Junior Department Music Festival, successes in prestigious national competitions and choir tours to New Zealand, Barcelona and Lisbon.

Fees per term (2008-2009). Senior Department £3,700, Junior Department £2,879.

The fees cover the regular curriculum, school books, stationery and other materials, choral music, games and swimming, but not optional extra subjects or special sports. All pupils below the Sixth Form take school meals for which the charge is £145 per term. The fees for instrumental tuition are shown in the Prospectus.

Financial Assistance. The GDST has its own Bursary Scheme that is means-tested and enables the school to accept bright girls whose parents would not be able to afford the fees.

Scholarships. There are, at present, available to internal or external candidates, a number of academic and music scholarships (up to 50% of fees) for entry at 11+. At 16+ we provide academic, art, drama, music and sport scholarships.

Charitable status. Putney High School is part of The Girls' Day School Trust, which is a Registered Charity, number 306983. The aim of the Trust is to provide a fine academic education for girls at a comparatively modest cost.

Queen Anne's School

6 Henley Road Caversham Reading Berkshire RG4 6DX
Tel: 0118 918 7333
0118 918 7400 (Finance & Administration)
Fax: 0118 918 7310
e-mail: admissions@qas.org.uk
website: www.qas.org.uk

Founded in Westminster 1698. Incorporated 1706. Reconstituted 1873. Established at Caversham 1894.

Governing Body of The Grey Coat Hospital Foundation:

Chairman of Queen Anne's School Council: Mr P Dunt

Governors:
Vice-Admiral P A Dunt
Mrs M S K Elliott, BSc
Mrs C Gray, BA
The Revd Canon Jane Hedges, BA
Prof B Kemp, BA, PhD, FSA, FRHistS
Lady Laws, BLitt, MA
Mr J Noakes, MA
Mr R Palmer
Mrs J M Timlett

Clerk: Mr R W Blackwell, MA

***Headmistress*: Mrs J Harrington**, BA Hons, PGCE, NPQH, Dip Counselling

Deputy Headmistresses:
Miss N Coombs, BEd Sussex
Mrs J L Furlonger, BA, PGCE London

Head of Sixth Forms: Mr J Owen, BA Oxon, MA Reading, PGCE Reading
Head of Fifth Forms: Mrs E Green, MA, PGCE Reading

Housemistresses:
Michell: Mrs H Rich
Holmes: Miss M Stamp
Wisdome: Mrs H Avramakis
Maddock and Ffyler: Miss A Freeman
Webbe: Mrs S Norman
Wilkins: Mrs S Hillier

Heads of Department:
The Revd Mrs H Benson, BA Manchester, PGCE Cantab, Dip HE Trinity College, Bristol (*Religious Studies*)
Mr A D H Garner, MA Cantab (*Classics*)
Mr M Norcross, MFA Reading, BA Cardiff, PGCE Reading (*Art*)
Mrs E Green, MA, PGCE Reading (*English*)
Mrs B Hough-Robbins, BA Cardiff, PGCE Bristol (*Modern Languages*)
Mrs G E Little, BSc St Andrews, PGCE Cantab (*Geography*)
Miss W Reynolds, BEd Liverpool (*PE*)
Mrs D C Nightingale, BA Oxon, PGCE Trent Polytechnic (*Mathematics*)
Mrs B Orpwood, LRSC, PGCE Reading (*Chemistry*)
Mr R Punter, BA Wales (*Drama*)
Dr A Lennard, BSc Lancaster, PhD Lancaster, PGCE Leeds (*IT*)
Mr D Talbot, MA Oxon, PGCE Greenwich (*History*)
Mr M Rich, MA Oxon, MA Kent, PGCE Loughborough, MIBiol, CBiol (*Science*)

Music:
Miss F Brewitt-Taylor, BA Liverpool, MA Nottingham, PGCE Liverpool, ARCO (*Class and Chapel Music*)

Chaplain: The Revd Mrs H Benson, BA Manchester, PGCE Cantab, Dip HE Trinity College, Bristol
Director of Finance & Administration: (*to be appointed*)
Librarian: Dr H Brand, MA Wits, PhD London, LDipLib Rhodes
PA to Headmistress: Mrs J Allen
Registrar: Mrs J Gallie
Marketing & Communications: Ms C Long, BA Hons Reading
Development: Mrs A Dudek, BA Canada, CFRE
School Secretary: Mrs S Gee
Senior School Secretary: Mrs B Livingstone
School Medical Officer: Emmer Green Surgery
Resident Nurse: Miss S Eatwell, SRN, PMRAFNS Retd

Queen Anne's is situated on a 35-acre campus just north of the River Thames and Reading, with excellent links by road and rail to London, the south-east and Heathrow. Providing a boarding and day school community, it offers a broad and balanced education with individual focus for girls aged 11–18. Founded in 1894 by the Grey Coat Hospital, it maintains its links with Westminster. There are approximately 320 pupils, about half of whom are boarders. The girls benefit from the school's vibrant and welcoming atmosphere, strong sense of community and wide range of opportunities available.

Pastoral organisation. Girls are assigned to Boarding, Day and Sixth Form Houses on the campus in the care of a Housemistress and House staff. The Sixth Form has two Houses, which provide greater independence and form a bridge between school and university. The school organises a full programme of weekend and evening activities. Weekly and flexi boarding options are available.

Curriculum. All girls follow a broad and varied curriculum up to GCSE. Separate subject sciences are taught, as well as Dual Award; Spanish or German may be taken from Year 9; Latin is studied from Year 8. Music, art, drama and HE form part of the girls' timetable until the end of Year 9. Information technology is taught throughout the school. A wide range of A Level subjects is offered. A programme of personal, social and health education is followed by all girls.

Careers. 100% of girls go on to higher education, many to the UK's top universities. Advice for university entrance is excellent and careers advice begins in Year 9.

Extra-curricular activities. Queen Anne's is reputed for many of its achievements. It offers good opportunities for sport, including tennis, cross-country, lacrosse (National Champions on many occasions) and rowing on the nearby Thames. Music and drama are very strong. The Duke of Edinburgh's Award, Young Enterprise, public speaking and debating (National and International finalists), dance, riding, socials and many more activities are available.

Admission. Girls are admitted at 11+, 13+ and at Sixth Form by Queen Anne's Entrance Examination or by Common Entrance. Sixth Form places are offered on the basis of GCSE results.

Scholarships. (*see Scholarship Entries section*). Academic Foundation scholarships are awarded each year at 11+, 13+ and 16+ as a result of performance in the Entrance Examinations. The top academic scholarship is valued at a maximum of 50% of day fees; further scholarships of up to 20% may be awarded.

Candidates may apply for scholarships in art, music, drama, sport and all-round ability and are valued at a maximum of 25% of day fees.

Fees per term (2008-2009). Boarding £8,195; Day girls £5,560.

Charitable status. The Grey Coat Hospital Foundation is a Registered Charity, number 312700. Its aims and objectives are the provision and conduct of two schools for girls in which religious instruction in accordance with the doctrines of the Church of England shall be given.

Queen Margaret's School

Escrick Park York YO19 6EU
Tel: 01904 728261
Fax: 01904 728150
e-mail: enquiries@queenmargaretsschool.co.uk
website: www.queenmargaretsschool.co.uk

Motto: *Filia Regis*

Board of Governors:

Chairman: Mrs Eleanor King

The Revd Rachel Benson
C D Forbes Adam, Esq
Sir James Crosby
Mrs M Gooder
J B Horsley, Esq
R L Hudson, Esq
Victoria Mather
C P Moorhouse, Esq
Mrs A Shelton
Mrs G Shepherd
D T Sheppard, Esq
Major-General M A Charlton-Weedy, CBE
I M Small, Esq
A G W Lewin, Esq
D Ward, Esq

Company Secretary & Clerk to the Governors: M D Oakley, Esq, Crombie, Wilkinson & Oakley

School Solicitors: Messrs Addleshaw Goddard
School Accountant: S Simpson, Esq, PricewaterhouseCoopers

***Headmaster*: G A H Chapman**, MA Oxon, DLitt et Phil SA, FRSA

Deputy Head: Mrs J King, BA Hons, PGCE Liverpool
Bursar: S P Bentley, LLB Hons Hull, ACA
Senior Master: C S Nettleship, MMus, BMus Hons Wales
Director of Studies: Dr A S Buchan, PhD Leeds, BSc Hull, PGCE
Head of Sixth Form: Miss C P Wood, MA Cantab, PGCE
Chaplain: The Revd R L Owen, BD Wales, PGCE
Doctor: Dr S J Butlin, MBChB, DRCOG, DCH

Art:
*G J Alcock, BA Bristol Polytechnic, PGCE
M P Baby, MA Leeds, DipAD West Surrey College of Art
Miss H L Colman, MA Newcastle, BA Hons Leeds, PGCE
Mrs L J Heaton, MA Leeds, BA Hons Trent Polytechnic
Mrs D Stewart, MA Leeds, BA Hons Wolverhampton, PGCE (*Design and Technology*)

Careers and Higher Education:
Mrs J R Price, MA York, BA Hons Liverpool, PGCE

Classics:
*W M Grant, MA Hons St Andrews, MSt Oxon, PGCE
Mrs J King, BA Hons Liverpool, PGCE
Mrs R Waugh, BA Hons York, MA Hull, PGCE

Dance:
*Miss A E Leadley, RAD, AISTDCBDip, UABPA
Mrs S Bolsher, AISTD
Miss A Pithers, AISTD
Mrs N Taylor, AISTD

Drama:
*Mrs D Whitcombe, BEd Hons London
Mrs V J Chapman, BA Hons Natal, PGCE
Technician: C D Ryan

Economics and Business Studies:
*Mrs S M P McDougall, BA Oxford Polytechnic, PGCE
Miss F Hopkinson, BSc Lancaster, MA Leeds

English:
*Ms J C Millhouse, MA Cantab, PGCE
I Giles, BA Hons Sussex
Mrs R M Doyle, MA York, BA Hons York, PGCE
Dr N J L Onyett, BA Hons, DPhil York, PGCE
M G Payton, MA Oxon, PGCE
Mrs M Greaves, CertEd, TESOL Cert London (*EAL Support*)

Food Technology:
*Miss G M Rickard, BEd Manchester
Mrs G Milnes, CertEd Newcastle, BA OU

Geography:
*Mrs L Seeney, BSc Hons Leicester, PGCE
Miss F J Whittle, BEd Hons Bedford CPE
NC Miller, BSc Hons Sheffield, PGCE
Miss A Proctor, BA Hons Oxon, MSc Dunelm, PGCE

History and Politics:
*Mrs C E S Batten, MA Michigan, BA Hons Queens Belfast, PGCE, DASE
Mrs G F Hobson, BA Hons Nottingham, PGCE
Miss H S Peacock, BA Hons Lancaster, PGCE

History of Art:
*Ms H Moore, MA UCL, BA Hons Bristol
Dr S Burnage, MA, BA Hons York

ICT:
*Miss K Anderson, BA Hons Huddersfield, PGCE
N C Miller, BSc Hons Sheffield, PGCE
Network Manager: G Mark, BScEE, MCSE
Systems Engineer: G M Howe

Mathematics:
*A Taylor, MA Cantab, PGCE
Mrs C I Herbert, BSc Hons Leeds, PGCE
Mrs B A Shaw, BEd Leeds
Mrs A Viant, BSc Hull, PGCE
Maths Support: Mrs J A Edwards, BSc Hons Dunelm, CMathMIMA, PGCE

Modern Languages:
*Mrs E A Hughes, BA Hons Reading, PGCE (*French, German*)
M T Baker, BA London, CertEd, AdvDipEd (*French*)
Mrs A J Debenham, BA Hons Newcastle, PGCE (*French, Spanish*)
*Mrs B Kirkham BA Hons Halle, Germany (*German*)
Mrs I L Leaf, BA Lyon, France, PGCE (*French*)
*Miss E Leclerc, BA Hons Leeds, PGCE (*Spanish*)

Music:
Acting Director of Music: J D J Bowyer, BMus Hons Manchester, FRCO, GRNCM, PGCE

C S Nettleship, MMus, BMus Hons Wales
Mrs D Pomfret, LGSM, DipEd

Part-time staff:
C Allison (*Bassoon, Clarinet, Saxophone*)
N A Bellamy, BA Hons Dartington, Exeter, RCO (*Piano*)
Mrs J Brewer, BA Hons York, PGCE (*Cello*)
Mrs D Clough, BA York (*Flute*)
Mrs K Cooper, BA Hons York, PGDipMus (*Singing*)
Miss L Evans, BA Hons Huddersfield, LTCL (*Flute*)
Mrs G Goodier, DipTCL (*Harp*)
J Herzberg, BA Hons Wolverhampton (*Percussion*)
J Le Grand, AGSM (*Clarinet, Saxophone*)
Mrs E Leaman-Brown, BA Hons Sussex, LTCL, GGSMD (*Recorder*)
J Mackenzie, BEng Hons, FTCL, FLCM, LGSM, LRAM, MIFireE (*Guitar*)
V Parsonage, BSc OU, PGDipMus, LTCL, CertExMus, DipABRSM (*Viola, Violin*)
B Robinson, BEd Sunderland (*Scottish Bagpipes, Snare Drumming*)
P Selwesiuk, MA Wroclaw (*Brass*)
Mrs J Sturmheit, GGSM MTC (*Singing*)
P Titcombe, BA Hons York (*Piano*)
Music Assistant: Mrs M Nettleship

Physical Education:
Director of Sport and Games: Miss A Davies, MEd Wales, CertEd Wales, PGCE
Asst Director of Sport and Games: Ms C Shaw, BEd Hons Liverpool
Miss J Bewers, BSc Hons Hull, PGCE
Mrs E Dathan, BSc Hons De Montfort, PGCE
Mrs J M Norman, CertPE Bedford CPE
Mrs L O'Grady, BEd Hons Bangor
Miss J L Whay, BEd Hons IM Marsh, Liverpool
Miss F J Whittle, BEd Hons Bedford CPE
Sports & Swimming Pool Technician: N S Allison, BA Hons Ripon & York St John
Riding: Miss G Sanders, BHSAI, CertEd
Tennis: Mrs C Place, LTA Coach, CertEd Bedford CPE

Religious Studies:
*The Revd R L Owen, BD Wales, PGCE (*Chaplain*)

Science:
*J Hazlewood, MA OU, BSc Aston, PGCE (*Head of Science*)
*Mrs S H Bullock, BSc Hons Dunelm, PGCE (*Biology*)
*Mrs E A Morton, BSc Hons London, PGCE (*Chemistry*)
Dr A S Buchan, PhD Leeds, BSc Hull, PGCE (*Chemistry*)
Miss A Lawrence, BA Hons York, PGCE (*Biology*)
Miss S McDermott, BSc Hons Leeds, PGCE (*Chemistry*)
Technicians: N Jackson, Mrs E Rust, Mrs K Hargreaves

Pupil Support:
*Mrs M Tate, CertEd Leeds
Mrs J Edwards, BSc Hons Dunelm, MA Leeds, PGDip Psych OU, PGCE
Mrs D Hill, BA Hons, PGCE

Librarian: Mrs S Hall, MA Teesside, BA OU, BLib Hons UCW, PGCE, MCLIP

Administrative Staff:
Headmaster's Secretary: Miss N Craig
Deputy Head's Secretary: Mrs J Pringle
Admissions Registrar: Mrs J A Gaunt, CertEd Manchester
Admissions Secretary: Mrs J Hallewell
Examinations Officer: Mrs M Randall
Receptionists: Mrs S MacGregor, Mrs J Hallewell
Database Administrator: (*to be appointed*)
Bursar's Assistants: Ms E Newman, Mrs H Brown, Mrs L A Walton
School Administration Secretary: Mrs M Quarmby
Buildings & Services Manager: Q A Cardy
Maintenance Supervisor: S Bramley

Resident Housemistresses:
UVI: Mrs S Robins, Mrs K Powell
LVI: Miss A Proctor, Mrs J Clark
V: Miss J L Whay, Miss F Hopkinson, Miss C Silverwood
IV: Ms M Richardson, Miss C Simoni
III: Mrs S Pickering, Miss E Stirk
II: (*to be appointed*)
I: Mrs W Lawson, Miss A Casey

Middle School & Seniors: Miss E Hawkins
Middle School: Miss R Jordan
Seniors: Miss C Goddard

Gap Assistants: Miss S Di Carlo, Miss C Foster

Medical Centre:
*Mrs G M Swinglehurst, RGN
Mrs J Crowther, RGN
Ms H Coyne, RGN

Foundation. Queen Margaret's School was established in Scarborough in 1901 by the Woodard Foundation. Following evacuation to Pitlochry during the First World War and to Castle Howard during the Second, the school came to Escrick Park in 1949.

In 1986, on the initiative of the Parents' and Friends' Association, a new company was established, which is registered with the Charity Commission.

Situation. Surrounded by sixty-five acres of parkland in the Vale of York, Queen Margaret's occupies a gracious country house with an attractive range of buildings linked to the main school. Girls live in year groups with broadening facilities and privileges each year. The first year girls live in Red House and the sixth form girls have study bedrooms in Cloisters, Carr House and adjacent cottages.

Numbers. Boarding 330; Day 25.

Admission is by Entrance Examination at 11+, 12+ and 13+. There is also entry at 16+.

Fees per term (2008-2009). Boarding £7,555; Day £4,787.

Curriculum. All girls follow a broad curriculum for three years before selecting at least nine GCSE subjects taken from a wide range of core and optional courses, providing all the strengths of the National Curriculum without its restrictiveness.

The Sixth Form at Queen Margaret's is strong. Most girls stay on from the fifth year and are joined by pupils from other schools, making a total sixth form of about 120 girls. Over 20 subjects are offered for A and AS Level in a wide variety of Arts and Science subjects. Candidates are prepared for all University entrance including Oxbridge. High academic standards are achieved at all levels.

Classrooms are modern and well equipped and ICT provision is widespread and up-to-date. There are seven science laboratories. Art, Design and Food Technology are located in a purpose-built centre. Pottery, sculpture, textile and fabric design, printing, as well as drawing and painting, are on the curriculum. In 2002 the new Centenary Building provided an ultra-modern theatre and new assembly hall and chapel.

Drama is important in the curriculum and school productions are mounted regularly. In addition girls can take classes in modern, tap and ballet dancing and individual tuition is available. Music plays a major role in school life at Queen Margaret's and there are three full time and twenty specialist music teachers on the staff. There are two orchestras and two bands, smaller ensembles, rock bands, chapel choir and junior choir. The school's choir provides the music for services in Chapel as well as the Parish Church and local concerts and regularly sings in York Minster and occasionally abroad.

Games. Games and Physical Education are an integral part of the curriculum. The school has first-class facilities for games including astroturf, sports hall and competition swimming pool. All-weather courts ensure year-round tennis of a high standard, and there are two squash courts and a nine-hole golf course. Main activities are lacrosse, hockey, netball, tennis, rounders, swimming and athletics with fixtures at all ages against schools and clubs of all types. Other clubs and societies cater for fencing, badminton, rowing, canoeing, martial arts and skiing.

The Riding School is situated within the grounds adjacent to the main school campus and offers riding to girls of all standards from beginners to Pony Club B Test level.

The School is divided into six Houses which compete in Games, Music, Drama, and other activities. Girls take part in the Duke of Edinburgh's Award Scheme at Bronze and Gold level.

Scholarships. (*see Scholarship Entries section*). Awards are made at 11+, 12+, 13+ and 16+. Music, Art and All-Rounder Scholarships are also available. For further details apply to the Admissions Office.

Charitable status. Queen Margaret's School, York is a Registered Charity, number 517523, which aims to provide high quality education for girls.

Queen Mary's School

A Woodard School

Baldersby Park Topcliffe Thirsk North Yorkshire YO7 3BZ
Tel: 01845 575000
Fax: 01845 575001
e-mail: admin@queenmarys.org
website: www.queenmarys.org

Queen Mary's is an all-girls boarding and day school for pupils aged 7 to 16. It has a co-educational Early Years and Pre-Prep department for day pupils aged 3 to 7. The total school roll is currently 226.

Queen Mary's has a unique family atmosphere with friendliness and concern for others being an important part of the school's ethos. The country setting provides a safe haven for girls to thrive and develop self-confidence.

Chairman of Governors: Dr M Denyer, MB BS, FRCP

***Headmaster*: R A McKenzie Johnston**, MA Trinity Hall, Cambridge

Deputy Head: Mrs D Hannam Walpole, BEd Hons

Miss E Abrahams, Mont Dip (*Year 1*)
Mrs J Almack, FIAB (*KS2 Maths/ICT*)
Mr P Bailey, BA Hons, PGCE (*Head of Mathematics*)
Mr N Carter, GRSM, ARCM, LRAM, LGSM, PGCE (*Director of Music*)
Mrs J Coles, BEd Hons (*Year 5, KS2 Science*)
Mrs D Coull, BA Hons, PGCE (*English*)
Mr A Cowey, BEd Hons (*Year 2, KS1 Coordinator*)
Mrs T Devenish, BEd, BA Hons (*Head of Design Technology*)
Mrs C Donaldson, BA Hons, PGCE (*Head of Art and Design*)
Miss E Fieldhouse, BSc Hons, PGCE (*Head of Physical Education*)
Mrs R Foster, BSc Hons, PGCE (*Year 4*)
Mrs V Foulser, BA Hons, MA, PGCE (*Head of Religious Studies*)
Miss S Gott (*Deputy Housemistres*)
Mrs M Grant, MA, PGCE (*Learning Support*)
Mrs S Grimshaw, BEd Hons (*Physical Education/Dance*)
Mr I Hamilton MA, PGCE (*Head of English*)
Mrs D Hannam Walpole, BEd Hons (*Deputy Head, PE, Maths*)
Mrs E Hopkins, CertEd (*Head of Modular Science, Learning Support Coordinator*)
Mrs H Knifton, BEd Hons (*English*)
Mrs K Manson, BSc Hons, PGCE (*Learning Support*)
Mr P Nuttall, BSc Hons, PGCE (*Director of Studies, Head of Science*)
Mr J Payne, BA Hons, QTS (*Head of Classics*)
Miss A Pearson, BA Hons, PGCE (*Head of History*)
Mrs A Petty, CertEd (*Special Needs*)
Mrs C Phillips, BEd, CertEd (*Head of Modern Languages*)
Mrs C Punshon, BA Hons, PGCE (*French*)
Mrs D Sheppard (*Teaching Assistant*)
Miss A Shepherdson, GRSM, PGCE (*Assistant Director of Music*)
Mrs C Sommerville, BSc, DipEd (*Head of Chemistry*)
Mrs K Kavanagh, BA Hons, PGCE (*Year 3*)
Miss A Teske, PGCE (*German/Spanish*)
Miss K Vaughan, BEd Hons, ALAM, UCPD (*Drama*)
Mrs C Wiggins, BSc Hons, PGCE (*Head of Geography*)

Early Years Department:
Head of Early Years: Mrs M-J Foster, BA, PGCE
Reception Assistant: Mrs J Tindall
Nursery Supervisor: Mrs L Welburn

Careers and Work Experience: Mrs D Gormley, BA Hons

Housemistress: Mrs P Johnson

School Chaplain: The Revd J Payne, BA
Roman Catholic Chaplain: Dom Charles McCauley, OSB

Drama: Mrs P M Coghlan, ALCM, LAM, Gold Medal (*Speech & Drama*)
Riding: Mrs P Ashworth

School Secretary: Mrs C Collin
Finance and Estate Manager: Mrs J Wright
Admissions: Mrs V Robeson

Location. Queen Mary's is situated at Baldersby Park in a beautiful Grade 1 Palladian mansion, with 50 acres of grounds, including formal gardens, playing fields, and riding stables. Despite its idyllic surroundings, it is only 2 miles from Junction 49 of the A1 and within ten minutes of Thirsk railway station. York and Harrogate are within easy reach and so are Leeds/Bradford and Teesside airports. Six minibuses, each covering a twenty-five mile radius, transport girls to and from home on a daily basis.

The Curriculum. The National Curriculum forms the basis of what is taught, and all pupils sit Key Stage tests at the appropriate age. However, pupils are offered much more in terms of breadth and depth of learning. Generous time is given to core subjects, English, mathematics, science and modern languages , but strong emphasis is also placed on the supporting subjects – geography, history, religious education, classics, ICT, design technology, music, art and a varied programme of physical education. Classes are kept deliberately small, which means that every girl can receive plenty of support from her teachers. The school has an excellent learning support department for those pupils who have specific learning difficulties. The two years leading up to GCSE are full and focused, with most girls taking nine or ten subjects at GCSE. The public examination results are outstandingly good and the school is one of the highest achieving non-selective schools in the country.

Pastoral care. All girls in school have personal tutors who oversee the academic, social and emotional development of each of their tutees. Building self-confidence and developing the individual talents of each pupil is seen as a vital aspect of the education offered. Each girl is encouraged to be self-reliant from an early age and pupils are taught a real concern for the needs of others. Girls in their final year at Queen Mary's undertake a number of important responsibilities to help the school community function smoothly.

Boarding. Queen Mary's offers a number of boarding options to suit the needs of parents and their daughters. Those who choose to board may be weekly or full boarders. The experience of boarding is considered to be valuable for all girls and, when space permits, day girls may board on a nightly basis to fit in with extra-curricular commitments or parental need. The boarding accommodation is all within the main building and the girls find their dormitories cheerful and comfortable. The full boarders, who stay at weekends, enjoy lots of varied activities and trips, often much to the envy of those who go home. The Housemistress, together with her colleagues, looks after the general health of the girls, while the school nurse and the school doctor oversee all medical care.

Extra-Curricular Activities. An impressive range of extra-curricular activities is available to all members of the school community. Choral and orchestral music are both huge strengths of the school; sport is good too with hockey, lacrosse and netball being played in the winter terms and tennis, rounders and athletics in the summer. Facilities include a modern indoor swimming pool and newly-installed astroturf pitch. Drama, debating and The Duke of Edinburgh's Award at bronze level are highly popular choices and the new, all-weather outdoor riding manège allows more than 90 girls to ride each week.

Religious Affiliation. The school is part of the Woodard Corporation, an Anglican foundation which promotes Christian education and high academic and pastoral standards within all its schools. The school has its own Church of England chapel. The school Chaplain prepares girls for confirmation. Girls of other denominations are welcome.

What happens after GCSE? Queen Mary's has no Sixth Form and this is seen as a real strength of the school. Specialist careers advice is offered throughout the senior school and well informed staff support the girls as they seek to make application to their new schools and colleges. Each senior girl is able to choose a school or Sixth Form college which can offer her exactly the courses and educational environment she requires for her Sixth Form studies. A healthy proportion of the girls join their new schools as scholars. A few girls will embark on GNVQs or vocational training. Queen Mary's girls can be found in the Sixth Forms of over 30 different schools and colleges.

Scholarships. Scholarships are offered at 11+, 12+ and 13+ to those candidates who show particular academic flair or have special talent in Music or Art. Examinations are held early in the Spring term.

Entrance. By interview with the Headmaster. Entry can be at most stages, subject to availability. An up-to-date prospectus will be dispatched immediately on request. The website (www.queenmarys.org) also provides useful information.

Fees per term (2008-2009). Nursery: £16.50 per half-day session; Reception £1,815; Years 1–2 £2,180; Year 3 £3,410, Years 4–6: £3,605 (day), £4,800 (boarding); Years 7–8: £3,875 (day), £5,090 (boarding); Years 9–11: £4,350 (day), £5,665 (boarding).

Extra subjects per term. Music £162, Speech and Drama £50, Riding £14.50 per lesson.

Charitable status. Queen Mary's School (Baldersby) Ltd is a Registered Charity, number 1098410. It exists to educate children in a Christian environment.

Queen's College, London

43–49 Harley Street London W1G 8BT
Tel: 020 7291 7070
Fax: 020 7291 7090
e-mail: queens@qcl.org.uk
website: www.qcl.org.uk

The College was the first institution to provide higher education and proper qualifications for young women. It was founded in 1848 by F D Maurice, Professor of Modern History at King's College, and in 1853 received the first-ever Royal Charter for Women's Education.

Today it is a thriving school of 380 girls aged from 11–18, of whom 95 are in the Sixth Form. Queen's College Preparatory School, opened in September 2002 at 61 Portland Place (020 7291 0660), takes girls from age 3–10.

Patron: Her Majesty The Queen

Visitor: The Rt Revd and Rt Hon the Lord Bishop of London

Council:
Chairman: Bernard Clow, FCA
Ms Sally Cass
Mrs Philippa Gitlin
Revd James Hawkey, MA, PhD Cantab
Lady Hopkins, AADip, HonFAIA, HonFRIAS
James Hutchinson, MA, MSc
Nicholas Inge, BA Oxon
Imogen Lloyd Webber, MA Cantab
Revd Dr Emma Loveridge
Mrs Gillian Low, MA Oxon
Daniel Peltz
Mrs Jessica Pulay, MA Oxon
Ms Claudia Rosencrantz
Mike Sharman, BSc
Professor J Somerville, MD, FRCP, FACC
Tom Shebbeare, KCVO, BA Exeter
Tim Streatfeild

Bursar and Secretary to the Council: Mr S Turner

***Principal*: Miss M M Connell**, MA Oxon

Headmistress of Queen's College Preparatory School: Mrs A-M Dempsey, BA London

Senior Tutor: T Lello, MA London

Deputy Senior Tutor and Senior Mistress: Mrs K Woodcock, BA Bristol

Admissions Secretary: Mrs S Hoenderkamp

Queen's College is situated in Harley Street, combining the beauty of four eighteenth century houses with modern facilities for science, languages, art, drama and ICT, as a well as a Hall and gymnasium. Two libraries, in the care of graduate librarians, offer the students some 17,000 books, with frequent new acquisitions, and we also preserve a unique archive recording the history of the college.

Curriculum. Class sizes rarely exceed twenty and the normal size of a year group is sixty, the three forms being grouped geographically or by parental request. The year group is streamed for mathematics and French during the first year and at a later stage for English, Latin and science.

The curriculum is wide, including French, Italian, German, Japanese, Spanish and Russian at GCSE and Advanced Level, as well as Latin, Greek and Classical Civilisation. Girls usually take nine subjects at GCSE, including a full programme of science. At Advanced Level it is possible to study Art History, Classical Civilisation, Economics, Music Technology, Politics, Psychology or Theatre Studies as alternatives to the subjects already taken at GCSE.

Regent's Park and Westminster University offer further opportunities for physical education, the traditional sports being supplemented by self-defence, yoga, badminton and other leisure pursuits as well as Dance GCSE. Sports fixtures are arranged against all the local schools. The Duke of Edinburgh's Award is organised at bronze and silver levels. Individual music lessons are offered in all instruments including voice, and the musical or dramatic productions and jazz concert are highlights of each year.

The location of the college means that theatre and other educational visits in London are an integral part of the curriculum, complemented by opportunities to travel abroad or to other parts of the country. Every year Year 7 visit Northumberland for a week and in recent years groups of girls have visited France, Greece, Germany, Italy and Russia, joining parties from Queen's College Preparatory School for skiing holidays in Switzerland.

Almost all the girls leaving Queen's proceed to university, including Oxford or Cambridge; several students each year choose to take an Art Foundation Course at one of the London colleges. Former students are prominent in medicine, education, writing and the media; they retain contact with each other and the college through the Old Queen's Society, which also gives bursaries to families in financial need.

Pastoral Care. Queen's College prides itself on its friendly and informal atmosphere, highly valued by girls, parents and staff. Pastoral care is strong and we have a full-time nurse to support the work of form tutors and pastoral staff. A specialist in various special educational needs works individually with pupils once the need has been identified. We send reports to parents at least twice each year and hold regular Parents' Evenings; contact with parents benefits from the rapid use of email by all members of staff. Parents also support the college through membership of the Parents' Association, giving practical and some financial assistance to college functions.

Admission. The college is a member of the North London Independent Schools Consortium for entry at 11+ and all candidates are interviewed individually. As well as high academic standards we value enthusiasm and creativity, and both music and art awards are available to 11+ entrants.

If vacancies arise we also welcome applicants at other ages, particularly after GCSE, where there is a long-standing tradition of accepting students to complete their school education at Queen's. Some scholarships are available on entry at this stage.

Fees per term (2008-2009). £4,370.

Charitable status. Queen's College, London is a Registered Charity, number 312726. It exists to provide education for girls. It is an Anglican foundation, open to those of all faiths or none who are prepared to subscribe to its ethos.

Queen's Gate School

133 Queen's Gate London SW7 5LE
Tel: 020 7589 3587
Fax: 020 7584 7691
e-mail: registrar@queensgate.org.uk
website: www.queensgate.org.uk

Governors:
Mr David Hurst (*Chairman*)
Mrs Elizabeth-Ann Reed (*Deputy Chairman*)
Mr Angus Cameron
Mr Michael Cumming
Mr William Gillen
Mrs Laura Marani
Dr Shirley A Radcliffe
Ms Elizabeth Reeves
Mrs Manina Weldon
Mr Geoffrey Wilmot

Staff:

***Principal*: Mrs R M Kamaryc**, BA Hons, MSc, PGCE (Queens, Belfast)

Director of Teaching and Learning: Mr M Alter, BSc, PGCE
Director of Pastoral Care and Head of Sixth Form: Mrs P Bleazard, BA Hons, PGCE
Senior Tutor: Mrs I Jones, BA Hons, PGCE

Art and Design:
Mr S Mataja, BA, PGCE
Miss E Cottrell, BA Hons, PGCE

Art, History of:
Mrs A Bridges, MA Cantab, MA

Physics:
Dr J Mercer, PhD, BSc, PGCE
Mr C Pollock, BSc Hons, ARCS, PGCE

Biology:
Miss N Mia, BSc Hons MSc, PGCE
Mrs C Mayne, BSc, PGCE
Mr C Seletto, BSc, Grad DipEd

Chemistry:
Mrs C Mayne, BSc, PGCE
Mr D Cheema, MSc

Classics:
Dr T Bell, MA
Miss L Boone, MA, PGCE
Mr R Moss, BA Hons, PGCE

ICT:
Mrs I Jones, BA Hons, PGCE
Dr A Harmer, BSc, PhD, PGCE

Design and Technology:
Mrs B Polanski, BA, ATC, PGCE
Miss C Murtagh, BA Hons, PGCE

Drama and Speech Training:
Ms L Arthur, MA Hons, MA RADA/London, Dip Teaching NZ
Ms R Reeves, MA
Ms J Doolan, MA
Miss E Gash, BA Hons, PGCE

English:
Ms C A Yates, MA, BEd
Mrs P Bleazard, BA Hons, PGCE
Mrs E Hansford, BA, PGCE
Miss R Wade, BA Hons, PGCE

Special Educational Needs:
Mrs P Scott, BSc, DipSpLD
Mr D Norfolk, BEd, DipSpLD

French:
Mme T Delbarry, L-ès-L Moderne
Mlle A Merin, Maîtrise de Littérature Afro-Américaine, PGCE
Dr M Cadei, Mod Lang Milan
Mme M Arnaud, Maîtrise d'Anglais, PGCE

Geography:
Mr M Crundwell BSc, MPhil
Miss S Scott, BSc Hons, PGCE, PCET, MEd

German:
Mrs I B Atufe-Kreuth, MA, Mag Phil, CertEd

History:
Mrs J S Ditchfield, MA
Miss N Townsend, MA, PGCE

Italian:
Dr M Cadei, Mod Lang Milan

Mathematics:
Miss M Newland, BSc Hons, GTP
Miss T McGregor, BA, HDE
Miss P Howe, BA Hons
Mr M Alter, BSc, PGCE

Music:
Miss R Mills, BA Hons, PGCE
Miss S Horcsog, BA Hons

Physical Education:
Miss B Ward, BEd Hons
Miss C Hurlbatt, BA Hons, PGCE

Mrs C Williams, BEd Sec Human Movement and Health Education
Mr M Soudey, BEd, MSc

PSCE: Miss E Gash, BA Hons PGCE

Religious Studies:
Mrs N Clear, BA Hons, PGCE
Mrs M White da Cruz, BA Hons

Sociology:
Mrs S E de Rougemont, BA Hons, PGCE

Spanish:
Miss S Gomez, Licenciada en Filología

Laboratory Technicians:
Mr D I Swan, BSc
Dr J Zhang, PhD
Mrs T Randle, BSc, MSc
Miss N Abbaas, BSc Hons

Librarian: Mrs L Lancashire, BA Hons

Fencing: Prof J Parkins, Maître de l'Academie d'Armes de France

Junior School:
Headmistress: Mrs N Webb, BA Hons, PGCE
Secretary: Mrs C Stevens

Form Tutors:
Mrs S Neale, BEd, ARCM, LTCL
Miss C Harris, CertEd
Miss E Allan, BA, BEd, PGCE
Mrs C Makhlouf, BEd
Mrs E Graham, BA Hons, QTS
Miss J Hasler, BSc Hons, PGCE
Miss G Davies, BA Hons, MEd

French: Mrs J Tweedie, L-ès-L Moderne, PGCE

Music Staff:
Mrs G Haynes, Mus USSR, DipAcc (*Piano*)
Mrs A Chua, MA, FLCM, LLCM (*Piano*)
Miss N Jackman, BMus (*Violin*)
Mr L Sollory, ALCM (*Guitar*)
Miss S Moore, BMus, DipARCM (*Flute*)
Mr M Grisdale, BMus Hons, PGDip (*Trumpet*)
Miss R Garland (*Oboe*)
Mrs S Mailey-Smith, BMus Hons (*Singing*)
Miss O Chaney, BMus, LRAM (*Singing*)
Miss R Nolan, BA Mus, BSc, LRAM (*Singing*)

Finance Director: Mr G Norman, BSc Econ, CPFA, ACIS
Bursar's Assistant: Lady Wilkinson
Registrar: Miss J Micklewright
Principal's Secretary: Miss I Brotherton-Ratcliffe, MVO
School Secretary: Mrs A Nissen, BSc Econ, DipEd

Queen's Gate School is an independent school for girls between the ages of 4 and 18 years. Established in 1891, the school is an Educational Trust situated in five large Victorian Houses within easy walking distance of Kensington Gardens, Hyde Park, the gardens of the Natural History Museum and many of the main London museums.

The aim of the school is to create a secure and happy environment in which the girls can realise their academic potential and make full use of individual interests and talents. We encourage the development of self-discipline and create an atmosphere where freedom of thought and ideas can flourish.

Close cooperation with parents is welcomed at every stage.

There is no school uniform except for games and gymnastics, but the girls are expected to wear clothing and footwear suitable for attending school and taking part in school activities.

Curriculum. Girls follow as wide a curriculum as possible and generally take GCSE in ten subjects which must include English, Mathematics, Science and a modern language.

A full range of A Level subjects is offered. Four or five AS Levels are studied in the first year and three (or four) of these are taken at A2 Level.

Games. Netball, Hockey, Tennis, Swimming, Athletics, Basketball and Volleyball.

Admission. By test and interview in the Junior School, The London Day Schools' Consortium Entrance examination at 11+, and the School's own Entrance examinations for second, third or fourth year entry. Applicants for the Sixth Form are expected to have passed five GCSEs at A–C Grade with A grades in those subjects they wish to pursue to A Level.

There is no entrance fee. Registration fee: £50.

Fees per term (2008-2009). £3,665–£4,485.

The Queen's School
Chester

City Walls Road Chester Cheshire CH1 2NN
Tel: 01244 312078
Fax: 01244 321507
e-mail: secretary@queens.cheshire.sch.uk
website: www.queens.cheshire.sch.uk

Founded 1878.

Governing Body:
Chairman: Mrs E J Lunn, BA, CPFA

Deputy Chairmen:
Mr S Denton, BSc, CEng, FIMMM
Mr E A Elliott, BSc, MRICS

The Rt Revd The Lord Bishop of Chester, Dr P Forster, MA, BD, PhD
Dr C H Laine, MSc, FRCR
Councillor M Jones, BSc Hons, Dip Elec Eng
District Judge C Newman, LLB
Mr P A W Roberts, MA, FCA
Mrs S Seys-Llewellyn, DipEd
Father D Chesters, OBE, FRSA, FSA Scot, BA Hons
Mr M Fearnall, FNAEA, FICBA
Mrs J Jones, BA
Mr K Sahni, MS, FRCSEd
Mrs M Yorke, MEd
Mr N S Mayfield, BA
Mr M Woodcock, BSc, MBA
Mr D Mason, LLE

Clerk to the Governors: Mr B Dutton, FCA

***Headmistress*: Mrs C M Buckley**, MA Oxon, PGCE

Deputy Headmistress: Mrs I Jones, BA Hons Leeds, PGCE

Headmistress's PA: Mrs C V O'Farrell
Secretaries: Mrs K Swinnock, Mrs L Amey, Mrs A Wallace
Admissions Officer: Mrs F J Taylor
Bursar: Mrs M Kelly
Bursar's Assistant: Mrs K Brown
Administrator: Mrs L Rushforth
General Services Manager: Mrs E Whittingham
Director of ICT: Mr P Foster
Librarians: Ms G Mayes, Mrs C A Roberts

Teachers:

Art:
Mr ATucker, BA Bristol
Mrs A J Latham, BA Loughborough College

Biology:
Dr J Threadgold, BSc Leeds, PhD
Mrs C Dillamore, MA Cambridge

Careers:
Mrs V Carpenter, BA Nottingham
Mrs W Marshall, BA Bangor

Chemistry:
Mrs F Costigan, BSc UMIST
Mr D Cripps, MSc Huddersfield
Mr I Abell, BSc Teesside

Classics:
Mrs E M L Griffiths, MA St Andrews
Mrs F M Culver, BA Newcastle

Design Technology:
Mrs P Moate, BSc Nottingham
Mrs S Bright, BA Leicester

Economics & Business Studies:
Mrs B Edwards, BEd Wales

English:
Mr R Ainsworth, BA Durham, BPhil Newcastle, ACP
Mrs S Chafer, BA Wales, ALCM
Mrs J Dunham, BA Hons Cardiff, PGCE London
Mr G Kelly, MA Liverpool
Mr S O'Meara, MA Durham

Geography:
Mr T Palfreyman, MA Liverpool
Mrs R Morrison, BA Hons, PGCE Exeter

History:
Mrs P Tolley, BA London
Mr M Robinson, BA Oxon

Home Economics:
Mrs G Hoyle, CertEd Madeley, BA OU
Mrs M Leigh, CertEd F L Calder, Liverpool

Information and Communications Technology:
Mrs E Furbur, BEd Hons NEWI, MA OU
Mr D McKeown, BEng Liverpool John Moores

Mathematics:
Mr I Armstrong, BSc Durham
Mrs S Osborne, BSc London
Mrs S Stinson, BSc London
Mrs J O'Donnell, BSc Lancaster
Ms S Gill, MA Hons Cambridge
Miss K Brown, BSc UMIST

Modern Languages:
Mrs Ketchell, BA Durham
Mrs C M Buckley, MA Oxon (*German; Headmistress*)
Mrs J Coupland, BA Oxford
Mrs V Carpenter, BA Nottingham (*French and Spanish*)
Mrs W Marshall, BA Bangor (*German*)
Miss S Racapé, BA Chester
Miss S Laloyer, Licence Arras, PGCE
Mrs M Hutchinson, BA Nantes
Mrs T Shi, MA Cardiff, BA Central China

Music:
Miss R O'Keefe, BA Royal Welsh College of Music & Drama
Mrs J Healey, BA Hons Salford, PGCE Manchester Metropolitan

Cello, Piano & Double Bass:
Miss C E Barker, BA Glasgow, LGSM

Piano:
Miss R Jones, GMus, RNCM, LRAM, ARCM, FLCM

Violin & Viola:
Mrs J Van Ingem, ATCL, ORAM
Mr A Rushforth

Woodwind:
Mrs E Dutch, BA Bristol, ARCM
Mr G C Macey, ATGL
Mrs J Riekert, ATCL, CTA, BRSM
Mrs J Holmes, BA Hons Liverpool

Brass:
Mr P Gregory, BMus Hons Huddersfield

Voice:
Mrs L Clayton, BA Hons Huddersfield

Percussion:
C Wharton, BMus Salford

Physical Education:
Mrs C E Moore, CertEd Coventry College
Miss S Littler, BEd, CertEd Astey College

Physics:
Mr C V Cook, BSc Wales
Mrs P Moate, BSc Nottingham
Mrs P Steventon, BSc Exeter

Psychology:
Dr J Russell, BA Keele, PhD UCL

Religious Studies:
Mrs H Daniels, BA Durham
Mr J Scherer, MA University of Wales, Bangor

Speech and Drama:
Mrs A Mistry, LGSM, ALAM

Drama:
Mrs K Larder, BA Hons Huddersfield, PGCE

Lower School, 55 Liverpool Road, Chester:
Mrs F Taylor, BA Hons OU, CertEd (*Head of Lower School*)
Mrs S Lindop, BEd Cambridge
Mrs C Tottey, BEd IM Marsh College of Physical Education
Mrs M Ainsworth, LLB Hons Leeds, PGCE
Mrs D Thomas, BEd Hons Sussex
Miss K Morris, BA Warwick, PGCE
Mr J Wheldon, BSc Ripon Carlisle, PGCE
Mrs M Corlett, BA Hons Royal Holloway College, London, PGCE
Ms A Latham, BA Hons Loughborough, PGCE
Miss E Hempsey, BSc & MA University of Chester

The Preparatory Department:
Miss R R Morgan, BA Hons Wales, PGCE (*Deputy Head of Lower School*)
Mrs F Carder, BEd Hons Exeter
Mrs D G Heron, BEd St Katherine's College, Liverpool
Mrs H Stockley, BSc Hons Derby, PGCIT Bangor
Mrs R Evans, BEd Hons St Katherine's College, Liverpool
Mrs J Callaghan, BEd Hons Manchester Poly
Miss A Adams, BA Chichester

Teaching Assistants:
Mrs S Talbot, NVQ 2 & 3
Mrs S Howell
Mrs H Singh
Mrs H Long ASA Level 1
Mrs K Davies, BA Bath, NVQ 3

Childcare Supervisor (*after school*): Mrs S Smith
Childcare Assistants (*after school*): Mrs T Wilde, Miss A Stocking

Secretaries:
Mrs K Hoare, BA Open
Mrs D Parry

The Queen's School is an independent day school for girls aged 4–18.

Senior School. Number of pupils: 400.

Situated in a central position within the city walls, the Victorian gothic building which houses part of the senior school was built on land donated by the first Duke of Westminster. In 1998, a neighbouring Georgian property was acquired and transformed into a sixth form centre, providing excellent facilities for both relaxation and work. Renamed MacLean House after a former headmistress, it comprises lower and upper sixth common rooms, an ICT room for private study, and a modern languages study room with satellite TV, a videotape library and access to the internet.

Lower School. Number of pupils: 180.

The lower school is within easy walking distance of Chester city centre. It occupies two spacious Victorian houses set in beautiful landscaped grounds, which include a large playing field and tennis courts. There is also an indoor swimming pool on site. Before and after school supervision is available.

Admission. Girls are admitted into the lower school at the start of the academic year (1st September–31st August) in which they will be five years of age. Each girl is invited for interview in the previous spring term, and her potential is evaluated, taking into account maturity, conversational skills, dexterity, concentration and memory. In addition, there is a limited entry into Year 3, the start of Key Stage Two (7–8 year olds) for which assessments also take place in the spring term. Vacancies in other year groups are sometimes available.

Girls wishing to enter the senior school in Year 7 take papers in English, mathematics and verbal reasoning in the spring term of Year 6. Candidates for entry at this stage should be under the age of 12 on 1st September in the year of admission.

Subject to obtaining satisfactory grades at GCSE, girls are also warmly welcomed into the sixth form from other schools.

Curriculum. A very broad curriculum, aimed at keeping options open, is taught throughout the school. Girls take 10 subjects at GCSE and 5 subjects at AS Level, including Critical Thinking in Year 13. They take 4 subjects to A2 Level in Year 13.

Sports which are offered include hockey, lacrosse, tennis, cross-country and swimming. Sixth formers can participate in a range of activities such as badminton, dance and fitness sessions, depending on demand.

Individual interests – whether musical, sporting or artistic – are all catered for in the extended curriculum.

Scholarships and Bursaries. The school has a number of bursaries and scholarships. Bursaries are awarded on a combination of academic merit and financial need. Further details may be obtained from the Clerk to the Governors.

Fees per term (2008-2009). Senior School: £3,140; Lower School: £2,200.

Music Lessons: All instruments £143 per term.

Lunch per day: Senior School £2.20, Lower School £2.10, Preparatory Department £2.05.

A term's notice of the intention to remove a pupil must be given in writing to the Head Mistress; otherwise payment for the next term will be required. No one is entitled to claim remission of fees on account of absence from school through illness, but parents may insure themselves against absence with a firm of underwriters; particulars of the scheme can be obtained from the Bursar.

The Governors reserve the right of requiring the withdrawal of a pupil at their discretion without any assignment of cause.

Visiting. Annual Open Days are held in the autumn term for Senior School and Lower School. Two evenings for prospective Sixth Formers are held in October and November. Taster days arranged to suit pupils of all ages.

The Queen's School Association (Old Girls).

Chairman: Mrs M Yorke, 1A Sandown Terrace, Boughton, Chester CH3 5BN.

Charitable status. The Queen's School is a Registered Charity, number 525935. Its aims and objectives are the advancement and provision of education for girls aged 4 to 18.

Queenswood

Hatfield Hertfordshire AL9 6NS
Tel: 01707 602500
Fax: 01707 602597
e-mail: go@queenswood.org
website: www.queenswood.org

Founded 1894.

Governors:

Chairman: Mrs M C A King, BA, ACA
Vice-Chairmen:
Mrs J K King, FRSA
W J Sykes

Miss S H Evans, BA, MA, PGCE
Mrs A C Dearle
Mrs S M Fazakerley (*Fellowship Representative*)
V R Hedley Lewis, FCA, FRAgS
A M Love, FCA
Mrs G Low, MA
Miss A M Rawlinson, MA
R H Reid, FCA
Mrs L A Robinson, BSc, MRICS
G Russell, MA
E M Sautter, MA
The Lord Stamp, MD, MSc, FRCP
Dr J A Usher-Smith, MA, PhD
Dr A J Vallance-Owen, MBA, FRCS Ed
Miss P M Wrinch (*OQA Representative*)

***Principal*: Mrs P C Edgar**, BA Hons London, PGCE

Clerk to the Governors and Director of Business Development: Mr P J Walker, CBE

Deputy Principal (*Pastoral*): Mrs J Wright, BA Hons Warwick, PGCE

Deputy Principal (*Academic*): Mr R J Morgan, BA Hons Swansea, MA London, PGCE

Housemistresses:
Upper Sixth: Mrs G M Dawson
Lower Sixth: Miss S Dee
Clapham North: Mrs J Brown-Hovelt
Clapham South: Dr A Seele
Hartley: Miss S Hardie (*Head of Boarding*)
Waller: Mrs A Wakefield
Upper Trew: Mrs V Castle

Administrative Staff:
Bursar: Mr S Lee
Director of External Communications: Mrs B M Havard, BA Hons Sussex, MBA Anna Maria College USA
Executive Assistant to the Principal: Miss H Langdon
Registrar: Mrs S K Wood
Marketing Manager: Mrs J Smith
Activities Development Director: Miss E A Needham
Academic Administrator & Examinations Officer: Mrs S Goodwin
Finance Manager: Mr R Balubuliza, BA Hons, ACCA
Accounts Manager: Mrs D Willmott
IT Manager: Mr G Lotter
Human Resources Manager: Mrs L Izzard
Senior Receptionist: Mrs M Park
Receptionist: Mrs J Higgens
Medical Staff:
Dr R J Elder, MBChB, MRCGP, DCH
Mrs A Davy (*Sister-in-charge, Medical Centre*)
Mrs S Hanton (*Sister, Medical Centre*)
Counsellor: Mrs D Meddes

School Shop Management: Chartwells
Works Manager: Mr B Owens
Estate Manager: Mr P Grigg
General Manager, Chartwells: Mrs A Halsey

Teaching Staff:
* *Head of Department*

Art and Design:
Mrs J Brown-Hovett, BA Westminster, CertEd (*Photography*)
*Mr J Hills, BA Hons Reading, MA London, PGCE
Miss V Lucas, BA Hons Westminster, PGCE

Business Studies and Economics:
*Mrs S F Mitchell, MA Hons Edinburgh, PGCE
Dr G J A Dawson, BA Hons Oxon, BPhil Liverpool, PGCE, PhD Keele
Mrs G M Dawson, BSc Hons Cardiff
Mr A Tárrega, BEng Hons Bradford, PGCE

Careers: Mrs J Kilsby, BA Hons UCL, PGCE

Design & Technology:
*Mr J Welch, MCIOB, MIFireE, DMS, PGCE
Miss M Dury, BA Hons Liverpool

Drama:
Mrs R Bell, BA Hons (*Drama*)
Mrs G Butlin, LLAM, ALAM (*Speech and Drama*)
Mrs M Finn, LUD London, ALCM (*Speech and Drama*)
Mrs R Goodman, LGSMD (*Speech and Drama*)
Mr S Jordan, BA Hons Middlesex (*Theatre Manager*)
*Mrs A Kelley, BA Hons Wales, MA Portsmouth (*Director of Drama*)
Mr N Kelley, BA Hons Oxon

English:
Mrs G Bonwick, BA Hons Bradford, TESOL (*English as a Foreign Language*)
Miss G Cocks
Mrs J Drysder, BA, CertEd Keele, DipSpLD OCR
Ms D Eastwood, BA Hons Leeds, TESOL (*English as a Foreign Language*)
Dr K Fleming, BA, MA, PhD, DipEd
Mrs M A Gourd, BA Hons Nottingham, MA London, PGCE
Mrs G Helks, BEd, AdvDipSEN, MA Ed Open, DipSpLD OCR, AMBDA
Mrs B Mole, BA Hons Manchester, PGCE
Mrs R Nolland, BA Hons Dunelm, PGCE
*Ms H Rossington, BA Hons Newcastle, PGCE
Mrs E Stott, CertEd

Geography:
Miss S Dee, BEd Hons Liverpool
*Miss H Hoyle, BA Hons Oxon
Miss P Sex, BA Hons Swansea, MA Ed Hertfordshire, PGCE

History:
Mrs P C Edgar, BA Hons London, PGCE
*Mr A Forrest, BA Hons Dublin, MA Oxon
Dr S Murray, BA Hons Warwick, MA Warwick, DPhil Oxon, AHEA
Mrs S Scriven, BA Hons Open, PGCE

History of Art:
*Dr W Bird, BA Hons Leicester, PGCE, PhD Reading

Information Technology:
Miss A Evison, CertEd, DipITE, MA Kings

Languages:
Mrs G M Darabi (*Italian*)
Miss M C Foster, BA Hons Manchester, PGCE
Miss S Hanlon, BA Hons Swansea, MA Sheffield, PGCE (**German and Japanese*)
Ms F Harvey, BA Hons Dunelm, PGCE (**French*)
Mrs J Kilsby, BA Hons UCL, PGCE
Mrs L Law, BA Hons Middlesex, PGCE (**Spanish, *Modern Languages*)
Ms E Moore, BA Hons Durham, PGCE
Mr R J Morgan, BA Swansea, MA London, PGCE
Miss A Munday, BA Hons Nottingham, PGCE
*Mrs V Renauden-Smith, BA Hons Keele, PGCE

Library:
Mrs H Beazley, BSc Hons UCL, MSc City (*Head of Library*)
Mrs D Gaffney
Mrs G Latham

Mathematics:
Mrs G Baker, BSc Hons Nottingham, PGCE
Mrs M Bromfield, BA, MA Oxon, PGCE
Miss H Nendick, BSc Hons Dunelm, PGCE
Mrs M Starling, BSc Hons Loughborough
*Mr P Vincent, BA Hons East Anglia, PGCE
Mrs K Ware, BTech, MPhil Bradford, PGCE
Miss G Wescott Hill, BSc Birmingham, PGCE

Music:
*Mr J Dobson, CertEd Hons, LRAM (*Director of Music*)
Miss J Kingsley-Smith, BA Hons Dunelm, PGCE
Mr C Kokkinos, BMus Hons RNCM, PGCE Specialist Strings

Instrumental Music Staff:
Mr A Brown (*Drums, Percussion*)
Mr R Carter, FRCO CHM, FTCL, ARCM, LRAM (*Organ*)
Mr G Caskie (*Piano*)
Miss J Clarke, BA Hons, GTCL, FTCL, LTCL (*Piano*)
Ms P Clifton-Everest, BMus Hons, GSMD, Licencium (*Violin*)
Mr A France, BMus Hons RAM, LRAM (*Brass*)
Ms E Frank (*Flute*)
Ms C Green, BMus Hons, PG Dip (*Clarinet*)
Ms M Keogh, ARCM (*Harp*)
Mr J Kirby, ARAM, LRAM, GRSM Hons (*Piano*)
Miss N Marshall, BMus Hons, MMus (*Flute*)
Mr G Owen, LGSM, MMus, Premier Prix (*Piano*)
Ms S Pilgrim, ARCM, DipRAM (*Singing*)
Mr R Ralph, Prof Cert RAM (*Piano*)
Ms J Rees, BA Hons, GRSM, ARCM (*Singing*)
Ms C Ricketts, LRAM (*Double Bass*)
Mr J Rodrigues (*Guitar*)
Mr M Smith, GRSM Hons, LRAM, ARCM (*Piano*)
Ms J Spotswood, GTCL Hons, LTCL (*Clarinet, Saxophone*)
Ms A Szreter (*Singing*)
Ms G Thoday, LRAM (*Cello*)
Mr M Townend (*Piano*)
Mr T Travis (*Saxophone*)
Miss A Turnbull, LRAM (*Oboe, Bassoon*)
Mr B Wragg (*Violin, Viola*)

Physical Education:
Mrs M Bullock, BSc Hons Loughborough, PGCE
Mrs K Coke, BSc Hons Loughborough, PGCE
Miss S Hardie, CertEd
Miss M Merrigan, BSc Loughborough, PGCE
Miss C Sluter, BA Hons Leeds Carnegie, PGCE
*Mrs J Wakeley, BEd Hons London (*Director of Sport*)

Peripatetic Staff:
Miss L Christian, BPhil Hons Durham, FISTD and Examiner (Cecchetti Ballet), DipLCD, Enrico Ceccetti Dip (*Dance*)
Miss A Holmes, BTF Coach, BGA Adv Club Coach (*Trampolining*)

Religious Studies:
Revd Mrs J Beer, CertEd London
Mrs A Goddard, BA Hons Warwick, PGCE
*Miss H Last, BA Hons, PGCE

Science:
Mrs M Adcock, BSc Hons Manchester, MEd Cantab, PGCE

Mrs D Copeman, BSc Hons London, PGCE (**Physics*)
Mrs M F T Davidson, BSc Hons Leicester, PGCE (**Chemistry, *Science*)
Mrs H M Giachardi, BSc Hons Leeds, PGCE (**Biology*)
Miss E Grover, BSc Hons Leicester, PGCE
Mrs D M Rowe, BSc Hons Bristol, PGCE
Mr M Sinclair, BSc Hons Victoria NZ, PGCE
Mrs A K Thompson, BSc Hons Birmingham, PGCE

Science Technicians:
Mrs C Culshaw
Mrs K Hayat
Ms C Newton
Mrs M Osborn
Mrs S Sapsed-Byrne

Tennis:
Mr D Drake, MSc (*Fitness Coach*)
Mrs P Hall, LTA CCA Coach (*Director of Tennis*)
Mrs S Langley, BSc Hons, LTA DCA Coach
Miss T Lilley, LTA PCA Coach
Mr K Mills, LTA DCA Coach
Mr A Pinter, BSc Hons, LTA CCA Coach, USPTR & USPTA Professional
Mrs J Singer, LTA DCA Coach

Artists-in-Residence:
Miss K Thomas (*Dramatist-in-Residence*)

Queenswood provides modern boarding and day education for about 420 senior girls. Situated in 120 acres of green belt, 17 miles north of central London, it is easily accessed by motorways, rail services and airports. Queenswood organises "in" weekends with planned activities and trips, home weekends and flexi weekends; for girls who stay at weekends, there are many activities on offer.

As well as a beautiful site, Queenswood has excellent educational facilities: an award winning theatre; swimming pool; library with over 20,000 items; refurbished science block; modern teaching block; 36 music teaching and practice rooms, concert hall; arts centre. The school site is networked for computer and internet access. Information Technology is integrated across the curriculum, laptop computers are used from Year 8.

Careers advice begins in Year 8 with work shadowing and continues throughout the school. Young Enterprise, Young Engineers and leadership training are arranged and almost all girls go to university.

Entrance to Queenswood is by the Independent Schools Examinations Board or Queenswood Entrance Examination and interview at 11+ or 13+ and by examination and interview into the Sixth Form. A report from the current school's Headteacher is also required.

The school is of Methodist foundation, with its own Chapel which plays a central part in community life, although the school welcomes girls of all faiths and none.

The international aspect of the school is a strength. Resident language assistants enrich the experience within the school and pupils can spend a term in schools in Canada, Australia, South Africa and New Zealand. Many girls take two modern languages at GCSE: French and either Spanish, Italian or Japanese. Regular overseas visits take place – for example: linguists to Spain, Costa Rica, Cuba, France, Austria and Italy, tennis players to Portugal, hockey players to South Africa and New Zealand, skiers to the USA, geographers to Iceland, historians to Russia and Alabama, art historians and musicians to Europe.

Physical Education and sport are an important part of the curriculum with the emphasis on health-related fitness and sport for all. The Queenswood/LTA Tennis Centre includes 12 'fast-dry' green clay courts as well as 16 astroturf courts and indoor acrylic courts, providing for the complete development of players for the modern game at this centre of excellence. The astroturf hockey pitch, grass pitches, athletics field, indoor sports hall, swimming pool, fitness suites and gymnasium provide opportunities to participate in many sporting activities at all levels or just for fun.

Two-thirds of the girls play a musical instrument. Ensembles, orchestra, choirs and various chamber groups regularly perform at home and abroad. There are annual school music performances and drama productions as well as studio presentations throughout the year and inter-house Music and Drama Festivals are annual events.

There are numerous extra-curricular activities including The Duke of Edinburgh's Award Scheme.

Scholarships. Scholarships (honorary) are available at 11+, 13+ and the Sixth Form. Tennis scholarships and bursaries, sports scholarships, drama and music scholarships (including organ) are also offered. Bursaries are means tested and reviewed annually. There is also an Old Queenswoodians' Bursary for the close relative of former students. Further information is available from the school.

Fees per term (2008-2009). Boarders: Sixth Form £8,495; Years 9–11 £8,145; Years 7–8 £7,790. Day: Sixth Form £6,560; Years 9–11 £6,280; Years 7–8 £6,005.

Further Information. A prospectus with full details is available on request and visits are encouraged.

Old Queenswoodians' Association (OQA) has over 3,000 members, organised in regional branches throughout the UK and in America, Canada, Australia and South Africa. The OQA can be contacted through the School.

Charitable status. Queenswood School Limited is a Registered Charity, number 311060, which exists to provide high quality education for girls.

The Red Maids' School

Westbury-on-Trym Bristol BS9 3AW
Tel: 0117 962 2641 (Headmistress)
0117 962 2641 (Admissions Office)
Fax: 0117 962 1687
e-mail: admin@redmaids.bristol.sch.uk
website: www.redmaids.bristol.sch.uk

The School was founded in 1634 for the daughters of freemen and burgesses of the city of Bristol and is the oldest girls' school in the country. Today it provides a modern education for up to 500 day girls, equipping them for higher education, professional working life and the challenges and opportunities of adulthood.

Governing Body:
Chairman: A K Bonham, BA, FCA, DL, MBE
There are 15 members of The Governing Body.

***Head Mistress*: Mrs I Tobias**, BA New Hall, Cambridge

Deputy Headmistress: Miss K Welham, BSc Bristol (*Mathematics*)

Assistant Teaching Staff:
Miss C Besterman, MA Cambridge (*Classics*)
Mr H Briggs, MA Bristol (*Theology*)
Mr S Browne, GRSM, LRAM, ARCM (*Music*)
Ms J Bryant, BSc Birmingham (*Physical Education*)
Miss H Cadogan, BSc Wales (*Physical Education*)
Mr R Cameron, BA Southampton (*History*)
Ms H Davies, CertEd Ilkley (*Food Technology*)
Mrs L Davies, BA Kent (*English*)
Mrs A Farthing, CertEd, MA Elizabeth Gaskell College of Ed, Manchester (*Textiles*)
Mr M Fielding, BSc Exeter (*Mathematics*)
Mr D Gibbons, BA Leeds (*Geography*)
Mrs J Goulden, BA Warwick (*History*)
Mrs J Gupta, BA Manchester (*Italian, Latin*)

Dr N Hanbury, PhD Reading (*Physics*)
Mrs G Hayward, CertEd Lady Mabel College of PE (*Physical Education*)
Mrs C Heard, BSc Bath College of HE (*Food Technology*)
Mrs S Higgins, BSc Hull (*Chemistry*)
Mr T Johnston, BA Bath College of HE (*3D Design Ceramics*)
Miss A Jones, BSc Salford (*Physics*)
Mrs R Killick, BA Liverpool Hope (*Music*)
Miss J Lowe, BSc Birmingham (*MFL*)
Miss R MacKay, BSc Glasgow (*Biology*)
Miss K Maclean, BA Bristol (*English*)
Mr A Newman, BA Bradford (*Modern Languages*)
Mrs S C North, BA Exeter (*French, Spanish*)
Miss C Peden, BA Warwick (*Theatre Studies, Drama, English*)
Mr E Psarros, MA Bristol (*Ancient History*)
Miss C Quainton, MSc Bristol (*Spanish*)
Mr D Seamark, BSc Imperial College, London (*Mathematics*)
Mr C Stainthorp, BSc Warwick (*Maths*)
Miss C Stephens, BSc UWIC (*History*)
Miss M Tomaszewski, BA Oxford (*French, Russian*)
Mrs J Trow, BEd Sunderland (*Design & Technology*)
Mr C Watson, BSc Leeds (*Chemistry*)
Mrs P West, BSc Bristol (*Geography*)
Miss R Wilson, MA St Andrews (*English*)
Mrs C Woodman, GBSM (*Music*)
Mrs P Wooff, BSc Sheffield (*Biology*)

Part-time Staff:
Mr T Angel (*Singing*)
Mrs M Appleton, BSc UWIST (*Economics*)
Mrs J Browne, LRAM (*Flute*)
Mrs J Evans, BMus, ARCM (*Flute*)
Mrs J Francis, GRSM, ARCM (*Cello*)
Mrs H Goodman, GRSM, ARCM (*Violin and Viola*)
Mr B Gruenvelt (*Double Bass*)
Mr G Jones (*Clarinet, Saxophone*)
Mrs K Lewis-Barned, MEd Bristol (*English*)
Ms A Lister, BEd Bristol College of St Matthias (*French*)
Mr P Mahon (*Electric Guitar*)
Mr C McCann (*Percussion*)
Miss R Newbold, BA St Mary's University College (*Religious Studies*)
Mrs Y Penn, BEd Wales (*ICT, Mathematics*)
Mrs L Pollock, BA Durham (*English*)
Miss J Ratcliffe, BA Bristol Polytechnic (*Art and Ceramics*)
Miss M Rhind, BSc London (*Biology*)
Mr P Riley, BA, ARCM (*Piano*)
Mr P Slade, BSc Worcester College, Oxford (*Physics*)
Ms F Trezevant (*Singing*)
Mrs I Trinner (*Oboe, Recorder*)
Mrs A Tyler, BA Cardiff (*Classics*)
Mrs N Weir BEd Trent Polytechnic (*Information Technology*)
Mrs T White, ARCM (*Brass*)

Head of Junior School:
Mrs G Rowcliffe, BEd Bristol

Teaching Staff:
Mrs L Brown, BSc Leicester
Miss S Browning, BA Manchester Metro
Mrs M Edbrooke, BEd King Alfred's College, Winchester
Ms B Fenton, BEd Bristol Polytechnic
Mrs S Hiley, BSc Lancashire
Mrs J Noad, BA Swansea
Mrs L Woodward, BSc Birmingham
Miss X Xu, MA York

Bursar: Mr K Gwinnell
Headmistress's PA: Mrs J Bell
Admissions Officers: Mrs S Boyce, Mrs F Evans

Character. Red Maids' is a friendly, purposeful school; intellectual curiosity, energy and enthusiasm are characteristic of pupils and teachers alike. Red Maids are encouraged to discover and develop their own abilities and strive for success whether this is academic, on the sports field, in the creative arts or in the practical technologies.

Facilities. Set in 12 acres of peaceful parkland, sports facilities are all on site with the latest addition, a new astroturf, opened in September 2005. Further investment, as part of the school's 5 year development plan, includes the exciting Junior School expansion opened in November 2007, the re-development of the Sixth Form Centre, new teaching rooms and expanded technology facilities all equipped with data projection facilities and ICT terminals.

Extended Day. The school offers an extended day at no extra charge. Girls may purchase breakfast from 7.45 am and can stay at school until 6.00 pm, taking part in the free After School Club, making use of supervised prep and/or participating in some of the numerous extra-curricular activities. These include: Young Enterprise, choirs, orchestras, The Duke of Edinburgh's Award, Public Speaking and a wide range of clubs, teams and societies.

School Life. The School Council and Sixth Form leadership positions encourage students to take responsibility for others. Peer support systems, clubs run by older students and staff and charitable fund-raising of all sorts also demonstrate the pupils' energetic involvement in their community.

Assemblies celebrate pupils' achievements, examine current affairs and topical issues and offer opportunities for thought, reflection and spiritual exploration.

Curriculum. Subjects taught include Religious Education, English, History, Geography, French, German, Italian, Latin, Russian, Spanish, Economics, Mathematics, Philosophy & Ethics, Psychology, Sciences (Physics, Chemistry, Biology), Design Technology, Food Technology, Textiles Technology, Art, Music, Drama, Sports Studies, Physical Education, Business Studies, Information Technology, Classical Civilisation, and Theatre Studies. Girls are prepared for GCSE, AS and A Level examinations and for entrance to university and other places of further education.

Mandarin is the modern foreign language taught in the Junior School.

Sixth Form. Sixth Form students enjoy both the continuity of excellent teacher relationships and the independence of the Sixth Form Centre which includes dedicated teaching rooms, common rooms and an ICT suite.

Students are enabled to achieve their full academic potential not only through challenging teaching but also through the encouragement to develop habits of independent study and academic rigour. Almost all students go on to study at University, including Oxbridge.

Sixth Formers have many opportunities both for new experiences of leadership within the school and for a broader understanding of the wider world through the varied community service programme and the general studies course.

Fees per term (2008-2009). Senior School £3,005, Junior School £1,850. School trips are included in this fee. The only extras are Music lessons (piano, clarinet, flute, viola, French horn, oboe, bassoon, violin, cello, saxophone, singing, trumpet, guitar) and Speech and Drama lessons.

Admission to Junior School. Girls wishing to enter the Junior School are assessed during a day visit when they also spend time with their peer group.

Admission to Senior School. Entrance to the Senior School for girls aged 10–11 depends on the results of an examination and interview. These are held at the end of January for admission the following September. There are also entries at 11, 12, 13, 14 and to the Sixth Form. For full particulars about fees, scholarships and admission procedures, application should be made to the Admissions Officers.

Scholarships. (*see Scholarship Entries section*). Academic, Music and Sport Scholarships are awarded for Year 7 entry with additional Headmistress's Scholarships available. A further discretionary scholarship may be awarded to those applying to the school for Year 9 entry.

Sixth Form Scholarships are available for the two-year Advanced Level Course. Applications for these are made in the Spring Term; they are open to those already in the school and those intending to join in the following September.

Charitable status. The Red Maids' School is a Registered Charity, number 1105017. It has existed since 1634 to provide an education for girls.

Redland High School for Girls

Redland Court Bristol BS6 7EF
Tel: 0117 924 5796
Fax: 0117 924 1127
e-mail: admissions@redland.bristol.sch.uk
website: www.redland.bristol.sch.uk

Motto: *So hateth she derknesse*

The School was founded in the year 1882, and established at Redland Court in 1884. The aim for which the School was instituted was to provide for the girls of Redland and its neighbourhood a non-denominational public school education of the highest class, fitting pupils for home life, for professional life, and for the Universities.

We hope to provide a broad and balanced education which will enable each girl to reach her potential, help her to form secure relationships and provide her with the skills and qualifications for a career and for creative leisure.

Governors:

School Council:
President: Mrs C Lear, BA
Chairman: Mr P J F Breach, BA, FCA, ATII, ACT, IIMR
Deputy Chairman: Mr J R Pool, MBE, MA, FRICS
Mrs L Brackstone, BEd
Mrs A M Ebery, BA
Mrs C Y Fleming, MA
Dr J S Littler, BA, BSc, MA, DPhil
Sir Alexander Macara, FRCP, FRCGP, FFPHM, DSc
Mrs C Melvin, BA
Mrs S Perry
Mrs P Pyper, BA
Mr M Whife, BSc, MRICS, MAPM, ACIArb
Mr D Alexander, MA, MBA
Mr S Clarke, BA (*Solicitor*)

Bursar and Clerk to Governors: Mr B W Blackwood, MSc Warwick

***Headmistress*: Mrs Caroline P Bateson**, BA UCL, PGCE London, MA UWE

Senior School Staff:

Deputy Headmistress: Mrs P Davidson, BA, PGCE Bristol
Director of Studies: Mrs S E Barnes, BA, Dip HE Bloemfontein
Head of Sixth Form: Ms D Heywood, BSc Bristol, PGCE Cambridge
Head of Lower School: Miss H A Drew, BA Leeds, PGCE Cambridge
Head of Year 11: Ms L Jenkins, BSc, Grad DipEd Charles Sturt University
Head of Year 10: Mrs K M McMahon, BA, PGCE Birmingham
Heads of Houses:
Rowan: Miss R L Nelson, BSc Montreal, PGCE Bristol
Maple: Miss R Lavery, BA, PGCE Wales
Willow: Mr M A K Sloan, BSc Bristol, PGCE Edinburgh
Chestnut: Mrs A Brake, BA, PGCE Nottingham

* *Head of Department*

Art including Ceramics, Fabric Craft and History of Art:
*Mr J E Icke, BEd Goldsmiths
Ms E Jennings, BA Central St Martins, PGCE Goldsmiths
Mr R A Pizzey, BA UWE
Mrs C Smith, BA Essex

Biology:
*Dr M Quick, BSc Liverpool, PhD, PGCE Bristol
Ms D Heywood, BSc Bristol, PGCE Cambridge

Careers:
Mrs A Brake, BA, PGCE Nottingham

Chemistry:
*Mrs L D Fletcher, BEd London, MRSC (*also Head of Science*)
Miss A McAxup, BSc, PGCE Southampton

Classics including Latin, Greek and Classical Civilisation:
*Ms S Knights, BA, PGCE Bristol
Mrs S Hook, BA Southampton, PGCE Oxford
Ms R M A Summers, MA St Andrews, PGCE Durham

Critical Thinking:
*Mrs A Brake, BA, PGCE Nottingham

Drama and Theatre Studies:
*Ms S McCormack, BA Manchester, PGCE Cambridge

Economics & Business Studies:
*Mrs K M Buff, BA, PGCE UWE

English:
* Mrs C Rodliffe, BA, PGCE Bristol
Mrs A J I Adams, MA St Andrews, PGCE Christ Church
Mrs P Davidson, BA, PGCE Bristol
Ms C Kitcatt, BA, MEd East Anglia, PGCE Southampton
Ms S McCormack, BA Manchester, PGCE Cambridge
Mrs J Nield, CertEd
Ms L White, BA Oxford, MA UWE, PhD Birmingham

French:
*Miss C M Douglas, BA Keele, PGCE Cardiff
Mrs C Barker, BA, MA, PGCE Oxford
Miss S Dujardin (*French Assistant*)
Mrs P M Hamilton, BA Belfast, PGCE Oxford
Mrs K M McMahon, BA, PGCE Birmingham
Ms E Sefer Mâtrise, LLCE Provence, PGCE Wales

Geography:
*Mrs J Neil, BSc, MSc Lancaster, PGCE Edinburgh
Mrs D L Alderson, BA Reading, PGCE Leicester
Mrs S M Argent, BA Worcester College, PGCE Exeter
Mrs A Brake, BA, PGCE Nottingham

German:
*Mrs K M McMahon, BA, PGCE Birmingham
Mrs P M Hamilton, BA Belfast, PGCE Oxford
Mrs K Roberts, BA Bern (*German Assistant*)

Government & Politics:
*Mrs D L Alderson, BA Reading, PGCE Leicester, TTCIT

History:
Mrs M Bishop, First Degree University of Venice, MLitt Cambridge, PGCE Bath
*Ms A L Earle, BA Brunel, PGCE Exeter
*Mrs S Knight, MA St Andrews, PGCE London

ICT:
*Ms J Gale (*Director of ICT*)
Mrs D L Alderson, BA Reading, PGCE Leicester, TTCIT
Mr A Chappell (*IT Support Technician*)
Mrs A Stean, BSc Leicester, PGCE Bristol Polytechnic

Library:
Mrs C J Spalding, BA Hull, ALA

Mathematics including Mechanics and Statistics and Further Mathematics:
*Mrs S E Barnes, BA, DipHE Bloemfontein
Mrs S Locke, BEd UWE
Mrs S M Spears, BA Cambridge, MSc Sussex, PGCE Reading
Mrs A Stean, BSc Leicester, PGCE Bristol Polytechnic

Music:
*Mr J N Davies, BMus, MA, FRCO, PGCE UCW Cardiff (*Director of Music*)
Miss N Cooper, BMus Cardiff, PGCE Bristol

Visiting Music Staff Junior & Senior Schools:
Mr D Ashby, FLCM, ARCM, LRAM (*Clarinet, Saxophone*)
Ms V Bremner, BA, ATCL, ALCM (*Voice*)
Mrs N Cooper, BMus Cardiff, PGCE Bristol (*Piano*)
Mr J N Davies, BMus, MA, FRCO, PGCE UCW Cardiff (*Organ*)
Mrs L Durrant (*Guitar*)
Mr B Fitzpatrick (*Drums*)
Miss V Hodges, BA, ALCM (*Clarinet, Saxophone*)
Mr A King, GBSM, ABSM, LTCL (*Oboe*)
Mrs S McKett, MA (*Piano*)
Mr A King, GBSM, ABSM, LTCL (*Oboe*)
Mrs S Phipps, LRAM (*Flute, Clarinet, Saxophone*)
Mrs A M Rump, GGSM (*Cello, Double Bass*)
Mr G Smith, LRAM (*Violin, Viola*)
Mrs H Stanley, BEd Manchester (*Piano, Violin, Guitar*)
Mr R Webb, BMus (*Brass*)
Mrs R Whitworth (*Violin*)
Ms H Williams, BMus, LTCL (*Piano*)
Ms I Windsor, BA, LRSM, LTCL (*Piano*)

Physical Education:
*Ms L Jenkins, BSc, Grad DipEd Charles Sturt University
Miss K Redman, BSc Exeter
Ms J Wood, BEd Sussex, MSc Leicester
Mrs S Thomas (*Tennis Coach, Junior & Senior School*)

Physics:
*Mr M A K Sloan, BSc Bristol, PGCE Edinburgh
Miss R L Nelson, BSc Montreal, PGCE Bristol
Mrs A Stean, BSc Leicester, PGCE Bristol Polytechnic

Psychology:
*Ms L Jephcote, BA Reading, PGCE Wales

Religious Studies:
*Miss H A Drew, BA Leeds, PGCE Cambridge
Mrs C Barker, BA, MA, PGCE Oxford
Mrs L Gillion, CertEd

Science Curriculum Support Staff:
Mrs J Boynton
Dr R Norris, BSc, MSc, PhD
Mrs Z Szczech

Spanish:
*Mrs E de la Fuente Lewis-Smith, LFL Valladolid, CAP Salamanca, Dip Chelsea College
Ms M E Rodriguez Dominguez, BSc Valladolid (*Spanish Assistant*)

Special Educational Needs:
Mrs A E Cartwright, BEd Oxon

Technology including Design, Food & Textiles:
*Mrs J E Yarrow, CertEd Gloucester College
Mrs T L Jones, BEd Bath College

Junior School:

Head Teacher: Mr J P Eyles, BEd Bath Spa

Deputy Head Teacher: Mrs A E Cartwright, BEd Oxon

Lower Foundation: Mrs J Nash
Upper Foundation: Miss K Smith, BSc, PGCE UWE
Early Years Assistant: Miss A Tippett, NNEB Bristol
Year 1 Teachers:
Miss K Carpenter, BSc Portsmouth, PGCE UWE
Mrs J Lear, BA UWE, QTS
Year 2 Teacher: Mrs E Scott, BA, PGCE Durham
Year 3 Teacher: Mr A Sandars, CertEd Plymouth
Year 4 Teacher: Mrs R Hayward, CertEd Bristol
Year 5 Teacher: Miss S F Rendall, BA Bristol, PGCE Bath Spa
Year 6 Teacher: Mrs K E George, BSc Bristol, PGCE Southampton
After School Care: Mrs H Ross, SVQ II & III
Ballet: Miss D Sims, ARAD, Adv TDip, LISTD, Dip RBS TTC
French: Mrs C Barker, BA, MA, PGCE Oxford
German:
Mrs K M McMahon, BA, PGCE Birmingham
Mrs P M Hamilton, BA Belfast, PGCE Oxford
ICT: Mr A Sandars, CertEd Plymouth
IT Assistant: Mrs J Trump, CTA3
Latin: Ms S Knights, BA, PGCE Bristol
Special Educational Needs: Mrs A E Cartwright, BEd Oxon
Classroom Assistants: Mrs A Doherty, Mrs H Ross, SVQ II & III, Mrs J Smith
Library: Mrs C J Spalding, BA Hull, ALA
Music:
Miss N Cooper, BMus Cardiff, PGCE Bristol
(*Visiting Music Teachers as for Senior School*)
Physical Education:
PSHE: Mrs A E Cartwright, BEd Oxon
Redland Rascals Holiday Club: Mrs H Ross, SVQ II & III
Science: Mrs K E George, BSc Bristol, PGCE Southampton
Speech & Drama: Mr J Butler, BA UWE

Administration:
Bursar: Mr B W Blackwood, MSc Warwick
Bursar's Secretary: Miss F Atkin
Payroll Officer: Miss A Brice, BA Portsmouth
Fees Officer: Mrs K L Gardner, FCCA
PA to Headmistress and Office Manager: Mrs A O'Callaghan
Admissions Secretary: Ms C Jenner
School Secretary: Mrs S Leonard
Junior School Secretaries: Mrs L Stannard, Mrs J Trump
Receptionist: Mrs H Kent
Development & Guild Coordinator: Mrs L Spencer-Small, BSc Bristol
Director of Marketing & Development: Mrs J F Butterworth, BSc London
Resources Technician: Mrs J Walker
Head of Maintenance: Mr D Edwards
Maintenance Staff: Mr M Cox, Mr C Everett, Mr W Gathercole, Mr K Harris
Catering and Cleaning: Ms H Tovey, Manager, Chartwells
Golden Hill Sports Ground: Mr and Mrs Cato

Redland High is an Independent School for girls between the ages of 3 and 18, with approximately 150 Juniors and 500 Seniors. All girls are given a broadly based education aimed at developing the ability and potential of each individual. The school is a friendly, purposeful, disciplined and caring community.

The Junior School is housed in Victorian houses close to the Senior School. We place due emphasis on ensuring that the Junior girls acquire excellent core skills but also devote time to many extras that are not part of the National Curriculum. Our extra-curricular activities programme (which includes Mandarin and chess club) ensures that girls throughout our age range can choose something to suit their interests whether sporting, musical, artistic, scientific or literary. We strongly encourage our pupils to try at least one activity to ensure she receives the benefit of a rounded education. Many educational trips are run through the year to enhance classroom learning. Class sizes are small to ensure each girl gets optimum attention and to enable the girls to express their individuality and know that they are special members of our close-knit community. We also offer after school care and our Redland Rascals Holiday club in support of working families. Visitors notice straight away that there is a buzz about this school that is to do with purposeful and innovative approaches to enhancing the girls' learning experiences. Because we are determined to 'reach' each and every pupil, we try lots of different methods so that each one of them will have the opportunity to find and develop her own learning style with enthusiasm and success. The Junior and Senior schools work very closely together enabling Junior pupils to benefit from specialist teachers for Music, Latin and Modern Languages and to use the Senior School facilities for Art, PE and Technology.

The Senior School is situated in a beautiful eighteenth-century mansion to which additional classrooms and excellently equipped laboratories have been added. There is a very impressive Art department housed in an Arts Centre, an ICT Suite, a Technology Workshop a well-equipped Home Economics unit and a gymnasium with a climbing wall and a large stage, well designed for dramatic productions. Music, which is a particular strength of the school, is housed in a dedicated Music School close by. Redland High has a fine tradition of very high examination results, effective and supportive pastoral care and a wide range of extra-curricular activities. The school's undoubted proficiency in encouraging all its pupils comes from outstanding teaching and having a school of optimum size: sufficient students to make a considerable subject choice viable but a low enough pupil to staff ratio for each individual pupil to be known well.

The school curriculum consists of Religious Studies, English Language and Literature, Drama, French, German, Spanish, Greek, Latin, Classical Civilisation, History, Geography, Mathematics, IT, Design Technology, Biology, Chemistry, Physics, Textiles, Art, Home Economics, Craft, Music and Physical Education which includes Gymnastics and Dancing, Hockey, Netball, Athletics, Tennis, Badminton, Squash, Cricket and Swimming. The recent introduction of Mandarin has proved extremely popular and is available to GCSE level. Additional subjects available in the Sixth Form are Business Studies, Critical Thinking, Government & Politics, Psychology, Theatre Studies and History of Art.

Students who enter the Sixth Form have the exclusive use of the Mary Crook Study Centre which provides excellent facilities and spacious accommodation for teaching and study; there is also a large common room available where the girls can relax. Sixth Formers do not wear uniform and are encouraged to develop their independence by sharing responsibility in the running of the school. The Senior School has a well-established link with a school in Marburg, Germany and pupils take part in the annual Bristol/Bordeaux exchange. Other educational trips are organised and girls may take part in the Duke of Edinburgh's Award and the Young Enterprise Scheme.

Girls throughout the school can learn a broad variety of musical instruments and there are Junior and Senior choirs and orchestras. Wide reading and individual work is strongly encouraged supported by generous library and computer provision in both schools.

Fees per term (2008-2009). Senior School: £2,960 (which includes stationery and books). Junior School: £1,770–£2,090. Nursery fees: £15 per half day session.

Scholarships. (*see Scholarship Entries section*). Particulars of Scholarships including School Bursaries and Music Scholarships in the school will be given on application.

Charitable status. The Redland High School for Girls is a Registered Charity, number 311734.

Roedean School

Brighton BN2 5RQ
Tel: 01273 667500; Admissions: 01273 667626
Fax: 01273 680791
e-mail: info@roedean.co.uk
website: www.roedean.co.uk

Founded 1885.
Incorporated by Royal Charter 1938.

President: Lady Patten of Barnes, BA (*OR*)

Vice-Presidents:
Mrs S Fowler-Watt (*OR*)
The Rt Hon Baroness Chalker of Wallasey, PC, FSS (*OR*)
Dr J M Peacey, MB, BS, MRCGP (*OR*)

Chairman of Council: C Jonas, CBE, FRICS

Vice-Chairman of Council: Mrs P Sinclair, JP (*OR*)

Council:
G Able, MA, MA
Ms J M Briggs, MA, PGCE, AdvDipBFM (CIPFA)
Mrs W Challen (*OR*)
Ms E Chapman, BA, MA, DipLib, FECert, FcLip
R H A Jenkyns, MA, MLitt
Mrs M Winckler
M Lyne, FCA
R G Mansfield, FCA
Ms D Patman, FRICS
Dr J M Peach, BSc, MA, DPhil
Mrs P Sinclair, JP (*OR*)
L Smith
Dr J H Thomas, BSc, PhD, CBiol, FIBiol

Clerk: Mr C L King, FCMA

President of the ORA: Mrs K Bourne

Staff:

***Headmistress*: Mrs F King**, MA Oxon, MA London, MBA Hull

Deputy Head: Mrs S Brett, BA Dunelm

Bursar: Mr C L King, FCMA

Head of Sixth Form: Miss C M N Carragher, BSc Southampton, PGCE

Head of Middle School: Mrs H Heron, BA London, PGCE

Head of Foundation Years: Mrs A Wilkinson, BEd Leeds

Heads of Department:

Mathematics: Mr P W Tarbet, BSc Durham, FRAS, DipEd

English: Mr M Back, BA Sussex, PGCE

Science:
Mr A S England, MA Cantab, PGCE
Biology: Miss A C Fraser, BSc London
Chemistry: Mr A S England, MA Cantab, PGCE
Physics: Dr D Fisher, BSc, PhD London, MInstP, CPhys, FRAS

Modern Languages: Ms A Fafalios, BA London

Geography: Ms A Rae, MA St Andrews, PGCE

Economics, Government & Politics: Mr K Thomson, BA Sheffield, PGCE

Classics: Mrs M Davis, BA London, PGCE

History/History of Art: Mr J M Davis, BA Lancaster, MA, MSc London, ARHistS, PGCE

Design Technology: Mrs P McNeill, BA Manchester

Art: Mrs S Stanway, Chelsea School of Art, DipAD, ATC London

ICT & Business Studies: Ms S Bakhtiari, BA, MA Brighton

Dance: Miss S Stidston, LISTD Dip, RAD Teaching Dip

Music: Miss V Fewkes, BA Bath, PGCE

Speech & Drama: Mrs K P Armes, BEd CSSD, MA Ed Southampton

Physical Education: Mrs J Chandler, BEd Sussex, CertEd

Careers Coordinator: Mrs M Davis, BA London, PGCE

Registrar:

Introduction. Roedean is primarily a boarding school with 400 girls aged 11–18, including approximately 80 day girls.

The three Lawrence sisters founded Roedean near Brighton in 1885. Their original aims were to give due emphasis to physical and outdoor education, to encourage independence and self-reliance, 'to give as much liberty as can be granted with safety' and to supply a sound intellectual training. Today the school community is made of 40 different nationalities and 18 religious faiths, and remains committed to the founders' emphasis on independent learning and the development of self-reliance in readiness for professional life. The school buildings are set on a 40-acre site dedicated to sport and leisure use and surrounded by a further 75 acres of farmland. The campus commands enchanting views of the English Channel.

Philosophy. The Roedean philosophy is for pupils to be self-reliant, to explore their talents, to strive for excellence, to develop their intellectual curiosity, to lead as well as to be part of a team and to appreciate cultural diversity. At the end of a girl's education at Roedean, she will have respect for herself and others, will look forward to an interesting career, and have the skills to balance the demands of her personal and professional life.

The boarding approach is ideally suited to carry out the school's 'whole life' philosophy by providing a rich and balanced programme of learning and activities in a context which is structured yet informal. Day girls benefit from this ethos and are well integrated into the House system. The single-sex environment has particular advantages for girls: it prevents stereotyping, raises expectations and develops self-confidence by offering many opportunities for leadership and responsibility.

Curriculum. Girls are given a structured grounding in basic skills and offered a very broad programme of knowledge and experience. Subject specialists work together in a coordinated approach to achieve maximum reinforcement and continuity across 30 subjects. The benefits of traditional subjects, including Latin, are balanced by Psychology, Design and Technology and Information and Critical Thinking.

Each girl's GCSE programme is individually tailored to provide a broad, balanced education and to ensure that requirements for Higher Education are met.

The strong Sixth Form offers an extensive range and combination of A and AS Levels covering 25 subjects. The school has developed a strong link with Sussex University enabling the most able Sixth Form mathematicians to study undergraduate modules alongside their AS and A Level courses.

Co-curricular Activities and Physical Education. The range of music, art and design, speech, debating, drama and dance opportunities within the curriculum are further supported by optional private tuition and club activities. There is also a special Scholars' Programme. The school is particularly strong in Performing Arts: music (choirs and orchestras), drama and dance.

The school has an excellent record in the Duke of Edinburgh's Award and Young Enterprise Business Scheme which offer girls opportunities to develop a spirit of discovery and independence and encourage links with the wider community.

Netball, hockey, tennis, swimming, athletics, cricket and rounders are the principal sports with lacrosse, badminton, basketball, volleyball, squash, trampoline, gymnastics, fencing, scuba diving and karate also available. Inter-school fixtures are part of all the major sport programmes and girls are encouraged to enter local, county and national tournaments.

Boarding. The House system is designed to provide the supportive and caring environment necessary for each girl, boarder or day, to flourish as an individual and a member of the community.

The two Main School Houses, Tanner and Lawrence (for girls 11 to 17) and the Sixth Form House, Keswick have a dedicated team of staff in close contact with parents. Facilities range from bedrooms for 3 or 4 younger girls to single study-bedrooms for students in the Sixth Form.

Continuity of individual guidance and care is ensured by the school's tutorial system. Tutors monitor each girl's academic progress and involvement in extra curricular activities and liaise with House Staff on a regular basis to maintain a balanced, realistic timetable which meets the individual's needs and abilities.

Health. The School Health Centre is run by a Registered General Nurse who is assisted by a team of similarly qualified nurses. Two doctors visit the School and hold clinics regularly each week. They are "on call" in case of an emergency. There is also a Counsellor who attends the school one day per week.

Religion. The School welcomes students of all faiths. Arrangements are made for Anglicans to be prepared for Confirmation, for Roman Catholics to attend Sunday Mass locally and for Jewish girls to receive instruction.

Facilities. All subjects are taught in specialist rooms. Over 250 internet computers offer school wide integrated learning and there is a main library and resources centre to support individual study. There are two art studios adjacent to a Design & Technology Centre, a multimedia Language Centre, a Performing Arts complex (theatre and studio, dance studios, music suite) and a Science wing with 9 laboratories for Biology, Chemistry and Physics. A multi-purpose sports hall, heated indoor pool, newly refurbished hard tennis (13) and netball courts, squash courts, ample playing fields and the use of two astroturf pitches close by support the PE/Sports programme.

School Year and Leave Out. There are three terms, beginning in September, January and April. The summer holidays last eight weeks and the other two up to four weeks each. Girls go home for half term and there are two weekend exeats each term. All boarders are free to go home at weekends – although the majority of girls choose to stay. The school provides a full boarding programme, but there is considerable flexibility to accommodate the individual needs of families.

Admission. Entry at 11+, 12+, 13+ and 16+ is through the Common Entrance Examination or Roedean Entrance Examination which can be taken at any time up to two terms before entry. A number of suitably qualified girls are admitted each year to the Sixth Form.

Scholarships and Bursaries. (*see Scholarship Entries section*). Roedean will set scholarship papers in January for 11+, 12+ and 13+ entry. Roedean Sixth Form scholarship papers will be taken in November.

Fees per term (2008-2009). Boarders £8,125–£9,050; Day Girls £4,550–£5,250. For girls entering the Sixth Form from other schools, there is an additional supplement of £750 per term (boarding). Parents who wish to pay a single composition fee should apply to the Bursar.

Extra fees are charged for individual tuition in musical instruments, speech training, ballet and some athletic activities.

For further details please contact the Registrar.

Charitable status. Roedean School is a Registered Charity, number 307063. It exists to provide quality education for girls.

The Royal High School, Bath (GDST)

Lansdown Road Bath BA1 5SZ
Tel: 01225 313877
Fax: 01225 465446
e-mail: royalhigh@bat.gdst.net
website: www.gdst.net/royalhighbath

The Royal High School is one of the 29 schools of The Girls' Day School Trust (founded in 1872). We are a Day and Boarding School for Girls aged 3–18. Our new co-educational Sixth Form College will open in September 2008.

For more information about the GDST, see p. xxiv.

Chairman of Governors: Mrs Carol Lear, BA Hons

***Principal*: Mr James Graham-Brown**, BA Hons, MPhil

Head of College and Vice-Principal: Mrs Rebecca Dougall, BA Hons, MA

Head of Junior School: Mrs H Fathers, BEd

Senior Resident Housemistresses:
Mrs J Trevithick
Mrs S Walworth

Admissions Secretary: Mrs D Lim

Number of Pupils. 810, including 180 in our Junior School and 174 in the Sixth Form.

Boarding. The Royal High School is unique among Trust schools in offering the enriching experience of boarding in the Senior School and Sixth Form College. This gives parents the flexibility to choose the type of education best suited to their daughter's needs. If family circumstances change, so too can school arrangements. Our boarding accommodation is comfortable, spacious and well equipped. The school enjoys a splendid location in beautiful grounds in the World Heritage City of Bath. Please note that Sixth Form boarding from September 2008 will be for girls only.

The Junior School includes a nursery in its own grounds. In addition to the core requirements of the National Curriculum, our juniors have the opportunity to learn French. The Royal High Junior School was the top performing independent junior school in the area in the latest Sunday Times 'Parent Power' guide. The school recently gained the Arts Council's Artsmark Gold award for its extensive provision in the expressive and performing arts. Many girls have individual drama or music lessons. Extra-curricular activities include judo, theatre club and pottery. We have an after-school care programme which enables pupils to stay in school until 6.00 pm.

The Senior School has seen substantial investment since opening in 1998. We have a new all-purpose sports hall, six new science laboratories and a new music centre. We have also recently opened a fourth ICT suite. In common with all GDST schools, academic standards are excellent. The broad curriculum includes a choice of four modern European languages plus Mandarin. Students can study three separate sciences at GCSE. Girls can also take Latin or Classical Greek.

Co-educational Sixth Form College. The Royal High Sixth Form College offers the International Baccalaureate Diploma Programme as an alternative to our 25 A Level courses. We are one of a growing number of approved IB World Schools, which share a commitment to high-quality, challenging, internationally-focused education. In addition to a choice of academic pathways, the college offers a real alternative to the traditional sixth form experience, with a greater measure of freedom and independence that will prepare students for the challenges of higher education and employment.

Extra-Curricular Activities. Students are encouraged to participate in our rich extra-curricular programme, including the many weekend activities. We have a strong tradition in music and drama, and put on a number of major performances each year, in addition to informal lunchtime concerts. Our students regularly win prizes in the local annual performing arts festival. We currently have record numbers of students participating in The Duke of Edinburgh's Award scheme.

Sport. We believe in nurturing all sporting talent, both in individual and team sports. A partnership with the University of Bath has resulted in undergraduate sport science students taking up resident coaching positions in the school. Students who prefer non-competitive sport are encouraged to join in other fitness activities, such as one of our dancing classes. Opportunities for sport and exercise are available every day at lunch times and after school and, as we are a boarding school, at weekends too. The school was recently awarded the prestigious Sportsmark by the Sport England Foundation for its extensive provision and commitment to sport. In recent years a number of our students have represented their country in a range of sports including swimming, diving, gymnastics, rowing, fencing and badminton.

Entry Procedures. In the Junior School, admission is by informal assessment. In the Senior School, entry at Year 7 is by examination and personal interview in January. For pupils currently in our Junior School, transfer to the Senior School is automatic, unless parents have been informed in writing, by the end of Year 5, that the transfer cannot be guaranteed. We have a few students who join later, subject to availability of places, usually in Years 9 and 10. Admission in these years is by entrance examination. A substantial number of students join us for the Sixth Form. All students entering the Sixth Form College are expected to have passes in at least 6 subjects at grades A*–B, with grade B or above in any subject they intend to study.

Fees per term (2008-2009). Senior School & Sixth Form College: £2,966 (day), £5,815 (full boarding), £5,162 (weekly boarding); Junior School £2,150; Nursery £1,776.

Scholarships and Bursaries. Scholarships are awarded at both 11+ and for entry into the Sixth Form College for all-round academic excellence or for outstanding promise in specialist areas such as art, music and drama.

Our bursary scheme ensures that the school is accessible to bright and talented students from families who require financial assistance towards the fees. Bursaries are awarded at 11+ and into the Sixth Form to girls who demonstrate outstanding all-round academic excellence or exceptional promise in a specialist area. A leaflet about our bursary scheme is available from the school.

Charitable status. The Royal High School is part of The Girls' Day School Trust, which is a Registered Charity, number 306983. The aim of the Trust is to provide a fine academic education for girls, which is distinguished by breadth, as well as depth.

The Royal Masonic School for Girls

Rickmansworth Park Rickmansworth Herts WD3 4HF
Tel: 01923 773168
Fax: 01923 896729
e-mail: enquiries@royalmasonic.herts.sch.uk
website: www.royalmasonic.herts.sch.uk

Governing Body: Royal Masonic School for Girls

Chairman of Governors: Mr K S Carmichael, CBE, FCA, FTII

Trustees and Governors:
Mr Carmichael
Mr J Gould

Colonel R K Hind
Mr R L Page

Governors:
The Rt Hon The Earl Cadogan, DL
Mr J Clappison
Mr D Ellis
Mr J Flecker
Mrs H Porter
Mr K Surry
Dr S J Tucker

Clerk to the Governors & Secretary to RMIG Endowment Trust: Mr B E Jones, MBA, DMS

***Headmistress*: Mrs D Rose**, MA Cantab

Deputy Headmistress: Mrs J Stearn, BA Herts
Director of Studies: Mrs E Couldridge, MA London
Chaplain: Revd J H Jenkins, BA Birmingham

Housemistresses:
Atholl/Sussex House: Miss K Davies
Cumberland: Miss A McDonald
Moira House: Mrs C Allen
Ruspini House: Mrs W McGowan
Zetland House: Miss K J Lord
Alexandra House: Miss K Batty

Heads of Year:
Miss H S Stanley, BEd Liverpool (*Year 7*)
Mrs C Bomford, BA Manchester, MA Greenwich (*Years 8 and 9*)
Miss C Adby, BSc Bradford (*Years 10 and 11*)
Mrs N Wade, BSc Newcastle (*Head of Sixth Form*)

Heads of Departments:
Miss C Adby, BSc Bradford (*Science*)
Mrs V Bannister, BCom Dublin, MBA (*Business Studies*)
Mrs R Bloomfield-Proud, MA London, BA Leeds (*Textiles*)
Mrs E Boast, MA, BA, Licence d'Anglais (*Modern Languages*)
Mrs S Booth, BA Bristol (*Politics*)
Mr D Buddie, BSc Dundee (*ICT Coordinator*)
Miss B A Champion, BA London (*Economics*)
Mr D Cox, BEng Brunel (*Mathematics*)
Miss M Dines, BA Bucks (*Design Technology*)
Miss T Duff, BA Kent, BEd Kent (*PSHCE*)
Mrs C E Freeman, BSc Durham (*Geography*)
Ms V C Gunn, BA Cape Town, South Africa (*English*)
Miss S Hards, BA Durham (*Religious Studies*)
Mr D Hyde, BMus Birmingham, ALCM (*Director of Performing Arts*)
Mrs P Kenyon, BA Keele (*Biology*)
Mr A Martin, MEng London (*Chemistry*)
Mrs A Ralph, BSc Lancaster (*Head of Learning Support*)
Mr D Spain (*Photography*)
Mrs S C Stephens, BEd Leeds Metropolitan (*Physical Education*)
Mrs S Reeve, MSc London (*Psychology*)
Mrs A Ratcliffe, BA Dunelm (*History*)
Mrs D Ronaldson, BEd Newcastle (*Home Economics*)
Mr T J Ward, BA London (*Art*)
Mrs J Whitbread, MA Trinity, LRAM, CertRAM (*Music*)
Mr N M Young, MA Oxon, MCIBS (*Latin & Classicial Civilisation*)

Preparatory Department:
Head: Miss L E Beckett, BEd Bucks
Deputy Head: Mrs A Brown, BA Reading

Visiting Music Teachers for bassoon, brass, cello, clarinet, drum kit, flute, guitar, oboe, organ, percussion, piano, saxophone, singing, steel pans, viola, violin.

Peripatetic Staff for Dance, SEN, Speech and Drama, Preparatory Learning Support, Extra English, Extra Mathematics.

Administration & Services Officer: Mrs J Heaven
School Doctor: Dr A C K Savani, LRCP, MRCS
Personal Assistant to the Headmistress: Mrs J Beal
Admissions Secretary: Mrs G Braiden

There are 768 pupils in school, of whom 185 are in the Preparatory Department and 158 in the Sixth Form. 133 of the current school population are boarders and integration of day girls and boarders is achieved through the Houses. The proportion of boarders to day pupils increases as girls come up through the School.

Premises and Facilities. Founded in 1788, the School came to Rickmansworth in 1934. It stands in 300 acres of parkland on an attractive site overlooking the valley of the River Chess. The buildings are spacious and well-appointed. They include an excellent ICT Centre, a well-equipped Science building, a Chapel and Library of exceptional beauty.

The Sports Hall is equipped to the highest international standards. There is a heated indoor swimming pool, 12 tennis courts, 4 squash courts and superb playing fields. The School has been awarded Sportsmark status.

Location. Central London is 15 miles to the south and Amersham is just north of the town. The M25 is 1 mile from the school and links it to London (Heathrow) – 30 minutes, London (Gatwick) – 50 minutes, and Luton Airport – 30 minutes. London Underground services (Metropolitan Line) and British Rail from Marylebone enable Central London to be reached by train in 30 minutes.

General Curriculum and Aims. The first three years of Senior School provide a broad general education which fulfils the requirements of the National Curriculum and reaches beyond it. As well as the traditional academic subjects of English, Mathematics, Science, History, Geography and Religious Studies, girls study Design Technology, Information Technology, Home Economics, Art & Textiles, Performing Arts, Physical Education and PSHCE. Language Studies begin with French or Spanish and Latin. In Year 8 German and Mandarin are also offered.

GCSE options are chosen from among all the subjects taught in Years 7 to 9 and new possibilities, such as Child Development, Expressive Arts, Drama and Business are introduced at this stage. Most pupils take nine or ten GCSE subjects and girls are guided in their choices by subject teachers, in full consultation with parents. Triple Science is available.

The Sixth Form. The School offers a wide range of A and AS Level subjects in flexible combinations. Politics, Economics, Performance Studies, Classical Civilisation, Photography and Psychology are all new additions to the curriculum at this stage. There are also practical and vocational courses leading to qualifications in Business and Health and Social Care. Virtually all sixth formers go on to higher education.

Religion. Girls of all faiths and none are welcome. School assemblies are traditional and inclusive in nature and Chapel Services for boarders are held according to the rites of the Church of England.

Health. The School Doctor attends the Medical Centre regularly. There are three Nursing Sisters and a Medical Assistant.

Admission. Applications should be made to the Admissions Secretary. The School sets its own entrance examinations at all levels. New boarding and day pupils are accepted into the Sixth Form where there are wide-ranging opportunities for girls of all abilities.

Scholarships. (*see Scholarship Entries section*). A number of scholarships are available at 7+, 11+ and 16+, and some bursaries. The former are for open competition; the latter are restricted to certain categories of pupils in need. There are a number of Foundation Scholarships available at 11+ for the daughters of Freemasons. These are based on academic ability.

Fees per term (2008-2009). Senior School: Boarders £6,585–£6,640; Weekly Boarders £6,420; Day Pupils £4,040–£4,260.

Preparatory Department: Boarders: £4,050 (Years 3 and 4), £4,170 (Years 5 and 6); Weekly Boarders: £3,980 (Years 3 and 4), £4,095 (Years 5 and 6). Day Pupils: £2,280 (Reception, Years 1 and 2), £2,660 (Years 3 and 4), £2,740 (Years 5 and 6).

Free places may be available for daughters of Freemasons in need of assistance.

Charitable status. The Royal Masonic School Limited is a Registered Charity, number 276784. Its aims are the advancement of education.

Royal School Hampstead

65 Rosslyn Hill Hampstead London NW3 5UD
Tel: 020 7794 7708
Fax: 020 7431 6741
e-mail: enquiries@royalschoolhampstead.net
website: www.royalschoolhampstead.net www.royalschool-nursery.net

Founded in 1855. Independent Day and Boarding school celebrating over 150 years of educating and caring for Girls.

***Headmistress*: Mrs J Ebner-Landy**, BEd Hons Cantab, MA London, PGDip Couns, Cert FT, NPQH

Deputy Head: Mr M Webster, BSc, PGCE

Head of Junior School: Mrs K Simon, BA, PGCE

Teaching Staff:
Mrs M Anastasi, BSc (*ICT*)
Miss C Bartram, BA, PGCE (*Geography*)
Mr B Benson, CertEd, CSSD Dip Acting (*Drama & Theatre Studies*)
Miss E Beresford, BEd, MSc (*Sociology*)
Miss B Borlinghaus, MA, PGCE (*German, French, Head of Sixth Form*)
Miss S Campbell, BA, PGCE (*Junior School Teacher*)
Mrs K Casper, MA (*Director of Music*)
Mme V Chenais, MA (*French*)
Miss C Clelland, PCGE (*English*)
Mrs A Davies, BSc, PGCE (*Science*)
Dr Z Dunn, BEd, PhD (*Deputy Head of Junior School*)
Miss C Eby, BEd (*Junior School Teacher*)
Mrs S Fisher, BEd (*Junior School Teacher & ICT Coordinator*)
Mrs A Green, BA, PGCE (*Art*)
Mr J Griffiths, BEd (*Junior School Teacher & Science Coordinator*)
Mrs J McKenna, NNEB (*Nursery Assistant*)
Miss S Nelson, BA, PGCE (*English*)
Mrs A Nicole, BEd (*Junior School Teacher*)
Ms K Philip, BSc (*Science & PE*)
Mrs L Pospisilova, MA (*PE*)
Ms S Ramery, BA, PGCE (*Junior School Teacher*)
Dr I Raptis, PhD, BSc, PGCE (*Science & Mathematics*)
Miss E Reeve, BEd (*Junior School Teacher*)
Mr K Saunders, BA, PGCE (*History*)
Mr R Shopland, MSc, PGCE (*Head of Science & Mathematics*)
Mr N Simon, BA, PGCE (*Geography, History & ICT*)
Mrs G Steiner, BSc, BA, PGCE (*Mathematics*)
Mrs A Theodoulou, MA (*Head of English*)
Miss C Walker, BA, PCGE (*Junior School Teacher & Literacy Coordinator*)
Mr M Webster, BSc, PGCE (*Mathematics*)

Visiting Teachers:
Mrs S Boudavi, BBA (*Economics*)
Mrs R Butcher, BSc (*Higher Mathematics*)
Mrs C Dodsworth, BA, CTEFLA (*EFL*)
Mrs J Bailey, BA, MA, PGCE, SpLD (*SENCO*)
Ms R Bird, BA, PGCE, RSA Dip SpLD (*Learning Support*)
Ms M Grunberger, BSc, PGCE (*Special Educational Needs*)
Ms L Rudolf, BA Hons (*Learning Support*)
Ms J Boulter, BA, PG Dip (*Speech & Language Therapist*)
Ms E Warin, BEd, BAP (*Psychoanalytic Psychotherapist, School Counsellor*)

Miss J Craig, BMus Hons, PGDip (*Adv*) (*Singing*)
Mr K Edman, BMus (*Cello & Piano*)
Mrs D Gaddas, PDTC, ARAD, AISTD (*Ballet*)
Ms J Griffiths, BA (*Piano & Violin*)
Miss P Hampson, AISTD (*Speech & Drama*)
Ms R Hand, BA (*Flute*)
Mrs E Kuenen, PGCE Performing Arts (*PC*), BPhil Hons, LRAD, LISTD, ARAD (*Creative Movement*)
Mr A Marmot, MA, MA (*Drums*)
Mr J Rowe, BMus (*Guitar*)
Miss E Sheldrake, BMus (*Piano & Violin*)

Residential Staff:
Miss D Pretty (*Manager of Boarding*)
Miss E Beresford, BEd, MSc (*Senior Housemistress*)
Ms M McGillicuddy, SEN
Miss S Campbell, BA, PGCE
Miss M Ponder
Ms K Philp, BSc
Miss F Treweeke

Administration:
Mrs M Shemtob (*Bursar*)
Miss K Moult (*PA to the Bursar*)
Mr P Vivek (*Finance Officer*)
Mrs L Woods (*PA to the Headmistress*)
Ms B Chidley (*Catering Manageress*)
Mrs S Gubbay (*School Nurse*)
Mr S Day (*Caretaker*)
Mr M Quaid (*Car Park Warden*)
Mr G Spriggs (*Car Park Warden*)
Keats Group Practice (*School Doctor*)

Support Staff:
Mr G Nourouzi (*IT Support Technican*)
Ms M Schlatter, MITI, MIL (*Librarian*)
Miss N Virdee (*Science Technician*)

The Royal School is the school with the heart in the heart of Hampstead.

The Royal School, Hampstead was founded in 1855 with the original aims to "nurse, board, clothe and educate the female children, orphans or not of soldiers in Her Majesty's Army who had served or were serving in the Crimean War". Today it is open to all girls.

Age Range and Number of Pupils. The Royal School is now a day and boarding school for 272 girls from 3–16 years, with boarders from 11 years.

Educational Philosophy. The school's aim is to provide an excellent education based on individual attention, in a happy, positive and secure environment, to allow each girl to develop her full potential and to become a self-confident, responsible young adult with a clear sense of duty towards others.

The Royal School is known for tailoring its education to each child as well as its work in the community and its caring ethos. Our aim is to ensure our girls are well educated, confident, polite and able to make their mark in society.

Location and Facilities. The school is situated in pleasant surroundings in the heart of Hampstead Village. It is a well resourced school, with spacious, light classrooms and comfortable modern boarding accommodation with panoramic views over London. The Royal School has a strong provision in the visual and performing arts, a wide range of extra-curricular activities and provides individual EFL teaching as part of our SEN department. There is also an Early Years Unit.

Curriculum. The Early Years Programme seeks to provide three to five year olds with a firm foundation upon which to build. This is developed and extended throughout the Junior School, where girls are offered a diverse curriculum within a positive and caring community. Pupils are encouraged to become confident independent thinkers who behave responsibly and courteously. Senior School girls follow a balanced curriculum, including 2 modern languages and 3 Sciences, leading to GCSE. The performing and visual arts are a particular strength of the school, for which the school holds an Artsmark, and charity work and life enrichment programmes are important aspects of the school's ethos, which feature strongly throughout the school. The school is consistently placed amongst the highest positions in the Value Added Key Stage 3 to GCSE Performance Tables.

All the girls are taught in small classes enabling them to develop a variety of skills to the best of their ability. There is an extremely high teacher/pupil ratio and girls are offered an excellent level of individual attention and positive help.

Extra-curricular activities feature widely in the school's daily routine, and include The Duke of Edinburgh's Award scheme, drama, art, music, ballet, dance and a wide range of games and sports.

Boarding. The school offers a homely and friendly boarding environment where girls thrive. Each new boarder is assigned a 'buddy' who acts as a companion and helper. Communication between parents and staff is excellent. Weekly boarding is a popular option; 'flexi-boarding' and 'sleepovers' can be arranged when required.

Fees per term (2008-2009). Day £2,560–£3,200; Weekly Boarding £5,290; Boarding £6,360; Flexi-Boarding £30 per night.

Admission. Girls are admitted throughout the age range although the majority are admitted at 3, 4, 11 and 13.

Entry Requirements. Girls applying to the Junior School are invited to attend school for a session of informal assessments. Admission to the Senior School at 11+ is through the Consortium of North London Independent Girls' Schools as the school is a member of the Girls' Schools Association, and also by an interview. Previous school reports are required for all pupils.

Bursaries and Scholarships. Bursaries may be awarded throughout all year groups including boarding – priority is given to British Armed Forces personnel. Scholarships are awarded at Year 7.

Religious Affiliation. All religions are welcome. The school is designated as Church of England.

Charitable status. The Royal School, Hampstead is a Registered Charity, number 312286, and exists for the purpose of educating girls.

Rye St Antony School

Pullen's Lane Oxford OX3 0BY
Tel: 01865 762802
Fax: 01865 763611
e-mail: info@ryestantony.co.uk
website: www.ryestantony.co.uk

Rye St Antony is an independent Catholic Boarding and Day School, founded in 1930.

Motto: *Vocatus Obedivi*

Governing Body:

Chairman: Mrs H Stafford Northcote, BA
Vice-Chairman: Mr T J Morton
Mr I Callaghan
Mr S Calnan
Miss J Clarke, FRCS
Dr T M M Czepiel
Mrs S Edmonds, BA
Revd Dr J F Jackson
Mr D Parke
Mrs M Shinkwin, BA, MEd, NPQH
Mr J Vaughan-Fowler

Clerk to the Governors: Mr A C Sinclair

***Headmistress*: Miss A M Jones**, BA York, PGCE Oxon

Deputy Headmistress: Mrs A Neil, BA Southampton (*History and Politics*)

Director of Studies: Dr C Rosser, BSc, PhD Leeds, MSc Oxon (*ICT*)

Senior School Staff:
Mrs J Bass, BA Southwest Baptist University, Missouri (*Mathematics*)
Mrs D Bates-Brownsword, BEd South Australian College (*Home Economics*)
Mrs M Birtill, MA Glasgow, DipEd Edinburgh (*Spanish, ICT*)
Mrs C Boyd, BA Middlesex (*Drama*)
Miss S Brookes, BA East London, PGCE Cantab (*Art and Design*)
Mrs E Caprotti, Italian Teaching Degree (*Italian*)
Mr A Coghlan, BSc East Anglia (*Mathematics*)
Mrs M Conway, MA Ulster, MEd Queen's, Belfast, CertEd London (*History*)
Miss J Croft, Maîtrise Strasbourg, BA, QTS Westminster (*French*)
Miss F Davison, BA Birmingham, PGCE Leeds (*Physical Education*)
Miss S Defoe, BA Loughborough (*Art and Design*)
Mrs P D'Souza-Eva, BA Essex, PGCE London (*Mathematics*)
Mrs A Evans, BA Nene University College, QTS Reading (*Drama*)
Mr M Evans, BA Durham, PGCE London, MEd Oxon (*Mathematics*)
Mrs P Evans, BA, MA Open, CertEd Leeds (*Religious Studies*)
Mrs J Ganly, BA Leeds, PGCE Bath (*French*)
Miss L Hailstone, BA Exeter (*English*)
Mrs K Harman, BSc Cardiff, RSADipTEFLA Bournemouth (*EAL*)
Miss A Hartnell, BA Oxon (*Chemistry*)
Miss L Howard, BA Oxon, PGCE London, MPhil Cantab (*Classics*)
Mrs M Jones, BA Cardiff, PGCE Oxon (*Music*)
Mrs C Lau, BA Hong Kong, MA Oxford Brookes (*Chinese*)
Mr S H Lau, BA Hong Kong, MPhil Hong Kong (*Chinese*)
Mrs A Newsome, BSc, MSc London, PGCE Reading (*Geography*)
Dr T Newsome, BSc Reading, PhD Stirling, PGCE Reading (*Biology*)
Mrs R Ockenden, BA Oxon (*German*)
Mrs J Owens, BSc Aberystwyth, CBiol, MIBiol, PGCE Lancaster (*Biology*)
Miss C Peck, BEd Leeds (*Physical Education*)
Mrs B Pillman, BA Brighton College of Art (*Learning Support*)

Miss F Pujos, Licence La Sorbonne Nouvelle, Paris, PGCE Oxford Brookes, Maîtrise Angers (*French*)
Mr J Rawlinson, BA Wolverhampton, PGCE Liverpool, MEd Oxon (*Art and Design*)
Mrs E Roberts, BA York, PGCE Cantab (*English*)
Dr F Ross, MA Glasgow, PhD Glasgow, PGCE Strathclyde (*English*)
Mrs S Savery, BA Cantab, CertEd London (*Economics, Business Studies*)
Mr B Sharland, BEd Cape Town (*ICT*)
Miss J Smail, BA Lancaster, MA Lancaster, PGCE Southampton (*History*)
Mrs F Stuart, MA, PGCE Oxon, ARCM (*Music*)
Dr P Tebbs, BA Oxon, MSt Oxon, MPhil Oxon, DPhil Oxon (*Music*)
Miss H Tomlinson, BEd Brighton (*Physical Education*)
Miss C Trenaman, BA Durham (*Physical Education*)
Mr A Vesty, BSc Manchester (*Chemistry and Physics*)
Mrs A Waterhouse, BA Univ of South Africa, Teaching Diploma Univ of South Africa (*ICT*)
Miss J Wells, BSc Southampton, PGCE Oxford Brookes (*Geography*)
Mr D Willcock, BA Oxon (*Religious Education*)

Junior School Staff:
Head of Junior School: Miss C Bishop, BEd Redland College, Bristol

Mrs S Blandy, BA Manchester
Miss K Dooley, HND Liverpool, PGCE Nottingham
Mrs A Dyar, MontDip Dublin
Miss K Gray, BA Canterbury, New Zealand
Mrs J Haigh, BSc London, QTS Reading
Mrs H Holland, BA Oxford Brookes, CertEd Warwick
Mrs M-E Judges, BA New York, BEd Oxford Brookes, PGCE Oxford Brookes
Dr C Kirtley, BSc Durham
Miss K Northcote, BA Birmingham
Miss J Parker, BA Ripon & York St John, MA Oxford Brookes
Mrs A Saunders, BEd Lancaster
Miss A Scott, MA St Andrews, PGCE Cantab

Nursery Department Staff:
Mrs B Crowther, BEd Toronto, BA Toronto
Mrs I Fenton, MontDip London
Miss K Repikova
Mrs E Stevens
Mrs A Utechin, MontDip Oxford

Visiting Music Staff:
Ms A M Ackrill, BA Music (*Flute*)
Ms A Bendy, LTCL, DipMusEd (*Guitar*)
Mr S Dunstone, BA Cantab, PGCE Durham (*Harp*)
Mr D Elsmore, BA Oxford Brookes (*Guitar*)
Miss B Evans, BA Bath (*Singing*)
Mr P Foster, LTCL (*Saxophone*)
Mr R Foster, BA Oxford Brookes University (*Drumkit*)
Mrs C Goodall, MA Oxford (*Clarinet and Piano*)
Miss E Hodson, MA, DPhil, PGDip (*Violin and Viola*)
Mrs P Miller, BA, LTCL (*Clarinet*)
Mrs F Purrier, BMus RNCM, PGDip RNCM (*Singing*)
Mrs C Rees, BMusEd, SRAsT (*Oboe, Piano*)

Librarian: Mrs E Kirby, BA Manchester
Assistant Librarian: Mrs A Goodall, BA Oxford Brookes

Medical Adviser: Dr M Holden
School Nurses:
Mrs S McIlvenna, RGN
Miss R Spedding, RGN Lancaster Infirmary

Administrative Staff:
Bursar: Mr A C Sinclair
Assistant Bursar: Mrs T Hudson
Finance Officer: Mrs N Sanhotra
Bursary Assistant: Mrs J Curl
School Secretaries: Mrs H Castle, Miss A Illingworth

Rye St Antony was founded in 1930 by Elizabeth Rendall and Ivy King, two school teachers who reached the decision to start a school of their own during a visit to Sussex and the Church of St Antony in Rye, in commemoration of which the School was named. In 1939 the School moved to its present site, twelve acres of exceptionally beautiful grounds a mile to the north east of the centre of Oxford on Pullen's Lane, overlooking the city.

A steady programme of building and development has provided excellent teaching and residential facilities, all new buildings being carefully harmonised with the architecture of the original handsome Victorian houses. King House was opened in 1986, the Art, Design and Technology centre in 1989, the Information and Communications Technology unit in 1991, the new wing of the Rendall Building in 1993 and the Sumpter Building with its Science laboratories in 1995. In recent years the computer network has been extended into all teaching and boarding areas, the Performing Arts centre was opened in February 2005 and the new Sports Hall will open in September 2008.

The School is highly regarded for its happy and purposeful atmosphere, its strong sense of community and its emphasis on the value of each member of the community as an individual. Pupils are helped to understand their strengths and weaknesses and the reasons for their successes and failures; they are encouraged to accept challenges and learn initiative and independence. They also have many opportunities to contribute to decision-making for the School, thereby learning how to play an active part in the school community and in future communities to which they will belong.

The School offers boarding and day places for girls aged 5–18, some day places for boys aged 5–8, and in Beech Tree Nursery School whole-day and half-day places for boys and girls aged 3–5. Short-stay and occasional boarding arrangements, varying in length from a single night to a whole term or more, can be made according to need.

Religious Life. The School's sacramental life is of fundamental importance, the Eucharist in particular uniting the School with Christ and his Church and giving a focus to prayer, both liturgical and private. Several Oxford priests regularly celebrate Mass for the whole School on special feast days and at the beginning and end of each term; they also celebrate the Sunday Masses, form Masses and weekday Masses. Religious Education is an integral part of the curriculum throughout the School, and all pupils are involved in the Christian life of the school community, not least its liturgical celebrations.

Senior School Curriculum. Academic standards and expectations are high, girls are offered many opportunities in music, art, drama and sport, and there is a busy programme of evening and weekend activities.

In the Senior School all girls follow a broad and balanced common course for the first three years, comprising English, Mathematics, Physics, Chemistry, Biology, Religious Education, French, History, Geography, Technology, Information and Communications Technology, Art, Music, Drama and Physical Education. Latin and Spanish are optional subjects. There is a cross-curricular Health Education programme.

Twenty plus subjects are offered as GCSE subjects. For the two-year GCSE course girls usually study 10 subjects, a mixture of options and core subjects (including Coordinated Science, a double award subject).

In the Sixth Form girls typically study four AS subjects in the first year of Sixth Form and continue with three of these subjects as A2 subjects in the second year, thus completing Sixth Form with certification in 3 A Level subjects and an additional AS subject.

Careers Guidance. The School's careers advisory service provides help and guidance for all girls, and there is a formal programme of careers advice throughout Years 9, 10 and 11 and Sixth Form. All girls go on to university and are helped to investigate thoroughly the Higher Education and careers options open to them, careful guidance being given concerning their applications and interviews. The support of the Headmistress, the Deputy Headmistress and other senior staff is available at all stages. Work experience placements are organised, and girls are encouraged to make particular use of this option at the end of their GCSE courses. The School belongs to the Independent Schools Careers Organisation and benefits from its many services. Visiting speakers give lectures on various higher education and careers topics; visits to appropriate conferences and exhibitions are arranged; and the School organises and hosts a biennial Careers Convention. The school has two well-resourced careers libraries of printed, video and computer-accessed information.

Junior School Curriculum. The Junior School and Senior School are closely linked, and Junior School pupils are steadily introduced to the specialist teaching and facilities of the Senior School. In the early years the teaching of most subjects is undertaken by the class teachers. In Years 5 and 6 girls are taught by subject teachers, some of whom also teach in the Senior School, and this arrangement gives girls the benefit of specialist teaching and encourages them to develop a feeling of confidence and continuity when the time comes for them to move into the Senior School. Use of the Senior School facilities is particularly valuable in Science, Art, Music, Physical Education and Drama. There is a Junior Library in Langley Lodge, and older Juniors may also use the King Library in the Senior School.

Performing Arts. The School has a strong tradition of debating and public speaking, and girls have many successes to their credit in city, county and regional competitions. A major drama production each year, and various smaller presentations give girls the opportunity to develop their skills in performing, directing, lighting, sound, stage design, costume design and make-up. There are frequent visits to Stratford, London and regional theatres including the Oxford Playhouse and some girls perform at the Playhouse in the annual schools' gala. The majority of girls learn one musical instrument and some learn two or more; there are two choirs, one orchestra and several smaller ensembles, and some girls are members of the Oxford Girls' Choir, the Oxford Youth Chamber Choir, the Oxford Schools' Symphony Orchestra, the Oxfordshire Youth Orchestra and the Thames Vale Orchestra. Instruments learnt include piano, violin, viola, 'cello, flute, oboe, clarinet, trumpet, bassoon, saxophone, French horn, guitar and percussion. Through musical productions, concerts and the liturgy there are many opportunities for girls to contribute to the musical life of the School. In both Drama and Music, pupils take the Guildhall School of Music and Drama examinations.

Sport. The School has good playing fields, all-weather hard courts and an outdoor heated swimming pool. The principal winter sports are netball and hockey; the principal summer sports are tennis, swimming, athletics and rounders. Girls compete regularly in local, county and regional tournaments.

Duke of Edinburgh's Award. The School has an outstanding record in the Duke of Edinburgh's Award, each year about 35 girls achieving the Bronze Award, 20 girls or so achieving the Silver Award and 20 or more girls achieving the Gold Award. The purpose of the Award is to give challenge, responsibility and adventure to young people, thus encouraging them to develop initiative and team skills.

Visits. Fieldwork, conferences, lectures, art exhibitions, plays and concerts give girls an interesting programme of visits within the UK. Visits abroad include study courses, exchanges, sports tours and skiing holidays, and the School regularly hosts visiting groups from schools overseas.

Health. The School Nurse works closely with the School Doctor who holds a weekly surgery at the School and who also sees girls at her nearby Health Centre. Dental and orthodontic treatment can be arranged locally, and the John Radcliffe Hospital is five minutes away.

Admissions. Admission to the Junior School is by interview and the School's own entrance tests. Admission to the Senior School is by interview and entrance examination (Common Entrance at 11+). Admission to the Sixth Form is by interview, school report and GCSE results. Scholarships are available at 11+ and 16+.

Fees per term (2008-2009). Full Boarders £5,050–£5,950; Weekly Boarders £4,750–£5,650; Day Pupils £2,240–£3,550.

Scholarships. Scholarships are offered at 11+ and 16+.

Charitable status. Rye St Antony School Limited is a Registered Charity, number 309685. Its purpose is the furtherance of Christian education.

St Albans High School

3 Townsend Avenue St Albans Hertfordshire AL1 3SJ
Tel: 01727 853800
Fax: 01727 792516
e-mail: admissions@stalbans-high.herts.sch.uk
website: www.sahs.org.uk

Motto: *The fear of the Lord is the beginning of wisdom*

Visitor: The Right Reverend The Lord Bishop of St Albans

Council:
The Dean of St Albans
Mrs S Ailles, BA, ACA
I Babbage, Esq, BSc, FCA
Dr P Barrison, MBBS
Mrs J F Boulton, MRICS (*Chairman*)
Mrs E Curtis
S C de Galleani, Esq
T de Pencier, Esq, BA, FILT
Mrs H Greatrex, BA, ACA
B Kettle, Esq
P Lawford, Esq, MA
Miss R Musgrave, MA, MA, FRSA
Dr D Porcelli
Mrs K Siviter, MA
Mrs J Stroud, MA
Mrs S Williams, FCA
Mrs J Woolley

‡ *Holder of Teacher's Diploma or Certificate*

***Head Mistress*: ‡Ms Jacqualyn Pain**, MA, MA, MBA, NPQH
from April 2009: Mrs Rosemary Martin, MEd, NPQH, FRSA

Bursar: Mr F Campbell, BSc Glasgow, FCMA

Head of Wheathampstead House: Mrs S Dunkerley, MA London, BEd Cantab

Deputy Head: ‡Mrs B Goulding, MA Ed Mgmt, BA London, BA Sheffield, NPQH

Director of Studies: ‡Ms C Cozens, BSc Exeter

Director of Marketing and Communications/Assistant Head: ‡Mrs J Ross, BA Manchester

Chaplain: The Revd Diane Fitzgerald Clark

* *Head of Department*
§ *Part-time*

Senior School:
‡Miss F E Alderman, BA Nottingham Trent
‡Dr G Alderton, BSc, PhD Leeds
Miss R L Aldgate, MSc Bristol
Miss M Bacon, BEd Exeter (**Physical Education*)

‡Mrs E J Beasley, MA Cambridge
‡Miss S M N Bordier, LLCE Orleans, France/Nottingham
‡Mrs S Bracey, BA Liverpool
‡Mrs S Brown, MA Manchester Metropolitan
Mrs D Browne, BEd Sussex
§‡Mrs A Bullen, BA Aberystwyth
‡Mr D J Carr, BA Southampton
§‡Mr N Chandler, BA Gothenburg
‡Mrs A Chapman, BA Exeter (**Classics*)
‡Miss S I R Clarke, MA St Andrews
‡Miss N Collins, BSc Brunel
‡Mrs S Cooper, BA Exeter
‡Mrs S Cubbon, MSc London
§Mrs E Davies, BA Warwick
‡Mrs G Davies, BSc, MSc Wales (**Design Technology*)
‡Mrs J Douglas, BA Durham
§‡Mrs S Dover, BSc London
‡Mr P Duddles, BEng Warwick
‡Miss H W Everett, BA Durham (**Modern Languages*)
‡Mrs R Frost, MA Ed Open, BEd Dundee, BA Open (*Senior Teacher*)
‡Mrs S Gillman, BSc Exeter
‡Mrs K Gorman, BA Birmingham (**English*)
Miss A A Hedley, BEd Edinburgh
‡Mrs A Jallport, BSc Hertfordshire
‡Dr S Legg, BSc Birmingham, DPhil Oxford (**Science*)
§‡Mr J Marney, BA Newcastle, BSc Herts
‡Miss R Marsh, BA Southampton
‡Miss S Matthews, BA London (**PSHE*)
‡Mrs C Mawston, BA Kent
‡Mr S McGuinness, BA Manchester Polytechnic (**Art*)
‡Mr S R Mew, MA Essex (**History*)
‡Mrs B Mitchell, BSc Sheffield
‡Mr S D Moore, BA Cambridge, MA Cantab
Mrs K Osborne, BEd Hons London
‡Mrs M Patel, BA Wales (**Religious Studies*)
‡Miss E A Pitcher, BA Oxford
‡Miss E Pritchard, BA York
§‡Mrs E Pyett MA Leeds
‡Mr S Ramsbottom, BSc Reading (**Geography*)
‡Mrs P Ray, BA Leeds
‡Mr I G Round, BA Oxford
§‡Mrs L Ryan, MA Cambridge
‡Dr N Springthorpe, BMus, PhD Surrey, FLCM, PGCertRCM Surrey (**Music*)
‡Mr J Stanford, BA York (**Economics*)
‡Mrs S Stewart, BSc Leicester
‡Miss K Sumner, BA Warwick (**Mathematics*)
‡Mrs J Taylor, MA Cambridge
Miss N Taylor-Imrie, BSc Hertfordshire, Dip SpLD Hornsby
§‡Mrs G Thompson, BA London
‡Mr I Thomson, BA London (**Sixth Form*)
§‡Mrs K Thomson, BSc London
Miss C Tweedie, BMusEd Cape Town
Mr P Vines, BA East Anglia QTS
§Miss E Wadey, BA Winchester
‡Mr C White, BSc London (*Examinations Officer*)
‡Miss H Whymark, BA Hull (**Drama*)
‡Miss P I Willmott, BA London
‡Miss H Woods, BSc Plymouth
‡Mrs C A Wright, BA Ulster (*ICT Coordinator*)

Librarian, Senior School:
Mrs C Day, BA Roehampton

Wheathampstead House (Primary School):
Head: Mrs S Dunkerley, MA London, BEd Cantab
Deputy Head: ‡Mr J Wadge, BA Durham
§‡Miss C M Allin, Licence LLCE Poitiers, France
‡Mrs S Beach, BA Essex
§Mrs J Bowskill, CertEd Loughborough
‡Mrs N Davies, BA London
‡Miss A Deacon, BSc Bath
‡Mrs S Edwards, GRSM
‡Mrs S E Fulford, BA Leeds
Miss D Hamalis, BEd Hertfordshire
‡Mrs W R Job, BEd Brighton
§Mrs J Julians, MSc Loughborough
Mrs C Kay, CertEd Lancaster, RSA SpLD
‡Mrs G E Lewis, BSc London
Mrs J Morrow, CertED Exeter
Mrs J Plenty, BEd Cambridge
Mr D Sayers, BA Winchester QTS
Miss A Scaife d'Ingerthorpe, BA Ed QTS
Mrs L Still, BA Ed Exeter
‡Miss S Styles, BA Surrey
Mrs C Sykes, CertEd Homerton College, Cambridge
‡Mrs K Turk, BA Leeds
Miss R Warren-Tape, BEd Cambridge

Classroom Assistants, Wheathampstead House:
Mrs P Bate, BA St Martins
Mrs A Gibbs, CertEd Sussex
Mrs S Holmwood, BA Manchester Polytechnic
Mrs J McMullen
Mrs S Smith
Mrs C Strang
Mrs L Wenham
Mrs J Whitaker

Librarian, Wheathampstead House:
§Mrs J Miles, LLB Hong Kong

School Medical Officer: Dr A E Margereson, MMBS London

Visiting Staff:
Music:
Miss J Bausor, BMus Hons, PGDipRAM (*Oboe*)
Mrs J Blinko, GRSM, DipRCM (*Flute*)
Mrs K Bradley, LRAM (*Violin*)
Ms C Charlesworth, BMus (*Flute*)
Miss S Dumbrill, BMus, PGDip (*Flute*)
Mrs E Fagg, LRAM, GRSM, MTC (*Piano*)
Mr I Gammie, MA, ALCM (*Guitar*)
Mrs C Heller-Jones, BMus, PGCE, PGCertGSM (*Singing*)
Miss P Jeppesen, PGDip Orch Studies GSM (*Violin*)
Mr S Jones, GTCL, LTCL, MTC (*Singing*)
Miss E Lane, GRSM, ARCM (*Singing*)
Ms A Le Hair, BMus, DipRCM (*Piano*)
Ms R Menday, BMus, LRAM (*Bassoon/Flute*)
Mrs M Miller, LLB, CTABRSM, LRSM, FRSM, ATCL (*Piano*)
Mr K Milton, AMusA AMB, DipT&P Sydney, Kunstl Dip Luebeck, MSc (*Violin*)
Miss C Morris Jones, AGSM, LRAM (*Harp*)
Mr I Muncey, AGSM (*Trumpet*)
Miss F Nisbett (*Cello, Piano, Double Bass*)
Mr M Onissi, LTCL (*Saxophone and Clarinet*)
Lady R Runcie, Hon ARAM, LRAM, ARCM (*Piano*)
Mrs H Shabetai, BMus (*Piano*)
Miss M Tsuji, BMus, DipPostgrad Perf RAM, LRAM (*Piano*)
Miss A Tysall, BMus (*Piano*)
Mrs B Valdar, AGSM (*Clarinet*)
Mr M Whittington, BMusPerf, LRAM (*Percussion*)

Physical Education:
Ms B Amos (*Tennis – WH*)
Mrs S Ashton (*Yoga*)
Miss N Cahn (*Aerobics*)
Mrs S Burton (*Squash*)
Mr I Gilbert (*Judo*)
Mr D Lawlor (*Tennis – WH*)
Mr G Marini (*Fencing*)
Mr W Rayden (*Fencing – WH*)
Mr H Shah (*Badminton*)
Mr A Wilkins (*Tennis Coach*)

Development Office:
Director of Communications & Marketing: Mrs J Ross, BA Manchester
Development Officer: §Mrs R Ramsay, BA Oxford
Marketing and IT Assistant: Miss J Evans, BA Leicester

Technicians:
§Mrs C Ametrano (*IT*)
§Mrs K Burchmore (*Physics*)
Mr P Gauntlett (*IT Resources Technician*)
Mrs A Hodsden (*CDT*)
§Mrs A Kellard, BA Hertfordshire (*Art*)
§Mr A Morris (*CDT*)
§Mrs N Phillips, BA Surrey (*Art*)
§Miss R Randall (*Biology*)
Mr C Veasey (*Chemistry*)

Administration:
Network Manager: Mr L Miles, BSc Glamorgan
Assistant Network Manager: Mr J Shackley, BA Gloucestershire
Account Manager: Mr M Langley
Domestic Bursar: Mrs H Stopps, MIH
Headmistress's PA: Mrs E Roberts
School Secretary: Mrs E Bullivant
Registrar: Miss S Nicholls, BEd Cambridge
Absence Clerk: Mrs H Paustian, BSc Nebrasca
Music Administrator: Mrs F Robinson, BA Sheffield Hallam

St Albans High School is a day school for 950 girls aged between 4 and 18. Since its foundation in 1889, it has been closely linked with the Cathedral and Abbey Church of St Alban and the Christian ethos is very important in the life of the School. Services are held regularly in School or at the Abbey. The School is only a few minutes' walk from the town centre.

The Primary School, which is based in Wheathampstead House – a distance of approximately 4½ miles away – is for girls aged 4–11, and numbers 310. It is a beautiful country house set in 18 acres of parkland. There are 19 full-time and 2 part-time members of staff as well as 8 classroom assistants. The curriculum covers all the primary school subjects in the National Curriculum in depth through a modern and lively approach. There is an extensive range of clubs from languages, including Mandarin, to music, sport and creative/fun activities.

The Senior School has facilities for the teaching of a wide range of subjects. There are nine modern science laboratories, a Design and Technology Centre, a Drama Studio, an Assembly Hall with a fully equipped stage, specialist rooms for IT, Art, Music, Textiles, Food Technology and all the usual academic subjects. The curriculum, which is kept under review, includes all the subjects of the National Curriculum as well as Latin, a second Modern Language and Drama. There are two well stocked libraries and a Sixth Form Centre to accommodate some 170 girls at the top of the School.

Girls are encouraged to participate in a wide range of extra-curricular activities, among which Sport and Music feature strongly, as well as the Duke of Edinburgh's Award Scheme, Young Enterprise and Community Service. Pastoral care is important at all levels of the School and girls are encouraged to feel that they are valued for their contributions to the life of the School community.

In the grounds of the Senior School there is a modern Sports Hall with adjoining leisure complex comprising indoor pool, fitness suite and dance studio. The main games field is ten minutes' walk from the School and there are eight hard tennis courts, two lacrosse pitches and a pavilion.

Pupils are prepared for GCSE examinations at the age of 16, for Advanced Level examinations, for Oxford and Cambridge entrance and for the examinations of the Associated Board of the Royal Schools of Music.

Fees per term (2008-2009). Reception £2,915, Years 1 and 2 £3,075 (inc Lunch); Junior Department (age 7–11) £3,075 (exc Lunch); Senior School (age 11–18) £3,705. Private music lessons, special tennis coaching, School lunch and daily School coaches are all optional extras.

Scholarships. (*see Scholarship Entries section*). A Music Scholarship is awarded annually at age 11 and Academic Scholarships at ages 11+ and 16+. There are bursaries to assist in cases of hardship.

Admission. Pupils are normally admitted in September at the age of 4, 5 and 7 for entry to the Primary School, 11 for the Senior School and 16 for the Sixth Form. Offers of places in the Sixth Form are provisional until the results of the GCSE examinations are known: girls are required to have a minimum of 5 subjects with A* or A grades including A* or A grades in the subjects to be taken at Advanced Level. Entrance examinations are held in the Lent Term for admission in the following September.

Charitable status. St Albans High School for Girls is a Registered Charity, number 311065. It exists to provide an education for girls "in accordance with the principles of the Church of England".

St Andrew's School
Bedford

Kimbolton Road Bedford MK40 2PA
Tel: 01234 267272
Fax: 01234 355105
e-mail: standrews@standrewsschoolbedford.com
website: www.standrewsschoolbedford.com

Founded 1897.
Motto: *Non Sibi Sed Deo et Alteria*

Governing Body:
Chairman: Mr K Sanders

Clerk to the Governors and Company Secretary: Mr D Johnson

Staff:

***Headteacher*: Mr S P Skehan**, BA, MA, NPQH

Deputy Head: Dr D J Pacini, BSc, PhD, MIEA, Adv Cert EdMgt

Miss J Bassett (*PE*)
Miss S Clark (*Art*)
Miss B Coleman (*Mathematics*)
Mrs K Dawson (*Mathematics*)
Mr B Heathcote (*History; Careers*)
Ms S Hammelev (*Speech and Drama*)
Mrs M Ireland (*Music*)
Ms G Jackson (*Science*)
Mr C Jones (*Mathematics; ICT*)
Mrs C Long (*German*)
Miss J Pearce (*Physical Education*)
Mrs J Randall (*Geography*)
Mrs H Ryan (*Science; Head of Senior School*)
Miss A Scorer (*Technology*)
Mrs K Searle (*Science*)
Mrs S Shepherd (*Mathematics*)
Mrs A Sprake (*English*)
Ms C Stewart (*Music*)
Mrs S Stott (*Drama*)
Mrs S Tribe (*Modern Languages; Careers*)
Mrs F Turner (*Physical Education*)
Mrs P Wilson (*Textiles*)
Mrs F Williams (*English*)
Mrs H Wittering (*Food Technology*)

Junior School:
Head: Mr N Hearn

Mrs D Berrington	Mrs L Wayles
Mrs K Joiner	Mrs G Ayres
Mrs M Jordan	Mrs M Frame
Mrs H King	Mrs A Howe
Miss L O'Dell	Mrs M Watt

Nursery Department:
Head: Mrs K Gamble
Mrs N Holt
Mrs J Tolhurst
Mrs J Satchwill

Learning Support Department:
Mrs J Prentice
Mrs R Scott
Mrs S Bosco
Mrs J Fitzgibbon
Mrs C Setchfield
Mrs M Hickey
Mrs T Carlisle
Mrs L Waller

Librarian: Mrs Y Owen (*Learning Support Assistant*)
Secretary to the Head/Admissions: Mrs S Heaney

There are a number of visiting Music staff and Speech and Drama staff, offering a wide range of individual tuition.

St Andrew's is a small day school for girls from the ages of three to sixteen and boys from three to nine who are taught in small classes.

A 19th Century house is at the heart of the School, which has expanded to provide modern facilities to meet the demands of the National Curriculum and beyond. The Preparatory Department occupies separate accommodation. The Nursery/Pre-Prep buildings cater for boys as well as girls.

The School prepares girls for the GCSE examinations and further education in the Sixth Form of local Independent Schools, Upper Schools or Colleges. There is an extremely wide range of extra-curricular activities, which includes sport, music, drama and The Duke of Edinburgh's Award Scheme.

For further details contact the School Office: Tel: 01234 267272; Fax: 01234 355105; e-mail: standrews@standrewsschoolbedford.com.

Fees per term (2008-2009). Nursery £1,950; Junior School: £1,950 (Reception to Year 2), £2,530 (Years 3–6); Senior School: £3,185 (Years 7–11).

Charitable status. St Andrew's School (Bedford) Limited is a Registered Charity, number 307531. It offers a broad based education to pupils of all abilities, who are encouraged to strive for excellence in all they do.

St Catherine's School
Bramley

Bramley Guildford Surrey GU5 0DF
Tel: 01483 893363
Fax: 01483 899608
e-mail: schooloffice@stcatherines.info
website: www.stcatherines.info

Founded as a Church of England School for Girls in 1885.

Governing Body:
Chairman: Mr P J Martin, BA, FRGS, FCCA
Vice-Chairman: Dr J F McGowan, MB BS, FCA
Mr C M R Campbell, MA
Mrs C M Dent
Mrs S M Fowler-Watt
Dr F Green
Mrs M Greenway
Dr J E Johnson, MA, DPhil
Mr M Ommanney
Mrs S Shipway
Mrs G Stuart
Mr J C M Tippett, BSc, FCA, TEP
Mr B M Way, DipArch, RIBA

***Headmistress*: Mrs A M Phillips**, MA Cantab

Business Manager: Mrs C Silver, BSc Durham, PGCE
Head of Prep School: Mrs K Jefferies, BSc Bridgewater, Massachusetts, PGCE
Head of Boarding: Mrs C Foord, BA, MPhil Birmingham, PGCE
Director of Studies: Dr S Pumphrey, PhD Imperial College, BSc, PGCE
Director of Staff: Mrs C Rose, BA Nottingham, PGCE
Senior Housemistress: Mrs M Banks, BA London, PGCE
Head of Sixth Form: Mrs C Wyllie, MA Durham, PGCE
School Administrator: Mrs H Bryn-Thomas, BSc Kent, PGCE
Director of Music: Mr G Field, DipRAM, GRSM, ARCO, LRAM
Deputy Head of Prep: Miss G Bradnam, MA De Montfort University, BEd
Director of Studies Prep: Mrs F Thomas, BA Victoria, New Zealand, Dip Tchg, TTC
Head of Pre-Prep: Mrs J Cochrane, BEd, CertEd Leicester, PGCPSE Open
Projects Director: Mr J Deane, FlnstLM, MBIFM

Registrar: Mrs J Corben
Development Director: Mr J Foord, MA Oxford
Association Director: Mrs K Stocks, MA Oxford
Chaplain: Revd Canon Colin Tickner, MA London

Senior School Teaching Staff:
§ *Part-time*

Mrs V Alexander, BEd Brighton (*Physical Education*)
Miss H Baig, BA Hons Cantab, PGCE (*Classics*)
Mrs M Banks, BA London, PGCE (*French*)
Miss G Barwood, BA, BEd, DipT Waikato, New Zealand (*English*)
§Mrs C Benson, BA Hons Manchester, PGCE Guildford (*Psychology*)
§Mrs S Berry, BA Canterbury, PGCE (*French*)
Mrs V Bingham, BA Oxon, PGCE (*Classics*)
§Mrs H Bowling, BA Warwick, PGCE (*English*)
Miss D Brown, BA Otago, Dip GradEd
Mrs H Bryn-Thomas, BSc Kent, PGCE (*Mathematics*)
Mrs J Collins, CertEd Bath College (*Home Economics*)
§Mrs M Creer, MA Kingston, BA Swansea, PGCE (*English*)
§Mrs L Crispin, BA Manchester (*Textiles*)
§Mrs H Crosbie, BSc Hons Durham, PGCE Twickenham (*Mathematics*)
Mr C Curtis, BSc UMIST, PGCE (*Chemistry*)
Mrs G David, BA Manchester, PGCE (*History & Politics/Marketing*)
§Mrs J Davies, CertEd St Osyth (*Home Economics*)
Miss L Dyball, BSc Cheltenham and Gloucester College, PGCE (*Physical Education*)
Mr G Field, DipRAM, GRSM, ARCO, LRAM (*Music*)
Mrs R Folley, BEd, DipEd Chelsea (*Physical Education*)
Mrs C Foord, BA Birmingham, MPhil, PGCE (*English*)
Mr P Friend, BSc Lancaster, PGCE St Martins (*Mathematics and Exam Officer*)
Mrs C Frost, MA Oxon, PGCE (*Biology*)
§Mrs F Gane, BA London, CertEd (*History*)
Mrs N Genzel, BA Roehampton, PGCE (*Food and Nutrition*)
Mr C Gladwell, BA London (*Politics/History*) PGCE

Miss L Godfrey, MA Hons St Andrews, PGCE Cambridge (*Spanish*)
§Mr D Goldsmith, MBE, BSc Oxon (*Mathematics*)
Mr M Greenfield, MA Oxon (*Physics*)
Miss L Grizzelle, BA London, PGCE (*Drama*)
Mrs S Hall, BA London, PGCE (*French with German*)
Mrs P Harris, BSc Edinburgh, PGCE (*Biology*)
§Miss L Hayat, MA Reading, PGCE London (*History of Art*)
Miss N Hindley, MA Hons Oxon (*Chemistry*)
Miss J Hilvert, BA London, PGCE, MA Middlesex (*Director of Drama*)
Mr J Ind, BA Oxon, PGCE (*Classics*)
Mrs E Jamieson, BCom Birmingham (*Physical Education & Business Studies*)
Miss H-A Jeans, BA Durham (*English*)
§Mrs J Keane, MA Greenwich, TEFL Trinity, AMBDA (*Learning Support*)
Mrs S Kelsall, MA Open, BSc Brighton, PGCE (*Mathematics*)
Dr O Kievit, Drs Nijmegen, Netherlands, PhD Yale (*Chemistry*)
§Dr E Kinsella, BSc Imperial College, (*Chemistry*)
Mr P Klein, BSc Cheltenham & Gloucester, PGCE (*Geography*)
Miss C Komor, BEd Wales (*Home Economics and PSHE*)
Miss T Kuchmy, MusB Manchester, PGCE, GRNCM, ARNCM, LRAM, ARCM
Mr A Lamb MA, MPhil Cantab, ARCO (*Music*)
Dr M Lee, BSc Hons KCL, PhD KCL (*Geography*)
Mrs S Mackness, BSc London, PGCE (*Geography*)
Mr A Mackinnon, BA Hons Surrey, PGCE Kingston (*History*)
Miss K McDowell, BA Durham, PGCE (*Spanish and Italian*)
Miss A McKane, MA Monash, DipE Monash (*English*)
Mr A McNally, BA Hons Queen's Belfast, PGCE (*Religious Studies*)
Mrs R McQuade, BA Oviedo, PGCE (*Spanish*)
Mrs K Meredith, BA London, AKC, PGCE (*Classics*)
§Mrs S Monks, BA Exeter, PG Sculpture City and Guilds (*English and Fine Art*)
Mrs N Moore, BA Wales, PGCE (*Physical Education*)
§Miss R Morgan, BA London, TCert, DCG (*Careers*)
Mrs L Munro-Faure, MA Oxon, PGCE (*Biology*)
Mrs S Murray, BSc London, AKC (*Physics*)
Miss E Nevin, BA Oxon (*French and German*)
Mrs H Noble, BA Cantab, PGCE (*German and French*)
§Mrs S Noy, BA Hons Nottingham (*Textiles*)
Mrs J Obaditch, BEd Hons Wales (*ICT*)
§Mr J Peters, BA Wales (*English*)
Mrs A Phillips, MA Cantab (*English*)
§Mrs L Pillar, BEd Surrey (*Religious Knowledge*)
Miss S Potter, BA Hons Durham, PGCE (*Classics*)
§Dr K Puech, BSc, PhD Dublin, PGCE (*Physics*)
Dr S Pumphrey, PhD Imperial College, PGCE (*Physics*)
§Mrs K Rayner, BSc Natal, DipEd Cape Town (*Biology*)
Mrs J Reid, BA Hons Oxon, PGCE (*Classics*)
Mrs C Rose, BA Nottingham, PGCE (*General Studies/History/Politics*)
Mrs A Rusholme, BSc Hons Durham, PGCE OU (*Mathematics*)
Mrs J Silk, Dip AD Bath Academy of Art (*Art & Ceramics*)
Mrs C Silver, BSc Durham, PGCE (*Mathematics*)
§Mrs S Small, BA Liverpool, PGCE, DipSpLD (*Learning Support*)
Dr J Spencer, BSc, PhD Birmingham, PGCE (*ICT*)
Mrs A Stortt, BSc Exeter, PGCE (*Geography*)
Mrs L Strong, BA Bristol, PGCE (*French and Italian*)
Mr C Taylor, MSc Oxon (*Biology*)
§Miss V Vinen, BA Plymouth, PGCE (*Art & Design*)
Mr N Watson, BA Ealing College of Higher Education, PGCE (*Economics/Business Studies*)
§Mrs S Weighell, BA Birmingham (*Business Studies*)
Mr D Weightman, BA Surrey Institute of Art and Design (*Photography*)
Mr A White, BA Winchester, CertEd (*Design & Technology*)
§Mrs A White, BSc Wales, PGCE (*Geography*)
Mr A Williams, MA Surrey (*Design & Technology*)
Mrs M Williams, Dip RCM Perf Hons, Dip PG, Adv Cert Chopin Academy
Mr J Worthen, BA Oxon, PGCE (*English*)
Mr A Wright, BSc Hertfordshire, PGCE (*Mathematics*)
Mrs C Wyllie, MA Durham, PGCE (*Theology*)
§Mrs N Wynne, MA Cantab, PGCE (*Mathematics*)

Librarian: Mrs S Lawrence, ALA

Preparatory School Teaching Staff:
Mrs C Berry, BA Southampton, PGCE (*General Subjects*)
Miss G Bradnam, MA De Montfort, BEd (*Science,Thinking Skills/VR*)
Mrs V Brown, BA Exeter, PGCE (*General Subjects*)
Mrs D Burton, BA Liverpool, PGCE (*General Subjects*)
Mrs S Carrington-West, BSc Hons Southern Maine, LLB Hons UWE
Mrs S Carter, TCert (*Physical Education*)
Mrs J Cochrane, BEd, CertEd Leicester, PGCPSE Open (*General Subjects*)
Mrs J Cowx, BEd Bedford College (*Physical Education*)
Mrs K Field, BA Cardiff, PGCE (*General Subjects*)
Mr M Hardman, BA York, PGCE (*General Subjects*)
Mrs D Hodgkiss, CertEd King Alfred's College (*General Subjects*)
Mrs J Hughes, BEd Birmingham (*General Subjects*)
Mrs J Keane, MA Greenwich, TEFL Trinity, AMBDA (*SENCO*)
Mrs P King-Fretts, BA WSIHE, PGCE (*General Subjects*)
Mrs R Lee, BA London, PGCE (*General Subjects*)
Mrs A MacVean, BEd King Alfred's College, Winchester, Dip Mont Hons (*General Subjects*)
Mrs T Marmion, BEd Hons, DipSpLD (*Mathematics*)
Mrs L Marriott, CertEd Homerton, Cambridge (*General Subjects*)
Mrs A May, Dip Art & Design Central School of Art & Design, Art TCert (*Art*)
Mrs H Pasley, BEd Lancaster (*Physical Education*)
§Mrs S Rolls, GTCL, LTCL, CertEd (*Music*)
Mrs F Thomas, BA Victoria, New Zealand, Dip Tchg, TTC (*General Subjects*)
Mrs A White, MA Oxon (*Music*)

ICT:
Network Manager: Mr J Watts, BEng Hons Sussex
Assistant Network Manager: Mr A Harris, MCP
Prep School ICT Coordinator and Trainer/Senior School ICT Trainer: Mrs K Chaventre

Teaching Assistants:
Miss G Ciampaglia
Miss R Harding
Mrs T Myners
Miss L Reynolds
Mrs L Silvester

Medical Centre Sisters:
Mrs T Brabin, RGN
Mrs L Green, RGN
Mrs L Pope, RGN
Mrs K Simpson, RGN

School Housemistresses:
Ashcombe: Miss C Komor
Merriman: Mrs R McQuade
Midleton: Mrs K Meredith
Musgrave: Mrs P Harris
Russell-Baker: Mrs S Hall
Stoner: Mrs M Banks

Boarding Staff:
Housemistresses:
Symes: Mrs H Church

Bronte: Miss S Phillips
Keller: Miss D Brown
Sixth Form: Miss A McKane

Visiting staff teach piano, string, wind instruments, brass, percussion, ballet, speech and drama.

The concluding paragraph of the October 2006 ISI Report on St Catherine's stated that 'Educational provision, in the full sense of these words, is outstanding because, above all, St Catherine's is a learning school in which a state of satisfaction with anything but the best is not on the agenda.' The outstanding results gained in public examinations by girls at St Catherine's School, Bramley secure them places at the top universities, in competitive disciplines like medicine and veterinary science, law and languages. This success comes not only as a result of the fine quality of the teaching, but is also due to the individual attention received by every girl. St Catherine's places great emphasis on creating a happy environment where every girl is encouraged to work hard to maximise her talents. The Inspectors found the atmosphere to be friendly and one in which children can 'develop and grow in a very stimulating environment'.

There are six Houses which are absolutely pivotal in the life of the School. The girls' loyalty and affection for their Houses is impressive with memories of inter-house plays, competitions and matches enduring long after their School days have ended.

The curriculum is broad and varied, and all pupils participate in many challenging and rewarding extra-curricular activities, at the same time raising impressive sums of money for charity each year.

The School's extremely flexible approach to boarding makes it increasingly attractive to busy, professional families where many girls enjoy the weekly boarding provision. Once again the ISI team picked out boarding as one of the outstanding features of St Catherine's.

Activities Week is held each year in the Summer Term. Pupils participate in outward bound ventures to Wales and Derbyshire, in an industrial heritage tour to the north and midlands, modern language courses in Europe whilst Sixth Formers focus on university choices. Activities Week is constantly evolving and always presents excitement; costs are included in the termly school fees.

International links are also very important. St Catherine's has an exchange programme with St Catherine's Melbourne and there are also links with schools in Kenya and Afghanistan.

St Catherine's has an unrivalled reputation in art, music, sport and drama; photography AS is a popular option amongst the Sixth Form, and younger girls are encouraged by an enthusiastic Art and Design department to take advantage of the superb facilities, and join after-school clubs.

Music is an important feature of school life, with several choirs, an orchestra and two concert bands rehearsing each week and performing regularly. Over half the girls learn to play a musical instrument, and there are flute choirs, string quartets, recorder groups and ensembles to cater for all levels of ability. Concerts and recitals are held regularly. An exciting venture has been the Organ Academy and the Jennifer Bate Organ Scholarship in conjunction with Guildford Cathedral. Our first 'Organ Scholar' took up her place in September 2007.

A large number of girls go on to represent the county in netball, lacrosse, swimming, squash and athletics and many St Catherine's girls have also played at national level. Every girl is encouraged to take part in sport at school, whatever her level of expertise. There are currently nine girls playing lacrosse for their national teams. St Catherine's has been granted full planning permission to build a brand new sports complex and assembly/performance hall, providing girls with facilities to match their talents and commitment.

Drama and Theatre Studies are extremely popular options and all girls are encouaraged to audition for the annual middle and senior school plays. As well as acting opportunities, pupils are also offered the opportunity to help backstage and front of house and learn many valuable skills as a result. LAMDA classes are offered to all year groups.

The Preparatory School offers a full academic and games curriculum; most girls join at 4 with a limited number of places available in other years. It aims to support families in helping younger pupils develop a strong sense of values, high standards of behaviour and consideration to others, as well as achieving excellent academic success. The girls benefit from specialist teaching, combining the best of traditional methods with modern technology to prepare them for the Entrance Examinations to all Senior Schools at 11+, including St Catherine's.

St Catherine's is situated in extensive grounds, in the heart of the attractive Surrey village of Bramley, three miles south of Guildford which has a main line station (Waterloo 35 minutes). There is easy access to Heathrow and Gatwick and travel arrangements are made for overseas boarders. Close proximity to London allows frequent visits to theatres and galleries and the miles of countryside on our doorstep is an asset to the many girls who take part in the Duke of Edinburgh's Award Scheme.

Fees per term (from January 2008). Day Girls (including lunch): Pre-Prep 1 £2,045, Pre-Prep 2 £2,475, Pre-Prep 3 £2,915; Prep School £3,370; Middle and Senior School £4,155.

Boarders: Middle and Senior Boarding and Tuition £6,840.

Entry. (*see Scholarship Entries section*). This is by Entrance Examination held in January. The Preparatory School also holds its entrance tests in January.

Entrance Scholarships are offered at 11+, together with a number of Sixth Form scholarships of one third fees. A number of music exhibitions, providing music tuition, music and instrument hire are also offered. A Sixth Form Art Scholarship is available.

Prospectus and School Visits. Please apply to the Registrar. The Headmistress will be pleased to see parents by appointment.

Charitable status. The Corporation of St Catherine's, Bramley is a Registered Charity, number 1070858. It exists to provide education for girls in accordance with the principles of the Church of England.

St Catherine's School
Twickenham

Cross Deep Twickenham Middlesex TW1 4QJ
Tel: 020 8891 2898
Fax: 020 8744 9629
e-mail: admissions@stcatherineschool.co.uk
website: www.stcatherineschool.co.uk

Motto: '*Not Words But Deeds*'

Chair of Governors: Mr D Sheath

***Headmistress*: Sister Paula Thomas**, BEd, MA

Deputy Head: Ms M Fisher, BA

Head of the Preparatory Department: Miss M M Regan, BEd Hons, CertEd

Bursar & Clerk to the Governors: Mr I G Stewart, BAcc, CA

Admissions Secretary: Mrs A Jones

Age Range. Girls 3–16 years, Boys 3–7 years.

Number in School. 340 Day Girls.

Founded in 1914 by the Sisters of Mercy, St Catherine's moved from its original site to its current location in 1919. Today the school is under lay management. St Catherine's is a Catholic School in the ecumenical tradition, and pupils of all denominations are welcome.

Aims. Our aim is to provide an excellent all-round education so that every pupil can achieve her personal best. We strive to provide a broad and balanced education within a stimulating and supportive environment which encourages learning without undue pressure. Success is achieved through personal responsibility, high expectations and a close partnership between parents and school. Emphasis is placed on self-discipline, responsibility and the importance of kindness, concern and respect for others. Since we are a relatively small school the staff are able to know the pupils as individuals. There is a strong sense of community and it takes no time at all for a girl to make friends.

Situation. The School enjoys an enviable position being located next to the River Thames. It is a short distance from the centre of Twickenham and approximately 10-15 minutes' walk from Strawberry Hill and Twickenham Stations. Both have regular services to London (Waterloo), Surrey, Berkshire and Middlesex. There are also a number of local bus routes.

Entrance. Main points of entry are at 3, 7 and 11 but girls are accepted at any stage subject to space. Places at the school are usually awarded on the basis of an interview, a report from the candidate's previous school and an assessment (examination in the senior school).

Scholarships and Bursaries. Academic Scholarships, up to the value of 50% of the fees, are awarded annually at 11+ on the basis of the entrance examination and interview. Music, Sports and Art Awards are also awarded annually following an audition/assessment and are conditional on the applicant achieving the School's academic requirement for entry.

A limited number of Bursaries are offered depending on need and funds available.

Curriculum. In the Senior School pupils follow courses in English, Mathematics, Science, Religious Studies, History, Geography, Drama, Music, Art, PSHE and Physical Education. All pupils in Years 7 to 9 study both French and German. Emphasis is also placed on the development of ICT skills and the school has two ICT Suites that can accommodate whole classes. Most pupils study nine or ten subjects to GCSE level.

There is a strong commitment to sports, music, drama and extra-curricular activities. The school has its own hockey pitch and indoor swimming pool as well as tennis and netball courts. Sports include swimming, netball, athletics, hockey, tennis, gymnastics and rounders and our pupils achieve considerable success at county, regional and national level.

Music plays an important part in the life of the school; all pupils are encouraged to participate in choirs, orchestras and ensembles, and the varied programme of concerts and informal performances. Drama is popular and regular theatre visits take place during the year.

Buildings. The Preparatory and Senior departments are on one site. The buildings include a large multi-purpose hall as well as a smaller assembly hall, a well-stocked Library, two ICT Suites, a spacious Art room with a Pottery and Photography room, and a Food Technology Room. The Music Centre has class and individual practice rooms. There are fully-equipped laboratories for Physics, Chemistry and Biology.

Extra-Curricular Activities. These play a significant role in the school. Activities include the Duke of Edinburgh's Award scheme, Spanish, Badminton, Science Club, Football, Rugby, Chess and Photography. Trips, both locally and abroad, add to the extensive range of activities on offer. Pupils also take part in community service and fund-raising activities.

Fees per term (2008-2009). Nursery £2,425, Reception £2,595, Prep 1–2 £2,660, Prep 3–6 £2,770, Years 7–11 £3,355 (excluding exam fees in Year 11).

Charitable status. St Catherine's School, Twickenham is a Registered Charity, number 1014651. It aims to provide for children seeking education in a Christian environment.

St David's School
Ashford

Church Road Ashford Middlesex TW15 3DZ
Tel: 01784 252494; 01784 240680 (Bursary)
Fax: 01784 248652
e-mail: office@stdavidsschool.com
website: www.stdavidsschool.com

Board of Governors:
Chairman: Mr S A Humphreys, BA Hons Open

Dr C J Barton
Mr S Bhasin
Miss C Cawston
Mrs R M Faulkner
Mrs H Fender
Mr S P Hannan
Mrs A Lacey
Mr J P Middleton
Mr A G Sloan
Mrs G Sloan
Dr W A Stevens

Adviser to the Governors: Mr N Finlayson

***Head*: Mrs T Smith**, BA Hons, PGCE, DipM, ACIM, MBA

Deputy Head (*Senior*): Mrs J Mackenzie, MA Double Hons (*French and German*)

Deputy Head (*Prep*): Mrs S Ralph, BEd

Bursar: Ms A M Dent, BA

Senior School Teaching Staff:
Mrs S Bhambra, BA Hons, PGCE
Mrs D E Bishop, BA Hons, PGCE (*Head of History, Year 6/7 Transfer Coordinator*)
Mrs L Clark, BEd (*Technology Coordinator*)
Mrs S Clerke, BA Hons, DipEd, BEd (*Head of English*)
Mrs C Coldicott, DipAD, PGCE (*Head of Art*)
Mr P Davy, BSc Hons, MA, ChB, PGCE (*Head of Science*)
Mrs A Deighton, BA, PGCE, RSA Cert, TEFL (*Psychology, Sociology, EFL*)
Mr R Geary, BSc (*Physics*)
Mrs A Gittins, BEd Hons (*PE & English*)
Mr S J Goodfellow, MA Oxon, PGCE (*Director of Studies*)
Ms M Habanyana, BSc (*Mathematics*)
Mr D Hymers, MA Cantab, PGCE (*Librarian, History*)
Mrs R Kareer, BSc Hons, PGCE (*Chemistry, Physics*)
Mrs S Mattock, BTech Hons (*Biology*)
Ms T Pacula, BA Hons, ATC, DHE (*Textiles*)
Mrs S M Pattison, Trinity College CertTEFL (*EFL*)
Mr B Pimley, BA Hons, PGCE (*Design Technology*)
Mrs B Reeves, RSACertTEFL (*EFL*)
Mrs R Sahota, BA Hons, AFC, PGCE (*Head of Business Studies & ICT*)
Miss V Sanchez, BA Hons (*Head of Modern Foreign Languages*)
Ms J Slocombe, BA Hons, MMus, PGCE (*Director of Music*)
Miss A Tatham, BSc Hons PGCE
Miss S Tredget, BSc Hons (*Director of Sport*)
Mr P Wilson, BEng, PGCE (*Head of Mathematics; Examinations Officer*)
Dr M Yacoot, BSc Hons, PhD, PGCE (*Mathematics*)

Visiting Music Staff:
Ms V Bajic, BMus, FLCM (*piano*)
Mr D Beaman (*guitar*)
Mrs S Bergquist (*trumpet, cornet*)
Mr I Brener (*singing*)
Mrs A Fogg, BA Hons (*piano*)
Mrs C Forkes, BA Hons (*flute*)

Mr R Frowde, MA, MMus, ARCO, Dip CHD (*violin*)
Miss L Goodhand (*clarinet, saxophone*)
Mrs H Head, BMus, MA, LTCL (*piano*)
Mrs R Hill, BA Hons, PGCE (*piano*)
Mr R Lane WCMD Hons (*percussion, drumkit*)
Mr R Woolley, ARCM,GRSM (*piano, organ, harpsichord*)

Mrs A Blair, MA, BEd Hons, RSA Dip SpLD, DIT (*Learning Support Unit*)

Boarding House Staff:
Senior Housemistress: Mrs J Cocks-Pursall
Secretaries:
Personal Assistant to Head: Mrs M Chapman
School Secretary: Mrs R Gill

Bursary:
Accountant: Mrs G Clifford
Assistant Accountant: Mrs S Lawrence

Medical Officer: Dr G McFarlane

St David's is an Independent School for girls which was founded originally in London in 1716 and moved to Ashford in 1857.

Offering all the benefits of an 'all through' school, St David's caters for girls from age 2½ to 18 and boys aged 2½ to 7.

St David's is a friendly and successful school set in 30 acres of superb green belt with a lake, playing fields and extensive sports facilities. Modern schooling is offered in historic surroundings and every girl is nurtured to realise her full potential in a happy and stimulating environment, upheld by a strong moral framework.

The school has both day pupils and boarders (weekly and full). The Boarding House accommodates some of the country's top gymnasts as the school is recognised as the most successful in the country for Acrobatic Gymnastics as a result of many successes at regional and national level.

The school is a 5-minute walk from Ashford station with direct links along the Windsor & Eton line as well as from London Waterloo. The school's own coach and mini bus service and convenient local bus routes make the school very accessible. For boarders Heathrow Airport is 15 minutes away, as are the main motorway systems linked by the M25.

The General Curriculum includes English, English Literature, Drama, Theatre Studies, Spanish, French, History, Geography, Mathematics, Physics, Chemistry, Biology, Religious Education, Information Technology, Business Studies, Food Technology, Art, Design Technology, Textiles, Music, PE, and Sport. We have a Learning Support Unit on site.

The Duke of Edinburgh's Award Scheme. There is a long standing commitment to this Scheme, promoting leadership, teamwork, initiative, survival techniques, public service and the spirit of adventure.

Music is encouraged throughout the school and this is epitomized in the St David's Day House Music competition when the school's Chapel is the venue for a variety of individual and group performances. Regular concerts take place throughout the year and a wide range of tuition is available.

Sport. Hockey and netball are the main Winter sports with athletics, tennis and rounders in the Summer. A wide range of other sports are played including volleyball, football, badminton and trampolining. Excellent links with local Gymnastics Clubs means that a wide range of skills are catered for in this discipline from elite athletes to fun gym. Our own lake offers the opportunity to canoe and swimming is available locally.

The Sixth Form benefits from its own well-equipped common room and study areas. The individual support and encouragement is particularly strong in years 12 and 13 with excellent careers advice and help with university applications. St David's achieved a 100% pass rate at A Level in 2007 with 77% of grades A–C.

The school is particularly proud of how St David's girls develop into confident individuals helped by the opportunities provided for girls to learn from a wide variety of experiences including community service, overseas trips, taking responsibility in the running of the school and a wide range of extra-curricular activities.

Fees per term (2008-2009). (*see Scholarship Entries section*). Senior School: Full Boarders £7,201, Weekly Boarders £6,650, Day Girls £3,888.

Preparatory School: Full Boarder £6,191, Weekly Boarder £5,640, Prep Day £2,878, Reception £2,755, Nursery £1,470/£2,755.

Charitable status. The Most Honourable and Loyal Society of Ancient Britons is a Registered Charity, number 312091. It exists to provide high quality education for girls from the United Kingdom and abroad.

St Dominic's Priory School

21 Station Road Stone Staffordshire ST15 8EN
Tel: 01785 814181/814411
Fax: 01785 819361
e-mail: enquiries@st-dominicspriory.staffs.sch.uk
website: www.st-dominics.co.uk

Founded 1836 by the Dominican Congregation of Catherine of Sienna.

Governors:
Chairman: Dr E M Court

Fr D Campbell
Mrs A Foxall
Dr T Gillow
Mr E D T Leadbetter
Mrs E Moran
Mrs H Phillips
Mr C Wilson
Sister Mary Pauline OP
Sister Mary Henry OP

***Headteacher*: Mrs P Adamson**, BA Hons, PGCE, CTC

Senior Department

Full-time Staff:
Mrs P Adamson, BA Hons, PGCE, CTC (*History*)
Miss B Capper, BEd Hons (*PE*)
Mrs J Deakin, BA, CertEd (*Sociology/Psychology*)
Mrs J Dunk, MBA, BA Hons, PGCE (*IT/Business Studies*)
Mrs A Hughes (*Learning Support*)
Mr R Jones, BA SecEd (*Geography/History*)
Mrs J Kirkland, BSc, CertEd (*Mathematics*)
Miss K Lynch, BA Hons, ABSM, GBSM, PGCE (*Music*)
Mrs A Wright, BA Hons, MA, PGCE (*Art*)

Part-time Staff:
Mrs V Burge, BSc, PGCE (*Chemistry*)
Mrs R Chatburn, BA, PGCE (*English/General Studies*)
Miss A Clarke (*Latin*)
Mrs J Cook, BA, PGCE (*RE*)
Mrs L de Cruz, BA Hons, PGCE, CCRS (*English*)
Mrs T Gauvin, BA Hons, PGCE (*French*)
Fr D Goodill, MA, MPhil (*RE/Chaplain*)
Mrs M Hignett, BSc, PGCE (*Biology*)
Mrs H Johnston, BEd (*French*)
Mr M Kirkland, CertEd (*Physics*)
Mrs M Kitchener, BA, PGCE (*French*)
Mrs L Leech, CertEd, BA Hons, ACP (*English*)
Mrs C Phillips, BA Hons, PGCE (*Italian/French*)
Mrs P Porter, BEd, CertEd (*Mathematics*)
Mrs S Whitehouse, BSc Joint Hons, PGCE (*Biology*)

Preparatory Department

Full-time Staff:
Mrs S Brunt, NNEB, BEd

Miss B Capper, BEd Hons
Mrs J Carey, BA Hons, PGCE, DipHEd
Mrs J Coombs, BSc Hons, PGCE, CCRS
Mrs S Dickson, LRAM
Mrs K Lanyon, NNEB
Mrs G Turner, CertEd

Part-time Staff:
Mrs A Borgman
Mrs R Borgman
Mrs S Bramwell (*Learning Support*)
Mrs J Holland
Miss F McDermid
Mrs E Stanhope (*Learning Support*)
Mrs A Whitfield, BEd Hons, CTC

Visiting Staff:
Mr M Davies (*Percussion*)
Miss J Hames (*Keyboard*)
Mr P Nevins (*Brass*)
Mrs B Oxlade (*Flute*)
Ms K Radcliffe (*Voice*)
Mr P Rogers (*Guitar*)
Mr C Walker (*Clarinet & Saxophone*)

Mrs Bird (*Ballet*)
Mrs A Alston (*Aerobics*)
Miss E Sawyer (*Speech & Drama*)
Mr J Trickey (*LTA Coach*)
Mrs L Gray (*Dyslexia Support*)
Mrs A Miller (*Dyslexia Support*)

St Dominic's Priory School is a Catholic Independent day school which welcomes pupils of all faiths. The School comprises three departments all of which are located on the same site: the Nursery/Infants Department for boys and girls from 2 to 7 years of age; the Preparatory Department for boys and girls up to age 11 and the Senior Department for girls only from 11 to 18. All departments occupy their own self-contained buildings but are united as one School by a common philosophy and approach to the education of young people.

Location. Centrally located within North Staffordshire, the School is easily accessible by road and several good local bus services. School coaches operate from Shropshire (Loggerheads) via Newcastle-under-Lyme and also from Stafford.

Premises/Facilities. Nursery and Infant classes are taught in purpose-built premises opened in 1996. The Preparatory Department occupies a large Victorian house renovated to a high standard and includes a networked computer suite. The Senior Department is located primarily within the original Convent buildings with additional classrooms in the Convent grounds including networked computer rooms.

Philosophy. The School is noted for its family atmosphere, small class sizes and individual attention given to each pupil. The School aims to promote academic rigour, a strong sense of personal responsibility based on enduring values and to foster a spirit of partnership between pupils, parents, staff and the wider community.

The School encourages pupils to develop as individuals so that they can fulfil their highest possible potential not just academically, but across the whole spectrum of school life. Our teaching is successful across the ability range using small teaching groups to ensure individual attention. Our teachers are highly qualified, dedicated and imaginative and at all times have the needs and talents of each child at heart.

Curriculum. Boys and girls are co-educated from the age of 2 within the purpose-built Nursery. The beginnings of reading, writing and number work are introduced at an early age.

The curriculum within the Preparatory Department encompasses all aspects of the National Curriculum with specialist teaching in many subjects including French. Great emphasis is placed on high standards of presentation and regular homework reinforces the work undertaken at School.

Girls join the Senior Department for a specialist girls-only education. Here the School aims to develop the capacity for independent thought through a rigorous and stimulating academic education. One of St Dominic's great strengths is taking a broad ability range of pupils and achieving outstanding A Level and GCSE results. Government research shows that a single-sex education adds significantly to girls' levels of achievement and the School's results are consistently amongst the best in Staffordshire. Again, with the benefit of small classes, teaching is geared to the needs of individual girls who are supported throughout by a strong pastoral care system. The School provides regular opportunities for all girls to take on positions of leadership and to develop a sense of their own worth and a determination to realise all their talents.

Religion. St Dominic's Priory is a Catholic School where children of all faiths are welcome and all religious observations are respected.

The Arts. The School is particularly strong in Speech and Drama, Art and Textiles and Music. Pupils regularly take part in public speaking competitions, plays, festivals, concerts, recitals and exhibitions both within and outside the School. A busy programme of events is a consistent feature of school life.

Sport. The School has a strong sporting tradition and facilities include a superb indoor tennis centre of international standard which is the LTA Centre of Excellence for Staffordshire. The main sports played are tennis, badminton, unihoc, netball, volleyball, gymnastics, athletics, football, tennis and cross-country running. Tennis coaching with an LTA Professional Coach is available all year round and there is a Parents' Tennis Club where parents can benefit from the Tennis Centre.

Extra-Curricular Activities. Numerous clubs and activities are held after school and during lunchtimes such as Dance, Chess, Drama, Duke of Edinburgh's Award, Music and Sport.

Sixth Form and Beyond. The School has an extensive and well-resourced careers programme which includes work experience, work shadowing, a Careers Library, help from school careers staff and advice from Connexions.

Admission. Admission to the Nursery and Preparatory Departments is by assessment day. Admission to the Senior Department is by Entrance Examination, interview and a report from the junior school. Senior girls are admitted at all ages.

Scholarships. Academic, Art and Performing Arts scholarships are available, along with Bursaries and Assisted Places throughout the School. Details can be obtained from the Headteacher's Secretary.

Fees per term (2008-2009). Nursery £1,716, Reception–Primary 6 £2,494, Seniors £2,736.

Further Information. The School welcomes visits from prospective parents and pupils. If you would like to visit or attend one of our termly Open Mornings, please telephone the Headteacher's Secretary on 01785 814181/814411.

Charitable status. St Dominic's Priory is a Registered Charity, number 271922, providing quality education for children aged 2 to 18 years.

St Dominic's School

Bargate Street Brewood Staffordshire ST19 9BA
Tel: 01902 850248
Fax: 01902 851154
e-mail: enquiries@stdominicsschool.co.uk
website: www.stdominicsschool.co.uk

St Dominic's is the leading independent girls' school in Staffordshire, achieving a 100% pass rate at GCSE for 7 consecutive years. We provide education for 300+ girls aged 2–18 years and boys aged 2–7 years and a belief in the development of the 'whole person' is at the heart of our school. We believe each child has special talents and we act to develop those gifts and talents so that they may achieve their full potential within a caring environment. Our school motto is 'Growth in mind, body and spirit' and we aim to develop the pupils academically, socially, creatively and spiritually. Our new Sixth Form Centre and Performing Arts Centre opened in September 2007.

Chairman of the Board of Directors: Mr P Lopez

***Headteacher*: Mrs S White**, BSc Hons, PGCE, Dip Comp, NPQH

Deputy Head: Mrs J Nield, MA, PGCE, BA Hons

Assistant Head (Pastoral): Mrs L Read, BA

Heads of Faculty:
Mathematics: Mrs R Cowley, BA, CertEd
Expressive Arts: Ms L Hovland, BEd Hons
Science and Technology: Miss N Mahi, BSc, PGCE
Communications: Miss R Mason, BA, PGCE
Humanities: Mrs J Mason, BA Hons, PGCE

Head of Foundation Years and KS1: Mrs K Grevett, BEd Hons, NCertEd, CertEd

Head of KS2: Mrs S Kirwan, BA, QTS

Bursar: Mr R Wallis, ACCA, ONC, HNC

Admissions Secretary: Mrs F Allen

School Secretaries:
Mrs J Marson
Mrs S Molloy

Teaching and Learning. Small class sizes facilitate individual attention and enable teachers to build a profile of each pupil: strengths and weaknesses are diagnosed and all work is tailored to match individual needs.

Teachers and pupils work closely together to make learning challenging, interesting and fun. We believe in close partnership with parents and always keep you informed about your daughter's progress.

Work is differentiated to challenge and support individual pupils and progress is closely tracked and monitored to ensure optimum learning opportunities.

As girls enter Year 7 they are taught by dedicated specialist subject teachers in small classes. They are encouraged to be independent learners and to take responsibility for managing their work. Encouraging pupils to think laterally and investigatively so that they work at the edge of their ability helps them to become life-long learners.

Curriculum. We offer a broad and balanced curriculum with enhancement and enrichment. The National Curriculum is taught throughout the school and this is further enhanced with additional subjects such as dance, drama and singing, which are integrated into the weekly timetable. A full range of 23 subjects is currently on offer at AS and A Level.

Expressive Arts. St Dominic's is renowned for its musical and dramatic excellence and is frequently approached by companies for our girls to audition in local productions. Our new Performing Arts Centre houses a Drama and Dance Studio, a Music Suite and a Recording Studio.

Girls are encouraged to join the choirs, play an instrument, take up dance or singing or tread the boards. Throughout the year there are a variety or performances ranging from the Christmas play, where children as young as 2 delight their audience, to the all-singing and all-dancing productions such as Bugsy Malone and Jesus Christ Superstar.

The girls participate in a busy schedule of competitions, local, regional and national. They regularly take part in local festivals and public speaking events. Many girls do LAMDA examinations and all Year 7 girls take English Speaking Board examinations.

Sports. We offer a broad and interesting curriculum which includes netball, hockey, dance, gymnastics, aerobics, football, volleyball, basketball, badminton, rounders, tennis and athletics.

Our all inclusive extra-curricular programmes provide further sporting variety and include kung fu, gymnastics, trampolining, modern dance and ballet, with all abilities encouraged to attend.

There is a comprehensive fixtures programme, as well as our competitive inter-house events including Annual Junior and Senior Sports Days.

The facilities used to deliver this popular subject include newly resurfaced and extended netball and tennis courts and our playing fields which include a hockey pitch, athletics track, football pitch and rounders pitches. We also have an excellent fully-equipped sports hall.

Extra Curricular Activities. Four days a week there is an all-inclusive after-school programme where the girls can undertake a variety of activities ranging from The Duke of Edinburgh's Award Scheme to Fencing to Japanese.

Throughout the year, girls are encouraged to become involved in fund-raising for local and national charities. These activities help each girl develop a good community spirit with respect and consideration for others.

Pastoral Care. Our outstanding pastoral care system and our Christian ethos create an atmosphere which fosters trust and mutual respect between pupils and teachers. Pupils feel relaxed and secure and develop their self-respect, self-confidence, personal discipline and consideration for others.

Examination Results. GCSE results are outstanding and we anticipate similar success at AS in Summer 2008.

Facilities. We have a whole school state-of-the-art ICT system and a purpose-built nursery and junior building, which encompasses a junior hall, IT room, DT and Art room, Home Economics room and a library. The Senior building has new fully-equipped science laboratories, IT room and a library. All classrooms have networked computers and several have interactive whiteboards. Plasma information screens are installed in the foyers. The Sixth Form and Performing Arts Centre is a modern, state-of-the art facility housing the latest technology in music, IT and the Performing Arts.

The new Sixth Form Centre has a common room with terraces and a well-equipped Library with wi-fi laptop technology.

Admissions. We draw our pupils from a wide ability range, which makes our record of results outstanding. Interview is followed by time spent in school (1 or 2 days) when assessment of potential can be made. Entry into the Senior department is through entrance exams and a place in the Sixth Form is conditional upon GCSE results.

Fees per term (2008-2009). Prep: £1,010 (5 mornings), Reception £1,890. Junior: £2,025 (Year 1), £2,205 (Year 2), £2,555 (Years 3–6). Senior: £3,100 (Years 7–9), £3,250 (Years 10–13).

Scholarships and Bursaries. Academic and Performing Arts scholarships are awarded for entry into Year 7. Sports scholarships are awarded for entry into Year 8 with a full range of scholarships awarded in Year 12. Bursaries are means-tested and are awarded at the discretion of the Directors.

For further information view our website which also contains a copy of our ISI Inspection report March 2007.

St Francis' College

Letchworth Garden City

The Broadway Letchworth Herts SG6 3PJ
Tel: 01462 670511
Fax: 01462 682361
e-mail: enquiries@st-francis.herts.sch.uk
website: www.st-francis.herts.sch.uk

Governors:
Mr P J McKay (*Chairman*)
Mrs P J Barlow
Mrs S Boardman
Mr AW Goodwin
Miss E Ismay
Mr C G Nott
Mr J Procter
Mrs M Rochester
Sister Joan Yates

***Headmistress*: Miss M Hegarty**, BA, HDipEd, DMS

Deputy Headmistress: Mrs P Wilkinson, BA, PGCE, NPQH (*Religious Studies*)

Headmistress of Preparatory Department: Mrs S Philpott, MEd, BA, CertEd, TEFL

Bursar: Mr M Collis, BSc

Senior Teacher: Mrs S Pope, BEd, AdvDipIT, NPQH (*IT Coordinator, Technology Coordinator*)

Sixth Form Coordinator: Mrs M Fenton, MA, BA, PGCE (**History*)

School Chaplain: Revd P Bennett BTh, SSC

Full-time teaching staff:
* *Head of Department*

Mr B J Eaton, MA, BEd (**Religious Studies*)
Mrs H Eaton, MA, BA, PGCE (**English*)
Dr I Fengler, Ph D, BSc, QTS (**Chemistry, Science*)
Mrs M Fenton, MA, BA, PGCE (**History, Sixth Form Coordinator*)
Mrs A Gillan, BSc, PGCE (**Geography, Examinations Officer*)
Mrs J Glanville, BSc, PGCE (*Biology, Science*)
Mrs J Grant, BSc, BA, DipEd (**Mathematics*)
Mr A Hetherington, BA, PGCE (*History, Careers Coordinator, PHSE Coordinator*)
Mrs L Hetherington, BA, PGCE (*English*)
Mr J Hobbs, MA, BA, PGCE (*English*)
Mrs C Moore, BA, PGCE, TEFL, TESL (**EFL*)
Mrs P Moore, BEd (*Physical Education*)
Mrs S Pope, BEd, AdvDipIT (*Senior Teacher, IT Coordinator, Technology Coordinator*)
Miss S Roberts, CertEd (**Physical Education*)
Miss V Semmens, BBS, DipBusAdmin, TTC (**Economics, *Business Studies*)
Mrs S Simpkin, BSc, PGCE (**Biology*)
Mr R Tabraham, BA, PGCE (*Art, Photography*)
Mrs A Taylor, BSc, PGCE (*Mathematics*)
Mr P Taylor, BA, PGCE, DPSE (**German*)
Mrs K Tipping, BSc, PGCE, MBA (**Science, *Physics*)
Mrs J Whyte, BA, PGCE (**Foreign Languages*)

Part-time teaching staff:
Mrs N Ashbrook, BA, TEFL, Cert TESOL (*EFL*)
Mr A Bond, BSc, PGCE (*Mathematics*)
Miss P Butcher, GRSM, ARCM, CertEd (*Music*)
Mrs E Carroll, BA, PGCE (*Co-Director of Music*)
Dr R Clarke, BSc, DPhil, PGCE (*Chemistry, Science*)
Mrs J Crittenden, HNC, AIMLS, CertEd, MIBiol, FIMLS (*Science*)
Mrs L Drake, BA, Cert TESOL (*EFL*)
Mrs K Elliott, BA, PGCE (*Religious Studies*)
Ms C Gaviria-Velez, MA, DEA, BA, PGCE (*French*)
Mrs D Hammond, CertEd (*PE, Games and Swimming*)
Mrs R Hayes, BA, PGCE (*Creative Textiles*)
Mrs A Hinnells, BA, PGCE (*Mathematics*)
Mr R Jones, BEd, ADB Ed (**Drama*)
Mr M Ketcher, MSc, BSc, PGCE (*Physics*)
Miss R Leek, BA (*Latin*)
Miss F McClymont, LTCL, GTCL, ARCM, PGCE (*Co-Director of Music*)
Mrs A Middleton, CertEd, CertCC (*Home Economics*)
Mrs S Sanders, BA, PGCE (*Geography*)
Mrs R Thompson, BA, PGCE (*French*)
Mrs J Thomson, BA (*Mathematics*)
Mrs S Twigg, RSA Dip (*Individual Needs*)
Mrs N Wait, BA, PGCE (*German, Business Studies*)
Mrs S York, MA, BSc, BA, MSTAT (*Psychology, Flute, Alexander Technique*)

Librarian: Mrs K Purchon, MA, BA
IT Technician: Mr P Monaghan, BEng

Preparatory Department Staff:
Mrs S Philpott, MEd, BA, CertEd, TEFL (*Head of Prep Department*)
Mrs E Brough, BEd (*Deputy Head of Prep Department*)
Mrs N Parsons, BA (*Kindergarten*)
Mrs J Day, BA (*Reception*)
Mrs V King, MEd, BEd, CertEd, CCRS (*Prep I Bumblebees*)
Mrs A Balcombe, BA, PGCE (*Prep I Butterflies*)
Mrs M Mitchell, CertEd (*Prep IIM*)
Miss S Naughton, BA, PGCE (*Prep IISN*)
Mrs D Hunt, DipPrimaryEd (*Prep IIIH*)
Mrs L Thayer, BA, QTS (*Prep IIIT*)
Mrs E Brough, BEd (*Prep IVLB*)
Mrs J White, CertEd (*Prep IVW*)
Mrs W Bailey, CertEd (*Prep VBE*)
Mrs M Elliot, BEd (*Prep VBE*)
Mrs H Stone, MEd, AdvDipEd, CertEd (*Prep VS*)
Mrs A Glew, BA, PGCE (*Prep VIG*)
Mrs G Hall, BEd, CertEd (*Prep VIH*)
Mrs D Bassnett, BA, PGCE (*Speech and Drama*)
Mrs E Carroll, BA, PGCE (*Speech & Drama*)
Mrs R Baldwin, BA, LTCL (*Music*)
Mrs A Greenhalgh, BA (*French*)
Miss S Roberts, CertEd (*PE, Games and Swimming*)
Mrs M Drew, CertEd (*PE, Games and Swimming*)
Mrs A Blomfield, BEd (*PE, Games and Swimming*)
Mrs P Moore, BEd (*PE, Games and Swimming*)
Mrs D Hammond, CertEd (*PE, Games and Swimming*)

Preparatory Department Classroom Assistants:
Mrs J Roseblade (*Kindergarten*)
Mrs J Watts (*Kindergarten*)
Mrs M Cornell (*Reception*)
Mrs J Eversden (*Reception*)
Mrs S Lockhart (*Prep I*)
Mrs T Worsley (*Prep I*)
Mrs M Shooter (*Preps II-III*)
Mrs R de Wolf, BA (*Learning Support Assistant*)
Mrs K Kandola (*After School Supervision*)
Ms P Keane (*After School Supervision*)

Residential Staff:
Mrs S Reed, FET Cert, TEFL, BPhil, CPP Hons (*Head of Boarding*)
Mrs D Heard (*Housemistress*)
Mrs L Everitt (*Assistant Housemistress*)
Mrs C Rogers (*Assistant Housemistress*)

Visiting Staff:
Mr R Atkinson, BA (*Electric Guitar*)
Mrs M Beecroft, BA, PGCE (*French Assistant*)
Mrs A Borner, BSc, CertABRSM (*Piano*)
Mrs S Card, LTCL (*Piano*)
Miss V Cheesman, LTCL, FTCL (*Clarinet*)
Mrs F Dearman, BA, CertEd (*Guitar*)
Mrs K Flowers, ANSM, LRAM (*Singing*)
Miss R Holbrow, GLCL, ALCM, LLCM, PGCE (*Saxophone, Clarinet*)
Miss D Jellis, FISTD CB, Dip ICDD, Enrico Cecchetti Dip, RAD, ISTD (*Ballet, Tap, Modern*)

Mrs A Kelly, ARCM (*Violin*)
Mrs C Lee, BA (*German Club*)
Mr P Marriott (*Drums*)
Mr P Maundrell, FTCL, GTCL, LTCL, CertEd (*Piano*)
Mrs G Miles, LTCL (*Oboe*)
Mrs M Mitchell (*Spanish*)
Mr A Robinson, ALCM, LLCM TD, PGCMT (*Brass*)
Miss M Roche, ARCM, CertEd (*Singing*)
Mr O Sirinathsingh, DipMusPerf (*Saxophone, Clarinet*)
Mrs R Thompson, BMus, LRAM, ARCM (*Violin*)
Mr T Turton, LWCMD (*Cello*)
Mrs S York, MA, BSc, BA, MSTAT (*Flute, Alexander Technique*)
Mrs L-M Yuen-Brooker, LRAM, CertEd (*Piano*)
Mrs D Wakeling, LAMDA (*Speech & Drama*)

Secretarial/Support Staff:
Mrs R Atkinson (*Bursar's Assistant – Payroll*)
Mrs S Cain (*Headmistress's Secretary, Admissions Secretary*)
Mrs C Cartwright (*Events Organiser, Office Assistant*)
Mrs S Circuit (*Bursar's Assistant – Accounts*)
Mr K Bray (*Site Manager*)
Mrs Y Deards (*Reprographics*)
Mrs T Dickerson (*Bursar's Assistant – Fees*)
Mrs D Gilbert, BSc (*Laboratory Technician*)
Mr G Haycroft (*Catering Manager*)
Mrs T Jesson (*Health Centre Administrator, Office Assistant*)
Mr J Jones (*Caretaker*)
Mrs M Kerr, BSc (*Laboratory Technician*)
Mrs C Lee, BA (*Lower Prep Secretary*)
Mrs H Lomax (*Office Assistant, First Aider*)
Mrs J Luggeri (*Reprographics*)
Mrs W Roskilly, BA (*Upper Prep Secretary, Prep Admissions Secretary*)
Mrs L Shaw (*Receptionist*)
Mrs G Wrigley (*Receptionist*)

The College was founded on its present site in 1933 by Sister Elizabeth of the Trinity, one of the Sisters of Charity of Jesus and Mary, an order of Roman Catholic Sisters based in Belgium. It grew steadily and flourished for the next fifth years until 1983 when the Belgian Order decided to reduce its educational commitment in the United Kingdom. The College was taken over by a newly-formed Educational Charity, The St Francis' College Educational Trust, and is administered by a Board of Governors, which is in membership of AGBIS. The Headmistress is a member of The Girls' Schools Association and the College is ISC accredited.

Within the ethos of the College the aim is to provide a modern education based on Christian principles. Pupils receive close individual care promoting spiritual, moral, intellectual and physical development. The College recognises the unique qualities of each pupil and encourages social responsibility and respect for others. With its Roman Catholic foundation and heritage, St Francis' is a Christian community, ecumenical in outlook, which has always welcomed pupils from other faiths. Religious Education plays a vital part of life in the College and remains part of the curriculum for all girls in the College. Organised community service is an important feature of the extra-curricular life of the College for pupils from Year 10 and 11 and girls in the Sixth Form.

Education is about encouraging talent and developing new interests. Small classes ensure that each girl is given individual attention and a professional and dedicated staff enable pupils to achieve success in a wide range of areas both academic and extra-curricular. St Francis' is committed to the provision of an all-round education where each girl is valued and each can contribute towards enriching the life of the community. There are 505 pupils on roll of whom about 40 are boarders.

Girls are prepared for GCSE and Advanced Level examinations as well as for Oxford and Cambridge entrance. The majority of girls take 10 GCSE subjects and stay on into the Sixth Form from where they proceed to University and Higher Education. The Sixth Form is housed in a newly-created Sixth Form centre, with common rooms, quiet study areas and tutorial offices.

Admission. (*see Scholarship Entries section*). Entrance to the College is by examination but due importance is also attached to school reports and interviews. Scholarships are available for entry at 7, 11, 13 and 16+.

Fees per term (2008-2009). Senior School: £3,505 (day), £6,895 (full boarding), £5,800 (weekly boarding 4 nights). Preparatory School: Kindergarten from £680 (half day) to £1,800 (full day including lunch); Infants (including lunch) £2,175; Prep III–VI: £2,605 (day), £5,955 (full boarding), £4,840 (weekly boarding 4 nights).

Charitable status. The St Francis' College Trust is a Registered Charity, number 287694. It has charitable status on three counts: it advances education, it provides an education founded on strong Christian ethos and it also helps many of its pupils financially by means of Scholarships and Bursaries.

St Gabriel's School
Senior School

Sandleford Priory Newbury Berkshire RG20 9BD
Tel: 01635 555680
Fax: 01635 37351
e-mail: info@stgabriels.co.uk
website: www.st-gabriels.w-berks.sch.uk

Church of England Independent Day School for Girls, in membership of GSA, AGBIS and IAPS.

Governing Body:
Mrs A Barnes
Mr S Barrett
Mrs S Bowen
Mr A C Cooper, FCA
Mr N Garland, BSc Hons (*Chairman*)
Mr A Hills
Mrs N Lee, LLB
Revd Mrs J Ramsbottom
Mr S Ryan
Mr M Scholl
Mrs M Steele

***Principal*: Mr A Jones**, LTCL, LWCMD

Vice-Principal: Mrs C Sams, CertEd London (*Mathematics, Critical Thinking*)
Bursar & Clerk to Governors: Mr N Erskine, MCIM, CDipAF
Director of Studies: Mr I Edwards, BSc Hons, PGCE (*Mathematics*)
Head of Pre-Prep Department: Mrs J Bindloss Gibb, MA, DipSEN, DipSpLD
Head of Junior Department: Mrs P Thompson, BSc, ALCM, CertEd
Pastoral Head, Years 7 & 8: Ms R Wright, BSc Hons, PGCE
Pastoral Head, Years 9, 10, 11: Mrs B March, BA Hons, PGCE, DipVG (*English*)
Head of Sixth Form: Mrs C Resegh, BA Hons, PGCE (*French*)

* *Head of Department*

Senior School Teaching Staff:
Mrs D Adlington (*Science Technician*)
Mr P Allen, MA, PGCE (*Politics, Psychology, Sociology*)
Mrs S Baxter, BEd, ACSD (**Drama*)
Mr C Bembridge, BTh Hons, PGCE (**Religious Studies*)
Mr J Brett, BA Hons, PGCE (*Classics*)

Mrs S Chappell, MA, BA Hons, CKME (**Music*)
Mrs S Cocker, BA Hons, PGCE (**History, *Politics*)
Mrs K Cook (*Art Technician*)
Mrs S Douglas (*Counsellor*)
Mr B Drew, BA Hons, QTS (*Art, Design Technology*)
Mrs S Egan, MA, BA Hons (**English*)
Mrs M Forsgren, BA Hons (*French & German*)
Mr J Franey, BSc, PGCE (*Science*)
Mrs S Gillow, BSc, PGCE (*Chemistry & Physics*)
Mrs M Goodhead, Cert SpLD (*Individual Needs*)
Dr D Hemsley, PhD, CPhys, BSc Hons, PGCE (*Physics*)
Mr R Hall, BA Hons, FE Cert (*Information Technology*)
Mrs A Hislop (*Art*)
Mrs R Horner, BEd Hons, DipSpLD (**Individual Needs*)
Mr M Ives, MA, PGCE (**Classics*)
Mrs A Jennings, MSc, PGCE (**Food Technology*)
Mrs P Joseph, MEd QTS (*Physical Education*)
Miss A Keenleyside, BEd Hons (**Art, *Photography*)
Miss H Kelleher, PGCE (**Dance*)
Miss H Kerr, BA Hons, PGCE (*Modern Foreign Languages*)
Mrs H Kirby, BA Hons, PGCE (*English*)
Mrs S J Lumley Kreysa, BA, CertEd (*Physical Education, Careers Advisor*)
Mrs P Lyons, BA Hons, PGCE (**Business Studies, Work Experience Coordinator*)
Mr J M Mannion, BA Hons, PGCE (**Information Technology, History*)
Mrs J Moulds, BEd (*Mathematics*)
Mrs H E Norris, MA, DipLib, MCILIP (*Examinations Officer, Librarian*)
Mrs H Porter, BSc Hons, PGCE (*KS3 Science Coordinator*)
Mrs J Ribiero, BSc Hons, PGCE (**Pyschology, *Sociology*)
Mrs C Roberts (*Food Technology*)
Mrs R Robinson, BEd (*English*)
Mrs W Rumbold, BA Hons, PGCE, DMA (**Modern Foreign Languages, Spanish*)
Miss C A Searle, BEd (**Physical Education*)
Mrs S Shedden, BSc Hons, PGCE (*Geography*)
Mrs S Sim, BSc Hons, PGCE (**Mathematics*)
Miss H Spiers, BA Hons (*Dance*)
Mrs S Syddall, BA, CertEd (*Mandarin*)
Mr A Symes, BA, CertEd (*Religious Studies*)
Miss A Tidy, BA Hons, PGCE (*Mathematics*)
Mrs R Vale, BA Hons, BEd (*English*)
Miss L Veasey, BA Hons, PGCE (*Modern Foreign Languages*)
Mrs S Vines, BEd Hons (*Textiles Technology*)
Mrs S Wade, BSc Hons, PGCE (*Science*)
Mrs J White, BSc, PGCE (**Science*)
Mrs R Wildsmith (*Support Assistant*)
Mrs P Willetts, BA Hons, PGCE (**Geography, * Economics*)
Mrs S Woodrow, MSc (*Science Technician*)
Mrs R Wright, BSc Hons, PGCE (*Physical Education*)
Mrs S Yeomans (*Technology Technician*)

Junior Department Teaching Staff:
Mrs P A Baker, BEd Hons, CertEd (*Mathematics, Form Tutor*)
Mrs S Cherrington, BA Hons, PGCE (*Modern Foreign Languages*)
Mrs A A Cope, CertEd (*PSHE, Science, Form Tutor*)
Mrs M Davidson, BEd Hons (*Art, Form Tutor*)
Mrs C Harding, BSc Hons, PGCE (*Form Tutor*)
Mrs P Highton, BA Hons, PGCE (*Drama*)
Mr A Kingston, GNSM, ARCM, CertEd (*Music*)
Miss E Lee, CertEd, DipSpEd Lang (*English, Form Tutor*)
Mrs C Moriarty, BEd Hons, CertEd (*French, Geography, Form Tutor*)
Mrs A Pasternakiewicz, BEd Hons (*History, Physical Education, Form Tutor*)
Mrs R Robinson, BEd (*Individual Needs, Form Tutor*)
Miss A J Smith, BEd Hons (*Information Technology, Form Tutor*)

Pre-Prep Department Teaching Staff:
Mrs P Dixon, CertEd (*Form Tutor*)
Mrs J Greenfield, CertEd (*Form Tutor*)
Mrs C Lawrence, BA Ed, PGCE (*Form Tutor*)
Mrs K Markides, MSc, BSc, PGCE (*Form Tutor*)

Teaching Assistants:
Ms C Adams
Mrs D Atkinson
Mrs S Bowden
Mrs J Brown
Mrs C O'Brien, NNEB
Miss N Williams

Visiting Music Staff:
Mrs E Begley, RGKNCM, CertEd (*Singing*)
Mr N Burrage, BA Hons (*Guitar, Drums*)
Mrs J Frith, CT ABRSM (*Flute*)
Mrs C Millar, BA (*Bassoon*)
Mr S Parker, ALCM, LLCM, CT ABRSM (*Clarinet & Saxophone*)
Mrs H Rawstron, BA, LTCL (*Oboe*)
Mrs H Rees, LRAM (*Violin*)
Mrs S Riddex, BA Hons, PECE, LTCHM, LESMD (*Cello*)
Mr N Streeter, CertEd (*Percussion & Orchestra*)
Mrs S Stringer, DipMusEd RSAM (*Piano*)
Mr P Tarrant, ARCM, CertEd (*Brass*)
Mrs V Toll, LRAM, CertEd (*Piano*)
Mrs A Wilkins, BA Hons (*Flute*)

Administrative Staff:
Mrs L Barlow (*School Secretary*)
Miss C Jackson (*PA to Principal*)
Mrs P Jones (*Assistant Bursar*)
Ms R Robson, BA Hons (*Registrar*)
Mrs S Thomas (*Bursar's Office Assistant*)

Number of Pupils. 515.

Visitors to St Gabriel's quickly recognise that this is no ordinary school. From Nursery to Sixth Form they are struck by the enthusiasm and sense of purpose of both staff and pupils. Some parents choose us because of our reputation for achieving exceptional academic standards, others welcome the individual attention which is given to all pupils.

The friendly and confident manner of our pupils is a reflection of the secure and caring environment in which they work. All pupils have the opportunity to take part in a wide variety of individual and team sports, music and creative arts. An extensive range of extra-curricular activities is offered – well over 50 each week.

Each of our pupils is unique and our primary objective is to develop individual strengths and interest. These culminate in the high quality of our GCSE results, which in 2007 was 98.44% A*–C. Our Sixth Form caters for a broad choice of individual subject requirements aimed at university entrance.

Junior Department. (*See entry in IAPS section*).

Fees per term (from April 2008). £3,720–£3,830.

Charitable status. The St Gabriel Schools Foundation is a Registered Charity, number 1062748. It exists to provide education for girls.

St George's School
Ascot

Ascot Berks SL5 7DZ
Tel: 01344 629900
Fax: 01344 629901
e-mail: office@stgeorges-ascot.org.uk

website: www.stgeorges-ascot.org.uk

Member of GSA, AGBIS, BSA.

Governors:
Mr T P Trueman (*Chairman*)
Mr G W P Barber, MA Oxon, LVO
Mr J S Calvert
Mr B Gallacher, OBE
Mr P Granger, FCA
Mr P James
Mrs A Laurie-Walker, BSc, MSc
Mr E Luker, FRICS (*Vice-Chairman*)
Mr J M G Markham, FCA
Mrs H Pheysey
Revd K Ramsay
Mr C Tongue, MA Cantab
Sarah, The Duchess of York

***Headmistress*: Mrs C L Jordan**, MA Oxon, PGCE (*Physics*)

Deputy Head: Miss S Moody, BSc Hons East Anglia, PGCE (*Mathematics*)

Assistant Head (*Pastoral*): Ms C Masters, TEFL, Dip Child Psych (*Head of Boarding*)

Assistant Head (*Sixth Form*) Mrs C Dyer, BA Hons OU, MA Edinburgh, PGCE (*History*)

Staff:
Miss H Barnett, BA Hons Durham, PGCE (*English*)
Mrs Y Barratt, BA Hons Reading, PGCE (*Geography*)
Mrs J Bennett-Rees, MA Oxon, CertEd (*Mathematics*)
Mrs A Bizior, BEd Hons, BSc South Africa, PGCE (*ICT, BCS, Geography, Head of Becket House*)
Mrs M Bruce, BSc Hons Bristol, TEFL Cert: RSA/UCLES (*TEFL Coordinator*)
Miss C Bunce, BMus Huddersfield, (*Music*)
Mrs A Bushill, BSc Hons Southampton, PGCE (*Biology, Psychology*)
Ms J M Cauldwell, BSc Hons London, MSc London, MA Reading (*Mathematics & ICT*)
Mr I Charnock, BA Hons Wales, MA London, PGCE (*History of Art, Film Studies*)
Mrs K Collingwood, BSc Hons Loughborough, PGCE, (*Physical Education, Duke of Edinburgh's Award Scheme*)
Mrs S Cope, Licence d'histoire Orléans, PGCE (*French*)
Mrs J Crossley, BA Hons Hull, PGCE, RSA DipEd in Drama (*Drama, Religious Studies*)
Mrs S Davies, Cert TESOL Trinity (*EAL*)
Mrs E Dawson, Licence d'Anglais Bordeaux, PGCE (*French, Spanish*)
Mrs A Dourountakis-Coultan, BA Hons Durban, PG Higher DipEd, ESL Diploma (*Religious Studies, History, Head of Churchill House*)
Mrs C Duval, BA Hons Sydney, PGDip English in Education Reading, PGDip Language Arts W Australia (*English, Film Studies, Critical Thinking*)
Mrs C A Fidler, BA Hons Wolverhampton, PGCE (*Art*)
Miss L Fontes, BA Hons Leeds, PGCE (*Classical Civilisation, Latin, French*)
Mr C Foreman, MA Durham, BSc Hons Edinburgh, PGCE (*Economics, Politics*)
Ms K Gilbert, BA Hons Chichester, PGCE (*Textiles*)
Mrs V J Green, MA Oxon, PGCE (*Mathematics*)
Mrs E Gregan, BA Hons Liverpool, PGCE (*Drama*)
Ms J Gregson, BMus Edinburgh, CertEd, ARCM (*Music*)
Mrs A Growcott, BEd Hons Cantab, CertEd (*French, Latin, Classics, Head of Darwin House*)
Mrs J Hadnagy, MA Budapest, TCert, ELTE (*Chemistry, Physics*)
Mrs R Harrison, BA, MCLIP (*Librarian*)
Mrs J Hayward, DipTh London, CertEd Cambridge (*Religious Studies*)
Mr I G Hillier, GLCM, FLCM, FCSM, FGMS, PGCE (*Director of Music*)
Mrs A King, MA Cantab, MEd OU, PGCE (*Geography*)
Mrs C Lilley, BSc Hons London, PGCE (*Mathematics*)
Miss K Lofthouse, PT1 Cert Army (*Physical Education*)
Ms R McGeoch, MA Hons Glasgow, MLitt Bristol, PGCE (*English*)
Mr N Mohammad, HDipE Dublin, MA Punjab, BSc Punjab (*Mathematics, ICT*)
Mrs A Morgan, BA Hons Dundee, PGCE (*Art, Textiles*)
Mrs W Moyles, BEd Hons London, CertEd (*English, Learning Skills*)
Mrs V J Potter, BA Hons Lancaster, PGCE (*French, History*)
Mrs E Rowe, BSc Hons Reading (*Science*)
Miss D Schmidt, MSc Pretoria, BEd South Africa (*Physics*)
Mr T Sharkey, BA Hons Exeter, PGCE (*History*)
Ms J Sherrard-Smtih, BSc Hons Westminster, PGCE (*Home Economics*)
Mrs J Smith, BEd Hons Reading (*Chemistry*)
Mrs J Spooner, BSc Hons Birmingham, PGCE (*Science, Psychology*)
Mr A Stafford, BA Hons Wales, MA London, PGCE, ARCM (*English*)
Miss E Townsend, BA Hons East Anglia, PGCE (*Art, Photography, Textiles, Head of Alexander House*)
Mrs M Welsh, BA Hons Barcelona, PGCE (*Spanish, Careers*)
Miss S Williams, BSc Canada (*Resident Lacrosse Coach*)
Mrs I Wright, BA Hons Manchester, PG Dip Drama in Education (*Drama*)

Visiting Staff:
Mrs K Baldwin, FETC Reading (*Chinese*)
Mrs L Barnard, MA Warsaw, DipIT C&G (*Russian*)
Mr N Burrage, BA Hons (*Electric Guitar*)
Mrs D Burt, LTCL, FTCL (*Flute*)
Mr J B Clark, BA (*Guitar*)
Mr J Ellwood, GBSM, ABSM (*Trumpet*)
Mrs A Farmery, BA Hons, DipMus, LTCL, ALCM, PGCE (*Clarinet, Saxophone*)
Mrs M Fitzgerald, DipS&D (*Speech & Drama*)
Mrs K Forrester (*Japanese*)
Mr L Frankel, LRAM, ARCM, CertGSM London (*Oboe*)
Mr F Jin, BA Hons, ABSM (*Cello*)
Mrs E Lee, MMus Moscow Conservatoire (*Piano*)
Miss P May, BMus Hons Edinburgh (*Singing*)
Miss L Ovett, BMus Hons Surrey (*Harp*)
Mr S Perkins, BMus (*Violin*)
Mrs E Roberts (*Italian*)
Mr R S Smith (*Percussion*)
Mrs K Stanley, BMus Hons (*Piano*)
Mr M Stanley, BMus, ARCM (*Piano*)
Mrs A P Watson, BMus (*Singing*)

Pastoral Staff:

Pastoral Senior Mistress: Ms C Masters, TEFL, Dip Child Psych

Housemistresses:
Ms J Black (*Lower Sixth*)
Miss C Bunce, BMus Huddersfield (*Lower School*)
Mrs A Mason (*Upper Sixth, Medical*)
Mrs I Marshall (*Deputy Middle School Housemistress*)
Miss V Shipley (*Middle School, School Shop, Library*)
Miss A van Ravenstein, BEd Canterbury, NZ (*Fifth Year*)
Miss T Walker, BA Hons Warwick, PGCE
Miss K Oatley (*Assistant Housemistress*)

Resident Tutors:
Miss K Bayley, BA Hons Kent
Miss R O'Lone, BA Hons Durham

Bursar: Ms J Hasnip, BA, ACA

Deputy Bursar: Mr M Heather
Bursar's Assistant: Mrs A Pearce

PA to the Headmistress: Mrs M Harman
School Secretaries: Mrs S Alexander, Mrs C Baker
Registrar & Marketing: Mrs R Lloyd, BA Hons London
Examinations Secretary: Mrs A Shevills

Domestic Services Manager: Mrs M Atkinson

School Doctor: Dr L Gardner, MB BS
School Nurse: Mrs S Horth, RNG General & Paediatric

Theatre Technician: Mr R Pearn, BA Hons Leeds

St George's is a School with approximately 300 girls, half boarders and half day girls. There are 80 in the Sixth Form. The boarders are arranged in house groups, dependent upon their age. The small size enables all the staff to take a personal interest in each pupil and each pupil is assigned a personal tutor. The school work is planned to give a good general education for girls in classes of 12–18. A high academic standard is maintained without subjecting the girls to undue pressure and there is a happy and friendly atmosphere. Both day girls and boarders benefit from a full programme of activities into the evenings.

The School stands on high ground with lovely views in a beautiful estate. There are 8 hard tennis courts, a heated swimming pool, an extensive sports field for lacrosse and athletics and a magnificent Sports Hall. Other sports played include netball, rounders and football. There are four science laboratories, music school and computer rooms. There is a computer network which provides each girl with her own e-mail address, computer/network access from every classroom, common room and senior bedroom. A multi-purpose Hall opened in September 2002 for Drama, Music performances and teaching. It is an extremely versatile space allowing a huge range of events to take place, such as Prize Giving, Parents Evenings and other school occasions.

The health of the girls is under the supervision of a registered nurse and the school doctor attends at least twice a week.

Curriculum. The curriculum includes English Language, English Literature, Drama and Theatre Studies, Mathematics, Information Technology, Combined Science, Biology, Chemistry, Physics, Latin/Classics, French, German, Spanish, Geography, History, Economics, Politics, Religious Studies, Psychology, Critical Thinking, Art, History of Art, Textiles, Music, PE. Girls are prepared for GCSE, and, in the Sixth Form, for AS and A2 examinations, as well as for Oxbridge entrance. Girls throughout the school also work towards the examinations of the Associated Board of the Royal School of Music, LAMDA in Acting and Verse and Prose, and Computer Literacy and Information Technology. Girls are given full advice about careers and Higher Education.

At weekends girls take part in a wide variety of recreational activities including drama, art, music, cooking, including a Tante Marie course, photography, sport, Duke of Edinburgh's Award Scheme, first aid courses, school matches and visits to theatres and concerts, art galleries, etc, in London. Girls are encouraged to follow some form of social service.

Entrance. Applicants take the Common Entrance examination for Girls' Independent Schools. The normal age range is 11+ and 13+. Sixth Form entry requires at least 6 GCSEs at A* to C, with preferably a B grade in subjects to be studied at A Level.

Fees per term (2008-2009). £8,450 Boarding, £5,480 Day.

Scholarships. Scholarships are available at 11+ and 13+ for outstanding potential, as evidenced by examination results. Music scholarships and instrumental awards are available at 11+ and Music, Drama and PE scholarships at 13+.

Extra Subjects. Other languages (including Mandarin), Music (most instruments), Speech and Drama, Ballet, Modern Stage and Tap Dancing, Individual Tennis, Dry Skiing, Riding and Yoga.

Charitable status. St George's School Ascot Trust Limited is a Registered Charity, number 309088. It exists to provide independent secondary girls' education.

St George's School for Girls
Edinburgh

Garscube Terrace Edinburgh EH12 6BG
Tel: 0131 311 8000
Fax: 0131 311 8120
e-mail: head@st-georges.edin.sch.uk
website: www.st-georges.edin.sch.uk

Council:
Chairman: The Hon Lady Smith, QC, LLB Hons
Vice-Chairman: Professor P Peattie, FRSA, MHSM, BSc, RGN, RSCN, RNT
Mr G Baird
Mr H F Ballard, LLB, CA
Ms W K Barrie, MHCIMA, MREHIS
Mrs M Contini, BSc, DipMan
Mrs K Cummins, MA Hons, DipLaw (*Solicitor*)
Mrs S Dollman, Dip Drama, Cert SecEd
Mr L Duguid, BSc, FRICS
Dr M M Macartney, MBChB, DPD, FRCGP
Mr A McGlynn, BA, MPhil
Mr J Oliver, MCIBS
Mr C Roxburgh, BA, CA
Miss K Targett-Adams, MA
Mr I Watford, BA Hons, MA
Mr S Woolman, QC

Secretary to the Council: Mr M F Sinclair, MA, CA
Treasurer to the Council: Mr J Chittleburgh, BSc Hons, CA

***Head*: Dr Judith McClure**, CBE, MA Oxon, DPhil Oxon, FRSA, FSA Scot

Deputy Head: Mrs H Mackie, BA Hons Birmingham, PGCE

Assistant Head, Student Welfare: Miss P Lancaster, MA Aberdeen, CertEd
Assistant Head, Learning Opportunities: Mrs A Armstrong, BSc Hons Edinburgh, PGCE
Assistant Head, Curriculum Planning: Dr A de Ville, BSc, PhD St Andrews, PGCE
Assistant Head, Boarding: Miss A Tomlinson, MTheol Hons St Andrews, PGCE
Facilities Director: Miss M Imlah, MA Aberdeen, MHCIMA
Head of Lower School: Mrs M Hall, BSc Hons St Andrews, PGCE

Upper and Lower School Staff:
* *Head of Department*

Mr M Adams, BSc Durham (*Assistant Head Lower School, Science*)
Mrs F Aiken, BEd Hons Moray House (*Physical Education*)
Mrs N Aitchison, BEd Hons Edinburgh (*Assistant *Physical Education*)
Dr J M C Alison, BSc, PhD Edinburgh, BA OU, PGCE (*Physics*)
Miss L J Allan, BEd Moray House (*PE*)
Miss N Barbier, BEng France, MA France, PGCE (*French, Head of Primary French*)
Mrs K Bargeton, BEd Moray House (*Physical Education*)
Miss K Barr, BA Hons Brighton, QTS (*Physical Education*)
Mrs L A Blencowe, MEd Edinburgh, BA OU, PGC Youth & Community Work Birmingham, CertEd Leeds (*Research and Development Fellow*)
Ms W Barrie, DipEd Queen Margaret College, NEBSM Cert Mgt Telford College, CertEd Edinburgh

Ms B Bianchi, Degree Foreign Languages and Literature Delgi Studi, Italy, MSc Edinburgh (*ESOL*)
Mrs J Boyle, BSc St Andrews, MSc Ed Edinburgh PGCE Cambridge (*Mathematics*)
Mrs E J Bryce, MA St Andrews, PGCE (*Mathematics, Head of Sixth Form*)
Miss H Burton, MA London (*History and Modern Studies*)
Miss L Campbell, MA Edinburgh, PGCE (**Modern Languages*)
Ms A Cordey, BA Oxford, MSc Edinburgh, PGCE Leeds (*History and Modern Studies*)
Dr R Daubenspeck, BSc Hons, PhD Heriot Watt, OND Esk Valley, Edinburgh, PGCE Secondary St Andrew's College, Glasgow (*Biology*)
Dr F R Dorward, MA, PhD Edinburgh (**Spanish*)
Mrs S Edwards, BA Hons Liverpool, PGCE Liverpool Hope, Cert Further Prof Studies Newcastle, PG CertSpLD Napier, MSc Edinburgh (**Support for Learning*)
Miss L C Emslie, DRSAMD Glasgow, CertEd (*Music, Head of Music Management*)
Mr J Fairhurst, BSc Heriot Watt, CertEd Edinburgh, FRSC (**Chemistry*)
Mrs J T Forbes, MA Aberdeen, DipEd (*English, Head of Lifelong Learning*)
Miss H B Gillard, MA St Andrews, PGCE (**English and Drama*)
Mrs L Gilmour, BSc Hons, PGCE (*Mathematics*)
Mrs J Goodman, MA Edinburgh, PGCE Edinburgh (*English*)
Miss R Gudger, BSc Hons St Andrews, PGCE Cambridge (*Head of Upper 5, Biology and French*)
Miss A Hamilton, BA Hons St Mary's Twickenham (*Assistant Librarian*)
Miss C Harvey, MA Glasgow, PGCE (*Classics*)
Miss S Herbert, BMus Edinburgh, PGCE Edinburgh (*Music*)
Mrs A Hesketh, BSc Hons Edinburgh, PGDE (*Physics*)
Mr J Hughes, BEd Hons Napier (*Head of Information Services and ICT*)
Mrs M Jackson, BSc Hons Edinburgh, PGDE (*Mathematics*)
Miss S Judge, BSc Edinburgh, PGCE Northumbria (*Physical Education*)
Miss N L Kerr, BEd DCPE (**Physical Education*)
Ms S Knox, BA Exeter, PGCE London (*Art, Coordinator of Primary Art*)
Ms M Knutt, MA St Andrews, PGDE Strathclyde (*Classics*)
Mr G Lamont, BTechEd Glasgow, HND Building Glasgow (*Coordinator of Design Technology*)
Mrs A Lawrence, BA Hons Stirling, DipEd (*English, Head of Communications*)
Ms M Lin, BA Hons Woverhampton, PGCE Sheffield, HND (**Chinese*)
Miss A MacDonald, MA Hons Edinburgh, PGCE Moray House (*Geography*)
Ms J Maclean, MA Hons Edinburgh, Cert SecEd Moray House (*French, Assistant Head of Languages*)
Mrs A Martinez, RSA Prep Cert TEFL, RSA Dip TEFLA (**ESOL*)
Miss K McColm, MA Hons Glasgow, PGCE Durham (*History and Modern Studies*)
Mrs S McGreehin, MA St Andrews, PGCE Edinburgh (*English*)
Mrs E McIlmoyle, BA Belfast, PGCE (*Geography*)
Mrs C McInally, MA Hons, PGCE (*Mathematics*)
Mr C Montgomery, BSc Heriot-Watt, PGCE (*Mathematics*)
Miss K Mulvey, BSc Glasgow, PGCE (**Geography, Head of Upper 4*)
Miss L Munn, BEd Edinburgh (*Physical Education*)
Miss J Nicholson, BSc St Andrews, MSc Napier, PGCE (*Chemistry, Academic Mentor*)
Mrs G O'Fee, MA Hons Edinburgh, PGCE (*English*)
Dr D E Oswald, BSc Hons, PhD (*Lower School Science Coordinator*)
Mrs S N O'Neil, BEd Edinburgh, HNC Telford (*Physical Education*)
Miss H Paredes, BSc Toronto, PGCE Edinburgh (*Biology and Psychology*)
Miss E Patrick, MA Hons St Andrews (**Social Science*)
Mrs D H Patterson, BSc Edinburgh, PGCE (**Physics*)
Ms E Poole, MA Cantab, PGCE QTT, Dip Japanese Sophia, Japan (*English*)
Mrs R Porteous, MA St Andrews, PGCE Edinburgh (*French*)
Miss J Ramage, BA Hons Bath, PGCE Jordanhill (*Art*)
Mr P K Redfern, BMus, ARCO (*Director of Music*)
Mr P Ricca, BSc, HND, PGCE (*Economics & Politics*)
Mrs S Robinson, BA Hons Dublin Higher Diploma Dublin (*History and Modern Studies*)
Mr K Rodger, BSc Napier, PGCE (*ICT*)
Miss R Shelbourn, BA Hons Wales, PGDE Edinburgh (*Drama*)
Mr N H Shepley, MA Cantab, MEd Edinburgh, CertEd (*Libraries and Head of Independent Learning*)
Mrs C W Steedman, BEd MHCE (*Physical Education*)
Mrs S Stenhouse, BA Hons Napier, PGCE Strathclyde (**Business and Enterprise*)
Mr S Stewart, BA Hons, PGDE (*Art*)
Miss A Strathdee, BSc Hons Heriot Watt, PGCE Edinburgh (*Mathematics, Remove Year Tutor*)
Mrs C Tate, L-ès-L Sorbonne, Agrégation d'Anglais (*French*)
Mr P Thomson, DipMusEd, PGCE RSAMD (*Music*)
Miss R Tomkins, BA Hons Kingston, PGCE London (**Art*)
Mrs E Traynor, MA Edinburgh, PGCE (**German*)
Mr P Verrecchia, MA Glasgow, BD Ireland, PGCE Glasgow (*Religion & Philosophy, Head of Lower 5*)
Mrs M E Walker, CertEd Durham (*French and Learning Support*)
Mr G Wallace, HNC Mgmt Glasgow, BA Paisley (*Design and Technology*)
Mrs M G Wardrop, BEd (*Physical Education*)
Miss C Waterhouse, BSc Durham, PGCE (**Biology*)
Miss J-J Zhao, MA Essex (*Chinese*)

Junior School:
Mrs M A Adams, BA MusEd Kingston upon Thames, PGCE
Mrs K Braham, BA Newcastle, Dip Arch Heriot-Watt, PGCE
Mrs K Coad, BEd Cambridge (*Music*)
Miss G Cordiner, BEd Primary Aberdeen
Miss L R Danzig, MA, PGCE (*Learning Support*)
Mrs H A Finlayson, MA Edinburgh, PGCE
Miss J M Forbes, DipPrimEd, Nat Froebel Cert, Infant Mistress and Nursery School Endorsement
Mrs S E Hay, BEd Edinburgh
Miss A Hippisley, BEd Cambridge
Miss K Hirst, MA Hons St Andrews, PGDE Edinburgh
Miss S Kumari, MS Ed California, PGCE Edinburgh
Miss C McCole, BEd Primary Edinburgh
Mrs C Midgley, MA Hons Edinburgh, PGCE Wales, TEFL Diploma
Mrs P Mouton-Sinclair, MA Aberdeen, PGCE
Mrs M Munro, DipEd Edinburgh
Ms J Paterson, DipEd
Mrs M J Peden, BA Edinburgh, PGCE
Mrs V A Pickup, CertEd, BEd
Mrs T Robertson, BEd
Mrs M Rushworth, DipEd, DipRSA
Mrs Z Siddle, BA Hons Lancaster
Miss R Sloan, D Psych Edinburgh, PGCE
Mrs P Stewart, BSc Edinburgh, PGCE Edinburgh
Mrs F C White, BSc Glasgow, PGCE

Early Years:
Head: Mrs E Stewart, MEd Edinburgh
Miss S Anderson, NNEB, NTC
Mr A McCarthy, BA Early Childhood Studies Cork, PGCE
Miss A McGregor, HNC
Mrs C Noble, NNEB

Miss H Paterson, MA Hons Cambridge, PGCE Edinburgh
Miss M I Robertson, NNEB, ND, RSH
Mrs J Watson, NNEB, ND

Headmistress's PA: Miss C McEwen (*Development & Operations*)

Leader of After School Care: Miss S Anderson

CCF: Mr Frank Henvey, Contingent Commander

St George's was founded in 1888 to provide a full education for girls and to take the lead in the advance of the women's educational movement in Scotland.

There are 584 girls in the Secondary Department, 267 in the Primary Department and 70 in the Nursery. There are 45 girls in the Boarding House.

The age range covered is from 5–9 in the Primary Department and from 9–18 in the Secondary Department. Entry is flexible at any stage by interview and assessment The Nursery Department accepts girls between the ages of 2 and 5 and boys from 2 to 4 years.

St George's, which is on the Register of Independent Schools and is a member of the Girls' Schools Association, is administered by its own Council. It stands in extensive grounds only ten minutes from Edinburgh City Centre. Hockey and Lacrosse pitches, an all-weather pitch and Tennis courts are contained in pleasant surroundings. A large modern Sports Hall accommodates an extensive array of indoor sports and activities and also has two squash courts. The heart of the school is the St George's Centre which contains dining facilities and drama/conference space. The science laboratories in all three areas of the school are modern and up-to-date, as is the Sixth Form reading room, the three school libraries and the Robertson Music Centre with its 200-seat auditorium, 12 music cells and two classrooms. There is an extensive IT network with Internet access across the whole site including the Boarding House.

St George's prepares pupils for Standard Grade, Scottish Higher and Advanced Higher and GCE A Level examinations, as well as offering a range of skills courses to meet individual needs.

Over 95% of leavers proceed to degree courses at Universities in Scotland and England including Oxford and Cambridge.

Fees per term (2008-2009). (The session has 3 terms.) Tuition: £2,065 (P1) – £3,370 (U6). Early Years: £1,065–£3,335, depending on child's age and number of half or full days. Boarding fee (in addition to tuition fee): £3,340.

The Registration Fee of £60 must accompany the Application Form.

When three or more sisters are pupils at the same time, the third and subsequent sisters will receive a discount of one-third on class fees. A comparable discount is given where families have three children at St George's and the Edinburgh Academy at the same time. A number of means-tested Bursaries is available.

Text books are provided by the School without charge for use during the Session. Extra subject fees are paid in full for each pupil.

Charitable status. St George's School for Girls is a Registered Charity, number SC012632. It exists to promote educational excellence for girls.

The School of St Helen and St Katharine

Faringdon Road Abingdon Oxon OX14 1BE
Tel: 01235 520173
Fax: 01235 532934
e-mail: info@shsk.org.uk
website: www.shsk.org.uk

The School (which was founded by the Community of St Mary the Virgin, Wantage in 1903) is a Church of England Independent School for day girls. There are 620 girls of whom 170 are in the Sixth Form.

Governors:
Miss J E Cranston (*Chairman*)

Ms A J Allden
Professor K M Burk
Mrs P E Cakebread
His Hon Judge H W P Eccles
Mr J Gabitass
Mrs R M Kashti
Mr D J Lea
Mrs D M May
Dr M Oppenheimer
Mrs P A Penney
Mr I Todd
Mrs M A R Varju
Mr A J Winckworth
Canon F J L Winfield
Mr J J H Wormell

Clerk to the Governors: Mrs K E J Wait

***Headmistress*: Miss R Edbrooke**, BEd Hons Bedford

Bursar: Lt Col A F M Douglas, MA Cantab, FCMI
Deputy Headmistress: Mrs R Gunn, MA Cantab
Deputy Headmistress Academic: Mrs B Stubley, MA Greenwich, PGCE
Chaplain: Revd J Herapath, MTh Oxon, Cert Eng Lit & Lang Oxon, PGCE
Head of Upper School: Mrs J Armstrong, BSc Leeds, PGCE, ACPSE (*Careers*)
Head of Middle School: Mrs C Townsend, BA London, PGCE
Head of Lower School: Miss A Ellis, BSc Imperial College, MSc London, PGCE
Head of Year 13: Mr O Hogben, BA Warwick, PGCE
Head of Year 12: Mrs J Edwards, BSc Nottingham, PGCE
Head of Year 11: Mrs C Russell, BSc London, PGCE
Head of Year 10: Mrs C Canlan-Shaw, BSc Loughborough, PGCE
Head of Year 9: Mrs L Fuller, MA Oxon, PGCE
Head of Year 8: Mrs C Eyles, MA Exeter, PGCE
Head of Year 7: Mrs K Taylor, BA Wales, PGCE
Head of Year 6: Mrs E Gale, BSc Manchester, PGCE
Head of Year 5: Mrs H Townsend, BEd Oxon

Art, Design and Technology:
Mrs J Jackson, BA Bristol, ATC
Mrs C Langston, BA Middlesex, PGCE
Mrs J McDonald, MA RCA, ATC London
Mr K Stiles, BA Falmouth, PGCE
Miss A Wardell, BA Derby

Business Studies:
Mrs C McKenna, BSc Manchester, PGCE
Mr C Rodda, BA Hull, PGCE

Careers:
Mrs J Armstrong, BSc Leeds, PGCE, ACPSE (*Careers*)
Mrs D Croft, Tech IOSH, MInstLM
Ms A Fogg, MA Maryland
Mrs D Laidlaw, BA London
Mrs S Marsh, BA London
Mr O Hogben, BA Warwick, PGCE
Mrs V Burbank, BA Bristol, PGCE

Classics:
Mr H Moore, MA Cantab, MA London, PGCE
Mrs E Poole, MA Cantab, CertEd
Mrs J Shearan, MA Oxon, PGCE
Mrs J Twaits, MA Cantab, PGCE

Drama and Theatre Studies:
Ms J Watt, BA Durham, PGCE
Mr O Hogben, BA Warwick, PGCE
Ms M Mason, BA Dublin, PGCE

Mr A Verjee, BA UEA

Economics:
Mr C Rodda, BA Hull, PGCE

English:
Mrs C Nash, MA Oxon, PGCE
Ms A Fogg, BA Columbia, MA Maryland
Revd J Herapath, MTh Oxon,Cert Eng Lit & Lang Oxon, PGCE
Ms M Mason, BA Dublin, PGCE
Mrs H Nash, BA Southampton, PGCE

Examinations Officer:
Mrs S Govier, BA Reading, DipEd

Food Studies:
(*to be appointed*)

General Studies:
Ms S Hayward, BA Durham, PGCE

Geography:
Miss E Phillips, BSc Queens, Belfast, PGCE
Mrs V Burbank, BA Bristol, PGCE
Mrs C Eyles, BSc, MA Exeter, PGCE
Mrs C Townsend, BA London, PGCE

History:
Miss D Smith, BA Durham, PGCE
Mrs F Fisher, BA Oxon, PGCE
Miss N Kerr-Boyle, MA Warwick, PGCE
Ms K Meuleman, BEd Eeklo, Belgium, PG Worcester
Mrs B Stubley, MA Greenwich, PGCE

History of Art:
Mrs N Levick, MA London

Information Technology:
Mr P Burnett, BSc Manchester, PGCE
Mrs J Dunwoody, CertEd Dartford
Mrs F Fisher, BA Oxon, PGCE
Mrs R Gunn, MA Cantab
Mrs C McKenna, BSc Manchester, PGCE

Library:
Mrs D Pocock Bell, BA Wales, MA London
Mrs K Gray, BSc Manchester, Dip IPM
Mrs E Greig, BSc Wales

Mathematics:
Mr C Morris, MA Oxon, PGCE
Miss N Copeman, BSc Coventry, PGCE
Mrs P Hall, BSc Exeter, PGCE
Mr D Ireland, BSc Leicester, FRAS, QTS
Miss S Kennedy, MA Cantab, PGCE
Mrs C Lewis, MA, MEng Cantab, PGCE
Mrs M Moore, BSc Lancaster, PGCE
Mrs C Russell, BSc London, PGCE

Medical:
Dr H Hodgson, MB BS
Mrs F Campbell, BEd Durham
Nurse A Dexter, RGN
Nurse C Swales, RGN

Modern Languages:
Mrs L Astbury, BA Birmingham, PGCE
Mrs M Delvaux-Abbott, CFS Liège, Dip French Alliance Française, Brussels
Dr G Clark, MA Cantab, DPhil Oxon, PGCE
Ms C Fisher, Milan, PGCE
Ms I Hichens, Sorbonne, PGCE
Mrs M A Lynes, LAUREA, BA Milan, PGCE
Mrs L Fuller, MA Oxon, PGCE
Mrs K Taylor, BA Wales, PGCE

Music:
Ms H Rakowski, BA, MA Oxon, PGCE
Mr A Knowles, MA Oxon, PGCE
Miss H Birt, BA Oxon, PG Dip Viola, PG Dip Baroque Violin (*Head of Strings*)
Mr A Bottrill, MA London, GGSM London (*Head of Keyboard*)
Mr P Foster, LTCL (*Head of Wind and Brass*)
Miss F Parker, BA Hons, LLCM (*Band Master, French Horn*)
Miss J Broome, MA Cantab (*Harp*)
Miss A Brunton, MA, BMus, LRAM, LGSM, PGCE (*Oboe*)
Mr R Burley, ALCM, LLCM (*Guitar*)
Mr R E Cutting, RMSM Kneller Hall (*Brass*)
Mrs V Findlay, MA Glasgow, LRAM (*Cello*)
Miss P Grant, BA Oxon (*Singing*)
Miss E Harré, LRAM, GRSM Hons, Dip Ex Sc (*Double Bass*)
Mrs H S Haskell, ARCM (*Violin and Viola*)
Miss E Hayes, Dip RCM, CTABRSM (*Piano*)
Mr N Long, GLCM Hons (*Percussion*)
Mrs S E Mears, MA Oxon, LRAM, PGCE,DipHSWOU (*Piano*)
Mr D J Rye, MA Cantab (*Clarinet*)
Mr N Somerville, BA, ARCM, LTCL, ABSM (*Brass*)
Miss A Strevens, MA, BSc Hons, SRAST M, BSCH (*Flute*)
Mrs M Thorne, BA MusEd, LGSM, MA London (*Clarinet*)
Mr R Thorne, BA Mus, A Mus A (*Flute*)
Mr R Thompson, PG Dip, BMus Hons, ATCL, ALCM (*Piano*)
Mr G Williams, LRAM, ARCM, FTCL, FLCM, MSTAT, PGCE (*Bassoon, Clarinet and Saxophone*)

Personal Social & Health Education:
Mrs F Fisher, BA Oxon, PGCE

Physical Education:
Mrs J Dunwoody, CertEd Dartford
Mrs J Chilvers, FTI
Mrs C Eyles, BSc, MA Exeter, PGCE
Mrs S Evans, IM Marsh CPE, CertEd Liverpool
Mrs J Harrison, CertEd Liverpool
Miss D James, BEd Exeter
Dr M Leigh, BSc, MSc, PhD Newcastle
Miss A Wisloski, BA Mary Washington, USA

Government and Politics:
Mrs E Poole, MA Cantab, CertEd
Miss N Kerr-Boyle, MA Warwick, PGCE
Mrs B Stubley, MA Greenwich, PGCE

Psychology:
Mrs C Canlan-Shaw, BSc Loughborough, PGCE

Religious Studies:
Ms S Hayward, BA Durham, PGCE
Revd J Herapath, MTh Oxon,Cert Eng Lit & Lang Oxon, PGCE
Ms K Meuleman, BEd Eeklo, Belgium, PG Worcester

Science:
Mrs J Bell, BSc Bristol, MSc Oxon, PGCE
Mrs J Edwards, BSc Nottingham, PGCE
Mrs P Yusuf, BSc London, PGCE
Mrs J Armstrong, BSc Leeds, PGCE, ACPSE (*Careers*)
Dr T Bainbridge, BSc Leeds, PhD London, PGCE
Mrs C Bullock, MA Cantab, PGCE
Miss A Ellis, BSc Imperial College, MSc London, PGCE
Mrs R Gunn, MA Cantab
Dr M Leigh, BSc, MSc, PhD Newcastle
Mr T Marjot, BSc London, PGCE
Mrs J Peat, BSc Hull, CertEd

Admissions Officer: Mrs J Wilmore
Headmistress's PA: Mrs J Pointer

The School is located on the outskirts of Abingdon with easy access from Oxford and surrounding villages; an extensive network of school buses facilitates access from as far afield as Newbury, Reading, Faringdon, Witney and Henley. The School is situated in extensive grounds which include tennis and netball courts, lacrosse pitches, athletics track and a heated open-air swimming pool.

The original building dates from 1906 with extensions being added at various times over the past 40 years. The School has an ongoing building programme, the most recent buildings being a Performing Arts Centre and Sports Centre. Specialist rooms exist for Art, Food Studies, Geography, Information Technology, Ceramic and Design Technology. These are complemented by a careers room, a library, Science laboratories, a concert hall, a language learning laboratory and a gymnasium and sports hall for indoor games. A new library is being planned and should be completed for January 2010.

The School encourages girls to maintain a broad and balanced curriculum as long as possible. Subjects included in the curriculum are: Art, Biology, Business Studies, Ceramics, Chemistry, Classics, Design Technology, Drama and Theatre Studies, Economics, English Language, English Literature, Food Studies, French, Geography, German, Government and Politics, Greek, History, History of Art, Information Technology, Italian, Latin, Mathematics, Further Mathematics, Music, Physical Education, Physics, Pottery, Psychology, Religious Studies, and Spanish.

There is a strong musical tradition in the school with many girls learning at least one instrument. Tuition is provided in all major instruments including the harp and organ. There are two orchestras, four choirs and numerous ensembles.

Mutually beneficial interchanges exist with two local boys' schools giving opportunities for joint activities in music, drama and debating. For selected subjects in the Upper School girls are taught with boys from Abingdon School.

A programme of citizenship and personal, social and health education encourages girls to be responsible for themselves and take care of others. Social service is emphasised and all pupils are encouraged to take part in the wide range of extra-curricular activities available at the School including: The Duke of Edinburgh's Award Scheme, Young Enterprise, debating, fencing, modern dance, sailing and rowing.

The School has its own Chapel in which a weekly Eucharist is offered to staff and girls.

Admission is at 9+, 10+, 11+, 13+ and 16+. An entrance examination is held in January for 9+, 10+ and 11+ and in November for 13+ for admission in the following September. Girls are accepted into the Sixth Form on the basis of their GCSE results and an interview. There may be occasional vacancies in other years of the school.

Bursaries are awarded at 11+. Governors' Scholarships are awarded at 11+, 13+ and 16+; Music Scholarships are available at 11+ and are awarded to girls already in the school from 14+.

Fees per term (2008-2009). £3,395.

Charitable status. The School of St Helen and St Katharine Trust is a Registered Charity, number 286892. The Trust was established to promote and provide for the advancement of education of children in the United Kingdom and elsewhere; such education to be designed to give a sound Christian and moral basis to all pupils.

St Helen's School for Girls

Eastbury Road Northwood Middlesex HA6 3AS
Tel: 01923 843210
Fax: 01923 843211
e-mail: enquiries@sthn.co.uk
website: www.sthn.co.uk

Founded 1899.
Independent Day School for Girls.
Member of GSA and IBO.

Council of Governors:
Chairman: Ms R Faunch, MSc Manchester
Dr D J Chivers, MA, PhD, ScD
Mr M Clark, MSc London
Mrs S Woolfson, BSc, FCA
Professor V Isham, MA, PhD Cantab
Mrs J Kirchheimer, MRCVS
Mr R Kumar
Mrs J Lewis, BSc, FCIPD
Mrs A Little, BA Cantab
Mr T R Roydon, BSc London, MBA Pittsburgh
Mrs H Leyser, MA Oxon

Staff:

***Head*: Mrs M Morris**, BA Hons London

Deputy Head: Mr P Tiley, BSc Bristol
Deputy Head: Miss J Dewhurst, BA Liverpool

Head of Sixth Form: Mr H Dymock, BA Durham, MA London
Head of Upper School: Mrs D Sinclair, MA London
Head of Middle School: Mrs L Landsman, BA Dublin
Head of Junior School: Mrs K Serinturk, BEd London
Head of Little St Helen's: Mrs J Chaventre, BEd West Sussex
Professional Development Manager: Mrs A Weaver, MA St Andrews

Director of IB: Mrs M Bowman, BEd Leeds
Deputy Head of Sixth Form: Miss E McKinley, BA Heriot-Watt; Mr N Elder, BA Stirling
Deputy Head of Upper School: Mrs K Gibbons, BSc Nottingham Trent; Mrs J Cox, BA Durham
Deputy Head of Middle School: Mrs C Hill, BA Newcastle
Assistant Head of Middle School: Mrs E Serrano, Gilologia Inglesa Degree Madrid; Miss L Starkey, BA De Montfort
Deputy Head of Junior School: Mrs L Tillston, BEd Herts; Miss A McCurry, BEd Melbourne
Deputy Head of Little St Helen's: Mrs S Begley, MPhil Pontypridd, MSc Bangor

* *Head of Department*

Art:
*Mrs V Wichel, BA Bristol

Miss L Starkey, BA De Montfort
Mr P Wiciel, CertEd
Mrs A O'Regan (*Technician*)

Careers:
*Miss E McKinley, BA Heriot-Watt
Mr H Dymock, BA Durham, MA London

Classics:
*Mr K Buck, BA Johannesburg
Dr A Berriman, PhD Nottingham Trent, BA Bristol

Miss E Elworthy, BA Nottingham

Design and Technology:
*Mr B Gee, MA OU
Mrs K Gibbons, BSc Nottingham Trent
Miss L Grover, BA Middlesex
Mr R Shaikh, BA Brighton
Mr L Boresta (*Technician*)

Drama:
*Mrs M Connell, BA Manchester
Miss K Archer, BA Loughborough
Mrs D Sinclair, MA London

Economics & Business Studies:
*Mrs M Bowman, BEd Leeds

Mrs F Britten, BEd UWE, BSc OU
Mr I Goodridge, BSc Surrey
Mr N Sennett, BA Reading

English:
*Mr R Johnston, BA Liverpool
Miss H Boobis, BA Cambridge
Mrs J Cox, BA Durham
Mrs S de Vaux-Balbirnie, BA Reading
Mr N Elder, BA Stirling
Mr T Gerig, BA Illinois
Mrs R Hershman, CertEd Froebel
Mrs V Lumley, MA Manchester
Mrs J Threlfall, BA Leicester

Geography:
*Miss E Rynne, MA London
Mrs C Beake, BA London
Mr J Rogoff, BA Oxford

History and Government and Politics:
*Mrs C Hill, BA Newcastle
Mrs F Ames, BA OU (*History of Art*)
Miss V Juckes, MA Oxford
Mr B Lewis, BA Cantab
Mr B Nemko, BA Bristol, MSc City
Mrs A Weaver, MA St Andrews
Mr P Whalley, BA Portsmouth

Information Technology:
*Mr M Hoffman, BA South Africa
Mr P Andersson, MA Brunel
Mr J Firestone, MA Brighton
Mr R Shaikh, BA Brighton
Mrs S Standen (*Technician*)

Mathematics:
*Mr D Soares, BA Hons Cantab, MA Hons Cantab
Mrs E Cadman, BSc London
Mr S Dawoodbhai, BSc Plymouth
Dr J Donovan, PhD London
Mrs S King, BEng Bristol
Mrs L Landsman, BA Dublin
Mrs J Malcolm, BA Oxon
Mrs S Michaels, BSc Manchester
Mrs M Moore, BA Cantab
Mrs T Onac, BSc London
Mrs A Pateli, CertEd St Mary's College
Mrs A Stiff, BA Liverpool
Mrs J Vann, BSc London

Modern Languages:
*Mr E Terris, BA London

French:
*Mr E Terris, BA London
Miss B Adamson, BA London
Mrs J Birkett, BA London
Mrs D Clayden, BA Leeds
Miss L Louisett, BA, MA Antilles
Mrs J Orme, BA Dunelm
Miss J Subra, BA Pau

German:
*Mrs J Birkett, BA London
Miss N Betts, BA Manchester
Miss J Dewhurst, BA Liverpool

Italian:
Mrs N O'Hagan, CertEd
Mrs M Trowell, BA Turin

Japanese:
Mrs M Ishikawa, MA London

Mandarin:
Miss N Betts, BA Manchester
Miss X Tian China

Spanish:
*Mrs E Serrano, Gilologia Inglesa Degree Madrid
Miss B Adamson, BA London
Mrs D Clayden, BA Leeds
Miss E McKinley, BA Heriot-Watt
Mrs J Orme, BA Dunelm
Miss R Roberts, BA Birmingham
Mrs M Salviaterra, BA Seville
Mrs C Gauci (*Language Assistant*)

Music:
Director of Music: Mr R Crowley
Head of Piano: Mrs R Yates, GRSM, LRAM, ARCM
Mrs K Palamarchuk, MA Krakow

Visiting Music:
Mr W Alexander, DipTCL
Miss C Barry, BA Mod, LTCL (*Cello*)
Miss R Bunn, Dip LRAM (*Violin*)
Mr P Dunn, MMus Surrey (*Piano*)
Mr J Dutton, Dip RCM (*Flute*)
Mrs L Fletcher, GRSM, ARCM (*Piano*)
Mr A Francis, LRAM (*Clarinet/Saxophone*)
Mrs S Furzey, ATCL, ALCM (*Piano*)
Mr A Gathercole, GGSM, ALCM (*Brass*)
Mr C Hooker, LRAM (*Oboe*)
Miss D Kemp, MA Oxford (*Violin, Viola*)
Mrs S Lawman, ARCM, GRSM (*Piano, Singing*)
Mr J Little, Dip TCM London Institute (*Guitar*)
Mr I Marcus (*Saxophone*)
Mrs D Martin, LRAM (*Flute*)
Mr N Martin (*Drums*)
Mr A McAfee, BA, PGCE (*Flute*)
Mr T Parks, BMus, ARCM (*Piano*)

Physical Education:
*Mrs R Jackman, CertEd Bedford
Mrs A Arnot, BEd Bedford
Mrs J Ball, BEd Crewe
Miss E Brown, BA Brighton
Miss K Gibbs, BSc Brunel
Miss S Heath, MA Brunel
Miss K Hudson, NVQ3 (*Dance Coach*)
Miss A Lloyd, BA Loughborough
Miss J Simmonds, BA Oxford Brookes
Miss J Southam, BSc Nottingham Trent

Psychology:
Dr S Brown, BA Reading, MA Lancaster, MA Brunel, MEd East Anglia, PhD Exeter

Religious Studies:
*Miss V Chamberlain, MA Cantab, MA Oxon
Mr H Dymock, BA Durham, MA London
Mr E McCartney, BSc London
Miss G Pearson, BA Oxon
Miss H Williams, MA Edinburgh

Science:
Head of Science: Mr S Inger, BSc East Anglia

Biology:
*Miss C Rhodes, BSc Wales
Miss K Baker, BSc Southampton
Mrs K Barnes, BSc Leeds
Mr J Salmon, MA Cambridge
Mrs V Wickens, BSc London
Mrs H Wooldridge, BEd Dundee
Dr A Young, BSc Leeds, PhD Reading
Mrs Z Alidina (*Technician*)

Chemistry:
*Mr M Reynish, BSc York
Mrs J Arthur, BSc Reading

Dr C Jones, PhD King's College London, BSc Nottingham Trent
Mrs T Kergon, BSc London
Mr P Tiley, BSc Bristol
Mrs Y O'Connor (*Technician*)
Mrs B Lee (*Technician*)

Physics:
*Mr S Inger, BSc East Anglia
Mr C Le Bas, BSc Edinburgh
Mrs S Wardley, BSc Southampton
Mrs S Williams, BSc Exeter
Mrs E Jacob (*Technician*)

Library:
*Ms E Howard, BA, ALA Chartered Librarian
Mrs F Ayache
Mrs S Gleave
Mrs G Hill, BA, DipLib (*Archivist*)

Junior Department:
Head: Mrs K Serinturk, Bed West Sussex
Deputy Head: Miss A McCurry, BA Melbourne
Deputy Head: Mrs L Tillston, BEd Herts
Mrs J Hunt, BEd Herts (*Art Coordinator*)
Mrs E Crawford (*Drama Coordinator*)
Mrs R Tukia, BEd New Zealand
Mr M Ronalds, BA Melbourne (*ICT Coordinator*)
Mrs M Grover, BA Cantab (*Mathematics Coordinator*)
Mrs N Lawson, BA Bath (*Modern Languages Coordinator*)
Mrs G Goulder, BA London (*Music Coordinator*)
Mrs S Kneller, MA OU (*Science & Technology Coordinator*)
Miss S Chandler, BSc Bristol
Miss L Fox, BEd Birmingham
Miss G Furphy, BEd London
Mrs A Groves, BA Brunel
Miss M Hammerschlag, BEd Herts
Mrs K Head, BEd LondonMrs L Morris, BA New Zealand
Mrs P Prosser, BEd Durham
Mrs L Bains (*Teaching Assistant*)
Mrs D Brooks, DipSW, BSc London (*Teaching Assistant*)
Mrs J Cheetham (*Teaching Assistant*)
Mrs T Hopkins (*Teaching Assistant*)
Mrs M Tanna (*Teaching Assistant*)
Miss J Van Krinks (*Teaching Assistant*)
Mrs A Gourley, BA Waikato (*Welfare Assistant*)

Pre-Preparatory Department (Little St Helen's):
Head: Miss J Chaventre, BEd West Sussex
Deputy Head: Mrs S Begley, MPhil Pontypridd, MSc Bangor
Senior Teacher: Mrs D Smith, BEd Warwick
Senior Teacher: Mrs T Wood, BA Surrey
Miss D Allsopp, Mont Dip London
Mrs H Corbett, BA Manchester Metropolitan
Mrs E Crawford
Miss L Crocker, BEd Cantab
Mrs C Davey, BA Brunel
Mrs G Goulder, BA London
Mrs G Hocking, BA London
Mrs R Hughes, BEd Manchester
Mrs N Johar, BA Brunel
Miss R Kansagra, BA Leeds
Mrs N Lawson, BA Bath
Miss H Manber, BA Birmingham
Miss D Masters, BEd Oxford
Mrs R Sirera, MA Manchester
Mrs C Smithers, HEd Junior Primary South Africa
Mrs M Da Rocha (*Teaching Assistant*)
Mrs G Davis, NVQ3 Early Years (*Teaching Assistant*)
Mrs P Edwards (*Teaching Assistant*)
Mrs F Gallagher, NNEB Uxbridge (*Teaching Assistant*)
Mrs K Milowski, NVQ3 Early Years (*Teaching Assistant*)
Mrs A Player, NNEB London (*Teaching Assistant*)
Mrs D Ransom, NVQ3 Early Years (*Teaching Assistant*)
Miss S Sharman, Mont Dip (*Teaching Assistant*)
Mrs E Speed, CLANSA (*Teaching Assistant*)
Mrs P Spokes, NVQ3 Early Years (*Teaching Assistant*)
Mrs D Thakrar, NVQ3 Early Years (*Teaching Assistant*)
Miss E White, NVQ2 Early Years (*Teaching Assistant*)
Mrs A Miah, NNEB Chiltern (*Welfare Assistant*)
Mrs A Stevens, NNEB Uxbridge (*Learning Support Assistant*)
Miss K Boden (*Gap Student*)

Boarding:
House Mistress: Mrs H Wooldridge, BEd Dundee
Assistant House Mistress: Mrs I Leach
Independent Listener: Mrs M Abedian

Administration:
Resources Director: Mr R Ukiah, MA Oxon
Team Secretary (Bursary): Mrs K Airey
Human Resources Manager: Mrs S Hart, BSc MIPD
Accountant: Mr D Dhrona, ACCA
Assistant Accountant: Mr A Shah
Domestic Bursar: Mrs L Toms
Estates Manager: Ms A Steele, BA Manchester
Marketing Manager: Miss K Ogden, BA Birmingham, DipM MCIM
Registrar: Mrs P Witterick
IT Systems Manager: Mr D Crawley
PA to the Head: Mr D McLaren
Head's Secretary: Mrs J Phillips
PA to Head of Junior School: Mrs J Botten
Administrative Assistant, Junior School: Mrs L Sheerin
PA to Head of Little St Helen's: Mrs L Jones, Mrs L Quilley
Administrative Assistants: Mrs L Hailey, Mrs S Page
Secretaries: Mrs F Kahan, Mrs A Nunes, Mrs V Sharwood-Smith
Accounts Assistants: Mrs C Jay, AAT , Miss D Stent
Resources Assistant: Mrs P Tailor
AV Technician: Mrs J Dean
ICT: Mr I Bremner, BEng Southampton, Miss M Edwards, Mr G Hartley, BSc Bournemouth
Junior School Technician: Mrs J Webb
Day Boarding Coordinator: Revd A Jacobs
Day Boarding Assistants: Mrs H Collen-Jones, Mrs D Bowles
School Doctor: Dr P R Goodwin, MB, BS
School Nurse: Mrs S Shackman, RGN
School Counsellor/Independent Listener: Mrs M Abedian

St Helen's School has a commitment to academic excellence that has given us an enviable reputation for over 100 years. We provide an excellent academic education for able girls, developing personal integrity alongside intellectual, creative and sporting talents. The staff are highly qualified and enthusiastic, the facilities are excellent, discipline is good and we know and care for every individual pupil.

Above all we encourage all the girls at St Helen's to chase their dreams and achieve a successful and fulfilling life.

The school is divided into three departments: Little St Helen's (3+ to 7), Junior School (7+ to 11) and Senior School (11+ to 18), enabling continuity and progression in the education of every pupil. Main entries are at 3+, 4+, 7+, 11+ and 16+.

St Helen's has an excellent academic record and girls achieve outstanding results in public examinations at all levels. In our flourishing Sixth Form there are approximately 200 girls. The International Baccalaureate Diploma and A Levels are offered in the Sixth Form, with girls able to choose from over 20 subjects. Most girls proceed to University and we send a significant proportion to Oxford and Cambridge each year.

The curriculum is designed to enable every girl to achieve intellectual and personal fulfilment and to develop her talents to the full. We support the aims of the National Curriculum, but offer a wider range of subjects and teach to greater depth, so enabling the girls to explore their interests and talents. The staff are subject specialists whose aim is to inspire a love of their subjects. They help the girls to learn how to study independently and develop good study habits, through stimulating and rigorous teaching. All girls study two modern foreign languages together with Latin. Science is taught throughout as three separate subjects. We expect the girls to study with commitment and we attach particular importance to the diligent and prompt completion of homework assignments. Music, Art, Drama and Sport are all an integral part of the life of the school and involve every girl. Many also take extra Music, Ballet, Speech and Drama lessons and Games coaching.

Girls take a full part in the broader life of the school and, through extra-curricular activities, discover interests to complement their academic achievements. Clubs and societies abound and we have a flourishing programme of optional outdoor and adventurous activities. A vertical House system also thrives which girls help to run, and all participate in interhouse competitions.

St Helen's is easily accessible using the Metropolitan Line. Northwood Station is less than five minutes from the school.

The School also runs extensive and flexible coach services from the surrounding areas.

Our popular day boarding programme allows girls to extend their day in the safety of the school environment until parents can collect them. Our highly qualified staff involve the girls in many activities, such as baking, games and paper craft, and enable them to complete their homework before they go home. Day boarding is housed in Longworthe House in familiar surroundings and tea and supper are provided.

Fees per term (2008-2009). Senior School: £3,985. Junior School (including Speech & Drama): £3,120. Little St Helen's (including Lunch, Ballet, Speech & Drama) Reception, Year 1 and Year 2: £2,980; Nursery (including Lunch, Ballet, Speech & Drama): £2,732.

Registration Fee: UK £50; Overseas £75.

Scholarships. Academic Scholarships are awarded to girls entering the Sixth Form and at 11+. Music Exhibitions at 11+ and Art Exhibitions at 11+ and 16+. Leader-Baker Scholarship awarded every four years at 14+. Bursaries are available.

St Helen's Old Girls' Club. *Secretary*: Mrs Sally Fleming, 2 Moneyhill Road, Rickmansworth, Herts WD3 2EQ.

Charitable status. St Helen's School for Girls is a Registered Charity, number 312762. It exists to provide quality education for girls.

St James Senior Girls' School

Earsby Street London W14 8SH
Tel: 020 7348 1777; Admissions: 020 7348 1748
Fax: 020 7348 1717; Admissions: 020 7348 1749
e-mail: enquiries@sjsg.org.uk
website: www.stjamesschools.co.uk

Motto: *Speak the truth. Live generously. Aim for the best.*

Governors:
Mr Jeremy Sinclair (*Chairman*)
Mr Michael Cranny, FCII, Chartered Insurer
Mr George Cselko, BA
Mrs Marion Gibbs, BA, M Litt, PGCE, FRSA
Mr Aatif Hassan, BSc Hons, CA
Mrs Mary Pickering, BA
Mr Jon Pickles BA, ACMA
Mr John Story, FRICS
Mr Hugh Venables, BSc, MBA
Mr Jerome Webb, MA, MRICS

***Headmistress*: Mrs Laura Hyde**, CertEd

Deputy Headmistress (*Academic*): Mrs S Labram, BA

Deputy Headmistress (*Pastoral*): Mrs J Andrews, RSA, Dip TLABE

Bursar: Mr William Wyatt

Teaching Staff:
Mrs M Abramson, BSc, QTS
Mrs G Addison, MA, TESOL, PGCE
Mr N Burrows, BSc, PGCE
Ms E Chadwick, MSc, PGCE
Ms M Chaudagne, Licence MA, PGCE
Mrs S Cooper, BA Art & Design, Assoc RSA
Dr J Craven, BA, MPhil, PhD
Mrs H de Mattos, BA, PGCE
Mr N de Mattos, BA, PGCE
Mrs D Downs BA, DipRS, AMI
Ms L Hernandez, BA
Mrs K Ibbett, BA, PGCE
Mrs E Jessup, BSc, MA
Mr W Jessup, BA Oxon, MA, MPhil
Mrs S Kuhrt, BA
Mrs S Kumar, BA Ed, MA Maths
Miss E Leppard, BSc Maths
Mrs Y Lewis, CNZLA
Mrs A Lubikowski, BA, MPhil, PGCE
Dr J MacRae, MSc, PhD, QTS
Mrs J Mason, MA Oxon, PGCE
Miss A Morgan, Dip Tabla
Mrs S Piegelin-Coles, Maîtrise, PGCE, MA BLT
Mrs A Pigott, MA, QTS
Mr S Powell, BSc, PGCE
Miss M Rahona-Solaz, BA Translation & Interpreting, QTS
Miss L Razzell, BA, LRAD, RTS, ISTD
Mr M Renison, MSc, PGCE
Miss C Rogers, BSc, PGCE
Ms S Shah, PGDip Man St, PGCE
Mrs J Skinner, BA, PGCE
Mr C Southwell, CertEd
Miss E Spence, CertEd
Miss C Willows, BA, PGCE

Visiting teachers:
Mrs R Al-Mushadani (*Needlework*)
Mrs R Downs (*Needlework*)
Mrs Y Lewis, CNZLA (*Librarian*)

Founded in 1975, St James Senior School for Girls is a day school for 270 pupils from age 10–18. It is situated on a spacious site in Olympia, West Kensington, shared by its own Junior School from which it receives half its pupils.

The School aims to nourish the mind and heart of a young person by drawing on the very best of our culture in all artistic and academic pursuits; to encourage the expansion of talents with a view to offering them for the benefit of others; to provide an intelligent balance of love and discipline leading to the development of self-discipline based upon a wise understanding of moral and spiritual principles; and to develop a young woman who is happy, strong, and steady in body, mind and emotion.

The school has strong spiritual and moral values, which lie at the heart of the education. Although the school is not of a particular religious denomination it gives emphasis to the Christian tradition through assemblies, beginning and end of term church services and the employment of a school chaplain. However, children of all religious and cultural backgrounds are welcome and a profound respect for the unity of faith and spirituality is actively fostered. Philosophy is taught to all pupils by the Headmistress: it provides access to the fine wisdom of great spiritual teachers from East and West. The aim is to inspire an admiration for wisdom together with an appreciation of the essential part it has to play in assisting the discovery of how to live happily, freely and in a spirit of unity. Opportunities for discovering inner quietude and stillness though contemplation and meditation are also offered.

The school aims to provide a broad and balanced education, which would promote happiness and fulfilment for each individual in its care. Pupils engage in a vigorous and stimulating programme of study in a friendly and harmonious environment. Whilst admission to the school is through a selective procedure, the school seeks to admit those candidates who are able and willing to make good use of the education offered. The school aims to foster creativity and intellectual curiosity, challenging its pupils to achieve excellence. Standards in public examinations are high: 98% of leavers proceed to Higher Education degree courses. 47% of these students achieve places at Russell Group universities. Academic subjects are frequently set by ability.

The Curriculum offers appropriate education in a range of personal, health, social and ethical issues as well as a full programme of Citizenship, Philosophy and Religious Studies. Emphasis is given to the cultivation of leadership training, public speaking and debating. Community Service runs throughout the school and is supported by a pupil Community Service Council. Career guidance is offered to all pupils from Years 8–13. All pupils also engage in Sports, Singing and Dance. Drama, Art of Hospitality and ICT are also taught to Years 6–9.

During the first two years pupils will study the subjects which are available at GCSE level although general science is taught prior to the three separate sciences which begin in Year 8. Years 6 and 7 also receive lessons in needlework.

Subjects available to GCSE: English (Language and Literature), French, Spanish, Latin, Greek, Sanskrit (St James Junior School pupils only), Maths, History, Geography, Physics, Biology, Chemistry, Art, Music, Drama. (Maths and the three sciences take IGCSE examinations.) Short course GCSEs are offered to Year 9 girls in ICT and Religious Studies.

All subjects available at GCSE can be continued to A Level with the exception of Drama which becomes Drama & Theatre Studies. Additional A Levels include Economics, History of Art (AS only), Further Mathematics and Critical Thinking (AS only).

The Sixth Form. Most pupils stay on to complete their education into the Sixth Form. This is treated as a very distinct stage in a young person's education, during which time support and encouragement is given to achieving responsible adulthood. Sixth Form students do not wear school uniform. An extensive programme of non-examination subjects is continued in order to preserve breadth and enjoyment of learning for its own sake. Emphasis is given to cultivation of social awareness and, in particular, leadership skills through assuming responsibility for younger pupils in the school. Sixth Form students engage in Millennium Volunteer projects within the local community. In Year 12 students are encouraged to engage in community service abroad.

Creative Arts. Music, Drama and Dance are strong features of the school. There is a strong tradition of choral and solo singing, as well as instrumental music making. A fully staged opera is performed biannually in association with our brother school (St James Independent School for Boys) – Gilbert and Sullivan's *Iolanthe* in 2006 and Purcell's *The Fairy Queen* in 2004. There are three choirs, four instrumental ensembles and girls are strongly encouraged to take up individual instruction with one of our visiting instrumental and/or vocal teachers. Approximately 60% of pupils participate in extra-curricular vocal or/and instrumental lessons. The latest dramatic productions include *The Caucasian Chalk Circle* (Year 12-13) and *As You Like It* (Year 9) – both productions were in full period costume with dances from the era. The Dance programme introduces pupils to a variety of dance forms: ballet, modern dance, ballroom and choreography. As well as extra-curricular lessons, pupils also have the opportunity to perform in the school's annual Dance and Music Festivals.

Physical Education. Sports and games are an important part of school life. Aerobics, Athletics, Fencing, Gymnastics, Lacrosse, Netball, Rounders, Tennis and Volleyball are all offered within the curriculum. Extra sports activities are also offered after school.

Extra-Curricular Activities. As well as a wide range of musical, sporting and other events, clubs include Art, Astronomy, Classics, Cookery, Dance, Drama, Science, St James Challengers (adventure training club) and The Duke of Edinburgh's Award Scheme.

Admission. By the North London Independent Girls' Schools Consortium Entrance examination for entry at 11+, and all candidates are interviewed individually; at Sixth Form, by the School's own entrance examination procedure and interview. There are occasional vacancies in Years 8/9. (St James own Junior School pupils transfer into the Senior School in Year 6.)

Fees per term (2008-2009). £3,700.

Bursaries. There are limited funds available for Bursary assistance. Awards are discretionary and based on full financial enquiry into parents' means by the Bursary Fund Committee. The funds are primarily to assist children already attending St James, but some help may be available to new parents in specific circumstances. Enquiries should be made in the first instance to the Bursar and completed application forms for the academic year 2009–2010 should be returned by 31st January 2009.

Charitable status. The Independent Educational Association Ltd, trading as St James Independent Schools, is a Registered Charity, number 270156. It exists to provide education for children.

St Joseph's Convent School

Upper Redlands Road Reading RG1 5JT
Tel: 0118 966 1000
Fax: 0118 926 9932
e-mail: mailbox@st-josephs.reading.sch.uk
website: www.st-josephs.reading.sch.uk

Motto: *Optima Deo*

Patron: Rt Revd Crispian Hollis, Bishop of Portsmouth

Board of Governors:
Mrs P Grainger (*Chairman*)
Sister Magdalena, Sisters of St Marie Madeleine Postel
Sister Helen, Sisters of St Marie Madeleine Postel
Revd Dominic Golding
Dr Margaret Cross
Mrs Kate Firth
Miss K Gripton
Mr D Hallé
Mrs D Mason
Mr T Nickson
Mr W Walker

Staff:

***Headmistress*: Mrs Maureen T Sheridan**, BA Hons, CertEd, MA Ed, NPQH

Deputy Head & Head of Sixth Form: Mr N A Crean, BA Hons, NPQH

Head of Preparatory Department: Mrs P Kennedy

Bursar: Mr R Vaux

PA to Headmistress and Registrar: Mrs D Kendrick

St Joseph's is an independent day school for girls aged 3–18 years and boys aged 3–7. The school was founded in 1894 by the Sisters of St Marie Madeleine Postel and welcomes pupils of all denominations and faiths. There are some 350 pupils on the school roll, making it large enough to offer a varied curriculum and excellent facilities but small enough to foster a strong sense of community.

St Joseph's is situated in the university area of Reading, convenient to the town centre and the M4. The Preparatory Department is housed in a purpose built complex, designed with the needs of small children in mind, which is adjacent to the Senior Department campus. Classrooms and laboratories throughout the school are well equipped and within the grounds there is a full range of outdoor sporting facilities, including an indoor heated swimming pool.

At St Joseph's we work in partnership with our parents. We create an environment that is safe and happy, in which academic and social skills, individual talent and consideration of the needs of others are developed. We are justly proud of the achievements of our girls, whether in the form of GCSE or A Level results or in seeing them grow in confidence and develop as young adults.

Curriculum. Tuition is organised in classes/tutorials/small groups. The average class size is 20 and there is a teacher/student ratio of 1:10.

St Joseph's academic life is not confined to the National Curriculum, but this forms the basis of the school's teaching. Preparatory Department pupils undertake Key Stages 1 and 2 testing in addition to regular monitoring. In the Senior Department the rigour of GCSE, AS and A Level requirements keep us close to the National Curriculum. For each Year Group there is regular testing with a Parents' Information Evening at the beginning of each academic year, plus two Consultative Evenings to discuss performance.

Academic standards are high and nearly all our Sixth Formers go on to higher education. In the summer 2007 examinations, a pass rate of 98% was achieved at Advanced Level. In GCSE, 97% of pupils achieved five or more passes at Grades A*–C and 89% achieved 8 or more passes at Grades A*–C.

Artistic talent and practical skills are encouraged at all ages. Original and exciting work is produced in Art/Textiles, in CDT and Food Technology.

The school has a strong music and drama tradition. There are various orchestras, musical groups and choirs, regularly touring abroad, with the most recent visits being to Italy, which included singing in St Peter's Basilica in Rome and St Mark's Basilica in Venice. The girls regularly give concerts and there are many opportunities to take part in Drama, Dance and Debating.

Sport is an important part of life at St Joseph's. A full range of activities, from Athletics and Swimming to team games, is offered. Girls are regularly chosen to represent their county in Athletics, Swimming, Tennis and Hockey.

Pastoral Care. Form Tutors form the backbone of the pastoral care system at St Joseph's. By developing an open and trusting relationship with their pupils, they can provide a receptive ear and the essential support and help that may be required.

Admission. Admission to the Preparatory Department is by interview. Entry to the Senior Department is by examination, interview and a report from the pupil's previous school. Good GCSE grades, an interview, plus a report from the previous school, are required for admission to the Sixth Form.

Scholarships. (*see Scholarship Entries section*). The school awards a number of scholarships each year. All candidates applying for entry into Year 7 are required to sit an entrance examination and are automatically considered for an academic scholarship. These scholarships are reviewed annually up to the end of Year 11. Scholarships are also awarded for music, drama, sport and on entry to the Sixth Form.

Fees per term (2008-2009). Senior £3,500; Preparatory £1,655–£2,390.

Charitable status. St Joseph's Convent School Reading Trust is a Registered Charity, number 277077. It exists to promote and provide for the advancement of education of children and young persons.

St Leonards–Mayfield School

The Old Palace, Mayfield, East Sussex TN20 6PH
Tel: 01435 874623 (Headmistress and Secretary)
01435 874600 (School)
01435 874642 (Admissions)
Fax: 01435 872627
e-mail: enquiry@stlm.e-sussex.sch.uk
website: www.stlm.e-sussex.sch.uk

St Leonards-Mayfield School seeks to realise the unique potential of each pupil within an inclusive community that is rooted in the Catholic tradition of the Society of the Holy Child Jesus.

An independent boarding and day school for girls aged 11 to 18 years, St Leonards-Mayfield is set in the heart of the beautiful Sussex village of Mayfield, near Royal Tunbridge Wells, surrounded by rolling countryside, yet conveniently located for Gatwick and Central London.

We offer an excellent all-round education and celebrate achievement, individuality and community spirit.

We provide an unusual breadth and balance in the curriculum, training for flexibility, adaptability and the qualities essential to leadership.

We teach a broad range of academic subjects at the same time as offering a good mix of creativity and activity – music, art, ceramics, drama, dance, debating, Duke of Edinburgh's Award and riding to name a few.

We encourage girls to make the most of the school day and beyond, and to this end promote a range of flexible boarding options from occasional to weekly and full boarding.

We aspire to give girls a sense of achievement and confidence by teaching them to think independently and learn effectively.

Governors:
Mr Crispian Collins (*Chairman*)
Mr Nick Bagshawe
Mrs Teresa Blaxland
Mrs Elizabeth Byrne Hill
Sister Mary Hilary Daly, SHCJ
Mr John Dilger
Sister Maria Dinnendahl, SHCJ
Mrs Sara Hulbert-Powell
Mrs Maureen Martin
Sister Judith Lancaster, SHCJ
Mrs Marie Quayle
Mr Christopher Storr

***Headmistress*: Miss Antonia M Beary**, MA, MPhil Cantab, PGCE

Deputy Heads:
Mrs M D McGovern, BA, CertEd
Ms S Gallagher, ABD Classics USA, BA, HDipEd, MA

Bursar: Lt Col A H Bayliss, MA Cantab, CEng, MICE

Lay Chaplain: Miss S Adams, BEd, DipEd Psych, MTheo

Director of Development & Communications: Dr T Eaton, BA, MA, PhD

Senior Manager Organisation: Miss J P Eales, BEd Cantab, CertEd

Head of Sixth Form & Careers: Mr P Kilbride, BA Oxon, MA

Teaching Staff:
Religious Studies:
*Mr P L Oxborrow, BA, MA, PGCE
Miss E Doherty, BA, MA, PGCE
Mr P Fisher, BA, MA, PGCE

English:
*Mr J Filkin, BA Oxon, MA, PGCE
Mrs C Tribe, BA, PGCE
Mrs N Evans, BA, PGCE
Mrs S Hudson, BA, PGCE
Mr M Harvey, BA

EFL:
*Mrs J D Sandoval, MA, DipTEFLA
Mrs S Balzarelli, BA, DipTEFLA
Mrs J Carter, BA, DipTEO, PGCE

Classics:
*Mrs M C Boothroyd, BA, MA, PGCE
Mrs S Herbert, BSc, PGCE
Mrs J King, BA, MA, PGCE

Modern Languages:
*Mrs A C von Wulffen, MA Oxon, PGCE
Mrs R E Boumediene, BA, PGCE
Mrs P A M Crook, MA, PGCE
Mrs M L Hockton, L-ès-L
Mrs M Criado, BA, PGCE

History:
*Miss N Clyma, BA, MA, RSA, CELTA, PGCE
Mr P Kilbride, BA Oxon, MA
Mrs M Bushell, BA, PGCE

Economics & Business Studies:
*Mr B McClelland, BSc, MSc, MPhil, PGCE

Geography:
*Mr S Gough, BSc, PGCE
Mrs F M Morris, BEd
Mrs C A Turner, BA, CertEd, PGCE

Mathematics:
*Mrs J Cuthbert, BA, MA, CertEd
*Mrs A Pullinger, BSc, PGCE
Mrs M D McGovern BA, CertEd
Mrs L Motoc, BSc, PGCE

Information Technology:
*Mrs C Barry, BSc, CertEd, LIPD
Mr S Gough, BSc, PGCE
Miss C Scully, CertEd
Mrs J Uren, TCOS RSA, CommTDip, CertEd

Sciences:
*Mrs L Varley, MA Oxon, PGCE
Dr L Love, BSc, MSc, PhD
*Mr J Stacey, BSc, MSc, PGCE
Miss R Jackson, BSc, PGCE
Miss T A Rakowska, BSc, PGCE
*Mrs J Tayler, BSc, PGCE
Miss L J Willmot, BSc, PGCE
Mrs J Gradon, BA, PGCE

Food & Nutrition:
*Mrs S Rothero, BEd, CertEd
Mrs C Davies, CNAA, BEd, PGCE
Mrs Y Nash, CB Dip

Art & History of Art:
*Miss J Thackray, BA, PGCE
Mrs J Sillem, BA, PGCE
Mrs A Sivyour, BA
*Mrs J Weddell, BA, MA
Mr R Lamb, BA, MA

Ceramics:
*Mr A Topliss, BA, PGCE
Mrs Y McFadyean, BA

Drama & Theatre Studies:
*Mrs J Upton, ALAM, LLAM, CertEd, PGCE
Mrs H Halliday, Hon Dip

Physical Education:
*Mrs H Miller BA, PGCE
*Mrs H Hyde BA, QTS
Miss J Barker, BEd, BHSII J, CertEd (*Director of Riding*)
Mrs F M Morris, BEd
Miss S Evans, BA
Miss S Mead, BA, QTS
Miss P Bentley, BA

Duke of Edinburgh's Award Scheme:
Dr L Love, BSc, MSc, PhD
Mrs J Carter, BA, DipTEO, PGCE

Music:
Director: Mr P Collins, GRSM, LRAM, ARCM, PGCE
Assistant Director of Music: Miss H Woodruff, BA Mus, MA

Boarding Housemistresses:
St Dunstan's: Mrs C Davies, CNAA, BEd, PGCE
Chapel: Mrs B J Flanagan, BA
Connelly: Mrs J Roberts, HND, CertEd
Leeds: Mrs C Barry, BSc, CertEd, LIPD

PA to the Headmistress: Mrs K L Bowles, BSc
Admissions Secretary: Mrs C Blomstrom, BA
School Doctor: Dr A Coates, BM, DROCG, Dip Therapeutics
Senior Nurses: Mrs D Streeter, RGN, Mrs S Ellis, RGN

There are 435 girls enrolled, with 102 of these in the Sixth Form. Just over one quarter of pupils are full or weekly boarders.

Organisation. There are boarding houses for years 7 and 8, for years 9 and 10, for year 11 and for the Sixth Form.

Curriculum. In the first three years the curriculum seeks to establish a good foundation in the different disciplines, to encourage initiative, investigation, and many varieties of creative activity, and the growth of self-discipline and self-motivation. The core for GCSE comprises English Language, English Literature, Mathematics, a modern foreign language, Physics, Chemistry and Biology (either as three separate subjects, or in Science/Additional Science), and Religious Studies. Three further subjects may be chosen freely from fourteen options. About twenty-four subjects are offered for AS and A2 Level. The importance of non-examination subjects is stressed, together with the need to develop inter-personal skills, to take responsibility for younger members of the school and those they help in the neighbourhood, and to achieve a proper balance between work and leisure. Virtually all proceed to higher education, over 90% to university.

The standard of Music is high. There are three choirs and one orchestra, and individual tuition is available in a large number of instruments. Teams and individuals compete at county, regional and national level in a wide variety of sports.

The school has a music school and a concert hall which is used for both music and drama. There is an all-weather hockey pitch, an indoor heated 25-metre swimming pool, a gymnasium, a dance studio, tennis and netball courts, playing fields, sand school and stables. Sports include hockey, netball, tennis, rounders, athletics, swimming, gymnastics, volleyball, squash, sailing, golf, riding and more.

Admission. At 11+ via the School Entrance Examination; at 13+ via the School Entrance Examination or Common Entrance Examination; at 14 (exceptionally) on school report; at 16 (for Sixth Form Course) with six good passes at GCSE and report from present head.

Registration fee: £100 (£200 overseas).

Fees per term (2008-2009). Full Boarders £7,520, Day girls £4,995.

Scholarships. (*see Scholarship Entries section*). Scholarships are offered for achievement and potential in academic subjects, music, art, drama and sport.

Charitable status. St Leonards–Mayfield School is a Registered Charity, number 1047503. It exists to provide education for girls in keeping with its Catholic foundation.

St Margaret's School for Girls
Aberdeen

17 Albyn Place Aberdeen AB10 1RU
Tel: 01224 584466
Fax: 01224 585600
e-mail: info@st-margaret.aberdeen.sch.uk
website: www.st-margaret.aberdeen.sch.uk

Founded in 1846.

School Council:
Mrs S Rutherford, LLB (*Chairman*)
Mr S R Bertram, MA, CA, Dip BA
Dr G A M Bruce, MBChB, DRCOG, FRCGP
Dr C M Carden, BSc, DIC, PhD, CEng, MEI
Professor J Harper BSc, PhD, CChem, FRSC
Mr B Hay, MA, CA
Mr D Heslop, BSc Hons, MSc
Mr J C Leheny
Mr B R W Lockhart, MA, DipEd
Mrs L Manders, BA, DipM, DipP, MCIM

Miss F Stevenson (*FP President*)
Mrs M A M Ruddiman, LLB, Dip LP
Miss M Weston, BEd
The Revd Dr A G N Wilson, MA, BD, DMin (*Chaplain*)

Clerk to the Council: Mr G Brown, BSc, Dip H-WU

***Headmistress*: Mrs Anne Everest**, BA Hons

Deputy Headmistress: Dr Julie Land, BSc Hons, PGCE, EdD (*Mathematics*)

Senior Staff:
* *Head of Department*
§ *Part-time or Visiting*

*Mr R Adair, BSc Hons, PGCE (*Sec*) (*Chemistry*)
*Miss K Barsby, BSc Hons (*Physics*)
Mrs S Chalmers, BA Hons, PGCE, QTS (*Modern Languages*)
§Mrs E Cordiner, LTCL (*Music, Piano*)
*Miss K Cowie, BA Hons, PGCE (*Art and Design*)
*Mrs E Crisp, BA Hons, PGCE (*Geography*)
*Mr Gavin Cunningham, MA Hons, PGCE (*History and Economics*)
*Ms P Davey, BA, DipT (*Geography, Modern Studies*)
Miss S Forgie, BA Hons, PGCE (*Modern Languages*)
§Mrs K Fowler, BEd Hons, QTS (*Physical Education*)
Mrs P Goodwin, BA Hons, CertEd, LTCL (*English*)
Mrs L Gurney, LTCL (*Music, Woodwind*)
§Mrs K Hudd, BA Hons (*History*)
§Mrs H Jennings, BD, PGCE (*RMPE, History and Philosophy*)
*§Mrs J Johnson, DipDomSc, DipSEN (*Food Technology*)
Mrs A Leiper, MA Hons, DipEd (*English*)
*Mrs S Lynch, MA Hons, PGCE (*Modern Languages*)
*Miss W Main, BA Hons, PGCE (*Latin & Classical Studies*)
Mrs C Middleton BSc Hons, PGCE (*Sec Sci*) (*Biology and Physics*)
*Mrs A Miller, BSc Hons, PGCE (*Biology*)
Mrs S Milne, BEd Hons, ATCL (*Music, PSE*)
Mr R Minett, MA Hons, DipEd (*Modern Languages, Library*)
*Mr I Murray, BSc (*ICT*)
Mrs K Norval, BEd Hons (*Physical Education*)
§Mrs C Ogg, BSc Hons (*Mathematics*)
*Mr Peter Parfitt, BA Hons, MMus (*Music*)
*Mrs G Parker, DipPE (*Physical Education, PSE*)
*Miss L Penrose, BEd (*Speech and Drama*)
Mrs N Pont, MA Hons, PGCE (*Mathematics*)
Miss S Reid, BA, LTCL (*Music, Strings*)
§Mrs J Richardson, BA Hons, PGCE (*Art and Design*)
Mrs R Scott, DipT Mus (*Music*)
*Mrs J Slater, DipComm (*Business Mgt, Admin, Word Processing, Guidance*)
*Mrs S Smith, BA Hons, PGCE (*Mathematics*)
§Mrs P Snape, BSc (*Chemistry, Biology, Careers*)
§Mrs J Stephen, DipPE (*Physical Education*)
*Mr J S Witte, MA Hons (*English*)

Junior Department:
Miss A M Bibby, DPE
Miss F Black, BEd Hons
Mrs C Bradbury, DPE
§Mrs C Davenport, MA
Ms A Dressel, BSc
Mrs L Easton, BEd
Miss A Lister, MA Hons, PGDE
*Ms S Hayles, BA Hons, MSt, PGCE, PGCSpLD, RSA, TEFL
§Mrs F King, BA Hons, QTS
§Mrs L Reilly, MA, CertEd
Mrs L Williams, BEd Hons

Classroom Assistants:
Mrs M Bentley
Mrs D Gregory
Ms A Robertson, BEd Hons

Daffodil Nursery:
Mrs A Paterson, BEd, DipSEN (*Nursery Manager*)
Miss W Fraser, HNC
Miss M McInnes, HNC Child Care and Education
§Mrs D Oswald, HNC Childcare and Education
Mrs C Spinelli, NNEB

Support for Learning:
*§Mrs L Williamson, MA, DPSE, SEN
§Mrs R Scott , DipT Mus

Administrative Staff:
Bursar: Mr G Brown, BSc, Dip H-WU
Assistant Bursar: Mrs M Raitt
PA to Headmistress: Mrs G Smith
Development Director: Mrs K Lindsay
Admissions/Marketing:
§Mrs K McCulloch, BSc, MSc, CIM, DipM (*job share*)
§Mrs C Sugden, BA Hons (*job share*)
Administrator: Mrs K Schmitz, Cert SocSci
Receptionist: Mrs A Murray
Art Technician: Mr C McGeachie, BA Hons
ICT Technician: Mr C Morris, BSc
Laboratory Technician: Miss K Mackie, ONC, HNC, Bio Sci
Reprographic Technician: Mrs S Ingram
Sports Coordinator: Dr A Low, BSc, PhD

After-School Care and Playground Supervision:
Ms A Robertson, BEd Hons (*Manager*)
Mrs Victoria Amedu (*After-School Care*)
Mrs M Bentley (*Playground Supervisor*)
Miss J Elder (*After-School Care*)
Mrs M Macdonald, HNC Childcare and Education (*After-School Care*)
Mrs A Murray (*After-School Care and Playground Supervisor*)

There are also visiting instrumental teachers for strings, brass and percussion and two modern language assistants.

Founded in 1846, St Margaret's School is the oldest all-through girls' school in Scotland and the Head is a member of the Girls' Schools Association and Scottish Girls' Schools Group. Education is provided for around 400 girls from 1 Junior to VIth Year. There is a Nursery within the main building to which boys and girls are admitted from the age of 3 years.

St Margaret's School is conveniently situated in the west end of Aberdeen. The school's excellent facilities include spacious, well-equipped science laboratories, a newly refurbished resource centre, dining room, art studio, an attractive music suite, a fine gymnasium and extensive playing fields at Summerhill. A new computer suite was installed in 2005. The whole school is networked.

Aims. The aims of the School are to provide the sound academic education essential for entry to higher and further education, to develop an appreciation of the arts, and to give each girl an education appropriate to her ability in an atmosphere conducive to the full development of her personality.

Curriculum. Girls are prepared for Standard Grade, Intermediate 2, Higher and Advanced Higher examinations of the Scottish Qualifications Authority. RSA Word Processing is also available. National examinations can be taken for awards in music.

The curriculum includes Art, Biology, Chemistry, Classical Studies, Computer Studies, Drama, Economics, English (language and literature), French, Geography, German, History, Italian, Latin, Mathematics, Modern Studies, Music, Office and Information Studies, Philosophy, Physics, Physical Education, Religious and Moral Education, Personal and Social Education and Word Processing.

Girls are encouraged to take part in extra-curricular activities which include piano, dance, swimming, drama, debating, computer club, science club, Scripture Union, junior and senior orchestra, woodwind ensemble, junior, senior and chamber choir, Duke of Edinburgh's Award Scheme, Young Enterprise, highland dancing, chess and Choi Kwang Do.

Admission. Girls are admitted to the School by informal or formal assessment.

Fees per term (2008-2009). Nursery (10 half-day sessions) £1,733; 1 Junior £1,733; 2 Junior £2,001; 3 and 4 Junior £2,574; 5, 6 and 7 Junior £2,746; I to VI Senior £3,023.

These include tuition fees, SQA examination fees and all books and materials for nursery and early years classes and are payable termly with an option to pay monthly. A reduction is made when three or more sisters attend at the same time.

Means-tested bursaries are available for entry to I Senior, V and VI Senior.

Charitable status. St Margaret's School for Girls is a Registered Charity, number SC016265. It exists to provide a high quality education for girls.

St Margaret's School
Bushey

Merry Hill Road Bushey Herts WD23 1DT
Tel: 020 8901 0870
Fax: 020 8950 1677
e-mail: schooloffice@stmargarets.herts.sch.uk
website: www.stmargaretsbushey.org.uk

Founded 1749.

Motto: *Sursum corda Habemus ad Dominuum*

Patron: Her Majesty The Queen

President: The Rt Revd C Herbert, Bishop of St Albans

Vice-Presidents:
The Lord Archbishop of Wales
The Lord Archbishop of York
The Lord Bishop of London
The Chaplain of the Fleet
The Chaplain-General, Army
The Chaplain-in-Chief Royal Air Force

Committee:
Chairman: Mr P R Faulkner, FRICS, FAAV
Vice-Chairman: The Revd O R Osmond

Members:
Mr J Baldwin
Mr C Maunder Taylor
Miss M Rudland
Mr P Walton
Mrs J Herbert
Mrs S Shepherd
Miss K Bower

Staff:

***Headmistress*: Mrs L Crighton**, BA Hons Manchester, PGCE Cambridge, NPQH

Deputy Head: Mr M Ferris, BSc Bristol, PGCE
Pastoral Deputy Head: Miss J Chatkiewicz, BA Wales, PGCE
Bursar: Dr K Young, PhD, ARSM, DIC, BSc Eng Hons
Examinations Officer/Senior Teacher: Mr R Aniolkowski, BSc Leeds, PGCE

Art:
Mrs L Stewart, BA Hons Central St Martins College of Art, PGCE Goldsmiths
Mrs R Howard, MA Hons Edin, PGCE Oxon

Classics:
(*to be appointed*)
Mr D Bowker, BA Cantab, PGCE

Drama:
Mrs E Janacek, BA CNAA Herts, BEd CNAA Herts
Miss P Mowll, CertEd, LLAM Teachers, ALAM Acting

English:
Mrs M Goodhew, BA London, TEFL Dip
Mrs R M Brennan, BEd Southampton
Mrs J Otlet, MA Hons Oxon, PGCE, Lic Phil et Lettres Brussels
Ms S Ahmed, BA Hons Essex, PGCE Homerton

Food Technology:
Mrs C Timms, BEd Bath

Geography:
Mr C Knox, BA Middlesex, PGCE, FRGS
Mrs J Faherty, TCert
Mr D Bowker, BA Cantab, PGCE

History:
Mrs A Harper, BA Liverpool, PGCE
Miss J Chatkiewicz, BA Wales, PGCE

Information Technology:
Mrs G Ilott, CertEd Greenwich
Mr M A Hammond, MA Cantab, PGCE Dunelm, FRCO, LRAM

Mathematics:
Mrs G Cook, BEd London, Dip Stat OU
Mrs S Cohen, BSc Hons London, PGCE London
Mr M Ferris, BSc Bristol, PGCE
Mr B Haines BSc Essex, PGCE
Mr M A Hammond, MA Cantab, PGCE Dunelm, FRCO, LRAM

Modern Languages:
Miss A Corbach, MA London, BA Cologne, PGCE
Miss C Hitchen, BA Hons Sheffield
Mrs P Milne, BA Hons Manchester, PGCE
Ms G Baudet, Rennes, France, PGCE London

Music:
Mr I Hope, BMus Edin, PGCE, LTCL
Mr M A Hammond, MA Cantab, PGCE Dunelm, FRCO, LRAM
The Music Department is supported by a wide range of visiting peripatetic Music Teachers.

Physical Education:
Mrs D Pimlott, BEd Hons Brighton
Mrs S Adams, BEd Bedford
Miss G Jackman, BSc Hons Brunel, PGCE Middx
Mrs J Faherty, TCert
(*to be appointed*)

Religious Studies:
Mr D Bowker, BA Cantab, PGCE
Mrs S Adams, BEd Bedford

Science:
Biology:
Miss V Jennings, BSc Hons London, PGCE Exeter
(*to be appointed*)
Chemistry:
(*to be appointed*)
Mrs T Feldman, MA Oxon, MSc London
Physics:
Mr R Aniolkowski, BSc Leeds, PGCE
Mr P Ingram, BEd London, CertEd
Laboratory Technician: Mrs C Shah, Mrs B Rixon

Social Studies:
Mrs C Rees, BA Wales, MA Leicester
Mrs B Blakemore, BA New York
Miss S Smith, BSc Hons London, PGCE Middx

Special Needs:
Mrs A Baker, LSC

Speech & Drama
Coordinator: Miss P Mowll, CertEd, LLAM Teachers, ALAM Acting
Mrs F Lester, LLAM Teachers, LLAM Acting, Grad IPD
Mrs L St Hilaire, Speaking of Verse & Prose Gold, Acting Gold
Mrs A Watson-Picken, LCST, MCST, LGSM, LRAM
Ms K Woods, BA Hons, LLAM Acting, PGC Acting, PGCE Primary
Mrs P Shah, BA Hons
Mrs J Joseph, BSc Hons, LLAM Teachers, ALAM Hons Public Speaking, ALAM Recital, LTCL Effective Speaking
Mrs C Saunders, BA Hons, LLAM

Textiles Technology:
Mrs R Howard, MA Hons Fine Art Edin, PGCEOxon

Preparatory Department:
Head: Mrs C Brothers, MAEd, CertEd Bedford, AdvDipEd
Mrs L Franklin, BEd Maria Grey
Mrs J Lee-Bratt, BSc, Adv DipEd, CertEd Retford, Notts
Mrs J Thomson, CertEd Newcastle
Mrs T Walsgrove, BEd Sussex
Teaching Assistants:
Mrs R Garry
Miss C Nickless

Infant Department:
Head: Mrs S Kingsford, DipMus Aberdeen, MA Brunel
Mrs L Carter, CertEd Exeter
Mrs K Kruger, BEd University of Saskatchewan
Teaching Assistants:
Mrs L Eastland
Mrs J Newall
Mrs L Ash, BA Hons Open, NQT Hertfordshire
Mrs S Hilton, BEd Hons

Senior School House Captains:
Gordon: Mrs P Milne, BA Manchester, PGCE
Nicholson: Miss J Chatkiewicz, BA Wales, PGCE
Raleigh: Mrs M Goodhew, BA London, TEFL Dip
Wesley: Mrs J Otlet, MA Hons Oxon, PGCE, Lic Phil et Lettres Brussels

Senior Housemistress:
Mrs J Faherty, TCert
Assistant Housemistresses:
Mrs R Howard, MA Hons Edin, PGCE Oxon
Mrs J Mulvihill
Mrs S Hooper

Duke of Edinburgh's Award Scheme:
Mrs P Beazley WGLA, BELA

Catering Manager: Mrs J Crawley, MHCIMA, CertEd Nutrition Dip
Finance Manager: Mrs S Jones
IT Manager: Mr M Graver, BSc Hons Middx, MBCS
Librarian: Mrs C Salmon, BA Econ Manchester, PGCE
Marketing Manager: Mrs M Brown
Medical Centre Sister: Mrs P Beazley, RGN, SCM, ONC
Sports Centre Manager: Mr C Sneddon, BSc
Administration Assistant: Mrs A Smith
Admissions Secretary: Miss G Morris
Bursary Secretary: Mrs J Curran
Finance Assistant: Mrs D Riordan
Head's PA/School Secretary: Mrs S Wright
Receptionist: Mrs J Fossey

St Margaret's provides a secure environment in which girls from 4 to 18 are enabled to develop to their full potential. A strong emphasis on pastoral care underpins a St Margaret's education which is rigorous and challenging, but also accessible. Small classes and highly professional staff lead to impressive public examination results at GCSE and A Level.

Founded in 1749 to educate the orphan children of the clergy, the School moved to its present site in 1896 where it has grown and developed into a thriving, multi-cultural community ideally located in rural surroundings, close to national and international transport links, preparing girls to play their part as active citizens of the 21st century.

The original main school building together with its chapel was designed by the Victorian architect Sir Alfred Waterhouse. New buildings have been added to the school complex and facilities have been considerably upgraded in recent years. The Library has been re-sited and re-designed and a new Resources Centre added. There are two new ICT suites and also modern Art, Technology and Careers facilities. The most recent building project is the new £3 million Sports Centre which includes a heated indoor swimming pool, sports hall, fitness centre and dance studio.

Although the majority of the pupils are day girls, the senior school admits full, weekly and occasional boarders which means that there is a busy, thriving community seven days a week. There is a wide range of sporting and cultural activities, for example, the Duke of Edinburgh's Award and the Young Enterprise Scheme as well as charitable fund-raising drives. The school has close links with fellow Comenius project partners in Germany, Hungary, Portugal, Iceland, Belgium, Poland and Norway, and there are regular field trips, outings and theatre visits. Other activities include choir, orchestra, speech and drama, drama, ballet and judo.

Fees per term (2008-2009). Senior and Lower School: Full Boarding £7,345, Weekly Boarding £6,295, Day £4,080. Preparatory: Day £3,560, Transition £3,235, Infant £2,710.

Means-tested bursaries are available and discounts for members of the Forces, Clergy and daughters of 'Old Girls'. Please contact the School for details.

Scholarships. Academic and Music Scholarships are awarded at Year 7 and Sixth Form at the discretion of the Head. An Art Scholarship is also available in the Sixth Form.

St Margaret's Guild (Old Girls' Association). *Secretary*: Mrs J Wilson, 43 Chase Ridings, Enfield, Middx EN2 7QE. Guild Membership available to any old girl of St Margaret's School.

Charitable status. St Margaret's School Bushey is a Registered Charity, number 1056228. It exists to provide high quality education for girls.

St Margaret's School
Edinburgh

East Suffolk Road Edinburgh EH16 5PJ
Tel: 0131 668 1986
Fax: 0131 667 9814
e-mail: contact@st-margarets.edin.sch.uk
website: www.st-margarets.edin.sch.uk

Honorary President: The Rt Hon Lord Cullen

Board of Governors:
Mr M L A Chiappelli (*Chairman*)
Mrs J Austin
Mr K Boyd
Mrs K Fairweather
Mr R Farley
Lord Kinclaven
Mr N Martin
Mr J McDonald
Mrs J Stevenson
Mr G Wilson

Acting Director of Finance: David Halliday

***Principal*: Eileen M Davis**, BA Hons, PGCE

Deputy Principals:
Seniors: Jennifer McGhee
Juniors & Early Years: Eileen Fisher

Senior School Staff:

Faculty of Creative Arts & Physical Education:

Art:
Jane Haddon, MA Hons, Cert Guidance, PGCE (*House Leader*)
Claire Reid

Drama:
Sameena Wright, DipEd Speech & Drama

Music:
Dorothy Millar, BMus, DipEd (*Head of Faculty*)
Jane Grime, BEd (*House Leader*)
Visiting Teachers for:
Piano, Flute, Violin, Cello, Viola, Oboe, Clarinet, Percussion, Guitar

PE & Sport:
Lyndsay Blackadder
Stephanie Chisholm, BEd Hons
Kim Christison
Julie Rizza

Faculty of Languages & Communication:

English:
Susan Easto, MA Hons, PGCE (*House Leader*)
Jennifer McGhee
Carol Magee, MA Hons, PGCE
Shelagh Rodger, MA Hons, PGCE (*Head of Faculty*)

Modern Languages:
Catherine Boscher
Bronwen McWhinney, MA Hons, CertEd
Louise Watson, MA Hons, PGCE (*Head of the Faculty of Pupil Support*)

English as an Additional Language:
Amelia Dorward, MA Hons

Faculty of Mathematics & Business Education:

Mathematics:
Hilary Ballantine, BSc Hons, DipEd (*Head of Faculty*)
Marianne Dalzell
Jean Gilmour, BSc Hons, DipEd, LTCL
Moira McLean, BEng, PGCE

Business Studies & Computing:
Jed Latif
Suzanne Turner

Faculty of Science & Technology:
Karen Grant
Alison Macleod
Iain Moffat, BSc Hons, CertEd
Louise Moyes, BSc, PGCE (*Coordinator of Careers & Social Activities, House Leader*)
Ann McKenzie, BSc Hons, DipEd
Claire Slowther, BSc Hons, PGCE

Home Economics:
Shena Glanvill, BA, CertEd

Faculty of Social Subjects:

History:
Phil Deans (*Head of Faculty*)
Gwen Mackinnon, MA, DipEd (*Citizenship Coordinator*)

Geography:
Eileen Davis
Anne Wood, MA Hons, DipEd (*Charities Coordinator*)

Modern Studies:
Steve Carlin

Religious Education:
Shona Mackinnon

Support for Learning:
Anne Hackland: DipEd, RSA Diploma, CELTA (*Coordinator*)
Kathryn Wawro, MA, PGCE

Nurses:
Fiona Davidson
Hilary Smith

Junior School & Early Years Staff:

Deputy Principal (*Juniors & Early Years*): Eileen Fisher

Lisa Bonar, BEd Hons (*Principal Teacher*)
Rachael Citroen
Jane Didcock, MA Hons, PGCE
Judith Douglas, BA Hons, PGCE
Julie Grant, MA Hons, PGCE
Gillian Hogarth
Elizabeth McGarva, BEd Hons
Caroline May
Sarah Ogden, BSc Hons, PGCE
Evelyn Ogilvie, Dip Primary Ed
Violet Provan, MA Hons, Dip Primary Ed (*Principal Teacher*)

A dedicated team of Nursery Nurses and Care Assistants support the Teachers in Early Years.

St Margaret's School ethos is built on the vision of its founder who was particularly interested in the development of girls as individuals. The current school is the product of several mergers, the most recent being with St Denis and Cranley School in 1998.

We believe in single gender education for girls, a belief stemming from over 100 years in the field, consistently excellent academic results and the achievements of our former pupils. The environment we create is based on '*challenge with support for the individual*' thus encouraging pupils to enjoy learning, to take part, to build their confidence and self-belief and to aspire to great heights. We strive to provide the best possible experiences to develop the talents of each young person. The result is assured, articulate and responsible young women, well equipped to exploit the many opportunities our modern day society affords.

A medium-sized school, in addition to early, primary and secondary education, we have a thriving facility offering extensive and flexible wrap-around care which covers 50 weeks of the year.

The complex of school buildings is situated in south central Edinburgh, easily accessible by public transport from all parts of the city and surrounding districts.

Residential. St Margaret's School offers a groundbreaking 'flexible' residential facility for both long and short stays. This exclusive service will continue to adapt to the changing needs of our parents.

Early Years. A dedicated team of specialist staff provide high quality pre-school education and care for girls and boys between the ages of 3 months and 5 years in an integrated, new and purpose-built environment. This is the core of a full service which runs for 50 weeks of the year; termly classes are supported by 'Early Birds', The After-School Club and Holiday Club.

The Junior School. (Girls 5–11; Boys to the age of 8.) Newly refurbished buildings and small classes provide an intimate and friendly atmosphere conducive to learning. The pupils follow an enhanced version of the Scottish 5–14 Curriculum. Full access to Senior School Facilities and our Extended Curriculum ensure a broad, all-round experience.

The Senior School. Girls move into Senior School aged 11 years, a year ahead of their counterparts elsewhere in Scotland. There are four main phases to secondary education at St Margaret's School. The first two years (Transition and Senior 1) provide a broad & balanced curriculum; Senior 2 and 3 follow the two-year courses leading to National Qualifications at Intermediate Level and Standard Grade; Senior 4 and 5 follow a programme of up to six Higher Levels; Senior 6 provides for the transition to higher education, the destination of most girls.

Curriculum. Tuition is available within five faculties as detailed in the Staff Lists above. The School is generously staffed with fully-qualified, GTCS Registered Teachers, who prepare girls for entrance to universities throughout Britain, for further education or for professional training of other kinds.

At the end of Senior 1 girls make choices and generally take eight subjects in which most of them are fast-tracked to National Qualifications, a year ahead of those in most schools. The preparation for Higher Level has been significantly extended to two full,academic sessions, to enable up to six subjects to be studied at the same time as providing much enhanced opportunities for personal development in the remaining time. The final Senior 6 year offers up to four Advanced Highers and a range of other qualifications, as well as opportunities for leadership and personal development.

There is good support for learning for pupils of all abilities and some with Additional Support Needs, as well as for those whose first language is not English. Candidates are entered for Scottish Qualifications Authority Examinations at all levels. We are committed to supporting other awards such as the Community Sports Leader Award and the Examinations of the Associated Board of the Royal Schools of Music; we strive to accommodate individual needs.

Personal Development and Career Guidance. A dedicated team of staff in the Faculty of Pupil Support assist pupils in all aspects of personal & social development, including career guidance. Extensive use is made of the Independent Schools Careers Service (ISCO) with appropriate web packages such as "Futurewise". Detailed and individual guidance is given on all forms of higher and further education, as well as other chosen career paths. A careers-orientated module is in place for all pupils from Transition to Senior 6, ensuring a broad spectrum of interest and opportunity.

Music and the Arts. There are two school orchestras (Junior and Senior), a wind band, jazz band and recorder groups. Tuition is available in a wide range of instruments. There are many facilities for Arts and Crafts, including well-equipped studios and a pottery kiln. There is an imaginative, annual Art Show, featuring drama and music.

Physical Education, Sport and Dance. Individual and team sports are promoted through a broad range of activities designed to cater for all tastes and abilities. The gymnasium is well equipped and use is made of the excellent facilities at the University of Edinburgh. School teams compete in Hockey, Swimming, Tennis, Athletics, Skiing and Riding, with facilities also available for Dancing and Gymnastics. Class swimming instruction is given from Primary 3 to 6 and as an option further up the School. Advantage is also taken of the facilities available at Hillend Dry Ski Slope and the nearby Commonwealth Swimming Pool.

Other Activities: the Extended Curriculum. Many pupils chose to utilise their leisure time developing new interests and hobbies. There is a wide choice of clubs and societies including Art, Drama, Debating, Film, Theatre, IT, Photography, Dance and Gymnastics; these change according to demand. The Duke of Edinburgh's Award Scheme is very successful at Bronze, Silver and Gold levels. The enthusiasm of the Charities Committee provides everybody with a sense of social involvement and many girls also take part in voluntary or community service. There is also a full programme of outdoor events, projects and clubs for all ages and interests; venues in school, locally or further afield are used to promote broader personal development.

Fees per term (2008-2009). Tuition £1,082–£3,179; Boarding (in addition to tuition fees) £3,504.

Scholarships and Bursaries. (*see Scholarship Entries section*). St Margaret's School offers the very best possible learning environment and is accessible to all – whatever your geographical location or economic background. You will be surprised how affordable providing your child with the best possible education can be. Your child's future will be the best investment your will ever make and we can help. For further details on Bursaries, Scholarships and Fee Concessions please visit our website or contact the Principal.

Capital Appeal Fund. A new Capital Appeal Fund has been recently launched in place of the Development Trust. The aim of the CAF is to ensure income generation through a number of methods, on an ongoing basis so that a rolling programme of capital investment ensures the future of the School. Please contact the Marketing & Development Director for more information.

Former Pupils' Club. The School has three former pupils associations which maintain links between School and its previous students. Social functions are arranged several times a year and news of former pupils is published in *Horizon* (the School Magazine).

Charitable status. St Margaret's School Edinburgh Limited is a Registered Charity, number SC002635. St Margaret's School exists to educate pupils in an inspirational and dynamic, yet caring and supportive environment. We aim to provide the best possible experiences and to develop the talents of individuals, so that they can meet the challenges of later years.

St Margaret's School
Exeter
A Woodard School

---

147 Magdalen Road Exeter EX2 4TS
Tel: 01392 491699 Headmistress/Admissions Secretary
01392 273197 School Office
01392 277132 Bursar
Fax: 01392 251402
e-mail: mail@stmargarets-school.co.uk
website: www.stmargarets-school.co.uk

For Girls and Boys aged 3–7; for Girls aged 3–18.

Part of the Woodard Corporation, St Margaret's aims to inspire girls with a love of learning, of every kind, within a caring Christian environment. The school seeks to develop the potential of all pupils giving them the confidence to respond to the responsibilities and opportunities offered by society.

***Headmistress*: Mrs S Cooper**, MA Hons Oxon, PGCE, LTCL (*Classics*)

Assistant Headteacher: Mrs L Grundberg, BA Hons King's College London, AKC, PGCE Exeter (*German and French*)

Assistant Headteacher: Mr L Bergin, BA Hons Hull, PGCE Newcastle, NPQH Manchester (*Geography*)

Bursar: Mr R Purkis, BA, MBA, ACA

Director of Sixth Form Studies: Mrs B Hutchings, BA, PGCE (*English*)

Chaplain: Mrs J Frost, BA Hons, PGCE

Headmistress's Secretary and Admissions Secretary: Mrs C Clapp

School Development Officer: Mrs J Benham

Foundation. St Margaret's was founded in 1902 and celebrated its centenary last year. In 1968 the School was brought into association with the Woodard Corporation and is one of the leading schools within the Corporation.

Situation. St Margaret's is situated a mile from the City Centre. The School consists of 8 large Georgian Houses in the Magdalen Road area. There is a Gym, Assembly Hall, specialist rooms and hard courts for tennis and netball. Playing fields are available in the locality for games. A Performing Arts Centre was opened in 1997, and a Learning Resources Centre was opened in September 1998. There are 3 full IT Suites and video conferencing facilities for specialist subjects. Four Science Laboratories were opened in 2003 by The Princess Royal.

Numbers. Total number of pupils 284. There are 62 pupils in the Sixth Form.

Admission. Entrance is by the School's own examinations, held in the Spring Term prior to entry in September. Entrance tests are from the age of 7 to the Junior House, through to the Lower Sixth, subject to GCSE results and report. Tests can be arranged at other times. Entrance to the Nursery and Pre-Prep is after a taster day and teacher observation.

Scholarships and Awards. (*see Scholarship Entries section*).

Religious Life of the School. As a Woodard school, St Margaret's follows Christian principles of the Church of England and the school has a Chaplain. Children of different or no faith are welcome.

Inspection. The Independent Schools Inspectorate visited the school in October 2006. In their summary they stated that "pupils leave the school as confident, mature, friendly and lively young adults" and that "the pupils achieve very well academically" and the "care for pupils' welfare . . . is outstanding".

Curriculum. Full ranges of subjects are studied at GCSE, AS and A2 Levels. There are fully-equipped Science laboratories, Food and Information Technology centres. All girls take the ECDL course in computer literacy. French, Spanish and German are available at KS3, GCSE and A Level.

St Margaret's excels in music, art and drama. The choir reached the finals in the 2006 BBC Radio 3 Choir of the Year Competition. The Chapel Choir also won its 5th successive Outstanding Performance Award at the National Festival of Music for Youth in July 2006. Last year St Margaret's joined all other Woodard Schools in Berlioz' *Te Deum* in the Birmingham Symphony Hall. Musical tuition can be offered in any instrument. Over 18 visiting music teachers are available for lessons.

The Drama department involves the whole school in its productions, Oliver being a recent example. The school's Loft Theatre group were the only theatre company in Devon to perform new pieces of theatre writing for the National Theatre.

Games. Competitive netball, hockey, tennis, football and rounders are played. Gymnastics, dance and swimming are part of the curriculum and there is a range of sporting activities as girls move up the school, including rowing.

Extra-Curricular Activities. There is a wide range of extra-curricular activities at St Margaret's including a thriving CCF department. The Duke of Edinburgh's Award scheme currently offers over 100 girls the opportunity to work towards Bronze, Silver and Gold awards. In 2007–8 18 girls achieved their Duke of Edinburgh's Gold Award. In 2007 29 girls girls travelled to India as part of their Duke of Edinburgh's Gold Award and 19 Girls competed in the Ten Tors Event. Each year foreign exchange visits to Germany, Spain and France are enjoyed.

Careers Advice. A fully-stocked careers library with internet access, and guidance and information is available. There is also a programme of work experience for Years 11 and 12 and opportunities for service to the community.

Fees per term (2008-2009). Senior £3,000; Junior £2,490; Pre-Prep £1,500–£1,600; Nursery by sessions.

Charitable status. St Margaret's School Exeter Limited is a Registered Charity, number 1103316. It exists to provide education for girls.

St Martha's Senior School

Camlet Way Hadley Wood Barnet Hertfordshire EN4 0NJ
Tel: 020 8449 6889
Fax: 020 8441 5632
e-mail: office@st-marthas.org.uk
website: www.st-marthas.org.uk

Governors and Trustees:

Chair of Governors: Mr Les Edgar

Father John Ball
Revd Michael Bycar
Mr Martin Grant
Mrs Maureen Howie
Mrs Catherine Lyons
Mr Terry Malone
Mr Michael McCann
Mr Joseph Medayil
Mr Seamus O'Sullivan
Mrs Bridget Sawyer
Mrs Jackie Williams

Trustees:
Sister Cécile Archer
Sister Christina O'Dwyer
Sister Janet Sinden
Mrs Mary Adam
Father Bernard Boylan
Mr Jonathan Hoare
Father Philip Law
Mr Michael McCann
Mrs Rosemary Robertson

School Staff:

***Headmaster*: Mr James Sheridan**, BSc, MA

Chaplain: Father D McGuire, BA, PGCE

Deputy Head: Sister T Roseingrave, CertEd, CTC

Bursar: Mr S Rayner

Assistant Bursar: Mrs E Boonzaier, BEd, BCom, HDE

Director of Studies: Miss C Rouse, BA, PGCE

Admissions & Headmaster's PA: Mrs M Maestranzi, BArch

Senior Teachers:
Miss E Monchaux, BA, PGCE (*Curriculum*)
Dr M Wall, BSc, PhD, PGCE (*Curriculum*)

House Mistresses:
Miss K Maestranzi, BA, GTP (*Avila*)
Miss R McGonagle, BA, PGCE (*Siena*)
Miss D Mela, GLCM, ALCM (*Lisieux*)

* *Head of Faculty*

Art & Design:
*Ms Y Cormack, BEd
Ms E Somerville, BA, PGCE
Mrs M Dixon (*Teaching Assistant*)

Catering:
Mrs P Meally

Classics:
Miss C Rouse, BA
Miss K Maestranzi, BA, GTP

Drama:
Miss R McGonagle, BA, PGCE
Mr E Whitmore, BA, MLS, PGCE
Ms G White, BA

English:
*Mr E Whitmore, BA, MLS, PGCE
Dr B Kavanagh, BA, MA, PhD, HDE
Miss L Steenson, BA

Geography:
*Mrs H Pestaille, BA, PGCE
Mrs G Neuhaus-Chalmers, MA
Miss K Thoburn, BA, PGCE

History:
Miss I Saenz-Some, BA, PGCE
Miss K Thoburn, BA, PGCE

Home Economics:
Mrs B Rodgers, BA, GTP
Sister T Roseingrave, CertEd, CTC

Information Technology and Business Studies:
*Mr J Boonzaier, BCom, HDE

Information Technology Manager:
Mr I Kay, BSc, ICM

Latin:
Mrs F Stamidou, BA, MA

Learning Resources:
Mr E Whitmore, BA, MLS, PGCE
Mrs V Annis (*Librarian*)

Marketing:
Mrs W Kolubayev, BA, MSc

Mathematics:
Mr L Kasza, B Eng, PGCE
Mrs M Platona-Basiel, BSc, PGCE
Mr J Sheridan, BSc, MA
Mr. R Hugill, BSc, PGCE

Modern Languages:
French:
*Mrs A Orr, BA, PGCE
Miss E Monchaux, BA, PGCE
Mrs L Corbett, BA, PGCE
Miss G Catherine, BA, MA (*Assistant*)
German:
Mrs G Neuhaus-Chalmers, MA
Spanish:
Mrs L Corbett, BA, PGCE
Miss I Saenz-Some, BA, PGCE

Music:
Mrs S Carter, GRSM, LRAM, ARCM

Physical Education:
Mrs F Casalaspro, CertEd, CTC
Ms A Herlihy, CertEd

Religious Education:
*Miss C Rouse, BA, PGCE
Mrs F Casalaspro, CertEd, CTC
Mrs D Mela, GLCM, ALCM
Father D McGuire, BA, PGCE

Science:
*Mr R Odell, BSc, PGCE
Miss F Agrotis, Dip Med Tech
Dr D Black, PhD
Mrs D Martin, BSc, PGCE, MSc
Mrs K McAlister, BSc, PGCE
Dr M Wall, BSc, PhD, PGCE

Sociology:
Mr P Hasell, BSc, MA, PGCE

Visiting Teachers:
Miss S Carney (*Violin*)
Mrs V Charles (*LAMDA Speech & Drama*)
Miss K Copeland (*Voice*)
Mr A McAtominey (*Drums*)
Miss K McDunnough (*Piano*)
Mrs L Shirm (*Clarinet, Saxophone*)
Mrs C Wilson (*Flute*)
Ms G White (*Dance*)

Administration:
Mr I Kay, BSc, ICM (*Admin Head*)
Mrs A Fitzpatrick, BA
Mrs G Halwani (*School Secretary*)
Mrs M Keane, BA

Site Manager: Mr C Heaney
Driver/Caretaker: Mr J Conway
Groundsman: Mr D Meally

Age Range. 11–18 Girls.
Number in School. 294 Day Girls.
Fees per term (2008-2009). £2,825.

St Martha's is a small independent Catholic school for girls welcoming all denominations, faiths and nationalities into our community. Located in the leafy environs of Monken Hadley Common, we treasure our picturesque rural surroundings yet benefit from close public transport links by tube and rail to central London.

We are renowned as a warm and friendly school that believes a demanding and challenging ethos can go hand in hand with a caring and supportive atmosphere. Intellectual endeavour and hard work should be part of an exciting, stimulating and enjoyable environment that inspires achievement. Our recent ISI inspection concluded: "*The school meets its aims and aspirations outstandingly well. The spiritual, moral, social and cultural development of the girls is excellent as is the provision for their pastoral care.*"

We base our work on Gospel values and encourage girls to see God in everything and everyone while fostering an appreciation of the joy derived from caring for others as is best expressed by our school motto '*Serve the Lord with Joy*'.

We are very proud of our girls' endeavours and achievements across the curriculum. They also engage in a surprising array of co-curricular activities which we believe is vital to their development as a whole person.

Please come along to our Open Day to see just what makes us so special and experience at first hand why so many parents are choosing St Martha's to educate their daughters.

Charitable status. Congregation of the Sisters of Saint Martha is a Registered Charity, number 233809.

Saint Martin's

Solihull

Malvern Hall Brueton Avenue Solihull West Midlands B91 3EN
Tel: 0121 705 1265
Fax: 0121 711 4529
e-mail: mail@saintmartins-school.com
website: www.saintmartins-school.com

Motto: *The Grace of God is in Courtesy*

Founded 1941. Independent Day School for girls aged 2¾ to 18.

Board of Governors:
Mr M Hope-Urwin (*Chairman*)
Revd J Bradford, BA, MEd, FRSA
Mrs N S Bridgewater, JP
Miss A Davies, BSc, FCA, ATII, MSPI
Mrs P Harbour, MA
Dr S Madeley, MSc, PhD, JP
Ms E Sewell, BA
Mr J Shepherd, FRICS
Mrs G Tillman, BSc

Clerk to the Governors and Bursar: Mr M Llewellyn, FCIS

***Headmistress*: Mrs J Carwithen**, BSc, MA London, PGCE

Deputy Headmistress Senior School: Mrs J Parker, BSc Reading, PGCE

Director of Studies & Head of Sixth Form: Mr M Richards, BMus Wales, MMus London

Staff:

English:
Mrs C Inns, BA Kent, PGCE
Mrs A Field, BA Nottingham, PGCE
Mrs S Watton, BA Hull, PGCE

Modern Languages:
German, French, Spanish: Mr P Delaney, BA Exeter, PGCE
French: Mrs C Gibney, DUT Nancy, MIL, PGCE
French: Mrs A Barrett, BA Hull, PGCE
French: Mrs J Golightly, BA Wales, PGCE
German, Spanish: Mrs I Jardon, DipIl, PGCE

Classics:
Mr K Carroll, BA Nottingham, PGCE
Mrs L Beaumont, BA Manchester, PGCE

History:
Mr M van Alderwegen, BA Leeds, MA Nottingham, PGCE
Mrs A Hanson, BA Oxon, CertEd
Mrs V Llewellyn, MA Edinburgh, PGCE

Geography:
Mrs F Fowles, BA Dunelm, MSc Reading, PGCE
Miss C Bednall, BSc Cheltenham, MSc London, PGCE

Religious Knowledge:
Miss H Levesley, BA Dunelm, PGCE

Mathematics:
Mrs H Barber, BA York, PGCE
Mrs J Carwithen, BSc, MA London, PGCE
Mrs R Lawson, BEd Warwick

Mrs R Linstead, BSc Dundee, PGCE
Mrs M Thompson, BA Open, CertEd
Mrs M Thompson, BSc Nottingham, PGCE
Mr D Wellings, BSc Birmingham, PGCE

Information Technology:
Mrs C Dance, BSc Keele, PGCE
Mrs A Short, BSc London, PGCE

Science:

Biology:
Mrs J Parker, BSc Reading, PGCE
Miss R Parkin, BSc Coventry, PGCE
Mrs J Waters, BSc Birmingham, PGCE

Chemistry:
Mrs B Ridley, BSc Wales, MA Ed, PGCE
Mr N Bray, BSc Wales, PGCE

Physics:
Mrs S Parker, BSc Leicester, PGCE
Mrs A Short, BSc London, PGCE

Business Studies and Economics:
Mrs M Hetherington, BA Coventry, MA

Psychology:
Mrs M Thompson, BSc Nottingham, PGCE

Food and Textiles:
Mrs E Enderby, CertEd

Art and Design:
Mrs L Dougall, BA Essex, PGCE
Mrs L Winnett, BEd Sheffield, CertEd

Speech and Drama:
Mrs C Kimpton, NCSDD, LUD Dramatic Art, LRAM
Mrs J Plain-Jones, BA Hertfordshire, CertEd

Music:
Mr P Allen, BA Liverpool, PGCE
Mr M Richards, BMus Wales, MMus London
Mrs E Williams, BSc Oxford Brookes, PGCE

Dance: Miss J Felix

Physical Education:
Mrs J Elston, CertEd Bedford College
Mrs B Waters, CertEd Bedford College
Mrs H Burgess, BA Birmingham, PGCE
Mrs S Trenchard, BEd London
Mrs H Bradbury, AIST, MSTA

Learning Support:
Mrs F Franklin, BA Trinity & All Saints

Deputy Headmistress, Junior School and Preparatory Dept:
Mrs K Woods, BA Lancaster, PGCE

Junior School:
Mrs D Gregory, BEd Bristol
Mrs D Griffiths, BA Open, CertEd
Mrs L Lotherington, BA Ed Exeter
Mrs T Marsh, BEd Bath College of Education
Mrs M Schofield, BA Dunelm, PGCE
Miss H Winn, LLB Manchester Metropolitan, PGCE
Miss E Wilkinson, BEd
Mrs J Crampton

Alice House Preparatory Department:
Mrs G Ginns, CertEd
Mrs L Campbell, CertEd
Mrs B Darby, BA Leeds, PGCE
Mrs P Haynes, BEd Birmingham Polytechnic
Mrs V Higley, BEd Christ & Notre Dame
Mrs E Pimlott, BSc Portsmouth, PGCE
Mrs E Rowley, CertEd

Librarian: Ms L Russell

Location. Saint Martin's is a well-established day school for approximately 520 girls situated in a beautiful twenty acre site in the south of Solihull. Solihull is about 8 miles from Birmingham and is on the edge of a rural district within very easy reach of Warwick, Coventry and Leamington Spa.

Buildings and Facilities. In addition to the main school buildings which are attached to the very fine Grade II listed Malvern Hall, there are separate, self-contained buildings for the Preparatory and Junior Departments; the Sixth Form is housed in renovated and extended listed buildings near to the main school. All playing fields, including tennis and netball courts, are on the premises and an exceptionally wide range of indoor and outdoor activities is offered. In addition, the all-weather facilities at nearby local sports and activities centres are frequently used. A 25 metre indoor swimming pool was opened in November 1999.

The school enjoys well resourced, specialist accommodation for teaching science, music, art, drama and technology. Following a recent building programme in the Senior School, new facilities include two ICT suites, a conference room and an enlarged library.

Curriculum. Girls receive a broad academic education with considerable opportunities for the development of individual interests and good academic standards are maintained. Emphasis is placed on hard work, discipline and independent learning. Courses leading to GCSE examinations are offered in all the usual subjects as well as ICT, Spanish, German, Latin, Classical Civilisation, Art and Music and all girls are required to continue with Mathematics, English Language, English Literature, a modern language and all three sciences. Classes are not streamed, but some subjects are taught in ability sets. In the Sixth Form, the majority of girls will study four Advanced Subsidiary subjects in the first year and complete three Advanced Level courses in the second year chosen from the same range as is offered at GCSE, with the addition of Economics, Business Studies, Psychology and Critical Thinking. Virtually all Sixth Form students go on to higher education and all senior pupils receive extensive careers education and advice and all take part in work experience in Year 11 and the Lower Sixth.

Extra-Curricular Activities. Sport, music, drama and public speaking are all strong in school: plays and concerts are held throughout the year at all ages and a very large proportion of girls study at least one instrument. A large selection of other extra-curricular interests is catered for, including Young Investigators' Science Award and Trampoline Club for younger girls and Young Enterprise and the Duke of Edinburgh's Award Scheme for the seniors. Clubs and societies are encouraged. There are many visits out in support of the curriculum, including regular field trips, and trips abroad to Fougères, Iceland, Brussels and New York among others.

Admission is by assessment for girls aged 5–10 and by interview and examination for older pupils. Girls are admitted to the Sixth Form on the basis of GCSE results and interview.

Fees per term (2008-2009). Nursery £1,895 (full time); R–Y2 £2,160; Y3 £2,270; Y4–6 £2,610; Senior School and Sixth Form £3,110.

Scholarships. (*see Scholarship Entries section*). A number of scholarships, including one music scholarship, are awarded annually for admission at 11+ and scholarships worth up to 50% of fees are awarded to girls entering the Lower Sixth or to enable a girl in the school to complete her education.

Charitable status. Saint Martin's (Solihull) Limited is a Registered Charity, number 528967. It exists to provide education for girls.

St Mary's Hall

Eastern Road Brighton East Sussex BN2 5JF
Tel: 01273 606061

Fax: 01273 620782
e-mail: registrar@stmaryshall.co.uk
website: www.stmaryshall.co.uk

President: The Right Revd The Lord Bishop of Chichester

Vice-Presidents:
The Right Revd The Lord Bishop of Horsham
The Right Revd The Lord Bishop of Lewes

Chairman of the Governors: Mr Andrew N Russell

Staff:
***Headmistress*: Mrs S M Meek**, MA

Deputy Head: Mrs O Ridge, BA

Bursar: Lt Cdr K F Mardon, MBE, MSc, RN Retd

Registrar: Mrs C A Johnson

Introduction. St Mary's Hall is a day and boarding school for girls aged 3–18. Established in 1836, St Mary's Hall is one of Britain's oldest schools for girls. Situated on extensive grounds overlooking the sea and within easy reach of Brighton & Hove's historic city centre, St Mary's Hall is very much a city school. The cultural buzz and artistic dynamism of Brighton & Hove make it one of the most exciting cities in Britain. London is 55 minutes away by train, Heathrow Airport easily accessible, and Gatwick Airport only a 40-minute drive away.

The School has over 300 students, a quarter of who are boarders. St Mary's Hall has a long tradition of educating and caring for students of many different nationalities.

St Mary's Hall offers a safe and happy environment where students are encouraged to realise their full potential in academic, sporting, cultural and social activities.

Age Range: Girls 3 to 18, Boys 3 to 11.

Statement of Purpose: Educating for Confidence. Our aim is to develop personal qualities necessary to make a positive contribution to a changing and unpredictable world. This requires each individual in the community to be ready for life-long learning, to be adaptable, to have the courage to face challenges, to acquire transferable skills, to be able to work independently and as part of a team, and to show self-discipline, commitment, flexibility and openness to change.

"The quality of the spiritual, moral, social and cultural development of pupils throughout the school is outstanding" – The Independent Schools Inspectorate.

At St Mary's Hall, we encourage a culture of learning, respect, knowledge and achievement, and focus upon the individual development of each pupil while preparing our pupils for life as young responsible adults. Great emphasis is placed on establishing sound personal relationships. Support and advice is given to integrate every student in the School community at all levels.

Curriculum. St Mary's Hall accepts pupils with a wide range of ability and has a very good record of helping all to achieve academic success. A wide range of subjects is on offer throughout the School at GCSE and A Level. Each pupil's programme is carefully monitored to suit the individual.

2007 pass rates: A Level = 98%, GCSE = 96%. Almost all of our A Level students go on to their chosen universities which have included Cambridge and Oxford.

One of St Mary's Hall's greatest strengths is its talented team of teachers. Heads of Department and Form Tutors work closely together to inspire and educate our pupils. The School provides a comprehensive training programme to develop teachers' skills and keep them up-to-date with curriculum developments.

Extra-Curricular Activities. There are many extra-curricular opportunities, which aim to give every pupil a chance to 'shine' in some respect.

In the Junior School extra-curricular activities during the week include ballet, modern and jazz dance, speech and drama, French club, swimming club, knitting club, choir, string quartet, orchestra and recorder ensemble. Children also have the opportunity to learn a variety of musical instruments.

Students in the Senior School are positively encouraged to supplement their academic studies with extra-curricular activities. The choice is wide to cater for individual aspirations and taste: a drama club for budding thespians, The Duke of Edinburgh's Award scheme for those who like challenges and Young Enterprise for the businesswomen of the future. The vibrant music department runs a chamber choir, senior choir, an orchestra, as well as a jazz group. For those with an artistic streak there is a pottery club.

Boarding. There are two boarding houses situated on the School grounds: Venn House and Elliott House which opened in September 2006. Elliott House houses our Sixth Form boarders primarily in single study-bedrooms close to individual shower rooms. St Mary's Hall offers boarding as early as the age of 8.

Students come from the local community and from all over the world to make St Mary's Hall their home. A caring, dedicated and friendly house staff provides a secure, comfortable and happy environment for our students.

The focus of boarding life at St Mary's Hall is the personal and academic development of each individual student. Boarding is about belonging to a community, sharing and learning to become a team player. Our community is a thriving one, enriched by the contribution of each individual.

Religion. St Mary's Hall welcomes students of all religious denominations or none. Arrangements are made, as far as practicable, for boarders to attend churches of their own denomination or worship in their own faith.

Facilities. The School's grounds are 6.3 acres (2.55 hectares). The School houses a multi-purpose Hall, science laboratories, two information technology suites, two design technology rooms, a music studio, the main library, careers centre and the ESL Department (English as a second language). The campus comprises an art centre, the modern languages department, the mathematics study centre, tennis/netball courts, an indoor, heated 25-metre swimming pool, sports field, a studio theatre, a beautiful chapel, two boarding houses, the Junior School and the Sixth Form Centre.

Elliott House is our newly developed Sixth Form Day Centre and boarding house. The Sixth Form Centre provides an attractive, spacious common room, a Study and IT area, a coffee bar and a wireless network system providing internet and intranet access.

Gloucester House is our new junior School which opened in January 2006. This modern two-storey building incorporates the Nursery (extended nursery provision, nursery education grants accepted), the Pre-Preparatory and the Preparatory Departments and as such offers our pupils a seamless primary education. There is a library, hall, ICT suite, dedicated music area and a Design Technology room.

ESL Department. Our pupils come from the local community as well as from around the world. Our cultural diversity is an asset. We have an English as a Second Language (ESL) Department for our overseas students. A team of talented and caring ESL specialist provides tailor-made tuition to allow a seamless integration of all nationalities into St Mary's Hall. Before entry, all students take an ESL written test. The result of this test will help determine the student's level of English. The ESL team will plan a programme of study to suit each individual student's needs.

"The teaching of pupils with EAL (English is an additional language) is excellent" – The Independent Schools Inspectorate.

Entrance. *Senior School*: Prospective pupils sit an assessment test. The School has its own assessment test, but the Girls' Common Entrance Examination is also accepted. For further details, please contact the Registrar.

Junior School: Where possible, prospective pupils are encouraged to spend a day, or part of a day, at the School, being assessed in class with their peers.

Scholarships and Bursaries. Two or three Open Scholarships are awarded to girls aged 11+, 12+ or 13+ on the results of an examination held in January. Sixth Form Scholarships are also awarded and details are available on request. In addition, there are Music, Sport, Drama and Art Scholarships and a limited number of Bursaries. Special Funds exist for the benefit of daughters of the Clergy or the Armed Forces.

Fees per term (2008-2009). Senior School: Boarders £6,939 (full), £6,652 (weekly); Day Girls Years 7, 8, 9, 12 and 13 £3,286, Years, 10 and 11 £4,203.

Junior School: Boarders (from age 8) £5,247 (full), £4,995 (weekly); Day Pupils £900–£2,528 depending on age. All fees inclusive of meals (lunch for day pupils), books and stationery.

Charitable status. St Mary's Hall is a Registered Charity, number 307062. It exists to provide high quality education.

St Mary's School Ascot

St Mary's Road Ascot Berks SL5 9JF
Tel: 01344 623721 (Main Switchboard)
01344 293614 (Admissions)
e-mail: admissions@st-marys-ascot.co.uk
website: www.st-marys-ascot.co.uk

Governing Body:
Chairman: Mr Mark Armour, MA
Mr Jonathan Agnew
Mrs Oonagh Berry
Mr Peter Davis
Mr Patrick Gaynor
Sr Cecilia Goodman CJ
Mr John Hickman, FRICS
The Hon Charles Martyn-Hemphill
Mr Frank Morgan, BSc, PGCE, MEd
Miss Margaret Rudland, BSc

Trustees:
Chairman: Mr Geoffrey van Cutsem, FRICS
Mr John Buckenham, MA
Baroness Sarah Hogg, MA
Sr Christina Kenworthy-Browne CJ, BA
Mrs Pauline Mathias
Mr Michael Milbourn
The Hon Mrs Olga Polizzi
Mr Brian Stevens

Management and Administration:

***Headmistress*: Mrs Mary Breen**, BSc Exeter, MSc Manchester

Deputy Headmistress: Mrs Virginia Barker, BSc Reading, PGCE
Deputy Headmistress Boarding: Miss Sheila Williams, CertEd, CTC Liverpool
Director of Studies: Mr Michael Clennett, MA Oxon, PGCE
Head of Sixth Form: Miss Laura Graves, BA Bristol, PGCE
Assistant Head of Sixth Form: Mrs Anna Curtis, BA OU, BSc Anglia, PGCE
Bursar: Mr Giles Brand
Assistant to Bursar: Mrs Julie Osborne
Sports Centre Weekend Supervisor: Mr Ross Fairclough, BA Oxford Brooks
Domestic Bursar: Mrs Wendy Woolaway
Clerk of Works: Mr Terence Ford
Accountant: Mrs Susan Chapman
Assistant to Accountant: Mrs Christine Cornish
Caterer: Mr Cliff Atkinson
PA to the Headmistress: Mrs Phyllida Dewes
Registrar: Mrs Sandra Young
Assistant to the Registrar: Mrs Christine Holland
Administrative Assistant: Mrs Christiane Scott, Lic Phil Zurich
Cover Supervisor: Mrs Joanna Meeson, BA East Anglia
Development Director: Mrs Wanda Nash, BA, MEd
Development Secretary: Mrs Catherine Leneghan
AOGA Secretary: Mrs Henrietta Currey
School Secretary: Mrs Frances Green
School Receptionist: Mrs Sheila Hickmott
School Doctor: Dr Gillian Tasker, MB BS, DRCOG
Senior Nursing Sister: Mrs Monica McGeown, RGN, SCM
Nursing Sister: Mrs Philippa Perera, RGN, RM
School Resident Chaplain: The Revd Dr Dermot Power, BA, BDSTL
CJ Chaplain: Sister Jane Livesey CJ, MA Cantab
Independent Listener: Mrs Julia Keys

Heads of House:
Mary Ward House: Mrs Brenda Vockings
Babthorpe: Mrs Helena West
Bedingfeld: Mr and Mrs Tom Parsons
Poyntz: Mrs Jo Brayton
Rookwood: Sister Michaela Robinson CJ
Wigmore: Mrs Valerie Hutchinson

Residential Staff:
Mrs S Ball
Miss Jane Bennett
Mrs J Bennett
Mrs C Candappa
Miss E Cuff
Mrs A Curtis
Miss K Horwood
Mrs J Hunt
Mrs S McLoughlin
Miss V Swire
Miss P Wallace
Miss P Walker

Academic Departments:

Art and Design:
Mr M Mitchell, BA Bristol Polytechnic, PGCE (*Head of Department*)
Mrs D Farrell, BA Middlesex, BTec Kent Inst Art & Design (*Textiles*)
Miss L Green, BA De Montfort, Reigate College of Art & Design, PGCE (*Art and Design*)
Mrs X Harrison, BA Wales, PGCE (*Ceramics*)
Mr T Parsons, MA York (*History of Art*)
Mrs M Place, BA OU, MA Reading, ALA London (*History of Art*)
Miss G Wigley, BA Coventry, MA Edinburgh (*Photography*)

Classics:
Mrs L Povey, BA Hons Nottingham, MPhil Classics London (*Head of Department*)
Mr M Clennett, MA Oxon PGCE
Miss M Fisher, BA Wales, PGCE
Mr K Rogers, BA London, PGCE

Drama:
Mr T Jelley, BA Surrey, PGCE (*Head of Department*)
Mrs J Brayton, BA Lancaster
Miss B Carr, BA Southampton
Miss A Margilewska, BA Theatre Studies Rose Bruford College, Guildford School of Acting
Ms L O'Callaghan-Mitchell
Ms V Dew (*Theatre Technician*)

English:
Mrs H Trapani, BA Leicester, MA Hong Kong, PGCE (*Head of Department*)
Mrs S Head, BA Nottingham, PGCE London
Mrs J McPherson, BA Western Australia, Grad DipEd Edith Cowan, MA Sydney

Miss H Owen-Frawley, BA Bristol, PGCE
Mrs K Parsons, BA York, MA Warwick
Mrs L Waltho, BA, MLitt Newcastle

Humanities:
Mrs K Holdich, MSc Kingston, PGCE (*Geography, Head of Department*)
Mrs E Hewer, MA Cantab, PGCE (*Geography*)
Mr D Hillman, BA Oxon, MSc Birkbeck, PGCE (*Economics and Politics*)
Mrs M Lake, BA Hatfield, PGCE (*History*)
Mr J Powell, BA Leeds, MSc Birkbeck, PGCE (*Economics & Politics*)
Miss H Rider, BA Bath, PGCE (*History*)
Mrs B Vockings, BA Wales, BSA Surrey, PGCE (*Geography*)

Information & Communications Technology:
Miss B Hudson-Reed, BA Natal Univ, HDE, FDE Computers in Education (*Head of Department*)
Mr T Francis (*IT Support Technician*)
Miss J Davis, BA Newcastle, PGCE, DipIT
Mrs V Hutchinson, BA University College, Cork, DipComSc, HDE, HDGC
Miss V Parsons, BSc Portsmouth
Mr G Planner (*IT Manager*)

Mathematics:
Mrs R Davies, BEd Homerton, Cambridge (*Head of Department*)
Mrs S Ball, BSc Liverpool, PGCE
Mrs V Barker, BSc Reading, PGCE
Mrs L Carlsson, BSc London
Mrs W Dutton, BSc Southampton, PGCE
Mrs L Matthews, BEd London
Mrs G Miles, BSc QMC, London, PGCE
Mrs E Whittaker, BA Wilhelms Universität, PGCE

Modern Languages:
Mme E Cook, DEUG Toulouse, AdvDip English Studies Portsmouth, CEMEA Toulouse, PGCE (*Head of Department, French*)
Dr C Bainton, BA London, PhD Cantab (*Spanish*)
Mrs S Boakes, MA Oxon (*German and French*)
Miss R Cabrera, English/Russian Translation Granada, QTS (*Spanish*)
Miss E Caretti, BA Milan, PGCE (*Italian*)
Mrs S Chasemore (*German Assistant*)
Mrs M Fernanda Dabbaj, BA London (*Spanish Assistant*)
Mlle V Feuillet, DEUG Sorbonne, MA, PGCE (*French*)
Mlle M Hervi, Licence d'Anglais, MA, FLE UHB Rennes, PGCE (*French*)
Mrs S Webb, BA Cantab, PGCE Reading, TESOL (*German, French*)

Music:
Director of Music: Mr D Andrew, MA Oxon
Asst Director of Music: Mr N Hutchinson, ARCO, ARCM, GBSM, LTCL, ABSM (*Organ*)
Dr F Neary, BMus London, PhD Ohio (*Piano*)
Mrs P Willard (*Secretary*)

Physical Education:
Miss G Eamer, BSc Coventry, PGCE (*Head of Department*)
Miss L Aylward, BSc Worcester, PGCE
Mrs G Bird, ACA (*Tennis*)
Mrs J Freeme BEd Johannesburg, PGCE
Miss A Haylett, Dip Sports Psychology Newcastle College
Ms L Stephenson (*Ballet and Tap Dancing*)
Mrs Z Warboys (*Modern Dance*)
Mrs A Wright, BA OU, CertEd Chelsea College of PE

Religious Education:
Miss R Toner, BA Cantab, MA London, PGCE (*Head of Department*)
Mr P Golden, BA Stirling, PGCE
Miss L Graves, BA Bristol, PGCE
Mr M J Hughes, PhB Rome, CertEd
Sister Michaela Robinson CJ, CertEd London, PG DipSpLD Dyslexia
Mrs M-T Slater, BA London, PGCE
Mrs H West, BA Surrey, PGCE
Miss S Williams, CertEd, CTC Liverpool

Sciences:
Mrs P Shaw, BSc Leeds, PGCE (*Head of Department*)
Mrs M Breen, BSc Exeter, MSc Manchester (*Physics*)
Mrs L Carlsson, BSc London (*Biology*)
Mrs M Clayton, BSc Birmingham, PGCE (*Physics*)
Mrs A Curtis, BA OU, BSc Anglia, PGCE (*Biology*)
Mrs H Hesp, BSc Manchester, PGCE (*Physics*)
Mr N Jones, BSc Swansea, MSc Swansea, PGCE
Mr R Kernley, BSc London, PGCE, GRIC (*Chemistry*)
Mrs J McCrudden, BSc Scranton, USA, QTS (*Biology*)
Mr D Riding, MPhys Sheffield, PGCE (*Physics*)
Miss C Roberts, MA Oxon, PGCE (*Chemistry*)
Mrs J Ford (*Laboratory Technician*)
Mrs S Meeks, BSc Southampton (*Laboratory Technician*)
Mrs L Weston, City and Guilds Cert (*Laboratory Technician*)

Miscellaneous:
Librarian and Careers Officer: Mrs C Norvill, BA Lib Hons, ALA Birmingham, CCEG
Reprographics: Mr R Liles
Examinations Officer: Mr M Hughes, PhB Rome, CertEd
Assistant Examinations Officer: Mr N Hutchinson, ARCO, ARCM, GBSM, LTCL, ABSM

Special Needs Coordinators:
Sr Michaela Robinson CJ, CertEd London, PGDipSpLD Dyslexia
Mrs W Dutton, BSc Southampton, PGCE

Duke of Edinburgh's Award Scheme:
Head: Mrs A Wright, BA OU, CertEd Chelsea Coll of PE
Mr R Godfrey, BA North Wales, PGCE, APIOL
Mr P Edmunds, CertEd, MA Oxford Brookes
Mr N Jones, BSc Swansea, MSc Swansea, PGCE

St Mary's School Ascot is a Roman Catholic boarding school founded by the Religious of the Institute of the Blessed Virgin Mary. St Mary's today is a self-governing, self-financing school.

Founded in 1885, the school is set in 55 acres within easy reach of London and Heathrow and close to the M4, M3 and M25 motorways.

Numbers on roll. Boarders 350, Day pupils 16.

Age range. 11–18.

Method of Entry. 11+ and 13+ School's own examination and interview. There is a small entry at Sixth Form.

Fees per term (2008-2009). (*see Scholarship Entries section*). Boarders £8,870, Day pupils £6,310.

Curriculum. All pupils follow a broad curriculum to GCSE including Religious Education, English, History, Geography, Maths, Biology, Physics, Chemistry, French, German, Italian, Spanish, Latin, Music, Drama, Art and Design, Information Technology and Physical Education. Tuition is also available in Piano, most String and Wind Instruments, Ballet, Tap Dancing, Fencing, Speech and Drama, Ceramics and Craft activities, Tennis, Photography.

All pupils are prepared for GCSE 16+ and typically take 10 subjects.

Sixth Formers have a choice of 25 AS/A2 level subjects and normally study 5 AS subjects including Critical Thinking in the Lower Sixth year. Interview, CV and course choice preparation is offered to all Upper Sixth including Oxbridge candidates. They are encouraged to undertake some of the many extra activities on offer and develop skills outside their A level curriculum. Sixth Formers also have their own tutor who liaises closely with the Careers Specialist. Careers advice forms an integral part of the curriculum. This is supported by work experience, work shadowing placements and talks from external speakers, including Ascot Old Girls. The majority of Sixth Formers go on to university, and preparation is offered to Oxbridge candidates.

The School is a member of ISCO (Independent Schools Careers Organisation).

Religious Education is an integral part of the curriculum and the chapel holds a central position in the life of the school.

Sport. Netball, Hockey, Gym, Swimming, Rounders, Tennis and Athletics.

New purpose built sports complex with sports hall, dance studio, squash courts and fitness suite.

Art, Music, Science, Modern Languages and English. Specialist buildings are provided for all of these subjects and all pupils are encouraged to develop their musical, artistic, scientific and linguistic skills.

Libraries. State of the art library with fully integrated information technology and access to school internet.

Other Activities. Senior pupils are encouraged to participate in Community Service Projects, and those interested may enter the Duke of Edinburgh's Award Scheme. There is a wide range of club activities for all ages, and, as a termly boarding school, generous provision is made for evening and weekend activities.

Charitable status. St Mary's School Ascot is a Registered Charity, number 290286. Its aim is to provide an excellent education in a Christian atmosphere.

St Mary's School
Calne

Calne Wilts SN11 0DF
Tel: 01249 857200
Fax: 01249 857207
e-mail: office@stmaryscalne.org
website: www.stmaryscalne.org

Visitor: The Lord Bishop of Salisbury

Governors:
Miss M Falk, BA
Mrs A Ferguson, OBE, BA, FCIM
The Revd A Griggs, BA
Mr S Knight, FRICS (*Chairman*)
Professor J G Buckingham
Mr P Allen
Mrs J Chesterton-Lam
Mr M Pipes, MA, MBA, CPhys, FInstP
Mrs C Lough
Mrs V Wilson

***Headmistress*: Dr Helen Wright**, MA Oxon, MA Leics, EdD Exeter, FRSA

Deputy Head: Mrs N Botterill, NPHQ, BSc Middlesex, MA London (*and Geography*)
Director of Studies: Mrs C Strudwick, L-ès-L Sorbonne
School Chaplain: The Reverend Peter Giles
Head of Admissions: Mrs C Fitt
Head of Marketing: Mrs C Depla, MA St Andrews

Teaching Staff:
* *Head of Department*
§ *Part-time*

History:
*Miss J Milburn, BA London, MA Bristol
Mrs S-J Socha, BA Bristol
Mrs T Bazen, BA Durham
§Mrs A Thornton, BA Teesside, MEd Leeds (*and IT*)
Mr A Jukes, MA Essex

English:
*Mrs M Footman, BA Bristol
Ms J Phippard, BA Bath, MSc Bristol
§Mrs S Stables, BA Swansea, MPhil Bath
§Mrs S Lindsay, DipSpLD, CertSpLD

Drama:
*Miss L Leadbetter, BA Lancaster
Ms M Forbes, MA Leeds
Mrs R Cochrane-Patrick

LAMDA:
§Mrs P Read
§Mrs A Chater-Davies
§Mrs R Cochran-Patrick
§Mrs R Patterson

Religious Studies:
*Mr D Martin, BA Warwick
Mr Y Dho, BTh Bangor

Geography:
*Mrs S J Froggatt, BA Leeds
Mrs S Hornby, BEd Worcester College
Mrs N Botterill, NPHQ, BSc Middlesex, MA London
Miss C Sear, BSc Bristol

Government and Politics
§Mr A Jukes, MA Essex

Classics:
*Mrs E Rothwell, MA Cantab
Mrs O Hetherington, MA Cantab
Mr P Liston, MA St Andrews

French:
Mrs C Strudwick, L-ès-L Sorbonne
Mrs H Malcolm, BA York, ABSM, ARCM
§Mrs C Foley, BA Ulster
Mrs M Bennett, CEP, BEPC

German:
§Mr V Malcolm, MA Oxon, MEd Bath

Spanish:
Mr J Rueda, MA Seville, MA Lancaster
Mrs M Marca-Norris, BA Peru, BA Bristol
§Mrs R Dempster, FAETC

Italian:
Ms B Albarelli

Chinese:
Mr B Chen, BA

Japanese:
Miss Y Higashikawa, BA Kobe

Mathematics:
*Mrs M Prescott, BSc Bristol, BA Open, DipComp Open
§Mrs J Moore, BSc York
Mr G Smith, MA Auckland
Mrs E Sheridan, BSc Strathclyde

IT:
*Mr A Howard, BEd Calgary
§Mrs A Thornton, BA Teesside, MEd Leeds (*and History*)
Mr N Zelnis, BA London

Science:
*Mrs P Maitland, BSc St Andrews

Physics:
*Mr R Auckland, BSc Manchester
Dr D Pearson, BSc Glasgow, PhD Cantab

Chemistry:
*Dr G Meredith, BSc Nottingham, DPhil Nottingham
Mrs C Taylor, BSc Salford

Biology:
Mrs J McKernan, BSc Open
Mrs P Maitland, BSc St Andrews

General Science:
Mrs L Dodd, BSc Surrey

Economics:
Mr A Poole, BA UWE

Librarian: Miss C Smith, BA Northampton

Art:
*Miss S Seville, BA Keele, BA UCE
§Mrs R Spicer, BA Cambridge College of Arts & Technology, FRGS

History of Art:
§Mrs A M Lowe, BA Reading

Music:
*Mr E Whiting, BA Oxford, ARCO
Miss P M Hobson, MA Cantab, ATCL, CTABRSM (*Singing, Piano*)
Miss A Lourens, BMU Pretoria

and visiting teachers for string, brass, percussion and wind instruments.

Physical Education:
*Miss H Carruthers, BEd De Montfort
Mrs C Cochrane, BA, QTS Brighton
Mrs E M Thompson, BA, QTS Surrey
§Mrs S C Foreman, BEd Sussex
§Mrs S Hornby, BEd Worcester College
Mrs J McKenzie, BSc Philadelphia

Extra-Curricular Activities: Miss J Dickson, BA Southampton
Medical Centre: Dr P R Harris, MBChB, DRCOG, FPCert
Bursar: Mr J McCausland

St Mary's School, Calne is noted for its academic excellence and offers its 300 girls, aged 11–18, a stimulating education in an attractive, informal and supportive environment. Great emphasis is placed on pastoral care and on traditional values which complement the modern curriculum, developing successful young women for the 21st century.

The twenty-six acre site school campus provides excellent facilities, not only for teaching, but also for a wide range of extra-curricular evening and weekend activities. Drama, Music, Art and Sport are strongly represented and the school has its own purpose-built theatre.

Small class sizes allow the highly-qualified teaching staff to focus on the needs of the individual and girls consistently achieve superb results in public examinations. All go on to higher education, with a good number each year successfully applying to Oxbridge. Around 16 subjects are offered at GCSE, while Sixth Formers have access to over 23 A Levels.

In 2007 at GCSE level, 82% of girls achieved grades A or A* in all their examinations, usually sitting between nine and eleven different subjects. At A Level, 75% of girls achieved A grades, with 60% achieving A grades in three or more subjects.

Anyone interested in learning more about St Mary's or wishing to receive a prospectus should contact the Admissions Department (Tel: 01249 857206, e-mail: admissions@stmaryscalne.org, Fax: 01249 857207).

Fees per term (2008-2009). Boarding £8,800, Day £6,300.

Scholarships. (*see Scholarship Entries section*).

St Margaret's Preparatory School. The co-educational day preparatory school is situated within St Mary's grounds and shares St Mary's School's excellent facilities. Tel: 01249 857220. Fax: 01249 857227. (*For further details, see entry in IAPS section.*)

Charitable status. St Mary's School (Calne) is a Registered Charity, number 309482 and exists for the education of children.

St Mary's School
Cambridge

Bateman Street Cambridge CB2 1LY
Tel: 01223 353253 Headmistress and School Office
Fax: 01223 357451
e-mail: enquiries@stmaryscambridge.co.uk
website: www.stmaryscambridge.co.uk

Founded in 1898 by the Religious Order of the Institute of the Blessed Virgin Mary (IBVM), St Mary's School today is an independent Catholic Day and Boarding School, located close to the centre of Cambridge, in its own grounds next to the beautiful University Botanic Gardens. The school maintains a strong Catholic tradition and ethos but welcomes girls of any creed or denomination, or none.

Governing Body:
Chairman: Mrs D Wilkinson

Mr S Anderson	Sr J Livesey, CJ
Mrs J Bates	Mr R Pearce-Gould
Mr P Chamberlain	Fr A Rogers
Mrs L Fairbrother	Sr H Sommer, CJ
Mr C Smart	Mrs P Walkinshaw
Mrs A Hickling	Mr J Woodhouse

Clerk to the Governors and Bursar: Mr D Askew

***Headmistress*: Miss Charlotte Avery**, MA Oxon

Deputy Head (Pastoral): Dr A Jackson, PhD Liverpool (*Chemistry*)
Deputy Head (Curriculum): Mr P Mitchell, BSc Newcastle (*Mathematics*)

Teaching Staff:
Mr R Atkinson, BSc London (*Chemistry*)
Dr T Bellamy, BSc, MSc, PhD London (*Chemistry*)
Mr D Bennett, BA Cantab, MA Cantab (*Theology*)
Mrs J Bevan, Dip Art Leicester (*Ceramics, Art*)
Mrs V Bevan, BA Hons Australia (*EFL*)
Dr JM Bock, DPhil York, BSc York, CPsych, QTS (*Psychology*)
Miss C Bowie, BA Sterling (*French*)
Mrs M Brown, MA St Andrews (*History*)
Mrs S Brown, MA Oxon (*Mathematics*)
Mrs A Chatterjee, PGCE London, BSc Hons London (*Biology*)
Mrs K Cicero (*EFL*)
Mrs A Clark, BSc Swansea (*Mathematics*)
Mrs G Clifford, BA Winchester, PGCE Middlesex (*Art & Design*)
Miss C Cooksey, BA Leeds, MSc Aston (*Italian, School Librarian*)
Ms J Cowan, BA Hons Cantab (*Geography*)
Mrs R d'Armada, BSc Manchester (*Mathematics*)
Mrs K Dodsworth, MA Lampeter (*Theology*)
Mrs J Drew, BA Durham (*English*)
Miss J Earley, BA Northampton (*Physical Education*)
Mrs J Emmans, BA Hons West Surrey College of Art and Design, PGCE London (*Art & Design*)
Mr P Fanourakis, BSc Dundee, MSc Cantab, PGCE De Montfort (*Mathematics*)
Miss A Fleming, BA Liverpool, MEd (*Religious Education*)

Mrs L Fleming, BA Kent, PGCE De Montfort (*Physical Education*)
Mrs J Francis, Lic-ès-Lettres Bordeaux (*French*)
Mrs W Galloway, BSc Sussex (*Science*)
Mrs H Garrett, MA Oxon (*English*)
Mrs S Gears, BA Hons Durham (*Director of Music*)
Mrs A George, BA London, PGCE London (*History, Head of Boarding*)
Dr C Goddard, MA Oxon, PhD Cantab (*Classics*)
Miss J Gregg, BA West Sussex Inst (*Physical Education*)
Mrs E Hall, BSc Hons UMIST (*Mathematics*)
Miss K Hall, BA Cantab (*Mathematics*)
Mrs F Hawken, CertEd Sheffield (*Physical Education*)
Mr J Hunnable, BA Hons Cantab (*Classics*)
Miss E Hunt, BSc Canberra (*Physical Education*)
Dr A Jackson, PhD Liverpool (*Chemistry, Deputy Head Pastoral*)
Mrs H Jackson, BEd Nottingham (*Textiles*)
Mrs M Jackson, BEd Newcastle (*English*)
Mr F Jeans, Dip Art & Design London (*Art & Design*)
Miss S Jones, BA Hons Anglia Ruskin University, PGCE Cantab (*Drama*)
Miss S Josiffe, BEd Bedford (*Physical Education*)
Ms C Klimaszewska, CertEd Homerton, MIBiol, CBiol (*Science*)
Mrs A Ladds, BEd London (*Textiles*)
Mrs D Larman, BA London (*English*)
Miss N Lees, BA Hons Oxon (*Spanish*)
Mrs S Leighton-Scott, BA Univ of Wales (*Geography*)
Miss E Levy, BA Hons Cantab (*Music*)
Mr P Mallabone, BA Hons St Mary's College (*Religious Education*)
Mrs H Marmion, BA Hons Exeter (*German*)
Mrs R McGuinness, BEng Portsmouth (*IT*)
Mrs Y McPartland, BA Hons York (*Business Studies*)
Dr G Miller, PhD Birmingham, BSc Manchester (*Physics*)
Mr P Mitchell, BSc Newcastle upon Tyne (*Mathematics, Deputy Head Curriculum*)
Mrs J Munday, Lic-ès-Lettres Sorbonne (*French*)
Mrs P Nicholson, BA Liverpool (*Economics & Business Studies*)
Mr R Peachey, BA Hons Oxon, PGCE Oxon (*Theatre Studies, Drama, English*)
Mrs C Priest, MA Cantab, PGCE Cambridge (*Biology, Chemistry, Science*)
Mrs K Ratcliffe, BSc Natal, S Africa, MSc London (*Biology*)
Mr P Richards, BA, MA Nottingham (*History*)
Mrs T Shercliff, MA Cantab (*Science, Physics*)
Miss F Spore, MA Cantab (*Geography*)
Mrs S Watling, MA SSSD, LLAM, LAMDA (*Drama*)
Mrs C Williams, BSc St Andrews (*Chemistry*)
Mrs A Wilson, BA Surrey (*IT*)

School Doctor:
Nursing Staff: Mrs C Green, Mrs F Myers, Mrs M Brightwell

Boarding Staff:
Mrs A George (*Head of Boarding*)
Mrs K Wayman (*Senior Housemistress, Pastoral*)
Mrs F Dolan (*House Matron*)
Miss C Clark (*Boarding Assistant*)
Miss A Whitehouse (*Housemistress*)
Miss A Duncan (*Gap Student*)

Visiting Staff:
Mr Q Benziger (*Piano, Organ*)
Mrs L Britton (*Piano*)
Mr P Britton (*Piano*)
Ms Julie Burrows (*Violin*)
Mrs A Bury (*Flute, Clarinet*)
Mr D Carter (*Clarinet, Guitar*)
Ms A Daniels (*Singing*)
Miss S Hill (*Flute*)
Mrs H Hymas (*Oboe*)
Mr J Landymore (*Saxophone*)
Mrs A MacKenzie-Mills (*Singing*)
Ms E Nallen (*Recorder*)
Ms G Oldham (*Cello*)
Ms R Platts (*Harp*)
Miss E Reeves (*Flute*)
Mr C Rutherford (*Trombone*)
Mrs R Stekly (*Speech & Drama*)
Mrs G Sutcliffe (*Violin*)
Ms J Burrows (*Violin, String Quartet*)
Mr A Vellacott (*Drums*)
Mrs K Weber (*Speech & Drama*)

Administrative Staff:
Head's PA: Mrs P Vallins
School Secretary: Mrs J Bauld
Registrar: Mrs A Cornell
Accountant: Mrs M Brown
Finance Assistant: Mrs S Couch
Accounts Secretary: Mrs J Doe
Careers Secretary: Mrs P Down
Marketing Manager: Miss S Longfield, BA Hons Oxon, CIM Dip
Marketing & Admissions Officer: Miss K Rigby
Reprographics: Mrs S Law
Receptionist: Mrs C Turner, Mrs D Stutely
Domestic Bursar: Mrs S Heath
Catering Manager: Mrs S Greenaway
Health and Safety Manager: Mr P Woods
IT (Systems) Manager: Mr D Fox
Senior IT Technician: Mrs A Earl, BA Hons London
IT Support Administrator: Miss E Stephenson, BA Hons Cambridge
Laboratory Technicians:
Mrs M Crammond, MIEH
Dr B Degnan
Miss K Lowbridge
Mrs E Miller
Art Technician: Miss J Debenham
Site Maintenance: Mr E Knight, Mr N French

Admission. The school's own entrance examination at 11+ and 13+. A few vacancies occur at other ages. Sixth Form entry is by examination and interview, conditional on 5 GCSE passes at A*–C, with B grade or more in those subjects to be chosen for A level.

Extra Subjects. Piano and Instrumental Music, Speech and Drama, and Dance.

Fees per term (2008-2009). Day Girls £3,875; Weekly boarding £6,825 inclusive; Full boarding £7,770 inclusive.

Scholarships. Academic, Music, Art, Drama, and Sport Scholarships are offered at 11+, 13+ and 16+.

Curriculum. Within the setting of a Christian community the school provides an 'all-round' education, enabling each girl to realise her full potential. Students are prepared for GCSE, A Level, Oxbridge Entrance, and for other forms of higher education and professional training in a wide variety of careers. The curriculum includes Religious Education, English, History, Geography, Latin, French, German, Spanish, Mathematics, ICT, Physics, Chemistry, Biology, Art and Design, Textiles, Theatre Studies, Music, Drama, PE and Games. Option schemes in Year 10 are arranged in such a way that each girl has a balanced programme without premature specialisation. In the Lower Sixth, students choose 4 or 5 subjects to study, making their choice from a total of 23 subjects. In the Upper Sixth, students continue their study of 3 or 4 subjects to A2 Level. All Sixth Formers follow a course of General Studies and have an enrichment programme.

The School stands in its own grounds, close to the centre of Cambridge and adjoining the University Botanic Gardens. The complex of buildings contains Science laboratories, assembly halls, gymnasium, library, specialist rooms for Geography, Music, IT, Art and Textiles Technology.

Sixth Form Centre. A Sixth Form Centre in a separate building provides an exclusive study facility with integral university reference/careers library and neighbouring work room with fully-networked computer suite, as well as common rooms and changing rooms.

Extra-Curricular Activities. The school provides a wide range of activities at lunch-times and after school – everything from Dance to Rowing and Arts Award, to The Duke of Edinburgh's Award Scheme and Young Enterprise Company.

Supervised Homework Club. Homework Club is available from 4–6 pm Monday–Thursday.

Boarding. We offer full as well as weekly boarding to pupils age 13+. All girls in Year 10 and above have attractive single study-bedrooms with internet access, whilst younger boarders share comfortable bedrooms (2–4 girls per room). Our weekly boarding facility is popular with both students and their parents as it offers the best of both worlds at school and at home.

Charitable status. St Mary's School, Cambridge is a Registered Charity, number 290180. It aims to promote and provide for the advancement of the education of children of any creed but particularly of the Roman Catholic faith.

St Mary's School
Colchester

Lexden Road Colchester Essex CO3 3RB
Tel: 01206 572544
Fax: 01206 576437
e-mail: info@stmaryscolchester.org.uk
website: www.stmaryscolchester.org.uk

Board of Governors:
Chairman: Mrs J Kimmance
Ms H Borgartz
Mr R V Borgartz
Mr A Brown
Mrs K Burns
Dr S Davidson
Mrs S Foakes
Mrs S Heath-Brook
Mrs J Jones
Mrs M Livingstone
Mrs S Masters

***Principal*: Mrs H Vipond**, BSc Hons Leeds, MEd Hatfield, NPQH

Vice-Principal, Senior School: Mrs A Mullen, BEd Portsmouth

Staff:
Mr C Baalham, BEd Homerton, MSc Essex
Mr M J Barrett, CertEd S E Essex
Mr E W Black, BA Oxon, MA Keele
Ms G Boardman, BA Southampton
Ms D Booth, BA Middlesex, MA Goldsmiths
Mrs G Boyd, DipEd Moray House
Mr P Burgoyne, BEd Anglia
Mrs A Bush, BEd Anglia
Miss F Clark, BEd Edgehill
Mrs H Clayton-Grainger, BA Lancaster
Mrs K Daines, CertEd Walsall, DipEdSpN Cantab
Mrs J Godfrey, CertEd Whitelands
Mrs V Hall, BSc Essex
Mr J Hammersley, BA East Anglia
Mrs R Harries, BA London
Mrs D Hart, DipEd Bingley
Mrs A Heather, BA Coventry
Mrs J Johnson, BEd Brighton
Mrs C Kurzynski, BEd Anglia
Mrs J Lindsey-Smith, BA Sheffield
Mrs M Loughhead, CertEd Edge Hill
Mrs K Margery, CertEd Eaton Hall
Mrs J Maydon, BEd Leicester
Mrs V Nicholson, BEd Anglia
Mrs J Nield, BEd London
Mrs S Oakley, CertEd Newcastle
Mrs C J Parry-Jones, CertEd CNAA, FETC
Mrs L M Pendle, CertEd Cambridge
Mrs C Pettman, CertEd Nonington
Mrs S Priestley, BA Keele
Mrs H Pritchard, BA Dunelm
Mr C A Ritson, BSc London, MSc UMIST, MInstPh
Mrs R Robinson, BA Newcastle
Mrs D Rose, BEd Doncaster
Miss L Sandu, BSc Bucharest, DipBio Bucharest
Mr J A Saunders, BA Wales
Ms K Saunders, BA UCL
Mr M Shah, BSc LSE
Mrs E Stanhope, GMus Colchester
Mrs S J Sutton, CertEd Sarum
Mrs L Taverner, CertEd Bedford
Mrs C Thompson, BA Leeds
Mrs L Tilly, BA Stirling
Mr N West, BA Griffith, Brisbane
Mrs L Whitehead, CertEd Bretton Hall
Mrs S Wilding, BA Glamorgan

Visiting Staff:
Mrs M Blanchard, BA CNAA, LTCL (*Flute*)
Mrs F Hill, BA Mus Essex, LGSM, LTCL (*Woodwind*)
Mr A Johnson, BMus (*Guitar*)
Mr C Matthews, LLCM, CertMusicEd, TCL (*Brass*)
Mr T Parr, CertMus CNAA, LTCL (*Piano, Singing*)
Ms C Simmons, LRAM (*Violin*)

Bursar: Mr S Cooke

Finance Manager: Miss A Walker

St Mary's is a day school for girls, founded in 1908, which currently has 500 pupils between the ages of 4 and 17.

The Senior School in Lexden Road is light and airy, and equipped with specialist teaching rooms including four laboratories, a Home Economics room, a Library and a careers information centre. Provision for physical education includes a gymnasium, tennis and netball courts, and a heated open-air swimming pool. These facilities are supplemented by the use of the local Sports Centre and playing fields.

A building programme, including a Performing Arts Studio, Music and Textiles facilities, new Art and Geography suites and two ICT suites, has recently been completed.

The Lower School is housed in nearby Stanway and is set in grounds of nine acres, with tennis and netball courts, sports field, adventure playground and nature trail.

Throughout the school each girl is encouraged to develop her personality and academic potential as fully as possible, and a broad-based curriculum is followed until Year 10, when a little more specialisation is necessary, to cater for GCSE courses. The forms are not streamed: setting is arranged as necessary. Optional extras include lessons in woodwind, brass, strings, piano, guitar and percussion instruments.

Lower School pupils are prepared for the 11+ examinations; Seniors are prepared for GCSEs.

Clubs and Societies meet in the lunch hour and after school, and music and the creative arts are encouraged.

Entry is by written assessment and interview.

The school prospectus will be sent on request and parents are always welcome at the school by appointment with the Principal.

Fees per term (from April 2008). Senior School: £2,870; Lower School: £1,450–£2,625.

Charitable status. St Mary's School (Colchester) Limited is a Registered Charity, number 309266. Its aims and objectives are to promote and provide for the advancement of education, and in connection therewith to conduct, carry on, acquire and develop, in the UK and elsewhere, any day or boarding school(s) for the education of children.

St Mary's School
Gerrards Cross

Gerrards Cross Buckinghamshire SL9 8JQ
Tel: 01753 883370
Fax: 01753 890966
e-mail: registrar@st-marys.bucks.sch.uk
website: www.stmarysschool.co.uk

Badge: *Ecce Ancilla Domini*

Founded by Dean Butler in 1872. Formerly at Lancaster Gate. Established in Gerrards Cross in 1937 as an Independent Day School catering for 320 day girls.

Governors:
Chairman: Mr D R Wilson, BA, FCA
Mr R J Burge
Mrs C Eilerts de Haan, MSc ChemTech Ingenieur, PGCE
Mr J R M Hanney
Mrs P Hurd, NDD, ATC
Mr J Loarridge, OBE, RD, BA
Prof S Machin, MBChB, FRCP, FRCPath
Mr N Moss
Mrs H Phillips, FCA

Bursar: Mrs J Wilson, MBA

Staff:

***Headmistress*: Mrs F A Balcombe**, BA Hons Southampton, PGCE, FRSA (*English*)

Deputy Headmistress: Dr J Ramsden, PhD, MSc UAE, BSc Hons Nottingham (*Physics*)

Middle School Tutor: Miss J H Miles, CertEd (*Mathematics*)
Upper School Tutor: Mrs S Vaughan, MA Oxford, PGCE (*Physics*)
Sixth Form Tutor: Mrs E Persaud, BA Hons Leicester, PGCE (*History, Careers*)

Senior School:
Miss S J Abbott, BA Hons Durham, PGCE (*Music*)
Miss F Alexander, BA Glasgow School of Art (*Art & Design*)
Mrs K Andrew, BEd Hons Reading, PGCE (*English*)
Mrs I Barrett, BSc Hons UMIST (*Mathematics, Information Technology*)
Mrs P Baggott, BPharm Hons Bradford, PGCE (*Science*)
Mrs J Cannon, BA Hons Newcastle, PGCE (*Spanish and French*)
Mrs M Christensen, Masters Law Nice, PGCE (*French*)
Mrs N Cooke, BSc Cardiff (*Biology, Chemistry*)
Mrs V Culmer, BA Hons Oxon, PGCE (*Drama*)
Mrs J Deadman, BEd Hons Exeter, PGCE (*Physical Education*)
Mrs J Dowling, HNC Microbiology (*Laboratory Technician*)
Mrs C Gandy, BA Hons Exeter, DipEd (*Geography*)
Mrs J V Giorgi, BA Hons Swansea, PGCE (*Geography*)
Mrs A Hadwin, BA Hons Oxford (*Religious Education*)
Mrs M A Hall, MA Hons Cantab (*ICT Technician*)
Mrs J E Halls, MA Oxon, PGCE (*Biology*)
Miss T Hancock, HND Music/Theatre (*Speech & Drama*)
Mrs K B Hills, BA Hons Bristol, PGCE (*Italian/German/ French/Latin*)
Mrs S Jones, MA Childrens Literature, BA Hons Reading, PGCE (*English*)
Mrs J L Kingston, BSc Hons Cardiff, MPhil Bath, PGCE (*Chemistry, Science*)
Mrs A MacDonald, BSc Strathclyde, PGCE
Mrs S Moore, BEd Sussex (*Physical Education*)
Mrs A Morrison, TCert Auckland, New Zealand (*Design Technology, Numeracy*)
Mrs G Newman, GRSC Chemistry (*Laboratory Technician*)
Mrs J Richards, CertEd Bath (*Home Economics*)
Mrs M Schwartz, BA Hons Leeds, PGCE (*Learning Support*)
Mrs C Stuart-Lee, MA Oxon, PGCE (*Learning Support Coordinator*)
Mr C Tucker, MA Oxon (*Mathematics*)
Mr J Walker, MSc London (*Information Technology*)
Mrs L Winter, BA Hons Nottingham, MBA (*Business Studies and Economics*)

Junior School:
Head of Department: Mrs A Maycock, BEd Hons Kingston (*General Subjects*)

Mrs S Brereton, BSc Leicester (*Combined Science*)
Mrs E Cook, BEd Hons Reading (*General Subjects, French*)
Mrs R Galustian, BEd Hons Brunel, PGCE (*General Subjects and Religious Education*)
Miss K Gilliland, BEd PrimEd QTSde Montfort (*Physical Education*)
Mrs C Hargadon, BEd University of London Inst of Ed (*General Subjects, French*)
Mrs C Hyett, PPA Dip (*Nursery Assistant, Paediatric First Aider*)
Mrs S Jenkins (*General Assistant, First Aider*)
Miss S Johnston, BA Ed Hons Exeter (*Maths, Design Technology*)
Mrs J Lukas, NNEB Cert (*Art, Nursery Teacher*)
Mrs H Mackinder, BA Hons PrimEd QTS Brighton (*General Subjects*)
Miss S Millar, NNEB (*Nursery Assistant*)
Mrs G Pierozynski, GRNCM, ARNCM, PGCE (*Music*)
Mrs J Redman, BA Hons (*General Subjects*)
Mrs J C Stone, BSc Hons Leicester, PGCE (*Science*)
Mrs C Wilson, ONC RSA, DipSpLD (*Learning Support*)

Visiting Staff:
Mr R Corden, ARCM, AI Kneller Hall (*Flute, Clarinet, Saxophone*)
Miss J Edworthy, GMus Hons RNCM (*Singing*)
Miss R Galustian, BACP (*School Counsellor*)
Miss K Harding, MA Hons, MPhil Cantab, LTCL (*Cello, Double Bass*)
Mrs J Holmes, BMus Hons, LRAM (*Piano*)
Mr J Keen, MIT (*Drumkit*)
Mrs J Miller, AISTD (*Ballet, Tap, General Dance*)
Miss J Stevenson, AGSM (*Singing*)
Mrs T Suggett, BA Hons Guildhall, PGDip Dist (*Singing*)
Mrs R Wheeler, ALCM, CT ABRSM (*Piano*)

Registrar & Headmistress's Secretary: Mrs C Pearcey

The School is situated in the attractive residential area of Gerrards Cross which is surrounded by beautiful countryside, 20 miles from London, close to the M25 and A40/M40, on the main bus routes and 10 minutes from the Railway Station.

The aim of the School is to provide an excellent academic and rounded education leading on to University for day girls between the ages of 3 and 18 and to enable each of them to develop their own talents and personalities in a happy, caring and disciplined environment, and to become successful, fulfilled young women.

Curriculum. Subjects offered include English Language and Literature, History, Geography, RE, Drama, Latin, French,

German, Spanish, Italian, Business Studies, Information Technology, Mathematics, Chemistry, Biology, Physics, Music, Art, Home Economics, Key Skills, Gymnastics, Hockey, Netball, Tennis, Rounders, Football, Rugby, Swimming, Media, Health and Social Care, Dancing and other sporting activities. Regular trips are made to places of educational interest, field courses are undertaken, foreign visits including a ski trip to the USA are arranged, and there is highly successful participation in The Duke of Edinburgh's Award Scheme and Young Enterprise. There is an excellent staff/pupil ratio.

Examinations. Girls are prepared for Entrance to the Universities and Colleges in all subjects; for the General Certificate of Education at AS, A2 and GCSE Level; RSA CLAIT Examinations, Associated Board Examinations in Music and examinations in Speech and Drama. Standardised tests are set at regular intervals in Junior House.

The Buildings are an attractive mixture of old and new and include 2 Libraries, Dining Hall, a Science Block with Laboratories and a Geography Room, a large open-plan Art Studio, a Home Economics Room, Textiles Room, 2 Computer Suites, a modern Sixth Form Centre, 2 Music Rooms, Drama Studio, Chapel and 2 Assembly Halls/Gymnasiums equipped to the highest standards. Junior House, in the grounds of the Senior House comprises a Nursery and two modern purpose-built blocks, with a Science Laboratory, Hall, Gymnasium and ICT suite. The lovely grounds include tennis and netball courts, a hockey pitch and an athletics lawn.

School Hours. The hours are 8.30 am – 3.40 pm. The School year is divided into 3 terms.

Reports. Full School Reports are sent to Parents at the end of each term and there are regular Parent/Staff meetings. The School also communicates with Parents via ParentMail.

Fees per term (2008-2009). £1,065–£3,825.

Scholarships are available at 7+, 11+ (including one for Music) and at 16+ in the Sixth Form. A means-tested Bursary scheme is in operation.

Charitable status. St Mary's School (Gerrards Cross) Limited is a Registered Charity, number 310634. It provides education for girls from Nursery to A level in a well-structured, academic and caring environment.

St Mary's School
Shaftesbury

Shaftesbury Dorset SP7 9LP
Tel: 01747 854005 Head and Admissions
01747 852416 School and Administration
01747 851188 Bursar's Office
Fax: 01747 851557
e-mail: admin@st-marys-shaftesbury.co.uk
website: www.st-marys-shaftesbury.co.uk

Governors:
Mrs J Dallyn, LLB (*Chair*)
Viscountess Asquith
Col R J M Carson, OBE
Mr M Catchpole
The Rt Hon Iain Duncan-Smith, MP
Mrs L Eeles
Vice-Admiral M P Gretton, CB, MA, FNI
Sister Jane Livesey, CJ, MA Cantab
Dr A-M May
Mr C C McCann
Miss J Taylor, BSc
Viscountess Asquith
Mrs B Quest-Ritson

***Head*: Mr R James**, BMus Hons London, ARCM (*Music*)

Deputy Head: Mrs S Raffray, BA Hons Manchester, MA Salford, PGCE Manchester, NPQH (*English, Religious Education & Faith Development*)
Bursar: Mr N M Peters, ACIB
Director of Studies: Mr D Cohen, BA Hons Aberystwyth (*English*)
Head of Boarding: Mrs A Salmon, CertEd Strawberry Hill (*Physical Education, Religious Education, PSE, Housemistress*)
Registrar: Miss J Walker, BEd Hons Sussex (*PSE, Physical Education, Senior Teacher*)
Chaplain: Miss A Le Guevel, BA Hons Dubliin, PGCE London, MA Paris, MPhil Manchester
Resident Priest: The Revd Andrew Moore

Teaching Staff:
Mrs M Andow, BA Hons Southampton (*History, Head of Senior School*)
Mrs S Barton, BA Hons North Staffs Polytechnic, PGCE Brighton
Mrs K Booth, CertEd Bedford College (*PE*)
Mrs J Bowe, BA Hons Lancaster, PGCE Manchester Metropolitan (*Head of Religious Education & Faith Development*)
Miss N Boyer, BSc Hons Cheltenham & Gloucester College, PGCE (*Head of PE*)
Mrs S Bramble, BA Hons Chester (*Geography*)
Ms R M R Brand, BA Hons Wales, MA Warwick, PGCE Lancaster (*Head of English, Drama*)
Mrs E Butterworth, BA Open (*History of Art*)
Dr G M Caunt, PhD, BSc Hons, PGCE (*Biology*)
Mrs D Clark, BA Hons London (*Classic, Careers, Examination Officer*)
Mrs G Cork, BA Hons Lancaster Polytechnic, PGCE Southampton (*French, Head of Middle School*)
Mr P Daley, BA Hons Exeter, Master of Studies in Latin Oxford, PGCE Secondary Classics King's College London (*Head of Classics*)
Mr P Davies, BA Joint Hons, MA Bristol, PGCE Leeds (*Head of Geography*)
Mrs R Davies, BA Hons Bristol (*Support Teaching Coordinator*)
Mrs C Drew, BSc Hons Open, PGCE (*Chemistry, ICT*)
Mrs V Emery, MSc Hons London, PGCE Bath (*Geography*)
Miss S Flower, BSc King's College London, PGCE Bath (*Biology*)
Mr T Goodwin, MA Oxon (*Head of History, Religious Education*)
Mrs G Götke, BA Hons London (*Spanish, French, Italian*)
Mrs J Hall, BSc Hons Open, CertEd Exeter (*Mathematics, ICT*)
Mrs A Hannam (*Art Technician*)
Mrs S Holdaway, BA Hons Wales, PGCE Wales (*English, RE and Faith Development*)
Mrs S Holman, DipAD Wimbledon (*Housemistress, Speech & Drama, PSE*)
Mrs D Kok, BSc, PGCE (*Mathematics, Physics*)
Mrs C Lane, BA Hons London, MA East Anglia, PGCE London (*Head of Sixth Form, Careers, Business Studies, Religious Education*)
Mrs A Lodder, BA Hons, PGCE (*German, French*)
Mrs A Maclaine, MA Hons Edinburgh, PGCE Craiglockhart (*Head of Modern Languages, RE*)
Mrs C Norton, BA Hons Liverpool, PGCE London (*English, Multiple Intelligences/G&T Coordinator*)
Mr J O'Hare (*Mathematics*)
Mrs S Pugh, BA Hons (*Head of Instrumental Music, Oboe/Recorder*)
Miss D Radford, FLCM, ARCM, LGSM, LLCM (*Director of Music*)
Mrs M Reddyhoff (*Business Studies, Duke of Edinburgh's Award Scheme*)

Mrs J A Ridgway, BA Hons Loughborough (*Head of Art & Design*)
Mr P Rigby, BSc Hons St Andrews, PGCE Cambridge (*Head of Science, Physics*)
Mrs J L Rose (*Assistant Lab Technician*)
Mr A Rowden, BA Hons London (*Mathematics*)
Mrs F M Rowland, BA Hons London, PGCE Southampton (*French, Housemistress*)
Mr J Rowland, CertEd St Paul's Cheltenham, DPE (*Art, Design, Photography*)
Mrs V Rushton, BSc Hons Liverpool (*Biology*)
Mr J Singleton, BSc Hons London, PGCE Southampton (*Webmaster*)
Mrs R Smith, BSc Hons London (*Head of Mathematics*)
Mrs T Spottiswood, BA Hons University of East Anglia, PGCE Open (*Housemistress*)
Mrs D Sudlow, CertEd Bristol Polytechnic (*Art, Design*)
Mr C J Sykes, BA Hons Dartington, PGCE Bretton Hall (*Drama, English*)
Mrs J Tidbury-Coates (*Art Technician*)
Mrs C Waddington (*EFL, Portugese*)
Mrs D Webb, BA UWE, PGCE Manchester (*French, Spanish, Housemistress*)
Miss S Williams, BSc Hons Open (*Flute, Psychology*)

Junior School:
Head: Mrs H Key, BA Hons Liverpool, PGCE Open
Mrs E Brown
Mrs S Holman, DipAD Wimbledon
Mrs J May-Laybourne (*Learning Support Assistant*)
Librarian: Ms S Walker, BA Hons Aberystwyth, PGCE Goldsmiths, DipLIB ALA, MCILIP

Nursing Staff:
Mrs S Savage, RN (*Head of Nursing*)
Mrs J Lewis, RN
Mrs A Lyons RN
Mrs P Ross-Hurst, RN
Mrs K Webber, RN

Administration:
Headmistress's PA: Mrs J Sampson
Assistant to the Registrar: Mrs S Awdry
Registration Secretary: Mrs K Day
Bursar's Assistant: Mrs P Bartram
Domestic Bursar: Mrs L Jones
School Office: Miss L Coffin
Accounts & Human Resources Bursar: Mrs M Gordon
Accounts Assistant: Miss D Williams
Accounts Assistant: Mr A Gordon
Database Manager: Mr C Norman
ICT Technician: Mr J Davies, BSc Hons Plymouth
Network Manager: Mr J Pearce, BSc Hons UWE Bristol
ICT Technician: Mr M Wollaston
School Office Evenings & Weekends: Mrs E O'Sullivan
Caretaker: Mr R A Pitman
Head Groundsman: Mr F King

Visiting Staff:
Mrs K Alder, BSc Bristol, LRSM (*Piano*)
Mrs D Binnington, GRSM, LRAM, ARCM, LTCL (*Piano, Voice*)
Mrs J Brookfield, BAPA (*Flute, piano*)
Mrs A Caunce, GRSM, LTCL, ARCM (*Piano*)
Mrs V Cross, LGSM, (*Singing*)
Mr J Gilbert (*Percussion*)
Mrs K Hawes, Julliard School, New York (*Violin*)
Mr W Hawes, LRAM (*Brass*)
Mr P Lester-Shaw, Dip Light Music Leeds (*Saxophone*)
Miss S Lockyer, GRSM, LRAM (*Clarinet, Saxophone*)
Mr S Lockyer, GRSM, LRAM (*Cello, Double Bass*)
Mrs L Lowndes-Northcott, BMus, LRAM (*Harp, Viola*)
Mr C Mahon, BA, ARCO, LRAM (*Pipe organ*)
Miss M Marton (*Singing*)
Mr D Mayo (*Acoustic, Electric Guitar*)
Mrs W Partridge, LTCL (*Classicial Guitar*)
Mrs F Riley, LTCL (*Flute*)
Mrs K Sheppard, ARCM (*Horn*)
Miss E Tolfree, BA Hons, LTCL MusEd, MA PsychEd London (*Clarinet, Saxophone, Bassoon*)

Founded in 1945, St Mary's School, Shaftesbury is an Independent Roman Catholic Boarding and Day School for girls administered by the Religious of the Congregation of Jesus, together with a Governing Body. It is situated on the A30 just outside Shaftesbury and stands in its own grounds of 55 acres.

Numbers on Roll. 316 Girls (two-thirds boarders, one-third day).

Age Range. 9–18 years.

Admission. (*see Scholarship Entries section*). The School has its own Entrance Examination, held in January, for 9+, 10+, 11+, 12+ and 13+ entry. Sixth Form entry is by testimonial and interview and is then conditional on 5 GCSE passes.

Fees per term (2008-2009). Boarders: £6,910 (9+–10+); £7,260 (11+–18). Day Girls: £4,750 (9+–10+); £4,990 (11+–18).

Aims and Curriculum. The School aims to give girls as broad an education, both spiritual, personal, academic and extra-curricular, as possible, thus enabling each girl to realise her own strengths in the various areas and build on them. Religious education is an integral part of the curriculum throughout the School. During Years 7–9 all girls follow a common curriculum which includes Religious Education, English, History, Geography, French, Latin, Mathematics, Information Technology, Science, Art, Textiles, Music, Singing, PSE and PE. From Year 10 both the core curriculum (RE, English Language and Literature, Mathematics, One Modern Foreign Language and either Single Sciences or Double Award Science) and options are arranged to ensure that each girl follows a balanced course suitable to her ability and interests.

The majority of girls remain for A Levels for which they have a choice of 22. The Sixth Form curriculum also includes RE, Information Technology, Desk Top Publishing, Current Affairs and PE.

The School is a member of ISCO (Independent Schools Careers Organisation) and all girls receive individual careers advice from the Head of Careers. All girls go on to some form of Higher Education and the majority to University.

Music. The Music Department is large and any orchestral instrument may be learned. In addition there are three school choirs, a chamber choir, orchestra and various instrumental ensembles. A new music block was opened in Summer 2003.

Sport. Winter: Netball, hockey, swimming and dance. Summer: Swimming, tennis, rounders, athletics. The School has its own Sports Hall, floodlit Astroturf and a 25m six-lane indoor swimming pool opened in 2006.

Extra subjects or activities. Speech and drama, ballet, riding, polo, tennis coaching, Duke of Edinburgh's Award, photography and a wide range of other Societies.

Charitable status. St Mary's School Shaftesbury Trust is a Registered Charity, number 292845. Its aims and objectives are to administer an independent Roman Catholic school for the education of children of any Christian denomination.

St Mary's
Worcester

Mount Battenhall Worcester WR5 2HP
Tel: 01905 357786
Fax: 01905 351718
e-mail: head@stmarys.org.uk
website: www.stmarys.org.uk

Independent Day School for girls (aged 0 to 18) and boys (aged 0 to 7).

Bursar and Clerk to the Trustees: Miss L Breeze, FCCA

***Headmistress*: Mrs S K Cookson**, BEd Hons, CertEd, Cert SpLD

Deputy Head: Mrs C Howe, BA Hons, PGCE
Head of Preparatory School: Mrs M Baker, BA Hons, PGCE

Mrs V Adams, BA Hons, MA, PGCE
Mrs E Amos, BSc Hons, PGCE
Ms J Bell, BSc Hons
Mrs M Burnham, MEd, ARCM, LTCL
Miss G Cleary, BA Hons, PGCE
Miss L Cooke, BSc Hons
Mrs J Davis, BSc Hons, PGCE
Mrs C Flannigan, BA Hons, PGCE
Mrs J Glazzard, CertEd
Miss A Hepplewhite, BSc Hons
Mr A Howe, BSc Hons, PGCE
Mrs T Howell, BSc Hons, PGCE
Mrs F Hudson, BA, LTCL, PGCE
Mrs J Hunt, BA Hons, PGCE
Miss R Lewis, BA, MA, PGCE
Miss C Ludlow, BSc, MSc, PGCE
Miss D Mahony, BA Hons, PGCE
Mr J McCumisky, BA, MA, QTS
Mrs M McCumisky, BA Hons, PGCE
Mrs S Parry, BA Hons, PGCE, LTCL
Mrs T Penny, BA Hons
Mrs S Reid, BA Hons, PGCE
Mrs S Ridge, BA Hons, QTS
Mrs M Robinson, BA Hons
Mrs C Rodgman, BEd Hons
Mrs E Stirling, BSc Hons
Mr G Stokes, BSc Hons, PGCE
Mrs N Thomas, BA Hons, MA, PGCE
Miss E Tyler, BA, MA, PGCE
Mrs J Von Anrep, BEd
Mrs B Woolley, BA Hons

Head of Early Years:
Mrs P Lowesmith, Montessori Early Years CertEd, Montessori SEN CertEd, HND Early Childhood Studies, NSPCC Cert Child Protection, Cert Supervisory Mgt

Learning Support:
Mrs A Chapman, Dip SpLD
Ms R Kutchinski, BSc, MPhil

PA to the Headmistress: Mrs Lorene Oliver

The school is housed in a fine Victorian mansion, a Grade II Listed Building, set amidst 15 acres of gardens and woodlands looking towards the Malvern Hills. The school has been sympathetically extended and updated to include up-to-date facilities and resources. A true oasis of tranquillity, it is conveniently placed just one mile from Worcester city centre. In addition the school has a 6.5 acre sports field as well as a dri-play hockey pitch, netball and tennis courts and three gymnasia.

The school's Early Years provision has been extended to include babies and is housed in its own secure and comfortable unit known as the Cottage Nursery. Boys and girls from 0–18 months are eligible to join the Cottage Nursery before proceeding to the Kindergarten Nursery and pre-school. Children may enter the Kindergarten from the age of 18 months and boys are accepted up to the age of 7. Children over the age of 7 take an entrance examination to assess potential.

At 11 years, girls transfer to the Senior School. Girls from other schools take the entrance examination/scholarship to gain entry to the Senior School. Girls are prepared for GCSE examinations in a full range of subjects. The academic record of St Mary's is excellent and the value-added score remains consistently high. In 2007 the GCSE pass rate was 100% with 95% of the Year 11 girls achieving 9 or more GCSEs at A*–C and 78% of all passes were at A*/ A or B grade. A 97% pass rate was achieved at A Level with 80% at grades A–C. However, pupils are not limited by the National Curriculum and those pupils who are capable of exceptional performance are always given the opportunities necessary to excel. Twenty subjects are offered at A Level. All girls go on to good universities including Oxford and Cambridge.

The school is an examination centre for the Associated Board of the Royal Schools of Music and LAMDA. Peripatetic teachers come into school to teach speech and drama, voice, pianoforte and a wide range of orchestral instruments. There are choirs and orchestras in both Junior and Senior Departments.

Academic and Music scholarships are offered at 11+ and Sixth Form. Sixth Form scholarships are also offered for humanities, arts and science.

At all stages, pupils are offered a well balanced curriculum that encompasses academic opportunities as well as drama, music, art and sport as it is our aim to educate the whole person. There is a wide range of extra-curricular activities and clubs on offer at lunch time and after school: junior and senior orchestras and choirs, string groups, wind groups, recorder ensembles, speech and drama, modern dance club, judo, tennis, netball, hockey, athletics, science and engineering, art, design and technology, computer club, The Duke of Edinburgh's Award, Young Enterprise, computer club, chess club, debating etc. We aim to capitalize on the talents and strengths of each girl and in so doing acknowledge the diversity and richness of our school community.

Fees per term (2008-2009). Kindergarten (inc lunch): £1,790 (full time), £395–£1,525 (part time 1–4 days), £295–£1,400 (part time 1-5 mornings); Preparatory School (inc lunch): £1,780–£2,675; Senior School: £3,105 (Years 7–11 inc lunch), £2,995 (Years 12–13 excl lunch). Lunches: £110 per term.

A midday meal is included in the fees for the Kindergarten (full time) and Preparatory School. Swimming lessons are also included in the fees for the Preparatory School.

Charitable status. St Mary's School Trust Worcester is a Registered Charity, number 1018889. Its purpose is the promotion of the Christian Education of girls from Nursery to University and boys up to the age of 7.

St Nicholas' School

Redfields House Redfields Lane Church Crookham Fleet Hampshire GU52 0RF
Tel: 01252 850121
Fax: 01252 850718
e-mail: headspa@st-nicholas.hants.sch.uk
website: www.st-nicholas.hants.sch.uk

Motto: *Confirma Domine Serviendo*

***Headmistress*: Mrs A V Whatmough**, BA Hons Bristol, CertEd

Deputy Head (Pastoral): Mrs E Johnstone, MA Glasgow, DipEd Glasgow, MEd

Director of Studies: Mrs C Moorby, BSc Hons Southampton, CertEd

Assistant Staff:
Mrs S Adams, CertEd Bedford
Miss N Brooks, BA Hons Exeter, PGCE Wales
Mrs J Brown, HND
Mr T T Burns, BA Hons West Surrey College of Art & Design
Miss S Chaffey, BEd Hons Southampton
Mrs J Dixon, BA Hons Bangor
Mrs C Egginton, BEd Hons London
Mrs S Fitzhenry, MEd, BA Gen, BEd Hons Johannesburg SA, PGCE
Mrs J Gardner, BEd Hons Kingston
Mrs A Glenn, CertEd Essex
Mrs K Goodfellow, BEd Hons London
Mrs B Green, CertEd South Yorkshire
Mrs M Hadnett, BA Hons Manchester
Mrs E Hague, BA Hons Lancaster, PGCE
Mrs L Harrison, BA Hons Liverpool, MBA Liverpool, SPELD NSW Australia
Mrs J Haysom, BEd Plymouth
Mrs V Helliwell, BEng Hons Liverpool, PGCE Reading
Mrs J Herridge, CertEd Kingston
Miss L Homer, BA Hons Wales, PGCE Oxon
Mrs S Hutcheson, BA Hons Reading, MA London, PGCE Reading
Mrs J C King, BEd Rolle College, Exmouth
Mrs J R King, BA Hons London, PGCE London
Mrs J Lagan, BEd Hons Strathclyde
Mrs A Lawrence, MA, PGCE Oxon
Mrs C E MacArthur, BA Hons Keele
Mrs I C McIvor, DipCE Hamilton College
Mrs M Morgan, NNEB
Mrs T Newton, BA Hons Open University, PGCE
Mrs T Perrett, BEd Chichester
Mr L Render, BA QTS Twickenham
Mrs A Rowe, CertEd Newcastle, MA Oxford Brookes
Miss J Selley, BA Hons Oxon, PGCE
Mrs P Semmens, BSc Hons Manchester, PGCE Southampton
Mrs P Simpson, BSc Hons Bath, PGCE
Mrs M Strevens, BEd West Midlands College
Miss J Wake, BA Hons Southampton, PGCE Southampton
Mrs L Walpole, BA Hons Hull, PGCE
Mrs E Ward, BA Hons, PGCE
Miss V West, NNEB

Music Department:
Mrs D White, BA Hons, PGCE, LGSM Leeds
Mrs A Franke, BMus Hons, MMus Surrey
Mrs W Busby, BMus Hons (*Voice*)
Mrs S Hosken, GGSM, ARCM, DipEd (*Violin*)
Mrs J Austin, ALCM, CertMusEd (*Piano*)
Mrs V Mitchell, LRAM (*Piano & Cello*)
Miss V Pearson, Perf Cert RAM, LTCL, ARCM (*Guitar*)
Mr A Pepper, ALCM (*Brass*)
Mr V Dean, ARCM, Dip RCM, RSA (*Violin*)
Mrs R Fox, Dip ABRSM (*Flute*)
Mr N Hickling, MMus, MMus (*Clarinet, Saxophone*)
Miss K Martin, HND (*Drums*)
Ms N Bailey, LRAM, ARCM (*Double Bass*)
Ms V Davies BA Oxon, PG Dip RAM, Dip ABRSM (*Harp*)
Ms S-A Emerson, MA Perf Queen's, New York (*Cello*)
Ms J Howarth, MSc, PG Dip RNCM (*Violin, Piano*)
Ms M Jenner, BA Hons Music (*Clarinet, Saxophone*)
Ms L Linge, Dip ABRSM (*Piano*)
Ms G Mortley, LRAM, ARCM (*Voice*)

Administrative Staff:
Bursar: Mrs C Taylor
Headmistress's PA: Mrs D Millar
Registrar & Marketing: Mrs T Johnson
School Office Assistant: Mrs D Dadswell
Accounts Secretary: Mrs D Davies
Laboratory Technician: Mrs M O'Donnell
Catering: Sodhexo Education Services Ltd
Maintenance: Mr P Sleet, Mr P White, Mr J Carrig
Caretaker: Mr R Crail
Uniform Shop: Mrs J Gibson

The School. St Nicholas' School is an independent day school for girls aged 3–16 and boys 3–7. Founded in 1935 at Branksomewood Road, Fleet, the school is now situated at Redfields House, Church Crookham, a large Victorian mansion set in 26 acres of parkland and playing fields. In December 2000 a new Olympic size sports hall was opened, which has widened the range of sporting activities on offer. A new art and textiles department opened in Spring 2006.

Pupils come from Hampshire, Surrey and Berkshire and school buses operate from Farnham, Odiham, Fleet and Basingstoke as well as Fleet Railway Station. There is easy accessibility from the A287 Hook to Farnham road and the M3 is a short distance away.

Religion. The school is Christian by foundation but children of other faiths are made welcome. Assemblies are held each morning and children are encouraged to show tolerance, compassion and care for others.

Curriculum. Our academic standards are high and we provide a balanced curriculum. Small classes place great emphasis on the individual and pupils are encouraged to achieve their full potential in every area of school life. The curriculum is kept as broad as possible until the age of fourteen when choices are made for GCSE. The option choices are varied year by year depending upon the girls' abilities and talents. On average each girl takes ten subjects at GCSE. Twenty subjects are offered at this level. A carefully structured personal development course incorporates a Careers programme. Our girls move confidently on to enter sixth form colleges or scholarships to senior independent schools. Choir, drama and music thrive within the school and performances are given frequently.

Physical Education. Pupils take part in inter-school and local district sports matches: hockey, netball and cross-country in winter; and tennis, athletics and swimming in summer. Rounders and lacrosse are also played. The new sports hall with granwood floor, viewing gallery and shower and changing facilities, offers participation in badminton, tennis, netball, volleyball and basketball throughout the year.

Entry. Children may enter at any stage subject to interview, school report and waiting list. Scholarships and Bursaries are available. For 11+ candidates there is an entrance examination.

Fees per term (2008-2009). Nursery £1,232; Infants (Reception, Years 1 and 2) £2,463; Juniors (Years 3 to 6) £2,804; Senior School £3,346.

Further Information. The prospectus is available upon request from the Registrar. The Headmistress is pleased to meet parents by appointment.

Charitable status. St Nicholas' School is a Registered Charity, number 307341. It exists to provide high quality education for children.

St Paul's Girls' School

Brook Green Hammersmith London W6 7BS
Tel: 020 7603 2288; Bursar: 020 7605 4881
Fax: 020 7602 9932; Bursar: 020 7605 4869
e-mail: admissions@spgs.org
website: www.spgs.org

Motto: '*Fide et Literis*'

The School is on the Foundation originally provided by Dean Colet in 1509 and is governed under the provisions of the Schemes of the Charity Commissioners dated 4 July 1879, and 16 June 1900. The Worshipful Company of Mercers are the trustees of the Foundation. The School was opened on 19 January 1904.

Governors:
Chairman: The Hon Henry William Palmer
Deputy Chairman: Ms Helen Alexander, CBE

Ms Kate Bingham
Mr Christopher Sands Clayton
Mr Richard Cawton Cunis
Mrs Pauline Davies
Mr Michael di Giorgio
Mr Daniel Houghton Hodson
Sir Alexander Graham, GBE, DCL
Ms Sarah Hamilton-Fairley
Ms Alice Hohler
Miss Judith Portrait

Appointed by The Mercers' Company in consultation with the University of Oxford:
(*position vacant*)

Appointed by The Mercers' Company in consultation with the University of Cambridge:
Dr Harriet E Harris, PhD

Appointed by The Mercers' Company in consultation with the University of London:
(*position vacant*)

Clerk to the Governors: Mrs Menna McGregor

Education Practice Manager: Mr Michael Marchant

***High Mistress*: Ms Clarissa M Farr**, MA Exeter, PGCE

Deputy Heads:
Pastoral Director: Mrs Wendy Furniss, MA Oxon, MA London (*History*)
Director of Studies: Mrs Kate Clanchy, MA Cantab, MBA Insead (*Modern Languages*)

Assistant Deputy Head:
Miss Amanda Triccas, MA London (*History*)

Head of Senior School:
Mrs Alex Hems, BA Oxon (*English*)

Miss Melanie Arr, BSc Loughborough (*Physical Education*)
Mr Stephen Arscott, BA Cantab (*Religious Studies*)
Mr Tim Askew, BA Oxon (*History and Religious Studies*)
Dr Howard Bailes, BA Adelaide, PhD London (*History*)
Miss Helen Barff, BA Goldsmiths College, MA Camberwell (*Art and Design*)
Mrs Hilary Barker, MA Oxon (*Modern Languages*)
Revd Vanessa Baron, MA Cantab, BSc City (*Religious Studies*)
Mr Wayne Barron, BA Cantab (*Classics*)
Miss Sandra Barth, BA Martin-Luther-Universitaet Halle-Wittenberg (*Modern Languages*)
Miss Mekhla Barua, BSc Warwick (*Mathematics*)
Mr David Benefer, BA Norwich School of Art (*Art and Design*)
Miss Carole Boothman, BA Liverpool (*Modern Languages*)
Miss Clare Brashaw, MA Leeds (*Art and Design*)
Dr Sophie Breese, BA Oxon, DPhil Oxon (*English*)
Mr Jonathan Bromley, BA Oxon (*History*)
Miss Gemma Caines, BA Cantab (*History*)
Ms Elizabeth Coutts, MA Oxon (*History*)
Mr Nicholas Dakin, BA Birmingham (*English*)
Mr Alexander Daglish, BA Plymouth (*Art and Design*)
Miss Camilla Darwin, BSc Bristol (*Mathematics*)
Dr Jane Dove, MScCalgary, PhD Newcastle (*Geography*)
Mr Anthony Ellison, BSc Nottingham (*Chemistry*)
Miss Katherine Evans, BA London (*History of Art*)
Miss Kate Frank, BA London, MA London (*Modern Languages*)
Mrs Hannah Fussner, BA Oxon, MA Stanford, USA (*Learning Support*)
Miss Penelope Garcia-Rodriguez, BA Oviedo, Spain, MA London (*Modern Languages*)
Mrs Marie-Laure Gillespie, Maîtrise (*Modern Languages*)
Mr Roger Green, MA Kent (*Mathematics*)
Mr Martin Hanak-Hammerl, BSc Graz, Austria (*Mathematics*)
Miss Rachel Harris, BA Durham (*Geography*)
Miss Victoria Harris, BA Lancaster (*English and Drama*)
Miss Marika Hatley, BSc Sheffield Hallam (*Physical Education*)
Dr Eilis Harron-Ponsonby, PhD, MSc, BA Cantab (*Chemistry*)
Mrs Emily Hedgecoe, MA Edinburgh (*Religious Studies*)
Dr Pascale Hewitt, PhD Queen's Belfast (*Mathematics*)
Miss Elizabeth Hodges, BA Wolverhampton Polytechnic, MA Royal College of Art (*Art and Design*)
Dr Anna Holland, BA Oxon, DPhil (*Classics*)
Miss Elizabeth Holley, BA Brighton (*Physical Education*)
Mrs Catherine James, BEd Homerton (*Geography*)
Miss Kulvant Kaur, BA Teesside (*Information Technology*)
Dr Joanna King, BSc, PhD London (*Chemistry*)
Mrs Manuela Knight, BA Milan (*Modern Languages*)
Dr Kingston Koo, BSc Warwick, PhD London (*Physics*)
Mr John Lee, BA Oxon, BA London (*Mathematics*)
Dr Kate Lee, BSc Witwatersrand, MSc Cape Town, PhD London (*Physics*)
Miss Kate Machemer, BA Connecticut College, USA (*Physical Education*)
Ms Lorna Macleod, BA Bristol, MBA Warwick (*Modern Languages*)
Mrs Christelle Maillot, Lic Ang Nancy, France (*Modern Languages*)
Ms Silvana Marconini, Turin, Italy (*Modern Languages*)
Miss Judith Marrinan, BSc London (*Biology*)
Mr William Martin, MA Surrey (*Classics*)
Mr Paul McDonald, BA Oxon, MSc LSE (*Mathematics*)
Mr Richard Michell, BA Bristol, MA Chelsea School of Art (*Art and Design*)
Dr Joanna Moriarty, BSc Birmingham, PhD Reading (*Biology*)
Miss Laura Morton, BA Oxon (*English*)
Mrs Irina Ninnis, BA Moscow and London (*Modern Languages*)
Dr Ezi Papakostopoulos, BSc Brunel, PhD Brunel (*Chemistry*)
Dr Jonathan Patrick, BA, DPhil Oxon (*English*)
Ms Jessica Potter, BA London (*Art History*)
Mr Anthony Richards, BSc, MSc Leicester (*Physics*)
Miss Jessica Richards, BSc Newcastle (*Biology*)
Miss Katie Roberts, BA Cantab (*Modern Languages*)
Ms Leonie Rushforth, BA Cantab (*English*)
Mrs Alexandra Shamloll, MA Cantab (*Mathematics*)
Dr Clare Sharp, MA, DPhil Oxon (*Classics*)
Dr Marcin Slaski, BSc Krakow, PhD Krakow (*Physics*)
Ms Divya Sunder, BSc University of Illinois, Ed M Harvard (*Chemistry*)
Miss Claire Suthren, BA Cantab (*Classics*)
Mr Michael Turner, BA Oxon (*Economics*)
Ms Paula Velez (*Modern Languages*)
Dr Sarah Wah, MA Leeds, DPhil Cantab (*English*)
Mr Mark Wardrop, MChem Oxon (*Chemistry*)
Miss Annabel Watts, BSc Bristol (*Biology*)
Mrs Susan Wilson, BA, MSc Oxon (*Mathematics*)
Mr Alun Yorath, BSc Bristol (*Biology*)
Ms Jane Zeng, BSc Guangzhan, China (*Modern Languages*)

Director of Music: Mr Yat-Soon Yeo, BA London, MMus London
Head of Curricular Music: Mr Mark Wilderspin, MA Oxon, MMus RCM, London

Senior Music and Head of Keyboard: Mr John York, AGSM, ARCM
Head of Singing: Miss Heidi Pegler, BA Cardiff, LTCL
Head of Strings: Miss Hilary Sturt, AGSM, ARCM (*Viola and Violin*)
Head of Wind & Brass: Miss Barbara McGregor, ARCM (*Clarinet and Saxophone*)
Music Administrator: Miss Alexandra Godfree, BA Oxon

Miss Rose Andresier, LLCM, FRSA (*Guitar*)
Mr Edward Barry, DipMus, LTCL (*Violin*)
Mrs Emily Bates, BA, MSTAT (*Alexander Technique*)
Mrs Anna Boucher, BA (*Singing*)
Miss Nicola Broke, ALCM (*Harp*)
Mrs Jane Clark-Maxwell, BMus London, AKC, LTCL (*Singing*)
Miss Gillian Cracknell, LRAM (*Piano, Aural*)
Mr Vivian E Davies, BMus (*Trombone, Horn*)
Mr Matthew Dickinson, BA, GGSM (*Percussion, Drum Kit*)
Mr Harold East, GRSM, ARCM (*Piano*)
Miss Jane Fisher, LTCL (*Flute*)
Miss Nicola-Jane Kemp, MA Cantab, MMus Opera, RSAMD (*Singing*)
Mr John Langley, BA (*Theory*)
Miss Joanna Lees, ARCM (*Oboe*)
Mr Carlos Lopez-Real, MA Oxon, LGSM (*Saxophone, Jazz Group*)
Miss Naadia Manington, BMus, LGSM (*Jazz Piano, Piano*)
Mr Andrew Mason, BMus (*Clarinet, Saxophone*)
Mrs Helen Mason, BMus RCM, PGDip Solo/Ensemble RCM (*Horn*)
Mr Alexander Mobbs, BMus (*Double Bass*)
Dr Susan Monks, BEd, MA Mus (*Singing*)
Miss Catherine Morphett, BMus (*Clarinet*)
Miss Amanda Morrison, BA (*Singing*)
Ms Helena Mowat-Brown, ARCM (*Harpischord*)
Miss Helen Neilson, BSc, PGDipAdv RCM (*Cello*)
Mr Libor Novacek, BMus, MMus GSMD (*Piano*)
Ms Jessica O'Leary, BMus, DipCSM, LTCL, LRAM (*Violin, Viola*)
Ms April Pierrot, MSTAT (*Alexander Technique*)
Miss Mandy Pollard, DipPA, BMus, LRAM (*Singing*)
Miss Julie Ryan, ARCM (*Trumpet*)
Miss Rachel Shannon, MA Cantab, RAM (*Singing*)
Miss Erica Simpson, ARAM, ARCM (*Cello*)
Mr James Sleigh, ARCM (*Viola*)
Ms Louise Strickland, BMus, MMus, LGSMD (*Recorder*)
Mrs Sarah Stroh, BMus, Dip Dist RAM, LRAM (*Singing*)
Ms Shelagh Sutherland, ARAM, LRAM, STAT (*Piano, Alexander Technique*)
Ms Gillian Tingay, ARCM (*Harp*)
Miss Judith Treggor, BMus Connecticut (*Flute*)
Ms Joanne Turner, DipRCM, ARCM (*Bassoon, Flute*)
Lady Walker, MSTAT (*Alexander Technique*)
Mr Simon Weale, MA Oxon, LGSM (*Piano and Organ*)
Miss Enloc Wu, ARCM, LRSM (*Piano*)
Mrs Fiona York, AGSM (*Piano*)

Bursar: (*to be appointed*)

Registrar: Mrs Lindy Hayward, BA Open

High Mistress's Personal Assistant: Mrs Patricia Mulcahy, BA Open

Librarian: Mrs Linda Kelley, BA Manchester, MSc UCE

The main ages of admission are 11 and 16. There are 710 girls in the school, 200 being in the Sixth Form. The school offers a balanced curriculum; both tradition and innovation are valued. A strong core of academic subjects is combined with Art, Design, Drama, Music, Information Technology and Sport.

Girls are prepared for GCSE, Advanced Supplementary and full Advanced Level examinations and for university entrance. Girls go on to major universities in the UK or overseas, approximately 40% to Oxford and Cambridge.

Sports facilities include a Sports Hall, a large heated swimming pool, lacrosse pitches and tennis and netball courts. The Library facilities are outstanding, as are those for Music, centred on the Gustav Holst Singing Hall. Drama takes place in the purpose-built Celia Johnson Theatre and Drama Studio. There is an ICT block with three fully-equipped classrooms. Twelve Science laboratories are housed in a separate Science block. There is a Sixth Form centre with its own ICT facilities, dining and relaxation areas, together with a Careers suite. We are continually modernising and adding to these facilities: six large, purpose-built specialist teaching rooms for English, Geography and Modern Languages opened in 2007.

Junior Academic Scholarships (11+) of a value of £100 per annum are offered to up to four candidates who perform exceptionally well in the First Year Entrance Examination.

Junior Bursaries (11+) to a value of up to full fee remission based on proven financial need subject to annual review are also available for up to eight successful candidates.

Junior Music Scholarships (11+) of the value of £100 per annum and free tuition in one instrument are awarded to up to four candidates on the basis of practical examination and interview, and candidates must be successful in the First Year Entrance Examination. (*see also entry in Music Scholarships section*)

Senior Academic Scholarships and Exhibitions (16+) of a value of £250 and £100 respectively are offered to up to eight present students on the basis of academic distinction demonstrated in a project completed at the end of the first year of Advanced Supplementary Level Study.

Senior Awards (16+) to a value of up to full fee remission based on proven financial need subject to annual review are available to up to four successful senior candidates who are currently in their final GCSE year at another school.

The Ogden Trust Science Scholarship (16+) is a means-tested award which may be available to a successful senior candidate who is a British national entering the school and who is currently in her final GCSE year at a maintained school and who wishes to study Physics and Mathematics at Advanced Level and at university.

Senior Music Scholarships (16+) of the value of £250 per annum and free tuition in two instruments are awarded on the basis of written and practical examinations and interview to up to two internal candidates and two external candidates. External candidates must be successful in the Senior School Entrance Examination.

The Nora Day Music Scholarship (16+) may be offered for entry in Autumn 2009 to an external candidate of outstanding musical ability on a keyboard instrument who is in her final GCSE year at another school and who has passed the Senior entrance examination for entry to the School for Advanced Level. The successful candidate is entitled to half the School's tuition fees as well as free music tuition in two instruments for her two years at the School. It would be expected that a candidate for the Nora Day Music Scholarship would meet the normal criteria for a Music Scholarship, but would, in addition, display outstanding talent and would be ready to participate in full in the musical life of the School.

(*see also entry in Music Scholarships section*)

Senior Art Scholarships (16+) of the value of £250 per annum are offered to up to two internal and two external candidates who are currently in their final GCSE year and who, if applying from another school, have previously been successful in the Senior School Entrance Examination. Candidates take part in a Saturday workshop and are also required to submit a portfolio.

Fees per term (2008-2009). £4,841 including lunches, excluding textbooks.

Registration & Examination Fee £120.

Charitable status. St Paul's Girls' School is a Registered Charity, number 1119613, and a Company Limited by Guarantee, registered in England, number 6142007. It exists to promote the education of girls in Greater London.

St Swithun's School

Alresford Road Winchester Hants SO21 1HA
Tel: 01962 835700
Fax: 01962 835779
e-mail: office@stswithuns.com
website: www.stswithuns.com

The School was founded in 1884 and moved to its present impressive site of 45 acres on the Downs on the outskirts of Winchester in 1931.

The School aims to give a broad, balanced academic education in which each girl has the opportunity to make appropriate choices which will enable her to develop her potential and give her the skills and confidence needed for adult life.

Within a framework of sensible discipline there is a remarkably friendly and caring atmosphere. Emphasis is placed on Christian values and consideration for others.

It is a school for both Day Girls, Full and Weekly Boarders and at present the Senior School (girls aged 11–18) has 257 Day Girls and 226 Boarders. There is an adjoining Junior School for girls aged 3–11 and boys from 3–7. years (*see entry in IAPS section*).

Visitor: The Rt Revd Michael Scott-Joynt, Bishop of Winchester

School Council:
Chairman: Mr J C Platt, FCA
The Mayor of Winchester (*ex officio*)
The Dean of Winchester (*ex officio*)
The Headmaster of Winchester College (*ex officio*)
Mrs S M Glasspool, DL, BSc
Mrs M S Greenway, LLB
Dr M A Gruffydd Jones, MA, PhD
Mr P Martin, MA
Dr H M Mycock, BA, MSc, PhD
Mr P H Radcliffe, FCA
Mrs R Randle, BA, MA Ed
Mr M Reid, MA, FCA
Miss R L E Rothman, BA, ACA
Dr H R Trippe, BA, BMS, FFPHM, PGCE
Prof J M A Whitehouse, MA, MD, FRCPE, FRCR
Mr M Wilson, BA

Bursar and Clerk to the Council: Mr G J Haig, OBE

***Headmistress*: Dr H L Harvey**, BSc, PhD London

Deputy Headmistress: Mrs J Tomlinson, BA Kent, MA Durham, PGCE York (*Religious Studies*)

Director of Studies: Mrs A Burns-Cox, BSc London, PGCE Southampton

Chaplain: Revd Katina Dykes, BA Bristol

Staff:

Religious Studies:
Mrs A Gibson, BA, PGCE Birmingham (*and Careers*)
Miss J Cox, BA Birmingham, PGCE Birmingham

English:
Mrs D Burgess, MA Oxon, PGCE Cantab, DipPSE CNAA
Mrs M Bond, MA Glasgow, CertEd Jordanhill, DipEd Glasgow
Mrs J Phillips, BA Oxon, PGCE Kings
Mrs N Young, BA Birmingham, PGCE
Miss J Askew, BA, DipEd NSW, Australia
Miss C Howard, BA, PGCE Leicester

History:
Miss J Thomas, MA Oxford, MA London, PGCE Oxford
Dr S Burt, BEd Durham, MA, PhD Southampton
Miss K Penny, BA West of England, PGCE Bristol

Geography:
Mrs H Jones, BSc London, PGCE Sussex
Mr J Brown, BA, PGCE Birmingham
Mrs L Parsons, BSc Liverpool, PGCE

Economics:
Mrs S Rothwell, BSc LSE, PGCE

Modern Languages:
Mrs E Lorge, BA London, PGCE London, MIL (*French*)
Mrs C Bewes, DEUG, Licence Maîtrise France, PGCE Southampton (*French*)
Mrs R Dhand, BA London, PGCE Southampton (*French*)
Mrs S Hayward, MA London, PGCE Durham (*German and French*)
Mrs C Glyn, MA Bochum, PGCE Durham (*German*)
Mrs M Grice, BA Germany, PGCE Southampton (*German*)
Miss H Herson, CertEd Bedford (*French*)
Miss N Lequang, Licence Spain, Maîtrise France, PGCE Bath
Mrs A Steer, MA Ed Frankfurt (*German*)

Classics:
Dr L Coles, MA, PhD Cantab, PGCE Southampton
Mrs P E Giles, BA Birmingham, PGCE Durham (*Careers and Head of General Studies*)
Mrs G Condell, BA Kings, PGCE Kings

Mathematics:
Mr S Power, BA Oxon, MSc Colorado, PGCE OU
Mrs C Bolger, BEng Exeter, PGCE Portsmouth, CEng, MIMechE
Mr P Debont, BSc Warwick, MSc Essex, PGCE Greenwich
Mrs L Thompson, BSc Exeter
Mrs R McCall-Tomlinson, MA, BSc, PGCE Oxon

Science:
Dr J Livy, BSc Liverpool, MSc, DIC, PhD London, CChem, MRSC (*Chemistry*)
Mr P Unitt, BSc Bristol, PGCE East Anglia (*Chemistry*)
Mr R Shah, BSc East Anglia, PGCE Southampton (*Chemistry*)
Mr A W J Smith, BSc Durham, PGCE Exeter (*Physics*)
Mrs P A Burley, BSc Swansea, PGCE Southampton (*Biology*)
Mrs S Evans, BSc London, MA OU, PGCE Bath (*Biology*)
Mr T Duncan, BSc, BEng Sydney, MEd Australia
Mrs H Fletcher, BSc, PGCE Bristol
Dr H Otter, PhD, BA, PGCE Cantab (*Science*)

Design and Technology:
Mrs H Jobling, BEng Exeter, PGCE Telford
Mr A Maskell, BEd Winchester

Careers:
Mrs A Campbell, BA Durham, DipRE Nottingham, PGCE Lancaster, CFPS Portsmouth, RSA DipTEFLA (*and Religious Studies*)
Miss J Webber, BA Wellington, NZ, Dip Teaching Christchurch, NZ, Cert Prof Studies CEG

Food Technology and Textiles:
Mrs N Sanvoisin, BSc, PGCE Cardiff

Art:
Mrs P Larrington, BEd, MA Southampton (*and History of Art*)

Mrs L Mason-Smith, BA, MA, PGCE
Miss C Campling, BA Winchester, PGCE Reading (*Art & Design*)
Miss F Gilchrist

ICT:
Mrs A Walker, BEd Leeds

Music:
Mr R Brett, MA, PGCE Cantab (*Director of Music*)
Miss J Richardson, MMus Perf, DRSAMD, RGN (*Head of Instrumental Studies*)
Mr R Patterson, MA, PGCE CfBT (*Head of Academic Music*)
Miss J Anderson, GRSM, LRAM, LTCL
Mr P White-Jones, BA Cantab, FRCO
Mrs V Stenning (*Administrative Assistant*)

Visiting Music Staff:
Mrs J Lloyd, ARCM, LGSM (*piano*)
Mr M Evemy, CT ABRSM, ATCL MusEd (*piano*)
Mrs J McKelvie, CertEd (*Piano*)
Miss S Vysniauskiene (*piano*)
Dr N Wilkinson, MMus, ARCM, HonARAM (*piano*)
Mrs J Kane, Dip RNCM (*violin*)
Mrs R Macdonald, ARCM (*violin*)
Mr P Sabberton, BMus, LRAM (*violin*)
Mr M Mace, DipRAM (*violoncello*)
Mrs V Harding, BSc Sothampton (*violoncello*)
Miss L Pope, BA Cantab, LRAM (*harp*)
Mr A Neville, ALCM (*guitar*)
Mr J O'Kane, LWCMD (*guitar*)
Dr J Satter (*oboe*)
Miss L Burns, MA Hons, PGDip (*flute*)
Mrs A McKay, BA London, PGCE Dundee (*flute*)
Mrs K Wills, GTC, LTGL, DipRAM (*flute*)
Mr A Collins, RA (*clarinet*)
Mrs J Paterson-Neild, BA (*saxophone*)
Miss E Innes, GGSM, AGSM Examiner to the GSMD (*bassoon and clarinet*)
Mrs F Brockhurst, ARCM (*French horn*)
Mr A Warren, BMus Hons, RCM, MMus, RCM (*trombone, tuba*)
Mr J Evans (*drums*)
Ms K Fenech, PPRNCM, BMus, RNCM (*voice*)
Mrs P Spencer, BA Hons (*voice*)
Mrs J Turner, MSAT (*Alexander Technique*)
Mrs J Bond, MSTAT, MGNI (*Alexander Technique*)

Drama and Theatre Studies:
Mrs T Spring, BA Hatfield, MA Middlesex, CertEd Birmingham
Mrs G Oakley, BA East Anglia, PGCE Southampton

Visiting Staff:
Mrs M Armstrong, BA Bretton Hall
Ms J Wilson, BA North London, PGCE Oxon, LRAM, LLAM
Ms C Price, LGSM, ALAM, SRD
Mr A Wieland, LLAM, ALAM

Learning Support:
Mrs M Hope, BEd, AdvDipEd, PGDipEd SpLD

Physical Education:
Mrs A Parker, CertEd Cambridge
Miss K Smith, BSc Cardiff
Miss D Fenn, BSc Swansea
Miss S Gilbert, BA, PGCE Chichester
Miss M Godfroy, BA Chichester, MSc, PGCE

Visiting Staff:
Mrs F Brooks (*Aerobics*)
Mr R Whitfield (*Judo*)
Mr S Budden (*Karate*)
Mr S Davey (*Fencing*)
Mrs P Francis (*Gym*)
Miss C Wyeth (*Yoga*)
Mr P Boyd-Leslie (*Tennis*)

ICT:
Mr A S King, BEd Warwick, MITT (*Head of ICT Services*)
Mr S Kerwood
Mr G Reed
Mr C Hume

Boarding Housemistresses:
Finlay: Miss J Webber
High House: Miss J Anderson
Hyde Abbey: Miss H Herson
Earl's Down: Mrs H Fletcher
Hillcroft: Mrs S Hayward
Le Roy: Mrs D Lugg

Day Housemistresses:
Caer Gwent: Mrs A Gibson
Venta: Mr J Brown
Davies: Mr R Shah
Chilcomb: Mrs C Bewes

Medical Staff:
Dr L Cole, MB BS, DRCOG
Mrs P May, RGN
Mrs J Deoweneley, RGN

Office Staff:
PA to The Headmistress: Mrs H Turner
Admissions Secretary: Mrs B Kingston

Aim. The School aims to provide a well-ordered and supportive environment in which each girl is encouraged to fulfil her intellectual, physical and creative potential. Spiritual, moral and cultural development allows the girls to gain the knowledge and wisdom that will facilitate the lifelong continuation of learning and development. Importance is placed on girls gaining an understanding of themselves and on promoting self-esteem to allow them to embark on adult life positively and with the ability to contribute fully to society.

Location. The School is on a rural site in Winchester's 'green belt' but only a short distance from the city centre. It is easily accessible from Heathrow and Gatwick airports and is one hour from London by car (via the M3 motorway). There is a frequent train service to London Waterloo (one hour).

Curriculum. The curriculum is designed with an emphasis on flexibility and individual choice. All girls take English and Mathematics at GCSE Level and are given a free choice for their remaining 7 subjects from a selection of 19, the only conditions being that they should include at least one science subject and a modern foreign language. They are also encouraged to include at least one humanity, (History, Geography, Religious Studies or Classical Civilisation) to ensure a breadth of knowledge and skills.

In the Sixth Form, girls are offered 23 subjects from which they choose 4. One of these will be normally followed to AS Level only while the remainder are taken through as full A Levels. Advice is given about the implications for their choice of university, degree course and career to ensure sensible combinations. Some girls choose to follow courses in subjects which are not offered at GCSE, eg Politics, Economics, History of Art. Over half the Sixth Form study at least one Science subject at A Level. To broaden their course further girls may take an additional subject to AS Level in the Upper Sixth and some will continue their 4 AS choices to full A Levels.

In addition, all Sixth Form girls take AS and A Level General Studies which, in its recognition of the connection between the various A Level disciplines, acts as a link between subjects. Contemporary, social, philosophical and political issues are explored through lectures, discussions, debates, visits and essays in a rolling programme which focuses in turn on music, science, technology, history of art, art and philosophy.

The curriculum is extended by exchange and educational visits to other countries.

Religion. The School is a Church of England foundation. There are close ties with Winchester Cathedral, where termly services and the annual Confirmation and Carol Services are held. A full-time Chaplain prepares girls for Confirmation and teaches in the School.

Music. The School has a strong musical tradition and there are frequent performances by the School choirs and orchestral groups. The Senior Choir sings Evensong in Winchester Cathedral twice a term, and chamber groups regularly enjoy success at national level.

Sports. There are extensive playing fields, a spacious modern sports hall and an impressive indoor swimming pool. Lacrosse players regularly attain national standard and a wide range of team and individual sports is offered.

Facilities. The original school building contains the main teaching rooms and libraries and has been extended and developed to provide specialist areas for Languages, Information Technology, Food and Textiles and Careers. The Science wing contains eight fully equipped laboratories, project rooms and a lecture theatre. In addition, there is an Art, Design and Technology Centre and a Performing Arts building was opened in 2003. This has a 600-seat main auditorium and two smaller performance spaces. A new Library, Careers and ICT facility was opened in 2007.

School Houses. There are 6 boarding houses and 4 day girl houses, each staffed by a housemistress and assistant who take pride in the high level of pastoral care offered to each girl. The Junior House is for girls aged 11 years who are then transferred to one of the Senior Houses after one year. They remain in the senior house until they have completed one year in the Sixth Form. The Upper Sixth House is for boarders and day girls together, with study bedrooms for boarders, study facilities for day girls and common rooms and galley for all.

Careers. Most girls continue to University, including Oxford and Cambridge, and all continue to some form of Higher Education and training. Each girl is counselled by one of our team of four Careers staff in a well-resourced department. Lectures and video presentations are organised frequently and a Careers Fair held annually.

Leisure Activities. There is an extensive range of extra-curricular activities and an organised programme of visits and activities at the weekend. Girls participate in the Duke of Edinburgh's Award Scheme, Young Enterprise and local Community Service work. The Sixth Form runs a range of Societies including a Green Society, a Debating Society and a branch of Amnesty International. There are cookery, dressmaking, craft and engineering clubs and each year there are drama productions as well as regular drama activities. There is an annual visit to a Geographical/Outward Bound Centre in Wales, ski trips and water-sports holidays.

Health. The School Sanatorium forms part of the main buildings. It is staffed by qualified RGNs and visited by the School Doctor twice a week.

Entrance. Entry is by means of the Common Entrance Examination for Independent Schools. The majority of girls enter the Senior School at the age of 11 or 13 years, but girls are accepted at other ages, including the Sixth Form, subject to satisfactory tests.

Scholarships and Exhibitions. (*see Scholarship Entries section*). These are awarded on the result of an examination at 11+ and 13+ and at entry to the Sixth Form. There are also Music Scholarships.

Fees per term (2008-2009). Senior School: Boarders £7,650; Day Girls £4,640. Junior School: £1,170–£3,000.

Charitable status. St Swithun's School Winchester is a Registered Charity, number 307335. It exists to provide education for girls aged 11–18 years.

St Teresa's School

Effingham Hill Dorking Surrey RH5 6ST
Tel: 01372 452037
Fax: 01372 450311
e-mail: info@stteresas.surrey.sch.uk
website: www.stteresasschool.com

Independent Day/Boarding School for 500 Girls aged 2–18 (Boarding 8–18).

A Different School for Every Girl

St Teresa's is a happy, thriving girls' boarding and day school with its own Preparatory School and Nursery. All departments of the school are responsive to the differing needs and latent talents of each individual girl, and each provides a warm and nurturing environment that recognises the girls as individuals with distinct personalities, needs and talents. St Teresa's is a flexible, 'can do' school that encourages every girl to explore her capabilities in her own way and provides whatever necessary to support each girl's interests and passions, both in and beyond the classroom. The school has a broad ability intake but was placed 12th in the country for adding educational value in the January 2006 DCSF Performance Tables and 149th in the UK in the 2008 Financial Times "Top 1000 Schools for A Level". It is also ranked 6th in Surrey for A Levels in 2008.

Chairman of the Governors: Mr P Grobel

***Headmistress*: Mrs L Falconer**, BSc Hons

Deputy Headmistress: Mrs J Elburn, BSc Hons, PGCE
Senior Teacher: Mrs J Gardner, BEd Hons, TCert
Director of Studies: Mrs D Dixon, BSc Hons, PGCE
Bursar: Mr P Large, BA
Head of Admissions and Marketing: Mrs J Shilling, BA Hons
Admissions Secretary: Mrs A Charles

Heads of Department:
Mr G Beynon, BEd Hons, MA (*Mathematics*)
Mr T Caister, GRSM, ARCM, PGCE (*Music*)
Mrs K Carpenter, BA Hons, PGCE (*English*)
Mr P Chatterton, BA, PGCE (*Economics & Business Studies, Careers*)
Mrs S Coughlin, BA Hons (*Design*)
Ms J Bartlett, BA Hons, PGCE (*History*)
Mrs J Leeming, BSc Hons, PGCE (*Geography*)
Miss S G Nelson, BEd Hons (*Physical Education*)
Dr R Peevey, STB, STL, STD (*Religious Studies*)
Mrs A Rogerson-Webb, BA Hons, MA (*Art*)
Miss H Vose, BA Hons (*Boarding*)
Mrs T Schaapkens, BEd (*Life Skills*)
Mrs J Snobel, BSc Hons, MA, PGCE (*Science*)
Mrs N C Wilson, BA Hons, PGCE (*Modern Languages*)
Mr M Woodward, BEd Hons, CertEd, MITT (*ICT*)

Foundation. St Teresa's was established in 1928 on what was originally part of a manor site recorded in the Domesday Book. The present Georgian house, dating from 1799, is the centre of the Senior School, now greatly extended to provide modern facilities for its high level of education. Although founded as a Catholic school, we welcome girls from diverse backgrounds and different faiths.

In 1953, St Teresa's Preparatory School (*see entry in IAPS section*) was established at Grove House, in the village of Effingham, about 1½ miles away, but will move to brand new, purpose-built premises on the Senior School site in January 2009.

Location. Situated amid beautiful, rural surroundings, approximately 22 miles from London, St Teresa's is located in 48 acres of grounds amongst the Surrey hills. The M25 is only four miles away. Both Heathrow and Gatwick airports are half an hour's drive and there is a good train service to London (Waterloo) from Effingham Junction Station and London (Victoria) from Dorking.

Facilities. We are constantly investing in new facilities. A magnificent, new indoor swimming pool complex and an all-weather pitch were completed in 2003. Music, drama and the arts now benefit from a £3 million performing arts theatre hall, incorporating the latest sound and lighting technology and its own recording studio completed in September 2005. The next phase of development will follow once the building of the new Nursery and Prep School is complete and will include a new Sports Hall and English and Maths rooms.

Years 7–11. Entrance at 11 is based on success in the Entrance Examination. Scholarships are available (see below). It is school policy to maintain small classes so that each pupil's progress is closely monitored.

St Teresa's is well-equipped in every way for the methods of GCSE teaching and excellent examination results bear this out. 19 GCSE subjects are on offer and most girls take 10 subjects.

Individual tuition is available in a variety of subjects, including singing, most musical instruments, dance and drama and a number of sporting activities. Parents receive reports regularly and they also have the opportunity to meet Staff on Parent's Evenings and are encouraged to approach the school whenever they feel it is necessary. Pastoral Care is provided at all levels by Form Tutors, Heads of Year and House Mistresses.

Sixth Form. As well as those who have come up through the school, every year St Teresa's Sixth Form welcomes girls from other schools. It has its own purpose-built accommodation in Magdalen House where girls live in a happy atmosphere in which high standards, responsibility and self discipline are encouraged. Currently 27 A Level subjects are on offer and each girl has a personal tutor. All girls follow a number of compulsory and optional courses, in addition to their main examination subjects. The Lower Sixth all do one or two weeks of work experience and also participate in the Young Enterprise Scheme and Voluntary Service. The Upper Sixth Economics and Business Studies students are given the experience of running the school's branch of a national clearing bank. All St Teresa's girls go on to higher education: most to first rank universities; others to the best art schools, drama schools, and music colleges.

Drama. At the end of the first term of the academic year, all of Year 7 perform in a seasonal production and later in the year, both Juniors and Seniors are involved in further productions. LAMDA examinations are taken by a high percentage of girls. Debating and Public Speaking is also an integral part of school life with notable successes in local and national competitions.

Music. St Teresa's has an excellent reputation for music. Music standards are high with girls attending Saturday sessions at London music colleges, playing in county orchestras and bands, and in children's and youth orchestras at national level. Choirs, ensembles and individuals are entered for competitions and festivals with a high degree of success.

Sport. St Teresa's has a 5-acre Sports Field for athletics, field events and cricket, several tennis courts, an all-weather hockey pitch, a new swimming pool complex, and a large sports hall. Hockey, netball and tennis are the main sports in which the school has a reputation in the local area, but numerous other sporting activities take place such as aerobics, self-defence and judo.

Boarding. St Teresa's offers full boarding in a happy relaxed atmosphere. Boarding facilities are first class with bright and attractive rooms. Boarding is organised on a year system and priority is given to providing a full programme of weekend activities. Extended day, weekly and flexi-boarding are also available to accommodate the varying requirements of parents and pupils.

Extra-Curricular Activities. Many extra-curricular activities are on offer including The Duke of Edinburgh's Award Scheme and the World Challenge Expeditions. School trips at home and abroad and school exchanges play an important part in broadening the girls' outlook as well as affording cultural and social benefits.

Fees per term (2008-2009). Day Pupils: Senior £4,040–£4,290. Includes lunch and most books/stationery and computer consumables. Boarding (additional fee): £2,465 (weekly), £3,010 (full).

Scholarships. Academic, Sport, Drama, Art and Music scholarships are available at 11+, 12+ and 13+ as well as in the Sixth Form.

STOGA. St Teresa's Old Girls Association meets regularly.

FOST. Friends of St Teresa's is a flourishing parents' association which engages in fund-raising through a variety of social events.

Prospectus. A fully illustrated prospectus is available on request or may be downloaded from our website.

Charitable status. St Teresa's School Effingham Trust is a Registered Charity. It exists to provide education for girls from 2 to 18 years.

Sheffield High School (GDST)

10 Rutland Park Sheffield S10 2PE
Tel: 0114 266 0324
Fax: 0114 267 8520
e-mail: enquiries@she.gdst.net
website: www.sheffieldhighschool.org.uk

Founded 1878.

This is one of the 29 schools of The Girls' Day School Trust. For further information about the Trust, see p. xxiv.

A more detailed prospectus may be obtained from the school and additional information may be found on the school's website.

Chair of Local Governors: Mrs P Liversidge, OBE, DL, FREng, CEng, BSc Hons, DEng, DSc, UnivD, FIMechE, FCGI, FRSA

***Headmistress*: Mrs V A Dunsford**, BA Manchester, NPQH

Deputy Head: Mr S Mozley, BA Oxford

Senior Tutor: Miss H Thorneloe, BEd Liverpool John Moores

Head of Pastoral Care: Mrs R Bennett, BA York

Director of Studies: Miss J M Goodwin, BSc Leicester

Assistant Head: Mr M J Getty, BA Northumbria, NPQH

Head of Junior Department: Mrs A Jones, BSc South Bank

Administrator: Mrs K White

Number of Pupils. 1,030: 295 (Junior Department), 570 (Senior School), 165 (Sixth Form)

The school was opened in 1878 and has occupied its pleasant site in the suburb of Broomhill since 1884. It draws its pupils from all parts of the city and from more distant rural and urban areas of Nottinghamshire, Derbyshire and Yorkshire, many travelling on special coaches.

The Junior Department, Senior School buildings and Sixth Form Centre are adjacent and share gardens, sports hall, hockey/rounders pitch, netball/tennis courts and a gymnasium on the site. An additional hockey and athletics field is situated a short bus ride from the school. In January 2007 the Junior Department acquired a new Infant building and ICT suite. Recent additions to the Senior School include a new IT suite, Science laboratories, additional Art & Design studios, Music facilities, a Drama studio, two new libraries and a language media suite.

Curriculum. The usual Junior subjects are taught plus French, Art, Computer Studies, Art/Technology, Drama, Music and PE. Most lessons are with form teachers but specialist staff teach older girls. In the Senior School, girls generally take 9 GCSE subjects from the range of usual options plus German, Greek, Latin, Drama, Russian, Spanish, Art and Design, Business Studies, Geology, Music and PE. Over 80% stay on to the Sixth Form and nearly all go on to Higher Education.

There are abundant sporting, musical, drama and other activities available at lunchtimes, after school and at weekends, including the Duke of Edinburgh's Award Scheme. A varied programme of residential trips and expeditions at home and abroad is offered, including Sport, Music and Art tours.

Fees per term (2008-2009). Senior School £2,966, Junior Department £2,150.

The fees cover the regular curriculum, school books, stationery and other materials, most extra-curricular activities, but not school meals for Senior girls.

Scholarships and Bursaries. The GDST makes available to the school a substantial number of scholarships and bursaries. The bursaries are means tested and are intended to ensure that the school remains accessible to bright girls who would profit from our education but who would be unable to enter the school without financial assistance.

A large range of scholarship and bursary support is provided at Sheffield High School. From Year 6, up to three prestigious Academic Scholarships and two Music Scholarships are provided each year with an additional means-tested HSBC Scholarship also available. In the Sixth Form, a range of Academic, Music, Art, Sport and Drama Scholarships are also made available to suitably talented girls.

Charitable status. Sheffield High School is part of The Girls' Day School Trust, which is a Registered Charity, number 306983. The aim of the Trust is to provide a fine academic education for girls, which is distinguished by its breadth, as well as its depth.

Sherborne Girls

Bradford Road Sherborne Dorset DT9 3QN

Tel: Admissions: 01935 818224
School: 01935 812245
Bursar: 01935 818206
Fax: 01935 389445
e-mail: enquiry@sherborne.com
website: www.sherborne.com

Sherborne Girls, founded in 1899, provides an outstanding education for 11 to 18 year olds in the beautiful county of Dorset, and is proud of its extra-curricular programme and exceptional pastoral care. Girls are admitted at 11+, 12+, 13+ and into the Sixth Form. There are around 380 girls, 345 Boarders, 30 Day girls. The International Baccalaureate Diploma is offered in addition to A Levels, which provides education tailored to each girl's needs. A close relationship with Sherborne School allows co-ed opportunities including some joint lessons in the Sixth Form, music, drama, activities, clubs and societies and social occasions. The schools have the same term dates. Scholarships and Bursaries are available.

Council:
Chairman: S H Wingfield Digby Esq, BSc, MBA
Mrs H Greenstock, MA
The Right Reverend T M Thornton, MA
S J Mabey Esq, MA, FCA
Mrs J Nicholson, BSc
Right Hon Oliver Letwin, MP
The Hon Mark Bridges, MA
Professor J M Brown, FRHistS
D J Pow Esq
Vice Admiral Sir Christopher Morgan, KBE
A J C Palmer Esq
Mrs S Tennant
Captain R J Fisher, RN
Air Vice-Marshal K D Filbey, CBE, FRAeS
Mrs I Burke, MB BS, MRCGP, DRCOP, DCH
Mr R H Robson Esq

Clerk to the Council: Mr Martyn J Steer, FCIPD

Senior and Pastoral Staff:

***Headmistress*: Mrs Jenny Dwyer**, BEd Hons Cantab

Bursar: Mr Martyn J Steer, FCIPD
Deputy Head Academic: Mr W J Penty, BA Hons Bristol, PG Dip Sheffield
Deputy Head Pastoral: Mrs Helen Lange, MA Sussex, BEd
Director of Studies: Dr G P Oliver, PhD London, BA Cantab
Director of Sixth Form: Mr H R MacNeary, BA Hons Wales, MA Winchester

Chaplain: Revd Rebecca Ayers-Harris, BA Hons Nottingham

Housemistresses of Boarding Houses:
Aldhelmsted East: Mrs E Poraj-Wilczynska, MSc Leicester, CertEd London (*PE*)
Aldhelmsted West: Mrs S Budd, BEd Massey, BSA Dip (*Mathematics*)
Dun Holme: Mrs A Taylor, BA Amsterdam (*Languages*)
Wingfield Digby: Mrs I Morley-Smith, BSc Bath Spa (*English*)
Reader Harris: Miss R Brown, BSc London, PGCE Bath (*Science*)
Kenelm: Miss M Dooley, CertEd Auckland, Dip Home Economics (*HE*)
Mulliner: Mrs L Parsons, MA Southampton, CertEd Bishop Otter (*PHSE*)

Staff:
* *Head of Department*

Art and Design:
*Miss J Newman, BA Norwich, ATC London
Miss J Wigley, BUWE
Mrs J A Baker, BA Leeds, ATD
Mr M D Chapman, MA Birmingham, BA Sunderland
Miss M Dooley, CertEd Auckland, Dip Home Economics
Ms A D Heron, BA Southampton
Mrs J Saurin, BA Sydney, MA Courtauld Institute, London
Mr T Taylor, CertEd Shoreditch College of Education
Mrs S H Wills, Dip Home Economics Aberdeen College (*Head of Fourth Forms*)
Miss T Farris, Leiths
Mr I McCarthy, BEng Leeds, PGCE
Miss L Gardiner, BA Arts Institute of Bournemouth, PGCE
Ms P Ellis, MA London, BA Courtauld Institute, London

Classics:
*Miss S Jones, BA Toronto
Mrs R M Allen, BA Birmingham (*Head of Middle Fifth*)
Mrs P English, MA Oxon (*Higher Education Adviser*)
Miss S Haslam, MA Cantab, PGCE

Drama and Theatre Studies:
*Mrs S Wolfenden, MA Roehampton Inst, Speech and Drama Diploma
Mr M Freestone, BA University of Natal
Ms J Moore, MA Warwick, BA Leicester, PGCE, DipEd Brighton
Mrs R Paige, CertEd Central School of Speech and Drama

English:
*Mr P R Cantrell, BA Nottingham
Mrs N Alper, BA Birmingham, PGCE (*CAS Coordinator*)
Mrs P Golovchenko, CertEd, RSA Dip SpLD
Ms K Chapman, BEd Southampton
Ms J M Seegers, BA OU, PGCE

Mrs C J Stones, MA Bristol, BA OU, Cert TEFL (*Head of EAL, International Coordinator, Archivist*)
Mrs J Ward, BA OU, SpLD Dip, TESL Toronto, AMI Toronto, PGCE
Mr S P Wood, BA Oxon
Mrs J Trew, BSc Bath, Dip Hornsby Int Dyslexia Centre (*Head of Learning Support*)

Geography, Economics and Business Studies:
*Mr G Collins, MA London, BA Reading, PGCE
Mr D Banks, BSc Cardiff, PGCE UWE
Mrs L Spears, BA London, PGCE
Mr P Richards, LLB Southampton, PGCE

History:
*Miss C Valeur, BA London
Mrs R M Allen, BA Birmingham
Mrs S Francis, MA Oxon

ICT:
Mr S Jefferson, MA Cantab (*Duke of Edinburgh's Award*)

Mathematics:
*Mrs M Wilson, BA York
Miss J Davidson, BSc UMIST, PGCE
Mr A Davies, BSc Cantab
Mr R Lavender, BSc Dunelm, PGCE
Dr A Moore, BEng, PhD Bristol, MA Nottingham
Miss T E Frith, MA Loughborough

Modern Languages:
*Mr M Felstead, MA Cantab
Mrs Y Bell, BA Birmingham
Mme M-D B Bonelli-Bean, Licence LLCE Paris
Mrs P J Fieldhouse, MA London, BA Rhodes, PGCE
Mrs D A Goldsack, BA Leeds
Mrs G Henderson, BA Exeter, PGCE
Mrs R Rogerson, Zurich
Mrs C Le Sueur
Mr A Osorio, Columbia

Music:
*Mr J M Jenkins, BA Dunelm, ARCO
Mr T J Urbainczyk, BA Dunelm (*Assistant Director of Music, Head of Strings*)
Mr S Clarkson, BMus Edinburgh, FRCO, ARCM (*Head of Academic Music*)
Miss Ana Manero (*Pianist in Residence*)
and 30 visiting teachers.

Musical tuition in:
Flute, Double Bass, Clarinet, Saxophone, Percussion, Singing, Alexander Technique, Oboe, Cor Anglais, Bassoon, Bass, Electric Guitar, Baroque Recorder, Classical Guitar, Brass, Viola, Cello, Percussion, Piano and Harp.

Physical Education:
*Mrs N Matthias, BEd St Peter & St Mary, Cheltenham
Miss J Brooker, BSc Gloucestershire
Mr J Brooker, BA London
Miss K Hoffman, BA North Carolina
Mrs K Stringer, BEd Crewe & Alsager College of PE
Mr M Stringer, DipEd St Luke's, Exeter

Religious Studies:
*Dr S D Loxton, PhD Seattle, BEd Sussex, MPhil Hull
The Revd Dr S Wood, PhD, MA Oxon
Mr P Woolway, BA Oxon, PGCE

Sciences:
*Dr J Ivimey-Cook, PhD Exeter
Miss P Abbott, BSc, Southampton
Mr D Buck, BSc London
Ms D B M Keating, BSc London, PGCE
Mr G Markham, BSc Dunelm, PGCE
Miss G Nelson, MSc East Anglia, BSc Dunelm
Mr P M Crabtree, BSc Leeds

Sanatorium Sister: Mrs J Hayes, SRN
Director of Admissions: Mrs F Clapp, BSc London, PGCE Oxon
Librarian: Miss P A Deacon, MA Oxon (*Director of IB*)
Marketing Coordinator: Miss K Nutland, BSc Bath Spa, ACIM
Web Producer: Miss Judith Seegers, BA OU, PGCE

Terms. Three terms of approximately 12 weeks each. Christmas holidays 4 weeks; Easter holidays 4 weeks; Summer holidays 8 weeks. Term dates are in common with those of Sherborne School.

Admission. (*see Scholarship Entries section*). Common Entrance Examination to Independent Schools. Scholarship Examinations and interviews. The School's own entrance examinations where Common Entrance is not possible. Girls should be registered in advance and reports will be requested from their current school. For entry into the Sixth Form girls are required to gain 5 good passes in relevant subjects.

Registration fee £100. A deposit of £750 is required before entry (a term's fees for overseas pupils) and credited to the last term's bill.

Fees per term (2008-2009). £8,800 for boarders and £6,400 for day girls.

Houses. There are five Houses for 13–17 year olds and one Upper Sixth House. 11 and 12 year old girls spend their first years together in a Junior House.

Religion. The School has a Church of England foundation, but it values the presence and contribution of members of all the Christian traditions and of other faiths. Regular services are held in the Abbey, some jointly with Sherborne School.

Examinations. Girls are prepared for GCSE, AS/A Levels and the International Baccalaureate Diploma. There is a wide choice of subjects to be studied. Some subjects at AS/A Level and IB are studied jointly with Sherborne School.

Games. Hockey and Lacrosse/Netball are played in the Michaelmas and Lent terms and Tennis, Rounders and Athletics during the Trinity term. Oxley Sports Centre in partnership with Sherborne Girls opened last year containing a 25m pool and state-of-the-art fitness suite. There are Squash Courts, floodlit Astroturf, Sports Hall, Dance Studio and Climbing Wall. Riding, Badminton, Cross-Country Running, Golf, Aerobics, Judo, Sailing, Trampolining are some of the alternative games.

Sherborne Old Girls Union (SOGU). All enquiries should be made to Mrs Diana Pring at the School, Tel: 01935 818329.

Prospective parents and their daughters are invited to the School for Open Mornings in the Spring and Autumn, or private visits by appointment. Please visit www.sherborne.com or telephone Admissions on 01935 818224 for further details.

Charitable status. Sherborne School for Girls is a Registered Charity, number 307427. It exists to provide education for girls in a boarding environment.

Shrewsbury High School (GDST)

Senior Department: 32 Town Walls Shrewsbury SY1 1TN
Tel: 01743 362872
Fax: 01743 364942
e-mail: enquiries@shr.gdst.net
website: www.gdst.net/shrewsburyhigh

Prep Department:
Old Roman Road Shrewsbury SY3 9AH
Tel: 01743 232132
e-mail: enquiries@shr.gdst.net

Pre-Prep Department:
33 Kennedy Road Shrewsbury SY3 7AA
Tel: 01743 271149
e-mail: enquiries@shr.gdst.net

Founded 1885. One of the 29 schools of The Girls' Day School Trust. For further information about the Trust, see p. xxiv.

In 2007 Shrewsbury High School merged with Kingsland Grange Prep School and has developed a new Prep Department with separate classes for girls and boys from September 2008. The school's website and prospectus contain comprehensive information.

Chairman of Local Governors: Mrs A Tudor, FCA

***Headmistress*: Mrs M Cass**, BA Exeter, MA EdMan Bath

Deputy Headmistress: Mrs H M Jones, BSc Liverpool

Joint Heads of Prep Department:
Mrs M Edwards, BEd Bedford, CertEd Primary Manchester
Mr M James, BSc, MSc London

Head of Pre-Prep Department: Mrs J Wallace, BMus Manchester

Head of Sixth Form: Mrs S Coppin, BSc Nottingham

Heads of Departments:

Art: Mr M Warner, BA Gwent
Biology: Mr B Brown, BSc Sheffield
Careers: Mrs D Higgs, BSc London
Chemistry: Mr D Payne, BSc Exeter
Classics: Mrs J Lashly, MA Oxford
Drama: Mrs C Evans, BEd Oxford
English: Mr C Steare, BA Cambridge
Geography: Miss J Campbell, BSc Hull
German: Mr S Cooper, BA London
History: Mr G Niblock, BA Belfast
Home Economics: Miss L Hughes, BA Liverpool
ICT: Mr T Curtis, BSc West London Inst, Brunel
Mathematics: Mrs J Mills, BSc Cardiff
Modern Languages: Miss R Smith, BA Durham
PE: Mrs R Sadd, BA Manchester
PSHE: Mrs S Merricks Murgatroyd, BA Manchester
Physics & Science: Dr S Richards, PhD London
Psychology: Mr A Ashley, BSc Open University, MA Keele, BSc Northumbria
RE: Ms E J Thomas, BEd Polytechnic of Wales

School Business Manager: Mrs B Lockley, BA
Admissions Officer: Mrs D Sutcliffe, BSc
Headmistress's PA: Mrs J Gittins
ICT Development Manager: Miss E Shaw
Network Manager, Mr L Hodgkinson, BA
Librarian: Mrs M Edmond
Marketing & Development Manager: Mr B Jason, BSc Manchester, MBA Manchester Metropolitan, MCIM
School Doctor: Dr L Houghton, MBBS, DCH, DRCOG, MRCGP
School Nurse: Mrs L Steeple, SRN

Number of Pupils. 803: 510 girls in Senior Department (age 11–18); 247 pupils in Prep and Pre-Prep Departments; 46 children in Nursery (age 2–4).

Shrewsbury High School is a high-performing school and its reputation as the county's premier girls' day school remains as strong as ever. The Senior Department extends along the Old Town Walls with gardens sweeping down the hill to the banks of the River Severn.

The merger with Kingsland Grange has led to a new structure from September 2008, on three sites all within walking distance. The Senior Department is unchanged, Kingsland Grange houses a new Prep Department for boys and girls, with separate classes for each across the core curriculum. Kennedy Road is now the Pre-Prep Department for children from age two to eight. It is expected that girls in the Prep will move up to the Senior Department at 11.

The school has invested considerably in key growth areas such as Information Technology. Other recent investments include a new Sports Hall and classroom complex for the Senior Department and a new Gym and classroom block at the Prep.

Curriculum. Alongside the academic subjects of the national curriculum, the school has excellent facilities for music, art and design, drama and sports. Public examination successes: 100% A level pass rate for six years, with 93.6% of A levels graded A–C in 2007. GCSE: 68.8% achieving A*/A grades, 98.6% grades A–C.

Sports include athletics, badminton, cricket, football, rugby, hockey, netball, rounders, swimming, tennis, rowing, canoeing, mountain-biking and volleyball. Opportunities exist for participation in debating, drama, Duke of Edinburgh's Award, music, public speaking, Amnesty, Young Enterprise at Senior School and ballet, judo, music, gym, crafts, ICT, chess and specialist speech and drama classes at the Junior Department.

Fees per term (2008-2009). Senior £2,966, Prep £2,417, Pre-Prep £2,150, Nursery £1,776.

The fees cover the regular curriculum, school books, stationery and other materials, entry fees for public examinations, choral music, games, and swimming, but not optional extra subjects or school meals. Full details are in the prospectus.

Admissions Procedures. Full details are available from the Admissions Officer.

Entrance Examinations. The 11+ Entrance Examinations are held in January. Sixth Form Scholarship Examinations are held in the Autumn Term of Year 11.

Open Days. Open Days are held from September to November each year, and also in April for the Prep and Pre-Prep.

Scholarships and Bursaries. The GDST provides a substantial number of scholarships and bursaries. Bursaries are means tested and ensure that the school remains accessible to bright girls who would profit from private education, but who would be unable to enter the school without financial assistance. They are available for entry at 11+. In cases of financial need bursaries may be available after entry to the Senior School.

Several scholarships are available each year for internal and external candidates for entry at 11+ or in the Sixth Form. Music scholarships for entry at 11+ are also available. Entrants must reach Grade 5 or above with their first instrument.

Charitable status. Shrewsbury High School is part of The Girls' Day School Trust, which is a Registered Charity, number 306983.

Sir William Perkins's School

Guildford Road Chertsey Surrey KT16 9BN
Tel: 01932 574900
Bursar: 01932 574910
Fax: 01932 574901
e-mail: reg@swps.org.uk
website: www.swps.org.uk

Founded 1725.

Board of Governors:
Chairman: Dr Alun Jones, CBE
Vice-Chair: Miss P W Triggs, FCA
Prof D W Holt, DSc Mech, FRCPath
Mrs M James, ALCM, MA
Revd T J Hillier
Mr A Eady, MA (*Solicitor*)
Mr M Sizmur, BSc, MIEE
Mrs D Stainbank, MA, FRSC
Mr D J Wareham
Mr I M F Balfour

Mrs K Clemo
Mrs C Jones
Mr G Want, EEng, MBA
Mrs M Walsh

***Headmistress*: Mrs S D Cooke**, BSc, MBA, PGCE

Deputy Headmistress: Mrs K Rowsell, BSc Bath
Director of Studies: Mr N Moughtin, BA Hons Leeds, MEd Nottingham
Head of Sixth Form: Mrs N Jenkin, MA

Staff:
* *Head of Department*

Mrs A Arnold, BA Keele
Mrs K Ball, BSc
Mrs S Bank, BA
Mrs C Bennett, BA
Miss E Bentley-Pattison, BA Newcastle, MA London, FRGS
Mrs E Bernard, BSc Birmingham
Mrs P A Berry, BA Manchester
Mrs S Bolton, BA East Anglia
Mrs M Bourne, BA Hull (**Geography*)
Mrs C Bowden, BA Bristol
Mr J Clatworthy, MA East Anglia (**English*)
Mrs E Collins, BA Warwick
Mrs C Cooper, BA Roehampton Inst, London (**French*)
Mrs J Creagh, BA Strathclyde (*Careers*)
Miss E Cross, BSc Bristol
Mr P Davies, CertEd Winchester (**Design and Technology*)
Mr A Dean, BA
Mrs P A Dennis-Jones, BA York (**Physics*)
Mr S Dodd, BSc Bath (**Chemistry*)
Mrs S Dodson, BA Wales (**German*)
Miss A Downey, BA, VCM, LRAM Music, LGSM, LLAM Drama, ADVS Voice
Miss C Duggan, BA Kent
Mrs H Eldridge, BA Leeds Metropolitan
Miss R England, BA Roehampton Institute
Miss V Gasston, BA
Mr M Gates, BMedSc Freestate, SA, MEd Freestate, SA
Miss H Golding, MMath
Ms A Gomez, BA Ealing College
Miss A Green, BA Roehampton
Mrs J Hamilton, MA St Andrews
Miss U Haring, MA
Dr I Harris (**Psychology*)
Mrs S Hay (**Home Economics*)
Mr P Holloway, BA Durham (**Music*)
Mrs E Hopes
Dr E Hudson
Miss C M Hudspith, BA Durham (**Classics*)
Mrs S Husselbury, BSc Natal
Miss H Jones, BA Leeds
Dr D Jordan, BA, PhD Brunel (**Religious Studies*)
Miss S Lawrence, BSc Birmingham
Mrs G Leese, MSc LSE
Mrs C Malcolm, BA Loughborough, MCLIP
Ms P Marriatt, BA Exeter
Dr C Masri, BSc London, PhD (**Biology*)
Mrs A Meecham, BSc Nottingham
Miss D Mugridge (**Physical Education*)
Mrs K Nessa, BA
Mrs S Page (**Business Studies*)
Mrs P A Parrish, BEd Manchester
Mrs S Pearson, MA London
Mrs G Penfold-Ward, MA
Mrs K Price, MA
Mrs B Rukuts
Mr I Russell, MA London (**Art & Design*)
Mrs T Scruton, BA LESM
Mrs E Searle, BEd Exeter
Mrs L Smith, BEd, MA Reading (**Information Technology*)
Mr R Staples, BSc London (**Science*)
Mrs C Steele, BSc Aberdeen (**Mathematics*)
Mrs M Stitt
Mrs S Sweeney, BA Wales (**Drama & Theatre Studies*)
Mrs F Synge, BA Hons London (**History*)
Mrs C Wells (*Counsellor*)
Mrs A White, BSc
Mrs J Wiggett, MA Cambridge
Mrs C Yarwood, BSc Birmingham

Bursar: Mr S Gallie
Head's Secretary: Mrs C Desai
Director of Communications & Admissions: Mrs S Hallsworth

Founded in 1725, the school was a voluntary controlled Grammar School before becoming Independent in 1978. It is a member of GSA. There are 580 day pupils between the ages of eleven and eighteen, drawn from a wide area.

Well served by bus routes and within five minutes' walk of Chertsey train station, five minutes drive of the M25 and M3. There are school bus services to and from the Windsor/Eton, Camberley and Twickenham areas.

Standing in twelve acres of gardens and playing fields, the school offers spacious accommodation, including Sixth Form, ICT and Language Centres. New facilities include improved art, dining, ICT, Science, Design Technology facilities and gym.

Curriculum. A well qualified, graduate staff teaches a modern curriculum aiming to provide a broad, balanced education. Most girls stay on in the Sixth Form, and nearly all Sixth Formers go on to degree courses; a number to Oxbridge.

Subjects offered include English, Mathematics, History, Geography, Economics, Business Studies, French, German, Spanish, Latin, Classical Civilisation, Greek, Biology, Physics, Chemistry, Science: Double Award, Design & Technology, Home Economics, Religious Studies, Art, History of Art, Music, Music Technology, Information & Communications Technology, Drama & Theatre Studies, Ethics & Philosophy, Critical Thinking.

Practical music and drama play an important part in school life. There is a strong instrumental and choral tradition with five choirs, orchestras, wind bands and many chamber ensembles. Dramatic and Musical productions are mounted annually. The school boasts 100% success rate in Victoria College of Music drama examinations. No other school, except a stage school, can offer this qualification and level of success.

Religious education is non-denominational. Pupils are expected to attend classes and a short act of worship in Assembly.

A wide variety of physical education activities is available. The Young Enterprise and Duke of Edinburgh's Award Schemes are well supported and very successful, and there are numerous clubs and societies.

Fees per term. Autumn Term 2008: £3,652, reviewed termly. Books and stationery are included. Private tuition in Music and Speech and Drama is extra. School lunch is available.

Entrance. Entry to Year 7 is by examination held in January for admission the following September. Entry at other levels, including the Sixth Form, is by academic record, examination and interview.

Scholarships. (*see Scholarship Entries section*). Some Scholarships and Bursaries are available, including Music, Academic and Foundation Scholarships.

Sir William Perkins's Former Pupils Association. Mrs Sheila Hallsworth, c/o The School.

Charitable status. Sir William Perkins's Educational Foundation is a Registered Charity, number 1060597, which exists to promote and provide for the education of children.

South Hampstead High School (GDST)

3 Maresfield Gardens London NW3 5SS
Tel: 020 7435 2899
Fax: 020 7431 8022
e-mail: senior@shhs.gdst.net
website: www.gdst.net/shhs

Founded 1876.

This is one of the 29 schools of The Girls' Day School Trust. For further information about the Trust, see p. xxiv. A more detailed prospectus may be obtained from the school.

Local Governors:
Chairman: Mr J Rosefield, BA Oxon, MBA Harvard
Mrs C Brill, CertEd
Miss E Clements, BA, BArch, RIBA, FRSA
Prof S Iversen, CBE, FMedSci, MA, PhD, ScD
Prof R Jackman, MA Cantab
Mrs N Perlman, LLB
Prof A Stevens, MA Cantab

***Headmistress*: Mrs J E Stephen**, BSc Leeds (*Chemistry*)

Deputy Heads:
Mrs A Lucas, BA Bristol, MA London (*History*)
Mr P M Keyte, MA Oxon (*Philosophy & Theology*)

Head of Sixth Form: Mrs D F Hugh, BA Manchester, MBA (*Modern Languages*)

Staff:
Mrs J Arundale, BSc Lancaster (*Physics*)
Mr P Arundale, BSc Manchester (*Chemistry*)
Mrs R J Banfield, BA Brighton (*Physical Education*)
Ms M Bastin, BMus, PG Dip Perf, LRAM (*Music*)
Mr M Bivand, MA London (*Art*)
Mrs V Boyarsky, BA Cantab, MPhil London (*History*)
Mrs J A Brown, BA Oxon (*English*)
Mr E Cabezas, Seville, Spain
Dr N Carling, PhD Cambridge, BSs Bristol (*Biology*)
Mrs J Coates, BA Bristol, MA Hawaii (*History*)
Mrs A Coker, BA Cantab, MA London (*English*)
Mrs E Curran, BA Reading, DipLib London (*Librarian*)
Dr B Davies, PhD London (*Mathematics*)
Mrs P Davis, BA Open (*ICT*)
Dr M M Egan, BA UCL, MA Essex, PhD UCL (*Politics and History*)
Mrs S Fanning, BSc London, Dip Arch RIBA (*Design Technology*)
Mrs C Finley, CAPES Toulouse (*Modern Languages*)
Mr K Fosbrook, BA Oxon (*Classics*)
Mrs L F Frank, BA York (*Mathematics*)
Ms R Furlonger, BA Cantab (*Classics*)
Mrs S Futter, DipAD Brighton, FCSD (*Design Technology*)
Mrs C E S Gibson, BSc Dunelm (*Mathematics*)
Mr B Harkins, BA Cantab, MA London (*English*)
Mr K C Harris, BSc Exeter (*Geography*)
Mr L Hearn, BSc Warwick, BSc Open (*Chemistry*)
Mr N Hunter, BA Liverpool (*Art*)
Mrs G Hurley, BA Brighton (*Physical Education*)
Mrs A S Johnson, BA Birmingham (*Religious Studies*)
Ms A Kennedy, BA Ulster, MA Philadelphia (*History of Art*)
Mrs S G Latto, MA Cantab (*Mathematics*)
Ms R Levick, MA Cantab (*English*)
Mr S Mackintosh, BA Oxon (*Economics*)
Mr E Meehan, MA Oxon (*English*)
Mrs S J Mitra, MA Bristol (*Religious Studies*)
Ms A Mobsby, BSc Wales (*Biology*)
Mrs P Morgan, MA Cantab (*History*)
Mr J C R Morris, BSc Open (*Chemistry*)
Ms S-J Mulcahy, BA (*Art*)
Mrs M C Pearce, M Des RCA (*Design Technology*)
Ms E Pierce, BSc Leicester (*Geography*)
Mrs L Raitz, MA Cantab (*Modern Languages*)
Mrs J Raitz (*Assistant Librarian*)
Mr S J Reid, MA Oxon, MMus Surrey (*Director of Music*)
Mrs H Rogers, BA Plymouth (*Physical Education*)
Mrs H Rose, BA Aberystwyth (*Drama*)
Miss S Shah, BA Cantab (*English*)
Mr M Smeaton, BA Leeds (*Spanish*)
Ms V M Spawls, BSc Westminster (*Biology*)
Mrs C Stevenson, MA London, MA Edinburgh (*Classics*)
Miss R J Stockdale, BHumMvemnt Tasmania (*Physical Education*)
Mr M Taylor, BSc Southampton (*Mathematics*)
Mrs P Tiger, BA Clermont Ferrand (*Modern Languages*)
Dr D J Walgate, BSc, PhD Cantab (*Physics*)
Mr D G Ward, BSc Nottingham, MA Open (*Physics*)
Mr M Weddell, BEng Brunel (*ICT Development Manager*)
Dr C J Woodward, BSc, PhD London (*Biology*)

Science Technicians:
Mrs C I Ezike, BSc
Mrs A Weekes

Junior Department:
Head of Junior Department: Mrs C Lough, MA Aberdeen
Miss A R Benjamin, Matriculation Leeds, CertEd
Miss C Collins, BA Middlesex
Mrs S C Cooper, BA Hull
Mrs M L Davenport, CertEd St Mary's
Miss Z Edwards, BA London
Miss N Fisher, BA Manchester
Miss J Franks, BA Birmingham
Miss A Fulton, BA Massey
Ms A L Harrison-Damms, BA Witwatersrand
Mrs B Honeyball, BEd Leicester
Miss A Luck, BA Nottingham Trent
Miss K Pidoux, BSc Bristol
Miss C Sousa, BA, BEd Brock

Teachers' Assistants:
Miss E Bartunekova
Miss S Silverstein
Miss R Ruiz
Miss A Javorkova
Mrs G Moris, MA

Visiting Staff:
Piano:
Ms J Clarke, BA, GRSM, LTCL, FTCL
Ms G Cracknell, LRAM
Mrs E Jones, LRAM
Mrs A Maneks, LRAM
Miss H Reid, BA, MA, ARCM
Ms H Seki, BA, ARAM, RecDipRAM, LRAM

Strings:
Ms C Cohen, BMus, LRAM (*Violin*)
Miss S Davis, BMus, MMus (*Cello*)
Ms L Moore (*Cello*)
Mr S Perkins, BMus, DipNCOS
Mrs R Wing, LRAM (*Violin*)
Ms S Young, GSMD (*Double Bass*)

Brass:
Ms D Calland (*Trombone*)
Mr D Clewlow, BA (*Trumpet, Trombone*)

Woodwind:
Ms F Carpos, ARCM (*Bassoon*)
Ms S J Clarke (*Clarinet*)
Ms K Corrigan
Mr I Judson, LRAM, LRWCMD (*Flute*)

Ms E Murphy, MMus, BMus, FTCL, LTCL (*Recorder*)
Miss E Tingey, LWCMD, ACC WCMD, TCM (*Oboe*)
Mr S West, GTCL, LTCL (*Saxophone*)

Percussion:
Mr T Marsden, BMus, MMus

Singing:
Miss K Bond, BMus, DipRAM, LRAM
Miss J Gardner Jones, MA, Dip ARCM
Miss C Hendricks, BMus
Mr V Kirk, ARCM
Ms H Mason, BMus
Mr M Miller, PhD, LGSM, ARCM (*Accompanist*)
Ms D Thomas
Miss M Vassiliou, BMus, ARCM

Theory: Ms J Clarke, BA, GRSM, LTCL, FTCL

Guitar: Mr R Fogg, BA

Administrative Staff:
School Business Manager: Miss A Forde
Accounts Manager: Mrs B Quilantang Ratcliff, BSc, CPA
Finance Assistant: Ms A Halai
Admissions Registrar: Ms P Karavla
Headmistress's Secretary: Mrs L Cripps
Deputy Heads' Secretary: Mrs S Halai
Junior School Secretary: Mrs F Badham
Teacher Resource Officer: Mrs S Bell
Receptionist: Ms Savani
Network Manager: Mr A Sumner
Network Support: Mr C Man
Audio Visual Technician: Mr J Parsotam
Site Supervisor: Mr M O'Connor
Caretakers: Mr D Lacey, Mr N Kingsley
School Nurse: Ms C Robinson

The school was opened in 1876 and is situated close to the Finchley Road and Swiss Cottage underground stations and to Finchley Road and Frognal railway station. It is also easily reached by bus from central, north and north-west London.

In the Senior School there are 573 pupils, including 142 in the Sixth Form. There are 242 girls in the Junior School. Entry to the Junior School is at 4 and 7; entry to the Senior School is at 11; occasional vacancies arise at other ages and new girls are welcomed into the Sixth Form if they achieve the necessary entrance qualifications. Full details of the admission procedures are available on written request.

The Junior School occupies two large houses with gardens about 5 minutes' walk from the Senior School. The Senior School premises, which are also used at times by girls from the Junior School, include a 4 acre sports ground, large sports hall, theatre, library, and specialist teaching accommodation including three Art studios, Design Technology rooms, Music and Music Technology rooms, Science laboratories and a fully computerised Modern Languages laboratory. The school is fully networked and the computer rooms are equipped with a wide range of software. The school minibus is used for expeditions and games transport. Sixth Form students occupy a large house on the Senior School site and their common room has its own kitchen, where they can prepare drinks and snacks. There is an extensive programme of visits and foreign exchanges, including work experience abroad.

The curriculum is planned to provide a wider general education and there is almost no specialism until the Sixth Form. The large compulsory "core" of subjects for GCSE includes three separate sciences or science with Additional Science, one modern foreign language and either History or Geography to which 2, 3 or 4 subjects are added. All girls in the Senior School are prepared for GCSE and Advanced level examinations and all leavers go on to university. Pupils are able and participate enthusiastically in an enormous number of extra-curricular clubs, societies and courses. Creativity in art, writing, music and drama is strongly encouraged at all stages. There are very many orchestras, ensembles and choirs. Tuition in almost any instrument and singing can be arranged and girls are prepared for the examinations of the Associated Board of the Royal School of Music. Large numbers of pupils participate in the Duke of Edinburgh's Award Scheme and Young Enterprise Business Scheme.

Fees per term (2008-2009). Senior School £3,700, Junior Department £2,879.

The fees cover the regular curriculum, games and swimming, but not school meals or instrumental/singing lessons. The fees for instrumental/singing lessons are detailed in the prospectus.

Scholarships and Bursaries. The GDST has made available to the school a number of scholarships and bursaries. The bursaries are means tested and are intended to ensure that the school remains accessible to bright girls who would profit from our education but who would be unable to enter the school without financial assistance.

There are at present available to internal or external candidates a number of Scholarships and Bursaries for entry at 11+ or to the Sixth Form.

Charitable status. South Hampstead High School is part of The Girls' Day School Trust, which is a Registered Charity, number 306983. The aim of the Trust is to provide a fine academic education for girls at a comparatively modest cost.

Stamford High School

St Martin's Stamford Lincolnshire PE9 2LL
Tel: 01780 484200
Fax: 01780 484201
e-mail: headshs@ses.lincs.sch.uk
website: www.ses.lincs.sch.uk

Founded by Browne's Hospital Foundation, of Stamford, 1876.

Motto: *Christe me spede*

Chairman of the Governing Body: Air Vice-Marshal P Dodworth, CB, OBE, AFC, BSc, FRAeS, DL

***Principal of the Stamford Endowed Schools*: S C Roberts,** MA

Vice-Principal, Head: Mrs Y L Powell, BEd, NPQH

Director of Studies: Mrs B A Szyjanowicz, BA, MEd
Guidance Coordinator: Mrs A J Horton, BA
CPD & Marketing Coordinator: Mrs D E Evans, BA
Head of Careers; Mrs S Killgren, BSc
Head of Sixth Form: Mrs C A Hawkins, BSc
SES Chaplain: The Revd M Goodman, BA, BTh, MTh
Director of ICT: N A Faux, MA
Librarian: Mrs A Virgo

Teaching Staff:

Miss K Ainsworth, BA
Miss K Allen, BSc, MSc
Mrs D Ashley, BA
Revd G B Austen, MA, MPhil
Mrs T R Bennie, BSc
M J Blissett, BA
P A Bowden, MA
Mrs C A S Boyfield, BA
Miss K Burghardt, BSc
Mrs C B Bysshe
Mrs M L Cade, BSc
Mrs L M Cannon, BSc
N S A Clift, BA
C Coles, MA
A J Cox, BA
Mrs A J B Cox, BA
Dr A Crookell, BSc, PhD
Mrs K Dexter, BA
A J Elliott, BEd
Mrs L Fisher, BA
Mrs Y Foreman, BA
R M Gale, BA
Mrs P A Galloway, RBTC
P Galloway, BA, Drama Dip
Mrs A P Gossel, BA
Miss J Hamphlett, BSc
Miss E A Hardy, BSc

G C Harman, BSc
Mrs L Harte, BSc
Dr T Hill, BSc, PhD
Mrs L Holden, BSc
Miss L Hornby, BA
Mrs J Husbands, BSc
Miss E L Jackson, BSc
Mrs A Johnson, MSc
Mrs L A Johnson, BSc
Mrs A Johnstone, MA
Mrs B Joint, BEd
Miss E Kerbrat, BA, MA
Mrs I M Matthews, BA
Mrs S Matthews, BA
Mrs G Moss, BSc
Mrs E Mount, BEd
Miss H Myles, BA
Miss F Pace, BA
Mrs A Rackham, BA
Miss A D Reilly, BSc
Mrs S Russell, MA
Mrs E Salt, BA
Mrs V Saunders, BA
M P Scriven, BA
J Stewart-Greatorex, BEd
Mrs C Vie, BA
Mrs N J Watson, BA
Mrs A Wenban, BA
C C M West-Sadler, MA
G J Whitehouse, BEd
C Williamson, BA
Mrs K Wilson, BEd
Mrs V Wilson, MA

Music Department:
G E Turner, BA (*Director of Music*)
D McIlrae, BMus, HED (*Assistant Director of Music*)
S Chandley, CT ABRSM (*Head of Brass*)
Mrs N Ingrams, GRSM, RAM, LRAM
D Leetch, MA, GRSM, LRAM (*Head of Strings*)
Mrs J E Roberts, GRSM, LRM, ARCM
N S Taylor, BA

Visiting Music Staff:
S Andrews (*Kit Drum/Percussion*)
F Applewhite (*Violin, Viola*)
J Aughton (*Flute*)
S Barber (*Organ*)
C Bell, BSc, LRAM, ARCM (*Guitar*)
Mrs M Bennett, LRAM, LTCL (*Singing*)
Mrs S Bond, GLCM, LLCM (*TD*), FLCM (*Singing*)
Mrs K Bentley, GTCL, LTCL (*Cello, Double Bass*)
F Black (*Singing*)
G Brown, BMus (*Oboe, Piano*)
Mrs H Brown, BA (*Clarinet*)
P J Casson (*Saxophone, Clarinet*)
Miss A Chalmers, LRAM (*Cello, Double Bass*)
Revd Mrs J Dumat, ARCM (*Clarinet*)
M Duthie, BSc, ARCO (*Organ*)
N Gray (*Electric Guitar*)
Mrs E Hanlon, ARMCM (*Pianoforte*)
Mrs C Lee, LRAM (*Violin*)
Miss F Maclennan (*Pianoforte*)
Mrs M Maclennan, LRAM, ARCM (*Pianoforte*)
Mrs A McCrae (*Bassoon, Pianoforte*)
Mrs E Murphy, GTCL, LTLL, PGCE (*Violin, Pianoforte*)
D Price, LRAM (*Brass*)
Mrs G Spencer, CertEd, ACRM (*Pianoforte*)
Mrs A Sumner, CertEd, ARCM (*Pianoforte*)
Mrs E A Taylor, BA (*Violin, Viola*)
Mrs L Williamson, LTCC (*Pianoforte*)

Boarding:

Welland House:
Mr & Mrs A Cox (*Houseparents*)
Mrs M Tyers (*Assistant Housemistress*)
Mrs J Rose (*Assistant Housemistress*)

Park House:
Mrs J Sanford (*Resident Housemistress*)
Mrs S Johnson, Mrs W Hartley, Mrs J Rose (*Assistant Housemistresses*)
Mrs S Kavanagh (*Deputy Housemistress*)

Medical Officer: Dr J Barney, MBChB, DAvMed, DOccMED, MRCGP

Introduction. Stamford High School is one of three schools within the overall Stamford Endowed Schools Educational Charity, along with Stamford School (boys) and Stamford Junior School, the co-educational Junior School.

Numbers and Boarding Houses. There are 620 girls aged 11–18 years including boarders. The main point of entry is at age 11 though applications are welcomed at any stage up to the Sixth Form. Girls who enter through the Junior School progress automatically on to the High School without further competitive entrance test. Boarders are received from the age of 8 (in the Junior School). There are two Boarding Houses for girls including a Sixth Form Boarding House where the girls have single or shared study bedrooms. The School accepts full and weekly boarders as well as considering flexi-boarding according to family need.

Fees per term (2008-2009). Day £3,616; Full Boarding £6,768; Weekly Boarding £6,732.

These fees include all stationery, text books and games. School lunches for day girls are at additional charge.

Registration Fee £50. Acceptance Fee £250.

Extras. Individual music lessons, Speech and Drama, Dancing (Riding for boarders only).

Curriculum. The curriculum is designed to ensure all girls have a balanced educational programme up to age 16 thus avoiding premature specialisation. The National Curriculum is broadly followed but much more is added to the curriculum to make it stimulating and rewarding. Most girls are entered for at least 9 GCSE examinations and for GCE AS and A Level examinations leading to university entry. In partnership with Stamford School, all Sixth Form girls have access to the full range of A Level subjects offered across the two schools providing an exceptionally wide range of subject choice.

Throughout their time in the school girls are prepared for the examinations of the Associated Board of the Royal Schools of Music in Music and The London Academy of Music and Dramatic Art for Speech and Drama. There is much scope for creative activities in Music, Art and Drama and state-of-the-art facilities for Information & Communication Technology, including access to the Internet. The Director of Music for the Stamford Endowed Schools ensures that the Music Department works very closely with Stamford School providing access to a wide range of activities of orchestras, bands, Chapel Choir and choirs. There are joint drama productions and a Performing Arts Studio was opened in September 1995.

Sport and Physical Education include Hockey, Netball, Tennis, Swimming, Golf, Judo, Athletics, Volleyball, Basketball, Badminton, Trampoline, Gymnastics and Squash. There is a very full programme of extra-curricular activities including Olympic Gymnastics, Athletics and TaeKwonDo. There is a heated, indoor swimming pool, a Sports Hall and a floodlit artificial hockey pitch. The Duke of Edinburgh's Award Scheme operates at Bronze, Silver and Gold levels with a considerable number of girls taking part each year. There is a thriving, mixed CCF offering RN, Army and RAF sections. There are many school clubs and societies and a thriving weekend activity programme.

Entrance Examinations are held in January.

Scholarships. (*see Scholarship Entries section*). Governors' Scholarships at 11+ and for the Sixth Form. Awards may be given for musical ability and art. Bursaries up to full fees are available.

Charitable status. As part of the Stamford Endowed Schools, Stamford High School is a Registered Charity, number 527618. It exists to provide education for girls.

Stonar School

Cottles Park Atworth Melksham Wiltshire SN12 8NT
Tel: 01225 701740
Fax: 01225 790830
e-mail: office@stonarschool.com
website: www.stonarschool.com

Governors:

Chairman: Mrs S Baldwin

Mr H Adam, BA, MCIPD
Mrs M Anderson
Mr C Beard
Mr D Butler, FRICS
Mr A Macpherson, BA, ACA, JP
Dame Elizabeth Neville, DBE, QPM
Mrs Sarah Outhwaite
Mrs E Prescott-Decie
The Venerable John Wraw

Bursar and Clerk to the Governors: Harriet Feilding, BA Oxon, ACA

***Headmistress*: Mrs Shirley Shayler**, MA, BSc Hons, PGCE

Deputy Headmaster: Mr T Nutt, MSc, BSc Hons, PGCE

Senior Staff:
Mrs S Adams, ALIA, MA London (*Librarian*)
Mrs S Askew (*Learning Support*)
Mr T Baddeley, MA Cantab, PGCE (*German*)
Mrs C Bennett, BA Hons UCL, PGCE (*Head of Geography*)
Mrs J Brighouse, BA Hons PGCE (*EAL, Houseparent*)
Mr S Butler, BA Homes, PGCE (*History*)
Mrs A Callow, BSc Hons Glos, PGCE (*PE & Dance*)
Mrs L Carolan, BA Hons Bath Spa, PGCE (*Art*)
Mrs J Cross, BEd Bulmershe College of HE (*English/SENCO*)
Miss C Deans, BA Bristol, TEFL Cert (*EAL*)
Dr S Divall, MA, PhD Cantab, PGCE (*Head of Physics*)
Mrs L Doliczny, BSc Hons Warwick, PGCE (*Mathematics*)
Mrs H Dziedzic, BSc Hons Wales, PGCE (*Head of Biology*)
Mrs A Fullalove, MA, BA, PGCE (*Mathematics*)
Mr N Goodall, BA Hons Notts, MMus, PGCE London (*Head of Music/IT*)
Mrs L Hawkins, BSc (*Mandarin*)
Mrs L Jones, BA Hons Leicester, BPhil, PGCE (*Head of English*)
Mrs M-P Jones, BA Hons OU (*French*)
Mrs P Lloret, BA Hons Birmingham, PGCE (*Spanish*)
Mr R Miller, BA Hons (*Director of Sport and PE*)
Mrs R Morgan, BEd (*Maths, Head of Boarding*)
Mrs J Mortlock, CertEd Liverpool (*Head of Home Economics*)
Mrs S Muir, BA Natal, DipEd (*Head of History & Careers*)
Mrs B Myers, BEd Hons Bristol (*Music/Religious Studies*)
Ms P Nix, BSc Hons Southern Mississippi, PGCE (*Chemistry*)
Mrs K Pickles, BEd Sheffield (*Head of Home Economics*)
Mrs V Power, BSc Cardiff, PGCE (*Science*)
Mr N Proud, BA Bath, PGCE (*Drama*)
Mrs E Reeves, BSc Hons, PGCE (*Chemistry*)
Mrs A Rivers, BSc Hons, PGCE Bristol (*Mathematics*)
Mrs G Sherman, BSc OU, ALA (*IT*)
Mrs L Smith, BSc Hons Wales, PGCE (*Geography/Mathematics*)
Mr C Stark, BSc Bristol, PGCE London (*Psychology*)
Miss J Storey, BHSI regd, ANCEBM (*Director of Equitation*)
Mrs N Teasdale, AENA L2 (*PE*)
Mrs K Watson, BA Hons, PGCE (*English*)
Mrs P Willcox, BA Hons Exeter, PGCE (*Learning Support*)
Mrs J Whymark, BA Hons (*Mathematics*)

Preparatory School & Nursery Department:
Head: Mr M Brain, BA Ed Hons Exeter
Deputy Head: Mrs A Thethy, BEd Worcester

Mrs S Askew (*Classroom Assistant*)
Mrs C Bath, CertEd London
Mrs F Box, CertEd, BEd Bristol
Mrs E Howard, NVQ3 (*Nursery Manager*)
Mrs G Johnson, TCert Hereford
Mrs S Musselwhite, BA Essex, PGCE
Miss E Paget, BSc Hons Durham, PGCE
Miss S van Gerwen, BA Ed Hons Canterbury
Mr A Walker, BA Hons Mus Bangor

Ethos. Stonar is a centre of academic excellence for girls, developing the talents and abilities of every individual and providing the breadth of opportunity to support and enable pupils of all abilities to achieve their potential across and beyond the formal curriculum. There is a positive work ethic and quality pastoral care. Curiosity, confidence and independence are encouraged so that pupils leave school well-equipped for the challenges of adult life and keen to contribute to the wider community.

Curriculum. A talented and committed staff offer students a broad and flexible curriculum, with literacy and numeracy firmly at the centre of the junior school timetable and an individual choice from wide ranging options in addition to the core of Science, Maths, English, a foreign language and ICT at GCSE. AS and A2 courses can include Psychology, Photography, Business Studies, PE and IT.

Science is popular and the new Head of Science has entered Stonar into the Royal Aero Society's human powered aircraft competition – the world's first female powered aircraft is expected to make a test flight in July 2008.

Results are good and students go on to university courses ranging from Medicine, Law and Accountancy to Geology, Veterinary Science and Music. Talented artists proceed to a variety of Art Foundation Courses. Young riders take up careers in eventing or go for the Equine Studies option. The BHSAI and a top-level Equestrian Competition Course are available in the Sixth Form.

Extra-curricular Activities. On site Sports Hall, Swimming Pool, Astroturf, Theatre, Music and Art schools and an internationally renowned Equestrian Centre offer first-class opportunities for sport, music, drama and riding. A timetabled tutorial period provides a rolling programme of careers advice, health education, study skills, first aid, self defence, citizenship and industrial awareness. Girls enjoy debating, dance, film studies, aerobics, cookery and camping. The Duke of Edinburgh's Award scheme flourishes at Stonar.

Boarding. Boarders live in comfortable, family style houses. The first phase of our new Sixth Form Centre will be complete by September 2008. Each girl has her own e-mail address for maintaining close contact with home, with the school's fibre optic network extending into every academic building and boarding house. Girls of any religion and of all nationalities are welcomed and can work towards IGCSE English, if this is not their first language.

Admission. Straightforward entrance procedures via Stonar entrance examinations, Common Entrance or school report at appropriate ages.

Fees per term (2008-2009). Prep Day £1,995–£3,220; Senior Day £3,895; Prep Boarding £5,890; Senior Boarding £6,860.

Scholarships and Bursaries. (*see Scholarship Entries section*). The school offers special Services bursaries and scholarships for riding, sport, music, drama, art, academic excellence and for the good all-rounder.

Charitable status. Stonar School is a Registered Charity, number 309481. It offers highest educational provision for girls.

Stover School

Newton Abbot South Devon TQ12 6QG
Tel: 01626 354505 (365279 out of hours)
01626 331451 (Preparatory School)
01626 335240 (Bursary)
Fax: 01626 361475

e-mail: mail@stover.co.uk
website: www.stover.co.uk

Board of Governors:

Chairman: Mr R Barlow, DL, FRICS
Chairman of Finance Committee: Mr R Wyatt-Haines, FCIB, MCIM, MBA
Vice Chair:
Mrs K Reece
Mrs M Batten, BSc

Members:
Mr H Akhtar
Mr H Anderson, BSc
Mrs A Anning
Miss F R Evans, CertEd
Professor R Hawker, OBE
Mr N Hole, BSc, RICS
Capt B Key, BSc RN
Dr P J Key, OBE, MB, BS
Revd C R Knott, BA
Mrs C Walliker, BSc MBA

***Principal*: Mrs Susan Bradley**, BSc, CBiol, MIBiol, PGCE

Assistant Principal Senior School: Mrs K Veal, BEd
Assistant Principal Preparatory School: Mrs C Coyle, BEd, MA
Head of Boarding: Mr C Housecroft, BSc, PGCE
Senior Teacher Academic: Mrs M Kearney, BEd
Head of Sixth Form: Mr T Wightman, BA, PGCE
Bursar: Mr S Drabble, BSc

Estates & Domestic Bursar: Mrs H Goodwin
Chaplain: Mrs F Wimsett, BA
Principal's PA: Miss D Robins, BA
Registrar: Miss F White
Senior School Secretary: Mrs B Lea
Preparatory School Secretary: Mrs F Martin
Administrative Assistants: Mrs H Symons, Miss L Lount
Bursar's Assistants: Mrs M Barnard, Mrs G Hanbury

Academic Staff:
Ms P Absalom, BA, PGCE (*English and Performing Arts*)
Dr D Allway, BSc, MSc, PhD (*Head of Science*)
Mrs M Ayela, DEUG, Licence ES, PGCE (*Spanish*)
Mr C Baillie, BSc, PGCE (*Psychology*)
Ms A Barr, BA Ed, HND, PG Dip (*Media Studies*)
Mr P Barter, BA, PGCE (*Head of History*)
Miss C Bennett, BA, PGCE (*Art*)
Miss K Broadhurst, BA, PG Dip, PGCE (*History*)
Mr C Brown, BA ODP (*Head of Physical Education, Stover Preparatory School*)
Miss C Bulford, BEd (*Physical Education*)
Mrs A Butler, BSc (*Head of Home Economics*)
Mrs M Corby, BSc, DipEd (*Head of Mathematics*)
Mrs H Coyne-Stacey, BA (*Modern Languages*)
Miss T Craven, BA, PGCE (*Head of Physical Education*)
Mrs L Creates, BA, MA (*Head of Geography*)
Mrs R Dawson, BA, MA, PGCE (*Learning Support Teacher*)
Mrs L Decamville, BA, CertEd (*Head of Access to Curriculum in English*)
Mrs V Elce, BA, PGCE (*Head of Religious Studies, Geography*)
Miss E Evans, BA, PGCE (*Head of Modern Languages*)
Mrs G Fletcher, CertEd ITEC (*Home Economics*)
Mr G Forsyth, BA, PGCE, TEFL (*English*)
Mrs K Gardner, BA, PGCE (*Mathematics*)
Mrs S Griffin, BEd (*Years 6 & 7*)
Mr J Haigh, MA (*Mathematics*)
Mrs M Hawkins, BEd, Cert SEN (*Learning Support Teacher*)
Mrs P Johnson, BEd (*Art, Learning Support*)
Mrs S Kensington, BA, AMBDA (*Head of Learning Support*)
Mr S Lea, MA, LTCL, GTCL, MA (*Director of Music*)
Mrs E Machin, BA, PGCE (*Head of ICT*)
Mrs V Mackie, BSc, PGCE (*Biology*)
Mrs M McVitty (*Learning Support*)
Mrs C Middleton, BA, MA (*ACE*)
Mrs J Middleton, BA, PGCE (*Head of English and Drama*)
Ms A O'Donovan, BEd, ALCM (*Music*)
Mr S Pillinger, BA, MA, PGCE (*Business Studies*)
Mrs A Richards, BSc, PGCE (*Physics*)
Mrs C Simmons, BEd
Mrs H Skuckova, BA, PGCE (*Mathematics*)
Ms S Trainer, Dip Theol, CertEd (*Head of RE*)
Mr D Veal, BA, PGCE (*Science and Head of Senior Boys PE*)
Miss H Warman, C&G 324 (*Learning Support*)
Mr T Wightman, BA, PGCE (*Head of Art & Photography*)
Mrs H Wills, ALCM (*Music*)
Mrs N Winston (*French*)
Mrs F Wimsett, BA (*RE, Chaplain*)

Visiting Staff:
Mr J Allnatt (*Double Bass*)
Mr J Baldwin (*Keyboard, Piano*)
Mrs A Brown (*Piano*)
Miss L Cordon (*Recorder and Piano*)
Mr S Douglas (*Drum kit*)
Mrs S Farleigh (*Voice*)
Miss C Hayek (*Violin and Viola*)
Miss Hiley (*Percussion*)
Mr P Hill (*Guitar*)
Mr M Holland (*Brass*)
Mr P Hurst (*Accompanist*)
Mr E Kingdom (*Drum Kit*)
Mr D Leaford (*Woodwinds*)
Mrs A O'Donovan (*Woodwinds, Piano, Keyboard*)
Mrs E Rainsford McMahon (*Piano*)
Mr T Unwin (*Jazz Piano*)
Mrs H Wills (*Cello, Piano*)
Miss J Berry, BA, MA (*Speech & Drama*)
Mrs R Dawson, BA, MA (*Speech and Drama, Learning Support*)
Mr R Bond, BTCA (*Tennis*)

Stover Preparatory School:

Assistant Principal: Mrs C Coyle, BEd, MA

Mr M Appleby, DipEd, BEd
Mr M Ayer, BSc
Mr C Brown, BA
Miss J Edwards, NNEB
Mr N Futrell, BA
Mrs M Hind, NVQ3, EYCE
Mrs S Holmes, BA, PGCE
Miss J Jamin, BEd
Mrs C Middleton, BA, MA
Mrs M Pallister, BEd
Miss S Pannell, BA Ed
Mrs J Parsons
Mr K Perkins, BA
Mrs R Reynolds, BSc, PGCE
Mrs J Sanders, NNEB
Mrs L Smale, BA, PGCE
Miss E Soper, BEd
Mrs S Stoddart, BA (*Head of Nursery*)
Mrs F Waring, CertEd, DELE

Nursery Assistants:
Mrs D Battershall
Mrs J Cross, NNEB
Mrs I McIntosh, NNEB
Mrs L Sharrock, NVQ3

Residential Staff:
Mr C Housecroft, BSc, PGCE (*Head of Boarding*)
Miss K Broadhurst, BA, PG Dip (*Housemistress*)
Mrs G Fletcher, CertEd, ITEC (*Housemistress*)

Miss M Leslie-Ellis, SEN SNR (*Assistant Housemistress*)
Miss C Bennett (*Assistant Housemistress*)

Each House also has attached Boarding Assistants:
Miss A Key
Miss E Bush

School Medical Officer: Dr D Milburn, MB, BS
School Nurses:
Miss S Edworthy, RGN
Miss M Leslie-Ellis, SEN SNR

Stover School is situated within a 60-acre estate that was once the seat of the Dukes of Somerset. Located just off the A38 on the southern edge of the Dartmoor National Park, Stover is easily accessible and surrounded by areas of outstanding natural beauty. The School has good access by road and rail to major cities and airports. Escort services are arranged.

Stover Senior School was founded in 1932 and was run as an all-girls senior school until 1995, when the First Steps Nursery was opened. Due to the rapid expansion, the Governors decided to open an all-girls Preparatory school in 1996 which grew rapidly and was joined by a new Boys section in January 2002, with a total now of 150 pupils. Facilities have been developed in line with this growth with a £50,000 extension to Stover Preparatory School having been completed in 2005.

A significant development was the introduction of boys into the Senior School from September 2005, turning Stover into a "diamond" school, where boys and girls in Year 3 to Year 11 are taught separately but mix for social and extra-curricular activities. The Pre-Preparatory School is co-educational and in September 2007 boys joined the Sixth Form for the first time and the Sixth Form is now co-educational.

Boarding facilities are currently provided for girls only; we are the only major girls' boarding school in Devon and Cornwall. Stover is well supported; total numbers are around 500 and the school has a fine reputation locally and nationally. Overseas boys who join Stover reside with host families and travel to school by bus.

The aim of the school is to prepare pupils for the twenty-first century by giving them a sound and flexible education and by encouraging them to develop initiative and self-discipline.

Throughout the school extra-curricular activities are given great importance and are designed to develop a wide range of skills and abilities. The Duke of Edinburgh's Award Scheme is well established as is Ten Tors and overseas expeditions have included trips to the West Indies, South Africa, Australia, Costa Rica, California, Paris and Barcelona with plans for an Art tour to New York in December 2008 and a sports tour to Barbados in July 2009.

The main building is an eighteenth century mansion in sixty acres of landscaped gardens and playing fields. Facilities are good and include six all-weather tennis courts, performing arts and music halls and a site wide computer network. Developments have included the Sixth Form Centre, to house an enlarged Sixth Form of between 50 and 60 students each year, and the opening of a £350,000 Art, Photography and Media Centre by HRH The Princess Royal in January 2001. A new £1¼m Science Laboratory building was completed for the start of the Autumn Term 2005.

Examinations. Public examinations set by all examination boards are taken at GCSE Level and at A level. Music examinations are set by the Associated Board of the Royal Schools of Music. Speech and Drama examinations are set by LAMDA.

Games. Hockey, netball, rugby, football and cross country are winter and spring term competitive sports. Gymnastics and dance are also compulsory elements of the Physical Education programme. There are six tennis courts and tennis is the major summer sport, but rounders, cricket and athletics are also important competitive summer activities. Inter-house and inter-school fixtures are played in all sports.

Optional subjects. In addition to a wide variety of activities organised by Stover's own staff there are specialist peripatetic staff for instrumental and voice tuition, speech and drama, riding and tennis coaching.

Fees per term (2008-2009). Senior School: Year 6: £2,775 (day), £4,950 (weekly boarding), £5,235 (full boarding); Years 7–13: £3,140 (day), £5,500 (weekly boarding), £6,495 (full boarding). Preparatory School: Day: £1,990–£2,435.

Entrance and Scholarships. Entrance examinations are set by Stover and all candidates who sit examinations in January are eligible for academic awards. Music, Art and Sport scholarships and Sixth Form scholarships are available. In addition there are means-tested Maurice Key Sixth Form scholarships, the Laurus scholarships and means-tested bursaries.

Health. Twenty four hours a day nursing care is provided by a team of SRNs and regular visits by a local GP.

Stover Portico Association. *Secretary*: Mrs E Shillabeer, c/o Stover School.

Charitable status. Stover School Association is a Registered Charity, number 306712. Stover School is a charitable foundation for education.

Streatham and Clapham High School (GDST)

42 Abbotswood Road Streatham London SW16 1AW
Tel: 020 8677 8400 (Senior Department & Sixth Form Centre)
020 8674 6912 (Junior Department & Nursery)
Fax: 020 8677 2001
e-mail: enquiry@shc.gdst.net
website: www.gdst.net/streathamhigh

Founded 1887.

This is one of the 29 schools of The Girls' Day School Trust. For further information about the Trust, see p. xxiv.

Additional information may be found on the school's website and a more detailed prospectus may be obtained from the school.

Chairman of Local Governors: Mrs A Maryon-Davies

***Head*: Mrs Susan Mitchell**, Oxon, PGCE, NPQH

Deputy Head: Ms Alexandra Hardy, BSc Hons UCL, PGCE Institute of Education, London, NPQH

Head of Junior Department: Miss Louisa Burke, BEd Hons, MA Ed, PG Dip Psych

Head of Sixth Form: Mrs Veronica Mills, BSc, MSc, PGCE

Admissions Secretary: Mrs Phyllis Warner

Pupil numbers. Senior Department 450; Junior Department 226; Nursery 18.

Streatham and Clapham High School GDST is a happy and successful school situated on two sites. The Senior Department is based on an attractive campus, surrounded by spacious grounds, next to Tooting Bec Common. The school is easily accessible to local mainline stations at Balham and Streatham Hill, and to numerous bus services from Streatham High Road. The Millennium Building, opened in 2003, adds a new Sixth Form Centre (to house the growing Sixth Form), Music Suite and Recital Room to the existing facilities, which include a magnificent Sports Hall, Art Studio and Fitness Centre. The Junior Department and Nursery, are based in nearby Wavertree Road and have large and well-equipped premises, including a new library. The Nursery moved in September from a separate site to be fully integrated into the school as part of the foundation stage area. The Nursery children now have their own specially designed indoor and outdoor space built specifically around their needs. The school has some of the best facilities in South London and attracts pupils from a wide radius, as well as from the immediate vicinity.

Streatham and Clapham High School figures prominently in the National League tables and is consistently ranked top in the league tables for Lambeth schools. Girls in both the Junior and Senior Departments enjoy a relevant and practical curriculum, culminating in preparation for GCE examinations at GCSE and AS/A2 Level, and for entrance and scholarship examinations to Oxford and Cambridge. The school has pioneered the study of AS/A Level subjects such as Law, Psychology and Sociology by Distance Learning. A wide variety of sports is offered by both Departments; some of these take place in lunch time activity slots alongside arts and music clubs. Arts are strong, with orchestras, choirs and various musical groups, and the proximity to central London makes possible many excursions to concerts, as well as to museums, art galleries and theatres. Regular trips abroad are offered, including foreign exchanges to France, Germany and Spain. Pupils can participate in the Duke of Edinburgh's Award Scheme and have substantial involvement with the local community, raising funds for charities.

The school has an excellent reputation for pastoral care. Two sixth-formers are assigned to each class to support new entrants. Parents are kept in touch with their child's progress through regular feedback. In-depth reports are sent home twice each year, there are regular parents' evenings, and Effort and Attainment grades are issued routinely. Prefects and a Head Girl are elected by the staff and senior school members. Girls' successes are celebrated at assemblies. There is a School Council and effective provision for special needs pupils.

Admission. There are five main stages for Admission: by assessment for the Nursery (3+ years), 4+ and 7+, by Entrance Examination at 11+ or at Sixth Form level. Occasional places sometimes arise at any age; interested parents are advised to contact the Admissions Secretary.

Fees per term (2008-2009). Senior Department £3,700, Junior Department £2,879, Nursery £2,221.

The fees cover the regular curriculum, books, school meals for Juniors, stationery and other materials, choral music, games and swimming, but not optional extra subjects.

Bursaries. Bursaries, which are means tested and related to academic ability, are available at 11+ and at Sixth Form entry. Applications for bursaries at other levels can be made to the Head in cases of financial need. All requests are considered in confidence.

Scholarships. Scholarships are available to internal and external candidates at 11+ and at Sixth Form level. These are awarded according to academic talent and for art and music, covering a maximum of 50 per cent of the fees.

Charitable status. Streatham and Clapham High School is part of The Girls' Day School Trust, which is a Registered Charity, number 306983. The aim of the Trust is to provide a fine academic education for girls, which is distinguished by its breadth, as well as its depth.

Surbiton High School (UCST)

Surbiton Crescent Kingston-upon-Thames Surrey KT1 2JT

(See entry in HMC section)

Sutton High School (GDST)

55 Cheam Road Sutton Surrey SM1 2AX
Tel: 020 8642 0594
Fax: 020 8642 2014
e-mail: office@sut.gdst.net
website: www.gdst.net/suttonhigh

Founded 1884. Celebrating 125 years in 2009.

This is one of the 29 schools of The Girls' Day School Trust. For general information about the Trust, see p. xxiv. A more detailed prospectus may be obtained from the school.

Chairman of Local Governors: Mrs Anne Pearcey

***Headmaster*: Mr S J Callaghan**, BA Durham, NPQH

Deputy Head: Mrs L Cole, BEd Hons Leeds, BA Hons, MA Open, NPQH

Assistant Heads:
Mrs D Holloway, BA Hons Open, MBA Open
Ms P Hutchinson, BEd Liverpool
Mrs K Crouch, BSc Leicester
Miss J Taylor, BSc Hons Nottingham

Head of Sixth Form: Mrs E Clark, BSc Econ Southampton

Head of Junior Department: Mrs E Wilson, BEd London

Deputy Junior Head: Mrs J Little, CertEd London

Administrative Staff:
School Business Manager: Ms E Wilson
Marketing and Communications Officer: Mrs N New
Admissions Secretary: Mrs J Ward

Sutton High School, founded in 1884, is a member of the Girls' Day School Trust and provides continuity of education for girls from 3 to 18 years. It has a strong reputation for providing a broad, balanced education for all girls in a happy working environment. Distinguished former pupils include the novelist Susan Howatch, BBC correspondent Sue Littlemore, and Ruth Kelly, MP.

There are 774 girls in the school: 322 aged 3–11 years in the Junior School and 452 aged 11–18 years in the Senior School. The Sixth Form is 105 strong. Girls enter the school aged 3+, 4+, 11+, 13+ or 16 after taking the school's own entrance tests. With occasional places available throughout the school year. Open Mornings take place in the Autumn, Spring and Summer Terms when girls provide enthusiastic and informative tours of the school and the Headmaster provides a welcoming talk and is available to answer questions. Further information and personal tours during the school day can be arranged by ringing the Admissions Secretary or e-mailing the school (J.Ward@sut.gdst.net).

Aims and Values. Sutton High School recognises that each girl is an individual. In a secure and friendly community we aim to identify and nurture potential in girls so their abilities and talents can flourish.

The school provides a broad and challenging curriculum in and beyond the classroom so that all our pupils develop a love of learning, self-confidence and respect for others.

Sutton High School enables girls to appreciate and enjoy the wider world while generating opportunities for themselves and for others.

Situation. The school occupies a central position in Sutton and is reached easily by train or bus from Dorking, Leatherhead, Epsom, Carshalton, Wallington, Worcester Park, New Malden, Wimbledon and Burgh Heath. A school bus services runs every morning from the Wimbledon area, picking up at 4 locations. The school is only 5 minutes' walk from Sutton Station. A new green travel plan for the school has been developed and is being supported by the London Borough of Sutton.

Facilities. The Junior and Senior Schools provide well-resourced accommodation for all major subjects. A large sports hall is located next to the indoor swimming pool and girls have access to astroturf pitches, netball and tennis courts. There is a dedicated music building and well-equipped art facilities.

The Sixth Form Centre – The Dene – provides the pupils with tutor rooms, ICT facilities, study areas, common rooms and a gym.

Curriculum. Girls are admitted to the Junior School from 3 years of age following an informal assessment and enter a Pre-Reception class prior to joining Reception at age 4. The National Curriculum creates a framework for teaching and Key Stage 1 and 2 SATs are taken. In 2007, 88% of those sitting Key Stage 2 English SATs achieved Level 5, 74% in Maths and 86% in Science. In Junior School there are many varied opportunities for extra-curricular activities including Music, ICT, Sport, Drama, Chess and Mandarin. Girls study French from 7 years of age and there is specialist teaching in many subject areas. Pre-school and after-school care is available form 7.30 am to 6.30 pm for all Junior School girls. Girls are encouraged to show kindness towards others, which is developed in our daily Act of Worship, our teaching, work in the local community and fund-raising for charity. The school recognises the need for independent learning and homework is set regularly.

In the Senior School girls follow an enriched version of the National Curriculum in preparation for entrance to university and the professions. The school regularly sends students to Oxford, Cambridge and other top universities where girls successfully study a wide range of courses. In 2008, 7 girls received offers from Oxbridge.

In Years 7-9 girls participate in a broad curriculum that, while encompassing Curriculum 2000, provides many extension opportunities. Two modern languages are studied from Year 7 and all girls study Latin from Year 8. It is a hallmark of the school that Science is taught as three distinct subjects by specialist teachers. At GCSE girls study 9 or 10 subjects including a core of English, ICT, IGCSE Mathematics, a Modern Language, Religious Studies and Sciences together with optional subjects from a wide range. Emphasis is placed on the use of ICT as a tool to enhance all aspects of education. Wherever possible, cross-curricular opportunities are exploited, such as in the French and Geography residential visit to Lille for Year 8 girls. Careers advice is given from Year 7 and all girls are able to take extra lessons in Speech and Drama and Music. Each year over 300 girls pass the Poetry Vanguard and Guildhall Speech and Drama Examinations and over 100 pass the Associated Board and Trinity College Music Examinations.

In the Sixth Form, students benefit from teaching styles that are supportive but provide opportunities for independent study. Students currently take four or five AS/A2 Levels from a wide range of disciplines. In 2007, the girls achieved a 100% pass rate at A Level, 91% gained A or B grades with 99% taking up places at University.

Extra-Curricular Activities. Each year an excellent and varied programme of concerts, musicals, plays, art exhibitions and festivals in both Junior and Senior Schools enables members of the drama groups, choirs and orchestras to perform in public.

An elected committee of girls, led by the Head Girl and her deputy, contributes to the smooth running of the school. The Sixth Form also runs societies, produces musicals and concerts in aid of charity.

Many girls take part in swimming galas, Hockey, Netball, Gymnastics, Badminton, Rounders and Tennis matches, including all major county tournaments; several girls reach county and national squad level each year.

A wide variety of clubs and activities are provided for girls during the lunch break and after school. In addition, parents run the Otter and Centipede Clubs which offer sports and coaching sessions. Staff regularly arrange cultural visits to places as varied as New York, Paris and Yorkshire and an exchange programme is now in place with the Fachhöch Schule in Tübingen, Germany. The Junior School organises annual residential visits in Years 5 and 6.

A number of girls take part in Mathematics challenges and competitions with an excellent record of success. The school has a good reputation for debates and public speaking. In the Sixth Form girls form their own companies and compete in the Young Enterprise competition and have won the Sutton and Merton area 'Best Company' award for the last two years.

Community Links. In addition to Harvest and Christmas parcel collections for the elderly, the whole school organises fund-raising activities for their chosen charities.

The school has a thriving Parent Staff Association – Connections – which arranges school fairs each year and a range of social activities. Money raised by Connections has been used on many projects including the upgrading of performance facilities in both the Junior and Senior Schools and the creation of the new 'Tops and Tails' before and after school care facility.

Close links with a local boys' school have resulted in such productions as 'Little Shop of Horrors', 'The Boyfriend', 'Grease', 'West Side Story', and in 2007 – 'Sweet Charity'.

In 2009, the school will be celebrating its 125th Anniversary with a year-long programme of events and special fund-raising activities supporting the school and the local community.

Fees per term (2008-2009). Senior School £3,700, Junior Department £2,879, Pre-Reception £2,221.

The fees cover the regular curriculum, examination entry fees, school books, stationery and other materials, games and swimming, but not optional extra subjects or lunch. Details of the fees for extra subjects, including instrumental music, and Speech and Drama, are available from the school.

Scholarships and Bursaries. Following the ending of the Government Assisted Places Scheme, the GDST has made available to the school a substantial number of scholarships and bursaries. The bursaries are means tested and are intended to ensure that the school remains accessible to bright girls who would be unable to enter the school without financial assistance. At present there are, available to internal or external candidates, part-fee scholarships for entry at 11+ and for entry at 16+ into the Sixth Form. Performance Scholarships are awarded at 11+ in Sport, Music and Drama and in the Sixth Form for Music, Drama, Sport and Art.

Charitable status. Sutton High School for Girls is part of The Girls' Day School Trust, which is a Registered Charity, number 306983. The aim of the Trust is to provide access to the very best education to as many individuals as possible.

Sydenham High School (GDST)

19 Westwood Hill London SE26 6BL
Tel: 020 8768 8000
Fax: 020 8768 8002
e-mail: info@syd.gdst.net
website: www.gdst.net/sydenhamhigh

Founded 1887.

This is one of the 29 schools of The Girls' Day School Trust. For further information about the Trust, see p. xxiv. Additional information may be found on the school's website and a more detailed prospectus may be obtained from the school.

Chair of Local Governors: Ms S Hanna, LLB

***Headteacher*: Mrs K E Pullen**, BA Warwick, MA London, PGCE

Deputy Head: Dr C Laverick, BA Swansea, MEd OU, PhD Hull

Head of Junior School: Mrs B Risk, CertEd Salisbury, MEd Bath

Assistant Head Teacher: Mrs S J McLellan, BA Durham, PGCE

Head of Sixth Form: Miss B Pakey, BA Lancaster, PGCE

Pupil numbers. Senior School 415, Junior School 250. Nursery opens in January 2009.

For over 100 years, Sydenham High School has been committed to the fundamental aim of providing a first class education for girls – grounded in a tradition of academic rigour and focused on developing in our pupils the skills and confidence to face the challenges and enjoy the opportunities of life in the twenty first century.

Occupying the grounds of a Victorian mansion we enjoy an open, leafy setting in a location that is easily accessible by public transport. Our Junior School enjoys its own recently refurbished facilities with ready access to those of the Senior School. The school is a distinctive blend of Victorian buildings and purpose-built accommodation refurbished to a high standard. Our facilities are impressive and include an extensive library with online facilities, two ICT suites and design technology centre. We have seven science laboratories, five of which have been recently refurbished. Our new Performing Arts Centre, featuring a new Theatre and Recital Hall, was opened in 2007.

Excellent on-site sports facilities comprise a Sports Hall and all-weather pitch, supplemented by extensive sports fields close by in Lower Sydenham. We produce fine sportswomen who compete in hockey, netball, tennis, and gymnastics to national level.

Curriculum. The school offers a broad curriculum, ensuring all our pupils arc stimulated and excited by learning. English and Mathematics provide a solid foundation while Languages offered include French, German, Spanish and Latin. Sciences include Biology, Chemistry and Physics. Separate Sciences are available at GCSE. Creative and practical subjects include Design Technology, Art, Physical Education, Music and Drama. Humanities include History, Geography, Religious Studies and Classical Civilisation. All pupils receive a thorough grounding in ICT, taught as a discrete subject and confidently used as a cross-curricular tool.

In the Sixth Form, Further Mathematics, Business Studies, Government and Politics, ICT, Theatre Studies, Physical Education and Sociology are offered in addition to the normal range of AS and A Level courses. Specifically focused preparation for entry to prestigious universities, including Oxford and Cambridge, is provided. Our New Horizons Programme brings in speakers and takes students out to visit exhibitions and industry. Huge opportunities are available for leadership through the Community Leader Sports Award, Young Enterprise, sports teams, administering clubs, and an extended prefect system.

Students make informed choices of GCSE, AS and A Level subjects, supported throughout by specialist staff. Work in Careers and PSHE also informs the decision making process. 100% of our students are offered places at universities, while some take gap years abroad. The breadth of extra curricular opportunities encourages all pupils to broaden their interests and develop personal skills. Drama is popular with numerous clubs and productions at the Junior and Senior Schools. A diversity of opportunity for making music is available to pupils whatever their instrument or level of expertise. Highly qualified peripatetic staff teach instrumental lessons. Specialist music staff train school ensembles, orchestra and choirs which perform in, and beyond, the school on a regular basis. Involvement in the wider community is encouraged through our successful Duke of Edinburgh's Award Scheme and charity work.

Fees per term (2008-2009). Senior School £3,700, Junior School £2,879.

School fees include textbooks, stationery and other materials, choral music, PE and swimming, ISCO and Careers counselling. They do not include instrumental music, speech and drama, and after-school clubs.

Scholarships and Bursaries. *Entrance Scholarships*: The Girls' Day School Trust provides a number of scholarships each year for entry to the Senior School at 11+ and directly into the Sixth Form. Scholarships are awarded on academic merit and no financial means test is involved.

Bursaries: The GDST Minerva Fund provides bursaries which are means tested and intended to ensure that the school remains accessible to bright girls who would benefit from our education, but who would be unable to enter the school without financial assistance. Bursaries are awarded on the basis of financial need and academic merit. An application form can be obtained from the Admissions Secretary. It is recognised that occasions will arise when some form of short-term assistance is required – a small fund exists to help pupils taking public examinations in such cases.

Sydenham High School Scholarships: Art, Music, Drama and Sports scholarships may be awarded on entry at 11+ in addition to our Academic scholarships.

Charitable status. Sydenham High School is part of The Girls' Day School Trust, which is a Registered Charity, number 306983. The aim of the Trust is to provide a fine academic education for girls, which is distinguished by breadth.

Talbot Heath

Rothesay Road Bournemouth BH4 9NJ
Tel: 01202 761881
Fax: 01202 768155
e-mail: admissions@talbotheath.org
website: www.talbotheath.org.uk

Motto: '*Honour before Honours*'

The School is an Independent School, founded in 1886 by private effort and transferred to Trustees in 1898 and is administered under a scheme drawn up by the Ministry of Education in 1903. It is a Church of England Foundation and pupils of all denominations are welcome. This School is committed to safeguarding and promoting the welfare of children and young people. The School is also committed to a policy of equal opportunity.

Governing Body:
Chairman: Mr S Tong
Vice Chair: Prof G Slater, MSc, MA, DPhil, FRSA
Dr T Battcock
Mrs M Day
Miss S Dennison, LLB
Mr G Exon
Mr R Kennedy
Mrs C Norman
Mr G Smith
Mr D Townend
Mrs S Trapnell, SRN

***Head Mistress*: Mrs C Dipple**, BA Leeds, M-ès-L Lille, FRSA, PGCE

Heads of Faculty:
Mrs T Magrath, MA York (*English*)
Miss J A Barrett, MA Oxon (*Classics*)
Mrs J Hooton, BSc Hons (*Mathematics*)
Mr A Hill, BMus Hons, FTCL (*Creative Arts & Technology*)
Mr M Gibson (*Science*)
Mrs S Baker (*Humanities*)
Mrs K D Leahy, BA Hons London (*Head of Junior Department*)
Miss H Hardy (*Physical Education*)
Miss E A Silvester, BA Hons Birmingham (*Modern Languages*)

Visiting teachers also attend for Piano, Violin, Violoncello, Double Bass, Flute, Clarinet, Oboe, Bassoon, Horn, Saxophone, Trumpet, Trombone, Tuba, Percussion, Singing,

Dancing, Speech Training and Voice Production, English for foreign students, French, Spanish and German Conversation.

Medical Officer: Dr S Kidman
Financial Manager: Mr A Johnson
Head Mistress's PA: Mrs I Richards

There are some 395 girls in the Main School, of whom 62 are in the Sixth Forms. There is a Junior Department for about 147 girls between the ages of 7 and 11. The Pre-Preparatory department caters for 120 boys and girls aged 3+ to 7.

Talbot Heath is among the longest-established schools in the Bournemouth area, with over a century of success. The school enjoys an attractive wooded site and outstanding facilities for Art, Drama, Music and the Sciences (new Art and Drama studios opened in September 2000, new Science Centre opened in March 1999) together with good ICT provision and extensive modern accommodation for a wide range of sports activities.

The school follows the best practice of the National Curriculum but does not undertake Key Stage testing at levels 1, 2 and 3.

Examinations. 21 subjects are offered to GCSE (including Core Subjects) and Advanced Level, and girls gain places at a variety of universities, including Oxford and Cambridge, or go on to other forms of higher education or professional training.

Admission. Girls are admitted into the Junior School by examination at 7 and above and into the Main School by examination at 11+, 12+ and 13+. The Entrance Examination is held annually in January and girls must be capable of working with those of their own age. Entry to the Pre-preparatory Department requires no examination.

Boarding Houses. St Mary's Boarding House is located in the School grounds, Miss Edwards being in overall charge.

Fees per term (from January 2008). Tuition: Junior School: £1,025–£2,635; Senior School: £3,231.

Boarding (in addition to Tuition Fees): £2,150 (full); £2,006 (weekly).

Scholarships and bursaries are available and there is also a discount for daughters of Service families and the clergy.

Charitable status. Talbot Heath is a Registered Charity, number 283708. It exists to provide high quality education for children.

Teesside High School

The Avenue Eaglescliffe Stockton-on-Tees TS16 9AT
Tel: 01642 782095
Fax: 01642 791207
e-mail: info@teessidehigh.co.uk
website: www.teessidehigh.co.uk

The School was founded in 1970 being an amalgamation of the Queen Victoria High School, Stockton-on-Tees, founded 1883 and the Cleveland High School, Eaglescliffe, founded 1939.

Board of Governors:
Chairman: His Honour Judge P J B Armstrong, MA Cantab
Mr R Anderson, BSc Hons
Mrs C R J Chapman, FCA
Dr K Farmery, BSc, PhD
Mr M J Graham
Mr S Merckx, BSc, CEng
Mr C G Neave, MA
Mr M C Smith, BDS, DGDP UK
Miss E M Vane, CertEd
Mr C G Watson, BA Hons, PGCE

***Headmaster*: Mr T A Packer**, BSc Hons, MSc Dunelm, FInstP, FCollP, NPQH

Bursar: Miss S Robson, ACIB

Senior Leadership Team:
Mr M C Abraham, BEd Hons Cheltenham (*Head of Preparatory*)
Mrs J Richardson, BEd Exeter, CertEd (*Head of Pre-Prep Section*)
Mrs A Vickers, CertEd Dunelm (*Senior Teacher Pastoral, SEN & Careers; PE*)
Dr A A Wardhaugh, BSc Hons, PhD London (*Senior Teacher Curriculum; Biology*)
Mr M K Wilkinson, MA Cantab (*Senior Teacher Assessment; Head of History*)

High School Staff:
Mrs R Aitken, BSc Hons Edinburgh (*Psychology, Biology*)
Mrs B Anderson, BSc Hons Kent, MSc CNAA (*Chemistry*)
Mrs M Barry, BSc Hons Salford, BEd (*Mathematics and IT*)
Mrs S Casey, BA Hons Hull (*History*)
Mrs K R Chamberlain, BA Hons Birmingham (*Geography*)
Mrs K A Crosby, BA Hons Staffordshire (*Economics & Business Studies*)
Mrs H M Dey, BSc Heriot-Watt (*Mathematics*)
Miss J Duffy, MA Jt Hons Glasgow (*Senior Tutor; English*)
Mrs K Edwards, City & Guilds (*Food & Nutrition*)
Mrs R Hancock, BA Hons York (*English*)
Mr J Harrington, BA Hons Newcastle (*French & German*)
Miss E Heather, MA Dunelm (*Art*)
Mrs S Jackson, BEd Hons (*Food/Nutrition & Textiles*)
Mrs R Kirk, BSc Newcastle, MSc Heriot-Watt (*Biology*)
Mrs L Kirton, BD Hons London (*Religious Studies*)
Mrs S C M Low, BA Hons Sunderland (*French and German*)
Mrs E Machan, BA Hons Teesside (*HE & Technology*)
Mrs K Mackenzie, BSc Hons Leeds (*Senior Tutor; Physics*)
Mrs S Parker, BA Hons Oxon (*Senior Sixth Form Tutor; English & Drama*)
Mr J A Perfect, MSc York (*Mathematics, IT*)
Mrs K Rawlinson, BSc Reading (*Geography*)
Mrs M Richardson, DipAD, ATD Liverpool (*Art and Design*)
Mrs V H Sherwood, MA Jt Hons St Andrews (*Classics*)
Miss N J Stephens, BA Hons York (*Physical Education*)
Mrs S Swalwell, BSc Hons Teesside (*Chemistry*)
Mrs J Thompson, BSc Hons Teesside (*IT*)
Mrs N Threadgold, BA Hons Leeds (*French and German*)
Miss V Turnbull, BSc Hons Gloucester (*Physical Education*)
Mrs G K Waddoup, BA Hons Dunelm (*German*)
Mr I Watson, BA Cambridge (*Chemistry*)
Mrs G Wilson, BSc Hons York, MSc Birmingham (*Senior Tutor; Physics*)

Music Department:
Head of Music: Mr P A Laverick, BA Hons Welsh College of Music & Drama, PGCE

Mr S J Bone, CT ABRSM, GSMDP Hons (*Clarinet, Saxophone*)
Mrs S A Burniston (*Flute*)
Mrs B Bury, ARCM, LRAM, PGDipRNCM (*Piano*)
Mr P Collumbine (*Guitar*)
Mr B Howitt (*Drums, Percussion*)
Mrs S Hunt (*Piano*)
Mr C J C Mackay, CertEd (*Brass*)
Mrs R Robinson, LGSM, DRSAM, DipCLCM (*Cello*)
Mr A Smith, GMus, PPRNCM (*Clarinet, Recorder*)
Miss E Smith, BMus (*Singing*)
Mr M Walton, BMus Hons RCM (*Violin, Viola*)

Speech & Drama:
Mrs J K Anderson, ALCM, LCST, MCST, CertEd
Miss C Kilvington, BA Hons Northumbria

Preparatory School:
Mrs H M Bennison, BEd Hons Southampton
Miss J Edwards, BEd Hons Liverpool
Mrs D Essex, BEd Dunelm

Miss R Farrell, BA Hons Southampton
Mrs C L Lara, CertEd Sheffield
Miss T A Lockerbie, BA Hons York
Mr F I Maude, BA Hons Bradford
Miss K J Neville, BA Hons Leeds
Miss H Pedley, BA Hons Durham (*PE & Games*)
Mr W Richardson, BEd Hons Exeter
Mrs J Todd, MA Durham (*Music*)
Mr D Winfield, BSc Hons Loughborough

Learning Resource Centre Manager: Miss R Ignirri, BA Hons Venice
Headmaster's PA: Mrs S Brown

Teesside High School, set in 19 acres of outstanding landscaped grounds, is an independent school for boys and girls aged 3 to 18. The School operates a unique 'Diamond' system with opportunities for girls and boys to learn separately as well as develop socially by means of some classes and activities being organised on a single-sex basis, with others mixed. It is easily accessible by road and rail from North Yorkshire, County Durham and the Tees Valley. The facilities are extensive including specialist state of the art areas for Art, Music, IT, Technologies and the Sciences. The Sports facilities are particularly fine, including an indoor Sports Hall and Gymnasia together with spacious playing fields idyllically placed on the banks of the Tees.

The School has a fine academic tradition regularly featuring in local and national league tables. Pupils study French from Year 4 whilst later on a further foreign language and Latin can be taken from Year 7. The Sciences are taught as three separate subjects throughout the High School and at all stages a full range of subjects is offered.

The taught curriculum is supplemented with a rich and varied activities provision alongside opportunities for individual music tuition as well as Speech and Drama, Ballet and Dance. Outdoor pursuits and the Duke of Edinburgh's Award Scheme are popular with pupils from Year 10 upwards.

The recently refurbished Sixth Form Centre offers girls and boys an exciting pre University experience. Individual study areas together with teaching rooms, IT suite and conference facilities are complemented with a Sixth Form cafe: the Hot Spot. A full range of A Level subjects is offered and pupils are expected to move on to University. A structured careers programme from Year 7 enables students to make informed choices at all stages.

There are about 400 pupils on site, 150 in the Preparatory School (3+ to 11). Admission is normally at 3+, 5, 11, 13 and 16, but may be at other ages if vacancies occur. The School takes part in the Nursery Voucher Scheme. A Bursary System is in operation. There is a full range of Scholarships. Details of entry requirements are available on application.

Fees per term (2008-2009). Preparatory School: £1,619–£2,732. High School: £3,333.

Charitable status. Teesside High School Limited is a Registered Charity, number 527386. It is established to provide the highest possible standard of education for girls and boys.

Thornton College
Convent of Jesus and Mary

Thornton Milton Keynes Buckinghamshire MK17 0HJ
Tel: 01280 812610
Fax: 01280 824042
e-mail: registrar@thorntoncollege.com
website: www.thorntoncollege.com

Chair of Governors: Sister J M Cuff, RJM

***Headmistress*: Miss A T Williams**

Deputy Headmistress: Mrs D Sheldon
Head of Junior School and Nursery: Sister M J O'Donohoe, RJM
Head of Boarding: Miss M Kelly
Chaplain: Father J McCormick
Bursar: Mr R A Inchley
Admissions Secretary: Mrs C Ballantyne
PA to Headmistress/Office Manager: Mrs L Tipping
School Secretary: Mrs L Try

Thornton College, Convent of Jesus and Mary, is a non-selective day and boarding school for girls aged 2½–16 years, with a nursery for boys and girls aged 2½–4+. The total number of pupils is 370, of which 55 are boarders.

Founded in 1917 by the Sisters of Jesus and Mary, Thornton College aims to provide a sound Christian education taking account of the aptitudes, aspirations and ability of each individual. We work in partnership with parents to develop the full potential of each child, both within the classroom and outside it. A Catholic foundation, girls of all denominations are warmly welcomed to Thornton.

School Mission Statement. 'To educate young people to meet the challenges of life courageously, to use their talents to the full and to live the values of Christ's Gospel.'

Location. Thornton College is situated in a rural location 5 miles from Buckingham and 11 miles from Milton Keynes. Whilst its setting is peaceful and secluded, Thornton College is close to excellent road, rail and air communications with Bedford, Northampton, Banbury and Aylesbury all within easy reach.

Extended Day 8 am – 8 pm. Crèche facilities provide after-school care for four to seven year olds and, from the age of eight, day pupils may stay for activities, supervised study and for supper.

Boarding Life. Girls are accepted as boarders from eight years of age (Year 4). Living in a relaxed, family atmosphere girls benefit from the constant companionship of other young people. Weekly and occasional boarding are popular options and GCSE pupils enjoy the privilege of individual study-bedrooms.

Academic Life. Classes are small; pupils receive individual attention and teaching is organised to allow each child personal success in all areas. Whilst keeping pace with the latest developments in education and the spirit of the National Curriculum, the best of traditional methods are employed in teaching literacy and numeracy skills.

Pupils enjoy a broad and balanced curriculum, which is both relevant and challenging. Highly qualified and committed staff bring wide-ranging knowledge and expertise to the classroom and pupils are encouraged to think for themselves and to become active learners.

We expect pupils to work hard at their studies and to participate fully in a wide range of extra-curricular activities. We equip our students to contribute effectively and responsibly to the community of which they are a part. Our pupils leave us prepared to meet future challenges and confident that they can make a difference to the world in which we live.

Our academic results are excellent and the majority of our girls go on to study A Level and progress to the University of their choice.

Careers Education and Guidance. Careers advice is provided throughout the Senior School. Delivered by our own careers staff and professional advisors, it is both up-to-date and informed. The Careers Library is well resourced and girls are encouraged to make full use of its facilities. Guest speakers are invited to talk to the girls about a wide variety of further education and careers options.

Time is set aside for group and individual counselling as girls prepare for GCSE options in Year 9 and for choice of sixth forms and further education courses in Year 11. Thornton girls are invariably offered the sixth form courses for which they apply, and each year a number obtain Scholarships or Exhibitions.

Extra-Curricular Activities. Pupils are encouraged to take part in a wide variety of extra-curricular activities. The school has an enthusiastic choir, orchestra and a number of instrumental groups that perform on special occasions within the school and in public. Drama is a popular activity at Thornton with many girls involved in the staging of large and small dramatic and musical productions. Dance is part of the PE curriculum and there are also opportunities for pupils to have lessons in ballet, tap and modern dance. Many pupils find pleasure and fulfilment in the creative arts. Girls may also choose to join a number of groups offering cooperative activity and fellowship. There are Art, Ceramics, Computer, French, Lace, Mathematics, Nature and Science clubs, Horseriding, Self-Defence classes and an active Christian Union. A group of senior girls work on the writing, illustration and production of the termly 'Thornton Times'. The School also participates in the Duke of Edinburgh's Award Scheme. Senior girls engage in a wide variety of indoor and outdoor activities while working for the Bronze Award.

There are opportunities for pupils to have lessons in ballet, dance, drama, elocution and music with peripatetic staff. The instruments currently available for study are: Cello, Clarinet, Flute, Guitar, Piano, Saxophone, Singing and Violin.

Sport. Sport is recognised as a vital part of every girl's education. It holds an important place in the curriculum and extra-curricular activities are plentiful. All pupils are encouraged to participate in individual activities and in team games. Not only do they gain immense enjoyment and a sense of achievement but also they develop the personal and social skills which come from team effort. We encourage each girl to recognise the importance of physical exercise as part of a healthy life-style.

Thornton boasts a magnificent sports hall, which is well equipped for gymnastics and indoor sports. The girls enjoy athletics, badminton, basketball, cross-country, dance, hockey, gymnastics, netball, swimming, tennis, trampoline and volleyball. There is a Gymnastics Club which gives displays and enters competitions. Outdoor games facilities are also excellent. There are two beautifully situated grass hockey pitches, six tennis courts, an outdoor swimming pool, and a further all-weather hockey pitch. The school offers a particularly strong fixture list. Every girl is offered the opportunity for competitive match play through the House system and House matches are always keenly contested.

Admission. Entrance is through interview with the Headmistress, satisfactory reports and availability of places. Prospective pupils spend a day in school with their peer group prior to the offer of a place.

Scholarships. Academic Scholarships of up to 50% are available for entry into Year 7. The scholarship examination for entry in September is held in March each year.

Fees per term (2008-2009). Day Pupil £1,960–£3,130; Weekly Boarder £3,250–£4,140; Termly Boarder £4,150–£5,150. Nursery fees range according to sessions required.

Friends of Thornton. All parents are automatically members of the parents' association, the Friends of Thornton. New parents are invited to a Cheese and Wine evening early in the school year where they have the opportunity to meet the Friends' Committee, other parents and members of the school staff.

Old Thorntonians Association. The Old Thorntonians can be contacted on oldthorntonians@aol.com and a reunion is held at Thornton College every May.

Charitable status. The Religious of Jesus and Mary is a Registered Charity, number 247358. Thornton College exists to provide education.

Thorpe House School

7 Yarmouth Road Thorpe St Andrew Norwich NR7 0EA
Tel: 01603 433055
Fax: 01603 436323
e-mail: office@thorpehouseschool.com
website: www.thorpehouseschool.com

Council of Management: Mr P Ramage (*Chairman*)

***Headmaster*: Mr A Todd**, BSc Hons

Head of Juniors: Mrs M Murphy, BSc Hons, PGCE

Senior Teacher: Mrs H Foulkes, MA, BSc Hons, PGCE

Director of Pastoral Care: Mrs M Younger, BA, CertEd

Age Range. 3–16.

Number of Pupils. 150 Day Girls aged 3 to 11; 150 Day Girls aged 11 to 16

Fees per term (2008-2009). £1,640–£2,480.

Thorpe House offers independent education for girls aged from 3 to 16 years and is a lively, friendly, cheerful school with a particularly caring atmosphere. It has a traditional educational philosophy and ethos. The school prides itself that every student achieves her full potential and the girls have a positive and responsible attitude towards their own education. The school adopts a firm position on behaviour, manners, courtesy and consideration for others and, as a whole, offers all girls the real advantages provided by a single-gender school.

The school was founded in 1897 and became an educational trust in 1963. The school is accredited by ISC; the Headmaster is a member of GSA and ISA and the Council of Management is a member of AGBIS.

The school is situated in 10 acres of gardens, woodland and playing fields and has excellent facilities. Located within 2 miles of Norwich City centre, Thorpe House has an indoor, heated swimming pool, a fully equipped gymnasium and a large sports hall, dance studio, school library, Art studio and fully equipped science laboratories. Hockey, tennis, rounders, athletics, swimming, cross country and badminton form part of the physical education curriculum, and the school enjoys success in many local, county and national competitions. The girls have access to a suite of 20 networked computers with secure Internet access and the entire site is networked for the provision of ICT in all subject areas. Tuition is also available in a wide range of musical instruments.

Girls are admitted to all years depending on the availability of places and subject to an interview with the Headmaster and a successful day visit. The Entrance Examination for admission to Year 7 is held in the Spring. Thorpe House also awards four scholarships annually of up to 25% of full fees. Applications are invited from girls from the maintained (state) sector or girls from other independent schools to enter Years 7, 8 or 9. The awards are reviewed annually and are subject to satisfactory academic progress, full contributions to the life of the school and to maintaining a high standard of attendance, behaviour and conduct. Scholarship interviews will normally take place in February.

The Headmaster is assisted by a dedicated staff of graduate and qualified teachers, and the school's Learning Support Unit provides personal learning programmes to those who need additional help.

Preparatory Department. The girls work in an informal atmosphere within a structured environment. The focus is on attaining high standards of literacy and numeracy and the curriculum includes timetabled lessons for Science, ICT, History, Geography, Speech and Drama, Ballet, Physical Education, RE, Art and Music.

Junior Department. The focus is on building on Key Stage I with a broad and balanced curriculum, including

English, Mathematics, Science, ICT, History, Geography, French, Design Technology, Speech and Drama, Physical Education, RE, Ballet, Art and Music. A number of these subjects are taught by specialist teachers from the Senior Department.

Senior Department. In Years 7 to 9 all girls study a broad and balanced range of subjects including English, Mathematics, Science, ICT, History, Geography, French, Spanish, Design Technology, Speech and Drama, Physical Education, RE, Art and Music. In Years 10 and 11 the girls are prepared for GCSE examinations offered by Edexcel. GCSE subjects include English, Literature, Mathematics, Double Award Science, ICT, History, Geography, French, Spanish, Food Technology, RE, PE, Art and Music. All girls also follow a programme of Personal Development, including Careers.

Charitable status. Thorpe House School (Norwich) Educational Trust Limited is a Registered Charity, number 311275. Its aim is to provide a good standard of education to girls.

Tormead School

Cranley Road Guildford Surrey GU1 2JD
Tel: 01483 575101
Fax: 01483 450592
e-mail: registrar@tormeadschool.org.uk
website: www.tormeadschool.org.uk

Academically selective independent school for 760 day girls from 4 to 18 years of age.
Founded 1905.

School Council:
Chairman: C W M Herbert, Esq, BSc Hons
Vice-Chairman: W T Gillen, Esq, MA

Governors:
Mrs J Bruton, BA, PGCE
J Dennis, Esq, DCAAE, AMIMI, OBE
Mrs D Forbes, MA
Mrs R Harris, BA Hons, ACA
The Revd Dr J M Holmes, MA, PhD, VetMB, MRCVS
Dr C Kissin, MB ChB, MRCP, FRCR
P J O'Keefe, Esq, RIBA, MCIOB, MIMgt
Cllr Mrs J Powell, JP
Dr N Rockcliff, BSc, PhD, FIMA, CMath, MWES
D M Williams, Esq, BA, FCA

Bursar and Clerk to the Governors: Mr M O'Donovan, BA Canterbury

***Headmistress*: Mrs S E Marks**, MA Oxon

Deputy Headmistresses:
Pastoral: Mrs D M Bendall, MA Ed Open, BSc, PGCE London (*Biology*)
Curriculum: Mrs L M Taylor, BSc, PGCE Nottingham, MBA Open (*Chemistry*)

Senior School Staff:
* *Head of Department*

Mrs A Arnold, BA, PGCE Keele (*French*)
Mrs E M Atkinson, MA Cantab, PGCE London (**Sociology, History*)
Mrs G Averill, BA, PGCE London (*History*)
Mr T Ball, BEd Nottingham, FCSM (**Director of Music*)
Mrs L Balls, BA Chichester (*Physical Education*)
Ms S Bennett, BSc Bath, PGCE Bath Spa (*Economics*)
Mrs H Boczkowski, BSc Bath Spa (*Food Technology*)
Ms C Brocvielle, MA Grenoble, PGCE Kingston (*French, Spanish*)
Mrs E A Burton, BA, PGCE Birmingham (*Mathematics, Physical Education*)
Mrs P Chambers, BA London, MA Birkbeck College, CertEd London (**History*)
Mrs S Clarke, MA Cantab, DipLib, MCLIP (*Senior Librarian*)
Mrs P Corbie, Cert Art & Design London College of Fashion and Clothing Technology (*Teacher in Charge of Textiles*)
Mrs S Culhane, BA Washington USA, PGCE Goldsmiths London (*English*)
Miss S E Darnton, MA Newcastle (**Art & Design*)
Mrs K R Dennison, BSc London, PGCE Leicester, Dip Psych London (**Psychology*)
Mrs C Don, MA Oxford, PGCE Surrey (*Mathematics*)
Miss J Downes, BA Surrey (*Physical Education*)
Mrs P Dreghorn, CertEd St Peter's Birmingham (**English*)
Mrs T A Dyer, BA Swansea, PGCE London (*Head of Upper School, Spanish, French*)
Mrs S Elmes, BA King's College, London, PGCE Cardiff (*Religious Studies*)
Mr R Ewbank, BA, PGCE Goldsmiths London (*Art, Technology, ICT*)
Mrs A Ferns MA Cantab (*Assistant Librarian*)
Mrs K Fletcher, BA UCL, CTEL, PGCE Trinity College London (*Classics*)
Mr I Frankland, BEd Portsmouth (*Physics*)
Mrs J Glazier, BSc Exeter, PGCE Gloucs (*Mathematics*)
Mrs A Haddock, MA Oxon, PGCE OU (*History, Sociology*)
Mrs S E Haddy, BSc Surrey (*Second in Charge of Mathematics, Assistant Timetabler*)
Miss J Hansen, BA Pace University, New York, PGCE Homerton (*Head of Lower School, Drama*)
Miss P Harris, BA Manchester Metropolitan, PGCE Manchester (*Teacher in Charge of Spanish, French*)
Mrs E Harrison, BA Leics, MSc Huddersfield (*Textiles*)
Mr P Heap, BA Hull, PGCE Manchester Metropolitan (*Teacher in Charge of Drama*)
Ms T Hetherington, BA Westminster, MA St Martin's College, PGCE Roehampton (*Art, 3D Studies*)
Miss J Hoffmann, BSc, PGCE Nottingham (*Mathematics*)
Mr M Holford, BMus Surrey, PGCE Roehampton, ARCO, LTCL (*Assistant Director of Music*)
Mrs M A Holtham, BEd Manchester (*Senior Examinations Secretary, *Food Technology*)
Mrs S Jones, BSc Surrey, PGCE St Mary's College (*Geography*)
Miss M Langlet, MA Toulouse le Mirail, PGCE Oxon (*Teacher in Charge of French, Spanish*)
Mrs D Ledgerwood, MA Oxon, PGCE Reading (*Head of Lower School Science, Chemistry*)
Mr J Lyng, MA London, BSc UMIST, PGCE Brunel (**Science *Physics*)
Mrs G M Mackay, BA, UED Rhodes (*English*)
Dr D Marriott, BSc, PhD Reading, MInstP, CPhys (**ICT, Network Manager*)
Mrs M Meats, BSc Leicester, MSc Open, CertEd (**Biology*)
Miss H Nelson, BA Warwick, PGCE Exeter (*Second in Charge of English*)
Ms E O'Brien, BA Liverpool, PGCE Durham (*Classics*)
Mrs M O'Brien, BA, HDEd PG Johannesburg, MA California (*Art & Design, Art History, Photography*)
Mrs K Perkins, BA Surrey (*Physical Education*)
Miss J Peterken, BA Durham, Dip Law City, PGCE Roehampton (*Teacher in Charge of Swimming, Physical Education*)
Mrs W Pomfrett, BSc, PGCE Bristol (**Chemistry, Science*)
Mr G Press, BSc, CertEd Brunel (*Teacher in Charge of Design and Technology*)
Mrs G Ralfe, BSc Aberystwyth, PGCE Exeter (*Geography*)
Ms J L Rawstron, BA, PGCE Liverpool (**General Studies, Psychology & Sociology*)
Mr J Rayner, BA Manchester, BMus Goldsmiths London, PGCE London (*Music Technology*)
Mrs E Robinson, MA Oxon, PGCE York (*Spanish*)

Ms L Rockhill, BA, PGCE Edith Cowans, W Australia (*Religious Studies*)
Miss M Rudge, BA Southampton (*Physical Education*)
Mr J E Sykes, BAWestminster, MSc LSE (*Government & Politics, Geography, DofE*)
Mrs Z Tan, BA Queen's Belfast, PGDip Tourism Management Surrey, PGCE Kingson (**Geography*)
Mrs M-C Taylor, Cert D'Aptitude Pédagogique (*French*)
Mrs L Head, BA Chichester (**Physical Education*)
Mrs M Torpey, BEd Chichester (*Director of Gymnastics, Physical Education*)
Miss O Toubkin, MA York, BA Cantab, CertEd Leeds (*English, Oxbridge Coordinator*)
Ms S Travis, MA, PGCE Cantab (*Chemistry*)
Mrs R Wallace, BEd Cantab (**Religious Studies, PSHE*)
Miss E Walshe, BSc Greenwich, PGCE Surrey (**Careers, Science*)
Mrs K R Ward-Close, BSc Birmingham, PGCE Durham (**Mathematics*)
Dr D A Watson, BSc, PGCE Birmingham, PhD Aston (*ICT Training and Development Advisor, Biology*)
Mrs J Welsh, BSc, PGCE London (*Head of Sixth Form, Biology*)
Mr K Wild, BA Bristol, PGCE Oxford Brookes (**Modern Foreign Languages, German*)
Mr P Wilkinson, MA Cantab, MSc UCL, MBA Brunel, CEng, CSci, MIChemE (*Science*)
Mr M Wilmore, MA Oxon, PGCE Cantab (**Classics*)
Miss C Wyatt, BSc Manchester, PGCE Sussex (*Mathematics*)

Junior Department Staff:
Miss K Tuckwell, MA Bath, BSc York, PGCE Lincoln (*Head of Junior Department*)
Mrs S Mortimer, CertEd, DipEd London, B Tech (*Deputy Head of Junior Department, KS2 Coordinator*)

Mrs R L J Bayne-Powell, BEd, CertEd Cantab (*Year 5 Class Teacher*)
Mrs G Blackburn, BSc Sussex, RSA Dip Helen Arkell Dyslexia Centre (*Special Educational Needs, Dyslexia*)
Miss M Colyer, BSc York, PGCE Cantab (*Year 5 Class Teacher*)
Mrs B E Deans, CertEd, DipEd Cantab (*Geography, Technology*)
Mrs S Doggett, NNEB Kingston (*Teaching Assistant*)
Mrs J J Fowler, BEd Wall Hall (*Year 1 Class Teacher, Extra-Curricular Activities Coordinator, KS1/Early Years Coordinator*)
Mrs H Frank-Keyes, BA Lancaster (*Teaching Assistant*)
Mrs S Heslop (*After-School Supervision*)
Mrs P Inskip, BSocSc, PGCE, CNAA (*Year 4 Class Teacher, Mathematics Coordinator*)
Mrs S Jordan, BEd Warwick (*Year 6 Class Teacher, Science Coordinator*)
Mrs C Langley, BA Ed Exeter (*Year 5 Class Teacher, English Coordinator*)
Mrs C Mead, CertEd Brighton (*Year 2 Class Teacher, KS1/ Early Years Coordinator*)
Ms C Nicholson, BA Kingston (*Year 3 Class Teacher*)
Mrs J L Norman, MPhil Reading, BSc Nottingham (*Teaching Assistant*)
Mrs P Oldroyd, CertEd Reading (*Teaching Assistant*)
Mrs K Perkins, BA Surrey (*Physical Education*)
Mrs I Phelps, BA Lancaster (*Year 4 Class Teacher*)
Mrs S Trott, BEd Reading (*Year 3 Class Teacher*)
Mrs S Vega, BA, PGCE Durham (*Music*)
Miss L Warden, BEd Hons Kingston (*Pre-Prep Class Teacher*)

Registrar: Mrs L Parsons
Headmistress's PA: Mrs W Houghton
Junior Department Secretary: Mrs D Adams

Tormead is an academically selective independent day school for girls, aged 4 to 18. Founded in 1905, it stands in pleasant grounds, close to the centre of Guildford. The atmosphere is lively and the teaching stimulating and challenging. Standards and expectations are high and girls leave the school as confident, articulate and self-reliant young women, ready to meet the challenges of university and beyond. Almost all girls leave Tormead to read for degrees at the university of their choice. On average, 11% gain an Oxford or Cambridge place each year.

An extensive extra-curricular programme provides further challenge and opportunity. We believe that a breadth of interests, skills and initiative are an essential complement to academic success for the future lives of our pupils. The school has a lively and active musical life with two orchestras, various chamber groups, ensembles and choirs as well as a highly popular and talented Jazz Band which has undertaken tours to various European countries. Drama, dance, public speaking and debating, Young Enterprise, the Access scheme and Duke of Edinburgh's Award are all very well supported and sixth form girls are regularly selected to join the British Schools' Exploring Society's summer expeditions to such remote and far flung destinations as Arctic Norway, China or Malawi. A wide range of sports is on offer and there is a busy programme of fixtures in Hockey, Netball, Rounders, Athletics and Swimming in all of which we compete with great success. Gymnastics has been a particular strength for some years with our teams competing successfully at national level.

International links. We believe that an international outlook is important. We have a partner school in Wanyange, Uganda and an established programme of exchange visits with schools in France, Germany and Spain; and gap students from Australia and South America who each spend a year with us as staff assistants.

Fees per term (2008-2009). Pre-Prep £1,785, Years 1–2 £2,020, Years 3–4 £2,995, Year 5 £3,095, Year 6 £3,280, Years 7–13 £3,745.

Scholarships and Bursaries. Academic, Music and Art Scholarships are offered at 11+ and 16+. Bursaries are available at 11+ entry and are dependent on the level of parental income.

Tormead Old Girls' Association. *General Secretaries*: Suzanne Hoddinott, tel: 01483 764582, email: s.hoddinott@tiscali.co.uk and Sally Hinkley, tel: 01603 720000, email: sally.hinkley@btinternet.com.

Charitable status. Tormead Limited is a Registered Charity, number 312057. It exists to provide education for able girls.

Truro High School for Girls

Truro Cornwall TR1 2HU
Tel: 01872 272830
Fax: 01872 279393
e-mail: admin@trurohigh.co.uk
website: www.trurohigh.co.uk

Founded 1880. Independent, formerly Direct Grant.

Governors:
President: The Rt Revd William Ind, BA, Bishop of Truro
Chairman: Mrs S Glover, SRN, SCM
Mrs N Bush, ASVA
The Honourable Mrs Evelyn Boscawen
Mr M Lowry, BA Hons
Mr J Nichols, MA, FRSA, FCollP
Mr N Parsons
Lieutenant Commander N Trefusis, RN, DL
Dr D West, BA, PhD
Miss K Whitford, LLB Hons

Mrs M Wilson-Holt, MB ChB, FRCA

***Headmaster*: Mr M A McDowell**, BA Hons, MLitt

Deputy Head: Mrs F Matthew, BA Hons
Assistant Deputy Head: Mrs M Smith, BA Hons
Head of Sixth Form: Mr N J Fee, BEd
Head of Preparatory School: Mrs A Mill, BSc Hons

Assistant Staff:
* *Head of Department*

Art:
*Mr R E Hunter, BA Hons, ATC
Mrs W A Williams, BA Hons
Miss C Rowe (*Art Technician*)

Business Studies: *Ms S Creed, MA

Careers & Work Experience:
*Mr R E Hunter, BA Hons, ATC
Ms S Creed, MA

Classics:
*Mrs S J Brown, MA
Mrs K Griffin, BA Hons
Mr M A McDowell, BA Hons, MLitt

English:
*Mrs J A Holland, BA Hons
Mr N J Fee, BEd
Mrs J A Lawrenson-Reid, BEd Hons
Mrs L May, BA Hons
Miss C Rawlinson, BA Hons
Mrs G Dowling BA Hons, TEFL

Geography:
*Mrs J Rice, BA Hons
Miss S Morris, BA Hons

History:
*Mr G Ford, BA Hons
Ms S Creed, MA
Miss S Morris, BA Hons

Home Economics/Textiles:
Mrs L Williams, BSc Hons
Mrs W Williams, BA Hons
Mrs S G Weiringa, BSc, MBA

ICT:
*Miss S T Coxen, BEd Hons
Mr C Beechey-Newman, BSc Hons (*IT Technician*)

Mathematics:
*Mrs A Hanson, BSc Hons
Miss S T Coxen, BEd Hons
Mrs A Lamble, BSc Hons
Mr S Townend, BSc Hons, BSc Hons, CMath, FIMA
Miss C Harding, BSc Hons
Miss C Lyle, BSc Hons
Mrs C Brownscombe, BSc Hons

Modern Languages:
*Mrs M Smith, BA Hons
Mrs F R Matthew, BA Hons
Mr A J M Taylor, BA Hons
Mrs S Murley, BA Hons
Mrs K Griffin, BA Hons
Mrs M M Hutton, L-ès-L

Music:
*Miss F Eagar, BMus, ARCM, LRSM, FTCL, QTS
Mr W Steyn, BMus, MMus (*Organ, Flute, Theory*)

Peripatetic Music Staff:
Miss K Allen (*Singing*)
Ms R P Beale (*Strings, Recorder*)
Mrs R Brenton (*Clarinet, Saxophone*)
Mr R Brokenshire (*Percussion*)
Mrs T Carleston (*Oboe*)
Miss S Carpender (*Piano, Theory*)
Mr M Davies (*Piano*)
Mr M Edwards (*Piano*)
Mrs J Edwards (*Violin, Viola*)
Mr G Graham (*Guitar*)
Ms F Hooper (*Flute*)
Ms J Kershaw (*Brass*)
Mrs V Lynn (*Flute*)
Mrs H Mee (*Singing*)
Mrs N Williams (*Guitar*)

Physical Education & Extra-Curricular Activities:
*Miss D Freeman, BEd Hons
Mrs J Barnfield, BEd Hons (*Director of Coaching*)
Mrs E Burnard, CertEd, FIST, AISC, ASTA, RLSSPLG (*Swimming Coach*)
Mrs G Tregay, CertEd (*Assistant Games Coach*)

Preparatory Department and Nursery:
Head: Mrs A J Miller, BSc Hons
Mrs J Ellis, MEd
Mrs Y Simpson, BEd Hons
Mrs E Symons, BA Hons
Mrs R Dunn, BA Hons
Miss H Mills, BEd Hons
Miss R Preuveneers, BA Hons
Mrs K A Roberts, BEd Hons
Miss T Kemp NNEB
Mrs G Redfearn, NVQ (*Level 3*)
Mrs P Herbert BA Hons (*Teaching Assistant*)
Mrs L Kingdon (*Teaching Assistant*)
Mrs C Pay (*Teaching Assistant*)

Religious Philosophy & Ethics:
*Mr P J Mothersole, BA Hons, MA
Mrs K Griffin, BA Hons

Science:
Miss E Bird, BSc Hons (**Biology*)
Mr M Patchett, BSc Hons (**Physics*)
Dr P Gill, BSc Hons (**Chemistry*)
Mrs M Cooper, BSc
Mr S Hawker, BEng Hons
Mrs A Letheren, BSc Hons
Mrs M Sharp, BSc Hons
Mrs J Spence (*Laboratory Technician*)
Miss R Moore, BSc, MSc (*Laboratory Technician*)

Special Needs:
*Mrs S Cunningham, BEd
Mrs H Butterfield, CertEd, AMBDA
Miss S Morris, BA Hons

Theatre Studies:
*Miss C Rawlinson, BA Hons
Mrs S Bradbury (*Speech and Drama peripatetic*)

Boarding:
*Mrs G Dowling, BA Hons (*Senior House Mistress*)
Mrs P Cassettari (*Assistant House Mistress*)

Librarian: Mr W F Rice, MA

Medical:
Dr M Proctor, MB BS, MRCS, LRCP, DRCOG, FPC
Mrs E Burnard, CertEd, SEN
Mrs C Vincent, SEN

Bursar: Mr G Mayhew, BA Hons, ACIB
Estates Manager: Mr T Bayton
Accountant: Mr M Brown
Assistant Accountant: Mrs D Tillgren
Headmaster's Secretary and Registrar: Mrs F Ellison
School Secretaries: Mrs S Stevens, Mrs J Nisbet, Miss K Cameron
Reprographics: Mrs S Boulter

Truro High School combines a Preparatory Department of approximately 120 girls aged 3–11 (Nursery: boys and girls aged 3–5) and a Senior School of approximately 320 girls (aged 11–19). Boarding accommodation is provided from the age of 8. Entry is based on the school's own selection procedure and Scholarships and Bursaries are available.

A broadly based curriculum is provided to GCSE including Art, Religious Philosophy & Ethics, English, History, Geography, Latin, French, German, Mathematics, ICT, Physics, Chemistry, Biology, Music, Art, Home Economics, Textiles, Theatre Studies and Physical Education. Further subjects at AS/A2 in the Sixth Form are Business Studies, Classical Civilisation, Greek, Spanish and Further Maths alongside an appropriate Key Skills programme. A Careers Department exists to advise girls and parents on openings available over a wide field including entrance to Universities and other institutions of Higher Education. Music forms an important part of the curriculum and there are two orchestras, numerous ensembles and a very strong choir. The school has good facilities: six well-equipped Science laboratories, a language laboratory, a Studio Theatre, Textiles and Cookery rooms, two Information Technology suites, indoor swimming pool, tennis courts and an all-weather hockey/athletics pitch. Pupils in the Sixth Form have their own Sixth Form Centre with individual cubicles for private study. A newly-refurbished boarding house opens in September 2008 followed by a new Modern Languages Department, including language laboratory, scheduled for opening the following summer.

There is a wide range of extra-curricular activities and all pupils are encouraged to participate. The school enjoys good relationships with other schools in the neighbourhood.

Fees per term (2008-2009). Tuition: Nursery £1,356 (part time), £2,025 (full time); Pre-Prep £2,165; Prep £3,040; Senior School £3,250.

Boarding (in addition to Tuition fees): £2,800 (weekly), £2,875 (full).

Truro High School Old Girls' and Alumni Association. *Membership Secretary*: Mrs B Cook. *Treasurer*: Mrs D Standen.

Charitable status. Truro High School for Girls is a Registered Charity, number 306577. It exists to give education to children.

Tudor Hall

Wykham Park Banbury Oxon OX16 9UR
Tel: 01295 263434
Fax: 01295 253264
e-mail: admin@tudorhallschool.com
website: www.tudorhallschool.com

Motto: *'Habeo Ut Dem'*

Board of Governors:
Mrs B Polk (*Chairman*)
B Ruck-Keene, Esq (*Vice-Chairman*)
Mrs K J Boult
Miss S Carrdus
Miss C Duncombe
C Dodson, Esq
M Fetherston-Dilke, FCA
Miss H Holden-Brown, BA
J W Lewis, FCA
Mrs L Mayne
Mrs S North, BA
P Whittle, Esq

***Headmistress*: Miss W Griffiths**, BSc Wales, PGCE London (*Zoology*)

Deputy Headmistress: Mrs H A Granville, BA London (*History*)
Assistant Head Curriculum: Mrs A Johnson, BSc, PGCE Dunelm (*Chemistry*)
Assistant Head Pastoral: Ms R Tandon, BA Birmingham, PGCE Manchester Met

Staff:
Mrs J Adkins, BSc OU, CertEd Oxon (*Physical Education, Learning Support*)
Mrs C F Beecham, BA Exeter (*English*)
Mrs J Benlalem, BMus Hons Kings College, London, PGCE (*Music*)
Dr A Bestaggini-Klemens, BA, PhD Oxford Brookes, MA London (*History of Art*)
Mr M Boden, BSc Greenwich (*Tennis Coach*)
Miss A Boswell, BSc Hons London, DipNA, PGCE, FIMA, CMATH (*Mathematics*)
Mrs S Bourne, BA Cantab, PGCE (*Classics*)
Mrs M C Boyns, BSc London QTS (*Mathematics*)
Miss A Brauer, BA Kent, PGCE Bedford (*Physical Education*)
Mrs E Buckner-Rowley, BA Hons Portsmouth, PGCE Leeds (*Spanish*)
Miss P Caddick, MPhilEd Birmingham (*Drama*)
Mrs S A Craske, BA Oxon, PGCE Manchester Poly (*Art*)
Mrs C Dawson, RSA DipSpLD, BSc London, PGD PRM OU (*Special Educational Needs*)
Ms A Eastwood, OCR Dip SpLD, CertEd Newcastle (*Learning Support*)
Mr J Field, MA Oxon, BA Oxon, PGCE Oxon (*English*)
Mr J Galloway, BA Middlesex, PGCE London (*Religious Studies*)
Miss A J Gamble, BA London, MA London, CPE Law (*History/Politics*)
Mrs H Gibbard, CertEd Nonnington College, BSc Hons Open (*Mathematics*)
Miss F Gow, BA Oxon, PGCE London (*Classics*)
Mrs K Hadfield, BA Leeds, PGCE Canterbury (*Geography*)
Mrs J Haggarty, City & Guilds Cookery Aylesbury (*Practical Cookery*)
Mrs J Hart, BA Nottingham (*Careers*)
Mrs K Hart, BA Manchester, PGCE Birmingham (*Textiles*)
Mrs D Hughes, BA Cardiff (*German*)
Doctor J Jackson, BA Ohio, MA Florida, DPhil Oxford (*School Chaplain*)
Mrs D Jones, BA Hons Sussex, PGCE Sussex, PGCE Sussex (*Art*)
Mrs F Jones, BEd Exeter (*Physical Education*)
Mr R L Jones, RAF Retd, CertEd, MIITTed, HNC Elec Eng
Mrs L Keyte, BA Nottingham, PGCE Warwick (*French*)
Mrs H Kidman, BA Portsmouth (*Textiles*)
Mr G Langer, BSc North Staffordshire, PGCE Oxon (*Physics & Combined Science*)
Mrs L Lea-James, BMus Hons, LTCL, ALCM Huddersfield, PGCE (*Director of Music*)
Mrs M Lucas, BA Lancaster, MA Bristol, PGCE (*French/Italian*)
Mrs S Malpass, BSc Hons Sheffield, MSc Durham, PGCE London (*Biology*)
Miss N Marshall, MA Oxon, PGCE Oxon (*Biology*)
Miss K J Martin, CertEd Bedford Coll of PE (*Staff Coordinator*)
Doctor B Murphy, BA Hons Wales, MA Wales, PhD Wales, PGCE East Anglia (*History*)
Mr J Murphy, BSc Manchester, PGCE Manchester (*Physics*)
Mrs H Peto, BA Oxford, MA London, PGCE London (*English*)
Mrs C Preston, BA Hons, PGCE Bangor (*Religious Education*)
Mrs R Pulvermacher, BA Hons Dunelm, PGCE UWE, (*SpLD Learning Support*)

Mrs L Pym, BA Manchester QTS (*Physical Education/ Mathematics*)
Miss B Robinson, BEd, DipPE Worcs (*Dance*)
Miss S Rogers, BSc Hons Plymouth, PGCE Exeter (*Geography*)
Miss E Rose, BA, Grad Dip Australia (*Dance/Art*)
Miss A Saunders, BA Hull (*Drama*)
Mr J Stead, BA Cumbria, PGCE Cardiff (*Design Crafts*)
Mrs J Stephens, BA Hons London, PGCE Middlesex (*Drama & Theatre Studies*)
Mrs K Stobbart, BEd Teesside (*Spanish*)
Miss S Taylor, MPhil St Andrews, MA St Andrews (*Classical Studies*)
Miss H Thomas, BA Hons Bath, PGCE Coventry (*Modern Languages*)
Mrs J M Thorn, BA Reading, DPhil Oxford (*Classics*)
Mrs C E Varney, BEd Oxon (*Business and Secretarial Studies*)
Miss J Webb (*Careers*)
Miss R Wilson, BA Australia (*Physical Education*)
Miss V L Wormell, BA Loughborough, PGCE Brighton (*CDT*)

Sanatorium:
Mrs H Bletchly, RGN (*Sister in Charge*)
Mrs J Middleton, RGN
Mrs Z Spring, RGN
Mrs J Stewart-Brown, RGN

Clerk to the Governors & Bursar: Miss H Jackson
Registrar: Miss A Brauer
Headmistress's PA: Mrs F George
Senior Administrative Secretary: Mrs H Mascall
Administrative Secretary:, Mrs P Snowden
Travel Secretary: Mrs C Thomas

Tudor Hall is an Independent Boarding School for Girls aged 11–18 years. The school was originally founded in 1850 and moved to Wykham Park in 1946. It is situated in spacious grounds 1½ miles from Banbury Station and is within easy access of London, Oxford and Stratford-upon-Avon – M40, Junction 11. This enables the girls to enjoy a wide range of cultural and educational activities.

The school accommodates approximately 225 boarders and 66 day girls. Its buildings comprise a 17th century and an 18th century manor with a modern purpose-built house for 78 Sixth Formers and extensive new facilities for academic purposes. These include laboratories for biology, chemistry, physics and general science; CDT workshop; 2 information technology rooms; music school; studios for art and pottery; textiles room; modern languages and domestic science rooms; gym and sports hall. There are tennis and netball courts, a swimming pool, squash courts, astroturf and pitches for hockey, lacrosse and rounders. A new classroom block has just been completed. Girls may also take riding and dancing lessons. All girls begin Latin and French with Spanish or German. Italian, Greek, Japanese and Russian, Polo and Sailing are also available in the Sixth Form. Music and Drama are strongly encouraged. The curriculum includes a full range of other academic subjects and, where possible, outings and fieldwork are arranged. Girls are prepared for GCSE and Advanced Level GCE, and appropriate certificates in optional extra subjects. There is a library and a careers room where advice is given about university entrance and further training.

Admission is by Common Entrance at 11+, 12+ and 13+. Entry may also be made to the Sixth Form where all girls pursue courses leading to higher education or vocational training and they are treated as students. Those entering at 11 are accustomed to being away from home by being housed separately in a smaller environment. Girls are divided into four competitive Houses but residence is with their own age group. Tudor Hall places great importance on having a friendly atmosphere, a lively and united spirit and high standards. Girls are expected to take an interest in a wide range of activities as well as following a broad educational programme. Involvement in the local community through the Duke of Edinburgh's Award and social service, and participation in events with other schools are encouraged. Debating and public speaking are strong and there is keen involvement in the Young Enterprise Scheme, Mock United Nations and European Youth Parliament. The school is Anglican but members of other religious groups are welcomed. There is a small chapel.

Fees per term (2008-2009). (*see Scholarship Entries section*). £7,865 for boarders; £5,112 for day pupils.

Wakefield Girls' High School

Wentworth Street Wakefield West Yorkshire WF1 2QS
Tel: 01924 372490
Fax: 01924 231601
e-mail: admissions@wghsss.org.uk
website: www.wgsf.org.uk

This is an Endowed High School under Management of the Governors of the Wakefield Grammar School Foundation established by Charter of Queen Elizabeth.

Motto: '*Each for All and All for God.*'

Governing Body:
The Governing Body, consisting of 13 co-optative Governors and 6 representative Governors, (including representatives of the Universities of Leeds, Bradford, Sheffield and Huddersfield), is the Wakefield Grammar School Foundation.

Spokesman: Mrs M M Waugh

Clerk to the Governors: Mr R C Hemsley, MA, FCA

* *Head of Department*
§ *Part-time*
‡ *Teaching Certificate*

***Head Mistress*: ‡Mrs P A Langham**, BA, MEd Leeds

Deputy Headmistress: ‡Mrs L M Staveley, BA Liverpool, MEd Leeds (*German*)

Academic Deputy: Mrs M K Davidson, BEd Queen's, MSc (*Mathematics*)

Assistant Heads:
‡Mrs A Bedford, BA Bristol (*Religious Studies*)
‡Mr D J Eggleston, BA Nottingham, MEd Leeds (*Business Studies & Economics*)

Teaching Staff:
* *Head of Department*

‡Miss P M Applewhite, BEd Sussex (*Examinations Officer; Physical Education*)
‡Mr D A Baker, MA Oxon (**Science*)
Mr S Besford (**Drama*)
Mrs J Borodina, BEd Ormsk, Russia, MA (*Art & Design*)
Mr B A Carlin, BSc Sheffield Hallam (*Design Technology*)
‡Mrs V E Carter, BA Leeds (**Classics*)
‡Mr D S Collett, BSc Sheffield (**Physics*)
Mrs A Craig, BSc Birmingham (*Chemistry*)
‡Mrs E A Cross, BA Manchester (*History & Classics*)
Mr J Cunningham, BSc Newcastle (*Mathematics*)
‡Dr M F Dabbs, BSc Swansea, PhD Keele (*Mathematics*)
Mrs V P Denison, PGDip Dyslexia Inst (*Learning Support*)
Dr S Duerden Brown, BSc Bradford, PhD (*Chemistry*)
Dr M Durrell (*Physics*)
Mr P Elmes, BEd Ripon & York St John (**Design Technology*)
‡Mrs S Fowler, BA Leicester (**General Studies; English*)
‡Mrs H M E Gill, BA Sheffield (*Learning Support*)

‡Miss J A Gore, BA Cardiff (*English; *Drama*)
‡Mrs R Gration, BEd Leicester (*Art & Design*)
‡Mrs D J Guthrie, BA Nottingham (*Modern Languages*)
‡Mrs D Hadfield, BA Open (**Mathematics*)
Mr H J Hargreaves, BSc Birmingham (*Geography*)
Mrs S L Harrison (*English*)
Miss E Hawkridge, BA Leeds (*Textiles; Head of Main School Careers*)
‡Mrs R Hesmondhalgh, BA Edinburgh College of Art, MEd Leeds (*Art & Design*)
‡Mrs S Hotham, BA Leeds (*Modern Languages*)
‡Ms L J Hutchins, BA Wales (*Head of Guidance Information & Support; Head of Sixth Form; Geography*)
Miss E James (*Classics*)
Miss K L Kendall, BSc Leeds (*Biology*)
‡Dr J C Korosi, MB, BS, BSc St Thomas' Hosp Med Sch (**Biology*)
‡Mr M Lassey, BA Leeds Metropolitan (*Information Technology*)
‡Mrs J Liddy, BSc Wales (*Biology*)
Mrs S Loftus (*English*)
‡Mrs E E MacGregor, BA Bedford College (*Physical Education*)
Dr L T McNamara, BA Lancaster, PhD (*English*)
Mr N Meredith, BA Cambridge, MMus Leeds (*Music*)
Mrs A J Murray, BA Leeds (*Modern Languages*)
Miss A O'Reilly, BA Birmingham (*History & Religious Studies*)
‡Mr S Paget, BA Christ Church College, Canterbury (*Information Technology*)
‡Miss J E Pick, BA Durham (**German*)
Mrs F D Preston (*Music*)
‡Mrs K Preston, BSc Sheffield (**Information Technology*)
Mrs J L Rees, BSc Sheffield (*Mathematics*)
Mrs R Relano, Licenciatura Madrid (*Spanish and French*)
‡Mrs C Richards, BA Newcastle upon Tyne (*Classics*)
‡Mrs V C Riddle, BSc Sheffield (*Biology*)
‡Mrs K F Robinson, BA Leeds Metropolitan (*Physical Education*)
‡Mrs D Russell, BSc, MSc London (*Physics*)
‡Mrs J Sadler, BSc Salford (**Spanish*)
‡Mrs C Scott, BA Durham (*History & Classics*)
Mr R Sewell (*Business Studies & Economics*)
‡Mr A D Shaw, BA Leeds (**History*)
‡Mrs A Singleton, BA Newcastle upon Tyne, MEd Leeds (**English*)
Mrs L A Slack, BA (**Modern Languages*)
Mrs K Stothard (*Geography*)
Mrs S L Taylor (*Mathematics*)
Mrs J A Tingle, BEd Leeds (**Physical Education*)
‡Mr D J Turmeau, BEd Bristol, MA York, LRAM (*Foundation Director of Music*)
‡Dr M F Uttley, BSc London, MSc, PhD (**Chemistry*)
Mrs J Ward, CertEd Liverpool (*Food Technology*)
‡Mrs G E Woods, MA Oxon (*English*)
‡Mrs L Wraight, BA Leeds (**Geography*)
‡Mrs C J Young, BSc Newcastle, BA Open, MSc Sheffield (**Psychology*)

Head's Secretary: Mrs L Maddick

Librarian: ‡Ms J Waterhouse, BA Bretton Hall College, MSc

Junior School
Head Mistress: Mrs D St C Cawthorne, BEd Sheffield, DipTEFL

Assistant Head: Mrs A Sutcliffe, CertEd Ripon and York St John

Teaching Staff:
Mrs J Baldock, BEd Trent
§Mrs J Banks, CertEd Sheffield
‡Mrs J Bellhouse, BA Reading
Mrs E Boid, BSc London, PGCE
Mrs C Castle, BEd Lancaster
Mrs S H Charlesworth, BEd Leicester
Mrs L Cholewa, DLC TCert
Mrs J Craggs, BEd NE Wales
Mrs J M Cunningham, CertEd Leeds
Mrs D C Day, OCR CertSpLD
Mrs V P Denison, PGDip Dyslexia Inst (*Special Needs Coordinator*)
Mrs M E A Denton, CertEd Ormskirk
Mrs K Dickens, BEd Liverpool
Mrs J Earnshaw, BEd Hons Leeds
Miss K Fear, BEd Leeds Carnegie
Mr P Ganley, BA Leicester, PGCE
Mrs P Gibbons, BEd Brighton
Mrs G Halton, BEd Bretton Hall College
Mrs V Hutchinson, BEd Leeds
‡Mrs H Judge, BA London
‡Ms K T O'Malley, BSc, Bradford
Miss M M Potts, BEd Manchester
Mrs R Pye, BEd Leeds
Mrs J E Ratcliffe, CertEd, GBSM London, MA Open
‡Miss L Roberts, BA Leicester
Mrs P Rodgers, TCert Nottingham
Mrs A Simon, CertEd Kingston, DipSpLD
Mrs V A Smith, BA Birmingham
Mrs S J Stringer, BEd Leeds
Mrs A J Sugden, CertEd Alnwick Coll of Education
§Mrs S Turmeau, BEd Bristol
‡Mrs A M Walters, BA Leeds
Mrs A M Wimbush, BEd Cambridge

Secretary: Mrs B Milne

Visiting Instrumental Musicians:
Mr D Allen, MSc, GCLCM Grand Dip (*Guitar and Bass Guitar*)
Mr C J Bacon, GMus (*Brass*)
Mrs S T Bacon, GMus (*Flute*)
Miss Z Barker, BMus (*Clarinet and Saxophone*)
Mr D Beckley, BA, LTCL, FTCL, ARCM (*Brass*)
Miss L Berwin, GRSM, LRAM, PGCE (*Piano and Keyboard*)
Mr P Bingham (*Piano and Keyboard*)
Mr P Birkby, GCLCM, LRAM (*Percussion*)
Miss L Emms, BMus (*Percussion*)
Mr J Gibson, BA RNCM (*French Horn*)
Miss Z Glossop, LRAM (*Oboe*)
Mrs C Hall, DCLCM, LTCL (*Clarinet*)
Mrs E Hambleton, GNSM, LRAM, CertEd (*Piano and Keyboard*)
Mr D Heathcote, BSc, PhD, RSA, MD (*Voice*)
Mrs M B Hemingway, ALCM (*Piano and Keyboard*)
Mr G Hirst, LRAM, ARCM, LTCL, CertEd (*Saxophone and Clarinet*)
Miss A Holmes, BA, LTCL, CertEd (*Saxophone and Clarinet*)
Mr D G Lewis (*Percussion*)
Mrs J D Maunsell, GBSM, ABSM, DipNCOS (*Violin and Viola*)
Mr D Mitchell, BMus, MA (*Guitar*)
Mr T Moore, BMus, MA (*Piano and Organ*)
Mr I Naylor, BMus (*Cello and Double Bass*)
Mr R O'Connell (*Voice*)
Miss K Price, BMus, MMus, PGDipMus (*Voice*)
Mr M Roberts, LGSM, DPLM (*Clarinet and Saxophone*)
Mr M Ryal (*Bass Guitar*)
Mr J Storer, BA (*Guitar*)

Wakefield Girls High School was founded in 1878 and has a long tradition of providing an education of the highest quality.

The school aims to give good all round education to each pupil, encouraging academic excellence, nurturing talents, developing an individual's potential, and emphasising traditional values in a modern context. These aims are pursued within a happy and stimulating environment.

The school occupies an extensive site in a conservation area near the centre of Wakefield, and is easily accessible by road and rail from a wide area. The Georgian house in which it began has been adapted and extended over the years as numbers have grown. A steady programme of building and the acquisition of nearby property have enabled the school to anticipate and meet the needs of succeeding generations of pupils.

Specialist facilities exist for all subjects. Recent developments have included the new all-weather hockey astroturf, Creative Arts Centre, Sports Pavilion, the Science and Technology Centre and the Hartley Pavilion – a Sports and Assembly Hall.

The first phase of the Creative Arts development has produced two quite stunning buildings which have retained the features of Victorian Villas but have been transformed into bright modern purpose built accommodation.

Hepworth House, named after our illustrious Old Girl, the Sculptress Barbara Hepworth, will be the home of the Art Department and provides excellent space for both the Sixth Form and the lower school with specialist provision for pottery, sculpture, 3D, textiles and photography.

Cliff House contains the Economics and Business Studies Centre, the Careers Centre and has additional facilities for the Sixth Form.

The second phase of the Creative Arts development opened in October 2004 and provides a drama studio, design and technology laboratories, a textiles workshop, a recording studio and a new English department.

All ICT equipment has been up-graded and now includes video-conferencing. There are plans to enhance the provision in the school even more.

The pre-preparatory school, Mulberry House, was completed in 2001. The Junior School occupies its own premises on the main school campus and share its facilities and some specialist staff. (*For further details, see Junior School entry in IAPS section.*)

There is a very strong tradition of sporting excellence at local, county and National level. At the playing fields, a short distance away, there are tennis courts, cricket, hockey and netball grounds.

The creative and performing arts play an important part in the life of the school as do extra curricular activities, with over 80 currently available. The Duke of Edinburgh's Award is taken by large numbers.

Curriculum. The school offers a grammar school education. All girls follow a broad and balanced curriculum which keeps the widest possible range of options open until A Level when there is a choice of any combination of 28 A Level subjects. Languages are a major strength with French, German, Spanish, Italian, Russian, Latin and Greek available. Sciences are also very strong with all girls doing Biology, Physics and Chemistry at GCSE and over half taking Mathematics or a Science at A Level.

Public examination results in 2007 were superb! At GCSE there was an overall pass rate of 100% with 72% at grades A* and A. Similar excellent results were achieved at A Level with another first division score of 76% of grades A and B. Most girls go on to university although some choose to go directly into management, the Forces or to RADA. There is a full Careers programme and well established links with industry.

The girls enjoy the best of both worlds. They benefit educationally from a single-sex environment but gain socially and culturally from the close cooperation with Queen Elizabeth Grammar School which has the same governing body. This means that there are many joint activities and some joint lessons at Sixth Form level.

School Hours. 8.45 am – 4.00 pm from Monday to Friday inclusive.

Admission. Boys and girls aged 3 to 7 years are admitted in order from the waiting list. Girls aged 7 years or older are admitted after passing an entrance examination. The main ages of entry are at 3, 7, 11 and 13 years. Some enter the school at 16 years to take A level courses; these girls need a suitable foundation of GCSE subjects.

Fees per term (2008-2009). Senior School £3,033; Junior School £2,275–£2,404; Pre-Preparatory and Nursery £2,203. Music lessons £175 for 10 lessons per term.

Scholarships and Bursaries. The Governors will consider providing a Foundation Award where the net parental income is less than £35,000 per annum.

11+ Peter Ogden Bursaries and Ogden Trust Sixth Form Science scholarships: one of these is awarded each year to help with fees up to 100%, uniform, travel costs and essential school trips.

Twelve Sixth Form Scholarships are awarded in recognition of academic work and GCSE results.

Charitable status. The Wakefield Grammar School Foundation is a Registered Charity, number 1088415. It exists to provide education for children.

Walthamstow Hall

Hollybush Lane Sevenoaks Kent TN13 3UL
Tel: 01732 451334
Fax: 01732 740439
e-mail: headmistress@walthamstowhall.kent.sch.uk
website: www.walthamstow-hall.co.uk

Walthamstow Hall was founded in 1838 as a Home and School for daughters of missionaries. It moved to Sevenoaks in 1882 and became a Direct Grant Grammar School, but is now independent. There are 297 day girls in the Senior School (11–18) and 210 girls in the Junior School (3–11) (*see Junior School entry in IAPS section*).

Governors:
Chairman: Ian Philip, Esq, FCA

9 Trust Governors, 3 nominated by Missionaries, 1 nominated by the Teachers and 2 nominated by the Parents.

***Headmistress*: Mrs J Milner**, MA Hons Oxford, PGCE

Deputy Headmistress: Mrs J Joynes, BA Hons Southampton, PGCE
Director of Studies: Mrs S F Cutter, BSc Hons London (*Head of Science and Chemistry*)
Head of Sixth Form: Mrs J East, BSc Hons Reading
Head of Junior School: Mrs P A Austin, BA Hons London, LTCL
Deputy Head of Junior School: Mrs A J Rotchell, BEd Hons Oxford

Senior School Assistant Staff:
* *Head of Department*
¶ *Former pupil*

Mrs E Benson, BA Liverpool (*Business Studies, Economics*)
Miss V Bower-Morris, BA Hons Surrey (*Drama*)
Miss E Bowman, BSc Hons Southampton (**Mathematics*)
Mrs F Y Brooking, L-ès-L Lille (*French*)
N Buckingham, Esq, BA Hons Reading, MA (**Classics*)
Miss K E Burtenshaw, BEd Westminster College (**Geography*)
Mrs J M Cox, MA Cambridge (**Biology*)
T J Daniell, Esq, BMus London AKC, MTC (**Music*)

Mrs A Earnshaw-Punnett, BA Hons Sheffield Hallam (*IT, PE*)
Miss L Eden, BA Hons Surrey (**ICT*)
Mrs H Evernden, BA Hons York (*English*)
Mrs E Fairhead, BA Hons Oxford (*Classics*)
Mrs S C Fitzmaurice, BSc Hons Manchester (*Biology*)
Mrs K Hofmann, MA Hons St Andrews (*MFL*)
Mrs L M Hogan, BSc Hons Durham (*Biology*)
Mrs M Holland, Dip Art & Design West Surrey College (**Textiles*)
Mrs H A Hook, BA Hons Aberystwyth (*English*)
Mrs K M Howlett, BEd Hons Sussex (*PE; Head of Lower School*)
Mrs C J Hughes, BA Hons West Surrey College (*Textiles*)
Mrs V A Jamison, L-ès-L Université de Sainte Etienne (*French and Spanish*)
Mrs S C Latham, BA Hons Oxford (*History*)
Dr P A Le Bas, MA Hons Cambridge, DPhil (**Physics*)
Mrs S Mackin, BSc Hons Sheffield (*Physics*)
Mrs E L Margrett, BA Hons Bristol, MA King's College, London (*Religious Studies*)
Mrs L A C Martin, BSc Hons Sheffield (*Mathematics; IT; Examinations*)
Mrs S M Miles, BSc Hons Imperial College (*Biology*)
Mrs E H Morgan, BA Hons Hull (*Spanish, French*)
Ms A H Murphy, MA Hons Oxford (*History, Politics*)
Ms A K Needham, MA Kent (**Religious Education*)
P J Newell, Esq, GRSM, Hons ARCM, ARCO, MTC (*Music*)
Miss S L Pearson, BA Hons Warwick (*Classics*)
Mrs J A Robertson, MA Hons Cambridge, MSc North London (*Geography*)
Mrs C Solan, BA Hons London (*Art*)
Miss A C Smith, BSc Hons Aberdeen (*Mathematics*)
Miss G A Smith, BA Hons London (**German*)
Mrs G M Smith, BA Nottingham College of Art & Design (*Art*)
D Swann, Esq, BSc Hons Christ Church College (*Mathematics*)
Miss B A Taylor, TCert Cambridge (**PE*)
Mrs M-F Waugh, L-ès-L Nantes, MA London (**French*)
Mrs H Wiffen, BA Hons Trent University, Ontario, BEd (*English*)
Dr S Wilkinson, DPhil Oxford (*Chemistry*)
Ms R J Wilson, BA Hons Rose Bruford College (**Drama*)
S R Wilson, Esq, BA Hons Sunderland (*Sociology*)
Mrs C M Winder, BA Hons Exeter, MA Kent (**English*)
Mrs M T Wood, BSc Hons Aberdeen (*Chemistry*)

Librarians:
Mrs H Evernden, BA Hons York
Mrs L White

Junior School

Director of Studies: Mrs P I Potter, BEd Southampton

Mrs N Armitage, BA Hons Nottingham
Mrs A Barber, CertEd De Montfort
Mrs S C Bishop, BEd Chelsea College of PE
Mrs J Bullman, BEd Hons Manchester
Mrs K Caine, BTEC
Mrs R K Dally, BA/BSc Hons Capetown, SA
Miss E C Dargie, Bed Hons Christ Church
Mrs L P Everitt, CertEd North Worcs College of Education
Miss S Harris, CertEd Lady Spencer Churchill College, Oxford
Mrs J D Haydock, CertEd Alsager College of Education
Miss S Lilliott, BA Hons Portsmouth
Mrs H E Malcolm, DipEd Aberdeen College of Education
Miss M R Murphy, BA Hons Swansea
Miss T Perry, NNEB Diploma
Miss A C Philip, BEd Hons Nottingham Trent
Mrs K Powell, BEd Hons
Mrs D Smith, SEN, NNEB
Mrs L Thompson, Montessori Gold Seal Dip
Miss A V Watson, BA Hons Reading
Mrs S P Wheeler, BA Hons Sussex

Administrative Staff:
Bursar: N Wood, Esq, MILog
Registrar: Mrs S Timms, GIPM
PA to the Headmistress: Miss K Lippiatt
Junior School Secretary: Mrs W Fahy

Medical Centre:
Mrs C A Kirwan, RGN
Mrs K A Schanche, RGN

The School stands in its own grounds and commands pleasant views of the North Downs and Knole Park. Girls are taught in modern buildings and the school has its own theatre, purpose-built libraries, squash courts, indoor swimming pool, science laboratories, sixth form centre, computer network, and the Erasmus Centre for Languages and Humanities.

Curriculum. Subjects taught include Religious Studies, English, History, Geography, Sociology, French, German, Spanish, Latin, Ancient Greek, Economics, Mathematics, Further Mathematics, Philosophy, Physics, Chemistry, Biology, Computer Studies, Art, Textiles, Music, Drama, Theatre Studies, Photography, Physical Education, Government and Politics, Fine Art, Business Studies, Classical Civilisation, Further Mathematics.

Girls are prepared for GCSE, AS and A2 Levels and for entrance to universities (including a good proportion to Oxford and Cambridge). The record of success in public examinations is excellent.

Religious Teaching is interdenominational.

Extra-curricular activities. Girls are encouraged to develop their individual interests in a variety of ways. These include the Duke of Edinburgh's Award scheme, Financial Literacy Challenge, public speaking, choirs, orchestras, Trinity Guildhall Drama, chess, dancing, science, Christian Fellowship, film and computer clubs. Sports offered include lacrosse, squash, judo, fencing, basketball, athletics, tennis, rounders, netball and swimming. There is a strong Schools' Voluntary Service Unit in Sevenoaks which enables the older girls to give service in the community. The School is also closely linked with the Union of Girls' Schools for Social Service and gives its support to the settlement at Peckham.

Admission. Admission to the Junior School is by interview and tests suitable to the age group. Admission to the Senior School for 11 and 13 year olds is through the School's own entrance examinations and interview. Suitably qualified girls are admitted to the Sixth Form. Parents are warmly invited to visit the School.

Fees per term (2008-2009). Senior School: £4,570. Junior School: Kindergarten £205 per session (2–10 sessions per week); Reception–Year 2 £2,690, Years 3–6 £3,330.

Scholarships. Foundation Scholarships are awarded annually to the candidates who show the greatest academic potential in the school's own 11+ and 13+ entrance examinations.

The Erasmus Scholarship, the Darwin Scholarship, the Tanner Mathematics Scholarship and Sixth Form Academic Scholarships are awarded annually to the candidates who show the greatest academic potential in the school's own Sixth Form Scholarship Examination.

Music Scholarships are awarded annually at 11+ and at 13+.

In addition, 13+ Art and Drama awards are available.

A Sports Scholarship is available from 2008.

The Lantern Award for Art is awarded annually to a Sixth Form candidate who demonstrates the greatest potential in art and textiles.

All awards are available to both internal and external candidates. In addition, a generous means-tested bursary scheme in the Senior School is provided.

Charitable status. Walthamstow Hall is a Registered Charity, number 1058439. It exists to provide education for girls.

Westfield School

Oakfield Road Gosforth Newcastle-upon-Tyne NE3 4HS
Tel: 0191 255 3980
Fax: 0191 255 3983
e-mail: westfield@westfield.newcastle.sch.uk
website: www.westfield.newcastle.sch.uk

Governors:
Chairman: Mrs O Forster
A C Coulson
Mrs J Hodgson
Mrs J Keep
C J Knox
P C M Lewis
M I Ranson, JP, FCA
Mrs J Robson
D Ronn
S Sharp
Mrs R Swinburne
P Walton
Miss L Winskell, LLB
Dr D Younger

***Headmistress*: Mrs M Farndale**, BA Hons London, PGCE Oxon, FRSA

Deputy Headteacher: Mrs B Dixon, CertEd Northern Counties, BA OU
Director of Studies: Mrs D Thompson, MA Hons Cantab, PGCE
Head of Sixth Form: Mrs C Gaynor, BEd Hons Warwick, DipManSt Bristol

Art/Design:
S Ratcliffe, LLB Newcastle, BA Hons Wimbledon School of Art, MFA Cranbrook Academy of Art, Michigan
Miss H McDougall, BA Hons London, PGDip Jordanston, PGCE

Biology: Mrs S Vallance, BSc Hons London, PGCE

Careers: Mrs D Thompson, MA Hons Cantab, PGCE

Chemistry: Mrs M Slack, BSc Leicester, PGCE

Drama/Theatre Studies: R Hersey, PDMus, AMus, PGCE

Business Studies: Mrs C Gaynor, BEd Hons Warwick, DipManSt Bristol

English:
R C Matthews, BA Allegheny Coll, MA, CertEd
Mrs C Speed, BA Warwick, PGCE
Mrs T Tough, BA Hons Durham, MA, PhD, PGCE

Food & Nutrition:
Mrs P J Ford, BEd Hons Newcastle, CertEd
Mrs S Woolley, BSc Northumbria, PGCE

French:
Mrs S Dodds, BA Hons Durham, PGCE
Mrs F Boyce, BA Hons Salford, PGCE
Mrs E Wise, BA Hons Newcastle, PGCE

Geography:
Mrs D Thompson, MA Hons Cantab, PGCE
C Dunns, BA Hons Cantab

German: Mrs E Wise, BA Hons Newcastle, PGCE

History:
Miss J Patterson, BA Hons Northumbria, PGCE
Mrs S Gibson, BA Hons Wales, PGCE

Information Communication Technology:
D Cairns, BSc Hons Northumbria, PGCE

Mathematics:
Miss K Welch, BSc Hons Northumbria, PGCE
Mrs F Swift, BA Cantab, MEng Cantab, PGCE
Mrs B Dixon, CertEd Northern Counties, BA OU

Music:
R Simmance, BA Hons Liverpool, BMus, LRAM, FTCL, PGCE

Physical Education:
Mrs K Nicholson, BEd Hons Plymouth
Miss N Baguley, BSc Lancaster, PGCE

Physics: Mrs A Hughes, MA Hons Oxon, PGCE

Religious Studies:
S Shieber, BA Hons Durham, PGCE, MA
Mrs B Dixon, CertEd Northern Counties, BA OU

Science:
Miss R Riley, BSc Newcastle, PGCE
Mrs J Scott, BSc Hons Napier, PGCE

Spanish:
Mrs J Mindham-Walker, BA Hons Newcastle, PGCE

Additional Learning Support:
Mrs L Robertson, MA Hons Aberdeen, PGCE

Junior House:
Head: Mrs M Branson, BA Hons Leeds, PGCE Newcastle
Assistant Head: Miss K Pugh, MA Hons Glasgow, PGCE

Teachers/Teaching Assistants:
Mrs A Botham
Miss J N Brown, BSc Hons Huddersfield, PGCE
Mrs F Collier, BA Hons Keele, PGCE
Mrs H Dean, BEd Hons Newcastle
Mrs N Gowdy, BA Hons Newcastle, PGCE
Mrs S Hann, BA Hons Hull, PGCE
Mrs M Johnson, CertEd Eastbourne
Miss G McKeating, BEd Hons York
Mrs L McNaught, BA Hons Staffs, NCFE2
Miss E Morgan, BSc Hons Bangor, PGCE
Miss K Pugh, MA Hons Glasgow, PGCE
Mrs A Rabey-Wilson, BA Hons London, PGCE
Mrs A Simmance, CertEd Lancaster
Mrs F Twaddle
Mrs A Winks, BEd Hons Newcastle

Visiting Staff:
Music:
B Alimohamadi, BA OU, LGSM, CertEd Newcastle
Mrs P Green, BA Hons Newcastle, CT ABRSM
Miss H Sander, LTCL
Mrs K Wakefield, CertEd St Hild's & Bede
Miss S Harrison, LTCL
M Dick
Mrs E Brown

Dancing: Miss G Quinn, RAD Int Children's Examiner, AdvTCert ARAD, MNCDTA
Tennis: Mrs F Twaddle
Fencing: G Thompson, BFA County Coach

Bursar: Mrs S Easton, BA Hons, ACMA, CPFA
Domestic Bursar: Miss D Sharp
Headmistress's Secretary: Mrs J F Jokelson
Junior House Secretary: Mrs C Park, BSc Hons Leeds
Laboratory Technician: Miss S Smith
ICT Technician: G Campbell

Westfield is a day school for 380 girls aged 3+ to 18, in Junior and Senior Houses situated on one campus in a very pleasant wooded site of over 6 acres. The School's aim is an uninterrupted education, a high academic standard and a wide curriculum offering scope and stimulus for individual development. There is a vast range of extra curricular activities with particular emphasis on Sport, Outdoor Pursuits, Music, Art and Drama. The Duke of Edinburgh's Award Scheme has a high profile and all senior girls are encouraged to participate. In addition to a sound grounding in basic skills, Junior House (3–11) offers specialist teaching in Art, Craft, PE, French and Music. So that every child may be assured of individual attention class sizes are restricted to a maximum of 20. Frequently, classes are further divided into smaller units.

Senior house (11–18), has first rate classroom and laboratory facilities with excellent specialist accommodation for Home Economics and Music. A wide range of subjects is taught by specialists. Initially all girls have lessons in the traditional academic core subjects, in English, Mathematics, Geography, History, Science (taught as 3 separate subjects) and French, as well as in Music, Drama, PE, Food and Nutrition, ICT and Design. German and Spanish are introduced in the second year. Girls are encouraged to aim for breadth in their choice of subjects at GCSE. Most girls achieve 9 passes in the A–C range of the GCSE, a number with straight A and A* passes. There is a carefully structured programme of Careers and Personal and Social Education and a well developed pastoral system.

The Sixth Form occupies a cottage block in the grounds and is under the direction of the Head of the Sixth Form.

There is a full range of AS, A2 and other courses and girls are prepared for University and other Higher Education courses, including Oxbridge, as well as for other courses and for employment. The A level pass rate is always over 90%, ensuring for most girls a place in their first choice of institute of higher education.

Sixth Formers have considerable responsibility within the School in addition to their own thriving academic and cultural life.

Westfield is a member of Round Square, a worldwide association of schools which share a commitment, beyond academic excellence, to personal development and responsibility through service, challenge, adventure and international understanding. Girls from Westfield have the opportunity to attend the Annual International Conference and to participate in exchanges with member schools from all over the world, and in the Round Square International Service Projects in developing countries.

Westfield is totally committed to producing happy, self-confident, well-balanced young women who are international in their outlook and fully prepared to face life in the 21st Century.

Admission to Westfield is by interview and examination. While children of all faiths are accepted, the religious life of the school is based on Christian principles.

Fees per term (2008-2009). In Junior House fees range from £1,140–£2,402 and in Senior House are £3,067.

Scholarships are available at 11+ and 16+. Some bursaries are also available in cases of financial need.

Charitable status. Westfield School is owned and administered by the Northbrian Educational Trust Ltd, which is a Registered Charity, number 528143. It exists for the purpose of education.

Westholme School

Meins Road Blackburn Lancashire BB2 6QU
Tel: 01254 506070
Fax: 01254 506080
e-mail: principal@westholmeschool.com
website: www.westholmeschool.com

Governing Body:
Chairman: Mr K J Ainsworth, FGA
Deputy Chairman: His Honour Judge E Slinger, BA

Mrs A Booth
Mr P Forrest, ARICS, FCIOB
Mrs A Gallacher
Mrs B Lees, JP
Mr B C Marsden, FCA
Mrs P S Marsden, BA Hons Manchester
Miss J Panton, MA Oxon, FRSA
Mrs S A Sharples
Professor R D Taylor, MA, LLM
Mr J R Yates, BSc

Clerk to the Governors: Mr J Whittaker

***Principal*: Mrs Lillian Croston**, BSc Hons Dunelm, PGCE Cantab, ALCM

Deputy Headteachers:
Mrs Anne Patefield, BSc Hons CNAA
Mrs Michele Emptage, BA Hons Leeds, PGCE Lancaster, MA Lancaster

Bursar: Mr J Henwood, BSc Hons, MA, FCMA

Westholme School comprises: Upper School (Girls aged 11–18), Middle School (Girls aged 7–11), Boys' School (Boys aged 7–11), Lower School (Boys and Girls aged 3–7), and The Nursery at Westholme (Boys and Girls from the age of 2).

Girls are guaranteed continuity of education through Westholme School to eighteen while boys are prepared for entry at 11 to the school of their parents' choice. A new nursery for 2–3 year olds opened in October 2006.

There are 1,089 day pupils at Westholme: 680 girls in the Upper School, 382 (257 girls, 125 boys) in the Preparatory Departments, and 33 boys and girls in the Nursery.

Westholme School, is administered by a Board of Governors which includes three nominated Governors representing current parents. Although the school is non-denominational, its Christian foundation is regarded as important, the emphasis being placed on the moral aspect of Christian teaching.

Upper School. The aim of the Upper School is to provide an atmosphere in which each girl can develop her abilities to the full and can excel in some field of activity. There is constant effort to widen interests and to instil a strong sense of individual responsibility. Most girls continue to the Sixth Form and then move on to Higher Education. Most pursue degree courses, a significant number at Oxford and Cambridge.

The Upper School offers an academic curriculum in English Language and Literature, Mathematics, Biology, Chemistry, Physics, Geography, History, French, German, Mandarin, Spanish, Food, Design, Information and Textiles Technology, Art, Business Studies, Classical Civilisation, Drama, Latin, Music, Ethics, Philosophy & Religious (EPR), Psychology, Sociology and Theatre Studies. Most of these subjects can be taken for the GCSE examination and at AS and A2 Levels; Oxbridge tuition is also offered.

Set in the countryside to the west of Blackburn, Westholme School offers excellent facilities. The premises have been regularly upgraded to give purpose-built accommodation for specialist subjects such as Art, Design and Information Technology and Music; six modern laboratories support the three separate sciences. Sporting facilities include a sports hall, indoor swimming pool, tennis courts and a large playing field with running circuit and hockey pitches. The Theatre, Concert and Assembly Hall opened in 1997, seats 700 and offers students outstanding production resources. The library has open-access multimedia giving students full research facilities on the Internet. The new sixth form wing opened in September 2003 complete with lecture theatre, common room, cafe and classrooms.

The Performing Arts are a special feature of the school. There are several school choirs and girls have the opportunity to learn a string, brass or wind instrument and to play in the school orchestras or wind ensembles. Extra-curricular drama includes the full scale spectacular musical, in the round productions, club and house competitions, while make-up and costume design are popular options at GCSE.

School societies and house teams meet on most days during midday break and girls are encouraged to participate in a variety of activities and in their house competitions. These provide younger girls with opportunities beyond the curriculum and older students with the chance to assume a leadership role.

Westholme Lower School, Westholme Middle School for Girls, Westholme Middle School for Boys. There is close cooperation between these schools and with the Upper School. A family atmosphere allows children to learn in a supportive and happy environment. Firm academic foundations are laid with the emphasis upon the basic skills of literacy and numeracy. Excellent facilities afford ample teaching space and resource areas; the Middle Schools (a new Boys' Middle School, ages 7-11, was opened in September 2003) have two halls, music rooms and specialist provision for Information Technology. Extra-curricular activities include public speaking, orchestra, choir, sports, societies and school visits. Music and sport are taught by specialists and all Departments use the swimming pool, sports hall, athletics track and outdoor pitches.

Admission. Pupils usually enter the school in September. Entry to the Middle and Upper Schools is by examination, and to the Lower School by interview. The normal ages of entry are at 2, 3, 4, 7, 11 and 16.

In view of the demand for places parents are advised to make an early application.

The Principal is happy for prospective parents to visit the school during normal working hours; appointments may be arranged through the Registrar, from whom application forms are available. Annual Open Days are held in October.

Private coaches run from Accrington, Blackburn Boulevard, Bolton, Burnley, Colne, Chorley, Clitheroe, Darwen, Leyland, Preston, Ribble Valley, South Ribble and the Rossendale Valley.

Fees per term (from January 2008). Upper School £2,510, Middle Schools £1,990, Lower School £1,990, Nursery £152 pw.

Bursaries are available at the Upper School for girls who show good academic ability.

Charitable status. Westholme School is a Registered Charity, number 526615. It exists for the education of children between the ages of 3 and 18.

Westonbirt

Tetbury Gloucestershire GL8 8QG
Tel: 01666 880333
Fax: 01666 880364
e-mail: office@westonbirt.gloucs.sch.uk
website: www.westonbirt.gloucs.sch.uk

Governing Body:
Chairman: Mr R Marriott, OBE, MA, FRSA
Vice-Chairman: Miss J Greenwood, BSc Hons, FRICS
Mr M Barrow, CBE
Lady Bland, JP
Mr R Boggis-Rolfe, MA Hons
Lady Anne Carr, BA Hons
Mrs S Castle, BSc Hons, RSA
Mr R Collinson, FCH, MBA, FCMC
Mr N Dale-Harris, BA Hons, MSc, FRSA
Mr S Fisher, MA, FCA
Mrs J Jones, BA Hons, MA
Mrs A R C Kershaw, BA Hons
Mrs P Leggate, BA Hons, MEd
Mrs H Metters, BSc Hons, PGCE
Mrs A Scott, BA Hons
Mr R G Tovey, CertEd Oxon

***Head*: Mrs M Henderson**, MA Hons St Andrews, PGCE Dunelm

Deputy Head: Mrs C Adler, BSc Hons North London, PGCE Bath

Senior House Mistress: Miss S Urquhart, BSc Hons Aberdeen, PGCE Glasgow

Chaplain: The Revd P Dixon, BSc Leeds, BA OU, DipEd Bath, DipTh Nottingham, DPS

Director of Studies: Mr M Gluning, BSc, PGCE Aberystwyth, MA Kingston

Heads of Department:

Art:
Mrs M Phillips, BA, FPSPhotog, CertEd Notre Dame, Liverpool

Business Studies:
Mrs A Sedman, BSc Dunelm, MSc Bath, PGCE UWE

Classics:
Mrs L Weeden, BA Hons Oxford, MA Surrey, PGCE Oxford

Drama:
Mr H Moss-Blundell, DipT Rose Bruford College

English:
Mrs D Browne, BA Hons University College, Wales, PGCE St Luke's, Exeter

Geography:
Mrs N Gill, BA Hons Manchester, PGCE Cambridge

History:
Mrs A Cowell, MSc Leicester, BA Hons University College Cardiff, PGCE Open

Food & Textiles Technology:
Mrs J Bell, BEd Hons Bath

Mathematics:
Mr D Thompson, BSc Hons St Paul & St Mary College, Cheltenham, PGCE West Sussex Inst of HE

Modern Languages:
Mrs C Rock, L-ès-L Université de Metz

Music:
Director of Music: Mr R Baggs, BMus Hons, GRSM, LRAM London, PGCE Reading

Physical Education:
Miss C Graham, CertEd Bedford, CPE

Religious Education:
The Revd P Dixon, BSc Leeds, BA OU, DipEd Bath DipTh Nottingham, DPS

Science:
Miss C Hinchliffe, BSc Hons Bristol, PGCE Leeds, MA East Anglia

Design Technology:
Mr J H M Sproule, CertEd London

Sanatorium Medical Officer: Dr A Walsh, MBChB, DRCOG

Sisters:
Mrs S Bath, RGN, RMN
Mrs J Brooker, RGN
Mrs C York, RGN

Housemistresses:
Badminton House: Miss G Fry, CertEd Birmingham
Beaufort House: Miss S Gould
Dorchester House: Miss S Gould

Holford House: Miss S Urquhart, BSc Hons Aberdeen, PGCE Glasgow
Sixth Form: Mrs C Stoker

Bursar: Mr P Story, MSOE, MIPlantE, RE

Registrar: Mrs B Holley, BSc Hons Coventry

Location. Set in a Grade I listed, historic Cotswold mansion within 250 acres of private parkland and garden, Westonbirt School provides a peaceful, safe and inspiring setting for education, within easy reach of major motorways, rail networks and airports.

Philosophy. Founded in 1928, Westonbirt School offers all the advantages of a small rural girls' school, within a happy, caring community and an exceptionally beautiful setting. Subject teachers, personal tutors and pastoral staff work together to provide a supportive, nurturing environment, rather than pressure of an academic hothouse. Consequently both girls to whom academic success comes naturally and those who require more coaching and encouragement achieve their full potential, both academically and in extra-curricular activities, but the school's focus is not solely on results. The pursuit of fulfilling recreational activities is actively encouraged, as are healthy, close relationships between staff and pupils.

The Curriculum. All pupils follow a broad, balanced course of study in line with the National Curriculum. The majority also learn at least two Modern Languages, Latin, Drama, Music, and all aspects of technology. They also play a great deal of sport.

They keep their options open for as long as possible and then take typically 9 GCSEs and 3 or 4 full A Levels. Virtually all will go on to a good university or art college for a degree course to suit their long-term career ambitions.

In addition they follow a Lifeskills programme from Year 7 onwards. This comprehensive programme addresses specific issues relevant to their age. It incorporates and adds value to the six Key Skills identified by the Department of Education that will make them especially able to succeed in the world of work: communication, working with others, improving one's own learning and performance, numeracy, information technology and problem-solving.

Music, Speech and Drama. The performing arts thrive at Westonbirt. Most girls play at least one instrument and there are four very active and growing choirs. Girls regularly take part in concerts and recitals at school and elsewhere. Musical instrument and singing lessons are timetabled for free periods wherever possible so that girls do not miss academic lessons.

Speech and Drama lessons and individual coaching are also very popular, and there are frequent opportunities for girls to take part in major school productions and to enter performing arts festivals. Many study for national qualifications such as LAMDA and ESB awards and take Drama and Theatre Studies to GCSE and A Level.

Sport and Leisure. The main winter sports are lacrosse and netball, and the summer sports are tennis and athletics, but girls have the chance to learn to play many other sports also, including hockey, cricket, rounders and golf on the school's own private nine-hole golf course. Those keen on equestrian sports may take polo lessons at the nearby Beaufort Polo Club and use the local riding school and the school frequently enters teams in equestrian competitions.

Careers Advice. Westonbirt is an accredited Investor in Careers. This award is given only to schools whose careers advice is of the very highest calibre. The Director of Studies plays a very active role in helping pupils choose the most appropriate public examination courses and to gain places at their preferred university. The school's work experience programme begins in Year 11 and continues into the Sixth Form.

Extra-curricular Activities. As well as organising frequent leisure outings at weekends, the school offers many extra-curricular activities with educational value in the broader sense. The school is an ardent supporter of the Young Enterprise Scheme in which participants set up and run their own business for a year and the school's company frequently wins awards. Under the Duke of Edinburgh's Award programme, many pupils pursue Bronze, Silver and Gold standard. The prestigious Leith's Certificate of Food and Wine is a popular sixth form option, and sixth formers may also have driving lessons timetabled for free periods. There are many interesting field trips and outings throughout the year. Recent overseas expeditions have included Geography trips to Iceland, a Classics tour of Italy, diving courses in the Red Sea and a Sixth Form trip to France to study European politics.

ELT (English Language Training). Although the vast majority of pupils are British, the school has a dedicated ELT Centre staffed by specialists for those whose first language is not English. The Centre offers individual and group coaching and self-help facilities. All overseas girls are taught in the mainstream school for all subjects except ELT, optimising their progress across the board and also ensuring effective integration with the rest of the pupils. The international contingent comes from all over the world, and the school respects and celebrates the cultural variety and cosmopolitan atmosphere that they bring to its community.

Learning Support. For those who need academic help, individual coaching can be arranged in all subjects. Pupils with learning difficulties such as dyslexia benefit from the superb Learning Support Department, and Westonbirt has an excellent track record of helping such girls achieve high academic standards and university entry.

Health Care. The school has its own Sanatorium constantly manned by experienced and sympathetic Sisters, supported by regular surgeries and an on-call service by the school's Medical Officer.

Spirituality. As a Church of England Foundation, Westonbirt School is underpinned by a strong Christian ethos, with morning prayers, evening vespers and Sunday services an important constant in the girls' timetable. Many girls choose to be confirmed, and all are expected to attend school worship as an act of school community, but pupils of other faiths are made to feel welcome and respected. Roman Catholics attend the local RC church regularly.

Facilities. Alongside the magnificent historic buildings at the heart of the school, there are excellent purpose-built facilities to provide for modern educational needs. The Francis Rawes Building includes spacious, airy art studios, well-equipped science laboratories, an extensive computer laboratory, enviable design and technology workshops, and a comfortable lecture theatre.

The school's private 250-acre estate includes extensive sports facilities. There are numerous outdoor pitches, courts and tracks immediately adjacent to the main school buildings, a nine-hole golf course, and the new £3 million Copland Sports Hall with indoor swimming pool, aerobics and dance room and fitness suite.

The self-contained music school includes 22 rehearsal rooms plus the charming Victorian Camellia House, recently completely restored and refurbished to create a delightful venue for rehearsals and intimate recitals which will be at the heart of the proposed new Music School. There are two pipe organs, one in the Great Hall and one in the School Chapel.

The two-tiered Orangery Theatre, with adjacent Green Room and Rehearsal Room, provides a versatile venue not only for the performing arts but also for special events such as fashion shows, charity events and socials.

The younger girls eat, sleep and socialise within the magnificent setting of Westonbirt House, while Sixth Formers are accommodated in single study bedrooms with shared common rooms, set apart from the main school above the Classroom Courtyard, cleverly converted from the former Carriage House and Stable Block and providing an excellent halfway house to university life. All the girls very much enjoy relaxing in the school's Grade I listed historic gardens.

Entrance Requirements. Girls normally join the school at 11, 12, 13 or 16, though they may do so at other ages in special circumstances. At 11+ and 13+ they must sit either the Common Entrance Examination or take the school's own entrance papers, attend an interview with the Headmistress, and provide a reference from their current school. Sixth Form entrants must have a minimum of 5 GCSEs at grades A*–C including the subjects they intend to study.

Fees per term (2008-2009). Boarding (full & weekly) £7,266–£8,300, Day £4,940–£5,760. The fee is inclusive of tuition, board, lodging, stationery and laundry. Day girls may stay one night per week free of charge and on additional nights for a small fee.

Scholarships and Bursaries. Scholarships and Bursaries are awarded at 11+, 12+, 13+ and 16+ entry. Scholarships may be awarded for academic prowess or for drama, art, music or sport, to a maximum of 25% of the annual fees. Means-tested bursaries may be awarded where financial need is proven, and families serving in HM Armed Forces are entitled to a bursary of 10%–20%, with each case considered individually. For the daughters of the Clergy there is a reduction of up to 30% in fees. When sisters are at school together, a 5% reduction is made for the elder. Full details are available on request from the Registrar.

Charitable status. Westonbirt School Limited is a Registered Charity, number 311715. It exists for the education of girls, in mind, body and spirit.

Wimbledon High School (GDST)

Mansel Road London SW19 4AB
Tel: 020 8971 0900 (Senior Department)
020 8971 0902 (Junior Department)
Fax: 020 8971 0901 (Senior Department)
020 8971 0903 (Junior Department)
e-mail: info@wim.gdst.net
website: www.gdst.net/wimbledon

One of the 29 schools of The Girls' Day School Trust. For further information about the Trust, see p. xxiv.

Additional information about the school may be found on the school's website. A prospectus may be obtained from the school.

Founded 1880.

Chairman of the Local Governors: Mr C Joubert, MA, MSc

***Headmistress*: Mrs H Hanbury**, MA, MSc

Deputy Head: Mrs J Mitchell, BSc

Head of Junior Department: Miss C Mitchell, MA

Director of Studies: Mr R Haythorne, MA

Director of Students: Ms P Preece, MA

Pupil numbers. Junior Department: 324 aged 4–11; Senior Department: 580, including 152 in the Sixth Form.

Wimbledon High School is a vibrant, successful and thriving community. It is above all a happy school. The ethos of the school is friendly and open. We encourage intellectual curiosity and independence of mind and ensure that all students are given every chance to be themselves, to grow in confidence and to achieve in the widest possible sense. We provide a secure framework of pastoral care, with the happiness and wellbeing of the girls our primary concerns.

Opportunities and challenges abound, with a wide programme of extension and enrichment in the classroom and a large choice of extra-curricular activities. Students participate in the Duke of Edinburgh's Award Scheme and World Challenge; clubs and societies include debating, chess, music, drama, art and Mandarin amongst many others. Sixth Form students can join the Young Enterprise scheme and practise leadership through the school council and by mentoring younger girls.

Our Junior and Senior Departments share one central Wimbledon site, with excellent facilities: a swimming pool and sports hall, the Rutherford Centre for the Performing Arts, opened in 2007 and the Hastings Centre for design and technology, opened in 2005. The playing fields are ten minutes' walk away at Nursery Road (the site of the original All England Lawn Tennis and Croquet Club) providing a full-size, all-weather hockey pitch and five netball/tennis courts. The Junior Department is housed in bright, purpose-built accommodation, with specialist rooms for art, ICT and science. Sixth Form House accommodates our older students.

Curriculum. Education is planned as a 4 to 18 continuum with an enriched and extended National Curriculum as the foundation. The Junior Department provides a broad and academic education in a happy and stimulating environment. There is a balance of class and specialist subject teaching and girls are set clear and challenging targets for their learning. The National Standard Tests are taken at the end of Key Stage 1 and 2.

The Senior Department continues the breadth and balance with German or Spanish as well as French in Year 7 and the addition of Latin in Year 8. Key Stage 3 also includes English and Drama, Mathematics, Sciences (taught separately); Humanities (Geography, History and Religious Studies), Art and Technology (including ICT); Music, PE and PSHE (Personal, Social and Health Education).

At Key Stage 4 all girls study English (Language and Literature), Mathematics, three separate sciences and ICT as well as PE, RS and PSHE (non-examined). The girls have a free choice of four other subjects, of which one must be a Modern Foreign Language with the possibility of adding Classical Greek as a fifth.

In the Sixth Form students may choose from the same subjects as on offer at GCSE (except PE), plus Economics, General Studies, History of Art, Psychology and Theatre Studies. In Year 12, most take four AS Levels and all take ICT Key Skills Level 3; the majority continue with three A2s in Year 13.

Admissions. 4+ girls are assessed in groups in a nursery-style environment; indication of a girl's potential is the key at this stage, rather than evidence of what has already been learnt.

7+ girls have a small group interview following formal assessments in English including comprehension and a story, mathematics and non-verbal reasoning.

11+ girls have a formal interview in the autumn term followed by English, Mathematics and non-verbal reasoning papers in January. The occasional entry examination has a Science paper.

16+ assessment comprises an interview and data analysis, English, Mathematics and verbal and non-verbal reasoning tests. Offers of places are usually conditional upon GCSE A-grades in their preferred A Level subjects, and at least C-grades in all other subjects.

Fees per term (2008-2009). Senior Department £3,700, Junior Department £2,879.

The fees cover the regular curriculum, school books, choral music, games and swimming, but not optional extra subjects.

Scholarships and Bursaries. Awarded to girls aged 11 or over; details and application forms available on request.

Scholarships are awarded on merit as measured by a girl's results in a competitive examination irrespective of financial means. The maximum value is 50% of the fees.

Bursaries take account of academic merit, but all are means tested and the value of the award is related to the income and financial resources of the girl's family. The maximum value is the full fee.

Charitable status. Wimbledon High School is part of The Girls' Day School Trust, which is a Registered Charity, number 306983.

Withington Girls' School

Wellington Road Fallowfield Manchester M14 6BL
Tel: 0161 224 1077
Fax: 0161 248 5377
e-mail: office@withington.manchester.sch.uk
website: www.withington.manchester.sch.uk

Independent (formerly Direct Grant)
Founded 1890.
Motto: *Ad Lucem*

Board of Governors:
Chair: Mrs E Lee, LLB
Mr D Illingworth, BA, FCA (*Hon Treasurer*)
Councillor J P Findlow, LLB, MBIM
Professor S B Furber, FRS, FREng, FBCS, CEng, MA, PhD
Miss J Lawley, BA
Lord Lee of Trafford, DL, FCA
Professor B J Pollard, BPharm, MB, ChB, MD, FRCA, MEWI
Mrs V Hempstock, BSc
Mr G Yeung, OBE, BA
Mr C E J Griffiths, BA, MA
Mrs L Sabbagh, BA

***Headmistress*: Mrs J D Pickering**, BSc Sheffield

Deputy Head: Mrs S J Haslam, BA Lancaster (*English*)

Director of Studies: Mrs J M Farrell, BSc Liverpool (*Chemistry*)

Assistant Staff:
Mrs C Air, BA Oxon (*History*)
Mrs J Arthan, BSc Birmingham (*Biology*)
Mrs L D Bailey, BSc Newcastle (*Mathematics*)
Mrs J Baylis, BA Leeds (*Theatre Studies*)
Mr S Boddy, MA London (*Economics, Politics*)
Miss K L Browning, BA London (*Geography*)
Mrs J Buckley, BA Durham (*Geography*)
Miss C J Davies, MA Open University (*English*)
Mrs CE Edge, MA Leeds (*English*)
Miss J E Ellis, BA Bath (*German*)
Mrs M Ferrol, BEd Dunfermline College (*Physical Education*)
Mrs Z E Goldman, BA Manchester (*Design Technology*)
Ms A B Hayes, BA Liverpool (*Art*)
Mr K G Hodgson, BSc Sheffield (*Mathematics*)
Ms L Holden, BA Edinburgh (*Classics*)
Miss A R H Holland, BMus Birmingham (*Music*)
Miss K Hollinshead, BSc Northumbria (*PE & Games*)
Mrs A Humblet, BA University of Dijon (*English*)
Mrs C Jones, BA Manchester (*English*)
Mrs R E Lamey, MEng Oxon (*Mathematics*)
Mrs R Lindsay-Dunn, MSc Manchester (*Physics*)
Mr I McKenna, BA Manchester (*Religious Studies*)
Dr S E Madden, PhD Newcastle (*Biology*)
Ms J C Maher, BA Sheffield (*History*)
Dr E A Maisey, PhD London (*Chemistry*)
Mrs Y T Menzies, MA Salford (*French, German*)
Mrs S I Mounteney, BSc London (*Mathematics*)
Miss B O'Neal, MSc MMU (*Psychology*)
Mrs C Ositelu, DEA-ès-L Nantes (*French*)
Ms J Renold, BSc Cardiff (*Information Technology, Physics*)
Mrs E K Robinson, MA Cantab (*Classics*)
Mrs G E Sargent, BMus London (*Music*)
Mr V Sharples, BA London (*Religious Studies*)
Mrs G A Smith, BSc Nottingham (*Biology, Chemistry*)
Mr A Snowden, BSc Warwick (*ICT*)
Dr C Spinks, BSc Edinburgh (*Chemistry*)
Mr O Syrus, BA Oxon (*French, German*)
Dr D Verity, PhD Hull (*Physics*)
Dr C P G Vilela, PhD Lisbon (*Biology, Chemistry*)
Ms N A West, BA Manchester (*English*)

Junior Department:
Mrs E S K Burrows, MA St Andrews (*Year 6*)
Miss S J Davies, BA Nottingham (*Year 5*)
Mrs H Stallard, BA Newcastle-upon-Tyne (*Year 4*)
Miss B Ward, BSc Northumbria (*Year 3*)

Part-time Staff:
Mrs M L Anderson, BSc Pennsylvania (*Computer Science, Spanish*)
Mrs J W Bowie, MA Dundee (*English, Psychology*)
Mrs S E Fletcher, BEd Brighton (*Physical Education, Mathematics*)
Mrs P M Gavan, BA Open University (*Mathematics*)
Ms A Godwin, BA Oxon (*Spanish*)
Mrs S E Hamilton, MA Aberdeen (*Geography*)
Mrs C Harris, BA Hull (*Politics*)
Mrs J Healey, BSc Newcastle (*FTT*)
Mrs J Howling, BA Cantab (*Classics*)
Mrs J Johnson, BA London (*English*)
Mrs J Manning, BA Newcastle (*History/Cover*)
Miss D J McGann, BA York (*English*)
Mrs G M Read, FRPS Ealing (*Photography*)
Mrs G A Smith, BSc Nottingham (*Biology and Chemistry*)
Mr M Speakman, MEd Manchester (*Art*)
Dr E L Terrill, PhD Oxon (*Mathematics*)
Mrs J L Walker, BA Manchester (*History*)
Mrs J C Wallis, BA Leeds (*Politics*)

Librarian: Mrs A Wells, BA, MCLIP Bolton
Network Manager: Mrs S Jenks, MCSE Manchester
School Nurse: Mrs M McNeill, RGN
Examinations Officer: Dr Y E Walls, PhD Bangor (*Chemistry*)
Development Director: Mrs H O'Donnell, BA Wolverhampton
Development Assistant: Mrs M F Spurgin

Administration:
PA to Headmistress: Mrs A Adshead
School Secretary: Mrs A Easton
Bursar: Mrs S Senn, BSc Hull, ACA
Financial Secretary: Mrs L Bennett

Since its foundation in 1890, Withington has remained relatively small, with about 650 pupils, 90 of whom are in the Junior Department and 160 in the Sixth Form. This size allows a friendly, intimate environment together with a broad and balanced curriculum. Withington provides a wide range of opportunities for girls, helping them to achieve their potential, academically, socially and personally. Withington attracts pupils from a wide geographical area and from many different social and cultural backgrounds, producing a diversity in which the school rejoices.

The school's A Level and GCSE results have been consistently outstanding. Girls who gain a place as a result of the entrance examination take at least 10 GCSE subjects, 4 AS Levels, 3 or 4 A2 Levels together with A Level General Studies. Studies are directed towards knowledge for its own sake as well as towards University entrance, including Oxford and Cambridge. All the girls go on to Higher Education.

The school enjoys excellent facilities and has an ongoing programme of major developments. Recent projects have included a new classroom wing, new Science Laboratories, and enhanced Language and Music facilities. The latest building project commenced April 2008 and will provide a new Sixth Form Centre and six additional teaching rooms for Summer 2009.

Withington fosters all-round development and the academic work is complemented by an extensive range of extra-curricular activities. Music is strong and very popular; there is a comprehensive range of choirs and orchestras, involving all age groups. Drama also thrives with regular productions including original works. In sport a variety of games are played, including hockey, lacrosse, netball, tennis, athletics, cricket and football. Pupils are regularly selected for county and national squads and there are regular sports tours within Europe and further afield. In addition to fixtures with other schools, games players compete within the school's House system. The four Houses, named after Withington's founders, also provide a focus for dramatic, musical and other activities.

The Duke of Edinburgh's Award and Young Enterprise Schemes, Model United Nations Conferences, voluntary work in the local community, Science and Mathematics Olympiads, residential activity weekends, foreign trips and local fieldwork all feature prominently in the school's provision. Numerous extra-curricular clubs and societies include Italian, Chinese, photography, bridge, literature, debating, mosaics, robotics, aeromix, fencing and dance. Awareness of the wider world is encouraged, girls participate in many fund-raising activities and the school has special links with a hospital and two schools in Kenya and a school in Uganda. Each December a party of girls depart on community projects to The Gambia; in 2009 expeditions will also depart to Uganda and Mongolia. Preparation for life after school starts early and involves a programme of careers advice, work experience and UCAS guidance.

Visitors are warmly welcomed at any time. Open Days are held in November. A number of means-tested Governors' Bursaries are awarded annually together with awards from various outside Trusts. Entrancc at agc 7–11 is by Entrance Examination, held in January, together with interview report from current school. Admission to the Sixth Form is by interview and is conditional upon GCSE results.

The School has DCSF-sponsored Art and Music Partnership programmes with local state schools and the Northern Chamber Orchestra.

Fees per term (2008-2009). Senior School £2,850, Junior School £2,130. Individual instrumental music lessons are charged separately.

Charitable status. Withington Girls' School is a Registered Charity, number 526632. It aims to provide an exceptional quality of opportunity, to encourage independence of mind and high aspirations for girls from seven to eighteen.

Woldingham School

Marden Park Woldingham Surrey CR3 7YA
Tel: 01883 349431
Fax: 01883 348653
e-mail: registrar@woldingham.surrey.sch.uk
website: www.woldinghamschool.co.uk

Independent School for Girls aged 11–18.

***Headmistress*: Mrs J Triffitt**, MA Oxon

Deputy Headmistress: Mrs S Tierney, BA Dunelm, PGCE Oxon

Bursar: Mr G Hunt

Registrar: Miss A McQuilkin, MA Cantab

Director of Pastoral Care: Mrs J Brown, BEd CNAA

Director of Studies: Mr D Murphy, BA Liverpool, MA London

Assistant Head: Mr D Murtagh, BSc Southampton, MA London

Head of Sixth Form: Miss A Hoyle, BA Dunelm

Marketing & Development Manager: Mrs J Hall

Teaching Staff:
Mrs H Baker, BA London (*Head of Classics; Head of Upper Sixth*)
Miss B Batchelor, BEd Exeter (*Head of Barat House*)
Mr M Bentley, BA Middlesex (*Head of Economics & Business Education; Head of Duchesne*)
Mrs A Benton, BA Camberwell Art School (*Head of Art*)
Mrs S Catley, BSc Leicester (*Examinations Officer; Head of Information Technology*)
Mrs K Connor, BSc East Anglia (*Head of Physics*)
Mrs N Craigdallie Green, BA UCA, MA Sussex (*Head of French*)
Miss M Creese, BA Manchester (*History; Head of Lower Sixth*)
Mrs W Crick, BA Exon, PGCE Primary Exon (*Head of Year 7*)
Miss B Fookes, BEd Southampton (*Head of Year 8*)
Revd Dr D Forrester (*Priest in Residence*)
Mrs J Hadley, BA Essex, MA London (*Head of History of Art*)
Mrs C Halpin, BPhil Birmingham (*Head of Year 9*)
Mrs G Haythorne, MA Oxon (*Senior Teacher i/c Staff Development*)
Dr G Hülsmann, BA Hons equivalent Münster (*Head of Modern Foreign Languages*)
Miss A Knowles, BSc Kent (*Head of Biology*)
Mrs J Langmuir, BA Leeds, TEFL Dip London (*Head of Year 11*)
Mrs J Mayhew, BA Canterbury (*Head of Government & Politics; Head of Stuart House*)
Mrs Y Mulhern, BA Madrid (*Head of Spanish*)
Dr J Murphy, BA Hons Southampton, MSc Birbeck, London, MPhil Oxon, DPhil Oxon (*Head of Religious Education*)
Mrs S Nuttall, BA Open University (*Head of Year 10*)
Miss A O'Neill, BEd London (*Head of PSHE*)
Mr H Patterson, BA Bristol (*Head of History*)
Mrs M Peake, Keele, MBA London Business School (*Careers*)
Mrs J Ruffle, BA Newcastle, MSc Kent, ALA (*Librarian*)
Mr M Saul, BEd Greenwich, CertEd (*SENCO*)
Miss E Sebastian, MA London (*Chaplain*)
Dr M Shipton, BSc Warwick, PhD London (*Head of Science*)
Miss R Tomlinson, BSc Dunelm, PGCE Dunelm (*Head of Geography*)
Mrs J Tower, BEd Hons CNAA (*Head of Physical Education*)
Mrs J Vivian, BA Wales, MEd Newcastle(*Head of English*)
Mr D Wahab, BA Brighton (*Head of Design Technology*)
Miss G Woollard, BSc Southampton (*Head of Mathematics*)

Foundation. Founded in 1842 by the Society of the Sacred Heart, the school has been sited at Woldingham since 1945. Today, under lay management, Woldingham is part of the international network of Sacred Heart schools.

Woldingham is a caring and supportive Christian community in which girls are happy, confident and inspired to meet challenges and to achieve excellence in whatever they choose to do. We encourage our girls to become independent, enquiring young women who forge lasting relationships, achieve academic success and become positive influences in the world they will enter.

Situation and Buildings. Woldingham is situated south east of London, inside the M25. The school is 35 minutes from London by train. Journey times to Gatwick and Heathrow airports are 20 and 45 minutes respectively. A stunning Jacobean house is the centre piece of the idyllic setting in a designated Area of Outstanding Natural Beauty. An intensive yet sympathetic buildings programme has now furnished the school with some of the most impressive facilities of any school or university in the country.

The Millennium Centre for the Performing Arts boasts state-of-the-art facilities. These include a 600 seat auditorium with orchestra pit, industry standard sound and lighting control rooms, scenery construction dock, wardrobe room for costume and prop construction and a fully-equipped studio theatre. In addition, the Centre hosts a Recital room, a MIDI computer room, keyboard studio, String and Woodwind rooms, numerous practice rooms and an exceptional eight-track digital recording studio. The purpose-built Art department comprises two large 2D studios, facilities for printmaking and a superb 3D area equipped with a range of power tools and two kilns. Design technology is taught in a fully-equipped workshop and studio, using state-of-the-art computer-controlled machinery. The Sports Centre includes a Sports Hall, 2 squash courts, Fitness Studio and a Dance/Gymnastics studio. In addition there are extensive outdoor playing areas, an indoor tennis dome, an indoor swimming pool and a new all-weather pitch.

Boarding accommodation is impressive. Shanley House, the Upper Sixth centre, is a newly completed block with en-suite accommodation. Berwick House is the Lower Sixth centre and provides single room accommodation. All girls from Year 10 have single study bedrooms in Main House. Marden House is a small, friendly junior house with welcoming accommodation for the first two years.

Size. The school accommodates 500 girls within the 11–18 age range, 350 of whom are boarders. 60% of boarders are from families living in London and Home Counties and 10% come from overseas. Approximately 7% of the intake are of nationalities other than British; these students enrich the school by bringing to it an international dimension and outlook.

Pastoral Care. This is a key strength of the school. In each year care of the boarding side of the school life is the responsibility of the Head of Year, who acts in loco parentis and ensures that each girl is known and cared for as an individual. The Head of Year is assisted by a deputy and academic Tutors each of whom is responsible for the girls' individual guidance. Buddy schemes ensure that girls provide support for each other.

Curriculum. All girls take a common course for the first three years. Year 7 students take introductory courses in both Spanish and German and continue with one of these languages (in addition to French).

It is expected that the majority of Years 10 and 11 girls will follow a total of 9 or 10 GCSE courses. The aim is to provide a "broad and balanced" curriculum for all up to the age of 16. All students take GCSE courses in English Language and Literature, Mathematics, Religious Education and a Modern Foreign Language. Science is also compulsory: most girls take it as a double GCSE subject, although some sit separate papers in Biology, Chemistry and Physics. As options, girls are recommended to choose an overall combination of subjects which includes Geography or History plus one creative or practical subject. Japanese is an option. Physical Education, Health Education and Information Technology are studied by all students, but are not necessarily examined at GCSE.

In the Sixth Form, girls study four AS Levels in the L6th and three A2 Levels in the U6th leading to three full A Levels and one AS qualification. A small number of girls take five AS and four A2 Levels. All students follow a General Studies programme which leads to an AS in Critical Thinking. Physical Education is also studied by all.

There is a 100% A Level pass rate. The school bucks the national trend in uptake of Science, Economics and Mathematics. Girls also achieve outstanding results in Humanities and Languages.

All leavers go to university or the equivalent, and in the last five years, 20 leavers went to Oxbridge.

Careers Guidance. The School attaches great importance to careers guidance. There is a well-staffed and stocked Careers Room with a wide range of materials available, including computer programmes helping students identify strengths, interests and options.

Music. Woldingham is well known for its strong and lively tradition of music. Over half the students play a musical instrument; there is a full school orchestra, a string orchestra, two wind bands and three choirs. School musical productions, public concerts and the church's liturgical celebrations provide scope for a variety of talent and performance.

Drama. Drama is run by dedicated professionals and is very impressive here. Girls are involved in local and professional theatre and may go on to become specialists in their chosen field of Drama.

Sport. There is a full fixture list of inter-school matches and girls are regularly selected for County and National Competitions. Sports such as Pop Lacrosse, Water Polo and Body Combat are also offered.

International Exchanges. Close links exist with Sacred Heart schools abroad. There is an excellent exchange programme to Germany, France and Spain.

Extra-Curricular Activities. Each term all boarders (and day girls who choose to do so) select options from the wide variety of indoor and outdoor activities available at weekends. Saturday morning features a packed programme of activities, "Saturday Active", run by professionals in their field. On offer is clay pigeon shooting, fencing and cookery, amongst others. The Duke of Edinburgh's Award Scheme is well-established; participants, and other girls, are regular helpers at local hospitals and centres for disabled people. The vigorous Debating Society has a successful record of achievement in inter-school competitions. Theatre visits and other short outings are very popular; several overseas tours for different age groups complement work done in class.

Exeats. Girls are allowed home any weekend from Saturday midday. There are two long weekends (from Friday evening) each term.

Health. There is an excellent Health Centre which has two resident nurses. Two doctors, a dentist and a physiotherapist attend regularly. There is a Health Education programme which emphasises healthy living. Our Wellness Centre provides support and a positive approach to matters of health.

Admissions. Main entry to Woldingham is via the Woldingham School examination in November for 11+, 13+ and 16+ applicants.

Students wishing to join the Sixth Form should be capable of taking at least four AS and three A2 courses and should have passed eight or more subjects at GCSE with grade B or better (ideally grade A in Sixth Form options).

Applicants for occasional vacant places in other year groups are also required to sit the school's own entrance examination.

Scholarships. Academic, Art, Music, Drama and Sport scholarships are offered at 11+, 13+ and Sixth Form.

Fees per term (2008-2009). Boarders: £8,290; Day £4,995.

Charitable status. Woldingham School is a Registered Charity. It exists for the education of girls.

Wychwood School

74 Banbury Road Oxford OX2 6JR
Tel: 01865 557976
Fax: 01865 556806
e-mail: admin@wychwood-school.org.uk
website: www.wychwood-school.org.uk

Board Members:
¶Mrs D Pluck, BA, FCA (*Chairman*)
N Talbot-Rice, Esq, MA, DipEd (*Vice-Chairman*)
Miss J Barker
[1]R Briant, MA
Mrs P Brims, MA, MPhil, PGCE
[1]Mr J Court, MCIB
[1]P Hall, Esq, BA
Mrs R Hayes, BA Hons, MA, PGCE, FRGS
[1]Dr C Nesling, MBChB
Mrs A Stewart
Mrs E Gorick
Mrs S Wingfield Digby, MA, PGCE

¶ *Old Pupil*
[1] *Parent or Past Parent*

Staff List:

***Headmistress*: Mrs S Wingfield Digby**, MA (Oxon), PGCE

Deputy: Ms M Crawford, BA Hons, PGCE

Mrs A Bennett-Jones, BSc, PGCE (*Mathematics*)
Miss J Bettridge, TESOLCert (*EFL, Dance*)
Ms M Bridgman, LDS (*Textiles*)
Mrs C Collcutt, DEUG (*French*)
Mrs H Corkhill, BEd Hons (*History*)
Ms M Crawford, BA Hons, PGCE (*English*)
Mrs S Cripps, MA (Cantab), PGCE (*Chemistry*)
Miss J Cotterill, BA Hons (*English, History*)
Mr J Cotton, MA (Oxon), PG Vocal Dip (TCM) (*Music*)
Mrs L Doughton, BSc Hons, MA (*Biology*)
Mrs E Forrester, BSc Hons, PGCE (*Geography*)
Mr M Fraser, MSc, BA Hons, PGCE (*Mathematics*)
Mrs J Gregory-Newman, BA QTS, BSc (*Business Studies*)
Mrs G Hale, MA (Cantab), PGCE (*English Support*)
Mr N Hodge, BA, PGCE (*Photography*)
Mrs J Hutchence, BA Hons, PGCE (*Drama*)
Ms A Jones, BA Hons, PGCE (A & D) (*Art & Design*)
Mrs J Marshall, MA(Ed), CertEd (*Craft, Textiles, PHSCE*)
Mrs M Nash, BA Hons, PGCE (*Psychology*)
Miss R Odlin, BSc Hons, PGCE (*PE, Sports Studies*)
Miss S Richards, BA Hons, CELTA (*Spanish, French*)
Mrs J Schiller, MA (Cantab), SpLD (Barts) (*Dyslexia Support*)
Ms N Scotcher, BSc Hons, PGCE (*Physics*)
Miss B Sherlock, BA, MEd (*English*)
Mr G Singh, BSc Hons, PGCE (*ICT/Network*)
Mrs J Williams, BA Hons, PGCE, SRN, RSCN (*History of Art*)

School Secretary: Mrs S Grainger
Admissions Secretary: Mrs E Plint
Bursar: Mrs A E Drake-Brockman
Housemistress, Head of Boarding: Mrs J Marshall, MA(Ed), CertEd
Assistant Housemistress: Mrs L Henk
School Doctor: Dr K Howie, MA, BM, BCh, MRCGP, DRCOG, DGM, DCH
School Counsellor: Mrs R Boswell

Wychwood School was established in 1897. It is a Charitable Trust set up for educational purposes and has 150 girls (ages 11–18), of whom about 50 are boarders. It offers small classes taught by qualified staff. Extra-curricular activities are a regular feature of the extended day and the school takes advantage of its central Oxford location.

Curriculum. All girls are expected to take up to 9 subjects at GCSE; most go on to work for AS and A2 and University entrance. The lower school curriculum includes: Religious Education, English, History, Geography, Mathematics, Biology, Physics, Chemistry, French, ICT, Textiles, Ceramics, Singing, Art, Photography, Dance, Music, Computing, PSE, Gymnastics, Spanish (from Year 9), Drama, Swimming and Games. Visiting staff teach other optional foreign languages and musical instruments; there is a school choir and chamber groups.

School Council. Day-to-day life is largely controlled by the School Council which meets weekly and consists of staff, seniors (elected by the school) and form representatives. This is a type of cooperative government, the matured result of a long series of experiments, which trains the girls to deal with the problems of community life and gives everyone, in greater or lesser degree according to her age and status, an understanding of, and a voice in, the rules necessary for a sensibly disciplined life.

Sixth Form. Members of the Sixth Form have considerable freedom yet play an active part in the life of the school. The choice of subjects at AS and A2 is wide, and classes are small and stimulating. Individual help with university applications and careers is a key feature of the Sixth Form. There are regular outside speakers and girls attend a variety of lectures, conferences, exhibitions and meetings. Their participation in school plays and concerts as well as School Council is greatly valued. Sixth Form girls may spend approximately 2 hours per week on community service. Optional computer courses are run after school. Sixth Form boarders have individual study bedrooms.

Conditions of Entrance. (*see Scholarship Entries section*). A personal interview is usually essential between the Headmistress and both a parent and the pupil, though this may be waived where circumstances make it impossible. There is an entrance test to satisfy the staff that the girl will benefit from an education of this kind; the opinion of the girl's former school is also taken into account, particularly in relation to non-academic qualities. Scholarships are offered in creative arts, art, music, science and academic areas.

Fees per term (2008-2009). Boarders £5,650, Weekly Boarders £5,375, Day Girls £3,475.

Charitable status. Wychwood School is a Registered Charity, number 309684. It exists for the education of girls from the ages of 11 to 18.

Wycombe Abbey School

High Wycombe Bucks HP11 1PE
Tel: 01494 520381
Fax: 01494 473836
e-mail: schoolsecretary@wycombeabbey.com
website: www.wycombeabbey.com

Founded in 1896.
Motto: *In Fide Vade*

Council:
President: The Rt Hon The Lord Carrington, PC, KG, GCMG, CH, MC, JP

Vice-Presidents:
Mr W P W Barnes, MA
Mr A K Stewart-Roberts, MA

Chairman of the Council: Mr A M D Willis, LLB, FCIArb

Mrs C M Archer, BA
Lady Sassoon, MA
Mr P E B Cawdron, FCA
Mr Keith Oates, MSc, BSc Econ, LLD, DSc
The Rt Hon Lord Justice May
Dr C A Seville, MA, BMus, LLM, PhD
Mr R N Strathon, MA, FRICS
Air Vice-Marshal T B Sherrington, CB, OBE
Mrs Penelope Lenon, BA
Mrs Gordon Hamilton, MA
Mrs Sue Singer, BA

Ms C Riley, MB, BA, MA, DBA
Miss Sue Carr, QC
Dr S V M Hordern
Mr D P Lillycrop, LLB, FCMI
The Rt Revd Dr Alan Wilson, MA, DPhil, Bishop of Buckingham

Senior Management Team:
***Headmistress*: Mrs C L Hall**, MA Oxon

Deputy Head: Mrs R Tear, BSc Exeter, PGCE London
Senior Housemistress: Mrs E C Best, BA Exeter
Director of Studies: Miss J Z Willmott, BA Dunelm, CertEd Cantab
School Bursar and Clerk to the Council: Mr J C O Luke, CBE, BSc London
Development Director: Mrs B M Armitage, MInstF

Senior Team (Curriculum):
Mrs R Tear, BSc Exeter, PGCE London (*Deputy Head*)
Miss J Z Willmott, BA Dunelm, CertEd Cantab (*Director of Studies*)
Miss R M Corderoy, BA Exeter, PGCE Manchester (*Registrar and Head of Admissions*)
Miss E Boswell, MA Oxon, PGCE Roehampton (*Director of Higher Education*)
Mrs M R Page, BSc, PGCE Reading (*Head of Examinations*)
Mr A Pawlowicz (*Director of IT*)
Mrs J A Pope, BSc, CertEd Bath (*Assistant Director of Studies, Curriculum Administration*)
Mrs O Raraty, BA Leeds, PGCE London (*Assistant Director of Studies, Curriculum and Learning*)
Ms J Winwood, BA Southampton, BPhil Oxon, Cert Ed (*Head of Sixth Form*)

Housemistresses Senior Team (Pastoral):
Clarence:
Miss A Wallace, MA MPhil Cantab, PGCE Oxon (*History*)
Dr A Yuasa, BA Oxon, PhD Reading, PGCE Cantab (*Music*)
Pitt: Mrs E Peers, BA, PGCE Liverpool (*History, Government & Politics*)
Rubens: Miss I Collier, MEd Manchester (*English, PSHE*)
Airlie: Mrs P Harrison, PGCE Liverpool, MIPM (*Mathematics*)
Barry: Dr L Jones, DPhil Oxon, BA, PGCE London, FRGS (*Geography*)
Butler: Mrs A Buxadé del Tronco, BA Southampton, PGCE Belfast (*English, French, Spanish*)
Campbell: Mrs Vivienne Langen, BA, BEd Johannesburg (*History*)
Cloister: Mrs V Ludwick, BA Dunelm, Maîtrise d'anglais & DEA Limoges, PGCE Exeter (*French, Spanish*)
Shelburne: Mrs S Jenkins, CertEd Wolverhampton, DipEd Reading, CPP Roehampton (*Physical Education*)
Wendover: Mrs S B Lafford, BSc Bristol, PGCE London (*Biology*)
Junior House: Mrs S Stevens-Wood, BSc, PGCE Manchester (*Biology*)

Chaplain: The Revd J Chaffey, MA Oxon, BA Durham

Heads of Department:
English: Mr D A W Forbes, MA Oxon, CertEd Exeter
Mathematics: Mrs H Warnick, BA Oxon, PGCE West Sussex
Science & Physics: Mrs S Jones, BSc Dunelm, PGCE Oxon
Chemistry: Mrs Z Edwards, BSc St Andrews, PGCE Dunelm
Biology: Mr M Whitely, BA Cantab, PGCE Canterbury
Modern Languages and French: Miss S Landsmann, Licence d'anglais La Sorbonne Nouvelle, PGCE Reading
German: Mrs N Wase, MA Cantab, MSc UCL, PGCE Oxford Brookes
Spanish: Miss L Orr, BA Heriot-Watt, PGCE Queen's
Classics: Miss S Lui, BA Oxon, PGCE Cantab
Religious Studies: Mrs A Khan, MA, PGCE Oxon
History: Mrs C Sherwood, BA Cantab, PGCE Bristol
History of Art: Mrs C Kwiatkowski, MA Edinburgh, MA London
Geography: Miss E Collins, BSc Lancaster, PGCE Cantab
Economics: Mrs K J Firman, BSc Bristol, MSc UCL
Information Technology: Mr A Porter, BSc, PGCE East Anglia, MA Reading, MBCS
Art and Design: Mr B G Lennon, BA Sheffield, ATD London
Drama: Miss C Livesey, BEd Cantab, AGSM Guildhall

Music:
Director of Music: Mr G Bevan, BMus, MMus, ARCM, ARCO CHM
Assistant Director of Music: Miss S McClure, BMus Wales, MA Birmingham Conservatoire, FTCL, PGCE Reading

General Studies:
Personal, Social, Health and Citizenship Education Coordinator: Mrs J A Pope, BSc, CertEd Bath
Physical Education:
Director of Sport: Miss R A Keens, BEd IM Marsh College of PE, Liverpool
Head of Physical Education: Mrs A Bamforth, BA Warwick, QTS

Careers and Higher Education Advice: Miss E Boswell, MA Oxon, PGCE Roehampton
Learning Support Coordinator: Mrs K J Kuhlmey, BA AKC London, PGCE Cantab
Librarian: Mrs C Cunningham, BSc London, MSc Loughborough
Performing Arts Centre: Dr G Bates, BSc Bath, PhD Aberdeen
Estates Bursar: Mr R S King, MRICS
Domestic Bursar: Miss K Wojciechowska

Numbers on roll. 552 Girls: 525 Boarding; 27 Day Girls.

Age range. 11–18.

Aims. Wycombe Abbey aims to provide an education in the widest sense and our pursuit of academic excellence goes hand in hand with our commitment to pastoral care. We believe the welfare and happiness of every girl to be paramount. Each individual is encouraged to achieve her full potential; she receives first-class academic teaching and has the opportunity to discover and develop her talents – artistic, creative, musical, sporting. She also learns to take responsibility for herself and to have respect for others. It is an intrinsic part of the School ethos that girls care for each other and offer service to the community. We also value close liaison with parents in all matters.

We hope that girls will leave us fully equipped not only to pursue the degree courses and careers of their choice but also to play a full part in the world as self-reliant, responsible and caring young adults.

Location. The School is conveniently situated for travel by road, rail and air. It is near the centre of High Wycombe, five minutes' drive from the M40, giving swift access to London and the West. Heathrow Airport is about half an hour's drive away and High Wycombe station with a frequent service to London is less than 10 minutes' walk from the School.

Buildings. The School buildings are all within the extensive grounds of 160 acres which include playing fields, woods, gardens and a lake.

Boarding Houses. There is a Junior House for 11 year olds. At 12, girls move to one of nine Houses, each accommodating around 45 girls, where they remain until the end of the Lower Sixth. Each House has a resident Housemistress who is also a member of the academic staff. This dual role ensures excellent communication in all matters concerning the girls. The mixed age Houses provide each individual with a secure framework and she is encouraged to take on responsibilities. The Lower Sixth girls take a major share in the administration of the Houses and the School as prefects and officers, developing invaluable skills in communication and management.

In the final year all girls move to the Upper Sixth House where they are encouraged to prepare for university life. They are relieved of House responsibilities but continue to join in general activities and to run School societies. They learn how to manage their own time during the day and are allowed considerable freedom at weekends. They cook some of their own meals and no longer wear uniform.

Religion. Wycombe Abbey is a Church of England foundation with its own Chapel. All girls attend morning prayers and a Sunday Service. (Roman Catholic girls can attend Mass and Jewish girls receive instruction from a Rabbi.) Christian principles inform the whole ethos of the School and a resident Chaplain oversees spiritual matters and plays a central role in pastoral care. Around forty girls are confirmed each year at the annual Confirmation Service.

Curriculum. The Lower School curriculum includes the study of English, English Literature, History, Geography, Religious Studies, French, German, Spanish, Latin, Greek, Mathematics, Biology, Chemistry, Physics, Information Technology, Design and Technology, Art and Craft, Textiles, Cookery, Drama, Music, Singing, Personal, Social and Health Education, a General Studies course and PE. In the Sixth Form, Economics, History of Art, Classical Civilisation, Government and Politics, Philosophy and Ethics, and Physical Education are also available. Critical Thinking AS is compulsory. Girls are prepared for the GCSE, AS and A2 level examinations and for University entrance.

The Modern Languages Department includes a number of specialist language teachers offering private tuition.

Teaching facilities are very good and have been extended and upgraded over recent years. For example, in Summer 2003 two additional laboratories were added to the Science wing (10 laboratories in total) and an extension to the Walpole wing significantly enhanced provision for English, Classics, Religious Studies and Philosophy teaching. A new multimedia language suite and lecture theatre opened in September 2007.

Physical Education. The School has excellent outdoor sports facilities, including five lacrosse pitches, an international size all-weather lacrosse pitch, a hockey pitch, an athletics track and twenty tennis courts, some of which are floodlit and used as netball courts in winter. A multi-purpose, state-of-the-art, sports complex opened in March 2004. It comprises swimming pool, Sports Hall, gymnasium, fitness room, four squash courts, indoor climbing wall, fencing piste and caféteria area.

Girls are taught a wide variety of sports: lacrosse, netball, tennis, athletics, swimming, gymnastics and dance. Hockey, health-related fitness, aerobics, squash, volleyball, badminton and basketball are offered to older girls. Extra-curricular activities – for which charges are made – include fencing, windsurfing, trampolining, karate, rowing, riding, golf, ballet, tap and modern dance, as well as extra tennis coaching.

Music. There is a strong tradition of music making. The Goodland Music School, opened in 1998, provides outstanding facilities for tuition and for recitals in the Archer Recital Hall, with its excellent accoustics. About three-quarters of the girls study at least one musical instrument and are taught by a large team of visiting specialists who provide tuition in a wide range of instruments, including voice. There are many opportunities for performing in orchestras and ensembles. In addition, there is a strong tradition of singing; the Chapel choir plays a central role in Chapel worship and undertakes annual overseas tours and annual choral concerts with other schools such as Eton.

Speech and Drama. Equally splendid facilities are available for the many girls who enjoy drama. A fully equipped theatre enables pupils to perform in a variety of plays and musicals. Over half of them take private Speech and Drama lessons, preparing for LAMDA and Poetry Society examinations.

Art, Craft, Design & Technology. Girls can pursue their interests in these subjects at weekends when the studios are open, as well as in curriculum time.

Other Activities. We encourage girls to participate in the Duke of Edinburgh's Award Scheme; large numbers take the Bronze Award, with many continuing to Silver and Gold. All Lower Sixth girls take part in weekly Community Service and many participate in Young Enterprise. Debating, Public Speaking and European Youth Parliament activities are also popular, as are social events with leading boys' schools.

Fees per term (2008-2009). The fees for boarders are £9,100 (£6,825 for day boarders). They are inclusive and cover, in addition to the subjects and activities already mentioned, lectures, concerts, most text-books and stationery.

Admission. Girls are admitted at the age of 11 or 13. Application should be made well in advance. The suggested procedure is given in the prospectus information booklet.

Sixth Form Entry: Competitive entry by examination for a limited number of places. Application must be made by the September preceding entry.

Scholarships. For details relating to Scholarships, please refer to the appropriate scholarship section.

Charitable status. The Girls' Education Company Limited is a Registered Charity, number 310638. Its aim is the provision of first class education for girls.

Wykeham House School

East Street Fareham Hampshire PO16 0BW
Tel: 01329 280178
Fax: 01329 823964
e-mail: office@wykehamhouse.com
website: www.wykehamhouse.com

Motto: *Vouloir C'est Pouvoir*

Staff:
***Headmistress*: Mrs L R Clarke**, BSc Hons, PGCE, PGDip Nottingham

Deputy Headmistress: Mrs J R Caddy, BEd Hons King Alfred's, Winchester
Head of Senior School: Miss H Wilson, BEd Hons Chichester Inst of HE
Head of Junior School: Mrs C Greenwell, BA Hons, PGCE King Alfred's, Winchester
Bursar: Mr D Bryant

Full-Time Staff:
Miss C Ball, NNEB
Mrs J A Briggs, BA Open, PGCE LSU Southampton
Mrs M E A Caple, Dipl PrimEd Aberdeen College of Education
Mr L Chapman, BSc Hons Sussex, PGCE Reading
Mrs J Corrigan, BA Hons Chichester Inst of HE
Mr S Dearden, BSc Leeds, PGCE, Loughborough College
Mrs J Disley, BSc Hons Aberdeen, PGCE King's College, London
Mrs Y C Dowse, BSc Hons Ed, CertEd, CNAA Portsmouth
Mrs C Flack, BEd Hons Westminster College, Oxford
Mr P Gago, BEd, Hons Sunderland Polytechnic

Mrs A P Higgins, BA Hons, PGCE Portsmouth
Mr D Jones, BMus Hons UCW Cardiff, QTS
Mrs L Jones, CertEd Portsmouth, BA Hons Open
Mrs P Knight, BSc, PGCE Surrey
Mrs O Pearson, BEd Hons Nottingham
Mrs J Shaw
Revd C R Prestidge, BEd Hons West Sussex Inst of HE, BA Hons Open, Dip Ministry and Mission Surrey STETS
Mrs M Reverse-Hayes, PGCE Licence D'Enseignement Histoire, France
Mr D Robertson, BA Hons, PGDip Duncan of Jordanstone
Mrs C Robinson, BEd Hons Southampton

Part-Time Staff:
Mrs S Beacon, BA Hons Exeter, PGCE St Mary's College, Twickenham
Mrs J Bristowe, BEd Rolle College, Devon
Mrs E Kay
Mrs G Kennard, BEd Hons Sussex
Mrs K Lincoln, BA Hons Sunderland, PGCE Southlands College, Wimbledon
Mrs M I Menendez, MA, BA Oviedo, Spain, PGCE Portsmouth
Mrs J Thimbelby
Mrs C E Noyce, BSc Hons, PGCE Bristol
Mrs N-K Reeve, BA Hons, PGCE Bristol
Mrs J Staniforth, BPrimEd Natal, Durban
Mrs A M Taylor, MA, PGCE St Andrews
Mrs A Todd, BSSc Hons Southampton, PGCE Portsmouth
Mrs E Webb

Classroom Assistants:
Mrs S Bell
Mrs V Finney
Mrs J French

Visiting Staff:
Mrs E A Burden, ARCM, BSc Hons
Mr G Elliott
Mrs J Flatman, LRSM, BA Hons
Mr and Mrs D Frankham
Miss L Gask
Mrs L Knapman, LLAM
Mr D Lewis
Miss J Purll

Headmistress's Secretary: Mrs L J Colbeck
School Administrator: Mrs M C Traynor
Assistant School Secretary: Mrs B M Rollo, NNEB

Wykeham House School has a reputation for outstanding pastoral care, excellent results and a dedication to small class sizes and individual attention. A day school for girls set in the heart of Fareham, the School provides spacious accommodation for 250 day girls aged between 2¾ and 16.

A recent Independent Schools Inspectorate Report praised the School for its high standard of education and outstanding pastoral care and complimented the teachers and the girls alike on their hard work, creativity and sense of fun.

The School's concept of education extends beyond the classroom with the aim of developing self-confident, self-disciplined and motivated girls. The excellent facilities at the School provide the opportunity to take part in art, music, drama, sport and other outdoor activities and emphasis is placed on courtesy and concern for others.

The Junior School (which includes the Foundation Stage), for pupils aged 2¾ to 11 years, has an individuality of its own which contributes greatly to the School's atmosphere and the sense of community. All the usual activities which are taught at Primary level are covered by the Junior Curriculum. The teaching methods employed place an emphasis on the acquisition of the basic skills of Literacy and Numeracy. Full opportunities are given for creative work, self-expression and individual development.

At the age of 9+ girls are introduced to a number of specialist teachers who teach across a wide curriculum leading to the 11+ Entrance.

The Senior School. The Curriculum aims to maintain standards and yet recognises the need to keep apace of educational developments and modern teaching techniques. The Curriculum is under constant review by the Headmistress and the Staff Committee. Specialist rooms and well-equipped laboratories and computer facilities are available; a set of laptops is also available for use throughout the curriculum, as well as interactive whiteboards.

The subjects taught in the Senior School cover a broad curriculum leading to GCSE.

An options system is in existence from the Fourth year but all pupils take English, Mathematics, a Modern Language, Science (either the separate subjects of Physics, Chemistry and Biology or as a double award) and a short course in RS, Philosophy and Ethics in their GCSE examinations. Private study periods are included in the option groups to encourage individual study skills and full use is made of the School Library and all girls study PSHCE and have PE.

Visits are undertaken to theatres, museums, art galleries, and other places of interest. Field work is an integral part of the study of Humanities and in Science while Modern Language study involves visits to Europe. Lecturers and performers are invited to the School while the girls are encouraged to take part in Music, Art and Drama as well as other leisure pursuits.

Senior girls participate in the Duke of Edinburgh's Award Scheme. In this way they test their own initiative, discover fresh challenging pursuits, make new friends and become aware of the needs of others.

Many activities occur during lunch times and after school such as the mathematics workshop, computer clubs, games practices, school choirs, instrumental groups, dramatic productions, first aid and cookery.

A member of the staff is responsible for careers advice in the School and there is an extensive library of careers literature freely available. Each girl is interviewed and receives information and advice on her own choice of career from the local Careers Advisory Officer who visits the School. Close contact is maintained with local sixth form colleges, further education colleges and other schools in the area.

The pastoral system is organised on a form basis while the girls also belong to four School Houses where the year groups mix socially and competitively.

Physical Education. The School supplements its Games facilities by hiring nearby local amenities.

Netball, Hockey, Tennis, Rounders and Athletics form the basis of the Senior Girls' Physical Education programme. Girls also have swimming lessons at the local pool.

Admission. Entry is by interview for the Infant Department and by assessment tests for the Junior School. Entry to the Senior School is through the School's own Entrance Examination in January.

Fees per term (2008-2009). Nursery: £1,200 (mornings only), £2,200 (all day); Infants £2,200; Juniors £2,360; Seniors £2,995.

Scholarships. (*see Scholarship Entries section*). Particulars regarding Scholarships at 11+ are available on application from the School and information can be found in the relevant section of this book.

Charitable status. The Trustee of Wykeham House School Trust is a Registered Charity, number 307339. It exists to provide education for girls.

Entrance Scholarships

The Abbey School (see p 505)
Academic Scholarships are awarded on entry to the Senior Department at age 11, and to the Sixth Form, on the results of the entrance examination.

Abbey School Assisted Places are available at age 11, and are on a sliding scale according to income.

Abbot's Hill (see p 507)
Minor awards of 5–10% of fees. Scholarships are awarded based on entrance examinations results.

Badminton School (see p 510)
Scholarships and Bursaries are available for girls entering Badminton in Years 7, 9 and 12. Girls who are awarded scholarships, are also eligible to apply for a Bursary, to a maximum of 100% remission of fees.

There are major and minor academic scholarships worth up to 20% of fees, all-rounder scholarships worth up to 10% of fees, music scholarships which cover tuition in two musical instruments and an art scholarship for Years 9 and 12 worth 20% of fees.

Closing date for scholarship applications is 20 October in the year prior to joining the Sixth Form and 1 December in the year prior to joining Years 7 or 9. Application forms can be requested by emailing admissions@badminton.bristol.sch.uk.

Bursaries are means-tested and awarded on the basis of parents' financial circumstances. Application forms are available by emailing bursar@badminton.bristol.sch.uk. Application dates are the same as for scholarship applications.

Bedford High School for Girls (see p 512)
Entrance Scholarships are available at 11+, 12+ and 13+. High School and Harpur Trust Bursaries are available, dependent upon parental income, and are reviewed annually. Sixth Form Scholarships are available to internal and external candidates.

Benenden School (see p 514)
Academic Scholarships – Lower School Entry (11–13). Substantial awards available. The level of examination will be determined not by date of birth but by intended Form of entry (11+ for Fourth Form, 12+ for Upper Fourth, 13+ for Lower Fifth). The examinations are held in January preceding the date of entry. For further information, please contact the *Admissions Secretary.*

Academic Scholarships – Sixth Form Entry. Substantial awards available. Examinations are held in November preceding entry in September. Candidates take three papers: a compulsory General Paper and two papers in subjects which they intend to study at A Level. For further information, please contact the *Admissions Secretary.*

Blackheath High School (see p 517)
Several academic scholarships are offered every year. Academic scholarships are awarded on academic merit as measured by the entrance examination. Particulars of the examination are available from the Admissions Secretary.

Bruton School for Girls (see p 524)
Scholarships and Awards are offered on entry to the Senior School at 11+, 13+ and Sixth Form.

Casterton School (see p 527)
There are a number of scholarships at 11+, 12+, 13+ and Sixth Form entry for academic, music or sporting ability. For details of how to apply please contact the Registrar.

Channing School (see p 530)
Academic Scholarships and Exhibitions are offered at 11+ and 16+. All candidates are eligible. Scholarships are occasionally awarded for academic prowess within the school. Awards are also offered to Sixth Form entrants, based on 'mock' GCSE results and contribution to the school for internal candidates or on test papers and interviews for external candidates. Particulars and the current Sixth Form Prospectus may be obtained from the School.

The Cheltenham Ladies' College (see p 531)
Junior and Sixth Form Scholarships are available. A Centenary Scholarship worth 40% of the annual fees and a number of other major and minor academic scholarships are offered annually.

Two Sixth Form Day Girl Awards, both worth 40% of the annual day girl fees, are also available.

Cobham Hall (see p 536)
The following Scholarships are offered annually:

Junior School Scholarships for pupils entering at age 11+ and 13+:

In all cases the Scholarships will be awarded as a result of performance in the School's own entrance examination, a full confidential report from the Head of the current school and an interview. Scholarships are awarded to candidates of outstanding ability in any field. Each candidate is considered individually. A willingness to work and contribute to the School community is vital.

Sixth Form Scholarships:

There are Sixth Form Scholarships available to students entering the Lower Sixth. An informal interview is always available to candidates unsure of their standard.

Cobham Hall Awards are awarded on a similar basis to scholarships, but less emphasis is placed on academic excellence. Girls who in the opinion of the School would benefit from and contribute to the education and ethos offered at Cobham Hall are eligible.

For further information contact The Registrar, Sally Ferrers, on 01474 823371.

Combe Bank School (see p 537)
Scholarships of up to half tuition fees at time of entry are awarded at 11+ and to the Sixth Form.

11+ Entry and Scholarship Paper – January, followed by interview.

Sixth Form Scholarships are awarded as a result either of Mock examinations internally or, for external pupils, an interview and predicted GCSE results.

Music Scholarships are available (see relevant section).

Sports Scholarships are awarded to suitable candidates subject to a satisfactory performance on the academic papers. Candidates should be able to demonstrate a high level in sport outside school (with club references) and within their present school.

Downe House (see p 544)
Scholarships are awarded to recognise girls with strong academic, musical, artistic or dramatic potential from a variety of backgrounds and who will benefit from the overall education offered by Downe House.

All Academic, Art and Drama Scholars will receive recognition in the form of £1000 per annum remission in fees. Exhibitioners will receive a remission of £600 per annum.

Music Scholars will receive free tuition in two instruments, which may include the voice, up to a maximum of 30 lessons per year. Exhibitioners will receive free tuition in one instrument, up to a maximum of 30 lessons per year.

Candidates who are successful in gaining an award, but require greater remission in fees in order to be able to take up their place may apply for an Academic, Art, Music or Drama means-tested Bursary, as appropriate.

Academic Awards. The Olive Willis Under 14 Scholarships, Under 13 and Under 12 Downe House Scholarships are awarded on the results of examinations and interviews with the Headmistress, Director of Studies and Head of Lower or Upper School, as appropriate, and are held each year in January. In addition to these major Awards, Exhibitions may be awarded in each age group. Further Minor Awards for excellence in specific fields may be made if candidates of sufficient merit present themselves. Candidates sit papers in English, Mathematics, Science, French (under 13 and 14 only), a General Paper, plus Latin (optional).

Sixth Form Scholarships are sat in November and candidates sit papers in two subjects of their choice, together with a General Paper. Candidates will also be required to undertake an interview with the Headmistress, Director of Studies and Head of Sixth Form.

Age of entry will normally be in line with general entry, ie 11+, 12+, 13+ and Sixth Form (16+). Candidates must be under 12, under 13 or under 14 on the 1st September following the examination. Girls sitting for entry to the Sixth Form must be in the final year of their GCSE studies or equivalent.

Music Awards will be made on the results of auditions and aural tests held at Downe House in February each year

Art Awards will be made on the results of a girl's portfolio and a practical test held at Downe House in June each year.

Drama Awards will be made on the results of a one-hour written paper and a one-hour practical examination.

A number of **Head's Scholarships** may be awarded, at the discretion of the Headmistress, to reward outstanding all-round performers.

For Music, Art and Drama awards junior candidates must be under 14 on the following 1st of September of the year of entry. Potential award holders are required to reach a satisfactory standard in the Common Entrance examinations for their age group before taking up their Award. Senior candidates (i.e. those entering the Sixth Form) must achieve Grade B or above in seven GCSE subjects before taking up their Award and at least an A/A* grade in the subjects they wish to pursue at A Level.

Edgbaston High School (see p 549)
Scholarships are available at 11+, including one for Music. They are awarded on the basis of performance in the entrance examination and in the case of Music there are additional written, aural and practical tests.

At 16+ there are further scholarships, offered in full or in part, to girls of outstanding ability. They include one for Music, one for Sport and one for the Arts. External candidates are examined by arrangement towards the end of the Autumn Term. Further particulars may be obtained from the School.

Farlington School (see p 551)
Scholarships are awarded on merit. There is no automatic fee reduction for scholarship awards; instead there is an automatic study support grant of £100 per term, payable directly to the Scholar. Scholarships will be held for the duration of the girl's time at Farlington, subject to annual review.

There will be public recognition of Scholars and all girls who maintain their scholarships until they leave will be further acknowledged on their final Speech Day.

Scholarships are available at three points of entry in the Senior School:

Entry into Year 7: Examination in January.

Academic, Music and Drama Scholarships are available. Both internal and external candidates need to apply for Music and Drama Scholarships. Candidates should be registered and entered by the first Friday in the preceding December. All girls who sit the Entrance Examination in January will automatically be considered for Academic Scholarships so there is no need to apply for these.

Entry into Year 9: Examination in January.

Academic, Music, Drama, Sport and Art Scholarships are available to both internal and external candidates who will need to apply in all cases. Candidates should be registered and entered by the first Friday in the preceding December.

Entry into the Sixth Form: Examination in October.

Academic, Music, Drama, Sport and Art Scholarships are available to both internal and external candidates who will need to apply in all cases. Candidates should be registered and entered by the first Monday in the October of Year 11 as the assessment will take place later that month.

Entrance Examination Day in 2009: Saturday 10th January.

Scholarship application forms may be obtained from the Registrar, Farlington School, Strood Park, Horsham, West Sussex RH12 3PN. Tel: 01403 254967 Fax: 01403 272258.

Farnborough Hill (see p 551)
Six Academic Scholarships are offered for entry at 11+. One of these is reserved for a Roman Catholic student. In addition one Music scholarship and one Sports Scholarship are awarded at 11+. There are also Bursaries for parents in need of financial assistance. Sixth Form scholarships are awarded for academic achievement, excellence in the performing arts, the creative arts and sports. An additional scholarship is awarded by Farnborough Hill Old Girls' Association.

Francis Holland School, London NW1 (see p 554)
11+ entry: One Academic Scholarship of value up to 25% of the current school fee for seven years.

Sixth Form: Two Academic Scholarships of value up to 50% of the current school fee for two years.

Francis Holland School, London SW1 (see p 555)
At 11+: 1 Academic and 1 Music scholarship, both up to the value of 25% of fees, are awarded.

Sixth Form: 4 Academic scholarships (3 internal, 1 external) up to the value of 50% of fees and 1 Music scholarship up to the value of 25% of fees are awarded for the two years leading to A Level.

Gateways School (see p 556)
Two Main School awards may be offered in each year group to pupils who attain exceptionally high standards in their entrance examinations or later in school examinations. Two Sixth Form scholarships may also be given to suitable candidates.

Scholarships in Art, Music, Drama and Sport may also be awarded to exceptional candidates.

The Godolphin and Latymer School (see p 558)
Music scholarships are available on entry to Year 7 and in the Sixth Form. They are worth up to 30% of fees and include free tuition in one instrument.

An Art scholarship is available in the Sixth Form, again worth up to 30% of fees.

For all awards, candidates must satisfy the academic requirements of the school.

The Godolphin School (see p 560)
11+, 12+, 13+ and Sixth Form scholarships, worth up to 50% of the boarding fees, are awarded for outstanding merit and promise in academic work, music or sport. Art scholarships are awarded at 13+ and Sixth Form only. Further particulars may be obtained from the *Admissions Secretary*.

Greenacre School (see p 562)
A limited number of Scholarships are awarded each year. An award equal to half the current fees is awarded at the 11+ level. Scholarships are also available for entry into the Sixth Form. These awards are available to internal or external candidates. Further particulars are available from the Headmistress.

Guernsey–The Ladies' College (see p 563)
The States of Guernsey operate an 11+ system and, annually, there are 23 selective places offered by the States of Guernsey.

Haberdashers' Monmouth School for Girls (see p 567)
Several scholarships of up to 50% fees are awarded to the most promising examination candidates entering the first year (11 year olds). Scholarships at 13+ also offered for academic potential or for Creative Arts and for Sport.

Sixth Form scholarships awarded to external candidates on the strength of school reports, interview and two subject papers.

Hethersett Old Hall School (see p 573)
Two Open Scholarships at 11+ of up to 20% of the tuition fee open to internal and external applicants.

Two Jubilee Bursaries at 11+ of up to 30% of the tuition fee (means-tested), open to external candidates only.

One Boarding Scholarship of up to 50% of the total fee available to pupils aged 11+ to 13+, open to external candidates only.

All the above are awarded as a result of the Entrance Assessments in the Spring term.

One Sport Scholarship for 11+ entry of up to 20% of the tuition fee, open to internal and external applicants.

Sixth Form: Three awards of up to 30% of the tuition fee. These are open to both internal and external candidates and awarded as a result of a scholarship examination in the Autumn term. New scholarships of up to 15% are available from March 2008 for pupils entering Year 12, who are able to demonstrate an ability to contribute significantly to a specific area of school life.

Highclare School (see p 574)
A number of scholarships are awarded each year for the 11+ age group for academic, artistic, musical and sports performance. These awards are at the discretion of the Headmistress.

James Allen's Girls' School (see p 581)
Scholarships are awarded every year to girls of 11 years of age on entry to the School. There are also Scholarships on entry into the Sixth Form. Scholarships are awarded for academic ability, but are also available for Music and Art. All Scholarships are augmented by a means-tested element where there is need. Sports Exhibitions are awarded at 11+ each year which include family membership of the JAGS Sports Club. The School has also introduced its own scheme to replace the Government Assisted Places Scheme.

Kent College Pembury (see p 582)
The Senior School offers Academic, Music, Drama, Art and Sport scholarships which can be worth up to 25% of tuition fees to pupils entering at 11+, 13+ and 16+.

King Edward VI High School for Girls (see p 586)
Up to two free place Scholarships may be awarded on the results of the Governors' Admission Examination to girls entering the first year, with a maximum of 50% for any individual scholarship. These are independent of parental income and are normally tenable for 7 years.

The Lady Eleanor Holles School (see p 591)
11+ Entry: Academic Scholarships. At least four awards are offered each year. These are expressed as percentages of the full fee and will thus keep pace with any increases. Awards are likely to be for 10%, dependent on parental circumstances. The awards are based on performance in the school's own Entrance Examination and subsequent interview.

Sixth Form Scholarships. A maximum of ten Scholarships worth 10% of fees (dependent on parental circumstances) over the two years of Sixth Form study are offered to internal and external candidates who sit the Sixth Form Entrance and Scholarship Examination in November of the year of proposed entry.

Governors' Bursaries. Candidates who sit entrance papers at any stage may be considered for a bursary award. These are means tested and subject to annual review.

Leicester High School for Girls (see p 595)
Bishop Williams Scholarships are awarded to girls at 11+ who show outstanding academic promise.

Leweston School (see p 596)
Scholarships are awarded at 11+, 12+, 13+ and Sixth Form entry. Academic scholarships are available as well as awards in Music, Art, Drama and Sport and are offered as a result of examination and interview. Dates of examinations: 24th and 25th November for Sixth Form scholarships, 2nd and 3rd February for others.

Further details and entry forms can be obtained from the Registrar, Leweston School, Sherborne, Dorset DT9 6EN.

Loughborough High School (see p 599)
The Governors offer a number of Scholarships at 11+ and 13+. The Scholarships are awarded on merit. In addition, some Governors' Awards are given at 16+. Further details of all these awards are available from the School.

Manchester High School for Girls (see p 602)
Entrance Scholarships: one or more Scholarships may be awarded for excellence in performance in the entrance tests taken at the age of 10 or 11 for admission to the Senior School in September. Such Scholarships will be awarded on merit only, not on the basis of parental income, and will provide part remission of fees.

Music and Sports Scholarships: Details are available from the Registrar.

Manor House School (see p 603)
Academic scholarships are offered each year. The awards are based on performance in the school's own Entrance Examination, which is held in the January prior to entry, and interview with the Headmistress. Art, Drama, Music and Sports Awards may be awarded to girls who show outstanding talent in these areas.

Means-tested bursaries may also be applied for.

Further details are available from the *Admissions Secretary*.

The Maynard School (see p 608)
Governors' Entrance Awards are available and Sixth Form Scholarships are available for Art, Music, Science and Sports.

Moira House Girls School (see p 611)
Ingham Academic Scholarships and Swann Exhibitions in Art, Drama, Music and Sport are open to internal and external candidates for entry into Years 7 and 9 and also the Junior School, who will take the examinations on the same day in early February of each year. Applications must be in by mid-January of the year in question.

A small number of sixth form scholarships are offered annually to deserving external students. Candidates are assessed on the basis of predicted GCSE results, interview and a reference from the student's current school.

Bursaries are available for daughters of Old Girls of the School and daughters of members of the Services.

Moreton Hall (see p 614)
A number of scholarships worth up to 10% of fees will be made to pupils at 11+, 12+ and 13+. Students may apply for more than one scholarship. Means-tested bursaries may be awarded up to the value of 100% of fees. Sixth Form Scholarships and bursaries, given in memory of Miss Bronwen Lloyd-Williams, are awarded to girls entering the Lower Sixth or to assist a pupil in the school to complete her education. Awards for Music, Drama, Art and for outstanding sporting talent are made at 11+, 12+, 13+ and 16+. For further details please contact the Principal.

The Mount School, York (see p 616)
Applicants may be awarded Scholarships at age 11, 13 and 16 on the basis of the Entrance Examination and interviews. All Academic Scholarships are fee related and are tenable while the holder remains at The Mount, provided that high standards of work and conduct are maintained.

Anniversary Scholarships, celebrating our 175th Anniversary, are available to maintained school pupils and are subject to a means-tested assessment.

Year 9 Scholarships are available in Science, Art and Design, Mathematics, Modern Languages, Music, English, Humanities and Drama.

New Hall School (see p 618)
At 13+: One or two of 50% of fees awarded on academic merit. Any Scholarships that are not awarded to the prospective Year 7 intake in a particular year will be transferred to external candidates for 13+ entry who would be joining that particular intake 2 years later.

At 11+:

One of 50% of fees – awarded on academic merit.

One of 50% of fees – candidate must be a Catholic who is currently attending an Independent Catholic School.

One of 50% of fees – candidate must be a Catholic who is currently attending a voluntary-aided Catholic Primary School.

Three of 20% of fees – awarded on academic merit.

At 16+ (Sixth Form):

2 at 16+ in the range 30-75% each (50+ part subject to means test) open to external applicants.

3 at 16+ following the results of the mock GCSE examinations. Total combined value will not exceed 75% of fees.

Various subject Awards are made to internal candidates in the following subject areas: Art, Drama, English, Geography, History, Languages, Latin, Mathematics, Music, Religious Studies, Science, Sport.

There is an award for the best GCSE results open to internal and external candidates worth 20% of day fees.

There is an internal award, "The Thomas More Award", for the greatest all-round contribution.

Newcastle upon Tyne Church High School (see p 619)
Two 11+ Governors' Awards, worth up to a maximum of 50% of the fees, are available. There is a Music Award at 11+. Further details are available from the Headmistress. Bursaries are also available, subject to criteria.

North London Collegiate School (see p 621)
A number of Scholarships, up to the value of 50% fees, are awarded each year on the results of the eleven year old entrance examinations and interviews.

Pipers Corner School (see p 639)
Pipers Corner School awards a number of Scholarships and Bursaries each year. Girls in the Prep Department and those from other Schools may apply for a Scholarship at 11+ in any one of the following areas: Academic, Art, Drama, Music and PE. Applications for Scholarships must be received by the end of November of the year preceding the intended entry to the School. Pipers Entrance Examinations are held early in January and potential scholars will be invited back shortly afterwards for further interview and assessment.

In addition, Sixth Form Scholarships are available to those already at Pipers. Examinations are held annually in November for student entry into the Sixth Form the following September. Short-listed candidates will be interviewed by members of the governing body, the Headmistress and the Deputy Head. There are five full Scholarships available. These cover all academic subjects, including Drama and Music.

Polam Hall (see p 640)
Academic Scholarships and Bursaries are offered at 7+, 11+, 14+ and 16+, with Music Awards at 11+, 14+ and 16+ and Sports at 16+. The maximum value of any scholarship is up to one-third remission of fees. Scholarships are awarded for academic excellence and for the promise or potential of academic excellence in the future. Examinations are held at the end of January for entry the following September. The 7+ Scholarship Assessments are held in June for entry the following September. For further details contact the School.

Bursaries are means-tested and awarded on academic merit.

Prior's Field (see p 642)
Academic Scholarships at 11+ and 13+ are awarded on the results of the Entrance Examination. These are valued at up to 50% of the current fees. Exhibitions for Academic Promise are also awarded for up to 25% fees.

Further details are available from the School, but applications must be with the school by the end of November of the year prior to entry.

Queen Anne's School (see p 647)
Academic Foundation scholarships are awarded each year at 11+, 13+ and 16+ as a result of performance in the Entrance Examinations. The top academic scholarship is valued at a maximum of 50% of day fees; further scholarships of up to 20% may be awarded.

Candidates may apply for scholarships in art, music, drama, sport and all-round ability which are valued at a maximum of 25% of day fees.

Further details are available from the Registrar.

Queen Margaret's School (see p 648)
Academic and All-Rounder Awards are made at 11+, 12+, 13+ and 16+. Details can be obtained from the School.

The Red Maids' School (see p 657)
Three Open Scholarships are awarded annually at 11+ for outstanding performance in the Entrance Examination. In addition discretionary Headmistress's Scholarships are awarded to girls who perform particularly well in one area of the Entrance Examination. A Year 9 Scholarship is available annually for outstanding performance in the Entrance Examination.

Sixth Form Scholarships, awarded on merit in subjects of choice, are available to Red Maids and to applicants from other schools wishing to join the Sixth Form. They are tenable for the two years of the Sixth Form where girls follow A Level courses.

Scholarships are not related to family income.

Redland High School (see p 659)
Scholarships are available for entry at 7+, 11+, 13+ and Sixth Form.

Academic, Art and Sport Scholarships. These are awarded annually to girls who display high academic potential at 7+, 11+, 13+ and for outstanding academic, artistic and sporting achievement at Sixth Form level. They are valued up to a maximum of half remission of fees and are awarded entirely on merit.

Music Scholarships. Scholarships are awarded to girls who are especially gifted in Music at 11+, 13+ and on entry to the Sixth Form. These are given irrespective of parental income and are valued up to a maximum of half remission of fees, or for free tuition on one or two instruments, as appropriate.

Bursaries are available.

A number of Bursary awards are available each year to those girls who show good academic ability and whose parents are in need of financial help to meet fees. The John James Bristol Foundation enables the school to provide annual Bursary Awards in its name to girls residing in the City of Bristol.

Roedean School (see p 661)
Junior Academic Scholarships. Examinations are held each January for entry into the school in the following September for candidates aged 11+, 12+ and 13+.

All scholarships at Roedean are worth 10% of the fees and can be supplemented by bursaries. The number and value of scholarships offered may vary according to the calibre of the candidates.

Junior Music Scholarships. Candidates are expected to play two instruments and to have reached at least Grade 5 in the first instrument. For the audition candidates should come prepared to perform two contrasting pieces on their main instrument and one piece on a second instrument. Should a candidate of outstanding ability wish to offer only one instrument, due consideration will be given. Candidates will also be required to do a practical test and to be interviewed. Any candidate who is uncertain about her eligibility is welcome to attend an individual pre-audition to obtain the opinion of the Music Department. Candidates will also sit the Roedean Entrance Examination and are required to produce evidence of a reasonable academic standard. Suitable music candidates will be called for interview at the same time as the academic candidates.

Junior Art and Performing Arts Scholarships. Candidates may be considered for a Performing Arts Scholarship in any combination of the following disciplines: Drama, Dance,

Music. (Music may only be offered as a secondary discipline for a Performing Arts Scholarship. There are separate Music Scholarships available for specialist musicians.)

For each discipline there is a separate assessment. Candidates must make clear in which disciplines they wish to be assessed. Candidates will also sit the Roedean Entrance Examination and are required to produce evidence of a reasonable academic standard.

Junior Physical Education Scholarships. Candidates will be expected to demonstrate their overall ability and excellence in one or two sports. It will also be important to have a track record of success at inter-school (IAPS) and county level. Candidates will also sit the Roedean Entrance Examination and are required to produce evidence of a reasonable academic standard.

Candidates should come prepared to participate in two of their main sports in order to show their ability and potential. Candidates will also be interviewed.

Sixth Form Scholarships, worth 10% of the fees, are awarded to candidates who show a high level of achievement across a number of disciplines as well as demonstrating both flair for their chosen subjects and the potential for further development. Individual subject scholarships are also awarded.

Details of the scholarships and past papers may be obtained from the Registrar.

The Royal Masonic School for Girls (see p 663)
Major and Minor Academic Scholarships are awarded annually at 11+ and 16+.

One Minor Scholarship is awarded at 7+, based on academic potential.

St Albans High School (see p 668)
Scholarships are offered annually at 11+ entry. These are awarded on academic merit shown in the entrance examinations and any subsequent interviews. The value of each Scholarship is up to 10% of the fees. Further Scholarships are offered on entry to the Sixth Form.

St Catherine's School, Bramley (see p 671)
11+ (Year 7)

Four Entrance Scholarships are available at age 11, awarded on the results of the Entrance Examination. Two scholarships are for one third of the fees payable and the other two for one sixth of the fees payable. These run through the Middle School and are extended through the Sixth Form at the discretion of the Headmistress.

A Music Scholarship of a third of the fees may be awarded annually to an 11+ candidate who shows exceptional musical talent.

Upper 5 & Sixth Form (Year 11)

There are 10 internal and three external academic Scholarships, one Sports Scholarship, one Music Scholarship and one Art Scholarship:

(i) *Margaret Kaye Scholarships*: There are four scholarships of one third of the fees payable awarded to run for three years (through Upper 5 and Sixth Form).
(ii) *Sixth Form Scholarships*: Six scholarships are available, each of one third of the fees payable. Awards are based on performance in the Lower Fifth year, the results of the June examinations at the end of the Lower Fifth, and an interview. Parents of girls in the Lower Fifth are sent full details at the beginning of the Summer Term.

There are three *External Academic Scholarships*. Awards are based on the results of the Entrance Examination and an interview. Candidates interested in applying should contact the Registrar for details.

Clare Gregory Scholarship: This is awarded for sporting ability and is for one third of the day fees in the Sixth Form.

Music Scholarship. There is one Music Scholarship for a pupil entering the Sixth Form, to the value of one third of the fees payable. Further details can be obtained from the Director of Music.

Art Scholarship. There is one Art Scholarship for a pupil entering the Sixth Form, to the value of one third of the fees payable. Further details can be obtained from the Head of Art.

Note: in each case the fees referred to are the fees payable by the parent for the term in question, whether boarding or day fees.

Music Awards. In addition there are five Music Awards available for free Music Tuition on individual instruments. Further details can be obtained from the Director of Music.

St David's School (see p 674)
Two scholarships worth 25% of fees are on offer to girls entering the school at age 10/11. Those wishing to be considered for these will be required to take a one hour extension paper on the day of the Entrance Examination and to have a short informal interview with the Head.

A number of Sixth Form scholarships are also available each year.

St Francis' College (see p 677)
A number of Scholarships are awarded at 11+ and 13+ following the entrance examinations held in February. These vary in value between 20% and 50% of tuition fees and are awarded on overall Academic ability.

St Joseph's Convent School (see p 690)
A number of scholarships are awarded each year. All candidates applying for entry into Year 7 are required to sit an entrance examination and are automatically considered for an academic scholarship. These scholarships are reviewed annually up to the end of Year 11. Scholarships are also awarded for music, drama, sport and on entry to the Sixth Form.

St Leonards–Mayfield School (see p 691)
Entrance at 11+, 13+ and 16+. These are open to any girls who show strong academic potential.

St Margaret's School, Bushey (see p 694)
Academic and Music Scholarships are awarded at Year 7 and Sixth Form at the discretion of the Head. An Art Scholarship is also available in the Sixth Form.

St Margaret's School, Edinburgh (see p 695)
Academic, Music, Drama, PE and Art Scholarships are available for entry into the Senior School. Further details can be obtained from the Principal.

St Margaret's School, Exeter (see p 697)
St Margaret's School wishes to attract and assist able pupils to join or continue their education at the school.

Academic awards are made on the basis of performance in entrance and other tests and their continued tenure is conditional on continued excellent academic performance. Awards are worth from 10% to 50% of fees.

Music Scholarships are awarded after audition and continued tenure is conditional on sustained commitment to school music.

Art Scholarships (Sixth Form only) are awarded on the basis of a portfolio submission. Continued tenure is conditional on sustained excellence in and commitment to Art.

Drama scholarships (Sixth Form only) are awarded after audition and continued tenure is conditional on sustained commitment to school drama.

Council awards are made on the basis of academic merit and parents' financial circumstances. Tenure thereafter is conditional on sustained academic progress and continuing financial need.

Parents who wish the school to consider their daughter for any of the Awards should complete the relevant section of the Pupil Registration Form. All Awards are reviewed annually by the Education Committee.

If you would like further information about the financial and practical support St Margaret's provides for its prospective and current pupils, please contact, in the first instance, the Admissions Secretary on 01392 491699.

Saint Martin's (see p 699)
A number of awards up to a limit of 50% of fees are offered each year for entry to the Senior School. Awards are made to candidates who show outstanding ability in the entrance examination and in interview.

Several scholarships up to a maximum of 50% of fees are awarded annually to pupils entering the Sixth Form. Candidates are required to sit papers assessing a variety of skills and their potential for further study. Those who are shortlisted are interviewed by the Headmistress and the Head of Sixth Form.

St Mary's School Ascot (see p 702)
At 11+ there are two Academic Scholarships available: the General Scholarship worth 5% of the boarding fees and the Mary Ward Exhibition worth 5% of the boarding fees.

At 13+ there is one General Scholarship available worth 5% of the tuition fees.

These awards may be augmented by a means-tested bursary of up to a further 25% of boarding fees. They are awarded on academic merit and interview based on the School's own entrance examination.

At 16+ there are two Academic Scholarships available: the General Scholarship worth 5% of the boarding fees and the Sixth Form Science Scholarship also worth up to 5% of boarding fees.

These awards may be augmented by a means-tested bursary of up to a further 25% of boarding fees. They are awarded on academic merit.

St Mary's School, Calne (see p 704)
Scholarships are awarded up to 40% of a Scholar's boarding or day fees, as applicable. Awards are granted solely on merit as the result of a competitive examination. To be able to allocate funds to those girls who would most benefit from them financially, only a proportion of the percentage offered – 5% – is awarded automatically. The remaining 35% – or any proportion thereof – is allocated, subject to a means test, at the Governors' discretion. This process will remain entirely confidential and parents may request the relevant forms at the time of the Scholarship award. In addition to the full Academic Scholarships, Exhibitions may be offered to internal or external candidates, showing outstanding ability in a single subject, each up to 10% of a scholar's boarding or day fees. Only 5% will be awarded automatically, the remainder being subject to a means test at the Governors' discretion. The following Scholarships are open to girls registered for entry to St Mary's; all rewards are retained until completion of the Sixth Form:

At 11+: One Music Scholarship and three Academic Scholarships will be awarded to girls who excel within the Scholarship entry group. Papers will be taken in English, Mathematics and Science.

At 13+: One Academic Scholarship, one Music Scholarship and one 'Bodinnar' All Rounder Scholarship will be awarded to girls who excel within the Scholarship entry group. Papers will be taken in English, Mathematics, Science and French and in addition, for 'Bodinnar', flair and ability must be presented in two or more disciplines selected from Art, Drama, Music and Sport.

At Sixth Form: Two internal Academic Scholarships awarded to current pupils in their final GCSE year at St Mary's for the duration of the Sixth Form.

One Open Academic Scholarship may be awarded to an internal or an external candidate for the duration of the Sixth Form.

Open Scholarships awarded for Art, Drama and Music may be awarded to an internal or an external candidate for the duration of the Sixth Form. Girls accepting one of these awards are expected to take the subject to A2 Level.

In addition to the full Academic Scholarships, up to two Exhibitions will be offered to internal or external candidates, each up to the value of £1,000, payable in two equal instalments of up to £500 at the beginning of Lower and Upper Sixth Forms.

Foundation Awards: Awards are available annually at 11+ and at Sixth Form to particularly gifted and talented pupils from the state sector. For more information, please contact the Admissions Department.

St Mary's School, Shaftesbury (see p 709)
11+ Academic, Music and Catholic Primary School scholarships are awarded.

13+ Academic, Music, Sport and Art scholarships are awarded.

Sixth Form Academic and Art scholarships are awarded.

Head's Scholarships can also be awarded at 11+, 13+ and 16+.

All Scholarships offer up to 10% remission of day or boarding fees with a further 40% available by a means-tested bursary.

Scholarship Examinations take place in January.

St Swithun's School (see p 715)
Entrance Scholarships are available for day girls and boarders entering the School at 11+. Scholarships are also awarded on the results of a competitive examination at 13+. The major award covers half of school fees. There are also a number of awards for Sixth Form entrants covering up to half of school fees.

Sherborne Girls (see p 719)
Academic Scholarships are offered at 11+, 12+, 13+ and 16+ annually as a result of examination and interview. There are also scholarships offered for outstanding promise in Music, Art and Sport (16+).

All examinations are held in January apart from Sixth Form in November and All-Rounder (13+) in February. Award holders are offered scholarships up to a maximum of 25% of fees. Scholarships may be combined with bursarial support. Bursarial support (up to 100%) may be available in cases of demonstrable need.

Sir William Perkins's School (see p 721)
Awards are offered each year to candidates who achieve an exceptionally high standard in the entrance examination for Year 7. Academic awards are offered for two years sixth form study on the results of a scholarship examination and interview. All awards will be worth up to half the academic tuition fees.

Stamford High School (see p 724)
There are Governors' Scholarships and Bursaries available on entry. These are predominantly for academic work, but also include Music and Art. For further particulars apply to the Head, Stamford High School, Lincolnshire PE9 2LL.

Stonar School (see p 725)
Academic, Music, Art, Sport, Drama, Riding and good All-Rounder Scholarships are offered from Year 7. 11+ Scholarship Examinations are held in January each year and Sixth Form Scholarships by the end of the calendar year. Other ages by arrangement.

Tudor Hall (see p 738)
Academic 11+/12+/13+ and 16+. These are awarded to candidates entering at 11+, 12+, 13+ on the basis of their performance at Common Entrance and interviews. At 16+ awards are offered on the basis of interview, school report and examination. The value of the award is up to £1,000 per annum. These awards are intended for the support of the pupil's academic interests.

Music 11+/13+ and 16+. These are awarded on the basis of ability and potential at 11+, 13+ and 16+. The value of the award is up to £1,000 per annum to entrants who show outstanding musical ability. Music awards exist in the form of free tuition in one or more instruments for the duration of the student's time at the school.

Art 13+/16+. These are awarded on the basis of ability and potential either at 13+ or 16+. The value of the award is up to

£1,000 per annum. These awards are intended for the support of the pupil's Art interests.

Drama 13+/16+. These are awarded on the basis of ability and potential either at 13+ or 16+. The value of the award is up to £1,000 per annum. These awards are intended for the support of the pupil's Dramatic interests.

Sport 13+/16+. These are awarded on the basis of ability and potential either at 13+ or 16+. The value of the award is up to £1,000 per annum. These awards are intended for the support of the pupil's Sporting interests.

Bursaries are awarded to new and current parents who are in financial need.

Wychwood School. (see p 750)
At 11+ one Scholarship worth £1,200 pa and two Scholarships worth £600 pa are offered.

At 16+ one Scholarship worth £1,200 pa and one Scholarship worth £600 pa are offered, and one Science Scholarship worth £1,500 pa.

Academic Scholarship will be awarded on the results of the general entrance paper.

Wycombe Abbey School (see p 751)
Lower School Entry: A variety of Scholarship and Exhibition awards are available for candidates under 12 and under 14 on 1st September of the proposed year of entry.

Some awards are also available for candidates entering the Sixth Form.

Academic and Music Awards may be augmented by means-tested bursaries.

For further information, please contact the Registrar.

Wykeham House School (see p 753)
A number of Scholarships worth a fixed amount each year towards the cost of books, tenable for five years, are awarded each year based on good 11+ entrance results and interview.

Music and/or Drama Scholarships

The Abbey School (see p 505)
Music Awards, giving free tuition on up to two instruments, are awarded at age 11 and on entry to the Sixth Form, following auditions.

Abbot's Hill (see p 507)
Music Scholarships of 5–10% of fees may be awarded.

Badminton School (see p 510)
Music Scholarships to a maximum of 20% remission of fees are available to all applicants. Auditions take place in January for girls entering Years 7 and 9 and November for girls entering the Sixth Form.

Bedford High School for Girls (see p 512)
Music Scholarships are available on entry to the Senior School or Sixth Form.

Benenden School (see p 514)
Lower School Entry (11–13): Substantial awards available. The examinations are held in January preceding the date of entry. Candidates should have reached the standard of Grade V (or equivalent) or show great potential. Those offering piano or singing as a principal study should be fluent in an orchestral instrument. Candidates will be required to do practical tests and will be interviewed; they are also required to show that they have reached the general academic standards of any entrant either by sitting qualifying papers, or by taking the academic scholarship examination. For further information, please contact the *Admissions Secretary.*

Sixth Form Entry: Substantial awards available. Examinations are held in November preceding entry in September. The requirements for a Sixth Form Music Scholarship are very much the same as for Lower School candidates (see above entry), but candidates should have reached the standard of Grade VII (or equivalent). Candidates are also required to show that they have reached the general academic standard required of any entrant by taking two qualifying papers in subjects which they intend to study at Advanced Level. For further information, please contact the *Admissions Secretary.*

Blackheath High School (see p 517)
Up to 2 Music Scholarships may be offered annually. Auditions are held following the entrance examination.

Bruton School for Girls (see p 524)
Music and Drama Scholarships include the Zhou Guang-Ren and Howard Music Exhibitions and Cumberlege Scholarships and Awards into the Sixth Form. The Besly and Palmer Music Awards are available to girls entering the School at 11+ and 13+.

Casterton School (see p 527)
A Music Scholarship (up to the value of 50% of full fees in exceptional cases) plus free tuition on two instruments, is available. Two Exhibitions of free tuition on two instruments are also offered. These awards are based on auditions which are conducted concurrently with the entrance examination.

Channing School (see p 530)
Academic and Music Scholarships and Exhibitions are offered at 11+ and 16+ entry. Music bursaries also awarded internally from Year 8 in the senior school. These cover lessons in school on one instrument for one year (renewable).

The Cheltenham Ladies' College (see p 531)
At Junior level, both Major and Minor Scholarships are offered. The major scholarship is worth 30% of the annual fees plus free instrumental tuition and the minor award 20% of annual fees plus free instrumental tuition. At Sixth Form level, one music scholarship is available and is worth 30% of the annual fees.

Combe Bank School (see p 537)
Music Scholarships are awarded to suitable candidates subject to a satisfactory performance on the academic papers. Candidates should be able to perform to Grade 3 standard or above. The audition will be mainly practical and designed to test musicianship and musical potential. Candidates are asked to play two contrasting pieces on their main instrument/voice, to take some aural and sight reading tests and to answer questions about their musical experience. They may also offer one piece on their second instrument/voice. A Music Scholar will be expected to play a full and active part in the musical life of the school and to be an ambassador for the subject among her peers.

Edgbaston High School (see p 549)
Two Music Scholarships are offered annually: one at 11+ and one at 16+. All scholarships can be combined with means-tested bursaries in cases of need. 11+ candidates must sit the main entrance test in January and then have written, aural and practical tests. Candidates at 16+ must attend an interview and sit a music examination in November. An Arts scholarship is available at 16+ to girls studying the visual, creative or performing arts. Applications are assessed by interview and a practical session. Further details may be obtained from the School.

Farlington School (see p 551)
Music and Drama Scholarships are available to both internal and external candidates entering Year 7, Year 9 and the Sixth Form.

Farnborough Hill (see p 551)
One Music Scholarship is offered at 11+. Applicants are auditioned and the award is made on the basis of overall potential and likely contribution to the musical life of the school. Sixth Form scholarships are also awarded for excellence in the performing arts.

Francis Holland School, London NW1 (see p 554)
11+ entry: One Music Scholarship of value up to 25% of the current school fee for seven years.

Sixth Form: One Music Scholarship of value up to 25% of the current school fee for two years.

Francis Holland School, London SW1 (see p 555)
1 Music scholarship at 11+ up to the value of 25% of the fees.

1 Sixth Form Music scholarship up to the value of 25% of fees is awarded for the two years leading to A Level.

The Godolphin School (see p 560)
11+, 12+, 13+ and Sixth Form Music scholarships are awarded for outstanding merit and promise. Candidates for music awards should have attained at least Grade 4 at 11+ (Grade 6 at 13+) on one instrument. They are also expected to reach an acceptable academic standard.

Haberdashers' Monmouth School for Girls (see p 567)
Music Awards are made to outstanding performers, junior and senior pupils of the School, following audition. Awards include the cost of tuition on up to two instruments while the pupil is at the school.

James Allen's Girls' School (see p 581)
Music Scholarships are available at 11+ and 16+. Candidates must satisfy the academic requirements of the school and pass an audition. Scholarships are on the same basis as academic scholarships but also include instrument tuition.

Kent College Pembury (see p 582)
Music and Drama scholarships each may be worth up to 25% of tuition fees and are available each year for girls entering at 11+, 13+ and 16+.

The Lady Eleanor Holles School (see p 591)
Both Major and Minor Awards for Music are available at 11+ and 16+. These are likely to be for 10% of fees (dependent on parental circumstances) and free tuition on one instrument. Candidates must satisfy academic requirements in entrance papers and attend on a further day for music auditions. Full details of requirements in these auditions are available from the school.

Leicester High School for Girls (see p 595)
A Music Scholarship is awarded at 11–18 available to all girls. An audition and interview is also necessary.

Leweston School (see p 596)
Music and Drama Scholarships are offered at 11+, 12+, 13+ and Sixth Form entry. Dates of Auditions: 25th November for Sixth Form candidates, 3rd February for others.

Further details and entry forms can be obtained from the Registrar, Leweston School, Sherborne, Dorset DT9 6EN.

Loughborough High School (see p 599)
The Governors offer Music Scholarships to musically promising and talented pupils who are successful in the Entrance Examination. Auditions are held during the week preceding the Entrance Examinations.

The Maynard School (see p 608)
Senior School Music Scholarships and Exhibitions are awarded each year. A Sixth Form Music Scholarship is awarded each year.

The Mount School, York (see p 616)
Music Scholarships are available at age 11, 13 and 16. These cover the costs of individual lessons.

Drama Scholarships are available at age 13.

New Hall School (see p 618)
1 at 11+: One Music of one-third fees and tuition in up to two instruments open to any applicant.

1 at 13+: One Music of one-third fees open to any applicant.

1 at 16+: One Music and one Drama Award open to internal or external candidates.

North London Collegiate School (see p 621)
A number of Music Scholarships, up to the value of 25% fees, are awarded each year.

Polam Hall (see p 640)
Music Awards are available at 11+, 14+ and 16+. A Minor Award normally involves free tuition in one instrument and a Major Award free tuition in two instruments. In exceptional cases some remission of fees may be made.

Prior's Field (see p 642)
Music Scholarships: First instrument, including voice, at approximately grade 3 Associated Board standard at age 11+ is expected and candidates will be required to perform as part of their interview. Candidates with strength in one instrument only may apply. The scholarship is valued at up to 25% of fees at 11+, 13+ and for the Sixth Form.

Drama Scholarships may be awarded valued up to 25% of the current fees at 11+, 13+ and for the Sixth Form. Girls are required to perform on the day of the examination and take part in a practical workshop.

Further details are available from the School, but applications for Scholarships must be with the school by the end of November of the year prior to entry.

Queen Anne's School (see p 647)
Music and Drama scholarships are available at 11+, 13+ and 16+ valued at a maximum of 25% of day fees.

Further details are available from the Registrar.

Queen Margaret's School (see p 648)
Music Scholarships plus free tuition on two instruments are available. There are also Music Exhibitions. The auditions are in February. For further details please contact the *Acting Director of Music*.

The Red Maids' School (see p 657)
Music Scholarships are awarded, usually at 11+. These cover a reduction of fees, or free tuition on one or two instruments, as appropriate.

Redland High School (see p 659)
Music Scholarships. Scholarships are awarded to girls who are especially gifted in Music at 11+, 13+ and on entry to the Sixth Form. These are given irrespective of parental income and are valued up to a maximum of half remission of fees, or for free tuition on one or two instruments, as appropriate.

The Royal Masonic School for Girls (see p 663)
There is one Music Scholarship, of value approximately one-third of the fees, available at 11+. A Music Scholarship of similar value is available at the Sixth Form level. The benefits of these Scholarships include free tuition on one instrument of the scholar's choice.

St Albans High School (see p 668)
One Music Scholarship is offered annually at 11+ entry. Candidates who have first reached the required standard in the entrance examinations are asked to attend the Music School for auditions.

St Catherine's School, Bramley (see p 671)
A Music Scholarship of a third of the fees may be awarded annually to an 11+ candidate who shows exceptional musical talent.

There is one general Music Scholarship for a pupil entering the Sixth Form, to the value of one third of the fees payable and the Jennifer Bate Organ Scholarship worth one-third fees payable plus organ tuition.

In addition there are five Music Awards available for free Music Tuition on individual instruments.

Further details can be obtained from the Director of Music.

St David's School (see p 674)
Two Music Scholarships are available annually on entry to the Senior School following auditions, with a value of up to 25% of fees.

St Francis' College (see p 677)
One Music Scholarship is awarded annually up to the value of 50% of the tuition fees plus free tuition on two musical instruments.

St Leonards–Mayfield School (see p 691)
At 11+, 13+ and 16+. These are open to any girls who show outstanding talent in Music or Drama.

Saint Martin's (see p 699)
A Music Scholarship is offered at 11+ to the value of one-third of full fees plus free tuition in one instrument.

St Mary's School Ascot (see p 702)
One Music Scholarship worth up to 5% of boarding fees is awarded annually to a pupil entering the School at 11+ or 13+. Candidates must have qualified to at least Grade V on the first study instrument at the time of application. This award may be augmented by a means-tested bursary of up to a further 25% of boarding fees. Free tuition is also given in two instruments.

St Mary's School, Shaftesbury (see p 709)
Music Scholarships are available at 11+ and 13+.

St Paul's Girls' School (see p 712)
Junior Music Scholarships (11+) of the value of £100 per annum and free tuition in one instrument for seven years. Candidates must be successful in the First Year Entrance Examination.

Senior Music Scholarships (16+) of the value of £250 per annum and free tuition in two instruments are awarded on the basis of written and practical examinations and interview. Candidates must be successful in the Senior School Entrance Examination.

The Nora Day Music Scholarship (16+) may be offered for entry in Autumn 2009 to an external candidate of outstanding musical ability on a keyboard instrument who is in her final GCSE year at another school and who has passed the Senior entrance examination for entry to the School for Advanced Level. The successful candidate is entitled to half the School's tuition fees as well as free music tuition in two instruments for her two years at the School. It would be expected that a candidate for the Nora Day Music Scholarship would meet the normal criteria for a Music Scholarship, but would, in addition, display outstanding talent and would be ready to participate in full in the musical life of the School.

St Swithun's School (see p 715)
Music awards (exhibitions) provide free tuition on up to two instruments. Music scholarships of up to 30% of school fees can be awarded each year to suitable candidates at 11+, 13+ and 16+.

Sherborne Girls (see p 719)
Music Awards (Junior and 16+): Major Awards of up to 25% of the current fees and Minor Awards of up to 20% (with free tuition in three instruments to a maximum of 2 lessons per week). Music Exhibitions offering free tuition. Further particulars may be obtained from Admissions.

Sir William Perkins's School (see p 721)
Music Scholarships will be worth up to 10% of the academic tuition fees.

Wychwood School (see p 750)
Two Music Scholarships are offered at ages 11+ or 16+ to cover instrument tuition. Candidates will be expected to play two prepared pieces on their instrument(s) and to do some sight reading and aural tests on the afternoon of the test day.

Wycombe Abbey School (see p 751)
Music Scholarships and Exhibitions of varying value are available to candidates under the age of 14 on 1st September of the proposed year of entry.

A Music Scholarship is also available to girls entering the Sixth Form.

Awards may be augmented by means-tested bursaries.

For details, please contact the Registrar.

Art and/or Design & Technology Scholarships

Abbot's Hill (see p 507)
Art Scholarships of 5–10% of fees may be awarded.

Badminton School (see p 510)
Art Scholarships to a maximum of 20% remission of fees are open to all applicants at 13+ and for Sixth Formers. Portfolios should be submitted in January preceding entry for 13+ and in October for Year 12.

Benenden School (see p 514)
Art and Design: Substantial awards available. Examinations are held in November preceding entry in September. The examination for the Art Scholarship will consist of one hour on a set-piece drawing followed by an interview based on the candidate's portfolio on which particular emphasis will be placed for evidence of commitment and enthusiasm. Candidates are required to show that they have reached the general academic standard of any entrant by sitting two qualifying papers in subjects which they intend to study at Advanced Level. For further information, please contact the *Admissions Secretary*.

Design and Technology: Scholarships are offered to girls who show exceptional promise and commitment in this area, supported by good academic results in the normal entry papers.

Applicants will be asked to produce evidence of three kinds: a record or portfolio of previous work or achievements; a response to a challenge set at Benenden; and an interview.

Candidates will be asked to identify and research the main purposes of packaging and to design and make a suitable container for a given object. They will use non-specialist materials and processes such as paper, pencils, card, scissors, glue. Research might be prepared at home or in their school, but the task of designing and making would be executed at Benenden.

Blackheath High School (see p 517)
One Art Scholarship may be offered annually. Art assessments are held following the entrance examination.

The Cheltenham Ladies' College (see p 531)
One Art Scholarship worth 20% of the annual fees is available to Sixth Form candidates.

One Art Scholarship worth 20% of the annual fees is available to Junior candidates.

Farlington School (see p 551)
Art Scholarships are available to both internal and external candidates entering Year 9 and the Sixth Form.

The Godolphin School (see p 560)
13+ and Sixth Form Art scholarships are awarded for outstanding merit and promise; candidates must present a portfolio. They are also expected to reach an acceptable academic standard.

James Allen's Girls' School (see p 581)
Art Scholarships are offered at 11+ and 16+ to girls who are successful in the Entrance Examination.

Kent College Pembury (see p 582)
Art scholarships may be worth up to 25% of tuition fees and are available at 11+, 13+ and 16+.

Leweston School (see p 596)
Art/DT Scholarships are offered at 11+, 12+, 13+ and Sixth Form entry. Dates of examinations: 25th November for Sixth Form scholarships, 3rd February for others. Candidates will be asked to bring a portfolio of work with them.

Further details and entry forms can be obtained from the Registrar, Leweston School, Sherborne, Dorset DT9 6EN.

The Maynard School (see p 608)
Two Sixth Form Art Scholarships are awarded annually.

New Hall School (see p 618)
1 at 16+: Award open to internal and external candidates.

Prior's Field (see p 642)
Art Scholarships are valued at up to 25% of current fees at 11+, 13+ and for the Sixth Form. Candidates are required to submit a sketchbook and two pieces of work. In addition, candidates will sit an examination and be interviewed by the Head of Creative Art.

Further details are available from the School, but applications for Scholarships must be with the school by the end of November of the year prior to entry.

Queen Anne's School (see p 647)
Art scholarships are available at 11+, 13+ and 16+ valued at a maximum of 25% of day fees.

Further details are available from the Registrar.

The Royal Masonic School for Girls (see p 663)
An Art Scholarship, of value approximately one-third of the fees, is available for competition at Sixth Form level.

St Catherine's School, Bramley (see p 671)
There is one Art Scholarship for a pupil entering the Sixth Form, to the value of one third of the fees payable. Further details can be obtained from the Head of Art.

St Leonards–Mayfield School (see p 691)
At 11+, 13+ and 16+. These are open to any girls who show outstanding talent in Art or Ceramics.

St Mary's School Ascot (see p 702)
One Art Scholarship worth up to 5% of boarding fees is awarded annually to a pupil entering the School at 11+, 13+ or 16+. This award may be augmented by a means-tested bursary of up to a further 25% of boarding fees.

St Mary's School, Shaftesbury (see p 709)
13+ and Sixth Form Art Scholarships are available.

Sherborne Girls (see p 719)
Art Awards (Junior and 16+): Major Award of up to 15% of the current fees and Minor Awards of up to 10%. Candidates will be required to bring a portfolio with them and would be asked to do some work in the Art Department whilst they are here.

Wychwood School (see p 750)
Two Creative Arts Scholarships are offered at age 11+ to candidates with outstanding ability in Music, Art or Creative Writing. One Scholarship worth £1,200 and the other £600.

(i) English: Candidates are asked to bring six different pieces of writing, including poetry, a story and a description. These will be discussed with the Head of English.

(ii) Art: Candidates are asked to bring six artistic compositions or craft items which will be discussed with the Head of Art. A short unprepared task will be undertaken on the afternoon of the test day.

Sports and/or All-Rounder Scholarships

Abbot's Hill (see p 507)
Sports Scholarships of 5–10% of fees may be awarded.

Badminton School (see p 510)
All Rounder awards for good academic potential and aptitude in areas such as the creative or performing arts or sport are offered with 10% remission of fees.

Benenden School (see p 514)
Sports Scholarships. Scholarships are offered to girls who show exceptional promise and commitment in this area, supported by good academic results in the normal entry papers.

Applicants will be asked to produce evidence of three kinds: a record or portfolio of previous work or achievements; a response to a challenge set at Benenden; and an interview.

Candidates will undertake a test to measure levels of fitness, participate in a range of games to show physical ability and tactical awareness, and be given an opportunity to demonstrate their chosen specialism

Bruton School for Girls (see p 524)
Sports and All-Rounder Scholarships include the Hobhouse Exhibition for 13+ entry and Cumberlege Scholarships and Awards for entry into the Sixth Form.

The Cheltenham Ladies' College (see p 531)
One Sports Scholarship worth 20% of the annual fees is available at 13+ entry. Two internal Sports Scholarships are also awarded at the end of Year 8.

Edgbaston High School (see p 549)
A Sport Scholarship is available at 16+.

Farlington School (see p 551)
Sport Scholarships are available to both internal and external candidates entering Year 9 and the Sixth Form.

Farnborough Hill (see p 551)
One Sports Scholarship is offered at 11+. Applicants are tested and the award is made on the basis of overall potential and likely contribution to the sporting life of the school. Sixth Form scholarships are offered for excellence in sport.

The Godolphin School (see p 560)
11+, 12+, 13+ and Sixth Form Sports scholarships are available.

Hethersett Old Hall School (see p 573)
One Sport Scholarship for 11+ entry of up to 20% of the tuition fee, open to internal and external applicants.

Kent College Pembury (see p 582)
Sport scholarships may be worth up to 25% of tuition fees and are available at 11+, 13+ and 16+.

Leweston School (see p 596)
Sport Scholarships are offered at 11+, 12+, 13+ and Sixth Form entry. Dates of examinations: 25th November for Sixth Form scholarships, 3rd February for others.

Further details and entry forms can be obtained from the Registrar, Leweston School, Sherborne, Dorset DT9 6EN.

The Maynard School (see p 608)
There are two Sixth Form Sports Scholarships awarded annually.

New Hall School (see p 618)
At 11+: One Sports Scholarship of 25% of fees open to any applicant.

At 13+: Two Sports Scholarships of 25% of fees open to any applicant.

At 16+: One Sports Award open to internal and external candidates.

Prior's Field (see p 642)
Physical Education Scholarships are valued at up to 25% of current fees at 11+, 13+ and for the Sixth Form. Candidates are required to take part in a practical assessment and interview with the Head of PE. A reference must also be submitted from their current school showing evidence of excellence in more than one sport or physical activity including achievements in team activities.

Queen Anne's School (see p 647)
Sports and All-Rounder scholarships are available at 11+, 13+ and 16+ valued at a maximum of 25% of day fees.

Further details are available from the Registrar.

The Royal Masonic School for Girls (see p 663)
One Sports and one All-Rounder Scholarship at 11+ of value approximately one-third of fees.

St Catherine's School, Bramley (see p 671)
Clare Gregory Scholarship: This is awarded for sporting ability and is for one third of the day fees in the Sixth Form.

St David's School (see p 674)
Gymnastic Scholarships are available at Year 7 entry. They have a value of 25% of fees and are awarded following trials. Applicants should supply a portfolio of achievements and a recommendation from their coach.

High performance Scholarships are awarded to girls recommended by the local High Performance Centres as having the potential to represent the UK at International level. These scholarships offer full boarding fees, but do not cover academic fees. They are available to both prep and senior school pupils.

Sports Scholarships are available, worth up to 25% of fees. Pupils will need to supply a portfolio of their achievements on the day of the Main Entrance Exam together with a letter of recommendation.

St Leonards–Mayfield School (see p 691)
Sports Scholarships are available at 11+, 13+ and 16+.

St Mary's School, Shaftesbury (see p 709)
13+ Sports Scholarships are available.

Sherborne Girls (see p 719)
All-Rounder Award (Junior): An award of up to 25% of the current fees. Candidates will sit papers in English, Mathematics and Science. The All-Rounder Award takes into account ability in two areas of activity outside of the classroom. Two All-Rounder Awards of up to 15% per annum may be awarded.

Sport Award (16+): Candidates will offer one or more sports, preferably reaching county standard or higher. One award of up to 10% reduction of the current fees may be awarded per annum. Means-tested bursaries can raise considerably the effective amount of an award.

Educational Awards/Bursaries

Badminton School (see p 510)
An Old Badmintonians scholarship is available for daughters/granddaughters of Old Badmintonians worth 15% remission of fees at Year 9.

The Baker Award for candidates currently studying at a girls' only prep school is also worth 15% remission of fees. Candidates will be considered for Academic or Art or Music.

Forces families receive 20% remission off fees.

Girls who are awarded scholarships, are also eligible to apply for a Bursary, to a maximum of 100% remission of fees.

Bursaries are means-tested and awarded on the basis of parents' financial circumstances. Application forms are available by emailing bursar@badminton.bristol.sch.uk. Application dates are 20 October preceding entry to the Sixth Form and 1 December for Years 7 and 9.

Bedford High School for Girls (see p 512)
The Headmistress's Award is available to girls who have outstanding ability in any area and/or who contribute to school life in an exceptional way.

Bruton School for Girls (see p 524)
Governors' Exhibitions exist to support pupils from families who would find difficulty in affording the full fees.

Casterton School (see p 527)
Bursaries for the daughters of Clergy are available (as the school was originally founded for daughters of the clergy). In addition, there are a small number of bursaries for the daughters of schoolmasters and very substantial bursaries for children from a Services background.

Channing School (see p 530)
Unitarians may apply for a Foundation Bursary in case of need. Some Bursary support is available to other girls on application and subject to need.

The Cheltenham Ladies' College (see p 531)
Applications for Means-Tested Bursaries are welcomed at all entry points, on entering for the examinations.

Edgbaston High School (see p 549)
A number of Bursaries at both 11+ and 16+ are available for candidates of good academic ability in financial need. They may cover part or full fees. Please apply to the Headmistress for further details.

Farlington School (see p 551)
The School offers means-tested Bursaries for all prospective and current pupils from Year 5 upwards.

The main bursary award process is carried out in the first half of the Spring Term and applications, therefore, should be made in the second half of the preceding autumn term.

Subject to available funds, applications for bursaries will be considered at other times of the year, on a half-termly basis if parental circumstances change unexpectedly.

Francis Holland School, London NW1 (see p 554)
The school is able to offer a limited number of bursaries at 11+ entry, of value of up to 100% of the current school fee. These bursaries are means tested and reviewed annually.

Francis Holland School, London SW1 (see p 555)
3 up to full fees Bursaries are available at 11+ and one at 14+.

For daughters of Clergy there is a remission of one-third of the School Fee.

The Godolphin School (see p 560)
Educational/Academic Awards

Six means-tested Foundation Bursaries worth up to 70% of the boarding fees, are available from time to time to boarding candidates from single parent, divorced or separated families who have been brought up as members of the Church of England.

Old Godolphin Bursary

A means-tested bursary, worth up to 50% of the boarding fees, is awarded from time to time by the Old Godolphin Association to the daughter of an Old Godolphin, either a girl of exceptional talent or an able, though not necessarily exceptional, girl who is in need of financial assistance.

Haberdashers' Monmouth School for Girls (see p 567)
E F Bulmer Sixth Form Award (means-tested) for a pupil from Herefordshire.

Hethersett Old Hall School (see p 573)
Bursaries are available, subject to means, to daughters of the Clergy and HM Forces Personnel, who satisfy the requirements of the Entrance Assessment of their age group.

Bursaries may be awarded, subject to means, by the Governors to some girls in the School who wish to continue their education in the Sixth Form.

Kent College Pembury (see p 582)
Fee assistance may be offered to those applying to the senior school. This fee assistance is for those girls who would benefit from all the school offers but whose parents cannot meet full fees. Such fee assistance is means tested on application.

Leicester High School for Girls (see p 595)
A limited number of bursaries are available throughout the school, including the Sixth Form.

The Maynard School (see p 608)
The 350th Anniversary Academic Award will be awarded to two students annually.

A number of Governors' Bursaries (means-tested) are awarded annually. Wolfson Foundation bursaries are awarded at Sixth Form level. Up to four Governors' Leaving Exhibitions are awarded in the Upper Sixth year.

The Mount School, York (see p 616)
Members of the Society of Friends are assessed under the Joint Bursaries Scheme for Friends' Schools and according to need may be helped by other Friends' funds in addition to School funds.

Bursary help is available for other candidates.

North London Collegiate School (see p 621)
Bursaries are offered in cases of financial need.

Prior's Field (see p 642)
A Bursary of 10% of fees is awarded on the results of our own examination to the daughter of an Old Girl. Further details are available from the School.

Academic Bursaries for day places in the Sixth Form are awarded up to 95% of fees.

Queen Margaret's School (see p 648)
Means-tested bursaries are offered at all levels.

The Red Maids' School (see p 657)
School Bursaries: Any student may apply for a school bursary at the point of which she applies for a place in the school. Bursaries are means tested in relation to family income. For further details please contact the Bursar.

Redland High School (see p 659)
Bursaries are available.

A number of Bursary awards are available each year to those girls who show good academic ability and whose parents are in need of financial help to meet fees. The John James Bristol Foundation enables the school to provide annual Bursary Awards in its name to girls residing in the City of Bristol.

The Royal Masonic School for Girls (see p 663)
Foundation Scholarships

Six Closed Scholarships, available only for girls who are the daughters of Freemasons, may be provided at 11+. The value of each of these is based upon a means test.

St Catherine's School, Bramley (see p 671)
OGA Bursary: There is an Old Girls' Association Sixth Form Bursary which is awarded to a daughter of a deserving Old Girl on criteria decided between the Headmistress and the Committee of the OGA.

For further details please contact the Registrar.

St David's School (see p 674)
Ashford Assisted Places: Two special Assisted Places, worth 90% of fees, are reserved for girls of high academic ability, living and attending a school in Ashford, entering the school in Year 7 whose families, under normal circumstances, would not be able to afford independent education.

Other Assisted Places: These are variable in number and value and are at the discretion of the Headmistress.

Welsh Bursaries: These are available to girls of Welsh parentage and have a value of £500 per term.

St Francis' College (see p 677)
Bursaries to assist parents of able girls may be awarded at the discretion of the Headmistress. Application for such assistance should be made to the Headmistress.

St Margaret's School for Girls, Aberdeen (see p 692)
Means-tested bursaries are available for entry to I Senior, V and VI Senior.

St Mary's School Ascot (see p 702)
The Ascot Old Girls' Bursary is awarded annually to a daughter of an Old Girl entering the Sixth Form and is worth 30% of boarding fees.

St Swithun's School (see p 715)
Bursaries are available on a means-tested basis.

Sir William Perkins's School (see p 721)
A limited number of Bursaries carry remission depending on need and funds available.

Wycombe Abbey School (see p 751)
The Seniors' Association offers a limited number of bursaries for the daughters and granddaughters of Members of the Association. Candidates are assessed by interview with representatives of the Seniors and with the Headmistress. The value is determined according to family financial circumstances and bursaries are held subject to the satisfactory conduct and progress of the recipient.

Further particulars are obtainable from the Secretary to the Bursary Committee, Miss Sue Davies, 13 Milnthorpe Gardens, Milnthorpe Road, Eastbourne, East Sussex BN20 7NW.

Applications should be made **at least two years** ahead of entry to the School.

PART III

Schools whose Heads are members of the Society of Headmasters and Headmistresses of Independent Schools

ALPHABETICAL LIST OF SCHOOLS

* co-educational schools

The following schools, whose Heads are members of SHMIS and HMC, can be found in the HMC section:

Ackworth School
Bedales School
Clayesmore School
King's School, Ely
King's School, Tynemouth
Kirkham Grammar School
Leighton Park School
Lord Wandsworth College
Reading Blue Coat School
Reed's School
Rendcomb College
Royal Russell School
Rydal Penrhos School
Ryde School with Upper Chine
St Bede's Senior School
St Columba's College, St Albans
St George's College
Seaford College
Shiplake College
Silcoates School
Tettenhall College
Wisbech Grammar School
Yarm School

The following schools, whose Heads are members of SHMIS and GSA, can be found in the GSA section:

Howell's School, Denbigh
King Edward VI High School for Girls
Moira House Girls' School
Stover School
Teesside High School

GEOGRAPHICAL LIST OF SHMIS SCHOOLS

Individual School Entries

Abbey Gate College

Saighton Grange Saighton Chester CH3 6EN
Tel: 01244 332077
Fax: 01244 335510
e-mail: admin@abbeygatecollege.co.uk
website: www.abbeygatecollege.co.uk

Founded in 1977, Abbey Gate College is a co-educational day school for 450 boys and girls from 4–18 years of age. The school is set in beautiful grounds at Saighton Grange some three miles south of the City of Chester. The history of Saighton Grange goes back long before the Norman Conquest. However, the most ancient portion of the present building is the red sandstone castellated gateway and tower, with its oriel window and spiral staircase, which was built in 1489. The remainder of the present building is Victorian and from 1853, the Grange was a residence of the Grosvenor family. Additional facilities include a large Sports Hall, playing fields and an Arts and Media Centre opened at Saighton receiving a high profile in March 2004 when it was officially opened by HRH the Duchess of Gloucester. A purpose-built Art and Design & Technology Centre and new science laboratory were completed in Spring 2008; a new Sixth Form Centre is due for completion in the summer. The Junior Department is sited in the former school at Aldford, a picturesque village only two miles from Saighton – facilities here include excellent playing fields and an ecology and wildlife area.

Motto: *Audentior Ito*

Visitor: His Grace The Duke of Westminster

Chairman of Governors: Mrs M Heywood, BA Hons

***Head*: Mrs L M Horner**, BA Hons Birmingham (*History and Physical Education*)

Deputy Head: D P H Meadows, BA Hons, PGCE (*History*)

Academic Staff:
G Allmand, BSc Hons, PGCE (*Geography*)
A Austen, BSc Hons, PGCE (*Geography*)
G Barton, BSc Hons, PGCE (*Physical Education*)
Mrs S Campbell-Woodward, BEd (*Modern Languages*)
M Cavallini, BSc Hons (*Mathematics*)
Mrs J Connor-Webb, MA, PGCE (*Modern Languages*)
C Cutler, BSc Hons (*Sport & Exercise Science, Psychology*)
Mrs S Dolan , BSc Hons, PGCE (*Biology/Chemistry*)
Miss S Fitzpatrick, BSc PGCE (*Physical Education*)
Miss E Flatman, BA Hons (*Physical Education*)
J P Gallagher, MA, DipEd (*Biology*)
K Gray, BSc Hons, PGCE (*Geography, ICT*)
A P Green, BEd (*Physical Education*)
Mrs C A Haines, BSc Hons, PGCE (*Mathematics*)
Miss K Hall, BA Hons, PGCE (*English & Drama*)
Mrs C Houghton, BA Hons, PGCE (*History*)
Mrs K Jackson, GTP, HDE (*English*)
Mrs J Jones, CertEd (*Home Economics and Careers*)
Mrs S J Kay, BSc Hons (*Mathematics*)
Mrs C Kingsley, BSc Hons, PGCE (*Mathematics*)
R Kitchen, BSc Hons (*Mathematics*)
P Lincoln, MA, BA Hons, PGCE (*History and Politics*)
Mrs N Moses, BA Hons, PGCE (*English*)
Mrs K Roden, BA Hons, PGCE (*English*)
Mrs C Russell, MA, PGCE (*English*)
Miss A Sa, PGCE (*Modern Languages*)
R A Slater, BSc Hons, PGCE (*Physics*)
S F Smith, BA, CertEd, ARCM, LMusLCM (*Music*)
D I Stockley, MSc, PGCE (*Technology*)
M Tempest, BEng Hons, PGCE (*Materials Science/Eng*)

Part-time Staff:
Mrs N Burton, BEd (*Art*)
Mrs M Curtis, MA, PGCE (*Modern Languages*)
Mrs S Hall, BA Hons, QTS ATS (*Learning Support*)
Mrs F Kay, BSc Hons, PGCE (*Science*)
Mrs S Parker, MSc, PGCE (*Geography*)
Mrs M Pilkington, BA Hons, PGCE (*Art*)
Mrs L Poyser, BSc Hons, PGCE (*Biology & Chemistry*)
Mrs P Selby, MA, PGCE (*Business Studies; Librarian*)
Miss V Thompson, BA Hons (*Art*)
Mrs J Townsend, CertEd (*PE*)

Junior Department:
Head of Junior Department: Miss M Smith, BEd Hons, PGCE
Mrs H Courtney, BEd Hons
Mrs J Dukes, BEd (*Music*)
Mrs J Gallagher, BSc Hons, PhD, PGCE
Mrs V Goodwin, BMus Hons, PGCE
Miss C Holman, BA Hons
Mrs L Lake, BA, CertEd
Mrs W Richards, BEd Hons
Mrs A Williams, BEd Hons
Mrs K Williams, BEd Hons

Musical Instruments Teaching:
Miss K Banerjee (*Junior Piano*)
L Hardwick (*Drums*)
E Hartwell-Jones (*Singing*)
A Lewis, DipMusTech (*Brass*)
G Macey (*Woodwind*)
P Oliver, BMus, LTCL (*Guitar*)
Miss R Owen (*Clarinet/Flute*)
P Rushforth (*Boys' Singing*)
S A Rushforth (*Violin*)
C Wharton (*Percussion*)
P Williams

Speech and Drama: Mrs C Faithfull, LRAM, ANEA

Bursar: W G Osmond, MSc
Finance Manager: Mrs P Rees
PA to Headmistress: Mrs J Gee
Bursar's Assistant: Mrs K Campion
School Secretary: Mrs S Knowles
Admissions Officer: Mrs S Boyd
Receptionist: Mrs A McCleary
Junior Department Secretary: Mrs D Humphreys
Matron: Mrs M Kirkaldie

Aims. The College encourages its pupils to aim for academic success; we provide a framework where every pupil will have the opportunity to develop their full potential. Outside the world of academia our objective is also to introduce our boys and girls to a wide range of extra-curricular activities. In addition much emphasis is placed on good manners and discipline; this is a friendly, family school particularly aware of the values of moulding character in conjunction with the search for excellence in the classroom. We provide a caring environment; we are proud of the relationship between the teaching staff and their pupils; we encourage a love of learning and ensure that children feel safe, happy and eager to do their best.

Academic Programme. The College aims to provide children with a broad general education through GCSE, AS and A2 Levels, to university, or other forms of higher education. In

Years 7 and 8 pupils study Art, Drama, English, French, German, Spanish, Home Economics, Geography, History, Mathematics, Music, Physical Education, PSHE, Religious Studies, Science, Spoken English, Design & Technology, Information and Communication Technology.

In Years 10 and 11 an option scheme takes effect: within the core, all pupils study English, English Literature and Mathematics, a modern foreign language and at least two Sciences. Study skills are developed and all pupils participate in sport and PSHE. To support their academic curriculum, Year 10 undertake a week's work experience and Year 11 participate in a Development Course designed to build teamwork, self-confidence and leadership skills.

Option subjects for GCSE are taken from the following: Art, Biology, Chemistry, Design and Technology, Drama, French, Geography, German, History, Music, Physics, ICT, Spanish and PE.

In the Sixth Form A2 Level (and AS Level) subjects available according to demand are: Mathematics, Further Mathematics, English Literature, English Language, History, Politics, Geography, Business Studies, Physics, Chemistry, Biology, French, German, Art, Music, Product Design, PE, ICT, Psychology and Theatre Studies. Sixth Form students follow a comprehensive PSHE programme, have the opportunity to study AS Critical Thinking and participate in sports.

In the Lower Sixth students may also join the Young Enterprise scheme which gives theoretical and practical knowledge of the business world. They enjoy an active community service programme. A number of outside speakers visit the school and regular trips to theatres, conferences or galleries are arranged. All the Lower Sixth students also attend a study skills and team building course in the Lake District in their first term which supports the transition from GCSE to A Level.

Music. The College is well known throughout Chester and North Wales for the outstanding quality of its music. The Chapel Choir has for several years undertaken week long summer visits to Cathedrals in various parts of the country including Ely, Gloucester, St Albans, Ripon, Tewkesbury, Hereford, Winchester, Durham, York and Bath, as well as touring Europe, including the Czech Republic in 2006 and the USA in 2003. Annually, the Chapel Choir has sung Evensong at St Paul's Cathedral or St George's Chapel, Windsor. The College also has a Concert Band and The Saighton Syncopators dance band.

Many pupils of all ages take music lessons and the pupils may take instrumental lessons with visiting staff and are prepared for the Associated Board Examinations.

Drama. There is one major dramatic production each year, usually alternating between drama and musical. Pupils are also prepared for examinations in Speech and Drama and regularly enter local competitions with great success. All pupils in Years 7–9 participate in the English Speaking Board scheme within the English and Drama curriculum, helping to develop their confidence and public speaking skills.

Sport. The College has extensive playing fields, tennis courts and sports hall. The latter offers four badminton courts, five-a-side soccer, volleyball, basketball, netball, indoor hockey, tennis and cricket nets.

All pupils participate in physical education and games. Boys play rugby, soccer, cricket and tennis; girls play hockey, netball, tennis and rounders. Athletics is also popular for both boys and girls and all sports provide full fixture lists for the various College teams. The local swimming pool is reserved each week for sessions with a fully-qualified instructor for the younger pupils.

The College competes in both Regional and National Independent Schools sports events, and has enjoyed great success in both athletics and swimming. Pupils are regularly sent for trials for Chester and District and County teams with players selected to represent Cheshire in hockey, cricket and rugby. A soccer tour to Malta, first undertaken in 1995, was repeated in 1997. The Senior Hockey Squad toured Holland in October 1997, the Isle of Man in 2000, and South Africa in 2004 in conjunction with a large football squad. The school's Ski Racing team trains weekly and is involved in many competitions including the annual British Championships in France where individual and team performances have been impressive. Recent developments include the setting up of an equestrian team which has gone from strength to strength.

Junior Department. Our Junior Department provides excellence in education with a broad based curriculum supported by a diverse extra curricular programme that gives children aged 4–11 a wide range of opportunities. These include choir, gymnastics, team games, Spanish, Ju jitsu, creative arts and drama to name but a few. There are frequent school trips and excursions that support the school experience, including a Year 6 residential outdoor and adventurous week at Glaramara in the Lake District.

Other activities. The College has a remarkable record of giving generously to Charities and the two Houses serve to raise money through sponsorship and tuck shops; Sixth Formers take a leading role in this. At weekends and during holidays many pupils take advantage of outdoor pursuits and many choose to follow the Duke of Edinburgh's Award Scheme; there are over 60 participants at present.

Admission. *Senior School*: Most pupils enter the College at age 11 following an Entrance Examination held in the Spring Term, although where occasional places occur in other year groups, assessments can be made mid year. Each pupil is allocated to one of the two Senior School Houses: Hastings and Marmion.

Junior Department: Pupils are admitted to the Junior Department at Aldford by means of short assessment and interview at ages 7, 8, 9 and 10. It is expected that children already in this part of the school will move directly into the College at age 11 if they pass the Entrance Examination.

Infant Department: Entry at ages 4, 5 and 6 is also available.

Sixth Form: Priority is given to existing pupils but places are offered to others and are conditional on satisfactory results at GCSE (Key Stage 4).

Scholarships. Two academic scholarships (means-tested) are awarded following the results of the Entrance Examination and one for sport.

For musical talent three awards are offered including Music Exhibitions at Year 7 and Sixth Form level and the Daphne Herbert Choral Scholarship.

Fees per term (2008-2009). Tuition: Infant Department £1,787; Junior Department £2,085; Senior School £3,046.

Old Saightonians. All pupils are encouraged to join the Old Saightonians' Association. Further details of the Association can be obtained from the Bursar at the College.

Charitable status. Deeside House Educational Trust is a Registered Charity. number 273586. It exists to provide co-education for children in the Chester and North Wales areas.

Abbotsholme School

Derbyshire

Rocester Uttoxeter ST14 5BS
Tel: 01889 594265 (admissions)
01889 590217 (main number)
Fax: 01889 591001
e-mail: admissions@abbotsholme.co.uk
website: www.abbotsholme.com

President: Mr Nicholas Wilford, FRICS

Chair of Governors: Mr Mark Wells

***Head*: Mr Steve Fairclough**, MSc

Bursar: Mr John Downes

Head's Personal Assistant: Mrs Linda Calvert

Registrar: Mrs Gill Mills

Abbotsholme School, on the Staffordshire/Derbyshire border, has been officially recognised as providing "a richly diverse and distinctive educational experience in which individual pupils are well known, very well cared for and enabled to flourish both personally and academically". These observations are contained in a glowing report in 2007 by the Independent Schools Inspectorate.

Abbotsholme School was founded in 1889 by Dr Cecil Reddie and was the first of a series of new schools to have considerable influence on European education. Today Abbotsholme is a co-educational, non-denominational boarding, weekly boarding and day school for girls and boys aged 5 to 18.

Abbotsholme is a small, friendly school of some 310 or so pupils, providing a modern, progressive education based on cooperation rather than competition, a compassion for others, and a whole-hearted respect for the environment. Abbotsholme is also a wholly inclusive school, where everyone in the community is valued for the individual contribution they make. We genuinely provide opportunities for self-discovery and personal development. This approach to education gives all our young people knowledge to facilitate success and achievement, commitment to nurture and care for the environment, challenges to build strength and test courage, cultural enrichment to widen perspective and responsibility for the needs of others. From this carefully planned curriculum emerge essential skills for life.

Location. Abbotsholme is located in a beautiful estate of some 140 acres on the banks of the River Dove in rural Derbyshire, close to the magnificent Peak District, easily accessible by road and rail and less than an hour away from three international airports.

Special Characteristics. Membership of the *Round Square* organisation (www.roundsquare.org) provides a strong international perspective. A world wide and unique association of schools committed to personal growth and responsibility through service, challenge, adventure and international understanding, members share one aim – the full and individual development of every pupil into a whole person.

Our *outdoor education* programme is both well known and well regarded. Its pioneering principles inspired such organisations as the Outward Bound Movement, the United World Colleges and the Duke of Edinburgh's Award Scheme. With adventures both close to home and internationally, it presents pupils with personal challenges, both physical and mental, and teaches them the importance of taking responsibility for themselves and others. Many pupils are involved in the Duke of Edinburgh's Award Scheme and all participate in summer camps and autumn hikes each year.

Abbotsholme is one of the very few schools in England to have a working *farm* upon which pupils are able to learn about animal husbandry and crop management and gain a healthy respect for the environment. In addition to the 70-acre farm, our British Horse Society approved *Equestrian Centre* is a popular place to be for our horse enthusiasts, who happily involve themselves in the upkeep of the stables and yard.

Music is a way of life at Abbotsholme. All pupils are encouraged to appreciate music in some way, either by learning to play an instrument or taking singing lessons or by simply attending some of the performances that are frequently organised. Both the orchestra and the choir comprise a mixture of staff and pupils, which fosters the special atmosphere so typical of Abbotsholme.

Drama flourishes, in and out of the classroom, with performances in the 120-seat theatre always oversubscribed. All pupils who are keen to be involved, whether on stage or behind the scenes, find regular opportunities to experience the fun and self-discipline characteristic of performance and improvised theatre.

The influence of the *Art* department is evident throughout school, where pupils' painting, drawing, pottery, ceramic, graphic design and 3D creations are permanently on display. In addition many pupils enjoy the facilities of the *Design and Technology* Department, which provides excellent opportunities for developing creative design into quality manufacture. Hours are also spent in the cutting edge *Film Studies* Unit, which enables pupils to design animation projects and create and edit film on computer, through digitisation.

We believe that the physical and mental disciplines of working together in a team are very important. *Sport* teaches the art of winning and losing with equally good grace, self-reliance and leadership, and the opportunities to compete are grasped by many of our pupils. Sports at Abbotsholme include: rugby, football, hockey, netball, tennis, swimming, athletics, squash, skiing, cross-country, horse riding, badminton and basketball.

Curriculum. Abbotsholme caters for a broad ability range. Academic standards are high with the majority of sixth formers going on to their first-choice university. Breadth and balance shape the curriculum, which aims to develop critical and creative thinking and self-discipline across a wide range of subjects at GCSE and A Level.

Activities. Abbotsholme firmly believes that a school should have a greater purpose beyond preparing students for College or University. As a result we seek not only to help all pupils realise their individual academic potential but also to develop in everyone a sense of responsibility for themselves and others through active participation within the community as well as a sense of adventure through challenges in and beyond the classroom. A comprehensive range of compulsory activities is integral to the curriculum, taking place on four afternoons a week. Each week's activities alternately include Outdoor Education and Farm/Conservation work, commitments to team sports, singers, and drama as well as a number of individual choices, including: art, bookworms, chess, debating, drama (major productions are staged every year), French for fun, music (including many concerts and recitals), Young Enterprise and Warhammer.

Home from Home. The boarding experience at Abbotsholme is a happy one, where staff and pupils know each other well and where every individual shares equal responsibility for the community's well being and progress. Small, friendly homes are run by resident houseparents as family units. Younger boarders share bright and comfortable dormitories in threes and fours whilst older pupils have single or shared study-bedrooms. A log cabin village has been added for sixth formers giving them opportunities to experience a greater degree of independence and privacy. Weekly boarding has become a popular option for families with busy lives and for our full boarders, a full programme of weekend activities provides plenty of choice and lots of fun, balancing academic work with social time. Our modern approach to boarding means that sleepover and flexi boarding are also options.

Facilities. These include: dedicated classroom areas, for each subject, including specialist science laboratories, art, music, design and IT centres (two suites), a purpose-built studio theatre for drama, film studies and films, a modern, multi-purpose sports hall, extensive playing fields and swimming pool, and a chapel, which combines as the venue for morning assembly as well as concerts.

Fees per term (2008-2009). Day £2,950–£5,450; Weekly Boarding £5,300–£6,700; Full Boarding £6,900–£8,000.

Scholarships. The 'Abbotsholmian Award' is offered at Year 7 and Year 12. The number of awards offered each year will be at the Head's discretion and on the basis of an all round aptitude and attitude – the essence of a true Abbotsholmian. Further details can be obtained from the Head's Personal Assistant either by telephone: 01889 590217 or by e-mail: headmaster@abbotsholme.co.uk.

The Abbotsholmians' Club. The Club currently has some 2000 members and is run by a Committee of Old Abbotsholmians, elected yearly. Members receive regular mail-outs, which give contact addresses and details of the adventures of OAs, young and old. There are also regular invitations to events, to help them keep in touch with each other and with current developments at the school. An enormous amount of networking takes place between OAs, often facilitated by the Club, ensuring that friendships are sustained and memories are relived.

The Club operates a small Bursary fund specifically aimed at helping to educate sons and daughters of OAs at Abbotsholme.

Abbotsholme Arts Society. The School is host to one of the country's most respected concert presenters in the country. Although embracing jazz, poetry and drama performances, its core programme of chamber music has brought a Who's Who of big-name musicians to the school over the years – Askenazy, Brendel, Galway, Hough, the Amadeus Quartet to name just a few. Pupils are able to attend any of the Arts Society concerts free of charge.

Abbotsholme Parents' Association. Run by parents, for the benefit of parents, children and school, the Parents' Association (APA) aims to help new families settle in and become quickly familiar with Abbotsholme and all that it has to offer. Keen to promote active parental involvement in the school, members regularly organise social activities and fund-raising events.

Charitable status. Abbotsholme School is a Registered Charity, number 528612. It exists to advance education and in particular to provide for children and young persons a broad, general education in accordance with the principles, traditions and aims developed since the school's foundation in 1889 by Dr Cecil Reddie.

Arts Educational School

Tring Park Tring Hertfordshire HP23 5LX
Tel: 01442 824255
Fax: 01442 891069
e-mail: info@aes-tring.com
website: www.aes-tring.com

Board of Governors:
Chairman: Mrs Juliet Murray
Mr Michael Geddes
Mr Jonathan Latham, BSc, MBA
Mr Mark Hewitt
Mrs Venetia Wrigley
Mr Andrew Dobbin, MA Cantab
Mrs Angela Odell
Mrs Mary Bonar
Ms Elizabeth Adlington

***Principal*: Mr Stefan Anderson**, MA Cantab, ARCM, ARCT

Deputy Principal: Mr Alex Walker, MA Oxon, PGCE

Director of Dance: Miss Rachel Rist, MA, FRSA
Deputy Director of Dance: Miss Teresa Wright, ARAD (Adv), FISTD (Cecchetti Branch) Dip

Director of Drama: Mr Edward Applewhite, BA Hons
Deputy Director of Drama: Miss Heather Loomes, BA Hons

Director of Music: Miss Elizabeth Hewett, BMus Hons, PGCE, ALCM
Deputy Director of Music: Miss Helen Reynolds, BMus Hons, PGCE

Director of Musical Theatre Course: Miss Donna Hayward, FISTD

Musical Director of Musical Theatre Course: Mr Simon Sharp, BA Hons, PGCE

Director of Academic Studies: Mrs Helen Wells, BA, PGCE
Deputy Director of Academic Studies: Mrs Janet Allen, BSc Hons, MSc, PGCE

Head of Learning Support: Dawn Sanders, CertEd, BEd Hons, MA EdMgt, PGCE, OCR Cert SpLD (*SENCO*)

School Administrator: Mrs Nicky Milne

Age Range. 8–19 years.

Number in School. Boarders: Boys 37, Girls 168. Day: 64.

Fees per term (2008-2009). Prep School: Boarders £6,335, Day £4,200. Aged 11–16: Boarders £8,365, Day £6,045. Sixth Form Entry: Boarders £8,950, Day £6,570.

Aided places are available under the Government's Music and Dance Scheme and Post 16 Dance and Drama Awards. School scholarships are available for Drama and Musical Theatre.

Arts Educational School, Tring Park, offers a unique opportunity for pupils from the age of 8 to 19 who show a particular talent in one or more of the Performing Arts, yet still wish to benefit from a sound academic education to A Level.

Tring is a small market town situated 30 miles northwest of Central London, within easy travelling distance of the major international airports and motorways. Set in 17 acres of attractive and secluded grounds, the School is principally housed in a superb mansion, formerly the home of the Rothschild family.

Dance, Drama, Musical Theatre and Music are taught to the highest level and pupils perform regularly in our excellent modern theatre as well as at prestigious venues in London and the South East. Many pupils go on to enjoy successful performing careers. Academic achievements at GCSE and A Level enable many of our students to progress to Degree courses in higher education.

Whatever the career or course chosen, the fusion of natural talent, creativity and personality with sound teaching and direction produces young communicators, well-equipped to take the many opportunities that lie ahead.

Charitable status. The AES Tring Park School Trust is a Registered Charity, number 1040330. It exists to provide vocational and academic education.

Ashford School (UCST)

Kent

East Hill Ashford Kent TN24 8PB
Tel: 01233 625171
Fax: 01233 647185
e-mail: registrar@ashfordschool.co.uk
website: www.ashfordschool.co.uk

Chairman of School Council: Mr P Massey, MA
Vice-Chairman: Mr R I Henderson, JP

Council Members:
Mrs J G Loudon
Mr H N L Blenkin, QPM
Mrs A Cottrell, JP
Mr W Peppitt, ARICS
Mrs E Rose
Mr P Anscombe
Mrs J A Webb, BA Hons
Mr A J Rawlins
Mr T Richards
Mr P B Smith, MA

***Head*: Mr Michael Buchanan**, BSc Hons London CertEd, CPhys, MInstP, NPQH

Head of the Prep School: Mr R Yeates, BA Hons Exeter

Deputy Head, Director of the Senior School: Mrs Y Howard, BA Hons Durham

Senior School:
Deputy Head, Director of Teaching: Mrs C Allum, BA Hons Durham, MPhil
Director of Learning: Miss L Allen, BA Hons London
Director of ICT: Mr F J Rossi, BA Hons Christchurch
Director of Boarding: Mr T Wilding, BA Hons Exeter
Director of Sixth Form: Miss H Semple, MA Hons Edinburgh

Prep School:
Deputy Head: Mrs P Willetts, BPrimEd
Head of Pre-Prep: Miss K Smith, BEd Eng & Ed

Ashford School was founded in 1898 as an independent, day and boarding school and now provides education for children from 3 months to 18 years. There are over 360 students in the Senior School (age 11–18), 170+ in the Preparatory School (age 7–11, boys and girls) and 180+ in the Pre-Preparatory School (age 3–7, boys and girls). As a growing school, Ashford is extending co-education, which has been such a success in the Preparatory School, into the Senior School and will be fully co-educational by 2009.

There are over 120 boarders (boys and girls) in the Senior School cared for by resident teachers and support staff in newly refurbished accommodation that includes en-suite rooms for many. Twenty-four nationalities are represented in the school and specialist English tuition is provided for those who require it. There are no lessons on Saturdays but all staff are expected to contribute to activities and to support the boarding life of the school including occasional duties at weekends.

Ashford School is a member of a group of independent schools run by the United Church Schools Trust which educates nearly 15,000 children across the UK. The Trust aims to be at the forefront of educational development, bringing the very best resources, both human and physical, to the children in its schools. Ashford School has a long history of providing an outstanding education for its pupils. While our Christian heritage and values are an integral aspect of the school we are not a church school and welcome people of all faiths and of none.

The Senior School occupies a 25-acre site in a prominent position close to the centre of Ashford and near to the International Rail Station. It is a green and secure haven in a busy and growing town. There are good rail, road and bus links to Ashford and the school operates its own bus services to outlying villages. The Senior School has playing fields on site, together with two gyms, an indoor swimming pool, a floodlit Astroturf, tennis and netball courts, boarding houses and dining hall. The School enjoys all the specialist teaching facilities you would expect of an independent school and we have embarked on a programme to refurbish and extend our facilities; in 2006 a new Learning Centre, Mathematics classrooms and student café were opened. The pre-nursery, Bridge House, is also located on this site as is the Pre-Preparatory School. Each benefits from the proximity to the Senior School and has their own dedicated and well-resourced accommodation and staff.

The Preparatory School is located in the rural village of Great Chart a few miles outside Ashford. Much of the site was refurbished in the summer of 2005 and further development is planned. As well as well-resourced classrooms, the pupils at the School enjoy specialist science, design technology and home economics laboratories, a music school and theatre, playing fields and tennis courts, an indoor swimming pool and sports hall. A Learning Centre equipped with open access computers was created in 2005.

There are normally three classes in each year of the Pre-Prep and Prep Schools. Many join from Bridge House. While the entry into the nursery at 3+ is non-selective it is most often the case that pupils from the Prep School move into the Senior School and so have to have the potential to achieve at a high academic level. Almost two-thirds of the students entering the Senior School at 11+ join direct from the Prep School and the remainder from other primary schools. There are then normally three classes through to GCSE and additional students join other years and the Sixth Form. Almost all students then go on to take degree courses at leading universities in the UK and abroad. In 2007, 90% of students leaving Year 13 achieved places at their first choice university, with 10% going to Oxford or Cambridge and 60% going to Russell Group universities.

The Senior School curriculum evolves to keep abreast of good practice and new technology, while maintaining a firm base in the more traditional disciplines, such as Latin. The school has electronic whiteboards in every teaching room. Up until the end of the Year 11, pupils follow a broad curriculum, to keep their options open. In addition to the core subjects – English, Mathematics, at least one Modern Foreign Language and all three Sciences – they may study additional languages, History, Geography, Classical Civilisation, Religious Studies, Information Technology, Art and Textiles, Music, Drama and Physical Education. Throughout the Senior School, subjects are set by ability where possible and there is a strong pastoral system based around six Houses.

External Examinations. At Key Stage 4 there is a full choice from all subjects for GCSE; most pupils take 9/10/11 subjects. Many A Level combinations are available to the Sixth Form, of whom nearly all go on to Higher Education before entering a varied range of careers including advertising, banking, engineering, journalism, law, management, the media, medicine and veterinary science. There is a consistently high external examination success rate and pupils are prepared for Oxbridge in all subjects.

Entry requirements. School report, tests and interview for the Sixth Form, supporting six or more A–C grades at GCSE. Written tests at Years 7 and 9. Places are generally available in all other years.

Scholarships. (*see Scholarship Entries section*).

Fees per term (2008-2009). Senior: £7,742–£7,941 (boarding), £4,368 (day); Prep £3,276 (day), Pre-Prep £1,880–£2,181. Nursery £380 (one full day per week).

Charitable status. Ashford School is a member of The United Church Schools Trust, which is a Registered Charity, number 1016538. It exists to provide education for boys and girls, aged between 3 and 18 years and to assist the local community where possible with the hire of school facilities and participation in local activities.

Austin Friars St Monica's Senior School

Etterby Scaur Carlisle Cumbria CA3 9PB
Tel: 01228 528042
Fax: 01228 810327
e-mail: office@austinfriars.cumbria.sch.uk
admissions@austinfriars.cumbria.sch.uk
website: www.austinfriars.cumbria.sch.uk

Austin Friars St Monica's School is an independent co-educational school, founded by members of the Order of St Augustine in 1951 and is one of the network of Augustinian schools in other parts of the world. Pupils of all denominations are welcome in the School, giving all the opportunity to embrace the Christian traditions on which the School is founded.

The School Motto is "*In Omnibus Caritas*". The word "caritas" embraces so much more than the accepted English translation "charity": it is indeed a summary of all the virtues and the School's Augustinian character is expressed in an inclusive way. Accordingly, Christian principles hold a central place in the life of the School with a pupil's faith creating a lively and effective influence on attitudes and activities.

The Senior School provides secondary education for 350 boys and girls aged 11–18. There are 150 children aged 4–11 in the brand new state-of-the-art Junior School and the purpose-built Nursery has places for 24 children aged 3–4. (*For further details, see Junior School entry in IAPS section.*)

Chairman of Trustees: Revd Dr Peter Tiplady, MB BS, MRCGP, FFPHM, FRIPH

***Headmaster*: Mr C J Lumb**, BSc, MEd, PGCE

Deputy Headmaster: Mr G R Barr, BA, PGCE
Director of Studies: Mr M C F Fielder, MA, PGCE
Head of Sixth Form: Mr S Parry, BSc, PGCE
Head of Junior School: Mrs F M Willacy
Bursar: Mrs J Murphy, MBA
Marketing & Admissions Manager: Mrs K R Walker, BSc, MATS

Heads of Department:
Art: Miss K Quinn, BA, PGCE
Science and Biology: Mr R Holden, BSc Hons, PGCE
Design Technology: Mr M Turnbull, BSc, NPQH
Chemistry: Mrs S A Blythe, MSc, PGCE
Classical Civilisation: Mr P Thornton, BA, PGCE
Drama: Mr M Judge, BA, PGCE
Economics: Mr S Cassidy, BA, PGCE
English: Mr P T Westmoreland, BA, PGCE
Geography: Mr S Parry, BSc, PGCE
History: Mrs S Maclean-Eltham, BA, PGCE
Mathematics: Mr N Barraclough, BSc Hons, PGCE
Modern Languages: Mrs C Castro, BA
Music: Mr C W J Hattrell, MA
Physical Education: Mr D R Smith, BEd, CertEd
Physics: Mr N Edmondson, BEd
Religious Studies: Mr K McNicholas, BA, PGCE

The School stands in its own grounds of 25 acres overlooking the historic City of Carlisle in North Cumbria. It is within easy reach of the M6 and there is excellent access to the North West and North East of England and to South West Scotland. There are also outstanding opportunities to take advantage of the cultural heritage of the area stretching back to Roman times and Hadrian's Wall, and for outdoor activities in the Lake District, Northumberland and north of the border in Scotland.

Austin Friars St Monica's School aims to foster the personal development of its pupils spiritually, academically, socially and physically to enable them to take their place creatively in society. The School has high expectations of its pupils and encourages them to develop their potential in a disciplined, happy, positive and productive atmosphere. Consequently, Austin Friars St Monica's School has established an enviable reputation for bringing out the best in each of its pupils. This means not only attaining high academic standards but realising sound spiritual and social values, self-discipline and the development of a sense of purpose for life.

The School is justifiably proud of its academic facilities, the breadth of its curriculum and its pupils' record in public examinations which are among the best in the North of England. The School's highly qualified staff, the close attention to the individual pupil throughout the school career and the nurturing of a positive attitude to work, ensure consistently good results and a sound preparation for higher education.

Both staff and pupils appreciate that school extends beyond the classroom and extra-curricular activities are a strong facet of Austin Friars St Monica's School. The School is an excellent centre for developing new and existing interests and talents and offers numerous opportunities for participation in cultural and leisure activities and involvement in charitable work. Each year the School produces a musical/play and termly concerts. There are regular visits to theatres, concerts and galleries and school visits to the continent. Qualified and enthusiastic staff provide coaching in team sports, and the School's record in inter-school competition is acknowledged far beyond Cumbria. Awards in the Duke of Edinburgh's Scheme are gained annually by a significant number of pupils, and other outdoor pursuits include canoeing, fell walking, sailing and ski trips to the USA.

The School has benefited from a large capital investment in the facilities over the last few years including a new Sixth From Centre, a dedicated Learning Support suite, a music recital, teaching and classroom area, new ICT facilities across the whole School and the Mendel building, a brand new science facility with 4 dedicated labs and technician rooms.

The Senior School is divided into three "Houses". Pupils have a Tutor in their houses. Smaller units are thus created so that each child can receive personal, individual attention.

Pupils are free to approach their Tutor to discuss whatever problems they may have. The Tutor is also responsible for discipline and they are in a position to relate a pupil's behaviour to the general picture of background and character. This ensures that discipline becomes more than an external observance of rules and traditions, and is seen by the pupils to be an integral part of their training and development. The School aims to form leaders in society who understand service and its value. Almost all pupils progress to higher education.

Studies. The following subjects are available to GCSE and/or A Level: English, Latin, French, Spanish, History, Geography, Economics, Mathematics, Further Mathematics, Physics, Chemistry, Biology, Art, Music, Classical Civilisation, Religious Studies, General Studies, Design Technology, ICT, PE, Drama, Philosophy and Photography.

The size of classes is restricted so that each pupil may receive close attention and be taught as an individual. Tutors supervise the studies of each pupil. They receive reports periodically from Subject Teachers. The Tutor keeps a watchful eye on the pupils' progress, the Sixth Formers are expected to learn to organize their time and their work in their own way. A dedicated Sixth Form centre was opened at the School in 2006 and has a common room, a games room and a study room, allowing the pupils to develop a sense of independence while still under the care of the Sixth Form Tutor and the rest of the staff. Specialist help is available for dyslexic pupils in the new Learning Resources suite.

The Library Resources Centre is well equipped and designed for serious study, access of information and relaxation. The Centre's Librarian assists pupils in developing their Information Handling Skills and supervise the Careers Library.

Activities. The Junior and Senior Schools Choir and the Dramatic Society's annual production provide important extra-curricular activities (a musical is performed every other year). The School Orchestra and Swing Band are also very active. Extra tuition in piano, woodwind, brass, percussion and elocution is provided by peripatetic teachers, who also run ensemble classes for groups of wind, brass and guitar. All this takes place in the new music facility at School

Societies include Chess, Fell Walking, Canoeing, Photography, Public Speaking, Duke of Edinburgh's Award Scheme, Outdoor Pursuits, Young Enterprise, Weight Training, Indoor Cricket and Rock Climbing. Pupils are encouraged to attend events outside the School in connection with their studies and interests. Outings are organised annually to the continent and to places of interest in Britain. Situated as we are in an area which is rich in Roman History, there are endless opportunities for visiting and studying historical monuments. There are also trips to the Lakes, which can be reached in half-an-hour. Other extra curricular trips offer the opportunity to travel abroad for further study including trips to New Zealand, Iceland, Borneo and Egypt.

Sport. Rugby, Hockey, Cross-Country in winter; Athletics, Cricket, Tennis in Summer. Badminton, Basketball, Swimming, Volleyball and Netball are available throughout the year.

The pupils regularly achieve county status in their various sports. Annual skiing trips take place to the continent and the USA.

Admission. The Senior School adopts a three-form entry policy. The majority of places are offered at 11+ with a small entry into the Sixth Form. Admissions at other ages are considered, subject to availability of places.

All pupils at 11+ sit the Senior School's entrance examination; entry to the Sixth Form is on the basis of performance at GCSE. At other levels, entry is on the basis of school reports and school-based assessment. The 11+ entrance examination takes place in late January prior to entry the following September. Prospective pupils undertake an entrance examination assessing their abilities in English, mathematics and non-verbal reasoning. All prospective pupils are screened for specific learning difficulties.

Fees per term (2008-2009). (*see Scholarship Entries section*). £3,418 (Years 7–13). Fees are inclusive of lunches.

There is a reduction of 5% for brothers/sisters in the School at the same time. Scholarships and Bursaries are available.

Junior School. *For information about Austin Friars St Monica's Junior School, see entry in IAPS section.*

Travel. Carlisle is a main stopping point for all London-Glasgow trains. It is equally well served from all other major centres. The M6 motorway connects Carlisle with the South, the Midlands and North Wales, and there are excellent links to the east. The A74/M74 is the continuation of the M6 to Glasgow. There is easy access to International Airports. School bus services run from several of the surrounding areas.

An invitation to see the School and meet the Headmaster is extended to all those who write for information.

Charitable status. Austin Friars St Monica's School is a Registered Charity, number 516289. It exists for the purpose of educating boys and girls.

Battle Abbey School

Battle East Sussex TN33 0AD
Tel: 01424 772385
Fax: 01424 773573
e-mail: office@battleabbeyschool.com
website: www.battleabbeyschool.com

Battle Abbey School is an independent, co-educational school for for 360 boys and girls between the ages of 2 and 18. Boarders (full and weekly) are accepted from the age of 11. The School is administered by BAS (School) Limited, a registered charity.

Governors:
Acting Chairman: Mr I S Mercer, CBE

Mr A P F Alexander
Dr G Baker, MB BS
Mrs A Caffyn
Mr C Champion
Mr S Hammerton
Mr J Harrison
Mr S J W McArthur
Mr D McIntyre
Mr C L Sangster
Mrs J M Smith
Mrs J Yeo, MBE

Clerk to the Governors: Miss S Collins, BA Hons

Senior Management Team:

***Headmaster*: Mr R C Clark**, BA, MA Ed

Deputy Head, Senior School (*Academic*): Mr A Payton, BSc Hons, PGCE
Senior Teacher, Senior School (*Pastoral*): Mrs D Durrant, BA Hons, CertEd
Head of Boarding: Mr R Patel, BA Hons QTS
Head of Preparatory School: Mrs J Clark, BA Hons, PGCE
Senior Teacher, Preparatory: Mrs P Corrigan, BEd Hons, CertEd, DPE

Bursar: Miss S Collins, BA Hons

Heads of Department:
Mr K G Anderson, BA Hons, PGCE (*Head of KS4*)
Miss S Broad, BA Hons QTS (*Head of Sport, Preparatory*)
Mrs L Hopkins, BA Hons, MA Ed, PGCE (*Head of Drama*)
Mrs S Hughes, BSc Hons, PGCE (*Head of PE*)
Mr J Langridge, BA Hons, Cert Ed (*Director of Music*)
Ms Z Malewicz, BSc Hons PGCE (*Head of Science, Head of Sixth Form*)
Mr P Reynolds, BEng Hons, PGCE (*Head of Mathematics, Careers*)
Miss J Simpson, BA Hons, PGCE (*Head of English*)
Mrs A Stewart, BA Hons CNAA, PGCE (*Head of Art*)
Mr P Usher, BA Hons, PGCE (*Head of IT, Head of KS3*)

Headmaster's PA: Mrs J Hinde
PA to the Preparatory School Headmistress, Prep School Administrator: Ms K Towers

The school is large enough to encourage healthy competition and to develop the social skills and awareness of others learnt by being part of a lively community, but it is small enough to have many of the attributes of a large family. The Head of Boarding lives within the main school building together with his wife and the Headmaster and his wife live within the school grounds. Caring supervision of the pupils is thus ensured at all times. Teaching classes are small throughout the school, allowing individual attention and the opportunity for all pupils to achieve their maximum potential.

The Senior Department (age 11 to 18) and the Boarders are privileged to occupy one of the most famous historical sites in the world, that of the 1066 Battle of Hastings. The main school building, with its assembly hall, dining-room, library, dormitories and common rooms is the 15th century Abbot's House belonging to the Abbey of St Martin founded by the Conqueror himself. It has been beautifully modernised, and is typical of the School's happy blend of traditional values with up-to-date facilities. The dormitories are bright and cheerful, many having magnificent views over the surrounding countryside. Boys and girls are in separate wings but the common rooms are co-educational making the school ideal for brothers and sisters. The Sixth Form pupils have study-bedrooms and their own common room and are treated very much as the young adults that they are. Grouped around this building are well-equipped specialist rooms including five science laboratories, a new art centre and technology areas. There is a computer room equipped with state-of-the-art, industry-standard hardware and software and a large, floodlit, artificial-grass, all-weather playing area.

The Nursery and Preparatory pupils (age 2 to 11) have their own separate premises within easy reach of the Abbey. Their elegant building, which has been recently refurbished, has spacious classrooms, a large multi-purpose hall, specialist rooms for Art and Design, and a state of the art IT suite. It stands in its own extensive grounds which include eight tennis courts, two games fields, two surfaced playgrounds and a 25 metre indoor heated swimming pool.

Battle is only 57 miles from London, on the main railway line to Hastings. Gatwick, Heathrow, and the Channel Ports are within easy reach. There is accompanied travel to and from London at the beginning and end of each term and half-term.

Fees per term (2008-2009). Nursery: £13 (per session), £30 (all day); Reception, Years 1 and 2 £2,075 (day), Years 3–6 £3,025 (day); Years 7–13: £4,200 (day), £6,930 (boarding)

There are Scholarships for pupils wishing to enter Year 3, 4, 5, 6, 7 and 9, generous Sixth Form Scholarships and there is an automatic 12% Bursary for serving members of Her Majesty's Forces.

The Joanna Lumley Scholarship for Performing Arts is open to applicants presently in State Education, and for entry into the Sixth Form.

Further details may be obtained from the School Secretary. If you can visit the School, please make an appointment to do so. Try to come in term-time, if possible, when you will be able to see Battle Abbey at its best, alive and in action.

Charitable status. Battle Abbey School is administered by BAS (School) Ltd which is a Registered Charity, number 306998. The objective of the Charity is to carry on a school or schools where students may obtain a sound education of the highest order, such a school to be carried on as an educational charity.

Bearwood College

Wokingham Berkshire RG41 5BG
Tel: 0118 974 8300
Fax: 0118 977 3186
e-mail: headmaster@bearwoodcollege.co.uk
Admissions: registrar@bearwoodcollege.co.uk
website: www.bearwoodcollege.co.uk

Bearwood College offers high-quality care and education to children aged from 3 months to 18 years through our Nursery, Pre-Prep, Prep and Senior Departments. With day pupils throughout the College and boarders from age 11 to 18, we are proud to engage each child in a wide range of experiences both in and beyond the classroom. Our expectations for effort, industry and achievement are high. Our focus is on personal success. Bearwood is a place where individuals thrive.

Bearwood's origins date back to 1827, its parent body being the Royal Merchant Navy School Foundation. The College has a Church of England foundation, which also welcomes and respects those of other faiths. Only 35 miles west of London near Wokingham in Berkshire, it is served by an excellent network of roads and railways. Heathrow airport is 35 minutes by car and Reading Mainline station is only 15 minutes away. On entering the College grounds the convenient proximity to London is at once forgotten. The Mansion House was once the residence of John Walter II, the original nineteenth century owner of The Times newspaper. Newer buildings have been added over the years including a beautiful Theatre with a 350-seat auditorium.

The College is a member of the Association of Governing Bodies of Independent Schools (AGBIS) and the Headmaster is a member of The Society of Headmasters and Headmistresses of Independent Schools (SHMIS).

Patron: Her Majesty The Queen.

President: HRH The Prince Philip, Duke of Edinburgh, KG, KT

Board of Governors:
Chairman: Mr J Bayliss
Mrs S R Cameron
Lieutenant Colonel C J Dawnay
Mrs A C Griffin
Mrs L Langley
Mr J Walter
Mr M Watts

***Headmaster*: S G G Aiano**, MA Cantab, PGCE, FRSA

Second Master: R P Ryall, BA, PGCE, FRGS

Deputy Head (*Curriculum*): I M Smith, BA, MA, NPQH, PGCE

Bursar: S A Jackson, BSc, MBA

Teaching Staff:
* *Head of Department*

Arts:
H B Browning, BA, PGCE (**English and Film Studies*)
S G G Aiano, MA Cantab, PGCE, FRSA (*English*)
Miss N M Line, BA, PGCE (*English*)
G Penlington, BA, Dip Teach (*English*)
Mrs P Phillips, BA, Dip RSA, PGCE (*English, Drama*)
H Macgregor, BA, PGCE, FRSA (*Theatre Studies*)
S Abery, BA, PGCE (**Art & Photography*)
Ms N Balfour, BA, PGCE (*Art & Photography*)
C E Enston, BMus, FRCO, LRAM, Dip RAM (*Director of Music*)
M J Rein, BA, GDE (*Music*)

Humanities & Languages:
J R Talbot, BEd, BA (**Geography*)
R P Ryall, BA, PGCE, FRGS (*Geography*)
D Leese, BSc, PGCE (*Geography*)
Ms N Jones, BA, PGCE (**History*)
I M Smith, MA, PGCE NPQH (*History*)
G P Watson, BA, GTP (*History*)
W P Stapelberg, BA, PGCE (**Business Studies*)
C M Woodward, BA, PGCE (**Modern Languages*)
Mrs C Ransom, BA, PGCE (*French, Spanish*)

Science & Technology:
M Ayoubi, MSc, PGCE (**Computing*)
M J Cheeseman, FETC (*Computing*)
S W Nichol, BSc, BEd (**Mathematics*)
Ms L A Baumberg, BSc, BEd, Dip Teach (*Mathematics*)
Ms W Desborough, BEng, PGCE (*Mathematics*)
R Knight, BPhEd, Dip Teach (*Mathematics*)
C A Bell, CertEd (**Design & Technology*)
K Lovell, CertEd (*Design & Technology*)
Ms S Barratt, BSc, PGCE (**Science*)
K N Buckler, BSc, QTS (*Physics*)
S King, BSc, QTS, MinstP, MIEE, FRAS (*Physics*)
R M Curtis, BSc, FETC, Adv DipEd (*Physics, Chemistry*)
R Sellick, BSc, Dip Teach, QTS (*Chemistry*)
Mrs A Beecham, BSc, PCEA (*Biology, Environmental Science*)
D Leese, BSc, PGCE (*Biology*)
S Quinn, BSc, MSc (*Psychology*)
Mrs M King, BA (*Textiles*)

Sports:
Ms C Briant, BEd (**Girls' Games*)
J C Dance, BEd (**PE and Boys' Games*)

Study Support/ESOL:
Mrs P Bell, BA, Dip RSA (**Study Support*)
S Quinn, BSc, MSc (*Study Support*)
Ms V Wreglesworth, BSc, MSc (*Study Support*)
Mrs A J Flintham, BA, PGCE, Cert TESOL (**ESOL*)
Mrs J Michel, BSc Cert TESOL (*ESOL*)
Ms S J Woodward (*ESOL*)

Pastoral Staff:
Chaplin: S J King, BSc, QTS, MinstP, MIEE, FRAS

Boys' Housemasters:
Blake House (*Boarding*): M J Cheeseman, FETC
Raleigh House (*Day*): R Knight, BPhEd, Dip Teach
Nelson House (*Day*): G Penlington, BA, Dip Teach
Jellicoe House (*Juniors Boarding and Day*): S Quinn, BSc, MSc

Girls' Housemistresses:
Drake House (*Boarding*): Ms W Desborough, BEng PGCE
Grenville House (*Day*): Mrs A Beecham, BSc PCEA

Matrons: Mrs M Bull, Mrs T Greenham, Mrs M Simmonds

Medical Centre:
Sister in Charge: Mrs K Kershaw, BSc, DipHe
Nurse: Mrs L Steele-Perkins, RN

Administrative Staff:
Registrar: Mrs D Birch
College Secretary: Mrs L Wood
Headmaster's Administrator: Mrs G Shepherd
Bursar's Secretary: Mrs L Sellings

Ethos. As the only co-educational day and boarding 'through school' within 15 miles, Bearwood College uniquely provides a stable yet evolving learning environment to meet the ever-changing needs of your developing child. Your child will gain great confidence from the College's ethos, staff and facilities throughout their school career. Age-appropriate pastoral care at every level ensures that personal development is supported, protecting childhood for younger pupils whilst fostering maturity in the upper years.

Academic Structure. At Bearwood College we expect your child to achieve his or her best. Each pupil works to an academic programme which is individually targeted and permanently monitored. It provides a structured, supported and demanding academic challenge appropriate to each pupil's capacity. The academic curriculum is based on and exceeds the guidelines of the National Curriculum. In the years up to GCSE, we provide a programme which offers choice, breadth of experience and the opportunity to develop particular academic skills.

A specialist Learning Support Unit is available for a limited number of suitable dyslexic pupils. ESOL lessons are similarly available for overseas pupils. An additional charge is made for these services.

In these all-important GCSE years, each pupil is continually assessed, and set realistic fixed-date targets for improvement by the subject teachers, in order to maximise individual potential.

Sixth Form pupils are able to choose from a wide range of subjects at A Level. They receive specialist attention in small teaching groups.

Pastoral. Day care and education is available for children from 3 months to 11 years. Once joining the Senior School the following day/boarding arrangements are available:

- Full boarding with continuous care and involvement for seven days a week.
- Weekly boarding with the chance to go home at weekends once College commitments have been fulfilled.
- Occasional or flexible boarding for limited or irregular periods to help busy parents.
- Day attendance, including Saturday mornings and one Sunday morning per term.

The House system

From the Prep School upwards the House system is at the core of virtually all College life outside the classroom. This arrangement provides all pupils with a contact for personalised pastoral care. It is the base for academic monitoring. It ensures a comfortable social environment and a structure within which games and many activities can thrive. The House is the focus of loyalty for the members.

Within the Senior School parents' first point of contact with the College on a day-to-day basis is the pupil's Houseparent. This is the person who pulls together all the different threads and weaves a coherent picture from the many strands of a pupil's varied existence at Bearwood College.

Houseparents are helped by their own team of House Tutors. The Tutor, who is an academic member of staff, assists in the general running of the House but is also in specific charge of a small group of tutees. Tutees meet with their own Tutors at least once a week. This may be for a personal chat about their progress, or a group tutorial. The House team is responsible for both encouraging and motivating those in their House to achieve their potential. All the Houses are supported by a skilled and dedicated group of ancillary staff the most important of whom are the Chaplain, the Medical Staff and the Matrons.

The Matrons are mainly responsible for the domestic arrangements but are also an important informal adult presence who may seem less official to those in need of a sympathetic ear.

Sport and Activities. All pupils take part in a wide range of games and activities outside the classroom. They enjoy a breadth of experience as well as being expected to discover specific areas in which to excel.

Everyone takes part in physical activities on most days. Sports and games give the pupils physical fitness, personal and team skills and recreation. They offer many opportunities to find a sense of achievement. On-site sports and activities on the extensive array of playing fields and facilities include all the usual field sports but in addition there are opportunities for: golf, equestrian sports, cycling and mountain biking, sailing, shooting, canoeing, to name but some.

Extra-curricular activities. Outdoor pursuits are encouraged at Bearwood. The pursuit of academic excellence is balanced by active encouragement of the pupils' extra-curricular involvement. The extensive grounds and lake are used for sailing, canoeing, mountain biking, camping, cross country and many other activities. Few schools can boast such a varied estate as that found at Bearwood College.

Combined Cadet Force. All pupils in the third and fourth forms of the Senior School join the Combined Cadet Force (CCF). Cadets learn self-reliance and teamwork, and develop their own leadership skills. The CCF also provides an unrivalled opportunity to experience outdoor pursuits. Two camps are held during holiday periods each year. The annual adventure training expedition provides boys and girls with the opportunity to experience environments that test and challenge their characters whilst under the supervision of highly qualified staff. Many cadets choose to continue their service in the cadet force during their fifth and sixth form years. At this time they take on the extra responsibilities of being senior cadets. The experience they gain from taking an active role in teaching and helping younger cadets provides a valuable insight into the qualities required from leaders.

The Duke of Edinburgh's Award Scheme. All pupils in the fourth year start the Duke of Edinburgh's Award at bronze level. This is organised partly in conjunction with the cadet force who help with the training for the expedition section. Senior pupils in the College are encouraged to continue with both silver and gold awards. The scheme provides pupils with an ideal opportunity to develop their own skills, fitness and commitment to others whilst fostering self-confidence and personal esteem.

Bearwood Outdoor Activity Club. Many of the pupils take part in other supervised activities away from the College at weekends during term time and in the holidays. Weekend events include jetskiing, water-skiing, hiking, long-distance mountain biking and gliding. We have a keen mountain marathon team who take part in annual events. Pupils in our first and second years are encouraged to develop a taste for adventure. The annual Junior Adventure Week to the South Wales coast at the start of each summer holiday is firmly established.

Music. Music is part of the life of every pupil, non-specialist and specialist alike. Everyone participates in music events including the House Singing Competition and the Choral Society. There are regular informal and formal concerts given by instrumentalists and singers. All pupils are encouraged to take up instrumental and vocal lessons with our team of professional peripatetic musicians. A number of ensembles can be joined: the College Choir, the Chapel Choir, the Jazz Band, the Wind Band, the Dance Band and the Junior Ensemble. Regular visits to concerts and other musical outings take place.

Theatre and Drama. Our Theatre represents the very best that is available for the pursuance of music and dramatic arts.

A busy programme of concerts, recitals and plays ensure that this 350-seat auditorium is continually in use. All pupils are expected to make a contribution to these productions. Performers from the College are supported by theatre technicians, lighting and sound engineers, stage crew and scenery builders. All have their part to play in the many productions.

Specialist tuition leading to LAMDA Speech and Drama grades and awards is available. These help to develop confidence and competence in acting, public speaking and general communication.

College Facilities. The Mansion House is the centre of the College around which all our other buildings are located. Historic rooms house modern facilities.

The Cook Library is situated in the former drawing room, one of the most beautiful rooms in the main mansion. It has a collection of both fiction and non-fiction books for loan and reference use. The library resource is further enhanced by modern personal computers with up to date reference CDs. Pupils are encouraged to read daily quality broad sheet newspapers to keep abreast of current affairs, politics and news. This learning resource is run by a full-time Librarian and supports all areas of the curriculum as well as providing for recreational reading.

The need for modern technology is supported by a new computer resource suite. All departments in the College have PCs which are linked to the pan-College network.

The range of facilities for pupils at Bearwood is extensive. A fully-equipped photographic suite, extensive sports pitches, a swimming pool, tennis courts, weights-training room, motor vehicle engineering workshop and rifle range are all found immediately adjacent to the main building.

The Pre-Prep and Prep Schools are located close to the main Victorian Mansion House, in a thoughtfully converted, listed coach house, known as Jellicoe House. The splendid surroundings of the wider campus combined with the intimate security of Jellicoe House allow children to explore, discover and learn in a safe and attractive setting.

The Nursery is adjacent to Jellicoe House in a purpose-designed building supplemented by a large Early Years unit for 0–3 year olds closer to the Mansion House. The Nursery enjoys unique facilities such as a farm area, a trike track and access to the extensive grounds.

Our grounds contain many additional features: two golf courses; a fifty acre lake and a well-equipped fleet of sailing dinghies, canoes and power boats; generous woodlands with a professionally-built obstacle course and fitness trail; a mountain bike course; stables and a skateboarding run.

Admission. Entry to the College is normally 11+, 13+ and the Sixth Form, but applications at other ages are accepted, subject to vacancies. Assessment is by interview and by Common Entrance where appropriate. Entry to the Sixth Form is normally conditional upon the achievement of a minimum of 5 GCSEs at C grade or above.

Fees per term (2008-2009). Nursery from £47.26 per day; Pre-Prep £2,515; Prep School: Day: £2,955 (Years 3–6), £4,185 (Years 7–8); Boarding (Years 7–8) £7,340; Senior School: Boarders £8,460, Day Pupils £4,930.

Charitable status. Bearwood College is a Registered Charity, number 285287, founded to provide education for young people.

Bedstone College

Bucknell Shropshire SY7 0BG
Tel: 01547 530303
Fax: 01547 530740
e-mail: admin@bedstone.org
website: www.bedstone.org

Bedstone College, founded in 1948, is a fully co-educational, independent, boarding and day school catering for children between the ages of 3 and 18 years. Set amongst the south Shropshire hills, the school enjoys a beautiful 40-acre campus within this idyllic setting.

The school comprises the Pre-Preparatory Department (for children aged 3 to 7 years), the Junior School (for ages 8 to 11 years) and the Senior College (for ages 11 to 18 years), all integrated within one campus. Almost 65% of the pupils in the senior school are full boarders.

Bedstone offers a broad and balanced curriculum offering over 17 subjects to GCSE, AS or A2. Over 95% of sixth formers proceed to their first-choice University and Bedstone is consistently one of the top Shropshire Schools, state or independent.

Our aim is to give individual attention enabling each pupil to achieve their potential. With a teacher:pupil ratio of 1:9, the smaller class sizes allow individual needs to be catered for. The well-qualified and highly-motivated staff believe that each child has a unique talent which it is their job to find and nurture.

Bedstone is very aware of the problems that learning difficulties, such as dyslexia, can cause and the highly-regarded learning support unit, led by its full-time director with the aid of fully-qualified staff, is central to the help provided.

Motto: *Caritas*

The Governing Body:

Chairman: Group Capt J Fynes, RAF

Secretary of the Trust: P R S Dutton, Esq

Members:
Mrs M Hughes, BA, DipEd
D Jones, Esq
J Jones, Esq
E J Murch, Esq, FRICS, FSVA
D Owens, Esq, JP
Mrs Y Thomas
A W Thornton, Esq
Dr P Treves
S Wright, Esq

Clerk to the Council and Bursar: A R Gore, Esq, AFA, FIAB, AIMgt

***Headmaster*: M S Symonds**, BSc, PGCE, CPhys, MInstP, FRSA

Second Master: N Bidgood, MA

Houseparents:
Pearson House: Mr & Mrs B Chadderton
Rutter House: Mrs A Richards
Bedstone House: Mr & Mrs C Braden
Wilson House: Mr & Mrs M Rozée

Competitive Housemasters:
Hopton: C Braden, BEd, QTS
Stokesay: K T Hatfield, BSc
Wigmore: Miss E Parkin, BA Hons, PGCE

Assistant Staff:
Miss P Beresford-Webb Cert Ed CTABRSM (*Acting Director of Music*)
Mrs K J Bidgood BSc, PGCE (*Junior Science*)
C Braden, BEd, QTS (*Head of Design Technology*)
Mrs D Bradfield,CertEd, Cert SpLD (*English*)
B M Chadderton,BA, PGCE (*Head of Modern Languages*)
Mrs J Dodd, CertEd (*Head of Sport*)
P Elkin, MSc (*Mathematics*)
D Fathers, BSc, PGCE, Cert CompSc (*Head of Physics*)
P J Gooderson, MA, PhD, MEd (*Head of History, Head of Careers*)
K T Hatfield, BSc (*Head of Science & Biology*)
P Lloyd, BA Hons, PGCE (*Head of ESL*)
J Lowe, MA Hons, PGCE (*Learning Support*)
J Lynch, BA, PGCE, MA Ed (*Director of Studies, Head of Geography*)

Miss E Parkin, BA Hons, PGCE (*Modern Languages*)
D M Rawlinson, BSc, PhD, PGCE (*Head of Mathematics*)
D M Rozee, BSc, PGCE (*Head of Chemistry*)
J P Smith, BA (*Head of Art*)
J R Simpson, BA Hons, QTS (*Sports Studies & PE*)
I Spencer, BA Hons, PGCE (*Head of Business Studies*)
M Wright, BA, PGCE (*Head of English*)
Preparatory Department:
Mrs J McPherson, CertEd (*Head of Preparatory Department*)
Mrs J Hatfield, BLib, ALA
Mrs J Richards, BA Hons, PGCE
P Wake, CertEd

Pre-Prep Department:
Mrs M Savery, Dip Montessori
Mrs E Pearson, BSc Hons, PGCE
Mrs L Meredith, NNEB

Lay Chaplain: A C Dyball, MA Cantab, DipEd

Visiting Instrumental Teachers:
Mrs M Rowlatt (*singing*)
Mrs M Williams (*flute & recorder*)
D Luke (*guitar*)
D Kirk (*drums*)
Ms L Davidson, ARCM (*woodwind*)
J Searle (*Brass*)
J Hargreaves (*piano*)
Mrs J Hargreaves (*strings*)

School Doctors:
Dr M Betts
Dr A Finter
Dr M Kiff
Dr A Lempert

School Sister: Mrs J M Fray, BSc, RGN
Catering and Domestic Supervisor: Miss M Jenkins
Transport Manager: A Jones
IT Network Manager: R Thomas
Maintenance Manager: R Mather
Headmaster's PA: Mrs P Davis
Director of Admissions & Marketing: Mrs C Reid-Warrilow
Accounts Administrator: P Downes
Accounts Clerk: Mrs S Gore

Character of the College. Many children who join Bedstone have done so because their parents feel that the individual strengths of their children have got lost in their current school; that the challenges and opportunities for fulfilling their child's unique talents do not exist, or that they wish for greater pastoral support and guidance for their children. All of them know that they want the education of the entire child – mind, body and spirit – and Bedstone provides that with the small class sizes and individual attention.

Family Education. There is a guarantee that once any member of a family is accepted at Bedstone, brothers and sisters will gain automatic entry by interview only. This is a relief for parents who wish all their children to be educated at the same school.

Accommodation. The main house, Bedstone Court, is a scheduled building of fine architectural merit and accommodates Junior and Senior Boys. It also houses the administration, library, dining hall and common rooms. Wilson House is a purpose-built Senior Girls' study-bedroom block and Bedstone House accommodates Junior Girls in homely surroundings with resident married staff as houseparents. Rees Court has Sixth Form study-bedrooms for boys as well as science teaching facilities. The Science laboratories and classrooms are in modern buildings. There is seating for 300 people in the Rees Hall and theatre. There is a well-equipped Sports Hall, Design Technology and Art Centre, Medical Centre with a resident RGN, a heated swimming pool and ample accommodation for a wide range of facilities. There is also a social bar/club for the Sixth Form. The College has a campus-wide wireless LAN with a satellite broadband connection. Each scholar has his or her own e-mail address.

Religious Education. Religious teaching at Bedstone is according to the tenets of the Church of England though other denominations are welcomed. Children, whose parents wish it, are also prepared for Confirmation by the Chaplain. There is a long choral tradition and the Choir enjoys an excellent reputation.

Curriculum. Pupils normally enter the Senior College at the age of eleven for a five-year course leading to GCSE, following which there are programmed courses in seventeen different subjects for a further two years up to A Level and University qualifications.

From the First Form to the Third Form (when a number join from the Preparatory Schools) the subjects taught are: Religious Knowledge, English Language and Literature, History, Geography, French, Mathematics, Biology, Physics, Chemistry, Design Technology, Art, Music, Physical Education, Computer Studies and German.

In the Fourth and Fifth Forms, in addition to the Core Curriculum of English, French, Mathematics and the three Sciences, options are: History, Geography, Art, Business Studies, Music, German, Design Technology, Sports Studies and ICT.

Throughout the College, whenever possible, it is endeavoured to set classes in each subject so that every pupil may achieve the best of which they are capable. There is no "cramming" at Bedstone, but considerable effort is required from each pupil; and with the aid of close tutorial support, a well-qualified staff and high staff/pupil ratio, good progress and examination success are assured. AS and A2 courses are offered in English, History, Geography, French, German, Business Studies, Art, Music, Design Technology, Mathematics, Physics, Chemistry, Biology, Sports Studies and General Studies. The British Horse Society Assistant Instructor qualification may also be pursued in conjunction with 2 A Levels.

The College has its own learning Support unit and EAL is available for those who require it.

Careers. There are specific Careers staff and a well-resourced Careers Room. Bedstone makes full use of the Independent Schools' Careers Organisation and all members of the Fifth Form take the ISCO Psychometric tests and have the opportunity to undertake work experience.

Games and Physical Education. There are 15 acres of playing fields, with an excellent Sports Hall and a variety of netball, tennis and squash courts. The success of the boys and girls in physical activity at school, county and district level has been nothing short of remarkable.

Rugby, Athletics and Cricket are the main sports for the boys and Hockey, Netball and Athletics for the girls. A rotation system ensures that all pupils, to a greater or lesser degree, have their share of such activities as Basketball, Cross-Country running, Squash, Swimming and Tennis. Nor are the individualists forgotten. Horse-riding is popular, as is Golf, and there are facilities for Fishing, Shooting, Badminton, Table Tennis and Mountain Biking, whilst the South Shropshire and Powys hills provide excellent opportunities for Duke of Edinburgh's Award activities.

Clubs and Activities. The Duke of Edinburgh's Award scheme flourishes and there is a wide range of out of class activity, including splendid dramatic and musical productions, debating, individual music tuition and an assortment of clubs to suit most tastes. Pupils are expected to know and observe all College rules and parents to cooperate in seeing that this is done. Prefects play an important part in the pastoral system of the College.

Bedstone Junior School is for boys and girls aged 3 to 11 years. The school is housed in its own accommodation and yet shares all the facilities of the senior school. Science, design technology, modern foreign languages, sport and music are all taught by subject specialists within specialist areas. The nursery school is based upon the Montessori system.

The Junior School is very much a part of the College and children find the transition to the Senior College seamless. Any child accepted within the Junior School is automatically accepted into the Senior College.

Scholarships. (*see Scholarship Entries section*). For entry to the Senior College, there is a scholarship examination, held at the College, and takes place on the first Saturday in March.

Fees per term (2008-2009). Senior: £3,730 (day), £6,750 (boarding). Junior: £2,690 (day), £4,560 (boarding). Pre-Preparatory: £1,250.

Old Bedstonian Society. *Hon Secretary*: Mr Frank Jones.

Charitable status. Bedstone College is a Registered Charity, number 528405. It is established for the education of young people.

Beechwood Sacred Heart School

Pembury Road Tunbridge Wells Kent TN2 3QD
Tel: 01892 532747
Fax: 01892 536164
e-mail: bsh@beechwood.org.uk
website: www.beechwood.org.uk

Set in 23 acres on the edge of the historic town of Tunbridge Wells, Beechwood is an independent school for boys and girls aged 3–18, with girls boarding from age 10–18. Of the 400 pupils, approximately 70 are boarders. Founded by the Society of the Sacred Heart, Beechwood has been a lay school since 1973, retaining a sound Catholic tradition whilst welcoming pupils from all nations and creeds.

From September 2008 there will be a transition to co-education in the Senior School, with boys joining Year 7 for the first time. An additional intake of boys into Year 9 in September 2009 and into Year 12 in 2010, means that it will be fully co-educational by 2011.

Governors:
Father Kevin Taggart, OSB (*Chairman*)
Mr Drummond Abrams
Mrs Helen Couldrey
Dr David Findley, BSc, PhD
Mr Patrick Holland, BA Oxon
Mrs Marie-France Mason
Lady Hilary Newman
Sister Moira O'Sullivan
Mr Graham Rodmell

Company Secretary and Clerk to the Governors: Mr Andrew Harvey

***Head*: Mr Nicholas Beesley**, MA Oxon

Deputy Head: Mrs Elaine Cox, BA Hons, PGDipEd (*Geography*)
Chaplain: Fr Peter Stodart
Curriculum Coordinator: Miss Lynda Wallens, BEd Hons (*ICT*)

Staff:
* *Head of Department*

Mrs Mary Allen, BSc Hons (*Biology, Careers, Junior Division*)
Mr Michael Awdry, BA Hons, PGCE (**Art & Design, Head of Senior Division*)
Mr Roy Bayliss, BSc Hons, PGCE (*Mathematics*)
Mr Joshua Brown, BA, LTCL, PGCE (**Music*)
Mr Tom Buzzard, MA, BA Hons (*History*)
Mrs Valerie Byrne, BSc Hons, MIPD (*Business Studies*)
Mrs Jill Childs, MA, PGCE (*English*)
Mrs Olga Clarke, PGCE, Maîtrise (MA) Licence/Deug (BA) (**Modern Languages*)
Mrs Kim Cook, BEd Hons, Primary DipEd (*Learning Support*)
Mr Paul Cotton, BA Hons, PGCE (**Geography*)
Mrs Mary de Vere Moss, DipEd, BEd, RSA (*EAL, Speech & Drama*)
Mrs Emily Fenech (*EAL, RE*)
Miss Mary Fox, BA Hons (*Law*)
Mrs Rosalind Gable, BA Hons, PGDip (*Textiles*)
Mrs Gwen Goodley, BA Hons, CertEd (*History*)
Mrs Teresa Goodwin, CertEd (*Mathematics*)
Mr Ian Harman, MSc, BEd (**EAL, English*)
Mr Gary Hatter, MEd, PGCE (*Art, ICT, Assistant Head of Junior Division*)
Mrs Hilary Hobbs, BA Hons, PGCE, HND (*Food Technology, Textiles*)
Mrs Anne Hopper, BSc Hons, PGCE (*Chemistry*)
Mrs Brigitte Jenner, L-ès-L La Sorbonne, Paris (*French*)
Mrs Sheila Kennedy, BA Hons (*Spanish*)
Mrs Jane Langdon, BSc Hons, PGCE (**Science, Biology*)
Ms Georgina Leake, MA, MEd, BSc (*Psychology*)
Mr John Legg, BA Hons, PGCE (*German*)
Mrs Virginia Letchworth, PGCE, PGDipSLD Dyslexia (**Learning Support*)
Mrs Helen McGill, BA, MA, PGDip (*Learning Support*)
Mrs Carol Mitchell, BA, PGCE (**Physical Education, Middle Division*)
Mr David Molloy, DMS, ACCA (*Accountancy*)
Mrs Candy Prodrick, BD, PGCE (**Religious Education, PSHE*)
Mrs Diana Ringer, BSc Hons, PGCE, MSc (*Mathematics, Public Examinations*)
Mr Stephen Ringer, BSc Hons, ACCA (*Mathematics*)
Dr Shahalam Siddiqui, PhD, BEd, MSc (*Physics*)
Mrs Bettina Terrell, StaatsEx QTS (*Religious Education*)
Mr Mike Truman (*Drama*)
Mrs Sandy Truman, MA (**English, Drama*)
Mrs Elizabeth Warburton-Smith, BA Hons, PGCE (*English*)
Ms Jemma Wyllie, BSc Hons, PGCE (*Food Technology*)

Preparatory School:
Head: Mrs Caron Peppard, BEd Hons
Director of Studies: Mrs Teresa Cutts, MA Cantab, PGCE
KS1 Coordinator: Mrs Susan Judge, PGCE

Staff:
Mrs Nicola Awdry, BEd Hons
Mrs Amanda Brooke, BEd Hons SpLD Dyslexia
Mrs Rachel Cruickshank, BA, HND Care
Mrs Kay Dooley, BSc Hons, PGCE, ME
Mrs Marie-Therèse Feeley, CertEd
Mrs Madeline Gammie, BA Hons, PGCE
Mrs Alice Greening, BA, QTS
Mrs Helen Hunter, CertEd
Mrs Cheryl Jude, Montessori DipEd
Mrs Samantha Michaelson-Yeates
Mrs Claire Parker, BA Hons
Mrs Sally Simm, BA Hons, PGCE
Mrs Jenny Thompson, BTEC, HND

Learning Support Assistants:
Mrs Catherine Chittock
Mrs Helen Doucy, BA Hons, PGCE
Mrs Susan Maynard
Mrs Fiona Pollack, BA Hons Cantab
Mrs Emma Rayner, BSc Hons

Nursery:
Mrs Tracy Dinnage, Cert Early Years Practice
Miss Karen Woodruff, Dip NAMCW

Boarding and Pastoral Staff:
Head of Boarding: Mrs Cecilia Rejbakoz
Housemistress (Seniors): Mrs Sue Dyke
Housemistress (Middles): Mrs Sandra Newman

Housemistress (*Juniors*): Mrs Michelle Newton
Assistant Housemistress: Mrs Mary Watts
School Nurse: Mrs Stephanie Holroyd, RGN

Pastoral Care. At Beechwood we educate in a happy, positive atmosphere. A strong partnership between family, staff and pupils encourages every child to develop and to excel at their individual talents. Small tutor groups allow for individual pastoral care with effective, careful monitoring of academic and social progress.

Curriculum. English, Mathematics and Science form the core of the curriculum at Key Stage 3 and GCSE. The emphasis is on sound teaching and encouragement, in order to give each pupil the understanding needed to enjoy these subjects to the full.

Music and Drama form an important part of life at Beechwood. More than half of the pupils have extra instrumental music lessons, many performing in groups such as Beechwood Singers, String Ensemble and Jazz Group.

In Art, drawing and painting form the cornerstone of the course. With these in place, students are encouraged to experiment with a variety of materials, including ceramics, textiles and photography, leading to Art GCSE and Fine Art A Level.

Modern languages are enjoyed by all pupils. French is studied in Year 7, with taster courses in German and Spanish in Year 8. In Year 9 all pupils study French and either Spanish or German which may be continued to GCSE and A Level.

Information Technology is provided as a cross-curricular discipline throughout the school. ICT skills are taught from an early age and the techniques acquired are quickly used as tools for projects, research and coursework in all areas of the school programme. There is a networked computer room and a newly installed wireless network provides Internet access from all classrooms.

At A Level, around twenty subjects are offered including Theatre Studies, Further Mathematics, Business Studies, Psychology, Accounting and Law. The Sixth Form curriculum is enhanced by an enrichment course that includes Current Affairs, Art and Music appreciation and comprehensive Careers advice.

Sixth Formers are encouraged to show initiative and take responsibility in areas such as the School Bank, the Tuck Shop and the Social Committee. They have opportunities for leadership in organising activities and clubs for younger pupils. The majority of our leavers take up places at universities, including Oxbridge, choosing a wide range of courses.

Our integrated Learning Development Unit caters for pupils with dyslexia and other mild specific learning difficulties, offers a comprehensive Study Skills Course at all levels, and coordinates programmes for gifted and talented pupils.

Examination Results. Our record in public examinations is particularly impressive for a non-selective school, with an A*–C pass rate of 90% at GCSE and 100% at A Level. Beechwood appears in the top 10% of schools nationwide in A Level league tables.

School Facilities. Academic facilities include: library, networked computer room, modern well-equipped science laboratories, art and pottery studio, food technology room, music auditorium, drama and dance hall. Sports facilities include: hockey and football pitches, netball, basketball and tennis courts, heated swimming pool, gymnasium, badminton and volleyball courts, a fitness area and playing fields. We encourage our pupils to experience a wide variety of sports, the emphasis being on fun and participation. Recent successes include being Kent County Basketball Champions.

Preparatory School and Nursery. Adjacent to the Senior School, the Preparatory School and newly equipped Nursery provide a sound beginning for every child in a supportive, family atmosphere. The curriculum stimulates enquiry, academic standards being maintained through regular monitoring and assessment. French is studied from Year 1 and all pupils also enjoy Food Technology lessons. In addition, by sharing the facilities of the Senior School, pupils participate in a wide variety of sports and can represent the school in matches. Instrumental music lessons are popular and pupils enjoy making music together in the choir and orchestra. After school club includes activities such as crafts, gardening and keyboard music making.

Entry Requirements. The school is non-selective academically, selection being based on interview with the Headmaster (where possible), previous school report and confidential reference. All enquiries and applications should be addressed, in the first instance, to the Registrar.

Fees per term (2008-2009). Full boarders £6,070–£7,315; Weekly boarders £5,215–£6,460; Day pupils £2,095–£4,315.

Scholarships. (*see Scholarship Entries section*).

Charitable status. The Sacred Heart School Beechwood Trust Ltd is a Registered Charity, number 325104.

Bethany School

Curtisden Green Goudhurst Cranbrook Kent TN17 1LB
Tel: 01580 211273
Fax: 01580 211151
e-mail: registrar@bethanyschool.org.uk
website: www.bethanyschool.org.uk

The School was founded in 1866 by the Revd J J Kendon. It is a Charitable Trust administered by a Board of Governors, a member of the Association of Governing Bodies of Independent Schools.

Governors:
C M Jackson, MA, MEP (*Chairman*)

Mrs R Bates
Mrs A Culley, CertEd
Miss C Bonnet
Lady Fenn
R Forsyth
Dr R Hangartner, BSc, MB BS, MBA, FRCPath
R M Harmer, BA
A Pengelly, MA, FRCS
G Radford
Mrs C Richards

Bursar and Clerk to the Governors: S J Douglass

Staff:

***Headmaster*: N D B Dorey**, MA Cantab

Academic Deputy: M F Healy, BSc

Pastoral Deputy: Ms S Bicheno, MA Ed

Chaplain: The Revd P Bentham, MTh

Assistant staff:
Miss K Berry, BA
C Bingham, BA
Mrs J Brett, BA
R Briggs, BMus
Mrs D Coley, MA
C Cooper, MSc
Mrs E Cornell, BEd
J M Cullen, BA
S Davies, BA
Mrs J Digby, BSc
Mrs H M Dorey, BA
Dr A Ducoulombier, BA, PhD
C Fisher, MA
Mrs D Gale, BSc
T P Hart Dyke, BA
Mrs G Hollman, CertEd
M W Hollman, BSc
Mrs F Johnson, CertEd PE
P Johnson
Mrs A C Kelly, BA
A A Khan, BA
Miss S King, BA
Mrs H Kirk, BA
Miss C Lager, MA
D Macdonald, BSc
Mrs P Macdonald, BSc
P G Marriott, CertEd PE
Mrs S Martin, CertEd, AMBDA
Mrs A J Mole, BEd
Miss N Nixon, BA
P Norgrove, BEd
M D G E Norman, BEd
M Payne, BSc
Mrs A Presland, BA
Miss R Rayner, BA
Miss C Romero, MA
D Schooledge, BSc
Miss K Shirley, BEd
G Simmons, BSc
G Stubberfield, BA

M Thomas, BSc
Mrs S Thompson, BA
G K Thorpe, BA
Mrs S Thorpe, BA
J Vickerman, BSc
Mrs A Wood, BEd

Medical Officer: Dr J N Watson, MBBS, MRCGP

Registrar: Mrs A Donelan

Headmaster's Secretary: Mrs L Lovelace

Bethany has 425 pupils, aged 11 to 18. 30% board on either a weekly or termly basis, with a varied weekend programme of activities available for termly boarders. A generous staff : pupil ratio of 1 : 8 ensures small classes and high quality pastoral care. Individuals are encouraged to develop their potential to the full in academic and all other respects. Most teaching takes place in modern classroom blocks, the result of an ongoing building development programme. Development in ICT has been a priority at Bethany: a wireless network enables pupils from year 8 to use laptops across the curriculum. The Sixth Form House offers single study-bedrooms with en-suite facilities for the Upper Sixth boarders, study rooms for day pupils and communal facilities for both Upper and Lower Sixth Form students. In 2005 a new Dining Hall complex was opened. More recent additions to the facilities include a state-of-the-art Food Technology Centre, a new Textiles Department and Modern Language classrooms. The new Science Centre is due to be opened before the end of 2008.

Situation. The School occupies a scenic, 60-acre site in the Weald of Kent, easily accessible from most parts of South-East England, an hour from Charing Cross (Marden Station) and with easy access to Gatwick and Heathrow Airports, the Channel ports and Ashford and Ebbsfleet International stations.

Admission. The normal age of entry is at 11 or 13 by the School's Entrance Examination and at Sixth Form level based on predicted GCSE grades but the school welcomes students to the Bethany community at other stages if places are available.

Fees per term (2008-2009). Boarders £6,959; Day Pupils £4,590.

Scholarships. (*see Scholarship Entries section*). Scholarships are awarded for Academic ability, Music, Art, Design Technology, Drama and Sport at years 7–9 and into Sixth Form. Children of members of HM Forces or Clergy receive at least 10% discount on full fees. Further means-tested bursaries are available.

Curriculum. The broad curriculum is based on the National Curriculum. The full range of subjects is taught including Information Technology from 11+ and Spanish from 13+. There are 21 GCE A Levels including Business Studies, Food Technology, Music, Photography, Textiles and Theatre Studies. The Double A Level in Business is also very popular and successful, as is the BTEC National Award in Sport. Almost all Sixth Form leavers proceed to degree courses at University.

Dyslexia. The Dyslexia and Learning Support Department, which enjoys an international reputation, has been supporting pupils of good-average intelligence for over 30 years.

Games and Activities. The School offers a wide range of sporting opportunities and enjoys an extensive fixture list, having established a long tradition of inter-school Sport. Facilities include a Sports Centre, climbing wall, fitness room, three squash courts, tennis courts, an outdoor heated swimming pool and a floodlit astroturf. There is a wide range of clubs and activities. The Duke of Edinburgh's Award Scheme is well established at Gold, Silver and Bronze levels.

Music. There are wide-ranging opportunities for instrumental tuition. There are sectional instrumental groups including: a Symphony Orchestra, Rock School, Jazz Band, Concert Band, Brass Consort and a Choir, all making use of the fine Music School with its recording studio and music technology area.

Careers. The School is a member of ISCO (Independent Schools Careers Organisation) and Careers Education is an important part of the Curriculum. Sixth Form students take part in the Coursefinder Analysis Scheme and receive detailed advice regarding Higher Education and Gap Year opportunities.

Chapel. The Chapel, built in 1878, is the focal point of School life and all pupils are expected to attend services. Confirmation classes are offered for those who wish to participate.

Charitable status. Bethany School Limited is a Registered Charity, number 307937.

Box Hill School

Mickleham Dorking Surrey RH5 6EA
Tel: 01372 373382;
01372 385002 (Registrar)
Fax: 01372 363942
e-mail: enquiries@boxhillschool.org.uk
website: www.boxhillschool.com

Warden: Vice-Admiral Sir James Weatherall, KCVO, KBE

Chairman of the Board of Governors:
Mr B Standring

The Board of Governors is a member of the Association of Governing Bodies of Independent Schools (AGBIS).

***Headmaster*: Mr Mark Eagers**, MA Cantab, MA Bath

Bursar: J Pratten

Registrar: Mrs K Hammond

Headmaster's PA: Mrs Jan Richards

The school was founded in 1959 and is looking forward to a year of Jubilee Celebrations to mark the 50th Anniversary in 2009. Box Hill School is different, and in many ways, unique. YES, we're a co-educational day and boarding school for 11–18 year olds. YES, we have a strong academic, artistic and sporting tradition that gets amazing results. But the difference at Box Hill School is that success and achievement aren't just measured in 'straight A grades', although we should say that the percentage of pupils achieving them at GCSE and A Level rose again in 2007, and we anticipate the same in 2008! The real difference we offer is in discovering and nurturing the talents and abilities of every student. Whether it's academically, through sport, on expeditions or from creative expression in music, art and drama, our outstanding pastoral care and personal attention means pupils really do succeed.

As Dana Farr, A Level student from Zimbabwe looking to enter a top UK University, says, "There's always someone to help with assignments or prep whenever you need it. You make really good friends and the structured day balances work with socializing and other activities. House staff support is invaluable."

A Great Boarding Environment. We offer flexible boarding and no Saturday classes, a great location that's convenient to Central London, Gatwick and Heathrow Airports. We're a caring community based upon the principals of Kurt Hahn founder of Gordonstoun in Scotland and Salem in Germany, now both sister schools of Box Hill. Hahn believed in confronting young people with both challenges and responsibility at an early age; *to learn through practical experience or IDEALS*: International understanding, Democracy, Environmental awareness, Adventure, Leadership and Service to community.

An International Academic Outlook. We've over 20 different nationalities in school and offer 24 subjects at GCSE Level and 20 at A Level; additional foreign languages may be added as an extra. Small classes and personal tutoring really benefit each student.

For overseas pupils, there's English Additional Language (EAL) specialised teaching to help improve vocabulary and overcome any difficulties.

NEW for Sixth Form 2008. From September 2008 all pupils starting Sixth Form will study (replacing A Levels) the **IB (International Baccalaureate) Diploma Programme** as preparation for their lives after school and, in particular, University, as in the UK more and more of them recognise the 'independent learning qualities' shown by IB Diploma applicants.

The IB Diploma is itself a positive attitude to learning; encouraging students to ask challenging questions, to critically reflect, to develop research skills, and to learn how to learn. Like the International Baccalaureate Organisation, we encourage exploration and community service as well as academic achievement in order that the students get the most from their time with us.

"We help kids to succeed in whatever they choose to do, and we're the first school in our area to introduce the IB Diploma – very exciting", Mark Eagers, Headmaster.

Accommodation. Box Hill stands in over 40 acres of grounds in Mickleham village in Green Belt countryside only 45 minutes from London. We have recently completed the brand new Dining Room to add to the extensive facilities already built and continuously updated. We have exciting plans for further new buildings in the next five years and the school has invested heavily in IT.

Pastoral Care. All pupils have a tutor who directs their academic studies and with whom they meet each morning. They also have a housemaster, housemistress or houseparents and all full boarding houses have an assistant and there are non-resident matrons. Relations between students and between students and staff are excellent – the school prides itself on being a friendly community.

Activities. Box Hill seeks to produce a well-rounded citizen capable of getting on confidently in adult life, working in a team, with a variety of interests and love of the outdoors. Every afternoon a wide range of activities, including the usual team sports, takes place. Pupils choose from within four areas, sporting, skills, service, and outdoor pursuits/expeditions. A week's activities may include a selection from swimming, tennis, photography, art, design/technology, and team games such as netball, hockey, soccer, cricket and athletics. Riding, judo and golf are available at extra charge. Over 100 pupils play musical instruments and take part in the Duke of Edinburgh's Award Scheme. A community service group visits local hospitals. Choirs and instrumental groups give regular performances in the school and the Eisteddfod (inter-house drama competition) and the inter-house music involves all pupils.

Expeditions. Expeditions are part of the curriculum in the first three years, combining academic work with expedition skills. As examples from previous years, Year 7 has been to the Brecon Beacons for a week, Year 8 to the Peak District and Year 9 to the Lakes. There are conservation weeks based on Box Hill and a Duke of Edinburgh's Award Scheme training week. All Years, particularly Years 12 and 13 (Sixth Form), go regularly to theatres, museums and drama workshops in London. Holiday trips are also offered, including language trips to the Continent and sports tours.

Round Square. Box Hill belongs to an international group of schools in England, Scotland, Canada, the United States, Australia, Germany, Switzerland, India and Africa. There is an annual conference at a member school attended by a delegation including senior pupils. Joint expeditions carry out project work in India, Thailand and South Africa. There are exchanges between schools and a mini-conference for the younger pupils.

Religion. The School is non-denominational. Sunday Church Services are planned largely by the Church Services Committee, a group of senior pupils and staff who invite speakers to address the School. The School Chaplain is also the Priest in Charge of Mickleham Parish, providing a close link with the parish. In certain cases overseas pupils may be excused Church attendance.

Fees per term (2008-2009). Years 7–11: Boarders £7,250; Weekly Boarders £6,250; Day Pupils £4,000–£4,300. Sixth Form: Boarders £7,625; Weekly Boarders £6,625; Day Pupils £4,700.

Weekly boarders are usually free to depart from 4.00 pm on Friday until Sunday evening or Monday morning.

Scholarships. (*see Scholarship Entries section*). A variety of awards are offered for entry to the Sixth Form, based on academic achievement and a contribution to school life through Art, Music, Drama, expedition work, or other appropriate activities. In Years 7 to 9 similar awards may be given in recognition of academic, musical, artistic or sporting potential. In cases of special financial need bursaries are available. Details from the Registrar.

Box Hill School Association. A supportive organisation of parents and friends of the school maintains links with the local community, and lays on social functions and fund-raising. Parents are strongly encouraged to join.

Method of Entry. Entry is based on an interview with the Headmaster, report from the pupil's present school, and written tests in Maths and English. Those from Preparatory Schools would be offered places based on our own entry tests. Sixth Form entry is based on report, interview and GCSE predictions. For overseas pupils the interview may be waived.

Location. In Mickleham village, just off the A24 Leatherhead to Dorking road, about 4 miles from the M25 and within easy reach of London, Gatwick and Heathrow.

Charitable status. Box Hill School Trust Limited is a Registered Charity, number 312082. It exists to promote the advancement of education.

Chetwynde School

Croslands Ratings Lane Barrow-in-Furness Cumbria LA13 0NY
Tel: 01229 824210
Fax: 01229 871440
e-mail: info@chetwynde.cumbria.sch.uk
website: www.chetwynde.co.uk

Chairman of Governors: Dr R G Baxter, BSc, PhD

Senior Management Team:

***Head of School*: Mrs I Nixon**, BA Hons York, MA Leeds, PGCE

Senior Teacher: Mrs P Curry, BEd Birmingham, TCert Worcs (*Biology*)
Head of ICT: Dr A Amos, PhD, BSc Bristol, EMIIT MIBiol (*Examinations Officer*)
Head of Primary School: Mr M Boyd, TCert Liverpool, ASA
Bursar: Mrs P Lightfoot

* *Head of Department*
† *Head of House*
§ *Part-time*

§Mrs G Allen, BSc Hons Nottingham, PGCE York (*Mathematics*)
Mr D Armitage, BSc Hons Manchester, PGCE Lancaster (*Physics*)
Mrs J Barrow, BSc Hons OU, PGCE (*Primary Teacher*)
Mr J Bates, BSc Hons Heriot-Watt, PGCE Lancaster (*Mathematics*)
Mrs M Beckett, BEd Manchester (*Head of Infants, Primary Teacher*)
Mr G Boardman, MA Durham, BA Hons Newcastle, PGCE Newcastle (**English, †Our Lady's House-boys*)

Mrs D Bowe, CertEd London, IT Dip, RSA (*Primary Teacher*)
Mrs D Barnes, BEd Liverpool, MA Southampton
Ms A Bradley, BA Hons Greenwich, PGCE London (*Primary Teacher*)
Ms J Duncalf, MA Wales, BA Hons Wales, PGCE London (**Art*)
Mr S Dutton, HND Farnborough (**Games, †Chetwynde House-boys*)
Mrs H Edmondson, BA Hons Reading, PGCE Westminster College Oxford, CFPS SEN Newcastle (*French, SENCO, †Our Lady's House-girls*)
Mrs L Foxen, BEd Manchester (*Primary Teacher*)
§Mrs A Fryer, BA Hons Oxon (*Mathematics*)
Mrs S Jeffreys, BA Hons London, PGCE (**RS and PSE, †Chetwynde House-girls*)
Dr C Mackey, PhD, BA Hons, PGCE Lancaster (**German*)
Mrs C Frankland, BA Hons Belfast, PGCE Lancaster (**Geography*)
§Mrs N Nield, BA Hons Exeter, PGCE Leeds (*Drama, Extra-Curricular Speech & Drama*)
§Mr J Munro BA Hons Oxon, MA Oxon, PGCE Oxon (*German*)
Mrs N Murray, BEd Manchester (*Primary Teacher*)
§Mr A Murray, BEd Hons Lancaster, PGCE Manchester (*Mathematics, ICT, and Football*)
Mrs K Greenall, BEd Hons Cheltenhan (*PE, Geography*)
Mrs C Parker, MA Glasgow, MEd Herts, CES Herts (**Modern Languages*)
Mrs C Penellum, NVQ3 (*Classroom Assistant*)
§Mrs J Petty, STA & LS (*Learning Support Assistant*)
§Mrs L Raine, NVQ3 (*Learning Support Assistant*)
Miss H Rann, BSc Hons Wales, PGCE Wales (*Science*)
Mr J Renton, BA Hons Wales, PGCE Newcastle (**Latin and Classical Studies, Assistant Examinations Officer*)
§Mrs J Sage, NNEB (*Classroom Assistant*)
§Mrs E Skinner, BA Hons Birmingham, PGCE Lancaster (*ICT*)
Mr S Spencer, MA Oxon, PGCE Lancaster (**History, Head of Sixth Form*)
Mr A Taylor, BSc Hons East Anglia, PGCE Birmingham (**Science*)
§Mrs J Taylor, GRSM, ARMCM, PGCE Reading (*Music*)
§Mrs A Williams, BA, PGCE Sheffield (*Humanities*)
§Mrs C Young, BA Hons Newcastle, PGCE Bath (*French*)

Administrative Staff:
PA to Head of School: Mrs A Bell
Senior Administrator: Mrs J Thomason
Administrative Assistant: Miss S Shimmin
Bursar's Assistant: Miss G Wardle

Introduction. Chetwynde, a non-selective, co-educational, independent day school for children aged from 3 to 18 years, was founded in 1936. It has charitable status administered by a Board of Governors. The school, although non-denominational, has a Christian ethos. There are currently 286 senior pupils and 144 kindergarten and primary pupils on roll.

Location. The school, situated in the Furness Peninsula, is on the edge of the Lake District on the outskirts of the coastal town of Barrow-in-Furness. The school operates two mini-buses to and from local villages and towns to the west and east.

Buildings and Facilities. The Senior and Primary Schools are housed in three main buildings set amongst gardens and woodland and adjacent to the school's large playing fields.

There are 4 purpose-built Science laboratories, 2 ICT areas, a Theatre, 2 Art rooms, a Library and Careers Resource Centre, Music rooms, a Sports hall, playing fields, courts and departmental resource areas. Substantial use is made of off-site sports facilities in the local area.

Curriculum. Chetwynde Primary School, comprises an Infant and Junior department catering for children aged 3–11 years. It is during these years that the solid foundations of future academic achievement are laid. The curriculum followed by Chetwynde Primary School is regularly reviewed and academic excellence is the school's main priority. However, particular attention is paid to meeting the individual needs and abilities of each pupil. Therefore, our aim in the early years at Chetwynde is to provide a secure and happy atmosphere within which children can develop into confident, well-balanced individuals with an enthusiasm for learning and a respect for others. We place considerable emphasis on moral, social, physical and aesthetic development as well as intellectual progress.

In Years 7–9 a wide range of academic subjects is taught: English, Mathematics, Biology, Chemistry, Physics, German, French, Latin/Classical Studies, Art, Music, History, Geography, Religious Studies and ICT. The curriculum is traditional, but the subjects are taught with a full awareness of new developments in teaching methods, and with an eye to catering for the varying levels of ability and need in any given class.

Pupils in years 10 and 11 usually follow GCSE courses in ten subjects, including the core: English, Mathematics and Science; and also at least one Modern Foreign Language. Courses in three separate science subjects are offered. In addition all pupils take an accredited IT course. GCSE Drama is offered as an extra-curricular subject. Balance in the curriculum is important and so, although the school is strongly academic, the children are encouraged to maintain interests in such activities as sport, drama and music, along with their academic studies. Above all, children should enjoy life at school.

At Chetwynde the Sixth Form course leads to academic AS and A Levels. Academic work takes priority and the excellent standard is maintained by the high quality of teaching in the Sixth Form. We know our students well and there is a strong work ethic. The academic results are consistently excellent and students go on to study a wide range of disciplines at universities throughout the country including Oxford and Cambridge.

The Sixth Form play an important role in creating an ethos based on hard work, courtesy and participation. They provide a good example within the school as a whole and the school environment provides opportunities for students to develop their leadership skills and independence. There are positions of responsibility including the Head Boy and Head Girl as well as House Captains and Games Captains. The Sixth Form benefit from a varied sports and activity programme including mountain biking and outdoor pursuits. They also enjoy a range of cultural visits, for example to Prague, Berlin and New York. Work experience is provided and modern languages students usually do theirs abroad.

Extra-Curricular Activities are very important in the school with an emphasis on participation, as you can see below:

Music is a very important aspect of the school with over 75% of pupils taking an active part in music making. Infant and Junior pupils benefit from a music specialist within the curriculum and there is a junior choir and junior orchestra. Several concerts are held during the year and there is a very popular House Music Competition which includes pupils from both junior and senior departments. There are several ensembles and pupils are encouraged to participate in these. The Music Department also contributes significantly to school productions which are held in both junior and senior departments.

Drama is included in the curriculum in Years 7 to 9 and is offered as a GCSE in Years 10 and 11 as an extra-curricular activity. There is at least one major production per annum involving pupils from across the school and members of the Drama Club and GCSE groups also perform in the RSC Shakespeare Festival as well as in additional drama evenings.

Sport. The school has a justifiably excellent reputation for sport at both junior and senior levels. In the last ten years the school has never failed to reach national finals in one sport or another. Junior swimmers are national record holders as Chetwynde is the only school to have reached the English National Swimming Championships for 12 years in succession, taking medals at every one. Senior netball teams, basketball teams and cross-country runners have all achieved distinction. Beyond this, of course, many individuals have gained county and north of England honours in football, rugby, cricket, rounders, tennis, orienteering etc. The emphasis is on participation and most children take part in something. The sport is run, not only by an excellent team of PE teachers and coaches but also by a large number of the teaching staff who support the extra-curricular programme.

Clubs and Activities include:

Senior: Senior Folk Group, Senior Choir, Chamber Group, String Orchestra Ensemble, Senior Orchestra, Senior Woodwind Ensemble, Senior Recorder Group, Senior Flute Group, Basketball, Chess Club, Computer Club, Croquet Club, Italian Club, Drama Club, Crossfire Christian Youth Group, Science Club, Debating Society, Study Games Club, Dance Club, Dance Class, Duke of Edinburgh's Award Scheme.

Juniors: String Quartet, Composers Group, Junior Orchestra, Junior Choir, Country Dancing, Engineers Club, Craft Club, Computer Club, Orienteering Club.

Infants: Dance and Drama Club, Yoga.

Chetwynde takes an active part in the community, attending and organising fund-raising events and concerts for a wide range of local, national and international charities. Since the Tsunami appeal the school have been twinned with the Matayama School in Sri Lanka.

Fees per term (2008-2009). £1,998–£2,332. 5% sibling discount. The Government nursery grant scheme is in operation for 3 and 4 year old children.

Uniform. The uniform code is strict and the uniform itself is unique to the school and can only be purchased from the on-site school shop.

Admission. Pupils entering the Senior School sit an entrance test in the January prior to joining the school. A scholarship of one term's fees is offered to the pupil with the highest score in the entrance test and there are limited Assisted Places available throughout the school. Acceptance of a pupil into the Primary or Senior School is dependent on a satisfactory school report giving particular reference to academic ability, behaviour, extent of parental support and any health or educational special needs.

Charitable status. Our Lady's Chetwynde School Limited is a Registered Charity, number 1048501.

Claremont Fan Court School

Claremont Drive Esher Surrey KT10 9LY
Tel: 01372 467841
Fax: 01372 471109
e-mail: jtilson@claremont.surrey.sch.uk
website: www.claremont-school.co.uk

***Principal*: Mrs A E Stanley**, MA, BA

Head of Senior School: Mr J Insall-Reid, BSSc, DipT, BArch Hons

Head of Upper Junior School: Dr J B Bradley, EdD

Head of Lower Junior School: Mrs J R Gordon, BA, DipT

Situation. Claremont Estate is one of the premier historic sites in the country. The original house and the famous Landscape Garden were first laid out by Sir John Vanbrugh for the Duke of Newcastle early in the eighteenth century. Later Capability Brown built the present Palladian Mansion for Clive of India. For over a century Claremont was a royal residence and played an important part in Queen Victoria's early years. In 1930 the School acquired the Mansion and now owns 96 acres of peaceful parkland. Esher is only 16 miles from London and almost equidistant from Heathrow and Gatwick airports with access points onto the M25 within 3 miles.

General Information. Claremont Fan Court School is a co-educational school for pupils from 3–18 years. The School consists of the Lower Juniors for pupils aged 3–7 years, the Upper Juniors for pupils aged 7–11 years and the Senior School for pupils from 11–18 years, each with its own Head, under the leadership of the Principal.

At Claremont Fan Court School high personal expectations and moral values are established and developed within small classes in a happy, positive environment, free from the excessive pressures sometimes placed on young people today. This in turn leads to growth in confidence, independence, self-motivation and self-discipline.

Aims. To provide a broad and forward-looking curriculum in which pupils are encouraged to think independently to meet the demands of a rapidly changing world. A balanced education develops the whole child and prepares the pupils academically, morally and socially for their future adult lives. Pupils have the opportunity to discover where their individual interests and contributions lie, enabling each pupil to achieve his/her full potential. They know that all their achievements, in whatever area they excel, are highly valued.

E-Learning. In September 2004 the School introduced an exciting and innovative e-learning programme through a phased introduction of laptops. Currently all pupils in Years 4 to Year 11 have their own laptop. This is much more than 'laptops on desks'. Each pupil in these year groups uses his/her own laptop both in the classroom and for work at home. Among their learning tools students have access to Internet, e-mail, CD-ROM, DVD-ROM together with specially selected software. The laptops are not replacing traditional teaching methods where they are shown to be effective, but are providing flexible resources that will enrich and support the students' learning experience.

Curriculum. The School educational programme is based on National Curriculum guidelines but the expectation of pupil achievement far exceeds the national average. Junior School classes have between 16–20 pupils. It is vitally important that children are secure and happy so that effective learning can take place and well-qualified staff encourage active, structured learning. Pupils are expected to meet new social and educational challenges with confidence and perseverance. Emphasis is placed on the acquisition and development of skills in numeracy and literacy while providing a wide and varied range of subjects to stimulate the joy and wonder of learning. Subjects include English, Maths, Science, History, Geography, Religious Studies, French, Design Technology, Food and Textiles Technology, Information Technology, Art, Music, Drama and Physical Education.

At the commencement of Senior School all pupils continue with the range of subjects offered in the Junior School and begin German or Spanish in Year 8. At GCSE all pupils take English Language, English Literature, Maths, Science and Religious Studies. The remainder of their subjects is chosen from a list, which includes French, German, Spanish, Geography, History, Technology, Drama, Art, PE and Music.

Many pupils excel in the sporting arena, where they can develop talents through fixtures against other schools as well as in county or national school championships. Annual tours, both nationally and overseas, give an added dimension to pupils' sporting education.

Music, Art and Drama are also important aspects of the daily curriculum. All contributions are valued, whether they be leading, supporting or backstage roles, in order for the participants to be given every opportunity for creative thought and individual expression and to develop an awareness of self-worth.

Sixth Form. The Sixth Form at Claremont is a vibrant and vital part of the School. It aims to form a bridge between the years of compulsory schooling and the more independent years of Higher Education. The many responsibilities our students take on, including leadership and organisational roles, provide an all-round experience of special value to universities, colleges and employers.

A wide variety of subject options from the traditional to the more contemporary subjects of Media Studies, Psychology, Photography and Music Technology, is available to the Sixth Form. Students will usually study four or five AS subjects in Lower Sixth converting three or four of them through to full A Levels via the A2 examinations at the end of their second year of study.

At Sixth Form, Claremont also welcomes external students, who meet our entry requirements. The Sixth Form Centre provides recreation and study facilities and is housed in the historic surroundings of White Cottage, designed by John Vanburgh in 1715.

Careers. Pupils receive careers advice from Year 8 onwards. The Careers Library is manned by the Head of Careers and operates an open-door policy. Pupils participate in Industry Days where representatives from industry and commerce organise topical workshops. There is training in the formulation of effective CVs. Advice and guidance is given regarding UCAS applications and to those pupils who choose to take a gap year. Mock interviews are organised for pupils and conducted by external advisors.

Extra-Curricular Activities. Making individual choices in the learning programme and developing a wide range of interests are both necessary preparations for lifelong learning. A wide range of clubs and extra-curricular activities is available throughout the School and pupils are actively encouraged to participate in a full and rich school experience.

For Junior School children extra-curricular activities include Chess, Touchtyping, Recorder, Gym Club, Choir, Jazz Dance, Country Dancing, Art Club, Fencing, Judo and a wide range of sporting activities. For older pupils opportunities are available in Art, Science Crest Award, Computing, Drama, Debating, Music, Duke of Edinburgh's Award, Cycle France, Young Enterprise and many sporting activities including Fencing.

Admission. The main intake of pupils occurs at 3+, 4+, 7+, 11+ and Sixth Form. Places are offered subject to a pupil reaching the School's entry requirements. Applications at other levels are welcome subject to a place becoming available.

Fees per term (2008-2009). Junior School: Nursery £1,217; Reception, Year 1 & 2 £2,434; Years 3–6 £3,133. Senior School: Years 7–8 £3,857; Years 9–11 & Sixth Form £4,072.

Scholarships. (*see Scholarship Entries section*). We offer Academic Scholarships at Year 3, 7, 9 and Sixth Form, Music Scholarships from Year 7, 9 and Sixth Form, Art and Drama Scholarships for Sixth Form entry, and Sport Scholarships at Year 7 and Sixth Form.

Charitable status. The School is owned and run by an educational foundation with charitable status, Registered Charity number 274664.

Cokethorpe School

Near Witney Oxfordshire OX29 7PU
Tel: 01993 703921
Fax: 01993 773499
e-mail: admissions@cokethorpe.org
website: www.cokethorpe.org.uk

The School was founded in 1957 and occupies a Queen Anne Mansion and substantial new buildings surrounded by almost 150 acres of parkland on the edge of the Cotswolds, two miles from Witney and ten from Oxford.

There has been a continuous building programme over the last few years, including new performing arts facilities in 2005, two Astroturf pitches and a Costa Coffee Internet café (for the Sixth Form) in 2006, and a reorganisation of classrooms and ICT, together with an expansion of the Library, in 2007. A new Dining Hall and Sixth Form Centre is due to be opened in 2009.

There are 650 pupils between the ages of 4 and 18 at the School. Class sizes are small and the individual attention and encouragement received enables pupils to maximise their achievements.

Governing Body:
Chairman: M StJohn Parker Esq, MA
Vice-Chairman: A W Baker Esq
D P Mason Esq, DL
Miss A C Jones, MA, FRSA
B Brown Esq, BA, DA, FCSD, FRSA
J R Hunt Esq, MEd, DLC
D Whibley Esq, LLB Hons
J Bond Smith Esq, FIMI
A C Burdall Esq, BEng, MICE
Professor D Macdonald, BA, MA, DSc
Mrs G Butt, MA
P Vaughan-Fowler Esq, MBA, BA
Sir John Allison, KCB, CBE, FRAeS
S K Dexter Esq, FCA

***Headmaster*: D J Ettinger**, MA, PGCE

Second Master: K Walton, CertEd
Director of Studies: D H Williams, BSc, CertEd
Bursar: Mrs S A Landon, BA, ACMA
Registrar: Mrs L M Berry, BA
Head of Junior School: Mrs C A Cook, BEd
Chaplain: Revd R Turner, BA, MA
School Nurse: Mrs L S Haste, RGN

Assistant Teachers:
* *Head of Department*
† *Housemaster/Housemistress*

W H C Daniels, BSc, PGCE (*Director of External Affairs*)
E J Fenton, BD, AKC, PGCE (*Senior Tutor; Examinations Officer*)
C Maskery, MSc, BA, PGCE, FBAPT (*Third Master; *Sport; †Gascoigne House*)
Miss P S M Townsend, BA, MBA, PGCE (*†Feilden House*)
Mrs S M Barton, BA, TEFL, DELTA
Mrs S E duFeu, BEd
Mrs M D Marchbank, BEd
Mrs J Legg, CertEd, DipSpLD
M T Jackson, BEd
Miss R G Ogilvie, BSc, PGCE
Mrs R J Simpson, BEd, DipSpLD
Mrs J L Rushton, BA
P Warner, BSc (*Professional Tutor*)
Mrs S R Edeson, BA, PGCE
Mrs L M Boulton, CertEd, BEd, DipSpLD
Mrs J Dow, CertEd
S J Rae, BA (**ICT*)
Mrs S E Saunders, BEd, DMS, DipSpLD
Mrs J Holmes, BA, LLB, PGCE, PG Dip BVC Barrister-at-Law (NP)
Mrs C Hooper, Dip Acting (**Drama*)
Mrs S F Martin, CertEd, BEd (**Learning Support*)
Mrs S M L Copeland, BA, PGCE, AdvDipPsych
B A Heaney, GMus RNCM, PGCE
Mrs H Lord, BA, PGCE, MA, BPhil
Mrs J L Pratley, MCertSpLD (*Third Mistress; †Vanbrugh House*)
H Van Zyl, BSc, BLaw, PGCE, MA
Mrs J Wheeler, DipSpLD
Mrs J Freeston, CertEd, BA, Dip SAID
J E Bown, BSc, PGCE (*†Swift House*)
Miss M M Taylor, BA, PGCE, NDDA, PGDC (**Art*)
T J Bostwick, BA (**History*)

Mrs J A Griffin, BA, PGCE
Miss F M M Hamon, BA, PGCE (*†Queen Anne House*)
Mrs J D Ryan, BA, DipEd
Mrs C S Scaysbrook, BSc, PGCE (**Mathematics*)
Mrs M R Martindale, MA (**Geography*)
Mrs D T Keegan, BA, DipCareers (**Careers*)
W G Lawson, BA, PGCE
Ms L Oliff, CertEd, CACDP
G J Rees, CertEd, RFU Coach Level 4 (*†Harcourt House*)
S D White, BA, PGCE (**English*)
S R Henderson, BSc, PGCE (**Music*)
Miss K J Anderson, BA
Miss S E Collis, BA
Mrs H J Butler, BA, PGCE
Miss D C H Jackson, BEd, DipEFL
Mrs R C G Jarrett, BA, PGCE, SHS Dip (*Nutrition*)
Mrs G E McHardie Jones, CertEd
M J O'Connor, BEd
Mrs J W Rees, CertEd
Dr T E Searls, PhD, MSc
O Harding, BSc
Mrs J E Neame, BSc, DipSpLD
M C Shingleton, BA, PGCE (*Head of Sixth Form; *Business Studies*)
A W Purdie, BSc
A W Hutchings, BEd, HNC (**Design Technology*)
M G Cooper, BA, PGCE
I M P Elkin-Jones, MBA, BA, PGCE
R D Hughes, BA
Miss S J Lapper, MSc, BSc, PGCE
Miss E Semenzato, DLitt, PGCE
A E Uglow, BA, PGCE
Miss S White, BA, PGCE
A Forsey, BA, PGCE
Mrs S Fraser-Paterson, BEd
Miss H Hiscox, BA
Miss N Larabí, BA, PGCE
M J Baldwin, BSc, PGCE
Miss M H Davis, BA, PGCE
Dr C Flaherty, PhD, MSc, BSc (**Science*)
Mrs H M Kenworthy, BSc, PGCE
M Schofield, BA, MA, PGCE (**Philosophy*)
Miss G R Ringham, MA, PGCE
T J Walwyn, BA
Miss M Bennett, BA, PGCE (**Modern Foreign Languages*)
J Capel, MA, PGCE
H Jennard, BA
T J Mann, BA
Mrs P Paterson, BA, PGCE
R Phillips, BA, PGCE

Visiting teachers for Piano, Violin, 'Cello, Guitar, Wind and Brass instruments, Timpani, Singing.

Admission. Pupils usually enter the Junior School at 4 or 7 (the latter based on an assessment day) and the Senior School either at 11, 13 or 16. Candidates at 11 are required to sit assessments in Maths, English and Reasoning, at 13 either assessments or Common Entrance and at 16 GCSEs or equivalent. Places are offered on the basis of these, plus interviews and school reports. A range of Senior School scholarships (means-tested) are assessed separately at each age.

Curriculum. Teaching is based on the National Curriculum until GCSE unless there are sound educational reasons why a particular subject should not be studied.

In Year 10 all pupils study core subjects of English, Maths and Science and have a wide choice of GCSE options which include Geography, History, Design Technology, Graphics, Art, Textiles, Drama, French, Spanish, Business Studies, Music, ICT, Physical Education and Psychology. There is also a full programme of personal, social and health education.

Pupils who may require learning support can be given extra help within the Learning Support Department, which is staffed by qualified specialist teachers.

After 16+ pupils join the Sixth Form and study at least four subjects to AS Level and at least three to A2 Level. The small size of teaching groups is particularly conducive to individual attention and encouragement. The usual courses are supplemented by Photography, Politics, Philosophy and Law.

All forms throughout the School are deliberately kept small.

Religion. The School has a joint Anglican and Roman Catholic foundation and there are regular services. Pupils of other faiths are welcome too. The whole School meets together for assemblies.

Sport. The School has a strong and successful sporting tradition. Rugby, netball, hockey, soccer, cricket, athletics, canoeing, clay pigeon shooting, tennis, badminton, golf, judo, squash, swimming and climbing are all available. All pupils do PE as part of the curriculum.

Other Activities. The AOB extra-curricular programme plays a prominent part in a pupil's timetable and includes Design Club, Canoeing, Music, Art, Ceramics, Cookery, Climbing, Library, Drama, Social Service, Computing, Film Club, Chess, Bridge, Horse Riding, Textiles, Young Enterprise Group, ACF and The Duke of Edinburgh's Award Scheme.

Music and Drama. All pupils are encouraged to learn a musical instrument and join the choir or one of the range of orchestras and ensembles, and the majority do so. Peripatetic teachers cover a very wide range of instruments, and there are regular concerts and recitals during the year. Drama flourishes with regular workshops and productions.

Careers. The School is a member of ISCO. Help and advice is given by experienced Careers teachers and the latest literature is available in the Careers Centre.

Fees per term (2008-2009). Junior School £3,095; Senior School: £4,295 (Years 7 and 8), £4,495 (Years 9–13). Extras are kept to a minimum.

The Cokethorpe Society. c/o *Director of External Affairs*: Warwick Daniels, Cokethorpe School (society@cokethorpe.org).

Charitable status. Cokethorpe Educational Trust Limited is a Registered Charity, number 309650. It aims to provide a first class education for each individual pupil.

Concord College

Acton Burnell Hall Shrewsbury Shropshire SY5 7PF
Tel: 01694 731631
Fax: 01694 731389
e-mail: theprincipal@concordcollegeuk.com
website: www.concordcollegeuk.com

Concord College is a highly successful international boarding college providing GCSE and A Level courses. Set in 50 acres of Shropshire parkland, the College combines outstanding facilities with first-rate academic performance. The College is regularly rated in the top 50 schools in the UK. Students are cared for by a dedicated staff in a safe and beautiful environment. UK day and boarding students are also welcome at the College. Concord is a community that celebrates national and cultural diversity while students and staff are united by the wish to set high standards. The result is a happy and open community in which students are polite, articulate and conscientious without ever losing their sense of fun.

The College dates back to 1949 and moved to its present site in 1973. In 1983 it became a charitable trust. Over the years, students from over eighty countries have attended Concord.

Chair of the Governors: Dr Iain M Bride

Clerk to the Governors and Bursar: Mrs Barbara Belfield-Dean

***Principal*: Neil G Hawkins**, MA Cantab, PGCE

Assistant Principal: John Leighton, BSc, DipEd

Senior Teachers:
Alfred Ellis, MA, PGCE
Jeremy Kerslake, MA
Tom Lawrence, BA PGCE

Registrar: Mrs Avril Bees

The College is a co-educational day and boarding school for students aged 13–19.

Number of students: 370 (approximately equal numbers of boys and girls) of whom 330 are boarders.

Facilities. Facilities at Concord College are superb. Based around an historic Main Building, there are many new additions as well as medieval ruins within the grounds. There is a stunning Theatre and Music School, an excellent Sports complex, indoor swimming pool as well as an outstanding Science facility (opened in 2005). Students eat their meals in the College Dining Room and select from a variety of international cuisine. Most students have individual study-bedrooms on campus, some with en-suite bathrooms. Students have a wide variety of facilities including a sports hall, internet café, social club and student kitchen.

Education. Teaching at Concord is undertaken in groups that average 16 at GCSE and 14 at A Level. Teachers are experts in their subjects.

At GCSE Biology, Chemistry and Physics are taught as separate subjects and emphasis is placed upon laboratory experience. Other compulsory subjects are Mathematics, English, Religious Studies and Physical Education. Optional subjects include Art, Business Studies, Geography, History, IT, Music, Spanish and Japanese.

At AS and A Level students normally study at least three A Levels and at least one further AS Level. Subjects include Art, Accounting, Biology, Chemistry, Chinese, Economics, English Language, English Literature, Geography, History, Law, Mathematics, Further Mathematics, Music, Physics and Spanish. All students who do not have GCSE English are expected to study English.

Lessons are taught in a variety of excellent classroom facilities. There is a purpose-built Science block with six superb laboratories. The English Department contains a modern digital Language Laboratory. Most teaching rooms are equipped with digital projectors.

In addition to their teachers, students have an individual tutor with whom they meet daily and who monitors their academic progress. Students also have a House Parent who is responsible for their well-being. Support is available to all students to develop their oral and discursive skills to ensure that they are able to express their ideas confidently especially at university interview.

Examination Results and University Entry. The College achieves excellent examination results with 85% A/B at A Level in 2007, placing Concord comfortably within the top 50 schools in the UK according to The Times and The Financial Times league tables. The College is highly successful in placing students into UK medical schools and other top UK universities. In 2007 8 students won places at Cambridge University, 8 at Oxford, 14 at Imperial College, London and 9 at the LSE. 28 students went on to read Medicine at UK medical schools.

Selection for Entry. The college selects applicants upon the basis of interviews, school record and entry tests. On line tests are arranged for overseas applicants. Students can be accepted for entry at all ages.

Fees per annum (2008-2009). Full Boarding £21,950, Day £10,428. Payable in 2 instalments.

Scholarships. A fee reduction of up to 20% of full fees is offered to students who have a particularly strong academic background. For entrants to GCSE classes, scholarship entry tests are administered. Bursaries are also available.

Holidays. Half term holidays involve only a long weekend (Friday to Monday evening). The Christmas holiday is one month and Easter is only two weeks. There is a long summer vacation from the end of June until early September.

The college remains open at half term and during the Easter holiday and there is no additional charge for holiday accommodation and meals.

The School Day. Lessons run from 9 am to 4 pm Monday to Friday with Wednesday afternoon allocated to sport and to a shopping trip to Shrewsbury. There is compulsory supervised study (prep) for two hours each evening Monday to Friday.

Saturday morning is used for whole-college testing. The public examination rooms are used for this purpose so that the rooms hold no terror for the students when the final public examinations are taken.

Reports to Parents. These are sent at half term in the first term and subsequently at the end of each term.

Clubs, Sports and Extra-Curricular Activities. Students at Concord can choose from a multitude of activities. Sports, music, dance and drama are all available in our own facilities. There is a Sports Hall, squash courts and gymnasium as well as outdoor facilities including football, athletics and tennis. A wealth of sporting activities is on offer ranging from archery to fencing and badminton to TaeKwonDo. For dancers, there is a purpose-built dance studio where ballet, modern, latin and ballroom and streetdance clubs take place. Musicians can join the orchestra, wind or string groups. Choir and singing club can develop all levels of vocal talent. Many other activities are also offered ranging from bridge and chess to horse-riding and mountain-biking. Students can take part in the Duke of Edinburgh's Award Scheme. Whatever their talents, students are able develop them at Concord.

Charitable status. Concord College is a Registered Charity, number 326279. It exists to provide high quality education for secondary age students.

Dover College

Effingham Crescent Dover Kent CT17 9RH
Tel: 01304 205969
Fax: 01304 242208
e-mail: registrar@dovercollege.org.uk
website: www.dovercollege.org.uk

Dover College was founded in 1871 and occupies the grounds of the Priory of St Martin, a 24 acre site in the centre of Dover. Another 20 acres of playing fields are nearby. The College Close is surrounded by a number of impressive medieval buildings. Pupils still use the original Refectory, and the School Chapel is a fine 12th Century building. The site has been occupied for nearly 900 years.

The College was granted a Royal Charter by His Majesty King George V in 1923 and the Patron of the College is the Lord Warden of the Cinque Ports.

Governors:
Members of the Council:
J T Sullivan, Esq (*Chairman*)
Revd Canon N P Nicholson (*Vice-Chairman*)

P Chadwick, Esq
M J Dakers, Esq
J P Gatehouse, Esq
M V P H Harrington, Esq
P A Koning, Esq
M G Krayenbrink, Esq
J G Ryeland, Esq
C M Tomson, Esq

Other Governors:
Ms S Capito
S Devalia, Esq
N J Drury, Esq
R D S Foxwell, Esq
M Goodridge, Esq
C P Hare, Esq

***Headmaster*: Mr Stephen Jones**, MSc, MLitt, FRSA

Deputy Head: Mrs Helen J Tresidder, BSc

Director of Studies: Mr D Ellerington, BSc, BA, MA

Head of Infant & Junior Department: Mrs H Miller, BA

Assistant Staff:
Mr M Algar, BA
Ms S Arbuthnot
Mrs E Aylward, BA
Mrs J Barnes, BA
M Beere, BSc
Mrs L Binfield
Mr G Came
Mr R Chohan, BSc
Mrs D Collis, CertEd
Mrs S Cook
Mr D Dales, BEd
Mr J Dewick, BA Hons
Mrs F Donnelly, CertEd
Mr P A H Donnelly, BA, DipTEFL
Miss C Dunbar
Mrs S E Eberlein, BEd
Mrs J Ellerington
Mr B Fairclough, BA
Mr B Farrant, BSc
Mrs J Gore, RSA
Mrs J Harris, Adv CertEd
Ms D Hassan, CertEd
Mr G Heppleston, BSc
Mrs J Heppleston, BEd
Mr G R Hill, MA
Mr N S Lockhart, MSc
Mr C Lockyer, BMus
Mr G Mees
Miss Y Ramadharsingh
Mrs E Repaska, MA
Mr N Roberts
Ms L Salter, MA
Ms A Simmons
Miss J Single, BA
Mr E Skates, BA
Mr R G Spencer, MA, FRCO
Ms A Squire, Montessori TDip
Ms S Stow, BSc
Ms T Taylor, BA, Dip de Cand
Dr P Turner
Mr M T Vanderhoeven, BA
Mrs P Vincent, CertEd
Ms W Wallis, CertEd
Mr P Wharton, MA
Mr P Young

Bursar and Business Manager: Col P Barry
Business Development & Admissions Officer: Mrs G Degrange
Headmaster's Secretary: Mrs D Kilvington
Medical Officer: Dr Barley
Medical Centre Sisters: Mrs C Hunt, S Robinson, S May
Medical Centre Assistant: Mr E Glayzer
IT Manager: Mr A Torrance, BSc

Co-education. Dover College (4–18) has been fully co-educational since 1975 and the 351 boys and girls are integrated at all levels. There are 124 boarders.

Organisation. The school divides into four parts: the Infant and Junior Department from age 4–11, Priory from 11–13, Lower College from 13–16, and Sixth Form. There are 7 Houses, all situated on the College Close, 4 for boys including 2 Day Houses and 3 for girls incorporating both day girls and boarders. Dover College's Junior Department is housed in a spacious self-contained building within the beautiful grounds of Dover College.

Catering. The catering team provides delicious, healthy, well-balanced homemade food.

Curriculum. Infants and Juniors study a wide range of subjects. Great importance is placed upon literacy, numeracy, information technology and key skills. French is taught from Year 1. Fourth and fifth form pupils study between six and ten GCSE subjects, depending on their level of ability. The curriculum at this level is flexible, enabling pupils to have an academic curriculum designed to suit individual needs.

All pupils are given very careful guidance when making their GCSE level choices, by their Academic Tutor, Housemaster/Housemistress, the Careers Department and by the Director of Studies.

At all stages of a pupil's time at Dover College, progress is carefully monitored. Assessment periods occur regularly, during which pupils are graded for achievement and effort. A merit/demerit system operates for pupils up to 16 years. Classes at Dover College are kept as small as possible. Class size up to GCSE are generally between 15–20 and at A level 10–15. Some A level sets are smaller.

Considerable emphasis is placed upon the breadth of education offered: music, art and drama are an integral part of the curriculum. All pupils participate in a variety of sports, with stress placed upon the development of leadership skills.

Sixth Form. Pupils in the Sixth Form are able to choose AS and A Levels from a list of over 20 subjects. BTEC Sports and AVCE Business Studies are also available. Traditional academic subjects are provided, as are the practical subjects of physical education, art, design and technology, drama and music.

Sixth formers wear a distinctive uniform, and are given more choice and freedom than junior pupils being expected to respond positively to their treatment as young adults. A well-equipped Sixth Form Centre is used by senior pupils as a meeting place and social club.

The School's Careers Adviser works in close liaison with Connexions to plan, deliver and evaluate an integrated careers' education and guidance programme. This enables pupils to gain the necessary knowledge, skills and understanding in order to make informed career plans before attending the universities of their choice.

International Study Centre (ISC). Dover College has recruited pupils from many parts of the world since 1957. The School's International Study Centre provides intensive English courses for pupils whose first language is not English. These courses vary in length and the aim is to enable all pupils to integrate fully into the life of Dover College as soon as possible after their arrival.

Individual Support. There is a Individual Needs Department in which pupils with learning difficulties (eg Dyslexia) receive 1:1 tuition. The College is registered with CReSTeD. Each pupil has a member of staff as a personal tutor. The tutor supervises his/her pupil's general academic progress.

Art and Technology. The Art Department is situated in a purpose built building which was opened in 1994. Fine Art, pottery and textiles are all available. Examination results are always excellent both at GCSE and A Level.

The Technology Department shares a building with the Art department and is situated in a large well-equipped open plan workshop. Pupils are encouraged to work with a range of materials (wood, plastic etc) and use CAD software. Design Technology is available at GCSE and A level. There are many opportunities for the students to use the workshop outside of curriculum time. There is a weekly Design and Technology Activity and also on various Activity Saturdays.

Music and Drama. Music plays a particularly important part in the life of the School. The well-equipped Music Department is located just off site. Extra curricular activities are numerous. The main one is the Chapel Choir, which meets three times a week and is the backbone of most concerts and services, but there are weekly rehearsals for the Choral Society, String group, Windband, and Madrigal group. There is a Concert at the end of each term, held in the Refectory and three Services a term, held in the Chapel. A House Music competition takes place annually.

Drama is a very active part of the cultural life of the School, as well as part of the Lower School curriculum. There is a major school production each year together with additional House productions. Drama is offered at A level and GCSE level.

ICT Centre. Pupils have access to high specification computers, which have excellent software. Each computer is linked to broadband internet and pupils have their own email address. A new Learning Resource Centre was opened in Summer 2004 providing cutting-edge facilities to all students, including a wireless network.

Sport. The School's playing fields are a short distance away. However on site are tennis courts and an astroturf facility. The School has an excellent modern Sports Hall with a gym. Sports include Athletics, Badminton, Basketball, Cricket, Cross Country, Running, Football, Hockey, Netball, Sailing, Tennis, Volleyball and various PE activities. Swimming takes place at the indoor swimming pool in the local leisure centre. Golf may be played on local courses and horse riding is also offered locally.

Extra-Curricular Activities. In addition to sport, pupils have an opportunity to take part in a wide range of activities including Adventure Training, Art, Chess, Computing, Debating, Duke of Edinburgh's Award, Electronics, Dancing, Fencing, First Aid, Language Clubs, Minerva Club, Music, Photography, Stage Management and Technology.

Pastoral Care. All pupils benefit from a carefully designed system of pastoral care. Every Dover College student belongs to a House and Boarders are provided with good quality accommodation in one of three boarding houses. All sixth formers have single study-bedrooms. A Housemaster or Housemistress, supported by a team of tutors, runs each House. It is their role to give pastoral support as well as supervising their academic progress.

There is a fully equipped medical centre, which can accommodate pupils overnight, staffed by two professionally qualified nurses.

Religious Life. The College has its own Chapel and is Christian in character. All pupils are encouraged to respect each other's beliefs and faiths from a position of tolerance and understanding.

Entry. Pupils are admitted at 4, 5, 7, 11, 13 or 16 but may come at any age. Entry into the Junior Department is by interview and an informal assessment carried out during a "Taster Day" at the school. The School has its own 11+ examination. 13+ pupils normally sit the Common Entrance at their own Preparatory School. Provision is made for direct entry into the Sixth Form for boys and girls. This is normally conditional upon GCSE results. Further information can be obtained from the Registrar.

Terms of Entry. Most pupils join the College in September, but entry in January and April is possible.

Fees per term (2008-2009). Junior Day £1,795–£2,615; Senior Day £3,010–£3,760; Senior Flexi Boarding £5,185–£6,180; Full Boarding £5,523–£7,622.

Scholarships. (*see Scholarship Entries section*). Academic, Music, Art, Sports and All-Rounder Scholarships are available. The scholarships are offered at 11+, 13+ and 16+. Scholarships may also be awarded to pupils entering at Sixth Form level based on a pupil's performance at GCSE level. Details can be obtained from the Registrar.

Location. Dover College is set in the heart of Dover, on the southeast coast of Kent. We are the closest school to continental Europe, with easy access via the Eurostar. Dover Priory Station and good road links are within easy reach of the School making London very accessible. London Heathrow and Gatwick airports are within two hours' travel by car.

Old Dovorian Society. *Secretary*: J K P Boorman, c/o Dover College.

Charitable status. Dover College is a Registered Charity, number 307856. The School exists to develop confidence and individual talents.

d'Overbroeck's College
(including Leckford Place School)

The Swan Building 111 Banbury Road Oxford OX2 6JX
Tel: 01865 310000 (Sixth Form)
01865 302620 (Leckford Place School)
Fax: 01865 552296 (Sixth Form)
01865 302622 (Leckford Place School)
e-mail: mail@doverbroecks.com
website: www.doverbroecks.com

***Principal*: Sami Cohen**, BSc (*Chemistry, French*)

Administrative Principal:
Richard Knowles, MA, DPhil (*Economics, Politics*)

Academic Head of Sixth Form:
Alasdair MacPherson, MA (*English**)

Academic Coordinator:
Alastair Barnett, BA, PGCE (*History**)

Head of Leckford Place School:
Mark Olejnik, BA, PGCE (*History*)

Deputy Head of Leckford Place School:
Jane Cockerill, BA, MEd, PGCE (*Music*)

Director of Studies, Leckford Place School:
Paul Wheeler, BSc, PGCE (*Geography*)

Teaching Staff:
* *Head of Subject*

Louise Arnould, BA, BTec (*Art*)
Rosie Astley, Froebel Dip, RSA SpLD (*Learning Support*)
Paul Baily, BA, CertEd (*Physics**)
Robert Beddow, BA, PhD (*History of Art*)
Christophe Brinster, M-ès-L (*French**)
Carol Brown, BSc, MSc (*Psychology*)
Frances Bucknall, BA, MA (*Drama & Theatre Studies*)
Clare Cameron BA, PGCE (*Business Studies*)
Chris Carter, BSc, PGCE (*Physics, Mathematics*)
Michael Carter, BSc, PGCE (*Mathematics, Religious Studies*)
Andrew Colclough, BA, MA (*Politics**)
Jon-Paul Davies, BSc, MA, PGCE (*Geography*)
Stephen Field, MA, PhD (*Chemistry*)
Andrew Gillespie, MA (*Business Studies*, Economics*)
Amy Godel, BA, PGCE (*Mathematics*)
Farhana Haque, BA, PGCE (*Physics*)
Keiko Harada, MA (*Japanese*)
Simon Harrison, BA (*Economics*, Business Studies*)
Richard Heelas, MA, DipAnth, MLitt, DPhil (*Geography*, Psychology*, Sport Studies**)
Christopher Holland, BA, MPhil (*English*)
Graham Hope, MA, DPhil (*Mathematics*)
Clare Horne, BSc, MA, DPhil, PGCE, PgDip (*Mathematics*)
Marc Howe, MA, PGCE, CPE, LPC, PCTHE (*Law*)
Ashley Inglis, MA (*Film Studies*)
Gwenaelle Joffin, BA, PGCE (*French*)
Adam Johnstone, MA, MSt (*Biology*)
Anne-Marie Jones, BSc, PhD (*Biology*)
Victoria Kallebrink, MChem, DPhil (*Chemistry, ICT*)
Susanne Kreitz, PhD (*German**)
Pascale Lafeber, MA (*French*)
Andrew Latcham, BA, DPhil (*History, Politics*)
Cam Lynesmith, BA, PGCE (*Art, Design Technology*)
Melanie Marshall, MA (*Classics*)
Christine Martelloni, MSc (*French*)
Kieran McIntyre, BSc (*Mathematics*)
Andrew McNeill, BSc, PhD (*Mathematics**)
Caroline McNicoll, BA (*History*)
Alan Milosevic, BSc, PGCE (*Mathematics, Computing*)
Carolyn Newton, BA, MPhil (*Communication and Culture*)

Jane Nimmo-Smith, BA (*Classics,* Ancient History**)
James O'Connor, BTEC HND (*Music Technology*)
Max Parsonage, BSc, PGCE (*Chemistry**)
Kate Parsons, BA, PGCE (*Drama**)
Jill Partridge, BSc, PGCE (*Biology*)
Mark Piesing, BA, PGCE (*Communication Studies*)
Selina Ramm, BA, PGCE (*Science*)
Wendy Rawding, BA, PGCE (*Art & Design*)
Nick Reeves, MA Cantab, PGCE (*Art*, History of Art**)
Martine Renauld, M-ès-L, PGCE (*French*)
Angus Roberts, BA, PGCE (*Mathematics, Physics*)
Ruth Robinson, JP, BA, PGCE (*English*)
Ana Rodriguez Nodal, BA (*Spanish*)
Patricia Santhanadass, MSc (*Psychology*)
Sarah Shekleton, BA, MA, PGCE (*Mathematics*, Leckford Place*)
Andrew Sheahan, BA (*Economics*)
Jasjeet Stone, BA, PGCE (*English, German*)
Oliver Stone, BA, PGCE (*Spanish*)
Tuncel Tack, BSc, PhD (*Chemistry*)
Jaimie Tarrell, BEd (*Biology**)
Mark Taylor, BA (*Sociology, Philosophy*)
Natalia Walker, BA (*Russian*)
Melanie Ward, MMus, GradDipTchg (*Music**)
Laurence Waters, City & Guilds (*Photography*)
Clare Wildish, BA (*Accounts, Business Studies*)
Martina Willimann, MA, MPhil (*Italian*)
Martin Winstone, BA, MLitt (*History, Politics*)
Sharon Wyper, BA, PGATC, MA (*Art & Design*)

Sport & Extra-Curricular Activities:
Jo Kalies, BSc
Jonathan Richards, BSc

Accommodation Office:
Felisa Deas, BA
Rebecca Rue, BA

College Counsellor: Catherine Bech, BA
Registrar: Bridget Norton, BA
Principal's PA: Pat Harris

Age Range. 11–19. Day: age 11–16 (Leckford Place School); Residential and Day: age 16–19 (d'Overbroeck's Sixth Form).

Number in School. 275.

Fees per term (2008-2009). Tuition: £3,850 (Leckford Place School); £5,615 (Sixth Form). Accommodation: £1,750–£2,775.

d'Overbroeck's is a co-educational school in Oxford for pupils aged 11–19. We are fairly evenly divided between residential and day students in the Sixth Form; but up to the age of 16 we only take day pupils. Pupils aged 11–16 join Leckford Place School which is part of d'Overbroeck's College, but which is located on a separate site from the Sixth Form.

Since the College was founded in 1977, we have established a reputation for providing an educational experience which is both excellent and, in a number of ways, distinctive.

Our academic approach is characterised by small classes (maximum of 10 students per class in the Sixth Form and 15 up to GCSE) and a strong sense of individual needs and personal attention.

Teaching is highly interactive and seeks to generate enthusiasm for the subject, sound academic skills and effective working habits – while at the same time providing a thorough preparation for public examinations and ensuring that the learning experience is fun.

A wide range of sporting and other extra-curricular activities is available (in the Sixth Form this is optional but strongly encouraged). Students can also benefit from the wide range of educational, cultural and social activities which Oxford has to offer.

Alongside academic achievement, there is a strong emphasis on personal development and on fostering a sense of individual responsibility, especially in the Sixth Form. We expect high standards of commitment and effort from our students and have a track-record of strong GCSE and A Level results, both in absolute terms and on a value-added basis. Students benefit from excellent teaching and a positive, encouraging approach which allow them to maximise their potential. The overwhelming majority of students go on to university and we have an excellent record of success with entry including Oxford and Cambridge, as well as medical, law and art schools.

All of our Sixth Form teaching is separate from the Lower School and we attract students from all over the UK to study with us for A Level. The Sixth Form provides an excellent bridge to university study.

Main Entry Points: age 11 and 13 into Leckford Place School; age 16+ into the d'Overbroeck's Sixth Form. Scholarships are available.

Duke of York's Royal Military School

Guston Dover Kent CT15 5EQ
Tel: 01304 245024
Fax: 01304 245019
e-mail: headmaster@doyrms.com
website: www.doyrms.mod.uk

The Duke of York's Royal Military School was founded in 1803. It is a co-educational boarding school for the children of Servicemen and Servicewomen.

Patron: HRH The Duke of Kent

Her Majesty's Commissioners:

Chairman: Major-General A L Meier, CB, OBE

Revd D E Wilkes, OBE, QHC
Miss C Cawston
Dr I Craig
Dr M A J Guzkowska, TD, AKC, BSc, MSc
Air Vice-Marshal M R Jackson, CB
Major-General R W M McAfee
Mrs R McCarthy
Dr L H Naylor
Brigadier M Nugent
R A Perrin, Esq, MA
Brigadier D Ralls
Dr G B Soar
Rear Admiral J A Trewby, CB, MA, CEng, FIEE
D H Webb, Esq, TD, BSc Eng, CEng, FIMechE, FIMgt
Prof M Wright, LLM, CIPD, FIMgt, FRSA

***Headmaster*: Mr C H Johnson**, MA, PGCE

Senior Deputy Head: Mrs B N Birchley, BSc, PGCE
Deputy Head (*Pastoral*): Mr S Saunderson, BA, PGCE
Assistant Head (*Teaching and Learning*): Mr S Haslehurst, MA Oxon, PGCE
Director of Studies: Mr J English, BSc, PGCE, FRGS
Bursar: Mr R Say, FCMA, ACIS, MIMgt
Assistant Bursar: Miss J Willis
Chaplain: The Revd Fr A D T Richards, FSC, BA, CPTS

Assistant Teachers:
* *Head of Department*
† *Houseparent/master/mistress*

English & Drama:
*Mr S Salisbury, BA, PGCE
Mr H R Brown, MA

Miss K Staff, BA, PGCE (**Drama*)
Mr A Clarke, BA
Ms E Kerry, BA, PGCE
Mrs H Hudgell, CertEd (*SENCO*)
Miss A F Jones, BA, PGCE
Miss E A McGregor, MA, PGCE
Mrs H Wallace, MA Ed, BA, PGCE

Mathematics:
*Mr J Marsh, BEng, PGCE
†Mr S Adams, BSc, PGCE
†Mrs B K Broughton, BEd
†Mr T Chihwayi, BSc, PGCE
Ms L Marley, BA, PGCE
Mr D S Vanderpeer, MSc, QTS

Science:
*Mr A W Bickerstaff, BEd
Mrs B N Birchley, BSc, PGCE
Mrs A A Devonport, BSc, PGCE
Mrs C J Dyer, BSc, PGCE
Mr D C Ferra, BSc, MSc, PGCE
Mr S J Head, MSci, PGCE
Mr A S Kanasewich, BSc
Mr M S Rixon, BSc, MA, PGCE
Mrs S T Taylor, BSc
Mr J D Wallace, BSc, PGCE

Modern Languages:
*Mrs A C Maclennan, LLB, DipPGCE, AInstLing
Mr S G Landmann, BA
Mrs C Maxwell, Tcert
Mr M Ripault, Lic d'Anglais, PGCE
Miss A Sheppard, BEd, Dip Fr

Humanities:
*Mr M B Carson, MA
Mrs M P Eddy, BSc, PGCE (**Geography*)
Mr J English, BSc, PGCE, FRGS
Mr A M Nunn, BEd (**Religious Education*)
Mr T R Porter, BSc, PGCE
Miss B Downes-Powell, BSc
Mr P Bush, BA, PGCE
Miss N L Waring, BA, PGCE

Technology & Art:
Mr D L Parsons, BA, TCert, DipSpPsy, FRSA (**Design & Technology*)
Mr D Froude, BA, PGCE (**Art*)
Miss A Ryder, BA Hons, PGCE
†Miss J J Shanks, MA
Mrs S V Tomenson, BDes, PGCE
Mr M Towers, BEd, LCG

Business Studies, IT and Vocational Education:
Mr D W Alexander, BA, CEdIEng
Mrs S Ganley, BA, PGCE
Mr N Phipps, TCert
Mrs C Purvey, BA, MA, PGCE (**Business Studies*)
†Mr A C Whale, BSc, PGCE (**ICT*)

Physical Education:
*Mrs J M Towers, BEd
Mr D J Bartley, BSc, PGCE
†Mr R D Jones, BEd
Mr G A D Vickery, ASACert

Music:
Mr I P Smith, BMus, LTCL, PGCE, CertRS (*Director of Music*)
Mr P K Kane, ARCM (Late 17/21L)
Mr J Metsapelto, BMus
Mr J W Robinson, BA, PGCE
Mrs L Simes, BA
Mr I Swatman, BA
Mr A Upton (Late RMSM)

Boarding Houses:
Alanbrooke Houseparent: Mrs J M Hyam
Haig Housemaster: Mr S J Adams
Clive Houseparent: Mrs L C Rixon
Kitchener Housemaster: Mr T Chihwayi
Marlborough Housemistress: Mrs B K Broughton
Roberts Housemaster: Mr R D Jones
Wellington Housemaster: Mr A C Whale
Wolfe Housemistress: Miss J J Shanks
Wolseley Housemaster: Mr S Saunderson

Careers: Mrs C Purvey, BA, MA, PGCE
Librarian: Mrs H Hudgell, CertEd, DipEd Lit
Assistant Librarian: Mr G A D Vickery, ASA Cert
School Doctor: Dr M Stevens
Headmaster's Personal Assistant: Miss K Smitton

General. The Duke of York's Royal Military School provides a unique education for the 11 to 18 year old children of those who are serving in the British Armed Forces or who have served for a minimum period of four years on regular engagements.

The school aims to provide a high-quality education and secure boarding environment with particular attention being given to the needs of Service children.

Situation. The school is well resourced and stands in 150 acres of attractive parkland, two kilometres north of Dover. Accommodation and facilities are maintained to a good standard. There are nine single-gender boarding houses serving the needs of some 500 pupils, all of whom are full boarders.

Curriculum. Academic work for 11 to 16 year olds follows the national curriculum. There is a broad based range of subjects leading to 6 to 10 GCSE entries per candidate in Year 11. With small class sizes and teacher pupil ratio of 1 to 10, the academic provision is comprehensive and success rate is consistently much higher than the national average.

In the Sixth Form a wide range of AS and A Levels is offered. The vast majority of Sixth Form leavers enter University. Careers education and guidance is provided as an integral part of the curriculum.

Boarding. The boarding environment gives a strong sense of community and stability for pupils who have had a very disjointed education and home life. Each of the nine boarding houses is generously staffed with teaching and support staff. House Tutors who are also qualified teachers look after between 12 and 15 pupils each.

The School Doctor is supported by resident nursing Sisters who provide 24-hour medical care.

Sport, Music and Drama. The school has excellent sporting facilities and an enviable sporting reputation.

Music and Drama have strong traditions in the school. Junior years receive lessons in Music and Drama. Both subjects are options at GCSE and A Level. There is a large Band, excellent Chapel Choir, Woodwind Band, Big Band and other groups. The school has an impressive theatre.

Other Activities. The range of clubs and activities is extensive. Pupils are given every opportunity to discover and to develop their various interests. There is a comprehensive programme of educational visits, international exchanges and trips and expeditions abroad.

There is a strong CCF and within the CCF there is scope for Adventurous Training and the Duke of Edinburgh's Award Scheme. The school has a unique ceremonial tradition with a large military band which, in addition to the other activities, enables pupils to develop teamwork, initiative and leadership skills.

Entry requirements. Examinations in English, Mathematics and good Headteacher's report.

Serving Parent or one who has served for a minimum of 4 years in the British Armed Forces.

Fees per term (2008-2009). All Boarding: £550 (serving); £2,411 (non-serving).

Ewell Castle School

Church Street Ewell Surrey KT17 2AW
Tel: 020 8394 3561 (admissions)
020 8393 1413 (main office)
Fax: 020 8786 8218
e-mail: admissions@ewellcastle.co.uk
website: www.ewellcastle.co.uk

Ewell Castle, a day school, was built as a castellated mansion in 1814. The gardens and playing fields cover some fifteen acres and were once part of Nonsuch Park. The Senior School is accommodated at The Castle. The Junior School now occupies two other premises in the village – Chessington Lodge, a Georgian house minutes from The Castle and Glyn House, the former Rectory to the parish church, opposite the Senior School. The school, which was founded in 1926, is registered as an educational charity and is administered by a Board of Governors, which is in membership of the Association of Governing Bodies of Independent Schools (AGBIS). The Principal is a member of the Society of Headmasters & Headmistresses of Independent Schools (SHMIS) and the Head of the Junior School is a member of IAPS (The Independent Association of Prep Schools).

Chairman of the Governing Body: D C M Hill

***Principal*: A J Tibble**, BSc, PGCE, NPQH

Head of Senior School: M Holder-Williams, MA, BA, PGCE, NPQH
Head of Junior School: Mrs H M Crossley, MA, BEd, CertEd

Deputy Head of Senior School: S D Bromley, BA, PGCE
Deputy Head of Junior School: Mrs S Radburn, MA, BEd

Assistant Staff:
* *Head of Department*

Miss M Affidi, BA, MA, PGCE, TEFL (*French*)
Miss K Ash, BA, PGCE (*Music, German*)
L Bader-Clynes, BA, RADA (**Drama*)
M C Bates, BD, PGCE (*Design & Technology*)
S J Bell, BEd (**Physical Education*)
J C W Blencowe, BA, PGCE (**History, RS*)
Miss S L Brack, BA, PGCE (**Music*)
S Casey, BA, BTEC (*Physical Education*)
Mrs R Din, BSc, PGCE (*Biology*)
C Donegan, BA, PGCE (*Science*)
J J D'Souza, BSc, PGCE (*Business Studies, Geography, Psychology*)
C Fitzgibbon, BSc, PGCE (**Mathematics, *Psychology*)
J Grindrod, BA, PGCE (*Physical Education*)
S Halpin, BA, PGCE (*Science, Physics*)
Mrs D Hillman, BEd (*Religious Studies*)
Ms V Kennedy, MA, PGCE (*French, German*)
P Krause, BBus, DipEd (**Business Studies, Government & Politics*)
S Leigh, BA, PGCE (*English*)
Mrs J Lovett, BA, CertEd (*French, German*)
Mrs K Mair, MSc, BSc, PGCE (*Mathematics*)
Mrs E McManus, MA, BA, PGCE (*English, Drama*)
Mrs E Morton, BA, PGCE (**Art & Design*)
K B Peto, BA, PGCE (*English, *PSHCE*)
C H Roffey, BSc, PGCE (**Chemistry*)
G Ryan, BSc, PGCE (*Biology*)
N Saadallah, BA, PGCE (**French*)
V S Sandhu, BSc, PGCE (*Geography*)
Mrs E Shepherd, BA (*Art & Design*)
V Singh, BSc, MTech (*Physics*)
Mrs C W Tapp, BA, PGCE (*Special Needs Coordinator*)
D P A Thompson, M des RCA, PGCE (**Design & Technology*)
Mrs R Tucker, BSc, Dip.Ed (*Mathematics*)
D Vijapura, BSc, PGCE (*Mathematics*)
Miss K Wallace, BA, PGCE (**English*)
Miss C Whiteley, MA, BA, PGCE (*Information Technology*)
Ms J Wilson, BSc, CertEd (**Information Technology*)
A Woodward, BA, PGCE (*History*)
Mrs S Young, BA, PGCE (*German*)

Junior School:
Miss M Affidi, MA, BA, PGCE, TEFL
Mrs K Burgess
Mrs S Colchester
Mrs L Fisher, STAC
Mrs S Fowler, BSc, PGCE
Mrs D Goff, CertEd
Miss K Hewitt, BA
Mrs J Higgs, BEd
E B Knowles, BEd
Miss C Leadbeter, MA, PGCE
Mrs C Leeds, NNEB, SEN
Mrs C Nightingale, BSc, PGCE
Miss S Puddicombe, BSc, PGCE
Mrs M Puri, CACHE Dip
Mrs A Royce, BEd
Miss P Spencer, BA, PGCE
Mrs J Targett, CACHE Dip, CertEd
N J Tinkler, BA, PGCE
P E Young, BA, PGCE

Registrar: Mrs D Bellenger
Bursar: G Holland
Assistant Bursar: Mrs M Kaegler
Clerk to Bursar: Mrs T Wilkins
School Secretaries: Mrs S Wood, Mrs J Dow, Mrs B Grierson
Careers Coordinator: Mrs E Thomson
Examinations Secretary: Mrs D Tibble
Network Manager: M J Coleman

The school comprises approximately 550 pupils in total with 360 pupils in the Senior School and 190 pupils in the Junior School.

Buildings. The school is located on three sites within the village of Ewell, accommodating The Junior School (Co-educational 3–11 years) and the Senior School (Boys 11–18 years). Academic departments are well resourced and accommodated. Recent improvements to facilities include: a sports centre, extensions to Science and Design & Technology facilities, the establishment of an ICT suite, a new music school, senior library and the acquisition of Glyn House.

Aims and Values. The aim is to achieve potential and excellence over a broad field: in academic, in sport, and the arts, and in numerous other extra-curricular activities and aspects of school life. The cornerstone of this small school is the strong pastoral care system and Christian values upheld, which enable the school not only to achieve its main purpose but also to maintain high standards of discipline, conduct and appearance.

A highly qualified and committed staff achieve very impressive results at KS2, KS3, GCSE, AS and A Level from pupils with a range of abilities. The School has enjoyed particular success in public examinations in recent years, with record levels being achieved at GCSE and/or A Level for the third successive year and has been recognised by the DCSF as the most improved independent school for GCSE results.

Classes are small, averaging fifteen at the Senior School, where setting is also adopted in core subjects, and seventeen at the Junior School.

Organisation. The Junior School is co-educational and accepts pupils from three years. Most boys transfer to the Senior School at 11+. Girls are prepared for entry to other Independent and selective/non-selective schools at 11+. Many Sixth Form classes are shared with pupils from a local girls' school.

Curriculum. National Curriculum requirements are incorporated into Senior and Junior School schemes, though the broad and flexible curriculum extends beyond such criteria. Breadth at KS3 (11–13 years) is replaced at KS4 (14–16 years) by a core of Mathematics, English, Science and Religious Studies supplemented by a wide ranging option scheme covering the languages, arts, humanities and technologies. There is an increased range of subjects available at AS and A Level in the Sixth Form (17–19 years).

Work experience is undertaken by pupils in Year 11 (16 years). Specialist HE/Careers guidance is available from Year 9 within the Senior School.

After the Sixth Form the majority of pupils proceed to Universities and Colleges.

Extra-Curricular Activities. The principal sports are rugby, soccer and cricket. In addition there are numerous pursuits which include: athletics, badminton, basketball, sailing, scuba diving, skiing, squash, table tennis, tennis and volleyball. There is an extensive music and drama programme and other activities such as the Duke of Edinburgh's Award Scheme. Regular language, sports and field trips embarked for America, Austria, Belgium, France, Germany, Ireland, Italy and Spain in the last two years.

The school benefits from a strong and active PTA.

Admissions. Boys and girls are admitted to the Junior School at the age of three. There are no entry requirements at this stage. Older children are invited to attend the school for a day's assessment, within a class, during which time they may undertake tests in English & Mathematics.

At the Senior School the standard points of entry are at 11+, 13+ and 16+. Subject to availability, there may be places at other levels. Entry requirements include interview, report from previous school and written assessments. At 13+ and 16+ the assessments may take the form of Common Entrance or GCSE respectively.

Visitors are welcome to the school on any of the Open Days or by appointment. Individual assessments are held by arrangement. Scholarship assessments are undertaken in January each year.

Scholarships. Scholarships are available for pupils entering the school at 11+, 13+ and 16+. At 11+ awards are made on the basis of competitive examination/assessment in the designated category. In the case of 13+ and 16+ awards are likely to be made on the basis of Common Entrance and GCSE performance respectively. Awards are made for academic excellence and also in the categories of Art & Design, Music, Sport and 'All-Rounder'.

Fees per term (2008-2009). Senior School £3,550, Junior School £1,100–£2,290.

Junior School. *For further information, see Ewell Castle Junior School entry in IAPS section.*

Charitable status. Ewell Castle School is a Registered Charity, number 312079. The aim of the charity is to achieve potential and excellence over a broad field: in academic, in sport, and the arts, and in numerous other extra-curricular activities and aspects of school life.

Friends' School

Saffron Walden Essex CB11 3EB
Tel: 01799 525351
Fax: 01799 523808
e-mail: admissions@friends.org.uk
website: www.friends.org.uk

Founded in London in 1702 by the Society of Friends (Quakers), the school moved to Saffron Walden in 1879. Today, it is a co-educational boarding and day school taking children from ages 3 to 18 years. There are currently 215 boys and 180 girls of which the majority are day pupils or weekly boarders.

Clerk to the Board of Governors: Tony Watson

***Head*: Graham Wigley**, BA, MA

Bursar: David Wood, ACIB
Senior Teacher: ‡Martin J Hugall, BSc
Assistant Head (*Curriculum*): William Mullen, PhD, BSc
Assistant Head (*Pastoral*): Sarah Westerhuis, BEd
Head of Sixth Form: ‡John Searle-Barnes, BA, MA

Teaching Staff:
‡ *Holder of PGCE*

Art:
‡Serena O'Connor, BA
‡Phillip Richardson, DipAD, ATC
‡Matthew Miller, BA, BTEC

Business Studies:
Carolyn White, MEd, BEd

Careers:
Julie Anderson, BEd

Critical Thinking:
§‡Brigid Vousden, BA

Design Technology – Product Design:
‡Jessica Armitage, BA

Design Technology – Food:
§Catherine Whyte, BEd
§Rosamund Burlinson, BA, CertEd

Drama:
‡Richard Smith, BA
Katie Stephens, BA (*Assistant*)

English:
‡Gillian Kinnear, BA
‡Graham Wigley, BA, MA
§Sue Lock, CertEd
§Joanna Matthews, BEd

ESOL:
‡Sarah Joseph, BA
‡Michelle Gillmore, BA
‡Jane Henfrey, BA

Film Studies:
‡John Searle-Barnes, BA, MA

Geography:
‡Alison Ainsworth, BA
‡Guy Martin, BSc

History:
‡John Searle-Barnes, BA, MA
‡Charlotte O'Neill, BA

ICT:
§Carolyn White, BEd
‡Jessica Armitage, BA

Library:
Judith Brown, MA, BA

Mathematics:
Colin McCrea, BEd, MEd
‡Richard Moss, BTEC
‡Geoffrey Curtis, BSc
‡Heather Douglas, MSc
Carolyn White, MEd, BEd

Modern Languages:
‡Gisèle Searle-Barnes, Licence, MA
‡Peter Fasching, BA
§‡Max Ford, BA

§‡Jane Pearce, BA

Music:
‡Gavin Greenaway, BA
Martin Wilson, BMus, ARCM, ALCM

Visiting Music Staff:
Mary Richardson, BA, PGCE, DipABRSM
Jason Meyrick, FTCL, LRAM, LTCL, Prof Cert
Alison Townend, BA, LLCM, LGSM, LTCL
Nicky Ogden, BA, PGCE, LRAM
Edward Dodge, MA, GRSM, ARMCM, PGCE
Philippa Hopewell, BSc, CT ABRSM
Steven Hynes, BTEC
Louis Thorne, BSc
Mark Townend, GRSM, LRAM, DipRAM
Sarah Clark, BTEC
Angela Lesslie, BMus, PGCE
Amy Klohr, BA, LRAM
Lorraine Patient, ATCL, LTCL

Physical Education:
Nicholas Batcheler, BEd, DipT
Jennifer Allwood, BEd
Raymond Mordini, BPHE

Psychology:
Glyn Huskisson, BA

Religious Studies & PSHE:
§‡Helen Golden, BA

Science:
Christine Sleight, BEd, CPhys, MInstP
‡Martin J Hugall, BSc
‡Leonard Mead, BA, DPhil
§Julie Anderson, BEd
William Mullen, PhD, BSc
Raymond Mordini, BPHE

Speech & Drama:
Susan McConnel, BDS, ALAM, LRAM

Study Centre – Learning Support:
‡Heather Carter, BA, MA
Vivien Spencer, DipSpLD, RGN
Heather Douglas, MSc
‡Brigid Vousden, BA, MPhil

House Staff:
Barbara Askew
Stephen Staerck, CertEd, Adv Dip Counselling & Welfare

Head of Junior School: Andrew Holmes, BEd, CertEd
Deputy Head: Sally Meyrick, BA

Junior Class Teachers:
Susan Westgarth, BEd
‡Kate Richardson, BSc
Jacqueline Branch, CertEd
‡Jane Manley, BA
Deborah Ballingall, BEd
Sue Powell

Infant Department & Early Years:
Sally Manser, CertEd (*Head*)
Robyn Doyle, BA
Claire Milner, BSc

Learning Support:
§Janet Bethune, BSc, CertSpLD

Nursery Coordinator:
Tiffany Johnson, NNEB

Our School is situated in the historic market town of Saffron Walden within easy reach of Cambridge, London, East Anglia and the Midlands and just 20 minutes from London Stansted Airport.

Friends' School is a small family-orientated school providing high standards of teaching and a flexible academic structure that enables children to reach their full potential. We believe that children need a broad educational foundation to prepare them for the future and, in addition to promoting academic success; we provide many opportunities for your children to develop creative, sporting and social skills. In line with our Quaker ethos of tolerance and mutual respect, there is dedicated Pastoral care to support the welfare of each individual.

The School has an excellent record of achievement at GCSE with a wide choice of subject options available; the latest DCSF league tables showed that 85% of Friends' School pupils achieved five or more A* to C grades, including Mathematics and English.

We have a strong Sixth Form with the majority of students continuing their education to degree level; most subjects are offered at AS and A Level with the addition of Business Studies, History of Art and Film Studies.

The School's 35-acre site has extensive playing fields and pupils enjoy hockey, football, rugby, tennis, cricket and athletics, as well as badminton and basketball in the sports hall and swimming year round in a heated indoor pool.

There is an extensive programme of extra-curricular and weekend activities for boarders and day pupils. Art, drama, music, cookery, computing, Duke of Edinburgh's Award Scheme are all popular. Pupils regularly stage drama and music productions and exhibitions at the School.

Admission. (*see Scholarship Entries section*). Open to Quaker and non-Quaker, determined by interview, an entrance test and school report.

The school is able to offer a number of Scholarships, at 11+, 13+ and Sixth Form, based on academic merit. Scholarships are also available to those who demonstrate excellence in Music, Drama, Art or Sport.

The Joint Bursary Scheme provides financial assistance, where needed, to help the children of Friends to attend the school. We also offer bursaries for boarding places to current serving members of HM Armed Forces.

Fees per term (from January 2008). Senior School: Full Boarding £5,210–£6,640, Weekly Boarding £4,995–£6,085, Day Pupils £4,265. Junior School: £2,595–£2,645. Infants: £1,925–£2,275.

Charitable status. Friends' School Saffron Walden is a Registered Charity, number 1000981.

Fulneck School

Pudsey Leeds West Yorkshire LS28 8DS
Tel: 0113 257 0235
Fax: 0113 255 7316
e-mail: general@fulneckschool.co.uk
website: www.fulneckschool.co.uk

Established on 1 September 1994 by the amalgamation of Fulneck Boys' School and Fulneck Girls' School, both originally founded in 1753, by the Moravian Church (a very early Protestant Church which has two schools in England and many more abroad) as part of a settlement on the slopes of a valley on the outskirts of Pudsey. Leeds and Bradford are both nearby; yet the valley is green and most attractive, with terraced gardens falling away from the School.

The Provincial Board of the Moravian Church is the Trustee of the School; the Governing Body of local people provides a range of professional expertise. The school is a member of SHMIS and AGBIS.

The Governing Body:
Chairman of the Governors: L Everett

Miss J Birch

Mrs A Bird
P Dean
Revd D Dickinson
Mrs V Hayton
E Marshall
C Robinson
T R Smith
C J Stern
D Stubbs

***Principal*: T Kernohan**, BA Hons, MEd Leeds, PGCE

Vice-Principal: Mrs G B Swallow, BA, CertEd Sheffield

Head of Junior School: Mr A P Boyer, BEd Hons

Staff:
D G Alcock, MA, BA Leeds, PGCE
Mrs E Aldridge, CertEd Hull
D I Andrew, MSc, BA Hons Stirling, PGCE
Miss H L Atkins, BSc Hons Sunderland, MSc Sheffield Hallam, PGCE
N A Barlow, BSc Hons Warwick, PGCE
Mrs P M Blackwell-Hamilton, BMus Hons Sheffield, MPhil, MEd, AdvDipEd Leeds, PGCE
Mrs J E Bleazard, BA Hons Lancaster, PGCE
Miss M H Brook, CertEd Chester
Miss E M Cabry, BA Hons Leeds, QTS
A D Chilvers, BA Hons London, PGCE
Miss S M Cunnie, BA Hons Leeds, QTS
N A Dixon, BSc Newcastle, PGCE
Mrs R Dooley, CertEd Bradford
Mrs K A Dunn, BA Liverpool, DipHE, AMBDA
Mrs J Freeman, L-ès-L Sorbonne, Paris
Mrs G Gautry, BEd Hons Bangor, CertEd
Mrs P Hardaker, CertEd Worcester College of Education
Mrs S Hardaker, CertEd Matlock College of Education
I C Harrison, BSc Hull, PGCE
C A Hewitt, BEd Leeds
Mrs S Hodgson, NNEB
Mrs L Holden, Teaching Degree University of Tomsk
S M Jacobs, BSc Hons Manchester, PGCE
Miss A Little, BA Hons Liverpool Poly, PGCE
T Luckman, DipAD Newcastle Poly, ATC Leeds Poly, ACP Wolverhampton Poly
Mrs M R Mulligan, BA Hons Canterbury, PGCE
D Needham, BSc Hons Loughborough, QTS
Miss A P Pateman, MA, BA Edinburgh, PGCE
Mrs D Y Postle, CertEd Leicester
Mrs C A Prytherch-Williams, BA Hons Canterbury, MA Leeds, PGCE, DipSpLD
J Rhodes, BA Open, CertEd
A N Robson, BA Hons Salford, PGCE
D P Roots, BA Hons Central Lancashire, PGCE
D Rose, MA, BA Hons Kent, PGCE
P A Rushfirth, BA Hons QTS Leeds
Miss R Smith, BA Hons Sunderland, QTS
P P Stapleton, BA Hons Durham, MA De Montfort, PGCE
I Stewart, BEd St John's College, York
Mrs C Strickland, BA Hons East Anglia, PGCE, Cert SEN
Miss S J Tooley, BSc Luton, PGCE
N R Townson, CertEd St John's College, York
Miss J A Trees, MA Leeds, BA Hons Leicester, PGCE
Mrs L Ward, BSc Hons Leeds, PGCE, CertEd
K Watts, BA Hons Leeds, PGCE
S A Wilde, BSc Hons Bristol, PGCE

Visiting Staff:
Mrs L Bentley, LTCL, DipMus, CertEd
Mrs J Clayton, GRSM, ARCM, ATCL, CertEd Leeds
Mrs E Green, ARMCM, ARNCM
Mrs V Jenkins, CertEd, ADB, LLAM, BPhil, MEd
J E Khan, Grad Dip Hons Leeds
S Norton, IDTA
Mrs A Palenski, LGSMD, MA
A Pryde, BA Hons Leeds
D Southcott

Principal's Secretary: Mrs J Rhodes
Catering Officer: Mrs S Barnes
Commercial Manager: I Martin

Originally founded for the education of the sons and daughters of ministers and missionaries, the school nowadays provides an education for about 400 pupils. Most of the pupils live in West Yorkshire and travel daily to School, but approximately 45 of them are boarders including some who board weekly and return home from Friday evening to Monday morning.

The School is co-educational and provides a modern, academic curriculum based on Christian principles. 20 A Level subjects are offered in the Sixth Form and the school has a fine record of success in public examinations. Class sizes rarely exceed 20, and most teaching groups are, in fact, smaller; in the Sixth Form groups seldom exceed 10.

Buildings. The main buildings of the School are part of the original settlement, yet other buildings on the campus have been added over the years. In September 2005 a new Junior Library with ICT facilities was opened and a new self-contained Sixth Form Centre established. The boys' boarding accommodation was extended and a new suite of Mathematics classrooms was created. In September 2003 a fourth Information Technology Centre opened adjacent to the brand new Senior Library offering additional computing facilities to enhance pupils' studies. Extensive playing fields and tennis courts are located on the site, which adjoins Fulneck Golf Club, and looks over to the Domesday village of Tong.

Pastoral Care. The staff work closely and effectively together, sharing in the duties and recreational needs of the School; their average length of service is over twelve years giving a very valuable degree of continuity and stability to the teaching. The School Nurses, who are both medically qualified, and other house staff take care of the boarders in conjunction with the resident teaching staff and the Principal, who also lives on the campus. Weekly and flexi-boarding are offered in addition to full boarding.

Sport. Netball, Hockey, Football, Cricket and Tennis are the main games of the School, but Athletics, Rugby, Basketball, Badminton, Cross-Country running, Golf, Rounders, Swimming and Table Tennis are all available to the pupils as part of a rapidly expanding programme of outdoor pursuits. Teams of various ages, in most sports, have full fixture lists with neighbouring schools. Dance classes are also run.

Activities. Music is very strong with 2 choirs, 2 bands, a jazz group, a flute group, and other orchestral groups. The Senior Choir performs in public. Drama is actively pursued with pupils involved in both lessons and Theatre Workshop productions.

There are a number of clubs and societies such as Art, Computer, Golf, Orienteering, Hockey, Netball, Table Tennis, Theatre Workshop, Chess, Debating and Sudoku.

The Duke of Edinburgh's Award Scheme is available to pupils over the age of 14, together with a wide range of trips and residentials, walking and skiing. A number of residentials and expeditions are organized in conjunction with the World Challenge organization.

Careers. The Careers teacher is on hand to advise, and most of the available literature on the whole range of courses and careers is stocked. All pupils complete a period of work experience.

Foundation Stage/Key Stage 1. This is housed within the main building and caters for children from the ages of 3 to 7.

Junior School (Key Stage 2). The Junior School is self-contained and caters for pupils from the ages of 7–11. Once a pupil is admitted he or she will usually progress into the Senior School, after examination at age 11. The Junior School has access to many of its own specialist facilities for Science, Art, Technology, Music, IT and Library.

Learning Support Unit. Specialist staff provide help on an individual or small group basis to children with dyslexia or other special needs. The Unit is CReSTeD approved.

Parents and Friends Association. There is a flourishing organization which acts as a fund-raising body, but supports the School in a variety of other ways and is a living example of the belief that education is a partnership between home and school.

Admission. (*see Scholarship Entries section*). Admission to the school is possible at any age depending on the availability of places, although the main intake is at the ages of 3, 7 and 11. Direct entry to the Sixth Form is also possible. Scholarships are available.

Fees per term (2008-2009). The fees are based on a scale relating to age and status (day, weekly boarding, full boarding or temporary boarding). Nursery (morning only) £1,090; Foundation Stage(all day) £1,780; Years 1 and 2 £1,930; Junior Day £2,400; Senior Day £3,165; Weekly Boarding £4,400–£5,270; Full Boarding £4,760–£5,790.

Fulneck Former Pupils' Association. *Secretary*: Mrs E Carruthers, Fulneck School, Pudsey, West Yorkshire LS28 8DS.

Charitable status. Fulneck School is a Registered Charity, number 251211. It exists to provide a traditional, Christian education for boys and girls between the ages of 3 and 18.

Grenville College
A Woodard School

Belvoir Road Bideford North Devon EX39 3JP
Tel: 01237 472212
Fax: 01237 477020
e-mail: registrar@grenvillecollege.co.uk
website: www.grenvillecollege.co.uk

The School was founded in 1954 by Walter Scott, who was also the first Headmaster. In 1964 the School became a member of the Woodard Corporation.

Motto: *Memento Creatoris Tui.*

School Council:
Mr M B Portman (*Chairman*)
The Rt Revd J D G Kirkham (*Provost*)
Mrs P H Adie, MBE
Mrs N G P Ansell
Mr P A Brend
Mr T G T Gale
Mr M S Hedges, MA, FCA, FRSA
Mr S D Hill, FREC
Capt N C H James, RN, JP
Mr J G Tomalin
The Hon J Rous

***Headmaster*: Mr Andy Waters**, BEd, MA

Deputy Headmaster: Mr S C Woolcott, BSc, ARCS

Senior Teacher: Mrs S E Davies, BSc

Assistant Staff:
Mr A V Argyle, MA
†*Mr C R Beechey, BA, MA
Mrs M Borsten, BA
Miss S Brown, BA
*Mr C J Charlton, BA
†Mr P R Claridge, BEd
Mr S J Cullingham, BEd
Mrs S E Davies, BSc
*Mr B Deegan, BA
*Mrs J Dodwell, BA
*Mr B D Edge, BA
Mrs F J Edmonds, BA
Dr S J Gurr, CSci, CChem, MRSC
Father Steve Hunt, CA
*Mr R H Ker, BSc
Mrs K M Klymow, BA, MA
*Mr A Lane, BEd, AMBDA, DipSpLD
Mrs J A Lewis, BA Hons, PGCE
Dr M Lynn, DipEd, PhD
Mrs K Makepeace, BA
Mr D Mason, BSc
Mr S Mathers, BSc
Mrs B Mingay, BA Hons, AdvDipSEN
*†Ms J A Monk, BSc
Mr M Norris, BSc
Miss M O'Shaughnessy, BA
Ms D Percy, BA Hons, MEd TEFL
Mrs S Roberts-Key, BEd
Mrs H Roome, BEd
Mrs L Stella, BA
*Mrs R Street, BA
Mr A Sturrock, BA Ed
*Mr K L Thompson, BA
Mr A Waters, BEd, MA
*Mr A D White, BPhil Ed (*Director of Music*)
Mr S C Woolcott, BSc, ARCS

Department of Music:
*Mr A D White, BPhil Ed
Mr D Bailey (*Drums*)
Mrs P Beechey (*Clarinet, Flute, Piano, Recorder and Saxophone*)
Mrs T Bennett (*Violin*)
Mrs D Body (*Voice, Piano, Brass*)
Mr A Duncan (*Rock, Bass and Folk Guitar*)
Mr R Norris (*Piano*)
Mrs A Prior (*Piano*)
Ms A Stolliday (*Cello*)
Mr M White, BA (*Technology/Music Technician*)

Visiting Coaches:
Mr J Davies (*Judo*)
Mr C Hold (*Tennis*)

Junior School
Head Teacher: Mrs E A Preece, DipEd

Assistant Staff:
Mrs M Maynard
Mrs J E Minhinnett, MEd SN
Mr C Isherwood, BEd
Ms J A Stonestreet, BA
Mrs G Violet
Mrs F Woolcott, BEd

Classroom Assistants:
Mrs S Stanford
Mr P Wilson
Mrs M Lock

Bursar: Mrs M Sena
Registrar: Mrs C G Bailey
Librarian: Mr A N Longman, CertEd

School Doctors:
Dr R G Ford, MB, BS, MRCS, LRCP
Dr K S Pritchard, MB, BS, DGM, MRCGP
School Nursing Sister: Mrs S Pittson, BSc, RGN, RSCN

Location. Grenville College is situated in the town of Bideford, an historic port beside the estuary of the River Torridge. The spectacular scenery of the North Devon coast is within walking distance and there is easy access to the National Parks of Exmoor and Dartmoor. The North Devon link road, which passes close to Bideford, provides a direct route to the M5 motorway.

Organisation. Grenville College is entirely co-educational and comprises the Senior School with approximately 325 pupils, aged 11 to 18 years, and the Junior School with approximately 85 pupils aged 2½ to 11 years.

Site and Buildings. Part of the College occupies an estate of about 55 acres on which stands Moreton House. Two Boarding Houses for boys and one for girls are situated within these beautiful grounds with immediate access to extensive playing fields, an all-weather hockey pitch, netball and tennis courts. Within these grounds are the Art and Design & Technology Departments with facilities for graphic design, fine art, metalwork, woodwork, ceramics and an indoor rifle range used by the small-bore rifle club.

Also on this site is the Junior School. (*For details please refer to the entry for Grenville College Junior School in the ISA section.*)

The Senior School site, at nearby Belvoir Road, houses the administrative centre, the newly-opened, state-of-the-art Sixth Form Centre and most of the other Senior School teaching areas. In recent years an ambitious programme of building has led to the provision of first-class facilities for science, ICT, drama, worship and dining. The new Library provides an excellent environment for study, research and career guidance. In addition, there is a gymnasium and tennis court.

Curriculum. For the first five years in the Senior School pupils study a core of subjects, including English, Mathematics, Biology, Chemistry, Physics, Modern Languages and Religious Studies. Subjects such as Geography, History, Art, Information & Communication Technology, Food & Nutrition, Textiles, Design & Technology, Drama, Music, and Moral & Health Education complete the programme of study for years one to three.

For GCSE, in addition to the core subjects, other courses available are Design & Technology, Food & Nutrition, Information & Communication Technology, Physical Education, Art, Business Studies, Statistics, Drama, Geography, History and Music.

In the Sixth Form there is a wide choice of AS and A Level subjects including English, Mathematics, Biology, Chemistry, Physics, Geography, History, Art, Design & Technology, French, German, Psychology, General Studies, Home Economics, Physical Education, Information & Communication Technology, Further Mathematics, Performance Arts and Music Technology.

In addition to these AS and A Level choices, GNVQ Business courses at Advanced Level (Vocational A Level) has proved both popular and successful.

The College has a long established and nationally recognised Department for helping pupils with dyslexia. Tuition in English for speakers of other languages is also available for overseas pupils.

Sport and Physical Education. Pupils are encouraged to participate fully both in individual and team games. All pupils, girls and boys, have an opportunity to participate in a large variety of sports including: rugby, hockey, netball, cross-country, athletics, cricket, dance, gymnastics, badminton, squash, volleyball, basketball, football, rounders, tennis, judo, swimming and health-related fitness. Rowing is fast becoming a very popular choice with both boys and girls.

Clubs and Activities. There is a range of extra-curricular activities each day which are organised and supervised by staff. Among these clubs are The Duke of Edinburgh's Award Scheme, electronics, computing, debating, art, music and shooting. In addition, a range of water sports is available including rowing, sailing, canoeing, windsurfing, surfing and swimming. Skiing parties are organised each year together with other expeditions and field trips in the UK and abroad.

Musicals, plays and concerts are regularly produced involving pupils of all ages.

Careers. From the Third Year onwards, pupils are offered a planned programme of careers education and guidance as part of the tutorial programme. This is complemented by presentations from visiting professionals, visits to careers events and close contact with Careers advisers from Connexions Cornwall and Devon. All pupils have access to the latest careers information in the School Library.

Religion and Pastoral Care. In common with every Woodard School, Grenville College has a Christian tradition. The School Chaplain conducts a Sung Eucharist on Sunday and at other times mid-week and pupils participate in weekday Assemblies.

In addition to their Year Heads, each pupil has a personal Tutor who is responsible for monitoring his or her academic progress and personal well-being. For boarding pupils, care is also the responsibility of the Housemaster or Housemistress.

Admission. Boys and girls are admitted to the Junior School from the age of $2^1/_2$ years. There are no formal tests.

Entry to the Senior School for pupils aged 11 and 12 years is by interview and written tests in Mathematics, English and Science, as well as a verbal reasoning test. These requirements do not apply to pupils with recognised learning difficulties. In such cases, entry is by interview together with an up-to-date educational psychologist's report.

For pupils aged 13 years admission is through the Common Entrance Examination or Scholarship Examination and interview.

For older pupils an interview together with a report from their present school is required.

Prospectus. A Grenville College prospectus and registration form are available from the Registrar, Mrs C G Bailey.

Visitors are most welcome to tour the School by appointment.

Scholarships. (*see Scholarship Entries section*).

Fees per term (2008-2009). Senior School: £6,885 (full boarders), £5,550 (weekly boarders), £3,380–£3,525 (day pupils including lunch).

Charitable status. Grenville College is a Registered Charity, number 1103317. It exists to provide high quality education for boys and girls.

Halliford School

Russell Road Shepperton Middlesex TW17 9HX
Tel: 01932 223593
Fax: 01932 229781
e-mail: registrar@hallifordschool.com
website: www.hallifordschool.co.uk

Halliford School was founded in 1921, moved to its present site in 1929 and was registered as a charity in 1966.

Brothers of existing pupils are usually accepted as long as they can benefit from a sound academic education. This policy creates a strong feeling of a family community and helps reinforce the close partnership that exists with parents.

Girls are admitted into the Sixth Form at Halliford.

The Governors are in membership of the Association of Governing Bodies of Independent Schools.

Governors:
J White Jones (*Chairman*)
C S Squire, FIHort (*Deputy Chairman*)
Mrs N F Cook, BA
M A Crosby, BSc, DipArch RIBA
R Davison, MA
W J Hargan, BSc
B T Harris, FIPD
Mrs T Harrison, BA
Mrs P A Horner, BA, LLB
A Lenoel
R J Parsons
Professor J P Phillips, BA, PhD, FRHS
P Roberts, BSc
Major General A P V Rogers, OBE, LLM, FRSA
Dr M Sachania
K Woodward, QPM

***Headmaster*: Philip V Cottam**, MA Oxon, FRGS

Deputy Head: Mr R C Talbot, BHum West London Inst, PGCE

Teaching Staff:
R Amod, BA
I P Bardgett, BA, PGCE
P N Booth, BSc, MSc, PGCE

S Bromley, BA, PGCE
B Brown, BA, PGCE
J E Carrington, BEng
G Cirillo, BA, PGCE
L Cupido, BEd
Mrs S Crosby, BSc, PGCE
N De Cata, CertEd
P Diamond, BEng, PGCE
R Dickinson, BSc, MSc
Mrs D Duffy, BSc, MBA, PGCE
Miss N Evans, BA, PGCE
Mrs P Fahey, NDD
Mrs K Gilbert, BEd
N Graham, BA, PGCE
S Graves, BA, MA
M Gray, BA, PGCE
Mrs R Greaves, BMus, PGCE
M Harris, BA, PGCE
Mrs P Heather, BSc, MSc, PGCE
D Henderson, BA, PGCE
D Howard, BSc, PGCE
A C Naish, BSc, PGCE
A Nelson, BSc, CertEd, CM, DMS, MBA
Miss V Redrup, BSc
S Slocock, BEd
B M Sunderji, MSc, DipEd, AFIMA, CMath, MIMA
P A Sweeting, BSc
Miss C Wilcockson, BA, PGCE

Part-time Staff:
Mrs K Beckerleg, BSc, PGCE
Mrs S Jurdic, BA, PGCE
Mrs S Regan, CertEd
Mrs A Wain, BA, PGCE
M Woolard, RSA Cert EFL

Visiting Staff:
A Hooley (*Clarinet, Saxophone, Flute*)
Ms S Jones (*Singing*)
K Miles (*Percussion*)
P Savides (*Guitar*)
S Tanner (*Piano*)

Administrative Staff:
Bursar & Company Secretary: Mr P Godfrey, MA, BSc, CEng, CPhys, MIEE, MInstP
Registrar: Mrs D Towse
Headmaster's Secretary: Mrs J A Davies
Leavers Secretary: Mrs J Pollock
Librarian: Mrs S Lewin, BA
Marketing & Publicity: Mrs A Cottam, BA
Matrons: Mrs M Hammond, Mrs C Brooks
Lab Technicians: Dr V Harrison, Mrs S Luterbacker
IT Technicians: Mrs S Bryant, J Bore
DT Technicians: R Seabrook, R Wiedemann

Visiting Chaplain: The Revd Christopher Swift, MA, Rector of Shepperton

Facilities. Halliford School is situated on the Halliford bend of the River Thames. The old house, a graceful eighteenth century building, which stands in six acres of grounds, is the administrative centre of the school. Some 500 yards from the school gate there are six additional acres of sports fields. Over the years there has been a steady development programme which has resulted in the addition of a Creative and Expressive Arts Block, a new classroom block housing four laboratories and a modern ICT department as well as bright and airy classrooms. In September 2001 the school opened an exciting new 320-seat theatre. Incorporated into this development is a kitchen, dining room and music practice facilities. In the Spring of 2003 three new classrooms and a new Science laboratory were added to the new teaching block. In September 2005 a new Sports Hall with new changing facilities, Library, Sixth Form Centre and additional classrooms were opened.

Admission. There are 400 pupils on roll with a three-form entry at 11+ through Halliford's own entrance examination. There is a further entry at 13+ through Common Entrance and admission is possible at other times dependent on the availability of places. Entrance is by examination and interview.

Curriculum. During Years 7, 8 and 9 all boys study a broadly based curriculum which includes Drama, Religious Studies, PE and Careers.

In Year 8 Maths and Languages are set in four groups to provide even smaller group teaching. In Year 9 all subjects are divided into four groups whether set or not. At least nine subjects are taken at GCSE with the top Maths set taking GCSE a year early and then starting on AS Maths in Year 11. The most academic also start a Critical Thinking AS course in parallel with their GCSE course.

In the Sixth Form some 24 subjects are available at A/AS Level and all teaching is co-educational.

Games. Rugby, Football, Cricket, Athletics, Rowing, Basketball, Badminton, Tennis, Volleyball, Swimming and Golf are available. There is also a Climbing Club which makes use of the climbing wall in the new Sports Hall.

Pastoral Organisation. There are three Houses and pupils are tutored in House groups. Parents receive six communications each year on their son's progress and there is a Prep Diary which parents are requested to sign each week. Tutors are always willing to see parents and the Headmaster can usually be seen at very short notice.

Out of School Activities. These include a very successful Drama Department which mounts some eight productions a year including a major whole school production at the end of the Spring Term. There are also lively Music and Art Departments.

There is a long list of clubs including Chess, Design, IT, Film, Creative Writing, Modern Languages, Science and Art. In addition there are Senior and Junior Debating and Academic Societies, a Philosophy Club and Interhouse Public Speaking and Unison Singing Competitions. The Duke of Edinburgh's Award is available as an additional activity.

School Council. Each Tutor group elects a representative to the School Council (19 members). This is not a cosmetic exercise and in recent times the School Council has effected real changes. Halliford believes that pupils do have good ideas which can be utilised for the well-being of the School as a whole.

Prospective Parents. In the Summer Term each year the School holds Open Days in March and May when the School is in session. In the Autumn Term the School holds an Open Day on a Saturday morning at the beginning of October and two days in November. Prospective parents are welcome at other times by appointment.

Fees per term (2008-2009). £3,400.

Scholarships and Bursaries. (*see Scholarship Entries section*).

Old Hallifordians. *Chairman*: Alex Lenoel, 5 Kingsworthy Close, Kingston, Surrey KT1 3ER.

Charitable status. Halliford School is a Registered Charity, number 312090. It exists to provide high-quality education.

Hampshire Collegiate School (UCST)

Embley Park Romsey Hampshire SO51 6ZE
Tel: 01794 512206 (Senior School)
01794 515737 (Junior School)
Fax: 01794 518737
e-mail: info@hampshirecs.org.uk
website: www.hampshirecs.org.uk

HCS is a completely new School, aiming to be a regional leader and formed of Embley Park & The Atherley. However, there has been a School at Embley Park since 1946. Its main building was the home of the Nightingale family, and Florence Nightingale lived at Embley until she went to the Crimea in 1854. The School estate is of the order of 120 acres, and more than £20 million pounds has been spent on new buildings in recent years, particularly in creating a 3–18 school on site.

The School is fully co-educational from 3 to 18. The Junior and Nursery School has its own new, purpose-built building on site.

The Governors are members of AGBIS and UCST is a registered charity, administered by a Council chaired by the former Archbishop, Lord Carey of Clifton, and headed by a Chief Executive, Sir Ewan Harper.

D A d'Arcy Hughes, Esq (*Chairman*)
Professor M J Clark, BA, PhD (*Vice-Chairman*)
P Brookes
R Butler
Professor G Griffiths, BA, MSc, CEng, MIEE, FRGS, FSUT
Dr J Lyon-Maris, BSc, MB, BS, MRCP, MRCGP
Mrs D Moody, AILAM
Mrs V Perry, QT
Revd P Salisbury, BSc, BTh
Professor R Thomas

***Principal*: Hector MacDonald**, BSc, MA, CChem, CSci, FRMS, FRSC

Vice-Principal: Mrs T M Rogers, MA Ed, CertEd
Head of Senior School: Mrs H Crawford, BSc
Head of Junior School: Mrs E Hooton, BA

Senior School

Director of Studies: Mrs W E Martin, BSc
Head of Sixth Form: Mr M Laverty, BA
Head of Boarding: Mr C Lowde, BSc

Pastoral Leader Year 7 and 8: Mrs M Bateman, BA
Pastoral Leader, Years 9 to 11: Mr C D Cates, BSc

Heads of Years:
Mrs E Driver, BA
Mrs J Leighton, MA
Mr R Smith, BSc
Mr R Hay, BA
Mrs A James, CertEd

Director of Sports and Activities: Mr R Martin, BSc
Head of Music: Mr G Tinsley, BMus
Head of Drama: (*to be appointed*)
Head of Mathematics: Mr A D Pearce, BSc
Head of English: Mr S Bowyer, MA
Head of Science: Mrs L Miller, BSc
Head of E-Learning: Mr P H Badham, MA (*Deputy Head of Boarding*)
Head of Geography: Ms N Healy, BA
Head of History, Government and Politics: Dr R Foster, BA PhD
Head of Art: Mrs J Pascoe, BA
Head of Design & Technology: Mr D M Adams, MET
Head of Learning Support: Mrs K Griffiths, MA
Head of Learning Development: Mrs B Jobson, CertEd

Assistant Teaching Staff:
Mrs D Birch, BA (*PSHE, Art*)
Mrs F Boorer, BSc (*Subject Leader of Chemistry, Science*)
Miss E Boutcher-West, BA (*PE*)
Miss J Bright (*Aerobics Instructor*)
Mr A J Brooks, BA (*Art, Head of Nightingale House*)
Mrs N Brown, BA (*Mathematics*)
Mrs C Cannadine, BEd (*Business Studies, ICT*)
Mrs M Chiverton, BA (*Subject Leader of French*)
Mrs B Clark, BA (*Geography*)
Mrs S Cornforth, BSc (*Mathematics*)
Miss G Cornick (*Girls' Sport Coach*)
Mrs H Cunliffe, CertLibPrac (*Librarian*)
Mrs J Ellis, BSc (*Science*)
Mrs E Glanville, BA (*PE and Games*)
Mrs S N Goodacre, BA (*French, German,*)
Mr S Gordon, BA (*Mathematics*)
Miss J Haim, BA (*English*)
Mrs S Hanson, BA (*Spanish*)
Mr R Hay, BA (*History*)
Mrs S Haywood Smith, BSc (*ICT*)
Mr J Hillier, BA (*English*)
Miss J Hoyle, BA (*Spanish*)
Mr J Irving, BSc (*Chemistry*)
Mrs M Jeffrey, BA (*Subject Leader of German, French, Spanish*)
Mrs T Johnson, BA (*Subject Leader Latin*)
Mr N Joisce, BA (*PE, Director of Rugby*)
Mr S Kent-Davies (*Music*)
Mrs D Lowde, BA (*Head of Girls' Boarding*)
Mrs H Lucas, BA (*Drama, English, Director in Residence*)
Miss D C Lulham, BA (*Head of Girls' Games*)
Mrs M Matlock, BA (*English*)
Mr A May, BSc (*IT*)
Mr J Oldham, BA (*English*)
Mrs J Penfold, BA (*French, German*)
Dr M Price, PhD (*Chemistry/Physics*)
Mr A P Scott, LLB (*Subject Leader of Law, Senior Head of House, Head of Austen House*)
Mrs W Rowntree, BSc (*Biology*)
Dr N Thomas, PhD (*Biology*)
Mr J Thomson, BA (*Mathematics, Deputy Head of Sixth Form*)
Mr S Trodd, BA (*Subject Leader of Psychology, Physics*)
Mr J Winship, BEd (*Design & Technology, Head of Chichester House*)
Mrs A Wolfe, MA (*English, RE*)

Junior School

Head of Junior School: Mrs E Hooton, BA

Deputy Head, Academic & Pastoral: Mr G King, BA

Head of Key Stage One: Ms F Adams, BA Ed
Head of Drama: Miss S Ashton, BEd
Head of Early Years: Mrs M Bower, BSc
Head of History: Mr A Cumming, BA
Head of English: Mrs C Fletcher, BA
Head of Music: Mrs K Francis, BEd
Head of Science: Mr T Marshall, BEd
Head of PE/Games: Mrs E Short, BA
Head of Art: Mrs K Stern, BA
Head of Mathematics: Mr R Tarlton, MA, BEd
Head of Modern Foreign Languages: Mrs V Worden, MA (*French*)
Head of ICT: Mr P Shuttleworth

Assistant Staff:
Mrs S Bartel, BEd (*Early Years Class Teacher*)
Mrs J Bell, BEd (*Academic Tutor*)
Mr T Brittan, BSc (*KS2 Class Teacher*)
Miss L Burlinson (*Classroom Assistant*)
Mrs L Chandler, BAGA Cert (*Classroom Assistant*)
Mrs P Chrismas, NNEB (*Early Years Assistant*)
Mrs T Collins, NVQ Level 2 (*Classroom Assistant*)
Mrs Y Cooke, BScc (*KS2 Class Teacher, Pastoral Tutor*)
Mrs M Corlass, CertEd (*Classroom Assistant*)
Mrs A Eaton, BSc (*Learning Support Teacher*)
Miss E Ellesley, BSc (*KS1 Class Teacher*)
Mrs C Green, BEd (*Early Years Team and Nursery Manager*)
Miss S Hardy, NNEB (*Early Years Teacher*)
Mrs A Jones, BSc (*Early Years Teacher*)
Miss H Martin (*Early Years Assistant*)
Mr P Meaden, BA (*Educational Visits Coordinator*)
Mrs T Moonsinghe, BA (*KS1 Class Teacher*)
Miss F Murray, NVQ Level 2 (*Teaching Assistant*)
Mrs Melissa Oxborrow (*Acting Head of Art – maternity cover*)
Mrs K Tibble, NNEB (*Early Years Nursery Nurse*)
Mrs S Sturgess (*Teaching Assistant and Learning Support*)
Mrs V Tozer, CertEd (*KS1 Class Teacher/Library*)
Mrs J Varndell, VA (*Teacher of MFL and Spanish Coordinator*)
Mrs F Walker, BEd (*KS2 Class Teacher*)

Mrs S Williams, MA Ed (*KS2 Class Teacher*)
Mrs F Winfield, CertEd (*Learning Support Teacher*)

Visiting Teachers:
Mrs M Bell (*Speech & Drama*)
Mr R Armstrong (*Percussion*)
Mr M Callow, Dip ABRSM (*Clarinet and Saxophone*)
Mr C Davey, BMus, CertEd (*Piano and Electric Keyboard*)
Mr K Dredge (*Drum Kit*)
Mrs P Glynn, DDME CertEd (*Classical Guitar*)
Mrs G Kuznicki, ALCM, LLCM (*Singing*)
Miss T Lucy (*Singing & Recorder*)
Miss N Land, ALCM (*Violin & Viola*)
Mrs S Newman, GTCL, LTCL, CertEd (*Piano and Cello*)
Miss C Williams, BA Hons, CertEd (*Piano & Keybaord*)
Mrs D Williams, BEd (*Music secondary*), ATCL, BA Hons, RSA DipSpLD (*Piano and Singing*)
Mr C Wickland, DipMus (*Electric Guitar*)
Mr P Wray (*Kit Percussion*)

Principal's PA: Mrs S MacLennan
Registrar: Mrs J Baird
Junior School Head's PA: Mrs J Piper
Deputy Bursar: Mrs L Rademaker, BCompt UNISA
Transport Manager & Finance: Mr B Dixon
Senior Matron: Mrs D Jarvis, RGNII
Assistant Matron: Mrs E Appleton, RGNII (*part-time*)
School Medical Officer: P J Burrows, BM, BCh, DObst, MRCP UK

Constitution. There are up to 900 pupils, with approximately 100 in the Sixth Form and 300 in the Junior School. Boys and girls are admitted at 11 and 13 by examination; and into the Sixth Form, at age 16, on GCSE results.

There are boarding places available for both boys and girls (11–18), and the whole School is divided into four houses. Day pupils and boarders are members of the same houses, thus obviating any feeling of division between boarding and day.

All senior pupils attend Assembly, often with Chapel and then commence nine 35-minute lessons (with a twenty-minute morning break and an hour lunch break). Following the academic routine, every afternoon and at lunchtime, games or activities are organized allowing day pupils to depart between 4.00 pm and 5.00 pm having experienced the daily routine and ethos of a boarding school. Many day pupils ask to board in their senior years.

Junior School lessons are from 8.45 am to 3.15 pm for Nursery, with staggered finishes, then to 3.35 pm for KS2, followed, again, by voluntary activities every afternoon.

Curriculum. The Junior School follows the National Curriculum in the main and as a basis but seeks to go beyond this in many areas using imaginative teaching and innovative cross-curricular projects. The use of ICT is increasingly embedded throughout the curriculum. In addition French is taught throughout the school and Spanish in the older age groups. There is a wide range of after-school clubs including sport, art, performance and music activities.

The GCSE curriculum offers a choice of many subjects (including separate subject sciences) and careful note has been taken of those elements of the National Curriculum considered vital to personal development. All pupils study French and Spanish in Year 7, and can choose German from Year 8. Each pupil must study a minimum of 1 foreign language to GCSE level. There is a wide range of subjects on offer. All pupils take a minimum of 9 GCSE examinations.

More than 20 AS and A Level subjects are available.

Careers guidance is given by tutors from the earliest days, and is backed up by professional advice. Work experience is undertaken in the summer of Year 10.

Games and Activities. Rugby, Football, Cricket, Hockey, Rounders and Netball are the main games, with Cross-Country, Basketball, Swimming, Tennis, Athletics, Lacrosse and Golf among others in a supporting role.

The School has a strong games tradition, achieving representation at County level, and beyond, a reputation for drama and a thriving musical life.

The School has its own practice golf course, floodlit pitch, lake, and 7,000 sq ft Sports Hall, all-weather playing areas, tennis courts under lights and swimming pool.

All Senior School pupils are encouraged to attempt the Duke of Edinburgh's Award Scheme and Asdan Scheme in citizenship; there are several expeditions each year in the neighbouring New Forest, or in Wales, in the mountains; and abroad, including two ski trips.

In the Junior School Year 6 take part in a residential activity week in Normandy.

Admission Procedures. Admission to the Junior School is by informal assessment and a 'taster day' for younger pupils and, for the older pupils, interview with the Head Teacher, satisfactory reports and assessments in English and Mathematics.

An examination is set at 11 + and an interview expected, plus report from present school (often a State Primary School).

At 13+ HCS Entrance examination and an interview and report.

At 16+ an interview and report including details of GCSE success are expected.

Places are occasionally available in other age groups.

Examination and interviews may take place at any time during the twelve months preceding entry.

Details from the Registrar.

Scholarships, Exhibitions and Bursaries. (*see Scholarship Entries section*). Awards are made for Academic ability, for Art, Music, Sport and Drama, and general All-Round contribution to the life of the School (including Sport) and Sixth Form.

Fees per term (2008-2009). Nursery: £1,553 (mornings only), £2,170 (full day). Payment by Termly Direct Debit: Junior School £2,478–£2,769; Senior School: £4,003 (day), £6,623 (boarding).

There is a reduction for brother/sister and children of the Clergy, HM Forces and Teachers.

65 points at GCSE (where A*=8 points), plus As and Bs in subjects to be taken to A Level, can achieve a 50% remission of the Sixth Form fee.

Location. Easily accessible from Eastleigh Airport (15 minutes), Southampton Parkway Railway Station (15 minutes) and M27 (5 minutes), HCS is 1½ miles north west of Romsey, on the Salisbury (A27) road. There is a railway station in Romsey.

Former Pupils. e-mail: info@hampshirecs.org.uk.

Charitable status. The United Church Schools Trust is a Registered Charity, number 1016538. It exists to educate children.

Hipperholme Grammar School Foundation

Bramley Lane Hipperholme Halifax West Yorkshire HX3 8JE
Tel: 01422 202256
Fax: 01422 204592
e-mail: secretary@hipperholmegrammar.org.uk
website: www.hipperholmegrammar.org.uk

Hipperholme Grammar School Foundation was founded in 1648 by Matthew Broadley (former pupils are Old Brodleians).

The Foundation provides a unique education in which children are educated to be the very best they can be. Alongside high academic standards, all children are provided with outstanding opportunities for their personal enrichment. A love of learning is developed alongside traditional values of politeness, good manners and strong moral code. The atmosphere that pervades through both schools is welcoming yet challenging: all visitors to the schools are given a very warm welcome and all students are provided with a range of academic and personal development challenges.

Hipperholme Grammar School Foundation is a registered educational charity with a board of Governors.

Officers of the Board:
President: J S Armitage, MBE
Chairman: C D Redfearn, BSc, DMS, MBIM
Vice-Chair: Mrs J F Milton, MBA

Foundation Contacts:
Headmaster: Dr John Scarth, BEd, PhD
PA to the Headmaster: Mrs S Furness
Bursar and Clerk to the Governors: Mr G Oliver

Grammar School Contacts:
Deputy Head: Mrs J Graham
Director of Studies: Mr P Rushton
Head of Lower School: Mrs J Sugden
Head of Upper School: Miss C Pickard
Head of Upper Sixth: Mr M Hendry
Leadership & Personal Enrichment Coordinator: Mr R Griffiths

Preparatory School Contacts:
Principal: Mrs J Pickersgill
Secretary: Mrs Jane Hall
Head of Infants: Mrs E Aggiss
Junior Coordinator: Mr H Tock
Junior Coordinator: Mrs C Roper

Organisation. The Foundation is a co-educational day school comprising The Preparatory School, for children aged 2–11 years, and The Grammar School, for children aged 11–18 years.

Although founded in the nearby Coley Parish Church, the Foundation is not specifically a church school. It has a Christian ethos which pervades its life but which welcomes those of all faiths. Assemblies and end-of-term services (at Coley) are Christian, as is part of the GCSE Religious Education course, all of which are compulsory.

The pupil roll stands at around 420 pupils, with 20 in each Form in The Preparatory School and 50 in each year group in The Grammar School. The schools are small enough to ensure individual attention for all children, yet large enough to provide a full range of subjects to GCSE and A Level.

Pupil Welfare. A great strength of the two schools is a strong commitment to provide outstanding pastoral care. Our small teaching groups, individual attention, teachers who genuinely care and excellent relationships with parents enable all children to blossom and fulfil their potential. Where necessary, individual learning programmes are devised and learning support staff ensure children make excellent progress.

Teaching and Learning. Our teachers enjoy teaching: they are enthusiastic, dedicated and exceptionally caring. Our curriculum is broadly in line with the National Curriculum to Year 9, after which students choose from a range of subjects leading to GCSE and later to A Level.

Personal Enrichment. Our Personal Enrichment programme builds self-confident and well-balanced young people with strong leadership skills. A wide range of activities is provided, including sports, music and drama, as well as a varied outdoor education programme and The Duke of Edinburgh's Award Scheme.

Admission. Admission to The Preparatory School is non-selective and places are given following an interview with the Principal and individual assessments, if appropriate. Entry to The Grammar School follows an entrance examination in January, with places offered for the following September. As important as performance on the entrance test is the Headmaster's interview: the Grammar School provides a unique education and children are selected for their personal qualities and desire to be at The Grammar School as much as academic performance. Entry to The Grammar School for other year groups depends on availability and admittance following a selection test and interview.

Fees per term (2007-2008). Little Lightcliffe (2 years) £165 per week; Nursery and Reception £1,550; Years 1–6 £1,850; Grammar School £2,665.

The Foundation operates a number of schemes that enable parents to spread the cost of school fees throughout the year. School meals, transport and individual music tuition are charged separately.

Bursaries and Scholarships. A number of Scholarships are awarded for entry at both Year 7 and Year 12 (Lower Sixth) for academic, musical and sporting achievement. Discounts are available for siblings and children attending The Preparatory receive a generous fee reduction on transfer to The Grammar School. Bursaries are available throughout the school to families in financial need.

Charitable status. Hipperholme Grammar School Trust is a Registered Charity, number 517152. It exists to provide education of a high calibre for the boys and girls aged 3–18 of the area and to help those who cannot afford fees, to finance such education.

Hull Collegiate School (UCST)

Tranby Croft Anlaby East Yorkshire HU10 7EH
Tel: 01482 657016
Fax: 01482 655389
e-mail: enquiries.hull@church-schools.com
website: www.hullcollegiateschool.co.uk

Governing Body: The Council of The United Church Schools Trust

Local Governing Body:
Mr K A Moffatt (*Chairman*)
Mrs C Levy (*Vice-Chairman*)
Revd Dr N D Barnes
Mrs J Ellery
Mr P Grimwood
Dr K Hammersley
Dr M Munro-Hill
Mr R Perry
Mr M Robson
Mr P Sexton
Dr A Swallow
Mr D van Rij

***Principal*: Mr R Haworth**, MA Cantab

Head of Preparatory School: Mrs K A Williams, BEd Cantab

First Director & Director of Studies: Mr S F Jolly, BSc Durham, PGCE
Director of Teaching & Learning: Mrs C A Holt, BA York, PGCE, NPQH
Director of Pastoral Care: Mrs G Hallgate, BEd Sussex, MSc
Business Services Director: Mrs J A Garnett
Deputy Head of Preparatory School: Mrs J Plewes, BA Hons Leeds, PGCE

Senior School Staff:
Mrs A Asbury, Dip LAMDA, BA Hull, PGCE
Ms A P Barnes, BA Hull, GTP
Miss S R Beddoes, BA Durham, PGCE
Mme C S Blanc, Men Psych, Nanterre, PGCE
Mrs K H Bloomfield, BA Hull, PGCE
Miss E A Butler, BSc Loughborough, PGCE

Mrs P J Carlisle, BEd Christchurch, Kent
Mr R J Chambers, BA Trinity & All Saints, Leeds
Miss A D Davis, BSc Birmingham, PGCE
Mr S M Doncaster, BA Leicester, PGCE
Mrs S A East, BEd Worcester College, MSc
Miss J K Eccles, BA Hull, PGCE
Mrs G M Evans, BSc Leeds, PGCE
Mrs D Feszczak, CertEd Sussex
Ms Z Fitzpatrick, BA Durham
Mrs S J Gibbs, BSc Leicester, PGCE
Mr B J Gilles, MA Oxon, PGCE
Mrs S Groves
Mr M T Haughton, BA International Christian College, MA, PGCE
Mrs D Heads, BSc Hull, PGCE
Mr F S Henderson, BSc York St John, GTP
Mr P D Holmes, BSc Hull, PGCE
Mrs N J Holvey, BEd Sheffield City
Mr G R Hughes, BA Coventry, MFA
Mrs M J Hugill, BSc UMIST, PGCE
Mrs P Jolly, MA Cantab, PGCE
Mrs S R Kelsall, BSc Bradford, PGCE
Miss S J Kielty, BA Aberystwyth, PGCE
Mr M E Kirby, BEd Ripon & York St Johns
Miss S McDowell, BA York, PGCE
Mrs G M Nicholson, MA Aberdeen, Dip Ed
Mr A D Norburn, BMus Birmingham, PGCE, LTCL, ALCM
Mrs J K North, BA Trent Poly, PGCE
Mr C F Owen, BSc Liverpool, PGCE, MIBiol
Mr S D Pearce, BSc Portsmouth, PGCE, CBiol, MIBiol
Mr M E Roper, BSc Bradford, PGCE
Miss R H Spencer, BA Durham, PGCE
Mr A F Stather, CertEd Hull
Mrs M A Steigmann, BSc Hull, CPhys, MInstP
Mr G R Stephenson, BA Newcastle, PGCE, DipEd
Mrs S D M Tatman, BMus Hull, ALCM
Mrs E L Tucker, BA Hull, PGCE
Mrs P C Vitta, BA Cantab, PGCE
Mr C M Wainman, BA Leeds, PGCE
Mrs E J Wallis, BA Leeds, PGCE
Mr R White, BSc Hull, PGCE
Miss L Wigglesworth, BA Leeds, PGCE
Miss R D Willie, BSc Sheffield, PGCE
Mr J W Windeatt, BSc Hull, GTP
Ms E Witty, BA Hull, GTP
Mr A F Woods, BSc Nottingham, MSc, GTP

Preparatory School Staff:
Miss L Ballard, NNEB
Miss C E Barley, BA Hull, MCD, PGCE
Mrs J Bousfield, CertEd Salisbury
Mrs Y Crabtree, BA Lancaster, PGCE
Mrs K Dent, BEd Durham
Mrs K Dewhirst, BSc Newcastle, PGCE
Mrs A Dinsdale, NNEB
Mrs C Dodgson, CertEd Cheltenham
Mr M Dyson, BA Staffordshire, PGCE
Mrs L Grunner, BSc Hull, PGCE
Mrs J Hamilton, BA Hull
Mrs A Haworth, NNEB
Mrs R Hazel, MA Oxford, PhD, PGCE
Mrs C Holtby, NVQ L2 Child Care
Mrs J Maltby, BEd Leeds
Mrs S Maynard, BEd Leeds
Mrs A Meltham, BA Sheffield, PGCE
Mrs A Nicholls, BA Lampeter, PGCE
Mr A North, BA St Pauls, MSc, PGCE
Mrs J Purdy, CertEd Hull
Mrs L Roebuck, BA Hull, QTS
Mrs K Rogers, BA Hull
Miss L Rymer, NVQ L3 Child Care
Mrs C Steele, NNEB
Mr R Stewart, BEd Brighton
Mrs E Stewart, BEd Sheffield
Mrs C Wood, BSc York, QTS

Music:
Mrs E Ashmead, LRAM, Dip NCOS (*Cello*)
Mr C Brown (*Guitar*)
Ms M Cross, ARCM, LGSM (*Flute, piano*)
Mrs R Dixon, MMus, BA, LRSM (*Clarinet, Saxophone*)
Mrs C Finney, BMus, Dip LCM (*Piano*)
Miss C Holdich, BMus, Dip ABRSM (*Singing*)
Mr G Keenan (*Drum Kit*)
Mr W Kremlicka, Austrian Teaching Diploma (*Violin*)
Mrs C Lyons, GRSM, LRAM, ARCM (*Piano*)
Dr R Mathieson, D Phil, BMus, BA, MSc, PGCE (*Piano*)
Mrs S Newton, BA, LGSM (*Woodwind*)
Mr G Oglesby, ABSM (*Brass*)
Mr J Parkin, BMus, LTCL, CertEd (*Piano, Violin, Keyboard*)
Mr J Savory, BMus, ATCL (*Piano*)

Age Range. 2½–18 Boys and Girls.

Number in School. 800.

Structure and Organisation. Hull Collegiate School is the result of the merger of Hull High School and Hull Grammar School and the pooling of their strengths under the forward-thinking management of United Church Schools Trust.

Fully co-educational, the school educates pupils from nursery to Year 13 on the delightful Tranby Croft site, a beautiful Victorian country house set in five hectares of mature, landscaped grounds, approximately four miles to the west of Hull and one mile north east of the Humber Bridge. The Preparatory School is a purpose-built facility opened in 2000, and the newly-merged Senior School opened in September 2005. This followed completion of a multi-million pound building project, providing the school with state-of-the-art classrooms and Science laboratories, a sports hall built to Sport England standard, workshops, a large open-plan art school and a new café-style refectory. In 2007 the school opened the Wilberforce Centre housing spacious sixth form common and study rooms, a drama rehearsal room and further classrooms.

Curriculum and Extra-Curricular Activities. Both Schools brought with them a history of consistently excellent academic results both at GCSE and A Level. The school boasts a very strong pastoral system and prides itself on preparing its pupils for entry to higher education. There is a wide choice of academic subjects available and the choice of extra-curricular activities is equally varied; participation in sport, music and drama is strongly encouraged, as the school plays a considerable amount of competitive sport and produces regular concerts and plays. There are many trips abroad every year, as well as numerous shorter visits to places of interest closer to home.

Admission. Hull Collegiate School welcomes pupils of a wide range of ability and all faiths. Admission is by pre-entry assessment, interview and report and subject to availability of a place. For further information please contact the Registrar.

Fees per term (2008-2009). Reception, Years 1–2 £1,747; Years 3–4 £2,015; Years 5–6 £2,424; Years 7–13 £2,898. Kindergarten: £16 per session (morning or afternoon); First Steps £13 per session.

Scholarships. Academic scholarships are available at 11+ and 16+ and sport, art and music scholarships are also available for outstanding individuals who demonstrate a level of excellence and commitment to these areas.

Charitable status. Hull Collegiate School is a member of The United Church Schools Trust which is a Registered Charity, number 1016538. It exists to provide education for boys and girls between the ages of 2½ and 18 years.

Immanuel College

87/91 Elstree Road Bushey Herts WD23 4EB
Tel: 020 8950 0604
Fax: 020 8950 8687
e-mail: info@immanuel.herts.sch.uk
website: www.immanuelcollege.co.uk

Immanuel College is an independent selective co-educational day school founded in 1990 by the late Chief Rabbi Lord Jakobovits to prepare pupils to live confident and loyal Jewish lives in the modern world. It aims to provide an excellent Jewish and secular education and strengthen Jewish values and practice. The College's ethos is characterised by attentiveness to individual pupils' progress, high academic achievement and the integration of Jewish and secular learning.

There are both Jewish and non-Jewish teachers at the school, the common element being enthusiasm for their work and concern for their pupils.

Motto: *Torah im Derech Eretz* (Jewish learning integrated with secular study)

Governing Body:
Chairman of Governors: The Hon Daniel Janner, QC
Mr Solly Abraham
Mrs Rhonda Alexander-Abt
Mr Shimon Cohen
Mr Michael Dangoor
Mr Russell Ereira
Mr Jeffrey Gordon
Mrs Elaine Kornbluth
Dr Laurence Lovat
Mr Richard Mintz
Mr Conrad Morris
Mr Daniel Peltz
Sir Harry Solomon, KB
Mr Richard Werth
Rabbi Dr Jeffrey Cohen, BA Hons, MPhil, AJC, PhD (*Rabbinical Adviser*)

Bursar & Clerk to the Governors: Mr Raymond Domnitz, FCA

***Headmaster*: Mr Philip Skelker**, MA Oxon (*English*)

Deputy Headmaster: Mr Richard Felsenstein, BA Hons Law, CertEd, UJIA Fellowship in Educational Leadership

Second Deputy Headmaster: Dr Millan Sachania, MA Cantab, MPhil, PhD, FRSA (*Director of Sixth Form, Music*)

* *Head of Department/Subject*
§ *Part-time*

Mr Paul Abrahams, BA Hons (**Modern Languages*)
Mrs Naomi Amdurer, BA Hons (*English, French*)
Mrs Alison Ardeman, BA Hons (**Art*)
§Miss Revital Azulay, First Degree (*BB*) (*Ivrit*)
Mr Danny Baigel, BA Hons (*Jewish Studies*)
§Mrs Nikki Bennett (*School Counsellor*)
Mr Mario Brzezinski, BSc Hons (**ICT, Senior Teacher*)
Miss Trudi Culverhouse, BSc Hons (*Head of Middle School, PE*)
§Dr Julia Cushnir, BSc Hons, PhD (*Chemistry*)
§Mrs Ruth Davis, BA Hons (*Mathematics*)
Mr Nick De Carpentier, BA, BEd (*Geography*)
Mr Paul de Naeyer, BSc Hons (**Geography*)
Mr Gideon Denby, BSc Hons (**Science*)
Mr Michael Drucker (*Director of Jewish Life*)
§Ms Laurel Endelman, BA Hons, RSA CertEFL, MA (*Drama*)
Mr Neil English, BEd Hons (*Design & Technology*)
Mrs Sue Fishburn, BA Hons, RSADipSpLD (*Head of Teaching & Learning*)
Mrs Joanna Fleet, BA (**Drama*)
Miss Sarah Friedgood, BA Hons (**History of Art, English*)
§Mrs Nurit Gance, BA, TCertSEN (*Ivrit*)
Mr Nicholas Garman, BA Hons (**Music*)
Mr Mark Gavin, MA (**Economics*)
Mr Michael Gillis, MA (**Biblical Hebrew*)
Mrs Shelley Gladstone, BA, RSA Dip (*Teaching & Learning*)
§Mrs Debra Glass, BSc (*Mathematics*)
Mr Daniel Goldblatt, BSc (**Mathematics*)
§Mrs Hinda Golding, CertEd (*Art*)
§Mrs Amanda Goodman, BMEd (*Assistant Librarian*)
§Mrs Yaffit Gordon, BSc Hons (*Mathematics*)
Mrs Judith Graham, BA Hons (*Head of Year 7, *History & Politics*)
Mrs Shuli Harris, BSc Hons (*Mathematics, Jewish Studies*)
Mr Roger Hazell, DMS, BA Hons, HNC (**Technology, Senior Examinations Officer, Senior Teacher*)
§Mr Edwin Hedge, BA (*History of Art*)
Miss Deborah Hensmans, MA (*French*)
Mr Robert Hibberd, BSc Hons (*Deputy Head of Science i/c Chemistry*)
Mr Frederick Isaac, BA, MA (*Jewish Studies*)
Mr Ben Jarman, BA Hons (*History*)
§Mrs Naina Kanabar, BSc Hons (*ICT*)
Mrs Beth Kerr, BSc Hons (*Director of Pastoral Education, PE & Games*)
§Mrs Janine Klein, BA Hons (*Art*)
Miss Laura Korn, BSc Hons (*Mathematics, Assistant Head of Middle School*)
§Mrs Janet Leifer, BA Hons, DipLib, MA, ALA (*Librarian*)
§Mrs Feigy Lieberman, Diploma (*Jewish Studies*)
§Dr Eleanor Lipman, BSc Hons, PhD (*Science*)
Rabbi Reuven Margrett, BA Hons (*Jewish Studies*)
§Mrs Joyce Mays, BSc Hons (**Psychology*)
§Mrs Eva McMillan, MSc(*Psychology*)
§Mrs Danielle Miller, BEd (*Biology*)
Mr Gideon Morrison Wood, BA Hons (*Mathematics, Jewish Studies*)
Mr David Moss, BA Hons (**PE*)
Mrs Angela Murphy, BA Hons (*French*)
Mrs Mazal Nisner, BEd (**Ivrit*)
§Mrs Emma Philips, BA Hons (**Sociology*)
Mr Lee Raby, BA Hons (**Boys' PE, Geography*)
Miss Susan Ribeiro, BA Hons (*Art*)
Rabbi David Riffkin, BA Hons, MA (**Jewish Studies*)
Mrs Sophie Rosenfeld, BSc Hons (*Chemistry*)
Mrs Vardit Sadeh-Ginsburg, BA Hons, MA, TDip (*Ivrit*)
Mrs Lily Schonberg, BA, BSc Ed (*French*)
Mrs Galia Segal, BA Hons (*Head of Upper School, English*)
Mrs Sharron Shackell, BA Hons (*History*)
Miss Camilla Shifrin, BSc (*Biology*)
Miss Celia Siegel, BA (*English*)
Mrs Maxine Skeggs (*Teaching and Learning*)
Miss Ruth Skelker, BA Hons (*Assistant Head of Upper School, English*)
Mrs Ruth Solomons, BSc Hons, MA Ed (*Science, Senior Teacher i/c Professional Development*)
Mr Gordon Spitz, BA, HDipEd, MA (**English*)
§Mrs Helen Stephenson-Yankuba, BSc Hons (*Psychology*)
Mr Daniel Tysman, BSc (**Biology*)
Mrs Deborah Unsdorfer, BSc (*Jewish Studies*)
Ms Neha Vadera, BA Hons (**Photography, Art*)
Mrs Annette Weinberg, BSc Hons (*Mathematics*)

Age Range. 11–18.

School Roll. There are 518 pupils on roll, of whom 251 are girls and 267 are boys. There are 138 pupils in the Sixth Form.

Buildings and Grounds. The school benefits from an attractive and well-resourced green belt campus. At its heart is Caldecote Towers, characterised by Pevsner as, "a crazy display like a hotel in Harrogate". The Joyce King Theatre opened in December 2003.

Admission. Boys and girls enter in September. Admission is on the basis of performance in the College's entrance examination and interview. The principal entry is at 11+. A number of boys and girls join the College in the Sixth Form; offers of places are gained by interview and are conditional upon GCSE results.

Fees per term (2008-2009). £4,068. Lunch £225.

Scholarships and Bursaries. Immanuel Jakobovits Scholarships are awarded to a maximum value of 25% of fees on a competitive basis to up to twelve outstanding 11+ entrants. These awards are subject to a yearly review throughout a pupil's time at the College. The parents of scholars are invited to apply for supplementary bursaries based on financial need. Exhibitions to the value of £2,000 per annum are awarded to pupils who show exceptional promise in Art or Music.

Means-tested bursaries are awarded to a number of boys and girls from less affluent families who are academically and personally suited to the education the College provides.

Co-education. Boys and girls are taught separately in Years 7 to 11. However, educational outings and journeys throughout the school are co-educational as are dramatic and musical productions. The Sixth Form is fully co-educational. It may therefore be said that Immanuel combines the benefits of single sex and co-education.

Curriculum. In Years 7 to 9, pupils follow a broad curriculum. In addition to English, French, Jewish Studies, Mathematics, Modern Hebrew and the Sciences, the College's core curriculum for Years 7 to 11, pupils study Art, Design and Technology, Drama, Geography, History, Information and Communications Technology and Music. Physical Education and Games are taught on the Sports Afternoons. There is a wide range of subjects available as GCSE options in Years 10 and 11. The great majority of pupils proceed to the Sixth Form to study three, four or five subjects to AS/A2 level.

Throughout a pupil's time at Immanuel, Jewish Studies forms part of her or his core curriculum. Jewish philosophy, history and religion are studied principally by way of close textual learning. There is a Torah Mitzion Kollel, an advanced Jewish learning institute, at the College.

Pastoral Care. The College prides itself on its attentiveness to the needs of individual pupils. The pastoral team includes form tutors, Heads of Year and the College counsellor, who in Years 7 to 11 work under the direction of the Director of Pastoral Education. The Director of the Sixth Form is in charge of a team of form tutors. Parental consultation evenings take place regularly. The School Council, which meets fortnightly with the Director of Pastoral Education and the Headmaster, gives pupils the opportunity to express concerns and make suggestions about improving school life.

Religious Life. Tefillah (prayer) and the celebration of festivals, both joyous and solemn, are an integral part of life at Immanuel. The College celebrates the intermediate days of Succoth, Chanukah, Purim and Yom Ha'atzmaut enthusiastically. On these festivals, pupils make a special effort to raise funds for charity.

The Teaching and Learning Department offers courses that enable pupils to become independent and successful learners. In addition to the programme followed by all pupils, the department provides small group teaching to a range of pupils whose learning needs are more specific. Pupils with a variety of learning difficulties are thereby helped to develop confidence and do justice to their potential.

Arts and Other Activities. All Year 7 pupils are offered tuition at a heavily discounted rate and the loan of an instrument for their first year at the College. Instrumental ensembles and choirs perform in school and at outside venues. There are regular dramatic productions. Pupils compete yearly for the Eli and Sonia Gottleib Art Trophy and in public speaking and debating competitions.

Games. The PE and Games staff involve pupils in activities that range from aerobics, golf, horse-riding and trampolining to athletics, cricket, football, hockey, netball and tennis. Physical Education may be studied for GCSE and A Level. Sports facilities include an all-weather surface and a Fitness Suite.

Educational Journeys. In Year 7 pupils stay in York for five days, in Year 9 they spend four weeks in Israel, in Year 10 they visit Jewish families in Strasbourg and Madrid and in Year 12 they spend eight days in Poland. A skiing trip to Colorado is held annually. These experiences encourage pupils to bond with one another and help them to understand the forces that have shaped contemporary Jewry.

Charitable status. Immanuel College is a Registered Charity, number 803179. It exists to combine academic excellence and Jewish tradition in a contemporary society.

Kingham Hill School

Kingham Chipping Norton Oxfordshire OX7 6TH
Tel: 01608 658999
Fax: 01608 658658
e-mail: admissions@kingham-hill.oxon.sch.uk
website: www.kingham-hill.oxon.sch.uk

Kingham Hill School is a thriving boarding and day school for 250 girls and boys from 11–18 years. Beautifully situated, it has offered many generations of students the best possible opportunity to flourish, enjoying their formative years and becoming successful, responsible and well-rounded adults.

The Headmaster and his dedicated staff team ensure that the school's special qualities benefit all:

- Christian values that permeate school life;
- Added value that enables so many to exceed all expectations;
- Family-style boarding houses and superb pastoral care.

Kingham Hill School nestles in 96 acres of rolling Cotswold countryside and enjoys wonderful sporting facilities.

Motto: *In virum perfectum.*

Governors:
M Stanley-Smith (*Chairman*)

Mrs C Anelay
Mrs V Ansah
Dr S Blake
Miss D Buggs
Mrs P Goodwin-Hudson
The Revd M Hepworth
D Monro
D M Orton
K Targett
Mrs G R Thorne
C Townsend
The Revd S Wookey

***Headmaster*: Revd Nick Seward**, BEng, MA

Deputy Headmaster: N Randay, MA, BSc, PGCE

Staff:
S Birnie
Mrs G Boyd, BA, PGCE
G Cape, DipEd
Dr P Carlin, BDS
Mrs J Chapman, BA Hons
Mrs S M Chesterton, CertEd, CertSpLD
T J Cottle, BEd
Mrs J Critchley
M Eyles, BSc Hons
Dr R Eyles, MBChB
Mrs J A Fowler, BEng Hons, PGCE
R N Fox, BA, PGCE
Mrs R G Hayes, BA, PGCE
Mrs C Heath
Mrs G Holliday
R Jones, MMus, BH Hons
G Lane, BSc Hons
Miss E Miller, BA Hons, MA

Miss R Nicklin, BSc Hons
P Parmenter, CertEd
Mrs J Parmenter, CertEd
E Pearson-Miles, BA Hons, PGCE
Mrs C Pearson-Miles, BA Hons
Dr A R Read, PhD, BSc, PGCE
B Sangster, BA, CertEd, AdDipEd
M Springett, CertEd, ACP
Mrs J A Stodart-Cook, BA Hons, DipM, PGCE, MSBT
Mrs I Swain, PGDip SpecEd
E Van Blerk, BA, BTh
Miss K Warner, BA

Chaplain: Revd A Savage
Deputy Chaplain: Miss D Moseley
Assistant Chaplain: Mr D Ritchie
Honorary Chaplain: The Revd Canon Geoffrey Shaw, MA

Administration:
Headmaster's PA and Registrar: Mrs K A Harvey, BA Hons
Director of Administration & Clerk to the Governors: M J B Hall
Domestic Bursar: T D Smith
School Secretary: Mrs J Cavan

Medical Officer: Dr D R Edwards, MB BS, DRCOG
Medical Centre: Mrs S Alexander

What would it take for your child to flourish?
Some parents know that their child could succeed but are frustrated that he or she is making slow progress. It might be because they:

- are going unnoticed in a large school;
- have a learning difficulty such as dyslexia;
- are struggling with difficult issues at home;
- seem to be developing later than their friends;
- lack confidence.

At Kingham Hill we are as keen as any school to accommodate the most able students, and we do it well. However, we revel in working with the average ability student, helping them to exceed expectations. There is something very satisfying about enabling a C grade student gain B grades, helping a second XV player make the first XV rugby squad and finding a place in the musical for the grade 3 clarinettist.

As a matter of principle we do not select students on the basis of their academic achievements. On assessment days and at interview the Headmaster and his team are looking to identify students who will flourish if offered timely affirmation, appropriate challenge and, sometimes, tender loving care. Many students surprise their parents, and more importantly, themselves, by what they achieve.

Securing this kind of success is hard work. It takes skill and dedication. It can only be found where the right values and ethos thrive. Drawing on 120 years of Christian commitment and outstanding pastoral care, we have a remarkable track record in helping students exceed all expectations.

Open Morning: 11th October 2008.
Assessment Day: 20th November 2008.

Fees per term (2008-2009). Boarding: £6,390 (Years 7 & 8), £7,200 (Years 9–11), £7,560 (Sixth Form). Day: £4,170 (Years 7 & 8), £4,700 (Years 9–11), £5,080 (Sixth Form).

ESOL tuition: £1,390. SpLD tuition: £1,320, SpLD for Sixth Form: £660.

Scholarships and Bursaries. The School is able to offer several categories of Scholarship: Art, Junior, Music, Performing Arts, Sixth Form and Sport. Generous Bursaries for sons and daughters of HM Forces personnel.

Charitable status. The Kingham Hill Trust is a Registered Charity, number 1076618, and a Company Limited by Guarantee, registered in England, number 365812. The school exists to provide education for girls and boys from 11 to 18.

Langley School

Langley Park Norwich Norfolk NR14 6BJ
Tel: 01508 520210
Fax: 01508 528058
e-mail: office@langleyschool.co.uk
website: www.langleyschool.co.uk

Langley School, formerly the Norwich High School for Boys, was founded in 1910. The School relocated from Norwich to Langley Park in 1946 and was renamed. It is the Senior School to Langley Preparatory School (IAPS), and the business affairs of both schools are managed by a Council of Management as a non-profit making educational charity.

In recent years the school has been steadily expanding and its facilities have been substantially enhanced. Recent developments include a complete refurbishment programme for boarding facilities, a new floodlit Astroturf pitch, a new 11-room Science Centre, a three-dimensional Art and Sculpture Studio, a multi-media suite for Modern Languages, a fully refurbished and extended Mathematics block and a multi-gym with fitness centre. Plans are in place for a new state-of-the-art block of sixteen classrooms to open in September 2009.

Langley admits boys and girls between the ages of 10 and 18 years to either day, weekly boarding or full boarding status. There are 475 pupils in the School, of whom around 100 are boarders. Situated in some 100 acres of playing fields and wooded parkland south of Norwich, Langley benefits from good accessibility by road, rail, air and sea.

Council of Management:

Chairman: Mrs Margaret M Alston, JP
Mr Richard Bacon, MP
Mr R G Basey-Fisher
Mr D J B Coventry, CA
Mr S P Rossall-Evans, LLB
Mr C E Self, FRICS, IRRV
Mr C Speake, MA Cantab
Mrs C Smith
Mr C Townsend
Mr G Pritchard
Mr J Fuller

***Headmaster*: Mr D K Findlay**, BEd Exeter, NPQH

Senior Deputy Head (*Pastoral*): Mr M Rayner, BA Hons Leeds, PGCE Oxford
Deputy Head (*Academic*): Mr F Butt, BEng Hons Bath, PGCE Roehampton

Staff:

Science:
Mr J Clegg, BA Hons Hull, PGCE UEA
Dr C A Lowery, BSc, PhD Birmingham, PGCE UEA
Mr R E Holmes, MA, CertEd Mansfield College, Oxford
Mr G A D Frost, BSc Hons, CertEd Cardiff, MIBiol
Mr J A Pearman, BSc Hons, AKC, PGCE King's College, London
Dr A Mason BSc, MSc, PhD MET University, PGCE UEA
Miss N Cowan BSc Hons, PGCE OU
Mr L Calvert, MChem Leeds, PGCE UEA
Mr G Oclee-Brown, BA Hons University of Wales

English & Drama:
Mr R Wood, BA Hons, MPhil, PGCE Liverpool
Mr J L McRobert, BA Jt Hons, PGCE Swansea
Mrs R Saunders, BA Hons Kent, PGCE CSSD
Miss A Hamill, MA Hons Dundee, PGCE Swansea
Mrs M Gordon-George, CertEd
Ms J Corser, BA, PGCE

Mathematics:
Mr W Baker, BEd Hons Manchester
Mr A Briggs, BA Hons OU, TCert
Mrs C A Feakes, BEd Worcester
Miss A Hanzelyova, MA Preston, QTS
Mrs K Skuse, BSc Hons UEA
Ms L White, BSc Hons Swansea, PGCE Southampton

Languages:
Mr T J Batchelor, BA Hons Nottingham, PGCE Homerton
Mrs J L Skelton, BA Hons Oxford Brookes, PGCE Leeds
Ms A Konig, CertEd Coventry
Mrs L Holmes, BA Hons, PGCE UEA
Mrs M Ellwood, BA Hons Roehampton, PGCE
Mrs A Yandell, BA Hons Newnham College,Cambridge, PGCE, Cert TEFL
Mrs J E Butt, BA Wolverhampton, Cert TEFL
Mrs D Harrington, BA Hons Durham, PGCE, RSA Dip TEFL
Mrs C Stewart, Cert Learning Support, Adult TCert
Mrs A Smith

Humanities:
Mr J Kempton, BA Hons Bristol, PGCE Bristol
Mr M Rayner, BA Hons Leeds, PGCE Oxford
Mr I Felton, BA Hons Portsmouth, PGCE UEA
Mrs G M Dover, BA UEA, PGCE St Johns, York
Mrs K Lambert, BA Hons Sussex, PGCE Nottingham
Mr M Vanston, BSc Hons Sheffield PGCE UEA
Mr D T Madgett, BA Hons, DipAcc City of London, PGCE Worc, Cert TEFL
Mr D Nichols, BSc Hons Stirling, PGCE Sunderland
Mr P Clark, BA Hons Northumbria, PGCE Sunderland
Mr S Read, LLB Cardiff
Mrs A Dain, BEd, MA, PhD, CertEd
Mr A Walker, BA Hons Brunel
Mrs H Day, BA Hons, PGCE UEA
Mr K Woodrow, BA Hons UEA, PGCE Middlesex
Mr C McAllister, BA Hons Bedfordshire
Mrs S O'Brien, BSc UEA, PGCE Manchester

Art:
Mr J N Ogden, BA Hons, PGCE Lancashire
Mr R J Wheeler, CIC Hons Brighton
Mr M Limbrick, BA St Martin's, MA Slade, PGCE Middlesex
Miss H Stewart, BA Hons, PGCE

Technology:
Mr F Butt, BEng Hons Bath, PGCE Roehampton
Mr S Daly, BEng Kingston, BA Greenwich QTS
Mr M J Holmes, BA, CertEd Brunel
Mr S Hughes, BA Hons Nottingham Trent
Mrs M Woolsey, CertEd Bath College of Educ
Mr D Innes, BA Hons Falmouth
Mr M Payne, BA Hons Warwick MA Leicester, PGCE
Mrs A Reynolds, BEd Hons Bristol

PE:
Mr C Greenhall, BA, PGCE Univ College, Wales
Mr C Cooper, PPC
Miss S Tea, BEd Hons Bedford, De Montfort
Miss A Davidson

Music:
Mr A Stratford, BA Hons Huddersfield, PGCE Oxford Brookes
Mr R White, ATCL
Mr D Howard
Mr S Durant
Mr A Cronin
Mr J Stephens

Learning Support:
Mrs P Lightfoot, BA Hons, PGCE London, DipSpLD
Mrs K Beaumont, Cert Learning Support
Mr R Hull CertEd
Mrs R Hull

Bursar: Mr P J Weeks, BEd, CertEd, CertSpLD, MCollP

Marketing Manager: Mr A F Barclay, Dip Ms, CertEd

School Medical Officers:
Dr P Barrie, MBChB, DRCOG, DCH
Dr A Guy, FPCert, MB, BS

Headmaster's PA: Mrs C Mayes

General. Langley School aims to provide a framework within which each pupil will develop effective learning skills and will achieve their maximum academic potential. A happy, secure and well ordered environment is maintained in a beautiful country house setting with extensive grounds and playing fields, where individuals are encouraged to set their sights high. Their progress is monitored by a strong tutorial system to ensure that they follow a course of study that best suits their individual skills and needs. Langley pupils are encouraged to identify their talents and to use and develop them whilst contributing to a wide variety of new experiences that will help them acquire the values of honesty, enterprise, independence and social awareness. Small classes and a well organised House system help our children to sample these new experiences with confidence. They will learn to take personal and social responsibility and will get ample opportunities to develop leadership qualities. We hope to produce young people who will be prepared to meet the demands of a rapidly changing and demanding world which will require versatile, adaptable, receptive and confident citizens of the future.

Academic Curriculum. Syllabuses and schemes of work are designed to complement the National Curriculum and the Common Entrance Examination Syllabuses up to Year 9.

Lower School (10–13 years): All pupils in these years study English, Mathematics, French, German, Geography, History, Biology, Chemistry, Physics, Design and Technology, Drama, Art and Ceramics, Information Technology, Music, Physical Education and Religious Studies. A programme of Personal and Social Education includes study skills and careers guidance. Pupils are setted on ability in the core subjects while in other subjects streaming may be applied.

Middle School (14–16 years): All pupils are prepared for the GCSE examinations. The School is an examining centre for a number of Boards, and this enables staff to select those syllabuses which they believe are most appropriate to the needs of their pupils. All pupils study English, Mathematics and the Sciences. A variable number of additional subjects are selected which enables the most able pupil to study up to eleven subjects. A brochure on GCSE courses is available on request.

Most students in the Sixth Form will study 4 AS Levels in the Lower Sixth from a choice of 28 subjects and continue with three of these to A Level in the Upper Sixth. Other permutations of AS and A Levels are possible to suit students of varying ability.

Monitoring Academic Progress. High priority is given to the monitoring of each pupil's progress and is the specific responsibility of the Heads of Year with a team of tutors. A combination of complementary short, medium and long-term recording systems are in use. This permits effective communication between teachers, and between the School and the parent.

Extra-Curricular Activities. The school offers a wide choice of sports, artistic, musical, dramatic, scientific, technical and literary activities to enhance students life-long learning. In total there are more than 80 such activities operating daily throughout the week. All staff and students are required to contribute to this programme. The major team games are rugby, football, cricket, tennis, athletics, hockey and netball. Sailing, fencing, judo, squash, basketball, climbing, shooting and golf are but a few of the other options.

The School has a thriving CCF (Army, RAF and Navy sections) and encourages participation in the Duke of Edinburgh's Award Scheme.

The self-confidence which can be acquired through participation in music and drama is immeasurable. Consequently, the school promotes participation by all in dramatic and musical events at a class, house and school level. An Arts Umbrella programme offers the opportunity for pupils to experience the theatrical and musical productions in London and other centres.

Admission. Pupils will be considered for admission to Langley at 10+, 11+, 13+ and into the Sixth Form. Entry may be possible at other levels when vacancies permit and is conditional on an interview followed by detailed and satisfactory school reports. At Sixth Form level, satisfactory performance in GCSE is required.

Scholarships. (*see Scholarship Entries section*). Competitive academic scholarships are awarded at 11+, 13+ and Sixth Form level. Music, Art, Drama, Design & Technology and Sports scholarships are also available.

Fees per term (2008-2009). Boarders: £5,550 (Year 6), £6,660 (Years 7–13); Weekly Boarders: £4,800 (Year 6), £5,550 (Years 7–13); Day Pupils: £2,525 (Year 6), £3,275 (Years 7–13).

Generous family and Forces discounts are offered.

Further Information. Please visit our website at www.langleyschool.co.uk. A School prospectus, Sixth Form brochure and GCSE brochure are available on application from the Headmaster's PA. Alternatively, you are invited to arrange to visit the school by telephoning the Headmaster's PA.

Charitable status. Langley School is a Registered Charity, number 311270. It exists to provide a sound education for boys and girls.

The Licensed Victuallers' School

London Road Ascot Berkshire SL5 8DR
Tel: 01344 882770
Fax: 01344 890648
e-mail: registrar@lvs.ascot.sch.uk
website: www.lvs.ascot.sch.uk

The School was founded in 1803 and was co-educational from the outset. The School is controlled by a Board of Governors on behalf of the parent charity, The Licensed Trade Charity.

Patron: Her Majesty The Queen

Principal: I A Mullins, BEd Hons, MSc, MBIM

***Head of Senior School*: G Best**, BA Hons

Head of Junior School: Mrs H Donnelly, BA, BEd Hons

Assistant Heads:
K Adams, BA, MA
P Bevis, CEd
Mrs C Farthing, BSc, BA, DipPsych, CEd
Mrs C Cunniffe, BA Hons
Mr D Hewson, BA Hons

Heads of Faculties:
Expressive Arts: Ms S Quant, MA, BA Hons, PGCE
Physical & Vocational Education: W Graham, BA Ed Hons
Mathematics: Mrs E Dowlen, BSc
Science: G Cunningham, BSc Hons, PGCE
Humanities: Mrs D Finch, BA Hons
Languages: Mrs E Owen, BA
Art & Design Technology: Mrs E Wigley, BPhil Ed

Heads of Houses:
Guinness: C Beswick, PhD, BSc Hons, MSc, PGCE
Carlsberg: Mrs J Liepa, GGSM Hons
Bass: G Blunt, BA Hons
Whitbread: S Clarkson, BA Hons, DipEd, MEd
Courage: Mrs S Riley, BA Hons
Bell's: N Preston, BA Hons, MA
Gilbey: A Monk, BSc Hons, PGCE

Art & Design:
P Cordeaux, BA Hons, PGCE
Miss M Stevens, BA Hons, MA Fine Art

Design Technology:
Mrs E Wigley, BPhil Ed
Ms G Heuchel, BEd
Mrs C Clarkson, BEd Hons
A Monk, BSc Hons, PGCE
J Swanepoel, BEd
P Hodges, PhD, MSc, BSc, PGCE

English and Media Studies:
Ms S Quant, MA, BA Hons, PGCE
S Clarkson, BA Hons, DipEd, MEd
Mrs J Liepa, GGSM, CertEd
Mrs J E Wren, BA
D Seymour, BA, PGQ
C Bryant, BA, PGCE
J Valente, BA, PGCE, MA
Miss S Vowles, BA Hons, PGCE

Drama:
Mrs J A Payne, CertEd
Miss T Deguara, BEd

Humanities:
Mrs D Finch, BA Hons
Mrs T Brass, BEd
Mrs C Farthing, BSc Hons, BA, DipPsych, CertEd
E G Smith, MA
N Preston, BA Hons, MA
Revd R F Walker, BSc Hons, BD ThM
P Veal (*Barrister*)
Miss H Lewis, BSc Hons, PhD, MSc
P J Brass, MA
Miss N Alam, BSc Hons, MSc
P Mallaband, PhD, MA, BA
Mrs T Bason, BA, PGCE

Information Technology:
G B Taylor, MA, BA
P Bevis, CertEd
Mrs L Cooper, MA
K Win, BSc Hons

Physical Education and Vocational Education:
W Graham, BA Ed Hons
Miss J M Holmes, CertEd, AdvDipEd
Miss H Pritchard, BA Hons
Miss L Seaton, BSc Hons, PGCE
A Towse, BA Hons
Miss L Stevens, BA Hons, PGCE
D Pike, BSc Hons
G Blunt, BA Hons

Languages:
Mrs E Owen, BA
Mrs E F Meyer, Licence d'Anglais
Mrs K A Potter, BA
J Roszykiewicz, BA, PGCE
Mrs M Davies, BA Hons, PGCE
I Arriandrago, PGCE, MA, BA
Mrs R Parry, BSc
A Fiol, BA, PGCE
Miss D Milner (*Spanish Assistant*)
Miss E Bernard (*French Assistant*)

Mathematics:
Mrs E Dowlen, BSc

Mrs A Buchanan, BSc
D M Newcombe, MA, BEd
S Miller, BSc, PGCE
D Pearson, BSc Hons, PGCE
P Cantor, BSc Hons, PGCE
S Tomlin, BA Hons
Miss L Betteridge, BSc, PGCE

Music:
Mrs Cunniffe, BA Hons, MMus
Mrs S P Riley, BA Hons, ARCM
A Cassar, MPhil

Science:
G Cunningham, BSc Hons, PGCE
K Adams, MA, BA
C W Beswick, PhD, MSc, BSc Hons, PGCE
Mrs V M L Beswick, BSc Hons, PGCE
E W Johnson, BSc Hons, PGCE
Mrs S Lucas, BSc Hons
A Wright, BSc, PhD
Mrs L Chappell, BSc Hons

Junior Department:
Mrs H Donnelly, BA, BEd Hons
Miss H C Buckett, BEd
Mrs E Earl, BEd
Mrs J Foster, BA Hons, PGCE, LTCL
Mrs L Rawlinson
Mrs H Sexton, CertEd
Mrs L Thomson, BSc Hons, PGCE
Miss R Maidment, BEd Hons
Miss L Gibson, BA Hons
Miss L Beck, BSc Hons
Miss L Williams, BEd Hons
M Donaldson, BA Hons, PGCE
Mrs E Aalders, BA Hons

Learning Support:
Mrs E Lawrence, OCR DipSpLD, PGCE, BSc Hons
Mrs F Hampson-Jones, BA Hons
Mrs L Wielenga, BEd
Mrs S Court

EAL:
Ms J Richardson, MA Hons, CTEFLA
Mrs L Toft, BEd Hons
Miss A Moores, BA Hons, PGCE

Instrumental Music:
Piano:
J Chantrey
Mrs K Stanley
Mrs G Tucker
A Konjhodzic
Woodwind: Mrs D Head
Percussion: G Brown
Guitar:
J Clark
P McKee
Rock Guitar: K Jenkins
Singing:
J Hatfield
D Manners
J Wood
A Watson
Brass: Miss K Dawkins
Violin/Viola: N Sharp

Medical:
Dr Kade (*Medical Officer*)
Dr C McDonald
Mrs L Wooldridge, RGN
Sister A Rossa, RGN, CertHEd

Technicians:
Computing:
A McGarry
Mrs G Marshall, BSc Hons
A Allen
C Read
D Hodgson
Science:
Mrs E Nicholson
Mrs Y Oliver
C Bushall
Mrs K Lavender
Art/Food Technology: Mrs D Brophy
Design Technology: M Montague
Drama: K Morgan, DipSM, TTP Hons
Audio-visual: D Gravett

Learning Resource Centre:
Manager: Mrs S Bastone
Mrs S Buckerfield
Mrs S Eaton, ALA
Mrs A Harris

Administrative Staff:
Examinations Officer: Mrs S Chapman
Headmaster's PA: Mrs L Humphreys
Registrar/Marketing Officer: Mrs M Dickinson
Reprographics Assistant: Mrs S Withers
School Secretaries:
Ms H Austin
Mrs L Reddy
Mrs S Silva
School Receptionist: Mrs A Davies

Housemothers:
Bass: Mrs H Blunt
Carlsberg: Ms J James
Gilbey: Mrs M Monk
Guinness: Mrs A Sawyer

Numbers. There are some 900 pupils in the school, of whom 200 are in the Junior Department (aged $4^1/_2$ to 11). Just over a quarter of the pupils are boarders (split equally between weekly and full boarding). The ratio of boys to girls is 60/40.

Location. The school lies to the north of the A329, approximately 1 kilometre west of Ascot Racecourse. It is readily accessible from the M3, M4 and M25 motorways as well as Heathrow and Gatwick airports. The school operates a bus service to connect with trains at Ascot Station.

Organisation. Pupils aged 4+ to 11+ (Years R to 6) are taught in a separate Junior Department. In the Senior School, pupils aged 11 to 18 (Years 7 to 13) are taught in groups which are setted by ability in each subject. In the senior school, all pupils belong to one of seven houses, of which four are for boarders and supervised by married couples and there is purpose-built accommodation for 2 and 4 in a room. All staff work within houses as tutors to small groups of pupils which meet daily. Junior Department pupils may board from Year 3 (age 7) in the mixed Junior House which is an integral part of the Junior School buildings.

Facilities. The school moved to its present location in the autumn of 1989 occupying purpose-built premises which were completely re-equipped at the time of the move. In addition to boarding accommodation and classroom blocks, there is a major sports complex and a new Performing Arts Centre, all located in 26 acres of landscaped grounds (which include a fishing lake). The school has extensive inter-linked computer facilities including three networked teaching rooms each with some 20 terminals, departmental mini-networks and stand-alone machines in classrooms and laboratories. Information technology is an integral part of class teaching from age 4+ onwards.

The new Sixth Form Centre opened in 2004 and ensures the best available resources for our 150 post-16 students. It also incorporates a new Learning Resource Centre which is available to all pupils.

Curriculum. All pupils in years 1 to 9 (ages 5 to 13) follow a broad foundation course which is compatible with the national curriculum. The school participates in testing arrangements under the national curriculum. Pupils may select their first foreign language from French or Spanish, and choose German as a second foreign language. In Years 10 and 11, all pupils follow a common core curriculum of English, Mathematics, Science, a first Foreign Language to GCSE, plus PE, PSE and Careers. A flexible blocking system allows considerable choice of further GCSE options from Technology, Art & Design, Geography, History, Food Technology, Music, Drama, Media Studies, Economics, Physical Education, Computer Science, Spanish, German or French. Set sizes average 15/16 pupils at GCSE. This approach allows the school to cope well with a wide intake ability.

A wide range of AS Level options is provided in Years 12 and 13, including Mathematics, Physics, Chemistry, Biology, Music, Geography, History, Economics, Business Studies, English, Art & Design, Theatre Studies, CDT, Media Studies, Photography, Psychology, French, Spanish, German, Computer Studies and Physical Education. A flexible blocking system allows considerable opportunity to mix arts and science subjects.

Games etc. The school has superb indoor and outdoor facilities including two sports halls, a 25 metre indoor pool and hard and artificial playing surfaces for outdoor team games and athletics. The school has achieved considerable success in providing County-standard players in a wide range of sports. Whilst all pupils play team games such as Rugby, Football, Cricket, Tennis, Netball, Basketball or Athletics in their early years, the range of options widens as pupils become older as the aim is to encourage fitness for life. Thus pupils row, ski, skate and play squash as well as follow the more usual team sports.

Clubs and Activities. The school offers a wide range of extra-curricular activities on a seven-day basis. The precise list depends upon the abilities and enthusiasms of staff and pupils, but includes Duke of Edinburgh's Award Scheme as well as a varied programme of physical, creative, cerebal and hobby activities such as music ensembles, newspaper club, riding, canoeing or riding.

Careers. The school is a member of ISCO and all pupils take part in careers lessons as part of the curriculum. Pupils receive guidance from the tutor team backed up by two specialists in Careers and Higher Education planning. The school operates a work experience scheme in Year 12.

Admissions. Entry is by reports and reference from current school, selection normally taking place in the December prior to the year of entry. The main entries are at ages 4½, 7, 11, 13 and 16 although small numbers enter at other years. There are frequent open mornings which take place on Saturdays to allow all members of the family to visit. Enquiries on admissions should be made to the Registrar, at the school.

Fees per term (2008-2009). Infants £2,385; Junior: £2,865 (Day), £6,110 (Boarding); Senior: £4,060 (Day), £4,495 (Extended Day), £7,245 (Full/Weekly Boarding); Sixth Form: £4,125 (Day), £7,245 (Full/Weekly Boarding).

Charitable status. The Licensed Victuallers' School is a Registered Charity, number 230011. It exists to provide education for boys and girls.

Lincoln Minster School (UCST)

The Prior Building Upper Lindum Street Lincoln LN2 5RW

Tel: 01522 551300
Fax: 01522 551310
e-mail: enquiries.lincoln@church-schools.com
website: www.lincolnminsterschool.co.uk

Lincoln Minster School is a co-educational day and boarding school for pupils from 2½–18. The Pre-Prep, Preparatory, Senior School and boarding houses are all closely situated in the heart of historic Lincoln, very close to the Cathedral and Castle.

School Council:
Chairman: R Childs

Members:
Revd Canon Gavin Kirk, MA, Precentor of Lincoln Cathedral

M Lamb
P Croft
E Mackay
Prof B Davies
R Murton
Dr K Fickling
R Buttery
Mrs A Crowe
Mrs K McFarlane

Ex officio:
Sir Ewan Harper, CBE
J Nicholson
C Rickart
K Maltby

***Principal & Head of Senior School*: Mr Clive Rickart**, BA Hons, PGCE

Head of Preparatory School: Mrs Karen Maltby, BEd Hons, MEd

First Deputy Head:
Mr M Jacob, BSc Hons, Cert Immunol, PGCE, MA, NPQH (*Director of Teaching, Learning and Curriculum*)

Deputy Head (*Pastoral*): Mrs C McKenzie, BSc Hons, PGCE

Director of Studies: Mr S Grocott, BSc Hons, PGCE

Head of Sixth Form: Miss T Chappell, BA Hons, QTS

Deputy Head of Preparatory School: Mr M Pickering, BSc Hons, PGCE

Head of Pre-Preparatory School: Miss J Bunker, BEd

Registrar: Mrs D Jenkinson

Examinations Officer: Mrs A Pullen, BA Hons, PGCE

Heads of Department:
Mrs E Alexander-Grocott, BA Hons, PGCE (*Modern Foreign Languages*)
Mrs E Barclay, BEd Hons, PGCE (*Learning Support*)
Mrs A Brown, BA Hons, PGCE (*English*)
Mr M Burnett, CMS, MACE, DipCG, NEBOSH (*Careers*)
Mr L Collins, BSc Hons, PGCE, FRGS (*Geography & Director of E-Learning*)
Mr J Drake, BA Hons, PGCE (*Business Studies*)
Mrs R Gladwin, BA, PGCE (*Religious Education*)
Mrs K Hutchings, BEd Hons (*Girls' Physical Education*)
Mrs H Jeffrey, CertEd, MA (*Food Science*)
Mr S King, BEng Hons, PGCE (*ICT*)
Mrs H Mason, BSc Hons, GGCE (*Science*)
Mr J O'Hara, BSc Hons, PGCE (*Mathematics*)
Mr A Prentice, MA Hons, PGCE, LTCL (*Director of Music*)
Mrs J Rhodes, BA Hons, PGCE (*History, Head of Year 7*)
Mrs C Servonat-Blanc, BA Hons, PGCE (*Art & Photography*)
Mrs J Wafer, BA Hons, PGCE (*Drama*)
Mr R Wenban, BEd Hons (*Boys' Physical Education, Head of Year 10*)

Structure and Organisation. Lincoln Minster School is the result of three independent schools pooling their strengths under the forward thinking management of United Church Schools Trust, which owns and manages schools and academies across England. There is no doubt that membership of a group of this size gives Lincoln Minster School stability and breadth of contact. Fully co-educational, the school educates pupils from nursery to A Level on several delightful sites situated very closely together in the historic centre of Lincoln. In ten years the school has almost trebled its number on roll without losing the marked friendliness and responsiveness which make it so attractive.

The third phase of major development – a £10 million music school, recital hall and sports hall – is currently underway and is due for completion in December 2009.

Class sizes, the quality of teaching and discipline are carefully controlled. There is excellent pastoral care and award-winning careers provision designed to equip youngsters for life beyond the classroom.

Curriculum. A full range of subjects is offered and the school is proud of its excellent track record of examination success.

The curriculum is supported by a wealth of trips, visits and activities, too numerous to list, plus a comprehensive sports programme to cater for all tastes.

Pupils of all ages are encouraged to develop intellectual curiosity, resilience and self confidence and to begin their lives within a Christian framework.

Music. As the Choir School for Lincoln Cathedral, Lincoln Minster School provides for the all-round education of boy and girl choristers. 27 music staff work in the department; approximately 70% of pupils receive individual instrument lessons. Music is a focal point of school life and opportunities for public performances abound. The strong musical and Christian ethic within the school is enhanced by daily use of the School Chapel and the Cathedral.

Boarding. Weekly, termly and flexible boarding is offered. The large family of boarders is very much at the heart of the School. The junior boarders live in a period residence within a minute's walk of the Preparatory School, the senior girl boarders in Lindum View, the senior boys in Pottergate, and Year 12 and 13 boarders enjoy a more independent environment in Hillside. Each house has an experienced team of staff who together provide a high quality of care and educational guidance. A fifth boarding house has recently been acquired, near to the Senior School site.

Admissions. Lincoln Minster School welcomes pupils of a wide range of ability and all faiths. Admission is by interview and report, and subject to availability of a place.

Voice Trials, open to boys and girls 7–10 years, are held in November and March. These are worth up to 50% of boarding and tuition fees. Other dates by arrangement. For further details apply to The Registrar.

Scholarships. Academic Scholarships are available at 7+, 11+, 13+ and 16+. Music Scholarships are available at 11+, 13+ and 16+. Choral Bursaries are available for members of the Cathedral Choir.

Fees per term (2007-2008). Day: Nursery £1,887 (all day); Early Years £2,170 (all day); Pre-Prep £2,159; Prep £2,799; Seniors £3,150. Weekly Boarding: £4,763 (up to Year 6), £5,516 (Year 7–13). Termly Boarding: £5,139 (up to Year 6), £5,961 (Year 7–13).

Fees for Reception class to Year 13 include lunches.

Charitable status. Lincoln Minster School is part of The United Church Schools Trust which is a Registered Charity, number 1016538. It exists to provide education for boys and girls between the ages of 2½ and 18 years.

Longridge Towers School

Berwick-upon-Tweed Northumberland TD15 2XQ
Tel: 01289 307584
Fax: 01289 302581
e-mail: enquiries@lts.org.uk
website: www.lts.org.uk

Motto: *Carpe Diem*

Board of Governors:
Chairman: Mr I G McCreath, MBE
Vice-Chairman: Lady Caroline Douglas Home

Mrs J Coats
Lt Col (Retd) H Culley
Dr J Fisken
Mr J A Houston
Lord Joicey

***Headmaster*: Mr A E Clemit**, BA, MA

Deputy Head: Mr T Manning, BSc, PGCE
Assistant Head (*Curriculum*): Mr R Notman, BCom, PGCE
Head of Junior Department: Mrs S Phillips, CertEd

Teaching Staff:
Miss E Beattie, BA, PGCE (*Girls Games, Sports Studies*)
Ms D Bryden, BEd (*Junior Department*)
Mr M Caddick, BA, PGCE (*German*)
Mrs I Cheer, DTM, (*Music*)
Mrs B Chynoweth, MA, PGCE (*Junior Department*)
Mrs J Chiles, BS, PGCE (*Science*)
Mrs C R D Clemit, L-ès-L, M-ès-L, PGCE (*Modern Languages*)
Mr R Davie, BSc, PGCE (*Mathematics, Computing*)
Mr I Dempster, BEd (*History, Games*)
Mr P Dodd, DIS, PGCE (*Mathematics*)
Mr R Glenn (*ICT Coordinator*)
Mrs C Krzysiak, BSc, PGCE (*Biology*)
Mrs L Lee, MA(*Ed*), CertEd (*English, Drama*)
Mrs J Masey, BSc, PGCE (*Science*)
Mr P McParland, BSc, MSc, PGCE (*Geography, Mathematics*)
Mrs S Murray, BA, PGCE (*Junior Department*)
Miss R Noble, BA, PGCE (*English*)
Mrs H Notman, BSc, MSc, PGCE (*Head of Sixth Form, Economics*)
Miss J Oates, MA, PGCE (*Junior Department*)
Mr A Phillips, BA, PGCE (*Boys Games, German, Sports Studies*)
Mr M Plunkett, BA, CertRAS (*Art*)
Miss J Roberts, BEd (*Careers, PSHE, Psychology*)
Mr P Rowett, BA (*RE, History, Geography*)
Mrs M Smith, BSc, PGCE (*Games, Science*)
Ms P Turner (*Special Needs*)
Mr A Westthorp, BEng, PGCE (*CDT, Computing*)
Mrs F Weightman, MA, PGCE (*Modern Languages*)

Boarding Staff:
Mr S Douglas (*House Parent*)
Mrs S Hewitt (*Assistant House Parent*)
Mrs M Robson (*Resident Matron*)

Visiting Music Staff:
Mrs P Bonia
Mr S Ferguson
Mr K McAllister
Mr S McCormick
Mr D McDonald
Mrs M Rowland
Mrs C Smith
Mrs B Taylor

Speech & Drama: Mrs J Wilson

Medical Staff:
School Doctor: Dr S Ruffe
Matron: Miss C Coates, SRN

Administration:
Bursar: Mr S Bankier, BA, ACMA, FCMA
Assistant: Mr D Burns
Head's Secretary: Mrs J Higgins
Reception: Mrs C Jobson

Site Manager: Mr L Caldwell
Catering Manager: Mrs C Krause

The school occupies a Victorian Mansion set in 80 acres of woodland in the beautiful Tweed Valley and enjoys excellent road and rail links with England and Scotland. Daily bus services operate within a radius of 25 miles from the school.

Longridge Towers, refounded in 1983 under its founder and President, the late Lord Home of the Hirsel, has grown from 113 pupils to more than 300 pupils. It is probably unique in offering the close personal relationships between pupils, staff and parents which are only possible in a small school together with the facilities normally found in much larger schools, eg large sports hall, library, theatre etc.

Specialities. Academic fulfilment is sought for all pupils and pass rates at GCSE and A Level exceed 90% and 95% respectively. It is usual for all Sixth Formers to be offered places at university. Sport figures strongly in the life of the pupils and over 20 each year gain representative honours at county level in a variety of sports, such as rugby, hockey, cross-country running, athletics, tennis and cricket. Art, Music and Drama are also very popular and successful activities. Almost half of the pupils take private instrumental lessons and the taking of grade examinations is encouraged.

Entry. The school caters for a wide spectrum of abilities among its pupils who are taught in small classes. Special provision is made for the needs of pupils with mild dyslexia and for the small proportion of pupils for whom English is their second language.

Assessments upon entry to the Junior and Senior Departments in Mathematics and English are diagnostic and have no fixed pass mark.

The school is divided into 2 departments, Junior and Senior, and caters for pupils throughout their school career, from four to eighteen years. Pupils may enter at any age provided that a vacancy exists. Classes are small with less than 20 pupils per teaching set, reducing to about half this in the Sixth Form.

Activities. Longridge Towers is a school where the development of the pupils outside the academic sphere is considered to be vital. To this end there is a very wide range of activities and clubs in which pupils may participate and are encouraged to do so. The major team games are rugby, hockey, tennis, cross-country running, athletics and cricket. Many senior pupils participate in the Duke of Edinburgh's Award Scheme. The musical activities within the school are varied and numerous. There are two Choirs, an Orchestra and various instrumental groups. No visitor to the school could fail to be aware of the variety and excellence of the artwork on display which includes clay modelling and photography.

Public Examinations. The school follows an enhanced version of the National Curriculum and enters pupils for Key Stage testing at Key Stages 1 and 2. Twenty-two subjects are offered at GCSE level, including Physics, Chemistry and Biology and 19, including Economics, Psychology, Sports Studies and Drama, are offered in the Sixth Form at A or AS Level.

Parents receive reports half-yearly and three-weekly Grade Cards ensure that they are kept up to date about their children's progress.

Boarding. The Boarding House has recently been refurbished, and pastoral care is in the hands of resident non-teaching house parents. There is medical and dental care. Pupils have access to telephones and e-mail and may send or receive fax messages using the facilities in the school office. Boarders may attend on a weekly or termly basis from age 8 years onwards. At weekends the boarders participate in a wide range of activities.

Scholarships and Bursaries. Academic awards at various levels are available annually to pupils aged 11, 13 and 16 (into Sixth Form). Music and Sports Scholarships are also available.

Bursaries are available to children of serving members of the Armed Forces.

Bursaries are also available to pupils seeking entry to Form 1 (NC Year 7); the value of these is determined after consideration of a statement of parental income.

Fees per term (2008-2009). Full Boarders: £6,205 (Junior), £6,630 (Senior). Weekly Boarders: £5,560 (Junior), £5,985 (Senior). Day pupils: £2,000 (Junior age 4–7), £2,735 (Junior age 7–11), £3,160 (Senior age 11–18).

Charitable status. Longridge Towers School is a Registered Charity, number 513534. It exists to provide an academic education for boys and girls.

Milton Abbey School

Near Blandford Dorset DT11 0BZ
Tel: 01258 880484
Fax: 01258 881194; Headmaster: 01258 881250
e-mail: info@miltonabbey.co.uk
website: www.miltonabbey.co.uk

Visitor: C J Driver, BA, BEd, MPhil

Governors:

Chairman: J K E Stanford, OBE

R D Barbour, FRICS
The Lady Elizabeth Barne
J E A Barnes, BA, PGCE
P H G Bradley, BA, BAI, ACA
¶A A B R Bruce of Crionaich
General Sir Jack Deverall, KCB, OBE, FRSA, FICPD
Mrs J C Dwyer, BEd
¶Captain N Hadden-Paton
P W McGrath, MA, MW
Mrs R A McKenzie-Johnston
Revd C W Mitchell-Innes, MA
D P O'Brien, QC, MA
¶P M G Stopford-Adams, FSI, FPSI, DL
Sir Philip Williams, Bt, MA, JP, DL
S J Young, MC, JP, FRICS, DL

Clerk to the Governors: Ms S J White
Finance Director: Mrs S Way

Staff:
***Headmaster*: W J Hughes-D'Aeth**, TD, BA

Second Master: N Arkell, BSc

M Benjafield, BSc
T Birkill, BSc, PGCE
S Bradbury, BA, MPhil
S J Brown, BSc
Mrs S Burton, BA
M S Clapper, BSc
Mrs R Dal Din, BSc, PGCE
Ms R Davies, BA, PGCE
†Mrs P Doubleday, CertEd, RSA
C Douchet, Maîtrise, DP, LPC, PGCE
Ms E Dudley, BSc
R Durrant, BA
R Edwards, FIH
Mrs J Emerson, FIL
Mrs H Goodinge, BA, CertEd
Mrs C Hallam, CertEd, CertSpLD
J Hinchcliffe, MA, RCA
Mrs F Hughes-D'Aeth, BA, MA
Mrs R Kerby, BA, RSA
†S Kibler, BA, PGCE
D E Lane, BSc, PGCE
P Lord, BA, MA
*H A Miéville, BA, MA, DipEdMan
*J D Milman, MA, DPhil, CertEd, MIBiol
D Mohamed, BSc, PGCE
R P L Nicholson, CertEd
†O Parkin, BSc
M Phipps, BEd
*A M Prior, BEd
Mrs M Raindle, MSc, BScEd
J Ratcliffe, BA
Mrs J Riley, BEd, CertEd
Ms J Roberts, BA, PGCE
M J Sale, CertEd, DMS
M D Sharp, BA, MA, CertEd
Miss R Sherbrooke, BA, PGCE
Dr F Shon, BA, MA, DPhil, PGCE
B N Shore, BA
R Simpson, BSc, PGCE
A Stroud
The Revd R Thomson, BA
M Watson, BSc, PGCE

*Miss K P Wightman, BA, PGCE, DipEd	†A Wilson, MA, BMus, FRCO, FTCL
†M Williams	†Mrs L Wingate-Grey
	P W Wood, BA

Foundation. Milton Abbey was founded in 1954 and comprises 219 boys aged 13–18 and 18 Sixth Form girls. It aims to provide a Christian education, to develop individual potential as fully as possible and to furnish wide opportunities for the exercise of responsibility. Milton Abbey helps to produce pupils who mature into balanced adults. Boys and girls who may find that a competitive environment drains their confidence can be judged by their own capabilities and encouraged to achieve their maximum potential. The school provides a framework of rigorous kindness in a safe but stimulating environment with a well-qualified and enthusiastic team of teaching and pastoral staff who know each individual well.

Situation. The School lies in a wooded valley on the site of a Benedictine Monastery (founded 1,000 years ago) and a short distance from the picturesque village of Milton Abbas. The nearest towns are Blandford and Dorchester. The campus provides ample space for playing fields and a nine-hole Golf course.

Buildings. The two remaining buildings of the Monastery are the Great Abbey, which is now the School Chapel, and the Abbot's Hall around which a Georgian mansion was built by the Earl of Dorchester in 1770. Today these great buildings form a perfect partnership to fulfil the needs of a boarding school. Outside the mansion house, the modern facilities which are on a par with those of a much larger school include Music school, Art Studio, Pottery, a Technology/Computer building, a 370-seat theatre, an all-weather pitch, an indoor heated 25-metre pool, a cricket pavilion, and a Design Technology centre and new Library.

Organisation. There are five boarding houses within the main building and a separate boarding house for girls. During the first year boys are housed in a dormitory of up to 4 boys. From the second year onwards the majority move into study-bedrooms for up to three occupants. In the Sixth Form pupils usually have single study-bedrooms. The School takes meals in the Abbot's Hall where the cafeteria service provides an informal atmosphere, but is well-disciplined.

Curriculum. All boys follow a broad and balanced curriculum up to GCSE. A boy is setted separately in most subjects, enabling him to work towards his academic goals at a comfortable pace. Most GCSE subjects are taken in year 10. Entry to the Sixth Form is dependent upon an interview, a literacy assessment test and team-building exercises with the Headmaster.

The Sixth Form offers a range of academic courses which incorporate traditional, bluechip ASs and A2s; vocational BTECs; and top-up GCSEs. Combinations are possible from: mathematics, further mathematics, physics, chemistry, biology, history, classical civilisation, English, French, Spanish, geography, religious studies, business studies, economics, art, music, music technology, design and technology, communication studies, drama, physical education; and these BTECs: Hospitality, Countryside Management, Sport and Exercise Science and Equine Studies.

Music. Individual tuition is available in all instruments, and in singing. A strong tradition of choral singing supports worship in the Abbey. Ensembles of all sorts perform music in a notably wide variety of styles.

Clubs and Societies. A wide range of interests and activities are encouraged in free time.

CCF and Community Service. The school's thriving CCF contingent has Royal Navy, Army and RAF sections, and enjoys close links with service establishments in the area. There are regular camps in the holidays. There are expeditions at home and abroad. Every weekend offers an opportunity for a boy to choose from caving, climbing, sailing, windsurfing and canoeing. Most boys take part in the Duke of Edinburgh's Award Scheme. Community service is the alternative to the CCF.

Games. Christmas Term: Rugby, Football, Hockey and Netball. Easter Term: Hockey, Lacrosse and Cross-Country. Summer Term: Cricket, Athletics, Dinghy Sailing and Racing in Portland Harbour, Tennis and Rounders. All year round: Swimming, Squash, Rifle Shooting, Basketball, Golf, Polo, Fencing, Riding, Canoeing and Clay Pigeon Shooting.

Admission. The flexible curriculum and the small size of classes enable the school to cater effectively for a wide spread of ability. A few qualify through the Scholarship Examination held in May. The majority sit the Common Entrance Examination in June for entry in the following Autumn Term. An average of 50% in the Common Entrance ensures a place but the School is also prepared to consider a few candidates who seem unlikely to reach this standard because their academic progress has been uneven. Sixth Form assessment day in February.

Fees per term (2008-2009). Boarding £9,060, Day £6,800.

Scholarships. (*see Scholarship Entries section*). Several Scholarships are awarded annually including ones for Academic, Music, Drama, DT, Art, Sailing and Sport. Bursaries may also be considered in cases of need.

Charitable status. The Council of Milton Abbey School Limited is a Registered Charity, number 306318. It is a charitable Trust for the secondary education of boys.

North Cestrian Grammar School

Dunham Road Altrincham Cheshire WA14 4AJ
Tel: 0161 928 1856
Fax: 0161 929 8657
e-mail: office@ncgs.co.uk
website: www.ncgs.co.uk

North Cestrian Grammar School was founded in 1951 to provide independent grammar school education for boys aged 11–16 with a co-educational Sixth Form. From September 2008 the School will become wholly co-educational.

As befits a School of 300 pupils attention to the individual is a reality, not an empty phrase. Over the years the School has acquired an enviable reputation for developing confidence and getting the best out of each child so that today's pupils come not only from the locality but from as far afield as North Manchester, Warrington, Macclesfield and the heart of rural Cheshire.

Board of Governors:

Chairman: Mr I T Parrott

Mr T D Brown	Mr J H Moss
Mr R Burdge	Dr A Pocklington
Mr D J Common	Mrs R Smart
Mrs S Forster	Mr N Swerling
Mr J-P Glaskie	Mr C D Wheeler
Mr D Merrell	Mr A Wong
Mr P F Morton	

***Headmaster*: D G Vanstone**, MA

Deputy Head: N Dunn, BSc

Assistant Staff:

F I Barclay, BA	R E Thompson, BSc
R A Pippett, BSc	M Whittam, BA, ATD
N G Brown, BA, MEd	D Cruxton, BA
M P Sharpe, BA	Mrs G R Piatkiewicz, BEd
P A Stott, BA	Mrs F Entwistle, BA
D J Bradley, MA	Ms J Sandy, BA
R W Horridge, BA	Mrs J James, BSc
C W Robinson, BA, DipEd	Mrs L Facchin, BA

P Stobbs, BA
K Jackman, BA
A Boswell, BA
A Heslop, BEng
Mrs E Holmes, BSc
P Robinson, BSc
D Healey, BA
Mrs C Varney, DipComm
Mrs R Boyd, MA, BM
Mrs R Kenyon, BSc
Mrs P Patterson, BSc

Dyslexia Specialists:
Mrs B Robson, MEd, TEFL, DipSLD, AMBDA
Mrs M Wheelan, PGDipSpLD, AMBDA

Bursar: Mrs M Ratcliffe, AAT, CIMA
Librarian: Mrs Y Stevenson
Office Staff: Mrs C Brown, Mrs S M Roby

Facilities. The School is housed in fine modern buildings constructed around an imposing Victorian mansion. Continuing investment in school facilities has provided excellent teaching accommodation including five laboratories, a computer suite, technology wing and language laboratory. A splendid new Library and an impressive Assembly Hall have recently been completed. Art has special provision for ceramics and photography and there are specialist suites for most departments. In addition to a well-equipped and spacious sports hall, the 20 acre sports grounds provide pitches for soccer, hockey and cricket, alongside an athletics track and tennis courts.

Academic. The School aims to provide a balanced curriculum offering each pupil a broad range of subjects. High standards of academic work are expected with an emphasis on individual guidance. The majority of pupils are prepared for 9 GCSEs, but a small group are offered the chance to follow a restricted curriculum of 7 subjects within small teaching sets and with additional learning support. There is a wide and expanding range of A Levels for students to choose from in the Sixth Form. These include recently introduced options such as Sports Science, Information Systems and Music Technology. Most students secure places at University.

Junior pupils are taught in parallel classes. Specialist dyslexia and support staff are available to give individual assistance by private arrangement. From Year 10 there is some streaming, based upon ability in Maths and English, with a view to accelerating the pace for the most able whilst providing smaller teaching groups for those who need most attention. There is also a comprehensive PSE and Careers Programme.

North Cestrian has a reputation for individual support and personal development in both academic and social terms and "added value" is closely monitored through the use of NFER assessment. Extensive success in this area has been recognised both statistically and in the School's most recent ISI inspection report.

Extra-Curricular Activity. A wide range of extra-curricular activities aims to allow each pupil to excel in some area, thus building his confidence and self-esteem. North Cestrian has a strong sporting tradition and there is an extensive programme of inter-school fixtures. National and county honours have been gained in hockey, athletics, swimming, football and basketball. Regular holidays are offered both in Britain and abroad and the Languages Department conducts a series of annual foreign visits to strengthen European awareness. The Duke of Edinburgh's Award Scheme is well supported and there is a series of outdoor pursuit trips for junior pupils. Public speaking, board games, music, drama and an extensive charity programme are a reflection of the care taken to oversee the development of the whole pupil in a friendly and supportive family atmosphere.

Admission. There is a competitive examination in February for entry at 11+ and 13+ and applications for the Sixth Form are considered on the basis of predicted GCSE grades. Entry into other years is possible when vacancies permit.

Scholarships. A limited number of Academic Scholarships are offered for admission to Year 7, based upon performance in the Entrance Examination. Bursaries based upon family income are made at the discretion of the Governors.

Fees per term (2008-2009). £2,490 (£7,470 per annum).

Location. The School is situated conveniently close to central Alrincham and there are few Manchester or Cheshire schools so easily accessible by either public or private transport. Ideally placed for mainline trains and buses which converge on Altrincham, the Metrolink provides a rapid link and regular service from Central Manchester whilst outlying districts are served by school coaches. Travel by car is equally easy as the School lies close to the A56 and within two miles of Junction 7/8 on the M56.

Further Information. A School Prospectus, Sixth Form Brochure and GCSE Options Booklet are available on application to the School Office. Parents and their children are welcome at twice yearly Open Evenings held in November and January, but alternative arrangements for a personal interview and tour of the School at any reasonable time can be made through the Office.

Charitable status. North Cestrian Grammar School is a Registered Charity, number 525925. It exists for the purpose of educating children.

Northamptonshire Grammar School

Pitsford Hall Pitsford Northamptonshire NN6 9AX
Tel: 01604 880306
Fax: 01604 882212
e-mail: office@ngs-school.com
website: www.ngs-school.com

Governing Body:

Chairman: Mr K Kruger

Mrs J Tice**
Mr P Corbishley
Mr M Adams
Mrs C Shirley**
Mrs S Norris
Revd S Trott
Mr J Lockhart
Mr J Kitchen
Mr G Shemeld*
Mr G Milner*

** *Foundation Governor*
* *Parent Governor*

***Headmaster*: Mr N R Toone**, BSc, MInstP, FRSA

Director of Studies: Miss S M Jackson, BSc
Head of the Junior School: Mrs J Cooper, BA

Mrs L Brown, BA (*Junior School*)
Miss T Calnan, BEd (*Junior School*)
Mrs L A Chacksfield, BEd (*Girls Games and RS*)
Mme M H Conroy, BA France (*Junior School*)
Mrs J Cowie, BA (*Junior School*)
Mr M E Dean, BSc (*Physics*)
Mrs J M Drakeford, BSc (*Chemistry and Biology*)
Mme C R Filliol, BA (*Modern Languages*)
Mrs S Goode, BSc Econ (*Junior School*)
Mr C Haines, BSc (*Physics, Boys Games*)
Mr D A Hallowell, BEd (*History*)
Mr J Hansford, BA (*Mathematics*)
Miss K Harkin, BA (*Junior School*)
Mrs F Jeffrey, BA (*Junior School*)
Mr A Lee, BA (*Art*)
Mrs J M Leeke, BSc (*Mathematics*)
Mr M J Lewis, BSc, FRGS, FRMetS (*Geography*)
Mrs L M Lyon, BEd (*Modern Languages*)
Mrs S E Matts, BSc, MA Ed, MIBiol, CBiol (*Biology*)
Mrs M Monaghan, BA (*Geography and Girls' Games*)
Mr A J Moodie, BA (*Music*)
Mrs S E Perin, BA (*Modern Languages*)
Mr J Saker, MA (*Modern Languages*)
Ms K Semus, MA (*ICT*)

Mr J Smorfitt, BA (*Economics*)
Mr C D Stanley, MA (*English*)
Mr C L Stoner, BSc (*Mathematics*)
Mr R P Tickle, BA, DipTh (*History and Religious Studies*)
Mr I Tovey, MSc (*Chemistry*)
Mr J A White, BA, DipTh (*English*)
Mrs J Willmott, BEd (*Junior School*)
Mrs L Wilson, BEd (*Junior School*)

Age Range. 4–18 Co-educational.

Number of Pupils. 360 boys and girls.

Fees per term (2008-2009). Junior School: £2,035–£3,300, Senior School: £3,532 Lunches: £200.

The School is set in 25 acres, four miles north of the county town. It was founded in 1989 and takes pupils from the age of 4 to 18. A full range of academic subjects through to GCSE, A Level and University entrance is taught. The curriculum draws on the best of the grammar school traditions of the past, makes them relevant to today's needs, and ensures that they are applicable to the demands of the future.

The School aims to educate the whole person and sets, expects and maintains high standards in all its disciplines and extra-curricular activities. Competition in both work and sport is encouraged and emphasis is placed on developing the highest personal and moral qualities. The School has not formed a particular connection with any one religious denomination, but strives to portray a living Christianity that reflects the whole range of denominations and it is sympathetic to other faiths. Assemblies, church services and religious education on the timetable ensure that moral and spiritual values underpin all the work. *Old Pitsfordians* leave as mature, sensitive individuals with an excellent academic grounding, a high level of self-discipline and a broad range of skills.

Pupils usually join at the age of 11, entering Year 7 either from the Junior School or from other local schools. The School enjoys a strong academic reputation, which is complemented with effective pastoral support and a wide range of extra-curricular activities. Entry to the Senior School is selective; the academic curriculum is designed to cater for the upper 40% of the ability range and the selection criteria is based upon this. It is expected that all pupils will take 10 GCSEs before transferring to the Sixth Form at the end of Year 11.

The Sixth Form is structured to provide a stepping stone from the discipline of the Senior School to the demands of Higher Education. Each Sixth Form student has his or her own tutor, who is normally one of their A Level teachers. Sixth Formers take a full part in the life of the School and many have positions of responsibility.

The extra curricular programme at Northamptonshire Grammar incorporates three elements: Service, Sports and Skills. In the main, these activities take place after school until 5.20 pm. The School currently has a junior percussion band, wind, string and guitar ensembles, two rock bands, a Senior and Junior choir and an emergent orchestra. A number of drama productions are staged every year, with usually a large musical performance every other year.

The Junior School was established in 1991 to act as a bridge for pupils to enter the Senior School at 11. All pupils are taught by class teachers and in addition, receive specialist teaching in Games, Gymnastics, French, Information Technology and Music. The sports taught include Rugby, Hockey, Cricket, Rounders, Tennis, Cross-Country Running, Netball and Athletics. All pupils are taught to play the recorder and encouraged to read music. Many learn to play other instruments. All pupils take part in Drama lessons and many enjoy extra Speech lessons.

A number of academic and other scholarships are awarded annually. Further details can be obtained from the School.

Charitable status. Northamptonshire Independent Grammar School Charity Trust Limited is a Registered Charity, number 298910.

Oswestry School

Upper Brook Street Oswestry Shropshire SY11 2TL
Tel: 01691 655711
Fax: 01691 671194
e-mail: enquiries@oswestryschool.org.uk
website: www.oswestryschool.org.uk

Oswestry School, founded in 1407, is the second oldest non-denominational school in England. It was founded by David Holbache and Gwynhyfar, his wife. The School is registered as a Charitable Trust and administered by a Board of Governors which is in membership with the Association of Governing Bodies of Independent Schools.

Governing Board:
Chairman: P T Wilcox-Jones
Vice-Chairman: B Morgan

Prof J Barrett
M Bebb
P M Bracegirdle
The Revd Preb D B Crowhurst
P D Edwards
Miss B Y Gull
W S Keable
J D Payne
Mrs J G Middleton
Mrs A Morris
B Stacey
M J Thorpe
A D R Wood
Mrs H P Yates

***Headmaster*: P D Stockdale**, BSc, MEd, PGCE, MIBiol, CBiol

Deputy Head (Academic): R G Evanson, BA Wales, PGCE London

Senior Master and Head of Sixth Form: N F Lambkin, BA Wales, MPhil Wales, PGCE

Director of Music: Mrs S J Morris, CertEd, ATCL

Business Manager: Mr S J Malkin, BSc, ACIS

School Medical Officer: Dr St John Taylor

Oswestry School is a co-educational day and boarding school for pupils aged 2 to 18. Pupils are taught on two closely situated sites. The Pre-Prep Department – Bellan House – which is situated in the town centre, takes children from Nursery to Year 4 and is for children aged 2 to 8+ (ie those who will be 9 by 31st August). The Senior School, located on the outskirts of the town, caters for Years 5 to 13, ages 9 to 18, both day and boarding.

The School moved to its present site in 1776. Its beautiful grounds and playing fields occupy a site of 50 acres. There is an ongoing programme of building and refurbishment. Most recently, the School opened a new dining hall, music centre and tennis courts. A new Sixth Form boys' boarding house was completed in January 2006. The School also has a 20-metre indoor heated swimming pool.

The School has a modern outlook but respects 'old fashioned' values and is proud of its warm, caring 'family' atmosphere. Its distinctive ethos allows the School to give much individual care and attention to pupils and to motivate them as they make academic and personal progress. Class sizes are small throughout the school and the teacher: pupil ratio is very generous, thus allowing every individual pupil to find the opportunity to excel. High quality teaching enables each pupil to reach their academic potential regardless of ability, but equally significant, they acquire skills, confidence and leadership qualities through participation in a broad range of activities and by taking on a variety of responsibilities.

The School aims to maintain discipline and good manners in all aspects, and operates as a community which seeks to safeguard the rights of the individual. Each member of the community should have the chance to grow in knowledge and self confidence, encouraged by staff and pupils alike. School rules are based on the fundamental tenet that individuals need to recognise their own responsibilities to others and conduct themselves with self-discipline. Rules are enforced firmly but fairly.

The School motto is 'We learn not for school but for life'.

Curriculum. The School aims to provide a broad general education up to GCSE with more specialised subjects in the Sixth Form. At present, the following subjects are taught to AS/A2 level: Art, Biology, Business Studies, Chemistry, Critical Thinking, Design Technology, English Literature, French, German, Geography, History, Information Communication Technology, Mathematics and Further Mathematics, Music, Philosophy, Physics, Psychology, Sports and Physical Education.

Special provision is available for those with learning difficulties in a purpose-designed Learning Support Unit. Most of our pupils proceed to the Sixth Form and virtually all our Sixth Formers then move on to university. The School ensures that all Sixth Formers are prepared for the transition to university.

Boarders. Boarders are accommodated in three houses: School House for boys up to Year 11, Holbache House for Sixth Form boys and Guinevere House for girls. Guinevere House has an annex attached for Sixth Form girls. Each house is headed by house parents who have overall responsibility for the welfare and general progress of the boarders.

School Chapel. The School Chapel, built in 1863, plays an important part in the life of the School. The School is non-denominational and services are as broadly based as possible within the Christian tradition. The School Chaplain has an important role in the pastoral structure of the School.

Games. The School has a strong tradition of participation in sports. All pupils are expected to participate in games unless medically exempt. Football, rugby, cricket, swimming, athletics and tennis are the main sports for boys while netball, hockey, rounders, football, swimming and tennis are available for girls. The School has extensive playing fields extending to some 30 acres and its own indoor swimming pool.

Out of School Activities. There is a wide range of extra-curricular activities including music, art, photography, debating, chess, mountain biking, sailing, kayaking, ballet, model making, swimming and computing. The School also has the Decimus Society which exists to promote all matters philosophical and to engage its members with the intellectual adventure of ideas. All boarders are encouraged to join at least two clubs.

CCF and Community Service. There is an active CCF contingent, membership of which is voluntary after two years' service; pupils can also pursue the Duke of Edinburgh's Award Scheme.

Admissions. Boys and girls are accepted into the Senior School from the age of 9, although applications are always considered for entry up to Year 10 and for Sixth Form. Scholarships are available at 9+, 11+, 13+ and 16+.

Registration fee: £50.

Fees per term (2008-2009). Day Pupils: £3,345 (Years 5 and 6), £3,745 (Years 7 and 8), £3,965 (Years 9–13). Weekly Boarding (age 9–18) £5,945. Boarding (age 9–18) £6,745.

Scholarships. (*see Scholarship Entries section*). The Governors offer a number of academic scholarships each year for conspicuously talented individuals, each of which remits up to 50% of the tuition fees. Scholarships are available at 9+, 11+, 13+ and 16+. Scholarships are also available in Art, Music and Sport.

Further details of all these Scholarships are available from the Headmaster.

Reductions for Services Families. Generous awards are available for children of Services personnel (when the child is in full-time education).

Old Oswestrians. Secretary: S G Hodge Esq, The Old Coach House, Bayshill Lane, Montpellier, Cheltenham, Glos GL50 3AX.

Charitable status. Oswestry School is a Registered Charity, number 1079822. It exists to provide education for boys and girls.

Our Lady of Sion School

Gratwicke Road Worthing West Sussex BN11 4BL
Tel: 01903 204063
Fax: 01903 214434
e-mail: enquiries@sionschool.org.uk
website: www.sionschool.org.uk

A thriving town school, we offer a complete education from Nursery to University entrance. Our aim is to encourage each young person in our care to be the best that he or she possibly can, and to prepare children for adult life, as citizens who can make a positive contribution to the world. At Our Lady of Sion, we seek to provide all our students with opportunities to achieve excellence in an atmosphere of tolerance and understanding. All members of the School Community are encouraged to embrace the school motto 'Consideration Always'.

Our school, established in 1862, has enjoyed a long and quietly illustrious history. Throughout this time, the school has always fostered its hallmarks of care and consideration, and unity within diversity. We are a fully co-educational school with all pupils enjoying the same opportunities in a small family community. Combining the very best of our traditions with a forward-looking approach enables us to meet the educational challenges of the 21st century. Our Staff to pupil ratio is excellent, and pupils are usually taught in groups of less than 20.

Our Lady of Sion School is one of a number of schools worldwide established by the Sisters of the Congregation of Our Lady of Sion, whose aims were simple: to foster bridge-building, tolerance and understanding. They were inspired by the ideals of reconciliation between Christian and Jewish faiths, promoted by their founders Theodore and Alphonse Ratisbonne.

Governors:
There are currently twelve governors: four are Sisters of Sion, appointed by the Provincial of the Congregation of Sion, and the remainder are drawn from a range of backgrounds, bringing invaluable expertise in many key areas to the school.

Mrs P Eggebrecht (*Chairman*)
Sr Margaret Shepherd nds (*Provincial of the Sisters of Our Lady of Sion, UK and Ireland*)
Mr S Alcock
Mr B Fielding
Sr Mary Camilleri nds
Mrs K Henwood
Sr Clare Jardine nds
Mr M Spofforth
Sr Elise Saudan nds
Mr G Taylor
Mr W Tree
Dr R Woodward-Court

School Management:

***Headmaster*: Mr M Scullion**, MA, BEd

Bursar: Mr K Woodcock, ACIB
Deputy Head, Senior School: Mrs P Starkey, BSc, PGCE
Deputy Head, Junior School: Mr J Summers, BA, PGCE

Senior School

Senior Teachers, Heads of Faculties, Year Group Coordinators:

Mr J Arnold, BEd (*Faculty Head, Geography; Assistant Examinations Officer*)
Mr P Baker, BSc Econ, PGCE (*Senior Teacher; History; Careers; Head of House*)
Mrs J Baker, BEd (*Faculty Head, PE; Year 10 Coordinator*
Mrs A Coe, BA, PGCE (*Faculty Head, Modern Languages*)

Mr M Hoarty, BSc, CertEd (*Senior Teacher; Faculty Head, Mathematics*)
Mrs J Monaghan, BA, PGCE (*English, Drama, Tear 11 Coordinator*)
Mrs A Paine, MA, PGCE (*Art; Year 7 Coordinator*)
Mr J Ramasami, BA, PGCE (*Religious Studies, PSCHE, Yr 9 Coordinator*
Mr K Tilley, MSc, PGCE (*Senior Teacher; Faculty Head, Science; Chemistry; Head of Sixth Form*)
Miss E Walker, MA, CertEd (*Faculty Head, English*)
Mrs A Whitchurch, BA, DipMus (*Senior Teacher; Director of Studies, Head of Music; PSCHE*)

Total number of Senior School Staff: 27 Full-time, 11 Part-time

Junior School

Heads of Department:
Miss S Dawson, NNEB (*Head of Nursery*)
Mrs L Leng, TCert, BEd (*Senior Teacher; Form Teacher Year 3*)

Total number of Junior School Staff: 11 Full-time, 9 Part-time

Our Lady of Sion is a fully co-educational school, taking boys and girls from age 2½ to 18 years. The school is divided into the Junior and Senior Schools, which are housed in separate buildings. Currently there are 553 pupils on roll, including 54 pupils in the Sixth Form.

Admission to the Junior School at Key Stage 1 is at the discretion of the Deputy Head following the child's introductory visit and an interview with his/her parents. Key Stage 2 pupils will be tested in English, Mathematics and Reasoning as well as spending 2 days in the school.

Admission to the Senior School is on a selective basis, and is offered on attainment of acceptable results in written examinations in English, Mathematics, Reasoning and French (for those who have already studied this subject), parent and pupil interview with the Headmaster and satisfactory references from previous schools. In the Sixth Form, admission for all pupils, both internal and external, is dependent upon GCSE results and satisfactory school reports. External candidates may be required to spend some time in school before the offer of a place is confirmed.

Fees per term (2008-2009). Senior School £2,930–£3,050; Junior School £1,905–£2,355. Nursery fees depend on number of days or half days attended. The school accepts the Nursery Grant for 3–5 year olds.

Curriculum. We pride ourselves on offering a balanced, relevant and flexible curriculum.

The Junior School works in close partnership with parents to ensure that children develop as individuals. A comprehensive curriculum enables all pupils to achieve their full potential, supported by highly qualified teachers. Pupils are taught in small groups and, in addition to the core subjects, French, Music, PE and Science are taught by specialist staff. Many after-school clubs and activities are offered, with supervision being available from 8.00 to 17.00.

In the Senior School, Years 7–9 pupils study a wide range of subjects, aimed at giving them a broad base from which to make their future choices. In 2008 we offer 22 subjects at GCSE Level and 19 subjects at AS/A Level. Mathematics, English Language, English Literature, a Modern Language, Religious Studies and currently at least one Science subject are compulsory at GCSE Level. From September 2008, we shall be offering A Level Law as an additional subject.

Languages: Pupils can take French, German, and Spanish at GCSE, and at A Level.

English Language and Literature are offered at GCSE, and English Literature at AS and A Level.

Science: Dual or triple Science Awards are offered at GCSE; Biology, Chemistry and Physics are offered at A Level.

ICT is taught across the curriculum as an integral part of each subject. We offer Applied ICT as a Double Award GCSE and AS and A Level ICT.

Business and Economics is offered at GCSE, AS and A Level.

Mathematics is offered at GCSE, AS and A Level.

Geography is offered at GCSE, AS and A Level.

History: Modern World History is offered at GCSE and History at AS and A Level.

Design & Technology: Resistant Materials is offered at GCSE and Product Design is offered at A Level.

Home Economics: Food and Nutrition is offered at GCSE.

Music: Every pupil is encouraged to discover and enjoy Music. Music is offered as a subject at GCSE, AS and A Level, with Music Technology being offered at AS and A Level. There is a vibrant extra-curricular music programme, which features regular formal and informal concerts. The Junior School award-winning Festival Choir performs several public concerts each year.

Drama and Dance are offered as GCSE options. Both departments aim to involve pupils actively in all aspects of drama and performance arts. Students can participate in productions, either by performing or being involved in vital backstage work. At least two major productions are staged each year, as well as performances of GCSE practical coursework.

Physical Education is offered at GCSE, AS and A Level.

Art and Design is offered at GCSE and A Level. The Art Department plays an integral part in supporting school events, providing exhibitions and display materials, and creating scenery and backgrounds for school music and drama productions.

Psychology is offered as an AS and A Level option.

Sport, Community Service and Clubs. Physical Education encourages a sense of fair play, sportsmanship and consideration, along with a positive attitude towards fitness and health. Activities range from traditional games, swimming galas and sports days to outdoor pursuits and ski trips. PE is offered as a GCSE and AS Level subject.

Clubs include a full range of Music and Sporting lunchtime and after school practices, plus Animal Action, Art Club, Dance Club, Debating Society, Gym Club and Design and Technology Club.

School Life. *Uniform*: All pupils, except those in Nursery, are expected to wear the Sion School uniform. Sixth formers are allowed to wear their own (suitable) clothes.

Houses: There are three Houses, corresponding to form groups. Houses have their own prefects, and compete against each other in academic, sporting and extra-curricular events. The House Cup is awarded, termly in the Junior School and annually in the Senior School, to the House having the highest number of house points.

Heads of School and Prefects: The Head Boy and Head Girl are appointed by a selective process, which allows all Sixth Form pupils to put themselves forward as candidates. Prefects are appointed to take specific responsibilities within the school. Year 6 pupils in the Junior School are allocated monitor duties.

Spiritual and Community Life. Our Lady of Sion School is a Catholic Foundation with an ecumenical spirit and outlook. We are rooted in the ideals of tolerance and understanding, welcoming children of different faiths and beliefs. We aim to create a strong educational community, promoting the highest academic standards and encouraging each child to develop to the best of their ability, while at the same time developing an atmosphere of mutual respect. We stress the importance of our awareness of the views, traditions and needs of others and the promotion of justice in the wider world. Religious Education and whole school assemblies are an integral part of the educational programme. In addition the school community supports a number of charitable causes, recognising our role in the world around us.

Discipline. We encourage and promote the highest possible standards, for the benefit and growth of everyone in the school.

In the Junior School, house points are awarded in recognition of good conduct, helpfulness or a high standard of achievement. Bullying, rough play or bad manners are not tolerated. In the Senior School, merit slips are awarded by the teaching staff to promote and publicise achievement, and encourage students to do their best. They can be awarded in recognition of good work, or for making a positive contribution to school life.

Charitable status. Our Lady of Sion School, Worthing is a Registered Charity, number 1121398. It exists to provide a high-quality education and spiritual framework for children and to prepare them for a positive role in the world.

Padworth College

Padworth Reading Berkshire RG7 4NR
Tel: 0118 983 2644
Fax: 0118 983 4515
e-mail: info@padworth.com
website: www.padworth.com

Founded 1963.

Padworth College is a co-educational boarding and day school for students aged 13–19 from the UK and all over the world. We aim to bring an informal tutorial-style atmosphere to school level education giving individual attention in very small classes underpinned by excellent pastoral care. The College's rural setting provides a peaceful and secure environment for study, yet the campus is within easy reach of the university town of Reading and just 45 minutes by road from Heathrow.

Senior Leadership Team:

***Principal*: Linde Melhuish**, BA, MA, PGCE, NPQH
Director of Studies: Simon Pinfield, BSc, MSc, PGCE, CELTA
Director of International Study Centre: Belinda Sumner, CertEd, RSA Dip TEFLA
Director of Easter and Summer School: Arthur Shields, MA, CertEd
Head of Boarding: Gordon Wilson, MA
Bursar: James Wilson

Academic Staff:

Accountancy:
Jane Joy, CertEd, RSA Dip

Art and Design:
Marianna Ziffo, BA, PGCE, Cert TEFLA
Roxana Shields, BA, MA

Business Studies:
Arthur Shields, MA, CertEd
Jane Joy, CertEd, RSA Dip

Design and Technology:
Stuart Boyd, BSc

Economics:
Janette Winnick, BA, MA, BCom, HDipEd

English:
Linde Melhuish, BA, MA, OGCE, NPQH
Gordon Wilson, MA
Kathryn Wills, BA, MA, PGCE

Geography:
Alexander Mitlehner, BSc, MSc, PhD, PGCE
Simon Pinfield, BSc, MSc, PGCE, CELTA

History and Politics:
David Peacock, BA, PhD, PGCE

History of Art:
Valerie Baker, BA, LL Dip

Information Technology and Computing:
Jane Joy, CertEd, RSA Dip
Clive Trinder, BA, PGCE

Law:
Valerie Baker, BA, LL Dip

Mathematics:
Maurice Biggs, BA, CertEd (*Head of Mathematics*)
Russell Bayliss, BA, MA, PGCE
Christine Cooper, BSc, PGCE
David Smith, BSc, PGCE
Julie Ward, BSc, PGCE

Modern Languages:
Lilia Knight (*Spanish*)
Dany Withers, L-ès-Lettres (*French*)
Heather Boraston, BA, PGCE, RSA Dip TEFLA (*Spanish*)
Nicola Ellis, BA, CertEd (*German*)

Music:
David Dennis, LTCL
Joanna Messenger, BMus, PGCE

Physical Education:
Tomasz Jadczak, QTS GTC, MA

Psychology:
Janette Winnick, BA, MA, BCom, HDipEd
Roxana Shields, BA, MA

Science:
Sally Lightowlers, BSc, PGCE (*Head of Science*)
Karen Hollox, MIBiol, MSC
Anthony Good, NDA, MA
Ingrid Jensen, BSc, MSc, DPhil, CertEd

Senior Tutor and Examinations Officer:
Christine Cooper, BSc, PGCE

UCAS Officer:
Alexander Mitlehner, BSc, MSc, PhD, PGCE

Careers Advisor:
David Smith, BSc, PGCE

International Study Centre:
Belinda Sumner, CertEd, RSA Dip TEFLA (*Director of ISC*)
Heather Boraston, BA, PGCE, RSA Dip TEFLA
Belinda Miljkovic, BA, PGCE Post Comp Ed Cambridge, CELTA
Sally Jeans, BA Hons, CELTA, CILIP
Jonathan Crook, BA Hons, MA, CTEFL

Number of Students. 120.

Academic. Padworth aims to provide a well-balanced curriculum with a strong academic core. We offer a broad-based Year 9 Foundation and a wide range of subjects at GCSE/IGCSE and AS/A Level as well as a one-year University Access programme. In addition, the International Study Centre provides short and long-term English Language courses for overseas students of all abilities.

Our curriculum aims to contribute effectively to the intellectual, physical and personal attainment and development of our students, according to their age and ability range, to prepare students for the next stage of education, training or employment and to provide the skills needed for life-long learning.

Pastoral Care. Outstanding pastoral care is provided by our experienced resident house staff whose role is to guide and support students. House staff also organise a varied extra-curricular programme in the evenings and at weekends for students to make the most of school life. Many sports and clubs are offered and students participate in the Duke of Edinburgh's Award Scheme.

Facilities. Boarding students are accommodated in comfortable single or shared bedrooms with sitting rooms and kitchen facilities. The campus offers a range of sports facilities including an outdoor swimming pool and tennis, basketball and volleyball courts. Modern classrooms and specialist science laboratories are complemented by a well-equipped IT room, library, art studio and day student centre.

Careers and Higher Education. Students are given individual careers counselling and guidance on their choice of course and university and support with the UCAS process.

Scholarships. A number of Academic Scholarships worth up to 50% of the fees are available for study at GCSE and A Level.

Admissions. Padworth welcomes students of a wide range of abilities. Admission is by interview and report from the previous school and subject to availability of a place.

A prospectus is available on request via the website www.padworth.com or by telephoning the College on 0118 983 2644. Prospective parents and students are warmly invited to arrange a visit and an appointment to meet the Principal.

Fees per term (2008-2009). Day Students £3,000, Weekly Boarders £5,300, Full boarders £6,950.

Charitable status. Padworth College Trust Limited is a Registered Charity, number 325023, which exists to promote and provide for the advancement of education.

Portland Place School

56–58 Portland Place London W1B 1NJ
Tel: 020 7307 8700
Fax: 020 7436 2676
e-mail: admin@portland-place.co.uk
website: www.portland-place.co.uk

Portland Place School was founded in 1996 in response to demand in central London for a mixed school that provided for pupils from a broad range of backgrounds and abilities. There are 348 boys and girls in the school aged from 11 to 18. The school is housed in an inner city location next to Broadcasting House and near to Oxford Circus, London W1.

***Headmaster*: Richard Walker**, BSc Loughborough, CSci, CChem, MRSC, FRSA, PGCE (*Chemistry*)

Deputy Head (*academic*): Victoria Low, MA London, BSc Otago NZ, MRSC,
DipGrad Teaching (*Chemistry*)

Deputy Head (*academic*): Philip Smyth, BSc Galway, PGCE (*Biology*)

Deputy Head (*pastoral*): Katherine Greenwood, BA London, PGCE (*Geography*)

Teaching Staff:
Simon Aaronson, BSc Perth, Australia, BEd (*Physics*)
Kirin Anulah, BA Brunel, PGCE (*English*)
Kamran Akhtar MSc London, PGCE (*Mathematics*)
Georgina Cauchi, BA Deakin, Australia (*Physical Education*)
Thomas Barnes, MA Cantab, PGCE (*English*)
Abbie Beard, BA Sydney (*Physical Education*)
Catherine Brahams, BA Durham, MA London PGCE (*English*)
Colin Bryce, BSc Glasgow (*Physical Education*)
Debra Brown, BMus Manchester, PGCE (*Music*)
Juan Caballero, MA Seville, PGCE (*Spanish*)
Janet Carruthers, BA Leeds, PGCE (*French*)
Aaron Columbus, BA Canterbury, NZ PGCE (*History*)
Penny Court, BSc Bath (*Mathematics*)
Susan Court, BA, MEd Natal, SA, PGCE London (*English*)
Julie Dunkley, BSc London (*Physical Education*)
Roger Dean, BEng London, MSc Imperial, London, MSc Kent PGCE (*Mathematics*)
Danielle English, MSc Queen Mary, London, MRSC, PGCE (*Chemistry*)
Isabel Fernando, BA Monash, Australia, PGCE (*English*)
Sarah Field, BA Otago, NZ, PGCE (*English*)
Rupert Gardner, BA Middlesex, PGCE Cambridge (*Music*)
Elizabeth Ghojefa, BA Brunel, PGCE (*Physical Education*)
Nicola Gridelli, BA Bologna, PGCE London (*Italian*)
Caroline Guest, BA Newcastle, PGCE (*Geography*)
Lisa Hunt, MPhil, MA London, PGCE (*History*)
Matthew Jones BA London, PGCE (*Art*)
Mital Kinderkedia BSc British Columbia (*Mathematics*)
Toby Langdon, BA King's London, PGCE (*Drama*)
Dalila Louni, MA St Etienne, PGCE (*French and Spanish*)
Chad Macfarlane, BA Goldsmiths London (*Design and Technology*)
Adrian Martijono, BSc London PGCE (*Chemistry*)
Jamie McLoughlin, BSc Brunel (*Physical Education*)
Caroline McMeekin BA Lancaster, PGCE (*Drama*)
Tim Mithen, BA Monash, Australia, PGCE (*English*)
Nicole Partington, BA Edith Cowan, Australia, PGCE (*English*)
Ruth Picado, BA Coruna, Spain (*Spanish*)
Helen Richards BSc Coventry, PGCE (*Geography*)
Leigh Rider, BSc Pretoria, PGCE (*Mathematics and ICT*)
Scott Rider, BA Brunel (*Physical Education*)
Graeme Rosie, BA Stirling, MA London, DipEd, PGCE (*Economics*)
Edna Scott, BSc Edinburgh, PGCE, GIBiol (*Chemistry*)
Patrick Smullen, BSc Open, PGCE (*Biology*)
Parwez Soogund MA London, PGCE (*Design and Technology*)
Alison Stringell, MA Slade, PGCE Goldsmiths (*Art*)
Klaus Wehner, MA LCP (*Photography*)
David Wellings, MSc LSE, PGCE (*Business Studies*)
Nader Yazdi, MSc Leeds, PhD UCL, MBA Imperial (*Mathematics and Computing*)

Visiting Music Teachers
Adam Blake (*Guitar*)
Zrinka Bottrill (*Classical Piano*)
Mike O'Neill (*Jazz Piano*)
Mark Cookson (*Clarinet & Sax*)
Balint Szekely (*Violin*)
Dan Ezard (*Bass*)
Siobhan Lavin (*Voice & Flute*)
Nicky Newman (*Voice*)
Jack Pollitt (*Percussion*)

Administration
Clemmie Studd (*School Secretary*)
Robyn Esterhuizen (*School Administrator*)
Helena Leinonen (*Bursar*)
Imelda Rafter-Phillips (*Admissions*)
Cheryl Jones (*Headmaster's Personal Assistant*)
Amanda Berrisford (*Librarian*)

Age Range. 11–18.

Number of Day Pupils. 260 Boys, 88 Girls.

Fees per term (2008-2009). £4,495.

General. Portland Place is housed in two magnificent Grade II* listed James Adam houses in Portland Place, London W1 with a separate Art, Drama and Science building and a senior school building close by in Great Portland Street. The school is a co-educational, independent secondary school for pupils aged from 11 to 18. Classes are small and all teachers are not only specialists in their subjects, but are chosen for their ability to enthuse and draw out the best in all students at all levels.

Aims and Philosophy. Portland Place is an inclusive and non-elitist school. We encourage pupils to excel in the arts, sport and in their academic studies. Discipline is firm, but compassionate. Our uniform is simple and functional. Teaching is structured. The relationship between teachers and pupils is courteously informal. We teach in small classes to offer every child individual attention. While we always strive for academic excellence, we never allow this to overshadow our dedication to nurturing natural intelligence or true potential. Each child's progress is followed through tests, homework and up to six reports a year. Parents are also encouraged to meet our staff to discuss any concerns at any time, as well as at a Parents' Evening every term. We are also a school in touch with the real world. The future of the children in our care comes first in all our decisions and the education every child receives is a journey to a successful later life.

Buildings. The school is ideally located right in the centre of the capital. Less than five minutes' walk from Regent's Park (where much of the outdoor sporting activities take place) and ten minutes walk from Oxford Circus. The buildings have been refurbished to an exceptionally high standard. Classrooms are supplemented by specialist rooms for drama, photography and computing. The Art, Drama and Science departments are housed in a separate building behind Portland Place in Great Portland Street. Senior pupils (Year 10 to 6th form) have many of their lessons in dedicated building directly behind the main school buildings in Portland Place.

Curriculum. The curriculum at Portland Place is developed from the English National Curriculum and offers a flexibility that puts the pupil first. Homework is supervised until 5.00 pm for those who want or require it and each pupil has a homework diary that details the homework programme for each week. Each child takes part in a comprehensive programme of physical education. Pupils in Years 7–9 have four PE sessions per week. Full advantage is taken of its central London location and excellent local facilities available. The outdoor programme takes place in neighbouring Regent's Park and includes athletics, hockey, football, rugby, tennis and cross-country. Indoor sports include basketball and fencing. Pupils represent the school in numerous matches against other London schools and in national tournaments. Class music is a compulsory part of the curriculum in Years 7, 8 and 9 and all pupils are encouraged, if they do not already play one, to take up a musical instrument and take advantage of the team of visiting instrumental teachers.

Sport and Extra-Curricular Activities. Our central London position means that we have easy access to world class facilities. All children are encouraged to participate in an interesting and varied physical education programme. Portland Place School offers a wide range of popular sport including: Athletics, Basketball, Cricket, Cross Country, Fencing, Football, Hockey, Netball, Rounders, Swimming, Tennis and Rugby. Outdoor sports such as football, netball, tennis, cricket and athletics take place in Regent's Park less than a ten minute walk from the school. Indoor activities including basketball and fencing take place at the University of Westminster gym just minutes away in Regent Street. Swimming is at the Seymour Centre, and in the summer we have nets at Lords indoor school. Optional after-school sport activities abound with senior and junior clubs for matches held with schools across London and the UK.

There is a wide and expanding range of extra-curricular activities that are offered at the end of afternoon school. Whole school productions, concerts, chamber groups and small dramatic workshops take place throughout the year and clubs ranging from politics and debating to games and Christianity all thrive throughout the year. During the last week of the summer term all pupils take part in an Activities Week that includes outdoor adventure centres and overseas trips.

Admission. Entry to the school (usually at 11+, 13+ and Sixth Form) is by examinations in English and Mathematics and interview. Interviews for September entry are held in the Autumn term prior to entry and the school's entrance examination is in January.

Scholarships. There are five half fee scholarships available for Year 7 (11+) candidates (Art, Music, Sport, Drama and Academic).

Governance. Portland Place School is part of the Alpha Plus Group of schools.

Princethorpe College

Princethorpe Rugby Warwickshire CV23 9PX
Tel: 01926 634200
Fax: 01926 633365
e-mail: post@princethorpe.co.uk
website: www.wcisf.co.uk

The school, which has a Catholic foundation, was founded as a boys' school in 1957 in Leamington Spa by the congregation of the Missionaries of the Sacred Heart (MSC), moving to its present site, a former Benedictine monastery, in 1966. The College became co-educational in 1996, and in September 2001 formed a partnership with Crackley Hall School in Kenilworth in order to provide continuous education from 2 to 18 years. Both schools are members of an independent trust – the Warwickshire Catholic Independent Schools Foundation.

Chairman of Governors: Professor Brian Ray, BSc, MSc, PhD, CEng, MIEE, CPhys, FInstP

***Headmaster*: John M Shinkwin**, MA Oxon, PGCE (*Physics*)

Deputy Head – Academic: Mrs Heather Harris, BA, PGCE, BPhilEd (*Religious Studies*)
Deputy Head – Pastoral: Mrs Susan Millest, BSc, PGCE, NPQH (*Chemistry and Physics*)
Assistant Head – Marketing and Operations: Alex Darkes, BEd (*Physics*)
Foundation Bursar, Company Secretary & Clerk to the Governors: Paul Shaw, JP, BA, ACIB
College Bursar: Mrs Anne Davey

Teaching Staff:
* *Head of Department*

Art:
*Paul Hubball, BA, PGCE
Mrs Susan Harris, BA, PGCE

Careers:
*Mike Taylor, BA, PGCE (**Geography*)

Design and Technology:
*Frank Gahan, BEd, MA, CertEd FIEA
Mrs Lesley McGaw, CertEd, GNVQ, ECDL
Mrs Sarah Sellars, BA, QTS

Economics and Business Studies:
*Peter Griffin, BA, PGCE (*Examinations Officer*)
Kenneth Owen, BSc

English:
*Christopher Kerrigan, BA, MA, PGCE
Miss Victoria Ball, BA, PGCE
Mrs Christine Carpenter, BA, PGCE
David Hare, BEd, Clait (*Assistant Head of Junior School*)
Mrs Emma Litterick, BA, PGCE, TESOL (*Assistant Head of Senior School*)
Mrs Helen-Leonie Pascoe-Williams, BA, PGCE (*Coordinator of Provision for the Most Academically Able*)

Ms Naomi Willard, BA, PGCE
Mrs Jane Winchester, JP, MA, CertEd, LGSM

Geography:
*Mike Taylor, BA, PGCE (*Careers*)
Jonathan Allen, BSc, PGCE
Miss Anne White, BSc, PGCE (*Assistant Head of Sixth Form*)

History and Politics:
*Dr Simon Peaple, BA, PhD, CGTC
Mrs Stephanie Bennett, BA, DipLIS (*Librarian*)
Mrs Tracey Hester, BA Oxon, PGCE
James Ridge, BA, PGCE

Information Technology:
David Smith, LLB, C&GAA, C&GIVA (*ICT Services Manager*)
Mrs Geraldine Spelman, BSc, PGCE

Latin:
Mrs Rachel Taylor, BA, QTS, IBT2

Learning Development:
*Dr Gill Watkins, BSc MA, PhD, PGCE
Ms Vikki Anderson, BA, PGCE, MEd, RSA, DipSpLD

Mathematics:
*Michael Conroy-Hargreaves, BSc, PGCE
Mrs Patricia Armitage, BEd
Mrs Karen Bannister, BSc, PGCE
Mrs Deborah Brookes, BA, QTS
Mrs Sarah McKeever, BEng, PGCE
Mrs Eileen Sharpe, BEd
Ms Tanya Sutton-Pryce, BSc, PGCE
Mrs Fenola Whittle, BEd

Modern Languages:
*Mrs Sarah Stewart, BA, PGCE, Cert TESOL (*French*)
Mrs Suzanne Ellis, BA, Cert TESOL (*French and German*)
Miss Juliette Francois (*French Language Assistant*)
Mrs Stella Keenan, MA, PGCE (*Spanish*)
Mrs Carlota Medina Diaz, BA, PGCE (*Spanish*)
Mrs Caroline Pavey, BA, PGCE, DEUG (*French*)
Mrs Margaret Robinson, BEd (*Head of Sixth Form; French*)
Mrs Brigitte Wood, CertEd (*French*)

Music:
*Mrs Susan Francis, DDME, CertEd, LTCL (*Director of Music*)
Mrs Felicity Coulson, GMus, PGCE
Mrs Susan Olden, LRAM, ARCM, LLCM TD, AMus TCL, ALCM

Visiting Music Staff:
Miss Alison Brierley, BA, GBSM, ABSM (*Clarinet, Bassoon, Piano, Keyboard and Theory*)
Mrs Felicity Coulson, GMus, PGCE (*Flute, Oboe, Saxophone, Clarinet and Piano*)
Carl Fletcher, BA (*Brass*)
Tim Fox (*Classical Guitar, Electric Guitar and Bass Guitar*)
Matthew Hopkins, BMus (*Vocal Studies, Piano and Keyboard*)
Nigel Hopkins (*Vocal Studies*)
Alistair Kennedy, BMus (*Violin and Viola*)
Andrew Kristy, BSc (*Piano, Organ, Music Technology, Composing and Keyboard*)
Nick Lee (*Classical Guitar, Electric Guitar and Bass Guitar*)
Adrian Moore, BA, ARCO (*Organ and Piano*)
Robin Payne (*Drum Kit and Percussion*)
Mrs Clare Rothwell, BMus (*Flute and Piano*)
Mrs Susan Shepherd, MA, ARCM, ARCO, LRAM, CertEd (*Piano*)
Ms Maja Todd (*Cello and Double Bass*)
Alan Wickett (*Drum Kit*)

Physical Education and Games:
Neil McCollin, BA, QTS (*Director of Sport*)
Jonathan Allen, BSc, PGCE
Mrs Karen Bannister, BSc, PGCE (*Mathematics*)
Miss Clare Bishop, BSc, PGCE
Mrs Deborah Brookes, BA, QTS
Ms Louise Champion, BSc, PGCE
Ms Sarah Cockayne, BA, PGCE
Michael Conroy-Hargreaves, BSc, PGCE (*Mathematics*)
Colin Dexter, MAAT
Jonathan Fitt, BSc, PGCE (*Master in charge of Rugby*)
Mrs Emily Johnson, BA, PGCE (*Girls' Games*)
Mrs Christina McCullough, BA, QTS (*Academic PE*)
Bernard Moroney, CertEd (*Biology, Head of Senior School*)
Edward Smith, BA, PGCE (*Religious Studies*)
Miss Joanne Smith, MChem, PGCE (*Chemistry*)
Symon Whitehouse

Religious Studies:
*Fr Alan Whelan, MSC, BA
Mrs Heather Harris, BA, PGCE, BPhil Ed (*Deputy Head – Academic, Chaplaincy Coordinator*)
Rodrick Isaacs, MA Cantab, MA, CertEd
Ian Lane, BA, PGCE (*PSHE Coordinator*)
Edward Smith, BA, PGCE

The Sciences:
*Dr Michael Tideswell, BSc, PhD, QTS (*Timetable Coordinator; Physics and Psychology*)
Mrs Anna Beech, BSc, PGCE (*Chemistry and Physics*)
Miss Clare Bishop, BSc, PGCE (*Psychology and Biology*)
Alex Darkes, BEd (*Assistant Head – Marketing and Operations; Physics*)
Mrs Susan Millest, HNC, BSc, PGCE, NPQH Applied Biology (*Deputy Head – Pastoral; Chemistry and Physics*)
Bernard Moroney, CertEd (*Biology, Head of Senior School*)
Sean Philpott, CertEd, BEd, MA, Adv Dip Ed (*Head of Junior School; Biology*)
Simon Robertson, BSc, PGCE (*Assistant Examinations Officer, Duke of Edinburgh's Award Coordinator; Biology and Chemistry*)
Mrs Gill Smith, BSc, PGCE (*Chemistry*)
Mrs Joanne Smith, MChem, PGCE (*Chemistry*)
Mrs Catherine Warne, BSC, PGCE (*House and Extra-Curricular Coordinator; Biology*)
Steve White, BSc, QTS (*Physics*)

Non Teaching Staff:
Maintenance: Michael Baron
Marketing Manager: Mrs Melanie Butler, BA
Housekeeping: Mrs Cynthia Carpenter
Assistant Bursar: Alan Chumbley
Bursar's Assistant: Miss Claudette Coleman
Registrar and Committee Secretary to Governors: Mrs Loretta Curtis
Senior Laboratory Technician: Mrs Ellen Davies, ONC
Library Assistant and ICT Technician: Mrs Shellagh Dodds
College Secretary: Mrs Lynne Dyke
Maintenance: Mostyn Evans
Catering Manager: Mrs Margaret Fuggle
Housekeeping: Lester Gibson
Purchasing Administrator: Mrs Ann Grant
Uniform and School Shop Manager: Mrs Angela Hales
Design and Technology Technician: Mrs Charlotte Hetherington, BEng
Headmaster's Personal Assistant and Office Manager: Mrs Carmel Hopkins
Senior Matron: Mrs Maria Lawless, SEN
Maintenance: Gerry Lovely
Gap Assistant: Laura Mason
Laboratory Technician: Mrs Angela Morris, CertEd
Estates: Joe Newton

Health and Safety Consultant: Matthew O'Farrell, Nat Dip, HEBOSH
Special Projects Officer: Mrs Gill Price
Estates: Tom Probert
Estates Manager: Edward Robertson
Maintenance: Gerry Rush
ICT Technician: Jonathan Sant
Secretary/Receptionist: Miss Naomi Taylor, BSc
House Manager: Mrs Judith Southam
Housekeeping: Mrs Judy Vick
Assistant to the Registrar: Mrs Elaine Warwick
School Counsellor: Mrs Tina Watkins
Gap Assistant: Tim Willis

Number in School. The school has about 760 day pupils from 11 to 18 years with 160 in the Sixth Form. An extensive network of private coaches transports pupils from a wide area.

Aims. The College provides a caring, Christian environment for children where their needs can be met and their talents, confidence and self-esteem developed. There is a healthy balance between freedom and structure and an emphasis on self-discipline through responsibility and trust, which develops confidence and independence.

The College draws on a rich tradition of Catholic teaching and the spirituality of the Missionaries of the Sacred Heart, whose ethos is central to its character and disciplinary system. In welcoming families of a variety of faiths, the school community is a living example of ecumenism. The College motto, *Christus Regnet* – let Christ reign – is a reminder of Christ's love, service, forgiveness and generosity of spirit.

Academic. A broad-based, stimulating curriculum satisfies a wide range of ability and fosters a love of learning. A favourable pupil-teacher ratio, permitting personal attention, contributes to impressive value-added achievements. High fliers are stretched and provided with intellectually challenging assignments, ensuring that they achieve at the highest possible levels. The curriculum is well supported by a magnificent library and ICT. Qualified specialists give tuition to dyslexic pupils.

Pupils in Years 7 to 9 have a broad-based curriculum which avoids early specialisation and usually go on to take nine or ten GCSEs.

Supervised homework and free extended day are offered until 6.00 pm.

The Sixth Form. A new £2.5m Sixth Form Centre opened at the end of 2007. Students in the Sixth Form are prepared for AS Level and A2 Level examinations after which the vast majority proceed to university. The Head of Sixth Form and the team of tutors monitor the academic progress of Sixth Formers through regular discussions with the students and their teachers. Visits to university Open Days, together with professional careers advice enables students to make the best choices about their next stage of education.

There is a strong emphasis on the acquisition of key skills and the education of the whole person. Sixth Formers are offered residential outward bound courses, training programmes and retreats which provide an opportunity for reflection and exploration, to develop a mature and balanced perspective. Guest lecturers, debates and theatre outings all enhance Sixth Form life.

All Sixth Formers enjoy privileges and have the responsibilities of leadership and example; certain members are elected to perform prefectorial duties. Prefects attend a leadership course and learn valuable management skills. They organise activities for younger pupils and chair the School Council, which offers a forum for lively discussion and gives the students an influential voice in the running of the College. Sixth Formers also act as Form Patrons, mentoring younger pupils and arranging outings for them. The House Captains have a pivotal role in the organisation of inter-house events.

Careers. The Careers Advice Programme commences in Year 9 and regular tutorials are held concentrating on option subject choices and developing careers awareness. Interview technique is developed and students are assisted with work experience placements which are undertaken at the end of Year 10 and Lower Sixth.

Art & Design. A feature which immediately strikes all visitors to the College is the outstanding display of canvases and ceramics. Superb examination results and successes in competitions are commonplace. The study of drawing, painting, graphics and ceramics are central and they are enhanced by using the work of great artists as stimulus material.

Technology includes Food, Graphics, Resistant Materials, Information and Communications Technology, Textiles and Electronics. Pupils can work with a variety of materials, realising their technical designs in the well-resourced workshops, which include CAD/CAM facilities.

Music and Drama. Music is studied by all pupils in their first three years and as an option at GCSE and A Level. The College choir gives regular performances and tours extensively overseas. Many pupils learn instruments and are encouraged to join the orchestra. Peripatetic staff offer tuition in most instruments. There are two well-equipped studios with digital recording facilities for Music Technology and there is an acclaimed Binns organ in the magnificent Chapel built by Peter Paul Pugin.

The College has a well-equipped theatre and regular productions are staged including pantomimes and revues, Shakespeare plays and adaptations from Dickens. Productions involve a large number of pupils and staff and provide an excellent way for pupils of different years to get to know each other. There are thriving Dance and Drama Clubs. Theatre Studies is offered in the Sixth Form.

Physical Education. All pupils participate in games and Physical Education classes. Physical Education can also be studied as an examination subject at GCSE and A Level. The major sports are rugby, netball, hockey, cricket, rounders, tennis and athletics; they are run in tandem with badminton, soccer, squash, basketball and trampolining. Off-site swimming and sailing are also available.

The Sports Centre has a sports hall, fitness gym and squash courts; a floodlit all-weather surface was laid in 2003. Extensive outdoor facilities include an internationally recognised cross-country course, tennis courts and over sixty acres of games pitches.

Extra-Curricular Activities. There is always a wide range of clubs, societies and activities such as art, board games, chemistry clinic, choir, computing, cookery, debating, drama, flight, history, jazz band, mathematics workshop, meditation, music workshop, orchestra, photography, Spanish, Warhammer, technology and textiles. The Duke of Edinburgh's Award Scheme and Outward Bound courses are also offered. The Arts Society provides a cultural programme of lectures, poetry evenings, music recitals and play readings.

Admission. Admission is by examination, usually in the middle of January, generally at 11 and 13 and at other ages as space allows. Students from other schools join the Sixth Form after their GCSE courses.

Scholarships. (*see Scholarship Entries section*).

Fees per term (2008-2009). £2,815 excluding transport and meals. Instrumental tuition, external examinations and some targeted support for those with learning needs are charged as extras.

Charitable status. Warwickshire Catholic Independent Schools Foundation is a Registered Charity, number 1087124. It exists solely for the education of children.

The Purcell School

Aldenham Road Bushey Hertfordshire WD2 3TS
Tel: 01923 331100
Fax: 01923 331166

e-mail: info@purcell-school.org
website: www.purcell-school.org

The Purcell School is one of the world's leading specialist centres of excellence and has a national and international reputation in the education and training of exceptional young musicians. There are 171 pupils, boys and girls, aged from 8 to 18, with 72 in the Sixth Form. Most pupils receive Scholarships under the Government's Music and Dance Scheme.

Patron: HRH The Prince of Wales

President: Sir Simon Rattle

Governing Body:
Mr Graham Smallbone, MA, ARCO, ARCM, FRSA (*Chairman*)
Mr Roy Cervenka (*Vice-Chairman*)
Ms Jenny Agutter
Mrs Fiona Ballantyne
The Hon Mark Bridges, GCMG
Mr Andrew Carter, CMG, MA, FRCO, LRAM, ARCM
Mr Simon Channing, BA Cantab
Mr Michael Garner, MA, FCA, FCT, FRSA
Ms Janice Graham, ARCM, AGSMD, ACT Julliard
Mrs Jean McGregor
Mr Philip Newman, FCA
Professor Curtis Price, AM, PhD, Hon RAM, FKC
Mr Martin Saunders, MA Cantab, FCA
Mr Michael Squires, BA
Professor John Wass, MB, BS, MD, MA, FRCP, MRCP
Mr David Woodhead, BA, FRSA

***Headmaster*: Mr Peter Crook**, MA, BMus, ARCO, LRAM

Deputy Head: Mr Paul Elliott, MA Hons Glasgow, PGCE

Director of Music: Mr Quentin Poole, MA Cantab, FRAM

Director of Finance & Administration: Mr Nicholas Rampley, BA Oxon, MBA London, DIC

Head of Sixth Form: Miss Elizabeth Willan, BA Hons London, PGCE

Music Department:
Head of Jazz: Mr Simon Colam
Head of Composition: Miss Alison Cox, GRNCM, DipAdvStdMus Comp, PGCE
Head of Keyboard: Mr William Fong, GMus RNCM, PPRNCM
Head of Academic Music: Mrs Miranda Francis, BMus, LRAM, ARCM, PGCE
Head of Music Technology/IT: Mr Aidan Goetzee, MSc, GRSM, ARCM
Head of Strings: Mr Ian Jewel, ARCM, ARAM Hon, HonDr Essex
Assistant Director of Music: Mr Edward Longstaff, BMus, MMus, PGCE
Assistant Head of Wind, Percussion: Dr Spencer Pitfield, BMus Hons, LMus Finland, PhD Sheffield
Director of Music/Head of Wind, Percussion: Mr Quentin Poole, MA Cantab
Accompanist: Mrs Deborah Shah, ARCM
Academic Music: Ms Marissa Thornton-Wood
Academic Music: Mrs Patta Tolputt, GRSM, ARCM, DipEd

Instrumental Staff:
Wind Department:
Head: Mr Quentin Poole
Assistant Head: Dr Spencer Pitfield
Anna Pope (*Flute*)
Barbara Law (*Recorder*)
Melanie Ragge (*Oboe*)
David Fuest (*Clarinet*)
Simon Stewart (*Saxophone*)
Naomi Sullivan (*Saxophone*)
Sarah Burnett (*Bassoon*)
Simon De Souza (*Horn*)
Tony Cross (*Trumpet*)
James Watson (*Trumpet*)
Steve Waterman (*Jazz Trumpet*)
Rob Workman (*Trombone*)
Daphne Boden (*Harp*)
Charlotte Seale (*Harp*)
Peter Beament (*Percussion*)
Tom Marandola (*Voice*)
Cassie White (*Voice*)
Roland Gallery (*Guitar*)
Mike Outram (*Jazz Bass*)
Stephen Wick (*Tuba*)

String Department:
Head: Mr Ian Jewel
Tony Cucchiara (*Violin*)
Evgueny Grach (*Violin*)
Erik Houston (*Violin*)
Mamedova Rashidova (*Violin*)
Carol Slater (*Violin*)
Krystof Smietana (*Violin*)
Nathaniel Vallois (*Violin*)
Ian Jewel (*Viola*)
Pal Banda (*Cello*)
Alexander Boyarsky (*Cello*)
Michal Kaznowski (*Cello*)
Natalia Pavlutskaya (*Cello*)
Martin Myers (*Double Bass*)

Keyboard Department:
Head: Mr William Fong
Piano:
Lidia Amorelli
Ilana Davids
William Fong
James Gibb
Gareth Hunt
Emily Jeffrey
Alla Kravchenko
Ching Ching Lim
Roshan Magub
Tessa Nicholson
Tatiana Sarkissova
Deborah Shah
Clare Sutherland (+ *Harpsichord*)
Valeria Szervansky
Charlotte Tomlinson

Jazz Department:
Head: Mr Simon Colam (*Piano*)
Oliver Hayhurst (*Bass*)
Carlos Lopez Real (*Saxophone*)
Steve Waterman (*Trumpet*)

Composition Department:
Head: Miss Alison Cox
Jonathan Cole
Alison Cox
Edward Longstaff
Simon Speare

Academic Music Department:
Head: Mrs Miranda Francis
Marissa Thornton-Wood (*Class Music*)
Edward Longstaff (*Class Music*)
Patta Tolputt (*Class Music*)
Simon Colam (*Jazz*)
Aidan Goetzee (*Music Technology*)

Alexander Technique:
Jean Mercer
John Crawford

Choirs:
Marissa Thornton-Wood (*Lower School Choir*)
Edward Longstaff (*Middle School & VI Form Choir*)
Quentin Poole (*Chamber Choir*)

Practice Coordinator:
Dr Spencer Pitfield

Practice Supervisors:
Cynthia Taylor
Ching Ching Lim

Academic Staff:
* *Head of Department*

Mrs Judith Simmons, BSc St Andrews, PGCE (*Art*)
Mr Phil Barrett, BA, ATC (**Art*)
Mr David Chappell, MSc York, BSc London PGCE Leeds (*Biology*)
Mr Kevan Taylor, BSc Hons, PGCE (*Biology*)
Mr Alan McKenna, BSc Hons, PGCE (*Chemistry*)
Mrs Eva Andrusier, BA Hons Manchester, CertEd, CertTEFL (*EFL*)
Ms Katherine Higgins, BEd Hons Warwick, RSADip (**EFL*)
Mr Andrew Leverton, BA Hons Tasmania, DipEd (**English*)
Mrs Sheila Young, BEd Glasgow, Dip SENCO Science (*English*)
Mrs Jocelyne Hazan, BA, MA Paris X (*French; Overseas Pupils Guardian Coordinator*)
Miss Elizabeth Willan, BA Hons London, PGCE (**French; Head of Sixth Form*)
Margaret Moore, BSc Hons (*Geography*)
Mrs Winifred Soutter, MA Glasgow, DRSAM, ARCM (*German*)
Mr Paul Elliott, MA Hons Glasgow, PGCE (**German/PSE*)
Mr Darrell Pigott, BSc Hons Bradford, PGCE (**History*)
Mrs Cherry Trotter, BEd Hons (**Juniors*)
Danielle Lewis, MA Oxon, MPhil Cantab (*Mathematics*)
Mr Martin Whitfield, BSc, PGCE (*Mathematics*)
Mrs Yvonne Tagoe, BA Hons, MBA, PGCE (**Mathematics*)

Mr David Grant, BAWLA Inst (*PE*)
Mr Panos Fellas, BSc Hons Surrey, MA ScEd (**Science/ Physics*)

Boarding Houses:
Gardner: Mr and Mrs Taylor
Dulverton: Mr and Mrs Henderson
Avison: Mr and Mrs Longstaff
Sunley: Mr and Mrs Francis

Administration Staff:
Art Technician: Ms Maggie Banks, BA Hons Herts
Pastoral Counsellor: Mrs Nikki Bennett
Foundation Director: Mrs Sue Hind-Woodward
Music Timetabler: Mrs Fiona Duce, BA
Music Department Secretary & Registrar: Mrs Karen Gumustekin
Catering Manager: Mrs Jennifer Henderson
Assistant Concerts Manager: Mrs Jane Hunt
Concert Manager: Ms Miriam Juviler, LRAM
Computing Assistant: Mr Simon Kingsbury
Librarian: Mrs Katerina Fellas, BSc Hons, PGCE London
Development Manager: Janette Shaw
School Nurse: Miss Andrea Napper, SRN
Receptionists: Mrs Jean Perkins, Mrs Jane Allen
Finance Officer: Mrs Susan Pickard, MAAT
Lab Technician: Mrs Susan Pitts, ASCT
PA to Headmaster/Office Manager: Mrs Gail Remfry, AIST, RSA
House Keeper: Mrs Stella Rendle
Assistant to Director of Finance & Administration: Mrs Tina Stewart

The Purcell School is the only specialist music school in London, with the benefit of all the capital's cultural and teaching resources. It offers exceptional opportunities to exceptional young musicians; the finest teachers, time and priority for musical activities, the opportunity to work with others of similar calibre, specialist education in a sane and balanced environment.

Music. The School provides teaching in all instruments including composition and voice. Great care is taken over the allocation of pupils to teachers and progress is carefully and regularly assessed by the Head of Departments, under the guidance of the Director of Music. Whilst there is an excellent and experienced instrumental staff at the School, pupils also have the advantage of established links with teachers from the Royal College of Music, the Royal Academy of Music and the Guildhall School of Music and Drama.

There are opportunities to take part in Masterclasses with eminent international musicians, to work with visiting members of Covent Garden, the London Symphony Orchestra or renowned chamber groups and to perform not only in the prestigious concert halls of London but also the concert halls of the Far East, Russia, America and all parts of Europe, on one of the School's regular foreign tours.

Academic Curriculum. In addition to specialist musical training the Purcell School offers a full academic education of the highest quality to GCSE and Advanced level. Examination results are outstanding.

Boarding. Pupils come from all over Britain and from all over the world. About 70% are boarders, all of whom live on the School campus.

The youngest pupils, aged between 9 and 11, live in Dulverton House looked after by Houseparents, with whom they live more or less 'en famille'.

There are two Houses, Sunley (girls') and Gardner (boys'), in the main building and the boarding accommodation has been newly modernised and refurbished to create comfortable, attractive and imaginative rooms. For the most part members of the Sixth Form have single rooms (or share with one other person) and can use their rooms for practice as well as for study. The Houses are run by a resident Housemistress and Housemaster, respectively, and there are also resident Tutors/ Practice Supervisors.

A Senior House, built in 1986, provides study bedroom accommodation for 20 members of the Upper Sixth who are in the care of their Housemaster and resident House Tutor.

Links between School and home are close and, with fax machines and e-mail, this is possible wherever in the world a pupil may live. In each half of the term there an exeat weekend when all pupils go home or to their guardian or to friends. There is also an extended half-term period in each of the three terms.

Admission. Entrance is by musical audition and interview and further details and a prospectus are available from the Registrar, Mrs Karen Gumustekin, who will be pleased to answer queries.

The School has a principle of taking young musicians whose exceptional musical ability merits them a place.

Fees per term (2008-2009). Day £7,709; Boarding £9,859.

Government Aided places are available. Bursaries and Scholarships are also available for those not eligible for aided places.

Charitable status. The Purcell School is a Registered Charity, number 312855. It aims to offer Specialist musical training, combined with an excellent general education, to children of exceptional musical ability.

The Read School
Drax

Drax Selby North Yorkshire YO8 8NL
Tel: 01757 618248
Fax: 01757 617432
e-mail: secretary@readschool.co.uk
website: www.readschool.co.uk

Chairman of Governors: C W Bayston

Bursar and Clerk to the Governors: Mr P W Thompson, RN (retd)

***Headmaster*: R A Hadfield**, BA, CertEd

Deputy Head: J A Sweetman, BSc, PhD, CertEd

Teaching Staff:
Miss K Allan, BA, CertEd (*Junior School*)
Mrs P Anderson, BEd (*Head of Junior School*)
Mrs C Barber, BA, CertEd (*Spanish and French*)
§N A Bellamy, BA (*Director of Music*)
Mrs S Bennie, CertEd (*Adamson Housemistress, Junior School*)
Miss S Barbour, BA, CertEd (*PE and Games, PSHE Coordinator*)
Miss J Bullock, BSc, CertEd (*English Additional Language*)
Ms S L Campbell (*Junior School*)
Mrs J Clark (*Brass instruments, Piano, CCF*)
§Revd D Cox, BA, CertEd, NEOC (*Chaplain, Religious Studies*)
Miss C Cross, BA, CertEd (*English*)
I T Edwards, BA, CertEd (*Drama, English*)
D H Evans, BA, CertEd (*PE & Games coaching*)
Mrs P Eyre, CertEd, BSc (*English*)
Miss V Fletcher, BA, CertEd (*Spanish, French*)
Mrs L Flinders, BA, MPhil, CertEd (*Head of MFL, French, Latin*)
§F Ford, CertEd (*Mathematics*)
B Garrard, BSc, CertEd (*Head of PE and Games*)
Mrs E Gilmore, BA, CertEd (*Spanish, German*)
D I Gisbourne, BSc, CertEd (*Director of ICT, Mathematics*)
Mrs H Haddock, CertEd (*Lower Junior School*)
Mrs D E Hadfield, CertEd, BA (*Head of Mathematics*)

Mrs H Hewson, BA, CertEd (*English*)
G Hill, BA, CertEd (*Upper Junior School*)
Mrs C Howarth (*Lower Juniors*)
R S Kendrick, BA, CertEd (*Mathematics, CCF*)
G J King, CertEd (*Senior Housemaster, PE, Mathematics*)
§Mrs L M Newman, BA, CertEd (*English, Religious Studies*)
§Mrs A Oliver, BA (*Latin, Classical Studies*)
R Osborne, BA, CertEd (*Upper Junior School*)
Ms C M Palmer, BSc, CertEd, MSc (*Director of Studies*)
Mrs K E Patrick (*Head of Inclusive Learning, Counsellor*)
C S Patrick, BSc, CertEd (*Special Needs, Basic Skills*)
Mrs S Scholefield, BSc, CertEd (*Head of Humanities*)
§Mrs E Stark, BSc, DipEd (*Biology, Chemistry*)
§R P Stark, BSc, DipEd (*Physics*)
J Staves, BSc, PhD (*Chemistry*)
R D Stobie, BSc (*Mathematics, Physics*)
Mrs S A Tolman, CertEd, CertMusEd (*Head of Lower Juniors*)
Mr P Vasey, BA, CertEd (*Business Studies, ICT*)
M A Voisey, BA, CertEd (*Head of English*)
Mrs R M Wake, BA, CertEd (*Upper Junior School*)
Mr P Whitcombe, BSc, CertEd (*Head of Science*)
R C Whyley, BA, CertEd (*History, Games*)
Mrs A Wightman, BA, LLB, CertEd (*Upper Junior School*)
Mrs J D Williams, BEd (*Girls' PE and Games*)
P Woodward, BA, CertEd, MA (*Design Technology*)
§Mrs C M Wynne (*Junior School*)
Ms S A Yates, BA, CertEd (*Art and Design, Tutor for Girls*)

Age Range. Co-educational 4–18 (Boarding 8–18).

Number in School. Total 360: Day 290, Boarding 70; Boys 210, Girls 150.

The school is pleasantly situated in the rural village of Drax and is very convenient for main rail (Doncaster, York) and road access (M62, M18, A1). Manchester is the nearest international airport (1½ hours distant). It is a relatively small school where children are well known to each other and to the staff.

The school has been a focal point for the education of boys in the Selby–Goole area for over 340 years, first as Drax Grammar School, and (since 1967) as The Read School. The school is now co-educational, offering a wide range of academic studies at GCSE and A Level, together with a full programme of Sports, Drama, Music, CCF and recreational activity. There is one class in each Junior School year from Early Years to Year 4 and two in Years 5 and 6. There are three classes in each of the Senior years (7–11). There is a small Sixth Form (30–40 pupils) following AS and A Level courses. High standards are expected in all aspects of endeavour, and in behaviour and manners.

Facilities. In addition to the refurbished Edwardian buildings there continued to be steady developments in the facilities and accommodation throughout the 1980s and 1990s. These include the fine Moloney Hall, Ramsker classrooms, Sports Hall, Coggrave Building for the Upper Junior School (Years 3–6), in addition to internal developments, especially in the provision of IT. The Shipley Building for music and mathematics opened in October 2002. The Lower Junior School and girls' boarding accommodation are situated on their own site in the village at Adamson House. New changing rooms have recently been completed and existing facilities refurbished. The dining room has been extended and modernised, together with the kitchen facilities. In 2007 a Multi-Use Games Area with Astroturf pitch was provided.

Fees per term (2008-2009). Boarders: £4,807–£5,884; Day: £1,947–£2,746.

Where brothers and sisters are in the school at the same time, a 10% reduction is allowed for the first younger brother or sister and a 20% discount for the second. Scholarships (up to 50% of tuition fees) are available by open competition held in January/February of the preceding year for entry into Year 7 and the Sixth Form.

Admission. An offer of a place in the school is made after interview (and verbal reasoning and mathematics tests for admission to the Senior School) and satisfactory report from the pupil's current school.

Charitable status. The Read School is a Registered Charity, number 529675. It exists to provide a proper education for boys and girls aged 4–18.

Rishworth School

Rishworth West Yorkshire HX6 4QA
Tel: 01422 822217 (Main School)
Fax: 01422 820911
e-mail: admissions@rishworth-school.co.uk
website: www.rishworth-school.co.uk

Rishworth is an exceptionally friendly, caring community, in which pupils are as strongly encouraged to rejoice in each other's achievements as to take pride in their own. The School succeeds in combining a disciplined environment with a relaxed and welcoming atmosphere.

While pupils are at Rishworth, we try to ensure that, in addition to the knowledge and skills acquired through academic study, they develop:

- A love of learning and the will to succeed.
- A sense of responsibility, self-discipline, purpose and fulfilment.
- A capacity for both self-reliance and cooperation.
- An appreciation of certain personal virtues and spiritual values, such as honesty, dependability, perseverance, commitment, humility and respect for others.

Visitor: The Most Reverend The Lord Archbishop of York

Honorary Governor: A J Morsley, Esq

The Governing Body:
Mrs D M Whitaker, JP (*Chairman*)
Dr C A G Brooks, Esq (*Vice-Chairman*)
G C W Allan, Esq
Revd Hilary Barber
M W Gledhill, Esq
E W Mitchell, Esq
Mrs A K Riley, ACA
The Right Revd Tony Robinson, Bishop of Pontefract
Mrs J C Slim
J G Wheelwright, Esq
T M Wheelwright, Esq
J S Whittaker, Esq

Clerk to the Board of Governors: R M Schofield, BA, ACA

Teaching Staff:
* *Head of Department*

***Headmaster*: R A Baker**, MA Cantab

Deputy Headmaster: P Seery, BSc, MEd (*Chemistry*)
Director of Administration: Mrs I Shelton, BA (**Art*)
Director of Studies: S Ogden, BSc Hons (*Geography, Mathematics*)
Director of Marketing & Registrar: Mrs S J Stamp, BSc (*Geography*)
Head of Heathfield: Mrs S M Temperley, GRSM, CertEd

T Anderson (*Sports Coach & Sports Club Manager*)
Miss N Andrews, BA (*Foundation Stage Teacher, Heathfield*)
N Appleton, BA, MA (**English*)
Mrs M T Arbelo-Dolan, BA (**Spanish*)
Mrs R Aujla, BA (**Geography*)
Mrs D F Baker, BA (**French*)
Miss S Beesley (*Out of School Care Deputy Manager & Foundation Stage Key Worker, Heathfield*)

Mrs H Bower, BSc (**PE & Sport, *Sport, Heathfield*)
Miss C E Bradberry, BA (**Psychology, Staff Mentor for Management, Assessment, Teaching & Learning*)
Mrs J Bradley, LTCL, GTCL (*Music Coordinator, Heathfield*)
Mrs J Bridges (*Teaching Assistant, Heathfield*)
D Bullock, BEd Hons (**Drama*)
Mrs S Chatterton, BEd Hons (*Director of Studies, Junior Class Teacher, Heathfield*)
Ms R Chatwin, BSc (*Teacher i/c Physics, Science*)
J A Davidson, BA, MA (*History*)
J Drowley, BA, MEd (*Physical Education & Sport, Housemaster Calder House*)
M L Dunn, BA (*Design Technology, IT, UCAS, HE & Careers Coordinator*)
Miss H A Fawcett, BA (*Junior Class Teacher, RE Coordinator, Teacher i/c Library, Heathfield*)
Ms K Foster, BA (*Part-time Foundation Stage Teacher, Heathfield*)
Mrs K Fraser, BA (*Art, Press Officer, House Area Mistress for Hanson House, Year 11*)
Mrs J Freeman (*Before-School Care Coordinator, Teaching Assistant, Heathfield*)
Miss K Greenwood, BA (*Junior Class Teacher, Sports Coordinator, Heathfield*)
Mrs E Gregory, BA (*Business Studies, *Economics, History, Assistant Housemistress Wheelwright House*)
Mrs J Higgins, NNEB (*Teaching Assistant, Heathfield*)
D I Horsfall, BSc (**Mathematics*)
Mrs J Hudson, BEd (*Learning Support & French Coordinator, Heathfield*)
R Hunwicks, BSc Hons, HREF (*Physical Education & Sport, Assistant Housemaster Calder House*)
P W Jones, MA (*Cantab*) (*Science Advisor, Master i/c Biology*)
Mrs A Jordan, DipAD, PGCE (*Junior Class Teacher, Art and Mathematics Coordinator, Heathfield*)
Mrs A M Kellett-End, BA, PGCLD (*Coordinator of Learning Support*)
Dr J Ladds, MChem, PhD, MEd (**Science, Teacher i/c Chemistry*)
Mrs S Lawrence (*After-School Care Assistant, Heathfield*)
P I Lynch, BEd (*Director of Music*)
F Majkowski BEd (**ICT*)
Mrs S M Marsden, BEd (*Reception Class Teacher, English Coordinator, Heathfield*)
Mrs L Meredith, BA, ARCM (*Music, English, Teacher i/c Provision for Academically Most Able*)
Mrs S Moore, BA (*English*)
D Newby, BTech (**Design Technology, House Area Master for Hanson House, Years 9 & 10*)
Mrs K Norris (*Teaching Assistant, After-School Care & Holiday School Coordinator, Heathfield*)
Miss L B Pots, BA (**Home Economics, Art, ICT, Design Technology*)
P I M Robinson, BEd (**Business Studies, Head of Sixth Form*)
Ms J Sheldrick, BSc (*Biology, Head of Middle School*)
Mrs S P Sheppard (*Librarian*)
M E Siggins, BA (*English, Coordinator of Enhanced Sixth Form Curriculum & General Studies*)
Miss H E A Stembridge, BEd (*Infant Class Teacher, PSHCE Coordinator, Section Leader Early Years, Heathfield*)
Mrs G Sunderland (*Senior Teaching Assistant, Heathfield*)
Mrs C Taylor BA (*Junior Class Teacher, Science Coordinator, Heathfield*)
P M Taylor, BSc (*Science, Mathematics*)
A J Thomas, BSc (*Director of Physical Education and Sport, Assistant Housemaster Calder House*)
Mrs J Thompson, BA (*EFL*)
Miss L Timlin, MSc (*Mathematics*)
Miss L V Turner, BA, MA (*French, EFL*)
J Western, BSc Hons (*Mathematics*)
Mrs A M R Wilby, BA (*Junior Class Teacher, KS2 English Coordinator, Heathfield*)
M Wilson, BA (**History, Head of Lower School*)
Mrs E J Wood, ABSM, LTCL, CertEd (*Infant Class Teacher, Humanities Coordinator, Early Years Mathematics Coordinator, Heathfield*)
Mrs L E Wood, BSc (*Physical Education & Sport, PSHCE Coordinator*)
Mrs D Van-Eda, BA (*Assistant Manager Out-of-School Care, Temporary Teaching Assistant, Heathfield*)

Instrumental Music Teachers:
Mrs R K Burbidge, GRSM, LRAM, ARCM, LTCL
Mrs B Slade, GRSM, ARMCM, ARNCM
C D Wood
Miss H Bywater, BMus, ABRSM, PPRNCM
P Brown, LGSM, GCLCM
J Moate
N Darwent, GMus
Ms F Farnworth, GGSM

Administrative Staff:

Bursar: R M Schofield, BA, ACA
Assistant Bursar: Mrs A C Martin, BA
Admissions Officer: Mrs D Keeble
Headmaster's PA: Mrs D Keeble
Matron: Mrs D K Robinson

General organisation. Founded in 1724, Rishworth is a co-educational day and boarding school comprising a nursery for children from age 3, a Junior School, Heathfield, which has its own separate site where children are taught up to the age of 11, and the Senior School up to age 18. Rishworth is a Church of England foundation, but welcomes children of all faiths, or of none. Numbers stand at about 585 pupils, of whom over 100 are boarders.

Facilities and Location. Superbly located in 130 acres of a beautiful Pennine valley, the School has a mix of elegant older buildings and excellent modern facilities including a capacious sports hall with fitness suite, a separate, newly-redeveloped Sports Club with 25-metre indoor swimming pool and squash courts, a large expanse of games pitches, a music block, 3 modern ICT suites, wireless (and cabled) Internet and Intranet connection across the whole site, a Performing Arts Theatre, a centre dedicated to sixth-form study, freshly-refurbished boarding houses and newly-installed, state-of-the-art science laboratories.

Access to the School by road is easy, with the M62 within five minutes' drive. School buses run to the Halifax, Todmorden, Rochdale, Oldham and Huddersfield areas.

Welfare and Pastoral. The unusually high degree of attention afforded to pupils by small teaching groups, the careful monitoring of progress, coordinated pastoral support and a close working partnership with parents enables pupils to build on their strengths and allows specific needs to be addressed. Each boarding pupil is under the direct care of a Housemaster or Housemistress, who is ably supported by assistant staff in each boarding house.

Teaching. Taught by a dedicated staff of qualified specialists, the curriculum, both academic and non-academic, is broad and stimulating, and offers every pupil the chance to be challenged and to excel. A general curriculum, broadly in line with the National Curriculum, is followed until Year 9, after which pupils select GCSE options in consultation with their parents, tutors and subject teachers. AS and A2 options are also selected via consultation.

Support is given by qualified specialists for certain special needs including dyslexia and English where this is not the pupil's first language.

Broader Education. In order to help our pupils to become the confident, balanced and considerate young men and women we wish them to be, we encourage participation in a wide range of activities outside the classroom.

Sports are well appointed and well taught, and each term boys and girls enjoy excellent results. The School also has a justly high reputation in music and drama.

Other activities range from The Duke of Edinburgh's Award to golf, skiing, diving, and many others.

Boarding. We have no dormitories. Boarders (from age 10 or 11, and sometimes age 9) are accommodated in individual study-bedrooms, almost all single or double occupancy, which allow pupils their personal space. These are located in spacious houses, overseen by house staff. The boarding houses have recently undergone major refurbishments which have ensured that the character of the historic buildings has been retained alongside the provision of top-rate modern amenities. A full programme of activities is arranged for the evenings and week-ends, and there are good recreational facilities reserved for the boarders, including dedicated social areas.

Admission. Places in the Junior School, Heathfield, are given, subject to availability, on individual assessments appropriate to each applicant's age and previous education. Entrants for Rishworth at Year 7 are asked to sit the School's own entrance assessment, which also forms the basis for the award of scholarships.

Those who wish to join the School at other stages are assessed individually.

Fees per term (from April 2008). Reception to Year 2 £1,635; Years 3 to 6 £2,395; Years 7 & 8: £2,940 day, £5,610 full boarding, £5,095 weekly boarding; Years 9 to 13: £3,195 day, £6,120 full boarding, £5,575 weekly boarding. The School operates a number of schemes, including monthly payments, to ease the financial burden on parents.

Scholarships and Bursaries. (*see Scholarship Entries section*). A number of scholarships are given for entrance at or after Year 7 for academic, musical, drama and sporting achievement. Substantial discounts are available for siblings of pupils in the School, for children of serving members of the Armed Forces and of ordained members of the Church of England. Bursaries may also be available in cases of financial need.

The Old Rishworthian Club maintains a fund for the grant of scholarships to children of ORs.

Charitable status. Rishworth School is a Registered Charity, number 1115562. It exists to provide education for boys and girls.

The Royal School Dungannon

1 Ranfurly Road Dungannon BT71 6EG Northern Ireland
Tel: 028 8772 2710
Fax: 028 8775 2845 Headmaster
028 8775 2506 Bursar
e-mail: info@rsd.dungannon.ni.sch.uk
website: www.royaldungannon.com

Founded 1608.
Motto: *Perseverando.* (*Never say Die*)
Voluntary Grammar School (GBA & SHMIS)
Pupils: 654. Teachers: 41 full-time and 2 part-time.

Board of Governors:
Chairman: D N Browne, MIB, MIMgt
Vice-Chairman: Mrs E Harkness, BL

Members:
Mrs J Archer
G A Cooper, OBE, BSc, CEng, FICE, FCIWEM, FIEI, MConsE
J C M Eddie
Revd A J Forster, BA, BTh
Miss J Garvin, BA, MEd, PGCE
M Girvan
D Graham, BSc Hons, MIR
Mrs I T Holmes, MBE, BSc, DASE
P S Kerr, BA, PGCE
The Revd K R Kingston, MA
Prof A E Long, BSc, PhD, DSc, CEng, FICE, MISE
Miss M E Macbeth, BSc
Lord Maginnis of Drumglass, PC
J C McCarter, BA, DipArch, RIBA
The Revd Canon W R D McCreery, BD, GOE
H McLean, LLB, MBA
Dr H G McNeill, BA, MB, FFARCSW
Mrs S McQueen
G D Nicholl, MA, PGCE
The Very Revd Dr A Rodgers, MA, DD
Dr F Shields, KM, BBS, MFGPD UK
G Smith
Mrs S Stewart
S Swaile
Revd A S Thompson, MA, BD
S Turkington
J G Willis, LLB

Secretary to the Governors: The Headmaster

***Headmaster*: P D Hewitt**, MA, DipEd, FRSA, FCIM

Teaching Staff:
* *Head of Department/Teacher-in-charge*
[1] *Form Master/Mistress*
[2] *Head of House*
§ *Part-time*

Deputy Head: Miss V S J Garvin, BA, PGCE, MEd

Vice Principal: R J Clingan, BSC, MEd, PGCE

Senior House Master: *P H Annesley, BSc, BAgr, DASE
Senior Form Master: *M A Batchelor, BEd, LRAM, LTCL
Senior Mistress: *A E Chestnutt, BSc, MEd, PGCE
Senior Resident Master: G D Nicholl, MA, PGCE

*[1]G R Black, BSc, PGCE
*[1]N J Canning, BEng, PGCE
[1]R E Chambers, BSc, PGCE
*[1]Mrs W Y Chambers, BSc, PGCE
*[1]Mrs M E Clingan, BA, ATD
Miss E V Fleming, BA, PGCE
§G Ferran, BSc, MA, PGCE
[1]J R Graham, BA, MSc, PGCE
Mrs R L Hampton, BSc, PGCE
J W Hunniford, BA, MA, PGCE
[1]Mrs J Hobson, BEd
*[1]Mrs S J Jackson, BA, PGCE
Mrs P L Johnston, BSc, PGCE
1Miss Z E Kelly, BA, PGCE
[1]Mrs C L Kerr, BA, PGCE
*[1]P S Kerr, BA, PGCE
G S R Lucas, BSc, PGCE
§Mrs P L Matthews, BEd, PGCE
Mrs J S McCarthy, BSc, PGCE
Miss D McCombe, BSc, PGCE
*[1]Mrs P McMullan, BEd, PGCTEd
*Miss H Montgomery, BSc, PGCE
*P G Moore, MA, PGCE, GC, TEFL
*[2]K D Patton, BEd
*Ms A M Prescott, BEd, MEd
*[2]D J Reid, MSc, DASE, MIB
*[2]A S Ritchie, BSc, PGCE
*Mrs A R Straghan, BSc Econ, PGCE
*Miss D Topley, BSc, PGCE
A T Turner, BSc, PGCE
Mrs E J Walker, BMus, PGCE
[1]G T Watterson, MSc, PGCE
Miss C A Weir, BA, MA, PGCE
J W Willis, BEd

Chaplain: Revd P Boyd, DipTh

Administrative Staff:
Bursar: Mr D Wheeler, BSc Econ, FCA

Headmaster's Secretary: Mrs A Cullen
Reception Office Supervisor: Mrs P Williamson

Matrons:
Mrs M Willis, SRN (*Day*)
Mrs P Lucas (*Evening*)
Miss M Trainor (*Evening*)

In 1608 James I made an order in Privy Council establishing six Royal Schools in Ulster of which Dungannon became, in 1614, the first to admit pupils. In 1983 plans were first drawn up to incorporate the neighbouring girls' grammar school and to use both campuses' excellent facilities for co-educational purposes. This development came to fruition in 1986. A £9 million building and refurbishment programme began in 2000 and was completed in 2003, providing very high-tech specialist accommodation in science, technology and IT. In 2007 an international standard Astroturf hockey pitch was completed with flood lighting and four new all-weather tennis courts were opened.

For nearly four centuries the Royal School has aimed at providing an education which enables its pupils to achieve the highest possible standards of academic excellence and at developing each pupil into a mature, well-balanced and responsible adult, well-equipped for the demands of a highly complex and technological world.

There are four Houses which foster the competitive instincts and idiosyncrasies of young people. Pastorally, each year is supervised by a Form Master or Mistress who guides his/her pupils throughout the child's career in a caring school environment.

There is modern accommodation for 50 Boarders with a normal residential staff of seven teachers and three matrons. Girls and Boys are housed in separate wings of the modernised Old School building of 1789. The establishment of good study skills and practices is considered to be of crucial importance. The size of the School ensures that no child is overlooked in any way.

The extensive buildings are a mixture of ancient and modern, with recently opened technology and science accommodation. In the late 1980s a half million pound renovation provided new careers, music and girls' boarding facilities.

Eight well-equipped Science Laboratories, Audio/Visual Room, two Libraries, Sixth Form Centre and Study Rooms, Technology, two Music and Art Studios and two Information Technology Suites are supplemented by a Boarding Department housed in luxury accommodation. Boarders are able to make use of a wide range of facilities such as Sports Hall, Computer Laboratory, Swimming Pool, Badminton Courts, Video Rooms, Television Lounges and extensive parkland walks. Situated in its own spacious grounds in a quiet residential area of this rural town, the School is linked directly by motorway to Belfast (40 minutes), two airports, cross-Channel ferries and railway stations.

Ab initio A level subjects are Economics, Computing, Art and Food Technology.

Pupils are prepared for GCSE and A levels under all the major UK Examination Boards and there is a tradition of Oxbridge successes as well as a high rate of entry to the University of Ulster, Queen's University Belfast and other leading British Universities. In most years over 85% of the Upper Sixth Form proceed into Higher Education. Many of the School's overseas students have chosen to enroll at the Province's two Universities, such is their affection for Northern Ireland.

Apart from three nursing Matrons, the School is medically attended to by a team of doctors and dentists which gives Boarders first priority in calls. A major hospital is less than 30 minutes from the campus. Many co-curricular pursuits are encouraged during lunchtime or after school, such as Choir, Orchestra, Duke of Edinburgh's Award Scheme, Chess, Photography, Debating, Public Speaking and many more.

Alongside the School's academic achievements in both Arts and Sciences may be placed its record in the sporting world: in Rugby, Hockey, Cricket, Badminton and Tennis many trophies have been awarded and the Shooting Team has won the UK Championship at Bisley.

Fees per annum (2008-2009). Day: £135. Boarding: £10,635 (non-EU passport holders), £5,750 (EU passport holders).

There are several valuable Entrance Scholarships awarded annually and tenable for at least five years. Reductions in fees are available for children of clergymen, of overseas missionary workers of any denomination or for families of the Armed Services.

Charitable status. The Royal School Dungannon is a Registered Charity, number XN46588 A. It was established by Royal Charter in 1608 for the purpose of education.

The Royal Wolverhampton School

Penn Road Wolverhampton WV3 0EG
Tel: 01902 341230
Fax: 01902 344496
e-mail: mo@royal.wolverhampton.sch.uk
website: www.theroyalschool.co.uk

Motto: *Nisi Dominus Frustra.*

Patron:
His Royal Highnesss, The Earl of Wessex, KG, KCVO

Vice-Patrons:
The Countess of Lichfield
The Duke of Sutherland

Board of Governors:
P Hill, Esq, FCMA, MIMC (*Chairman*)
D Swift, Esq, BEd (*Vice-Chairman*)
R H Etheridge, Esq
P H Freeth, Esq, ACIB
P Gough, Esq, FRICS
Cllr R Hart
H V Hilton, Esq, LLB, ACIS
Mrs J Lawson, BA, ACIB
B Maybee, Esq, MA Oxon, JP
Prof R Moreton, BA Hons, MTech, FBCS
Mrs K Y Podmore, BA, MBA, PGCE, CEM
A T Sharp, Esq
Mrs B J Dixon

***Headmaster*: S M Bailey**, MA, BA Hons, PGCE

Deputy Head (Academic/Administrative): (*to be appointed*)
Head of Junior School: Mrs M Saunders, CertEd
Administrator, Clerk to the Governors and Secretary to the Foundation: D R Penn, BSc
Boarding Coordinator: D P Ireland, BEng Hons, PGCE
Lichfield Housemistress: Mrs M Johanesen, BA Hons

Senior School Staff:

Arts, Craft, Design & Technology:
M Allison, BA Hons, PGCE, BTec National Diploma (*Head of Art*)
P E Holliday, BEd (*Head of Design and Technology*)
Miss A M Atherton, BA, PGCE (*Head of Food Technology*)
Mrs L Fabre, BA Hons, PGCE

Business Studies:
C J Walker, BSc Hons, PGCE (*Head of Year 10; Head of Business Studies*)
Ms J Tate, BA Hons, HND, MAAT, PGCE (*Head of Year 7*)

Divinity:
(*to be appointed*)

English:
D P Boag-Munroe, CertEd, BA (*Head of Year 11; Head of English*)
Mrs B Bee, BA Hons, PGCE (*Head of Sixth Form*)

Geography:
Miss C Cadwallader, MSc, BSc (*Head of Geography*)

History:
M G White, CertEd (*Head of History*)

Information Technology:
R Watkins, BSc Hons, PGCE (*Head of Information Technology*)

Mathematics:
A Long (*Head of Mathematics*)
D Ireland, BEng Hons, PGCE (*Boarding Coordinator*)
W Duckworth, BSc Hons

Modern Languages:
Mrs A Goodlad, BA Hons, PGCE (*Head of Modern Languages*)
Mrs R Boden, BA Hons, PGCE

Physical Education:
G W Beckett, BSc Hons, PGCE, FIST, AISC (*Head of PE; Surmaster*)
Mrs R L Ingerfield-Lapsley, BA Hons, PGCE (*Head of Girls PE; Head of PSCHE/Careers*)
Miss A M Atherton, BA, PGCE
M Taylor, BA Hons (*Dartmouth Housemaster*)

Psychology/Sociology:
Miss C Martin, BSc, MSc (*Head of Sociology*)

Science:
R C Bissell, BSc, PGCE (*Head of Science*)
Miss H Prosser, BSc, PGCE
Dr W Chhabra, MPhil, BSc, MSc, BA Ed
R Beardsmore, BSc Hons, PGCE
Mrs S Tappin, CChem, MRSC (*Laboratory Assistant*)

TEFL:
Miss J L Kyle, BA, PGCE

Junior School Staff:
R Alder, BA Hons, PGCE (*Head of French, Year 4 Teacher*)
Miss C Galbraith, BA, PGCE (*Year 3 Teacher*)
Miss K Atkins, BA Hons, HBO Hons, PGCE (*Year 1 Teacher; Key Stage 1 Coordinator*)
Miss J Hall, BTEC, NVQ3, Cert EYP (*Year 2 Assistant*)
Mrs K Harris, BA Hons, PGCE (*Reception Teacher*)
Mrs J Higgins, NCFE Cert (*Year 3-4 Assistant*)
Mrs J Hocknull, BEd Hons, CertSpLd (*Special Educational Needs Coordinator*)
Mrs C D Howes, BEd (*Head of Maths & ICT, Year 5 Teacher*)
Mrs C Ireland, BA Hons, PGCE (*Head of English, Year 6 Teacher*)
Miss E Jackson, DCE Cert EYP (*Year 1 Assistant*)
Mrs K Jefferson, BEd Hons (*Year 2 Teacher, Head of Junior Library*)

Nursery:
Mrs S Lawrence, NNEB (*Head of Nursery*)
Mrs J Cooper, BTEC (*Nursery Nurse*)
Mrs P Brannan (*Assistant*)
Miss S Colley, BTEC (*Nursery Nurse*)
Mrs P Davies, NNEB (*Nursery Nurse*)
Miss L Fletcher, BTEC (*Nursery Nurse*)
Mrs S Page (*Assistant*)
Mrs E Wood, BTEC (*Nursery Nurse*)
Miss A Wylde BTEC (*Nursery Nurse*)

Music Staff:
Mrs C Fellows, BMus, GNCM, ANCM, FRNCM (*Director of Music*)
I Hackett, BMus Hons, PGCE (*Assistant Director of Music; Head of Year 9*)

Visiting Music Staff:
Mrs J Davis, LCM Hons (*Keyboard/London College of Music Rep*)
C Fletcher, BA Hons (*Brass*)
Miss A Finch, BMus, PG Dip (*Strings*)
Miss R Lakeland, CertEd, ALCM (*Singing/Harp*)
Mrs M Morton, GRSM, ARCM, LRAM, PGCE
B Perkins, ABSM (*Guitar*)
Miss R Perry, BA Hons (*Flute*)
D Rosina, BMus Hons, PG Dip (*Woodwind*)
S Terry (*Keyboard/Drums*)
G Walker, BA Hons, ARCO, FRSA (*Piano*)

Administrative Staff:
Registrar: Mrs M Orton
Secretary to the Headteacher: Mrs L Berry
Secretary to the Administrator: Mrs N Warmer/Mrs K Marsden
Junior School Secretary: Mrs A P Jackson
Administration Office Manager: Mrs D Hall, MAAT
School Fees: Mrs M Wilkinson
Accounts Assistant: Mrs K Bastable
Receptionist: Miss R Marsh
Resource Centre Manager: Mrs M Leigh, ALA
Head of International Office: Mrs L Penn
Overseas Liaison: S Chung, FCIOB, FBEng, JP

Medical Staff:
Dr D DeRosa, BSc, MB, CLB, MRCGP
Mrs C Dinham, RGN, RSCN
Mrs A Astley, BSc Hons Nursing
Mrs H Burrell, RGN

Estates Supervisor: J O'Hara
Catering Manager: C Cooke

The Royal Wolverhampton School occupies a 28-acre site in a pleasant residential area to the west of Wolverhampton. Easy access is afforded by road, train or air from the local area and further afield. A daily school transport service is organised for pupils locally and the school arranges airport transfers for pupils from other areas of the country and abroad.

The Royal Wolverhampton School provides an education for boys and girls aged 2 to 18 years. The Royal Wolverhampton Junior School and The Young Royals' Nursery has approximately 180 pupils and the Senior School 290 pupils. Pupils can attend the school on a daily basis or they can be admitted as weekly, full or flexi boarders. The School can accommodate 170 boarders, most of whom are in the Senior School and Sixth Form.

Founded in 1850, The Royal Wolverhampton School celebrated its 150th Anniversary in the year 2000. The prefix "Royal" was granted by Queen Victoria in 1891.

Facilities. The School has been transformed since its days as an orphanage and the elegant ivy-clad main school building having been continually updated and augmented with a number of substantial modern developments. Over the past ten years, the School has spent over £10 million on improvements to the School buildings and equipment. Today, The Royal Wolverhampton School offers tradition combined with modern facilities, including a brand new swimming pool and sports complex, a new sixth form centre and internet café, an art, craft and design centre, a dining room and kitchens, a library, modern boarding houses, 5 refurbished science laboratories, 3 information technology suites, and a floodlit astroturf.

The School's boarding accommodation houses boys and girls separately, according to their age. Younger children share with 2 or 3 others of the same age and pupils in the Sixth Form either have a single study-bedroom or a twin room. All boarding houses have a lounge, where pupils can meet and relax, as well as a kitchen and a launderette. Pupils are carefully supervised by the School's residential staff at all times.

The School's own catering staff serves a variety of meals to suit all tastes. A cooked lunch is provided for day pupils and boarders can enjoy breakfast, lunch and dinner in the modern dining room. Special dietary requirements, for religious or medical reasons, can be accommodated.

Religion. The Royal Wolverhampton School has its own Chapel within the School grounds. This fine building forms a focus for School life, with daily assemblies and important events in the School calendar being held there. Such events include Speech Day, The Advent Service of Light, Remembrance Sunday and Founder's Day. Although the School has a religious affiliation to the Church of England, it welcomes pupils of all religions. Staff will assist pupils of other religions in pursuing their beliefs during their stay at the School.

Pastoral Care. The well-being of all pupils in the School is of prime importance and pastoral care is a universally recognised strength of the School. Both day and boarding pupils are allocated to "houses" under the guidance of a housemaster or housemistress. All pupils have a Tutor responsible for overseeing their pastoral and academic welfare, although all staff are expected to take corporate responsibility for pupil welfare and pupils are entitled to consult any member of staff regarding matters of concern.

In case of illness, the School has a fully equipped sanatorium, which provides 24 hour healthcare.

Curriculum. Use of IT is integral to the curriculum from Reception onwards. It is planned that the Senior School will move to conducting the majority of its pupil work and reporting via a virtual learning environment with individual pupil laptops during the academic year 2008/9.

The School offers a broad education at all levels, which is based on the National Curriculum. Recent additions to the curriculum include Mandarin in Years 7 to 9 and Psychology and Sociology at GCSE and A Level. Pupils in Year 10 study four compulsory subjects (English and English Literature, Mathematics and the Sciences) plus four optional subjects, out of a total of sixteen. Pupils of higher ability may take separate Sciences and additional Mathematics, both taught within the standard timetable. At the end of Year 11 all pupils take GCSE examinations.

At A Level students are advised on the quantity and type of subject they should choose by Sixth Form staff, bearing in mind their proposed university course and career. Twenty-two different A Level courses are available to choose from. The School has strength in a variety of areas and on three occasions pupils have finished in the top five in the UK in one of their A Level subjects (Physics and MFL).

Sixth Form. The School prides itself on the great care it takes in advising Sixth Form students on careers and universities. The School organises its own universities' exhibition each year, where students can discuss various options with representatives from Higher and Further Education. At least 95% of pupils continue their education at university.

In addition to the School's other facilities, which can be used by all pupils, Sixth Form pupils have their own study area, sixth form centre and internet café where they can meet, study and relax.

The School is currently broadening the activities available for sixth formers and intends that all should work towards an ASDAN award. This will not only ensure their rounded development but in addition is worth UCAS points.

Sixth Form Scholarships are available. (*See Scholarships section entry.*)

Music and Drama. The School has an excellent reputation for its musical standards and is a recognised examination centre for the London College of Music. Our active Music Department, equipped with the latest technology, provides pupils with an opportunity to learn how to play 20 different instruments. In addition, pupils are encouraged to take part in the School's choir and to perform in a wide variety of events, including at the National Indoor Arena in Birmingham.

The Music Department organises regular Performing Arts festivals at which pupils of all ages perform. One of the highlights of the School calendar is the Variety Show, which presents the best of the School's dramatic and musical talents to parents and other guests.

The School awards a number of Music and Performing Arts scholarships each year. (*See Scholarships Section entry.*)

Sport and Extra-Curricular Activities. The School aims to educate well-rounded individuals and a wide variety of extra-curricular activities are enjoyed by all pupils from age 7.

Pupils can choose from fifteen different sports and matches are frequently arranged both inter-house and against local schools. The School basketball team has achieved major successes nationally in the past and became City Champions in 2007.

The School has a very strong Combined Cadet Force with Army and RAF sections. The shooting team has finished in the top ten in the UK in the RAF Assegai shooting competition for seven years in succession and regularly wins trophies in Army "March and Shoot" competitions. Pupils are also given the opportunity to participate in the successful Duke of Edinburgh's Award Scheme and various other community projects.

The School ethos promotes compassion towards those less fortunate than ourselves and considerable amounts of money are raised for local and national charities.

(*See Scholarships Section entry.*)

Entrance. The School holds three entrance examinations each year for entry to Year 7, one in November, one in January and one for late applicants in February. Scholarships will be offered to the pupils achieving the best grades in these examinations. Individual entrance testing can be arranged to suit specific applicant needs (for full details please contact the Registrar). In addition the School can offer support via its Bursary Scheme. Foundation places are available for pupils facing difficult family circumstances and are awarded to pupils who fulfill the Foundation's criteria. (*For further details regarding all awards please see Scholarships Section entry.*)

The minimum entry requirement for Sixth Form is five GCSE passes at Grade C or equivalent.

Fees per term (2008-2009). Senior School: Full Boarders £7,420; Weekly Boarders £6,615; Day Pupils £3,730. (Prompt payment discount available.)

Day fees include: lunch, text books, stationery, compulsory teaching materials and personal accident insurance cover. In addition to the above, boarding fees include: full board accommodation, laundry, dry cleaning, medical attention and nursing in the Sanatorium.

The children of Serving Personnel in the Armed Forces receive a Bursary of £1,500 per term. The children of Old Royals receive a reduction of 25% off the basic fees and discounts are also available for siblings.

Old Royals' and Old Rowans' Association. The Association regularly organises reunions for former pupils. Founders' Day in June and Remembrance Sunday are also popular times for Old Royals and Old Rowans to return to the School. For further information, please contact Mr Mike Masters, 139 High Street, Coleshill, Birmingham B46 3AY; Tel: 01675 463093; e-mail: mike_masters@talk21.com.

Charitable status. The Royal Wolverhampton School is a Registered Charity, number 1092221. It exists solely to provide an education for children.

Ruthin School

Ruthin Denbighshire LL15 1EE
Tel: 01824 702543
Fax: 01824 707141

e-mail: secretary@ruthinschool.co.uk
admissions@ruthinschool.co.uk
website: www.ruthinschool.co.uk

The School was originally founded in 1284. Refounded in 1574 by Gabriel Goodman, Dean of Westminster, the School was a centre of academic excellence in North Wales, and was granted a Royal Charter.

Motto: *Dei gratia sum quod sum*

Visitor: Her Majesty The Queen

Patron: Sir William Gladstone, Bt, KG, MA

Council of Management:

Chairman: J P Williams
Prof C Adams
A R Bale
A D Douglas
N Jones
Mrs T Kerrigan
Mrs J Oldbury
R N E Raven, JP, MA, MBE
P Retout
S H Sington (*OR*)
G M Swift (*OR*)
I J C Trigger (*OR*)

Bursar and Clerk to the Council: T J Belfield, MA Cantab

***Headmaster*: J S Rowlands**, BSc, PGCE

† *Housemaster/Housemistress*

Senior Management Team:
I Welsby, BSc, MIBiol, PGCE, DipEd
†Ms J Higham, MA, PGCE, CPE

Assistant Staff:
N J Blandford, BA, MA, PGCE
Mrs R Crowther, BA, PGCE
M Davies, BSc, PGCE
Mrs J Duffy, BA, PGCE
Miss S L Evans, BEd
S J H Foster, MEng, PGCE
†Miss K A Goodey, MEd, TESOL, BEd, CETFLA
J P Hamer, BA, PGCE
Dr M D Hannant, PhD, PGCE
Miss A Hayling, BEd
J R Henry, BA, PGCE
D J Heywood, BA, PGCE
Mrs R J Maher, BA
A V McGibbon, BEd
Ms S Morley, BEd
†D Owen Booth, BEd
I M Rimmer, BSc, PGCE
Dr J A Roberts, BSc, MSc, PhD
Mrs S Rowlands, CertEd
O Sammons, BMus, PGCE
†Mrs E Thomas, BA, PGCE, TEFL, AMBDA
Miss P Warburton, BEd

Visiting:
Mrs J Aldridge (*Violin*)
Mrs P Almond, CertEd (*Special Learning*)
Mrs G Bolton, GMus RNCM (*Piano*)
Mrs P Evers-Swindell (*Speech and Drama*)
M Lewis (*Tennis*)
M Hamilton (*Guitar*)
M H L Hewer, MA, DipEd (*EAL*)
D Hughes (*Clarinet*)
G Knight (*Judo*)

Officer Commanding CCF: Major D Owen Booth
School Secretaries: Mrs E Eccles, Mrs A Pierce
Matron: Mrs C Bland, RGN

The School. Ruthin School is co-educational with some 200 pupils in the School comprising 60 boarders and 140 day pupils. Just under a third of the pupils are girls. The emphasis is on the individual. Good manners, personal discipline and respect for others are of supreme importance, as is a thorough grounding in central subjects of the curriculum. We believe that social responsibility can be developed in a small community with a family atmosphere, comprising a wide range of academic and other talents. This is reflected in our entry policy. Ruthin School is committed to providing an education of the highest quality, endeavouring to develop the potential of all pupils in all spheres of education. The pupils develop self-confidence through recognising and building upon their strengths as well as identifying and striving to improve their weaknesses. They are thus prepared to face the challenges of the changing world beyond school.

Organisation. Weekly and full boarding places are offered to boys and girls in the Senior School (11 to 18). Day places are offered from 3 to 11 in the Junior School and throughout the Senior School.

The two boarding houses – Gladstone (boys) and Wynne (girls) – have their own House system under the guidance of resident House staff and tutors.

The School operates a 5-day week from 8.40 am to 5.00 pm.

Admission. The normal method of entry to the Junior School is by interview, and to the Senior School by interview, examination, and reports.

Activities. A wide range of non-curricular activities is provided and has included car maintenance, fitness training, basketball, swimming, Welsh, yoga, judo, TaeKwonDo, drama, rock climbing, sailing and canoeing, mountain biking, stage management, shooting, weight training, table tennis, badminton, conservation, gardening and tennis. Boys and girls are encouraged to participate in the Duke of Edinburgh's Award Scheme at the age of 14 until they have completed the Bronze Award; several go on to complete the Silver and a few aspire to the Gold Awards. A lively mix of traditional and contemporary musical and dramatic productions is a feature of the school year and half the pupils receive individual instrumental tuition from the professional music staff. A programme of excursions is organised for boarders in the evenings and at weekends and these are open to all pupils.

Bursaries and Awards. (*see Scholarship Entries section*). In addition to academic awards, there are awards for Art, Music, Sport and Design Technology and remissions are available for siblings, children of members of the armed forces, of the clergy and of Old Ruthinians.

Curriculum. A wide curriculum is offered in the Junior School with emphasis on the basic skills of reading, writing and arithmetic.

In the Senior School the curriculum includes English, Mathematics, History, Geography, separate Biology, Physics and Chemistry, Information Technology, Art, Music, Design Technology, French, and German. PE and Business Studies are added at GCSE level. Psychology is added at AS Level and Further Maths is available in Year 12.

An option scheme operates for Year 10, but English, Mathematics and at least one Science are compulsory. The BTEC in Public Service has been added as an option through the CCF.

Careers. Guidance begins in Year 9 of the Senior School and a comprehensive programme evolves through Years 10 and 11 and the whole of Year 12 is devoted to research and visits before university applications are made. Virtually all members of the Sixth Form gain university places. Work experience is undertaken in Year 10 and Year 12.

CCF. Pupils join either the Army or the RN Section at the end of their second year in the Senior School and may opt to continue membership in the Sixth Form. There are opportunities to attend courses and camps.

Games. Rugby, basketball, football, cross-country, netball, tennis and athletics all feature in the coaching programme. A new Sports Hall was opened in January 2004.

Fees per term (2008-2009). Junior Day £1,000–£2,000; Senior Day £2,750–£3,500; Senior Boarding £5,000–£6,500.

Transport. The School provides daily transport to and from the North Wales coast, Holywell and Mold.

Ruthin School Association. This parents' association of which all parents are members is very active and plays an important supportive role in the School community.

The Old Ruthinian Association fosters close links between past and present pupils of the School. The *Secretary* is Mrs B Tremayne, c/o Ruthin School, Denbighshire LL15 1EE.

Charitable status. Ruthin School is a Registered Charity, number 525754. It exists to provide education for boys and girls.

St Christopher School

Barrington Road Letchworth Garden City Herts SG6 3JZ
Tel: 01462 650850
Fax: 01462 481578
e-mail: school.admin@stchris.co.uk
admissions@stchris.co.uk
website: www.stchris.co.uk

Fully co-educational from its foundation in 1915, St Christopher has always been noted for its friendly informality, breadth of educational vision, good academic standards and success in developing lifelong self-confidence. There are now some 540 pupils from 2 to 18. Boarders can start from age 11. There are full and weekly boarders. We aim for our young people to develop competence and resourcefulness, social conscience and moral courage, a capacity for friendship and a true zest for life.

The School was founded in Letchworth's infant Garden City by the Theosophical Educational Trust, whose object was to support schools 'where members of different faiths shall be encouraged to mix together and in this way learn a respect and tolerance for ideas other than their own'. The School in its present form developed under the Quakers, Lyn and Eleanor Harris and their son Nicholas from 1925 to 1980, and the same continuity of purpose was sustained by Colin Reid who retired in 2004. The School is now an educational charity conducted by a Board of Governors, all of whom have a close knowledge of the School.

Board of Governors:
Garth Pollard (*Chairman*)
Vernon McClure (*Vice-Chairman*)
William Armitage
Christopher Brown
Ian Cotterill
Kevin Jones
Meher Pocha
Veronica Raymond
Cath Smith
Helen Szirtes

***Head*: Richard Palmer**, BEd, FRSA

Deputy Head: Emma-Kate Henry, BA (*from January 2009*)
Director of Studies: Dennis Rix, BA, MA, PGCE
Director of Pastoral System: Andy Selkirk, MBA, BSc, DipPhy
Director of Activities: Edwin Gruber, MagPhil, PGCE
Director of Marketing & Admissions: Ed Peters, BA, AKC, MCIM, FIDM
Junior School Head: Sue Rix, BA, PGCE, Adv DipEd
Registrar: Maire McAlister

Teaching Staff:
Sylvester Beecroft, BA, PGCE (*French, Examinations, Careers*)
Julie Bolter, BSc, MEd Mgt (*Head of Mathematics, Faculty Coordinator, HE Adviser*)
Michael Clement, BEd, MEd (*Arts Faculty Coordinator*)
Michael Collins, BA, MA, PGCE (*History, Politics*)
Wendy Cottenden, CertEd (*PE, Games*)
Chris Drayton, BSc (*Mathematics, Outdoor Pursuits*)
Denise Eades, BA (*Geography*)
Gavin Fraser Williams, BA, MA (*Design & Techology*)
Saida Goutel, BA, MA (*French, Spanish*)
Edwin Gruber, MagPhil, PGCE (*Director of Activities*)
Anthony Harris, BSc, PGCE (*Mathematics*)
David Ilott, BA, DipEd (*Head of English, Head of EFL*)
Paul Kelly, BEd (*Head of PE*)
Andrew Lambie, BA, PGCE (*Chemistry*)
Samantha Lloyd, BSc, PGCE (*Biology*)
Penny Main, BA, MA, PGCE (*History, English*)
Mario May, BA, MA, PhD, PGCE (*Head of History, Faculty Coordinator*)
Liz Mayes, BA (*History, Politics*)
Isabelle Mills, Licence d'Anglais, PGCE (*French, Spanish*)
Linda Moore, BSc, PGCE (*Mathematics*)
William Norris, MPhil, BMus, AKC (*Music Assistant*)
Angeles Ojeda, Licendiada (*Spanish, German*)
Andy Owen, BSc, PGCE (*Head of Science Faculty*)
Dennis Rix, BA, MA, PGCE (*English*)
Emma Roskilly BA, PGCE (*English*)
Jennifer Savage, MA, PGCE (*Head of Geography*)
Andy Selkirk, MBA, BSc, DipPhy, PGCE (*Biology*)
Emma Semple, BA, MA, PGCE (*Head of Art*)
Cyrille Simon, Maîtrise (*Head of Modern Languages, French, Spanish*)
Pat Themistocli, BA, PGCE (*History, Head of Special Needs*)
Phil Thomas, BSc, PGCE (*Physics*)
Ben Wall, BSc, PGCE (*Head of Design & Technology*)
Linda Wallace, BSc, PhD, PGCE (*Biology, Chemistry*)
Ian Warder, MA, MSc, PGCE (*Mathematics*)
Terence Watson, BSc, PGCE (*Physics, Astronomy*)
Michael Watts, BSc Econ (*Economics, Business Studies*)
Jenny White, BEd (*PE and Games*)
Richard White, BSc, PGCE (*Biology*)
Hamish Wilson, BA, MA (*Drama*)
Susan Woollard, BSc, MSc (*Psychology, Head of Sixth Form*)
Jonathan Wright, BSc (*PE, Games*)
Naz Yeni, BA, MA (*English, Drama*)

Junior School and Montessori Department:
Head: Sue Rix, BA, PGCE, Adv DipEd
Christine Percival, CertEd (*Senior Teacher*)
Bryan Anderson, BEd
Anne Holland, BA, PGCE
David Jackson, BA, PGCE
Adam McAndrews, BA
Sam Selkirk, BEd
Alyson Shiel, CertEd
Claire Slater, BEng, PGCE
Carly Smith, BA, PGCE
Sally Wall, BA, PGCE

Lesley Edwards (*Nursery Manager*)
Sarah Brown
Wendy Gwilliams
Valerie Olton
Lucy Pinkstone

Director of Music: Martin Goodchild, GRSM, LRAM, PGCE

Community Coordinator: Jane Edwards, BA
Librarian: Linda Aird, ALA
Performing Arts Technician: Robert Johnson
School Doctor: Anthea Bond, MBChB, DRCOG
School Nurse: Caroline Dorrington
Special Needs Consultant: Anthea Briggs, BA, DipEd, PGCE

Bursar & Clerk to the Governors: William Hawkes, MA

Boarding Staff:
Arundale: Chris and Cecilia Drayton, Angeles Ojeda, Adam McAndrews
Arunside: Malcolm and Pippa Hodgson, Paul and Sue Kelly, Melanie Calin

The School provides for children of average to outstanding ability. All who are admitted to the Montessori Nursery (for 2 to 4 year olds) or to the Junior School (for 4 to 11 year olds) may continue through the Senior School, subject to performance. Entry to the Sixth Form is dependent on GCSE results and the ability to cope with the AS/A Level programme.

Academic Programme. The Montessori has its own very particular curriculum. Close attention is given to the transition to the Junior School which follows a programme which includes extensive enrichment built around the core elements of the National Curriculum. The Junior School offers small classes and a wide range of opportunities, including the use of specialist teachers and facilities for the older children. In the Senior School a wide-ranging programme continues to the age of 16, including the separate study of all three sciences to Double Certificate level of the GCSE. In Modern Languages everyone visits one of our exchange schools in France or Spain. The creative and expressive arts are particularly encouraged.

The Sixth Form. Although St Christopher is not a large school, the Sixth Form is a good size (generally numbering 100) with excellent facilities in its Sixth Form Centre. 21 AS/A level courses are on offer with all the usual Arts and Science subjects and in addition Theatre Studies, Psychology, Economics and Design Technology. There is a lively extra-curricular programme.

Learning through experience. There is an emphasis on learning through experience both with regard to academic subjects and more generally. There are many opportunities for practical and community work and for Outdoor Pursuits. At the end of the Summer Term the timetable is suspended for all pupils to undertake an extended project, generally away from the School campus. Each year two groups of sixth formers visit development projects in the Indian desert province of Rajasthan. There are also long-standing international projects in Kosovo and Ladakh. In 2006 the School was awarded the International School Award by the DCSF through the British Council.

A humane and global outlook. There is no uniform (except for games). All children and adults are called by their first names. Internationalist and green values are encouraged and the School was re-awarded the Eco-Schools Award in 2008. The School's diet has been vegetarian from the foundation. People of different religions and of none feel equally at home; there is a significant period of silence in every assembly.

Self-Government. The informality of the School encourages openness: children speak up for themselves – and for others. Everyone, child and adult, is represented on the School Council which is chaired by an elected senior pupil. The elected Major Officials and Committees look after different aspects of community life.

Treating children as individuals. From the outset the School has sought to treat children as individuals. In consequence, the ethos is an encouraging one and suits children who enjoy a broad education and who will thrive in a non-competitive academic environment. In our Tutorial Centre individual and group help is available. We also deal individually with those of very high ability and children are placed "a year ahead" or "a year behind" according to their needs.

Creative and Performing Arts. The School has an excellent tradition in these areas and has fine purpose-built facilities that reflect this. There are several productions a year in the Theatre which has tiered seating and full technical resources. Similarly there are regular concerts and recitals in the Music Centre. A Music Technology Suite opened in 2007. In the Arts Centre there are studios for fine art, for design and for ceramics, together with individual Sixth Form work areas and a lecture theatre for Art History.

Technology and Computing. The School benefits from an ICT Centre, opened in 2004. Internal online resources for teaching and learning have been developed.

Clubs and Societies. There are plentiful activities for pupils to join in with, taking place after School and at weekends. Staff share their enthusiasms and pupils too can take the lead in their own areas of interest.

Health, Fitness and Physical Education. The diet has been vegetarian from the outset and considerable pride is taken in the catering. There is a resident nurse with relief staff on call. The PE programme is full and varied, making use of playing field, gym, sports hall, all weather surface and a 25m covered swimming pool. Matches take place against many other schools.

Full collaboration with parents. The Parents' Circle was founded in 1921 and the School has throughout valued the close involvement of parents, who are welcome in the School not just for consultation about their children but also to take part in evening classes and in sharing the many performances and information evenings. We want parents to share in the education of their children and in the School community.

Boarders. There are up to 50 boarders living in 2 boarding houses. The provision for younger pupils has a strongly domestic feeling, with each under the supervision of resident house staff. The accommodation for sixth formers in a newly refurbished Sixth Form house is along student lines with almost all in single rooms. Apart from four 'community' weekends each year, most boarders go home each weekend on Friday evening.

Day Pupils. Day pupils benefit from the residential nature of the community, sharing in the evening and weekend life and taking meals in the School when they wish. Sixth formers have their own study areas in the Sixth Form Centre.

Fees per term (2008-2009). Day Pupils £1,050–£4,500, Boarders £6,125–£7,900. There are discounts of 10% for second and subsequent children, so long as they have an older sibling in the School. A range of financial assistance is available.

Admission Procedure. The most usual ages of admission are at 2 (into the Montessori Nursery) at ages 4, 7, 8 or 9 (into the Junior School) and at 11 or 13 (into the Senior School). A number also enter at Sixth Form level. Our assessment procedure includes diagnostic tests and interview. Assessment for Years 7 and 9 entry takes place in January.

Situation and Travel. The School has an attractive 35-acre campus on the edge of the Garden City with excellent communications. The A1(M) is a mile away and London (King's Cross) is 35 minutes by train. Stansted Airport is 35 minutes and Heathrow 60 minutes by car.

Old Scholars. The Membership Secretary of the St Christopher Club is David Cursons who can be reached c/o The School. The Annual Reunion is held over a weekend each July.

Charitable status. St Christopher School is a Registered Charity, number 311062. It exists to provide education for boys and girls, aiming to treat all as individuals and to develop their proper self-confidence.

St David's College

Llandudno North Wales LL30 1RD
Tel: 01492 875974
Fax: 01492 870383
e-mail: hmsec@stdavidscollege.co.uk
website: www.stdavidscollege.co.uk

Governors:
David J Rawlinson, LlB OD (*Chairman*)
Peter J Caldwell, FRICS, FRVA (*Vice-Chairman*)

***Headmaster*: Chris Condrup**, MSc

Senior Management Team:
S Hay, BSc, PGCE (*Deputy Head*)
H W Lomas, BSc, CertEd (*Assistant Head, Curriculum*)
A Russell, BSc, PGCE (*Assistant Head, Pastoral*)
Mrs J Buckley, BA, MEd, PGCE, Cert Further Prof Studies SpLD, AMBDA (*SENCO*)
Revd T R Hall, BA, LTh (*Chaplain*)
Ms J Leslie, BSc, ACIS (*Bursar*)

Headmaster's Secretary/Admissions: Mrs S Hold

The School. Education should be challenging and fun! With the sea on one side and Snowdonia on the other, St David's sits astride the gateway to both academic achievement and unrivalled outdoor activities. We number some 250 boys and girls, both boarders and day pupils, accommodated in a combination of a 16th century mansion (updated!) and modern buildings that reflect the site's listed status. Organisation is based on the traditional house system, with dedicated houseparents, year heads and tutors catering for pupils' pastoral care and individual needs.

Academic Studies. A broad curriculum offers 21 subjects to GCSE and with a staff/pupil ratio of 1:5, our target class sizes are no more than 12. At A Level, we offer up to 17 subjects, along with a range of BTEC National Awards. With a state-of-the-art Design Technology Centre, we have a particular expertise in Computer Aided Design (CAD), where career opportunities are limitless.

Art, Drama and Music. The practical and visual arts are strong, winning national awards for our students. Music and drama have leapt ahead in recent years, leading to Associated Board and LAMDA qualifications; some three-quarters of the School now study individual musical instruments and new stage facilities provide greater opportunity for drama productions.

Learning Support. Our Cadogan Centre is recognised nationally for its teaching of SEN children, particularly Dyslexia, on a 1:1 or small group basis; the majority of staff have specialist qualifications and, unique to St David's, additional training in classroom techniques appropriate for dyslexics.

Outdoor Education and Sport. Another of our specialities, our curriculum-based outdoor education programme is designed to develop pupils' confidence and self-esteem, which then translates into the classroom. Our range of expeditions – 15 are planned for this year – the Duke of Edinburgh's Award Scheme and environmental activities all contribute to development of the 'whole person', our stated aim. On the sports field, we offer the usual range of independent schools' sports, with opportunities for representative selection at national level.

Religious Life. Our Christian foundation, teaching and values form an integral part of School life, shaping our expectation of personal standards. Assemblies are held daily and there is a lively Chapel service on Sundays, bringing worship to young people in a relevant and contemporary way. There is an annual option for pupils to be confirmed.

Clubs and Activities. Apart from outdoor pursuits, the host of clubs and activities is based on demand, currently ranging from astronomy, through kite-buggying to skating. Again, activities are timetabled, so that every pupil has the opportunity to explore new events.

Community Service. A natural extension of our foundation is recognition of those less fortunate than ourselves and how our work in the community can help. The St David's family is involved in a number of charitable activities locally, from hospices to sky-diving; but our influence spreads wider: our 'Uganda Link' is a much-sought-after chance for pupils to experience living with and helping some of the world's poorest peoples.

Admission. Entry is by selection or scholarship exam following Headmaster's interview; the majority join at age 11–13, with others joining the Sixth Form for A Levels.

Scholarships and Bursaries. Academic scholarships of between 10–50% of full fees may be awarded, with smaller awards available for drama, music, sports and other talents. Means-tested bursaries may also be applied for.

Fees per term (2008-2009). Boarders: £5,995–£7,555. Day Pupils: £3,475–£5,070.

Discounts are available for siblings in School, children of clergy and members of the Armed Forces.

Charitable status. St David's College Trust is a Registered Charity, number 525747. It exists to provide whole person education within a Christian framework.

St Edward's School

Cirencester Road Charlton Kings Cheltenham Glos GL53 8EY
Tel: 01242 538600
Fax: 01242 538610
e-mail: headmaster@stedwards.co.uk
website: www.stedwards.co.uk

Formed from two former Grammar Schools in 1987, St Edward's is a fully co-educational Catholic day school for 11 to 18 year olds. Proud of its Roman Catholic foundation as the Carmelite boys' school Whitefriars and the girls' convent school Charlton Park, St Edward's is now lay-run and warmly welcomes all denominations. Pupil numbers have risen in recent years, with 485 pupils currently on roll of whom 116 are in the Sixth Form. The School is set in 17 acres of beautiful grounds on the southern outskirts of Cheltenham. The site was originally a hunting lodge of King Edward the Confessor, and the main building dates from the 18th century. The School has a warm Christian ethos built on a firm Catholic foundation. There is a full-time Priest Chaplain. The School promotes academic excellence and all-round cultural and physical development.

Motto: *Quantum Potes Aude*

Chairman of Trustees: Mr P Walsh

***Headmaster*: A J Nash**, MA, PhD

Organisation. On entry to the Senior School at age 11, the students are allocated to one of three or four Forms. They are taught in four teaching groups which are 'setted' for the principal subjects of Mathematics, English, French and Science. The pastoral system of the School is based on Sections for the different age groups, with Section Heads leading teams of Tutors. The Sixth Formers have their own Study and Common Room and play a vital role in the organisation and promotion of the School.

Developments. Recent years have seen: a major development of the ICT facilities; a new extension containing additional changing-rooms and a new Maths suite; an additional Science laboratory and refurbishment of existing laboratories; CCF headquarters; additional Art rooms; an extra Technology workshop; and an additional Sixth Form study room. A major new building housing a modern Dining Hall, Drama Studio and extra teaching rooms opens in September 2008, together with a refurbished Sixth Form 'Café 6' Careers Centre and refurbished Art Studios.

Academic Curriculum. A broad range of subjects is offered to GCSE with over 25 at A Level. During the first three years all pupils study Art, Drama, English, French, Geography, History, Information Technology, Latin, Mathematics, Music, Physical Education, Religious Studies, Science and Technology (including Resistant Materials, Food and Textiles). German, Spanish and Mandarin are offered as second foreign languages from the second year, with Classical Civilisation as an additional option. The Sciences are studied as discrete subjects in the third year.

The compulsory subjects for GCSE are English Language, English Literature, Mathematics, Religious Education (short course), Science (the three separate GCSEs or the new Science and Additional Science GCSEs) and a foreign language (French, Spanish, German, Mandarin). Up to three further subjects are studied from Latin, Classical Civilisation, French, German, Spanish, Mandarin, History, Geography, Music, Drama, Art, Design & Technology, PE, Home Economics.

The Sixth Form AS and A2 subjects offered are: Mathematics, Further Mathematics, English, History, Geography, Religious Studies, Biology, Chemistry, Physics, French, German, Spanish, Latin, Classical Civilisation, Critical Thinking, Art (including Photography), Music, Music Technology, Theatre Studies, Design Technology, Food Technology, Computing, Business Studies, Psychology and Physical Education.

Spiritual. There is a full-time Priest Chaplain (shared with our Junior School). Every day starts with prayers, whether in School Assembly or Form time. Whole school Masses and other liturgies are celebrated several times a term.

Careers. There is a specialist Higher Education Counsellor to guide Sixth Formers through the university application process and an Oxbridge Adviser. There is a careers guidance programme for the lower Years. In Year 11, pupils participate in a Work Experience week.

Sport. The principal sports for boys are Rugby, Hockey, Soccer and Cricket; for girls Hockey, Netball and Rounders. The School also competes very successfully in Swimming, Tennis, Basketball, Athletics, Badminton, Golf and Cross-Country. There are regular sports tours, most recently to Austrialia and South Africa.

Facilities include four rugby pitches, three hockey pitches (including one synthetic-turf), cricket square, several tennis courts, two sports halls, a fitness centre and a large indoor swimming pool.

Clubs and Activities. There is a thriving CCF contingent with both Army and RAF sections. The Duke of Edinburgh's Award Scheme is also flourishing. The School has a high reputation for the quality of its Drama and Music (the Choir and Orchestra regularly perform both at school and in the community). Other societies range from debating and chess to creative writing and Bridge. Pupils are encouraged to take full advantage of the many activities which take place both at lunch time and after school. Supervised homework is available after school every day until 5.30 pm. Trips abroad are a major feature of school life, including: an annual Ski Trip; a tour of the Normandy battlefields; a French cuisine trip; German, Spanish and French exchanges; a residential Art course; trips to Iceland and Costa Rica; expeditions to Patagonia and Zambia.

Admission. The main entry to the Senior School is at age 11 (the entry examination takes place in November), although some join the School at age 13 and into the Sixth Form.

Fees per term (2008-2009). £3,163–£3,708. Discounts are offered for a third, fourth and subsequent children. The Senior School offers Assisted Places and a number of Scholarships for entry at age 11 and age 16.

Junior School. St Edward's Junior School, with over 400 boys and girls aged 2½–11, is on a separate nearby site with its own extensive buildings and 40-acre grounds containing the main sports fields which are used by both the Senior and Junior schools. It is very well equipped with its own Science Laboratories, new library, technology room, music rooms etc. Admission to the Junior School is possible at any age depending on ability and the availability of places. With an emphasis upon sound learning of basics (French is studied from Kindergarten), yet with a broad range of opportunities, pupils are fully prepared for entry to the Senior School.

The Kindergarten, in a separate modern building, takes children from the age of 2½ and is open nearly all year round.

(*For further details, see entry in IAPS section.*)

Old Edwardians' Association. Secretary: Mrs P Hemming, St Edward's School, Cirencester Road, Charlton Kings, Cheltenham, Glos GL53 8EY.

Further information. A School prospectus is available on request from the Headmaster's PA & Registrar. You are warmly invited to arrange a visit to the School by telephoning her on 01242 538600. Our website is: www.stedwards.co.uk.

Charitable status. St Edward's School is a Registered Charity, number 293360. It exists to provide for the education of children of any creed with preference to those who are of the Roman Catholic faith.

Saint Felix School

Southwold Suffolk IP18 6SD
Tel: 01502 722175
Fax: 01502 722641
e-mail: schooladmin@stfelix.suffolk.sch.uk
website: www.stfelix.co.uk

Founded 1897.
Motto: *'Felix Quia Fortis'*

Patrons:
Mrs V Bottomley, MSc, JP, MP
The Rt Hon Christopher Patten
Sir Colin Davis, CBE
The Lady Prior of Brampton, JP
Sir Philip Foreman, CBE
Sir Brian Jenkins, GBE, MA, DSc

Board of Governors:
Chairman: Mrs Margaret Angus, MSc, TCert
Vice-Chairman: Mr John Whyte
Mr Alan Burgess
Miss Sian Dawson, BA Hons, MA, MCMI, FRSA, JP
Mr Andrew Kendall, MA
Dom Anthony Sutch
Mr Tom Webster
Mrs Lynda Al-Nakeeb (*Parent Governor*)
Mrs Helen Collis (*Parent Governor*)

***Headmaster*: Mr David A T Ward**, MA

[1] *PGCE/DipEd qualification*

Deputy Heads:
[1]Miss M F D'Alcorn, BA Hons Birmingham, MA UEA
Mrs Sue Duckett, NNEB, CertEd
Miss Sue Greenfield, BEd

Senior School:

Art & Design:
Mrs S Bassett, BA Hons East London
Mrs V Burns, BEd London
[1]Mrs L Roberts, BA Hons Leicester

Business Studies:
[1]Mr M Surridge, BA Hons Warwick, MA Ed UEA

Classics:
Mr B Harrild ACP, CertEd London

Design Technology:
Mr R Kay, BEd Hons, MPhil

English:
[1]Miss J Ashford, BA Hons Durham
Miss L J Branson, BA Hons OU, CertEd Bedford College
Miss N Peatchey, BA Hons, LLAM (*Speech and Drama*)

English as a Foreign Language (EFL):
Mrs S Hammond, BA Hons UEA
Ms A Eastaugh, MA Hons Edinburgh

Geography:
Mr I McLean, BSc Hons UEA

History:
[1]Miss M F D'Alcorn, BA Hons Birmingham, MA UEA
[1]Mrs J Camburn, BSc Hons Loughborough

Home Economics:
Mrs J Anderson, BA Hons, CertEd

ICT:
Mr T Ellard, HND Applied Physics, Grad Inst Physics
Mr M Grunnell, BEd Exeter

Mathematics:
Dr J Dodsworth, PhD Bath, BEd Hons Cantab
[1]Mr P J Duxbury, BSc Hons London, ARCS, MSc London, DIC, Dip ABRSM, LRSM
Mr J Cowan BSc Hons Sheffield Hallam

Modern Languages and EFL:
Mme C Cazergue-Sagaz, MA Montpellier III
[1]Miss L Hepenstal, BA Hons Manchester (*French and Spanish*)
Mlle A Nivanen, MA L'Université du Littoral

Music:
Miss R Moakes, BA Hons University of Cambridge
Mr V Scott, BA Hons Liverpool, DipEd Mus

Physical Education:
Miss L Baldwin, ASA Swimming Assistant, BSc Hons Exeter
Miss S Fenwick, BA Hons Warwick
Mrs G Nash, CertEd Sussex
Mr T O'Connell, BSc Hons Exeter
Ms S Purchase, ASA Swimming Coach
Mr B Collis
Mr N Brooker

Science:
Mr D Bryanton, BSc Hons Swansea, MA London
Mr A Hill, BSc Wales, MA OU (*Physics*)
Dr M Woodward, PhD Warwick (*Chemistry*)

Technicians: Mrs C Tyler, Mrs S Weldon

Careers & Sixth Form:
[1]Miss M F D'Alcorn, BA Hons Birmingham, MA UEA
[1]Miss J Ashford, BA Hons Durham

Learning Support:
[1]Mrs J Camburn, BSc Hons Loughborough
Mrs J Campbell, CertEd, Adv Dip CSN
Mrs J Poole, BA Hons
Mrs P Webb, CertEd

Chaplain: Mrs S B Slatter, CertEd Liverpool

House Staff:

Pre-Prep Houseparents: Mr & Mrs Laughland
Head of Boarding: Mr M Coombs, BSc Hons, MSc Newcastle
House Tutors:
Miss R Moakes, BA Hons University of Cambridge
Mrs G Nash, CertEd Sussex (*Sixth Form*)
Dr M Woodward, PhD Warwick (*Boys' Housemaster*)
House Matrons: Mrs J Tindle & Mrs W Tarr

Sanatorium:
Sister A Carr, RGN
Sister Y Proctor, RGN

School Medical Officer: Dr M Niemeijer

Management Support:
Secretaries: Mrs D Whittington & Ms B Weatherill
Registrar/Headmaster's Secretary: Mrs J Ellard
Assistant to the Registrar: Miss M Bridgman
Bursar: Mr T Chapman
Assistant to the Bursar: Mrs E Raw
Bronte House Secretary: Mrs D Whittington
Bursary Assistants: Mrs E Wells & Ms L Koehler

Preparatory & Pre-Preparatory Schools:
[1]Mrs N Burrows, BA Hons, MA
Mrs J Campbell, CertEd, Adv Dip CSN
Mme C Cazergue-Sagaz, MA Montpellier III
Miss A Colloby, BTec Level 3 (*Class Assistant*)
Miss J Cooke, NNEB (*Class Assistant, Bronte House*)
Mrs I Cooke (*Classroom Assistant*)
[1]Mrs R Crane, BA Hons (*French Teacher p/t, Bronte House*)
Miss K Craven, HNC, HND (*Nursery Assistant, Bronte House*)
Dr J Dodsworth, PhD Bath, BEd Hons Cantab (*Mathematics, Latin, Games Teacher*)
Miss T Doy, CCE, DNN (*Nursery Assistant, Bronte House*)
Mrs S Duckett, NNEB, CertEd (*Head of Pre-Prep, Form Teacher*)
Mrs A Evans, BA Hons (*Form Teacher*)
Miss S Greenfield, BEd (*Deputy Head, Form Teacher*)
Mr D Goddard, BA Hons, MEd (*Form Teacher*)
Mr B Harrild, CertEd (*Latin Teacher p/t*)
Mrs J Heal, Cert EYP (*Open*) (*Class Assistant, Bronte House*)
Mrs S Hunting (*Toddler Care Assistant, Bronte House*)
[1]Mrs P Kinsella, BA Hons (*Form Teacher*)
Mrs L Laughland, CCE, DNN (*Nursery Supervisor, Bronte House*)
Miss A Lee (*Nursery Assistant, Bronte House*)
Mr S Marsden, BEd Hons (*Form Teacher, Boys PE/Games*)
Miss R Moakes, BA Hons University of Cambridge (*Music Teacher*)
Mlle A Nivanen, MA L'Université du Littoral (*French Teacher*)
Mrs A Nunn (*p/t Year Teacher/Art*)
Mrs E Scoggins, NNEB (*Nursery Nurse, Bronte House*)
Mr V Scott, BA Hons (*Music Teacher*)
Mrs J Waters, NVQ2 (*Nursery Assistant, Bronte House*)
Mrs A Watling, CCE, DNN (*Nursery Nurse*)
Mrs P Webb, CertEd (*Enhanced Learning*)
Mrs D Whittington (*Bronte House Secretary*)
Mrs E Wilson, NNEB, CertEd (*Nursery Coordinator, Bronte House*)
[1]Mrs S Yates, BA (*Art Teacher p/t*)

Peripatetic Staff:
Mrs L Buncombe, ARCM, LRAM
Mr B Carben (*Woodwind*)
Mrs C Cliff, DipEd Music (*Piano, Recorder, Cello*)
Miss A Evans, GRSM, ARCM, ATCL, MTC (*Piano, Singing*)
Mrs S James (*Flute*)
Mrs J Joliffe (*Judo Coach*)
Mrs T Marriott, MIDA, SIPBE (*Ballet, Modern Dance*)
Mr D Miles (*Electric Guitar*)
Miss N Peatchey, BA Hons, LLAM (*Speech & Drama*)
Mr R Simmons (*Brass*)
Mrs M Smith (*Brown Owl*)
Mr D Strauss, GRSM, LRAM (*Piano*)
Mrs R Turner, LRAM (*Violin & Viola*)
Mr R Whiley (*Guitar*)
Mrs V Wise, BMus, STD, PDO, PDM, LRSM, UPLM, RCMAC, ACRM, APC Nice (*Singing & Choir*)

Age Range. 1–18.

Number of Pupils. 456.

Saint Felix School was founded in 1897 and is set in 75 acres overlooking the Blyth Estuary near the picturesque town of Southwold in Suffolk. The extensive buildings are purpose built and well equipped.

As a co-educational day and boarding school Saint Felix offers boys and girls a broad and balanced curriculum from the age of 1 to 18. A through school from the Nursery and Pre-Prep (ages 1–6) to the Preparatory (ages 7–11) through to the Senior School (ages 11–16) and then into the Sixth Form.

Academic. A well-structured timetable, and a broad and balanced curriculum, encourages children in the Pre-Prep and Preparatory Schools to achieve their personal best, both academically and socially. Small class sizes and specialist teaching staff ensure excellent SATS results together with happy, well-mannered and confident pupils.

In the Senior School, each individual child is encouraged to achieve the highest grade attainable, made possible by the expertise of committed, skilled and motivated teachers working in small class groups. A wide and distinctive range of subjects can be studied at GCSE, AS and A Level. Sixth Form students this year achieved 100% pass rate at A Level, enabling entry into many of the country's finest Art, Drama and Music colleges, and universities such as Cambridge. In addition the school's system of pastoral care ensures that children have continuous support and mentoring throughout their time at Saint Felix.

Music. Music is popular with over half taking peripatetic lessons. There is a variety of musical groups including chapel and chamber choirs, choral societies, orchestras as well as several chamber ensembles, eg piano trio, string quartets, jazz group and a rock band with electric guitar and drums especially popular. All Preparatory pupils are encouraged to learn an instrument and the Pre-Prep pupils learn the recorder. A 'Music in Residence' group encourages pupils to take up instruments. Music can be studied at GCSE and A Level. The department has 18 practice rooms and a performance area.

Sport. Facilities include an 25m indoor swimming pool, sports hall/theatre complex, squash courts, fitness suite and a 25-acre equestrian cross-country course.

A wide variety of sports are on offer including tennis, rugby, cricket, football, netball, hockey and rounders. Swimming is particularly strong throughout the school resulting in pupils competing in county, regional and national championships and achieving national recognition. An extensive range of other sports is available including squash, sailing, basketball, table tennis, aerobics, wall climbing and horse riding.

Arts. The school promotes the Arts with regular exhibitions and displays and eagerly-awaited school productions throughout the year. The combination of Art, Music and Drama is actively encouraged through an Arts Week. Photography and Art throughout the school is of a very high standard with excellent results at both GCSE and A Level. The school has been awarded the prestigious 'Gold Artsmark' for its outstanding achievements in creative subjects. A new Performing Arts Studio will be completed later this year to further enhance the provision for drama, dance and music and lecture facilities.

Extra Curricular Activities. There is an extensive list of activities available. All pupils are actively encouraged to take part in the Duke of Edinburgh's Award Scheme. A similar scheme runs in the Preparatory school. The school day is extended to include activities. The Army Cadet Force is very popular.

Community. The school actively encourages the local community to get involved in school life and various clubs are closely linked to the school (Norwich City Football Club, Guides, Brownies, The Choral Society, Southwold Rugby, Netball and Tennis Clubs) enabling pupils to be involved in groups outside school.

Fees per term (2008-2009). Day: £1,695–£3,995; Boarding: £4,145–£5,645 (weekly), £5,495–£6,995 (full).

Scholarships. (*see Scholarship Entries section*). The School offers Academic Scholarships of 50% maximum of fees and Exhibitions of 25% maximum on entry at 11+, 13+ or into the Sixth Form. The Hess Music Scholarship, for outstanding promise in music, is awarded annually, value 33% of the fees. Academic, Art, Drama, Music and Sport Scholarships at 16+ are also available. Forces Boarding School Allowance available.

Charitable status. Saint Felix School is a Registered Charity, number 310482. It exists to promote and advance education.

St George's School
Edgbaston

31 Calthorpe Road Birmingham B15 1RX
Tel: 0121 625 0398
Fax: 0121 625 3340
e-mail: admin@sgse.co.uk
website: www.sgse.co.uk

Council:
Chairman: Mr S M Topman

Mr D J Corney, FCA, MSPI, MIPA
Mr C J Goodier, MA Oxon
Mr C Keil, BSc Eng, CEng, MRAeS
Mr J Kumar, MBBS, FRCS, FACS
Dr M Kumar, BDS, MFGDP
Mr S Lewandowski, BSc
Mrs R Plevey, BSc Hons, PGCE
The Revd S Thorburn, BSc, MA
Mrs J Uff, BA, CPFA
Mr B Warner

Clerk to the Council and School Bursar: Mr D F Baker

***Headmistress*: Miss Hilary Phillips**, MSc Brunel

Deputy Head: Mr Russell Collier, BSc Hons Leeds, PGCE
Head of Sixth Form: Mrs Tina Kenwood, BA Hons London, PGCE
Head of Learning Support: Mrs Carolyn Hayes, CertEd London, MA Ed (SE/IE), PGCert SEN Coordination

Upper School:

English:
Mrs Pia Abbott, BA Hons Kent, CertEd
Miss Rebecca Hodge, BA Hons Warwick, PGCE
Mrs Vanessa Johnson, BA Hons Dunelm, PGCE
Mr Stephen Abbott, BA Hons London, PGCE

Mathematics:
Mr Mike Adams, BSc Hons Birmingham, PGCE
Mrs Jane Furneaux Smith, BEd Birmingham
Mrs Balvinder Gill, BA Hons Bath,GTP
Mr Geoff Thompson, BEd Hons Lancaster
Mrs Sally Powell, BSc Hons, PGCE

Science:
Mr Keith Bruce, BSc Hons Leeds, PGCE
Mr David Lai, BSc Lancs, PGCE
Mrs Gillian Lyth, BSc Hons Aston, PGCE
Dr Jane Thomas, PhD Bristol, PGCE
Mr Mark Williams, BSc Hons Bradford, PGCE

Design Technology:
Mrs Michelle Harbott, , BA Hons Wolverhampton, PGCE

Information Technology:
Miss Jennifer Davis, BSc Hons Plymouth, PGCE
Mrs Julie Glover, BTec Nat Cert Caring Services
Mrs Michelle Fowler, BSc Hons Birmingham, PGCE

Business Studies:
Mr Martin Morgan, ACIB, PGCE Wolverhampton

Psychology:
Dr Vanessa Parson, PhD Aston, BSc Hons Bangor

Modern Languages:
Mr Arséne Abitbol, Lic Langues Étrangères Appliquées Paris, PGCE
Mrs Tina Kenwood, BA Hons London, PGCE
Mrs Sue Sandys, AIL, MIL, PGCE

Religious Studies:
Mrs Hannah Girling, BA Hons Birmingham, PGCE

History:
Ms Sally Allder, BA Hons Essex, PGCE
Dr David Brown, BA Hons Manchester, MA, PhD, PGCE
Mrs Eleanor Webster, BA Hons Leicester, PGCE

Geography:
Mrs Emma-Jane Rawlings Smith, BSc Hons Sussex, MSc Sheffield, PGCE

Food Technology:
Mrs Margaret A Gough, CertEd Chelsea

Art and Ceramics:
Mrs Claire Hackett, DipAD Wolverhampton, ATD
Mrs Ursula Westwood, BA Hons Brighton, PGCE

Music:
Mrs Sarah C Russell, MA Cantab, PGCE

Theatre Studies:
Mr Michael Venables, BA Hons Lancaster, PGCE, ACE

Physical Education:
Mrs Sheila Foley, CertEd Birmingham
Mr Paul Ferris, BSc Hons, QTS Brunel
Miss Ann Hollman, BSc Hons QTS, Brunel

Learning Support:
Mrs Debra Arnold, NVQ 3 Child Care & Education
Ms Katherine Livall, BSc Hons Swansea, PGCE
Mrs Finulla Harrison, BA De Montfort
Mrs Wendy Nash, NVQ 3 Early Years Care & Education
Mrs Karen Parker, BA Hons Lancaster
Mr Gavin Passmore, BSc Hons Leeds
Miss Louise Passmore
Mrs Beverley Rance
Mrs Marieanne Stoke
Mrs Helen Taylor, CertEd Liverpool, BEd Hons Liverpool
Miss Kate Towers, BA Hons Durham
Mrs Pamela Varma, BA Hons, NVQ 2 Teaching Asst
Mr Matthew White, BA Hons, BEd Newcastle, Australia
Miss Joanna Walisiak, BA Hons MA
Mr Aarron Wynne
Mrs Sandra Wynne

Head of Lower School
Mr Mark McLuckie, BEd Hons Alsager College

Lower School Staff:
Mrs Christine Russell, CertEd Brunel
Mr Martin Russell, CertEd Brunel
Mrs Merâl Barlow, BEd Hons Birmingham
Mr Jason Evans, BA Hons QTS University of Central England
Mrs Lindsey Reid
Mrs Sally Roberts, NNEB, MontDip
Mrs Tracy Rose
Mrs Parminder Gill, ISC Dip Child Daycare
Mrs Sayima Shaheen
Mrs Patricia Tonks, BEd Hons Birmingham
Mrs Lynn Williams, CertEd Liverpool
Miss Denise Wood, NVQ3 Childcare & Education
Mr Timothy Wurr, BA Hons Birmingham,PGCE

Technical Staff:
Miss Lisa Allen, MSc Newcastle upon Tyne
Mrs Barbara Murdock, BSc Herts
Mrs Marilyn Jones

Librarian: Mrs Louise Walker & Mrs Marieanne Stoke
Bursar: Mr David F Baker
Registrar and Head's PA: Mrs Maureen Fahy
Secretarial Assistants:
Mrs Anne Jordan (*Upper School*)
Mrs Michelle O'Reilly (*Upper School*)
Miss Jennifer Parkes (*Lower School*)
Caretakers: Mr Patrick Ryan, Mr Michael Bridgens

The school opened in September 1999 as the amalgamation of Edgbaston Church of England College for Girls and Edgbaston College. The school is open to boys and girls of all faiths, but has a strong Christian ethos, and prides itself on the warm family atmosphere where each child is known as an individual. Entry to the Upper School is by selection at 11+ and most pupils are expected to move into Higher Education when they leave. Entry into the Lower School is by an informal interview and visit.

Location. Although the School is within a mile of the City Centre it occupies extensive grounds, providing excellent facilities for Football, Hockey, Tennis, Rugby, Athletics, Basketball, Netball and Rounders. In addition to good local transport services, the School has privately organised school coaches to transport pupils from more distant residential areas. The School takes full advantage of the first class facilities offered by the City and University of Birmingham and pupils are given the opportunity to visit exhibitions, plays, concerts and lectures to enhance their academic and cultural development.

Accommodation. A comprehensive building programme has provided additions to the original school building to meet educational demands.

Curriculum. The aim of the curriculum is to provide each pupil with a broad education appropriate to their age and to enable them to develop their own skills and talents as they mature. The School pays heed to the requirements of the National Curriculum, while offering a wider range of subjects than those prescribed. At Advanced Level there is a corresponding breadth of subject choice. The Sixth Form has its own centre which gives the students a degree of independence. Sixth Formers all take part in the School organised scheme of service in the local community. The majority of pupils continue their education after leaving the School through entry to University and vocational training.

Extra Curricular Activities. Pupils are encouraged to join the lunchtime and after-school activities which cover the spectrum of Music, Drama and Sports for which there is no extra charge. Instrumental Music, Speech and Drama, Ballet and Fencing lessons are available as 'extras' and the examinations of the Associated Board and LAMDA are taken.

Fees per term (2008-2009). £1,575–£3,100. Full details may be obtained on application to the School. We will be pleased to forward a copy of the prospectus and to arrange an opportunity for parents to visit the School to discuss their child's education with the Headmistress.

Charitable status. St George's School, Edgbaston is a Registered Charity, number 1079647. It exists to provide a quality education for boys and girls within the Birmingham area.

St James Independent School for Senior Boys

Pope's Villa 19 Cross Deep Twickenham Middlesex TW1 4QG
Tel: 020 8892 2002
Fax: 020 8892 4442
e-mail: admissions@stjamesboys.co.uk
website: www.stjamesschools.co.uk

The School, founded in 1975, is registered as an educational charity and is administered by a Board of Governors. The headmaster is a member of the Society of Headmasters and Headmistresses of Independent Schools (SHMIS) and also of the Independent Schools Association (ISA). These Associations require that excellence is assured by regular inspections by the Independent Schools Inspectorate which is itself monitored by Ofsted.

The school has 310 students – all boys, aged between 10 and 18. There is a small weekly boarding option.

Chairman of Governors: Jeremy Sinclair

***Headmaster*: David Boddy**, FIoD

Deputy Headmasters:
James Glover, BSc, CMath, FIMA, PGCE (*Mathematics*)
Koen Claeys, BA, GLSE Belgium (*French, German*)

Assistant Headmaster: David Hipshon, BA Hons, MPhil Cantab, PhD, PGCE (*History*)

Director of Studies: David Lacey, BA Mod, HDipEd, CPhys, MInstP (*Head of Science*)

Head of Sixth Form: Christian Daw BA Hons, PhB, STB, QTS (*Divinity*)

Head of Years 9–11: Koen Claeys, BA GLSE Belgium (*French, German*)

Head of Lower School: William Wray, RBTC Dip (*English*)

Full-Time:
David Beezadhur, BA Hons, MA, GTTP (*Ancient History*)
Kevan Bell, MA, MSc, BEd (*Sports Performance Director*)
James Carlyle, BA Oxon, PGCE (*Head of Classics*)
Anne-Helene Choimet, BA France, FLE, MFL, PGCE (*French, German*)
Patricia Collman, BA Hons, PGCE (*English, Librarian*)
Peter Crompton, BEng NZ, MSc Oxon (*Mathematics*)
Christian Darwent, BSc, PGCE (*Geography*)
Richard Fletcher, BSc Hons, GTTP (*Head of Sport*)
Nic Lemprière, MA, PGCE (*English*)
Neil MacKichan, BSc Hons, PGCE (*Head of ICT, Computing*)
David Marshall, MA, PGCE (*Acting Head of English*)
Pardeep Marway, BSc Hons, PGCE (*Science*)
Sam Moss, MA Hons (*Classics*)
Elizabeth Munro, BA Hons, PGCE (*Science*)
Philip Nicholls, BSc, PGCE (*Mathematics*)
Angus Pearson, MA Hons, PGCE (*Head of Mathematics*)
Andrew Pilkington, BSc, PGCE (*Head of Geography*)
Virginie Quartier, BA, GLSE Belgium (*Head of French*)
Julia Russell, BSc Hons, QTS (*Art*)
Derek Saunders, BA Hons, PGCE (*Director of Music*)
Oliver Saunders, BA Hons, QTS (*Head of History*)
Mark Saunders, BA, HND Art & Design (*Head of Art*)
Yolanda Saunders, BA Hons, PGCE (*Classics*)
Lorraine Soares, MSc Hons, PGCE (*Science, Head of Chemistry*)
David Stollar, BA Hons, ATC (*Head of Sanskrit*)
Miriam Stollar, NNEB (*Sanskrit*)
Marie Wood, BA Hons, PGCE (*Drama*)

Part-Time:
Jonathan Lewis, MA, LLB Hons, PGCE (*Law*)
Katerina Ridge, MSc, PGCE (*Science*)

Learning Support:
Talit Khan, BSc, PGCE (*Head of Learning Support*)
John Brook, LCST, MSc, BAF
Abby Gumbrell, BA Hons Early Childhood Studies
Sarah-Jane Hipshon
Cora Wren, BA Hons

Boarding Staff:
Andrew Pilkington, BSc, PGCE (*Head of Boarding*)
Sam Moss, MA Hons (*Houseparent*)
Isabel Moss, MA Hons (*Houseparent*)

Location. St James Independent School for Senior Boys is situated on one of the most beautiful stretches of the River Thames, opposite Ham Common and between Swan Island and Eel Pie Island. The building is on the site of Alexander Pope's Villa (c1720), of which only the famous Grotto remains.

Aims and Values. St James offers a distinctive education, uniting a philosophical approach to the development of life skills with academic excellence. The approach aims to unfold the twin powers of love and reason so that a boy may grow into a man who knows what he thinks, does what he says and is a friend to all.

The curriculum lays open the great cultures of East and West through Greek, Latin, Sanskrit and weekly lessons in Philosophy. Interest is also taken in the great scriptures of all traditions. The teaching of all the Sciences and Mathematics inspires a sense of the miraculous nature of the world in which we live, along with the desire to care for it. Meeting the finest examples of English literature, poetry, classical music, art, plus singing for all pupils, opens the emotional realm; while viewing History through the stories of great men and women gives boys a sense of the size of their human potential. Modern Languages, Geography, ICT, Drama, three afternoons of sport per week and an Adventure Pursuits programme, help ensure that the school day is rich in content and yet full of fun. It is important that every boy achieves more than he thinks is possible.

St James holds high expectations for its pupils. They are encouraged to discover the happiness that comes when we serve and care for the world, not just take from it; when we work to inspire harmony and cooperation among people of *all* faiths and cultures. The world is a challenging place, and St James tries to prepare its pupils to play leading roles. A quiet time for stillness and meditation is offered daily.

Academic Standards and Successes. Academic standards are high, but we also measure success to the extent that boys surpass their own expectations. 2007 results were: GCSE Pass Rate 100%, A*ABC 93%, 5+ A*ABC 93%. A Level Pass Rate 100%, ABC 82%. The Whitbread Memorial Prize for the best GCSE student in an ISA school was awarded in 2007 to a St James student, who achieved 12 A* grades. Another student gained five A grades at A Level, coming in the top ten in the UK for Computing.

Extra-Curricular Activities. Boys are offered an adventure pursuits programme designed to challenge the young men in terms of fitness, endurance, courage, leadership skills, service, self-esteem and confidence. Cadets (239 Para detachment), Duke of Edinburgh's Award Scheme, Skiing, Sailing Club, Climbing Club, Community Service and Task force are amongst the activities offered.

Philosophy. Each class throughout the school has one period of Philosophy per week. The boys are opened up to the great ideas relating to human values and relationships. Broadly, the themes prepare boys through different stages of development – Years 6 to 8: the correct use of mind, the power of attention; Years 9 to 11: aspiring to a great vision of Man and exploring human relationships and personal mastery; Years 12 to 13: living the philosophical life, making it practical, the importance of service.

Educational Trips. These are fairly regular and frequent for the Lower School, but there is an Activities Week in June when Year 6 are taken out daily to experience the sights and places of interest in London, Year 7 are introduced to sailing on the Solent; Year 8 go to Greece to further their studies of Classical Civilisation; Year 9 stay in Paris for a week with French families, speaking the language and being introduced to French culture; and Year 10 spend some time in Lucca in Italy for leadership training and aspects of teamworking, then move on to Florence to study Renaissance art and architecture.

Meditation and Quiet Time. The importance of inner stillness is recognised in the school and the school day begins and ends with 10 minutes' meditation and reflection. Every lesson begins and ends in a quiet moment of stillness and rest.

Admissions. Year 6 is made up mostly from boys from our Junior School in Olympia. We add some local 10+ boys to this class in the September intake. Apart from this the standard entry is at 11+, 13+ and 16+. Boys applying for entry to Year 7 take an Entrance Exam in January and also are all interviewed by the Headmaster shortly afterwards. Boys are not judged solely on their exam results. At 13+, we favour the Common Entrance route, but the number of places available is dependent upon whether spaces have become available. We welcome applications to our Sixth Form at 16+. Good GCSE performance and satisfactory interviews will be the basis of selection.

Fees per term (2008-2009). £3,700.

Open Days and Visits. Every year we hold two Open Days in late October/early November. We also encourage parents to come and see the school in session. This takes the form of a tour around the school during normal classes.

Charitable status. The Independent Educational Association Limited is a Registered Charity, number 270156.

St John's College

Grove Road South Southsea Hampshire PO5 3QW
Tel: 023 9281 5118 (Upper School)
023 9282 0237 (Lower School)
Fax: 023 9287 3603
e-mail: info@stjohnscollege.co.uk
website: www.stjohnscollege.co.uk

Founded in 1908 by the De La Salle Brothers, St John's seeks to provide an excellent all-round day and boarding education to boys and girls of all abilities. The school has a strong Christian ethos inspired by the teachings of St John Baptist De La Salle, the patron saint of teachers. Children of all Christian denominations, those of other faiths and those with no formal religious affiliation but who are in sympathy with the values of the school – all are welcome.

Chairman of Governors: Mr G W Warren OJ

***Headmaster*: Mr N Thorne**, BEd, MSc, FRGS, FRSA

Deputy Headmaster: Mr A J Steele, BA, MA, FRSA
Head of Lower School: Mr R Shrubsall, MA Ed
Head of Nursery: Mrs L Short, NNEB

Senior Teacher (*Director of Studies*): Dr G D Goodlad, PhD, BA
Senior Teacher (*Pastoral*): Mr B Saunders, BEd
Senior Teacher (*Boarding*): Mr M Renahan, BA
Senior Teacher (*Examinations*): Mr R Forshaw, BA

Heads of Department:
English: Miss A Bailey, BA
Mathematics: Mr G Burwood, BSc
Science: Miss V Matthews, BSc
Art and Design: Mr C H Wear, DipAD
Design and Technology: Mr P Harris-Deans, BEd
Drama: Miss E Morley, BA
Economics & Business Studies: Mr M Field, CertEd
Geography: Mr P Hyde, BSc
Government & Political Studies: Dr G D Goodlad, PhD, BA
History: Mrs K Audsley, BA
Learning Support: Mrs L Gorham, BA, DipSpLD
Modern Languages: Mr G Walker, MA
Music: Mr A Howes, BA
Physical Education: Mr A Tart, BA
Religious Studies: Mrs J Turner, BA, MA

Bursar: Mrs H Angel, MAAT

Head's PA/Admissions: Mrs J L Mengham

Number of Pupils. Boys 425, Girls 191, Boarders 122.

Situation. St John's main day and boarding campus is located in the heart of Southsea, an attractive and thriving seaside suburb of Portsmouth. The College's 34 acres of sports fields are located on the outskirts of the city, with transport being provided to and from that site.

Approach and Ethos. Academically, St John's is a non-selective school, its aim being excellence for every pupil according to their personal potential. All children who are able and willing to benefit from the curriculum provided are welcome to join the school community. The school's academic record – by all measures – is outstanding.

The pastoral care offered to boarders and day pupils is of very high quality. The commitment of the staff to the welfare and progress of each pupil is second to none. In return, honest effort and application is expected from the children – in order to meet the challenging standards set in academic work, sporting endeavour, behaviour and self-discipline.

Nursery. The Nursery occupies self-contained premises within the Junior (Lower) School. It has its own entrance and secure playground. The Nursery caters for children aged from two to four years and is open 51 weeks of the year. The children are actively involved in a carefully constructed pre-school programme. Great emphasis is placed on creative artwork, outdoor play and educational visits – as well as on acquiring foundation skills and concepts relating to numeracy and literacy.

Junior (Lower) School. The Lower School is also a self-contained unit within the main College campus. This enables younger children to make daily use of all the College's excellent facilities and to benefit in some areas from specialist tuition by Upper (Senior) School staff. The broadly-based curriculum incorporates and extends the National Curriculum. Great emphasis is placed on English, mathematics and science – which is taught in well-equipped laboratories. Musical talent is also carefully nurtured, with all pupils learning a musical instrument from the age of seven. The Lower School Choir and Orchestra provide opportunities for ensemble playing and performance.

Upper (Senior) School. The Senior School curriculum again incorporates and extends the National Curriculum. All subjects are taught by appropriately qualified specialists in well-resourced subject areas. A wide range of GCSE subjects is offered. Instrumental tuition is encouraged and the Upper School Choir and Orchestra are open to all pupils. Drama has a high profile within the school, with all pupils encouraged to be involved. Sport – principally rugby, cricket and netball – is strong at all levels. Pupils' progress in all areas is assessed formally each half-term, with formal examinations being held twice yearly.

Sixth Form. As the progress into the Sixth Form, older students are enabled and encouraged to become independent and self-motivated learners – in preparation for Higher Education. The teaching and pastoral staff continue to work closely with parents, who are kept fully informed of progress and achievement. A wide range of AS and A2 Level subjects is offered.

The College ensures a good student/teacher ratio, allowing for close and constant monitoring of the performance and effort of each student. Preparation for Oxbridge entry is available. Students are also offered practice interviews for University and job applications and a full careers service.

Beyond the formal curriculum, a wide range of sporting, academic, dramatic, cultural and social activities is available. The Politics Society, administered predominantly by Sixth Form students, enjoys a national reputation.

Admission. Pupils are accepted and placed on the basis of a formal assessment and previous reports.

Fees per term (2008-2009). Lower School: £2,025–£2,180 Upper School: £2,750. UK Boarding £6,050, Overseas Boarding £6,425.

Occasional Boarding (including bed, breakfast, evening meal): £30 per day.

Music fees are extra.

Scholarships and Bursaries. Academic and other scholarships and bursarial awards are available.

Charitable status. St John's College is a Registered Charity, number 232632. It exists to provide excellent education and pastoral care to boys and girls.

St Joseph's College

Birkfield Ipswich Suffolk IP2 9DR
Tel: 01473 690281
Fax: 01473 602409
e-mail: registrar@stjos.co.uk
website: www.stjos.co.uk

A co-educational independent day school providing Christian education for 2–18 year olds with boarding facilities. High academic expectation and national achievement in sport, performing arts and community service.

Set in a beautiful wooded parkland site the College is situated just ten minutes' walk from Ipswich station or alternately just ten minutes' drive from the A12/A14 interchange.

Governing Body:
Chairman: Mrs J Lea, MA
Vice-Chairman: Mr R Stace, LLB
Mr P Clement, BSc Hons
Mr A Goulborn
Mr J Hehir, OBE, BSc Hons, IPFA, FCMA
Mr G Kalbraier, BSc, FInstD, FIMgt
Mr S Davies, FREng, BSc, CEng, FIEE
Dr P Woods
Mr M Howes

Clerk to the Governors: Mrs J Blemings

***Principal*: Mrs S Grant**, BMus Hons

Vice-Principals:
Mrs D Clarke, BA Hons
Mr R Harris BA Hons

Senior School:
Mr P Andrew, BA (*Head of RE*)
Mrs J Bailey, BA (*Geography*)
Mr C Boucher, BSc (*Mathematics; House Leader*)
Mrs A Bowden (*Food Technology*)
Sr Carmel (*Chaplain; Religious Education*)
Mr R Bradford (*Mathematics*)
Mr C Branch (*Director of Cricket*)
Mr N Chandler (*Politics & History; Duke of Edinburgh's Award; Careers Officer*)
Mr D Cole, BA (*Music*)
Mr B Crisp, BA (*Art*)
Mr M Davey, BA (*Head of Sixth Form; English; i/c Cricket*)
Mr J Dewhurst (*English*)
Mrs K Drake, QTS (*English*)
Mr D Edwards (*Business Studies*)
Mrs M Felton, BSc, MSc (*Head of IT*)
Mr A Fisher (*English*)
Miss L Green, NQT (*English; History*)
Mr K Hirst, BEd (*Head of Biology; CCF Contingent Commander*)
Mr M Hockley, BSc (*IT; i/c Charity Projects; House Leader*)
Mr T Hunter, MA (*TEFL; German; Science; Head of Boarding*)
Mrs B Jousiffe, CertEd (*Girls' PE; TEFL*)
Mr P Jousiffe, CertEd (*Design & Technology; Head of Fourth Form*)
Mrs L King (*Dance Teacher*)
Mr M King (*Drama/English*)
Mrs J Lauder, CertEd (*Head of Girls' PE & Games*)
Mrs A Lee, BA (*EFL Overseas Liaison Officer*)
Mrs S Lindridge (*SENCO*)
Mr C Long, BEdSc (*Physics*)
Mrs J Marston (*Mathematics and RE*)
Mr C McNicholas (*Director of E Learning*)
Mr A Miller, CertEd (*Head of Design & Technology*)
Mr M Patterson (*Director of Sport*)
Mr A Reavill, BSc (*Head of Humanities Faculty*)
Ms C Renshaw, BA (*Design & Technology; House Leader*)
Mrs J Rothwell, BA (*Modern Languages; TEFL; Head of Year 11*)
Mrs G Rowlands, BA (*Modern Languages*)
Mrs J Scott (*History*)
Miss E Self (*Drama*)
Mrs M Simmonds, BA (*Modern Languages; Head of Year 10*)
Mrs M Stiles, BSc (*Geography; Asst Head of Sixth Form*)
Mrs J Thomas (*MFL*)
Dr C Tinker, PhD, ARCM (*Head of Performing Arts Faculty*)
Mr P Twist, BSc (*Biology; Chemistry; House Coordinator*)
Dr S Waitkins, PhD, FRCPath (*Head of Science & Technology Faculty*)
Mr N Walkinshaw, MSc (*Head of Mathematics*)
Miss A Ward (*English*)
Mr N Watson, BEd (*PE & Mathematics; Examinations Officer*)

Junior School:
Dr M Hine (*Head of Primary Dept*)
Mrs J Branston, CertEd (*Infants*)
Miss E Dance (*Infants*)
Mr M Davies, BEd (*PE & Games*)
Mrs P Garnet (*KS2 Teacher*)
Mrs L Ireland (*KS2 Teacher*)
Mrs Z James, BA Hons (*Nursery Coordinator*)
Mrs T McGinn (*Classroom Assistant*)
Mrs J Weale (*Music*)
Mrs M Sharpe, Certed (*Curriculum & Assessment Coordinator*)
Mr G Weaver (*Infants*)
Mrs H Hutchinson (*Infants*)
Mrs V Gilliard (*Classroom Assistant*)

Visiting Staff:
Miss M Dulgarn (*Piano*)
Mrs A Baker (*Piano*)
Ms S Maxwell (*Guitars*)
Mr G Gillings (*Percussion*)
Mr R Reavill (*Voice*)
Mrs Tinker (*Piano*)
Miss S Wilkinson (*Classroom Assistant*)

Administrative Staff:
Office Manager: Mrs S Bosher
Management Information Systems: Mrs M Turner
Registrar: Mrs S Gregory
Administration, Junior School: Mrs R Leech

School Secretary/Reception: Mrs H Philpot
Principal's PA: Mrs J Blemings
Business and Finance Manager: Mrs D Baber
Accounts: Mrs N Cordle
Accounts: Mrs K Hayhow
Accounts: Mrs D Merrick
Receptionist: Mrs B Donovan
Marketing & PR: Mrs B Hudson
Lab Technicians:
Mr C Stevens
Mr F James (*Design & Technology*)
Mrs M Turner (*Biology*)
Mrs E McKay (*Reprographics*)
Facilities Manager: Mr G Allen
Catering Manager: Mr D McGinn
Medical Staff:
School Nurse: Sr J Debenham, SRN
Junior School Nurse: Mrs L Gilbert

Ethos. We believe that successful education depends upon a three-way partnership between the child, their parents and the College. Effective communication is at the heart of this, hence our extensive assessments and reporting system. We instil in our pupils a sense of responsibility, whilst encouraging self-reliance with a willingness to cooperate as part of a team.

St Joseph's prides itself on its pastoral care and the individual support and guidance it gives each child as he or she progresses through the school. This ethos, along with the pursuit of excellence, is reflected in all aspects of life at the College whether it is academic, sporting, cultural or spiritual.

Developments. In May 2006, St Joseph's College received a glowing inspection report, following a week-long ISI inspection by eleven inspectors. Their conclusions were that the College provides a well-rounded education of high quality and is committed to academic success within the context of fully developing all the talents and skills of its pupils. The report stated that "high standards of behaviour are the norm, pupils are contagiously enthusiastic about the educational opportunities offered by the school; examination results are a success story" and concluded that St Joseph's is a school which is "going places".

Never a school to rest on its laurels, further development and success have followed. Demand for places continues to rise and the school is expanding rapidly. In January 2008, the innovative new Junior school building was formally opened. This fascinating curved building with its Maltings-style windcatcher towers provides a highly stimulating environment for pupils between 2 and 11 years of age and is resourced with the latest technological and physical resources.

Boarding. Although primarily a day school, we also offer flexible and full boarding facilities in family-run, spacious and warm boarding houses.

The College has two boarding houses, Senior 14–18, and Junior 11–14, which have undergone extensive modernisation to provide single study-bedrooms for the seniors and small, 3–4 bed rooms for the juniors.

Curriculum. The curriculum is designed to provide a broad and balanced education for all pupils from 2 to 18. Strong foundations in the core skills of reading, writing and numeracy, are laid down in the Infant Department. The Junior Section continues the process of preparing the children for their secondary education by concentrating further on the core skills. In addition to these subjects, Science, French, Music and PE are taught and the children are introduced to a wider curriculum, including Design and Technology, Art, History, Geography, RE, IT and Games.

The Senior School prepares pupils for entrance to universities, other forms of higher education and the professions. Pupils are set according to ability in certain subjects. In Years 7–9 the emphasis continues to be placed on the core subjects whilst developing knowledge, skills and experiences necessary for the GCSE courses. In addition to the mainstream subjects, all students follow an RE and PSHE course. Languages studied at the College include Mandarin, French and Spanish.

GCSE studies maintain a broad and balanced curriculum but with the introduction of a degree of specialisation. Mathematics, English Language and Literature, Double Science Award, a Modern Foreign Language and RE are compulsory. Once again core subjects continue to be set by ability.

To cater for developing interests and abilities there is a wide range of further choices from Graphics and Photography to Art, Dance and PE to Business Studies. In addition all students follow a short course GCSE in RE, which focuses on moral and current issues and combines with the PSHE course. PE and Sport complete the curriculum in the GCSE years.

The majority of our pupils continue into the Sixth Form to complete their A Level courses before going on to university. There is a wide range of subjects available in the Sixth Form and students choose 4 AS Level subjects for examination in the Lower Sixth, reducing to 3 A2s for completion in the Upper Sixth. General Studies are an integral part of the post-16 curriculum at the College, with a wide range of sporting and other leisure and cultural opportunities.

A Learning Support department operates throughout the College to provide support individually or in small groups particularly for Dyslexia and the more able child.

There is comprehensive careers guidance from Year 9 and extensive help with university admission in the Sixth Form.

Extra-Curricular Activities. Sport, Art, Music and Drama are strongly encouraged, together with participation in the CCF and The Duke of Edinburgh's Award scheme. A large number of extra-curricular clubs meet weekly. Regular ski trips, activity holidays and language exchanges are organised throughout the College.

Admission. Entry to the College is normally at 4+, 7+, 11+, 13+ and the Sixth Form, with applications for occasional vacancies at other ages. The entry process includes an interview, a test and a report from the applicant's previous school. For the Sixth Form, the test is replaced by GCSE results.

Fees per term (2008-2009). Nursery: £34 (per full session); Infants: £2,095; Juniors: £2,645 (day), £4,360 (weekly boarding), £4,675 (overseas boarding). Senior School: £3,125–£3,535 (day), £5,375–£5,875 (weekly boarding), £5,625–£6,115 (full boarding), £5,625–£7,005 (overseas boarding).

Scholarships and Bursaries. The College offers a number of Academic Scholarships each year for different points of entry, as well as Scholarships for Music, Sport and Drama. A number of bursaries are also available in cases of need. Please contact the Registrar for further information.

Charitable status. St Joseph's College is a Registered Charity, number 1051688. It exists to provide high quality education for children.

Scarborough College

Filey Road Scarborough North Yorkshire YO11 3BA
Tel: 01723 360620
Fax: 01723 377265
e-mail: admin@scarboroughcollege.co.uk
website: www.scarboroughcollege.co.uk

IB World School Scarborough College is a co-educational day and boarding school for some 550 students aged 3–18. The College and its junior school occupy a magnificent site on the slopes of Oliver's Mount, overlooking the South Bay of Scarborough. Study and recreation facilities are of the highest quality and in 2005 the three boarding houses underwent a £2 million refurbishment programme.

(*For further details about Scarborough College Junior School, see IAPS section.*)

Motto: *Pensez Fort*

Governors:

S J Chittock, BSc, MBA (*Chairman*)
Dr M J Abrines, MA, BM, BCh, MRCGP, DRCOG, DPD
Mrs G Braithwaite
Ms C J Cullen, BA, MA York (*Deputy Chairman*)
J M Green
A S Green
Mrs L Griffin
Mrs Z Harrison
D M Hastie, FRICS
Dr M Precious, MA, MPhil, DPhil
Dr I G H Renwick, MB, BS
Mrs G Ricketts
Prof S Westland
P Worsley, QC, MA

Bursar and Clerk to the Governors: P F Harriott, BA

***Headmaster*: T L Kirkup**, MA, ARCM

Deputy Headmaster: D R Woodhead, BA
Deputy Head (*Curriculum*): Ms B Kelly, BA Hons
Head of Sixth Form: Mrs J M Drury, BSc
Head of Junior School: G Twist, BEd, BA, NPQH

Assistant Staff:
* *Head of Department*
† *Boarding Housemaster/mistress*
‡ *Head of Year*
§ *Part-time*

W Adams, BEd (*Physical Education, Mathematics*)
Mrs H A Barker (*English, †Willersley*)
Mrs C Bates, BA (*§Music*)
T Brough, BSc (*Physics*)
Miss J Brown Forden, BA (**Drama, Physical Education*)
G C Brownridge, BA (**RE, French, German*)
Miss S Clyde, BSc (*Mathematics*)
J Davies, BMus, LGSM, ACertCM (**Director of Music, †Denys Crews*)
Mrs A Evirgen, BA (*IB Director, TESOL*)
J A Fraser, MSc (**Biology*)
Mrs C Graham, BSc (**Physics*)
S D Harvey, BSc (**Science, *Chemistry*)
F Hopkins (*†Weaponess*)
S Hutton, BSc, CertEd (*Director of Cricket, ICT*)
W A Jefferson, BA (**Modern Languages*)
Dr A Kehrli (*Chemistry*)
‡Mrs C Lucas, BA (*German, French*)
Mrs R A Macdonald, BA (*French*)
Mrs E A Mack, BA (**English*)
P J Mack, BA, CertEd (*Examinations Officer, Mathematics*)
J U McMillan, BA (*Director of Sport*)
C J Meyler, BA (**Art, †Weaponness*)
Mrs K Noble, CertEd, DipSpEd (**§SEN*)
N H Pettitt, CertEd (**§ICT*)
‡S D Phillips, MSc (*Biology, Science*)
J M Precious, BA (*Assistant Head of Sixth Form, *Business Studies*)
Miss H S Ramsey, BA (*Physical Education, Geography*)
Mrs D Raper (*†Willersley*)
Mrs J Robinson-Beswick (*§Learning Support Assistant*)
R J Robson, MSc, CertEd (**Geography*)
R L Scott, BA (**History, Government & Politics*)
A Skailes, BSc (**Mathematics*)
Miss J Shillaw, BA (*History, Government & Politics*)
Miss H L Waldram, BA, CertEd (*French, German*)
Mrs J Walsh, MA, CertEd (*§English*)
Miss A H Williams, BA (*Art*)
‡P J Wilson, BEd (*Careers Coordinator, Business Studies, Psychology*)
Mrs A M Woodhead, BA (*§English*)

The Music Department is assisted by visiting instrumental teachers

Medical Officer: Dr J Adamson, MSBS, DRCOG, MRCGP

Headmaster's PA/Admissions: Mrs A Courtney

Entry. (*see Scholarship Entries section*). Boys and girls are admitted to the Senior school at 11 and 13 years old, following an Entrance Examination in November, or through Common Entrance, or through special arrangements. Students are admitted to other years, subject to recommendation from their previous school, an interview, and, where appropriate, satisfactory performance in a College examination. Means-tested 11+ and 13+ Scholarships and Exhibitions are awarded. There is a separate Sixth Form entry, conditional upon satisfactory performance at GCSE.

The Curriculum. All students follow a broad-based curriculum, but study both French and German from the age of 11 and Spanish from the age of 13. At GCSE, students take English and English Literature, Mathematics, Science (3 separate sciences), at least one Modern Foreign Language, and four other subjects. Sixth Formers are prepared for the IB Diploma.

Care of Students. Scarborough College is a stimulating and happy school where boys and girls are taught to live cooperatively together, to develop their talents to the full, and to respect one another. Students are allocated a tutor who is responsible for coordinating and monitoring all aspects of a child's welfare and maintaining regular communication with parents. Tutors are responsible to Heads of Year.

Religion. The College seeks to cultivate in its students, by all means possible, a developing awareness of what lies beyond the informative, the material and the explainable.

Games. High standards are reached in sport, with many students representing the County and a few playing for England. The College offers expert coaching in Rugby, Hockey, Cricket and Tennis for boys; and Hockey, Netball and Tennis for girls. The College has its own full-size, all-weather pitch.

Other Activities. Drama and Music flourish at all levels of the College (the Janet Martin Music School opened in 2003), and regular performances occur throughout the year. Educational expeditions play an important part of the general curriculum, and there are language exchange opportunities with France, Germany and Spain. An extensive programme of weekday and weekend activities enables all students to participate in an exciting programme outside the classroom. The College boasts a popular Duke of Edinburgh's Award Scheme and a thriving Combined Cadet Force (Army and Navy sections).

Transport is provided to outlying districts and occasional and weekly boarding are popular options with many parents.

Fees per term (2008-2009). Senior School: £3,119–£3,478 (day), £5,060–£5,786 (UK full and weekly boarding), £5,304–£5,999 (Overseas full and weekly boarding). Junior School: £1,860–£2,833 (day), £4,135 (full and weekly boarding from Year 5). Remissions for brothers and sisters and members of the Old Scardeburgians Society.

Charitable status. Scarborough College is a Registered Charity, number 529686. It exists to provide a first-class education for boys and girls.

Shebbear College

Shebbear North Devon EX21 5HJ
Tel: 01409 281228
Fax: 01409 281784
e-mail: registrar@shebbearcollege.co.uk
website: www.shebbearcollege.co.uk

Shebbear College, set in 85 acres of healthy Devon countryside, was founded in 1841 by the Bible Christians. It is now part of the Board of Management for Methodist Residential Schools. It is fully co-educational for children between the ages of 3 to 18 years. The secure, happy family atmosphere at Shebbear, free from urban distractions, offers pupils full, weekly, occasional and daily education. We aim to give our pupils self confidence; we teach our pupils to be self disciplined and they leave the College with excellent qualifications. Thus offering all our pupils "*A foundation for life*".

Chairman of the Governors: M J Saltmarsh

***Headmaster*: R S Barnes**, BA

Deputy Headmistress: Mrs A Farrell, MEd, BEd

Chaplain: Revd Y Jaiyesimi, BSc, PGCE

Financial Bursar: Mr B Horn, ACMA, ACIS

Teaching Staff:
* *Head of Department or Subject Leader*

Mr A Barlow, BSc
Mrs J Barnes, BA (**Modern Languages*)
Mrs E Bearpark, LLB (**Mathematics*)
Mr A Bryan, CertEd
Mr J Buist, MA Ed
Mr I Burnett, BA
Mr S Chapman, BA Hons (**Physical Education*)
Mrs S Chapman, BA Hons (**Learning Support*)
Mr J Colpus, BEd (**History*)
Dr S Crook, BSc, PhD (**Chemistry*)
Mrs J Foster, BSc
Mr J Freeman, BEng (**Physics*)
Mrs A French
Mrs V Hale (*Food Technician*)
Mrs F Lovett, YTEFLA, CELTA (**ESL*)
Mrs C Olsson, BA Hons
Mr K Parker, GRSM (**Music*)
Mrs L Parker, GRSM, LRAM
Mrs A Partridge
Mr K Petley, BSc (**Biology*)
Mrs K Purdew, CertEd
Mr M Quirk (*CDT*)
Mr J Scotney, MEd, BEd, CertEd (**Geography*)
Mr A Steel, BSc
Mrs P Thomas, BA (**IT*)
Mrs J Welby, ALA (*Librarian*)
Mr M Wildridge, BA (**Art*)
Miss C Wilkinson, BSc

Senior House Staff (Boarding):
Mrs L Quirk, BSA (*Head of Boarding & Pastoral Care*)
Mr and Mrs A Bryan (*Pollard Houseparents*)
Mr and Mrs B Harman (*Pyke Houseparents*)

Junior School Teaching Staff:
Mr B Harman, BSc (*Head of Junior School*)
Mrs J Burnett, BA
Mrs F Goode, CertEd
Miss T Martin
Mrs J Harman

Kindergarten: Mrs J Biddlecoombe

Registrar: Mrs J Rowe
Marketing Coordinator: Miss E Burwood

Medical Department:
Dr A Aldoori, MBChB, MRCGP, FPCert
Sister R Light, SEN, RGN DipPart1

Visiting Music Staff:
Ms T Bennett
Mrs R Cornish
Mr A Davies
Mr G Goodwin
Mr J McAvoy
Mrs A Morphy
Ms H Riches
Ms R Slater-Lyons

Number in College. In the Senior School there are 250 pupils, of whom 100 are boarders, and a total of 80 pupils in the Junior School.

Situation and Location. Shebbear College borders on Dartmoor National Park and stands in 85 acres of unspoilt countryside. It can be easily reached by main road and rail links; only 40 miles west of Exeter and 30 miles north of Plymouth. Both cities have their own regional and international airport.

Buildings. The main College buildings include Prospect House, Lake Chapel, Beckly Wing, Shebbear College Junior School, Science Department, Music School, Sixth Form Centre, Language Centre and Sports Hall. There are 2 senior boarding houses and 1 junior boarding house. (The junior girls have a separate area within the senior girls house).

In recent years there has been an impressive record of school building projects. The latest work has been to refurbish the Science Block and Sports Hall. The Junior School also has a new multi-purpose play area.

Admission. The Kindergarten accepts children from the age of $2^1/_2$ where boys and girls are admitted to the Junior School from the age of five. Entrance to the College at 11 years from other schools is by examination in January for entry in September. Pupils are also admitted at 13 or 14 after submitting Common Entrance Examination papers, but if they wish they may sit our own entrance papers instead. Entry into the Sixth Form is conditional upon GCSE performance.

Houses. Every pupil belongs to a House – Ruddle, Thorne or Way. These Houses organise activities and games competitions throughout the year. Our boarders also belong to an additional boarding house – Pollard House for senior boy boarders, Pyke House for junior boy boarders and Ruddle House for girl boarders – each having a Senior Houseparent and two assistants who "live-in". The House Tutors watch each child's progress academically as well as their general development.

Curriculum. All pupils at Shebbear College follow the National Curriculum until the age of 14. A wide choice of subjects is available in the following two years, leading to GCSE, but everyone is obliged to take English, Mathematics, Science and, usually, a foreign language. In the Sixth Form there is not only a wide choice of A2 and AS levels, but there is particularly flexible timetabling which enables students to mix Arts and Science subjects.

Sport. With more than 25 acres of playing fields, modern sports hall with multi-gym, squash courts, cricket nets, tennis and netball courts, and indoor climbing centre, pupils have the security to exercise within the school grounds confidently. The main games covered for the boys are rugby, football, hockey and cricket, in which we have fixtures with most of the major schools in the South West of England. For the girls, we have teams in netball, hockey, rounders and tennis. All pupils are also offered tennis, basketball, squash, athletics, swimming, cross-country, badminton, table tennis and horse riding. All pupils up to the 4th Form have one afternoon of games plus an additional one period of PE every week.

Music and Drama. Pupils are strongly encouraged to participate in music and drama. Our choir has over 40 members and our orchestra, which represents most instruments, also has over 40 members. Players perform regularly in concerts and instrumental ensembles. Every term candidates proudly achieve Honours and Distinctions with The Associated Board of the Royal School for Music. Also, every term, a theatrical production is performed to a very high standard. The traditional staff and sixth form pantomime, offers light relief during the Spring Term.

Societies and Activities. All pupils participate in at least 4 afternoons a week of extra-curricular activities. This widens their interests and develops their self-confidence. The list of activities is endless and includes the usual and unusual. We are fortunate to house our own photographic studio where excellent work is produced and displayed around the school. Shebbear's rural position enables outdoor pursuits to be very popular. Many pupils enjoy getting involved with Ten Tors training, hill-walking, camping, sailing, canoeing, surfing and rowing. The newly-formed Army Cadet Corp is proving to be very popular.

Many are involved in the Duke of Edinburgh's Award scheme.

Careers. Careers advice is taken very seriously. Staff help our students prepare for their chosen career. The College is a member of ISCO. Individual attention is given at appropriate levels and a team of Old Shebbearians covering many professions visits the school regularly and helps with work experience and placement.

Scholarships. (*see Scholarship Entries section*). Scholarships and Bursaries are offered.

Fees per term (2008-2009). Junior School: Day £1,575–£2,300, Weekly Boarding £3,534–£3,834, Full Boarding £4,305–£4,632. Senior School: Day £3,176, Weekly Boarding £4,885, Full Boarding £5,904.

Charitable status. Shebbear College is a Registered Charity, number 306945. It exists to provide high quality education for children.

Sibford School

Sibford Ferris Banbury Oxon OX15 5QL
Tel: 01295 781200
Fax: 01295 781204
e-mail: admissions@sibfordschool.co.uk
website: www.sibford.oxon.sch.uk

Founded 1842.

A Co-educational Independent Boarding (full/weekly) and Day School. Membership of SHMIS, BSA, AGBIS.

There are 420 pupils in the school aged between 4 and 18: 351 pupils in the Senior School and 69 pupils in the Junior School, Orchard Close.

There are 44 full-time and 27 part-time teachers plus visiting staff.

Chairman of School Committee: Judith Weeks

***Head*: Michael Goodwin**, BA

Deputy Head: Maggie Guy, BA (*English*)

Senior Master: Tony Skeath, BSc (*Science*)

Senior School:
* *Head of Department*
§ *Part-time*

Simon Baker, BSc Econ (**Geography*)
Stephen Ball, BSc, MSc (*Mathematics*)
Derek Bottomley, BSc (*Mathematics*)
Angela Bovill, BEd, CertEd (**Horticulture, Countryside/ Environmental Sciences*)
Simon Chard, BA (*PE, Vocational Education*)
John Charlesworth, MA (*Director of Studies, *Science*)
Ruth Chinn, BSc (*Science*)
§Tammi Choudhury-Fieret, BSc, PhD (*Mathematics & Physics*)
Debra Collins, BSc (**Mathematics*)
Zoë Connor, BA, MA, AKC (**Religious Studies, Philosophy & Ethics*)
§Claire Darlington (*English*) (*Maternity cover*)
Pat Davies (*Instructor, Librarian*)
§Kate Davison (*Classroom Assistant*)
§Totoya Dew (*Spanish*)
Debby Evans, CertEd PCE, Cert SpLD (Dyslexia) (**Information Technology*)
§Vanessa Evans, CertEd, Dip TS (*RS*)
Claire Ferley, BSc, GTTP (*PE, Vocational Education*)
§Rebecca Flynn, BA, MA, CTEFL (*Psychology, EAL*)
Andrew Foakes, MA, BA (*English, Media*)
Andrew Glover, Dip SpLD, BA, Dip TEFL (*Dyslexia*)
Fay Godwin, BA, CertEd (**Dyslexia*)
Yvonne Greene, LLB, GradIPD, MBA (*Director of Vocational Studies, Business Studies*)
§Alan Greenslade-Hibbert, LLB (*EAL*)
Victoria Hall, BA (*English, Media, Careers, PSHE/ Citizenship*)
§Cath Harding, BSc (*Science*)
Julian Harris, ABSM (*Director of Music*)
Susan Hinde, BSc (*Mathematics*)
§Stephen Jacobi (*English*) (*Maternity cover*)
Shelley Jarvis (*PE*) (*Maternity cover*)
§Jane Kenehan (*Learning Support, Dyslexia*)
Clare Kent, BSc, Adv Dip SEN, Dip Developing Inclusive Curricula (*Curriculum Access & Learning Support Manager*)
Tracy Knowles, BA Ed (*Assistant Deputy Head, English, Activities Coordinator*)
§Jo Mayes (*EAL*)
Mary Memarzia, BA, MA (**Head of Sixth Form, Media Studies, English*)
Andrew Newbold, BSc, PhD (*Director of Studies (Examinations*) Science)
Lesley Norton, CertEd (*Textiles*)
Dolores Papin, Licence Anglais, Maîtrise Anglais (*Modern Foreign Languages*)
Nichola Patterson, MA, BA, AMBDA Literacy & Numeracy (*Dyslexia*)
§Richard Phethean, BA, PGATC (*Ceramics*)
Sally Pickering, BA (**EAL*)
Dan Pigott, BEd (**PE*)
§Matthew Platt, Grad Dip Music, LGSM Teaching Dip (*Music*)
§Elisabeth Pronost, Cert de Formation Pedagogique (*Modern Foreign Languages*)
Anna Jo Righton, BA (*Director of Studies (Teaching and Learning*), *Humanities, History)
§Jeremy Ross, MA (*History*)
§Jonathan Seagroatt (*Music Technology, Woodwind*)
Iona Smith, MA (*Geography, Vocational Education, PE*)
Michael Spring, BEd (**Expressive Arts Faculty*)
Penelope Spring, BA (**English*)
§Debra Staley, BSc (*Science*)
Victor Stannard, BA, BA Des (**Design & Technology*)
§Justine Tibbetts (*Classroom Assistant*)
Lyn Usher, BEd, TCert, CertRSA SpLD, PG Cert SpLD & Numeracy (*SpLD Mathematics, Science*)
Trevor Walters, BA, TESOL (**Drama*)
§Angela Way, CertEd (*Food Technology*)
§Ginette Wheeldon (*Senior Classroom Assistant*)
Janet Woodcock (*Mathematics*)
§Emma Worsley (*Design Technology, Textiles*)

Junior School:
Vanessa Cranke, BA, QTS Drama (*Year 4*)
§Rachel Dumbleton, CertEd, BDA, DipSpLD (*Dyslexia*)
Patricia Howes, BSc (*Year 6*)
§Jane Kenehan (*Classroom Assistant*)
§Trudy Koochit, BA, CNAA, PGDip Mandarin, DipTEFL (*Year 6*)
§Gill Newbold, TCert (*Dyspraxia, PE*)
Edward Rossiter, BSc, PG Dip Social Sciences (*Year 5*)
§Claire Solesbury (*Classroom Assistant*)
§Jen Unwin, TCert Music, Arts & Drama (*Music*)
Jayne Woolley, BA, TCert (*Year 3*)
Elizabeth Williams, BA, BTech Nat Dip Art (*Reception*)

Visiting Staff:
Celia Bolton King
Matthew Bosworth
Richard Hamel
Ilone Jones
Lucy Mason, BMus
Clifford Pick, ABSM
Peter Pontzen, BSc
Martin Quinn
Hazel Rafter, RAF SoM
Miranda Ricardo
Dittany Stirling
Mickey Woodcock

Admissions Secretary: Janet Dunkin

Curriculum. Mainstream curriculum with emphasis on the performing and creative arts. Renowned dyslexia tuition and support for a small number of pupils with other learning difficulties.

Junior Department (age 4–11): a wide-ranging curriculum with an emphasis on outdoor education is provided to children in small groups. Literacy, numeracy, science and technology skills are emphasised alongside art, music, drama and PE. Enriched Curriculum in Year 6 with Senior School Staff. Specialist teachers help individual children with specific learning difficulties.

Senior School (age 11–18): all pupils follow courses leading to GCSE, in a curriculum expanding on the National Curriculum. Information Technology is introduced at an early age and the use of laptop computers is widespread.

Dyslexic pupils have special tuition in small groups on a daily basis. Highly regarded Specific Learning Difficulties (Dyslexic) Department provides specialised support within the timetable. Personal and Social Development runs through the school.

All Sixth Form students take A Levels and/or AVCEs. The Sixth Form curriculum leads to higher education, and offers a particularly wide range of opportunities for further study.

Entry requirements. Admission to the Junior School, Senior School and Sixth Form is by interview and internal tests. Where applicable a report from the candidate's current school is required. No religious requirements.

Examinations offered. A Level, GCSE, AVCE, Associated Board Music Examinations, Oxford and Cambridge IELTS Examinations.

Academic and leisure facilities. Exceptional Performing & Creative Arts in purpose-built facilities, multi-purpose Sports Centre, squash courts, 25m indoor swimming pool, well-equipped Library and Information Technology Centres, Design Technology Centre, Business Studies Centre, wide range of indoor and outdoor activities, 55-acre campus set in beautiful North Oxfordshire countryside.

Easy access to Stratford, Oxford, Cheltenham, Birmingham, London.

Religion. The School has a distinctive Quaker ethos. It welcomes pupils of all faiths, backgrounds and nationalities, encouraging in each of them genuine self-esteem in a purposeful, caring and challenging environment.

Fees per term (2008-2009). £6,774–£6,909, Weekly Boarders £6,309–£6,434, Day Pupils £3,488–£3,556.

Junior School: Day Pupils £2,216–£2,680.

The fee for a full term of learning support is £1,236.

Scholarships and Bursaries. The School offers general Academic scholarships and specific scholarships in Art and Music. A limited number of bursaries is offered to both Quaker and non Quaker children.

Charitable status. Sibford School is a Registered Charity, number 1068256. It is a company limited by guarantee under number 3487651. It aims to give all pupils a vehicle to educational and personal success.

Sidcot School

Winscombe North Somerset BS25 1PD
Tel: 01934 843102
Fax: 01934 844181
e-mail: admissions@sidcot.org.uk
website: www.sidcot.org.uk

Sidcot School traces its roots to 1699 and was re-founded in 1808 for the education of the children of members of the Society of Friends (Quakers) and others. It admits boys and girls from a wide variety of backgrounds, but about a tenth of the pupils come from Quaker homes. The school estate of about 180 acres is set on high ground sheltered by the Mendip hills. The school is under the management of a Board of Governors appointed by a General Meeting of Friends, held annually.

Chairman of the Committee: Paul Whitehouse

***Headmaster*: John Walmsley**, BSc, PGCE

Deputy Head: Elizabeth Burgess, BSc, BEd

Head of Junior School: Rosie Craig, BEd, DCE

House Staff:
Christopher Bateman, CertEd and Janice Bateman, BA (*Combe House*)
Paul Coates, BSc (*Wing House*)
Jane Chambers, CertEd, BEd (*School House Girls*)
Christopher Potts, MA Ed (*School House Boys*)
Alison Sinclair (*Newcombe House*)

Director of Finance: Christine Edwards

Admissions Secretaries: Alison Thomas & Valerie Kennedy

Situation and Accommodation. The school is half a mile from Winscombe Village and 15 miles from Bristol. It is situated in beautiful unspoilt countryside, which the pupils are encouraged to explore.

There are 520 pupils, boys and girls in approximately equal numbers. 160 boarding pupils are accommodated in 5 Houses including two wings of the main building. The main building complex provides leisure and refectory facilities. Most of the class teaching is done in a separate classroom block. The Science Block has been enlarged and re-built. There is also a self-contained Music School, drama studio and a study block with special facilities for Sixth Formers. There is a 10-acre playing field, a new sports complex (with swimming pool, sports hall, squash court and multi-gym) and eight tennis courts. A new Library and Resource Centre was opened in 1999. A new visual and performing arts block will open in the Autumn 2008.

Aims. The aims of the school are to give boys and girls a top-class academic and liberal education, and to educate them to think and behave ethically, in the light of the principles of the Society of Friends.

We encourage our students to reflect upon moral issues and to seek "that of God" in everyone, whatever their faith.

We hope that our students will leave Sidcot with the power and determination to play an active part in the life of their communities, and a desire to continue to learn about the world and about themselves.

Curriculum. The School broadly follows the National Curriculum. Within this there is a basic course of the usual subjects for all pupils in the first 3 years, 7, 8 and 9. German and Spanish are offered as a second foreign language in Years 8 and 9. Latin is also introduced in Year 8. In Years 10 and 11 English Language, Literature, Mathematics, Dual Science, French, RE, IT, Games and Computing are normally chosen from a wide range of options to give a balanced curriculum.

The school enters candidates for several GCSE Examining Boards. The Sixth Form provides a two-year course through AS to A level or VCE for 130 students and most of these then proceed to Further and Higher Education.

Pupils are given every encouragement to find and follow leisure time pursuits. Riding and orienteering feature amongst a very wide range of sports and outdoor pursuits. There is much active drama work and interest in art and music is particularly strong. Over half of the pupils learn at least one instrument. There is an orchestra, a concert band, a jazz band, a dixie band, rock bands and 5 choirs. Visits to concerts and theatres, and excursions to places of interest are a regular feature of each term. The Music Department tours abroad bi-annually.

Sidcot's Junior School accommodates 3–11 year olds in a self-contained campus adjoining Sidcot. Currently some 130 pupils are enrolled.

Admission. Sidcot is not a school that selects a narrow academic ability for baseline assessment purposes, but pupils are admitted after interview with the Head and receipt of a previous school report. Pupils are admitted at any stage from the age of 9 up to Sixth Form entry. There is an Entrance Test but pupils entering from preparatory schools can be admitted on the basis of Common Entrance.

Scholarships. (*see Scholarship Entries section*).

Fees per term (2008-2009). Day: Junior School £1,400–£2,700, Senior School £3,950. UK/EU boarding £6,600, Overseas boarding £7,100, Sidcot Academic English School £8,100.

Charitable status. Sidcot School is a Registered Charity, number 296491. The aim of the school is the education of children in a Quaker and caring environment.

Stafford Grammar School

Burton Manor Stafford ST18 9AT
Tel: 01785 249752
Fax: 01785 255005
e-mail: headsec@staffordgs.plus.com
website: www.stafford-grammar.co.uk

Stafford Grammar School was founded in 1982 in response to demand for independent education in Stafford. The School, which is co-educational, is registered as an educational charity and the Board of Governors is in membership with the Association of Governing Bodies of Independent Schools.

Motto: *Quod tibi hoc alteri*

Patrons:
The Right Hon The Earl of Shrewsbury
The Lord Stafford
The Right Hon The Earl of Lichfield

Governing Body:
B K Hodges (*Chairman*)

J Archer, TD, FCIS, JP
B Baggott
Mrs C Churchill
Mrs S Flatters
J W Griffiths, LLB
Dr A Kratz, BA, PhD
J Lotz, FRCS
D Pearsall
Mrs P Pearsall
Mrs H Watson Jones
D White
A Wright

***Headmaster*: M R Darley**, BA

Deputy Head: M P Robinson, BA, DipEd Man

Senior Teacher: Mrs L I Robson, BA
Senior Teacher: Dr PA Johnson, BSc, PhD

Assistant Staff:
Mrs S Appleford, BA
Mrs E Ayirebi, BA
D R Beauchamp, BSc
Mrs R Beauchamp, BA
G Beckett, BSc
Dr H Blakeman, BA, MA, PhD
Miss S Brereton, BMus, LRAM
D Craig, BA, UED
Dr F G Crane, BSc, PhD
Miss L Elias, BA
Mrs J A Fletcher, BA, ADB
Dr R Foster, BSc, PhD
E Gill, BA, BEd
Mrs L J Gill, BA, AdvCert Art Ed, DipRSA
S Godwin, MSc, BA
R C Green, BA
Miss H Hackett, BSc
L J Harwood, BEd
Mrs M M Hinton, BA
A C Johnson, BSc
Mrs L Johnstone, BA
T Kirsch, BSc
Mrs A Lonsdale, BSc
Mrs P Mawman, BA
Mrs E Paton, BA
Mrs H Robinson, BSc
Mrs B Robson, BSc
G Robson, BSc
Mrs A M Saxon, BEd, MA
B K Sharman, CertEd
Miss D Shaughnessy
Mrs J Smale, BEd
J Smith, BA
Mrs A J Taylor, BA
Mrs T Whyte, BSc, MSc
D R Williams, BSc
Mrs L Williams, BA

Chaplain: Prebendary R Sargent, MA

Bursar: B Astbury, MA, DipSchMan

Headmaster's Secretary: Mrs S M Pickavance

Number in School. There are 414 pupils, of whom 250 are boys and 164 girls. There is a Sixth Form of around 115.

Stafford Grammar School is housed in a fine Victorian manor house, designed by Augustus Pugin, standing in 22 acres of grounds with sports pitches, tennis courts and extensive additional specialist accommodation. Recent additions have included a sports hall and music centre, cafeteria, additional classrooms, two further ICT rooms, broadband internet and network access across the site, mezzanine floor library and refurbished reception and conference suite. A large new Science and Sixth Form Centre opened in 2007. A further 16 acres of sports land have recently been purchased to enable further development of team sports' facilities.

Curriculum. In Year 7 and Year 8 all pupils follow a common course consisting of English, Mathematics, Science, French, German, Geography, History, Music, Art, Drama, Computing, Design, Technology, Religious Education and Physical Education. Year 9 sees Science divide into separate subjects.

Pupils in Years 10 and 11 study nine subjects at GCSE: English (2), Mathematics, Sciences and a language, together with three options chosen from some twelve available. Physical Education continues and Careers and Life Skills are introduced.

There is setting in Mathematics from Year 8, but most subjects are taught in parallel groups. Classes are kept small (maximum 20) so that pupils can receive individual attention.

In the Lower Sixth Form students study three, four or five A level subjects (AS) leading to three or four A level subjects (A2) in the Upper Sixth Form. Approximately 20 A level subjects are available.

Creativity and the Arts. The School has an extensive Art and Design Department. Pupils' powers of observation and awareness are developed through practical skills and theoretical studies involving areas as varied as painting, printing, 3-D work, photography and textiles. There are frequent competitions and exhibitions of work as well as projects linked with other departments.

Music plays an important part in the life of the School. There is an orchestra and a choir which perform on many occasions in musicals, church services and concerts. Ensembles, both instrumental and vocal, are encouraged. Original incidental music is composed for School productions. Pupils have the opportunity to learn to play a wide range of musical instruments with tuition provided by peripatetic teachers.

Drama enables pupils to gain confidence and self-understanding. It is particularly effective in the early years in the

School. Two annual School Plays are major productions on the School's excellent stage and involve a large number of pupils.

Art and Drama are available at GCSE and A level.

Sport and Activities. Whilst sport plays a prominent part in School life, the emphasis is very much on training for future leisure time.

The School has outstanding sports facilities and the following sports are available: Soccer, Hockey, Rugby, Cricket, Tennis, Squash, Badminton, Basketball, Netball, Volleyball, Athletics, Gymnastics, Rounders, Table Tennis, and Health-related Fitness, as well as Swimming at Riverside.

The School plays a large number of matches against other schools, both state and independent, and is fully involved with local school leagues. Individuals regularly secure places in Staffordshire and Midlands teams.

Our range of activities is deliberately wide since we believe that every child is good at something and that it is our job to discover and develop talent in any direction.

There are many Clubs and Societies of widely differing kinds and a large number of pupils are working for the Duke of Edinburgh's Award Scheme.

At present there are 15 inter-House competitions. These range from Technology to Public Speaking and from Football to Hobbies, and include some which are specifically for younger pupils.

The intention of these is not only to enable as many pupils as possible to represent their Houses, but also to stress that we value excellence in any area.

Pastoral Care. In its pastoral organisation, the School seeks to nurture the potential of every child giving both support and encouragement in an overt and practical way. The School is divided into three houses, the Head of House being the key figure in the academic and personal development of each child. Tutor groups are kept small and are based on the House to maintain continuity and to strengthen communal bonds. Tutors maintain strong links with each pupil using a programme of active tutoring which includes scheduled interviews. We place great emphasis on close contact with parents, believing that lack of progress and other problems are best addressed jointly and as early as possible.

In the Sixth Form a slightly different system operates. Although retaining the same House Tutor, the pupil will have a Form Tutor from a specialist team of Sixth Form Tutors. Additionally one of the Senior Teachers is attached to this team. Further to this is the opportunity for each pupil to choose a Personal Tutor with whom to build a special rapport.

Sixth Form. The Sixth Form is the ideal environment in which to foster confidence, responsibility, leadership, initiative and self-discipline.

The keynote of the Sixth Form is freedom with responsibility. At this stage pupils still need help in planning their time and in establishing good working habits, and the guidance of an understanding tutor can mean the difference between success and failure.

Careers. Considerable attention is paid to career advice, and there are frequent visits by speakers from industry and the professions. From Year 10 onwards, individual advice is given by our own careers staff, and pupils are also encouraged to consult the County Careers Service.

Religion. Although we welcome pupils of all faiths, or none, the School is a Christian foundation.

The School seeks to live by the Christian ideal, in particular by being a community in which members genuinely care about each other.

Admission. Entrance is by examination and interview in order to ensure that pupils have sufficient reasoning ability to be able to attempt GCSE in a reasonable range of subjects.

Entrance to the Sixth Form is by GCSE results and interview.

Scholarships and Bursaries. The Governors have allocated funds to enable pupils of exceptional ability or limited means to join the school.

Fees per term (from January 2008). £2,839.

Stafford Preparatory School opened, in purpose-built accommodation, in September 2007 admitting pupils into Year 5 and Year 6. We will be admitting pupils into Year 4 from September 2008. This will provide exciting opportunities for pupils and staff to prepare for selective senior school education at Stafford Grammar School or elsewhere.

Charitable status. Stafford Independent Grammar School Limited is a Registered Charity, number 513031. It exists to provide education for children.

Stanbridge Earls School

Romsey Hampshire S051 0ZS
Tel: 01794 529400
Fax: 01794 511201
e-mail: admin@stanbridgeearls.co.uk
website: www.stanbridgeearls.co.uk

Number of Boys: 148 aged 11–18.
Number of Girls: 26 aged 11–18.

Governors:

Chairman: D J Beeby

C Bulman
J Chandler
R Crockett
Mrs M Da Cunha
J Glen
P C Goodship
R Grime
A J Knight
Mrs N Moss
Mrs S Warner
M J Woodhall, FRICS

Director of Finance and Secretary to Governors: B R Taylor, Fellow ACCA

***Headmaster*: G P Link**, CertEd, MEd Exeter

Deputy Head Curriculum: D J Durnell, BSc, PGCE London
Deputy Head Pastoral: R J Bailey, BA Canterbury, CertEd

Assistant Staff:
† *House Master/Mistress*

Mrs M Adams, BSc, PGCertDys
Ms J Baigel, RCSLT, ASLTIP, HPCUK (*Speech & Language Therapy*)
Mrs H Bedford, BA Hons Leeds, PGCE Hull
Mrs R E Blencowe, CertEd Bath
Miss Z E Boyle, BMus Hons, PG Cert Perf, LTCL (*Director of Music*)
Mrs E M S Cole, CertEd, BEd, DipSpEd King Alfred's College (*i/c ALC*)
Mrs J Coleman, CertEd London, AMBDA
Mrs G Coppock, BA Hons Southampton, DipOT (*Occupational Therapist*)
Mrs C M D'Urso, RCSLT, PATOSS, CPSM (*Speech & Language Therapist*)
Mrs D A Dutfield, CertEd Avery Hill, London
Mrs L Edwards, CertEd Hull College, PGDipDys Kingston
Mrs G Ford, BEd Cape Town
Mrs J H George, CertEd St Osyth's College, DipAESSpN King Alfred's College
Mrs M Grubb, DipCE, Dip Fashion & Textiles, LRPS
R D Hancock, BEd
Mrs P R Hollingsbee, CertEd
Dr C F Hughes, BSc Hons, PhD
Miss J S Hughes, BA Exeter, CertEd Bangor
Mrs M A Mackay, BEd London, DipBDA
Miss L Mann, BA Greenwich, London
Mrs S Martinelli, BSc Reading
Mrs W L Molyneaux, BA, BEd Toronto
Dr F E Myszor, PhD Southampton, BA, PGCE Nottingham

P Neethling, BA, B Hons, BEd Dip Stellenbosch, SA
L Nicholson, MA Southampton, TCert St Luke's, Exeter
Mrs E A Nye, MAEd Open, CertEd LSU, PGDipSEN
N A Parker, CertEd
G A Pearce, BA Hons, PGCE Birmingham (*†B House*)
P C Pellatt, BA Leicester, MAEd Open, CertEd Liverpool
Mrs S L Puffitt, BEd, TEFL
Mrs K Richardson, BEd, TCert Warwick (*†C House*)
D J Rose, BA QTS Bristol
Ms S L Rowe, BA Warwick
C F Rowney, BA Bangor, CertEd Southampton (*†A House*)
J Stephens, BA Cardiff, PGCE Oxford
G P Taylor, BA Ed, MA SEN Liverpool John Moore's (*†D House*)
Mrs S B Taylor, BEd Hons Southampton
Mrs S J Thomson, BA Kent, PGCE Reading
M C Townend, BSc Warwick, CertEd Coventry
Mrs D Trotman, DipEd London
Mrs L Upson, CertEd
Mrs A J Visser, BA Southampton, PGCE Leeds
Dr J Wait, CertEd, MA, PhD Sheffield
N Walsh, BSc London, CertEd Chester
Mrs K Woodrow, BSc CNAA, CertEd Oxford

Visiting Staff:
Ms E Clarke, BMus Hons (*Violin, Viola*)
Mrs F Howard, LRAM, PGCE, BMus Hons
P M McKenna (*Drums*)
S Newman, GTCL, LTCL, PGCE (*Strings*)
T A Norris, BA Ed Hons, LRSM (*Brass*)
Mrs S Ormiston, BA Hons Cardiff, PGCE Reading (*Piano*)
C Pearce, BA Hons (*Guitar*)
Mrs M Shearer, GTLC Hons, LTCL, PGCE
Mrs A Venning (*Keyboard Skills*)
Miss M Williams, BA, PGDip

Warden, Goulds: Mrs F Callender (*Head of Senior Girls*)
Houseparent, Agora Junior Boys: Mrs E Neethling, BA, HEd Soc Stellenbosch, SA
Houseparent, Forum: N A Parker, CertEd
Houseparent, John Attlee: Mrs P Jones
Houseparent, Cornock-Taylor: Mrs J Taylor
Houseparent, A Annex: C F R Rowney
Houseparent, B Annex: Mrs A Visser
Houseparent, C Annex: Mrs K Richardson
Houseparent, Acropolis: F E Myszor

Administrative Staff:
Finance Officer: Ms J A Ramsay
Headmaster's PA: Mrs A Cox
Medical Officer: Dr Scriminger
Registrar: Mrs A Spicer, BTec
Sister-in-Charge: Miss J L Thompson, RGN, RNS
School Nurses:
Mrs M Bavington, RGN
Mrs A O'Neill, RGN
Mrs N Atkins, RGN

Foundation and Purpose. Stanbridge Earls was founded in 1952 by Mr Anthony Thomas, the original Principal, and his wife with funds granted by the Graham Robertson Trust. The aim of this Trust was to encourage art, music and drama, and these activities have always played an important part in the life of the school. The school has over the years evolved its own special purpose, which is to offer parents a distinctive alternative to the large, traditional Independent Schools and to State Education.

It exists to serve those who are seeking a small and intimate school with a particularly high staffing ratio, individualised teaching methods and qualified additional staff for special needs English and Mathematics. The academic objectives are high GCSE grades for all, A Level for most, and entrance to university or other higher education for those capable of profiting from such courses. It is a particularly suitable school for boys or girls of good academic potential who, for one reason or another, have up to the time of entry not achieved that potential.

Special Needs. Since 1962 the school has been helping pupils with specific word-learning difficulties (dyslexia) and has a custom-built Accelerated Learning Centre where 16 qualified staff are able to help pupils overcome their problems on a one-to-one basis. Dyslexia is not seen as a reason for failure. The internationally-recognised specialist help, together with a whole school approach, means that success is not only possible but expected. There is also a well-established department to help those pupils who have a problem with Maths. Speech communication, EAL and Occupational Therapy are other specialisms on offer. CReSTeD rating "SP".

Entry. There is no entrance examination. The report of an Educational Psychologist may be required in some cases. In others, a pupil's current work may be asked for. A full confidential report must be received from the pupil's current Headmaster or Headmistress, to cover character, interests, ability at work, games or other skills.

Parents and child must attend the school for interview with the Headmaster prior to final acceptance.

Curriculum. The curriculum covers all the basic academic skills and such further courses as can be offered from the skills and enthusiasms of the current staff, such as Automotive Studies. There are 20 subjects taught to GCSE Level. The following are taught at AS and A2 Level: English, History, Geography, Mathematics, Biology, Physics, Chemistry, Art, Textiles, Drama, Media Studies, Music, Design, French, Sports Studies, Leisure & Recreation, Business Studies and ICT.

In the Sixth Form, apart from the above subjects, there is also an emphasis on preparing students for adult life outside school.

Recreation. The school is unusually well equipped for its size for sport. There is a heated, indoor swimming-pool for all-year use, a sports hall, large motor vehicle workshop, a fitness suite, one squash court, two hard tennis courts and a normal games field. Soccer, rugger, cricket, tennis, badminton, basketball, netball, squash, swimming, athletics, TaeKwonDo, riding and golf are provided. A chain of small lakes offers fishing. Many hobbies are encouraged. There is no CCF or other cadet force but interested pupils join the ATC in Romsey and there is a Duke of Edinburgh's Award scheme.

Girls. At present there are 40 boarding places, but there is no limit to the number of day girls. The normal ages of entry is either 11 to 13 years for a full career or into the Sixth Form for A Levels.

Fees per term (2008-2009). Boarding: £7,870 (13+), £7,055 (11+). Day: £5,910 (13+), £5,295 (11+). Remedial tuition and lessons on a musical instrument are extras.

Scholarships and Bursaries. The Headmaster may award a number of Bursaries to deserving cases.

Charitable status. Stanbridge Earls School is a Registered Charity, number 307342. It exists to provide education for boys and girls.

Sunderland High School (UCST)

Mowbray Road Sunderland SR2 8HY
Tel: 0191 567 7674
Fax: 0191 510 3953
e-mail: info@sunderlandhigh.co.uk
website: www.sunderlandhigh.co.uk

Junior School:
Tonstall House Ashbrooke Road Sunderland SR2 7JA
Tel: 0191 514 3278
Fax: 0191 565 6510

e-mail: info@sunderlandhigh.co.uk
website: www.sunderlandhigh.co.uk

Motto: *Timor Domini Principium Sapientiæ*

Co-educational Day School established by the United Church Schools Trust and opened in 1884.

Number of Pupils: 261 Girls, 325 Boys.

Governing Body: The Council of the United Church Schools Trust

Local Committee:
Revd Canon S Taylor (*Chairman*)
D C Barnes, Esq, FCA
S Lundy, Esq
T Maxfield, Esq
K S Moore, Esq
D K Sherwood-Smith, Esq
J Ward, Esq
V Ward

***Head*: Dr Angela Slater**, BA, PhD

Head of Junior School: Mr C Bulmer, MA Ed, NPQH, CertEd

Full-time Staff:
Miss N Badcock, BA
Miss A Berry, BA, PGCE
Miss J Bruce, BA, PGCE
Mrs J Craven, BA Sunderland
Miss A Dargan, BEd
Mrs J A Donald, CertEd
Mrs J Dunn, TCert
Mrs P Gibbs, BA OU, CertEd
Mr M Giron, Lic-ès-Lettres, PGCE
Mr J Gowland, CertEd Manchester
Miss K Grenfell, BSc, OTS
Mr D Hair, BA Hull, MA, PGCE
Mr W G Hedley, BSc Leeds, PGCE
Mrs J Hill, BSc, MA, PGCE
Mrs S E Hope, BA, PGCE
Mrs R Keating, BA Hons
Mrs M Lewis, BSc Manchester, DipEd
Mrs D Mahon, BEd
Mr I McDonough, BScEd Hons
Mrs D McVay, CertEd
Miss S Minto, BA Newcastle, PGCE
Miss H R Morrison, BA Belfast, PGCE
Mr R D Paine, BA, PGCE (*Deputy Head*)
Mr R Phillips, BA, PGCE
Mr G Prior, BA, PGCE
Mrs G Prior, BA, PGCE (*Deputy Head Junior School*)
Miss S Probets, BSc London, PGCE
Mrs M Reed, CertEd (*Head of Nursery*)
Mr T Render, BEd Newcastle, ATCL
Mrs J Robson, BA Liverpool, PGCE
Mrs M M Roddy, BA Leicester, PGCE
Dr H Sarson, BSc, PhD, PGCE
Mr A Smith, PGCE
Mrs C Summers, BA Hons
Mr A Temple, BSc, PGCE
Mrs J A Thompson, BEd Southampton
Mrs A E Wayman, BA Sunderland, CertEd
Mr P Wayman, BSc, PGCE

Part-time Staff:
Mrs A Bovill, BA
Mrs V Dixon, MA
Mrs L Hallam, MA, BA, PGCE
Mrs B Harratt, BA, PGCE
Mrs A Hedley, BA Newcastle, DipEd
Mr M Hudson, BSc, PGCE
Mrs S James, BSc, PGCE
Mrs J Newby, BSc, PGCE
Mrs L Taylor, BEd Ord
Mrs T Wilson BA, PGCE

The school is situated in the centre of the town close to the bus and railway stations. Pupils travel from Gateshead, Chester-le-Street, Washington, South Shields, Peterlee, Houghton-le-Spring and Durham. Transport services are good. School buses are organised from South Shields, Washington, Peterlee, Houghton-le-Spring and Durham.

The Junior School, for Nursery, Infant and Junior boys and girls, was opened by HRH The Princess Royal in May 1994. The building has specialist rooms for Science, Art, Computers and Music as well as a fully equipped Sports Hall. Outside sports facilities include a full sized, floodlit all-weather pitch and grass pitch. These sports facilities are shared by Junior and Secondary pupils for their games programme which includes hockey, netball, football, rugby, cricket, tennis, rounders and athletics. All boys and girls in the Junior School, including the Nursery, have swimming classes also.

The Nursery admits boys and girls on a full or part-time basis and prepares children for school through constructive educational play.

The Infant and Junior Departments provide a sound education for boys and girls. The special feature of the Infant and Junior programme is the Early Language Programme in which German is core curriculum for all pupils from the age of 4+. Junior School pupils enter the Senior School on the recommendation of the Head of Junior School, and they may take a scholarship test at that point. These scholarships are awarded on academic merit. There is also a music scholarship awarded at this stage.

The Senior School (Years 7 to 11) in Mowbray Road has three sites. The Centenary building provides excellent classrooms, four science laboratories and a networked Information Technology Room. The original building includes a fifth laboratory, a second networked Computer Room, library, art room, Design and Food Technology Centre, careers room and further classrooms.

Clifton Hall is especially equipped for Year 7 and Year 8 pupils. Each classroom is equipped with an interactive w/board. There are specialist Music and Drama facilities. Langham Tower and the Armstrong James teaching block were acquired in 2004.

The Curriculum. The school is small enough for all pupils to be in close contact with the staff. Classes are limited in size and allow for teachers to deal with individual needs.

The Curriculum is designed to provide a broad education from 4+ to 18+, in line with the requirements of the National Curriculum. Pupils are encouraged to acquire the right qualifications for further study, an independence of spirit, a self awareness of their personal qualities and a sensitivity to the needs of others.

In the Junior School, core subjects are taught in forms with specialist subjects being added as pupils get older. German is taught to pupils from the age of 4+ as part of the school's European awareness policy.

In the Senior School, there are some twenty subjects which pupils study from the age of 11. Pupils receive guidance in Year 9 to enable them to make a wise and balanced choice of subjects for the GCSE courses. In Year 11 Work Experience is organised after the GCSE examinations.

Music, drama and sport are strongly encouraged as well as extra-curricular activities, including the Duke of Edinburgh's Award Scheme. Regular ski trips, activity holidays and visits abroad are organised for both junior and senior pupils.

The Sixth Form. The Sixth Form is housed in a separate Sixth Form Centre. Boys and girls are admitted to the Sixth Form subject to a satisfactory standard at GCSE. Most students take four AS level subjects in Arts and/or Science, leading to three A2 levels. A General Studies programme is also offered. Extra courses, such as the CSLA and Young Enterprise, are part of the General Studies programme. All students are encouraged to help in the organisation of the school. Most students proceed to University and other areas of Higher Education. Scholarships are available on entry to the Sixth Form.

Admission. Entry to the school is normally at 4+, 7+, 11+, 13+ and the Sixth Form, but applications at other ages are accepted, subject to vacancies. Entrance is partially selective and may include an interview, written tests and a reference from the applicant's previous school.

Fees per term (2007-2008). (*see Scholarship Entries section*). Infants £1,741; Juniors £2,130; Seniors (including the Sixth Form) £2,494. The fees include all books, stationery, equipment. Lunches are extra.

Foundation Assisted Places are also available.

Additional Subjects. Music, Speech, Karate, Dancing (Fees on request).

Charitable status. The United Church Schools Trust is a Registered Charity, number 1016538. It is a charitable trust existing to provide high quality education in keeping with the teaching of the Church of England.

Thetford Grammar School

Bridge Street Thetford Norfolk IP24 3AF
Tel: 01842 752840
Fax: 01842 750220
e-mail: enquiries@thetfordgrammarschool.fsnet.co.uk
website: www.thetgram.norfolk.sch.uk

Refounded in the 17th century by Sir Richard Fulmerston, Thetford Grammar School can however show an unbroken roll of Headmasters from 1119 and traces its origins to the 7th century. In more recent times it was voluntarily controlled until, augmented by the adjacent girls' grammar school, it returned to independence in 1981. Today it is a two-form entry 3½–18 co-educational day school with 320 pupils drawn from a radius of 30 miles across the Norfolk/Suffolk border. We seek to combine worthwhile academic standards with a tradition of care and support for the individual and commitment to the breadth of educational experience. A member of SHMIS (elected 1996), ISC and AGBIS, the school is administered by the Governors of the Thetford Grammar School Foundation, acting as Trustees on behalf of the Charity Commission.

The Governing Body:

Chairman of Governors: Dr J E J Altham, MA, PhD
Vice-Chairman: Mrs B Garrard, MA, BSc
I M Clark
J G Crisp
J R Edwards, TD, JP, MA, DMS
Mrs L Hobden-Clarke
Mrs V Hutchby
T J Lamb, BSc Econ
Mrs J Large, JP, FBCO
Major T MacMullen, BA, TCD
P J Price, MBA
Mrs J M Sinclair
Mayor of Thetford (*ex officio*)
Cllr R Kybird, Breckland District Council (*co-opted*)

Bursar and Clerk to the Governors: Wing Cdr P J McGahan, MCMI, MInstLM

***Headmaster*: G J Price**, MA Oxon

Deputy Headmaster: J S Campbell, BSc Nottingham
Deputy Headmistress & Director of Music: Mrs J Huntington, ARAM, GRSM, LRAM, CPSEd
Head of Junior School: Ms K A Dennis, MEd Melbourne

Assistant Staff:
Mrs A Alecock, BA Manchester
Miss D Blake
I M L Blundell, BSc UEA
Mrs J Bull, BA Leicester
Mrs R Dimminger, CertEd Zimbabwe
A M Durling, BA UEA
Mrs A Durling, BA Warwick
Mrs J Fifield, BA University of Wales
Miss F Foster, BA Warwick
Mrs T E Granger, BSc Wolverhampton
M Hill, BA Bedfordshire
I Holby, BA Southampton
Ms G Irving, BA Exeter, MA Lancaster
Mrs J Kidd, BA Surrey
C Kingsnorth, BSc London, DPhil Oxford
J A Law, BEd Loughborough
R Maringue, MA Clermont-Ferrand University
J C Mead, BEd Hons, CSci, CPhys, MInstP
Ms L Perry, BA Sussex
Mrs A Poole, BA Open University, CertEd Dartford
Mrs H Pringle, BA Teesside Polytechnic
S Ratcliffe, BA Hons Portsmouth Polytechnic
Miss F Ridgwell, BA Hons De Montfort
Mrs M Rolton, CertEd Bretton Hall
C M Shepherd, BSc Liverpool
Ms A Sherring, BA Camberwell
S R Simpson, BSc Birmingham
S G Spencer, MA Open University
Mrs P J Stockwell, CertEd Bromley
Ms Stratford, BA York
Miss C Sulley, BA Surrey
Mrs A M Vant, BA Cork
A Ward, BSc Hons London
Mrs V S Webber, BA Hons Open University, CertEd Brighton

Classroom Assistant: Mrs D C Sims, FD, CertEYP Open

Visiting Music Staff:
Miss N Absolum (*Piano*)
M B Clarke, BA Sussex, MA Illinois (*Clarinet, Saxophone*)
Mrs P Clarke, MM UEA (*Flute*)
I Payne (*Brass*)
Ms F Levy, LLCM TD, ALCM (*Violin*)
B Metcalfe, GNSM (*Strings*)
Miss R Platts, BEd (*Harp*)
Mrs J Rickard, GRSM, LRAM (*Oboe*)
J Rowland (*Drums*)
A H Salazar, GSMD, PGC, PGAdvDip TCM (*Voice*)
B Smith (*Guitar*)
Mrs J G Weeks, GRSM, ARMCM

Dyslexia Support:
Miss A Harrold, PGCertSpLD
Mrs K E Jones, BSc, DipSpLD

Headmaster's Secretary: Ms E Morrell
School Secretary: Ms S Summers

Buildings and Situation. Situated close to the centre of Thetford, the school occupies a well established site graced by several buildings of architectural interest and the ruins of a medieval priory. An active Development Programme has seen the impressive refurbishment of buildings to provide improved facilities. Music, Art, English, Technology, the Junior School and its pre-prep, Goldcrest, are among recent beneficiaries of this process while the Thomas Paine Library both commemorates an Old Thetfordian and extends private study facilities. A new Sixth Form Centre and Performing Arts Studio has recently opened. There are extensive playing fields with a refurbished pavilion within walking distance of the main buildings.

Organisation. Junior School pupils (3½–7 Goldcrest; 8–10 Junior Department) are taught primarily in their own premises with independent facilities. Older juniors, however, have contact with specialist teachers in several subject areas and benefit from similar integration into many other aspects of school life. Main School education from 11 follows a two or three-form entry pattern with setting in core subjects to GCSE. Sixth Form students, who have their own Common Room, play a full part in the life of the school.

Curriculum. Junior School teaching follows National Curriculum lines with strong emphasis on the English/Mathematics core and the range of specialist subjects in support. Music and Drama are important within the Department, while a full programme of PE and Games allows for the development of team sports and individual fitness.

Main School education through to GCSE is based on a common core of English, English Literature, Mathematics, a Modern Language (French or German) and the Sciences. Options allow students to develop skills and interests in History, Geography, RS and Business Studies, languages, the expressive arts, physical education and technology. IT is strongly represented across the curriculum. AS and A2 courses are offered in all these subjects, including the separate sciences, with the addition of Psychology. Mathematics and Science lead a strong pattern of results at this level and sixth form students proceed to university degree courses.

Sport and Extra-Curricular Activities. The life of the school extends widely from the classroom into sport, community service, dramatic and musical presentation; the lessons taught by the pursuit of excellence through individual commitment and teamwork are greatly valued.

Winter sports are Rugby, Soccer, Hockey, Netball and Cross-Country with Cricket, Tennis, Rounders and Athletics in the Summer. Popular indoor sports such as Basketball, Aerobics, Badminton, Volleyball and Gymnastics are also followed.

A majority of pupils take part in training for the Duke of Edinburgh's Award Scheme. Musically, a lively concert programme supports individual instrumental tuition and choral rehearsal while opportunities for theatre are provided termly by House and School productions.

A popular Activities Week is run biennially at the end of the Summer Term encompassing expeditions and foreign visits.

Admission. Admission into the Junior School follows a day in school with the appropriate year group during which an assessment is made. Admission into Main School is by formal examination with interview and school report. Sixth Form entrance is on the basis of interview and school report, with subsequent performance at GCSE taken into consideration. The main Entrance Examination is held in January but supplementary testing continues through the year. Full details from the Headmaster's Secretary.

Fees per term (2008-2009). £2,624 (Goldcrest), £2,915 (Junior Department), £3,173 (Main School) including books and tuition, but excluding uniform, lunches, transport, examination entry fees and some specialised teaching such as instrumental music lessons.

Scholarships and Bursaries. (*see Scholarship Entries section*). Within the limits of available funds the Governors are able to provide financial support with the fees in case of need. Such bursaries are based on a declaration of family income and can be up to 100% of the fees. They are available from Year 7 upwards. They are dependent of course on the pupil fulfilling the entrance requirements of the school. Six scholarships of an honorary nature will be awarded to the top performers in the entrance examinations. Music scholarships are available on entry in Year 7 or 9 which will provide free instrumental or voice tuition. Four scholarships are also available into the Sixth Form for both internal and external candidates. These can provide 25% reduction in fees for two years and are awarded as the result of a scholarship paper sat in January or in recognition of outstanding GCSE performance in the summer.

Details of all awards may be had from the Headmaster.

Charitable status. Thetford Grammar School is a Registered Charity, number 311263. It exists to provide education for boys and girls.

Warminster School

Church Street Warminster Wiltshire BA12 8PJ
Tel: 01985 210100 (Senior School)
01985 224800 (Preparatory School)
Fax: 01985 214129
e-mail: admin@warminsterschool.org.uk
website: www.warminsterschool.org.uk

The original boys' school was founded in 1707 by the first Viscount Weymouth, an ancestor of the present Marquess of Bath. It became an Independent Educational Trust in 1973 formed by the amalgamation of the Lord Weymouth School with the long-established local girls' school, St Monica's, founded in 1874. The School is a Limited Company whose Directors are Trustees elected by and from within the Board of Governors which is in membership of the Association of Governing Bodies of Independent Schools.

Patron: The Most Honourable the Marquess of Bath

Chairman of Governors: R Payn, MA Oxon

Staff:

***Headmaster*: M J Priestley**, MA Oxon

Deputy Head (*Academic*): Mrs O Bourne, BEd
Deputy Head (*Pastoral*): Mrs S M Marklew, BA, PGCE

Head of Sixth Form: Mr G McQueen, MA, PGCE
Head of Middle School: Ms N W Davies, BSc Hons, PGCE
Head of Lower School: Mr J R Bonnell, BSc, CertEd

Examinations Officer: Dr M Martin BSc Hons, PhD, PGCE, MIBIOL

Heads of Department:
Mrs S Barns-Graham, BA, LLB Hons, Dip LP (*Modern Languages*)
Mrs F Beck, BSc Hons, PGCE (*Psychology*)
Mrs M Caron-Courtney, MA SEN, BA Hons, RSA DipSpLD, CertEd (*Learning Support*)
Mrs L Clayton, MA, PGCE (*Art*)
A Ellison, BSc SocSci, ACMA (*Business Studies*)
Ms J Hallam, BA Hons, PGCE, RSA Dip TEFL (*EFL*)
Dr D Hankey, BSc, PhD, MRSC (*Science*)
C Knight, BEd Hons (*Director of Sports*)
R Lincoln, BA, CertEd (*Mathematics*)
Mrs S Marklew, BA, PGCE (*History*)
B Martineau, BA Hons, PGCE (*Director of Music*)
J Mawer, BSc (*Geography*)
Mrs C Morgan, BEd Hons (*D&T*)
I Newman, BScEd (*IT*)
Mrs J North, BA Hons, HEd, QTS, ATCL (*RS*)
M Thompson, BA Hons, PGCE (*English*)
D Todres, BA Hons, PGCE (*Drama*)

There are 30 other full-time and part-time staff.

House Staff:
Mr and Mrs J Bonnell (*St Boniface*)
Mr and Mrs G Knapman (*Stratton House*)
Mrs S M Marklew (*St Denys*)
Mr & Mrs Doyle-Davidson (*Old Vicarage*)
Mr & Mrs B Sustek (*Northdown*)
Mrs H Arter, RGN (*School Nursing Sister*)

Bursar & Clerk to the Governors: Mrs A C Martin, MBA, FMAAT
Admissions Registrar: Mrs G Webb

General. Founded in 1707, the School is a co-educational day and boarding school numbering some 640 pupils (150 in the Sixth Form) from 4 to 18, of whom 250 are boarders. The Preparatory School of 160 pupils works in close cooperation with the Senior School and enjoys many of the same facilities. (*For further details see Warminster Preparatory School entry in IAPS section.*)

The School is situated along the western periphery of the town, looking out over open countryside, while its buildings are linked by extensive gardens and playing fields.

It is easily accessible by rail (via Warminster or Westbury) from London, Heathrow, the South Coast and the West, and by road (via the M3, M4 and M5).

Aims and Philosophy. The School aims to provide a stimulating and caring environment in which all pupils develop as individuals and achieve their potential in as many areas as possible. We encourage our pupils to have respect for the rights and beliefs of other people, and wish to provide for them the opportunity to acquire social, academic and personal qualities which will enable them to live happy and productive lives, both within the School and as part of local, national and global communities. The School is proud of its reputation for friendliness and the close working relationship between staff and pupils.

The School is a Church of England foundation, and welcomes pupils of all denominations and faiths, and hopes that, whatever their religious background, they will learn tolerance and concern for other people.

Buildings. As befits a school with a long history, there is a wide variety of historic buildings. The History department, for example, teaches in the School's oldest building, School House, which was founded by Viscount Weymouth in 1707. The school boasts one of the oldest working Fives courts in England.

A multi-million pound development programme has taken place in the last few years and has included a new state-of-the-art science centre, a new library, design technology centre as well as additional boarding facilities. Existing boarding accommodation has been extensively refurbished.

Boarders are cared for by Housemasters or Housemistresses, Resident Tutors and Matrons. Pupils typically enjoy single study-bedrooms in the Sixth Form.

Curriculum. In the first three years of the Senior School, all pupils follow a broad curriculum and GCSE pupils study a full and varied range of subjects. All pupils are involved in PE and Games, and Health and Social Education, as well as a comprehensive programme of Careers advice.

In the Sixth Form greater individual freedom and responsibility are encouraged, and at least 18 different A Level subjects are offered. Although the vast majority of pupils will be aiming for University, with over 95% winning places at leading institutions including Oxford and Cambridge, some will pursue gap years or enter business or the Armed Services directly. The School is now accredited as an IB World School offering the International Baccalaureate Diploma as an alternative to A Levels. This is an increasingly popular choice for many of our pupils with others joining the Sixth Form from elsewhere to study the Diploma.

The overall pupil/staff ratio is under 10:1. Pupils receive an exceptional amount of individual attention and are encouraged to realise their full potential in as many areas as possible. There is an extensive tutorial system and a strong sense of the importance of the individual within the community. A small learning support unit is staffed by dedicated specialists.

Activities. A very wide range of activities is on offer, and pupils are encouraged to involve themselves fully. The School has a strong tradition of drama, and the musical activities, including choir, orchestra and jazz band, are a real strength. There are currently over 40 hobby activities available.

The School enjoys close links with the Services, and the CCF, though voluntary, is traditionally strong. There is also a large involvement in the Duke of Edinburgh's Award Scheme, while a number of pupils are actively engaged in Community Service in Warminster and the local area.

Games. Sports offered include Soccer, Cricket, Athletics, Basketball, Squash, Rugby, Netball, Hockey, Cross-Country running, Rounders, Tennis, Swimming, Badminton, and Volleyball.

There is a spacious Sports Hall with squash courts, hard tennis courts, heated swimming pool, an Astroturf all-weather pitch and an indoor shooting range. Pupils have access to the local Golf Club and Riding stables.

Admission. Pupils are admitted to the Preparatory School from the age of 3. Boarders are admitted from the age of 7. Pupils who enter after the age of 8 will be required to sit the Warminster School entrance examinations relative to the proposed year of entry. The examinations comprise English and Maths papers, Verbal and Non-Verbal Reasoning Tests and a spelling test.

A report from the Head of a pupil's present school will always be requested. Older pupils who qualify by good GCSE results and school report may be admitted directly to the Sixth Form. Scholarships are available for entry at 7+, 9+, 11+, 13+ and 16+. Examinations for Scholarships are held in May and November. Details may be obtained from the Headmaster.

Progress throughout the School, including the transfer from the Preparatory to the Senior School, is not necessarily automatic but will be based on the School's assessment at key points of each student's ability and will always be dependent on the student's continued commitment and progress in all areas of activity.

Great care is taken to consider individual needs and circumstances. The School provides a Special Support Facility for pupils who are mildly dyslexic, or who have other similar needs. Parents of such pupils should ask to meet Mrs Caron-Courtney, who is the SENCO.

Please telephone the School (01985 210160) to arrange a visit, and to meet the Headmaster and the Head of the Preparatory School.

A Registration Fee of £30 is payable and, upon the acceptance of a place, a guarantee fee of £350 for UK based parents and £1,000 for overseas based parents, credited to the final account, will be payable.

Fees per term (2008-2009). Day: Preparatory School £2,000–£3,200; Year 7 to Sixth Form £4,028. Boarding: Preparatory School £4,660; Years 7 to Sixth Form £6,880.

Fees are as inclusive as possible, covering meals, stationery and textbooks. The Bursar welcomes consultation with parents over fees, insurance and capital payment schemes. As the School is an Independent Educational Trust, any financial surplus is used exclusively for the further improvement of the School. Fees are kept to the minimum required to run the School effectively, employ first-rate staff and keep the facilities and resources up to the level expected by parents.

Charitable status. Warminster School is a Registered Charity, number 1042204. It exists to promote the education of boys and girls.

Wentworth College

College Road Bournemouth Dorset BH5 2DY
Tel: 01202 423266
Fax: 01202 418030
e-mail: enquiries@wentworthcollege.com
website: www.wentworthcollege.com

Wentworth College is a co-educational day school for students aged 11 to 18 years. In addition we currently offer weekly, flexi and full boarding for girls only. For over 125 years the school has been providing excellence in education and is the joint foundation of Wentworth School, Bournemouth and Milton Mount College, Crawley.

Motto: *Vive ut postea vivas*

Governing Body:
Mr D Morris, BA, FCA (*Chairman*)
Mr R Haynes, BA Hons
Mrs C Meachin
Mrs K Oliver
Mr J D H Richardson
Mr G Rolfe, MA Oxon, DipEd
Mrs R Simmons, BSc, PGCE
Dr D E Williams, MB BS, MRCGP
Mrs S Williams, BA Hons, CQSW

Staff:
[1] *Resident Staff*

***Headmistress*: [1]Miss S Coe**, BA Hons, PGCE, FRGS

Deputy Head: Mr C Hancock, BEd, CertEd (*Biology*)

Assistant Head: Miss Katherine Castle, BA Hons, PGCE

Director of Boarding: Mrs C Waters, BSc, CertEd

Bursar: Mr J Willis

Clerk to the Governors: Mrs G Strange

Medical Officer: Dr S Walker-Date, MB BS London

Chaplain: Revd M Evans

Teaching Staff:
Mr M Adamson, BSc, MSc (*Business Studies*)
Mr P Allen, BEd, MA (*Physics*)
Mrs A Baffos, BA Hons, PGCE (*French*)
Mr V Blow, TCert (*Design & Technology; Science; Engineering Ambassadors Link Teacher*)
Miss E Bradwell, BSc Hons, PGCE (*Biology, Science; Service Learning Coordinator*)
Miss S Camponeschi, BA Hons (*Physical Education*)
Mrs R Cole, BSc Hons (*Psychology*)
Mr G Coleshill, BA Hons (*Religious Studies; Psychology*)
Mrs C Crane, BA Hons, PGCE (*Geography; Careers/Higher Education Adviser*)
Mr C David, BSc Hons, PGCE (*Biology*)
Mrs A Davies, BA Hons, PGCE (*History*)
Ms K Garcia, BA Hons, TCert (*Spanish*)
Mrs M J Goodman, BA Hons, PGCE, ARCM (*Music*)
Mr R Harrison-Poole, BSc, QTS (*Physical Education*)
Miss P Hayes, BEd (*Information Technology; Mathematics*)
Mrs J Hayward, BA, PGCE (*English, Drama; Farrell House President*)
Mrs J Kolaczkowski, BEd Hons, CertEd (*History; Religious Studies; Critical Thinking*)
Dr B Mason, BSc, PhD, PGCE (*Chemistry*)
Mrs S McCaffrey, BEd Hons (*Home Economics – Food*)
Miss D T McClellan, BA Hons (*Art & Design; Davie House President*)
Mrs S North, LRAM, LCCMD, CertEd (*Speech & Drama*)
Miss J Nussey, BA, CertEd, Dip Dys (*Learning Support Coordinator*)
Mrs J Oldale, MA, PGCE (*German*)
Mrs B Partridge, BEd (*English; Theatre Studies*)
Miss J Poore, BSc Hons, PGCE (*Physical Education*)
Mrs C Rixon, Licence d'Anglais, PGCE (*French*)
Mrs C L Rutherford, BSc Hons, CertEd (*Mathematics; Hadland House President*)
Mr R Sheehan, BA Hons, MA Hons, DipEd (*English*)
Mrs S Stoddard, BSc, PGCE (*Mathematics*)
Mrs N Stride, BSc Hons (*Physical Education; Outdoor Education*)
Mrs L Wedge, MA, TEFL (*English as an Additional Language*)

Housemistresses:
[1]Mrs E Anderson
[1]Mrs S Barber

Independent Listener: Mrs J Henshaw, Mrs B So
Nursing Sister: [1]Miss J Tseung, SEN
Head's Secretary: Mrs M Hardwick
Registrar: Mrs C Bland
Assistant to Bursar: Mrs J Mulcrone
Head Chef: Mr A Windle

plus Visiting Staff.

Our aims. Our staff and governing body are dedicated to providing a caring, close-knit community in which each student may reach their full potential. We aim to develop happy, confident young people who are proud of their academic success and equipped with important life skills.

General information. Wentworth College stands in extensive grounds on a cliff top close to the centre of Bournemouth. It houses approximately 200 students of which one third are either full or weekly boarders. The school makes full use of its proximity to clean beaches, safe waters and the New Forest for field trips and outdoor activities. Day students and boarders integrate well and belong to one of three houses.

Facilities include a well-equipped teaching block with excellent science laboratories, art studios, music school and design and technology workshop. For physical recreation the school has an all weather astro pitch, four tennis courts, a hockey pitch and athletics field and track. Our large sports hall is equipped for netball and volleyball matches, badminton and gym. There is also a separate 25 metre heated indoor swimming pool.

Dormitories are small and comfortable with communal areas for evening recreation. Senior girls occupy study-bedrooms.

Pastoral Care and Health. The school is founded on Christian principles and has close links with the United Reformed Church. However, students of all denominations and other faiths are welcomed into our community.

A team of residential house staff fulfils an important social and pastoral role for the boarders. Each student is assigned a tutor who will monitor progress. The school chaplain and independent listener provide a confidential service while older students become proctors to new students, helping them through the first few weeks at school.

Personal and social education is part of the curriculum for every student in the school and provides a forum to discuss issues which particularly affect young people today.

A medical wing is staffed by matron and the school doctor holds weekly surgeries in the school for non-urgent medical problems. Meals are taken in a 'family-style' atmosphere and careful attention is paid to diet.

Curriculum. Well qualified staff prepare pupils in a variety of studies, beginning with a three-year foundation course which provides the opportunity to study three sciences and three foreign languages, as well as mathematics, English, history, geography, religious education, art and music, drama, food and textiles technology, information technology, design and technology, use of library, and physical education. Special support is available for dyslexic pupils. For their GCSE course, a flexible option scheme allows students to make a varied but balanced selection from 19 subjects. Our Sixth Form offers a wide range of arts and science subjects at GCE Advanced Level. Ninety-seven percent of students enter university or choose some other form of higher education which will prepare them for their chosen career.

Optional extras. Musicians are prepared for the Associated Board of the Royal Schools of Music examinations. Students may take LAMDA examinations in Speech and Drama. RSA Computer Literacy and Information Technology qualifications and work toward the Duke of Edinburgh's Award and their individual Diploma of Achievement.

Wentworth Plus provides special tuition for overseas students whose first language is not English.

A wide choice of clubs and after school events includes canoeing, photography, drama, cookery, self-defence and forensic science.

Communication. The school believes that communication and cooperation between school and home ensures the successful development of each student. Parents receive reports twice a year, regular grade cards and are able to discuss their child's progress at meetings specially dedicated to their year group. Parents are encouraged to attend plays, concerts, sporting events and inter-house competitions. The Friends of Wentworth College – run by parents for parents – stage a number of social events through the year.

Entry. Candidates may take the School's own entry tests at 11+ and 12+ and the Common Entrance Examination at 13+. If places are available, students may join the school at any stage, including the Lower Sixth, on successfully completing the school's own entrance examination.

Fees per term (2008-2009). Boarders and Weekly Boarders £5,975; Day Students £3,645.

Scholarships. (*see Scholarship Entries section*). A number of awards and bursaries are available each year for students with all-round academic ability, or clear potential in either music, art, drama or sport. Internal and external awards are also available for Sixth Form candidates. Full details of these and other bursaries, including grants for children of ministers and lay members of the United Reformed and Congregational Churches, are given in the prospectus. Please contact the Registrar for a copy and details of special events for prospective parents and students.

Charitable status. Wentworth Milton Mount Ltd is a Registered Charity number 306322, promoting excellence in education.

Windermere St Anne's School

The Lake District Windermere Cumbria LA23 1NW
Tel: 015394 46164
International +44 15394 46164
Fax: 015394 88414
e-mail: admissions@wsaschool.com
website: www.wsaschool.com

A unique and inspiring education that develops well-rounded individuals

Chairman of Governors: Peter Redhead

***Head*: Allan Graham**, BA Durham, HNTD Port Elizabeth

Deputy Head: Miss J Parry, MPhil, BSc Hons Liverpool, PGCE Manchester

Junior Department:
Headmaster: Mr B C Freeman, BEd Hons Bristol
Deputy Head: Mr N Stanley, BA Hons, PGCE Charlotte Mason

Administrative Staff:
Bursar: Mr P Flint
Head's PA: Mrs J Jones
School Secretary: Mrs S Dougherty
Elleray Head's PA: Miss S Ingham
Registrar: Mrs H Pethica
Director of Marketing: Mrs S Devir

Windermere St Anne's, is an independent co-educational boarding and day school, founded in 1863, and is an Educational Trust administered by a Board of Governors. It is divided into the Senior School (ages 11 to 18) and the Junior School (ages 3 to 11).

Located In the heart of the English Lake District National Park, our school offers a rich environment in which young people flourish. It combines the beauty and tranquillity of a wooded campus overlooking the mountains and lake with the hustle and bustle of a thriving Cumbrian community. This combined with the rich literary and cultural heritage of the Lake District provides a unique setting for study, self-development and fulfilment.

At Windermere St Anne's we aim to maximise each child's academic potential, and believe we can offer a truly unique space in which children can grow and develop as well rounded individuals.

Even with its breathtaking location, the school has easy access to the motorway network, main rail lines and major airports.

The Senior School is housed at Browhead, and the Junior School is nearby at Elleray, with grounds of over 70 acres in total. There is a modern Sixth Form House with single and double study-bedrooms, plus a Boys (11–16) Boarding House with magnificent views south and west over Lake Windermere and the mountains.

Numbers. There are approximately 420 pupils in total. The Senior School has approximately 270 pupils, of whom 40% are boarders. The size of the community has the advantage of providing a friendly atmosphere of understanding and fosters good staff-pupil relationships. There is a 4-house system for competitions and games.

Curriculum. The curriculum offered at Windermere St Anne's reflects the belief that students should be exposed to as many opportunities as possible and leave the school as well-rounded individuals.

Recognition that learning and communication skills are as important as subject content underpins the way the curriculum is delivered.

The curriculum is tailored to the needs of each child, with small class sizes the norm. Sixth Form students have the opportunity to undertake the internationally recognised International Baccalaureate Diploma, as well as the uniquely practical Venture Baccalaureate Programme.

Music, Art, and Drama play an important part in the life of the school. There are two choirs, and individual instruction leading to chamber groups and orchestra. Students are prepared for the written and practical music exams of the Associated Board of the Royal Schools of Music. The school participates in the local Music Festival. The Central School of Speech and Drama and LAMDA's examinations are also taken in Speech and Drama. Art, Pottery and Design Technology provide considerable scope and opportunity. The Art Studios contain facilities for History of Art and an Art History Library. Drama classes are included in the timetable, and there are several productions staged each year.

Extra-Curricular Activities. Windermere St Anne's has a water sports centre, Hodge Howe, which is located right on the shores of Windermere, providing a wide range of opportunities for pupils during the school's timetabled curriculum and as part of the extra-curricular activity programme. The centre has accreditation from the British Canoeing Union and the Adventure Activities Licensing Authority, as well as being a Royal Yachting Association Teaching Centre.

Service. Windermere St Anne's has a strong tradition of Community Service. The school has an active role in Age Concern, SCOPE, and the Cheshire Home, and supports many other charities including local Hospices, NSPCC, Tiger Kloof in South Africa and the Save The Children Fund.

Religion. The school is Christian in outlook and welcomes other denominations.

Medical. The health of the pupils is under the care of the School Doctors and full time nurse. There is a regular surgery, and dispensary twice daily.

Societies. More than 40 Clubs and Societies provide a variety of interests for out-of-school hours.

Uniform. Senior School – Navy uniform for all pupils during the day; home clothes may be worn at weekends. The Sixth

Form wear dark suits and they may wear home clothes in the evenings and at weekends.

Junior School – Girls blue kilt and striped blazer plus checked shirts in the winter. In the summer the kilt is worn with a navy and white flowered short-sleeved blouse and pale blue sleeveless slipover. Boys wear grey trousers, pale blue shirts and sweater, the school tie and blazer.

Boarding. There is a strong boarding tradition at Windermere St Anne's School that benefits the whole school community. We aim to provide a safe and caring extended family environment where pupils can flourish academically, socially and personally, giving our students the life skills and experiences necessary for adulthood.

Round Square. The School is a member of the international Round Square group of schools. Exchanges and Overseas Service Projects are regularly arranged between the schools involved in Australia, Canada, Germany, India, Switzerland, South Africa and USA and Brunei.

Junior School at Elleray. Elleray is in the care of a Headmaster, and takes boarders and day children. There is also a Nursery School for children from age 2. Elleray is integrated with the Senior School giving continuity of teaching programmes and children in the two parts of the school meet frequently.

(*For further details, see entry in IAPS section.*)

Entry. Pupils are accepted into the Senior School from Prep and Junior schools at 11 or 13+, or by direct entry into the Sixth Form. In other circumstances students may be accepted at other times. In the Junior School, pupils are taken at various stages, from Nursery onwards.

Fees per term (2008-2009). Day (including lunch): £3,695 (Years 7–8), £4,170 (Years 9–13). Boarding: £7,020–£7,098 (weekly), £7,388–£7,466 (full).

Scholarships. Academic, Performing Arts, Visual Arts and Sport Scholarships are available. For more information please contact Admissions on admissions@wsaschool.com or check our website www.wsaschool.com.

Charitable status. Windermere Educational Trust Limited is a Registered Charity, number 526973. It exists to provide education of the highest quality.

The Yehudi Menuhin School

Stoke d'Abernon Cobham Surrey KT11 3QQ
Tel: 01932 864739
Fax: 01932 864633
e-mail: admin@yehudimenuhinschool.co.uk
website: www.yehudimenuhinschool.co.uk

The Yehudi Menuhin School was founded in 1963 by Lord Menuhin and is situated in beautiful grounds in the Surrey countryside, close to London and within easy reach of both Gatwick and Heathrow.

The School provides specialist music tuition in stringed instruments and piano to over 60 musically gifted boys and girls aged between 8 and 18 and aims to enable them to pursue their love of music, develop their musical potential and achieve standards of performance at the highest level. The School also provides a broad education within a relaxed open community in which each individual can fully develop intellectual, artistic and social skills. We are proud that our pupils develop into dedicated and excellent musicians who will use their music to inspire and enrich the lives of others and into friendly, thinking individuals well equipped to contribute fully to the international community.

President: Daniel Barenboim

Vice-Presidents:
Elizabeth, Duchess of Hamilton & Brandon, OBE, DL
A N Hollis, OBE, DFC
Barbara R-D Fisher, OBE

Governor Emeritus:
Daniel Hodson
Anne Simor

Governors:

Chairman: Sir Alan Traill, GBE
Vice-Chairman: Sir John Burgh, KCMG, CB

Mr Noel Annesley
Mr Gavin Barrett
Sir Peter Beale, KBE
The Hon Zamira Menuhin Benthall
Prof Sebastian Forbes
Mr Oscar Lewisohn
Mrs Susan Mitchell
Lord Moser, KCB, CBE, FBA
Mrs Alice Philips
Dr Andreas Prindl, CBE
Mr Adam Ridley
Mr Mark Sheldon, CBE
Mr Graham Smallbone
Mr Peter Willan

Staff:

***Headmaster*: Mr Nicolas Chisholm**, MA Cantab

Director of Music: Mr Malcolm Singer, MA Cantab
Director of Studies/Mathematics: Mr Richard Tanner, MA

Academic Staff:

Art & Craft: Mrs Patsy Belmonte, BA Hons
Biology & Science: Mrs Karen Lyle, BSc Hons, PGCE
English & Drama: Mr Joseph Bennett, MA Hons Edin
French: Mrs Annie Perkins, M-ès-L, MA
German & Russian: Mrs Petra Young, MA
History: Miss Sarah Warren, BA Hons, PGCE
Junior Subjects: Mrs Janet Poppe, BA Hons, PGCE
Mathematics: Mrs Mary Draper, BA Hons, PGCE
EFL: Mrs Hazel Brier, CertEdm MA TESL

Music Staff:

Violin:
Mrs Natalie Boyarskaya, Dip Solo Performance
Mr Simon Fischer, AGSM
Miss Akiko Ono, 1st Cert Dip Mus & Perf Arts, Vienna
Mr Berent Korfker, Dip Solo Cologne, Amsterdam
Miss Sara Struntz
Miss Anna Harpham, BMus Hons

'Cello:
Mr Pierre Doumenge, BMus, PGDip
Mr Thomas Carroll, Cert Munich Hochschule

Bass:
Mrs Caroline Emery, LTCL, GTCL, CertEd

Piano:
Mrs Ruth Nye, DipMusPerf, Melbourne Conservatory
Mr Marcel Baudet Groningen Cons
Mr Graham Caskie, BA Hons, ABSM, DipRAMRCM
Ms Zoe Mather, AGSM

Harpsichord:
Miss Carole Cerasi

Coach Accompanist:
Mr Julian Dyson, ARCM, DipRCM
Mr Nigel Hutchison, BMus Hons

Chamber Music:
Mr Ioan Davies, MA Cantab
Mr Malcolm Singer, MA Cantab
Mr Peter Norris, BMus, ARCM

Orchestra:
Mr Malcolm Singer, MA Cantab

General Music:
Mr Malcolm Singer, MA Cantab
Mr John Cooney, BMus Hons
Mr Nathan Williamson, BMus, Master Mus Dist, Master Musical Arts Yale
Mr Tom Armstrong BA Hons Mus, DPhil Composition
Mr Oscar Colomina i Bosch, BMus, MMus

Choral:
Mr Christopher Bucknall, MA

Alexander Technique:
Mrs Hannah Walton, NNEB, MSTAT

Administrative Staff:

Bursar: Dr Angela Isaac, PhD
Headmaster's PA: Ms Angela Stockbridge
Concert Secretary: Mrs Catharine Whitnall, MA Cantab, LTCL
Housemistress: Mrs Lucyann Palmer, BA Hons, PGCE
Housemaster: Mr Joseph Bennett, MA Hons Edin
Matron: Mrs Joan Clarke, SRN, SCM
Estate Manager: Mr Brian Harris
Receptionist: Ms Kim Anderson

Music. At least half of each day is devoted to musical studies. Pupils receive a minimum of two one-hour lessons each week on their first study instrument and at least half an hour on their second study instrument. Supervised practice is incorporated into the daily programme ensuring that successful habits of work are formed. All pupils receive guidance in composition and take part in regular composers workshops and concerts. Aural training and general musicianship studies are included in the music curriculum. To awaken feeling for good posture, training in Alexander Technique is provided. GCSE and A Level Music are compulsory core subjects for all pupils.

Regular opportunity for solo performance is of central importance to the musical activity of the School, and pupils also perform chamber music and with the String Orchestra. Concerts are given several times each week within the School and at a wide variety of venues throughout the United Kingdom and overseas. The most distinguished musicians have taught at the school, including Boulanger, Perlemuter, Rostropovich and Perlman. Lord Menuhin visited the school regularly. Selection of pupils is by stringent audition which seeks to assess musical ability and identify potential. Special arrangements are made for applicants from overseas, who now account for almost half of the School's pupils.

The School has just opened a state-of-the-art Concert Hall seating 315 with excellent acoustics. Concerts and outreach programmes will now be presented in this new facility.

Academic Studies and Sport. The curriculum is designed to be balanced and to do full justice to both the musical and the general education of each pupil. Academic studies including the understanding of art, literature and science are considered vital to the development of creative, intelligent and sensitive musicians. All classes are small with excellent opportunities for individual attention, and as a result GCSE and A level examination grades are high. To broaden their artistic and creative talents, all pupils work in a wide variety of artistic media including painting, ceramics, jewellery and textiles. Pupils from overseas with limited English receive an intensive course in the English Language from specialist teachers.

The extensive grounds allow plenty of scope for relaxation and sport, including tennis, badminton, football, running, swimming, rounders and yoga.

An International Family. The international reputation of the School brings pupils from all over the world who find a happy atmosphere in a large musical family. Pupils live in single or shared rooms and are cared for by the resident House Staff, the Matron who is a qualified nurse, and the School Doctor. Special attention is paid to diet with the emphasis on whole and fresh food.

Fees and Bursaries. All pupils fully resident in the UK are awarded an Aided Place through the Music and Dance Scheme which is subsidised by the Department for Children, Schools and Families (DCSF). Parents pay a means-tested contribution to the school fees based on their gross income assessed on a scale issued by the DCSF. Pupils from overseas pay full fees for two full calendar years until they acquire the residence qualification needed for support through the Music and Dance Scheme. The school has some bursary funds available to assist with fees for pupils who are not eligible for the Music and Dance Scheme.

Admission. Entry to the School is by music audition, and prospective pupils are auditioned at any time during the year. Candidates may audition at any age between 7 and 16, though the main age for entry to the School spans the years 8 to 14.

Charitable status. The Yehudi Menuhin School is a Registered Charity, number 312010. It exists to provide musical and academic education for boys and girls.

Scholarships and Bursaries

Ashford School (see p 772)
Academic and Music scholarships are available at Year 4 for the Prep School. Academic, Art, Sport, Drama (Year 12 only) and Music scholarships are available at Years 7, 9 and the Sixth Form for the Senior School. Details may be obtained from the Head.

Austin Friars St Monica's School (see p 773)
At 11+:
2 Academic Scholarships, open to all.
2 Sports Scholarships, open to all.
2 Music Scholarships, open to all.
At 16+:
Bursaries are available.

Bearwood College (see p 776)
Open and Closed (British Merchant Navy and Old Royals) Scholarships can be awarded annually in Art, Drama, Music, Sport, General Academic Ability and Sixth Form Entry to those boys and girls reaching the required competitive standard in CEE or College Entry Tests. Sixth Form awards are made on GCSE Grades. A special fees package is available for HM Forces.

Discretionary Bursaries are available in cases of financial hardship.

Personal discussions with the Headmaster are very much encouraged. Full details from the Headmaster, Tel: 0118 974 8300; Fax: 0118 977 3186.

Bedstone College (see p 778)
Bedstone offers Academic, Sport, Music and Art scholarships at 11+/13+ and 16+ with the maximum award being 15% remission of fees. The school is also able to provide "top up" scholarships for exceptional pupils. Valuable Sixth Form scholarships are also available for successful GCSE candidates.

Beechwood Sacred Heart (see p 780)
Scholarships and awards are available: Academic, Music, Art, Sport and Drama at 11+, 13+ and 16+. Major awards up to 50% of the tuition fees and other minor awards. 11+ and 13+ Entrance and Scholarship Days take place in the Spring Term and 16+ in November. Further details are available from the Registrar.

Bethany School (see p 781)
Academic Scholarships are awarded based on performance in the Entrance Examination. Scholarships are also available in Art, Music, Sport, Design Technology and Drama at the main points of entry: Years 7 and 9 and into the Sixth Form. Further details available from the Headmaster. Members of HM Forces and the Clergy receive a 10% fee discount.

Box Hill School (see p 782)
A variety of awards is offered for entry to Year 7, Year 9 and the Sixth Form, based on academic achievement and a contribution to school life through Art, Music, Drama, expedition work, or other appropriate activities. For details, apply to the Registrar.

Claremont Fan Court School (see p 785)
Academic Scholarships are offered at Year 3, to continue through to the end of Year 6, and at Year 7 and Year 9 to continue through to the end of Year 11. Offers are based on a written examination and interview. Sixth Form Academic Scholarships are offered for the two-year course with the minimum requirement of six Grade A passes at GCSE.

Music Scholarships are available for Senior School applicants. As a guide, scholarship candidates should be working at the following levels before applying: Year 7 – Grade 4, Year 9 – Grade 5, Sixth Form – Grade 6. Sixth Form Scholarships will be awarded for the two-year course. Year 7 and Year 9 Scholarships will be awarded through to the end of Year 11.

Both Art and Drama Scholarships are available to candidates applying for a Sixth Form place and are awarded for the duration of their two-year course. Applicants need to present a portfolio for Art which they will be asked to discuss at interview whilst those applying for Drama will need to show evidence illustrating an active and ongoing involvement in drama and theatre.

Sports Scholarships are awarded for pupils of exceptional sporting ability. Sixth Form Scholarships are awarded for the two years of the course. Year 7 Scholarships are awarded through to the end of Year 11.

Dover College (see p 788)
(a) Academic Scholarships are awarded for academic quality ranging up to 50% of the full boarding fee.
(b) Other Scholarships are available for Music, Art, All-Rounder and Sport ranging up to 50% of the full boarding fee.

Scholarships are available to pupils at 11+, 13+ and 16+. Scholarships are not awarded to pupils in the Junior Department.

Sibling Bursaries (10%) and Service Bursaries are automatically awarded. Members of HM Armed Forces and the Diplomatic Service who are eligible for the boarding allowance only pay a parental contribution of 10% of the full boarding fee.

Further details may be obtained on application to the Headmaster, Dover College, Effingham Crescent, Dover, Kent CT17 9RH.

Friends' School (see p 794)
Scholarships are available to internal and external candidates.

Academic awards of up to 50% of the day fee are made in Years 7 and 9. In addition, there are awards made for Art, Drama, Music and Sport.

Sixth Form Scholarships are awarded at the Head's discretion to young people who would contribute substantially to the life of the School.

Further details are available from the Head's Secretary.

Fulneck School (see p 795)
Scholarships are available to both internal and external candidates.

Seniors: Two Fulneck progression scholarships, each worth 20% remission on the Senior School day fees are available to pupils entering the Senior School who have attended Fulneck Junior School. In addition there are five external scholarships awarded at age 11: two general academic scholarships and one scholarship each for Sport, Music and Art. Each scholarship is worth 20% remission on Senior School day fees. Normally the scholarship covers the pupil's whole Senior School career to GCSE, subject to satisfactory progress and behaviour.

Sixth Form: Up to 5 academic scholarships are available worth 20% of day school fees, awarded on the basis of performance in GCSE examinations.

Grenville College (see p 797)
Entrance Scholarships are offered annually at ages 11, 12 and 13 on the basis of the results of entrance tests held each January/February. A maximum of ten Academic Scholarship awards can be made each year; an exceptional candidate can receive an exceptional award. Awards are also available where candidates show outstanding ability in Music, Art, Drama, Design & Technology, and/or Sport. Applications should be made to the Headmaster by the first week in January of the year of entry. Sixth Form Academic Scholarships are awarded on the basis of GCSE performance.

Halliford School (see p 798)
The School offers up to six scholarships to the value of 10% of the annual school fees for entry at 11+. The scholarships are awarded for academic, artistic, musical and sporting excellence. All those taking the 11+ entrance examination will be

considered for the academic scholarships. Means-tested Bursaries are available on application.

Sixth Form Scholarships and Bursaries: Three scholarships to the value of 10% of the annual school fees are available for external candidates showing excellence whether musical, artistic, dramatic or sporting. In addition there are means-tested Bursaries. These are available on application and are awarded either to support scholarships or to candidates with potential.

Hampshire Collegiate School (see p 799)
Scholarships and awards are available to both internal and external candidates at 9+, 11+, 13+ and 16+. An entrance examination takes place in January.

Scholarships of up to 50% of the fees in value may be awarded for Academic, Musical, Artistic, Dramatic, Sport and All-Round ability. Bursaries and Exhibitions of lesser value may also be awarded.

Sixth Form Scholarships are awarded on the basis of GCSE and all-round contribution (actual and potential) to internal and external candidates. These may all be worth up to 50% of the fee.

Langley School (see p 806)
A total of 17 Entrance Scholarships may be awarded annually. The assessment takes place in the Spring Term.

Competitive academic scholarships are awarded at 11+, 12+, 13+ and at 6th Form entry.

Two scholarships may be awarded in each of Music, Sport, Art and Design/Technology.

Further details and a Scholarships brochure may be obtained from the Headmaster.

Milton Abbey School (see p 812)
Academic scholarships (held in May); Music, DT, Art, Sailing and Sport scholarships (held in February). Candidates must be under 14 on 1 September. Scholarships also awarded at Sixth Form entry level. Full particulars from the Admissions Office, e-mail: admissions@miltonabbey.co.uk.

Oswestry School (see p 815)
The Governors offer a number of academic scholarships each year for conspicuously talented individuals, each of which remits up to 50% of the tuition fees. Scholarships are available at 9+, 11+, 13+ and 16+. Scholarships are also available in Art, Music and Sport.

Further details of all these Scholarships are available from the Headmaster.

Princethorpe College (see p 820)
There is a variety of Scholarships available for particularly able or talented candidates ranging from Academic, Art and Music and All-Rounder. Additionally for the Sixth Form there is an Academic Scholarship and Sport Scholarship.

Academic Scholarships: As a guide, there are eleven Academic Scholarships available. Three scholarships providing a reduction of one half of tuition fees, four scholarships providing a reduction of one third of tuition fees and four providing a reduction of one quarter of tuition fees may be awarded to external candidates aged 11+, 12+, 13+, or 14+.

In addition a Sixth Form Academic Scholarship – awarding up to one half of tuition fees – is open to all external candidates who are expected to be top achievers at GCSE. A Sixth Form Scholarship examination is held in the middle of March each year.

Art Scholarships: One scholarship providing a reduction of one third of tuition fees and one scholarship providing a reduction of one quarter of tuition fees may be awarded to candidates aged 11+, 12+, 13+ or 14+. Candidates must submit a portfolio and attend an Art Scholarship day, usually in early January.

Further details and an Art Scholarship application form are available from the Registrar.

Music Scholarships: Instrumental and Choral

Four music scholarships may be awarded annually, either for instrumentalists or choristers. Two scholarships offer a reduction of one third of tuition fees and two offer a reduction of one quarter of tuition fees.

Additionally, one scholarship, providing a reduction of one half of tuition fees may be awarded to an organ scholar, either internally or externally.

Timing of auditions is usually staggered over a week in early January. Further details and a Music Scholarship application form are available from the Registrar.

Sixth Form Sport Scholarship: A Senior Sport Scholarship offering a reduction of up to one half of tuition fees may be awarded to an internal or external candidate entering the Sixth Form. Full details are available from the Registrar.

Rishworth School (see p 825)
Scholarships & Bursaries are available, the former on merit, the latter for demonstrable financial need. The extent to which these awards can be offered will also be determined by other factors, such as the School's own circumstances and the nature of a given cohort of applicants.

Scholarships may be awarded, up to a value of 50% of Tuition fees, for excellence in academic work, sport, music or drama. For Year 7 entry scholarships, applicants are formally assessed. For Year 12 entry, awards are made on the basis of an individual's past record (including examination results).

Most awards are made to applicants at these entry levels. However, suitable candidates at any stage will be considered.

More information from: The Admissions Officer Rishworth School, Rishworth, West Yorkshire HX6 4QA. Tel: 01422 822217, Fax: 01422 820911, e-mail: admissions@rishworth-school.co.uk.

The Royal Wolverhampton School (see p 828)
Scholarships and Bursaries

Academic: Merit scholarships are available each year to pupils entering Senior School at age 11 or 13. Pupils gaining the best grades in the School's entrance examination will be awarded such scholarships.

Music: A certain number of Music scholarships are available to pupils entering Senior School at age 11 or 13. Such scholarships are awarded following an examination organised by the Director of Music. The audition consists of two contrasting pieces on the pupil's chosen instrument plus aural, listening and theory tests. Future musical potential is also assessed. Similar assessments take place for those with skills in Drama or Dance. The amount of the award can be up to 25% of school fees plus tuition in one instrument.

Sports: The School offers a small number of Sports scholarships. Candidates will be expected to have achieved distinction in at least one sport and show potential for future development. Candidates will be assessed by the Head of PE.

Sixth Form: Academic scholarships at Sixth form level are normally awarded on the basis of GCSE grades. The amount of the award depends upon the academic ability of the pupil concerned.

Orphan Foundation: Orphan Foundation Scholarships are available to children who have lost one or both parents, whose father or mother is incapacitated through illness or who are from single or divorced families. A need for a boarding education normally has to be established. Foundation Scholarship entry forms are available from the Clerk to the Governors.

Full details of Scholarships and Bursaries can be obtained from the Registrar. Awarding of such concessions takes full account of the Charity's requirement to deliver "public benefit".

Ruthin School (see p 830)
Academic Scholarships are offered for entry at 11, 13 and 16 and are worth up to a maximum of half-fees. Sixth Form scholarships are awarded on GCSE grades and subject papers taken during the year prior to entry. Auditions for the Music Scholarship (open to external candidates aged between 11 and 16) take place in the February of the year of entry. Drama, Sports, Art

and Design Technology Scholarships are also available. Further information may be obtained from the Headmaster, Ruthin School, Ruthin, Denbighshire LL15 1EE (Telephone: 01824 702543).

Saint Felix School (see p 835)
Saint Felix School seeks high-calibre candidates, who will contribute very positively and proactively to the life of the school community. The maximum award for an academic scholarship is 50% and for an exhibition 25% of the fees.

Academic awards at 11+ and 13+. All applicants will sit competitive academic examination papers. Awards will be made to high flying candidates, who demonstrate flair and the potential to excel in their academic studies. Exhibitions are awards given for candidates who show promise but do not attain the exacting standards demanded of scholars.

Margaret Isabella Gardiner Scholarship for candidates aged 11+ and 13+. Outstanding candidates may be eligible for this highly prestigious award, worth up to 75% of the fees. This scholarship will be awarded only to a candidate of sufficiently high calibre and not necessarily on an annual basis.

Examinations. Applicants for academic awards at 11+ and 13+ will sit examination papers in English, Mathematics, Science and Aptitude. Topics will be closely linked to those covered in Key Stages 2 and 3.

Music Scholarships for candidates in Year 5 to Year 10. These will be awarded on the basis of an audition, voice test and interview with the Director of Music and members of the Scholarship Selection Committee. Candidates will be asked to offer two instruments, one of which should be an orchestral instrument.

Sixth Form Scholarships and Exhibitions. Scholarships and exhibitions for Academic Studies, Art, Drama, Music and Sport are available for talented Sixth Form applicants, as the result of a competitive examination, trial or audition.

Full details of all awards, including Founder's Scholarships, Remissions and Swimming Scholarships may be obtained from the Registrar. Further information on Bursaries (available to current parents only) are available from the Bursar.

Scarborough College (see p 842)
A number of means-tested Scholarships and Exhibitions, normally up to the value of 30% of the fees, are offered each year for entry at 11, 13 and 16. Outstanding candidates are invited to the College for written papers and interview.

Shebbear College (see p 843)
Scholarships up to the value of half fees are awarded as follows:

(1) For the Junior Department: on interview and written assessment.
(2) At 11+: All candidates take the Entrance and Scholar-ship Examination in February.
(3) At 13+: The Scholarship Examination is held in the Spring Term. Awards are also made following Common Entrance Examination results.
(4) For Sixth Form candidates, scholarships are awarded on the basis of interview, school report and GCSE performance.

Further details may be obtained from the Registrar.

Sidcot School (see p 846)
There are several entrance scholarships available at age 11 and 13, of up to 50% of the boarding fees, awarded by competitive examination. Ten Sixth Form scholarships of 20% of the fees are awarded on the basis of GCSE results.

Sunderland High School (see p 849)
Entrance Scholarships are available at 11+. These are awarded on academic ability and are approximately 1/4 fees. Scholarships are also available to students wishing to join the School at 16+. These are awarded according to academic ability (interview and test).

A Music Scholarship of approximately 1/4 fees is available to pupils on entry to the School at age 11.

A reduction in fees is available to children of Clergy families and awarded by the United Church Schools Trust.

Thetford Grammar School (see p 851)
Within the limits of available funds the Governors are able to provide financial support with the fees in case of need. Such bursaries are based on a declaration of family income and can be up to 100% of the fees. They are available from Year 7 upwards. They are dependent of course on the pupil fulfilling the entrance requirements of the school. Six scholarships of an honorary nature will be awarded to the top performers in the entrance examinations. Music scholarships are available on entry in Year 7 or 9 which will provide free instrumental or voice tuition. Four scholarships are also available into the Sixth Form for both internal and external candidates. These can provide 25% reduction in fees for two years and are awarded as the result of a scholarship paper sat in January or in recognition of outstanding GCSE performance in the summer.

Details of all awards may be had from the Headmaster.

Wentworth College (see p 853)
Awards are offered to pupils who join the school at 11, 12 or 13+. They are awarded to students with all-round academic excellence or special ability in music, art or sport.

A Sixth Form award may also be available.

Children of ministers and lay members of the United Reformed and Congregational Churches may be eligible for a bursary from the Milton Mount Foundation.

We also offer bursaries to students whose parents are members of the Armed Forces.

Society of Headmasters and Headmistresses of Independent Schools

Additional Members

PETER JONES
Headmaster
Old Swinford Hospital, Heath Lane, Stourbridge, West Midlands DY8 1QX
Tel: 01384 817300, e-mail: reception@oshsch.com
website: www.oshsch.com

PAUL SPENCER ELLIS
Headmaster
Royal Alexandra and Albert School, Gatton Park, Reigate, Surrey RH2 0TD
Tel: 01737 649000, e-mail: admissions@gatton-park.org.uk
website: www.raa-school.co.uk

MELVYN ROFFE
Principal
Wymondham College, Wymondham, Norfolk NR18 9SZ
Tel: 01953 609000, e-mail: enquiries@wymondhamcollege.org
website: www.wymondhamcollege.org

Additional Members Overseas

WENDY ELLIS
Principal
The British International School Bratislava, Peknikova 6, 841 02 Bratislava, Slovakia
Tel: 00 421 2 6930 7081, e-mail: info@bisb.sk
website: www.bisb.sk

DR WALID EL-KHOURY
Principal
Brummana High School, PO Box 36, Brummana, Lebanon
Tel: 00 961 4 960 430/1/2, e-mail: info@bhs.edu.lb
website: www.bhs.edu.lb

ALASTAIR J REID
Principal
Hebron School, Lushington Hall, Ootacamund 643 001, Tamil Nadu, South India
Tel: 00 91 423 2442587, e-mail: admin@hebronooty.org
website: www.hebronooty.org

AMY FAFA AWOONOR
Head
The Roman Ridge School, PO Box GP 21057, Accra, Ghana
Tel: 00 233 21 780456/780457, e-mail: enquiries@theromanridgeschool.com
website: www.theromanridgeschool.com

ADRIAN PALMER
Headmaster
St Andrew's Senior School Turi, Private Bag, Molo 20106, Kenya
Tel: 00 254 51 721283, e-mail: office@turimail.co.ke
website: www.standrews-turi.com

PART IV

Schools whose Heads are members of IAPS (Independent Association of Prep Schools)

ALPHABETICAL LIST OF SCHOOLS

* co-educational schools

GEOGRAPHICAL LIST OF IAPS SCHOOLS

Alphabetical List of IAPS Heads

The following is a list of IAPS member Heads and Deputy Heads of Schools appearing on pages 877–1124.

Individual School Entries

Abberley Hall

Worcester WR6 6DD
Tel: 01299 896275
Fax: 01299 896875
e-mail: john.walker@abberleyhall.co.uk
website: www.abberleyhallschool.co.uk

Chairman of Governors: The Hon David Legh

***Headmaster*: J G W Walker**, BSc QTS University of Surrey

Assistant Headmaster: R Wesley, BEd Cheltenham

Age Range. 2–13.

Number of Pupils. Prep School: 197 (133 Boys, 64 Girls; 115 Boarders, 82 Day Pupils).

Pre-Prep & Nursery: 94 (57 Boys, 35 Girls).

Fees per term (2007-2008). Prep: Boarders £5,490, Day Pupils £4,100–£4,380. Pre-Prep: £1,090–£2,450.

Abberley Hall is co-educational. It is situated 12 miles north-west of Worcester, with easy access to the M5. It is a boarding school for boys and girls aged 8–13 years, and is set in 100 acres of gardens and wooded grounds amid magnificent countryside.

Pupils are prepared for all Independent Senior Schools. Although there is no entry examination, the school has a strong academic tradition with consistently good results in scholarships and Common Entrance, thanks to a highly-qualified staff, favourable teacher/pupil ratios and small classes. This also helps encourage the slower learners, for whom individual attention is available.

The school's facilities include an indoor swimming pool, a chapel, library, music school and concert studio; two new science laboratories, technology room, DT centre and extensively equipped computer centre; an art studio and pottery rooms; a multi-purpose hall with permanent stage, rifle range and climbing wall; a sports hall, hard tennis courts, a Ricochet court and ample playing fields for the major games and athletics, including a large Astroturf pitch. The school also owns its own French chalet where children go on three-week blocks for total immersion into the French language and way of life.

The pupils are also encouraged to take part in a wide range of hobbies and activities including archery, chess, fishing, golf, horse riding, fencing, model-making, printing, ballet, mountain-biking, woodwork and many more.

The school aims to combine a friendly atmosphere with the discipline which enables pupils to achieve their full potential and learn to feel responsibility for themselves and others.

Charitable status. Abberley Hall is a Registered Charity, number 527598. Its aim is to further good education.

The Abbey

Church Street Woodbridge Suffolk IP12 1DS
Tel: 01394 382673
Fax: 01394 383880
e-mail: office@theabbeyschool-suffolk.org.uk
website: www.woodbridge.suffolk.sch.uk/the_abbey

Chairman of the Governors: Air Vice-Marshal P J Goddard, CB, AFC, FRAeS, RAF (Retd)

***The Master*: N J Garrett**, BA, PGCE

Age Range. Co-educational 4–11.

Number of Pupils. 330 Day pupils.

Fees per term (2008-2009). Pre-Prep £2,200; Prep £3,300.

Religious affiliation. Church of England (other denominations accepted).

Entry requirements. Entrance test according to age.

The Abbey is the Preparatory School for Woodbridge School for which boys and girls are prepared for entry. A small number of pupils go elsewhere. There is a highly qualified teaching staff of thirty, with additional visiting music and other specialist teachers. The academic record has been consistently good: scholarships are won regularly both to Woodbridge and to other schools. The teaching is linked to the National Curriculum and emphasis is placed on pupils reaching their full academic potential whilst also benefiting from a broad education. The school enjoys strong links with a number of European schools and exchange visits take place. Music is regarded as an important part of school life with a large number of pupils receiving individual music lessons and in Year Four all pupils receive strings tuition as well as their class music lessons. In Games lessons boys play soccer, rugby, hockey and cricket and girls play netball, hockey and rounders. Children also have the opportunity to swim, play tennis and take part in athletics, cross-country, horse riding and sailing. In lunch breaks and after school, pupils are able to participate in a whole range of extra-curricular activities and hobbies.

The School is set in its own beautiful grounds of 30 acres in the middle of the town. Apart from the fine Tudor Manor house, it has a well-planned and high quality classroom and changing room block. Another major development includes a multi-purpose hall and classroom block. Recent developments have included an upgrade of Music, ICT, Art, DT and Science facilities. The grounds are extensive and include playing fields, an all weather surface games area and a science garden. The Pre-Prep Department is at Queen's House, situated on the periphery of the Senior School's grounds, a short walk from The Abbey. Here the pupils enjoy spacious accommodation and excellent facilities. The Department is led by Mrs Jan King.

Parents of Abbey pupils are eligible to join the Parents' Association and there is a close contact maintained between parents and school.

Charitable status. The Seckford Foundation is a Registered Charity, number 1110964. It exists to provide education for boys and girls.

Abercorn School

Infants: 28 Abercorn Place London NW8 9XP
Tel: 020 7286 4785
Fax: 020 7266 0219
e-mail: a.greystoke@abercornschool.com

Lower Prep: The Old Grammar School 248 Marylebone Road London NW1 6JF
Tel: 020 7723 8700
e-mail: togs@abercornschool.com

Upper Prep: 7b Wyndham Place London W1H 1PN
Tel: 020 7616 8989
e-mail: wyndham@abercornschool.com
website: www.abercornschool.com

***High Mistress*: Mrs A Greystoke**, BA Hons

Age Range. 2½ to 13+ Co-educational.
Number of Pupils. 390.
Fees per term (2008-2009). £2,345–£4,345. Fees include all extras, apart from lunch.

Abercorn School provides quality education in a happy caring atmosphere. Both branches are housed in gracious Victorian listed mansions. Children are in the senior building from age 6+.

Pupils flourish in the small classes (average size is 16) and the high degree of specialist teaching. As a result, the children achieve excellent entrance results to further schools, including St Paul's, North London Collegiate, South Hampstead High School and Westminster.

Before and after school care is available.

Aberdour School

Burgh Heath Nr Tadworth Surrey KT20 6AJ
Tel: 01737 354119
Fax: 01737 363044
e-mail: enquiries@aberdourschool.co.uk
website: www.aberdourschool.co.uk

The School is an Educational Trust run by a Board of Governors.

Chairman of the Governors: R C Nicol, Esq, FCA

***Headmaster*: Mr S D Collins**

Deputy Headmaster: R G Moss, BA Hons, PGCE
Deputy Headmaster: G Clark, BEd Hons
Deputy Headmistress: Mrs T Thomas, BEd Hons
Head of the Pre-Preparatory School: Mrs K Evans, BEd Hons, RSADipSpLD

Age Range. 2–13.
Number of Pupils. 259 Day Boys and Girls.
Fees per term (2008-2009). £925–£3,430 fully inclusive.

Children are taken at 2 years old into the pre-preparatory department and transfer to the preparatory school at age 7. Children are prepared for all the major Senior Schools and many scholarships have been won. A special point is made of music. There is a school orchestra and a concert band as well as a large school choir. There are ample playing fields with a large sports hall and indoor heated swimming pool. There are two science laboratories and a design technology room. All the usual games are coached and the general character of the children is developed by many interests and activities.

Charitable status. Aberdour School Educational Trust Limited is a Registered Charity, number 312033. Its aim is to promote education.

Abingdon Preparatory School

Josca's House Kingston Road Frilford Abingdon Oxon OX13 5NX
Tel: 01865 391570
Fax: 01865 391042
e-mail: registrar@abingdonprep.org.uk
website: www.abingdonprep.org.uk

The School was founded in 1956. In 1998 it merged with Abingdon School to become part of one Charitable Foundation with a single Board of Governors.

Chairman of the Governors: Mr C R Dick, MA, CEng

***Head Master*: C J Davies**, BA, PGCE

Age Range. 4–13.
Number of Pupils. 250 Day Boys.
Fees per term (2008-2009). £3,090–£3,470.

Main entry points are at age four and seven. Boys are prepared for senior school entrance examinations. A strong majority goes on to Abingdon School.

Abingdon Preparatory School is a thinking and learning school – as well as a teaching school. Pupils' needs are served by providing a happy and stimulating environment where the children are encouraged to develop self-reliance and a sense of responsibility. Considerable emphasis is placed on helping pupils to develop good working patterns together with sound organisational and learning skills.

The school opened stunning new facilities in September 2007, which include new classrooms, an art studio, sports hall and changing rooms. There has also been substantial refurbishment to many of the existing facilities such as the swimming pool, library, CDT and classrooms. Current facilities include new computer and science laboratories, a multi-purpose hall, and a substantial music department.

Sport is a major strength of the school outside the classroom. The splendid amenities, which include an indoor swimming pool, thirty acres of playing fields and an adventure playground, enable every child to participate in a wide range of sports and activities. There are regular fixtures against local schools in the main school sports of rugby, football, cricket, tennis, and athletics. All pupils swim at least once a week. There is a range of after-school hobby clubs, which includes amongst many others, orchestra, choir, art, science, judo, golf, fencing, gardening, chess, computers and drama.

A regular number of academic, music, drama and all-rounder awards are gained every year – the majority to the senior school, Abingdon.

A large number of trips are organised for all year groups during the year and the oldest boys go abroad for a week on completing their Common Entrance examinations.

Charitable status. Abingdon School is a Registered Charity, number 1071298. It exists to provide for the education of children aged 4–18.

Aiglon College Junior School

CH-1885 Chesières-Villars Switzerland
Tel: 00 41 24 496 6161
Fax: 00 41 24 496 6142
e-mail: info@aiglon.ch
website: www.aiglon.ch

Chairman of Governors: Mr Peter Armitage

***Headmaster*: Didier Boutroux**, L-ès-L, M-ès-L (Nancy)

Age Range. 9–13.
Number of Pupils. Boys 40, Girls 40, Boarders 55, Day Children 25.

Fees per annum (2007-2008). (CHF): Day children: 27,000–36,800; Weekly boarders: 44,300–47,800; Full boarders: 50,300–55,800.

Setting. The Aiglon College Junior School provides a warm family atmosphere in the beauty and peace of the Swiss Alps for children from all over the world – with around 25 different nationalities. The intimate and caring community spirit encourages self-discipline, thought for others and joy in learning. Aiglon College Junior School's buildings and life are kept quite separate from those of the Senior school. However, it shares part of the campus of Aiglon College, and follows the principles of the founder, John Corlette. Ultimately we aim at ensuring a smooth and well-prepared transition into the Senior School.

Pastoral Care. Having a place of their own allows us to concentrate on issues most significant to this age group, such as creating and developing good habits in a positive and encouraging environment. Our main goal is to create a caring environment and, through carefully chosen experiences, build up the whole person and develop the many talents that all our pupils possess. We also aim at making the transition from Junior to Senior School a comfortable one. Learning to live and grow up with peers, listening to each other, and acquiring a taste for discovery and independence within a supportive environment; all these skills contribute, using moral and spiritual beliefs in a constructive way, to the foundation of a healthy attitude towards the challenges of teenage life. Moral principles are developed within school "meditations" (morning assemblies) especially and spiritual life is encouraged in chapel services.

Curriculum. For children aged between 9 and 11 whose mother tongue is English or French, lessons are taught in either of the two languages. French, Geography and History are taught in French, while the other subjects are taught in English. The school also offers an ESL programme for all non-English speakers aged 10–12. From age 11, the Junior School curriculum includes English, Maths, French, Science, Geography, History, Art, Music, Physical Education, Drama, Religious Studies and ICT. Strong pastoral care and individual attention allows for a curriculum which has its roots in the British National Curriculum but caters for the international diversity of our recruitment. The Learning Support department aids children with special learning needs and tests all children on a yearly basis.

Sports and expeditions. Sports and "expeditions" form an essential component of a well-rounded approach to the development of our children's personality and character. There is a range of sports teams to choose from and we encourage full participation. "Expeditions" take place at weekends and activities include walking, map reading and orienteering, cycling, canoeing, gorge walking and rock climbing. Children participate in camping, hiking or skiing "expeditions" under expert and qualified supervision. Apart from learning to enjoy and understand nature, being outdoors together, come rain or shine, reinforces children's team spirit and respect for each other and their environment as they learn to live a little closer to nature!

Extra curricular activities. There is a wide variety of extra-curricular activities called "Options", which encompass sports, art and craft activities, music clubs, choir and bands (including a Samba & Salsa Band), as well as quieter pastimes.

Further information. Further information may be obtained from the Headmaster or the Director of Admissions.

Aiglon College is a non-profit making organisation, accredited by ECIS.

Aldenham Preparatory School

Aldenham Road Elstree Herts WD6 3AJ
Tel: 01923 851664
Fax: 01923 854410
e-mail: prepschool@aldenham.com
website: www.aldenham.com

Chairman of Board of Governors: J S Lewis, DL, FCIS

***Head of Preparatory School*: K J Whiskerd**, BA

Age Range. 3–11.

Number of Pupils. Total 171: 111 Boys, 60 Girls.

Fees per term (2008-2009). Nursery: £21.68 (per morning or afternoon session); Pre-Prep: £3,041; Prep: £3,363.

At Aldenham Preparatory School, we provide a warm, happy and nurturing environment where quality learning takes place and the needs of each individual child are fulfilled.

The Preparatory School is a co-educational day school encompassing the Nursery (3–4 years), the Pre-Prep Department (4–7 years) and the Prep Department (7–11 years). It forms an integral part of the main school which was established in 1597 and remains on the same glorious site, set in over 100 acres of countryside yet only 12 miles from the centre of London.

Our primary aim is to provide an excellent all round education, presenting all of our pupils with exceptional opportunities. The school is dedicated to ensuring the flexibility for each child to develop their own individual abilities, whether they are academic, creative or sporting. We offer high quality teaching from enthusiastic, motivated and caring staff.

An inspection commissioned by the Independent Schools Inspectorate (ISI) praised the school for being "*. . . a lively, happy community in which young children thrive. They benefit from a high standard of education and very good care in all year groups. Children's attitude to learning and their behaviour are exemplary. Relationships between children and staff are friendly and courteous.*"

We believe that the pastoral care at Aldenham is second to none, providing the children with a nurturing environment in which they flourish. We also place great importance on personal and social growth and strive to ensure that our pupils are confident and responsible members of the community.

Small class sizes (16 in the Pre-Prep and 20 in the Prep) and expert teaching from an early age ensure that academic attainment is high. The requirements of the National Curriculum and preparation for entry into senior schools are blended into a broad based curriculum. This along with an excellent staff/pupil ratio enriches our children's learning and encourages them to work to the very best of their ability.

The accommodation for both Pre-Prep and Prep Departments is first class with pupils resident in newly purpose-built classrooms, having access to their own science and DT laboratory, library, music rooms and computer suite. We are also able to share the Aldenham School campus as a whole, enabling us to enjoy use of the extensive grounds and facilities, including the Sports Complex, Artificial Turf Pitch, Music School, Chapel, Dining Hall and School Hall. (*For further information about the senior school, see Aldenham School entry in HMC section.*)

We have high expectations of all our pupils and encourage initiative, independence and self-confidence. We also insist on good manners and consideration for others, as a result there is a strong sense of community at Aldenham.

Entry is primarily at 4+, although there are also a number of places available at 7+.

Our excellent established Nursery facilities provide a structured lively and stimulating introduction to Aldenham School with morning and afternoon classes or full day care.

Charitable status. The Aldenham School Company is a Registered Charity, number 298140. It exists to provide high quality education and pastoral care to enable children to achieve their full potential in later life.

Aldro

Lombard Street Shackleford Godalming Surrey GU8 6AS
Tel: 01483 409020 (Headmaster and Admissions)
01483 810266 (School Office)
Fax: 01483 409010
e-mail: hmsec@aldro.org
website: www.aldro.org

Chairman of the Governors: M W Sayers

***Headmaster*: David W N Aston**, BA, PGCE

Age Range. 7–13.

Number of Boys. 220: 60 Boarders, 160 Day.

Fees per term (2008-2009). £6,265 (Boarders), £4,870 (Dayboys) inclusive.

Aldro is a boys' boarding and day prep school set in a beautiful rural location yet within a mile of the A3 and 45 minutes of central London, Gatwick and Heathrow airports.

Aldro aims to offer boys an exceptional all-round education in a happy, purposeful community. It has a Christian foundation and this underpins the values and ethos of the school. Each school day starts with a short service in the lovely Chapel, beautifully converted from an eighteenth century barn.

The school is fortunate in having a spacious site including a lake and about 30 acres of playing fields. There are also four hard tennis courts, a squash court, two shooting ranges and a covered games area. The facilities are excellent and there has been much investment in new buildings over the past ten years. The Centenary Building opened in 2000 and houses most of the classrooms, the ICT centre, an outstanding library and, in the basement, changing rooms and a large common room. The Crispin Hill Centre incorporates a Music School, theatre and sports hall. Two science laboratories and the Art and Design Technology Centre have been developed in eighteenth century buildings either side of the Chapel. The Argyle Building including a new dining hall and kitchen was opened in late 2003. The dormitories in the main building have recently been refurbished. The boarders enjoy high quality pastoral care and a varied programme of activities in the evenings and at weekends.

In the classroom, there is a balance between the best traditional and modern approaches, whilst firm and friendly encouragement of each individual has led to an outstanding academic record of success at Common Entrance and Scholarship level. Thirty academic awards have been won in the last four years to leading schools such as Charterhouse, Eton, Sherborne, Winchester, Radley, Shrewsbury and Wellington College.

Aldro is committed to giving boys real breadth to their education and much emphasis is placed on extra-curricular activities. There are many opportunities for the arts, with a good record of success in Art and Music scholarships – 20 awards have been won in the past four years. Many boys learn musical instruments and there are three choirs, two orchestras and numerous ensembles. Drama also features prominently with several productions each year.

The major sports are rugby, soccer and hockey in the winter, with cricket in the summer. Athletics, tennis, swimming, cross-country running, squash and shooting are secondary sports and high standards are achieved. A huge range of activities are available including cubs and scouts, badminton, bottle digging, fly fishing and petanque. The school has an enviable record for Chess with 8 teams winning National championships in the past five years.

Boys at Aldro are treated as individuals with talents to develop. They lead cheerful and purposeful lives, and are well-prepared for a wide range of leading senior schools.

Charitable status. Aldro School Educational Trust Limited is a Registered Charity, number 312072. It exists to provide education for boys.

Aldwickbury School

Wheathampstead Road Harpenden Herts AL5 1AE
Tel: 01582 713022
Fax: 01582 767696
e-mail: head@aldwickbury.herts.sch.uk
website: www.aldwickbury.org.uk

Chairman of Governors: N Buchanan, Esq

***Headmaster*: V W Hales**, BEd (Exeter)

Age Range. 4–13.

Number of Boys. Main School: 220 (including 35 weekly boarders). Pre-Prep: 96.

Fees per term (2007-2008). Boarders £4,067–£4,097; Day Boys: Main School £3,195–£3,225; Pre-Prep £2,745.

Boys are prepared for Independent Schools' Entrance and Scholarship examinations at 13 plus.

There is a full-time teaching staff of 31, with qualified visiting teachers for remedial work, speech training, singing, woodwork, piano, and orchestral instruments. Art, music, drama, IT and CDT are included in the curriculum.

Many boys board in their final years and they are all encouraged to take part in a wide variety of activities throughout their time in the school.

The School is exceptionally well equipped. Recent additions include two new classroom blocks, a block for science, computing and music, a Gymnasium, a heated indoor Swimming Pool, a Hall and Chapel and a new kitchen. The playing fields are on the spot and large enough for all boys to play games every day. Boys are taught Association and Rugby Football, Hockey, Athletics, Cricket, Swimming, Gymnastics, Tennis and Basketball. Skiing parties are taken to the Alps during the Christmas holidays.

The Pre-Preparatory Department is accommodated in a building opened in 2001.

Charitable status. Aldwickbury School Trust Ltd is a Registered Charity, number 311059. It exists to provide education for children.

Alice Smith Primary School

2 Jalan Bellamy 50460 Kuala Lumpur Malaysia
Tel: 00 603 2148 3674
Fax: 00 603 2148 3418
e-mail: klass@alice-smith.edu.my
website: www.alice-smith.edu.my

Chairman of Governors: Mr Andrew Barber

***Principal*: Steve Caulfield**, BSc Hons, MEd, LPSH

Age Range. 3–11.

Number of Pupils. 780 (Pre-School to Year 6).

Fees per term (2008-2009). Pre-School RM7,100, Reception RM10,000, Years 1–2 RM10,500, Years 3–6 RM10,800.

Location. The Alice Smith Primary School at Jalan Bellamy is situated in a beautiful area adjacent to the Royal Palace, just 10–15 minutes from the major residential suburbs on the west side of the capital.

Facilities. The Primary School offers a specialised learning environment and benefits from the following facilities:

- Well-resourced, air-conditioned classrooms and large shared year group learning areas
- Gymnasium
- 3 Libraries
- Design & Technology Room
- Multi-purpose Hall
- Hard and grassed playing areas
- 20m swimming pool
- Playground with climbing frames
- 3 ICT suites
- New purpose-built Years 5 and 6 Block
- New purpose-built Years 3 and 4 Block

Curriculum. We offer a rigorous British education in an international context while celebrating the culture and natural environment of our hosts, the people of Malaysia. The English National Curriculum enables us to develop the essential knowledge, skills and concepts our international students need in a broad programme that encompasses English, Mathematics, Science, Design Technology, Information Technology,

Modern Foreign Languages (from Year 4), History, Geography, Music, Drama and Physical Education.

Children have specialist teachers for Music, Physical Education, Learning Support, Foreign Languages and Swimming. All classes carry a maximum of 22.

The school undertakes the NCT assessments in Years 2 and 6 and the non-statutory NCT tests for Years 3, 4 and 5. Standards and expectations are high and regular In-service Training and Inspections are undertaken with UK based Inspectors/Advisory teams.

Staff. At the heart of a good school is the staff, both teaching and non-teaching. Our teaching staff are well qualified, caring and experienced professionals, recruited mainly from the UK.

All classes benefit from a full-time assistant in addition to the class teacher.

Extra-curricular programme. Our main curriculum is enhanced by a full programme of extra-curricular sporting, performance and cultural activities. Older children are regular participants in National and International expeditions, competitions and trips, while our younger students participate in frequent visits to local places of interest. A busy Saturday Sports programme ensures children have recreational opportunities on many Saturdays throughout each term. An intensive after-school swim programme exists for a Torpedoes Club, who train 5 evenings a week.

All Hallows School

Cranmore Hall Shepton Mallet Somerset BA4 4SF
Tel: 01749 880227
Fax: 01749 880709
e-mail: info@allhallowsschool.co.uk
website: www.allhallows.somerset.sch.uk

***Headmaster*: I A Murphy**, BA Hons (Durham), PGCE (Durham)

Age Range. 4–13 Co-educational.

Number of Pupils. 285. Boys: Boarding 35, Day 120. Girls: Boarding 25, Day 105.

Fees per term (2008-2009). Boarding £5,700, Day £3,800 (over 7), £1,950 (under 7). There are no compulsory extras.

True education is preparation for life in all its facets. It is all the better if it's also challenging, exciting, caring and great fun. We strive for the academic achievement of each individual to go hand-in-hand with spiritual growth, friendship, confidence, respect and a sheer love of life.

All Hallows pioneered Catholic boarding co-education for preparatory school age children and the school continues to be very innovative and quite distinct.

Christian principles are integrated into daily life so that all denominations are welcomed into the ecumenical life of this Roman Catholic foundation. Professionally qualified, energetic and family-orientated staff, many of whom reside in the school, provide for the academic and pastoral welfare of the children.

Distinctive opportunities, at no extra cost, exist for both the academically gifted and those with learning difficulties through the Learning Support Centre and/or specialist teachers. The school has a happy and deliberate mix of boarders and day pupils. Attractive flexibility exists between boarding and day arrangements. There is an extensive and exciting Activities Programme for all children each evening after school, with weekend highlights.

The school enjoys regional and national sporting success in rugby, hockey, tennis and athletics, as well as regular competitive fixtures for children of all abilities against local opposition in the traditional team sports. Excellence within a framework of sport for all is our aim. Riding, golf and fencing are activities that are becoming increasingly popular. Our Tennis Academy attracts some of the most gifted players in the region and other talented children from other parts of the country, but it is available to every child in the school.

Music and the Arts thrive, ranging from the grace of the chapel choir to the creativity and performance of dance and drama. Exceptional facilities allow the children and staff to discover talent and develop potential, including an astroturf, floodlit tennis courts, sports hall, covered swimming pool, cycle track, Chapel, art studio, brand new classroom block, networked information technology centre and three impressive science laboratories. We are able to offer a specific environmental education, utilising the school's special outdoor teaching area and private wood. Our Junior children follow a specific Forest School curriculum also.

All Hallows' independent status from any one particular senior school, plus adherence to the Common Entrance and prep schools' scholarship syllabus, enables parents and the Headmaster to select the most appropriate senior school to suit a particular child's needs and talents. In the last few years we have sent pupils to over forty different schools. 2007 witnessed an impressive scholarship record, 40% of the leavers! We offer a range of scholarships and bursaries.

Charitable status. All Hallows is a Registered Charity, number 310281. The school is a Charitable Trust, the raison d'être of which is the integration of Christian principles with daily life.

Alleyn Court Preparatory School

Wakering Road Southend-on-Sea Essex SS3 0PW
Tel: 01702 582553
Fax: 01702 584574
e-mail: acitsuite@tiscali.co.uk
website: www.alleyn-court.co.uk

***Headteacher*: Mr G Davies**, BA, PGCE

Age Range. 2½–11.

Number of Pupils. 311 Boys and Girls.

Fees per term (from April 2008). £1,643–£2,829 according to age.

Throughout the school pupils learn to live as members of a community while developing their individual personalities in a happy and structured environment. Former pupils make an outstanding contribution to local and national life: there are two present MPs, a member of the House of Lords, a novelist of international renown, a prize-winning playwright, a pop star and international representatives in all major sports. The school celebrated its centenary two years ago.

Admission is between 2½ and 4 years to the Pre-Prep Department and at 5 years to the Main School (or at other ages by arrangement). Entry is by interview; there are no tests applied. Pupils are prepared for local selective school examinations at 11+ and for entrance and scholarship entry to independent schools. French is taught from 4 years. Scholarships to major independent schools and results of National Curriculum Tests are consistently above the national average.

Academic facilities include: library, fully equipped science laboratory, modern computer suite with 21 multimedia computers and internet access, Arts Centre.

Sports facilities include: extensive playing fields, Sports Hall, cricket nets, tennis courts, cross-country course.

Other facilities include: attractive grounds, dining hall, 200 seat assembly hall.

Extra-curricular activities include: art, drama, computers, dance, chess as well as various sports training sessions.

Academic, Artistic, Music and Sports scholarships are available annually for pupils aged between 6 and 9 years. Some Bursaries are available according to need.

Pre-Prep. Located on the main site and on a separate site in Westcliff, the twin Pre-Prep departments offer an education based on Montessori principles for boys and girls $2^1/_2$–5 years old.

Alleyn's Junior School

Townley Road Dulwich London SE22 8SU
Tel: 020 8557 1519
Fax: 020 8693 3597
e-mail: juniorschool@alleyns.org.uk
website: www.alleynsjunior.org.uk

Chairman of Governors: R J R Cousins, BSc Eng, FICE, FRSA

Headmaster: **Mark O'Donnell**, BA, PGDDes, MSc Arch, EdM Harv, PGDES Oxon

Age Range. 4–11.

Number of Pupils. 224 boys and girls.

Fees per term (2008-2009). £3,567-£3,714 to include lunches and out of school visits.

The school is part of the foundation known as 'Alleyn's College of God's Gift' which was founded by Edward Alleyn, the Elizabethan actor, in 1619.

Opened in 1992 to provide a co-educational Junior School for Alleyn's School and sharing the same excellent green site, Alleyn's Junior School provides a happy and lively environment in which well-qualified teachers and well-motivated boys and girls follow a broad and academic education. Boys and girls work together with their teachers in a calm and structured way to develop their potential and self-confidence as they pursue the highest standards across a curriculum which embraces many opportunities for Art, German, drama, music, French, ICT and a wide range of sports. Entry to the school is at 4+, 7+ and 9+. The overwhelming majority of our children move on to Alleyn's senior school at 11+.

Within small classes and with a balance of class and specialist subject teaching, children are set clear and challenging targets for their learning. Children perform at above average level in KS1 and KS2 tests. The school enjoys a strong extra-curricular life offering children varied and exciting opportunities to extend their learning beyond the classroom.

Progress is carefully monitored and individual differences appropriately met. Competition has its place in the encouragement of the highest academic, artistic and sporting standards, but it is always tempered by an emphasis on values of thoughtfulness, courtesy and tolerance. All members of the school community are expected to maintain high standards in their behaviour, manners and appearance, showing pride in themselves and their school.

The school enjoys excellent support from its parent body. Regular meetings and reports keep parents informed of academic progress and pastoral matters and The Alleyn's Junior School Association works tirelessly to promote social cohesion within the school and to support the charity, sporting, dramatic and extra-curricular programmes. It also organises an After School Care scheme through which children can be supervised at school each day during term time until 6 pm.

Charitable status. Alleyn's College of God's Gift is a Registered Charity, number 1057971. Its purpose is to provide independent education for boys and girls.

Alpha Preparatory School

Hindes Road Harrow Middlesex HA1 1SH
Tel: 020 8427 1471
Fax: 020 8424 9324
e-mail: sec@alpha.harrow.sch.uk
website: www.alpha.harrow.sch.uk

Chairman of the Board of Governors: Mr A Bloom

***Headmaster*: P J Wylie**, BA, CertEd

Age Range. 3–11.

Number of Pupils. 200 boys and girls (day only).

Fees per term (2007-2008). Inclusive of lunch, with no compulsory extras: Nursery £810–£1,775; Pre-Preparatory £2,350; Main School £2,570.

The School, situated in a residential area of Harrow, was founded in 1895, and in 1950 was reorganised as a non-profit-making Educational Charity, with a Board of Governors elected by members of the Company; parents of pupils in the School are eligible for membership.

The majority of children enter the Main School at the age of 4 by interview and assessment but there can also be a few vacancies for older pupils and here entry is by interview and/or written tests, dependent upon age.

There is a full-time staff of 16 experienced and qualified teachers, with additional part-time teachers in instrumental Music. The main games are Football and Cricket, with cross-country, athletics, tennis and netball. Extra-curricular activities include Drama, Piano and Violin instruction.

Religious education, which is considered important, is non-sectarian in nature, but follows upon the School's Christian foundation and tradition; children of all faiths are accepted.

Outside visits to theatres, concerts and museums form an integral part of the curriculum and during the Lent Term pupils in Year 6 visit the Isle of Wight.

Regular successes are obtained in Entrance and Scholarship examinations, with many Scholarships having been won in recent years.

The School has its own Nursery (Alphabets) for children aged 3 in the term of entry. Further details can be obtained from the Registration Secretary.

Charitable status. Alpha Preparatory School is a Registered Charity, number 312640. It exists to carry on the undertaking of a boys and/or girls preparatory school in Harrow in the County of Middlesex.

Amesbury

Hazel Grove Hindhead Surrey GU26 6BL
Tel: 01428 604322
Fax: 01428 607715
e-mail: enquiries@amesburyschool.co.uk
website: www.amesburyschool.co.uk

Chairman of the Governors: D Wenman

Headmaster: **Nigel Taylor**, MA

Age Range. 2–13.

Number of Pupils. Main School: 225 Day pupils. Pre-Preparatory Department: 100 Day pupils.

Fees per term (2008-2009). Day Pupils £3,520–£3,825, Pre-Prep £2,495.

Amesbury is a co-educational day school founded in 1870. The main building is unique, as the only school to be designed by Sir Edwin Lutyens, and stands in its own 34-acre estate in the heart of the Surrey countryside.

Classes are small guaranteeing individual attention. Study programmes currently lead to Common Entrance or senior school scholarship examinations at 11+ (for girls only) and at 13+ (for girls and boys). We have a proud tradition of academic, sporting and artistic achievement. The school has excellent purpose-built facilities.

For further information please contact the Headmaster's Secretary.

Charitable status. Amesbury School is a Registered Charity, number 312058. It exists to provide education for boys and girls. It is administered by a Board of Governors.

Appleford School

Shrewton Nr Salisbury Wiltshire SP3 4HL
Tel: 01980 621020
Fax: 01980 621366
e-mail: secretary@appleford.wilts.sch.uk
website: www.appleford.wilts.sch.uk

***Headmistress*: Ms S M Wilson**

Age Range. 7–13, Boarders from 7.

Number of Pupils. 34 (day), 59 (boarding). Girls 18, Boys 76.

Fees per term (2008-2009). Day £4,877; Boarding £7,177.

Founded in 1988, Appleford is a co-educational boarding and day specialist school for pupils aged 7–13. Teaching is in small groups.

Appleford School provides a stimulating, structured and varied curriculum for the dyslexic child, with the emphasis on literacy and numeracy skills.

Appleford offers a whole-school approach to Dyslexia:

- research-backed multi-sensory programmes designed to encourage increased self-confidence and self-esteem
- on site Speech and Language Therapy and Occupational Therapy
- qualified DCSF teachers with a high ratio of specialist qualifications
- experienced and caring houseparents in friendly, structured boarding houses, encouraging the development of personal organisation and life skills within individual care plans
- an extensive games and fixtures programme, numerous challenging and exciting after-school activities from art to archery, cooking to croquet, putting to pottery. Judo, swimming and tennis also take place after school. Participation in music and drama is encouraged. There is a carefully planned and stimulating weekend programme for the full boarder.

Appleford is approved by the Council for the Registration of Schools Teaching Dyslexic Children (CReSTeD) and the DCSF and accredited by the Independent Schools Council. It is a Corporate Member of the British Dyslexia Association and accredited by IAPS.

Appleford's stated aim is to return the pupils to mainstream education as soon as possible and, since its foundation, over 80% of the children have achieved this goal. Some dyslexic pupils still need considerable support at senior school and advice is given on future placements. It is crucial that the foundations laid at Appleford are carefully and sympathetically built upon at the next stage of education.

Aravon Preparatory School

Old Conna House Bray Co Wicklow Ireland
Tel: 00 353 1 282 1355
Fax: 00 353 1 282 1242
e-mail: aravon@indigo.ie
website: www.aravon.ie

The oldest school of its kind in Ireland, Aravon was founded in 1862.

It is a Charitable, Educational and Scientific Trust administered by a Board of Governors.

***Principal*: Mr K W J Allwright**

Location. Aravon is located 2.5 km from Bray, approximately 19.5 km south-east of Dublin City and three-quarters of an hour from Dublin Airport.

The house stands on an elevated site overlooking 15 acres of terraced lawns and playing fields. It is surrounded by mature woodland and an 18 hole Championship golf course.

The school has seven newly-built classrooms, independent from the main building.

Pupils. Inter-Denominational, Co-Educational, Boarding and Weekly Boarding (from 9 to 12 years) and Day Preparatory School (from 4 to 12 years). Pre-School Montessori (3–4 years), and Extended Day available from 1–5.30 pm.

Syllabus. All pupils are prepared for entry to Irish Secondary and all independent senior schools. The Irish National Curriculum is followed.

The range of core subjects taught at Infant level is extended to encompass additional French and Irish: Junior Science, Mathematics, English, History, Geography, RE and Recorder from Forms I to III; Experimental Science (Physics, Chemistry and Biology) Forms IV to VI. In addition each form averages two periods of Art per week.

Outings to Theatres and Concerts are considered an integral part of the English and Music curricula, developing an early appreciation of Literature and the Arts. Outings are also arranged throughout the year by the Geography, History and Science Departments, and the Languages Department has cultural exchanges with overseas schools.

Science. Large, well equipped laboratory. General Science is taught in Forms I to IV and Experimental Science – Physics/Chemistry/Biology in Forms V to VI.

Computers. Computer studies are a part of the curriculum for all pupils. There is a well-equipped computer room and all classes are equipped with their own computer on the network. There are five interactive whiteboards.

Languages. Irish and French from Junior Infants to Form VI. Annual Exchanges with a school in Bourg en Bresse for senior pupils, and several days in an Irish speaking area of Ireland. Bi-annual trip to Gaeltacht school is undertaken in top classes.

Drama. Drama is an integral part of language teaching and there is also a major school production every year and each child is involved in some way in productions through the year.

Special Needs. Full time professional Remedial help is available as an extra for those pupils who require it.

Music. School Orchestra, Chamber Groups, Senior and Junior Choirs, a Chamber Choir. A wide range of musical instruments is taught: Flute, Oboe, Clarinet, 'Cello, Violin, Viola, Piano, Guitar, Recorders and Percussion.

Sports. Hockey, rugby, cricket, tennis, football, basketball, athletics, netball, PE, cross-country running, swimming. The school has a large astroturf area for hockey/tennis/football/netball, in addition to grass rugby/hockey/cricket pitches.

Aravon has a 25-metre outdoor pool for Summer use, but also avails of 25-metre indoor facilities where swimming takes place throughout the school year.

Extras. Horse-riding, Ballet and Modern Dance, Music, Carpentry, Tennis coaching, Wood turning (4 lathes).

Parent Teachers Association. Aravon has an active and enthusiastic PTA and a School Development Committee.

Fees per annum (2007-2008). Junior Infants €4,000; Senior Infants €5,000; Form 1 €6,000; Form 2 €6,300; Senior: Day €7,650; Boarding and Tuition: €19,600 (7 day), €15,400 (5 day). There are three terms in the school year.

Charitable status. Aravon School Limited is a Registered Charity, number 59277. It exists to provide education for children from the age of 3 to 12+.

Ardingly College Pre-Preparatory School – The Farmhouse
A Woodard School

Haywards Heath West Sussex RH17 6SQ
Tel: 01444 893300
Fax: 01444 893301
e-mail: admin@ardingly.com
website: www.ardingly.com

Chairman of School Council: Mr R Alston, CMG

***Headmistress*: Ms J L Adkins**, MA Ed, BA Hons

Age Range. 2½–7 Co-educational.

Number of Pupils. 85 Day Boys and Girls.

Fees per term (2008-2009). Reception, Years 1 & 2: £2,200; Nursery (half day) £1,300; Nursery (full day) £2,000; Pre-Nursery £25 per session or £40 per full day; Before and After-School Care available until 6.00 pm on school days.

The Farmhouse provides children with the perfect introduction to their education. Safely yet idyllically situated within the College estate, our Pre-Preparatory is housed within carefully restored Grade 2 listed Victorian farm buildings. We have full use of the College facilities, including swimming pool, sports hall, playing fields, chapel and full medical on-site care. The school grounds provide us with a wealth of resources for many different purposes.

We aim to lay the basic foundations – academic, social, physical and spiritual – upon which every child can build a sound education, all within a caring yet challenging and well-organised atmosphere.

The Farmhouse caters for children from 2½ to 3 years in our Pre-Nursery, 3 to 4 years in our Nursery and from 4 to 7 in the Pre-Preparatory classes.

The Pre-Preparatory children are taught in small classes of about 15 pupils, benefiting from a high teacher/pupil ratio, whilst the Nursery may cater for up to 25 children (four mornings are compulsory, with full day available).

Our school is run from Monday to Friday. There are no boarding facilities at this age but a Before and After-School Care service is available.

After-school activities include Hockey, Badminton, Country Dancing, Choir, Maths Club, Tennis, Chess, Art and Cricket in the summer term.

All children have full use of the College swimming pool and a wide variety of sport is included in the curriculum.

French is taught from the age of 4 years.

The Farmhouse has its own qualified staff under the direction of the Headmistress and the School has access to specialist staff.

We offer Government funding.

Charitable status. Ardingly College Limited is a Registered Charity, number 1076456. It exists to enable all boys and girls to develop their love of learning, academic potential and individual talents in a caring community which fosters sensitivity, confidence, a sense of service and enthusiasm for life.

Ardingly College Prep School
A Woodard School

Haywards Heath West Sussex RH17 6SQ
Tel: 01444 893200
Fax: 01444 893201
e-mail: registrar@ardingly.com
website: www.ardingly.com

Chairman of School Council: Mr R Alston, CMG

***Headmaster*: Mr C B Calvey**, BEd Hons

Age Range. 7–13.

Number of Pupils. Approximately 230. There are 20 weekly boarders and flexi-boarding is a popular option.

Fees per term (2008-2009). Day pupils: £3,150 (Years 3–4), £3,900 (Years 5–6), £4,000 (Years 7–8), including meals. Boarders: £5,150 (Years 5–8). Casual boarding: £40 per night.

Ardingly College Prep School is the Preparatory School for Ardingly College Senior School (*see entry in HMC section*). Boys and girls are admitted after they have reached the age of 7. Boarders from age 9.

Details of Scholarships available may be obtained from the Registrar.

The Prep School shares extensive grounds with the Senior School and benefits from the College's Chapel, Music School, Dining Hall, Design Technology Department, Gymnasium, a new Sports Hall, 25m indoor Swimming Pool, Squash Courts, Astroturf, Medical Centre (with 24 hour nursing cover) and school shop and it is organised as a separate unit. The Prep School has its own classrooms, Drama Studio, Library, Art Department (with pottery), new ICT suite, changing rooms and boarding accommodation.

Children are prepared for KS2 SATs, CE and PSS.

There are four live-in boarding staff, four resident Gappers and a full time Matron to look after the boarders.

A wide range of extra-curricular activities is encouraged. They include Study Skills, Drama Club (there are termly productions), Maths Club, Chess, Gardening, Leadership Challenge, Cookery, Board Games, Cubs, Riding, Art, various musical groups from Orchestra and strings to Jazz Band and plenty of sporting activities.

The Senior School boys concentrate on Soccer but Prep School boys will experience Rugby as well as Soccer. Girls play Netball and Rounders and both boys and girls enjoy Hockey, Athletics, Cross-Country, Cricket, Basketball and Squash. Ardingly College Prep School is an Activemark Gold school (Sport England recognised).

Children are streamed at the top end of the school and setted in core subjects. Prep is done at school. ICT is strong.

Religious Education is in accordance with the teaching of the Church of England.

Charitable status. Ardingly College Limited is a Registered Charity, number 1076456. It exists to provide high quality education for boys and girls aged 3–18 in a Christian context.

Ardvreck

Crieff Perthshire PH7 4EX
Tel: 01764 653112
Fax: 01764 654920
e-mail: headmaster@ardvreck.org.uk
website: www.ardvreck.org.uk

Chairman of the Governors: A K Miller

***Headmaster*: Peter R B Sutton**, AKC, BD, MTh

Age Range. Co-educational 3–13.

Number of Pupils. Main School: 100 Boarders, 35 day. Pre-Prep 22. Nursery 12.

Fees per term (2007-2008). Main School: £5,186 (boarders), £3,450 (day); Pre-Prep £1,617.

Admission is by interview with the Headmaster. A Scholarship and several Exhibitions or Bursaries are awarded each year following a competitive examination in early March. Service Bursaries are also available.

Ardvreck stands in extensive grounds on the edge of Crieff, having been purpose built and founded in 1883. The School has a long tradition of providing academic excellence as well as outstanding achievement in sport and music. There are 17 full-time and 3 part-time members of the teaching staff and classes are no larger than 16. Health and domestic arrangements are under the personal supervision of the Headmaster's wife and she is assisted by four full-time Matrons – one of whom is the resident, qualified school Nurse.

The School Doctor visits regularly and dental and orthodontic treatment can be arranged if necessary.

Boys and girls are prepared for senior schools throughout Britain. In recent years, all have passed the Common Entrance to their schools of first choice and over 30 scholarships have been won in the past four years.

Rugby, Netball, Hockey, Cricket, Rounders and Athletics are the main games and on several Saturdays in the summer, pupils are provided with picnic lunches enabling them to explore the surrounding countryside, accompanied by members of staff, where they can study the wildlife, fish in one of the rivers or lochs, climb, sail or canoe. Other activities include Golf, Riding, Tennis and Shooting, a sport for which the School has a national reputation for excellence having won the UK Prep Schools Championship for the last fifteen years.

A modern and well-equipped Music School provides the best possible opportunities for music-making. There is an orchestra and choir both of which regularly achieve distinction at music festivals. Visiting music specialists teach a wide range of instruments including the Pipes. Music and Drama play an important part in the life of the School and a major production is staged annually with several smaller productions and numerous concerts taking place throughout the year.

There is a heated, indoor swimming pool (all children are taught to swim), an Astroturf surface for hockey, tennis and netball, and a superb sports hall.

Most full-time staff live within the School grounds and a special feature of Ardvreck is that there are two senior boarding houses – one for girls and one for boys – where pupils gain a little more independence and are encouraged to show greater personal responsibility in readiness for the transition to senior schools.

Many boarders live overseas and they are escorted to and from Edinburgh Airport; all necessary documentation can be handled by the School if required. Overseas pupils are required to have a guardian in the UK with whom they can stay during exeats.

Charitable status. Ardvreck School is a Registered Charity, number SC009886. Its aim is to provide education for boys and girls.

Arley House PNEU School

8 Station Road East Leake Loughborough Leics LE12 6LQ
Tel: 01509 852229
Fax: 01509 852229
e-mail: office@arley-pneu.eastleake.sch.uk
website: www.arley-pneu.eastleake.sch.uk

Chairman of Governors: Mr C M McDowell, FCIB, FCIBS

***Headteacher*: Mrs Charlotte Anderton**, BSc, PGCE, Dip SpLD

Age Range. 3–11 Co-educational.

Number of Pupils. 81: 40 Boys, 41 Girls.

Fees per term (2008-2009). Tuition: £2,185–£2,325. Lunch now included.

Arley House PNEU School was established in East Leake in 1939 and is conveniently situated near to the centre of the village, enjoying beautiful, rural surroundings.

Visitors are immediately struck by the friendly atmosphere in the school; buildings are grouped around what used to be a large private house which has retained its warmth and intimacy.

Children are taught in small groups by well-qualified and experienced staff with a caring attitude shown towards each individual child.

The school is non-denominational and children of all faiths, or none, are welcome.

The thriving Early Years Unit has a nursery where children may enter the term after their third birthday, on a part time or full time basis. Entry into other year groups is according to vacancies. The school has an excellent academic record of children passing entrance examinations to independent senior schools.

French is taught from Nursery upwards and residential visits to France take place every two years. Individual music lessons are available for a wide range of instruments; the school has its own music group and choir.

The school has a purpose-built Science and Design room, a refurbished Library and a networked Computer Room with internet provision and wireless access around the school. The school has a field and a netball court.

Off-site facilities include the all-year-round use of a local sports hall and tennis courts. Swimming lessons take place at a local pool. Many friendly matches are played in a wide range of sports and teams participate in local tournaments.

A wide range of extra-curricular activities is offered. Recently clubs have been available for various Sports, Computing, Athletics, Gymnastics and Chess.

Charitable status. Arley House is a wholly owned subsidiary of Trent College Limited, which is a Registered Charity, number 527180. It exists to provide education for children.

Arnold House School

1 Loudoun Road St John's Wood London NW8 0LH
Tel: 020 7266 4840
Fax: 020 7266 6994
e-mail: office@arnoldhouse.co.uk
website: www.arnoldhouse.co.uk

Chairman of the Board of Governors: A T N Warner Esq

***Headmaster*: V W P Thomas**, BEd, MA

Age Range. 5–13.

Number of Boys. 250 (Day Boys only).

Fees per term (2008-2009). £4,620 including Lunch.

Arnold House is an independent day school for boys founded in 1905.

Most boys join the school after their fifth birthday. A few join at other ages.

The Arnold House website gives full details of recent developments in the school's curriculum and facilities. These include the complete refurbishment and extension of the main teaching facilities at Loudoun Road (2001) and the introduction of an innovative research and ICT based learning programme for pupils in Years 5 and 6 (2003). At the school's playing fields at Canons Park, Edgware, the existing pavilion hall has been adapted to become an auditorium seating 150 with a fully equipped stage and associated facilities. The Canons Park Activity Centre has become an important addition to the excellent facilities at Loudoun Road.

Boys transfer to their chosen independent senior schools at the age of 13. Arnold House has an enviable record of success in placing each boy in the school that is right for him. More than half of the boys move on to the most sought-after London day schools: Westminster, St Paul's, Highgate, UCS, Mill Hill and City of London. Others transfer to boarding schools: Eton,

Winchester, Marlborough, Rugby and Bryanston have been popular destinations in recent years. Arnold House takes a long view of a boy's education. Academic breadth, a balance between study, sport, music, the arts and activities together with excellent pastoral care constitute the foundations of the school's philosophy and success.

Charitable status. Arnold House School is a Registered Charity, number 312725. It exists to provide education for boys in preparation for transfer to senior independent schools at 13.

Arnold Junior School (UCST)

Lytham Road Blackpool Lancashire FY4 1JG
Tel: 01253 346391
Fax: 01253 336251
e-mail: juniorheadmaster@arnoldschool.com
website: www.arnoldschool.com

Chairman of Governors: J M Wooding, OBE, BSc, CEng, FRAeS

***Head*: P Hopkinson**, BA, PGCE

Age Range. 2–11 years.

Number of Pupils. 148 Boys, 139 Girls.

Fees per term (2008-2009). Infants and Juniors £2,126, Kindergarten £20 (per half day session). (Reductions in fees for siblings.)

Arnold Junior School is an integral part of Arnold School, with its own buildings and separate organisation. The School houses a Kindergarten, Infant and Junior Departments and has recently developed its facilities to include: Kindergarten play area, enlarged classrooms, a dedicated Science/Art area, a Resource Room, ICT facilities throughout and changing rooms for PE and Games.

Academic standards are high and progress is well monitored throughout the school. The majority of pupils proceed to the Senior School without the need to complete the entrance examination at 11 years. (*See also Arnold School entry in HMC section.*)

Computers are routinely used in every classroom and all pupils receive weekly, dedicated ICT tuition in our up-to-date ICT suite.

Music has a valued place in school life. Children have the opportunity to learn wind, string or brass instruments, playing in group ensembles or the Junior School Orchestra. There is a choir and musical events are held each term.

French is taught from the age of 6 years and an annual visit to France is organised for older pupils.

The school competes successfully in local and regional sports activities – football, rugby, hockey, netball, cross-country, athletics, cricket and swimming.

There is a thriving programme of extra-curricular activities, including sport, chess and ICT. A wide variety of educational visits is offered, many taking advantage of the school's own outdoor pursuit centre in the Lake District.

The Arnold Summer School offers sporting and educational courses for children aged 4–14 years in July and August.

In our school we aim to provide a happy and caring environment where the individual child may flourish. We are proud of our academic standards but we also strive to give a broad and balanced education. Above all, we want our boys and girls to use and develop their different gifts and to enjoy the success this brings.

Charitable status. The United Church Schools Trust (to which Arnold School belongs) is a Registered Charity, number 1016538. Its aims and objectives are to provide pupils with a sound education based on and inspired by Christian principles.

Arnold Lodge School

Kenilworth Road Leamington Spa Warwickshire CV32 5TW
Tel: 01926 778050
Fax: 01926 743311
e-mail: info@arnoldlodge.com
website: www.arnoldlodge.com

***Principal*: Mrs Elizabeth Hickling**, MA

Age Range. $2^1/_2$–13 Co-educational.

Number of Pupils. 320 (including Kindergarten).

Fees per term (2007-2008). £2,620 (Years 5–8), £2,560 (Years 3–4), £2,115 (Reception–Year 2), Kindergarten: £1,800 (full time), £990 (half day).

Arnold Lodge was founded in 1864 and is the oldest Preparatory School in Warwickshire. Since that time the school, which is co-educational, has been extended and recently refurbished.

There are 33 permanent members of the teaching staff and pupils enjoy the benefits of a strong tradition of effective student care. Parents are encouraged to become actively involved in all aspects of their children's education.

Pupils are prepared for the boys' and girls' Common Entrance Examinations and Scholarships to Independent Senior Schools at 11+ and 13+. Potential scholars are grouped together and many awards have been won in recent years to a variety of Independent Schools.

Arnold Lodge boasts unique resources for Information and Communications Technology and has developed its own Website as well as home-school links through its Intranet. Students are taught to use IT to support learning and to integrate it into their work when practicable.

There is a strong tradition of Music at the school with a range of visiting specialist teachers. The Choir is affiliated to the RSCM and undertakes a full programme of engagements and recitals.

Association and Rugby football, hockey, netball, lacrosse, cricket, rounders, swimming and athletics are all on the curriculum, but other sports such as judo, tennis, gymnastics, outdoor pursuits and equestrian eventing are all part of the very wide range of optional activities. Many sporting tours are organised, most notably in the recent past to Japan, USA and Canada. We have also hosted tourists from Nairobi.

The fine assembly hall doubles as a theatre, and the school has its own Academy of Dance and Drama. The school has a strong dramatic tradition and hosts playwrights in residence to write and produce plays. The School has performed at the Fringe in Edinburgh. The Visual Arts Department is particularly thriving. Pupils are encouraged to develop their interests through the various hobby clubs and to take advantage of the educational visits and field trips that are offered.

Each year a group of students and staff visit France for an enjoyable and rewarding educational residential experience.

Arundale School

Lower Street Pulborough West Sussex RH20 2BX
Tel: 01798 872520
Fax: 01798 875202
e-mail: arundale@easynet.co.uk
website: www.arundale.w-sussex.sch.uk

Chairman of Governors: Mr S Watson, MA

***Headmistress*: Miss K M Lovejoy**

Age Range. 2–11 Co-educational.
Number of Pupils. 96: 59 Day Girls, 37 Day Boys.
Fees per term (from April 2008). Flying Start (2 year olds): £15 per session. Nursery: £955 (5 half days per week), £1,910 (5 full days per week); Reception: £1,325 (5 half days per week), £2,470 (5 full days); Form I £2,550, Form II £2,640, Form III £2,755, Form IV £2,870, Form V £2,955, Form VI £3,040.

Set in the heart of Pulborough, Arundale School has an enviable reputation for providing an excellent, pupil-centred education in a small and friendly environment which caters for each individual pupil. At Arundale the children are prepared for entry to senior school at age 11 when it is usual for all pupils to gain entry to the senior school of their choice, often with a scholarship. In 2007, 11 scholarships/awards were gained by 6 of the 11 pupils going on to senior school. The School prizes and teaches traditional values including courtesy, respect, good manners and caring for others.

From 2003–2006 Arundale was ranked between 53rd and 56th each year in a national survey of Prep Schools conducted by the Sunday Times. In addition, Arundale was the only prep school in West Sussex to appear in the survey.

Among Arundale's many strengths is the Music department and all children at Arundale enjoy class music, choir and orchestra. A wide range of individual instrumental lessons are taken and range from cello for 3 years upwards and piano to saxophone and drums. Many of the children take singing lessons and reach Grade III or IV whilst at Arundale.

Regular visits to theatres, musical concerts and places of historic or natural interest plus drama and science workshops in school are part of every term's activities. Sport including swimming, netball, football and tennis are built into the curriculum and regular matches against local schools are arranged. There are a number of lunch-time and after-school sclubs available such as Tennis, Cooking, Football, Art, Modelling, Cricket and Technology Club. All pupils learn French from the age of five and use computers in the IT suite.

Pupils in Year 6 (10–11 years) are given leadership responsibilities and duties to prepare them for their future schools; additional privileges include a residential activity week. The confidence pupils gain from "life at the top" is evident in their success both at Arundale and in their transition to senior school.

A hot midday meal is freshly prepared on the premises from locally sourced produce for all children from 4–11 years every day and is included in the fees. Pre- and after-school care is available.

Charitable status. Arundale School Trust Limited is a Registered Charity, number 307049. It exists to provide education for children.

Ashdell Preparatory School

266 Fulwood Road Sheffield S10 3BL
Tel: 0114 266 3835
Fax: 0114 267 1762
e-mail: headteacher@ashdell-prep.sheffield.sch.uk
website: www.ashdell-prep.sheffield.sch.uk

Girls Day Preparatory.

Chairman of Council of Management: Ian Walker

***Headmistress*: Mrs A B Camm**, BEd

Deputy Head: Mr L Guntrip

Age Range. 4–11 years.
Number of Pupils. 120 girls.
Fees per term (2008-2009). £2,240–£2,580.

Ashdell has an excellent reputation for academic success and for providing its pupils with a friendly, caring environment in which to flourish. We aim to develop each girls unique potential and are able to achieve this through small class sizes (average 17) and our careful attention to the basics. The school maintains a high pupil teacher ratio and the cosy atmosphere ensures that all children are well known and individual needs are catered for. We have programmes to support learning and to develop the talented or gifted child. Girls are prepared for entrance examinations to Independent Senior Schools at the age of 11.

Girls study a broad range of subjects including English, Mathematics, Science, French, ICT, Music, Swimming, Tennis, Drama, PE, Ballet, Pottery, Fencing, Judo, Cookery and Woodwork. The School has an excellent music programme with a choir orchestra, flute choir and string group. Individual lessons are offered in a variety of instruments and there are many opportunities for pupils to perform.

Ashdell was founded in 1948, and whilst its traditional values of responsibility, respect and role in the community continue to be fundamental to our ethos, we love to have fun and realise that happiness at school is key to achieving a girl's potential, be it academic, artistic, personal or social.

Accommodated in a beautiful Victorian building our Pre-Preparatory Department caters for the 4–6 year olds. It has its own Art and Design Technology room, ICT facilities, garden and play area. The Prep School boasts excellent ICT, music and practice rooms, a science lab, Art room and large gym.

A rich Physical Education programme makes good use of local university sports facilities for swimming, netball, hockey and tennis.

Meals are cooked in house by our own staff and pupils eat lunch in family style groupings. We offer a breakfast club which starts at 7.45 am and after-school care runs from 3.30 until 5.30 pm to cater for working parents.

Our fee schedule reflects our all inclusive policy but excludes individual music tuition and the many extra curricular clubs such as gym, drama, cookery, art, and Spanish.

Charitable status. Ashdell Schools Trust Limited is a Registered Charity, number 529380. It was founded for the education of girls.

Ashdown House

Forest Row East Sussex RH18 5JY
Tel: 01342 822574
Fax: 01342 824380
e-mail: headmaster@ashdownhouse.com
website: www.ashdownhouse.co.uk

The School is registered as an Educational Trust with a Board of Governors.

Chairman of Governors: His Honour Judge Richard Hayward

***Headmaster*: A R Taylor**, BA Hons, PGCE

Deputy Headmaster: J C Taylor, BA Hons, PGCE

Age Range. 7–13.
Number of Pupils. 155 (97 boys, 58 girls).
Fees per term (2007-2008). £6,224.

The School (full boarding with day pupils welcome in Years 3, 4 & 5) is a Latrobe house situated in its own grounds of 35 acres, a mile from the main road. A large new Science classroom block with its own lecture theatre was completed in 2002. The 180-seat Centenary Theatre and Arts Centre allows all children to perform on stage at least once a year. There is an indoor swimming pool and a golf course.

There are 26 full time members of teaching staff, most of whom live within the grounds. Music of all kinds is studied under resident and peripatetic teachers and Art, DT and ICT are part of every child's curriculum. Scholarships are regularly won in all disciplines.

Games. Major sports for boys are cricket, soccer, rugby; the girls play netball (U12 National Prep School champions this year) and rounders. Hockey and athletics are prominent for both girls and boys. In addition there are huge numbers of other sporting opportunities, including swimming, tennis, riding, golf, squash, polo, archery and cross country.

Mr & Mrs Taylor, assisted by houseparents, three senior matrons, three assistant matrons and two State Registered Nurses, look after all pastoral and domestic arrangements.

Charitable status. Ashdown House is a Registered Charity, number 269929.

Ashfold School

Dorton Aylesbury Bucks HP18 9NG
Tel: 01844 238237
Fax: 01844 238505
e-mail: katrina.hartley@ashfoldschool.co.uk
website: www.ashfoldschool.co.uk

Chairman of Governors: Mr R Williams

***Headmaster*: M O M Chitty**, BSc

Age Range. 3–13.

Number of Pupils. Age 7–13: 170 boys and girls (day pupils and weekly boarders). Pre-Prep (3–6 years): 108 boys and girls.

Fees per term (2007-2008). Weekly boarders £4,590; Day £4,050; Pre-Prep £1,030–£2,905.

Ashfold is housed in a magnificent Jacobean mansion set in thirty acres of parkland and playing fields in the heart of the countryside between Oxford and Aylesbury.

Ashfold aims to deliver confident and fully prepared young children ready to meet the challenges of their chosen secondary schools. Its emphasis remains upon the broadest possible education so, in addition to satisfying the academic requirements of preparing them for Common Entrance and Scholarship examination to Senior Independent Schools, every encouragement and opportunity is given to children to develop a wide range of sporting, musical (instrumental and choral), artistic, countryside and other interests (for many years National Clay Pigeon Champions). Children are also prepared, as required, for the LEA 11 plus examination to local grammar schools.

Ashfold is a small, close-knit Christian-based community, holding strong family values. With class sizes averaging just 14, the 31 mainly resident qualified staff are able to give each child the individual attention and encouragement they need. Recent developments include an ICT Centre, Performance Studio, new Library, Junior Department, expanded boarding wing and Astroturf pitches.

Charitable status. Ashfold School Trust is a Registered Charity, number 272663. It exists to provide a quality preparatory school education, academically and in other respects, for all the children entrusted to its care.

Ashford Friars Preparatory School (UCST)

Great Chart Ashford Kent TN23 3DJ
Tel: 01233 620493
Fax: 01233 636579
e-mail: ashfordfriars@ashfordschool.co.uk
website: www.ashfordschool.co.uk

Co-educational Day School.

Chairman of School Council: Mr P Massey, MA

***Head*: Mr R Yeates**, BA Hons

Age Range. 3–11.

Number of Pupils. 368: 158 Boys, 210 Girls.

Fees per term (2008-2009). Day: Nursery £380 (one full day per week), Nursery (full-time) and Reception £1,880, Years 1 and 2 £2,181, Years 3–6 £3,276.

Ashford Friars Prep School is part of the United Church Schools Trust and as such has benefited from significant recent investment, including extensive refurbishment and new facilities. The school believes in the importance of focusing on the development of the individual through a broad education in which every child can find success whilst developing confidence, motivation, self-esteem and emotional intelligence.

A focus on pastoral care and the pursuit of excellence go together with high standards of discipline and a strong Christian ethos.

Situated in a rural setting, Ashford Friars Prep School (Years 3–6) lies in some 20 very attractive acres. The Prep School enjoys both classroom-based and excellent specialist teaching with well-designed facilities for science, art, music, PE, ICT and design technology. The School is fully networked and has exceptional provision for ICT with ACTIVboards in all classrooms, a computer room capable of accommodating entire classes and broadband access to the Internet throughout.

The Pre-Prep School (Nursery–Year 2) is set in its own pleasant grounds on the Ashford site and boasts a new, full-size artificial hockey pitch, sports fields and a gym, as well as use of the school's indoor swimming pool, tennis and netball courts and sports hall. There is a well-equipped playground. The thriving Nursery operates on a flexible basis and the school offers full, wrap-around care from 7.30 am to 6.00 pm for all our children. The school operates Mondays to Fridays. Holiday Clubs operate during school breaks on both sites.

Throughout the school, team sports include hockey, netball, football, rounders, athletics and cricket. Regular fixtures are held with other local schools. Children also participate in PE and swimming as part of their curricular programme.

An extensive range of clubs and activities is provided, both at lunchtime and after school. Individual music tuition with a wide range of instruments is available. Music, drama, dance and public speaking are all important opportunities; productions and presentations are performed by all age groups to a high standard and take place throughout the year. The choir and orchestra meet regularly.

A programme of educational trips and visits provides a stimulating and important addition to the all-round education and development of the 'whole' child.

Children normally progress to Ashford Senior School without the need to take an entrance test unless they wish to sit scholarship exams. The Prep School has had considerable success in preparing children for scholarships to leading independent schools as well as other entrance tests including the 11+.

Charitable status. Ashford Friars Preparatory School is a member of The United Church Schools Trust which is a Registered Charity, number 1016538.

Austin Friars St Monica's Junior School

Etterby Scaur Carlisle Cumbria CA3 9PB
Tel: 01228 528042
Fax: 01228 810327
e-mail: office@austinfriars.cumbria.sch.uk
admissions@austinfriars.cumbria.sch.uk

website: www.austinfriars.cumbria.sch.uk

Chairman of Trustees: Revd Dr Peter Tiplady, MB BS, MRCGP, FFPHM, FRIPH

Headmaster: Mr C J Lumb, BSc, MEd, PGCE

***Head of Junior School*: Mrs F M Willacy**

Marketing & Admissions Manager: Mrs K R Walker, BSc, MATS

Age Range. 3–11.

Number of Pupils. Junior School: 150; Nursery: 24.

Fees per term (2008-2009). Junior School: £1,667 (R–Year 2), £1,930 (Years 3–4), £2,262 (Years 5–6). Nursery: £4.30 per hour, plus £1.40 for lunch.

Austin Friars St Monica's Junior School offers a wide and varied curriculum, which encourages academic achievement alongside sporting, musical, cultural and creative development, thus allowing each child's talents and potential to be fully pursued.

The importance of good primary education cannot be over emphasised and the junior school commits itself to this purpose.

The teaching staff form a capable and highly motivated team totally dedicated to the aims and ethos of the school.

Pupils benefit from specialist teaching in subjects such as ICT, music, drama, modern languages and sports and games. Learning support is an integral part of the curriculum for those who will benefit.

Academically, the school has a fine reputation within the City of Carlisle and beyond, with a record of many scholarship successes at age 11.

Music, speech and drama have a high profile.

Annually Junior 1 (Year 3) pupils are given a musical instrument to learn and enjoy specialist tuition.

Juniors take LAMDA Verse and Prose Speaking Examination achieving consistently high grades.

Good use is made of the extensive grounds surrounding the school, including Astroturf, providing ample scope for PE lessons as well as hosting matches against local school teams.

The junior school is an Ofsted registered provider of Nursery Education Grant for three and four year olds. Reception follows the Foundation Stage curriculum.

A wide range of extra curricular activities is offered from 4.00–6.00 pm, including history, chess, hockey, art, science, computing, young engineers, French, football and netball.

Due to the expansion of pupil numbers, a new £3.1 million state-of-the-art Junior School is due for completion early in 2008.

Austin Nursery occupies a spacious detached two-storey house, adjacent to the main school.

Set within its own grounds and bordered by a mature garden, the Nursery provides pupils with excellent facilities, including an interesting garden bordered by mature trees and all weather safety play area. The secure building and grounds offer parents an opportunity to educate three year olds within a natural and comfortable setting.

The main aim of the nursery is to provide a caring and stimulating environment, endowing children with a positive attitude to learning which will serve them through their formative years. The curriculum is based on the guidelines for Foundation Stage covering six areas of learning. Through carefully structured and well planned, play based activities pupils are encouraged to develop their own ideas and to learn sound spiritual and social values by being cooperative and aware of others. Nursery pupils are taught to listen carefully, to make friends, share, take turns and be polite and to use good manners.

Admission. Children are admitted into the Nursery in the 3–4 age range. 24 places are available per session.

Entry into the Junior School at all levels, except Kindergarten, is by formal assessment of English, mathematics and non-verbal reasoning; prospective pupils spend a taster day in School. All prospective pupils are screened for specific learning difficulties. Entry into Kindergarten is by interview and a taster afternoon.

Senior School. *For information about Austin Friars St Monica's Senior School, see entry in SHMIS section.*

Charitable status. Austin Friars St Monica's School is a Registered Charity, number 516289.

Avenue House School

70 The Avenue Ealing London W13 8LS
Tel: 020 8998 9981
Fax: 020 8991 1533
e-mail: avenuehouseschool@btinternet.com

Co-educational Day School.

Chairman of Governors: Mr David Immanuel

***Head*: Mrs C M Self**

Age Range. 3–11.

Number of Pupils. 140.

Fees per term (2007-2008). £1,560–£2,600.

Avenue House School provides a small, caring environment where children gain the confidence to flourish in all areas of the curriculum. Good manners, mutual respect and a caring community are prevalent at all times.

Children are taught in small classes conducive to the development of an excellent work ethos and achieve high standards in academic subjects as well as an appreciation and understanding of Drama, Art, Music and Sport.

Avenue House School does not test children at entry to Reception as we feel that each child develops at their own individual rate. Extra support is available in small groups for English and mathematics. All pupils are monitored and assessed individually throughout the year and frequent meetings between parents and school occur as we believe a positive approach leads to excellence.

The children are prepared for the competitive entrance examinations to the London Independent Day Schools.

Pupils also have access to our own small library and gymnasium. For ICT the school has the latest laptop computers with wireless broadband internet connection and whiteboards installed throughout the school.

Avenue House School prides itself on the many musical and drama productions that are put on throughout the year for Nursery children to Year 6.

Physical Education is an important part of our curriculum and all children go swimming every week. Children in the Nursery, Reception and Year 1 have Physical Education in our Gymnasium and small playground. From Year 2 the children have their weekly sports lessons at GlaxoSmithKline sports and social club. We have a network of local schools with whom we play regular sports matches throughout the year. The traditional annual sports day for the whole school is also held here.

Extra curriculum activities form a valuable and important part of our education. Apart from the daily homework club other activities include football, drama, touch rugby, ICT, art, tennis (Summer Term) and ballet. After School care is provided until 6 pm for parental convenience.

Educational visits play an important role in helping children relate their class work to the real world. For this reason pupils are taken on outings each term where they can benefit from having first hand knowledge of London and its surrounding areas. Children have the opportunity to go on residential trips which include skiing, The Black Mountains in Wales, the Golden Hinde, Paris and the Isle of Wight.

Aysgarth School

Bedale North Yorkshire DL8 1TF
Tel: 01677 450240
Fax: 01677 450736
e-mail: enquiries@aysgarthschool.co.uk
website: www.aysgarthschool.com

Chairman of Governors: The Marquess of Downshire

***Headmaster*: C A A Goddard**, MA (Emmanuel College, Cambridge)

Assistant Headmaster: P J Southall, BA (University of Hull), PGCE (St Mary's College, Twickenham)

Age Range. 3–13.

Number of Pupils. 185. Pre-Prep Department: 65 boys and girls aged 3–8. Prep School: 120 boys aged 8–13.

Fees per term (2007-2008). Boarders (full and weekly) £5,580, Day £4,530, Pre-Prep £1,750–£2,220.

The Prep School is a boarding school for boys set in 50 acres of grounds in Wensleydale about 6 miles from the A1. It attracts boys from all over northern England and southern Scotland, and boys go on to the country's leading independent senior schools, many of them in southern England. Some boys start as day boys or weekly boarders to enable them to adjust to boarding gently. For exeats, boys are escorted on trains from Darlington to the north and south and there are coaches to and from Cumbria and Lancashire.

Boys of all abilities are welcomed and academic standards are high. All boys are prepared for Common Entrance and several gain scholarships. Before entry, each boy is assessed to ensure that any special needs are identified early and given fully integrated specialist help where necessary. Class sizes are typically around 12. There is a newly equipped computer centre and every teacher has a laptop to link to digital projectors and interactive whiteboards in most classrooms.

The activities in which boys can participate are enormously varied. The facilities include a new heated indoor swimming pool, a modern sports hall, tennis, fives and squash courts, 17 acres of excellent playing fields and a floodlit all-weather pitch. Cricket, Soccer and Rugby Football are the main school sports, and there are opportunities to participate in a wide range of other sports. Music is one of the strengths of the school with more than 75% of boys playing a musical instrument and several boys have been awarded music scholarships. There are three choirs and the school musicians have regular opportunities to perform both in the school and locally. Each term different year groups produce a play or musical. Art and Craft and Design & Technology are taught by specialist teachers.

The school has a fine Victorian chapel, and boys are encouraged to develop Christian faith and values in a positive, caring environment. Pastoral care is the first priority for all staff. The headmaster and his wife, a housemaster and his wife and three matrons, are all resident in the main building. A wide range of exciting activities in the evenings and at weekends ensure that boys are keen to board, and they are encouraged to do so particularly in their last two years as preparation for their next schools.

The school aims to encourage boys to be well mannered and courteous with a cheerful enthusiasm for learning and for life and a determination to make the most of their abilities.

There is also a flourishing Pre-Prep Department including a Nursery for day boys and girls aged 3 to 8.

Charitable status. Aysgarth School Trust Limited is a Registered Charity, number 529538. Its purpose is to provide a high standard of boarding and day education.

Babington House Preparatory School

Grange Drive Chislehurst Kent BR7 5ES
Tel: 020 8467 5537
Fax: 020 8295 1175
e-mail: enquiries@babingtonhouse.com
website: www.babingtonhouse.com

Chairman of Governors: Mr T N Guise

***Head*: Mrs S V Gore**, CertEd

Age Range. Girls 3–11, Boys 3–7.
Number of Pupils. 187: 127 Girls, 60 Boys.
Fees per term (2008-2009). £1,090–£2,940.

At Babington House Preparatory School we provide a happy, family atmosphere, where children can flourish, develop their academic potential and enjoy success in a wide range of other activities.

We believe that children learn best in a caring, friendly environment, where they feel valued as individuals and confident in themselves.

Our expectations are high, encouraging good behaviour, a strong work ethic and an awareness of the wider community. Pupils engage with each other with respect and an appreciation of diversity, following a curriculum designed to promote curiosity and stimulate a desire to learn about the world in which they live.

High-quality teaching effectively supports pupils to become creative and critical thinkers, who can employ different learning styles to improve their understanding.

We recognise that every child is unique and we greatly value the contribution they each have to make to our school. Babington House School pupils have a reputation for being articulate, enthusiastic and well-mannered.

The Preparatory School is housed in new purpose-built accommodation linked to the Senior School, thus ensuring close liaison and smooth transition between the two. We are proud of the exciting series of developments providing facilities to enhance the impressive standards for which our pupils have become known.

At each Key Stage our pupils achieve results for above the National Standards and are well prepared for the next stage of their education.

Charitable status. Babington House School is a Registered Charity, number 307914.

Bablake Junior School

Coundon Road Coventry West Midlands CV1 4AU
Tel: 024 7627 1260
Fax: 024 7627 1294
e-mail: jhmsec@bablakejs.co.uk
website: www.bablakejuniorschool.co.uk

Chairman of Governors: B Connor

***Headmaster*: N A Price**, BA Hons, PGCE

Age Range. 7–11.
Number of Pupils. 190 Day Pupils.
Fees per term (2008-2009). £2,115.

Bablake Junior School offers an outstanding environment for young people. Pupils enjoy coming to school and are given broad opportunities to develop and learn and acquire skills and interests that will equip them for life and their future learning.

We are a small school where people are nurtured as individuals. This helps them to achieve all that they are capable of academically, creatively and on the games field. Most of our pupils continue their education at Bablake until they complete their A Levels. Throughout the school we ensure they make the most of their abilities and the outstanding opportunities that exist here for them. (See www.bablake.com)

We encourage our pupils to take on many positions of responsibility within the school and to supplement this we spend some exciting times at various residential centres. This all helps the children's growing sense of themselves and their role within a community. A wide variety of other trips and expeditions also help reinforce the learning experience.

Admission is at age seven, or older if space exists, and all pupils have to pass an Entrance Exam. Scholarships and Bursaries are available. We follow a broad and balanced curriculum – lessons are interesting and our academic results exceptional. Our teachers' commitment to helping everyone achieve their potential is reflected in the support of our parents and the hard work our pupils put into their studies.

All of our pupils receive expert coaching in sport and have the opportunity to take part in a wide range of activities. We share the swimming pool, games fields, sports hall and astroturfs with our Senior School and make use of Bablake's fantastic theatre and other specialist facilities. All achievement; academic, creative or sporting, is recognised and celebrated.

Charitable status. Coventry School Foundation is a Registered Charity, number 528961. It exists to provide education for boys and girls.

Badminton Junior School

Westbury-on-Trym Bristol BS9 3BA
Tel: 0117 905 5222
Fax: 0117 962 3049
e-mail: alloyd@badminton.bristol.sch.uk
website: www.badminton.bristol.sch.uk

Chairman of Governors: Mrs Alison Bernays

***Headmistress*: Mrs A Lloyd**, MA Ed Open, CertEd Oxford, LGSM

Age Range. 4–11.

Number of Girls. 114.

Fees per term (2008-2009). £2,230–£3,270 inclusive of lunch.

Educational Philosophy. The style of Badminton Junior School reflects the traditions of the Senior School – a combination of discipline and warmth. Children come to school to learn how to concentrate, how to think and how to get on with other people. This process happens best in a stimulating environment where high standards of work and behaviour are expected. A girl also needs a welcoming and friendly atmosphere so that she can feel emotionally secure and her own particular talents and abilities can blossom. Key notes in our philosophy are the development of self-confidence, respect for the individual and the nurturing of inquiring and critical minds.

Children are happiest when they are kept busy and so we try to create a balance between hard work in the classroom, plenty of physical exercise, a range of extra-curricular activities and opportunities for recreational play.

Facilities. The Junior School is well appointed with light airy classrooms, dedicated rooms for Art and French, a new science laboratory, networked computer room, a library and an Assembly Hall/Dining Hall.

The girls have use of the 25m indoor swimming pool, gymnasium and new all-purpose sports pitch which are all on site, and have expert coaching from the very beginning. There are excellent facilities for music which plays an important part both inside and outside the curriculum.

With our extended day facilities we aim to provide a warm and caring home from home to suit the needs of a variety of pupils and their parents.

For further information on Badminton School, see entry in GSA section. A prospectus is available on request to Miss Karen Balmforth (admissions@badminton.bristol.sch.uk).

Charitable status. Badminton School Limited is a Registered Charity, number 311738. It exists to provide education for children.

Ballard School

Fernhill Lane New Milton Hampshire BH25 5SU
Tel: 01425 611153
Fax: 01425 622099
e-mail: admissions@ballardschool.co.uk
website: www.ballardschool.co.uk

The School is a non-profit making Educational Trust under a Board of Governors.

Chairman of the Board of Governors: Mr W Howard

***Headmaster*: Mr S P Duckitt**, MA, BEd, BSc, NPQH

Age Range. 1½–16.

Number of Children. 590 day children.

Fees per term (2008-2009). Senior £3,586, Middle £3,456, Years 4–5 £3,402, Year 3 £3,251, Pre-Prep £1,999, Kindergarten £1,869. Day fees include the cost of School lunches.

The School is situated 2 miles from the sea and on the borders of the New Forest in its own very spacious grounds and woodlands.

Ballard School has key departments catering for the specific needs of the pupils. These departments include the Nursery (1½–3), Pre-Prep (3–7), Prep (7–11), Middle (11–13) and Senior (13–16) sections.

There are over 60 qualified teaching staff plus a Learning Support Unit with 9 teachers. Academic results are excellent at all stages (7+, 11+, 13+ and GCSE) with many pupils gaining scholarships. The School offers a broad curriculum with further strengths in music, art, performing arts, and sport. More than 60 extra-curricular activities are offered.

Facilities are excellent, including 5 science laboratories, large art department, 3 computer suites, 3 libraries, large music department including a recording studio, technology laboratory, home economics laboratory, large sports hall, extensive playing fields, with tennis courts, netball courts, heated outdoor swimming pool and Performing Arts Centre.

The School has a Christian foundation and the aim of the School is to provide an all round education where traditional values and standards are valued combined with facilities to prepare children for the 21st century.

Charitable status. Ballard Schools Ltd is a Registered Charity, number 307328. It exists for the education of children.

Bancroft's Preparatory School

High Road Woodford Green Essex IG8 0RF
Tel: 020 8506 6751
020 8506 6774 (Admissions)
Fax: 020 8506 6752
e-mail: prep.office@bancrofts.essex.sch.uk
website: www.bancrofts.essex.sch.uk

Chairman of the Governors: Major General A W Lyons, CBE

***Headmaster*: C M Curl**, MA, BEd

Age Range. 7–11.

Number of Pupils. 216 Day pupils: 102 girls, 114 boys.

Fees per term (2008-2009). £2,920.

Bancroft's Preparatory School was established in September 1990 in the attractive grounds of Bancroft's School in Woodford Green (*see entry in HMC section*).

This expanding Prep School currently has 12 classrooms including its own hall, library language and art room as well as provision of laptops taking ICT to the classroom. The class teacher has a key role to play and there is also an increasing emphasis on specialised teaching, particularly in the top two years. The Prep School is self-contained but has the advantages of using Senior School facilities including the new Sports Hall (2007), Music Facilities, Performing Arts Studio (2007), Chapel, the Catering Facility (2006) and Hard Play Area.

Children are assessed for entry at the age of seven visiting the school in small groups and being assessed in a friendly and low-key way. Once accepted they have guaranteed places in Bancroft's Senior School (on the same site) at the age of eleven. Academic standards are high with a broad, structured curriculum which includes Drama, Music, Games, Art & Craft and Design & Technology. As well as establishing a strong academic base the school is very much concerned with providing an excellent all-round education for each child which includes encouraging good manners and respect for others and for property. Pastoral Care is seen as key and children are encouraged to take part in a wide range of extra-curricular activities at lunch times, after school and at weekends. Older children are given the opportunity to take on responsibilities around the school such as "playground buddies" and various house duties.

In March 2007 the whole school (including the staff) took part in a production of the musical "Oliver!" which was produced by the Headmaster and performed in two casts to four packed audiences.

The curriculum and administration of the Prep School and Senior School are closely linked and the Headmaster of the Prep School is a member of the Senior Management Team of Bancroft's School.

Charitable status. Bancroft's School is a Registered Charity, number 1068532. It exists to provide a rounded academic education for able children.

The Banda School

PO Box 24722, Nairobi 00502, Kenya
Tel: 00 254 20 891220 / 891260 / 3547828
Fax: 00 254 20 890004
e-mail: bandaschool@swiftkenya.com
website: www.bandaschool.com

Chairman of Governors: Mr D G M Hutchison

***Headmaster*: Mr M D Dickson**, BA Hons Worcester

Deputy Head: Miss W Rutter, CertEd Leeds

Age Range. 1–13.

Number of Children. 400 (Day and Weekly Boarding).

Fees per term (2007-2008). Tuition: Kshs 244,000 (Years 3–8 including lunches). Weekly Boarding: Kshs 70,000 in addition to Tuition Fees. Sliding fee scale Year 2 and below.

The School was founded in 1966 by Mr and Mrs J A L Chitty. It is 9 miles from Nairobi and stands in its own grounds of 30 acres adjacent to the Nairobi Game Park. Boys and girls are admitted in equal numbers and are prepared for Independent Senior School Scholarship and Common Entrance Examinations to leading secondary schools in Kenya, South Africa and the UK. The Staff consists of 40 teachers with the vast majority being graduates. The teacher-pupil ratio is about 1:10.

Facilities include a modern Weekly Boarding House, new Pegasus Pre-Prep building, Science laboratories, ICT rooms, Art room, Music rooms, Hall with well-equipped stage, two Libraries, Junior Art Room and a Dance Studio, specialist rooms for Mathematics, French, History and Geography, Design Technology, audio-visual room, three Tennis courts, two Squash courts and a six-lane 25-metre Swimming Pool with three new diving boards.

Sports include Rugby, Football, Hockey, Cricket, Tennis, Swimming, Netball, Rounders, Athletics, Sailing, Squash and Cross-Country. A wide range of other activities including Instrumental lessons and Dancing is also available. Music, Art and Drama are an important part in the life of the school.

Barfield

Runfold Farnham Surrey GU10 1PB
Tel: 01252 782271
Fax: 01252 781480
e-mail: admin@barfieldschool.com
website: www.barfieldschool.com

The School is an Educational Trust, administered by a Board of Governors.

Chairman of Governors: Mr Andrew Christmas

***Head*: Mr Robin Davies**, BSc, PGCE

Age Range. 3–13 Co-educational.

Number of Children. 250.

Fees per term (2008-2009). Prep £3,620–£3,740, Pre-Prep £870–£2,650.

Barfield, set in 12 acres of beautiful grounds, is a first class IAPS Day Preparatory School for girls and boys. The Pre-Prep Department has earned an enviable reputation for its high standards and caring staff. It is based in its own self-contained unit, close to Senior School facilities, which include Science Laboratory, Library and Information Centre and a Multi-Resource Centre, incorporating an Auditorium, Music and Music practice rooms, ICT Suite, and facilities for Art and DT.

The school has a flourishing PE and outdoor pursuits department, with most major and minor sports covered. There is a magnificent indoor heated swimming pool and a Par 3 golf course. Children are encouraged to participate in a wide range of evening activities from Synchronised Swimming to Adventure Training. The team also runs activity courses throughout most of the school holidays.

Girls and boys, taught in small classes, are prepared for their respective Common Entrance and Scholarship examinations and for Grammar School entry. Visitors are always welcome.

Charitable status. Barfield is a Registered Charity, number 312085. It exists to provide a quality education for boys and girls.

Barnard Castle Preparatory School

Westwick Road Barnard Castle Co Durham DL12 8UW
Tel: 01833 696032
Fax: 01833 696034
e-mail: secretary@barneyprepschool.org.uk
website: www.barnardcastleschool.org.uk

Chairman of Governors: Mr M McCallum

***Headmaster*: Mr E J Haslam**, ACP, DipTeach

Age Range. 4–11 years.

Number of Pupils. 195 girls and boys, including 30 boarders.

Fees per term (2008-2009). Prep: £4,331 (Boarders), £2,327 (Day). Pre-Prep: £1,492.

"The Community of Barnard Castle Preparatory School will encourage and challenge our pupils to reach their full educational potential within a secure and happy teaching environment."

Barnard Castle Preparatory School is the Junior School of Barnard Castle School and offers an all round, high quality education for boys and girls aged between 4 and 11 years. The School offers both day and boarding places and is situated in a beautiful setting on the edge of a traditional English market town.

The campuses of the two schools are adjoining, allowing shared use of many excellent facilities. At the same time the Preparatory School is able to provide a separate, stimulating environment, with small classes, a wide range of extra curricular activities and an exciting school excursion programme. The school has recently benefited from an extensive building and refurbishment programme. This has included the construction of a new hall and greatly improved art, design, IT and library facilities.

The School is well served by a bus network system and supervision is given to those day children waiting for transport home. The boarders reside in a newly developed boarding house, which creates a warm and friendly environment supported by a full range of facilities including the School's medical centre.

Our Director of Studies oversees a carefully designed curriculum. It incorporates the National Curriculum and aims to create further learning experiences for the children. Sport, drama and music occupy important places in the life of the School. All children have numerous opportunities to participate in each of these area. The School also offers a qualified learning support service to those children who require further assistance.

Charitable status. Barnard Castle School is a Registered Charity, number 527383. Its aim is the education of boys and girls.

Barnardiston Hall Preparatory School

Nr Haverhill Suffolk CB9 7TG
Tel: 01440 786316
Fax: 01440 786355
e-mail: registrar@barnardiston-hall.co.uk
www.barnardiston-hall.co.uk

***Headmaster*: K A Boulter**, MA Cantab, PGCE

Age Range. Co-educational 2–13.

Number of Pupils. Day 204, Boarding (full and weekly) 50.

Fees per term (2008-2009). Day Pupils £2,700–£3,450; Weekly Boarders £4,845; Full Boarders £5,265.

Barnardiston Hall, set in 16 acres of grounds on the borders of Suffolk, Essex and Cambridge, offers an individual all-round education for boys and girls, both day and boarding. High standards are achieved by small classes taught by graduate and teacher-trained staff, a caring approach and close liaison with parents.

The School has good facilities, including a Pre-Preparatory Block and Art Room complex, a very modern and well equipped computer room, assembly hall, tennis/netball courts, music room, science laboratory, library and extensive sports fields. For the boarders, the dormitories are bright, uncluttered and home-like.

The curriculum is designed to allow pupils to reach Common Entrance standards in the appropriate subjects. The best of traditional methods are mixed with modern ideas to provide an enjoyable and productive learning environment. French and computers are taught from the age of 3; Latin from age 7. The School is CReSTeD registered.

Sports in the Michaelmas and Lent Terms are hockey, swimming and cross-country/orienteering for all pupils, rugby for the boys and netball for the girls. During the Summer, all do athletics, cricket/rounders, and tennis/short tennis.

There is a wide range of clubs and societies including 3 choirs, an orchestra, pet corner, recorders, chess, horse-riding, painting, drama, basketry, weaving, carpentry and science award. Ballet, speech and drama, piano, woodwind, brass, string and singing lessons are also offered.

Throughout the term, there are weekend activities for boarders (optional for day pupils) which include mountain walking. Derbyshire Dales at 6, Ben Nevis at 8, camping, visits to museums/historic buildings and other places of interest and theatre trips. There is an annual trip to Europe.

Barrow Hills School

Roke Lane Witley Godalming Surrey GU8 5NY
Tel: 01428 683639/682634
Fax: 01428 681906
e-mail: info@barrowhills.org.uk
website: www.barrowhills.org.uk

Chairman of the Governors: Mr Stephen Mulliner

***Headmaster*: Mr Matthew Unsworth**, BEng Hons, PGCE

Age Range. 3–13.

Number of Pupils. 260.

Fees per term (2008-2009). £1,625–£3,605.

A co-educational day school for children aged 3 to 13 years set within 40 acres of attractive gardens and playing fields some 8 miles south of Guildford. It offers children a stimulating curriculum which is sensitive to the needs of the individual. There are strong links with many senior schools such as Ampleforth College, Charterhouse, Cranleigh School, King Edward's School Witley, Prior's Field, The Royal Grammar School, St Catherine's, Tormead and Wellington College.

Our extensive Art and Design Centre offers children superb facilities to develop their creative talents in numerous disciplines including textiles, print-making, ceramics, food technology and photography. We have a modern well-equipped computing suite in the main building and all classrooms have computing resources. In 2006 a new classroom block was opened with extensive facilities including a new computer suite. Science is taught in a dedicated science laboratory. The study of languages is important too; French is taught from the age of 3 whilst older pupils also study Latin. Music and drama play a large part in the life of the school. Many children study a musical instrument and we have a chapel choir. Each term there is a major drama production in the school hall.

The school has a Roman Catholic foundation but pupils from all denominations are most welcome. All children can participate in assemblies and other services which are held in our splendid chapel.

A wide range of sporting activities is offered including rugby, football, hockey, cricket, netball, tennis, athletics, judo and riding. The school has its own heated swimming pool. Educational visits, both locally and overseas, enhance the rich curriculum which is provided in school.

Charitable status. Barrow Hills School Witley is a Registered Charity, number 1000190. It exists to provide high quality education for both boys and girls.

Bassett House School

60 Bassett Road London W10 6JP
Tel: 020 8969 0313
Fax: 020 8960 9624
e-mail: info@bassetths.org.uk
website: www.bassetths.org.uk

Motto: *Quisque pro sua parte* (From each to the best of his or her ability).

Chairman of Governors: Mr Anthony Rentoul

***Head*: Mrs Andrea Harris**, BEd London, CertEd London, CEPLF Caen

Age Range. 3–11 Co-educational.

Number of Pupils. 160.

Fees per term (2007-2008). Nursery (5 mornings) £1,830, Prep-Prep £3,610, Prep £3,780.

Bassett House School was founded in 1947. As a member school of the House Schools Group, it has two sister schools, Orchard House School in Chiswick and Prospect House School in Putney, both of which, like Bassett House School, take both boys and girls from the age of 3 or 4 until the time they leave for their next senior or, in some cases, intermediate preparatory schools. Bassett House takes children from age 3 to age 11. Entry is, in the younger years, non-selective. Aspects of the Montessori method are used in the Early Years. The school has some 160 pupils in eleven classes.

The school was built towards the end of the 19th century and what was originally designed as a large family house now provides classrooms that are spacious, brightly lit and well heated and ventilated. The entire building was substantially rebuilt in 2001 to a very high standard. The school premises include the church hall at St Helen's Church, just around the corner from 60 Bassett Road, providing an assembly hall with a stage and gymnasium, three classrooms, a kitchen and a garden. The main school building has a playground which doubles as a basketball or netball court.

Bassett House provides a thorough grounding in the usual educational subjects and the children are prepared for the entrance examinations to leading day and boarding preparatory schools. In recent years the entrance examination results to these schools have been excellent. The reason this school has enjoyed such a long track record of success is mainly due to its happy yet purposeful atmosphere... indeed, this is a hallmark of Bassett House: the school believes that only if a child is happy and actively wants to come to school will his or her potential in the widest sense be maximised. The school does not stint to obtain the very best staff and to support them with the best in resources. Within a friendly but nevertheless structured and disciplined academic environment, the school aims to bring out the best in every one of its children.

Beachborough

Westbury Nr Brackley Northants NN13 5LB
Tel: 01280 700071
Fax: 01280 704839
e-mail: office@beachborough.com
website: www.beachborough.com

The School is administered as a non-profit-making Educational Trust by a Board of Governors.

Chairman of Governors: H F Thuillier, BSc

***Headmaster*: J F Whybrow**, BEd (Exeter)

Age Range. 2½–13.

Number of Children. Main School 140 (40% flexi boarding), Pre-Prep 95.

Fees per term (2008-2009). Day: £2,690 (Reception, Years 1 and 2), £3,890 (Years 3 and 4), £4,235 (Year 5–8). Nursery £230 per session per term. Flexi-boarding £22 per night.

The school is fully co-educational with a balanced mix of girls and boys throughout. The flourishing Pre-Prep, which moved into purpose-built accommodation in September 2006, takes children from 2½ years old with a Nursery Class allowing the youngest children to build up sessions during their first year. With an average class size of no more than 16, children are prepared for a wide range of Independent Senior Schools. A balance between work and play is achieved through the provision of a wide-ranging programme of co-curricular activities, coordinated by a Deputy Head, specifically appointed for this purpose.

The school occupies a fine Manor House in the small village of Westbury and enjoys 30 acres of grounds, playing fields and woodland. A major refurbishment programme of the boarding and teaching facilities in the prep school has recently been completed. Consequently, the teaching facilities, which previously allowed a broad curriculum, have been considerably enhanced.

The Beachborough Association, run by parents and staff, arranges many events during the year.

Charitable status. Beachborough is a Registered Charity, number 309910. It exists to provide quality education for children.

The Beacon

Chesham Bois Amersham Bucks HP6 5PF
Tel: 01494 433654
Fax: 01494 727849
e-mail: enquiries@beaconschool.co.uk
website: www.beaconschool.co.uk

Chairman of the Governors: W I D Plaistowe, Esq

***Headmaster*: M W Spinney**, BEd, CertEd

Age Range. 3–13.

Number of Boys. Upper School 280; Lower School 144.

Inclusive Fees per term (2008-2009). Upper School £3,820, Middle School £3,620, Lower School £1,420–£2,810.

The Beacon is a Charitable Trust which provides education for some 420+ boys. Its buildings are a delightful blend of old and new; the school is centred around a 17th Century farmstead whose barns provide a lovely Dining Hall and a Library. Classroom accommodation is almost all purpose-built, and the excellent facilities include a large Sports Hall/Theatre, Music Technology suite, ICT labs, Art Room, Design and Technology suite and a new Modern Languages laboratory opened in September 2008. As well as the 16-acre grass games field there is an Astroturf pitch for Hockey and Tennis, and a 20-metre outdoor Swimming Pool.

Most boys join the Nursery at age 3, or Reception at age 4. There are 24 boys in the Nursery, and two Reception classes with 20 boys in each. Each class teacher has an assistant. At age 5 and 6 the boys are based mainly with their form teacher in classes of 20. From age 7 class sizes are a maximum 20.

The aim of the school is to provide breadth of opportunity. The daily timetable contains a broad range of subjects, and there is a strong emphasis on participation in sport, music, drama, art and technology. There are teams for Rugby, Soccer, Hockey, Basketball, Cricket, Tennis, Swimming and Athletics, while the Music Department has 2 Choirs, an Orchestra, Strings and Wind Bands and some 18 visiting teachers to cater for individual tuition.

The School's examination record is excellent, both at 11+ into Buckinghamshire Grammar Schools and at 13+ to senior independent day and boarding schools, with a number of academic, music, art and sports scholarships being won.

Charitable status. The Beacon School is a Registered Charity, number 309911. It exists to provide education for boys.

Beaconhurst School

52 Kenilworth Road Bridge of Allan Stirling FK9 4RR
Tel: 01786 832146
Fax: 01786 833415
e-mail: secretary@beaconhurst.stirling.sch.uk
website: www.beaconhurst.com

Chairman of Governors: R G Lawson, BSc, CA

***Headmaster*: I W Kilpatrick**, BA, MEd, FRSA

Age Range. 3–18.

Number of Pupils. 407: 46 (Nursery), 152 (Junior School), 209 (Senior School); 213 Boys, 194 Girls.

Fees per term (2007-2008). £2,030–£2,745.

Beaconhurst is a co-educational day school, situated in Bridge of Allan, an attractive country town near Stirling in Central Scotland. The Ochils rise behind the school offering marvellous countryside for outdoor pursuits while the MacRobert Centre at nearby Stirling University hosts a wide range of musical and theatrical events. There are excellent road and rail links and both Edinburgh and Glasgow airports are less than one hour's drive away.

There has been a school on the current site at Bridge of Allan since 1919, when the Beacon School for Girls was established. In the same year, Hurst Grange, a boys' school in Stirling, opened and the two schools merged to form Beaconhurst Grange in 1976. This ran as a boarding prep school until the decision was taken in the early 90s to develop an all-through day school providing high-quality education to pupils from three to eighteen years of age.

With this came the vision to redevelop the school site to accommodate a Nursery, Junior School and Senior School. Our compact campus now provides all the facilities expected in a modern, dynamic school community.

Beaconhurst has forged an identity of delivering a personal, flexible educational experience by offering an integrated curriculum from three to eighteen, in which focus on the individual is paramount.

Learning should be fun, challenging and above all engaging – features that Beaconhurst pupils embrace every day. A school should be a community in which everyone is listened to, provided for and nurtured to achieve their potential – reasons why parents choose Beaconhurst for their children.

A prospectus with full details is available from the Headmaster.

Charitable status. Beaconhurst Grange is a Registered Charity, number SC005753. Its aim is to provide a flexible educational experience for all.

Beaudesert Park

Minchinhampton Stroud Gloucestershire GL6 9AF
Tel: 01453 832072
Fax: 01453 836040
e-mail: office@beaudesert.gloucs.sch.uk
website: www.beaudesert.gloucs.sch.uk

Chairman of Governors: R S Trafford, Esq, MA

***Headmaster*: J P R Womersley**, BA, PGCE

Age Range. 4–13.

Number of Pupils. Boarders 60, Day Boys and Girls 220, Pre-Prep Department 120.

Fees per term (2008-2009). Boarders £5,620, Day Fees £2,980–£4,295, Pre-Prep £2,270.

The School was founded in 1908 and became an educational trust in 1968.

Beaudesert Park is a preparatory school for boys and girls from 4–13. The school is very well equipped with indoor and outdoor swimming pools, sports hall, art centre, design technology and music departments. There are also astroturf tennis courts and hard courts which are situated in beautiful wooded grounds. The school stands high up in the Cotswolds adjoining 500 acres of common land and golf course. Despite its rural location, the school is within half an hour of the M4 and M5 motorways and within easy reach of the surrounding towns of Gloucester, Cheltenham, Cirencester, Swindon, Bath and Bristol.

There is a strong academic tradition and all pupils are encouraged to work to the best of their ability. There is great emphasis on effort and all children are praised for their individual performance. Pupils are prepared for Common Entrance and Scholarship examinations. They are given individual attention in classes which are mostly setted not streamed. Over the last five years an average of 10 scholarships a year (in 2006 20 awards) – academic, art, music, sport and technology – have been won to leading Independent Senior Schools. The staff consists of 42 full time teaching staff and 12 music teachers, all of whom take a personal interest in the children's welfare.

Good manners and consideration for others are a priority. Beaudesert strives to create a happy and purposeful atmosphere, providing for the talents of each child in a wide range of activities, cultural, sporting and recreational. There are thriving drama, art, pottery and music departments. Sporting activities include cricket, soccer, rugby, hockey, netball, rounders, tennis, swimming, athletics, golf, badminton, fencing, dance, judo, riding and sailing. A wide number of societies and clubs meet each week.

Charitable status. Beaudesert Park is a Registered Charity, number 311711. It exists to provide education for boys and girls in a caring atmosphere.

Bedford Modern Junior School

Manton Lane Bedford Bedfordshire MK41 7NT
Tel: 01234 332513
Fax: 01234 332617
e-mail: info@bedmod.co.uk
website: www.bedmod.co.uk

Chairman of the School Committee: I McEwen, BPhil, MA, DPhil

***Head of Junior School*: N R Yelland**, BEd Oxon

Age Range. 7–11 Co-educational.
Number of Pupils. 152 Boys, 54 Girls.
Fees per term (2008-2009). £2,468.

The Junior School is housed in its own separate buildings adjacent to the main school. Facilities include specialist rooms for Art and Science, ICT Centre, Design Technology Suite, library, designated Year 3 classrooms and play area and a superb state-of-the-art School Hall.

The whole site overlooks the School playing fields and the Junior School has extensive views over the Ouse Valley. Many of the Main School facilities are available to the Junior School, including full use of the playing fields, Sports Hall, Gymnasium, covered and heated Swimming Pool, Tennis and Squash Courts. The Main School Hall provides facilities for full scale Drama productions and extensive use is made of the Music School.

There is a strong Choral, Instrumental Music, Dramatic and Sporting tradition.

Pupils are admitted to the Junior School at 7, 8, 9 and 10, after sitting an Entrance Examination in English and Maths which is held in January each year. Pupils proceed automatically to the Main School at 11, unless special circumstances mean that this is inappropriate.

(*See Beford Modern School entry in HMC section.*)

Charitable status. The Bedford Charity (The Harpur Trust) is a Registered Charity, number 204817. It includes in its aims the provision of high quality education for boys and girls.

Bedford Preparatory School

De Parys Avenue Bedford MK40 2TU
Tel: 01234 362271/362274
Fax: 01234 362285
e-mail: prepinfo@bedfordschool.org.uk
website: www.bedfordschool.org.uk

Chairman of Governors: H H Judge Simon Brown, QC

***Headmaster*: C Godwin**, BSc, MA

Deputy Head (*Pastoral*): Mrs C Boughton, BA
Deputy Head (*Academic*): G J Wickens, MA

Age Range. 7–13.
Number of Boys. Dayboys 452, Boarders 18, Weekly Boarders 4.
Fees per term (2008-2009). Day £3,104–£4,068, Full Boarding £5,138–£6,102, Weekly Boarding £4,898–£5,862.

Bedford Preparatory School combines the two schools formerly known as the Preparatory School and the Bedford Lower School. An extensive building programme has been completed offering excellent facilities: three purpose-built and well-equipped Science Laboratories, an Art Studio, excellent computing resources, specialist teaching rooms, a new library and a spacious Assembly Hall.

Curriculum. Boys are prepared for the Bedford School 13+ Entrance Examination, which is allied to Common Entrance, but under normal circumstances boys transfer automatically. The curriculum is otherwise carefully tailored to match and prepare for the curriculum followed in the Upper School, and includes in addition to the usual subjects: French, Information Technology and Design/Technology from the age of 7 and Latin, Spanish and French from the age of 11.

The boys enjoy full use of the facilities available to Upper School pupils: the Recreation Centre, incorporating an excellent theatre, an indoor swimming pool and a large sports hall; the Technology Centre; superb playing fields, all-weather pitch and tennis courts. All the usual games are played to a high standard and boys are often selected to play in county or national teams.

Many boys play musical instruments, and orchestra and bands perform frequently. There are good School Choirs and selected boys sing alongside Upper School pupils in the Chapel Choir trained in the English Cathedral tradition. There are several theatrical productions each year in the theatre or hall, often in conjunction with girls from sister Harpur Trust Schools.

Boarding. Full boarders and a small number of weekly boarders live in the new purpose-built Boarding House in the grounds of the Preparatory School. Boys are cared for by the Housemaster and his wife, two resident house-tutors and a full-time matron.

Pastoral Care. The progress and well-being of pupils are carefully monitored, and parental involvement and contact are maintained through reports and Parents Evenings and other formal and informal meetings. A competitive House system is in use.

Financial Assistance and Scholarships. Designed to open up new opportunities and bring out the best in every boy, Bedford's radical new Access Award and Scholarship Scheme is changing the face of independent education. Bedford now offers some £1 million per year of funding in recognition of academic potential to provide a wealth of opportunites for boys irrespective of background.

For more information please call our freephone helpline 0800 432 0084 or visit our website www.bedfordschool.org.uk.

Charitable status. The Bedford Charity (The Harpur Trust) is a Registered Charity, number 204817. It aims to provide high quality education for boys.

Beech Hall School

Tytherington Macclesfield Cheshire SK10 2EG
Tel: 01625 422192
Fax: 01625 502424
e-mail: secretary@beechhallschool.freeserve.co.uk
website: www.beechhallschool.org

Chairman of Board of Governors: Mr E McGrath

***Headmaster*: T J G Scott**, BA, MA, NPQH, PGCE

Age Range. 6 months–16 years.
Number of Pupils. 241.
Fees per term (2008-2009). Pre-Prep £1,895, Transition £2,290, Junior School £2,720, Senior School £2,780 (including lunch).

Kindergarten, Infant, Junior and Senior departments offer education between 8.30 am and 4.00 pm with further supervised sporting and leisure activities available until 5.00 pm. If required, there is supervised care up until 6.00 pm for all children.

Beech Hall is a co-educational Day school situated in spacious and attractive grounds with extensive playing fields, a heated outdoor swimming pool and many other facilities.

Boys and girls are prepared for entry to a wide variety of Independent Schools and local Independent Day Schools. Classes are kept small – the school has a maximum class size policy of 20 pupils – making individual attention possible in every lesson.

There is a very popular Kindergarten and Reception department, consisting of children between the ages of 6 months and 6 years under the care of their own specialist teachers. These classes were started with the objective of giving boys and girls a good grounding in reading, writing and arithmetic.

Beech Hall aims to provide a sound all-round education and children are encouraged to sit for academic, music and art scholarships. There is a school choir, a high standard of drama and the children produce their own school magazine.

Rugby, Association football, hockey and netball are played in the winter terms. The school also has a good cross-country course. In the summer, cricket, athletics, rounders and tennis. Swimming is taught throughout the year. Other activities include squash, badminton, archery and ju-jitsu.

The school is situated off the main Stockport–Macclesfield road, within easy reach of Manchester International Airport and the M6 and M62 motorways.

Further details and illustrated prospectus are obtainable from the Headmaster.

Charitable status. Beech Hall School Trust Limited is a Registered Charity, number 525922. It exists to provide education for boys and girls.

Beechwood Park

Markyate St Albans Hertfordshire AL3 8AW
Tel: 01582 840333
Fax: 01582 842372
e-mail: hmsecretary@beechwoodpark.herts.sch.uk
website: www.beechwoodpark.herts.sch.uk

Chairman of Governors: D J Pirie, Esq, BSc, CEng, MICE

***Headmaster*: Patrick C E Atkinson**, BSc, MIBiol, PGCE

Age Range. 2½–13.

Number of Pupils. 469: 45 boarders (aged 8–13), 255 day boys and 169 day girls (aged 4–13). In addition there are 44 pre-school children at the newly-acquired Montessori Nursery which is at a separate location less than one mile from the main school.

Fees per term (2008-2009). Day pupils: Senior £3,801, Junior £3,111, Reception £2,779. Boarders (in addition to day fees) £1,030. No compulsory extras

Beechwood Park occupies a large mansion, with a fine Regency Library and Great Hall, in 38 acres of surrounding grounds. Modernisation has added kitchens, changing rooms, Science laboratories, language rooms, Design Technology workshop, dormitories, gymnasium and sports facilities, including a large sports hall and two squash courts, hard tennis courts and two heated swimming pools. Three purpose-built classroom blocks house the Middle Department, Junior Forms and Reception classes. A Music Department has a music chamber and 14 practice rooms. More recently a Performance Hall and an all-weather pitch have been added.

Day pupils use private buses serving Harpenden, St Albans, Luton and Dunstable and the surrounding villages. Many subsequently convert to boarding under the care of the Housemaster, Mr O S C Bullock.

Maximum class size is 20; major subjects are setted. Qualified class teachers teach the Juniors; older children are taught by subject specialist graduates. There is a resident Chaplain. The Director of Music has a staff of visiting instrumentalists.

Common Entrance results affirm a high standard of work, against a background of every kind of worthwhile out-of-class activity. Music is distinguished.

Soccer, Rugby, Cricket, Golf, Hockey, Netball, Swimming and Athletics and an unusually wide range of minor sports are coached by well-qualified PE Staff.

Beechwood Park is a non-profit-making trust administered by governors of wide professional and educational experience.

Charitable status. Beechwood Park School is a Registered Charity, number 311068. It exists to provide education for boys and girls from 2½–13.

Beeston Hall School

West Runton Cromer Norfolk NR27 9NQ
Tel: 01263 837324
Fax: 01263 838177
e-mail: office@beestonhall.co.uk
website: www.beestonhall.co.uk

Chairman of Governors: D D Marris

***Headmaster*: I K MacAskill**, BEd Hons

Deputy Headmaster: A V L Richards, BSc, PGCE

Bursar: M R Braybrook

Age Range. Co-educational 7–13 years.

Numbers of Pupils. 177: 96 Full Boarding, 81 Daily Boarding. 107 Boys, 70 Girls.

Fees per term (2007-2008). £5,525 Boarding, £4,125 Daily Boarding.

Religious Denomination. Mainly Church of England; 15% Roman Catholic.

About Beeston. Beeston Hall was established in 1948 in a Regency house set in 30 acres in North Norfolk, close to the sea and surrounded by 700 acres of National Trust land. Beeston's reputation for being a happy, caring family school is in no small part due to the real sense of community which pervades throughout. The strength of the Pastoral Care system ensures that every child is closely watched over and cared for. Although there is no compulsory boarding, 95% of the children experience boarding before they leave, the majority moving on to boarding schools such as Ampleforth, Downe House, Eton, Gordonstoun, Gresham's, Harrow, Oakham, Oundle, Queen Margaret's York, Radley, Rugby, Stowe, Tudor Hall and Uppingham. In addition to the normal subjects, Music, DT, ICT and Drama are all timetabled, providing the children with a wide curriculum and the opportunity to find an activity in which they can excel. The school enjoys great success at scholarship level, with 59 scholarships won in the last 4 years. Extra help is given on a one-to-one basis in English, Mathematics and French; Dyslexics are looked after by trained staff. There is a positive emphasis on the traditional values such as courtesy, kindness, industry and awareness of others, and at every stage of their education the children are encouraged to maximise their potential and think and act for themselves. Drama and Music are considered important for every child: each takes part in at least one play production each year. 110 children are in three choirs and ten different music groups meet every week. The school is equally proud of its record on the sports field where all children are coached regardless of ability by a dedicated team of staff, and where all are, at some stage, given the opportunity to represent the school. It has a particularly impressive record in Rugby, Netball, Rounders, Cross-Country, Hockey, Cricket and Athletics, whilst a comprehensive activities programme provides opportunities to suit all tastes: camp craft, shooting, sailing, golf, debating, French cuisine, chess and archery, to name but a few.

The 2004 ISI Inspection Report comments: "happy community in which pupils thrive... results at 13+ are impressive... an environment in which all pupils flourish."

Charitable status. Beeston Hall School Trust Limited is a Registered Charity, number 311274. It exists to provide preparatory education for boarding and day boys and girls.

Belhaven Hill

Dunbar East Lothian EH42 1NN
Tel: 01368 862785
Fax: 01368 865225
e-mail: headmaster@belhavenhill.com
website: www.belhavenhill.com

Chairman of Governors: Mrs J Harper

***Head Master*: I M Osborne**, MA Cantab

Age Range. 8–13.

Number of Pupils. 70 boys, 55 girls. Boarders 105, Day 20.

Fees per term (2007-2008). Boarders £5,495, Days £3,810.

The School is a Charitable Trust, under a Board of Governors, catering mainly for boarders but with some day pupils. The boys live in the main building and the girls in a separate house that is newly built and very attractive.

The handsome buildings are surrounded by extensive playing fields and stand in sheltered grounds with a golf course, to which children have access, between the school and the sea. There is a full-time teaching staff of seventeen, and the school has an excellent record of academic success, with a number of Awards to leading English and Scottish Senior Independent Schools in recent years. There are other teachers for Art, Carpentry and Instrumental Music. The policy of the Governors has been to keep the school a comparatively small one in order to retain a family atmosphere. The emphasis is on bringing out the various talents of all the pupils and encouraging high standards in all that they undertake. Three full-time Matrons and two Assistants take care of the children's health, and the School Doctor is always available in case of emergency.

The chief team games for the boys are Rugby, Hockey and Cricket and there is some Football in the winter terms. The girls play Netball, Hockey and Rounders. There is Swimming in the school's heated outdoor pool in the summer and in the indoor pool in Dunbar during the winter terms. The school has two grass tennis courts and four on an all-weather pitch. Athletics, Tennis and Golf are professionally coached and sports such as Badminton, Judo, Croquet and Surfing are available. The Sports Hall is used during lessons and free time for Drama, Gymnastics, Scottish Country Dancing, Indoor Cricket Nets and Rollerblading. Every sort of hobby and activity is practised and encouraged: Debating, Mastermind, Singing, Model-making, Computer Programming, Gardening, Fishing, Bird-watching and many others.

Prospectuses are available from the Head Master.

Charitable status. Belhaven Hill School Trust Ltd is a Registered Charity, number SC007118. Its aim is to educate children in the full sense of the word.

Belmont
Mill Hill Preparatory School

The Ridgeway Mill Hill London NW7 4ED
Tel: 020 8906 7270
Fax: 020 8906 3519
e-mail: info@belmontschool.com
website: www.belmontschool.com

Chairman of the Court of Governors: Sir Robert Balchin, DL

***Head*: Mrs L C Duncan**, BSc, PGCE

Deputy Head (*Curriculum*): L Roberts, BA, PGCE
Deputy Head (*Pastoral & Administration*): Mrs C Adler, BA, Dip Dys Inst

Age Range. 7–13.

Number of Pupils. Day: 249 Boys, 149 Girls.

Fees per term (2007-2008). £4,151.

Belmont is situated in the Green Belt on the borders of Hertfordshire and Middlesex, yet is only ten miles from central London. It stands in about 35 acres of its own woods and parkland and enjoys the advantages of a truly rural environment, but at the same time the capital's cultural facilities are easily accessible.

Belmont is part of the Mill Hill School Foundation; the Pre-Prep Grimsdell and Mill Hill School are situated less than a quarter of a mile away. Opened in 1912, Belmont takes its name from the original mansion built on the Ridgeway about the middle of the eighteenth century. Successive alterations and additions have provided a chapel, a gymnasium, music-rooms, science laboratories and a fully resourced ICT room, ample games fields, five all-weather cricket nets, two all-weather cricket pitches, and six hard tennis courts. A major building and refurbishment programme has recently been undertaken to provide a large new multi-purpose hall, junior classroom block, a new resources centre, design technology room, additional music teaching space and catering facilities.

Use is made of the five courts, and the indoor heated swimming-pool at Mill Hill School.

The School became co-educational in 1995 and in September 2005 40% of the pupils were girls.

The usual age of entry is at 7 or 11 years, but 8, 9 and 10-year-olds are considered as vacancies occur. It is expected that most children will pass to Mill Hill at the end of Year 8 via a competitive examination, but some may be prepared for entry to other senior schools.

There is a permanent teaching staff of 40, with 20 visiting teachers for Instrumental Music, supportive English and Mathematics, Ballet and Fencing. There is a full-time Matron and a visiting counsellor while the school's catering is entrusted to a national company.

The main games are Rugby, Soccer, Cricket, Hockey, Netball and Rounders, but minor sports also flourish, as do instrumental and choral music, drama, and many out-of school activities. There are French exchanges with Belmont's 'twin' school in Rouen, and all the children take part in the Summer Activities Programme, which includes for senior children a Geography field trip and an outward bound week.

Charitable status. The Mill Hill School Foundation is a Registered Charity, number 1064758. It exists to provide education for boys and girls.

Belmont School

Feldemore Holmbury St Mary Dorking Surrey RH5 6LQ
Tel: 01306 730852
Fax: 01306 731220
e-mail: schooloffice@belmont-school.org
website: www.belmont-school.org

Chairman of the Governors: Mr N Butcher

***Headmistress*: Mrs H Skrine**, BA Hons Exeter, PGCE London, NPQH, FRSA

Age Range. 2–13.

Number of Pupils. 260 Boys and Girls: Day, Weekly and Flexible Boarding.

Fees per term (2008-2009). Day Pupils: £3,425 (Years 3 to 8), £2,260 (Years 1 and 2), £2,010 (Early Years pro rata). Boarding: £1,615 supplement.

Founded in London in 1880, the School is now established in 65 acres of wooded parkland overlooking the picturesque village of Holmbury St Mary, between Guildford and Dorking. The main house, Feldemore, was completely refurbished in the early 1990s so that the school now boasts an historic building with a purpose-built interior. Outstanding facilities include a brand new Early Years building, impressive sports hall, a well-equipped theatre, two state-of-the-art computer suites, newly-refurbished Science lab and woodland adventure courses. These, together with our friendly, talented staff and confident, happy boys and girls, make Belmont the very best choice you could make for your child.

We offer co-educational day education for boys and girls aged 2 to 13, and optional weekly boarding or flexible boarding arrangements. We prepare children for Common Entrance and Scholarship examinations to a wide range of schools, and will assist children in preparing for other Senior Schools that have their own admissions procedures.

Here, every child matters and we look to develop children as individuals, seeking to inspire, to encourage self-esteem and to unfurl the hidden strengths of every boy or girl. There is a happy, industrious atmosphere and high expectations pervade throughout all aspects of school life. In addition, we have a challenging curriculum and an extensive array of extra-curricular opportunities which together are designed to captivate the imaginations of every boy and girl. Creativity is a particular strength of the school and pervades throughout the curriculum. The teaching staff is well qualified and healthy pupil : staff ratios have enabled us to develop a flexible setting system within a small school.

The curriculum covers all the required Common Entrance subjects plus Drama, Art, DT, IT, Music, PSHCE, PE and Games. Sports include Netball, Rugby, Football, Hockey, Tennis, Swimming, Cricket, Athletics and Rounders depending upon the sex of the child.

Moon Hall is our tenant specialist school offering expert help for children with dyslexia. Operating within the grounds of Belmont School, it is able to draw upon all the resources and facilities we have. Pupils at Moon Hall integrate with those in the main school for Games, PE, assemblies, design classes, lunch and break times. They also take part in many of the school's extra-curricular activities such as the theatre productions. Many of the Moon Hall pupils board at Belmont. If a pupil is able to, he or she may transfer to the main school, usually into Year 6, and continue to have full support in English through Years 7 and 8. He or she can also continue to go to Moon Hall as often as necessary to ensure their continued progress.

Children are assessed prior to entry and this requires a half day or full day visit to the school, depending on age. Further details can be obtained from the Registrar, Mrs Kaye Gabriel. Children who are extremely dyslexic may be required to enter via Moon Hall (*see also Moon Hall School entry.*)

Charitable status. Belmont School (Feldemore) Educational Trust Limited is a Registered Charity, number 312077.

Berkhampstead School

Pittville Circus Road Cheltenham Glos GL52 2QA
Tel: 01242 523263
Fax: 01242 514114
e-mail: head.berkhampstead@btconnect.com
website: www.berkhampsteadschool.co.uk

Chairman of Governors: Mrs R Hope

***Headmaster*: T R Owen**, BEd, MA

Age Range. 3–11 co-educational.

Number of Pupils. 250 day pupils.

Fees per term (2008-2009). Nursery £900–£1,352. Pre-Prep: £1,674 (Reception and Year 1), £1,908 (Year 2). Prep: £2,079 (Year 3), £2,231 (Year 4), £2,335 (Years 5 and 6). Lunches: £179.

Berkhampstead School was founded over 60 years ago and continues to thrive today. Most of our pupils enter the school in the Nursery, which has its own team of teachers and nursery nurses and is situated in a purpose-built block that has recently been extended.

Parents comment on the wonderful, happy atmosphere and the stimulating environment that exists throughout the school.

Classes are small, never exceeding 18, and the curriculum is wide-ranging and offers many opportunities for individuals to develop their talents.

All major team sports are taught and a range of after-school sports clubs extend the activities offered. Gymnastics and swimming are core elements of the PE curriculum.

There are several choirs and bands and pupils have the opportunity to learn a variety of instruments in addition to their music lessons.

Drama is taught throughout the school and all pupils are involved in stage productions.

Art is another successful subject, and pupils are encouraged to enter local exhibitions.

The school has an enviable academic reputation, with over 20% of its pupils gaining Scholarships to many senior independent schools every year.

Pastoral care is also of a very high standard and a simple knowledge of Christ is woven gently into the life of the school.

In 2003 the Prep Department opened a new Art and Music block with extra classrooms and other facilities. A new Early Years centre opened in 2007.

Charitable status. Berkhampstead School is a Registered Charity, number 325018, which exists for the development of excellent education for children.

Berkhamsted Collegiate Preparatory School

Kings Road Berkhamsted Hertfordshire HP4 3YP
Tel: 01442 358201/2
Fax: 01442 358203
e-mail: prepadmin@bcschool.org
website: www.berkhamstedcollegiateschool.org.uk

Chairman of Governors: Mr P J Williamson

Principal: Dr P Chadwick, MA, PhD, FRSA

***Head*: Mr A J Taylor**, BA, CertEd

Deputy Head: Mrs J L Howard, CertEd
Second Deputy: Mr D Brown
Head of Pre-Prep: Mrs M Hall, BA, CertEd

Age Range. 3–11.

Number of Pupils. 225 boys, 231 girls.

Fees per term (from April 2008). Nursery: £1,030 (half day), £2,190 (full day). Preparatory: £2,585–£3,453.

Berkhamsted Collegiate Preparatory School opened in September 1998 as a new co-educational school, offering first-class facilities for the 3 to 11 age group, in conjunction with the highest standards of teaching and educational development. All classes offer a happy, caring environment where children are encouraged to investigate and explore the world around them. Classes at all levels have access to computers. Key features include a new multi-purpose hall, modern dining facilities, a full range of specialist classrooms (eg Science laboratory, ICT suite) and nursery units. The Preparatory School also has use of Senior School facilities including extensive playing fields, tennis courts and swimming pool. A new Sports Centre and swimming pool opened in April 2004.

A recent ISI Inspection (February 2006) noted outstanding strengths in spiritual and moral development, excellent behaviour and results which place the school in the top 5% nationally.

Nursery. "Stepping Stones is an excellent nursery" *Ofsted report.*

The Stepping Stones department has provided nursery education for boys and girls aged 3 and 4 since 1991. It continues to grow in popularity with parents and is housed within a recently refurbished building, St David's House. A carefully structured curriculum encourages the development of basic skills with a broad and balanced programme of learning and play. Literacy and numeracy are taught from the entry class onwards and scientific thinking is developed through experiment and problem solving. Children are also encouraged to express themselves through art, music and drama.

Infants and Juniors. All children are encouraged to develop to their full potential and grow in confidence and independence. The School's general approach is progressive, while retaining traditional values and standards; courtesy and politeness towards others are expected at all times. Academic achievement is of great importance, but the emphasis on other activities such as sports and music ensures that pupils receive a well-rounded education.

At this level, literacy and numeracy are the key foundation skills, but subjects such as science, history, geography, religious studies, French, art, design, information technology, music and drama gain increasing prominence. Form teachers take overall responsibility for each child's social and academic progress and are supported by specialist teachers covering subjects such as science, music and sport.

A wide range of extra-curricular activities are offered at lunch-time, the end of the school day and on Saturday mornings, including art, drama, music and sport. Choirs and orchestras perform in concerts and services throughout the year and sports teams compete successfully.

Charitable status. Berkhamsted Collegiate School is a Registered Charity, number 311056. It is a leading Charitable School in the field of Junior and Secondary Education.

Bickley Park School

24 Page Heath Lane Bickley Bromley Kent BR1 2DS
Tel: 020 8467 2195
Fax: 020 8325 5511
e-mail: info@bickleyparkschool.co.uk
website: www.bickleyparkschool.co.uk

Chairman of Governors: Mr J S Tiley

***Headmaster*: P M Ashley**, MBA, BA, CertEd

Age Range. Boys 3–13, Girls 3–4.

Number of Pupils. 380 Boys, 20 Girls.

Fees per term (2008-2009). From £1,345 (Nursery) to £3,800 (Boys in Years 7 & 8). There are no compulsory extras.

Bickley Park School, founded in 1918, occupies two sites in Bickley, the Prep at 24 Page Heath Lane and the Pre-Prep at 14 Page Heath Lane. The school has excellent modern facilities to complement the original Victorian buildings. Both sites are extremely attractive and the school's sports field is on the opposite side of the road.

The Nursery provides a very caring and stimulating environment for children to start their school lives. At Pre-Prep level, the children are cared for by a class teacher with the addition of specialist teaching for Music and Games. Classes are kept small with none exceeding 18 in total.

In the Prep Department, the children are introduced to more specialist teaching and setting for Mathematics, English, Science and French is introduced. The curriculum is broad with the emphasis being placed on encouraging the children to develop their potential to the full in a very caring environment. There is a wide range of extra curricular activities and a full sports programme. The major sports played are football, rugby and cricket, whilst athletics and tennis are also offered.

The majority of children leave at 13+ through the Common Entrance or Scholarship examinations whilst a small number leave at 11 to join local Grammar Schools.

The Parents Association, run by parents and staff, arrange events, both social and fund-raising, during the year.

Visitors are made very welcome.

Charitable status. Bickley Park School Limited is a Registered Charity, number 307915. It exists to provide a broad curriculum for boys aged 3–13 and girls aged 3–4.

Bilton Grange

Dunchurch Rugby CV22 6QU
Tel: 01788 810217
Fax: 01788 816922
e-mail: hmsec@biltongrange.co.uk
website: www.biltongrange.co.uk

The school is registered as an Educational Trust under the Charities Act and is controlled by a Board of Governors.

Chairman of Governors: J B Greenhalgh, Esq

***Headmaster*: J P Kirk**, BSc, FRSA

Senior Staff:
Deputy Headmaster: Giles Tollit, BA Hons
Assistant Headmaster: Paul Nicholson, BA Hons, PGCE
Director of Studies: (*to be appointed*)
Head of Pre Prep: Adrian Brindley, BSc, MA, PGCE

Age Range. 4–13.

Number of Pupils. 340 boys and girls of whom 55 are boarders. Preparatory (8–13 year olds): 210 pupils; Pre-Preparatory (4–7 year olds): 130 pupils.

Fees per term (from April 2008). Preparatory: Boarding £5,900, Day £4,230–£4,800. Pre-Preparatory: £2,510–£3,020.

Bursaries for those whose parents cannot afford full fees, for Service children, third child and scholarships are also available.

Bilton Grange, Warwickshire aspires to be the foremost co-educational prep school in the country.

The school, which was established in 1887, prides itself on bringing out the very best in every child. Children are extremely happy at the school, and in a nurturing, inspiring and caring environment, children confidently find their true potential.

Bilton Grange offers a diverse range of opportunities all designed to support individual accomplishments. Here, children share common values of respect, awareness of others and courtesy. They are usually 'all-rounders', willing to take advantage of all the opportunities open to them – be it on the sports field, on an adventure weekend or in the classroom.

This sense of pride in the school was recently confirmed by external inspection. Bilton Grange was rated 'Outstanding' for quality of education, spiritual, moral, social and cultural development, facilities, boarding provision, leadership and management in the 2008 ISI inspection report. Ofsted boarding Inspectors also rated Bilton Grange as 'Outstanding'.

According to ISI Inspectors, "Pupils enjoy a rich childhood; they are articulate and imaginative, enthusiastic and confident, friendly and courteous. Outstanding provision begins in Reception and this is maintained throughout years 1 to 8. A quarter of all lessons observed by Inspectors were outstanding. The school provides an environment where pupils grow and blossom. The high calibre of the teaching staff has a direct bearing on the quality of education provided. The governance, leadership and management have transformed the school since the previous ISI inspection."

The school has 340 children aged 4–13 and is set in 160 secure acres of sports fields, woods, and landscaped gardens dominated by a 19th Century Pugin mansion. A Montessori Nursery school caters for the 3 to 4 years olds in morning and afternoon sessions.

Both full and flexible boarding are offered – with around 55 boarders divided equally between boys and girls.

Bilton Grange is not academically selective. Class sizes rarely exceed 16 and all classrooms are fitted with interactive whiteboards and the highest level of IT resources.

Children are entered for the Common Entrance Examination and Eton, Oundle, Rugby, Uppingham, Wycombe Abbey are the principal schools to which Bilton Grange children progress. Approximately 25%–30% of Year 8 children win senior school awards in any one year.

Bursaries are available for children aged 7–11 in recognition of academic, music, artistic or sporting potential. Fee reductions of 90% are available subject to income. Bursary selection day takes place around the third Saturday in February.

Facilities include a 9-hole golf course, shooting range, theatre, indoor heated pool and chapel. Hockey is a particular strength of the school.

Music is also a very important part of school life and Bilton Grange is one of very few prep schools to have a CD of its own original music.

Out-of-school activities include international tours, outward bound activity, sporting and creative opportunities.

In 2008, parents rated the school very highly for providing a happy and secure environment, offering outstanding breadth of opportunity, having a talented, dedicated and friendly team of staff and offering excellent resources.

We encourage all prospective parents and children to visit the school to see and experience teaching and learning of the highest standards in an inspiring setting.

Charitable status. Bilton Grange Trust is a Registered Charity, number 528771. It exists to provide education for boys and girls.

Birchfield School

Albrighton Wolverhampton WV7 3AF
Tel: 01902 372534
Fax: 01902 373516
e-mail: office@birchfieldschool.co.uk
website: www.birchfieldschool.co.uk

Chairman of the Governors: B Frankling

***Headmaster*: Richard Merriman**, MA, BSc Hons

Age Range. 4–13.

Number of Pupils. 156 of whom 19 are weekly boarders. Preparatory (8–13 year olds) 104. Pre-Prep (4–7 year olds) 52.

Fees per term (2007-2008). Weekly boarding £4,587, Day: Years 3–8 £3,412, Year 2 £2,842, Juniors (Reception–Year 1) £2,130.

These are exciting times for Birchfield School. The last Independent Schools Inspectorate report in October 2007 described us as a 'very welcoming community with outstanding pastoral care and relationships'.

Birchfield's academic staff consist of many subject specialists who operate from well-equipped classrooms and modern facilities such as a music suite, science laboratory, design and technology workshop and art studio, and library. There are two ICT suites with networked PCs.

Sport is a fundamental part of school life and with superb playing fields, floodlit sports area and an outdoor swimming pool, Birchfield enjoys a national sporting reputation. From September 2008, Birchfield will boast a new synthetic sports surface which will be used for a variety of sports and by all age groups.

Birchfield also encourages self-expression through music, drama, art and design technology. The Music Department holds regular concerts and our musicians have performed with professional bodies in major productions. The pupils are also involved in a wide-range of extra-curricular activities.

The school has a well-resourced Learning Enhancement department with two members of staff who provide excellent support for pupils with special educational needs. For those demonstrating strong academic prowess a scholarship form is in place during the final years.

Birchfield has a fine reputation for its all-round holistic education.

In recent years senior pupils have achieved numerous scholarships and awards. There is a rich and challenging programme for pupils up to the age of 13, including the opportunity to board in the final years. When the time comes to say goodbye, senior pupils are prepared for entry into a wide range of independent senior schools and local grammar schools which suit best the individual's needs.

The headmaster's wife is in charge of catering and domestic arrangements and there is a full-time school nurse.

Co-educational nursery Prepcare (managed by Prepcare LLP) opened on the Birchfield School site in September 2005. It welcomes children from 6 weeks to 4 years old, all year round (except weekends and Bank Holidays) from 8.00 am until 6.00 pm. Girls joined our reception class in September 2006 and are progressing through the school.

Set in 20 acres of attractive grounds and playing fields, Birchfield School is close to Wolverhampton and Telford and boasts excellent transport links.

Charitable status. Birchfield School is a Registered Charity, number 528420.

Birkdale Preparatory School

Clarke House Clarke Drive Sheffield S10 2NS
Tel: 0114 267 0407
Fax: 0114 268 2929
e-mail: prepschool@birkdaleschool.org.uk
website: www.birkdaleschool.org.uk

Chairman of Governors: Revd S A P Hunter, JP, MA

***Acting Head of Preparatory School*: J R Leighton**, BEd
Head of Preparatory School (*from January 2009*): C J Burch, BA, PGCE

Age Range. 4–11.

Number of Boys. 267 day boys.

Fees per term (2008-2009). Pre-Preparatory Department £2,267; Preparatory Department £2,682.

Birkdale has grown and developed since the post war years into a school offering a continuous curriculum for boys aged 4 to 18 and girls in the Sixth Form.

This expansion led to the reorganisation of the school and in 1988 a new Preparatory School was established at Clarke House, situated in a pleasant residential area near the University and close to the Senior School. The school has a firm Christian tradition and this, coupled with the size of the school, ensures that the boys develop their own abilities, whether academic or otherwise, to the full.

The Pre-Preparatory Department is accommodated in a self contained wing of the school but enjoys full use of the well-resourced facilities of the Preparatory School. Specialist subject teaching across the curriculum starts at the age of 7 and setting in the core subjects in the final two years enhances, still further, the pupil teacher ratio.

The school has its own Matron and pastoral care is given high priority. Boys are encouraged to join a wide variety of clubs and societies in their leisure time. Music plays a significant part in school life, both in and out of the timetable. There is a large choir, brass band and orchestra and there are strong choral links with Sheffield Cathedral where many of the choristers are Birkdalians.

Cricket, Association and Rugby Football are played on the School's own substantial playing fields, which are within easy reach of the school. Instruction in Tennis and Judo are available as part of the extensive extra curricular programme.

The majority of boys pass into the Senior School.

Charitable status. Birkdale School is a Registered Charity, number 1018973, and a Company Limited by Guarantee, registered in England, number 2792166. It exists to provide education for boys.

Bishop's Stortford College Junior School

Maze Green Road Bishop's Stortford Herts CM23 2PH
Tel: 01279 838607
Fax: 01279 306110
e-mail: jsadmissions@bsc.biblio.net
website: www.bishops-stortford-college.herts.sch.uk

Chairman of Governors: J R Tee, MA

***Head*: J A Greathead**, BEd Bangor

Age Range. 4–13.

Number of Pupils. 31 boarders and 513 day pupils.

Fees per term (2008-2009). Full Boarders £4,376–£4,761; Weekly Boarders £4,332–£4,713; Day £3,221–£3,613; Pre-Prep £2,112. There are no compulsory extras.

Bishop's Stortford College is a friendly, co-educational, day and boarding community providing high academic standards, good discipline and an excellent all-round education.

There are 50 full-time members of staff, and a small number of Senior School staff also teach in the Junior School. Being on the same campus as the Senior School, many College facilities (language laboratory, art and technology centres, music school, computer room, sports hall, swimming pool, all-weather pitches, dining hall, medical centre) are shared. The Junior School also has its own buildings, with the main building containing multi-purpose Hall, laboratories, IT centre and classrooms and a more recent building containing library, art room and classrooms. An innovative, interactive science centre was opened in 2006.

The Junior School routine and curriculum are appropriate to the 7–13 age range, with pupils being prepared for Common Entrance and Senior Schools' Scholarships, although most children proceed to the College Senior School. There are 29 forms streamed by general ability and setted for Maths. High standards of work and behaviour are expected and the full development, in a happy and friendly atmosphere, of each child's abilities in sport and the Arts is actively encouraged. A strong swimming tradition exists and many of the Staff are expert coaches of the major games (rugby, hockey, cricket, netball, rounders and tennis). The choirs and orchestra flourish throughout the year, and two afternoons of Activities provide opportunities for pupils to participate in many minor sports, outdoor pursuits, crafts, computing and chess. Six major dramatic productions occur every year.

A Pre-Prep Department for 4–6 year olds was opened in 1995 and new purpose-built accommodation for the Pre-Prep opened in September 2005.

The Junior School is run on boarding lines with a six-day week and a 5 pm finish on four days with Wednesdays ending at 4 pm and Saturdays at 3 pm. The 7 and 8 year olds have a slightly shorter day and separate classrooms.

Entry tests for 7, 8, 9, 10, 11 year olds are held each January; Academic, Music and Art Scholarships are available at 10+ and 11+, as are Bursaries.

Charitable status. The Incorporated Bishop's Stortford College Association is a Registered Charity, number 311057. Its aims and objectives are to provide high quality Independent Boarding and Day education for boys and girls from age 4 to 18.

Bishopsgate School

Englefield Green Surrey TW20 0YJ
Tel: 01784 432109
Fax: 01784 430460
e-mail: headmaster@bishopsgate.surrey.sch.uk
website: www.bishopsgate-school.co.uk

Chair of Governors: Mrs H Matthews

***Headmaster*: A H Cowell**, BEd

Age Range. 2½–13.

Number of Pupils. 320, 14 Weekly Boarders.

Fees per term (2008-2009). Weekly Boarders: £900 (4 nights in addition to Day fee). Day: £3,715 (Years 5–8), £2,425–£3,285 (Reception–Year 4); Nursery £2,280 (full-time).

Set in beautiful woodland, close to Windsor Great Park, Bishopsgate is blessed with a glorious learning environment. The heart of the school remains a large, Victorian house, but recent developments have included a multi-purpose hall, brand new classroom blocks for both Lower and Upper Schools, and an all-weather pitch. A new library and performing arts centre opened in 2007. Bishopsgate is superbly equipped with Science Laboratory, Art and Design Studio, Music School, ICT Suite, heated swimming pool and extensive playing fields.

Children may enter Bishopsgate from the age of 2½ into our cosy Pre-Nursery or at 3 into our Nursery. Our trained staff and well equipped rooms ensure that each child is given the best possible start to life. There is a warm family atmosphere as we recognise how important it is for children to feel happy and secure. We place great emphasis on building a solid foundation of social skills and a love of learning, which will enable each child to settle confidently to school life. A wide variety of activities is on offer with plenty of opportunities for healthy outdoor learning.

Beyond Nursery, a class teacher remains at the core of your child's learning. Emphasis is placed on establishing a firm foundation in literacy and numeracy, but the curriculum is broad with a range of educational visits planned to enrich and extend the children's learning. Good use is made of our glorious grounds as a learning resource. The teaching of French, Music, PE, Singing and Dance is provided by specialist teachers.

Form-based teaching continues in Years Three and Four, but by Year Five all teaching is by subject specialists. Programmes of study in Upper School are full and varied, covering the traditional academic subjects as well as Art, Design, Music, Information and Communication Technology, PSHE and Physical Education. The children are prepared carefully for entrance to a range of senior schools and we are proud of our record of success. We prepare children for 11+ entry to senior schools, but we prefer our children to remain with us to 13.

In Upper School, opportunities to represent the school in sports teams, plays, choirs and instrument groups are all part of the 'Bishopsgate Experience'. In addition, a busy programme of extra-curricular activities ensures that all children have the opportunity to shine at something.

Music plays an essential part in the life of the school with many of our pupils enjoying individual music lessons. There are choirs and ensembles. Participation by children of all abilities, with ample opportunities to perform, is our aim. Dramatic productions, dance and public speaking events all provide additional occasions when the children can perform on stage.

Our vibrant Art and Design Department occupies a spacious studio equipped with a kiln for ceramics and a printing press for design projects. There is an annual art exhibition for both Lower and Upper Schools and the children's work is displayed proudly around the school and in our annual school magazine. There is a popular after-school Art club for children and regular workshops for parents.

Team Games, Athletics, Dance, Tennis, Gymnastics, Tae Kwon Do, Swimming and much more are all included in a varied and exciting sporting programme within the school day. An extensive programme of inter-school fixtures is arranged each term and we like to see as many parents in support as possible! We like to win, but our priorities are participation, enjoyment and teamwork.

Bishopsgate is a thriving community and we encourage the active involvement of our parents.

Weekly boarding (Monday to Thursday) is available.

A prospectus and further details can be obtained from the School Office.

Charitable status. Bishopsgate School is a Registered Charity, number 1060511. It aims to provide a broad and sound education for its pupils with thorough and personal pastoral care.

Blackheath Nursery & Preparatory School

4 St German's Place London SE3 0NJ
Tel: 020 8858 0692
Fax: 020 8858 7778
e-mail: info@blackheathprepschool.com
website: www.blackheathprepschool.com

Co-educational Day School.

Chairman of Governors: Mr Hugh Stallard

***Headmistress*: Mrs P J Thompson**

Age Range. 3–11.

Number of Pupils. 166 Girls, 163 Boys.

Fees per term (2008-2009). Nursery: £1,400–2,250; Reception–Year 2 £2,700; Years 3–6 £2,940.

The school is located in an attractive residential area close to Blackheath village, overlooking the heath itself and borders of Greenwich Park. The five-acre site includes attractive playing fields, cricket nets, tennis courts and two playgrounds, providing enviable sporting opportunities and room for children to play.

A rigorous refurbishment and building programme has resulted in an attractive learning environment. Lessons may take place in one of the 17 form rooms; in addition there are dedicated specialist rooms for Science, ICT, Art, DT, Maths and Music. A most attractive library encourages a real love of literature. A new spacious multi-purpose hall and music suite have increased opportunities for music, drama, sport and leisure activities.

Most children join the school in the nursery at the age of three and progress through the Pre-Prep (4–7) and Prep (7–11) before leaving to transfer to selective senior schools. Academic standards are high and pupils are well prepared for selection at 11 and achieve consistent success in obtaining places at their first choice of grammar or independent senior school.

The form teacher of every class is responsible for the pastoral welfare of each child. In the Nursery and the Pre-Prep the key worker and the form teacher are primarily responsible for teaching the children. However, there is a strong emphasis on specialist teaching from the very beginning. Music, French, PE and dance are introduced in the nursery. As the children progress through the school, more specialist teachers are responsible for ICT, Drama, Design Technology, Maths, English and Science.

The quality of teaching has been recognised as one of the many strengths of the school. The dedicated and committed staff enjoy excellent relations with their pupils who achieve very good standards by the time they leave the school. Pupils display real pleasure in their learning.

The school positively encourages parental involvement in the daily life of the school. The strong ethos and vision of the school is underpinned by the considerable enthusiasm of all involved and by the very strong sense of community.

The Blue Coat School

Somerset Road Edgbaston Birmingham B17 0HR
Tel: 0121 410 6800
Fax: 0121 454 7757
e-mail: admissions@bluecoat.bham.sch.uk
website: www.bluecoat.bham.sch.uk

Founded 1722. Co-educational Day Preparatory School. Accredited by the Independent Schools Council.

Chairman of Governors: Professor J N Hay, DSc, BSc, PhD, CChem, FRSC

***Headmaster*: A D J Browning**, MA (Cantab), PGCE

Deputy Head: C R Lynn, MA, MIL

Age Range. 2–11.

Number of Pupils. The total enrolment is 549 children. Pre-Prep has 284 girls and boys from 2–7 years, while Prep has 265 from 7–11 years.

There is a graduate and qualified full-time teaching staff of 36 and 12 part-time teachers, giving a teacher/pupil ratio of 1:12.

Fees per term (2007-2008). Pre-Prep: £1,925–£2,415; Prep: £2,855–£2,965. The fees quoted include lunches and morning and afternoon breaks. A range of some 50 activities may be taken as extras.

Assisted Places are available at greatly reduced charges to children with a demonstrable financial need.

Scholarships are offered for academic and musical excellence from age 7+.

The School is set in 15 acres of grounds and playing fields just 2 miles from the centre of Birmingham. Its well-designed buildings and facilities comprise the Chapel, the Administrative Building, the Prep Teaching Centre, the Pre-Prep Department, the Pre-School, sports pitches, tennis courts and a superb multi-purpose Sports Centre with a heated 25m swimming pool. After-school care is provided in two spacious, purpose-designed Houses.

Additional features include the School Library and specialist facilities for Science, Art, Design and Technology and ICT.

Children are prepared for scholarships and examinations to prestigious local schools. The school enjoys particular success in the 11+ examinations to Birmingham's grammar schools and the schools of the King Edward VI Foundation. The National Curriculum is incorporated at Key Stages 1 and 2 as part of a wider academic structure.

The school places great emphasis on Music, basing its approach on the Kodály Concept. The robed Chapel Choir is affiliated to the RSCM, and there are three further choirs, a School Orchestra and a significant number of instrumental groups. The school benefits from *Sibelius* software, used in the teaching of composition, and from a Steinway Concert Grand.

The main sports are Hockey, Netball, Rounders, Rugby, Soccer, Cricket, Tennis, Athletics and Swimming. The teams enjoy considerable success in inter-school competitions and all children have the opportunity to develop their skills.

Extra-curricular activities include Mandarin Chinese, Gymnastics, Judo, Ballet, Drama, Sign Language, Speech Training, Chess, Table Tennis and Dance. Excursions and field courses are available each year, together with a leadership training programme.

Charitable status. The Blue Coat School, Birmingham is a Registered Charity, number 528805. It exists to provide education of quality for children of Preparatory School age.

Blundell's Preparatory School

Milestones House Blundell's Road Tiverton Devon EX16 4NA
Tel: 01884 252393
Fax: 01884 232333
e-mail: prep@blundells.org
website: www.blundells.org

Chairman of Governors: His Hon Judge W E M Taylor

***Headmaster*: Mr N A Folland**

Age Range. 2½–11 years.

Numbers of Pupils. Boys and Girls: Prep (aged 7–11) 135; Pre-Prep (aged 2½–7) 148.

Fees per term (2008-2009). Prep £2,775 (Lunch £217), Pre-Prep £546–£2,115 (Lunch £185).

Blundell's Preparatory School is a family school and all the staff adopt a personal interest in every child and work in partnership with the parents. The school places great emphasis on children being happy, secure and confident, thus offering individuals every opportunity to achieve their full potential within a caring family atmosphere.

The School has been established for over seventy years and is part of the Blundell's Charitable Trust. It enjoys its own separate site within the very extensive Blundell's campus. This rural setting is within easy reach of the market town of Tiverton and is conveniently placed less than ten minutes from the M5 motorway and Tiverton Parkway Station.

The School has an excellent reputation for providing the essentials. Sound academic standards are based on providing the core subjects of Maths, English and Science taught to an extremely high standard. Added to this is the bonus of a wide range of supplementary subjects, well taught by specialist teachers. The School has recently had a major redevelopment and a significant extension. This includes a fully-equipped Art & Design Centre and a new Food Technology Suite.

Drama, music and art flourish at Blundell's Preparatory School with all the children participating fully both in lessons and as part of extra-curricular activities. Specialist music teachers offer an extensive variety of different instruments. The Drama and Music department have their own dedicated facility.

The sports department has an enviable reputation of producing good all-round sporting pupils, as well as nurturing and extending those with talent. Amongst the sports offered are rugby, football, netball, hockey and cross-country in the winter and cricket, rounders, tennis, athletics and swimming in the summer. The Preparatory School has access to the extensive sporting facilities within Blundell's campus.

There is an comprehensive choice of extra-curricular activities offered to the pupils which includes ballet, chess, fencing, golf, choir, judo, environment club and woodwork.

Priority entrance to Blundell's is given to its Preparatory School pupils but the school's autonomous position ensures that, if wished for, the pupils are prepared for entrance, including scholarships, to a variety of other senior schools.

(*See also Blundell's School entry in HMC section.*)

Charitable status. Blundell's School is a Registered Charity, number 1081249. It exists to provide education for children.

Bodiam Manor School

Bodiam Robertsbridge East Sussex TN32 5UJ
Tel: 01580 830225
Fax: 01580 830227
e-mail: office@bodiammanorschool.co.uk
website: www.bodiammanorschool.co.uk

***Headmaster*: S P Flutter**, BEd

Age Range. 3–13.

Number of Pupils. 147: 80 Boys, 67 Girls.

Fees per term (2008-2009). Nursery (3–4 yrs) £1,804, Reception (4–5 yrs) £1,990, Form 1 (5–6 yrs) £2,184, Form 2 (6–7 yrs) £2,310, Forms 3–4 (7–9 yrs) £3,469; Forms 5–8 (10–13 yrs) £3,599.

Bodiam Manor is a co-educational school with an integral nursery and pre-preparatory department.

Overlooking Bodiam Castle and set in 11 acres of beautiful countryside on the East Sussex/Kent border, Bodiam is a family-run school founded in 1955. School finishes at 4 pm for younger pupils and all extra-curricular activities finish by 5.30 pm for older pupils. There is no Saturday morning school but activities such as trampoline, swimming, mini-rugby and cricket are available on Saturdays.

The curriculum is geared to Common Entrance examinations to senior independent schools and Cranbrook Grammar. Over the years many pupils have achieved scholarships at the senior level.

Bodiam has the reputation of being a happy school. Given the right conditions, children who are happy will enjoy learning and will want to achieve.

The opportunities offered to pupils are wide and varied and the school day is a very busy one, as was highlighted in our recent inspection. Music, dance, drama, gymnastics, swimming and trampolining are particularly strong. The annual school ski and barge holidays and a wide range of clubs and outings are all very much part of life at Bodiam. During their time at Bodiam children are encouraged to experience a range of activities and to develop their own individual potential to the full.

Boundary Oak School

Roche Court Wickham Road Fareham Hampshire PO17 5BL
Tel: 01329 280955
Fax: 01329 827656

e-mail: secretary@boundaryoak.co.uk
website: www.boundaryoak.co.uk

Chairman of Governors: Dr C Hargreaves, BM

***Headmaster*: S R Symonds**, BA Ed Hons

Age Range. 2½–13.

Number of Pupils. 20 Boarders, 150 Day Pupils.

Fees per term (2007-2008). Full Boarders £4,750–£5,490; Weekly Boarders £3,590–£4,890; Day Pupils: £2,130–£3,430 (Reception–Year 8), Nursery £1,030–£2,010 (all day).

The school was founded in 1918 and moved to Roche Court in 1960. A new 99 year lease was secured in 1994. The school is set in 22 acres of pleasant, self-contained grounds between Fareham and Wickham in Hampshire and enjoys extensive views of the countryside around.

Boundary Oak is now fully co-educational in all respects with girls' boarding established in totally refurbished accommodation.

The Nursery Department takes children from the age of 2½ to rising 5 and this group is housed in a purpose-built centre offering the most up-to-date facilities. This department is structured to the needs of this age group and the day can extend from 8.00 am to either 12 noon or 5.30 pm.

The Junior Department has its own purpose-built buildings and other facilities within the school, a staff of nine teachers, and caters for children from rising 5 to 8 years of age.

At 8 years the children move to the Senior Department where they remain until they are 13+. Full and weekly boarding are offered to all from the age of 7 years and the school has a policy of admitting boarders in a flexible system that is of great benefit to all. Pupils are prepared for a wide number of independent schools throughout the United Kingdom in a friendly and caring environment.

Apart from the historic main house of Roche Court where the boarders live, there is the Jubilee Block of classrooms, two laboratories and a Geography room in a separate building, the Widley Block, Library and the Music Centre, which incorporates a computer centred music generating complex. The School has a new ICT Suite and a recently built Art and Design Technology Centre that incorporates work areas for Photography, Pottery and Carpentry. The school has a fine Assembly Hall that is also used for Drama and Physical Education.

As well as extensive playing fields with woods beyond for cross country, three new astroturf tennis courts and a netball court, there is an outdoor swimming pool and the indoor Fareham Pool is within very easy reach with our three minibuses.

Most sports are taught and there is a wide selection of clubs and activities run in the school for both day and boarding pupils including judo, horse riding and sailing.

For a copy of the prospectus and full details of scholarships, please apply to the Headmaster, or view us on the internet at www.boundaryoak.co.uk.

Charitable status. Boundary Oak School Trust Ltd is a Registered Charity, number 307346. It exists to provide education for boys and girls.

Bow, Durham School

South Road Durham DH1 3LS
Tel: 0191 384 8233
Fax: 0191 384 1371
e-mail: bow@durhamschool.co.uk
website: www.durhamschool.co.uk

Chairman of Governors: A MacConachie, OBE, DL

***Headmaster*: R N Baird**, BA, PGCE

Age Range. 3–11 Co-educational.

Number of Pupils. 136 Day Pupils (girls and boys).

Fees per term (2008-2009). £1,790 (Nursery), £2,100 (Reception, Years 1 & 2), £2,520 (Years 3–6).

Bow, Durham School (formerly Bow School) is Durham School's preparatory school and caters for girls and boys aged from 3 to 11. It has been situated on its present site, half a mile from the Senior School and overlooking the cathedral, since 1888. Bow has its own extensive facilities including a fully-equipped science laboratory, IT suite, sports hall and library. An extensive modernisation and improvement programme was completed in September 2006 when Bow became co-educational. Bow pupils are also able to use all the excellent facilities at the senior site, such as the swimming pool, all-weather sports surface, the chapel and the theatre.

Academic. Bow has a fine record of academic achievement over the years and results in externally-marked examinations, such as the Key Stage 1 and 2 tests, are regularly impressive. Pupils are prepared for the Durham School 11+ entrance examination, as a result of which valuable awards are available and the overwhelming majority of pupils move into the Senior School at the age of 11. A high pupil-teacher ratio is maintained and small classes are considered vital as we seek to ensure that each child fulfils his or her academic potential.

Sport, Music and Drama. Bow has an outstanding tradition in competitive sport, many former pupils having represented their country. A wide range of sports is on offer to all pupils.

Music and drama form an integral part of life at Bow, with an active choir, jazz band and fiddle group performing regularly. In addition to their weekly class music lessons, each child has the opportunity to take part in a wide range of musical pursuits. Large numbers of pupils learn individual instruments and instruments are available for hire.

There are three drama productions each year: a nativity play (Reception, Years 1 and 2), a production for Years 3 and 4 and the senior play. Pupils are encouraged to take part in these productions whether it is on the stage or behind the scenes.

Extra-Curricular Activities. Bow offers a wide range of extra-curricular activities which are seen as a vital ingredient in the daily diet of every Bow pupil. In addition further activities and hobbies are available as voluntary after-school clubs.

Admission. Admission is possible at any age and entry is based on an interview with the Headmaster and (if appropriate) an assessment test.

Adamson Scholarships are available at Years 3 and 4 and financial support in the form of bursaries can also be offered where necessary at any age. There are generous concessions for brothers and sisters (either at Bow or at the Senior School) and for children of the Armed Forces and the clergy.

Charitable status. Durham School is a Registered Charity, number 1023407. The aim of the charity is to advance education in the North-East.

Bradford Grammar Junior School (Clock House)

Keighley Road Bradford West Yorkshire BD9 4JP
Tel: 01274 553742
Fax: 01274 553745
e-mail: chsec@bradfordgrammar.com
website: www.bradfordgrammar.com

Chairman of the Board of Governors: A H Jerome, MA

***Headmaster*: G Lee-Gallon**, BTech

Deputy Headmaster: N H Gabriel, BA, DipArch

Age Range. 6–11.

Number of Pupils. 137 boys, 55 girls.

Fees per annum (2008-2009). £7,424.

Bradford Grammar Junior School is located on the same site as the senior school, in the original seventeenth century manor house, Clock House. The manor house has been extended and refurbished and the thoughtful blending of the old with the new has created a school of style and spaciousness.

The school offers pupils a wide range of specialist facilities, including a swimming pool, theatre, instrumental music tuition, dedicated ICT and DT rooms and science laboratories. In Years 2, 3 and 4 the pupils are taught mostly by their form teachers, in Years 5 and 6 they are taught by specialist teachers within Clock House, though some specialist teaching from staff in the senior school also takes place in Art, Science, PE and Games. The girls and boys are given a good grounding in all subjects, which prepares them well for what is required in the senior school.

Extra-curricular activities take place at lunchtime. There is a long tradition of excellence in sport, music and drama. Winter sports include rugby, netball, hockey, swimming, cross-country and football. In the summer children play cricket, rounders and take part in athletics and a variety of other sports.

The Junior School is a very busy place but pastoral care permeates all the school does. Our aim is to provide young boys and girls with a wide range of educational experiences and to develop the right attitude to learning so that they fulfil their potential, in a safe, friendly, tolerant and caring environment utilising all the resources and facilities the school has to offer.

Boys and girls can enter the school at the start of Years 2, 3, 4, 5 and 6 having satisfied our entrance requirements; an informal assessment for Years 2, 3 and 4 and an entrance examination for those joining in Years 5 and 6. Invariably most of our pupils transfer to the Senior School and the close relationship between the two schools enables us to make the transition as smooth as possible.

There are excellent transport links to the school along the Wharfe and Aire Valleys and the Metro train station is a five-minute walk away, thus putting the school within easy travelling distance from Skipton, Ilkley and Keighley. The school also operates its own bus service from Huddersfield, Halifax and Leeds.

Charitable status. The Free Grammar School of King Charles II at Bradford is a Registered Charity, number 529113. It exists to provide education for children.

Braeburn School

PO Box 45112-00100, Gitanga Road, Lavington, Nairobi, Kenya
Tel: 00 254 20 3872300-2
Fax: 00 254 20 3872310
e-mail: scott.webber@braeburn.ac.ke
website: www.braeburn.com

***Headteacher*: Mr Scott Webber**

Age Range. 3–13.

Number of Pupils. 642.

Fees per term (2007-2008). Tuition: Kshs 84,600–209,500.

Braeburn is the largest British Curriculum School in Kenya, catering for children from over 70 nationalities.

At Braeburn School, our children come first. We believe that it is our responsibility to provide opportunities for all children, from the Early Years to Year 8, to excel academically and socially. Our school is a community and we recognise that each individual is important and has a valuable contribution to make towards the quality of life enjoyed by the people within it. We continually stress the importance of honesty, trust, fairness and self-discipline, mutual respect and self-esteem. We endeavour to encourage and praise good behaviour and help all children to appreciate that this is the normal expectation.

In Early Years, the curriculum is based on the "Early Learning Goals". Here we have two classes for 3–5 year-olds in 2 age groups, a dedicated play area, daily morning Nursery class, full-day provision for Reception Class, afternoon Crèche facilities. The children start learning Music, PE and Swimming and also have library time and cooking.

Our school follows the British National Curriculum. Our teaching is a combination of whole class, group and individual teaching with more specialised teaching in the subject areas of ICT, French, Swimming, PE and Music. We have a learning support team that works with individual children or small groups within a class or year group. Core subjects are: English, Mathematics, Science and Information Communication Technology (ICT). Foundation subjects are: French, History and Geography, Religious Education, Art & Design Technology, Music & Drama, Personal, Social & Health Education (including Sex Education), PE and Swimming.

Beyond the primary years, we extend into Key Stage 3 (Year 7 and Year 8). Our students enjoy the expertise of subject-based teachers as well as the pastoral support of a form tutor.

At Braeburn, we enjoy excellent facilities and resources. We have a well-stocked and up-to-date library, a centre for music, 2 computer suites, a design technology workshop, science laboratories, an art room and a fine arts and ceramics room. We also boast 2 wonderful theatres seating 120 and 420 people respectively.

Provision for sports is superb. A good-size playing field complements 3 swimming pools, 3 squash courts, 2 tennis courts, a dance studio and a large indoor sports hall.

A large and varied programme of extra-curricular activities is offered. Various martial arts, ballet, origami, squash, golf, horse riding and sailing are but a few of the activities available at lunch time, after school and at weekends.

Brambletye

East Grinstead West Sussex RH19 3PD
Tel: 01342 321004
Fax: 01342 317562
e-mail: admin@brambletye.com
website: www.brambletye.com

Chairman of Governors: A F Beazley, Esq

***Headmaster*: H D Cocke**, BA, CertEd Oxon

Deputy Headmaster: A C Callender, CertEd

Age Range. 2½–13.

Number of Pupils. 255 co-educational boarding/day pupils.

Fees per term (2008-2009). Boarders £6,180, Day Pupils £4,690–£5,930, Pre-Prep £2,410, Nursery £2,110.

Brambletye is an independent day and boarding preparatory school for boys and girls aged 7-13½ years, situated in beautiful grounds in rural Sussex. There is a pre-preparatory/nursery department which takes boys and girls from the age of 2½ years to the age of 7 years.

Brambletye is a large country house in its own wooded estate of 140 acres, overlooking Ashdown Forest and Weir Wood Reservoir. The school stands one mile south of East Grinstead. Gatwick Airport is only 20 minutes by car and Heathrow is an hour away. London is 30 miles by road and 50 minutes by rail. There is escorted travel to and from London at the beginning of all exeat weekends and half-term holidays.

The school has outstanding sporting, music, drama and arts facilities. These include an up to date Arts Room and Design Technology workshop, an extensive Library, an ICT room, a large theatre and music rooms. There is also a new Sports Hall, tennis and netball courts, two squash courts, a swimming pool and several playing fields. We aim to produce happy, confident, all-rounded children who work hard and enjoy drama, games and music, play a part in some of the numerous societies and hobbies and take a full share in the daily life of the school. These facilities in conjunction with high quality teaching staff, generate regular awards for the children from the schools that inherit them.

Brambletye has always been run along family lines, with a distinctive warm and friendly atmosphere. Traditional values such as high standards of manners and good behaviour provide a platform for academic and personal development. As a co-educational day and boarding school, pupils enjoy and benefit from living and working in a community. At weekends, there is a full programme of activities for the boarders and children are encouraged to make constructive use of their spare time. The environment is inspirational and pupils develop a love of learning which creates a positive interaction with the staff and a curiosity about the world around us.

The Nursery and Pre-Preparatory Department is situated in a self-contained purpose-built state-of-the art building. The main aim of the Department is to provide a secure, friendly and structured environment in which all children are encouraged to achieve their full potential and to develop at their own rate.

Children may join the Nursery class at the age of two and a half before progressing to Reception at four. Boys and girls transfer to the Preparatory Department at the age of seven. All children acquire the basic skills, while following the breadth of the National Curriculum. Religious Studies, Physical Education, Art, Music, Science and Technology are all integrated into the weekly timetable. Children have swimming lessons throughout the year in the indoor pool, and teachers from the Preparatory Department visit regularly to teach Music and to coach games.

Enquiries about admissions, our music scholarships and bursary programme are welcomed throughout the year. Please contact the Headmaster's Secretary for a prospectus.

Charitable status. Brambletye School Trust Limited is a Registered Charity, number 307003. It aims to provide an all round education for the children in its care.

Bramcote Lorne School (UCST)

Rectory Lane Gamston Retford Notts DN22 0QQ
Tel: 01777 838636
Fax: 01777 838633
e-mail: enquiries.bramcotelorne@church-schools.com
website: www.bramcotelorneschool.co.uk

Chair of Governors: Mrs A Kay, BA

***Headmaster*: Mr Richard M Raistrick**, BA Hons, PGCE

Age Range. 3 months – 13 years.

Number of Pupils. 10 Boarders, 170 Day Pupils.

Fees per term (2007-2008). Nursery (full-time) £1,717, Pre-Prep £1,840, Prep £2,538–£3,055. Boarding (in addition to Tuition fee): £1,017 (weekly), £1,311 (full).

Bramcote Lorne has a reputation for providing an outstanding education. It has a tradition of high standards which challenge young people not just academically but in all areas of their development within a spiritual framework. This ensures that every child has the opportunity to discover talents that they may not have realised they possessed and create friendships and relationships which will enable them to grow with confidence into adult life.

Bramcote Lorne is a day and boarding school for pupils aged three months to 13 years of age. The school is part of United Church Schools Trust, an organisation that is renowned for its high quality schools where every child is seen to be important and where each child's achievements are celebrated as a success. All involved at Bramcote Lorne share a passion for the quality of teaching and learning. Our key objective is to bring out the best in every child in an atmosphere in which they feel safe and valued, where they are happy and challenged. Our curriculum offers a broad and balanced learning experience designed to ensure that every pupil has a wide range of skills which will enable him or her to succeed in life and work.

The school enjoys exceptional ICT provision, with interactive whiteboards and provision for Design, Technical Drawing and Food Technology. Other specialist facilities include a spacious Science Laboratory, an Art Studio and Dyslexia Unit. Games facilities are excellent with a Sports Hall and extensive games fields on site. Our thriving Pre-Nursery and Nursery School feed our well-resourced Pre-Prep Department.

Within the setting of a small country estate on the fringe of one of Nottinghamshire's finest villages we enjoy excellent communications along the A1 and the rail link to London making the school very accessible for boarder parents. The school operates bus routes from villages within Nottinghamshire, Lincolnshire and South Yorkshire.

Charitable status. Bramcote Lorne School is a member of The United Church Schools Trust, which is a Registered Charity, number 1016538.

Bramcote School

Filey Road Scarborough North Yorkshire YO11 2TT
Tel: 01723 373086
Fax: 01723 364186
e-mail: info@bramcoteschool.com
website: www.bramcoteschool.com

Chairman of Governors: H A Bethell, Esq, ACA, BA Hons

***Headmaster*: A G W Lewin**, BA Hons, PGCE

Deputy Headmaster: A R Snow, BSc, PGCE

Age Range. Co-educational 4–13.

Number of Pupils. 64 boys, 60 girls.

Fees per term (2007-2008). Boarding £5,300, Day £1,995–£3,805.

Bramcote is a boarding and day preparatory school for boys and girls aged between 4 and 13 years. The school is set in its own grounds close to the sea on Scarborough's South Cliff. The school was founded on its present site in 1893 and became an Educational Trust in 1957, administered by a chairman and nine governors of wide professional and educational experience.

A girls' wing was opened twelve years ago and other recent developments have included the complete refurbishment of the boarding accommodation, improvements to the teaching facilities and a sports hall, which can be used as an indoor tennis court. The latest addition is the opening of a new Pre-Prep Department in September 2006.

The curriculum is based on the Scholarship and Common Entrance requirements for major Independent Schools throughout the country. Although the experienced, full-time teaching staff of 14 ensures that the academic standards for which Bramcote has long held a high reputation are maintained, the school caters for children of mixed ability and classes are small with extra help available where needed by the school's qualified specialist.

Bramcote's facilities and position allow a wide range of extra-curricular activities in the evenings and at weekends. Facilities include the sports hall, a modern music and art centre, theatre, fully equipped computer room, indoor swimming pool and floodlit tennis court and play areas. Frequent visits are made to the theatre and concerts, whilst the seaside and nearby National Parks give opportunities for more adventurous pursuits such as orienteering, canoeing and rambling.

The school has excellent playing fields, where football, netball, rugby, hockey, lacrosse, rounders and cricket are played as major sports, with a wide variety of alternative opportunities including tennis, athletics, squash, dance, shooting, clay pigeon shooting, golf, sailing and riding.

The school has a strong musical tradition and tuition is available for the full range of orchestral instruments and choir. The department is run by a Director of Music with 10 peripatetic staff and all pupils learn to play at least one musical instrument. The Chamber Choir visited Rome in 2007, singing at St Peter's Basilica.

Pastoral and health care is supervised by the Headmaster's wife and the Head Matron, with one medical and three assistant matrons.

For further information, parents are invited to write or to telephone the Headmaster or the school secretary for copies of a prospectus and current magazine or to arrange a visit to the school.

Charitable status. Bramcote School is a Registered Charity, number 529739. It exists to provide education for boys and girls.

Bramley School

Chequers Lane Walton-on-the-Hill Tadworth Surrey KT20 7ST
Tel: 01737 812004
Fax: 01737 819945
e-mail: office@bramleyschool.surrey.sch.uk
website: www.bramleyschool.co.uk

Chairman of Governors: Mrs A Morrell

***Headmistress*: Mrs P Burgess**, BEd Hons, MA, NPQH

Age Range. 3–11.

Number in School. 120 Girls.

Fees per term (2007-2008). £1,220–£2,666 including lunches.

Bramley was founded in 1945 as an independent pre-preparatory and preparatory day school and became an Educational Trust in 1972. A registered charity, the school is administered by a Trust Council and all income is used for educational purposes. The school has been accredited by the Independent Schools Council and the Headmistress is a member of IAPS (The Independent Association of Prep Schools).

The strength of Bramley School lies in its commitment to developing happy, confident, self-motivated pupils with a lifelong love of learning. An excellent teacher/pupil ratio; a caring friendly atmosphere; highly qualified, specialised and enthusiastic staff, and a genuine concern for each child's welfare contribute to academic success. Bramley achieves excellent examination results at 11+ and many girls gain places and scholarships to prestigious senior schools within both the independent and maintained sectors. Alongside this, children are encouraged to develop their own interests and talents and a wide range of extra curricular activities are offered.

Throughout the school girls work in small classes, according to their age group, with particular attention being paid to meeting the specific needs of individuals. All children in the Pre-Preparatory Department are taught by dedicated class teachers who have full responsibility for their classes, whilst older children benefit from specialised teaching staff, for example in Mathematics, English, Science, ICT, Music, PE and Art. A specialist teacher teaches French from the age of 5. The Preparatory Curriculum is constantly being developed to keep abreast of educational changes in the National Curriculum, whilst retaining the excellence of well-tried methods.

The Little Bramley Nursery Department is an ideal starting point for school life with literacy and numeracy skills fostered through play in a safe and nurturing environment. Children from three years of age settle quickly and happily and the newly refurbished premises allow the early curriculum to take place outdoors as well as indoors.

The Headmistress welcomes visitors to the school.

Charitable status. Bramley Educational Trust Limited is a Registered Charity, number 270046. Its aim is to provide an excellent educational establishment for 3–11 year old girls.

Brandeston Hall
Framlingham College's Preparatory School

Brandeston Hall Woodbridge Suffolk IP13 7AH
Tel: 01728 685331
Fax: 01728 685437
e-mail: office@brandestonhall.co.uk
website: www.framlingham.suffolk.sch.uk

Chairman of Governors: A W M Fane, MA, FCA

***Master*: M K Myers-Allen**, BSc Hons, PGCE

Second Master: R Sampson, BA Hons, PGCE

Age Range. $2^1/_2$–13 Co-educational.

Number of Pupils. 250: Boarders 50, Day 200; Pre-Prep 50, Nursery 25.

Fees per term (2008-2009). Boarding £5,748, Day £3,574 (inc lunch), Pre-Prep: Day £2,055 (inc lunch), Nursery: £33 (full day session inc lunch), £16 (half day session exc lunch).

Brandeston Hall is a co-educational preparatory school for $2^1/_2$–13 year olds offering boarding, and day education in an idyllic, rural setting. The school is located in a Jacobean style building dating back to the sixteenth century and it stands in its own grounds of 26 acres on the banks of the River Deben.

Boys and girls are prepared for the ISEB Common Entrance at 13 to give them the widest choice of senior schools; most enter the Senior School, Framlingham College (*see HMC entry*).

The school is very well equipped, reflecting the large number of improvements to the site over many years. There are 18 purpose-built classrooms, a Junior Science and Technology Laboratory, an Arts Studio and Ceramics Centre, a Design and Technology Centre, a specialist Music Room and self-contained Nursery and Pre-Preparatory Departments. In addition there are two Senior Science Laboratories, a well-equipped ICT Centre, music practice rooms and a generous recreation area for boarders. A large, modern multi-purpose hall further enhances the school's provision.

The school provides a friendly, caring and safe community in which each individual is encouraged to strive for the very highest levels of achievement across a broad front. The boarding facilities are warm, homely and very friendly and our experienced house-parents nurture and care for children as if they were their own. Girl boarders share homely dormitories in a purpose-built wing and boys are housed in comfortable family dormitories in the main building.

The sports facilities, which include extensive playing fields, a covered swimming pool, a full-size floodlit all-weather pitch (hockey/tennis/netball courts) and a nine-hole golf course, serve the pupils well. In addition pupils have use of the facilities at Framlingham College including the indoor swimming pool and astroturf pitch.

The main winter games for boys are Rugby and Hockey, and Hockey and Netball for girls. In the summer Rounders and Cricket predominate with Tennis, Golf, Athletics and Swimming available for all. Skilled coaching is given and a full programme of matches is arranged at all levels in major and minor sports.

Strong Music and Drama opportunities are also available including a number of music and drama productions, music recitals and drama workshops with visiting artists.

Scholarships are available for 11+ entrants in Music, Academic and Sports.

The local parish church, located within the school grounds, is used regularly by the school and is a focus for community activities.

Charitable status. Albert Memorial College is a Registered Charity, number 1114383. It exists for the purpose of educating children.

Breaside Preparatory School
Cognita Schools Group

41-43 Orchard Road Bromley Kent BR1 2PR
Tel: 020 8460 0916
Fax: 020 8466 5664
e-mail: info@breaside.co.uk
website: www.breaside.co.uk

***Headmaster*: Mr Nigel D Kynaston**, BEd Hons

Age Range. 3–11 Co-educational.
Number of Pupils. 240.
Fees per term (2008-2009). £1,438–£2,865.

Breaside is an independent IAPS co-educational day school for children aged from 3 to 11. On the Chislehurst side of Bromley it is easily reached from many parts of south-east London. We offer a rich learning environment aimed at preparing children for entry to Independent Senior and Grammar schools, and our broadly-based curriculum is complemented by a wide range of sporting and creative opportunities.

Breaside is a happy school and it is our main priority to see that all our children enjoy school and look forward to going there each day. We believe that a child with a high self-esteem will want to learn and will want to succeed. At Breaside, we offer our children many opportunities to develop and to discover their talents and we am keen to see that all our pupils take full advantage of what we provide.

At Breaside we pride ourselves on our good behaviour and discipline. As a result, the children are keen to work hard in a warm, friendly environment where expectations and boundaries are clear and well understood. We believe in getting the basics right and teaching the core subjects with a mixture of traditional teaching styles with the more modern approaches to learning. Coupled together with a strong work ethic and an enriching learning environment, we are confident that we help each child to develop towards its full potential.

We strongly believe in promoting the "3 Rs" – **R**espect for oneself, **R**espect for everyone else and taking full **R**esponsibility for one's own actions.

Breaside provides a rich learning environment for boys and girls. The curriculum prepares children for senior schools, but in addition we attach great importance to providing all our children with a balanced and broadly based education, from their first days in the kindergarten through to the age of 11.

We are very aware that learning takes place in and outside the classroom and we offer a wide range of opportunities where the children can not only do well, but can excel at what they do. In this way, our children develop their confidence and high self-esteem.

Finally, education is a three-way partnership amongst parent, teacher and pupil and at Breaside we are keen to develop and promote this important relationship.

Breaside is proud to be part of the Cognita Schools Group (www.cognitaschools.co.uk).

Brentwood Preparatory School

Middleton Hall Middleton Hall Lane Brentwood Essex CM15 8EQ
Tel: 01277 243333; Pre-Prep: 01277 243239
Fax: 01277 243340
e-mail: prep@brentwood.essex.sch.uk
preprep@brentwood.essex.sch.uk
website: www.brentwoodschool.co.uk

Chairman of Governors: C J Finch, FRICS

***Headmaster*: Mr N Helliwell**, MA, BEd Hons

Head of Pre-Prep: Mrs S Wilson, BEd, CertEd

Age Range. 3–11.
Number of Children. Prep 242, Pre-Prep 146.
Fees per term (2008-2009). Nursery £1,615, Pre-Prep and Prep £3,229.

Brentwood Preparatory School and Brentwood Pre-Preparatory School have their own buildings and grounds quite distinct from Brentwood School (qv) but close enough to share the use of its chapel, indoor swimming pool, Sports Centre and all-weather pitch.

The co-educational Pre-Preparatory School, which opened in 1995, educates children from age 3 to 7 in a spacious building with very well-equipped classrooms. Entrance is by an informal assessment at age 3.

The Preparatory School is housed in elegant buildings and has its own spacious grounds and sports pitches. Entrance is at age 7 by an academically selective test; candidates come from a wide range of schools as well Brentwood Pre-Preparatory School. Small class sizes and a team of well-qualified teachers provide a caring and challenging environment. Specialist rooms for art, design technology, drama, French, ICT, music and science provide outstanding facilities and a stimulating environment in which children can thrive.

There is an extensive programme of house and inter-school sports matches. Three choirs, two orchestras and variety of ensembles perform regularly both in and out of school. Every child has the opportunity of taking part in a major drama production. There is a wide range of lunchtime and after-school clubs, and a late stay scheme for children to complete homework at school. Many day visits to museums and places of interest in London complement school-based work and children enjoy annual residential trips in the holidays.

The Preparatory School, which was founded in 1892, has a strong academic tradition and a reputation for providing an excellent all-round education. The vast majority of pupils transfer to the Senior School (founded in 1557) at age 11.

The Pre-Preparatory and Preparatory schools recently underwent an inspection by the ISI. The majority of the aspects in the report were judged as 'outstanding' or 'excellent' and all were rated good or better. The opening sentence of the conclusion provides the best summary of the inspectors' views: '*Both the pre-prep and the prep are successful in achieving the aims of Brentwood School to provide a first class education for all its pupils.*' The 2008 report acknowledges the progress the schools have made since the last inspection in 2002, particularly the significant investment in ICT resources, the increase in facilities that the 'new' building has brought and the continuing improvement in academic standards.

Charitable status. Brentwood School (part of Sir Antony Browne's School Trust, Brentwood) is a Registered Charity, number 310864. It exists for the purpose of educating children.

Bricklehurst Manor

Stonegate Wadhurst East Sussex TN5 7EL
Tel: 01580 200448
Fax: 01580 200998
e-mail: office@bricklehurst.co.uk
website: www.bricklehurst.co.uk

***Headmistress*: Mrs C Flowers**, CertEd, BEd Hons

Age Range. 3–11.

Number of Pupils. 146.

Fees per term (2008-2009). Kindergarten £1,200; Years R, 1 and 2 £2,500; Years 3–4 £2,700, Years 5–6 £2,750.

Bricklehurst Manor was founded in 1959. It now operates as a co-educational school for boys and girls from 3 years old. Children are prepared for Common Entrance or equivalent standard entrance examinations at 11.

Bricklehurst stands in 3 acres of mature gardens and grounds. Previously a private house, the school retains many home-like characteristics, not least a friendly, family atmosphere which helps young children bridge the gap between home and school, and build up their confidence in the comfort and security of familiar surroundings.

The school has eight main classrooms and a purpose-built Kindergarten. The big panelled schoolroom is used for PE, Dancing, Drama, Music and any other activity requiring space. There is an Art/Science room, a reference library and a Music Room. Computers are used in all classrooms.

For outdoor playtime there is an orchard with an Adventure Playground, swings and sandpit. In the games periods the older children play hockey, netball, football, tag rugby, rounders and cricket; tennis coaching is available all year round and all the children learn to swim in our own heated and covered pool.

Curriculum. In the Kindergarten 3 and 4 year olds are given a happy introduction to school life learning to mix with others of the same age, to play contentedly together as one of a group, and generally to act in an orderly manner. Through using carefully structured equipment they also learn their letters and numbers, make a start at reading and gain simple number concepts.

From Reception Class onwards children stay all day. Gradually their curriculum is extended, subjects such as History, Geography, Scripture, Nature Study, Science and project work are introduced, and there are specialist teachers for Art and CDT, Drama and all musical activities. French is taught from Year 1 onwards. A variety of after-school activities is offered, including Spanish and Pottery. Mathematics is set from Year 3 and reasoning skills introduced from Year 4.

Bricklehurst has a reputation for sending children on to their next schools with a sensible attitude towards learning, and the ability to work independently and with enjoyment. A high standard of behaviour is expected, with emphasis on the gradual development of self-control, a sense of responsibility and real consideration for the needs of others.

Brigg Preparatory School (UCST)

Bigby Street Brigg North Lincolnshire DN20 8EF
Tel: 01652 653237
Fax: 01652 658879
e-mail: joan.simpkins@church-schools.com
website: www.briggprepschool.co.uk

***Head*: Mrs J Simpkins**, CertEd

Age Range. 2½–11 years.

Number of Pupils. 44 Boys, 40 Girls.

Fees per term (2007-2008). £1,827 (Lunches £103); Nursery £1,519 (Lunches £96).

Brigg Prep School is a well-established independent school situated in pleasant walled grounds in the centre of the small market town of Brigg. There are excellent access routes via motorway and there is a thriving airport nearby.

The school is part of the United Church Schools Trust, which gives close links with neighbouring sister schools at senior level in Hull and Lincoln.

Our Nursery class is stimulating and exciting and encourages enquiry and learning. Our children all receive an excellent start to their formal education. Nursery funding is available.

We offer a wide curriculum, including French and a range of extra-curricular activities, including sport and drama. Pre-school and after-school care are available, meaning that school is open from 8.00 am until 5.45 pm. Breakfast and tea are available on request.

We employ specialist teachers for Music and Sport and also a Special Needs teacher to support more and less able children when appropriate. Classes are small and our excellent pastoral care is based on our commitment to a Christian ethos.

Charitable status. Brigg Preparatory School is a member of The United Church Schools Trust which is a Registered Charity, number 1016538. It exists to provide children with a full Christian education.

Brighton College Prep School

Walpole Lodge Walpole Road Brighton East Sussex BN2 0EU
Tel: 01273 704210
Fax: 01273 704286
e-mail: paprep@brightoncollege.net
website: www.brightoncollege.net

Chairman of Preparatory School Governors: R F Jones, DipMS, IPFA

***Headmaster*: Brian D Melia**, MA Cantab, PGCE

Deputy Heads:
Alison Hills, BEd
Neil Anderson, BEd

Headmistress of Pre-Prep: Sue Wicks, MA, GTCL, LTCL, PGCE

Director of Admissions: Mary-Anne Brightwell

Age Range. 3–13.

Number of Pupils. Prep 297, Pre-Prep 190.

Fees per term (2008-2009). From £1,423 (Pre-Reception) to £4,442 (Year 8).

Brighton College Prep School is a co-educational school, which offers a broad curriculum taught to high standards by dedicated and energetic staff. The Pre-Prep School cares for children from 3–8 years in a modern, purpose-built building overlooking the playing fields of Brighton College. The Prep School is situated adjacent to the Senior School on its own site. The site is urban, but enjoys close proximity to the sea, the Downs and the vibrant sports and culture of Brighton, where an annual arts festival is held in May.

The excellent facilities provided by Brighton College are shared by the Prep School. These include the Chapel, swimming pool, a sports hall, two areas of playing fields, a purpose-built Performing Arts Centre and The Great Hall, which doubles as a large theatre for Prep School's annual senior musical. The Prep School itself has many specialist rooms including a well-equipped ICT suite, a large design technology room, art room, science laboratories, home economics room, library and hall. Art and DT are both key subjects on the timetable for all year groups.

Academic standards are high and are one of the foundations upon which school life is built, along with the broad range of subjects and activities. A variety of teaching methods is used – the key principle being that children enjoy their lessons and thus develop a love for learning. For details on assessment procedures and scholarships available at 11+ and 13+, please contact the Director of Admissions.

The school also caters for able dyslexic pupils who are fully integrated into classes. The Dyslexia Centre attached to the school provides specialist teaching; dyslexic pupils are given extra support in small groups and may be withdrawn from French.

Sport is a very important part of the life at the school. Major girls' games are netball, hockey, athletics and rounders. Girls' football and cricket as options, are a feature of the school. Major boys' games are soccer, rugby, cricket, athletics and tennis. Swimming is on the curriculum for all pupils.

The Prep School is well known for its musical strength with a suite of specially designed music rooms and practice areas. Two orchestras, a concert band and two choirs are organised by the director of music and thirty-one visiting music teachers provide tuition for the large number of pupils who learn a wide variety of instruments including piano, violin, saxophone, clarinet and drums.

Drama clubs and coaching are available for every year group and there are opportunities for children to perform during the academic year through assemblies, recitals, chapel services and also through annual drama productions.

The Brighton College School of Dance, based in the Performing Arts Centre, is thriving and many pupils attend classes on Saturdays and after school during the week.

The Prep School runs a large range of clubs and activities after school and at lunchtimes. There is a range of school bus routes. Further details on bus routes are available from the Director of Admissions.

Charitable status. Brighton College is a Registered Charity, number 307061. It exists to provide high quality education for boys and girls aged 3–18.

Bristol Grammar Lower School

Elton Road Bristol BS8 1SR
Tel: 0117 973 6109
Fax: 0117 974 1941
e-mail: lshead@bgs.bristol.sch.uk
website: www.bristolgrammarschool.co.uk

Chairman of Governors: L Perrin

***Headmistress*: Dr Alison F Primrose**, MA Cambridge, PGCE, MEd, FRSA

Age Range. 7–11.
Numbers in School. Boys 145, Girls 53 (all day children).
Fees per term (2008-2009). £2,173.

The Lower School is an independent co-educational day school. It was founded in 1900 and occupies a self-contained building on the same site as the Upper School, Bristol Grammar School (*see entry in HMC section*). Its own facilities include a Hall, Library, Music, Art, Science and technology rooms. Some facilities are shared with the Upper School, particularly the Sports Complex, Theatre and Dining Hall. The school now thrives on the happy and purposeful demands of approximately 200 girls and boys aged 7–11 years.

Entry is by test at seven or eight years old (and other ages, subject to the availability of places) and thereafter to the Upper School at eleven by an open competitive examination in which the Lower School's record of success is outstanding. Peloquin Scholarships and bursaries are awarded annually, the latter being means tested. The school aims to provide a rich, broad and balanced curriculum. Science and Music are taught by specialists to all pupils in all years, Art and Drama are particularly encouraged and there are many clubs such as Chess, Dance, Orchestra, Choir, many sports, outdoor pursuits and cookery.

A wide range of sports is offered to the pupils at our superb playing fields on the outskirts of the city and at our extensive on-site sports complex.

Discipline and pastoral care are provided by the Form Tutors and Deputy Head, supported by all teaching staff and the Headmistress.

Communication with parents is a regular feature of school life and includes the use of written reports, consultation evening and weekly newsletters.

Charitable status. Bristol Grammar School is a Registered Charity, number 1104425. The object of the Charity is the provision and conduct in or near the City of Bristol of a day school for boys and girls.

The British International School, Cairo

Junior School

PO Box 137, Gezira 11211, Cairo, Egypt
Tel: 00 202 2736 5959
Fax: 00 202 2736 4168
e-mail: info@bisc.edu.eg
website: www.bisc.edu.eg

Chairman of Governors: Eng Ahmed Ezz

***Head of Junior School*: Mr Michael Higgins**, BEd Hons, MA

Age Range. 3–11 Co-educational.
Number of Pupils. 320.
Fees per term (2007-2008). £1,123–£2,126.

British School of Houston

4211 Watonga Boulevard, Houston, TX 77092, USA
Tel: 00 1 713 290 9025
Fax: 00 1 713 290 9014
e-mail: admissionsbsh@britishschool.org
website: www.britishschool.org

***Head of School*: Alison Norris**

Age Range. 3–18 Co-educational.
Number of Pupils. 578.
Fees per annum (2007-2008). $8,955–$19,775.

The British School of Houston was established in 2000 with approximately 50 pupils. Since then the school has grown quickly, now accepting pupils from age 3 to 18. It is the largest school in the British Schools of America network, a division of World Class Learning Systems and Schools (WCLS) which includes Fieldwork Education. This thriving organisation now has five schools altogether, the others in Boston, Chicago, Washington DC and Charlotte.

Our mission is to provide a high-quality education in a structured, positive and caring environment, which meets the needs of all pupils. The school community draws strength from its British identity and its American home; however, with over 30 nationalities represented the school has an international outlook and encourages global awareness and understanding through the curriculum. The School offers a challenging, broad curriculum based on the National Curriculum (England and Wales) and focuses on the development of the whole child, aiming to equip every pupil with the essential skills for life-long learning. The school is also accredited by the International Baccalaureate Organisation and we offer the IB Diploma course to our oldest pupils.

Our position, as both an independent and international school, allows us to offer teaching which, in all cases, goes above and beyond government stipulations. We aim to provide a stimulating learning environment to enhance the learning experiences of all our pupils. The school maintains benchmarks of quality through membership of the European Council of International Schools (ECIS), the Independent Association of Prep Schools (IAPS) and the Council for International Schools in the Americas (CISTA).

The school's highly skilled and dedicated teaching staff is UK trained and has several years' experience teaching the National Curriculum. A number of teachers have previous international school experience. Excellent standards of teaching and high expectations challenge pupils and allow all our children to reach their full academic potential, becoming responsible, confident, articulate and industrious individuals.

Learning beyond the classroom is very important to us. We look to enhance the curriculum as often as possible through field trips as well as providing all pupils from the age of 8 with the opportunity to take part in a residential stay. We encourage community service projects through the International Award and CAS elements of the IB course, as well as having our pupils take part in charity events throughout the year. Our well-developed pastoral curriculum is designed to provide a holistic education, valuing the whole child. Finally, we have a well-organised and highly-motivated student council involving pupils from the very early years, giving them the chance to work as partners with staff to develop a caring school community and skills such as problem-solving, organisation, decision-making and leadership.

The British School in The Netherlands

Junior School Assen

Lottingstraat 17, 9406 LX, Assen, The Netherlands
Tel: 00 31 (0)592 344 590
Fax: 00 31 (0)592 370 998
e-mail: junior.assen@britishschool.nl
website: www.britishschool.nl

Chairman of Governors: Mr P Bayliff

***Headteacher*: Michala Warner**

Age Range. 3–11 years.

Number on Roll. 65: 33 Boys, 32 Girls.

Fees per term (2008-2009). Foundation 1: €1,940 (part-time), €3,900 (full-time); Foundation 2–Year 6: €3,850.

The BSN Junior School Assen (The Helen Sharman School) is purpose-built and located near Groningen, serving the needs of expatriate families in the north of The Netherlands.

The school follows an internationalised version of the British National Curriculum. Dutch is taught from the age of 5 and French from the age of 7 and themed topics are introduced relevant to the needs of the cultures within the school.

The school has an excellent teacher : pupil ratio and follows a comprehensive academic programme, which can be adjusted to individual needs and school experience. With children from over 18 different countries; our staff are very experienced in accommodating children from a variety of educational backgrounds.

Great advantage is taken of being located in The Netherlands and there are frequent educational visits to local places of interest. The school has Art, Music and Language rooms and has a well-sourced ICT suite with interactive whiteboards and networked computers in each classroom. The Physical Education and Sports curriculum is delivered both on-site and by using excellent local sports facilities. Specialist support for English as an Additional Language is available and the school has its own Special Needs Coordinator. The school also has an Extended Learning Policy, furthering its commitment to comprehensive education of individual children.

The school, named after the first British astronaut, frequently quotes Helen Sharman's advice to 'aim high'. The wish is to provide a world-class education to pupils of all nationalities, to ensure a smooth transition into the curriculum, and to foster self-discipline, mutual respect and harmony between all cultures.

There is a lively and varied after-school activity programme which is run by both parents and teachers. Activities include drama, art, guitar and chess clubs, and a monthly 'fun run' for the whole school community in the nearby countryside.

Children may join the school at any point during the academic year, from Nursery (Foundation 1) to Year 6. Great care is taken to ensure the smooth and friendly integration of each child into the academic and social life of the school.

The British School in The Netherlands

Junior School Diamanthorst

Diamanthorst 16, 2592 GH, The Hague, The Netherlands
Tel: 00 31 (0)70 315 7620
Fax: 00 31 (0)70 315 7621
e-mail: junior.diamanthorst@britishschool.nl
website: www.britishschool.nl

Chairman of Governors: Mr P Bayliff

***Headteacher*: Mr Paul Ellis**

Age Range. 3–11 Co-educational.

Number of Pupils. 350.

Fees per term (2008-2009). Foundation 1: €1,940 (part-time), €3,900 (full-time); Foundation 2–Year 6: €3,850.

The Junior School Diamanthorst is a place where children can thrive and grow, develop and study, play and perform and, above all, discover the enjoyment of learning. We aim to help children understand the value of both work and leisure and encourage them to become confident, happy individuals.

The site is located in a residential area in the north of The Hague. The facilities include a Media Library Centre, Food Technology Room, Hall/Gym, Design Technology Room, Wild Garden, Dance/Drama Studio, IT suite and Music Room. All classrooms are equipped with interactive whiteboards and computers. The school has a wireless network system throughout.

The learning programme includes the three core subjects Mathematics, English and Science, together with the foundation subjects, geography, history, design and technology, art & music, information technology and PE with the addition of Dutch from entry into the School and taster courses in French, German and Spanish from Year 5.

Our Foundation classes follow the English Foundation Curriculum with particular emphasis on acquiring literacy, numeracy and social skills.

In Key Stages 1 and 2 specific schemes of work outline the progressive skills and knowledge which are taught, and all work is closely monitored to ensure that pupils are making progress matched to their abilities. In the case of children who display unusual talent or ability, extension material is given to motivate and challenge their intellectual growth. All children enjoy a variety of experiences, visiting places of interest in the immediate locality, performing in dance, drama and choral activities and engaging in a wide range of extra-curricular programmes.

As children progress through the Junior School subject teaching becomes more defined, especially in the core subjects of English, Mathematics and Science. Children are carefully prepared for the subject-orientated approach evident in the Senior School where they are expected to become more independent in the planning and completion of tasks and time management.

The British School in The Netherlands
Junior School Vlaskamp

Vlaskamp 19, 2592 AA, The Hague, The Netherlands
Tel: 00 31 (0)70 333 8111
Fax: 00 31 (0)70 333 8100
e-mail: junior.vlaskamp@britishschool.nl
website: www.britishschool.nl

Chairman of Governors: Mr P Bayliff

***Headteacher*: Mr Anthony Berwick**

Age Range. 5–11 years.
Number on Roll. 752: 383 Boys, 369 Girls.
Fees per term (2008-2009). €3,850.

At the heart of all learning there must be sound, happy relationships and a feeling of self esteem. Children learn best when they feel secure, respected and valued. Our staff are totally committed to working in partnership with parents to provide a welcoming, challenging and stimulating environment for children to explore, experiment, learn, laugh and reflect. Our ultimate aim is to foster in each of our pupils an excitement and a love of learning which will remain with them for the rest of their lives.

The Junior School Vlaskamp is situated close to the centre of Den Haag on a tree-filled site with extensive green play areas and modern facilities designed to meet the academic, technological and recreational requirements of each age group.

All the classrooms are light and airy overlooking the grounds and landscaped gardens. Facilities include music rooms with adjoining practice cells, a main hall, a circular drama studio, library, IT studio with a comprehensive network of computers linking each classroom and fully equipped rooms for craft, design technology and science.

The learning programme includes the three core subjects, mathematics, English and science, together with the foundation subjects, geography, history, design and technology, art and music, information technology and PE with the addition of Dutch from entry into the School and French from Year 6.

In the Key Stage 1 and Key Stage 2 Curricula, specific schemes of work outline the progressive skills and knowledge which are taught, and all work is closely monitored to ensure that pupils are making progress matched to their abilities. In the case of children who display unusual talent or ability, extension material is given to motivate and challenge their intellectual growth. All children enjoy a variety of experiences, visiting places of interest in the immediate locality, performing in dance, drama and choral activities and engaging in extra-curricular programmes. As children progress through the Junior School subject teaching becomes more defined, especially in the core subjects of English, mathematics and science, and more extensive use is made of the science laboratory and technology room. Children are carefully prepared for the subject-orientated approach evident in the Senior School where they are expected to become more independent in the planning and completion of tasks and time management.

The Foundation School for 3–5 year olds is based just 4 minutes' walk away providing a secure and stimulating environment for the youngest children.

The British School of Paris
Junior School

Junior School Bougival:
Chemin du Mur du Parc, 78380 Bougival, France
Tel: (00 33) 1 39 69 78 21
Fax: (00 33) 1 30 82 47 49
e-mail: jsb@britishschool.fr

Junior School Croissy:
38 Quai de l'Ecluse, 78290 Croissy sur Seine, France
Tel: (00 33) 1 34 80 45 94
Fax: (00 33) 1 39 76 12 69
e-mail: ssc@britishschool.fr
website: www.bsparis.net

Chairman of Governors: Mr P Kett

Headmaster: R J Woodall, MA (Edin)

***Head of Junior School*: Mrs A Tardivel**

Type of School. Co-educational Day School.
Age Range. Bougival site: 4–11 (Reception to Year 6).
Croissy site: 7–11 (Year 3 to Year 6).
Number of Pupils. 500.
Fees per annum (2007-2008). €13,958–€16,390.

The Junior School Bougival occupies a beautiful wooded site overlooking the Seine valley and has many modern facilities including an indoor swimming pool and a large outdoor play area. Pupils follow the British National curriculum, with its emphasis on English, Maths and Science plus daily instruction in the French language. Various sports, music and drama, together with many extra-curricular activities are also provided.

The Junior School Croissy, adjacent to the Senior School, provides for the increasing demand for a British education in Paris at Key Stage 2 (age 7–11). Following closely the structure of the National Curriculum children are taught by a Class Teacher and also by specialists in French, Music and PE. Staff and pupils are able to make use of the specialist facilities available on site.

For further details and applications, please contact the Registrar, e-mail registrar@britishschool.fr.

The British School in Tokyo

1-21-18 Shibuya, Shibuya-ku, Tokyo 150-0002, Japan
Tel: 00 81 03 5467 4321
Fax: 00 81 03 5467 4322
e-mail: admissions@bst.ac.jp
website: www.bst.ac.jp

***Headmaster*: Mr Michael G Farley**

Age Range. 3–14 Co-educational.
Number of Pupils. 520.
Fees per annum (from January 2008). Yen 1,400,000 (Nursery), Yen 1,990,000 (Reception–Year 10).

The British School in Tokyo is the only British school in Japan. Our unique position provides our pupils with unprecedented opportunities for academic achievement within the rich cultural soil that is Japan. The best of British education is our aim, with all children being offered the stimuli to reach their full potential within the School's disciplined and caring environment. Set this aim in the context of one of the most exciting and vibrant cityscapes in the world and it is easy to see why our pupils are the beneficiaries of a truly memorable educational experience.

The BST is an independent co-educational two-site day school, offering a high quality English National Curriculum education. The School is a non-profit organisation; administered by a Board of Trustees representing the British and international community in Tokyo. Her Britannic Majesty's Ambassador to Japan is the School's patron.

Being a British School, the majority of pupils are from the UK, but pupils from all nationalities are welcome, provided that each child, relative to age, is fluent in English. There are on average over 30 nationalities represented within the School community.

The ethos of a busy 'community' school is reflected in the high degree of parental involvement. Parents are encouraged to play a full and active role in school, offering support in the classrooms, on educational visits and on residentials and through the activities of the PTA and Parent Advisory Group.

Broadwater Manor School

Worthing West Sussex BN14 8HU
Tel: 01903 201123
Fax: 01903 821777
e-mail: info@broadwatermanor.com
website: www.broadwatermanor.com

***Headteacher*: Mrs E K Woodley**, BA Hons, CertEd

Head of Prep: Mr N Gunn, BA Hons, PGCE
Head of Nursery and Toddlers: Mrs C O'Rourke, BEd Hons & Mrs C Flower

Age Range. 2–13 Co-educational.

Number of Pupils. Day only: Prep 150, Pre-Prep 91, Nursery 63 and Toddlers 12.

Girls occupy about 40% of the places throughout the school.

Fees per term (2008-2009). (inclusive) Prep (age 8–13) £2,560; Pre-Prep (age 4–8) £2,174; Nursery (age 3–4) £2,030 (full-time), Toddlers (age 2–3) £220.

There are 19 full-time and 8 part-time teachers on the staff.

Pupils are prepared for entry to a variety of senior schools and scholarships are frequently gained. The school has a thriving musical tradition and a strong PE department. Soccer, Hockey, Netball, Tennis, Rounders and Athletics are all played. As well as computers in every classroom there is a well equipped Information Technology room. CDT is also a strong aspect of the school.

Brockhurst School

Hermitage Newbury Berkshire RG18 9UL
Tel: 01635 200293
Fax: 01635 200190
e-mail: info@brockmarl.org.uk
website: www.brockmarl.org.uk

***Headmaster*: D J W Fleming**, MA (Oxon), MSc

Age Range. 3 to 13.

Number of Boys. 55 Boarders, 105 Day Boys.

Fees per term (2007-2008). Boarding £5,510, Day £3,910–£4,150. Pre-Prep School (Ridge House): £1,250–£2,470.

Established in 1884, Brockhurst is situated in 500 acres of its own grounds in countryside of outstanding beauty, but is only four miles from access to the M4. The school is located on the same site as Marlston House Girls' Preparatory School which occupies separate, listed buildings. Boys and Girls are educated separately, but the two schools join forces for drama, music and many hobbies. In this way, Brockhurst and Marlston House aim to combine the best features of the single-sex and co-educational systems: academic excellence and social mixing. The schools have built up a fine reputation for high standards of pastoral care given to each pupil within a caring, family establishment. (*See also entry for Marlston House School.*)

The Pre-Prep School, Ridge House, is a co-educational department for 75 children aged 3 to 6½.

Boys are prepared for entry to all Independent Senior Schools and there is an excellent scholarship record.

All boys play Soccer, Rugger, Hockey and Cricket and take part in Athletics, Cross-Country and Swimming (new 25m indoor heated pool). Additional activities include Riding (own ponies), Fencing, Judo, Shooting (indoor rifle range) and Tennis (indoor court and three hard courts). Facilities for gymnastics and other sporting activities are provided in a purpose-built Sports Hall. The schools also have their own Château near Bordeaux where they practise their spoken French.

Music and art are important features of the curriculum and a good number of pupils have won scholarships to senior schools in recent years.

Where appropriate, pupils can be transported by members of staff to and from airports if parents are serving in the armed forces or otherwise working overseas.

Bromsgrove Preparatory School

Old Station Road Bromsgrove Worcs B60 2BU
Tel: 01527 579600
Fax: 01527 579571
e-mail: admissions@bromsgrove-school.co.uk
website: www.bromsgrove-school.co.uk

Chairman of Governors: T M Horton, BA

***Headmaster*: Richard Evans**, BEd, Adv Dip Ed Man

Age Range. 7–13.

Number of Pupils. 460: 229 Day Boys, 178 Day Girls, 38 Boy Boarders, 15 Girl Boarders.

Fees per term (2008-2009). £2,815–£3,675 day, £5,600–£6,935 full boarding, £3,815–£4,675 weekly boarding. Forces Bursaries and, from 11+, scholarships are available.

Bromsgrove Preparatory School feeds the adjacent 800 strong Senior School. (*See Bromsgrove School entry in HMC section.*) The sites covering 100 acres offer exclusive and shared facilities, with over £23 million pounds having been invested in the last ten years. A new £2.5 million teaching block for Years 3, 4 and 5 was opened in 2005. Teachers working in both Senior and Preparatory Schools ensure continuity of ethos and expectation.

Academic, sporting and cultural facilities are extensive and outstanding.

Pupils are admitted at the age of 7+ with another substantial intake at 11+, but pupils including boarders are admitted throughout the age range up to 13. Admission to the school is by Entrance Test (English, Maths and VR) supported by a report from the current school. At the end of Year 6 pupils sit examinations which allow them to be guaranteed a place in Bromsgrove Senior School two years later. Pupils admitted at age 11 are also guaranteed entry to the Senior School.

The separate boys', girls' and mixed junior boarding houses are lively, homely environments where pupils are cared for by resident houseparents and a team of tutors. The school aims to make a boarder's first experience of life away from home enjoyable and absorbing.

Parents can choose either a five or six day week for their children. All academic lessons are timetabled from Monday to Friday with Saturdays offering an optional and flexible programme of activities.

The aim of the school is to provide a first-class education, which identifies and develops the potential of individual pupils, academically, culturally and socially. It prepares them to enter the Senior School with confidence.

In the Preparatory School there is a purposeful and lively atmosphere. Mutual trust, respect and friendship exist between staff and pupils. The high-quality and dedication of the teaching staff, favourable teacher/pupil ratio and regular monitoring of performance ensure that the natural spontaneity and inquisitiveness of this age group are directed purposefully. The pastoral care system, rooted in the school's Christian heritage, is firmly founded on the form tutor. It is designed to ensure that every pupil is recognised as an important individual and that their development is nurtured.

Charitable status. Bromsgrove Preparatory School is a Registered Charity, number 1098740. It exists to provide education for boys and girls.

Brontë House

The Junior School of Woodhouse Grove

Apperley Bridge Bradford West Yorkshire BD10 0PQ
Tel: 0113 250 2811
Fax: 0113 250 0666
e-mail: general.enquiries@brontehouse.org.uk
website: www.woodhousegrove.co.uk

Chairman of Governors: G B Greenwood, JP

***Headmaster*: S Dunn**, BEd

Age Range. 2½–11 Co-educational.

Number of Pupils. 290 Boys and Girls (including 8 boarders).

Fees per term (2008-2009). £5,500 (boarders), £4,940 (weekly boarders), £2,490–£2,830 (day). Ashdown Lodge: Nursery and Reception £2,030 (full day), £1,265 (half day), Years 1 & 2 £2,280.

These are graduated according to age. The day fee covers an extended day from 8 am to 6 pm; there are no extra charges for breakfast, tea and the majority of supervised activities after lessons.

The School is situated in its own grounds, a short distance from the Senior School, on the slopes of the Aire Valley at the edge of the urban area of Bradford and Leeds. The moors are within view and access to the Dales National Park and the international Leeds/Bradford Airport is swift.

The School is of Methodist foundation, but children of other denominations and faiths are willingly accepted. Morning assembly is run on broad ecumenical lines, and school services are held in the Chapel of Woodhouse Grove.

Normal entry is in September via the Entrance Tests held the previous January, but assessment and entry at other times in the year can be easily arranged if places are available. Academic, art and music scholarships may be awarded to children who display special merit, and the School now offers bursaries in lieu of the defunct Assisted Places scheme. Entry to the Foundation and Key Stage 1 classes merely requires registration of the child. Part-time places are available in the Nursery. The Early Years Department offers holiday provision for all school holidays.

The work of all age groups is based on the National Curriculum; this is supplemented by a European Studies course in French, German and Spanish, plus a special emphasis on Music and Sport. Children automatically transfer to the senior school, Woodhouse Grove, and there is continuity of schooling from 3 to 18. Regular standardised testing takes place in all year groups, and the national Key Stage 1 and 2 Tests (for seven and eleven year olds) are taken. All staff, both full-time and visiting, are fully qualified. Individual tuition is encouraged in piano, string, wind and brass instruments and also in speech and drama, with the two choirs and orchestra participating regularly in assemblies and concerts. (Over 70% of the children learn to play an instrument). There is a Dyslexia Unit, run by specialist staff, for a maximum of 16 children of above average ability.

The curriculum includes compulsory physical education for all children. Those with ability and enthusiasm are coached in athletics, cricket, cross-country running, football, rugby, rounders, tennis and netball; there is a comprehensive fixture list with other schools in the area, and regular participation in local and regional tournaments. All children learn to swim; teaching and training takes place weekly in the full-size pool at Woodhouse Grove.

In addition to training sessions in sport, clubs and activities include art and craft, chess, computers, dance and model railway. Expeditions are made to the Dales and the Lake District, as are cultural outings into Bradford, Leeds and York. An annual ski trip takes place during the Easter holidays.

For a copy of the detailed prospectus, please apply to the Secretary.

Charitable status. Brontë House School is a Registered Charity, number 529205. It exists to provide independent primary education within the pastoral environment of a Methodist Residential School.

Brooke Priory School

Station Approach Oakham Rutland LE15 6QW
Tel: 01572 724778
Fax: 01572 724969
e-mail: info@brooke.rutland.sch.uk
website: www.brooke.rutland.sch.uk

***Headmistress*: Mrs E S Bell**, BEd Hons

Age Range. 2.8 to 11 years (co-educational).

Number of Pupils. 230: 196 (age 4+ to 11); 34 (Nursery, age 2.8 to 4).

Fees per term (2007-2008). £1,560–£2,090.

Staff. There are 20 graduate and qualified members of the teaching staff.

Brooke Priory is a day Preparatory School for boys and girls. The school was founded in 1989 and moved into its own purpose-built building in February 1995. Since then it has doubled its classroom provision and established a fully-networked Computer Room, well-resourced Library and Drama Room.

Brooke Priory provides a stimulating, caring environment in which children are encouraged to attain their highest potential. Class sizes are optimally 16 in parallel forms and children are grouped according to ability in Mathematics and English.

The school delivers a broad and varied curriculum, where every child will participate in Art, Drama, French and Music. Over 50% of children in the Prep Department enjoy individual music lessons and are encouraged to join the Choir and Ensemble.

Brooke Priory enjoys a high success rate at Common Entrance and Senior Independent School Entry Examinations, with many children being awarded scholarships. With this solid foundation pupils move confidently on to their chosen senior schools.

Sport is an important part of the curriculum. Children swim weekly throughout the year and are coached in a wide variety of games by specialist staff. The main sports are Soccer, Rugby, Hockey, Netball, Cricket, Rounders and Athletics

The school offers a wide choice of extra-curricular activities.

Before and after school care is available.

Brooklands School

167 Eccleshall Road Stafford ST16 1PD
Tel: 01785 251399
Fax: 01785 236987
e-mail: enquiries@brooklandsschool.com
website: www.brooklandsschool.com

Chairman of Council: Lady Mitting

***Headmaster*: D R Williams**BA Hons, PGCE Cantab

Age Range. 3 months–11 years.

Number of Pupils. 170.

Fees per term (2008-2009). Pre Nursery £31.60 per day; Nursery £1,320–£1,795; Lower School £2,345; Upper School £2,645.

Brooklands is a thriving co-educational day prep school for 170 children aged 3 months to 11 years. Situated on the edge of the town it looks onto a delightful conservation area but is also only 1 mile from Junction 14 of the M6 affording excellent accessibility from within Stafford and the surrounding areas.

The philosophy of the school is to provide a secure, stimulating and structured environment where each child is encouraged to achieve as high an academic standard as possible whilst at the same time developing individual interests and talents in a wide range of areas. The children learn to live as happy and caring members of a school community, which values their personal contribution, and also the needs of others, all within a Christian framework.

A committed and enthusiastic staff of qualified teachers ensures that each child receives maximum individual attention in small class sizes.

Brooklands is well equipped with Science & Technology buildings, Computer Suite with interactive whiteboard and specialist rooms for music, art, drama, PE and library. The sports field enables us to provide an exciting mix of traditional boys and girls games throughout the year and all children from the age of 6 have the opportunity to learn to swim at the Stafford Leisure Centre.

Our broad and dynamic curriculum gives each child the chance to flourish in many aspects of School life. Subjects taught are those required by the National Curriculum and for Entrance/Scholarship examinations to Senior Independent Schools. 24 Scholarships have been awarded to Brooklands pupils in the last five years. Opportunities to represent the School in sports teams, performing arts, choirs and instrumental groups are all part of the "Brooklands Experience".

The School recognises the importance of a child feeling happy, secure and motivated. The Form Tutor is of prime importance – overseeing the development of each child academically, socially and emotionally – but is supplemented with our 'House' system and care worker organisation. Close links with home provide even greater value to being part of the community as a whole. To help busy parents we provide early arrival care, including breakfast, from 8.00 am daily and a wide range of After School activities and child care are provided until 6.00 pm. The School and pre-nursery unit are open 48 weeks of the year with a dedicated Holiday Club running throughout the holiday periods.

Charitable status. Brooklands School is a Registered Charity, number 528616. It exists to provide quality education and care for boys and girls with bursarial help according to need.

Broomwood Hall

74 Nightingale Lane London SW12 8NR
Tel: 020 8682 8800
Fax: 020 8675 0136
e-mail: broomwood@northwoodschools.com
website: www.broomwood.co.uk

Principal: Mrs K A H Colquhoun, BEd, DipT

***Head of Upper School*: Mrs C Jenkinson**

Age Range. Girls 4–13, Boys 4–8.

Number of Pupils. Lower School (4–7): 200 girls, 160 boys; Upper School (8–13): 150 girls.

Fees per term (2007-2008). £3,445–£4,205.

Broomwood Hall is an independent pre-prep and preparatory school for boys and girls from the ages of 4–8 (boys) and 4–13 (girls). Boys have an automatic right of entry at 8 to Northcote Lodge (day preparatory school on Wandsworth Common, in the same ownership as Broomwood Hall) subject to an interview with the Headmaster.

Broomwood Hall has expanded from 12 children to nearly 500 in five substantial Victorian Houses sprinkled round the south side of Clapham and Tooting Commons, but the school's approach and values have remained constant. Broomwood believes that a young child does not benefit from long drives across London (hence the catchment rule), that single-sex education works best after 8, and that the traditional virtues of self-discipline, a sense of responsibility and good manners are the core of a good education. The upper school is unique in London in providing an education for girls specifically aiming for boarding at 13.

There are four separate sites: a pre-prep of 110 children at Garrad's Road SW16, another pre-prep of 220 – sub-divided into two neighbouring buildings – at 192 Ramsden Road and 50 Nightingale Lane, SW12. And finally, the Upper School – 150 girls aged 8–13 – based in the gracious Victorian mansion at 68–74 Nightingale Lane, SW12.

Teaching (in small groups) is strong throughout. Mixed ability classes, but setting in maths and English. An extended day because homework is done at school. A variety of clubs – karate, mini-rugby, chess, pottery are on offer.

Art is particularly lively. Strong music, with two music lessons a week, a Chamber choir, wind ensemble and brass band. Lots of drama – everyone takes part in two productions a year. Netball, hockey, PE, football, touch rugby, athletics, cricket, rounders and tennis taught on site or nearby (five courts within walking distance), with inter-house competitions and external matches. Swimming at local baths, with swim squad once a week. Very good library. Sophisticated ICT, with state-of-the-art computers, permanent high-speed internet connection and an email account for every child above class 2.

A Christian school with regular RE, morning assembly and church attendance once a week. Happy to welcome all faiths (special arrangements for Catholics to attend Mass and days of obligation), but all pupils must attend services. Pastoral care extremely well thought through at every level. From class 5 girls have a personal tutor (chosen by themselves), whom they meet weekly to discuss social and personal issues as well as work. The tutor liaises with parents, helps plan revision, sorts out friendships and writes report. Social skills as important as academic ones and manners definitely a priority.

One compulsory – though much enjoyed – course is the weekly Leiths cookery lessons for girls in years 7 and 8. Lunches – prepared on site – are accompanied by the teachers for the younger children to ensure that table manners are observed and food is finished.

Entry requirements. Entry takes place in September following a child's fourth birthday. Admission is by personal interview with both parents and the child at the age of 3. Parents must live locally (Clapham/Battersea/Wandsworth/Tooting/Streatham).

Examinations offered. Boys' preparatory schools, girls' Common Entrance and Scholarship examinations at 11+ and 13+ (12+ where applicable) and London day schools' examinations. Pupils may also take Associated Board examinations (music).

Bruern Abbey School

Chesterton House Chesterton Oxfordshire OX26 1UY
Tel: 01869 242448
Fax: 01869 243949
e-mail: headmaster@bruernabbey.org
website: www.bruernabbey.org

Chair of Governors: Mrs Sarah Austen, BA Hons

***Headmaster*: Mr P F Fawkes**, CertEd, MBA(Ed)

Age Range. Boys 7–13.
Number of Pupils. 60.
Fees per term (2008-2009). Day £5,006, Boarding £6,168.

Bruern Abbey is situated in twenty acres of Oxfordshire countryside, ten miles north-west of Oxford and within easy commuting distance of London, from where a bus brings boys to school on Mondays – and takes them back on Fridays.

The School's raison d'être is to prepare boys who have dyslexia, or some other form of learning difficulty, or who, for whatever reasons, may not be flourishing at their present schools, for Common Entrance to the major English and Scottish independent senior schools. Bruern boys graduate to a range of independent schools, which have included in recent years, Winchester College, Tonbridge, Stowe, Harrow, Canford, Rugby, Gordonstoun, Shiplake, Milton Abbey and Uppingham.

Its purpose is to provide quality education in safe and pleasant surroundings, to ensure that the work of every child is recognised and appreciated, and to build confidence, in the firm belief that confidence is the key to academic success.

Bruern believes that it has found the right balance between the traditional and the progressive. All boys are permitted, and indeed, positively encouraged, to use a laptop, and for those who have difficulty in expressing themselves as swiftly or as coherently on paper as they do in speech, this proves a huge advantage. There is a focus on literacy and numerical work, with ten periods of English and Mathematics each a week, but with little or no withdrawal, and small groups of rarely more than four or five boys taught by specialists in the field of dyslexia, dyspraxia and dyscalculia. Alongside the traditional, with boys climbing trees and building dens in the twenty acres of woodland, and sport every afternoon, are several examples of the cutting edge of education, the use of ICT across the range of the curriculum being just one.

The boarding accommodation and the care shown by staff are of the highest standard. This is reflected in the growing number of boarders. The School is steadfast in the teaching of traditional values, dear to all, and places an emphasis on good manners and self-discipline, and encourages boys to share their aspirations and their anxieties.

The Buchan School

Castletown Isle of Man IM9 1RD
Tel: 01624 820481
Fax: 01624 820403
e-mail: secretary@buchan.sch.im
website: www.buchan.sch.im

Chairman of the Governors: S G Alder, BA, FCA

***Headteacher*: Mrs A Hope Hedley**, BEd Hons, NPQH

Age Range. 3–11.
Number of Pupils. 242 (130 boys, 112 girls).
Fees per term (2007-2008). Day £2,381–£3,104 according to age.

After more than a century of independence, mainly as a Girls' School, The Buchan School amalgamated, in 1991, with King William's College to form a single continuous provision of Independent Education on the Isle of Man.

As the Preparatory School to King William's College (*see entry in HMC section*), The Buchan School provides an education of all-round quality for boys and girls until the age of 11 when most pupils proceed naturally to the Senior School although the curriculum meets the needs of Common Entrance, Scholarship and Entrance Examinations to other Independent Senior Schools.

The school buildings are clustered round Westhill House, the centre of the original estate, in fourteen acres of partly wooded grounds. The whole environment, close to the attractive harbour of Castletown, is ideally suited to the needs of younger children. They are able to work and play safely and develop their potential in every direction.

There are 20 full time and 5 part time staff. Classes are small throughout, providing considerable individual attention. A well-equipped Nursery provides Pre-School education for some 40 children. At the age of 5, boys and girls are accepted into the Pre-Preparatory Department. They work largely in their own building in bright, modern classrooms and also make use of the specialist Preparatory School facilities where they proceed three years later.

Facilities are first class, including laboratories for Science and Technology, Library, Computer Room, large Games Hall and Art, Design Centre. The School is particularly well-equipped with ICT facilities extending down to the Pre-Prep Department. Outside, the school grounds provide a natural gymnasium. There is a Pavilion with fields marked out for a variety of team games and a multi purpose area which is used for Netball, Tennis and Hockey.

There is emphasis on traditional standards in and out of the classroom, with an enterprising range of activities outside normal lessons. Music is strong – both choral and instrumental – and there is energetic involvement in Art, Drama, Sport.

The school strives for high academic standards, aiming to ensure that all pupils enjoy the benefits of a rounded education, giving children every opportunity to develop their individual talents from an early age.

Entry is usually by Interview and School report and the children may join The Buchan School at any time, providing there is space. The School is a happy, friendly community where new pupils integrate quickly socially and academically.

Charitable status. King William's College is a Registered Charity, number 615. It exists for the provision of high quality education for boys and girls.

Buckingham College Preparatory School

458 Rayners Lane Pinner Middlesex HA5 5DT
Tel: 020 8866 2737
Fax: 020 8868 3228
e-mail: office@buckprep.org
website: www.buckprep.org

Chairman of Governors: Mr Robert Brock

***Headmaster*: Mr Laurence Smith**, BA Hons, MSc, LCP, PGDE, CertEd

Age Range. Boys 4–11.
Number of Pupils. 119.
Fees per term (2007-2008). £2,095–£2,740.

Buckingham College Preparatory School (BCPS) is a small 'family school' which offers its pupils a very high level of pastoral care. Indeed, a recent ISI Inspection found that:

"The overall provision for the pupils' spiritual, moral, social and cultural development is very good and is a strength of the school."

With a maximum class size of 20 throughout the school, individual attention is thus assured.

The School also believes in forging a strong Parent/Teacher partnership so that parents feel as if they have a vital role to play in the education of their child. A thriving Parent/Teacher Association also organises as many as four major fund-raising events during the academic year.

BCPS produces excellent academic results year in, year out, due to the expertise and professionalism of its dedicated and highly qualified teaching staff. Indeed, in 2007/2008, an impressive 8 scholarships/bursaries were achieved from its Year 6 class of 16 pupils. Moreover, in the past 10 years, the School has always managed to place every member of Year 6 in at least one of the prestigious Senior Independent Schools in the area – a remarkable achievement.

BCPS also prides itself in its results in other areas of the curriculum, namely Sport, Music and Drama.

Such is the enthusiasm for sport in the school that the PE/Games Department organises Inter-School competitions in Swimming, Athletics and Cross-Country. The School also competes in sports such as football, rugby, hockey and cricket at Under 9 and Under 11 levels. With a Judo squad of over 40 and a very comprehensive after-school programme of 16 sports and recreational pursuits, pupils at BCPS have every opportunity of developing their individual and social skills.

Music also plays a very important part in the life of the school with approximately 60% of pupils playing an orchestral instrument, some as young as 5. With an orchestra currently 35 strong and 7 peripatetic staff on call, it is unsurprising that pupils frequently achieve examination results as high as Grade 5. Music scholarships are now a regular occurrence.

Drama holds a high profile at BCPS, too. The School presents four major productions in the academic year, one being at the Music and Drama Festival at a local theatre. The Expressive Arts Week, when pupils have the opportunity of participating in approximately 14 categories of events, is also a focal point of the academic year. Once again, Drama scholarships feature highly.

Charitable status. The E Ivor Hughes Educational Foundation is a Registered Charity, number 293623.

Butcombe
Clifton College Pre-Preparatory School

Guthrie Road Clifton Bristol BS8 3EZ
Tel: 0117 3157 591
Fax: 0117 3157 592
e-mail: apurnell@clifton-college.avon.sch.uk
website: www.cliftoncollegeuk.com

Chairman of College Council: A R Thornhill, BA, QC

***Headmistress*: Wendy E Bowring**, BEd HODS, ADB Ed, MEd, PhD

Age Range. 3–8.
Number of Pupils. 250 (150 day boys and 100 day girls).
Fees per term (2008-2009). £1,310–£2,845.

Butcombe is one of three schools that form Clifton College, independent in terms of running and organisation. However, it benefits from being governed by the same Council as the Preparatory School and Upper School, and enjoys the considerable advantages of sharing many of the College's extensive facilities. These include swimming pool, sports hall, gymnasium, multi-activity hall, Chapel and Theatre. The school is situated in two buildings either side of a superb playground with a variety of play equipment.

The school caters for children in the Foundation Stage (Nursery and Reception), Key Stage 1 (Y1 and 2) and Year 3, the first year of Key Stage 2. The nursery has up to 50 children on roll, with a staff pupil ratio of 1 : 8. Attendance in the nursery may be either five mornings, five afternoons, three days or full-time. Morning sessions include lunch at no extra cost. Butcombe is a member of the Bristol Early Years Partnership and accepts the government's nursery grant for the majority of 3 and 4 year olds. The nursery staff are either qualified teachers or nursery nurses.

There are three classes of 16 children in Reception, each with a class teacher and teaching assistant, three classes in each of Year 1 and Year 2, and four classes in Year 3, where there is always a big intake. In all there are 18 full-time and 14 part-time staff. Qualified specialist class teachers deliver a topic-based curriculum, with specialist teachers for music, dance (ballet, jazz dance, tap), sports, French and IT. Piano and instrumental lessons are available from Year 2, and all children in Years 2 and 3 learn the recorder and sing in the choir. Some sports activity takes place every day.

Life at Butcombe is busy and challenging. Year 2 and 3 pupils may take part in a range of co-curricular activities at lunchtimes or after school, when around sixteen clubs and societies are held. These change termly, and may include a variety of sports, sewing, puppet-making, junior detectives, zoo club, chess etc. Termly services and concerts are held in the Chapel, and an annual musical is performed in the Redgrave Theatre. There is a full programme of visits and outings for all ages, including a youth hostelling trip for Year 3.

The school has excellent provision for children requiring learning support.

New scholarships are available for entry to Year 3 (age 7) with a value of up to £1000 off fees per year. Please contact the secretary for details on how to apply.

Charitable status. Clifton College is a Registered Charity, number 311735. It provides boarding and day education for boys and girls aged 3–18.

Bute House Preparatory School for Girls

Bute House Luxemburg Gardens Hammersmith London W6 7EA
Tel: 020 7603 7381
Fax: 020 7371 3446
e-mail: mail@butehouse.co.uk
website: www.butehouse.co.uk

Chairman of Governors: Mr W O Clarke

***Headmistress*: Mrs S C Salvidant**, BEd Hons (London)

Age Range. 4–11.
Number of Pupils. 307 Day Girls.
Fees per term (2008-2009). £3,585 inclusive of lunches.

Bute House overlooks extensive playing fields and is housed in a large bright modern building. Facilities include a science laboratory, art room, technology room, music hall, 2 drama studios, multi-purpose hall and a large well-stocked library. A well-qualified, enthusiastic and experienced staff teach a broad curriculum which emphasises both the academic and the aesthetic. Information Technology is an integral part of the curriculum and the school has a wireless network. The classrooms are all equipped with multimedia machines. Laptops are also widely used for individual or class work. Monitored access to the internet is available. French is taught from Reception.

Sports include swimming, gymnastics, dance, tennis, lacrosse, netball and athletics which are taught on excellent on-site facilities. Full use is made of all that London has to offer and residential trips further afield are also offered to older girls.

Girls are encouraged to take full part in the school life from an early age. There is a democratically elected School Council and regular school meetings run by the girls when all pupils are able to put forward their views as well as to volunteer for duties around the school. A wide variety of extra-curricular activities is available.

The school aims at academic excellence in a non competitive, happy environment where girls are encouraged to be confident, articulate and independent and where courtesy and consideration are expected. There is a flourishing Parents Association. Entry is by ballot at age 4 and by assessment at age 7.

Caldicott

Farnham Royal Bucks SL2 3SL
Tel: 01753 644457
Fax: 01753 649325
e-mail: office@caldicott.com
website: www.caldicott.com

Chairman of the Board of Governors: G Puttergill

***Headmaster*: Simon Doggart**, BA

Age Range. 7–13.
Number of Boys. 130 Boarders and 120 Day Boys
Fees per term (2007-2008). Boarders £5,867, Day Boys: Middle School £4,316, Junior School £3,990.

Caldicott, founded in 1904, is an Educational Trust. The School is situated in 40 acres of grounds and playing fields adjacent to more than a thousand acres of permanent woodland. It is conveniently placed close to London between the M40 and the M4 and within 20 minutes of Heathrow Airport.

The school is forward-looking in its approach and the development of the buildings and playing fields is seen as a continuous process. The facilities are, therefore, modern, spacious, well-designed, well-maintained, and conveniently situated in and around the main building. They include a well equipped Technology Department and Computer Room, Music School, and an extensive Sports and Recreation centre which includes a Sports Hall and Squash Courts.

In September 2004 the Centenary Hall was finished giving the school excellent drama and concert facilities.

There is a high proportion of qualified teaching staff to boys. Classes are therefore kept as small as possible and each boy is able to receive individual help and attention. Our teaching methods combine what we believe to be the best in modern ideas with the more traditional ways we know to be indispensable. Throughout the school we insist on a high standard of work, and we offer all subjects necessary for the Common Entrance and Scholarship examinations to the Independent Senior Schools.

The school has a Christian ethos. The day begins with a short Chapel Service on weekdays, and on Sundays parents are welcome to join in the Services.

All day boys are expected to board from the age of 11 for their last two years in preparation for boarding at their Senior Schools.

Much emphasis is placed on creative activities such as Music, Art, Design, Modelling, Photography and Drama, and through the tutorial system every boy is encouraged to use his leisure time sensibly.

The principal games are Rugby, Hockey, and Cricket. Other sporting activities include Squash, Football, Swimming, Athletics, Tennis, Cross-country, Basketball and Gymnastics.

The prospectus is available on application to the Headmaster, who is always pleased to meet parents, discuss with them their sons' particular needs, and arrange for them to look around the school.

Charitable status. Caldicott is a Registered Charity, number 310631. Its purpose is to provide education for the young.

Cameron House

4 The Vale London SW3 6AH
Tel: 020 7352 4040
Fax: 020 7352 2349
e-mail: info@cameronhouseschool.org
website: www.cameronhouseschool.org

Founded in 1980.

***Principal*: Miss Josie Cameron**, BSc, DipEd

***Headmistress*: Miss Lucie Moore**, BA Hons, PGCE

Age Range. 4–11 Co-educational.
Number of Pupils. 105.
Fees per term (2007-2008). £4,150.

Based in a beautifully designed Edwardian building, just steps from London King's Road, Cameron House School prides itself on sending pupils to some of the most sought after schools in the country.

At 11, boys go on to Colet Court, King's College, Westminster Under and other day schools, and girls leave for St Paul's, Godolphin and Putney High, as well as a number of leading boarding schools.

The school is designed to be completely child-centred, modern and warm, creating the right atmosphere for learning. Yet it is not a hot house: its programme is designed to develop each child's personality and to stretch his or her individual talents. A high teacher/pupil ratio is essential to Cameron House's success. Excellent provision is made for children of exceptionally high IQ, or unusual ability, eg a Native French Speakers' Club, and Artists' Group.

The aim is to instil a firm sense of self, a passion for exploration and a freedom to express creativity, balanced by good manners, kindness and a selfless interest in others.

One of the first tasks is to foster a joy of reading, which Cameron House believes is the best foundation in each class. All pupils can access the school's own intranet, interactive whiteboards and the extensive computer suite.

From their earliest years, music, art and sport form an integral part of the children's school life and excellent local facilities allow the pupils to engage in a wide variety of sports. Unusually, a large majority of children learn karate, which builds physical confidence. Verbal communication skills are also developed, leading to English Speaking Board Examinations or Guildhall Examinations. Other popular clubs include Lunchtime Latin, Chess, Ballet, Tap and Fencing.

Two active choirs, as well as singing and percussion classes, composition and musical appreciation classes, and individual instrument lessons, lead to grade examinations of the Association Board of the Royal Schools of Music.

There is a genuinely open dialogue between parents and teachers, also fostered by The Friends of Cameron House. This contributes to the welcoming feel of the school. The Head of Cameron House is always delighted to give parents a tour of the school so that they can experience its special qualities for themselves.

Cargilfield

Barnton Avenue West, Edinburgh EH4 6HU
Tel: 0131 336 2207
Fax: 0131 336 3179
e-mail: admin@cargilfield.com
website: www.cargilfield.com

Chairman of the Board of Governors: Mrs Pamela Gray MA, Dip LE, FRICS

***Headmaster*: Mr John Elder**, MA Hons Edinburgh, PGCE

Bursar: Mrs Angela Favell

Assistant Headmaster: Mr David Walker, BA Hons

Deputy Heads:
Dr James Wilson, BA, PhD
Miss Emma Wallis, BEd

Age Range. 3–13.

Number of Children. 290.

Fees per term (2008-2009). Boarding: £5,000 (full), £4,800 (weekly). Day Pupils: £3,650–£3,950, Pre-Prep £2,500, Nursery £1,360.

The School is ideally situated in spacious grounds five miles from the centre of Edinburgh, just off the A90 and close to Edinburgh Airport. The staff consists of 29 teachers, both full-time and part-time, a senior matron and one assistant matron. Pupils, who are taught in small groups (between 12 and 16), are prepared for all independent secondary schools: the majority of leavers move on to the major Scottish boarding and day schools, in particular Fettes, Merchiston, Loretto and Glenalmond, but a number go south of the border and, in recent years, children have gone to Ampleforth, Downe House, Eton, Harrow, Oundle, Queen Margaret's York, Radley and Rugby. Suitable candidates are encouraged to enter for Scholarships, and 50 awards have been gained in the last six years, with a very strong showing in Classics (including Greek), Maths, English and Music. Rugby, Netball, Hockey, Cricket, Rounders, Tennis and Athletics make up the main part of the Games Programme and a wide variety of activities are organised, for example Skiing, mainly on the Hillend Dry Ski Slope, Riding, Sailing, Squash, Fencing, Judo, Archery, Swimming, Golf, Gymnastics, Climbing, Cookery and Chess. There is a very active Music Department: a thriving Pipe Band; Wind, Strings, Guitar, Flute groups and an Orchestra meets each week. There is both a Chapel Choir and a Junior Choir. The School is at the forefront of ICT with two suites and 60 PCs in both the Upper School and Pre-Prep. Other facilities include a lovely War Memorial Chapel, Theatre, new Science Department, a new classroom block, Music School, Girls' Boarding House, Art Studio, Design Workshop, Gymnasium and a superb multi-purpose Sports Hall; there are excellent playing fields and a floodlit Astroturf.

Our $2^1/_2$ million pound Pre-Prep and Nursery for boys and girls between the ages of three and eight feeds in directly to the Upper School. In the Upper School there are 60 boarders, but day children may board on a flexi-boarding system and all play a full part in the life of the School.

The pastoral system is centred on the Division Leader, Form Teacher and Tutor and we teach them about courtesy, appreciation of values (spiritual and social); we try to develop any talent and develop it to the full; we teach them about kindness, humour and honour.

Well-equipped games rooms offering snooker, table tennis, bar football and a host of board games and cosy and friendly bedrooms create a very strong family atmosphere. The staff have great fun here, the challenge of youth is ever present and although we have plenty of new buildings and equipment – the latest £1.5million development was completed in 2007 – a boarding and day preparatory school is much more: to learn to help others, to enjoy ourselves; these are top priorities.

Fee concessions are offered for third and fourth siblings and also for children of members of the Armed Forces. Scholarships are awarded each year for Academic work, Drama, Art, Music and Sport. Bursary support is available.

Charitable status. Cargilfield School is a Registered Scottish Charity, number SC005757. It is under a Board of Governors and is run on a non-profit-making basis; it exists solely to provide a first-class education for boys and girls.

The Carrdus School

Overthorpe Hall Nr Banbury Oxon OX17 2BS
Tel: 01295 263733
Fax: 01295 263733
e-mail: office@carrdusschool.co.uk
website: www.carrdusschool.co.uk

***Headmistress*: Miss S T Carrdus**, BA

Age Range. Boys 3–7, Girls 3–11, Nursery Class for children $3–4^1/_2$.

Number of Day Pupils. 151 (122 girls, 29 boys)

Fees per term (from April 2008). £350–£2,730. Compulsory extras: Insurance £3.70; PTA membership £5.

Overthorpe Hall is a day preparatory school for girls and a pre-preparatory school for boys. The large house stands in 11 acres of beautiful grounds.

The teaching staff consists of nine full-time qualified teachers and fifteen part-time specialists. Girls are prepared for 11+ Common Entrance and the school has an excellent record of success in this and all other examinations, sending girls to many well-known Independent Senior Schools in recent years. We take National Curriculum KS1 and KS2 tests. Boys are given a good grounding for their preparatory schools.

There is a heated outdoor swimming pool, a tennis court and a purpose-built sports hall. We have regular sporting success in local and regional events.

The aim of the school is to produce confident, well-disciplined and happy children, who have the satisfaction of reaching their own highest academic and personal standards. This is made possible by an organisation flexible enough to achieve a balance between new methods of teaching and sound traditional disciplines.

Castle Court Preparatory School

The Knoll House Knoll Lane Corfe Mullen Wimborne Dorset BH21 3RF
Tel: 01202 694438
Fax: 01202 659063
e-mail: office@castlecourt.com
website: www.castlecourt.com

Chairman of the Governors: Mr Michael J Cuthbertson, MA

***Headmaster*: Richard E T Nicholl**, BA Dunelm, CertEd

Deputy Headmaster: J J Hett, BA

Age Range. 3–13.

Number of Pupils. 346 (216 boys, 130 girls) including Pre-Preparatory, Reception and Badgers (Nursery).

Teaching Staff. 28 full time, 25 part time.

Fees per term (2008-2009). £2,375 (Reception to Year 2), £4,315 (Years 3 to 8). Nursery fees on application.

Castle Court is a day preparatory school for boys and girls aged 3 to 13, situated in 35 acres of beautiful grounds and woodlands within easy reach of Bournemouth, Poole, Blandford and the Isle of Purbeck. A gracious Regency house forms the heart of the school and contains the Reception rooms, dining rooms, offices and some of the junior classrooms. The Badgers, Reception and Pre-Preparatory departments (for 3 to 7 year olds) are all self-contained and, like the senior classrooms, are all purpose-built. Planning Permission has been granted (April 2008) to rebuild ten classrooms and to add a new dining room. There is a spacious hall for Assembly, drama and gymnastics, with a music department attached; an extension has provided a light and attractive school library. A science and art complex provides laboratories, art studios, design and technology room and the IT centre. All classrooms also have a bank of computers and an interactive whiteboard. New buildings include poolside sports changing rooms, an academic block with four classrooms, offices and Special Skills rooms. There is an outdoor heated swimming pool and extensive playing fields including an all-weather synthetic hockey pitch, for tennis in the summer.

While Castle Court is a day school, from the age of 9 children are encouraged to stay on for tea followed by prep or activities, before going home at 6 o'clock. There is a wide range of informal activities such as chess, computing, cookery, drama, electronics, photography, pottery, woodwork etc.

The normal curriculum includes English, mathematics, science, French, Latin, history, geography, religious studies, information technology, design and technology, art, music, and sport, with speech and drama for some years. All the children are prepared for the Common Entrance or Scholarship exams to senior independent schools, as well as for entry to local grammar schools. The school has a strong musical tradition with its own Orchestra, Band, Choir and various ensembles. Sport also forms an important part in the life of the children with rugby, soccer, hockey and cricket for the boys, and netball, rounders and hockey for the girls, with athletics, cross-country, gymnastics, dance, swimming and tennis for all. There are opportunities for sailing instruction, riding, fencing and golf. Trips include visits to local places of interest, camping weekends, and expeditions to the continent.

Our goal at Castle Court is to provide an outstanding day education based upon strong Christian values, and ensure that all the children here do the best they can and find their natural talents.

A prospectus (with details of the school bus service if required) will be sent on application to the Admissions Secretary; further information may be found on our school website.

Charitable status. Castle Court School Educational Trust Limited is a Registered Charity, number 325028. It aims to provide a first class education for local children.

Castle Park School

Castle Park Road Dalkey Co Dublin Ireland
Tel: 00 353 1 280 3037
Fax: 00 353 1 230 0936
e-mail: admin@castleparkschool.ie
website: www.castleparkschool.ie

Chairman of the Governors: Mr Alexis FitzGerald

***Headmaster*: D A McSweeney**

Age Range. 3–12 Co-educational.

Number of Pupils. 283: 175 Prep, 108 Pre-Prep.

Fees per term (2007-2008). €2,440.

The staff consists of 18 graduate teachers. Peripatetic staff teach musical instruments.

The School, which is a charitable trust, was founded in 1904. Children are prepared for entrance and Scholarships to Independent schools in Ireland, England and Scotland.

Facilities include 12 acres of attractive grounds overlooking Dublin Bay, a heated indoor swimming pool, an all-weather surface for hockey and tennis, cricket and soccer fields, artificial cricket wicket, art and craft room, a science laboratory and computer room.

Games: Hockey, Soccer, Cricket, Tennis, Swimming, Athletics, Rounders, Gaelic Games.

Hobbies: Riding, craft, computing, construction, cookery, sailing, drama, dance.

Music plays an important part in the curriculum with woodwind, percussion, piano, guitar, voice lessons.

A Junior Montessori School for 3–6 year olds under fully qualified staff is incorporated. Fees: €1,270–€1,515 per term. Extended Day facilities are available.

Caterham Preparatory School

Mottrams Harestone Valley Road Caterham Surrey CR3 6YB
Tel: 01883 342097
Fax: 01883 341230
e-mail: prep-enquiries@caterhamschool.co.uk
website: www.caterhamschool.co.uk

Chairman of Governors: W R Broadhead

***Head Teacher*: H W G Tuckett**, MA

Age Range. 3–11 years.

Number of Pupils. 283: 160 Boys, 123 Girls.

Fees per term (2008-2009). Pre-Preparatory £1,341–£2,250, Preparatory £2,872–£3,451. Lunch £162.50.

The School stands in 80 acres of grounds in the green belt on the slopes of the North Downs, approximately 1 mile outside Caterham.

In 1994 the School became co-educational and the Nursery and Pre-Prep Department provides excellent facilities for younger children joining the School.

The curriculum offers the normal range of subjects including Technology and Science in well equipped laboratories. In addition, French is taught from age 4. There is a full PE programme including Soccer, Netball, Cricket, Rounders, Athletics, Tennis, Swimming and Gymnastics. Regular use is made of the new sports hall, astroturf and 25m indoor swimming pool.

Over 30 clubs and extra-curricular activities take place each week including Computer Club, Sailing, Drama, Short Tennis, Judo, Needlework, Choir, Orchestra and facilities for instrumental tuition.

All classrooms are equipped with their own multimedia computers and are fully networked with screened internet access. There is also a separate ICTSuite with 20 computers.

The Preparatory School enjoys close liaison with Caterham School, to which pupils normally proceed at age 11. In 1995 Caterham School became fully co-educational and a member of The United Church Schools Trust. This heralded an exciting series of developments providing the facilities for all pupils to continue achieving the high standards for which the School is well known.

Charitable status. Caterham School is an Associate School of the United Church Schools Trust and is a Registered Charity, number 1050847.

The Cathedral School Llandaff
A Woodard School

Llandaff Cardiff CF5 2YH
Tel: 029 2056 3179
Fax: 029 2056 7752
e-mail: registrar@cathedral-school.co.uk
website: www.cathedral-school.co.uk

Chairman of the Council: Mr P S Davey

***Headmaster*: S W Morris**, BA, MEd, PGCE

Age Range. 3–16 Co-educational.

Number of Pupils. 650 (436 Boys and 214 Girls), including 40 in Nursery, 129 in Infant Department.

Fees per term (2007-2008). Senior Day (Years 7 & above) £2,890, Years 5 & 6 £2,750, Year 4 £2,550, Year 3 Pupils £2,235, Years 1 & 2 £2,010, Reception £1,970, Nursery £28.70 per day or £23 per morning session.

Academic, Music and Sports Scholarships and a number of means-tested bursaries are available for children currently in Year 6.

The Cathedral School Llandaff, with a 120 year tradition of academic excellence, is one of the leading independent schools in Wales, offering an outstanding and broad education to boys and girls aged 3–16 years.

During the last ten years The School has grown from a small preparatory school of 280 pupils to one of the leading co-educational establishments in Wales with 635 pupils.

More than £1 million has been spent on new buildings in recent years. The investment provides outstanding facilities, which benefit every pupil, and the environment available to each child has been greatly enhanced. The School's facilities include four science laboratories, five computer laboratories, an Art and Design Technology department in the old boarding house, a fine purpose-built Music Department including a recording studio and practice rooms, a specially designed Drama centre for workshops and performances, a Sports Hall, on-site games fields and an impressive Nursery building with appropriate areas for work and play activities. After-school activities happen daily and there is after-school care available until 6.00 pm.

For the fourth consecutive years pupils at The Cathedral School, Llandaff have achieved outstanding GCSE results. Overall the percentage of exams passed with A* or A Grade was an astonishing 67%, whilst 73.5% of the pupils gained 5 or more A* and As. 98% of pupils achieved 5 or more A* to C grades.

In addition to the high academic standards, the School is well-known for its astonishing wide range of extra-curricular activities. Music (10 choirs and over 20 instrumental ensembles) is exceptionally strong and the School also provides choristers (boys and girls in two choirs) for Llandaff Cathedral. In Sport there are extensive opportunities for pupils both in terms of the traditional games (where competing teams have an outstanding record of success) and with regard to such activities as Rowing, Judo and Rock-climbing. In addition, pupils can opt for such diverse activities as Drama, Dance, Archaeology Club, Yoga, Judo and Cookery.

The only way, however, to experience the true atmosphere of the School is to meet the staff and pupils and to see us in action. We warmly welcome you to visit us.

Charitable status. The Cathedral School Llandaff Limited is a Registered Charity, number 1103522. It exists to provide a high standard of education for girls and boys between the ages of 3 and 16 years.

The Cavendish School

31 Inverness Street London NW1 7HB
Tel: 020 7485 1958
Fax: 020 7267 0098
e-mail: admissions@cavendish-school.co.uk
website: www.cavendishschool.co.uk

Chairman of Governors: Mrs E Chesswas

***Head*: Mrs Teresa Dunbar**

Age Range. 3–11.

Number of Children. 160 Day Girls.

Fees per term (2007-2008). Reception–Year 6: £3,380; Nursery £1,700–£3,180 depending upon number of sessions. Fees include lunch and outings.

The Cavendish School is a small friendly IAPS preparatory school with over a century's experience in providing a lively well-balanced academic education in a caring Christian environment. The school is housed in a spacious Victorian school building and a modern teaching block. There are two secluded playgrounds. There is a large, well-kept library, separate Science and DT/Art rooms and an IT teaching room.

The Cavendish School is administered by a charitable educational trust. The Headmistress is a member of IAPS and the school is inspected and accredited by ISC. The Cavendish School is a Catholic foundation. Children of other denominations are welcomed and their beliefs are respected.

Particular attention is given at The Cavendish School to each child's individual needs. Throughout the school a pupil's progress is carefully monitored so that, in consultation with parents, talents may be encouraged or difficulties overcome with small group or supplementary specialist tuition. In addition to the usual range of subjects, The Cavendish offers tuition in conversational French to all pupils from four years.

There is an extensive programme of extra-curricular activities including Spanish conversation, ballet, IT, gym, rounders, judo, pottery and folk dancing. Pupils participate in the BAYS science, BAGA gymnastic, St John's Ambulance First Aid and ASA swimming award schemes. The school operates an after-school care service.

The school attaches great importance to maintaining strong yet informal links between home and school. The Headmistress and her staff are available weekly for consultation. There are also 2 termly written reports and annual parent-teacher meetings. There is a parents' association to which all parents belong. Parents are encouraged to participate in school outings, to join their children by invitation on numerous less formal occasions, and to contribute their expertise to supplementary activities.

Senior pupils are prepared in small tutorial groups for entry to a wide range of senior schools. The highly experienced and dedicated staff aim to make the pupils' years at The Cavendish a happy and purposeful experience so that they will transfer to their senior school at the age of eleven with confidence and ease.

Charitable status. The Cavendish School is a Registered Charity, number 312727.

Chafyn Grove School

Salisbury Wiltshire SP1 1LR
Tel: 01722 333423
Fax: 01722 323114
e-mail: info@chafyngrove.co.uk
website: www.chafyngrove.co.uk

Chairman of Governors: G Osmond, Esq

***Headmaster*: Mr Eddy Newton**, BA, PGCE (Cantab)

Age Range. 2½–13.

Number of Pupils. 312: 222 Boys, 90 Girls.

Fees per term (2007-2008). Boarding supplement £1,480. Day Children: Main School (Years 4–8) £4,175, Transition (Year 3) £3,145, Pre-Prep (Years R–2) £2,095, Nursery £15.30 per session.

Chafyn Grove is set in 14 acres of grounds on the edge of the historic city of Salisbury – just an hour and a half from London by road, with easy access to air and rail links. The children thrive in an ambitious academic environment, where good sports facilities; extensive Art, Music and Drama opportunities and a commitment to extra-curricular activities encourage your child to discover their interests and their strengths.

Chafyn Grove has a happy family atmosphere that is created by a caring pastoral system and a team of talented and committed teachers. Pupils at Chafyn Grove School enjoy a good relationship with our staff; there is mutual friendship and a healthy respect. Our children also develop good relationships with other pupils, whether younger or older. Assemblies, chapel and tutor time all foster an understanding of how people should treat one another.

We have a mix of day and boarding pupils. Our boarding enhances the sense of community and is all about making the most of your time at school, developing independence and making friends for life – our aim is to provide a caring and happy environment in which children thrive and grow. Our boarders benefit from a secure and homely atmosphere and are accommodated in cosy, brightly decorated dormitories, often creatively decorated with their own pictures and posters, their own bedding and of course a teddy or two! There is a full weekly activity programme for boarders as well as a full weekend programme where both boarding and teaching staff are fully involved with the children creating a strong bond between staff and pupils.

Small class sizes (maximum 16) and a commitment to high standards allow our pupils to perform impressively in the classroom. All pupils reached the school of their choice last year and 17 scholarships have been awarded so far to our pupils to Senior Schools in 2007. Pupils go on to many well-known Senior Schools including Canford, Marlborough, Bryanston, Godolphin and Winchester. Pupils are also prepared for 11+ to the two Grammar Schools in Salisbury and a record number of Year 6 pupils made the grade last year, although some opted to stay at Chafyn! Scholarships to Chafyn are awarded in Years 2, 4, and 6, and take place in February.

Our facilities include ten acres of playing fields, a large astroturf pitch, 25-metre heated swimming pool, 2 tennis courts, 2 squash courts, sports hall, music school, creative arts centre, two science laboratories and a computer centre. A new library block with a computerised resource centre and 8 classrooms opened in May 2006.

Charitable status. Chafyn Grove School is a Registered Charity, number 309483. It exists to provide an excellent education for children.

Chandlings School

Bagley Wood Kennington Oxford OX1 5ND
Tel: 01865 730771
Fax: 01865 735194
e-mail: office@chandlings.org.uk
website: www.chandlings.org.uk

Chairman of the Governors: The Rt Hon Lord Wakeham, DL

***Headmistress*: Mrs Sophia Ashworth Jones**, BSc Jt Hons QTS Leeds

Age Range. 3–11 Co-educational.

Number of Pupils. 426 Day Pupils: Pre-Prep: 110 boys and 76 girls. Prep: 146 boys and 94 girls.

Fees per term (2008-2009). £2,850–£3,750.

Staffing. 46 full-time and 10 part-time qualified staff teach the 27 classes.

Location. The school is set in a beautiful sixty-acre site, with lakes, woods and extensive grounds which provide a stimulating educational environment. Situated on the outskirts of Oxford one mile from the ring road and A34, it is easily accessible from all directions.

Facilities. The facilities include modern and well-equipped classrooms and science laboratories, excellent IT facilities, brand new dedicated music department, art, food technology, textile and pottery rooms, a large hall for sport, music and drama, extensive playing fields, tennis courts, a 9-hole golf course, riding school, indoor and outdoor swimming pools.

Aims. The warm family atmosphere at the heart of Chandlings ensures each child is valued and cared for as an individual. This creates a happy environment in which children are well motivated and keen to learn. It also develops courteous and considerate children who each contribute their special strengths to Chandlings.

Chandlings seeks to provide quality in the education it offers, with a well-balanced curriculum and high academic standards to promote the development of the whole child. Children are given a strong educational foundation through sound teaching methods and challenging work. This is all delivered in an exciting and stimulating way which fosters a love of learning which will last them a lifetime.

Children are well prepared for entrance to independent senior schools in the area with a high number of scholarships being awarded.

Small classes ensure good progress, individual attention and support. Our aim is to encourage each child to develop a sense of achievement and self-worth together with a positive attitude and high expectations.

This approach continues beyond the academic. Chandlings offers a wide range of educational activities which give breadth and balance to the children's learning and also provides opportunities for them to develop their own personal strengths and skills; these include ballet, judo, riding, golf, individual music lessons, swimming and tennis. Further activities include orchestra, choir, computer club, team practices and sport, plus variations such as pottery, chess, drama, table tennis, snooker and gardening. French is taught from the age of 4 years and is a particular strength of the school. Children in their final year spend a week in Normandy.

The school encourages close links between parents and school and there is a strong Parents' Association, PACH.

Charitable status. Chandlings is governed by Cothill Educational Trust, which is a Registered Charity, number 309639. Its main object and purpose is the advancement of education.

Cheam School

Headley Newbury Berkshire RG19 8LD
Tel: 01635 268381
Registrar: 01635 268381
Fax: 01635 269345
e-mail: office@cheamschool.co.uk
website: www.cheamschool.com

The School, originally founded in 1645, is a charitable trust controlled by a Board of Governors.

Chairman of Governors: A F Gibbs, MA

***Headmaster*: M R Johnson**, BEd College of St Mark & St John, Plymouth

Assistant Headmaster: T C Haigh, BA Birmingham, PGCE

Age Range. 3–13.

Number of Pupils. 96 boarders, 302 day children.

Fees per term (2008-2009). £6,845 Boarders; £2,900–£5,070 Day children.

The School became co-educational in September 1997. A merger with Inhurst House School, formerly situated at Baughurst, and which re-located to the Headley site in 1999, offers parents the opportunity for education from 3–13+ for their sons and daughters.

Scholarships are offered annually for 8 year olds.

Classes are small (maximum 18) and pupils are prepared for the major senior independent schools with Eton, Harrow, Radley, Marlborough, Sherborne, Wellington, Downe House, St Mary's Calne and Sherborne Girls' featuring frequently. Recent improvements include excellent facilities for Design Technology and Information Technology, a new dedicated Science Building, a refurbished Chapel and new Teaching Block, a new Music School, a new Sports Hall (opened September 2003) and much improved boarding facilities. Dormitories are comfortable, carpeted and curtained.

Rugby, Soccer and Cricket are the major team games for boys; Netball, Rounders, Hockey and Lacrosse for girls. A heated outdoor swimming pool, 6 all-weather tennis courts and a 9-hole golf course in the extensive 80-acre grounds allow a wide range of other sports and pastimes to be enjoyed.

The School is situated half way between Newbury and Basingstoke on the A339 and is within easy reach of the M3 and M4 motorways and the A34 trunk route from Portsmouth, Southampton and Winchester to Oxford and the Midlands. London Heathrow Airport is within an hour's drive.

Charitable status. Cheam School Educational Trust is a Registered Charity, number 290143. It provides high-class education for boarding and day pupils; traditional values; modern thinking; education for the 21st century.

Cheltenham College Junior School

Thirlestaine Road Cheltenham GL53 7AB
Tel: 01242 522697
Fax: 01242 265620
e-mail: ccjs@cheltcoll.gloucs.sch.uk
website: www.cheltcoll.gloucs.sch.uk

President of Council: The Revd J C Horan

***Headmaster*: A C Morris**, BEd Hons

Age Range. 3–13.

Number of Pupils. 430 (55 boarders, 375 day boys and girls).

Fees per term (2008-2009). Boarders £4,900–£6,395; Day Boys and Girls £2,000–£4,920.

Cheltenham College Junior School is a co-educational preparatory school from 3 to 13. The Pre-Prep Department called Kingfishers is located in a self-contained purpose-built department.

The School stands in a beautiful 15-acre parkland site near the centre of Regency Cheltenham; the town itself being well served by both motorway and rail networks. Excellent facilities include: all weather pitches, athletics track, squash courts, tennis courts, art block, computer centre, CDT centre, drama studio and music school. In 2001 a spacious multi-purpose Assembly Hall was opened and in 2002 a new six-classroom teaching block was completed. Some facilities are shared with the senior school including the Chapel, Science School, 25m indoor swimming pool, floodlit astroturf and outstanding sports hall.

The curriculum is a wide and stimulating one with all pupils being prepared for Common Entrance and Scholarship examinations. Apart from the normal academic subjects, all study Art, Music, PE, Information Technology, CDT and Drama. The excellent facilities are backed by a team of professional and dedicated teachers. French is taught from the age of 3 in Kingfishers, Latin from age 10.

A wide range of sports are available including: Rugby, cricket, hockey, football, cross-country, netball, badminton, athletics, archery, golf, gymnastics, squash, ballet, sailing, swimming, tennis and orienteering. Sporting skills are taught from an early age and include swimming for the whole school.

The school aims to give a well-rounded education in preparation for senior school. The environment is secure and caring, allowing each individual to meet his/her full potential. The boarding house aims to provide a 'home from home', with excellent pastoral care and a wide range of extra-curricular activities under the supervision of the House Parents. Regular contact with parents is encouraged with exeats every third weekend. Three weekly progress reports are issued and full reports at the end of each term.

Visitors are welcomed and further information available from the Headmaster's Secretary, who will also arrange an appointment to tour the school and meet the Headmaster.

Charitable status. Cheltenham College Junior School is a Registered Charity, number 311720. It exists to provide education for boys and girls.

Chesham Preparatory School

Two Dells Lane Chesham Bucks HP5 3QF
Tel: 01494 782619
Fax: 01494 791645
e-mail: secretary@chesham-prep.bucks.sch.uk
website: www.chesham-prep.bucks.sch.uk

Chairman of Governors: Mr J T Axon, FCA

***Headmaster*: J D B Marjoribanks**, BEd Hons, Dip d'Et Fr

Deputy Head: S J Dilley, MEd, CertEd

Age Range. 4–13.

Numbers of Pupils. 390 boys and girls.

Fees per term (from January 2008). £2,500–£3,200 (incl lunch).

Situated in the Green Belt between Chesham and Berkhamsted and surrounded by open countryside, Chesham Preparatory School is the leading co-educational Preparatory school in South Buckinghamshire.

A twenty year programme of development has seen numbers rise from 150 to 390 and the construction of purpose-built classrooms, Library, Science Lab, ICT room, Art and DT room, Dining room, Changing rooms and All-weather Tennis courts. The construction of a Music Block and a full-sized Sports Hall was completed in April 2004.

There is a two-form entry at Reception level; a further form is added at Year 3. Maximum class size is 20. Entry into Reception is on a 'first come, first served' basis. Entry into Year 3 is via a screening and assessment process. The school has a learning support department for children who need a little extra help and encouragement.

The curriculum is traditional and includes English, Maths, Science, Spanish, French, History, Geography, RE, Music, PSHE, Art, DT, ICT, PE, Games and Swimming. Music and Drama are important areas of school life. Instrumental tuition is available and the Choir numbers some 60 children. Art displays are a feature of the school. Regular trips are organised throughout the year including ski trips, trips abroad and more locally.

At the centre of the school's ethos is the determination that all children will be happy and confident so that they thrive in the school environment, benefit from the broad and balanced curriculum and are fully prepared for their Secondary education.

Children go on to the Senior Independent Schools at 13+ via Common Entrance, Scholarship or local Independent School exams. Buckinghamshire County Council runs the 11+ selection process to Grammar Schools. About half the children enter the Grammar Schools at 11+.

Charitable status. Chesham Preparatory School is a Registered Charity, number 310642. It exists to provide education for boys and girls.

Chigwell Junior School

Chigwell Essex IG7 6QF
Tel: 020 8501 5721
Fax: 020 8501 5723
website: www.chigwell-school.org

Chairman of the Governors: C P de Boer, Esq

***Head of the Junior School*: Mrs J Gwinn**, BSc, CertEd

Age Range. 7–13.

Number of Pupils. 329 Day Pupils.

Fees per term (2008-2009). £2,797–£4,301 plus Lunch/Tea £228.

The Junior School is housed in a purpose-built building on the same site as the Senior School, with which it shares the use of a wide range of activities and facilities including Chapel, Science laboratories, Music School, Arts and Technology Centre, Theatre, Gymnasium, Swimming Pool, Sports Hall and 70 acres of playing fields, only 10 miles from the heart of London.

The curriculum and administration of the Senior and Junior Schools are closely linked.

Pupils sit a written test for entry to the Junior School and are normally admitted to the Senior School (*see entry in HMC section*) without further examination.

Charitable status. Chigwell School is a Registered Charity, number 1115098. It exists to provide a rounded education of the highest quality for its pupils.

Chinthurst School

Tadworth Surrey KT20 5QZ
Tel: 01737 812011
Fax: 01737 814835
e-mail: enquiries@chinthurst.surrey.sch.uk
website: www.chinthurst.surrey.sch.uk

The School is an Educational Trust, administered by a Board of Governors.

Chairman of Governors: A Bisset, Esq

***Headmaster*: T J Egan**, MEd

Deputy Headmasters:
M S Roylance, BEd
P Mulhern, BEd
T Button, BEd

Age Range. $2^1/_2$–13.

Number of Boys. 250.

Fees per term (2007-2008). Nursery (age $2^1/_2$–$4^1/_2$) £1,025, Pre-Preparatory (age $4^1/_2$–7) £2,090, Preparatory (age 7–13) £2,890. Lunch is provided at a cost of £180–£185.

The School is set in modern and attractive rural surroundings with spacious games facilities.

Boys are prepared for all Senior Independent Schools, by way of the Common Entrance or Scholarships. A very experienced and well qualified staff ensure a high standard is achieved both academically and on the games field. Chinthurst has a 'family' ethos, aimed at the achievement of high academic standards allied to a purposeful and active school life within a happy environment.

Charitable status. Chinthurst School is a Registered Charity, number 271160 A/1.

The Chorister School

Durham DH1 3EL
Tel: 0191 384 2935
Fax: 0191 383 1275
e-mail: head@choristers.durham.sch.uk
website: www.choristers.durham.sch.uk

Chairman of Governors: The Dean of Durham, The Very Revd Michael Sadgrove

***Headmaster*: I T A Hawksby**, BA Leeds

Age Range. 3–13.

Number of Pupils. 174 (20 Chorister-boarders, 9 full/weekly boarders, 145 day pupils, including 49 in Pre-Prep.) The school became co-educational in 1995 and there are girls in every year group.

Fees per term (2007-2008). Choristers (including piano lessons) £2,520, Full/Weekly Boarders £4,800, Day Pupils £2,920, Pre-Prep £2,140, Nursery £15 per half day session. Reductions are available for the children of CofE clergy and for younger siblings. Fees are inclusive of all normal requirements; there are no compulsory extras.

The Chorister School is situated in a beautiful corner of Durham Cathedral Close and is overlooked by the magnificent Norman tower of the Cathedral. Choristers take a voice trial; for non-chorister pupils musical ability is not, of course, expected.

Pastoral care is the responsibility of all members of the staff, with the boarders' needs attended to by the five house staff and the Headmaster and his wife. Day pupils may take advantage of the extended boarding day, taking part with boarders in a wide range of clubs and activities after lessons are over. Art club, school choir, ballet, chess, sports clubs, speech and drama, karate and textiles are some of the popular ones. Flexible boarding is also available.

Our curriculum introduces French from Pre-Prep level, where each of the classes has its own class teacher. In the Prep School class-teaching of the core curriculum is gradually replaced by subject-specialist teaching as children are prepared for Common Entrance and Scholarship examinations to senior schools. The school has a reputation for academic success, but cherishes all its pupils, whatever their academic attainment. Its curriculum, which includes RE, PE, swimming, Art, Technology and Music, is designed to ensure that academic edge does not lead to academic narrowness.

Games are an important element in the curriculum. The Chorister School competes at various levels with other schools in athletics, cricket, netball, hockey, rounders, rugby, football and swimming. Badminton, volleyball, basketball, tennis, indoor football and netball (in our large Sports Hall) are also played. The Chorister School has its own sports fields, tennis court and play areas, and uses the indoor swimming pool at Durham School.

Individual instrumental music lessons are available in almost all instruments, and all pupils take class music in which they sing and learn about musical history, musical instruments, simple analysis and some famous pieces.

Entry is by English and Maths test graded according to age or by informal assessment during a 'taster' day, as seems best for the age of the individual child. Competitive voice trials for aspiring Choristers are held twice a year, and at other times by arrangement. Please write or telephone the Registrar for a prospectus and to arrange a visit to the school.

Next School. Children move from The Chorister School to a wide range of maintained and independent secondary schools throughout the North East and further afield. The school advises and guides parents in the appropriate choice of next school and aims to secure a successful transition for every pupil. In the past six years every child has won a place to the senior school of choice, with between 43–72% winning an academic or subject scholarship or a competitive entry place.

Charitable status. The Chorister School and Durham Cathedral enjoy charitable status (exempt from registration) and the school exists to provide boarding education for the choristers of Durham Cathedral and day or boarding education for other children aged 4–13.

Christ Church Cathedral School

3 Brewer Street Oxford OX1 1QW
Tel: 01865 242561
Fax: 01865 202945
e-mail: schooloffice@cccs.org.uk
website: www.cccs.org.uk

Governors: The Dean and Canons of Christ Church Cathedral

***Headmaster*: Martin Bruce**, BA, MA, FCollP

Age Range. Rising 3–13.

Number of Boys. About 22 boarders, all of whom are Cathedral Choristers (who must board) and 142 day boys.

Fees per term (2008-2009). Day boys £3,555 (including lunch); Pre-Prep £2,430 (including lunch); Cathedral Choristers £2,195–£2,425 (fees are subsidised by the Cathedral); Nursery £1,110–£2,060.

Christ Church Cathedral School is a boarding and day Preparatory, Pre-Preparatory and Nursery School for boys.

The School provides Choristers for the choirs of Christ Church Cathedral and Worcester College, and is governed by the Dean and Canons of Christ Church, with the assistance of lay members drawn from the city's professional community, some of whom are past or current parents.

It was founded in 1546 when provision was made for the education of eight Choristers on King Henry VIII's foundation of Christ Church on the site of Cardinal Wolsey's earlier foundation of Cardinal College. In the latter half of the nineteenth century, at the initiative of Dean Liddell, father of Alice Liddell, the inspiration for 'Alice in Wonderland', the boarding house was established at No 1 Brewer Street, and in 1892, during the Headship of the Reverend Henry Sayers, father of Dorothy L Sayers, the Italian Mediaeval scholar and creator of Lord Peter Wimsey, the present building was erected.

The School is centrally situated off St Aldates, and two hundred yards from Christ Church. It therefore not only enjoys the unique cultural background provided by Oxford itself, but also has the advantage of excellent recreational facilities on Christ Church Meadow. Buildings include a former residence of Cardinal Wolsey and the Sir William Walton Centre which contains a recital hall in addition to spacious classrooms.

Churcher's College Junior School

Midhurst Road Liphook Hampshire GU30 7HT
Tel: 01730 236870
Fax: 01428 722550
e-mail: ccjsofffice@churcherscollege.com
website: www.churcherscollege.com

Chairman of Governors: M J Gallagher, Esq, DipArch Hons, RIBA, MIOD, FIMgmt

***Head*: Mrs S M Rivett**, CertEd, DipDrama (London)

Age Range. 4–11 Co-educational.

Number of Pupils. 220.

Fees per term (2008-2009). £2,195–£2,340 excluding lunch.

Churcher's College Junior School provides a happy, stimulating, safe and secure environment in which every child feels valued and is able to develop personally, socially and academically. Each child should be nurtured and taught to hold a high regard for others and themselves.

We view education as a joint partnership between teachers, parents and pupils, and strive to develop a team spirit in which every member gives of their best. We hold high expectations of staff and pupils and aim to create an environment that values individuals, applauds success, strives to encourage questioning, lets pupils explore, be controversial and be special.

The Junior School enjoys a newly developed and modernised site in Liphook approximately 8 miles from the College, but continues to have strong links with the Senior School in Petersfield.

The school is set in beautiful rural surroundings providing extensive grounds for sports practices, three separate playing areas and a nature garden. Latest computer technology, networked classroom computers and interactive whiteboards are all used by staff and pupils to enhance curriculum studies. The school has a fully-equipped ICT suite, science laboratory and dedicated music and art rooms. A current building project will provide a new Performing Arts wing – due for completion in Autumn 2008.

The wider curriculum is valued, offering additional depth and scope in all subjects and pupils are encouraged to take part in a broad range of experiences both in and out of the classroom.

Churcher's College Junior School provides pupils with:

(a) a broad based and challenging curriculum that enables all pupils to achieve their individual potential in all areas and caters for their individual abilities, needs and interests.

(b) a functional education in which pupils are able to develop transferable skills and a love of learning that will enable them to succeed in the ever changing world.

(c) experiences of an aesthetic, creative and spiritual nature.

Teaching and learning activities cater for the varying needs of our pupils and allow all to achieve their full potential in a wide variety of areas – academic, creative, sporting, etc.

We maintain a broad and balanced curriculum in which pupils experience a wide range of activities to maximise their learning opportunities. Teaching is grounded in pupils past experiences and they are helped to see the importance of each area of study.

The school is seen as a continually evolving organisation and we constantly reflect upon practice as a means of self improvement.

Charitable status. Churcher's College is a Registered Charity, number 307320.

City of London Freemen's Junior School

Ashtead Park Surrey KT21 1ET
Tel: 01372 822474 (Secretary)
01372 822418 (Admissions)
Fax: 01372 822415
01372 822416 (Admissions)
e-mail: admissions.clfs@cityoflondon.gov.uk
website: www.clfs.surrey.sch.uk

Co-educational Day and Boarding School.

Chairman of Governors: R A Eve, Deputy

***Head*: Mr I D Thorpe**, BA(Ed), MA(Ed)

Age Range. 7–13.
Number of Pupils. 360.
Fees per term (2008-2009). Tuition £3,395–£3,576.

The City of London Freemen's Junior School was established formally in 1988 as an integral part of CLFS and it prepares girls and boys for entry to the Senior School in Year 9. It shares a magnificent 57 acre site in Ashtead Park, Surrey, where the many outstanding facilities are available to all pupils (*see separate entry in HMC section*).

With its broad based curriculum and modern purpose-built facilities, the Junior School offers a challenging and unique atmosphere for all new entrants. There is a Junior School Head with specialist teaching staff and a clearly defined academic and pastoral structure to ensure that all pupils know what is expected of them. On average there are about 20 pupils in each of the three parallel classes in each year group. In Year 7 the year groups rises to four classes. Junior pupils benefit greatly from seeing their Form Prefects, who are Sixth Formers from the Senior School, on a daily basis.

For the first four years, in Key Stage 2, Heads of Year work in liaison with the subject coordinators and the Heads of Senior School Departments to ensure that the programmes of work are compatible and progressive. The aim is to establish a secure foundation in traditional core subjects within a curriculum which will broaden experience and excite the imagination of each child. In Years 7 and 8 the teaching programme is managed by the Heads of the Senior School Departments using specialist teachers for all of the subjects. Whilst academic excellence throughout the Junior School is still a major aim, there is also a very full programme of extra curricular activities including drama, music and sports.

Fully integrated into whole school routines, the Junior School takes full advantage of Ashtead Park's facilities. Extensive playing fields, the floodlit all-weather pitch, the sports hall and the modern swimming pool ensure that the sports facilities available are second to none.

There are three Houses in the School providing pastoral care and supervision whilst also promoting healthy competition in many activities. In both the Senior and the Junior School outstanding work and good progress, inside and outside the classroom, are recognised by the award of appropriate merits and distinctions.

Admission to the Junior School is through entrance examination, interview and feeder school report. Progression to the Senior School is based on continuous assessment with no separate qualifying entrance test and as such is almost always automatic for Junior School pupils. Pupils are constantly reviewed and can be assured that they will move through to the Senior School with many familiar faces around them.

Claires Court Schools

Ridgeway

Maidenhead Thicket Maidenhead Berkshire SL6 3QE
Tel: 01628 411490; Registrar: 01628 411472
Fax: 01628 411465
e-mail: registrar@clairescourt.com
website: www.clairescourt.com

Principals:
H StJ Wilding, BA, MCIM, FRSA (*Bursar*)
J T Wilding, BSc, FRSA (*Academic Principal*)

***Head of Ridgeway*: Mrs K M Rogg**, BEd

Age Range. 4–11.
Number of Boys. 235 Day Boys.
Teaching Staff. 19 full time, 11 part time, 5 visiting.
Fees per term (2008-2009). £2,145–£3,120.

The ethos of Ridgeway lies in the provision for its pupils of a thorough education in all senses so that in time the challenges of the future will be met with confidence. A rich and full programme of study and activity leads to academic success, sporting accomplishment and cultural fulfilment, within a firm structure based on friendship and self-discipline. Boys are accepted into the School from 4+ to 11.

Ridgeway is situated in Maidenhead Thicket set in its own extensive grounds. The curriculum embraces the Government's National Curriculum and includes Music, Art and Craft, practical Science, and the major games and PE as well as a thorough, caring preparation for normal academic subjects. At 11+ boys transfer to the Senior School, Claires Court.

Specialist pre-prep accommodation was added in 1991 and further new buildings to accommodate the school's expansion were added in 1994. A new sports hall was completed in 2005.

Ridgeway is the Boys' Junior School of Claires Court and its provision is complemented by the provision for Girls' education at The College. The Nursery is situated at The College, where 100 places exist for pre-school children. The coordination of all arrangements from transport to teaching across the three sites forms an integral part of the day to day school management.

The extensive playing fields, which provide ample facilities for the playing of major games such as Mini-Rugby, Soccer, Cricket and Athletics, also include a conservation area and the School swimming pool. Among the many activities run after school are Archery, CDT, Chess, Choir, Computing, Cookery, Drama, Electronics, Judo, Model-making, Pottery, Science Club and Study in addition to a very wide variety of sports.

The School is multi-denominational.

A Prospectus, containing further information, may be obtained by telephoning the Registrar at Claires Court on 01628 411472 and prospective parents are always welcome to visit the School.

Clayesmore Preparatory School

Iwerne Minster Blandford Forum Dorset DT11 8PH
Tel: 01747 811707
Fax: 01747 811692
e-mail: smorris@clayesmore.com
website: www.clayesmore.com

Chairman of Governors: Dr R Willis, MA, BM, BCh

***Headmaster*: R D H Geffen**, BEd

Age Range. 2½–13.

Number of Pupils. 295 (Boarders 80, Day 215).

Fees per term (2007-2008). Boarders: £5,248 (Year 3), £5,751 (Years 4–8); Day Pupils: £2,100 (Pre-Prep), £4,001 (Year 3), £4,271 (Years 4–8).

Clayesmore Preparatory School was founded in 1929 at Charlton Marshall House by R A L Everett. In 1974 it moved to Iwerne Minster to occupy purpose-built premises close to Senior Clayesmore. A comprehensive development programme in recent years has provided the School with outstanding facilities for Sport, Music, Drama and the Arts, while the 62-acre parkland campus in one of the most beautiful parts of Dorset is the ideal environment for children to grow up in. In September 2008 a brand new state-of-the-art classroom building will be opened. This will comprise five classrooms which will accommodate Years 3 and 4 and two new Science laboratories.

Day children can join the Pre-Preparatory Department at 2½; the youngest boarders usually arrive at the age of 8. Admission is normally by interview and report from a child's previous school. Older children may be asked to take a short entry test to assist in setting. The School is fully co-educational.

Academic, Art, Music, Sporting and All Rounder Scholarships are offered each year, together with 11+ Continuity Scholarships for candidates intending to complete their Sixth Form education at Senior Clayesmore.

The school is particularly proud of its long association with HM Forces and offers a number of service bursaries. There are also many children from expatriate families amongst the boarding community and the School is well versed in handling all the arrangements necessary for overseas travel.

The curriculum – with its strong emphasis on sound foundations – is typical of most good Prep Schools, but at Clayesmore each day is greatly enriched by the wide range of facilities and activities offered within the timetable. Younger children spend most of their time with their Form Teacher but by the age of ten all children are being taught by specialist subject teachers. In the Upper School the children are setted for Mathematics and Languages and work in their form groups for most subjects, which allows them to proceed at their own level and pace. Though the pressure of academic work increases as examinations approach, every child's programme includes a full range of Art, Music, Design Technology and Games and also gives time for play and relaxation.

The main games for boys are Rugby, Hockey and Cricket; for girls Netball, Hockey, Tennis and Rounders. A well equipped Sports Hall with a 25 metre heated pool, a floodlit all-weather hockey pitch and extensive playing fields give every opportunity for games to reach the highest standards. The School also enjoys considerable success at Athletics, Football, Swimming and Orienteering, with international swimmers and runners. Many other minor sports are also available.

Approximately 200 children learn instruments and music is held in high regard. The Chapel Choir has toured in Italy, France, Germany, USA, Spain and South Africa during the 90s and more recently Prague and France. The Prep School has two orchestras – sometimes three – and there are several instrumental ensembles. The Concert Band which draws the best woodwind, brass and percussion pupils from both schools is in hot demand in the locality and also tours abroad. Art, too, is very strong. The Prep School has its own Art Department with separate pottery, and holds an 'Arts Week' every year.

Boys and girls are prepared for Common Entrance and Senior School Scholarship examinations. The Prep School has an outstanding reputation for supporting pupils with dyslexia through its "all through" approach to teaching such pupils. All staff receive regular training so that the work of the Learning Support specialists is fully understood by the subject specialist staff and the form teachers. Communication is absolutely the key element in this.

Charitable status. Clayesmore School Limited is a Registered Charity, number 306214. It exists for the purposes of educating children.

Clevelands Preparatory School
GEMS Education

425 Chorley New Road Bolton Lancashire BL1 5DH
Tel: 01204 843898
Fax: 01204 848007
e-mail: clevelands@indschool.org
website: www.clevelandsprepschool.co.uk

Co-educational Day School.

***Headteacher*: Mrs L Parlane**

Age Range. 2–11.

Number of Pupils. 173: 81 boys, 92 girls.

Fees per term (2008-2009). £1,818.

Clevelands Nursery and Preparatory School offers a traditional academic education in a caring, stimulating environment. The school and new nursery department is open to boys and girls between the ages of 2¾ and 11 years.

We aim to give our pupils a stimulating and challenging curriculum linking strong, traditional values with the best of new educational initiatives. The range of experiences on offer ensures that our pupils have a broad curriculum which combines the National Curriculum with our own successful Educational programme. It also ensures that emphasis is placed on developing and celebrating each child's individual talents.

The school's family values are built on kindness, a sense of belonging, mutual respect and consideration of one another. The pupils spend each day in a happy, caring, work orientated environment in which their needs are prioritised and catered for by dedicated and highly qualified teachers.

Pupils have a proud record of academic success in entrance examinations and scholarships for entry into the leading day senior schools.

They also excel in other fields such as art, drama, music and sport. A significant number of pupils play at least one musical instrument.

Clevelands children compete successfully in local, regional and national sporting competitions.

Pupils are taught by specialist teachers from Nursery upwards. This teaching increases as the pupils move through the school.

Facilities at Clevelands include a fully networked Computer Suite. In the art /design and technology studio pupils can explore all media. The science laboratory is fully equipped with the latest technology. Our sporting facilities include a netball court and football pitch.

A myriad of extra-curricular activities takes place during lunchtimes and after school. A thriving programme of external Educational and Theatre visits exists as well as the opportunity for the children to encounter a variety of new and exciting experiences internally. Skiing trips and Outward Bound courses take place annually.

Our pupils develop into well rounded, self-assured, competent young people who will meet the challenges of life with enthusiasm and vigour.

Before and after school care is available to all.

Most pupils enter the main school in September of any year, but the Headteacher is happy to consider requests for admission for children of any age during the academic year, should circumstances so warrant.

Entry to the Nursery is ongoing throughout the year as a child reaches the appropriate age.

Clifton College Preparatory School

Bristol BS8 3HE
Tel: 0117 3157 502
Fax: 0117 3157 504
e-mail: lwoodward@clifton-college.avon.sch.uk
website: www.cliftoncollegeuk.com

Chairman of College Council: A R Thornhill, BA, QC

***Head Master*: J Milne**, BA, MBA

Age Range. 8–13.

Number of Pupils. 375: 51 boarders, 324 day pupils.

Fees per term (2008-2009). Boarders £5,970–£6,190, Weekly Boarders £5,700–£5,915, Day Pupils £3,750–£4,090.

There is a full time teaching staff of 50, all of whom are qualified. A wide range of subjects is included in the normal curriculum.

The majority go on to the Upper School with whom there is cooperation on curriculum matters, but a number are prepared for and win scholarships to other schools. Over 60 awards have been won in the past three years. Pupils can be prepared for the Common Entrance examination to other schools.

The administration of the School is entirely separate from the Upper School, but some facilities are shared, including the Sports Hall and Indoor Swimming Pool, the Gymnasium, Chapel, Squash and Rackets Courts and 93 acres of playing fields, which include Astroturf pitches and a new indoor Tennis and Netball Centre. The School has its own Art & Design Centre. The School possesses one of the most advanced Information Technology Centres in the West of England.

The House system operates for both boarders and day pupils. Three houses cater for the boarders, each under the supervision of a Housemaster or Housemistress assisted by wife or husband, house tutor and matron. The remaining five Houses cater specifically for day pupils. No House contains more than 60 pupils and the smallest has 30. Boys and girls are in separate Houses, all recently reconditioned.

Out of school activities supplementing the main School games are many and varied, the aim being to give every child an opportunity to participate in an activity from which he or she gains confidence and a sense of achievement.

The youngest boys and girls (aged 3–8) work separately in the Pre-Preparatory School called Butcombe under the care of their own Head and teachers. (*See separate IAPS entry for Butcombe.*)

Charitable status. Clifton College is a Registered Charity, number 311735. It provides boarding and day education for boys and girls aged 3–18 years.

Clifton High School Lower School

College Road Clifton Bristol BS8 3JD
Tel: 0117 973 8096
Fax: 0117 923 8962
e-mail: admissions@cliftonhigh.bristol.sch.uk
website: www.cliftonhigh.bristol.sch.uk

President of School Council: Mr H Stebbing, BSc, FRICS, FBIFM, FRSA, FICPD

***Head of Lower School*: Mr Anthony Richards**, MBE, BSocSc Hons Birmingham, PGCE

Age Range. Rising 3 to 11.

Number of Pupils. 247: 162 Girls, 85 Boys; Nursery 46, Preparatory 92, Junior 109.

Fees per term (2008-2009). Nursery (Rising 3–4 years) £905–£1,705; Prep (4–7 years) £2,260; Junior (7–11 years) £2,380.

There are three separate but inter-dependent sections of the Lower School, each has its own building, its own staff and its own character but there is a sense of belonging to each other and being part of a great school.

The Upper School, for girls only (age 11–16) with the Sixth Form (age 16–18) becoming co-educational from September 2008, is on the same campus (*see entry in GSA section*).

The Nursery Department has outstanding facilities for your child's introduction to school life. Within an informal and secure environment the children take part in a varied programme of activities that develop confidence, self esteem, a sense of responsibility, consideration for others and a willingness to approach challenges and learning with a sense of excitement. A qualified nursery teacher and nursery nurse in each small class ensure your child's progress in the key areas of the Foundation Stage.

The Nursery takes boys and girls from rising three, who may attend from three mornings up to five full days.

Highly praised by Ofsted and ISI Inspectors, the Nursery is justly proud of its fine reputation.

The Preparatory Department. Our Reception and Years 1 and 2 are housed within the spacious Preparatory Department. Close links with the Nursery ensure your child progresses smoothly in the key learning areas of the Foundation Stage and beyond.

The Preparatory Department has excellent facilities and a dedicated, well qualified staff to provide that essential early grounding in a stimulating, happy and secure environment.

With small classes there is the time and space to attend to each child's needs and the capacity to extend each child's ability. Literacy and Numeracy are the main focuses but all classes benefit from a weekly ICT lesson in the Prep's own computer room, Gym, Music and Swimming.

The Junior Department has grown into a large, flourishing co-educational department for the four year groups, Years 3–6.

Art, Drama, French, Latin, Gym, ICT, Music, RE, Singing and Swimming are all specialist taught for the most part in specialist areas. Games are taught at the Coombe Dingle Sports Centre where the facilities include all-weather pitches and indoor tennis courts.

Academic standards are high but there is time and consideration for each individual, whatever her/his needs or abilities.

The Junior Orchestra, Windband and choirs, the girls' and boys' teams in a variety of sports and after-school clubs ranging from TaeKwonDo to Textiles, Art, Drama and Music Technology provide a range of extra-curricular opportunities for the children.

Charitable status. Clifton High School is a Registered Charity, number 311736. It exists to provide education for pupils.

Clifton Pre-preparatory School

York YO30 6AB
Tel: 01904 527361
Fax: 01904 527304
e-mail: enquiries@cliftonprep.york.sch.uk
website: www.st-peters.york.sch.uk

Chairman of the Governors: J D Pike

***Headmistress*: Mrs P Arkley**, MA, BSc, CertEd

Age Range. 3–8 co-educational.

Number of Pupils. 97 boys, 74 girls.

Fees per term (2008-2009). Nursery (full time), Reception, Years 1 & 2: £2,080, Year 3: £2,185.

Clifton Pre-preparatory School is the Pre-prep of St Peter's School, York. The school has large modern buildings on the St Peter's School site which occupies 47 acres in the centre of York

Curriculum. All aspects of the National Curriculum are covered but the syllabus at the school is broader and more challenging. Individual development in all subjects is a priority, particularly in literacy and numeracy. Small classes, individual attention and after-school activities enable high standards to be achieved.

Music and Drama. Nursery children have a session of music and movement, and all other classes have weekly lessons with a specialist teacher. From Year 2, children have the opportunity to learn to play the recorder, piano, violin or guitar at school. Each year there are opportunities for children to participate in performances to a wider audience. All classes have weekly drama lessons, and there is the opportunity for Y2 and Y3 to do speech and drama as an after school activity.

Sport and Extra-Curricular Activities. Physical Education starts in the Nursery. As children grow older games and swimming are added. The pupils at Clifton Preparatory School have access to the Sports facilities at St Peter's School. Extra-curricular activities include gymnastics, board games, swimming club, country dancing, football club, short tennis, choir, drama, Art, Design and Technology Club and Computer Club.

Assessments. Throughout Nursery and Reception children work towards achieving the Early Learning Goals, culminating in the completion of the Foundation Stage Profile. Work is assessed continuously and children's progress is discussed at monthly staff meetings. There is ongoing communication between parents and staff through a reports system, invitations to visit the school and parent evenings.

After the recent ISI inspection, the inspectors reported that: "The School provides a high-quality education, which is outstanding in several important respects".

Charitable status. St Peter's School York is a Registered Charity, number 529740. It exists to provide education for boys and girls.

Colet Court (St Paul's Preparatory School)

Lonsdale Road London SW13 9JT
Tel: 020 8748 3461
Fax: 020 8746 5357
e-mail: HMSecCC@StPaulsSchool.org.uk
website: www.coletcourt.org.uk

Chairman of Governors: Alderman Sir Alexander Graham, GBE, DCL

***Headmaster*: T A Meunier**, MA, CChem, FRSC, PGCE

Deputy Headmaster: C G Howes, MA, PGCE

Senior Tutor: J Barlow, BSc, PGCE
Director of Studies: Miss A J Gordon, BA, PGCE
Director of Administration: A P C Fuggle, MA
Head of Juniors: S R K Bailey, BA, QTS

Age Range. 7–13.

Number of Boys. 436.

Fees per term (2008-2009). £4,363.

Colet Court is very closely linked with St Paul's School (*see entry in HMC section*), to which almost all the boys go on. The two schools are in separate, but adjacent modern buildings on the south bank of the Thames, and share many amenities – dining hall, sports centre and playing fields.

The work is organised to fit in with that of the Senior School. A normal Preparatory School curriculum is followed, except that boys are not specifically prepared for scholarships to senior schools other than St Paul's. There are excellent facilities for all games and sports, for Art, DT, Science and IT. Music is also very strong and there are two orchestras, three choirs, and many other smaller instrumental ensembles.

Entrance is normally at either 7 or 8 by competitive examination and registration for this is essential. Approximately twenty places are also available at 11 by examination. Up to ten of these places may be offered to pupils from maintained schools who can opt to sit an examination at 10+ and defer their arrival for one year. Means-tested bursaries are available at all points of entry.

Charitable status. St Paul's School is a Registered Charity, number 1119619. The object of the charity is to promote the education of boys in Greater London.

Colfe's Preparatory School

Horn Park Lane London SE12 8AW
Tel: 020 8852 0220 (Prep)
020 8297 1709 (Pre-Prep)
Fax: 020 8297 2941
e-mail: prep@colfes.com
website: www.colfes.com

Chairman of the Governors: Mr Ian Russell, MBE

***Head of the Preparatory School*: Mr John Gallagher**, BA Hons, MBA

Age Range. 3–11.

Number of Pupils. 356 boys and girls.

Fees per term (2008-2009). Prep £3,189 (excluding lunch); Pre-Prep £3,006 (including lunch); Nursery £2,745 (including lunch).

Colfe's Preparatory School is a co-educational day school under the general direction of the Governors and Headmaster of Colfe's School (founded in 1652). It is academically selective, offers a broad curriculum and aims to provide an excellent all-round education. Children normally enter at the ages of 3, 4 or 7 although the occasional vacancy arises at other times.

The Preparatory School is housed in modern purpose-built accommodation with spacious and well-equipped classrooms. Small class sizes and a team of well-qualified teachers provide a caring and vibrant environment. Excellent library facilities and specialist accommodation for art and design, ICT and science provide boys and girls with a stimulating environment in which to learn. Full use is made of the school's swimming pool, sports centre, visual and performing arts centre and extensive on-site playing fields.

PE specialists teach a wide range of sports. There is an extensive programme of house and inter-school sports matches. A school choir, orchestra, strings group and numerous ensembles perform frequently both in and out of school. Drama productions normally take place each term. There is a wide range of after-school clubs on offer (over 50 each week for the 7–11 year olds) and a late school scheme until 6 pm.

The school has a strong reputation in the local area for excellence within a friendly and caring atmosphere.

Charitable status. Colfe's School is a Registered Charity, number 1109650. It exists to provide education for children.

Colston's Lower School

Stapleton Bristol BS16 1BA
Tel: 0117 965 5297
Fax: 0117 965 6330
e-mail: celiapullin@colstons.bristol.sch.uk
website: www.colstons.bristol.sch.uk

Chairman of Governors: D J Marsh

***Head*: Mrs C Aspden**, MA, PGCE

Age Range. 3–11.

Number of Pupils. 220 Day Pupils.

Fees per term (from January 2008). Reception, Year 1 and 2 £1,745; Years 3 and 4 £2,225; Years 5 and 6 £2,540; Nursery from £18 per session. Scholarships are offered from 7+.

Colston's Lower School is located in Stapleton village which is within the city of Bristol. It is less than one mile from Junction 2 of the M32 and therefore easily accessible from north Bristol and South Gloucestershire. In addition to its own specialist facilities for Science, ICT, Music, Design & Technology, Art and Games, the Lower School has full use of facilities at the neighbouring Upper School including 32 acres of playing fields.

The majority of pupils move from the Lower to the Upper School (*see entry in HMC section*). They work in small classes on a broad curriculum that extends beyond the requirements of the National Curriculum, incorporating the full range of academic subjects together with French, Spanish, Design and Technology, ICT, Art and Music. There is also a Learning Support Unit.

Music and Drama flourish in the Lower School, with a choir and orchestra, regular concerts, school plays and music competitions.

In addition to PE lessons there are two afternoons of Junior Games each week. The boys principally play rugby, hockey and cricket, and the girls play hockey, netball and rounders. Pupils also enjoy opportunities to take part in football, tennis, swimming, athletics and badminton.

Colston's Lower offers a wide range of clubs and activities, and pupils are able to stay on at school under supervision for an extended day or start with Breakfast Club. There are numerous visits and trips including skiing and adventure activities.

Charitable status. Colston's School is a Registered Charity, number 1079552. Its aims and objectives are the provision of education.

Copthorne School

Effingham Lane Copthorne West Sussex RH10 3HR
Tel: 01342 712311
Fax: 01342 714014
e-mail: office@copthorneprep.co.uk
website: www.copthorneprep.co.uk

Chairman of Governors: James Abdool

***Headmaster*: C J Jones**, BEd Hons

Deputy Headmaster: B J Coombes

Age Range. 2½–13.

Number of Boys and Girls. 300 (20 Boarders).

Fees per term (2008-2009). Day: Pre-Prep £2,165, Year 3 £2,960, Year 4 £3,390, Years 5-8 £3,750. Weekly Boarding £4,700. Occasional Boarding £25 per night.

Copthorne is a flourishing IAPS Prep School with approximately 300 boys and girls from 2½ to 13. The school has grown by over 40% within the last 3 years. Children are prepared for Independent School Scholarships or Common Entrance. In the last 3 years Copthorne children have been awarded 31 Scholarships or Awards to a variety of Senior Schools.

We believe that, in order to learn, children must be happy and feel secure in their environment. Copthorne Prep School is full of happy children and the environment is caring but still allows children the freedom to develop as individuals.

The school helps to develop each child's confidence, to raise self-esteem and to make children feel good about themselves. Nothing does this more than children enjoying success in all areas of school life. This is why Art, Music, ICT, DT, Drama and Sport are all just as important as the pursuit of academic excellence.

We provide opportunities for children to achieve success in all areas of the curriculum and we always celebrate their achievements.

We recognise that all children have talents, and every child is encouraged to realise their true potential, whatever that may be, in whatever area of school life.

We demand and set high standards, and our children respond by always giving of their best.

Put simply, our mission is to:

Develop **C**onfidence – Provide **O**pportunity – Realise **P**otential – in every single child.

The school is very proud of its history of over 100 years, and retains all the important traditions of the past whilst developing a very forward thinking approach. The children receive a "child-centred" education, where their individual needs come first, in an environment that is "parent-friendly", with very high levels of communication and pastoral care.

Charitable status. Copthorne School Trust Limited is a Registered Charity, number 270757. It exists to provide education to boys and girls.

Cothill House

Nr Abingdon Oxon OX13 6JL
Tel: 01865 390800
Fax: 01865 390205
e-mail: office@cothill.net
website: www.cothill.net

Chairman of the Governors: The Rt Hon Lord Wakeham, DL

***Headmaster*: N R Brooks**

Age Range. 8–13.

Number of Boys. 225.

Fees per term (2008-2009). Boarders £6,800 inclusive.

Charitable status. Cothill Educational Trust is a Registered Charity, number 309639. Its main object and purpose is the advancement of education. The Trust includes the day school Chandlings Manor, Kitebrook House, Mowden Hall and the Château de Sauveterre in France.

Cottesmore School

Buchan Hill Pease Pottage West Sussex RH11 9AU
Tel: 01293 520648
Fax: 01293 614784
e-mail: schooloffice@cottesmoreschool.com
website: www.cottesmoreschool.com

Independent Co-educational Preparatory Boarding School.

***Headmaster*: T F Rogerson**, BA, PGCE

Age Range. 7–13.

Number of Pupils. 100 Boys, 50 Girls.

Fees per term (2008-2009). £5,970 (boarding), £4,480–£5,375 (weekly/day boarding).

Cottesmore is a boarding school, situated a mile from Exit 11 of the M23, ten minutes from Gatwick Airport and one hour from Central London and Heathrow Airport.

The school is now offering Weekly and Day Boarding.

Curriculum. Boys and girls are taught together in classes averaging 14 in number. The teacher/pupil ratio is 1:9. Children are fully prepared for Common Entrance and Scholarship examinations.

Music. The musical tradition is strong – more than 80% of children learn a variety of instruments; there are three Choirs, a School Orchestra and several musical ensembles.

Sport. The major games are Association and Rugby Football, Cricket, Hockey, Netball and Rounders. Numerous other sports are taught and encouraged. They include Tennis, Squash, Golf, Riding, Athletics, Cross-Country Running, Swimming, Windsurfing, Fishing, Boating, Gymnastics, Shooting, Judo and Archery. The School competes at a national level in several of these sports.

Recent Developments. Our Technology Centre houses a constantly developing Information Technology Suite, a Design Technology room for metal, woodwork, plastic and pneumatics, a Craft room, Kiln, two Science laboratories and Art Studio.

Hobbies and Activities. These include Pottery, Photography, Stamp Collecting, Chess, Bridge, Model-Making, Model Railway, Tenpin Bowling, Gardening, Rollerblading, Ballet, Modern Dancing, Drama, Craft, Carpentry, Printing, Cooking and Debating.

The boys and girls lead a full and varied life and are all encouraged to take part in as wide a variety of activities as possible. Weekends are a vital part of the school life and are made busy and fun for all.

Entry requirements. Entry is by Headmaster's interview and a report from the previous school. For a prospectus and more information, please write or telephone the Headmaster's Personal Assistant, Miss Janine Scola.

Coworth–Flexlands School

Valley End Chobham Woking Surrey GU24 8TE
Tel: 01276 855707
Fax: 01276 856043
e-mail: sholmes@coworthflexlands.co.uk
website: www.coworthflexlands.co.uk

Joint Chairmen of Governors:
Mr Peter Wynter Bee and Mr Peter R Harris

***Headmistress*: Mrs Sandy Stephen**

Age Range. Boys 3–7 years; Girls 3–11 years.

Number of Pupils. 155 day girls, 20 day boys.

Fees per term (2007-2008). £1,145–£2,825.

Coworth-Flexlands School is located in delightful rural surroundings on the outskirts of Chobham Common. The lovely Edwardian house has been enhanced by a superb new extension. The school nestles in 13 acres of Surrey countryside.

The popularity and affection, which the school enjoys with parents and pupils alike, is reflected in the positive, happy atmosphere. Small classes and experienced staff have ensured that academic excellence thrives. Coworth-Flexlands encourages high personal expectations and moral values and we believe that happy children will achieve their best. The excellent staff to pupil ratio ensures children receive individual attention. Where needed, special coaching for accelerated learning and specific learning difficulties is offered.

In addition to all the usual National Curriculum subjects, Drama, Technology, Music, French, Art and Sport feature strongly in a broad curriculum, and the school has its own orchestra. Every class goes on an outing each term and residential trips are arranged for the older children. Many extra curricular activities (after-school clubs) can be enjoyed including chess, dance, tennis, Rainbows and Brownies, orchestra, art, choir, gymnastics and Spanish. An after-school Homework Club is also available for older children. There is a strong emphasis on pastoral care throughout the school.

Girls and boys are admitted into the Nursery in the term of their third birthday. Trained Nursery staff are sensitive to the younger children's needs and provide the foundation for all future learning in a happy and enjoyable environment. Boys stay at the school until they are 7 and the girls are prepared for their entrance examinations leaving for their senior schools at the age of 11.

There is an active Parents' Association and parents have access to the Headmistress and all the staff whenever required. Prospective parents are warmly invited to tour the school with the Headmistress. All enquiries and appointments should be made via the school secretary on 01276 855707.

Charitable status. Coworth–Flexlands School is a Registered Charity, number 309109. It exists to provide an excellent, balanced education with a strong emphasis on pastoral care.

Craigclowan School

Edinburgh Road Perth PH2 8PS
Tel: 01738 626310
Fax: 01738 440349
e-mail: headmaster@craigclowan-school.co.uk
website: www.craigclowan-school.co.uk

Chairman of Governors: James Bax, Esq

***Headmaster*: A R Rathborne**

Age Range. 3–13.

Number of Pupils. 280: 140 boys, 140 girls; Pre-Prep 50.

Fees per term (2007-2008). £2,700.

Craigclowan is a co-educational, day school situated in 15 acres of its own ground on the outskirts of Perth. It is administered by a Charitable Trust.

Boys and girls are prepared for Common Entrance and scholarship for independent schools in both England and Scotland. In the recent past children have entered Glenalmond, Strathallan, Loretto, Merchiston Castle, Fettes, Gordonstoun, St Leonards, Ampleforth, Downe House, Sherborne, St Mary's Ascot, Malvern, Queen Margaret's York, Haileybury, Rugby, Stowe and Eton as a result of Common Entrance or Scholarship. In the last five years a total of 62 Scholarships have been gained covering academic, music, art, sport and all rounders.

Much attention is paid to each individual child in their preparation for academic success throughout the school and much energy is directed to a wide range of extra-curricular activities with games, music, drama, debating and art high on the list. The games played include rugby, hockey and cricket for boys, tennis, hockey and netball for girls, whilst everyone swims and takes part in athletics and skiing. Instrumental tuition takes in all the orchestral areas and children regularly participate in productions at the local Repertory Company. The children have won National Competitions in Rugby, Netball, Swimming, Skiing, Debating and Choir. Recent developments have included the construction of a dry ski slope, full-size astroturf for hockey and tennis and in September 2005 a one million pound classroom block.

The HMIE Inspection Report published in September 2004 gave significant praise to the school for the high standards achieved in key areas of school life. The major strengths identified by the Inspectors were:

- The school's positive ethos, including the strong partnership with parents.
- Attainment in English language.
- The high quality of pastoral care for pupils.
- The extensive range of extra curricular activities which provided opportunities for pupils to broaden their achievements.
- The commitment of staff and the polite, well motivated pupils.
- The quality of leadership provided by the Headmaster.

In addition, the Care Commission has inspected the Pre-school four times in the past three years, endorsing all that is being achieved within the Pre-school.

Charitable status. Craigclowan School Limited is a Registered Charity, number SC010817. It exists to promote education generally and for that purpose to establish, carry on and maintain a school within Scotland.

Cranford House Junior School

Moulsford Wallingford Oxfordshire OX10 9HT
Tel: 01491 651218
Fax: 01491 652557
e-mail: admissions@cranfordhouse.oxon.sch.uk
website: www.cranfordhouse.oxon.sch.uk

The School is a Charitable Trust run by a Board of Governors.

Chairman of the Governors: Mr R S Bray

***Head of the Junior School*: Mrs H Osborn**, CertEd

Head of the Lower School: Mrs G Smeeton, BSc, QTS

Age Range. Girls 3–11, Boys 3–7.
Number of Pupils. 324.
Fees per term (2008-2009). £861–£3,155.

Children are admitted from 3 years old into the co-educational Lower School (pre-preparatory) which includes a purpose-built Nursery. Girls transfer to the Junior School (preparatory) at age 7.

Children are taught by specialist teachers for Music, Drama, PE, French and Religious Studies from the start of their time at Cranford. More specialist teaching is introduced in the Junior School to aid a smooth transition to Senior School education. In Form 3 there are two qualified teachers per class for English and Mathematics. All Junior pupils work in small ability groups for English and Mathematics to maximise achievement in these core subject areas. There is a full choir, chamber choir and orchestra and pupils are encouraged to take an active role in this as well as in school drama productions. A wide-reaching programme of extra-curricular clubs and activities ensures the all-round development of our pupils. Junior and Lower School pupils take part in sporting tournaments and competitions both at home and away. The curriculum includes a great number of curriculum+ activities and trips to enhance each child's learning experience in and out of the classroom.

Charitable status. Cranford House School Trust Limited is a Registered Charity, number 280883.

Cranleigh Preparatory School

Horseshoe Lane Cranleigh Surrey GU6 8QH
Tel: 01483 273666
Fax: 01483 277136
e-mail: pa@cranprep.org
website: www.cranprep.org

Chairman of Governors: J A V Townsend, MA

***Head*: M T Wilson**, BSc

Age Range. 7–13.
Number of Pupils. 280 (50 Boarders, 230 Day).
Fees per term (2008-2009). Boarders £5,775; Day Pupils: £3,795 (Forms 1 & 2), £4,675 (Forms 3–6). These are genuinely inclusive and there are no hidden or compulsory extras.

The school stands in its own beautiful and spacious grounds of 35 acres. Cranleigh Preparatory School is a co-educational boarding and day school. A teaching staff of 38 enables classes to be small. The Head and his wife live in the school, as do the boys' boarding master and his family and the girls' housemistress. They are fully involved with the health and happiness of the boys and girls, together with pastoral staff, including matrons. A great source of strength is the close partnership with Cranleigh School 'across the road'. The Preparatory School has use of Senior School sports facilities, including an indoor pool, artificial pitches, the stables and golf course.

The boys and girls are prepared for Common Entrance and many Scholarships are won. Through these exams about three quarters of the children move on to Cranleigh School and the remaining one quarter to a wide variety of other independent senior schools.

Boarding life is busy and fun and pupils are welcome to be full boarders, returning home at fortnightly exeats, or weekly boarders. There is also the opportunity to flexi board for two or more nights during the week.

The curriculum is broad, balanced and covers all and more than that laid down by the National Curriculum. The school teaches computing, and technological problem solving is encouraged. Art (including design, pottery, woodwork and various craft skills) and Music are included in the curriculum at all levels and individual instrumental lessons are available. There are choirs, orchestras, a band and several ensembles. Boys and girls are given every incentive to develop spare time interests and a choice of activities is built into the timetable.

The school is fortunate to have excellent facilities including a large sports and drama hall, a dance studio, a music school, light airy classrooms and laboratories. The school has recently undergone a very large refurbishment programme and all facilities are extensive and modern. Boarding accommodation is bright and cheerful and fully modernised. Additions and improvements to the facilities are ongoing.

Rugby, football, hockey, netball, lacrosse, cricket, athletics, tennis, swimming, rounders, shooting, squash, cross country, basketball, fencing, riding, golf, Eton Fives, badminton, are among the sports.

Normal entry age is at seven or eleven. Boarding places are occasionally available in the intervening year groups.

Charitable status. Cranleigh School is a Registered Charity, number 1070856, whose Preparatory School exists to provide education for boys and girls aged 7–13.

Cranmore School

West Horsley Leatherhead Surrey KT24 6AT
Tel: 01483 280340
Fax: 01483 280341

e-mail: office@cranmoreprep.co.uk
website: www.cranmoreprep.co.uk

Chairman of Governors: The Very Revd Mgr J Scott, LCL, MCL

***Headmaster*: M P Connolly**, BSc, BA, MA, MEd

Deputy Head: Mrs S Walker, CertEd
Assistant Head: T Hallett, BA Hons, QTS
Head of Pre-Prep: Miss S Head, MA, PGCE

Age Range. 3–13.

Number of Boys. 500 Day Pupils.

Fees per term (from January 2008). Nursery £1,250, Pre-Prep £2,775, Prep £3,350.

The School is situated midway between Leatherhead and Guildford, whilst Dorking and Woking are equally accessible.

There are 37 full-time members of staff, 16 part-time members and 19 visiting teachers for instruments in the Music department.

A Nursery school (3–4 yrs) with separate morning and afternoon sessions prepares boys for entry to the Junior Pre-Prep section of the school (4–8 yrs) where each boy plays a full part in the life of school, using the sports hall, gymnasium, swimming pool and other sports and music facilities. A new junior teaching block was completed in January 1994. Pupils enter the Senior Department at 8+ years and are taught by specialist subject teachers. At the end of their second year in the Senior School each year group is divided into a Scholarship set and two parallel Common Entrance sets.

Boys are prepared for entry to a wide range of Independent Schools via the Common Entrance or Scholarship examination. We have an impressive track record in our pupils gaining academic, music, sport and all-rounder scholarships, all to a wide variety of schools.

A new senior teaching block was completed in April 1998 and comprises 3 large well-equipped science laboratories, 4 classrooms, a second ICT laboratory and a chapel. At the same time the gymnasium has been completely rebuilt, the swimming pool refurbished, 4 new astro tennis courts put in place and a large playground with playground furniture, all on a rubberised surface large enough to take two tennis courts, for 5-a-side football or 6-a-side hockey. There are 24 acres of playing fields, a sports hall (Badminton, Basketball, Cricket nets, Volleyball etc) and 4 squash courts, cross-country and athletics. 2004 saw the opening of yet another major development consisting of a new entrance hall, reception area, two libraries, art room and Design Technology room. In 2007 a second astroturf was completed and we opened a 6th form common room.

School swimming and tennis teams compete in a wide variety of galas and tournaments. Inter-School and Inter-House competitions allow all boys to take part in organised games. Rowing, golf, tennis, ski clubs and many other sporting clubs operate through the term. There is also a Bridge Club, Technology Club, Board Games Club, etc, which occur weekly. A thriving chess club competes in a local schools' league and a number of honours have been won in recent years. The School has three ICT laboratories with the most up-to-date equipment. There is a site intranet and the school has broadband internet connection. Many of the subject teachers use the ICT facility for the use of back-up subject specific software.

A Drama, Speech and Music school incorporates a large Auditorium, two specialist teaching rooms and 7 practice rooms. Individual tuition in a wide variety of instruments is available; there are 2 orchestras, 8 choirs and various ensemble groups. A number of music scholarships are obtained each year.

Many other out-of-school activities are offered including skiing and rowing clubs. There are annual PGL, skiing and French holidays.

Many of the boys are Catholic although entry is open to boys of all denominations who are warmly welcomed.

Charitable status. Cranmore School, as part of the Diocese of Arundel & Brighton, is a Registered Charity, number 252878. It exists to provide education for boys.

Crescent School

Bawnmore Road Bilton Rugby Warwickshire CV22 7QH
Tel: 01788 521595
Fax: 01788 816185
e-mail: admin@crescentschool.co.uk
website: www.crescentschool.co.uk

Chairman of Trustees: Mr N Lines

***Headmaster*: Mr R H Marshall**, BSc Hons (Wales), PGCE

Age Range. 3–11.

Number of Pupils. 156 Day Boys and Girls (69 boys, 87 girls).

Fees per term (2008-2009). £2,060–£2,270.

The Crescent School is an independent co-educational preparatory school for day pupils aged 4–11 years. In addition, there is a Nursery for children from the age of 3. The school was founded in 1947, originally to provide a place of education for the young children of the masters of Rugby School. Over the years the school has steadily expanded, admitting children from Rugby and the surrounding area. In 1988, having outgrown its original premises, the school moved into modern, purpose built accommodation in Bilton, about a mile to the south of Rugby town centre. The buildings provide large and bright teaching areas, with a separate annexe housing the Nursery and Reception classes. There are specialist rooms for Science, Art, Design Technology, ICT and the Performing Arts. In addition there is also a spacious Library and Resource Area. The multi purpose hall provides a venue for daily assemblies, large scale music making, is fully equipped for physical education and has all the necessary equipment to turn it into a theatre for school productions. The school is surrounded by its own gardens, play areas and sports field.

The requirements of the National Curriculum are fully encompassed by the academic programme and particular emphasis is placed on English and mathematics in the early years. All pupils receive specialist tuition in Information and Communication Technology, Music and Physical Education. Specialist teaching in other subjects is introduced as children move upwards through the school. Spanish is introduced in Reception, followed by French in Year IV and Latin in Year V. The pupils are prepared for the local 11+ examination for entry to maintained secondary schools, including local grammar schools, Common Entrance and specific entrance examinations also at 11+ for independent senior schools.

The performing arts are a particular strength of the school and lessons are given in speech and drama, singing, percussion, musical theory and appreciation and recorder playing. Instrumental lessons (piano, brass, woodwind and strings) are offered as an optional extra. There is a school choir, orchestra, brass, string and wind ensembles and recorder groups.

Charitable status. The Crescent School Trust is a Registered Charity, number 1120628. The object of the charity shall be the provision and conduct of a day school for children of the inhabitants of Rugby and the surrounding district.

The Croft Preparatory School

Alveston Hill Loxley Road Stratford-upon-Avon Warwickshire CV37 7RL
Tel: 01789 293795
Fax: 01789 414960

e-mail: office@croftschool.co.uk
website: www.croftschool.co.uk

Principal: Mrs L K M Thornton, CertEd London

Chairman of the School's Council: A Wolfe, LLB

***Headmistress*: Dr P A Thompson**, MA, DLitt, GRNCM, ARMCM, PGCE, FICPD, FRSA

Deputy Headmaster: Mr M Cook, BSc Hons, PGCE
Principal Teacher – Prep: Mrs M Crocombe, BA Hons, PGCE
Principal Teacher – Pre-Prep & Early Years: Mrs L Dudley, BSc OU, PGCE Primary

Age Range. 2–11.
Number of Pupils. 468: 253 boys, 215 girls.
Fees per term (from January 2008). £415–£2,870.

The Croft is a co-educational day school for children from 2 to 11 years old, situated on the outskirts of Stratford upon Avon. Founded in 1933, the School occupies a large rural site with superb facilities and extensive playing fields, offering children some of the most exciting educational opportunities in the area. There is also a nature conservation area with lake.

A family-based school, The Croft provides specialist teaching in small groups, where good discipline and a wider knowledge of the world around us, both spiritual and geographical, is encouraged. Music, Sport and Drama each play an important part in the curriculum. The resulting high educational standards provide the all-round excellence which is at the heart of the School.

In May 2007, the School opened Mundell Court, a two-storey building which provides additional, spacious teaching areas for ICT, DT, Mathematics, and a Multimedia Room, available to every subject and age group. It also incorporates a small-scale performance space. The concept underpinning the design is 'problem solving' and the development of thinking skills, vital for children in the 21st Century and beyond.

Children are prepared for 11+ entry either to the local Grammar Schools or Senior Independent Day Schools, or to go on to Boarding Schools.

Entrance requirements. Children can be accepted in the Nursery from the age of 2 years. Children above Reception age are assessed.

Crosfields School

Shinfield Road Reading Berks RG2 9BL
Tel: 0118 9871810
Fax: 0118 9310806
e-mail: office@crosfields.com
website: www.crosfields.com

Crosfields became co-educational in the Pre-Prep Department in September 2007 and will be fully co-educational from September 2008.

Chairman of Governors: Mr R G Sutherland

***Headmaster*: Mr J P Wansey**, BA, CertEd

Deputy Headmaster:
S C Dinsdale, MA Ed Open, BA Hons Chichester, FLCM, LTCL, LLCM, PGCE Open

Age Range. 3–13.
Number of Pupils. 430.
Fees per term (2007-2008). £2,200–£3,400 including lunches, school visits and after-school care. No compulsory extras.

Crosfields became independent under its own Board of Governors in 1957. It combines the important features of traditional education with the sounder forms of modern practice. Together they contribute to this vital stage of education which is at the same time a part of a lifelong process. Christian principles underlie the curriculum and a broad-based opportunity is considered the right of every child.

There are 40 qualified staff and 6 part-time staff. The buildings and facilities are outstanding. Recent additions include a Sports Centre (1999), a Music School (2000), and new classroom block for Reception classes (2002), Performing Arts Centre (2005), new Library, IT Suite, Design & Technology lab and six classrooms (2007).

These lie in 40 acres of parkland and 1 mile from the M4 motorway Junction 11.

Most children enter senior schools via the Common Entrance Examination and a significant number of children gain academic, games, art, music and drama awards through scholarship examinations.

Charitable status. Crosfields School Trust Limited is a Registered Charity, number 584278. The aim of the School is solely to provide education for children between the ages of 3 and 13.

Culford Preparatory School

Culford Bury St Edmunds Suffolk IP28 6TX
Tel: 01284 729308
Fax: 01284 729146
e-mail: preparatory@culford.co.uk
website: www.culford.co.uk

Chairman of Governors: Dr R R McLone, MA, PhD, FIMA

***Headmaster*: T J Collins**, BA

Age Range. Co-educational 7–13.
Number of Pupils. 195 (Day), 35 (Boarders).
Fees per term (2008-2009). Day £2,835–£3,975, Boarding £5,460–£5,840.

Admission is by entrance examination at all ages, though the majority of pupils enter at age 7 or 11. Scholarships at 7+ and 11+.

Culford Preparatory School has its own staff and Headmaster, but remains closely linked to the Senior School. This allows the School to enjoy a significant degree of independence and autonomy whilst benefiting from the outstanding facilities of the whole school, which is set on a site of 480 acres.

The Preparatory School is situated in its own grounds, within Culford Park. At the heart of the School is the quadrangle in the centre of which is the Jubilee Library. The two Science laboratories allow all children to benefit from specialist facilities and teachers. The pupils also enjoy splendid ICT facilities with the two dedicated ICT suites and the Prep School is fully networked with interactive whiteboards in all classrooms.

Beyond the quadrangle there are magnificent playing fields and a well equipped adventure playground. The pupils also benefit from Culford School Sports Centre which offers a 25m indoor pool, cricket nets, squash courts, fitness suite, sports hall and a new specially designed climbing wall as well as floodlit Astroturf for hockey and tennis. An Indoor Tennis Centre will open in 2008.

Pupils are given a thorough grounding in the essential learning skills of Mathematics and English and the curriculum broadens beyond the confines of the National Curriculum. Work in the classrooms is augmented by an extensive Activities Programme which offers pupils a wide range of opportunities and experiences. Music and drama play a significant part in school life with a variety of theatrical performances, choirs and ensembles (some in the new Studio Theatre) taking place throughout the year. Speech and drama lessons are also offered.

Boarders live in Cadogan House, a mixed boarding house located next to the School and overlooking the extensive playing fields and the adventure playground. There is a comprehensive programme of weekend activities and children are looked after by a team of dedicated staff under the direction of the Housemistress.

Religious affiliation: Methodist (pupils from other denominations are welcome).

Charitable status. Culford School is a Registered Charity, number 310486. It exists to provide education for boys and girls.

Cumnor House School

168 Pampisford Road South Croydon Surrey CR2 6DA
Tel: 020 8660 3445
Fax: 020 8660 3445
e-mail: admin@cumnorhouse.com
website: www.cumnorhouse.com

***Headmaster*: P Clare-Hunt**, MA, CertEd

Age Range. Boys 4–13. Co-educational Nursery 2–4 years.

Number of Boys. 370.

Fees per term (2007-2008). £2,150–£2,800 (including lunch).

Cumnor House is one of Surrey's leading Preparatory Schools. Pleasantly and conveniently situated, the School prepares boys for scholarships and common entrance examinations to leading senior independent schools and local grammar schools.

Scholarships have been won recently to Dulwich, Epsom, Westminster, Charterhouse, Tonbridge and the local senior independent schools, Whitgift, Trinity and Caterham.

Music, Art, Drama and Games play a large part in the life of the School and all contribute to the busy, happy atmosphere.

Choir, sports tours and matches, ski trips, regular stage productions and a broad spectrum of clubs and options, give the boys the opportunity to pursue a wide range of interests.

Religious denomination: Christian.

Entry requirements: Assessment test and interview.

Cumnor House School

Danehill Haywards Heath West Sussex RH17 7HT
Tel: 01825 790347
Fax: 01825 790910
e-mail: office@cumnor.co.uk
website: www.cumnor.co.uk

Chairman of Governors: S Cockburn, Esq, MA (Oxon)

***Headmaster*: C St J S Heinrich**, BA Hons, PGCE
Deputy Headmaster: M N P Mockridge, BSc Hons, PGCE

Age Range. 4–13.

Number of Pupils. 358: 187 boys, 171 girls; 90 in the Pre-Prep; 50 boarders.

Fees per term (from April 2008). £5,735 (Boarding), £4,830 (Day); £2,555 (Pre-Preparatory). There is a reduction of 5% for each younger brother or sister at the school.

We aim to provide a happy and purposeful atmosphere in which children learn to set themselves high standards. Individuality is encouraged and equal esteem is given to achievements in and out of class.

The School has a strong tradition of scholarship, and many awards have been won at a wide range of senior schools, primarily academic but also in art, music and sport.

Out of school we offer children many opportunities for sports and cultural activities. Girls and boys in the Prep school all play sport every day. Each term children are given a choice of 20 or so supervised hobbies, from which they choose three. Much music and drama takes place: 95% of pupils in the Prep school learn an individual instrument and the choirs perform regularly. There are two orchestras and a wind band, as well as much singing and ensemble work. Each Summer term 50 or more children are involved in the annual production of a Shakespearean play in our open air theatre. Our rebuilt Sussex barn is used both as a school hall and as a local arts centre for concerts, lectures, exhibitions and winter term plays. A purpose-built theatre complex opens in September 2008 to enhance further the provision for the Arts. Set in 50 acres of fields and woodland, the school has a Sports Hall, four tennis courts and a heated outdoor pool, with a new 25m indoor pool completed in Spring 2004. Old farm buildings have been converted into blocks for science, music, art, ICT and home economics whilst additions of a new boarding wing, new kitchens and laundry are all recent. A new barn conversion in 2006 has provided 6 additional classrooms and a design technology centre and all classrooms have interactive whiteboards. The boarding staff includes a full-time qualified nurse. Boarding, entirely elective, is on a bi-weekly basis, allowing time for full weekends both at home and at school.

Charitable status. Cumnor House School Trust is a Registered Charity, number 801924. It exists for the advancement of education.

Dair House School

Bishop's Blake Beaconsfield Road Farnham Royal Buckinghamshire SL2 3BY
Tel: 01753 643964
Fax: 01753 642376
e-mail: info@dairhouse.co.uk
website: www.dairhouse.org.uk

Chairman of Governors: Mr P Geach

***Headmaster*: Mr Terence Wintle**, BEd

Age Range. 3–11.

Number in School. 120 Co-educational Day pupils.

Fees per term (2007-2008). £849–£2,405.

Located on the A355 at Farnham Royal we are conveniently placed for the Farnhams, Gerrards Cross, Beaconsfield, Stoke Poges and surrounding villages.

The School has excellent facilities – a large playing field, a multi-purpose playing surface, a gym with stage and lighting, a fully-equipped science and technology room, a separate art room, a music room, a dining room and a library. The classrooms are fully resourced and have a computer and interactive whiteboards. The children in Key Stage 1 and 2 are taught in classes up to 14 so individual attention is assured. The syllabus is wide and varied giving children 'a sure foundation from the start'. We provide a happy, caring environment where all children can flourish. Well-qualified and experienced staff will take the time to ensure the children have the best of learning experiences. All abilities are catered for with extra help given, by qualified staff, when needed. Peripatetic staff visit the school for weekly music and dancing lessons.

There are 'Before and After School' care facilities and activities available until 5.00 pm Monday to Friday. A recently completed extension to the school accommodates the under 5s in light and spacious classrooms and they have their own safe enclosed play area.

Charitable status. Dair House School Trust Limited is a Registered Charity, number 270719. Its aim is to provide 'a sure foundation from the start'.

Dame Bradbury's School

Ashdon Road Saffron Walden Essex CB10 2AL
Tel: 01799 522348
Fax: 01799 516762
e-mail: info@damebradburys.com
website: www.damebradburys.com

Dame Bradbury's is a co-educational day school, founded in 1525. It is an educational charity managed by a Board of Governors.

Chairman of Governors: Dr J Burch

***Headmistress*: Mrs J Crouch**

Age Range. 3–11.
Number of Pupils. 304 Day Pupils (144 boys, 160 girls).
Fees per term (2008-2009). Nursery: £985 (mornings only), £885 (afternoons). Main school: Reception (4–5 years): £2,210 (mornings only), £2,640 (full time); 5–7 years £2,640; 7–11 years £2,760. Lunches £190.

Children are accepted from 3–11 years and are prepared for Common Entrance and entry into both independent and state schools.

A high teacher/pupil ratio is maintained and the fully qualified staff, augmented by part-time specialists and in the younger forms by teachers' assistants, work as a team to provide a stimulating educational environment. The curriculum is designed to give a broad general education of a high standard and covers the National Curriculum. French is introduced at the age of 3 and taught by a specialist. The school has a musical tradition and creative potential is encouraged in all the arts.

The spacious buildings provide room for the Nursery, large classrooms, a Performing Arts Theatre (created 2006), a multipurpose Sports Hall (opened 2003), a well-equipped Science Laboratory and environmental garden with dipping pond (created 2007), a Teaching Garden (2008), a DT area, Music and Art Rooms, a spacious Library and Special Needs rooms and a main Dining Room. IT is fully integrated within the school with a wireless network, interactive whiteboards and an extensive IT suite (opened in 2004).

There are spacious grounds and playing fields, 2 hard tennis/netball courts and an Astroturf court (from September 2007). Physical Education features strongly in the curriculum and includes gymnastics, tennis, netball, football, rugby, hockey, cricket, athletics, rounders and swimming. There is an extensive programme of extra curricular activities which includes orchestra, choir, football, cricket, netball, drama, chess and pottery.

The Headmistress will be pleased to provide further details and meet interested parents.

Charitable status. Dame Johane Bradbury's School is a Registered Charity, number 1070780. It exists to provide education for boys and girls.

Danes Hill

Leatherhead Road Oxshott Surrey KT22 0JG
Tel: 01372 842509
Fax: 01372 844452
e-mail: registrar@daneshillschool.co.uk
website: www.daneshillschool.co.uk

Chairman of Governors: The Rt Hon Dame Angela Rumbold, DBE

***Headmaster*: Mr William Murdock**, BA

Age Range. 2½–13 co-educational.
Number of Children. 880.
Fees per term (2008-2009). £1,535–£4,256.

As a co-educational school, Danes Hill prepares boys and girls for Scholarship and Common Entrance examinations to senior schools (girls at 11, 12 and 13 and boys at 13). A high academic record (23 awards this year from a year group of 84) combines happily with a strong tradition of sporting prowess to ensure that all children are exposed to a kaleidoscope of opportunity on a peaceful 31 acre site set well back from the main Esher–Leatherhead road. The Pre-Preparatory Department takes children from 2½ to 6 years and is situated separately, but within easy walking distance of the Main School.

Extensive facilities include 2 state of the art IT suites and a science block with 4 fully equipped laboratories. Both Pre-Prep and Main School sites have covered swimming pools. There is a transport system available to take children both to and from school.

The curriculum is broad and a wide range of extra-curricular activity is encouraged. Languages are a particular strength of the school. All children learn French from age 3 and in addition choose German or Spanish in Year 4. All scholars and most Common Entrance pupils also study Latin, and Greek is a further option. Twenty-three pupils reached the final of the National Language Challenge in 2005 and scholars are encouraged to sit one or more language GCSEs in their final term at the school.

Pastoral care and pupil welfare are closely monitored. The school's Learning Support Centre provides a high level of support both for those with specific learning difficulties as well as those of exceptional ability in one or more areas.

Residential and day trips are seen as an essential part of the school experience. The school operates a well-established exchange programme with a German school, and there are language trips to centres in Spain and France. The annual Trips Week is a very special feature of the school calendar with over 500 children leaving the site to a range of residential destinations in the UK and abroad. There are also annual ski trips, as well as rugby, netball and hockey tours. Easter and Summer Holiday activity courses are very popular with both Pre-Prep and Prep children.

Sport is a major strength and a team of 12 specialist games staff ensures that all the major sports are expertly coached. There are extensive programmes of inter-school fixtures for all age groups. Every child is encouraged to participate and in 2005 the school fielded 27 rugby and 21 netball teams against other schools. A floodlit astroturf pitch allows all-weather training. Team spirit is valued alongside ability and three games dinners are held annually.

Former pupils are keen to stay in touch with the school. In 2004 a past pupils' society was founded, 'The Old Ravens', with over 3000 members on the database so far. A regular newsletter and a range of reunion dinners and events have proved extremely popular.

Charitable status. Danes Hill School (administered by The Vernon Educational Trust Ltd) is a Registered Charity, number 269433. It exists to provide high-quality education for boys and girls.

Daneshill School

Stratfield Turgis Basingstoke Hampshire RG27 0AR
Tel: 01256 882707
Fax: 01256 882007
e-mail: office@daneshill.hants.sch.uk
website: www.daneshill.hants.sch.uk

***Headmaster*: S V Spencer**, CertEd, DipPhysEd (St Luke's College, Exeter)

Age Range. 2½–13.

Number of Pupils. Day Boys 120, Day Girls 171.

Fees per term (2008-2009). Nursery £1,300 (5 mornings); Reception & Year 1 £2,500, Year 2 £2,700, Year 3 £2,800, Years 4–6 £3,050. Lunch included.

There are no compulsory extras.

The school was founded in 1950 and moved to Stratfield Turgis in 1979.

Daneshill School has a very happy atmosphere that can be attributed to the sensitive and sensible way in which the staff teach the children. This approach creates a successful, stimulating environment that is both conducive for learning and also allows the children to take full advantage of opportunities and experiences in these enjoyable formative years.

Our aim is to develop enthusiastic learners who will make a strong contribution to their senior schools as good citizens and as pupils who are prepared to work hard in order to achieve success. Children are valued as individuals and taught in a way that is appropriate to their needs. The School has an excellent record in achieving scholarships to leading independent schools.

A new Junior School and Nursery block was opened in March 2002 and an all-purpose astroturf pitch was added in 2005.

Davenies School

Beaconsfield Bucks HP9 1AA
Tel: 01494 685400
Fax: 01494 685408
e-mail: office@davenies.co.uk
website: www.davenies.co.uk

Chairman: C Dodds

***Headmaster*: C Watson**, BEd, MA

Age Range. 4–13.

Number of Boys. 330 (Day Boys only).

Fees per term (2007-2008). £3,200–£3,850.

Davenies is situated in the heart of Beaconsfield, a Georgian town on the edge of the Chiltern Hills, close to the M40 and only thirty minutes from the centre of London by rail and car. Founded in 1940, the school aims to provide a broad education for day boys between the ages of 4 and 13. It enjoys a 'family' atmosphere, confident and courteous pupils and enthusiastic and committed staff.

The large site includes modern, airy classrooms, a purpose-built Science Laboratory, DT facility and Art Studio and a fully modernised IT Suite and Music Wing. A state-of-the-art Sports Complex incorporates an indoor swimming pool, Sports Hall and Performing Arts Centre. Boys are taught Rugby, Football, Cricket, Hockey, Athletics and Swimming and compete regularly against other schools.

Davenies follows a broad curriculum and there is a strong emphasis on numeracy and literacy from an early age. Specialist subject teaching begins in Year 3. French is taught from Year 1 and Latin from Year 6. There is an exciting array of over fifty extra-curricular activities each week which cater for individual interests; these include jazz band, mountain biking, rock climbing, snowboarding, photography, electronics, cookery and media. The school also has its own Cub Pack.

Once they leave the Pre-Prep Department, the academic and pastoral welfare of the boys is undertaken by a network of form teachers. The Deputy Head and two of the Assistant Heads oversee the management of this care and ensure that regular, detailed communication with parents takes place, both formally and informally.

Some pupils move on to local Grammar Schools at the end of Year 6, although many choose to stay on to enjoy the hugely popular programme that Davenies offers its senior pupils before they move on to Senior Independent Schools at 13. As well as individual attention in the classroom, senior boys take part in the school's Senior Activity Programme (SAP) which introduces them to challenging, often unusual activities, whilst promoting team building and character development. SAP activities include paintballing, go-karting, sailing, skiing, water skiing and golf. Senior boys also have opportunities to go on skiing and adventure holidays, outward bound weekend and a wide variety of education trips. They also have the opportunity to participate in various sports tours, both at home and abroad.

Developing the whole individual is paramount at Davenies, where great emphasis is placed on the value of courtesy, good manners and consideration for others, encapsulated in the school's motto: 'singulus pro fraternitate laborans' (one working for the good of all).

Charitable status. Beaconsfield Educational Trust Ltd is a Registered Charity, number 313120. It exists to provide high standards and the fulfilment of each child's potential.

Dean Close Pre-Preparatory School

Lansdown Road Cheltenham Gloucestershire GL51 6QS
Tel: 01242 258079
Fax: 01242 258005
e-mail: squirrels@deanclose.org.uk
website: www.deanclose.co.uk

Chairman of Governors: Mrs P G Napier

***Headmistress*: Mrs S E Bennett**, CertEd

Age Range. 2–7 Co-educational.

Number of Pupils. 147.

Fees per term (2008-2009). £2,070–£2,135.

The Pre-Preparatory School of Dean Close is a co-educational, Christian family school which occupies the same campus as Dean Close Preparatory and Dean Close School and is, therefore, able to share such outstanding facilities as the swimming pool, sports hall, tennis courts, computer centre and art block.

The Pre-Preparatory School moved into a new, purpose built school building opened by Lord Robert Winston in June 2004. The school has a large hall surrounded by classrooms on two floors. There are two playgrounds – one for the Nursery and Kindergarten and one for Reception and Years 1 and 2.

The curriculum within the Pre-Preparatory school offers a wide range of learning opportunities aimed at stimulating and nurturing a child's development and interests in an intellectual, physical, spiritual, social and emotional sense. Speech and Drama, Dance, Tennis, Music and Judo are available as extra-curricular activities. All children participate in Forest School, which teaches them about the trees and plants in the forest.

Charitable status. Dean Close School is a Registered Charity, number 1086829.

Dean Close Preparatory School

Lansdown Road Cheltenham Gloucestershire GL51 6QS
Tel: 01242 512217
Fax: 01242 258005
e-mail: dcpsoffice@deanclose.org.uk
website: www.deanclose.co.uk/prep

Chairman of Governors: Mrs P G Napier

***Headmaster*: The Revd Leonard Browne**, MA

Age Range. 7–13.

Number of Pupils. 285: Boarding Boys 34, Boarding Girls 35, Day Boys 112, Day Girls 104.

Inclusive Fees per term (2008-2009). Boarders £4,870–£6,165, Day Boarders £3,380–£4,770, Day Pupils £2,920–£4,310.

The Preparatory School of Dean Close is a fully co-educational, Christian family school which occupies the same campus as Dean Close School and is, therefore, able to share such outstanding facilities as the Chapel, gymnasium, swimming pool, theatre and extensive playing fields, including hard tennis courts, artificial astroturf hockey pitches and the new sports hall with indoor tennis, cricket nets, large gymnasium and dance studio.

Although the Preparatory School is administered by the same board of Governors, it has its own Headmaster and Staff. The Staff complement consists of 48 who either hold Degrees or Diplomas of Education, including a Director of Music and there is a team of excellent peripatetic musicians.

There are three boarding houses, each with resident House-parents, a House Tutor and a resident matron.

The day pupils are accommodated in three purpose-built houses. Each is run by a Housemaster/Housemistress, assisted by house tutors.

The School follows a curriculum which embraces the National Curriculum and Common Entrance, preparing boys and girls for entry to the Senior School at 13+ by CE and internal transfer procedures. A few transfer to other Senior Independent Schools.

The main games for boys are Rugby, Hockey and Cricket and for girls, Hockey, Netball, Rounders and Tennis. Swimming, Athletics and Cross-Country Running are taught as well and use is made of the School's Covered Playing Area. Golf is available at a nearby course and Shooting is available in the school grounds.

Camping, Canoeing, Hill-walking and Orienteering are catered for and a wide range of activities is available including, among others, Trampolining, Badminton, Judo, Climbing, Computing, Cooking, Watercolour Painting and all forms of Dance. Special Activity courses are part of the curriculum.

There is a special music school and a purpose built hall for dramatic and orchestral performances. There is a separate Art, Pottery and Technology centre and a dining hall and kitchens.

The main classroom block consists of 10 specialist teaching rooms including 2 laboratories and a computer centre. This building is joined to the newest teaching block by the admin centre. This block has 7 purpose-built classrooms, together with day house facilities, the staff Common Room, a new Library and Art and Technology block.

The new purpose-built Pre-Prep School was opened in June 2004. (*See separate entry for Dean Close Pre-Preparatory School.*)

Charitable status. Dean Close School is a Registered Charity, number 1086829. It exists to provide education for children.

Denmead

Wensleydale Road Hampton Middlesex TW12 2LP
Tel: 020 8979 1844
Fax: 020 8941 8773
e-mail: secretary@denmead.richmond.sch.uk
website: www.denmead.richmond.sch.uk

Chairman of Governors: A J Roberts, CBE, BA, FRSA

***Headmaster*: M McKaughan**, BEd

Age Range. Boys 2½–11, Girls 2½–7.

Number of Pupils. 180.

Fees per term (2008-2009). Kindergarten (2½–4 years): £1,295 (mornings), £2,590 (all day). Pre-Prep (4–7 years): £2,780. Prep (7–11 years): £2,990 including lunch for full day pupils.

The School is situated in a quiet, leafy part of Hampton and is easily accessible by road and rail. The School merged with Hampton School in September 1999 to become the Hampton School Trust's preparatory school. Although there is still no expectation for pupils to select Hampton as their first-choice secondary school, at least 50 per cent on average each year transfer there. Both schools are served by the same Board of Governors and the Headmaster of Denmead now reports to the Headmaster of Hampton School. The amalgamation produces economies of scale from which Denmead benefits.

Further developments have taken place over the last academic year. Boys now transfer to senior schools at 11+ rather than 13+. The school will be adding a second class to its Year 3 intake, ultimately to have 16 to 18 pupils, who will be set for English and Maths. From September 2004 Hampton has been offering assured places for 11+ entry via a 7+ assessment to boys from Denmead Pre-Prep and to those starting in Year 3 of the Preparatory Department. Also those boys who perform very well in the 11+ Hampton entry exams, but who do not gain an award from Hampton, will be considered for the W D James Award made by Denmead, which will be in the form of a reduction in the child's first term's fees at Hampton.

The Pre-Prep is housed on its own site in the homely atmosphere of two residential houses offering space and security. Rooms are well-appointed and there are 20 pupils per class. The Preparatory section which backs on to an attractive public park, boasts its own games field and purpose-built teaching facilities including a multi-purpose hall. Major school sports are Football, Rugby, Cricket and Athletics. An extensive programme of extra-curricular activities includes art club, chess, debating, judo, computing and a variety of minor sports. There is a School choir, an orchestra, and a flourishing tradition of drama. Individual music tuition is also provided.

Parents share in the life of the School as fully as possible and there exists a very active parents' association.

Please contact the School Office for a prospectus.

Charitable status. Denmead School is part of the Hampton School Trust, which is a Registered Charity, number 1120005. It exists to provide a school in Hampton.

Derwent Lodge
The Schools at Somerhill

Somerhill Tonbridge Kent TN11 0NJ
Tel: 01732 352124
Fax: 01732 363381
e-mail: office@schoolsatsomerhill.com
website: www.schoolsatsomerhill.com

Derwent Lodge is one of the three Schools at Somerhill under the care and control of The Somerhill Charitable Trust.

Chairman of Governors: Mr Philip Thomas

Principal: Mr J T Coakley, MA

***Headmistress*: Mrs E Hill**, BEd, CertEd

Age Range. 7–11 years.

Number of Pupils. 141 Day Girls.

Fees per term (2007-2008). £3,450.

Extras: individual music lessons, recreational outings, minibus service from Tunbridge Wells, West Malling and Brenchley area, residential study visits.

Derwent Lodge was founded in central Tunbridge Wells in 1952 and moved to its present parkland setting on the southern outskirts of Tonbridge in 1993.

The school is noted for its strong academic tradition and for its caring, happy atmosphere. High standards of work, manners and courtesy are expected of each girl. There are specialist facilities for science, art, music, IT and sport.

The curriculum is designed to give a sound basic general education which will prepare pupils well for entry to the grammar or independent schools chosen by their parents. Pupils regularly gain scholarships to secondary schools.

An optional extended day is offered. There is a full programme of extra-curricular clubs and activities. Girls in their final year at the school are offered residential study visits to the Isle of Wight and Saint Omer.

Admission to the school at 7+ is by interview and a report from the previous school. For entry at later stages, girls spend a day at the school for informal assessment before the offer of a place is confirmed. Girls from the pre-preparatory school at Somerhill may proceed to Derwent Lodge automatically.

Charitable status. The Somerhill Charitable Trust Limited is a Registered Charity, number 1002212. It exists for the purpose of providing education for children.

Devonshire House Preparatory School

2 Arkwright Road Hampstead London NW3 6AE
Tel: 020 7435 1916
Fax: 020 7431 4787
e-mail: enquiries@devonshirehouseprepschool.co.uk
website: www.devonshirehouseschool.co.uk

***Headmistress*: Mrs S Alexander**, BA Hons, PGCE

Age Range. Boys 2½–13, Girls 2½–11.

Number in School. 530: 292 Boys, 238 Girls.

Fees per term (2008-2009). £2,150–£4,150.

Devonshire House School is for boys and girls from three to thirteen years of age and the School's nursery department, the Oak Tree Nursery, takes children from two and a half. The academic subjects form the core curriculum and the teaching of music, art, drama, computer studies, design technology and games helps to give each child a chance to excel. At the age of eleven for girls and thirteen for boys the children go on to their next schools, particularly the main independent London day schools.

Devonshire House pursues high academic standards whilst developing enthusiasm and initiative. It is considered important to encourage pupils to develop their own individual personalities and a good sense of personal responsibility. There is a wide variety of clubs and tuition is available in ballet, judo, fencing, speech and communication and in a range of musical instruments. High standards and individual attention for each child are of particular importance.

The School is located on the crest of the hill running into Hampstead Village and has fine Victorian premises with charming grounds and walled gardens.

The Headmistress is a member of IAPS and ISA and the school is accredited by the Independent Schools Council.

Dolphin School

Hurst Berkshire RG10 0BP
Tel: 0118 934 1277
Fax: 0118 934 4110
e-mail: omnes@dolphinschool.com
website: www.dolphinschool.com

Founded in 1970.

Principal: Dr N Follett, BA, MA, PhD

***Head*: Veronica Gibbs**BSc, PGCE

Registrar: Mrs J Vernon

Age Range. 3–13.

Number of Pupils. 265: 136 Day Boys, 129 Day Girls, Montessori Nursery 34.

Fees per term (2008-2009). Nursery: £2,395 (core session), £2,475 (full day); £3,170 (Reception, Years 1 and 2); £3,285 (Years 3–8).

"An exciting, challenging, dynamic learning environment" according to the 2004 ISI Inspection Report of Dolphin School. "The warmth of the greeting everywhere is striking and genuine", noted the Good Schools Guide review.

We believe that children have special gifts and talents, which too often remain hidden forever. Dolphin School offers an environment which encourages these gifts to flourish. Children leave Dolphin with confidence in themselves, a strong sense of individualism, the ability to adjust well in school and social situations, at least one area in which they can feel pride in their own achievement and a strong sense of curiosity and enjoyment in learning. Throughout life, in an ever more quickly changing world, they will have the skills and the confidence successfully to pursue their ambitions and interests and to lead happy and fulfilled lives.

Dolphin children are allowed to develop as individuals and encouraged to fulfil their various potentials in small classes under the careful guidance of specialist teachers. Abundant academic, artistic, social and sporting stimulation is provided through an extremely broad, well-rounded programme. We encourage lateral thinking and the ability to cross reference. Expectations for all children are high and academic rigour is a key component in all lessons. We provide an education that suits the needs of able children.

Dolphin School provides the friendly, family atmosphere of a small school. All members of staff are actively concerned with the pastoral care of all the children, but each form teacher assumes special responsibility for the daily well-being and the overall progress of a very small group of children. In addition children in their final three years have a personal mentor. Class sizes average sixteen. Children learn both to talk and listen to each other, to evaluate and tolerate the opinions of others and to take pride in each other's achievements. They are also encouraged to accept responsibility and to develop their leadership abilities.

Courses offered. All children are taught by graduate specialists from age six in most subjects. In the early years we provide a firm grounding in English-based skills throughout all humanities subjects. French begins in Nursery, Latin in Year Five and German, Spanish and Greek in Year Eight. Laboratory science is taught from age seven. Mathematics, geography, history, ICT, classical studies, art, design technology, drama, music and PE are taught throughout the upper school.

Architecture, astronomy, philosophy, thinking skills, religious education, current affairs, environmental studies and history/ geography in French are included in some years.

The "Dolphin Scheme" for teaching ICT is now used in more than 80 schools throughout Britain. It was invented and developed in our ICT Department. The subject is now integrated into all areas of the curriculum.

Activities. A unique strength of Dolphin School is our residential field trip programme in which all children participate from age seven. The work related to these trips forms major sections of all departmental syllabuses. Principal annual field trips visit East Sussex, Dorset, Ironbridge, North Wales, Northumbria and Italy, while departments organise residential trips to Boulogne, York, Normandy and Stratford. We also offer an extensive mountain-walking programme. We have a large number of trained British Mountain Leaders. Staff and children participate in a graded fell walking programme. Locations range from the Lake District and Brecon Beacons to Snowdonia and the Alps. We also organise sports tours and a "custom made" outward bound course.

We believe in 'hands-on' learning, whether in or outside the classroom, and children participate in a very wide range of day trips to museums, theatres, archaeological sites and many other venues.

Almost all costs associated with field, walking and day trips are included in the fees, as are lunch-time and after-school clubs which include: athletics, tennis, short tennis, judo, rounders, cricket, embroidery, computing, cycling proficiency, swimming, football, netball, gymnastics, craft, hockey, chess, cross country, rugby, art, table tennis, orchestra, windband, string group, choir, orienteering, gardening, cookery, drama and classics.

We field teams at all levels in football, rugby, cricket, chess, netball, rounders, tennis, short tennis, swimming, cross-country, athletics, hockey and judo. We are well represented at county level.

Facilities. Our hall offers a splendid venue for school concerts and plays. We stage several major productions each year. Grounds include a swimming pool, all weather tennis courts and playing fields. Cricket matches are played at Hurst, a neighbouring county standard ground.

Entry. Nursery at age 3, Reception at age 4+, and throughout the Upper School as places become available.

Internal and external scholarships are available to children aged 10–13 in the performing arts, art, creative writing and sport. Academic bursaries are also available.

Examination results. Our examination results are outstanding and we regularly win major scholarships to senior independent schools, including St Paul's, Eton and Winchester. We have a thriving Old Delphinian organisation. Most past pupils gain good degrees and a high proportion attend Oxbridge colleges.

Donhead

Edge Hill Wimbledon London SW19 4NP
Tel: 020 8946 7000
Fax: 020 8947 1219
e-mail: office@donhead.org.uk
website: www.donhead.org.uk

Chairman of Governors: Mr Michael Blundell

***Headmaster*: Mr Christopher McGrath**, BA Hons, PGCE, MBA Ed

Age Range. Boys 4–11.
Number of Pupils. 220.
Fees per term (2008-2009). £2,300–£2,485.

Donhead is a small, friendly Jesuit preparatory school for boys aged 4 to 11, providing a lively well-balanced academic education in a caring Christian environment. A broad, balanced and differentiated curriculum is delivered by a very experienced and fully-qualified staff team committed to the provision of stimulating, focused and challenging teaching, preparing the boys for entry into the top state and independent schools in SW London and beyond. Particular attention is given to each child's individual needs with an emphasis on the importance of pastoral care. The school maintains strong yet informal links between home and school. There is also an extensive programme of extra-curricular activities.

Our games provision is a strong feature of the school, and we enjoy a national reputation for the strength of our rugby teams. During the last rugby season our U11A team were winners of The Prior Park International Rugby Festival, The Surrey Cup, The Northern Sevens and the St Benedict's 7s Tournament.

A dramatic period of rapid development has changed the face of Donhead in the last two years. July 2006 saw the completion of its extensive £1.5 million building development programme with the new St Ignatius Building providing a sports hall, ICT suite, music room and art room. In addition, the Pre-Prep Department opened in September 2006 and now boasts a Reception, Year 1 and Year 2 class.

Charitable status. The Society of Jesus Trust of 1929 for Roman Catholic Purposes is a Registered Charity, number 230165.

Dorset House

The Manor Church Lane Bury Pulborough West Sussex RH20 1PB
Tel: 01798 831456
Fax: 01798 831141
e-mail: headmaster@dorsethouse.w-sussex.sch.uk
website: www.dorsethouseschool.com

Chairman of Governors: C S Major, Esq, BSc

***Headmaster*: R C M Brown**, BA Hons, MA, PGCE

Age Range. 2–13 Co-educational.
Number of Pupils. 130.
Fees per term (2007-2008). Boarding £4,645–£5,220, no unavoidable extras. Day £2,142–£4,320.

Founded over 200 years ago, Dorset House is an educational trust, thus assuring the continuity and financial security of the school.

Being a small school, it has been possible to create a home from home atmosphere in which individual attention is more easily devoted to each pupil, both in and out of the classroom. The school introduced a very successful nursery in 2004 which has admitted girls and boys since 2006.

Bury Manor stands in beautiful grounds set in pasture and woodland. On the banks of the river Arun and at the foot of one of the most attractive stretches of the South Downs, the surroundings offer unlimited opportunities for recreation and adventure.

There is a full-time qualified and experienced staff of 20. Classes are small rarely exceeding 18. Self-discipline and a love of learning are stressed. The School has an almost unbroken run of success in Common Entrance examinations, together with many scholarships. Every effort is made to bring out the best in every boy, whatever his ability and interests. Music, art and drama are major features whilst the school has a fine choir and orchestra. The school enjoys a very high reputation for chess.

On the sporting front, the school offers all the traditional games and sports, plus judo, squash, shooting and golf.

All boarding is now on a weekly basis, but the school is flexible about boarding arrangements. The Headmaster's wife takes a close interest in all aspects of the school. Entry is by interview.

Charitable status. Bury Manor School Trust Limited (Dorset House School) is a Registered Charity, number 307035. It exists to provide a first class education to boys and girls.

The Downs, Malvern College Preparatory School

Colwall Malvern Worcs WR13 6EY
Tel: 01684 540277
Fax: 01684 540094
e-mail: enquiries@thedowns.malcol.org
website: www.thedowns.malcol.org

Chairman of Governors: Adrian G Silcock, Esq, MA, DipEd, FRSA

***Headmaster*: A P Ramsay**, BEd, MSc

Age Range. 2½–13 years.

Number of Pupils. 180 boys, 120 girls.

Fees per term (2008-2009). Boarding £3,500–£5,403; Flexi-boarding £25 per night; Day £2,900–£4,082; Pre-Preparatory £1,700–£2,300; Kindergarten £17.50 per half day session; Nursery £38.25 per day.

Located 3 miles west of Malvern, 4 miles east of Ledbury, 15 miles from the M5 motorway, on the main line from Paddington and extensively served by Malvern College transport, the school is set in 55 acres of attractive rural countryside on the western slopes of the Malvern Hills.

The school has been formed as a result of a carefully-planned merger between two well-respected educational establishments, The Downs, Colwall and Malvern College Prep School. The new school continues to value its surroundings along with traditions from both schools, but also has taken the opportunity to move with the times, striving to exceed the confines of the National Curriculum in academic, as well as cultural, sporting and social accomplishments. The Downs, Malvern College Prep offers a broad curriculum challenging the academically gifted and supporting those with special needs.

The youngest pupils can attend the Montessori based Early Years Department in its own purpose-built, open-plan, building surrounded by wonderful grounds and then move seamlessly into the Pre-Prep, Prep and on to Malvern College, providing continuity from 2½ to 18 years.

Over the past decade pupils have moved to a variety of senior independent schools on the basis of scholarship or common entrance examinations and, whilst the option for independent choice is still there, the direction has changed. The Downs is the main feeder school for Malvern College and the emphasis in Years 7 and 8 is not only a preparation for scholarships and Common Entrance, but should allow a smooth transition to the College academically and socially.

Sports, especially team games, are also a serious part of the curriculum, as is Music. 80% of the pupils learn a musical instrument. There is a wide and expanding hobbies programme which includes railway engineering as well as Speech and Drama, Dance, Design Technology and Art.

Boarding. The newly refurbished Boarding House provides a home for up to 60 boarders with a professional boarding team of House Parents and Matrons who have responsibility for their care. Boarding can be full, flexi or a one-off experience with a published programme of evening and weekend activities.

Facilities. There is a wide range of facilities including a 300-seat capacity Concert Hall, a self-contained Music School; new Science laboratories; a Design and Technology suite, Pottery studio and wired computer network with white-boards. A brand new sports complex is due to open in April 2009 and this is supplemented by an astroturf Hockey pitch, 3 Netball/Tennis courts and 55 acres of grounds set aside for games pitches, forest schools' lessons and relaxation. The school has its own 9½" narrow gauge steam railway!

Scholarships and Exhibitions are awarded to pupils who show academic excellence and/or who show academic competence as well as having a particular talent in Art, Music, Drama or Sport.

Bursaries are available offering assistance to parents subject to completion of a means test form.

Charitable status. The Downs, Malvern College Prep School is a Registered Charity, number 1120616. It exists to provide education for girls and boys from 2½–13 years.

The Downs School

Wraxall Bristol BS48 1PF
Tel: 01275 852008
Fax: 01275 855840
e-mail: office@thedownsschool.co.uk
website: www.thedownsschool.co.uk

Chairman of Governors: A N J Currie

***Head Master*: Marcus Gunn**, MA Ed, BA, PGCE

Age Range. 4–13.

Number of Pupils. 250: 159 boys, 91 girls.

Fees per term (2008-2009). £2,450–£3,950 including lunch.

The Downs School was founded in 1894 in a house near The Downs in Bristol. In 1927 it moved six miles due west to the idyllic country setting of Charlton House and in the Autumn of 2002, the School was bought from the late Lord Wraxall's estate.

The Downs is a co-educational preparatory school for children from 4 to 13 years old. The children enjoy an all-round education, achieving high academic standards and they are recognised nationally for their success in sport, particularly, rugby and hockey.

Through highly skilled teaching we create an exciting and stimulating environment for learning, and by developing the talents of each child we believe that every pupil can succeed. The children are encouraged to become independent thinkers and to use their own initiative with confidence. They are prepared for Common Entrance and scholarship examinations to a wide range of public and independent schools.

In the happy, caring Pre-Prep Department (from 4 to 7 years old) the girls and boys play imaginatively and grow in confidence. Each child is nurtured to establish a sound social and academic foundation for their future education.

The School has over 50 acres of playing fields, a sports hall, a walled garden for tennis and an outdoor heated pool. The children play and compete in athletics, cricket, netball, rounders, rugby, rugby sevens, swimming and tennis. Outdoor pursuits include abseiling, caving and canoeing and a broad range of activities include cricket, ballet, cooking, sculpture and chess.

Major drama and musical productions, as well as more frequent informal music, poetry and drama evenings are staged throughout the year.

For further information or to arrange a visit to see the children at work and play, please contact The School Office on 01275 852008.

Charitable status. The Downs School is a Registered Charity, number 310279. It was established for the education of boys and girls aged 4–13.

Downsend
Cognita Schools Group

Leatherhead Surrey KT22 8TJ
Tel: 01372 372311
Fax: 01372 363367
e-mail: admissions@downsend.co.uk
website: www.downsend.co.uk

Headmaster: **F Steadman**

Age Range. 2–13 co-educational.

Number of Pupils. Day: 580 (aged 6–13), 329 (aged 2–6).

Fees per term (from April 2008). Pre-Preparatory £695–£2,625, including lunch for full-time pupils. Preparatory: £2,880 (Year 2), £3,495 (Years 3–8), including lunch.

Downsend is a co-educational day school for children aged between 2 and 13 years.

The main school stands on a pleasant, open site just outside the town, surrounded by its own playing fields and tennis courts. The Sports Complex includes a large indoor swimming pool and a new artificial pitch was completed in 2007. The newly styled library and the expanded, networked ICT provision, are available to support children's learning and development.

Pre-Preparatory (age 2 to 6). There are three co-educational pre-preparatory departments in Ashtead, Epsom and Leatherhead. Here pupils work in a small and friendly environment, where they are encouraged to achieve their individual potential through a wide range of activities. Outings, sport, music and drama all play an important part in school life. French is enjoyed by Second Steps Nursery to Year 1 children. Our extended day facility provides after-school care to 5.30 pm which is especially useful for working parents. At 6 the majority of the children move on to the main Downsend site where they are joined by children from other local Independent and State schools.

Preparatory (age 6 to 13). Founded in 1918, Downsend is not only a traditional academic prep school which prepares children for Common Entrance, Scholarship and High School examinations, but also a thriving community where many other opportunities are provided.

The standard of work is high and the school is particularly proud of its scholarship record. Recently an average of 30 awards a year has been achieved.

There is a wide curriculum and the children study, in addition to the normal Common Entrance subjects, Art, Drama, Food Technology, Health Education, ICT, Music, Technology and Textiles. Parents are kept informed of their children's progress through regular Parents' Evenings and termly reports, and are welcome at all times to communicate with members of staff.

The school has a strong reputation for its music, with regular concerts throughout the year, and a large number of children learn a variety of musical instruments. Drama is equally important and there are several productions each year. Pupils can take part in a full range of sports not only in school but also at local, regional and national level. Regular visits occur outside school and holidays abroad are also arranged.

Our holiday activity scheme, Downsend+, gives pupils access to exciting and absorbing workshops and courses, Masterclass coaching by professional sports people and thrilling days out. This is available to children aged 5–13 from 8 am to 5.30 pm, including breakfast, lunch and tea as appropriate. We also now offer Downsend Nursery+ as a dedicated facility for children aged 2–5 at our Leatherhead Lodge.

Dragon School

Bardwell Road Oxford OX2 6SS
Tel: 01865 315400
Fax: 01865 311664
e-mail: admissions@dragonschool.org
website: www.dragonschool.org

Chairman of Governors: D T R Lewis

Headmaster: **John Baugh**, BEd

Age Range. 4–7 (Dragon Pre-Prep), 8–13 (Dragon).

Number of Pupils. Day: 597 (384 boys, 213 girls); Boarders: 258 (189 boys, 69 girls).

Fees per term (2008-2009). Day £2,760–£5,080; Boarding £7,270.

The Dragon School, just north of Oxford city centre, enjoys a leafy setting on the banks of the River Cherwell. Traditional buildings, contemporary facilities and extensive playing fields are the setting for an exceptional all round education for day and boarding pupils. Dragons are noted for a spirited informality and a confident, enthusiast approach to all they do. A culture of learning how to learn and the appreciation of effort of every kind, result in all round academic, sporting and cultural excellence. A non-selective school, the Dragon regularly achieves an impressive list of scholarships and awards (over 50 in 2007) and children go on to the country's finest Independent Senior Schools.

A sizeable school, the Dragon is composed of small, friendly communities. A dedicated building for Year 4 (E block) with its own playground offers children a gentle introduction to a preparatory school that is large enough to grow with them. Boarding is the heart of the school where warm support and a caring ethos are enjoyed by boarders from the local community and around the world. Nine homely boarding houses of varying sizes provide a gradual transition to life at senior schools.

The extensive curriculum is taught by highly qualified and individual staff whose innovative lessons and high standards led to the Dragon being deemed 'outstanding' on many fronts in its 2006 Inspection. A very strong sporting tradition is mirrored by rich creativity in drama, music and art.

Extra-curricular activities encompass games, languages, sports, debates, drama, music and much more. Dragons are seasoned travellers and many expeditions and trips are made to destinations ranging from local woodlands to Brazil and including Sri Lanka, Switzerland, South Africa and Morocco. There is a regular exchange programme with schools in New York and Tokyo.

The Dragon Pre-Prep Lynams is a short distance away in Summertown with its own staff and facilities for Reception and Years 1, 2 and 3.

Bursaries of up to 95% of fees are offered and a well-established development programme exists to support growth in this area.

For further information or to arrange a visit please contact the Registrar on 01865 315405.

Charitable status. The Dragon School Trust Ltd is a Registered Charity, number 309676. It aims to provide education for boys and girls between the ages of 4 and 13.

Duke of Kent School

Peaslake Road Ewhurst Surrey GU6 7NS
Tel: 01483 277313
Fax: 01483 273862

e-mail: dok.school@virgin.net
website: www.dukeofkentschool.org.uk

Chairman of the Governing Body: Air Vice-Marshal M J Gardiner, OBE, BSc, FRAeS, RAF (Ret'd)

***Headmaster*: A D Cameron**, MA, PhD (University of Edinburgh)

Age Range. 3–13 co-educational. To include Years 9 to 11 from September 2009.

Number of Pupils. 185 including 50 full/part boarders.

Fees per term (2008-2009). Boarders £4,735–£5,665, Day Pupils £1,385–£4,170. Entrance scholarships are available for admission to the Main School for both day and boarding pupils. Special discounts are available for Service Boarders to supplement the CEA.

The Duke of Kent School stands in magnificent surroundings in the Surrey Hills and is within easy reach of Central London, the M25 and Heathrow and Gatwick Airports. The School offers Nursery, Pre-Preparatory and Preparatory education for children aged 3–13. Though predominantly a day school in total numbers, the School retains a thriving boarding section and day pupils are frequently involved in evening and weekend activities. The Pre-Prep School was fully refurbished in 2001 and opened by HRH, the Duke of Kent.

There is a full-time qualified teaching staff of 23 and pupils are prepared for Common Entrance to a wide range of distinguished senior schools. In addition to the standard academic subjects, art, drama, music, CDT and computer studies are included in the curriculum, all delivered by specialist teachers.

The School has very good facilities which include a classroom block with 2 science labs, a computer room and a library. There is also a music-block with 9 teaching/practice rooms. Specialist tuition is available in a wide range of musical instruments. There are very extensive playing fields, a heated and covered swimming pool and all-weather tennis courts. A full-sized sports hall allows a wide range of indoor sports, including hockey and gymnastics.

Charitable status. The Duke of Kent School is a Registered Charity, number 1064183.

Dulwich College Junior School

London SE21 7LD
Tel: 020 8299 9248
Fax: 020 8299 9248
e-mail: info@dulwich.org.uk
website: www.dulwich.org.uk

***Head of Junior School*: Mrs P A Horsman**, CertEd

Dulwich College Junior School is part of Dulwich College. *For further details, see Dulwich College entry in HMC section.*

Charitable status. Part of the Foundation, Alleyn's College of God's Gift, Dulwich College is a Registered Charity, number 312755. It exists for the education of children.

Dulwich College Preparatory School

42 Alleyn Park Dulwich London SE21 7AA
Tel: 020 8670 3217
Fax: 020 8766 7586
e-mail: registrar@dcpslondon.org
website: www.dcpslondon.org

The School was founded in 1885 and became a charitable trust in 1957 with a board of governors.

Chairman of Governors: Mr D Pennock

***Headmaster*: G Marsh**, MA, CertEd

Age Range. Boys 3–13, Girls 3–5.

Number of Boys. 785 day boys, +/-30 girls, 25 weekly boarders (aged 8–13).

Fees per term (2007-2008). Tuition: Day boys £1,347–£4,194 (inclusive of lunch – there are no compulsory extras). Weekly boarders: £1,959 in addition to tuition fee.

Boys are prepared for Common Entrance and scholarships to a wide range of independent schools where 30–35 scholarships are won annually. DCPS is an entirely separate school from Dulwich College, though between a third and a half of the boys continue their education at the College every year.

The school is divided into a Nursery School for 140 boys and girls aged 3–5, a Pre-Prep for 140 boys aged 5–7, a Lower School for 200 boys aged 7–9 and the Upper School for 360 boys aged 9–13.

Over the past twenty years an extensive programme of building and development has provided the school with facilities that it can be proud of. These include two well equipped computer suites, three large, modern science laboratories, a spacious art studio, a design technology workshop, a studio theatre and a large music school. All academic subjects are taught in modern, spacious classrooms and there are well-stocked libraries in each section of the school. A new "four-court" sports hall and state-of-the-art Nursery were commissioned in September 2006.

There are extensive playing fields a short walk from the school and all normal games are played. All boys aged 5 and over are taught to swim in the school's own 25-metre heated, indoor pool.

Boarders. There are up to 30 weekly boarders in the 8–13 age group in the school's boarding house, Brightlands, situated on Gallery Road, 10 minutes' walk from the main school site. The boarding house shares 13 acres of grounds with the Nursery School, with tennis courts and playing fields available in leisure time.

Charitable status. Dulwich College Preparatory School is a Registered Charity, number 312715. It exists to provide education for boys.

Dulwich Preparatory School

Coursehorn Cranbrook Kent TN17 3NP
Tel: 01580 712179
Fax: 01580 715322
e-mail: registrar@dcpskent.org
website: www.dcpskent.org

Chairman of Governors: D R M Pennock

***Headmaster*: S L Rigby**, BA, PGCE

Age Range. 3–13.

Number of Boys and Girls. Day: 263 (Upper School), 194 (Little Stream), 64 (Pre-Prep). Boarders: 11.

Inclusive Fees per term (2008-2009). Day: £4,178 (Years 5–8), £3,572 (Years 2–4), £2,781 (Year 1), Pre-Prep: £1,425–£2,781 (full day), £1,425–£1,689 (mornings). Boarders: £33.50–£36.60 per night.

The School, which is one mile from the country town of Cranbrook, has extensive grounds (50 acres) and offers a broad and varied education to boys and girls from 3 to 13+. To ensure that children receive the personal attention that is vital for this age range the School is divided up into three separate, self-contained, departments. These are Nash House (3–5 year olds),

Little Stream (5–9 year olds) and Upper School (9–13 year olds). Each department has its own staff, teaching equipment, sports facilities, playgrounds, swimming pools, etc. Pupils are prepared for Common Entrance or Scholarship examinations to any school of their parents' choice, and there is a strong emphasis on up to date teaching methods. The wide scope for sporting activities – Football, Rugby, Cricket, Hockey, Netball, Rounders, Athletics, Cross-country, Swimming, Tennis – is balanced by the importance attached to Art, DT, Drama, ICT and Music. Over 200 pupils learn the full range of orchestral instruments. There are two Orchestras, Wind and Brass Bands, Jazz Band, and four Choirs. The boarders are divided into two houses, boys and girls, each under the care of House staff. The happiness of the boarders is a particular concern and every effort is made to establish close and friendly contact between the School and the parents. There is a flourishing Parents Association, and regular meetings are held between staff and parents.

The School is a Charitable Trust, under the same Governing Body as Dulwich College Preparatory School, London, although in other respects the two schools are quite separate. The link with Dulwich College is historical only.

Charitable status. Dulwich College Preparatory School Trust is a Registered Charity, number 312715. It exists for the provision of high quality education in a Christian environment.

Dumpton School

Deans Grove House Wimborne Dorset BH21 7AF
Tel: 01202 883818
Fax: 01202 848760
e-mail: secretary@dumpton.com
website: www.dumpton.com

Chairman of Governors: Dr M R Sadler

***Headmaster*: A W Browning**, BSc, PGCE, MA(Ed), CChem, MRSC

Age Range. 2½–13.

Number of Pupils. Boys and Girls: 212 (aged 7–13); 127 (aged 2½–7).

Fees per term (2008-2009). Prep School £3,985; Pre-Prep £2,230; Nursery (per session): £190. Monday to Friday with some Saturday fixtures. All fees include meals. There are no compulsory extras.

In a beautiful rural setting, the school is nevertheless only one mile from Wimborne and there are daily school bus runs to and from the nearby towns of Bournemouth, Poole, Ringwood and Blandford.

Despite record numbers in the school class sizes are small, averaging 16–17 in the Prep School and 13–14 in the Pre-Prep.

Children enjoy excellent teaching as well as incomparable opportunities for Music, Art, Drama and Sport in which the school excels. Dumpton is renowned for its caring approach in which every child is encouraged to identify and develop his or her abilities and personal qualities as fully as possible. It is a very happy and successful school and children regularly win scholarships to their Senior Schools or places at the local Grammar Schools.

Recent developments have included a full-size Astroturf, climbing wall and environmental area, complete with ponds, pontoons and pupil allotments. A new Science Centre will open in 2008.

For a copy of the prospectus, please apply to the Headmaster.

Charitable status. Dumpton School is a Registered Charity, number 306222. It exists to provide education for boys and girls.

Dunhurst

Bedales Junior School

Petersfield Hampshire GU32 2DP
Tel: 01730 300200
Fax: 01730 300600
e-mail: jjarman@bedales.org.uk
website: www.bedales.org.uk

Interim Co-Chairmen of Governors:
D T Handley, CMG, BA
A Redpath

***Head*: Mrs P A Watkins**, BA

Age Range. 8–13.

Number of Pupils. 195: 105 girls (77 day, 28 boarders), 90 boys (66 day, 24 boarders).

Fees per term (2007-2008). Boarders £5,874, Day £4,565.

Dunhurst, the Junior School of Bedales, was founded in 1902 and occupies a part of the Bedales estate. It follows the same general ethos as Bedales and is properly co-educational and non-denominational. The atmosphere is happy, relaxed, friendly and purposeful with a great amount of tolerance, trust and genuine rapport between teachers and pupils. There is much emphasis on personal responsibility and a sense of community.

Dunhurst aims to achieve high academic standards and follows a broad educational programme built around the "core" subjects of English, Mathematics and Science, but giving equal importance to Physical Education, Art, Pottery, Textiles, Workshop, Computing, Comparative Religion, Current Affairs, Geography, History, Dance, Drama and Music. In addition to Class Music for all, pupils' practice time for individual instruments is supervised and fitted into their daily timetable. The aim is to achieve breadth of opportunity and experience as well as the chance to achieve excellence in many different areas.

Matches against other schools take place regularly in Athletics, Cricket, Football, Hockey, Netball, Rounders, Rugby and occasionally Swimming and Tennis. A wide range of other sports and outdoor activities is also offered, including judo and golf.

Dunhurst makes full use of the first rate facilities at Bedales which include the Bedales "Olivier Theatre", a Sports Hall, an all-weather pitch and covered swimming pool. This and the similarity of ethos, makes for an easy transition for pupils moving from Dunhurst to the Senior School at the age of thirteen.

There is a strong boarding community at Dunhurst. A large proportion of older pupils are full boarders and provision is made for flexible boarding for day pupils.

Applicants for both boarder and day places sit residential entrance tests. The main points of entry are at 8+ and 11+. Entry at other ages is dependent on the availability of places.

For information about Dunannie, the Pre-Prep (3–8 years), see the Bedales entry in HMC section.

Charitable status. Bedales School is a Registered Charity, number 307332. It exists to provide a sound education and training for children and young persons of both sexes.

Durlston Court

Becton Lane Barton-on-Sea New Milton Hampshire BH25 7AQ
Tel: 01425 610010
Fax: 01425 622731

e-mail: secretary@durlstoncourt.co.uk
website: www.durlstoncourt.co.uk

Chairman of Governors: Dr A Girling, BDS, LDSRCS

***Headmaster*: D C Wansey**, MA(Ed), CertEd

Age Range. 2–13 Co-educational.

Number of Pupils. 320 Day Pupils.

Fees per term (2008-2009). Kindergarten £1,145; Pre-Prep £2,295; Prep: £3,440 (Year 3), £3,965 (Years 4–8).

Durlston Court Preparatory School, founded in 1903, is a happy and successful day school set in a beautiful campus with impressive facilities.

The school is committed to providing a first-class academic education within the framework of a broad curriculum. Music, Art, Sport and Drama are all strengths of the school and a wide range of clubs and activities is on offer.

Feeding many of the South's leading Senior Schools, Durlston has an enviable academic reputation. Small classes and dedicated teaching have resulted in excellent exam results. Scholarships are offered each year to pupils entering the school who can show Academic, Music, Artistic or Sporting Excellence. Scholarship exams take place at the end of January each year.

Bus services cover routes from the Bournemouth, Brockenhurst, Christchurch, Ferndown, Ringwood, Lymington and Lyndhurst areas.

Parents are most welcome to visit the school by making an appointment or by attending an Open Morning. They may also wish to take advantage of arranging for their child to spend a trial day at Durlston, without obligation.

Further details of the school are available by visiting the school's website or by contacting the Headmaster's Secretary by phone or e-mail, as above.

Charitable status. Durlston Court School is a Registered Charity, number 307325, which exists to provide quality education for children from 2–13 years.

Durston House

12 Castlebar Road Ealing London W5 2DR
Tel: 020 8991 6532
Fax: 020 8991 6547
e-mail: info@durstonhouse.ealing.sch.uk
website: www.durstonhouse.org

Chairman of Governors: A J Allen

***Headmaster*: N I Kendrick**, MA, BEd Hons

Academic Deputy Head: M Turner, BA, PGCE
Administrative Deputy Head: W J Murphy, BA, DipTchg (NZ)
Head of Junior School: C L Englefield, DipTch (NZ)
Head of Pre-Prep: Mrs H L Wyatt, MA, PGCE

Age Range. 4–13.

Number of Boys. 380 Day Boys.

Fees per term (2008-2009). £2,850–£3,830.

An educational Trust, Durston House has charitable status and is ISC accredited. The school has a long history of academic success reflected in Scholarships won at many of the leading senior schools. The emphasis is on high standards of work and targets that commensurate with each pupil's personal development.

Pre-Prep and Junior School (boys aged 4–8) cater for three classes of about sixteen boys in each year group. There is generous ancillary staffing and learning support for specific needs.

In Middle and Upper School (boys aged 9–13) the Headmaster is helped by two Deputy Heads and a team comprising graduate specialist Heads of Department for English, Classics, Mathematics, Modern Languages, Science, ICT, History, Geography, Music, Art, Physical Education and Religious Studies.

Throughout the school there are Activities Programmes offering a wide range of cultural, recreational and sporting pursuits. One of the two playing field complexes has floodlit all-weather facilities and there has been much sporting success in recent years. Extensive use is made of local facilities, especially for drama and swimming. There are fixtures with other prep schools, full participation in IAPS events, and regular expeditions at home and abroad.

Entry assessment procedures take place some six months before boys are due to enter, which is usually in September at age 4, or later if there are vacancies. Durston House is currently seeking to increase its provision of bursaries for boys who would benefit from an education at the school.

Charitable status. Durston House School Educational Trust Limited is a Registered Charity, number 294670. Its aim is the provision and promotion of education.

Eagle House

Sandhurst Berkshire GU47 8PH
Tel: 01344 772134
Fax: 01344 779039
e-mail: info@eaglehouseschool.com
website: www.eaglehouseschool.com

Chairman of Governors: Rear Admiral H A H G Edleston, RN

***Headmaster*: A P N Barnard**, BA Hons, PGCE

Age Range. 3–13.

Number of Children. 293: 24 Boarders, 269 Day Children.

Fees per term (2007-2008). Main School: £5,550 (boarders), £4,125 (day pupils). Pre-Prep: £2,575 (Year 2), £2,500 (Year 1 & Reception). Nursery: £1,485 (5 mornings including lunch).

Eagle House was founded in 1820, and has been on its present site since 1886. The School is administered by a board of governors under the overall control of Wellington College.

Children are prepared for Scholarship and Common Entrance examinations to senior Independent Schools. There are 41 members of staff and two matrons. The average class size is 15.

The school is situated between Sandhurst and Crowthorne in over 30 acres of playing fields which include a large all-weather sports area, a Sports Hall, an indoor heated swimming pool, extensive woodlands, adventure playground and a small lake. The principal games are rugby, netball, hockey, soccer, rounders and cricket. Other sports include athletics, swimming, tennis, cross country, squash, judo, basketball, archery, golf, riding and badminton.

Much emphasis is placed on the Arts and there are excellent facilities for music, art, design and drama. Music scholarships are available for outstanding young musicians.

The school has its own chapel.

Recent major building works have provided a new classroom block, Art Centre and additional computer facilities.

Charitable status. Wellington College is a Registered Charity, number 309093. Eagle House School is owned by Wellington College and is part of the same charity registration.

Eaton House The Manor Pre-Preparatory School

58 Clapham Common Northside London SW4 9RU
Tel: 020 7924 6000
Fax: 020 7924 1530
e-mail: admin@eatonhouseschools.com
website: www.eatonhouseschools.com

Principal: Mrs H Harper

***Head*: Mrs S Segrave**

Age Range. 4–8.
Number of Pupils. 160 Boys.
Fees per term (2008-2009). £3,695.

The quality of an Eaton House The Manor education means that all of the boys leaving the Pre-Prep and Preparatory Schools go on to their first choice of senior school with several winning scholarships. Our approach, which teaches according to ability in small groups, means that we succeed in bringing out the best in each child, fostering a lifelong enthusiasm for learning and attaining the highest academic results. Pupils go on to the most prestigious independent schools including Eaton House The Manor Prep, Westminster Under School, Colet Court, Dulwich College Prep, Westminster Cathedral School, The Dragon School, Ludgrove and Summer Fields.

The curriculum at Eaton House The Manor Pre-Prep is traditional. Strong moral values and a concern for others are emphasised in the classroom and through the House system. Care is taken to develop each childs confidence, and instil a healthy pride in achieving personal goals as well as participating in team games and competitions.

Pupils are taught in a vibrant environment on an exceptionally large site opposite Clapham Common. A recent multi-million pound investment to extend and improve facilities means they benefit from the latest computer technology in the new ICT lab, lavish art and design rooms, an extended library and extremely good music facilities.

The children enjoy many day and weekend trips as part of the curriculum and are encouraged to take part in a host of extra-curricular activities. Displays, concerts and dramatic performances in the school theatre and gym always prove popular, as do the many parent vs pupils sporting events. Parents are encouraged to be closely involved in their children's education, and to take part in many of the children's activities.

Admission to Eaton House The Manor Pre-Preparatory School is non-selective and on a first-come, first-served basis. Parents wishing to enrol their children in the School are advised to register them at birth.

Eaton House The Manor Preparatory School

58 Clapham Common Northside London SW4 9RU
Tel: 020 7924 6000
Fax: 020 7924 1530
e-mail: admin@eatonhouseschools.com
website: www.eatonhouseschools.com

Principal: Mrs H Harper

***Head*: Mr S Hepher**

Age Range. 8–13.
Number of Pupils. 160 Boys.
Fees per term (2008-2009). £4,470.

The quality of an Eaton House The Manor education means that all of the boys leaving the Prep School go on to their first choice of senior school, with several winning scholarships. Our approach, which teaches according to ability in small groups, means that we succeed in bringing out the best in each child, fostering a lifelong enthusiasm for learning and attaining the highest academic results. Pupils go on to the most prestigious independent schools including Westminster, St Paul's, Eton, Harrow, Radley, Charterhouse, Marlborough and Dulwich College.

The curriculum at Eaton House The Manor Prep is traditional. Strong moral values and a concern for others are emphasised in the classroom and through the House system. Care is taken to develop each child's confidence, and instil a healthy pride in achieving personal goals as well as participating in team games and competitions. Every day, children at the Prep School enjoy a reading period after lunch and can attend a supervised homework club at the end of the day.

Pupils are taught in a vibrant environment on an exceptionally large site opposite Clapham Common. A recent multi-million pound investment to extend and improve facilities means they benefit from the latest computer technology in the new ICT lab, lavish art and design rooms, an extended library and extremely good music facilities.

The children enjoy many day and weekend trips as part of the curriculum and are encouraged to take part in a host of extra-curricular activities. Displays, concerts and dramatic performances in the school theatre and gym always prove popular, as do the many parent vs pupils sporting events. Parents are encouraged to be closely involved in their children's education, and to take part in many of the children's activities.

Entry to the Preparatory School is at 8 years of age by examination and interview. Places are offered at 7+ and 8+. Interviews occur a year before the child's projected start date, backed up by a report from their current Pre-Preparatory School.

Eaton House The Vale

2 Elvaston Place Kensington London SW7 5QH
Tel: 020 7584 9515
Fax: 020 7584 8368
e-mail: admin@eatonhouseschools.com
website: www.eatonhouseschools.com

Principal: Mrs H Harper

***Head*: Mr Robin Greenwood**

Age Range. 4–11 co-educational.
Number of Pupils. 100.
Fees per term (2008-2009). £3,695.

Centrally situated in South Kensington, near Hyde Park, Eaton House The Vale offers a personalised education of exceptional quality to both boys and girls. Conveniently situated in a beautiful building, its pupils benefit from being near the centre of one of the most vibrant and exciting cities in the world, and undertake a traditional curriculum that is brought alive by the many trips and visits they enjoy. A recent Ofsted report commented on the excellent teaching and pastoral care of the children (view it in full at www.ofsted.gov.uk).

Eaton House The Vale takes children from the age of 4 and from the beginning emphasises the core subjects of Maths and English. Intensive teaching methods mean that all pupils attain a high academic standard and receive a strong grounding in a whole range of subjects from a very early age. The high teacher/pupil ratio and amount of individual attention each child can therefore expect means Eaton House The Vale pupils are independent thinkers whose creativity and spirit are encouraged in a caring environment.

Boys take their Preparatory School entrance examinations at 8 and are very successful in achieving their first choice of school. Many go on to our sister school, Eaton House The Manor Preparatory School, while others achieve places at London Day Schools such as Colet Court, Sussex House, Westminster Under School and Westminster Cathedral Choir School, as well as notable boarding schools such as Ludgrove, The Dragon and Windlesham House.

Girls are thoroughly prepared for both the London Day Schools and Common Entrance exams at 11, with excellent results. Teaching is in classes of no more than 10, and a small number of places are available for girls to join at 9 and enjoy the advantage of our intensive preparation. Girls move on to highly-regarded academic institutions such as St Paul's Girls' School, The Godolphin and Latymer School and Francis Holland School among the day schools and St Mary's Calne, Heathfield St Mary's and Woldingham among boarding schools.

Eaton House The Vale is a non-selective school; admittance is on a first-come, first-served basis at the age of 4 and early application is advised. Girls wishing to join at 9 are assessed via a written paper.

Eaton Square School

79 Eccleston Square London SW1V 1PP
Tel: 020 7931 9469
Fax: 020 7828 0164
e-mail: admissions@eatonsquareschool.com
website: www.eatonsquareschool.com

***Headmaster*: Mr Paul David**, BEd Hons

Age Range. 2½–13 Co-educational.

Number of Pupils. 529: 280 boys, 249 girls.

Fees per term (2007-2008). Nursery £765–£3,410, Pre-Prep £4,400, Prep £4,450.

Entry. Early Registration for Nursery places, Early registration and assessment for Pre-Prep and Prep School admissions. Priority given to internal Nursery candidates.

Contact. *Pre-Prep & Prep*: Penelope Stitcher, Registrar, e-mail: admissions@eatonsquareschool.com.

Nursery: Rohan Kara, Assistant Registrar, e-mail: rohan.kara@eatonsquareschool.com.

Ethos. Eaton Square School is one of the few co-educational day schools in the heart of London offering nursery, pre-preparatory and preparatory education. The School maintains high standards and encourages in every child an enthusiasm for learning, good manners, self-discipline and, in all things, a determination to do their best and realise their potential. The ISI inspection (2005) indicated that personal development of pupils was a notable strength of the school. The School offers a stretching, challenging approach to learning that emphasises achievement and builds confidence. Great emphasis is placed on experiential learning including ski trips, classical tours of Rome and Pompeii, and a half term spent in a French château in Sauveterre in Year Seven.

Academic Life. The form teachers teach general subjects to their classes up to the age of 8. Thereafter, specialist subject teachers continue the curriculum in preparation for the Common Entrance Examinations for senior English Independent Schools, for girls at age 11 and boys at age 13. A wide range of subjects is encompassed in the curriculum, including English, Mathematics, Science, History, Geography, French, Latin, Art, Drama, Music and Physical Education. ICT is introduced from the age of 3 and it is an integral part of the syllabus. The various parts of the school are served by a school wide network, allowing pupils and staff to access their work from any computer. There is a computer suite in each of the three school buildings. In addition, all Prep School classrooms are equipped with interactive whiteboards and data projectors. The School also benefits from a new Art and Science block with separate Science laboratory and a wonderfully equipped Art, Design and Technology Studio.

Pupils are prepared for entry into both selective London day schools and leading boarding schools through London Day School examinations at 11+ and Common Entrance examinations at 13+.

Sport & the Arts. Sport and Physical Education include Swimming, Fencing, Gymnastics, Football, Rugby, Cricket and Tennis and the School has successful teams competing against other London schools. Music is a flourishing department within the School. Appreciation of music, singing, composition, music theory and recorder tuition are taught by specialists at all ages. There is an active School Choir, an orchestra and a variety of ensembles that rehearse throughout the week. Instruction in Music, Art and Design Technology is included for all children from Nursery School upwards, as part of the Curriculum. Individual Music lessons on a wide variety of instruments are available during the day and after school (for an additional fee) from Year 2 upwards. Drama is integrated within the curriculum and each child takes part in at least two public productions every year. The Prep School production for children in Years 4–8 is held at a West End Theatre during the Summer Term. The Art and Design room provides an outstanding resource and is equipped with a wide selection of facilities, including a kiln for ceramic work. Projects undertaken in Design and Technology include work with resistant materials, textiles, ceramics, electronics, mechanisms and computer control. The Art syllabus includes painting, drawing, printing, sculpture and sketchbook work.

Further information and a prospectus may be obtained from the Registrar.

Edenhurst Preparatory School

Westlands Avenue Newcastle-under-Lyme Staffordshire ST5 2PU
Tel: 01782 619348
Fax: 01782 662402
e-mail: headmaster@edenhurst.co.uk
website: www.edenhurst.co.uk

***Headmaster*: N H F Copestick**, BSc (University of St Andrews), CertEd (The Queen's College, Oxford)

Age Range. 3–13.

Number of Pupils. Boys 110, Girls 100.

Fees per term (2008-2009). £2,233–£2,877.

A family run day school established in 1961 by the present Headmaster's father.

The Victorian main building is set in a pleasant suburban area and boasts many purpose built additions, notably a well-equipped laboratory and an ITC centre.

Edenhurst has an enviable local reputation in preparing pupils for entrance examinations to local independent secondary schools and also for the Common Entrance 13+ Examinations. Results in National Curriculum tests have demonstrated consistently high standards of pupil achievement.

Particular strengths of the school include the music department which offers tuition in nine instruments. The orchestra and choir perform publicly many times throughout the year.

The new Full Day-Care Nursery offers places to babies from 3 months in a brand new centre providing quality care in an exciting yet safe environment.

Edge Grove

Aldenham Village Radlett Herts WD25 8NL
Tel: 01923 855724
Fax: 01923 859920
e-mail: headmaster@edgegrove.indschools.co.uk
website: www.edgegrove.co.uk

The school is a non-profit making Trust administered by a Board of Governors.

Chairman of Governors: N A Shryane, MBE, BA, MPhil

***Acting Headmaster & Second Master*: K A Doble**, BA, PDM, PGCE

Headmaster from January 2009: M J Davies, BA Hons, PGCE

Age Range. 3–13.

Number of Pupils. Day: 120 (Pre-Prep), 194 (Prep); Boarders 63.

Fees per term (2008-2009). Pre-Prep £1,415–£2,665; Day £3,495–£4,185; Boarding (weekly/full) £4,675–£5,705.

Edge Grove is situated in 28 acres of glorious Hertfordshire parkland. We are approximately 5 minutes' drive from both the M1 and M25 motorways and only 15 miles from Central London. Heathrow and Luton airports are 30 minutes' drive by car.

The Pre-Prep (Hart House) caters for children between the ages of 3 and 7 and is situated within the grounds, close to the main Preparatory school. The Early Years Department was moved into a new wing of the building in 2007. The children use many of the main Preparatory School's facilities. The main points of entry are at Nursery (3+) and Reception (4+).

Boys and girls normally join the Preparatory department, Edge Grove, at 7+ and all are prepared for the Common Entrance and Scholarship Examinations. Pupils are taught in co-educational classes and they move on to a wide variety of Senior Independent schools across the country. There is an excellent record of Scholarship and Common Entrance success; indeed, forty Scholarships were gained between 2005 and 2007. The Music, Art and Sport are also strong and there is a great range of extra-curricular activities on offer.

Facilities include a modern teaching block, purpose-built Pre-Prep, Science Laboratories, School Chapel, Music School and Sports Hall. We have two ICT suites and the school has further upgraded its ICT facilities to incorporate mobile trolleys of laptops. Edge Grove has two Art studios, a heated swimming pool and nine acres of games fields, as well as an artificial sports surface.

The main sports are Netball, Rounders and Hockey for girls and Football, Rugby, Cricket and Hockey for boys. Swimming, Cross-Country, Archery, Tennis and Squash are also popular and are played by both boys and girls. Twenty-five pupils currently represent the county and the Region in a variety of different sports.

Charitable status. Edge Grove School Trust Ltd is a Registered Charity, number 311054.

Edgeborough

Frensham Farnham Surrey GU10 3AH
Tel: 01252 792495
Fax: 01252 795156
e-mail: office@edgeborough.co.uk
website: www.edgeborough.co.uk

Chairman of Governors: T Elliott, FCA

***Headmaster*: R A Jackson**, MA Cantab, PGCE
***Headmistress*: Mrs M A Jackson**, BEd Hons London

Age Range. 2–13.

Number of Children. Boarders 70, Day 207, Pre Prep 96, Nursery 44.

Fees per term (2008-2009). Upper Prep £4,325, Lower Prep £3,885, Pre Prep £2,655. Weekly Boarding £1,230.

Edgeborough is an independent school which focuses on the individual and offers a wealth of opportunities. The school's motto is *Carpe Diem*. Founded in 1906 in Guildford, Edgeborough moved to its current site, the beautiful Frensham Place, in 1939. With its 50 acres of mixed woodland and playing fields, Edgeborough offers a wonderful environment for children.

The school is distinctive in its setup and comprises of four departments: Nursery (2–4), Pre Prep (4–7). Lower Prep (7–10) and Upper Prep (10–13), all closely linked yet with their own character and individuality. This specialism enables us to tailor carefully the academic programme to the ages and stages of the pupils, and the aim is to provide an all-round education of high quality for all. From Edgeborough, boys and girls go to a wide range of top Independent Schools at 13+ via Common Entrance or Scholarship and we expect 20% of our pupils to gain scholarships and other awards in their final year.

As well as the spacious grounds and playing fields, the range of facilities is a strength of the school. They include well-equipped classrooms for all the departments, a stunning new Science and Technology Building, Art and Pottery Centre, fully-equipped Theatre with adjoining Dance and Drama Studio, large Sports Hall, floodlit Astroturf, heated Swimming Pool, Golf Course, Children's Farm and Adventure Playground. This enables the school to pursue a wide and varied programme of extra-curricular activities including sport, music, art and drama. In addition to the main sports of rugby, soccer, cricket, hockey, netball, rounders, lacrosse and athletics pupils can also participate in golf, basketball, badminton, tennis, swimming, climbing, gymnastics and canoeing. There are numerous school visits organised for the pupils, including a residential week in France, an annual ski trip, and sporting and cultural tours to South Africa.

Weekly or flexible boarding is a very popular option, and Edgeborough's distinctive warm and friendly atmosphere is rooted deep in its traditional family values of courtesy and care for the individual, developed over many years.

Entry to the school is by interview and informal assessment. Further information and a prospectus can be obtained from the Admissions Secretary.

'*Edgeborough provides an all-round education of high quality for all pupils*.'

Charitable status. Edgeborough Educational Trust is a Registered Charity, number 312051.

The Edinburgh Academy Junior School

10 Arboretum Road Edinburgh EH3 5PL
Tel: 0131 552 3690
Fax: 0131 551 2660
e-mail: juniorschool@edinburghacademy.org.uk
website: www.edinburghacademy.org.uk

Chairman of Directors: S A Mackintosh, MA, LLB, WS

***Headteacher*: Mrs C S Bashford**, BA Edinburgh

Age Range. 2–11.

Number of Pupils. 320 (Primary 1–6), 90 (Nursery).

Fees per term (from April 2008). Nursery £1,240–£1,950; Primary 1–6 £1,950–£2,440.

The Edinburgh Academy Junior School was founded in 1824 and the Headteacher is a member of IAPS. The Junior School is in a separate location but is an integral part of The Edinburgh Academy. (*Further information about The Edinburgh Academy will be found in the HMC section.*)

The whole school is now fully co-educational.

The Early Years Department takes boys and girls from age 2 to $7^1/_2$, the Upper Years Department from $7^1/_2$ to 11. A Nursery Class for boys and girls aged 2 and over is attached to the Early Years Department.

Boys and girls are prepared for entry to the Senior School and work is arranged to ensure a smooth transition from one to the other at the age of about 11.

The School is situated in a most attractive part of the city, with its own rugby and cricket pitches, sports centre and athletics track on site. The Edinburgh Academy Junior School produces very high levels of performance in all areas due to small classes and a dedicated teaching staff. The extra-curricular activities are extensive.

The School encourages pupils to enjoy life in a very real and participative sense.

Prospectus from and enquiries to The Admissions Secretary.

Elleray Preparatory School
(Junior School of Windermere St Anne's)

Windermere Cumbria LA23 1AP
Tel: 015394 43308
Fax: 015394 46803
e-mail: elleray@wsaschool.com
website: www.wsaschool.com

Chairman of Governors: Mr Peter Redhead

***Headmaster*: Mr B C Freeman**, BEd Hons, PGDip

Type of School. Co-educational Day and Boarding School with Nursery.

Age Range. 2–11.

Number of Pupils. 82 girls, 64 boys.

Fees per term (2008-2009). Day (including lunch): Pre-School and Reception £2,040, Forms 1–2 £2,735, Forms 3–6 £3,695. Boarding: £6,210 (weekly), £6,560 (full).

The Purpose of the School. Windermere St Anne's and Elleray School – a community with an international outlook which develops courageous, responsible and inspiring individuals. Elleray is an Independent Preparatory School for boys and girls from 2–11 years, set in 17 acres of grounds in the heart of the English Lake District.

At Elleray we aim to ensure that our children enjoy the excitement of learning and surprise themselves by the standards they are able to achieve. A school of 150 means that the 'family-feel' of Elleray is shared by everyone. Children are given the opportunity to make the most of their childhood in this outstanding location which is at once safe and inspiring – and which gives us all the opportunity to explore – in the widest sense of the word. We learn about the world and ourselves in surroundings of exceptional beauty and interest.

Academic Ethos. Elleray offers a truly broad curriculum and gives your child a head start in life. All our Form Tutors are specialist primary teachers and their skill and experience ensure a good understanding of the core learning necessary for real academic progress. The majority of pupils achieve results well ahead of the national average in the Standard Attainment Tests at seven and eleven years and are successful in winning places at the secondary schools of their choice, whether by passing a school's own Entrance Examination or Common Entrance papers. Elleray children shine in interviews. We offer both Extension Learning and Educational Support if necessary. Subject specialists teach Art, Drama, Dance, French, Games, Design and Technology, Music, Physical Education, and our unique Adventure! lessons. Our children enjoy lessons. They recognise their own progress and learn to take joint responsibility for it with their teachers and parents.

Sport for All. Elleray offers a wide range of challenging and enjoyable sports for all, taught by specialist staff: Football, Netball, Dance, Sailing, Swimming, Cricket, Rounders, Hockey, Adventure Playground, Gymnastics, Athletics, Tag Rugby, Cross-Country Running, Rugby, Tennis.

Clubs and Activities. *The Arts*: Art Club, Choir, ICT, Drama, Infant Cookery, Individual Music lessons including piano, strings, woodwind, brass and guitar, Le Club Francais, Library, Orchestra, Recorder groups, Craft Club.

Sporting Activities: Athletics, Judo, Badminton, Gym Club, Cricket, Dance (tap, jazz, modern, ballet), Fell walking, Football, Netball, Rounders, Sailing, Swimming, Tennis coaching, Tag Rugby, Rugby, Adventure Club, Dens.

Pastoral and Boarding. At Elleray we take good care of children. A zest for life and a sense of humour are encouraged. Sound discipline and clear boundaries encourage appropriate behaviour. Elleray children are friendly. Elleray boarders live in at the Senior School, Windermere St Anne's, with their own bedrooms, bathroom and sitting room and a resident houseparent. They are very much part of life in the evenings and weekends.

At Elleray, children are encouraged to understand themselves and to change what they do not like. Leadership and teamworking skills are constantly developed and there is a thriving School Council and House System.

We are an International School and courtesy, thoughtfulness towards other people and care of ourselves are all part of the Elleray spirit.

Charitable status. Windermere Educational Trust Limited is a Registered Charity, number 526973. It exists to provide education of the highest quality.

Elm Green Preparatory School

Parsonage Lane Little Baddow Chelmsford Essex CM3 4SU
Tel: 01245 225230
Fax: 01245 226008
e-mail: admin@elmgreen.essex.sch.uk
website: www.elmgreenschool.co.uk

***Principal*: Mrs A E Milner**, BTech Hons, MSc

Age Range. Co-educational 4–11 years.

Number of Day Pupils. 220: 115 Boys, 105 Girls.

Fees per term (from April 2008). £2,266.

Religious affiliation. Non-denominational.

Elm Green was founded in 1944 and enjoys a lovely rural setting, surrounded by National Trust woodland.

Children enter in the September after their fourth birthday and in their final year are prepared for scholarships, entry to other independent schools and for entry to maintained schools. Many of the pupils take the Essex 11+ and the school has an excellent record of success in this examination.

The school maintains a high standard of academic education giving great emphasis to a secure foundation in the basic subjects whilst offering a wide curriculum with specialist teaching in many areas.

Information technology and design technology form an integral part of the curriculum and there are flourishing art, music and PE departments. The school competes successfully in a wide range of sports – football, rugby, netball, swimming, cricket, gymnastics, athletics, rounders and tennis.

There are many extra-curricular activities and all the children are encouraged to work and to play hard in order to fulfil their potential.

The school aims to foster intellectual curiosity and to encourage individual and corporate work. Kindness and thought for others are given a high priority.

The Elms

Colwall Malvern Worcestershire WR13 6EF
Tel: 01684 540344
Fax: 01684 541174
e-mail: office@elmsschool.co.uk
website: www.elmsschool.co.uk

Founded 1614.

Chairman of the Governors: Mr C F R Potter, OBE, MA

***Head Master*: L A C Ashby**, BA Hons, CertEd

Age Range. 3–13.

Number of Pupils. Main School: 133: 79 Boys, 64 Girls. 89 boarders. Pre-Prep: 57.

Fees per term (2008-2009). Full board £5,960; Day board £5,510; Pre-Prep (3–7) £2,125–£3,525. Fees are payable termly. There are no compulsory extras.

The Elms is run as a charitable, non-profit making company with a Board of Governors. Children are taken in the Main School from the age of rising 8 and there is a Pre-Preparatory Department for 3–7 year olds.

An experienced staff and small classes ensure attention to each pupil's special needs and a high academic standard is maintained to CE and Scholarship levels. Small numbers help to create a family atmosphere with comfortable accommodation and a resident Headmaster and staff.

Gardens, fields and woodland with stream in 150 acres surround the school, beautifully set at the foot of the Malvern Hills, and include fine playing fields for Rugby, Association Football, Hockey, Cricket, Athletics. Netball and Rounders. Facilities include a Sports Hall, Tennis Courts, Laboratory, Computer Room, new teaching block, CDT Centre and an Art Room with facilities for Pottery. There is also a heated indoor swimming pool. The children manage a small farming enterprise; and many ride on school ponies or bring their own.

Bursaries available for sons and daughters of Servicemen, clergymen and schoolmasters, and there are competitive awards.

Charitable status. The Elms (Colwall) Limited is a Registered Charity, number 527252. It exists to provide education for boys and girls.

The Elms
Junior School to Trent College

Derby Road Long Eaton Nottingham NG10 4AD
Tel: 0115 849 4942
Fax: 0115 849 4943
e-mail: elms.school@trentcollege.net
website: www.elmsschool.net

Chairman of Governors: C M McDowell, FCIB

***Head*: K B Morrow**, BA Hons QTS, NPQH

Age Range. 3–11 co-educational.

Number of Pupils. 330: 175 Boys,155 Girls.

Fees per term (2007-2008). £1,981–£2,146.

The Elms was opened by Trent College in September 1999 and has enjoyed incredible success in its expansion to a two-form entry, gender-balanced, co-educational primary school.

Adopting Trent College's vision of a broad and balanced curriculum, The Elms offers academic, artistic, personal and sporting challenges for children in the early stages of their lives, whilst aiding their development as sensitive and caring members of the school community.

The Elms comprises 2 main locations on the campus: Elms Lower School, including the new Bungalow Nursery, and Elms Upper School, a newly constructed building for our 8–11 year olds. Facilities include Science lab, Music rooms, ICT suite and library as well as bright, airy and well-resourced classrooms.

In The Elms Lower School we are proud of the extensive and outstanding Foundation Stage provision allowing us to plan an exciting and stimulating learning environment for our youngest pupils.

High standards of teaching and pastoral care ensure that our pupils' needs are met and the close relationship we have with parents encourages a true partnership for educational development.

In the David Wigglesworth building at The Elms Lower School we have a spacious, well-equipped hall/gym while for Games we access the all-weather surfaces and games fields as well as the Trent College swimming pool.

Music is an essential part of the school curriculum with over 90% of our Key Stage 2 pupils playing orchestral instruments, taking part in concerts and ensembles. Our ISC inspection report testifies to the excellence of our music curriculum and teaching.

The Elms benefits from the rural nature of the huge Trent College campus yet is close to all the local amenities of road networks. School buses shared with Trent College allow some of our older pupils to travel independently to and from school while our before and after school care systems provide extended day provision for busy families.

For our Juniors there is a wide range of lunch-time and after-school activities and a very comprehensive fixture list with a range of local schools.

Charitable status. Trent College is a Registered Charity, number 527180.

Elstree School

Woolhampton Reading Berks RG7 5TD
Tel: 0118 971 3302
Fax: 0118 971 4280
e-mail: secretary@elstreeschool.org.uk
website: www.elstreeschool.org.uk

The School is an educational trust controlled by a Board of Governors.

Chairman of Governors: Nicholas Bomford, Esq

***Headmaster*: M J Sayer**, MA Cantab

Deputy Headmaster: S C Bates, BEd

Age Range. Boys 3–13, Girls 3–7.

Number of Pupils. Prep School (age 7–13): 190 boys (100 boarders, 90 day boys); Pre-Prep School (age 3–7): 70 boys and girls.

Fees per term (2008-2009). Boarders £6,450, Day Boys £4,900, Pre-Prep School £2,810.

Elstree is set in its own 150 acres in the beautiful Berkshire countryside, a quiet location but very accessible. The School moved to Woolhampton, between Reading and Newbury, in 1939, after nearly 100 years at Elstree, Hertfordshire. At the heart of the School is a magnificent Georgian house which has been modernized and extended. Facilities and accommodation are of a very high standard.

Elstree prepares boys for entrance to Britain's leading independent senior schools and has a fine Open Scholarship record. Boys play Football, Rugby, Hockey, Cricket and many other sports. Equal emphasis is given to an appreciation of music, art, drama and to life skills such as Information Technology.

Charitable status. Elstree School Limited is a Registered Charity, number 309101. It exists to establish, maintain and carry on schools for the education of boys and girls and to give such pupils general or specialised instruction of the highest class, and as an educational charity to promote education generally.

The English School
Kuwait

PO Box 379 13004 Safat Kuwait
Tel: 00 965 563 7205/7206
Fax: 00 965 563 7147
e-mail: admin@tes.edu.kw
website: www.tes.edu.kw

Sponsor: M A R Al-Bahar

Chair of the Governing Committee: Brigadier James Mackaness

***Headmaster*: J A Allcott**

Age Range. 2–13.
Number of Pupils. 530.
Fees per annum (2008-2009). Nursery (PreKG and KG) KD1,305; Pre-Preparatory (Rec, Year 1 and Year 2) KD2,125; Preparatory (Years 3–8) KD2,530.

The English School, founded in 1953 under the auspices of the British Embassy, is the longest established school in Kuwait catering for the expatriate community. The School operates as a non-profit making, private co-educational establishment providing the highest standards in education for children of Pre-Kindergarten to Preparatory School age. The roll is predominantly British as are the resources and texts. With the exception of foreign language teachers, all teaching staff are British and qualified in the United Kingdom. Following its relocation to new premises, The English School is housed in well-resourced and spacious, fully air-conditioned buildings in a pleasant residential suburb of Kuwait City.

Responsibility for the School is vested in the Governing Committee whose members are appointed and serve in a voluntary capacity.

The curriculum is British-oriented, aiming for a blend of traditional standards and contemporary innovations. The National Curriculum for England and Wales is used as the core for the curriculum. Formal End-of-Key Stage assessment of attainment takes place in Years 2 and 6. In addition the pupils are prepared for entrance tests to other schools, including Independent Schools Examinations Board (Common Entrance) Examinations at 11+, 12+ and 13+. Class teachers are supported by specialist coordinators in Art and Design and Technology, Information Technology, Music, Library and PE and Games. Music is taught to all ages and French is introduced in Year 4.

The School seeks to provide a learning environment within which the children will be stimulated to develop their individual capacity for achievement to its fullest potential. Each individual is directed towards self-discipline and respect for himself/herself and for others. Strong emphasis is placed on academic study, together with a wide range of non-academic activities to provide a balance. The School aims to ensure that, by achieving standards equivalent to those of independent schools in Britain, our pupils are well prepared for the subsequent stages of their academic development whether in Britain, Kuwait or elsewhere in the world.

All applications for entry are addressed on a personal and individual basis. The Headmaster and teaching staff are always happy to meet prospective pupils and their parents. A visit to the School, where possible, is encouraged in order for each family's needs and requirements to be discussed.

Eton End School

35 Eton Road Datchet Slough Berkshire SL3 9AX
Tel: 01753 541075
Fax: 01753 541123
e-mail: admin@etonend.org
website: www.etonend.org

Chairman of Board of Governors: D Losse, Esq

***Headmistress*: Mrs V M Pilgerstorfer**, BA Hons, PGCE

Age Range. Girls 3–11, Boys 3–7.
Number of Pupils. 205: 168 girls, 37 boys.
Fees per term (2008-2009). £1,380–£2,930. Lunch: £2.70 per day.

The school is a day school set within six acres of spacious grounds. All the classrooms are purpose-built and modern, offering excellent facilities, including specialist rooms, eg art and craft, music, science laboratory, large library. There is a large well-equipped gym, two hard tennis/netball courts, a football and sports field. Boys are prepared for all preparatory schools in the area. Girls leave after the 11+ Entrance Examination often gaining Scholarships. Small classes allow each child to reach their maximum potential in a happy caring environment.

The school's origins lie in the traditions inspired by educationalist, Charlotte Mason, who founded the PNEU movement.

Charitable status. Eton End School Trust (Datchet) Limited is a Registered Charity, number 310644. The aim of the charity is to provide a well-balanced education for children whose parents wish them to attend Eton End School.

Eversfield Preparatory School

Warwick Road Solihull West Midlands B91 1AT
Tel: 0121 705 0354
Fax: 0121 709 0168
e-mail: enquiries@eversfield.co.uk
website: www.eversfield.co.uk

Chairman of Governors: Dr S J Chamberlain

***Headmaster*: R Yates**, BA, PGCE, LPSH

Age Range. 2½–11 Co-educational.
Number of Pupils. 260.
Fees per term (2008-2009). £826–£2,733 according to age and inclusive of lunch and books.

Eversfield is a Day Preparatory School on an attractive site in the centre of Solihull preparing boys and girls for entry to the leading Senior Schools in the West Midlands and beyond.

The curriculum values academic excellence and prepares pupils for National Curriculum Tests and 11+ examinations. At the same time it nurtures the creative, sporting, technical and social skills of each pupil. There are excellent facilities and opportunities for sports, music, the arts, and a programme of extra-curricular and holiday activities.

The School encourages a strong sense of community where small classes, a well-ordered routine and good pastoral support help pupils to feel secure and develop their self-confidence. Eversfield promotes high moral standards and responsible attitudes based on clear and relevant Christian teaching.

Charitable status. Eversfield Preparatory School Trust Limited is a Registered Charity, number 528966. It is under the direction of a Board of Governors and exists to carry out the work of an Independent Preparatory School.

Ewell Castle Junior School

Glyn House Church Street Ewell Surrey KT17 2PA
Tel: 020 8394 1440
Fax: 020 8394 2220
e-mail: juniorschool@ewellcastle.co.uk
website: www.ewellcastle.co.uk

Chairman of Governors: D C M Hill

Principal: A J Tibble, BSc, PGCE, NPQH

***Head of Junior School*: Mrs H M Crossley**, MA, BEd, CertEd

Deputy Head of Junior School: Mrs S Radburn, MA, BEd

Age Range. 3–11.
Number of Pupils. 200 Boys and Girls.
Fees per term (2008-2009). £1,100–£2,290.

Ewell Castle Junior School is a co-educational day school, located on two sites in the heart of Ewell Village. Nursery to Year 2 pupils (3–7 years) are based at Chessington Lodge in Spring Street, while Years 3 to 6 (7–11 years) are based at Glyn House in Church Street, opposite the Senior School (360 boys, 11–18 years), with which a close liaison is maintained.

Those entering the Nursery may attend for a half-day until they are ready for full-time education. There are no entry requirements for Nursery children, but older pupils attend the school for a day's assessment, which will include tests in Mathematics and English. Girls are prepared for local independent senior schools, whilst boys may proceed to the Senior School, for which a number of aided places and scholarships are available at 11+ entry. All pupils are prepared for entry at 11+ to selective state schools. The National Curriculum is incorporated within a broad curriculum.

The creative arts play an important part in School life. Apart from the timetabled music lessons, there is the opportunity for pupils to learn a variety of instruments under professional teachers. Drama productions take place regularly. Pupils' art work can be seen on display in the local community and is always to be found decorating the School walls. All pupils join in various sporting activities as part of the weekly curriculum. In addition, a wide variety of activities are available after school and during the holidays.

All pupils use the 5 acres of attractive gardens and playing fields at Glyn House for outdoor play and games lessons. In addition, Junior School pupils benefit from full access to the excellent sporting facilities, including a sports hall and playing fields on the 15 acre site at The Castle. The main games are football, netball, cricket and tennis. There are also athletics and cross country events, including a School sports day. All pupils receive swimming instruction.

Outside speakers include police liaison officers and actors and authors who conduct workshops with pupils. A number of visits occur to places of interest which are relevant to a particular area of study. There are regular School visits abroad.

The School also enjoys close links with St Mary's Church, where regular assemblies are held throughout the year.

The Junior School aims to provide a caring, responsive and stimulating environment in which pupils are able to fulfill their potential. Hard work and high standards together with courtesy and consideration to others are of prime importance.

Charitable status. Ewell Castle Junior School is a Registered Charity, number 312079. It exists to provide education for boys and girls.

Exeter Cathedral School

The Chantry Palace Gate Exeter Devon EX1 1HX
Tel: 01392 255298
Fax: 01392 422718
e-mail: reception@exetercs.org
website: www.exetercs.org

Chairman of Governors: The Dean of Exeter

***Headmaster*: B J McDowell**

Age Range. 3–13.
Number of Pupils. 19 Boarders, 177 Day Pupils.
Fees per term (2008-2009). Day Pupils (excluding lunches): £1,688–£2,856. Boarding (in addition to Day fees): £1,814 (full), £1,612 (weekly).

Founded in 1159, the Cathedral School provides the Boy and Girl Choristers for Exeter Cathedral and educates 150 other pupils to the same high standard.

Entry is normally at 3 or 4 to the Pre-Preparatory Department or 7 or 8 years into the Prep School, though pupils may be accepted later. Entrance assessments for 7+ or later entry are by arrangement with the Headmaster.

Voice Trials for Choristers are held in November, or by arrangement, and successful applicants become probationers, upon completion of which they enter the Choir.

There are 18 scholarships available for Boy Choristers and probationers which can be worth up to 25% of the tuition fee. Scholarships of up to 20% are also available to Girl Choristers. Awards are also available to non-choristers, details of which can be given on application.

Pupils are prepared for Scholarship and Common Entrance to Independent and Maintained Senior Schools by a full-time staff of 17, assisted by other part-time teachers including 11 teachers of musical instruments.

There are no Saturday lessons, though day pupils sometimes join boarders in weekend or after school activities. The curriculum encompasses all National Curriculum and Common Entrance subjects, including Modern Foreign Languages, Latin and Greek.

In the Michaelmas Term, rugby football and netball are the team sports. Netball, soccer and hockey are played in the Lent Term. During the Trinity Term, cricket, rounders, athletics and swimming are all pursued competitively. Swimming takes place all year round.

Musical activities, including school choir, orchestra and ensembles for string, woodwind, brass and jazz instrumentalists are available to all pupils.

Daily morning worship takes place in the Cathedral or in The Chapter House led by the School Chaplain or Lay Pastor.

The buildings are located around the Close and include a Science Laboratory, a gymnasium and Kalendar Hall (the music and drama school), as well as a large portion of the 14th Century Deanery. There is a Food Technology Centre, Pottery and Design and Technology Department and Computer Centre.

For games, use is made of playing fields, swimming baths and other facilities situated short distances away in the city.

Charitable status. Exeter Cathedral School, as part of the Foundation of the Chapter of Exeter which is an ecclesiastical charity, is a Registered Charity and exists to provide education for boys and girls.

Exeter Junior School

Victoria Park Road Exeter Devon EX2 4NS
Tel: 01392 273679
Fax: 01392 498144
e-mail: admissions@exeterschool.org.uk
website: www.exeterschool.org.uk

Co-educational Day School.

Chairman of Board of Governors: Mrs B Meeke, LLB

***Headmistress*: Mrs Alison J Turner**, MA

Age Range. 7–11.

Number of Pupils. 178: 111 Boys, 67 Girls.

Fees per term (2008-2009). £2,800.

Exeter Junior School is housed in a spacious, Victorian building in the grounds of Exeter School. The close proximity of the Junior School to the Senior School enables the pupils to take full advantage of the facilities on site, which include a chapel, music centre, science laboratories, sports hall with dance studio, fitness suite and squash courts, outdoor heated swimming pool, playing fields, all-weather astroturf arena and tennis courts.

In addition to this the Junior School retains its own playground and green space, therefore giving the School a separate and clearly recognisable identity.

Liaison between Junior and Senior staff is a positive feature of the thriving and expanding Junior School.

The School aims to offer, in academic, cultural and sporting terms, the widest possible range of opportunities thus helping each pupil to identify the activities which will give the greatest scope for development and fulfilment in years to come. Music, drama, art, sport and expeditions all have an important part to play in the life of the school.

Pupils enter the school at age 7 or 8, and entrance is by informal assessment in January. This includes a report from the child's previous school, classroom sessions in the company of other prospective pupils, and literacy, numeracy and general intelligence tasks.

Pupils are offered an academic programme which incorporates the National Curriculum model with the addition of French which is introduced from Year 3.

Specialist teaching is offered from the outset, with the additional support of Senior School staff in science, French, music and ICT.

A wide variety of clubs are available during the week including textiles, cookery, calligraphy, football, hockey, netball, rugby, chess and drama.

(*For further information about the Senior School, see Exeter School entry in HMC section.*)

Charitable status. Exeter School is a Registered Charity, number 1093080. It exists to provide education for children.

Fairfield Preparatory School

Leicester Road Loughborough Leics LE11 2AE
Tel: 01509 215172
Fax: 01509 238648
e-mail: admin@fairfield.leics.sch.uk
website: www.fairfield.leics.sch.uk

Chairman of the Governors: H Michael Pearson, BA(Econ), LLB, ACIS

***Headmaster*: R Outwin-Flinders**, BEd Hons

Age Range. 4–11.

Number of Pupils. 260 Boys, 236 Girls (all day)

Fees per term (2007-2008). £2,259. Lunches and individual music lessons extra.

Fairfield School is the Preparatory School of the Loughborough Endowed Schools, the two Upper Schools being Loughborough Grammar School for Boys (*see HMC entry*) and Loughborough High School for Girls (*see GSA entry*).

The three Schools are governed by the same Governing Body and share a fine campus to the west of the Leicester Road, with their private roads free of through traffic.

The aim of Fairfield is to give a broad-based education appropriate for the needs of the children in our care. In the process, they will be prepared for their secondary education. For most this will mean either Loughborough Grammar School or High School, although some children move elsewhere.

Our intention is also to teach children how to live together in a community and to show respect for the property and feelings of others. We hope that time spent at Fairfield will be thoroughly enjoyable.

Whilst our children are prepared for entry to the Upper Schools, this is certainly not our only goal. In addition to all National Curriculum subjects French is taught and there are specialist rooms for ICT, Science and Music. Our Gymnasium is extremely well equipped.

The children are introduced to a wide variety of sporting and recreational activities. Team games are encouraged for the spirit of cooperation and working together which the School aims to foster. Activities of a more individual nature also play an increasing part in the life of the School. Winter games include Soccer, Netball, Cross-Country Running and Hockey. In the summer Cricket, Tennis, Rounders, Athletics and Short Tennis are played. The children swim throughout the year in the Endowed Schools' indoor, heated pool.

Music and Drama are considered very important areas of School life. In addition to class music lessons, children have the opportunity to receive tuition on a variety of musical instruments and many take advantage of this. The School Orchestras perform on a regular basis, there are also two Choirs, two Recorder Groups and numerous additional instrumental ensembles. The completed £4 million state-of-the-art whole school Music School opened in September 2006.

Music is coordinated by the new Loughborough Endowed Schools Director of Music and the music curriculum includes traditional music teaching, using extensive ICT in the modern facilities.

Dramatic productions play a major part in the life of the School. Here children are given the opportunity to express themselves and experience the excitement of performing before an audience.

There is a whole range of other activities in which children are given the opportunity to participate. Success and enjoyment in these invariably help to boost confidence and widen horizons generally.

Lunchtime and after-school clubs include Brownies, Cycling Proficiency, Drama, Pottery, Photography, Technology, Green Fingers Club, Latin and Mind Sports (Chess, Mini Bridge, Go), as well as the sporting and musical activities already mentioned.

The main ages for entry to the School are at 4+ and 7+ although a few places are available at other ages.

The examination for entry at 7+, 8+, 9+ and 10+ takes place in January each year whilst assessments for entry at 4+ take place in late January.

The Prospectus and further details can be obtained from the Headmaster's Secretary and the Headmaster will be happy to show prospective parents around the School and more information can be found on the school website www.fairfield.leics.sch.uk.

Charitable status. Loughborough Endowed Schools is a Registered Charity, number 1081765, and a Company Limited by Guarantee, registered in England, number 4038033.

Fairstead House School

Fordham Road Newmarket Suffolk CB8 7AA
Tel: 01638 662318
Fax: 01638 561685
e-mail: secretary@fairsteadhouse.co.uk
website: www.fairsteadhouse.co.uk

***Headmistress*: Mrs D J Buckenham**, CertEd

Age Range. Co-educational 3–11.
Number of Children. Day: 61 Boys, 64 Girls.
Staff. 9 full-time, 9 part-time.
Fees per term (2008-2009). Nursery: from £684 (for a minimum of 3 sessions per week), lunches £1.60 per day; Main School: £2,288–£2,452 including lunches.

Fairstead House School provides a lively and stimulating environment in which children develop into happy, confident and knowledgeable young people. All pupils have the benefit of a fulfilling and well-rounded education, providing them with every opportunity to develop individual interests and talents from an early age. Music and Drama are great strengths. Many extra-curricular activities are offered along with pre-school and after-school care.

Sport plays an important part in school life, with a new sports pavilion and field close by.

Classes are small and Pre-Prep children have the benefit of a teaching assistant in addition to the class teacher, enabling each child to receive individual help and attention. Extra help is available within the school for children experiencing difficulties in specific areas of the curriculum, or alternatively when a child requires further challenges. As well as National Curriculum subjects, each child is encouraged to develop an enjoyment and understanding of the value of French and specialist Music.

The progress of each child, both academic and social, is carefully monitored by means of ongoing assessment. The Common Entrance and Key Stage 2 tests are the targets for pupils in Year 6. 100% pass rate has been achieved for entry into first-choice schools for the past eight years.

A continuous and ongoing programme of development has ensured the provision of first-class facilities throughout the school. A 'state-of-the-art' Music & Drama Centre with specialist facilities is the latest in a series of major developments. Other recent projects have included an ICT suite, a Science, Design & Technology room and the introduction of interactive whiteboards into the classrooms.

A Bursary Fund has recently been set up to help families in need and an academic scholarship is awarded to a child at 10+ for their final year. Scholarships in sport, music and drama are awarded to talented children entering school in Year 4.

Charitable status. Fairstead House School Trust Limited is a Registered Charity, number 276787. It exists to provide independent education for children.

The Falcons Schools
Alpha Plus Group

Boys School: 2 Burnaby Gardens London W4 3DT
Tel: 020 8747 8393
Fax: 020 8995 3903
e-mail: admin@falconschool.com

Girls School: 15 Gunnersbury Avenue London W5 3XD
Tel: 020 8992 5189
Fax: 020 8752 1635
e-mail: admin@falconsgirls.co.uk

Boys Prep School:
41 Kew Foot Road Richmond Surrey TW9 2SS
Tel: 0844 225 2211
Fax: 0844 225 2212
e-mail: prep@falconschool.com
website: www.falconschool.com

***Principal*: Mr B H Evans**, BEd

Age Range. Boys School 3–7; Girls School 3–11; Boys Prep 7–13.
Number of Pupils. 188 Boys; 121 Girls; Boys Prep 270.
Fees per term (2007-2008). Boys School: £1,780–£3,495. Girls School: £1,720–£3,150. Boys Prep: (2008-2009) £3,695–£3,770.

The Falcons Schools enjoy a well-deserved reputation for excellence. Results to the leading London Day Schools are impressive, as too is the specialist teaching on offer throughout the schools. The schools provide a safe outdoor space for play and sport and a school hall for, gym, assemblies and lunch. Nearby sports facilities are used to enhance an exciting sports program. There are well-equipped libraries, music rooms, ICT suites, with a much-admired art and science facility. Our overriding emphasis is on achieving excellence in numeric and literacy whilst offering a broad and creative curriculum. The Falcons is a uniquely caring and stimulating environment, where learning is seen as fun and the pursuit of excellence is embraced by all.

Our Preparatory School for Boys opens in September 2008 with Year Three and Four classes. When full, the School will have up to 270 pupils.

Falkner House

19 Brechin Place London SW7 4QB
Tel: 020 7373 4501
Fax: 020 7835 0073
e-mail: office@falknerhouse.co.uk
website: www.falknerhouse.co.uk

Principal: Mrs Flavia Nunes

***Headmistress*: Mrs Anita Griggs**, BA Hons, PGCE

Age Range. Girls 4–11, Co-educational Nursery (ages 3–4).
Number of Girls. 170.
Fees per term (2008-2009). £4,200.

Falkner House provides a strong academic programme within a supportive family atmosphere. The broad curriculum taught by highly experienced staff results in girls achieving success at 11+ to top day and boarding schools.

Excellent facilities include a science laboratory, art room, IT centre, good libraries and large playground. The school has a strong musical tradition as well as an excellent sporting record. Pre/post school care is offered, as well as a wide range of after school activities.

Entrance at 4+ is by assessment and interview.

Falkner House Nursery caters for boys and girls aged 3–4 years. Extensive facilities and a team of specialist teachers create an ideal pre-school environment. Main school staff are on hand to enrich the Nursery School's curriculum.

Farleigh School

Red Rice Andover Hampshire SP11 7PW
Tel: 01264 710766
Fax: 01264 710070

e-mail: office@farleighschool.co.uk
website: www.farleighschool.com

Chairman of Governors: Michael Dawson

***Headmaster*: Fr Simon Everson**

Age Range. 3–13. Boarding from age 7.

Number of Pupils. 75 Boarders (36 boys, 39 girls), 303 Day.

Fees per term (2008-2009). Boarders £5,505–£6,115, Day £1,290–£4,695. 15% discount for Forces boarders. A junior boarding discount of 10% is offered for children in Years 3 to 6.

Originally founded in 1953 as a Roman Catholic boys' boarding school, Farleigh is now a fully co-educational boarding and day school which welcomes children of all faiths. Situated in a Georgian country house standing in 60 acres of magnificent parkland and landscaped woodland in the Test Valley of Hampshire, Farleigh is just over an hour from London and within easy reach of Southampton and London airports.

High standards are achieved both in and out of the classroom and excellent academic results are the norm, with leavers going to a large number of leading senior schools and many obtaining scholarships.

Farleigh has outstanding facilities, including a spacious and light Art and Design Technology building, three science laboratories, two well-equipped computer rooms with Apple Macs and PCs, a theatre with tiered seating, music suite, spacious recreation rooms, a fine Chapel, gymnasium, outdoor swimming pool, 22-metre heated indoor swimming pool, squash courts and purpose-built Pre-Prep and Kindergarten.

The teaching staff is complemented by a committed pastoral team including Year Heads, House Parents and two qualified matrons. Many staff are resident, giving the school a welcoming family atmosphere, often commented upon by visitors. A recent Ofsted inspection of the school's boarding provision reported that "Farleigh School offers a good standard of care, guidance and support to its boarding pupils."

The school provides a vibrant and active evening and weekend activity programme for boarders. Barbecue parties, 'pop stars' competitions, theatre trips, karaoke, quiz nights, bowling, Chinese takeaway nights, London museum visits are just some of the weekend events organised for pupils. Weekday activities include building dens in the woods, winter cricket nets, chess, community service, swimming, water polo, tennis, football, uni-hockey, board games, jewellery making, art and craft.

Drama, music and art have important places in school life. A programme of major drama and musical productions, and informal concerts weave variety into the school year and the children's artwork is always displayed around the school for all to see.

The major sports for boys are rugby, football, cricket, athletics and cross-country; for girls they are netball, hockey, rounders, athletics and cross-country. Swimming lessons and tennis coaching are available throughout the year.

Charitable status. Farleigh School is a Registered Charity, number 307340. It exists for the purpose of educating children.

Farlington Preparatory School

Strood Park Horsham West Sussex RH12 3PN
Tel: 01403 282566
Fax: 01403 272258
e-mail: baggsj@farlingtonschool.net
website: www.farlingtonschool.net

Chairman of Governors: J L McGuffog

***Headmistress*: Mrs Joy K Baggs**, BEd Hons, CertEd

Registrar: Mrs E V Healy

Age Range. 3–11.

Number of Girls. 200.

Fees per term (2008-2009). Tuition: £1,971–£3,505. Boarding (in addition to Tuition fees): £2,342 (weekly), £2,477 (full).

Farlington Pre-Prep Department is housed in a brand new courtyard building opened in September 2008. This purpose-built accommodation comprises a new nursery, large infant classrooms and an innovative play area. The large hall and separate dining facilities are enjoyed by all of our Prep Pupils. The Junior School girls are also housed in purpose-built classrooms that mirror the architecture of the Mansion House in the School grounds. Younger children quickly feel at home in this close-knit community, and the older girls have the opportunity to learn responsibility and have status in "their" school by becoming prefects and house captains in Prep 6.

Early school days that are happy and secure, provide a sound basis for learning and for life. At Farlington, we aim to achieve high academic standards in our Preparatory School, with the emphasis on encouragement and confidence-building. The philosophy of the School is based on Christian ethics but we also welcome girls from a wide range of religious and cultural backgrounds.

We have a staff of well-qualified and dedicated teachers. They form a wonderfully good-humoured team, who support fully the ethos of the School. Literacy and numeracy are the building blocks of education, and this is the basis of our teaching. Scientific and aesthetic skills are developed in a challenging way, using exploration and experiment, as well as practice and problem-solving.

We follow the National Curriculum but offer far more in terms of subject content, and, of course, individual attention. As girls become older, they are taught some subjects by specialist teachers (for example French, Spanish, German, PE/Games, Drama, Music, Art). In Prep 6, Science is taught in the well-equipped laboratories in the Senior School. The Prep School has its own Director of Music who runs a variety of musical activities. Individual tuition can be arranged for most instruments.

All girls can enjoy the beautiful 33 acre parkland setting for play and for learning.

The Prep School offers a wide range of extra-curricular activities which take place at lunchtimes and after school. These range from sporting clubs such as tennis, trampolining, golf, judo and horse riding. Musical activities take place on a daily basis and include choir, orchestra, recorder groups and a samba band. We offer chess tuition, pottery, ballet, jazz dance and many more! Although school finishes at 3.20 pm for girls in Reception to Prep 2, they can stay on at school until 5.00 pm supervised by members of staff.

The older girls finish their lessons at 3.45 pm and can do activities and supervised prep until 5.45 pm. Parents are encouraged to consult their daughters' teachers regularly and we hope that they will take an active part in their education. Parents are invited to Prep outings and are keen supporters of junior teams. Farlington has a very active PTA and a Parents' Forum.

Boarding is available to girls from the age of 8. Our Boarding House is friendly and run on family lines.

Prospective parents are always welcome to come and meet the Headmistress and have a tour of the School. Please telephone for an appointment and we will be delighted to forward a current prospectus.

Charitable status. Farlington Preparatory School is a Registered Charity, number 307048. It exists solely for the purpose of educating girls.

Felsted Preparatory School

Felsted Essex CM6 3JL
Tel: 01371 822610
Fax: 01371 822617
e-mail: info@felstedprep.org
website: www.felsted.org

Chairman of the Governors: Mr J H Davies

***Headmistress*: Mrs J M Burrett**, BA

Deputy Head: T J Searle, BSc

Age Range. 4–13 Co-educational.

Number of Pupils. 310 day pupils (85 of whom flexi-board), plus 120 4–6 year olds in the Pre-Preparatory Department.

Fees per term (2008-2009). £3,361–£4,417; Pre-Preparatory: £2,019; Boarding £5,646.

The staff, excluding the Headmistress, consists of 50 full-time qualified teachers and there are additional part-time teachers for instrumental music and games. There are four matrons and two sisters in charge of the Medical Centre.

The Preparatory School, set in its own grounds, is separate from Felsted School itself, with all its own facilities, including a modern well-equipped library, an excellent theatre/assembly hall, music practice rooms, a sports hall, open-air heated swimming pool and floodlit, multi-purpose, hard-play games area. Use is made of Felsted School's extra amenities at regular times so that small-bore rifle shooting, squash courts, indoor swimming, two Astroturf hockey pitches, Music School and another indoor sports hall are also available to the pupils.

Rugby football, netball, hockey, cricket, tennis, swimming, rounders, athletics and cross-country have been the major sports. Music plays an important part in the School's life, and there is an excellent Chapel choir. Regular instrumental, orchestral and rock concerts are given. The School has a deserved reputation for its drama productions, while Art, Design and Technology, PSHE, and Computing are part of the weekly timetable. Out-of-class activities include public speaking and debating opportunities, horse riding, chess, fishing, public speaking, aerobics, cookery and dance/ballet, among others.

Pupils joining at 11+ can be guaranteed assured transfer to Felsted School at 13, as can pupils of a similar age already at the Preparatory School, following successful completion of assessment tests. The majority of pupils proceed to Felsted School itself, but a number regularly move on to other major independent senior schools, having taken Common Entrance, and there is an excellent record of academic, art, music, drama and Design & Technology scholarships. (*For further information about Felsted School, see entry in HMC section.*)

Scholarships (up to 50% of fees, depending on ability and financial circumstances) and Outstanding Talent Awards are open to pupils joining Felsted Preparatory School at ages of 11+ in the September of the year of entry.

Charitable status. Felsted School is a Registered Charity, number 310870. It exists to provide education for boys and girls.

Feltonfleet School

Cobham Surrey KT11 1DR
Tel: 01932 862264
Fax: 01932 860280
e-mail: office@feltonfleet.co.uk
website: www.feltonfleet.co.uk

Chairman of Governors: G D Ashbee

***Headmaster*: P C Ward**, BEd Hons

Age Range. 3–13.

Number of Pupils. Nursery/Pre-Prep 72, Years 3–8 288, of whom 45 are Boarders.

Fees per term (2008-2009). Boarders £5,900; Day Pupils £2,930–£4,290; Nursery £1,565.

Feltonfleet School was founded in 1903 and became an Educational Trust in 1967. The School is situated in 20 acres of scenic grounds close to the M25 between Heathrow and Gatwick Airports. There are 50 full-time and 4 Gap Year members of the teaching staff. The School became fully co-educational in September 1994 and offers both weekly (Monday to Friday) boarding or day education, as well as a flexible boarding option. There is a flourishing, purpose-built Pre-Preparatory Department, Calvi House.

Ethos. It is the School's strongly held belief that if children are happy they will fulfil their potential, and by recognising the individual in a child this is more likely to happen, which is why it is committed to fostering a small school atmosphere centred on family values. The School does its best to place the children first, to meet each child's needs on an individual basis, to encourage and nurture the positive aspects of 'self': self-discipline, self-confidence, self-motivation, self-reliance and self-esteem. High-achieving children, irrespective of their real potential, are those who have a high self-esteem – without it very little can be achieved.

Pastoral. Caring for each other matters at Feltonfleet. From a child's first day, the adult community provides care, direction and confidence. The form tutor is the welcoming face on a daily basis and a secure link with daily routine, a familiar and reassuring presence, a trusted confidant and role model. Small classes make quality pastoral care much more certain. Once pupils join the Main School, the Head of Year provides further direction and guidance. The boarding house is run by two house parents, seven boarding house tutors and two matrons who promote the personal, family atmosphere on which Feltonfleet prides itself.

Entry. Children are admitted from the age of three into the Nursery in the Pre-Preparatory Department and, having moved into the Main School at the age of seven, are prepared for Common Entrance or Scholarship examinations to a wide range of independent senior schools. In the Main School there is a staff : pupil ratio of 9.5 : 1, with the average class size of 16.

For entry into the Main School pupils are required to sit an entrance assessment and interview. Academic, Art, Music, Drama, DT, All-Rounder and Sports Scholarships are offered at 11+.

Facilities. Well-equipped Science, Art, DT and ICT Departments, Library and Performing Arts Centre, where dramatic productions are performed by all year groups. The Pre-Prep, Calvi House, has recently undergone a major refurbishment with the addition of its own hall and ICT suite. Plans are in place for the building of a new swimming pool complex.

Sport. The Sports Department prides itself that is able to encompass both excellence and sport for all within a very busy prep school environment. All pupils receive high quality teaching and coaching in a variety of sports and activities in a positive and safe learning environment. Facilities include a magnificent sports hall, sports fields, two squash courts, cricket nets, floodlit courts for tennis, hockey, football and basketball, swimming pool and two shooting ranges (air weapon and .22 rifle).

Games played are rugby, football, hockey, netball, athletics and cricket.

Extra-Curricular Activities. The School has an active policy of preparing children for the challenges of today's world and an exceptional activities programme is offered to all pupils during the school day as often as possible. Pupils in the main school are offered the opportunity to attend residential activity courses as well as subject-related overseas trips. In the final two years pupils attend residential leadership courses. After Common Entrance examinations, Year 8 pupils take part in a varied programme of activities, lectures and trips in preparation for leaving Feltonfleet and moving on to their senior schools.

In recent years sporting teams have visited Belgium and Spain and the Drama Department has performed at the Edinburgh Fringe Festival.

Charitable status. Feltonfleet School Trust Limited is a Registered Charity, number 312070.

Fettes College Preparatory School

East Fettes Avenue Edinburgh EH4 1QZ
Tel: 0131 332 2976
Fax: 0131 332 4724
e-mail: prepschool@fettes.com
website: www.fettes.com

Chairman of Governors: David McMurray, Esq, MA

Chairman of Preparatory School Committee: Mrs Elaine Ross, CBE, BA

***Headmaster*: A A Edwards**, BA Hons, PGCE

Age Range. 7–13.

Number of Pupils. 149 (58 boarders, 89 day pupils), 77 boys, 68 girls.

Fees per term (2008-2009). Boarders £5,913, Day Pupils £3,777, including all meals and text-books.

Founded in 1974 as the Junior School of Fettes College taking pupils from the age of ten, it became a Preparatory School in 1999 when the age of entry was lowered to eight and its own Headmaster was appointed.

The College grounds occupy some 80 acres of parkland just 20 minutes walk away from the centre of Edinburgh. The Senior School occupies the original College building and the Prep School is about 200 metres away. It has therefore all the advantages of the excellent facilities of the Senior School along with the ability to be a complete unit of its own.

The curriculum is an extension of the Scottish 5–14 curriculum and, although pupils going on to the Senior School do not take Common Entrance, they are capable of so doing and the more able sit the 13+ Scholarship examinations. Class sizes range from 10 to 18.

Formal coaching is given to boys in rugby, hockey, athletics and cricket and to girls in hockey, netball, rounders, athletics and tennis. Each year pupils from the school represent their district in these sports. Swimming is taught as part of the PE programme and lessons are available in judo, fencing, squash and shooting. All these take place in the new Westwoods Health Centre. There is an extensive activities programme with clubs ranging from knitting to flat water speed kayaking.

Music and Drama flourish. The School Choir and School Orchestra give concerts each term, and choirs and instrumental groups participate successfully in musical competitions. Year group concerts, too, are regularly held. Each year there is a large-production School Play, younger pupils produce their own pantomime, and shorter plays are performed in French and Latin.

There is an annual trip to France and other tours are regularly organised. All twelve year olds receive leadership training and the top two year groups are involved in a programme designed at the school to increase and improve skills in various areas including resourcefulness, initiative and personal challenge.

Entrance. Entrance at the age of seven, eight or nine is by assessment tests and at 10+, 11+ and 12+ by the Entrance and Scholarship examinations, taken in early February.

Further information and a prospectus can be obtained from the Admissions Secretary, Fettes College, Carrington Road, Edinburgh EH4 1QX (tel: 0131 311 6744, fax: 0131 311 6714, e-mail: admissions@fettes.com, website: www.fettes.com), who will be very happy to arrange a visit.

Charitable status. The Fettes Trust is a Registered Charity, number SC017489. It exists to provide education for boys and girls.

Finborough Preparatory School

The Hall Great Finborough Stowmarket Suffolk IP14 3EF
Tel: 01449 773600
Fax: 01449 773601
e-mail: admin@finborough.suffolk.sch.uk
website: www.finborough.suffolk.sch.uk

Co-educational, Day and Boarding School.

Principal: Mr John Sinclair, BSc(Econ) Hons, FCA

***Head of Preparatory School*: Mr A Roberts**, BSc, PGCE

Age Range. 2½–11 years.

Number of Pupils. 73: 36 girls (8 boarders), 37 boys (10 boarders).

Fees per term (2007-2008). Day £1,740–£2,860, Boarding £3,620–£5,670.

Finborough Preparatory School is situated in 60 acres of its own playing fields, gardens and woodlands. Finborough Hall is an 18th Century manor house with modern extensions.

Classes are small, maximum 20, and often 15, taught by well-qualified staff. Subject specialists are used from year 3. The school teaches traditional values in education, manners and respect, whilst maintaining a friendly family atmosphere. Pride is taken in having pupils who are happy, and who benefit from staff whose mission is to help each child maximise his or her potential. The curriculum covers the full range of subjects, making full use of new facilities including library and ICT suite.

The school offers a full sporting programme, a wide range of after-school and weekend activities, regular competition in art, speech and music, and a new on-site equestrian centre.

Full, weekly or occasional boarding is available from the age of 7, in a secure and friendly environment.

A thriving Parents Association organises social events for parents and children at least once a term.

The school is situated 2 miles west of Stowmarket, on the main London–Norwich railway line, and is a 5-minute drive from the A14.

(*See also Finborough School entry in ISA section.*)

Finton House

171 Trinity Road London SW17 7HL
Tel: 020 8682 0921
Fax: 020 8767 5017
e-mail: admissions@fintonhouse.org.uk
website: www.fintonhouse.org.uk

Co-Founders: Terry O'Neill and Finola Stack founded Finton House in 1987.

Chair of Governors: Mrs Clare Clark

***Headmaster*: Mr A E Floyd**, BSc, PGCE

Age Range. 4–11.

Number of Pupils. 102 Boys, 183 Girls.

Fees per term (2008-2009). £3,450–£3,750.

Entrance. No testing – first come/first served.

Exit. Boys at 7, 8, 9, 10, 11 for both London Day and Prep. Girls at 11 for London Day and Boarding.

Strong policy of inclusion with a percentage of children with Special Needs – Cerebral Palsy, profoundly deaf, language development. Employs a full-time Speech and Language Therapist and Special Needs Assistants. Aims to give an all-round education, developing the whole child with individual teaching to fulfil each child's potential. Music, Art and Sports are all taught to a very high standard. A stimulating environment which encourages all children to learn and gain confidence in their own ambitions. Non-denominational but teaches a moral belief encouraging respect and self-discipline.

Charitable status. Finton House is a Registered Charity, number 296588. It exists to provide an broad, inclusive education for children.

Fonthill Lodge

Coombe Hill Road East Grinstead West Sussex RH19 4LY
Tel: 01342 321635
Fax: 01342 326844
e-mail: enquiries@fonthill-lodge.co.uk
website: www.fonthill-lodge.co.uk

Chairman of Governors: Mr P Cockburn

***Headmistress*: Mrs M Neal**

Age Range. 2–11.

Number of Children. 178.

Fees per term (2008-2009). £1,260–£3,757.

It is hard to imagine a more perfect setting for a child's first school than Fonthill Lodge, set in large and peaceful grounds, a mile from East Grinstead. With excellent facilities and a caring staff, Fonthill Lodge is a unique school. Parents choose Fonthill Lodge for their sons and daughters because of its warm family atmosphere, the provision of co-education and single-sex education, high academic standards and the choice it gives them when selecting the next stage of their child's education.

The school combines co-education for the Nursery and Key Stage I children and single-sex education at Key Stage 2. In this unique environment, the children share the social benefits of co-education while being challenged in single-sex classrooms.

Our Aims.

- High standards in academic and personal education.
- To make each child's early experience of school, rich and stimulating, both in its own right, and as a full preparation for the next stage of their education.
- Individual personal care and support given to enable each child to feel valued and develop high self-esteem.
- To make learning enjoyable, and encourage our pupils to become independent, responsible, caring and courteous, in an attractive, well-resourced environment.
- To teach good manners and respect for others and to develop self-discipline and self-esteem through praise and encouragement.

Curriculum. The school offers a broad and balanced education in average class sizes of 12. The National Curriculum is followed and outstanding results are achieved in Key Stage 1 and Key Stage 2 examinations. The children are prepared for Common Entrance and individual Senior school examinations.

Drama, Gymnastics, Ballet and Music are taught to a high standard and all children participate in the school productions, which are acclaimed. All children are encouraged to learn the recorder and may choose to learn the piano, flute, clarinet, guitar, violin and drums.

The three nursery classes are a vital part of the school. Within a comfortable and secure environment, the children enjoy learning and playing together and are introduced to the basic skills required for reading, writing, mathematics and ICT. Imaginative play is an essential part of the day and they also enjoy PE, Music, Ballet and Football.

Special Needs. A specialist teacher, employed by the Dyslexia Institute, attends the school to give lessons to the boys and girls who are found to be Dyslexic. Extra individual help is given to children in the classrooms by support teachers.

Sport. In the safety of the beautiful grounds athletics, cricket, hockey, football, golf, karate, netball, rounders and rugby are played. An indoor sports hall and astroturf facilities are used at the East Grinstead Sports Club which is adjacent to the school. Swimming lessons are given each week at Ardingly College.

Extra-Curricular Activities. At the end of each day there are a number of activities in which the children can participate: Chess, Cricket, Drama, Football, Golf, Gymnastics, Netball and Rugby.

Before and After School Care. Early drop-off care and breakfast are available before school starts and there is after-school supervision until 6.00 pm in addition to the wide range of extra-curricular activities.

Charitable status. Fonthill Lodge is a Registered Charity, number 325071. It exists to provide education for boys and girls.

Foremarke Hall

Repton Preparatory School

Milton Derbyshire DE65 6EJ
Tel: 01283 703269
Fax: 01283 701185
e-mail: registrar@foremarke.org.uk
website: www.foremarke.org.uk

Chairman of Governors: J M Fry

***Head*: P G Watson**, MA, PGCE

Age Range. 2½–13.

Number of Pupils. Boys: 49 boarders, 234 day; Girls: 29 boarders, 130 day.

Fees per term (2008-2009). Prep: £5,630 boarding, £4,240 day; Pre-Prep £2,555, Reception £2,305, Nursery £2,190 (full-time), £219 (part-time per session).

Foremarke Hall is under the control of the Governors of Repton School. Boys and girls are prepared for all Independent Schools but about two-thirds choose to continue to Repton.

The school is situated in a fine Georgian mansion surrounded by 50 acres of woods, playing fields and a lake. The facilities include all that the school requires including a new classroom building to house mathematics, three science laboratories, sophisticated computer technology with full time IT specialist, large art room with pottery facilities, Design Technology department, an extensive library run by a chartered librarian, an indoor competition sized swimming pool, a sports hall and a floodlit sports artificial turf surface.

Great importance is attached to pastoral care where boarders have their own dedicated staff and space for themselves. There is an imaginative and varied programme of activities making most use of the grounds including outdoor pursuits. The games programme is extensive and includes athletics, cricket, football, rugby, hockey, rounders, swimming and tennis. We also have an extensive and varied after school activities programme.

We seek to bring out the most in every pupil, to provide a rounded education and a range of experience and skills that will be a preparation for life. We value our 'family atmosphere' and strong sense of community, the spacious grounds and happy environment.

Foremarke is situated in undisturbed countryside in the centre of England. It is easily reached by the M1, M42 and Birmingham and East Midland airports.

Charitable status. Repton Preparatory School is a Registered Charity, number 1093165. It exists to provide high quality education for boys and girls.

Forest Preparatory School

College Place Snaresbrook London E17 3PY
Tel: 020 8520 1744
Fax: 020 8520 3656
e-mail: prep@forest.org.uk
website: www.forest.org.uk

Co-educational Day School.

Chairman of Governors: J W Matthews, FCA
***Head*: Mrs E Garner**, BA Hons London, MEd Cantab

Age Range. 4–11.
Number of Pupils. 215.
Fees per term (2008-2009). £2,690–£3,242.

Forest Preparatory School is part of Forest School (HMC), with which it shares a 30-acre site at the foot of Epping Forest on the East London/Essex border. Its aims are to offer an education of high quality, and to encourage and develop each child academically, physically and creatively. From the age of 7, pupils are taught in single-sex classes, and at age 11 they proceed to the boys' and girls' sections of Forest School (*see separate entry in HMC section*).

Entry to the school is by selection at age 4 by means of informal assessment and, at age 7, by entrance examination.

The Pre-Prep Department is co-educational, with forms of 16 pupils who are taught predominantly by form teachers and supported by classroom assistants. Music and PE are taught by specialist teachers. From the age of 7, forms become single-sex and number around 22 pupils. Form teachers teach the main curriculum subjects, while specialists teach modern foreign languages – French, Spanish and German – ICT, music, drama, design and technology, physical education and games. In the final two years an element of setting is introduced in English and mathematics. Scholarship and music awards are available to pupils for entry at age 11 to the Boys' and Girls' Schools at Forest.

Sport and music are strengths of the school. The main sports played are football, cricket, netball and rounders, and teams compete locally and regionally. Athletics, swimming and cross-country are all coached to a high standard. The musical life of the school is enriched by its three choirs, orchestra and several chamber groups, and all pupils in Years 2 and 4 are provided with free tuition in a musical instrument. There are endless opportunities for pupils to perform in concerts or recitals throughout the year, and Chapel services, form assemblies and school competitions provide occasions for public speaking and performance. Activities take place at lunchtime, with a wide variety of extra-curricular clubs on offer. Breakfast club opens at 7.30 am, after-school care is available up to 6.00 pm, and an extensive school bus service is in operation.

Charitable status. Forest School Essex is a Registered Charity, number 312677. The objective of the school is education.

Forres Sandle Manor

Sandleheath Fordingbridge Hampshire SP6 1NS
Tel: 01425 653181
Fax: 01425 655676
e-mail: office@fsmschool.com
website: www.fsmschool.com

***Headmaster*: R P J Moore**, BA, PGCE

Deputy Head: M R Brearey

Age Range. 3–13.
Number of Pupils. Prep: 180 (half of whom are boarders, and half boys). Pre-Prep: 90 (all are day children, half are boys).
Fees per term (2008-2009). Prep: Boarders £6,100, Day pupils £4,495; Pre-Prep £230–£2,425.

Forres Sandle Manor is situated on its own beautiful 35-acre estate on the edge of the New Forest. The main school building is a large manor house and the grounds are perfect for children – extensive and well-maintained playing fields, woods, a stream and plenty of space for even the most active individual! Facilities include a fine multi-purpose hall, heated swimming pool, Technology Centre, a superb Coach House Art Studio, and there are plans for various exciting developments in the near future.

The School has a fine academic record and achieves an impressive number of Awards to Independent Senior Schools. There is an exceptionally dynamic teaching staff who teach in spacious, light classrooms and who prepare children for Common Entrance and scholarships at 13+ whilst delivering the National Curriculum wherever possible. It is our aim to develop in children a true enjoyment and involvement in their work and this is aided by our efforts to link various subjects together and to the wider world in general.

Music is an especially strong feature of the school with all children encouraged to play and to become confident in performance. Sport, too, is an important part of school life as are the extraordinary range of activities available to both boarders and day children. It is the school's policy to make weekends the best part of a thoroughly enjoyable week!

The Headmaster, his wife and family, are all fully involved in the school and it is the main aim of all who live and work at Forres Sandle Manor that the community be happy, confident and caring. Great care is taken to ensure the happiness of every child and to maintain the family atmosphere which has always been the basis of the school's tradition.

Charitable status. Forres Sandle Manor Education Trust Ltd is a Registered Charity, number 284260. It exists to provide high quality education for boys and girls.

The Froebelian School

Clarence Road Horsforth Leeds LS18 4LB
Tel: 0113 258 3047
Fax: 0113 258 0173
e-mail: office@froebelian.co.uk
website: www.froebelian.co.uk

Chairman of Governors: Mr E V Brown, LLB Hons
***Headmaster*: Mr J Tranmer**, MA, PGCE, FCollP

Age Range. 3+ to 11+ years (3–4 years half days, optional afternoons).

Number of Pupils. 187 (92 boys, 95 girls).

Fees per term (2008-2009). £1,280–£1,920. Compulsory extras for full-time pupils, such as lunches and swimming, amount to approximately £170 per term.

Bursaries (income-related fee reduction) may be available.

Religious Affiliation: Christian, non-denominational.

Entry Requirements: Interview and assessment; written tests for older children.

Entry is usually at 3+, but limited places are sometimes available throughout the school.

Every child is respected as an individual and pupils are able to reach their full potential in the purposeful atmosphere of this caring, disciplined school. High standards are achieved in all areas of the school – academic work, creative arts, music, sport, behaviour and manners. Early progress in language and mathematics is sustained and broadened in the junior curriculum, which includes French, information and design technology, drama and outdoor pursuits.

The school enjoys an envied reputation for success in entrance and scholarship examinations at 11+. A flourishing Parent Teacher Association supports the school and a growing database helps to keep former pupils in touch.

Situated to the north-west of Leeds, and close to Bradford, the school is well served by major transport links. 'Wrap-around' care is available from 7.30 am to 6.00 pm in the form of Breakfast Club, Little Acorns and Homework and Activities Club and there is a holiday club during the breaks.

Charitable status. The Froebelian School is a Registered Charity, number 529111. It exists to provide education of the highest quality at affordable fee levels.

Garden House School

Turk's Row London SW3 4TW
Tel: 020 7730 1652 (Girls)
020 7730 6652 (Boys)
e-mail: info@gardenhouseschool.co.uk
website: www.gardenhouseschool.co.uk

Principal: Mrs J K Oddy

Headmistress (*Upper School*): **Mrs Janet Webb**, CertEd (Southampton)

Headmistress (*Lower School*): **Mrs Wendy Challen**, CertEd (Froebel)

Headmaster (*Boys' School*): **Mr Christian Warland**, BA Hons

Age Range. 3–11 Girls, 3–8 Boys.

Number of Pupils. 288 girls, 161 boys, taught in single-sex classes.

Fees per term (2008-2009). Kindergarten £3,100, Reception–Year 6 £5,150–£5,295. There is a 10% reduction for siblings.

Buildings and facilities. The School is housed in a charming, light and airy listed building. Original artwork hangs in every classroom, and facilities include libraries for different age groups, a ballet/performance/drama hall and dedicated science and art rooms.

The school has its own garden within the grounds of the Royal Hospital where children enjoy science lessons and attend a Gardening Club.

School drama productions are ambitiously staged at the Royal Court Theatre in Sloane Square.

Aims, ethos and values. Garden House provides a thorough and balanced education in a lively and purposeful environment. Our children achieve high academic results in a calm and constructive manner, being encouraged to have inquiring and independent minds. Emphasis is placed not only on academic, sporting and artistic ability but on manners and consideration to others. Our Kindness Code is adhered to and constantly re-emphasised.

Curriculum. Literacy, Numeracy, Science, History, Geography, Religious Education, French (from Kindergarten), Latin, Computers/Design Technology, Current Events, Art, Drama, Singing and Music, Dancing, Fencing and Physical Education (netball, tennis, rounders, gym, swimming, athletics, cricket, pop lacrosse, rugby and football). We have many sports squads, sports clubs and matches. Children with learning difficulties are catered for in small groups, taught by two full-time and many visiting specialist teachers. 80% of children learn at least one musical instrument. The school boasts four choirs and a chamber orchestra.

A diverse range of after-school clubs include touch-typing, Mandarin, Chess, and Sculpture.

Benefiting from our central London location, visits to museums, galleries and churches form an essential part of the curriculum, as do annual field study and outward bound trips. Girls spend a week in France after Common Entrance and boys enjoy a camping expedition.

School Successes. Girls are prepared for the Common Entrance, with the majority leaving for the premier girls' schools, 50% to leading London senior schools, 50% to major boarding schools. Boys leave us at 8, having been well prepared for entrance to leading London prep schools and 25% to top boarding preps. Our children achieve several scholarships each year.

Entrance. We encourage you to visit the school. Girls and boys join Garden House in the September after they reach 3 or 4 years of age. An Application Form can be obtained from the School Office and once completed, and returned with the relevant fee, your child's name is placed on the waiting list. Entry interview is held one year before entry. We look forward to welcoming you and your children to Garden House School.

Gateway School

1 High Street Great Missenden Buckinghamshire HP16 9AA
Tel: 01494 862407
Fax: 01494 865787
e-mail: headteacher@gateway.bucks.sch.uk
website: www.gatewayschool-bucks.co.uk

***Principal*: S J Y Wade**, MA, PGCE

Age Range. 2–12.

Number of Pupils. Day: 178 Boys, 123 Girls.

Fees per term (2007-2008). £796–£2,623.

- Montessori based Early Years Unit
- Funding for 3 and 4 year olds plus childcare vouchers
- High academic standard with a broad curriculum
- Wide range of sporting activities
- Extensive ICT provision
- Vibrant music department
- Day and overnight trips at home and abroad
- Provision from 8.00 am to 6.00 pm for 48 weeks p.a.

Gayhurst School

Bull Lane Gerrards Cross Bucks SL9 8RJ
Tel: 01753 882690
Fax: 01753 887451
e-mail: gayhurst@gayhurst.bucks.sch.uk
website: www.gayhurst.bucks.sch.uk

Chairman of the Governors: Mr A Middleton

***Headmaster*: A Sims**, MA (Cantab)

Age Range. 4–13.

Number of Boys. 300.

Fees per term (2007-2008). £2,517–£3,198 inclusive of lunch for all boys. A small extra charge is made for some text books.

The School is a day school for boys aged 4+ to 13+. It aims to include the important features of a traditional education but also introduces boys to a wide range of experiences. The School is in country surroundings and stands in a 5 acre playing field with some woodland and a further 4 acre field beyond, all of which play important roles in the overall education.

The 22 classrooms include well-equipped specialist subject rooms for all academic subjects, including two Science Laboratories and an IT Laboratory. In addition there is a modern multipurpose Hall (Sports, drama, music), an Art room, Music Room, two libraries and an all-weather, astroturf pitch. The School has just benefited from a £2,000,000 redevelopment plan. Rugby, Soccer, Cricket, Cross-country, Hockey, Swimming, Tennis, Athletics and Basketball are taught. Boys also take part in a wide range of extra-curricular activities.

There are 27 full-time, qualified teaching staff. There are also 2 part-time teachers and a large number of peripatetic instrumental music teachers and specialist games coaches.

Entry to the School is by interview, and boys go on to both Day and Boarding Independent Schools via the CEE and to local Grammar Schools. The School has a good record of examination results and scholarships to Independent Schools are won regularly.

Charitable status. The school is a Registered Charity, number 298869. It exists to provide education for boys.

Giggleswick Junior School

Giggleswick Settle North Yorkshire BD24 0DG
Tel: 01729 893100
Fax: 01729 893150
e-mail: juniorschool@giggleswick.org.uk
website: www.giggleswickschool.co.uk

Chairman of Governors: M H O'Connell, BA, FCA

***Head*: M Brotherton**, BEd Hons, NPQH

Age Range. 3–11 Co-educational.

Number of Pupils. 80.

Fees per term (2008-2009). Boarders £4,878, Day Pupils £1,929–£3,970.

Giggleswick Junior School offers a co-educational day and boarding education within a secure, happy, family atmosphere. Day pupils are fully integrated into the life and ethos of the school. The Head and family live on site and the Boarding Housemaster and his family live in the boarding house. There is an experienced team of academic staff and matrons to care for the children. The modern dining room serves particularly good food.

There is a clear sense of purpose and development. Facilities are excellent: a new sports hall was completed in 2005 and there are extensive playing fields. The Junior School enjoys superb, modern self-contained grounds with a full range of facilities, in addition to sharing Giggleswick's Swimming pool, Chapel, Food Technology, Design Centre, and all-weather pitch. Our ICT facilities, including email and supervised internet access, are constantly upgraded. The great majority of pupils progress to Giggleswick (*see HMC entry*). In the centre of Britain, in the Yorkshire Dales, Giggleswick is within 75 minutes drive of Manchester and Leeds, their airports and railway stations. Airport transfers are organised.

Music and drama are integral to school life, as is participation in major team and individual sports and outdoor pursuits. Pupils with particular educational needs are offered private individual or group lessons with the on-site specialists. Art and Music are particularly strong, with both an inclusive atmosphere and an excellent standard. Music and sports tours alternate, with expeditions both around the UK and abroad.

Visits and "taster" stays are warmly encouraged and contribute to new pupils' sense of involvement while being part of the living school.

Charitable status. Giggleswick School is a Registered Charity, number 1109826. It exists to provide education for boys and girls.

Glebe House School

Cromer Road Hunstanton Norfolk PE36 6HW
Tel: 01485 532809
Fax: 01485 533900
e-mail: admin@glebehouseschool.co.uk
website: www.glebehouseschool.co.uk

Chairman of the Governors: Mr Chris Armstrong

***Headmaster*: J P Crofts**, BA, PGCE

Age Range. 6 months to 13 years.

Number of Children. 55 Boys, 53 Girls, Nursery 77.

Fees per term (2008-2009). Prep £3,85; Pre-Prep £2,650; Weekly boarding £4,500.

Glebe House School and Nursery was founded in 1874 as a preparatory school and is surrounded by 12 acres of playing fields.

The Junior School children are accommodated in a purpose-built building. The Senior School has specialist areas for all academic subjects and music, sport and drama are a significant part of a child's life at Glebe House. Our 25 metre indoor heated swimming pool, tennis and netball courts, adventure playground, gym, music school and performance hall all help to ensure that the core academic subjects are supported by a balanced and stimulating curriculum. With the senior school working until 5.50 pm, there is an after school club for the pre-prep from 3.30 pm until 5.50 pm, and with the Breakfast Club from 7.45 am this gives additional benefit to working parents organising their day.

Aims and Values. At the heart of Glebe House is our emphasis on supporting and valuing the individual. We encourage the traditional values of courtesy, consideration for others, self discipline and a desire to contribute to society.

Academic Life. We are committed to the achievement of high academic standards, harnessing the best of modern educational practice. Class sizes remain small and every child is encouraged to achieve their full potential. Close supervision, with one-to-one support where necessary, is maintained and progress is carefully monitored through regular standardised testing and classroom assessments. The broad curriculum both incorporates and exceed national requirements, including offering a second modern language in addition to French from year six. Glebe House enjoys a high success rate at Common Entrance and in Independent Scholarship Examinations and with this solid foundation our pupils move confidently on to a wide range of senior schools.

Sport and Activities. We offer a wide sporting programme aimed to encourage fitness and a healthy enjoyment of sport that will remain with the children for life. Rugby, hockey and cricket are the main sports for boys and hockey, netball and rounders for girls. We also encourage involvement in many activities including athletics, cross country, football, golf, swimming and tennis. The Glebe House Award Scheme encourages children to strive for high standards in acquiring skills that will prepare them for the future. We offer a wide range of activities during the summer holidays, including football, swimming, craft, music and drama workshops, tennis, and sailing.

Pastoral Care and Boarding. Relations between children and staff are respectful but relaxed and the children know they are free to talk to all staff, one of the great advantages of a school this size. All pupils belong to one of three houses and have a tutor who sees them each morning and is the first point of contact for parents. Good communication is crucial and we operate an open door policy to parents. The school offers 35 weekly boarding places and flexibility in choosing from one to four nights.

Travel. Our minibus picks up in the morning and takes home at 3.30 pm and 6 pm to Kings Lynn and surrounding areas.

Further Information. Prospective parents and children are most welcome to contact the School Administrator to meet the Headmaster and tour the school.

Charitable status. Glebe House School Trust Limited is a Registered Charity, number 1018815.

The Gleddings Preparatory School

Birdcage Lane Savile Park Halifax West Yorkshire HX3 0JB
Tel: 01422 354605
Fax: 01422 356263
e-mail: TheGleddings@aol.com
website: www.TheGleddings.co.uk

***Headmistress*: Mrs P J Wilson**, CBE

Age Range. 3–11 Co-educational.
Number of Pupils. 187: 85 Boys, 102 Girls.
Fees per term (2007-2008). £1,015–£1,695.

Glendower Preparatory School

87 Queen's Gate London SW7 5JX
Tel: 020 7370 1927
Fax: 020 7244 8308
e-mail: office@glendower.kensington.sch.uk
website: www.glendowerprep.org

Chairman of Governors: Mrs Nicola Horlick, BA Hons (Oxon)

***Headmistress*: Mrs R E Bowman**, BA (Warwick), PGCE

Age Range. Girls 4–11.
Number of Girls. 190.
Fees per term (2008-2009). £3,950.

Preparatory school for girls aged 4–11+ years. Pupils are prepared for the Common Entrance examinations and to the London Independent Day Schools at age 11.

French is taught throughout the school by a native speaker. Emphasis is laid on fluency and purity of accent. Science is taught in the purpose-built laboratory by a specialist, Latin is taught at age 10. ICT, Art and DT are included in the curriculum and taught in specialist rooms. All blackboards/whiteboards in KS2 classrooms have been replaced by plasma screens and every room has at least one computer.

In addition to class music lessons under a Director of Music, girls may learn piano, violin, recorder, viola, voice and flute; any other instruments by arrangement. Class drama is taught by a specialist and there are Drama Clubs for enthusiasts. Various club activities take place after school every day between 4pm and 5pm.

Physical Education includes Swimming, Netball, Gymnastics, Dance, Tennis and Athletics. The School values highly the close interest of parents, and staff are readily available by appointment as well as for regular Parent-Teacher discussion evenings.

The school had a successful ISI Inspection in 2005.

Charitable status. Glendower School Trust Limited is a Registered Charity, number 312717. It exists to provide high quality education for local girls.

The Godolphin Preparatory School

Laverstock Road Salisbury Wiltshire SP1 2RB
Tel: 01722 430652
Fax: 01722 430651
e-mail: prep@godolphin.wilts.sch.uk
website: www.godolphinprep.org

Chairman of the Governors: G Fletcher, Esq

***Headmistress*: Mrs P White**, BEd

Age Range. 3–11.
Number of Pupils. 70 Day Girls.
Fees per term (2008-2009). £1,653–£3,210.

Godolphin Prep is a purpose-built, compact school for girls aged from three to eleven. It is a mainstream academic school which focuses on the strengths of its pupils, values their potential as individuals and nurtures the girls to become caring members of society.

Many of the varied visitors to the school comment on the friendly atmosphere which they encounter. It is within such an environment that the girls are encouraged to have high expectations, good work habits and an active desire to take advantage of all that is on offer to them. Early specialist teaching across the curriculum is available from the age of 7, taught by people who are both dedicated and enthusiastic about their subjects. The high standard of teaching is reflected in the National Curriculum assessment results, as well as the scholarship awards gained by a significant number of pupils at eleven. There is an ambience of learning which comes from the 'work hard–play hard' ethic.

Courtesy and good manners are an implicit part of daily life at Godolphin; the basic precept is '*Never be the cause of another's unhappiness*'.

The school opened in 1993 as a part of the development plan of the Godolphin School. Following an inspection in 1996, which resulted in IAPS accreditation and then DCSF registration two years later, the Prep has continued to thrive.

Godolphin Prep is a day school where outside interests are encouraged and weekends are perceived as family time, however, there is a programme of afterschool activities which creates opportunities for those who travel considerable distances to school by bus. This arrangement offers an element of choice which ensures that the girls develop as well-balanced individuals.

About 60% of the pupils move to the Godolphin School, following Common Entrance. Others move to boarding schools slightly farther afield or transfer to the local girls' grammar school.

Charitable status. The Godolphin School is a Registered Charity, number 309488. Its object is to provide and conduct in or near Salisbury a boarding and day school for girls.

Godstowe Preparatory School

Shrubbery Road High Wycombe Bucks HP13 6PR
Tel: 01494 529273
01494 429006 Registrar
Fax: 01494 429009
e-mail: head@godstowe.org
website: www.godstowe.org

Motto: *Finem Respice*
Founded 1900.

Chairman of the Governors: A Kemp, BA Econ, ACA (*Current Parent*)

***Head*: Mr David Gainer**, BEd Hons London

Age Range. Girls 3–13, Boys 3–7.

Number of Pupils. Preparatory: 254 (boarding and day). Pre-Preparatory: 106.

Fees per term (2008-2009). Boarders £6,110, Day Children £2,670–£4,160. Nursery: £1,210–£2,400.

The School. Since its foundation in 1900, Godstowe Preparatory School has been at the forefront of education. It has a distinguished tradition as the first British boarding preparatory school for girls, in a foundation that includes Wycombe Abbey, Benenden and St Leonards.

Today, Godstowe is a flourishing boarding and day school with over 350 pupils, enjoying an unparalleled academic reputation. It has a Pre-Prep department for boys and girls aged between three and seven, and a Preparatory School for girls from seven to thirteen years old. Class sizes are small allowing children to benefit from individual attention.

Academic Record. Godstowe enjoys an excellent and unparalleled academic reputation amongst British independent schools. Despite its non-selective entry policy, Godstowe consistently achieves unrivalled academic results. Over a third of girls left the School with a Scholarship in 2008. By the age of nine, pupils are taught by specialists in 16 subjects across the curriculum. Language teaching includes French, Spanish and Latin. Sport, ICT, art and music are all outstandingly taught within first-rate facilities.

Boarding. Girls' boarding life is focused within three houses in the grounds, one of which is a dedicated junior house. Each has four resident staff and a warm and supportive atmosphere. A combination of professional and caring staff and beautifully refurbished accommodation ensures a safe and relaxing environment. Each house has its own garden and tennis court, reinforcing the feeling of 'going home' at the end of the school day. Weekends are packed full of activity and fun, with many weekly boarders often choosing to stay at School for the weekend.

The **Enrichment Curriculum** is an extended school day from 7.30 am to 7.30 pm, with some 50 after-school activities scheduled each week. The 'E-Curriculum' gives children the chance to try many exciting and challenging new pursuits including fencing, rock climbing, rowing, football and song writing. In addition, supervised homework sessions are offered every evening. Day children may join the boarders for breakfast and supper. Other than those sessions supervised by outside instructors all activities are offered free of charge. An Enrichment programme is also in place for Pre-Prep children.

Charitable status. The Godstowe Preparatory School Company Limited is a Registered Charity, number 310637. It exists to provide education and training for young girls and boys.

Grace Dieu Manor School

Grace Dieu Thringstone Leics LE67 5UG
Tel: 01530 222276
Fax: 01530 223184
e-mail: registrar@gracedieu.com
website: www.gracedieu.com

Chairman of Governors: Fr B E Cuddihy

***Headmaster*: Mr C E Foulds**, BA (University College, Swansea)

Age Range. 3–13 Co-educational.

Number of Pupils. 329: Pre-Prep 74, Infants 58, Seniors 197.

Fees per term (2007-2008). £1,949–£3,009.

Grace Dieu, set in one hundred and twenty acres of grounds, is situated in the heart of the countryside. It is a co-educational Roman Catholic School, accepting children of all denominations from the age of 3. The School is divided into three departments, Pre-Prep (3–5), Infants (5–7) and Seniors (8–13+), each operating its own timetable. Entry is by interview and assessment.

The School has an excellent reputation academically and has a strong tradition in games and music. The School has its own indoor swimming pool and sports hall. There is a full programme of major sports (football, rugby, hockey, netball, rounders, cricket, tennis, swimming and athletics) as well as some minor sports (including volleyball and golf). The curriculum also includes Music and Drama, and school productions are performed annually. Many children receive individual music tuition as an extra-curricular activity. A range of clubs operates during the lunch break or after school. There is an annual skiing trip, as well as an annual Jersey cricket tour. Other tours for senior pupils also take place. The School offers before and after school care (8.00 am to 6.00 pm) at no extra charge. In addition, other activities for children are run on the premises during some holiday periods, though there is an extra charge for this service.

Charitable status. Grace Dieu Manor School is a Registered Charity, number 1115976. It exists to provide education for boys and girls.

The Grange
Monmouth School Preparatory School

St James Street Monmouth NP25 3DL
Tel: 01600 710408
Fax: 01600 7710441
e-mail: grangese@monmouth.monm.sch.uk
website: www.habs-monmouth.org

Chairman of Governors: J B S Swallow, MA, FCA

***Head*: Mrs E G Thomas**, BA

Age Range. 7–11.

Number of Pupils. 105 boys.

Fees per term (2008-2009). Boarding £5,197, Day £2,643.

The Grange provides the friendliness and close pastoral care of a small school together with the outstanding resources of a large school through its association with Monmouth School, a Haberdashers' school for boys aged 11 to 18. There are also strong links with the other schools in the area belonging to the family of Haberdashers' Monmouth Schools – Haberdashers' Agincourt School (for boys and girls aged 3 to 7), Gilbert Inglefield House (for girls aged 7 to 11) and Haberdashers'

Monmouth School for Girls (for girls aged 11 to 18.) In their final year at The Grange boys take the General Entry Examination for Monmouth School. There is a very high pass rate and a significant number of boys gain scholarships – both academic and music. A wide and very popular extra curricular programme combines with high academic achievement to provide a vibrant and stimulating educational experience.

Aims. The aims of The Grange are to provide an excellent education as the foundation for future achievement and to develop personal qualities of confidence, independence and social conscience.

Location. The Grange is an historic Georgian building occupying its own site very near Monmouth School in the heart of Monmouth.

Staffing. 8 full-time and 8 part-time staff, all of whom are fully qualified, teach the 7 classes, in addition to peripatetic teachers and specialist coaches for extra curricular activities.

Facilities. The Grange has its own well-equipped classrooms, assembly hall, art studio and computer suite. The garden and grounds provide a safe, spacious area for recreation, games and outdoor projects. In addition The Grange shares the facilities of Monmouth School which include the School Chapel, large playing fields, Sports Complex, Drama Studio and a new Performing Arts Centre – the Blake Theatre.

Curriculum. The curriculum is broad and takes account of, though is not constrained by, the National Curriculum. Subjects include English, Mathematics, Science, Information and Communication Technology, History, Geography, Religious Education, Art, Design Technology, Music, Physical Education, Games and Drama. French is added to the curriculum in Year 5 and 6. There is subject specialist teaching throughout. A part time learning support teacher provides extra help on an individual or small group basis for boys who need it.

Extra-Curricular Activities. There is a full programme of activities which take place both in the lunch break and after school. These vary slightly according to the season though in any one year will include rugby, football, cricket, tennis, swimming, golf, cross-country running, string orchestra, wind band, choir, fencing and chess. There is a good record of boys playing at county and national level in rugby, cricket, fencing and chess.

Entry. Entry is usually at 7+ following assessment, though occasionally in the other year groups if a space becomes available.

Charitable status. William Jones Monmouth Schools is a Registered Charity, number 525616. Its aims and objectives are to provide an all-round education for boys and girls at reasonable fees.

Grange Park Preparatory School

13 The Chine Grange Park London N21 2EA
Tel: 020 8360 1469
Fax: 020 8360 4869
e-mail: office@gpps.org.uk
website: www.gpps.org.uk

Day School for Girls.

Chair of Governors: Mrs Susan Ross

***Head*: Mr Ashley Martin**

Age Range. 4–11.
Number of Girls. 105.
Fees per term (2007-2008). £2,400.

Grange Park Preparatory School is a long established, happy and successful school that provides a broad and stimulating education. It is situated in the pleasant residential area of Grange Park.

Hidden behind what was once a residential house lies a purpose built school with excellent facilities for the modern curriculum, including a fully equipped ICT suite and facilities for science, art, design technology and pottery. There are two libraries, one for KS1 and the other for KS2. The younger children are taught PE and games within the school grounds. Years 5 and 6 make use of off site facilities for netball and tennis. From Year 2 girls swim at a local pool.

Classes are small and the school has an excellent reputation for pastoral care and for nurturing the individual child.

We have a very broad curriculum and encourage excellence throughout, academically, in sport, art, dance and drama and in music.

In KS1 the children are taught mostly by form teachers with specialist teaching being introduced gradually in KS2. From Year 1 specialist teachers teach games, French, music and dance. Individual music tuition is available.

The girls are taught by experienced and well qualified staff.

The curriculum is enriched by a comprehensive programme of visits, which take advantage of the artistic and cultural opportunities of London, as well as local facilities for field studies. A ski trip takes place annually and Year 6 girls go on an outdoor pursuits weekend.

Girls are prepared for examinations for a wide range of secondary schools, both selective state schools and independent schools.

The school has a healthy eating policy. Lunches are cooked in school using only fresh ingredients. No processed food is used. There is always a vegetarian option and salads and fresh fruit are available daily.

The school is non-selective and places in Reception are offered after the Head has met with parents and daughters. Children taking up chance vacancies in other classes will be invited to spend a day in school to ensure they will fit into the class successfully.

Charitable status. Grange Park Preparatory School is a Registered Charity, number 268328.

The Grange Preparatory School
Chile

Av Principe de Gales 6154, La Reina, Santiago, Chile
Tel: 00 562 586 0131
Fax: 00 562 586 0147
e-mail: hmprep@grange.cl
website: www.grange.cl

Co-educational Day School.

***Head*: Mr Michael Freeman**

Age Range. 4–12.
Number of Pupils. 1,009.
Fees per annum (2008). Ch$3,710,905–Ch$4,221,624 (roughly £4,000–£4,600) payable in one annual sum or 11 monthly instalments. There is a one-off incorporation fee, payable on entry, of about £3,200 for the first child entering the school and £2,100 for each subsequent child.

The Grange Preparatory School is the junior section of The Grange, founded in 1928 by John Jackson and based upon the British independent school which he had attended.

The Prep School is divided into the Lower Prep, which takes children from the age of 4 to the age of 8, and the Upper Prep, taking children from 8 to 12. Almost all pupils will transfer into The Grange senior school.

The ethos of the school is strongly based on giving a broad, all-round educational experience to find strengths for each child. The school may be very large but each child is valued as an individual within the team.

Entry to the school is usually at the age of 4, though entry at ages over 4 may be possible as vacancies occur in the course of the year. All teaching is in English except in those areas where the Chilean National Curriculum requires that they be taught in Spanish. The majority of the pupils are Chilean and begin an immersion course in English upon entry.

International assessment criteria are used at various stages of each pupil's career, with NFER testing in English and mathematics. The core curriculum is based largely upon the National Curriculum of England and Wales, fully encompassing and surpassing the local National Curriculum. Teaching is mainly by class teachers, though older children will find themselves being taught by specialists in many subjects. All heads of department are specialists. Approximately 30 of the teachers are ex-patriates.

Over the last few years strong progress has been made in the areas of Science, ICT, Music, Drama and Art and Design Technology, with new rooms having been dedicated to these subjects. There is a comprehensive after-school extra-curricular programme in which children from the age of 7 upwards are strongly encouraged to take part.

The Granville School

2 Bradbourne Park Road Sevenoaks Kent TN13 3LJ
Tel: 01732 453039
Fax: 01732 743634
e-mail: evans@granville-school.com
website: www.granville-school.com

Chairman of Governors: Mr R Campin

***Headmistress*: Mrs Jane Scott**, BEd Hons Cantab

Age Range. Girls 3–11, Boys 3–5,

Number of Pupils. 197.

Fees per term (2008-2009). Nursery £1,315, Transition £2,265, Reception, Years 1 & 2 £2,670, Years 3 & 4 £3,015, Years 5 & 6 £3,400. Lunch included for Transition–Year 6.

Extras. Private Lessons: Pianoforte, Violin, Cello, Oboe, Clarinet, Flute £211 per term.

Shared Lessons: Recorder £26.10, Ballet £51.25 per term.

Charitable status. The Ena Makin Educational Trust Limited is a Registered Charity, number 307931. Its aim is to run any school as an educational charity for the promotion of education generally.

Great Ballard

Eartham Chichester West Sussex PO18 0LR
Tel: 01243 814236
Fax: 01243 814586
e-mail: admin@greatballard.co.uk
website: www.greatballard.co.uk

***Headmaster*: R E T Jennings**, CertEd

Age Range. 2½–13 co-educational.

Number of Children. 195: 102 Boys, 93 Girls (including 77 in Pre-Prep and approx 35 Boarders).

Fees per term (2008-2009). Weekly Boarding £4,325, Day £3,275–£3,600, Pre-Prep £1,000–£2,175. The boarding fees for HM Forces are reduced by £150.

The school stands in 30 acres of wonderful countryside on the South Downs between Arundel and Chichester.

Children are prepared for the Common Entrance and Scholarship examinations to Independent Senior Schools, but the emphasis is on ensuring that all children achieve to their potential both in and out of the classroom. The average number of children in a teaching group in the main school is 16.

Outdoor activities include: Soccer, Rugby, Hockey, Cricket, Netball, Rounders, Tennis, Athletics, Swimming, Archery, Golf, Mountain Biking, Trampolining and Volleyball.

Facilities include: theatre, three main libraries, fully computerised science laboratories, main ICT suite and ICT facilities in all areas of the school and a studio for pottery. There is an extensive range of clubs and activities organised both in and outside the school grounds.

There are also regular visits to a château in France for intensive language studies and Geography field work.

Children who show real potential in Art, Drama or Music are able to take advantage of excellence classes during the day.

Appreciation of Music is encouraged and a wide range of instruments is taught. There are three choirs and various ensemble groups, many of the children participate in local festivals and sit a range of musical exams. Importantly, all children perform and enjoy performing in regular concerts.

Drama is a timetabled subject and every child appears in a form play at some time during the year, some are on stage rather more frequently. LAMDA classes are also on offer.

Art is another strength of the school, many children build up portfolios of real quality to take to their next school and scholarships are won regularly. The constantly changing displays throughout the school are a testament to both the quality and the children's enthusiasm for Art.

The Pre-Prep Department, for children aged 2½–7, is housed in a lovely walled garden area with plenty of space for play activities. The curriculum is delivered by well qualified, enthusiastic form teachers with extra input from Main School specialists in PE, Music and ICT.

There is an 'after hours' club for children from Nursery age upwards, enabling parents to work a full day.

Boarding remains popular and many children take advantage of the flexible arrangements. The boarding facilities have been redesigned and decorated, partly by senior children, with super results.

There is a rolling programme to continually update the impressive provision for ICT and the heated swimming pool has become a super indoor pool. There are plans for a new Sports Hall, which will allow the present gym to be transformed into an Arts Hall.

Important though these facilities are, the happiness and safety of our children remain the top priority.

This is supported by the ISI Inspection report of 2007 that states that "the quality of relationships between the pupils and staff is outstanding".

Great Houghton Preparatory School (GDST)

Great Houghton Hall Northampton NN4 7AG
Tel: 01604 761907
Fax: 01604 761251
e-mail: office@ghps.co.uk
website: www.ghps.co.uk

Founded in 1955.

This is one of the 29 schools of The Girls' Day School Trust. For further information about the Trust, see p. xxiv.

***Headmaster*: R O Barnes**, MA, BEd Oxon, FRSA

Deputy Head: Mrs P J Yates, CertEd, NPQH

Age Range. 1–13.

Number of Day Pupils. 224 boys, 90 girls.

Fees per term (2008-2009). Years 4–8: £3,466 (Lunch £175); Reception to Year 3: £2,061–£2,840 (Lunch £160).

Great Houghton Hall is a mainly Georgian house (Grade II) of architectural distinction. The school benefits from being easily accessible while providing delightful, secure, rural surroundings of 26 acres in a conservation area.

GHPS is a well-established school with many strengths, combining a very broad, inclusive approach with specialist expertise. The emphasis of the school is on the encouragement of the whole child: via assemblies that are Christian in ethos, in the classroom, on the games field, in relationships and through responsibilities. Children develop confidence and courtesy, self-discipline and self-knowledge in a happy, purposeful environment. Our most recent ISI inspection report observed that our pupils 'are notably well behaved, polite and hard working'.

Boys and girls join our 'outstanding' (Ofsted Report) Early Years department from age 12 months and most transfer to day or boarding, co-ed or single-sex Senior Schools at 13+ via Common Entrance or Scholarship. These include: the Bedford Schools, Bloxham, Kimbolton, Malvern St James, Northampton High School for Girls, Northamptonshire Grammar School, Oakham, Oundle, Rugby, Stowe, Uppingham and Wellingborough. Form teachers and subject specialists maintain high academic standards in line with and beyond the National Curriculum, supported where appropriate by an expert Special Educational Needs Department.

The buildings provide large, light classrooms, as well as a Science Laboratory, Theatre/Gymnasium, Library and dedicated facilities for ICT, Art, Pottery, DT and Music. The school places strong emphasis on performing and visual arts.

In addition to basketball, badminton, gymnastics and table tennis in the gym, the grounds offer an all-weather surface, tennis courts and excellent pitches for: rugby, netball, hockey, football, cricket, athletics and rounders. The range of extra activities includes: art, ballet, dance, band, chess, choir, choristers, cookery, drama, individual music tuition, instrumental groups, Girls' club, reading club and team training.

Nutritious lunches are cooked in the school kitchen, while breakfast and tea are available to fit in with parents' busy lives: we are open from 08.00 to 18.10. A lively programme of social events complements regular charity fund-raising, directed amongst other worthy causes towards Outspan School, Kampala, Uganda, where we sponsor two pupils' education.

The school has a contemporary outlook and a traditional ethos.

Charitable status. Great Houghton Preparatory School is part of The Girls' Day School Trust, which is a Registered Charity, number 306983.

Great Walstead School

Lindfield Haywards Heath West Sussex RH16 2QL
Tel: 01444 483528
Fax: 01444 482122
e-mail: admin@greatwalstead.co.uk
website: www.greatwalstead.co.uk

Chairman of the Board of Governors: M J Olliff-Lee

***Headmaster*: Revd J J N Sykes**, MA

Deputy Head: J Crouch, BA Hons, CertEd

Age Range. $2^1/_2$–13.

Number of Pupils. Boys: 21 Weekly Boarders, 129 Day Boys. Girls: 7 Weekly Boarders, 64 Day Girls. Pre-preparatory Dept: 76 boys, 53 girls, Nursery: 58 boys, 55 girls.

Fees per term (from January 2008). Day £1,910–£3,775. Weekly Boarding (in addition to Tuition): £310–£860 (1–4 nights).

In 1927, Mr R J Mowll, who founded his school in 1925, moved his pupils from Enfield to Great Walstead. He came to a Victorian country house set in over 260 acres of fields and woodland where children could both enjoy and learn from the unspoilt countryside around them.

From those beginnings, Great Walstead has developed into a thriving co-educational prep school, catering for children from $2^1/_2$ to 13. It is a school which above all values children as people and regards it as vital that they develop their potential: in the academic sphere, in sport, in all things creative, socially and spiritually. The school stands for secure Christian values which provide an essential foundation for the whole of education and life.

The Nursery welcomes children from the ages of $2^1/_2$ until it is time to enter the Pre-Prep at age 4. It provides a full, rich and varied nursery education and lays firm foundations in basic skills and understanding for future learning. The Nursery is open both mornings and afternoons to provide maximum flexibility of hours for children and parents.

The Pre-Prep covers the years from 4 to 7 within its own section of the school. It has its own library, hall and playground. The aim here is to ensure that the foundation skills of reading, writing and maths which the National Curriculum endorses are taught and learnt while at the same time adding the breadth of interest which the staff are able to provide. For example children learn French, Computer skills, and have specialist Music tuition.

Children enter the Junior School at 7, either from the Pre-prep or from other schools. For the next two years they will have a class teacher who supervises them closely for a good proportion of the day, but have specialist teachers for French, music, computers, art, craft, design technology and PE. They have games or outdoor activities each day and gradually learn to become more independent.

Children in the senior age group are taught by graduate specialist teachers for the most part and are prepared primarily for the Common Entrance examination and senior school scholarships at 13, but also for other examinations. In the past ten years over 90 scholarships to senior schools have been won. A newly opened Woodland Wing provides classrooms and subject rooms for the senior children. There is also a computer room (with 21 linked PCs), a new and extremely well-equipped Science laboratory, and a fine library.

Acres of farmland, playing fields and woodland make many outdoor activities possible. The children build camps in the Summer term and the log cabin gives boarders an enjoyable chance to camp out! The purpose-built Challenge Course gives enormous pleasure all the year round! In addition there are opportunities to go on expeditions.

The Art, Craft and Design Technology department is housed in old farm buildings which have been adapted to make fine modern workshops and studios. All children encounter all parts of the programme each year and in addition can gain further experience in their spare time.

The school's spacious grounds provide opportunities for a wide range of sports. All the year round swimming is encouraged using our own outdoor heated pool and local indoor pools. The superbly equipped sports hall and extensive outdoor facilities make it possible for a large number of different team games to be played as well as other more individual sports.

The school has a Referral Unit where staff with dyslexia training are able to give the extra support required by children who are referred to them and to provide training and techniques of learning that all need.

Music has long been a strength at Great Walstead. A high proportion of the children learn instruments in the Music School. They play in groups, bands and orchestras. Singing is encouraged. Music and drama often come together for performances. All children have opportunities to act. As well as major productions, there are shorter form plays with large casts.

The girls' and boys' boarding areas (which cater for weekly boarding only) provide a comfortable home under the care of a married couple assisted by other boarding staff. Matron sees to the health of all children in the school. The school provides flexible holiday, pre- and after school care as well as other holiday activities to meet the needs of today's parents.

Parents are always made most welcome at the school. There is a thriving parents' organisation which provides a number of most successful social events and raises substantial sums for the benefit of the school.

Academic and Music Scholarships are offered at 7+, 8+, 9+, 10+ and 11+, and Sports Scholarships at 8+, 9+, 10+ and 11+.

Charitable status. Great Walstead School is a Registered Charity, number 307002. It exists to provide a good education on Christian foundations.

Greenfield

Brooklyn Road Woking Surrey GU22 7TP
Tel: 01483 772525
Fax: 01483 728907
e-mail: schooloffice@greenfield.surrey.sch.uk
website: www.greenfield.surrey.sch.uk

Chairman of the Governors: Dr Geoffrey Smith

***Headteacher*: Mrs Janis Radcliffe**, BSc

Age Range. 3–11 years.
Number of Pupils. 87 day girls, 90 day boys.
Fees per term (2008-2009). £1,428–£3,000.

Greenfield is firmly co-educational, boys and girls being equally represented in all year groups. The school is one wherein a happy balance between the formal and informal is achieved in all areas of the curriculum, and an expectation of courtesy and good manners goes hand in hand with a collective sense of comraderie and good humour.

Whilst there is no written admission test or examination, children are assessed at entry, thus appropriate teaching is ensured. All are thoroughly prepared for examinations – SATs at eleven, 11+ senior school entry and Common Entrance. Informed advice regarding senior schools is available to parents at all times.

Music is a particular strength at Greenfield, which has an orchestra, jazz band, choirs and a variety of groups involving wind, strings, percussion and steel band. All Year 2 pupils enjoy free violin tuition.

Sport is eclectic, thus pupils enjoy a wide range of activities which include swimming, hockey, netball, football and athletics.

ICT is undertaken by all pupils from 5 years in networked suites.

School visits are integral with the curriculum and all day trips and residential field trips are included in school fees; the National and Tate Galleries, London Zoo and Hampton Court are typical venues. France, Germany, Holland, Devon and Wales are typical locations for residential visits.

A prospectus is available on request; prospective parents are welcomed individually by the Headteacher, who undertakes an initial information interview followed by a tour of the school.

Charitable status. Greenfield is a Registered Charity, number 295145. It aims to offer an excellent education to children of all abilities.

Gresham's Preparatory School

Holt Norfolk NR25 6EY
Tel: 01263 714600
01263 714575 Pre-Preparatory School
Fax: 01263 714060
e-mail: prep@greshams.com
website: www.greshams.com

Chairman of Governors: A N G Duckworth-Chad, OBE, DL

***Headmaster*: J H W Quick**, BA Hons Durham, PGCE

Age Range. 3–13.
Number of Pupils. 375: Boarders 50, Day pupils 325.
Fees per term (2008-2009). Boarders £5,870, Day £4,465. Pre-Prep: £2,225–£2,470.

Gresham's Preparatory School is part of the family of Gresham's Schools, which are located in the busy market town of Holt in a beautiful and tranquil part of North Norfolk. Some pupils enter the school from the Pre-Preparatory School, which is based on a separate site half a mile from the Preparatory School, but many others enter the school from elsewhere. Most pupils move on to Gresham's Senior School, but the school has a very good record of winning scholarships and gaining excellent Common Entrance results to other major Independent Schools.

The school has excellent facilities including extensive playing fields, an Art and Technology Centre (opened in 2001) and a modern and well equipped Music School. The use of two Astroturf Hockey pitches, the swimming pool, sports hall and many other excellent sports facilities are shared with the Senior School.

Boarders are accommodated in modern, comfortable bedrooms in Crossways House (girls) or Kenwyn House (boys). Flexible boarding is available and is extremely popular.

The school prides itself on the breadth of its curriculum. Sport, Drama and Music play an important part in the lives of all pupils. The school has built up a considerable reputation in these areas in recent years. There is a wide arrange of extra-curricular activities available in the evenings.

Above all the school wants children to enjoy the process of growing up and developing their talents to the full and to establish the strong roots that will help them become self assured and well balanced adults.

Entry Requirements. Entry is by assessment in Mathematics and English and the recommendation of the child's previous school. Entry is possible into all year groups. Scholarships and Bursaries are available for entry into Year 7.

Pre-Preparatory School. Co-educational, age 3–7, Day pupils only.

Headmistress: Mrs J Davidson

The Pre-Preparatory School is housed in the beautiful setting of Old School House. It is a vibrant and dynamic school that puts great emphasis on the development of the whole child as well giving children an excellent academic grounding.

Charitable status. Gresham's School is a Registered Charity, number 1105500. It exists for the purpose of educating children.

Grimsdell

Mill Hill Pre-Preparatory School

Winterstoke House Wills Grove Mill Hill London NW7 1QR
Tel: 020 8959 6884
Fax: 020 8959 4626
e-mail: office@grimsdell.org.uk

website: www.grimsdell.org.uk

Co-educational Pre-Preparatory Day School.

Chairman of Court of Governors: Prof M R E Proctor, ScD, FRS

***Head*: Mrs P E R Bennett-Mills**, CertEd

Age Range. 3–7.

Number of Pupils. 184: 111 Boys, 73 Girls.

Fees per term (2008-2009). £3,570 (full day), Nursery: £1,936 (mornings only), £1,642 (afternoons only).

Grimsdell is situated in the Green Belt on the borders of Hertfordshire and Middlesex but only ten miles from central London. It stands adjacent to Mill Hill School's 120 acres of land, enjoying the advantages of a rural environment. Grimsdell is part of the Mill Hill School Foundation. It provides a happy, secure and rich learning environment for boys and girls aged 3 to 7. Belmont, the Mill Hill Preparatory School, is less than a quarter of a mile away and educates pupils from 7 to 13, the majority of whom move on to the senior school, Mill Hill.

The boys and girls at Grimsdell learn through hands-on experience. With the support and guidance of professional, caring staff and excellent resources and equipment, each child is encouraged to reach their full potential. Our approach combines traditional skills of reading, writing and mathematics with the breadth and balance offered by an enhanced National Curriculum. Every pupil can enjoy many opportunities offered by learning through Science, Technology and Computing. They also gain much from Art, Drama, Music, PE and French lessons.

The school is housed in a large Victorian building with its own secure play areas and adventure playgrounds, taking advantage of further facilities on the Mill Hill site including sports fields, swimming pool and theatre.

The usual age of entry is at 3 and 4 years, but 5 and 6 year olds are considered as vacancies occur. It is expected that most children will pass to Belmont at the end of Year 2.

Charitable status. The Mill School Foundation is a Registered Charity, number 1064758. It exists to provide education for boys and girls.

Grimwade House

67 Balaclava Road, Caulfield, Victoria 3161, Australia
Tel: 00 61 3 9865 7800
Fax: 00 61 3 9865 7888
e-mail: grimwade@mgs.vic.edu.au
website: www.mgs.vic.edu.au

Chairman of School Council: Mr C G Clark, BComm Melbourne, DipAgEcon Reading

***Head*: Mr Andrew Boyd**, DipT, BEd, MEdPA Monash, MACE

Age Range. 5–12.

Number of Children. 680 girls and boys, all day pupils.

Fees per term (from January 2008). Prep–Year 6: A$4,080 ($16,320 per annum). There are four terms to the school year.

Grimwade House, the co-educational junior school of Melbourne Grammar, is located in Caulfield, about 7 kilometres from the Senior School and Wadhurst. It opened as a school in 1918, following the gift of a fine old Victorian home, "Harleston", to Melbourne Grammar by the Grimwade family.

Grimwade House has its own Chapel, Assembly Hall, two Libraries, two Art and Craft areas, a Science Laboratory, Music School, PE Centre including an indoor pool and gymnasium, playgrounds and modern classrooms.

A full-time qualified staff of 50 teach a core curriculum including English, Mathematics, Science, Art, Technology, Religious & Values Education, Music, Physical Education and Mandarin Chinese. Computers are used at all levels and notebook computers for each student are an integral part of the curriculum in Years 5 and 6. There are also a School Counsellor, Chaplain and Learning Strategies teachers. The emphasis is on learning as a positive and challenging experience.

The School has its own orchestra and choir as well as many smaller instrumental and choral groups. Sporting activities include Australian rules football, soccer, hockey, cross country, athletics, cricket, basketball, tennis and swimming.

All students in Years 5 and 6 attend the School Camp at Woodend, some 80 kilometres from Melbourne.

Grosvenor School

Edwalton Grange Nottingham NG12 4BS
Tel: 0115 923 1184
Fax: 0115 923 5184
e-mail: office@grosvenorschool.co.uk
website: www.grosvenorschool.co.uk

***Headmaster*: C G J Oldershaw**, BEd

Age Range. 4–13.

Number of Pupils. 160 boys and girls.

Fees per term (2008-2009). £2,350–£2,600.

Grosvenor School was founded in 1876. It is a co-educational day Prep School, which is easily accessible on the south side of Nottingham. A broad curriculum is taught which is designed to give the children a preparation for life while covering requirements for entry to Senior Schools at 13+ and 11+. There is a newly-equipped laboratory, an IT centre, dedicated Art, Pottery, Music and Design Technology rooms, as well as Junior and Senior Libraries. A wide range of individual music tuition is offered. Soccer, Hockey, Cricket, Rugby, Netball, Rounders and Athletics are the main sporting activities. Swimming lessons are given to all pupils over 7 years. Tennis, Badminton and Golf coaching is available. There is a comprehensive programme of clubs and after-school activities.

"A traditional school for today's child."

Guildford High School Junior School (UCST)

London Road Guildford Surrey GU1 1SJ
Tel: 01483 561440
Fax: 01483 306516
e-mail: alex.kearney@church-schools.com
website: www.guildfordhigh.surrey.sch.uk

Chairman of Local Governing Body: Mrs L M Keat

***Headmistress*: Mrs S J Phillips**, BA Hons (Reading)

Age Range. Girls 4–11.

Number of Pupils. 285.

Fees per term (2007-2008). £2,198 (Reception–Year 2), £2,998 (Years 3–6).

The Junior School at Guildford High School is situated on the same site as the Senior School. It is a modern, bright, self-contained school with the third floor especially designed for art, music, science, IT and the Library.

The girls normally start in the Reception classes (4 years) or at Year 3 (7 years), however, they are welcome in any year group depending on spaces available, and work their way through the Junior School with natural progression on to the Senior School at Year 7 (11 years).

The breadth and depth of the curriculum encompasses 15 fast paced subjects, with an embedded thinking skills programme. Three modern foreign languages are included, with Spanish starting in Year 1 for the five year olds. Music, drama and sport play an important part in the curricular and co-curricular programmes. Specialist teachers and resources are employed throughout the Junior School. Parents and teachers work closely together to ensure excellent differentiation and a nurturing environment with strong pastoral care.

Guildford High Junior School girls of all abilities and temperaments are confident, happy and well-prepared for entry to the Senior School.

Charitable status. The United Church Schools Trust (to which Guildford High School belongs) is a Registered Charity, number 1016538.

The Haberdashers' Aske's Boys' Preparatory School

Butterfly Lane Elstree Herts WD6 3AF
Tel: 020 8266 1779
Fax: 020 8266 1808
e-mail: office@habsboys.org.uk
website: www.habsboys.org.uk

Chairman of Governors: Mr M D G Wheldon, FRICS

***Head*: Miss Y M Mercer**, BEd, Dip Adv Ed

Deputy Head: Mr M G Brown, BSc

Age Range. 5–11.
Number of Boys. 270.
Fees per term (2008-2009). £3,225–£4,285.

The Preparatory School is housed in a delightful purpose-built building, on the same campus as the Main School. The boys are able to share the facilities and grounds of the Main School, the Sports Centre, the heated indoor Swimming Pool, the Music School and the Dining Room.

A broad and balanced curriculum is delivered. In addition, the Preparatory School offers a wealth of extra-curricular and holiday activities in which all boys are encouraged to participate.

Boys enter the Preparatory School each September after assessments at the age of 5+ and 7+. Boys are expected to move into the Main School at 11.

For further details, please see entry in HMC section.

Charitable status. The Haberdashers' Aske's Charity is a Registered Charity, number 313996. It exists to promote education.

The Hall

23 Crossfield Road Hampstead London NW3 4NU
Tel: 020 7722 1700
Fax: 020 7483 0181
e-mail: office@hallschool.co.uk
website: www.hallschool.co.uk

Chairman of Governors: Dr A G Hearden, OBE

***Headmaster*: P J Lough**, MA (Oxon), PGCE (Dunelm)

Age Range. 4–13.
Number of Pupils. 450 Day Boys.
Fees per term (2008-2009). £3,450–£4,190 (inclusive).

Founded in 1889, the school is on three sites within close proximity. The majority of boys join Reception or Year 1 at the age of 4 or 5, but a few places are usually available in later years. The average class size is 18.

In 2004 the Reception department was extensively refurbished and now provides excellent facilities.

The Junior School (Years 1–3) was extended recently and provides up-to-date computing, science and music facilities. The Senior School underwent a major programme of refurbishment in 2000/01 to give a new library, improved music, DT, pottery and computing facilities, and new changing rooms. Boys in the Junior School use the sports hall, located in the Senior School, and have lunch in the dining hall which serves the whole school.

From the Junior School, boys transfer to the Middle School for Years 4 and 5. During that time they make the transition from classroom based teaching to subject based teaching. Boys are taught by subject specialists from Year 5.

The Hall prides itself on the breadth of education it offers. Senior School boys study Art, Drama, Music, Pottery, ICT, Design Technology and Current Affairs within the timetable and there is a broad range of after-school activities.

Team games, soccer, rugby and cricket are played mainly at the Wilf Slack Memorial Ground, and in recent years fencing has developed as a major sporting strength. Hockey, squash, athletics, golf and other sports are also offered.

The school is not linked with any particular senior school. Over half the boys proceed to London day schools, such as Westminster, St Paul's, Highgate, City of London and UCS, and others proceed to leading boarding schools such as Eton, Harrow, Winchester and King's Canterbury. In recent years numerous academic scholarships have been won at these and other schools. Other awards have been won in areas such as music and sport.

The school was last inspected in October 2004 and the report may be found at www.isi.net.

Charitable status. The Hall School Charitable Trust is a Registered Charity, number 312722. It exists entirely for the purposes of education.

Hall Grove

London Road Bagshot Surrey GU19 5HZ
Tel: 01276 473059
Fax: 01276 452003
e-mail: office@hallgrove.surrey.sch.uk
website: www.hallgrove.co.uk

***Headmaster*: A R Graham**, BSc, PGCE

Deputy Headmaster: I Adams

Age Range. 4–13.
Number of Children. Pre-Preparatory (age 4–7) 99. Preparatory (age 7–13) 221.
Fees per term (2008-2009). Pre-Preparatory £2,545; Preparatory: £3,200 (Years 3–5), £3,525 (Years 5–8). Fees inclusive of meals and all essential extras including field trips.

Hall Grove is a thriving co-educational school for 4–13 year olds. Weekly/Flexi boarding is offered for up to 12 pupils. The main entry ages are 4, 7 and 11. There is a separate nursery in the grounds for children from the age of 2.

The school was founded in 1957 by the parents of the current Headmaster. At its centre is a most attractive Georgian house set in beautiful gardens and parkland. Recent additions have provided some modern rooms and specialist teaching areas, an impressive computer facility and new classroom blocks. Despite this building programme, the character and atmosphere of a family home has been retained.

The academic standards are high and there is a very strong emphasis on Sport and Music. A wide range of activities flourish; woodwork, drama and a host of major and minor sports including soccer, rugby, hockey, netball, rounders, cricket, tennis, athletics, swimming, golf, judo, basketball, badminton and dance. Riding and stable management is an added attraction with the opening of Pony Grove in the school grounds in 2006.

The school day continues until 5.40 pm for Years 7 and 8 and older children may stay overnight on a regular basis. There is also provision for after-school care and a full programme of evening activities.

Hall Grove has its own residential field study centre situated on the South Devon coast called Battisborough House and there are many field trips and expeditions both in Devon and overseas. Battisborough is available for hire by other schools and can accommodate up to 30 in comfort.

Hallfield School

48 Church Road Edgbaston Birmingham B15 3SJ
Tel: 0121 454 1496
Fax: 0121 454 9182
e-mail: admissions@hallfield.bham.sch.uk
website: www.hallfieldschool.co.uk

Founded 1879.

Governing Body: The Hallfield School Trust

Chairman of Governors: Dr N Fisher, MA, MLitt

***Headmaster*: J A Shackleton**, BEd, MA

Deputy Head: J P Thackway, BA Hons, PGCE

Age Range. 3 months to 11 years.

Number of Pupils. Upper School (7–11 years): 198 Day Boys and Girls. Pre-Preparatory Department (3½–7 years): 207 Day Boys and Girls. Nursery (2½–3½ years): 58 Boys and Girls, Hallfield First (3 months to 2½ years).

Fees per term (2007-2008). Hallfield First and Nursery on application; Pre-Prep £2,425; Upper School £2,885. Lunches are included in the fees.

The school is divided into four sections: Hallfield First for children aged 3 months to 2½ (newly opened in May 2006), the Nursery for children aged 2½ to 3½, the Pre-Preparatory Department for 3½ to 7 years and the Upper School for children aged 7–11 years. The well qualified staff consists of 24 teachers and a teaching assistant in the Upper School, 16 teachers and 6 teaching assistants in the Pre-Prep Department, 12 Nursery Nurses and Assistants in the Nursery and 4 Nursery Nurses and a Nursery Manager in Hallfield First.

The majority of pupils enter the School through the Nursery. Direct entry into the Pre-Prep and Upper School is by means of an entrance test and interview. There is no automatic entry from Nursery to Pre-Prep and from Pre-Prep to Upper School. Children are appropriately assessed prior to the proposed move into either Pre-Prep or Upper School and are expected to perform at a level that will enable them to adjust to the new demands and expectations without difficulty.

Hallfield has a fine academic record, including an impressive list of Scholarship successes, and sets as its goal "striving for excellence" in all fields. The wide curriculum satisfies and goes well beyond the demands of the National Curriculum.

The major sports are association football, rugby and cricket for boys; rounders, netball and tennis for girls. Other sports include athletics, swimming, gymnastics and basketball. The playing fields, which form part of the School grounds, provide sufficient space to accommodate all the major seasonal sporting activities. Music is given a high profile and many pupils learn musical instruments.

Pupils are prepared for entry to local selective day schools at 11; a few pupils move on to boarding schools. All pupils are encouraged to strive for excellence in all that they do and high standards of work, dress, behaviour and courtesy are expected at all times.

The School occupies a fine 20-acre site in a very pleasant area of the City. Classrooms are bright and well equipped and class sizes rarely exceed 18. Over the past twelve years an extensive development programme has added a range of new facilities to the original late Georgian buildings, including a purpose-built Nursery, six additional Pre-Prep classrooms, two impressive laboratories, Sports Hall, Music School and an all-weather pitch. Recent developments have provided a new ICT Suite and Art & Design Room as well as larger and refurbished classrooms for Upper School. A new sports pavilion opened this summer.

A wide range of extra-curricular activities is available. At the moment these include: art, athletics, ballet, badminton, basketball, brass group, chess, choir, cricket, cross-country, drama, information technology, Lego, orchestra, orienteering, quiz, recorders, sailing, football, string band, speech and wind band. During the summer and Easter breaks there are also successful holiday clubs.

There is an active Parents' Association which organises a number of social events each year, as well as raising funds for equipment to enhance the education of children in the School. Pupils are encouraged to maintain their links with the School by joining the Old Hallfieldian Society.

Charitable status. Hallfield School Trust is a Registered Charity, number 528956. It exists for the purpose of providing education for children.

Halstead Preparatory School for Girls

Woodham Rise Woking Surrey GU21 4EE
Tel: 01483 772682
Fax: 01483 757611
e-mail: registrar@halstead-school.org.uk
website: www.halstead-school.org.uk

Chairman of Governors: Mrs A Murray

***Headmistress*: Mrs S G Fellows**, BA Hons

Age Range. Nursery–11.

Number of Pupils. 200 Girls.

Fees per term (2007-2008). Nursery (flexible) from £720; Kindergarten to Year 2 £2,678; Years 3–6 £3,136.

The fees from Kindergarten to Year 6 are inclusive of tuition, books, and lunches.

Halstead School was founded by Mrs Olive Bidwell in 1927 at Halstead Place, near Sevenoaks, Kent. During the war it moved to Devizes, Wiltshire, before re-opening at the present location in Woodham Rise, a leafy part of residential Woking in 1947. The main school building is a large Edwardian house to which modern facilities have been added including a spacious, purpose-built Pre-Preparatory Department, a new gym/performing hall and music room. A happy, friendly atmosphere pervades giving the feel of a home with desks in it, where girls go out into the garden to play; there are no hard play areas.

Each child is treated as an individual and given a broad education in line with the National Curriculum but with many extras and the advantage of an excellent adult/child ratio. The philosophy of the school is to educate "the whole child" so that creative, physical, social, emotional and spiritual aspects of each girl's development are considered as well as her academic ability. Every child has the opportunity to take part in one of the many sports teams, choirs or the school orchestra. There have been notable successes recently in musical and sporting competitions and academic scholarships are regularly achieved.

Outside, and sometimes during, the school day, there are many optional extras such as Judo, Art and Craft Workshops, Computer Clubs, Tennis Coaching and individual Music lessons on a whole range of instruments. Before and After School Care is also available for a modest additional charge for all pupils from Nursery upwards.

Charitable status. Halstead (Educational Trust) Limited is a Registered Charity, number 270525. It exists to provide a high quality all-round education for girls aged 3–11.

Hampshire Collegiate Junior School (UCST)

Embley Park Romsey Hampshire SO51 6ZA
Tel: 01794 515737
e-mail: info@hampshirecs.org.uk
website: www.hampshirecs.org.uk

Chairman of the Local Council: Mr David d'Arcy Hughes

Principal: Hector MacDonald, BSc, MA, CChem, CSci, FRMS, FRSC

***Head*: Mrs Elaine Hooton**, BA, PGCE, FRGS

Age Range. 2¾–11 Co-educational.

Number of Pupils. 307 Day Pupils: 156 Boys, 151 Girls.

Fees per term (2008-2009). Nursery: £1,553 (mornings only), £2,170 (full day). Junior School £2,478–£2,769.

The school operates an extended day from 8 am to 5.30 pm offering comprehensive care to support busy, modern family living.

The school has its own Nursery taking children from 2 years 9 months and is very flexible in session bookings to suit parents' working patterns and family life. The Reception to Year 2 pupils enjoy small class sizes with an emphasis on careful monitoring of progress in the core subjects and early intervention in the event of any identified learning needs. A broad curriculum is offered, including French, Music and PE taught by specialists and weekly access to a fully networked computer suite.

Within Years 3 to 6 the focus is on careful monitoring of progress, development of potential across the curriculum and work in preparing for the challenges of senior schooling and associated scholarships. The school seeks to provide, through small class sizes, teaching expertise and support staff, a broad education tailored to the individual needs of the children in the school. There is both a clear and effective learning support structure and policy to help children experiencing difficulties, as well as challenge those who are our most able children.

There is a strong tradition of musical achievement in the school with two choirs, an orchestra, rock band and recorder ensembles. Children compete in a wide range of sports within curriculum time and as part of the busy House and extra-curriculum programme. Drama is promoted via its inclusion within the weekly timetable for all children, annual LAMDA preparation and in the end of year productions. Our annual art exhibition showcases artistic talent in the school and regular linked work with local artists encourages enthusiasm for the visual arts. Each year our two oldest year groups undertake residential visits. Year 5 experience geographical studies and outdoor pursuits in Devon, whilst Year 6 travel to Normandy to experience a week's immersion in a wide variety of activities, all conducted in French.

The school seeks to achieve a high standard of academic achievement and to encourage attitudes of tolerance, adaptability, invention, persistence, responsibility, confidence, compassion, flexibility and creativity coupled with a lifelong love of learning and endeavour. Our last ISI inspection highlighted the school's pastoral care as a 'outstanding'.

Charitable status. The United Church Schools Trust is a Registered Charity, number 1016538.

Handcross Park School

Handcross Haywards Heath West Sussex RH17 6HF
Tel: 01444 400526
Fax: 01444 400527
e-mail: info@handxpark.com
website: www.handxpark.com

Where potential is nurtured and success is celebrated in a friendly learning environment.

Chairman of Governors: Mrs T J B Hutchings

***Headmaster*: W J Hilton**, BA, CertEd

***Head of Pre-Prep*: Mrs S Harper**, MA, CertEd

Deputy Heads:
N K Cheesman, BSc, PGCE
T W P Hills, BA, QTS

Age Range. 2–13 Co-educational.

Number of Pupils. 273: Boys 153, Girls 120.

Fees per term (2008-2009). Nursery: £530 (for minimum 2 morning sessions), Pre-Preparatory: £2,692, Preparatory: £3,937 (Years 3–4), £4,517 (Years 5–8). Weekly Boarding: £5,293.

Handcross Park is a non-selective pre-preparatory and preparatory school, set in beautiful surroundings but conveniently located just off the A23 and close to Haywards Heath, Horsham, Gatwick and Crawley. The School provides a first-class education for children from 2 to 13 in a happy family atmosphere within a caring Christian framework.

The School unashamedly takes pride in the pursuit of excellence for all its pupils. Alongside academic endeavours staff believe ardently in educating children to become well-rounded, compassionate and articulate citizens.

The modern Nursery, situated in the Secret Garden and accommodated in well-designed and purpose-built classrooms, offers a wonderful environment in which to begin the exciting adventure of a child's school career. Activities are specially designed to help young minds investigate and find solutions for themselves and the cleverly planned classrooms allow children the opportunity to pursue interests both inside and outdoors. With an excellent staff to pupil ratio throughout the Early Years and small class sizes right the way through the school, the emphasis is on helping the individual to flourish as part of a supportive, vibrant and happy community.

Handcross Park has a proven academic record with many Year 8 pupils gaining scholarships to Senior Schools both locally and further afield and a 100% pass rate at Common Entrance. But as well as a deep and broad knowledge of the curriculum, pupils also develop an understanding of the role they can play in society as informed and caring citizens.

Alongside the provision of a high quality academic education for all children, the School's well-qualified, friendly staff focus on nourishing the creative, musical and sporting aptitudes of the pupils. With a vibrant Music Department, inspiring Art Studio, excellent sports coaching and facilities and well-equipped Science, IT and Design Technology Rooms, pupils are offered the best opportunities to foster and showcase their talents.

The 'home away from home' accommodation at Handcross Park has been refurbished, revamped and rejuvenated and early in 2008 received an excellent report following an Ofsted inspection. With a variety of activities to choose from the focus is on having fun in a structured environment. Both flexi and weekly boarding are available and are very useful elements in the package of flexible pre and after school care offered to parents.

From the Nursery through to Year 8 the School 'offers exceptionally supportive pastoral care for its pupils' and this, coupled with a focus on achieving high academic standards, 'results in confident and happy pupils who leave the school very well-prepared for the next stage in their education' (ISI Inspection Report 2007).

Charitable status. Newells School Trust is a Registered Charity, number 307038. Handcross Park School exists to provide a high-quality education to children aged 2 to 13.

Hanford School

Childe Okeford Blandford Dorset DT11 8HN
Tel: 01258 860219
Fax: 01258 861255
e-mail: hanfordsch@aol.com
website: www.hanfordschool.co.uk

Chairman of Governors: The Hon Mark Bridges, GCMG

***Headmaster*: N S Mackay**, CertEd (Zimbabwe)

Age Range. 7–13.

Number of Girls. 100.

Fees per term (2007-2008). Boarders £5,500, Day Girls £4,500.

Hanford School, which was founded in 1947 by the Revd and Mrs C B Canning, is an early 17th Century manor house standing in about 45 acres and situated in the Stour valley, half way between Blandford and Shaftesbury. The amenities include a Chapel, Laboratories, a Music School, an Art School, a Gymnasium, a Swimming Pool, a Handwork Room, two Netball/Tennis Courts (hard) and a covered Riding School. Pupils are prepared for entry to all Independent Senior Schools.

Charitable status. The Hanford School Charitable Trust Ltd is a Registered Charity, number 1001751.

Haslemere Preparatory School

The Heights Hill Road Haslemere Surrey GU27 2JP
Tel: 01428 642350
Fax: 01428 645314
e-mail: office@haslemereprep.co.uk
website: www.haslemereprep.co.uk

Chairman of Governors: Mr M Pavia

***Headmaster*: P Wenham**, MA Cantab, PGCE

Age Range. Boys 2–13, Girls 2–4.

Number of Pupils. 215 Day Boys including 64 boys in Pre-Prep. Nursery: 61 boys and girls.

Fees per term (2007-2008). £2,199–£3,145. The school offers sibling discounts and Scholarships annually in academics and the arts.

The Heights is committed to giving each individual boy the best possible start to his education.

The school is a boys' independent day school for 4 to 13 year olds, with a Nursery Department which opened in September 2001 to cater for boys and girls aged 2+. The school is set in a stunning location, within walking distance of Haslemere town centre.

Academically it has an excellent reputation for producing well rounded, well mannered, confident young men. The majority of boys move on to senior schools such as the Royal Grammar School, King Edward's, Churchers, Lord Wandsworth, Charterhouse and Cranleigh, many with scholarships. The Heights seeks to encourage all boys to find the best within themselves by creating a safe and stimulating environment in which they can learn. A highly dedicated and professional staff teaches a well balanced curriculum, that includes not only the core subjects but also a wide range of extra-curricular activities, catering for all. Each individual's performance is closely monitored. Class sizes are small, with a maximum of 16. Minibus travel is provided from local areas and Haslemere railway station. After school care is provided until 6 pm. The Heights encourages an active involvement of parents in achieving its success.

For a copy of our prospectus, please contact the Headmaster's Secretary.

Charitable status. Haslemere Preparatory School Trust is a Registered Charity, number 294944.

Hatherop Castle Preparatory School

Hatherop Cirencester Glos GL7 3NB
Tel: 01285 750206
Fax: 01285 750430
e-mail: admissions@hatheropcastle.co.uk
website: www.hatheropcastle.co.uk

Chairman of Governors: Mr M StJ Parker, MA

***Headmaster*: Mr P Easterbrook**, BEd

Age Range. 2½–13. Kindergarten/Transition 2½–4½.

Number of Pupils. Prep and Pre-Prep: 110 Day Boys, 80 Day Girls, 21 Boarders (boarding from age 7). Kindergarten/Transition: 26 Day Boys, 23 Day Girls.

Fees per term (2008-2009). £2,045–£3,400 (Day), £4,965–£5,240 (Boarding), Kindergarten/Transition up to £2,177.

Founded in 1926, Hatherop Castle is a co-educational day and boarding prep school for children between the ages of 2½ and 13. Children are prepared for Common Entrance and Scholarship Examinations at 11+ and 13+; the children move on to a wide range of senior independent schools. Weekly boarders are accepted and the boarding facilities are homely and well furnished. A family atmosphere exists throughout the school. The curriculum spans a wide range of subjects and there is a great variety of sports and extra-curricular activities.

Set in 25 acres of beautiful Cotswold countryside, Hatherop Castle enjoys a superb setting and is a happy environment in which the pupils learn. The classes are housed in well-equipped rooms and the pre-prep and kindergarten/transition have their own self-contained areas where the pupils enjoy playing and working in a welcoming and stimulating atmosphere. The ICT Suite opened in October 2007 has impacted across the curriculum.

Charitable status. Hatherop Castle School Ltd is a Registered Charity, number 311710. It exists for the education of children. Fund-raising for home and overseas charities takes place throughout the year.

Hawkesdown House School

27 Edge Street Kensington London W8 7PN
Tel: 020 7727 9090
Fax: 020 7727 9988
e-mail: admin@hawkesdown.co.uk

website: www.hawkesdown.co.uk

Pre-Preparatory Day School for Boys.

***Headmistress*: Mrs C J Leslie**, BA (USA), CertEd

Age Range. 3–8.
Number of Pupils. 135 Boys.
Fees per term (2008-2009). £3,650 (age 3), £3,950 (age 4), £4,200 (age 5–8).

In December 2003, the Headmistress was the first Head of a free standing pre-preparatory school to be elected to membership of IAPS (The Independent Association of Prep Schools).

Early literacy and numeracy are of prime importance and the traditional academic subjects form the core curriculum. A balanced education helps all aspects of learning and a wide range of interests is encouraged. The School finds and fosters individual talents in each pupil. Boys are prepared for entry at eight to the main London and other preparatory schools. The Headmistress places the greatest importance on matching boys happily and successfully to potential schools and spends time with parents ensuring that the transition is smooth and free of stress.

Sound and thorough early education is important for success, and also for self-confidence. The thoughtful and thorough teaching and care at Hawkesdown House ensures high academic standards and promotes initiative, kindness and courtesy. Hawkesdown is a school with fun and laughter, where boys develop their own personalities together with a sense of personal responsibility.

The School provides an excellent traditional education, with the benefits of modern technology, in a safe, happy and caring atmosphere. Many of the boys coming to the School live within walking distance and the School has become an important part of the Kensington community.

There are clear expectations and the boys are encouraged by positive motivation and by the recognition and praise of their achievements, progress and effort. Individual attention and pastoral care for each of the boys is of great importance.

Hawkesdown House has a fine building in Edge Street, off Kensington Church Street.

Religious Denomination: Non denominational; Christian ethos.

Parents who would like further information or to visit the School and meet the Headmistress, should contact the School Office for a prospectus or an appointment.

The Hawthorns

Pendell Court Bletchingley Surrey RH1 4QJ
Tel: 01883 743048 (Prep); 01883 743718 (Pre-Prep)
Fax: 01883 744256
e-mail: admissions@hawthorns.com
website: www.hawthorns.com

Motto: *Love God, Love Your Neighbour*

The School is an Educational Trust controlled by a Board of Governors.

Chairman of Governors: Mr L J Baart

***Headmaster*: T R Johns**, BA, PGCE, FRGS

Age Range. 2–13.
Number of Pupils. 553 Day Pupils.
Fees per term (2008-2009). From £1,230 (Nursery 5 mornings) to £3,333.

Founded in 1926 near Redhill, The Hawthorns moved in 1961 to the haven of its present impressive site, a Jacobean manor set in 35 acres below the North Downs, with a catchment area from East Grinstead to Coulsdon and Dorking to Westerham.

The prospectus reflects the rich and diverse nature of our school. Recent developments include an innovative Nursery Ark, the Bull Centre for Science and ICT, a new Sports and Swimming complex, All-Weather Pitch and the Holman building for art and languages. The curriculum, incorporating the National Curriculum, Common Entrance and Scholarship goals, blends modern and traditional methods with emphasis on thorough grounding in English, Maths, Science, ICT and Languages. In Music, DT, Art and Textiles specialist centres are very well equipped. The strong Music Department fields three choirs and two orchestras, with a wide range of individual instrumental tuition available. Public recitals and regular competition entries are encouraged, with good scholarship results. The co-educational commitment to PE and Games is of great importance with major sports including soccer, netball, rugby, hockey, pop-lacrosse, cricket, tennis, cross-country, athletics, swimming and gymnastics. The grounds contain four sports areas, tennis courts and 5 acres of woodland for outdoor pursuits. An extensive programme of extra curricular activities is offered including sailing, high wires, squash, golf, ballet, modern dance, model-making, film-making, fashion design and cooking.

A flourishing Parent/Toddler group runs during term time with Extended Day facilities and a comprehensive Holiday Activity Programme.

We believe firmly in hard work encouraging excellent results and providing breadth of opportunity. This includes trips, exchanges, Schools of Swimming and Dance (open to the local community) and triathlon. Life Skills such as touch-typing, time management, teamwork, survival and service are all taught. Equal opportunities, enjoyment and success are sought for every child. Boys and girls gain entry as day pupils between the ages of 2 and 13 and are prepared for the Common Entrance examination and/or Scholarships at 11+ and 13+.

The staff consists of 35 full-time teachers, graduates or qualified in their particular field, and 7 part-time teachers. Mrs Johns oversees the domestic arrangements and personally supervises the children's health, aided by assistant matrons. The school is a living, happy, working community and a visit is essential.

Charitable status. The Hawthorns Educational Trust Limited is a Registered Charity, number 312067. It exists to provide education for girls and boys of 2 to 13 years.

Hazelwood School

Wolfs Hill Limpsfield Oxted Surrey RH8 0QU
Tel: 01883 712194
Fax: 01883 716135
e-mail: registrar@hazelwoodschool.com
website: www.hazelwoodschool.com

Chairman of Governors: A J Baulf, FCA

***Headmaster*: R McDuff**, BEd Hons, MA

Age Range. 2½–13.
Number of Pupils. 400 co-educational.
Fees per term (2007-2008). Day Pupils from £1,195 (Nursery Class) to £3,700.

Founded in 1890, Hazelwood stands in superb grounds, commanding a magnificent view over the Kent and Sussex Weald.

Pupils usually enter at 3+ into the Pre-Prep School, or at 7+ to the Prep School, joining those pupils transferring from the Pre-Prep to the Prep School. Entry at other ages is possible if space permits. 2004 saw the opening of a Pre-Nursery class allowing children to join at 2½.

A gradual transition is made towards subject specialist tuition in the middle and upper forms. All teaching staff are fully qualified. Pupils are prepared for the Common Entrance examinations at 11+ and 13+, and also for Scholarships to Senior Schools. 125 academic, all-rounder, sporting, music and art awards have been gained since 1995.

Extra-mural activity is an important part of every pupil's education. Excellent sports facilities, which include games fields, heated indoor swimming pool, gymnasium and many games pitches, tennis courts and other hard surfaces, allow preparation of school teams at various age and ability levels in a wide range of sports. A fully-equipped Sports Hall was completed in May 2004. Our aim is that every pupil has an opportunity to represent the School.

Art, Technology, Music and Drama are on the curriculum as well as being lively extra-mural activities. Our Centenary Theatre incorporates a 200-seat theatre, music school and Chapel. Extra-mural activities on offer include tap, ballet and jazz dance, judo, orchestras, choir, brass group, wind group, saxophone group, recorder group, sports coaching in many different sports, art, electronics, computing, modelling and chess.

Charitable status. Hazelwood School Limited is a Registered Charity, number 312081. It exists to provide excellent preparatory school education for boys and girls at Oxted, in Surrey.

Hazlegrove
King's Bruton Preparatory School

Hazlegrove Sparkford Yeovil Somerset BA22 7JA
Tel: 01963 440314
Fax: 01963 440569
e-mail: office@hazlegrove.co.uk
website: www.hazlegrove.co.uk

Senior Warden: Air Chief Marshal Sir Peter Squire, GCB, DFC, AFC, FRAeS

***Headmaster*: Richard Fenwick**, BEd, MA

Deputy Headmaster: Martin Davis, BEd

Head of Pre-Preparatory Department: Ellie Lee, BEd

Age Range. 2½–13.

Number of Pupils. 355 boys and girls of whom 90 are boarders. Preparatory (7–13 year olds) 262 pupils; Pre-Preparatory (2½–7 year olds) 93 pupils.

Fees per term (2008-2009). Preparatory: Boarders £4,835–£6,169 (fees are inclusive, there are no compulsory extras); Day pupils £3,413–£4,352

Pre-Preparatory: £2,147. Nursery: £22.85 (morning session); £17.35 (afternoon session) plus £3.05 for lunch.

Scholarships and Bursaries: Academic Scholarships are available for entry at 7+ and 11+. Music and Sport awards and Armed Forces Bursaries to serving members are also available.

The school is located within a 200-acre park and is based around a country house built by Carew Hervey Mildmay in 1730. The entrance to the school is situated on the A303 at the Sparkford roundabout opposite the turning to Yeovil and Sherborne. The Preparatory School has a strong boarding ethos which is reflected in the full days and Saturday morning lessons from Year four. There is a full range of activities for boarders and those day pupils who wish to join in during the evenings and at weekends.

Hazlegrove is a happy and purposeful school with an established tutor system. The curriculum provides a varied and exciting experience for pupils as they progress through the school and includes specialist taught Art, Design and Technology, Drama, Music and Outdoor Education. Latin is introduced in Year five for all pupils. The main sports are Rugby, Hockey, Cricket, Netball, Rounders, Tennis, Athletics and Swimming. Squash, Golf, Horse Riding and Kayaking are also available.

Streaming and setting is introduced as pupils progress through the school with a scholarship stream in the top two years. Pupils are entered for Common Entrance or Scholarship Examinations. About half go to the senior school, King's School Bruton (*see entry in HMC section*). Others move on to major secondary schools such as Sherborne, Sherborne School for Girls, Millfield, St Mary's Shaftsbury, King's College Taunton, Bryanston, Marlborough and Winchester. Between 15 and 20 scholarships and awards are gained by pupils each year. Extra support is available to those pupils who have specific learning difficulties or who are gifted.

Pupils have achieved considerable success at regional and national level in recent years through sport, in team and individual performances. In addition, the choir reached the finals of the BBC Radio 3 Children's Choir or the Year competition and pupils won the Exmoor Challenge last year.

Hazlegrove has outstanding facilities. These include a comprehensive Computer Network, the Theatre, a Sports Hall, a 25m Indoor Heated Pool, two Squash Courts, the Design Centre and an extensive Music School. Outside, the extensive playing fields include a 6-hole Golf Course, hard Tennis Courts and a synthetic pitch.

Pastoral care for Boarders, which is overseen by the Headmaster's wife, is provided by three sets of House Parents, four Matrons and a Nurse. The school has considerable experience of meeting the needs of pupils whose parents are in the Services or who live and work overseas. Flexible boarding can also be arranged to meet individual needs.

The school shop, which is on site, provides most necessary clothing and games kit.

Pre-Preparatory Department. Located in a purpose built facility within the grounds, the Pre-Preparatory Department provides a carefully structured curriculum which encourages the development of the basic skills within a balanced programme of learning and play. Full use is made of the Preparatory School facilities. After school care is available.

Charitable status. King's School, Bruton is a Registered Charity, number 1071997. It exists to provide education for children.

Headington Preparatory School

26 London Road Headington Oxford OX3 7PB
Tel: 01865 759400
Fax: 01865 761774
e-mail: admissions@headington.org
website: www.headington.org

Chairman of Board of Governors: Mr R G Barnes, BSc, MBA

***Headmistress*: Miss A J Bartlett**, BEd Hons London

Age Range. Girls 3–11.

Number of Pupils. 280.

Fees per term (2008-2009). Day: L3 and U2 £3,190; L2 and I £2,835; Transition and Kindergarten £2,510; Pre-Kindergarten and Nursery £2,190. Boarding (L3 and U2 only): £6,370–£6,590 weekly, £6,915–£7,125 full.

Headington Preparatory School occupies its own three-acre site just two minutes' walk from Headington School. The main building is a fine Victorian house, with several purpose-built additions, including a Foundation Stage Building for the Nursery and Reception classes and a new science block (2005). The grounds comprise gardens, an adventure playground, a hockey pitch, netball court and a special new children's garden for which pupils are responsible. The proximity of the Senior

School allows for use of their facilities, such as the heated indoor pool, where Preparatory School pupils from the age of five swim weekly.

The Nursery and Reception classes lay the basis for the pupils' future education, developing confidence, curiosity and social skills, and gradually introducing simple reading, writing and mathematics. Also housed in purpose-built classrooms, the four Key Stage 1 classes build on previous learning, and a broad range of topics are gradually introduced. In Key Stage 2 the girls prepare for their eventual transition to secondary education. ICT is taught from the Nursery upwards by a specialist teacher, and French is introduced at age seven.

Throughout the school emphasis is placed on the breadth of education. There are a considerable number of after school clubs, ranging from Cross Country to Chess Club, a programme of visiting speakers and workshops for all age groups, as well as a Creative Arts Week. Numerous educational outings are offered, including a residential stay in France for pupils in Year 6, and an outdoor activity week for Year 5. Drama plays an important role, with each year group staging an annual production. Most children learn at least one musical instrument and the Chamber Choir is highly acclaimed. The PE curriculum in Key Stage 2 includes hockey, netball, dance, gymnastics, swimming and rounders. Other sports, such as kwik cricket, judo, trampolining and fencing are optional after-school activities. After-school care is provided daily.

Entry to the school is by registration only until the age of seven. Thereafter candidates are invited to the school for a short assessment and informal interview. The main years of entry are at age 3, 4 and 7. The majority of pupils continue to Headington Senior School, with a number of girls being awarded scholarships every year. (*See Headington School entry in HMC section.*)

Charitable status. Headington School Oxford Limited is a Registered Charity, number 309678. It exists to provide quality education for girls.

Heath Mount School

Woodhall Park Watton-at-Stone Hertford Hertfordshire SG14 3NG
Tel: 01920 830230
Fax: 01920 830357
e-mail: registrar@heathmount.org
website: www.heathmount.org

The school became a Trust in September 1970, with a Board of Governors.

Chairman of Governors: Mrs L Haysey

***Headmaster*: R W Middleton**, MSc, BEd

Deputy Heads:
Mrs A Greer, BEd Hons
Mrs P Hawkins, MA (Hull), BEd Hons, CertEd

Age Range. 3–13.

Number of Pupils. Boys 207, Girls 150. Flexi/Sleepover boarding offered.

Fees per term (2007-2008). Weekly Boarders (4 nights): £5,090–£5,225; Boarding (in addition to Day fee): £365 (1 night), £725 (2 nights), £1,090 (3 nights). Day Pupils: Years 3–6 £3,685, Years 7–8 £3,820. Pre-Prep £2,850; Nursery £1,115–£2,520.

There is a reduction in fees for the second and subsequent children attending the School at the same time.

The School, situated five miles from Hertford, Ware and Knebworth, is a Georgian mansion with its own Chapel and Music School. It stands in glorious grounds of over forty acres in the middle of a large private park. From 1817 to 1933 Heath Mount was at Hampstead before moving to Woodhall Park. The excellent facilities include a new swimming pool, several games pitches, tennis courts, a nine-hole golf course, hard-play area and a Sports Hall within the grounds. The main house contains an imaginatively developed lower ground floor housing modern science laboratories and rooms for art, pottery, textiles, film making, computer-assisted design, food technology and design and technology. There is a further information technology room and well-stocked research and fiction libraries. A Pre-Prep and Nursery Unit was opened in 1991 and a Girls' Boarding House was opened in 1993.

The School has an excellent record of scholarships to leading independent senior schools.

Charitable status. Heath Mount School is a Registered Charity, number 311069.

Heatherton House School

Copperkins Lane Chesham Bois Amersham Bucks HP6 5QB
Tel: 01494 726433
Fax: 01494 729628
e-mail: admissions@heathertonhouse.co.uk
website: www.heathertonhouse.co.uk

Chairman of the Governors: Mr David Bracey

***Headmaster*: Mr P H Rushforth**, BEd, MA

Age Range. Girls 2½–11, Boys 2½–5.

Number of Pupils. 156.

Fees per term (2007-2008). £375–£2,975 inclusive of all but optional subjects.

Founded in 1912, the school is set in an attractive green and leafy location on the outskirts of Amersham.

Heatherton provides an excellent all-round education. Very high-quality facilities combined with an experienced staff of specialist teachers encourage each child's individual academic and emotional development. High standards are achieved across a broad curriculum with small classes (max 20), a caring ethos and a close relationship with parents.

Excellent results are produced at all stages of school performance tests: and at 11 pupils progress to both local independent girls' senior schools, often with scholarships, and Buckinghamshire grammar schools.

Musical, artistic and sporting talents flourish at Heatherton. A thriving orchestra, individual instrument lessons and many drama, ballet and music productions are an important part of life in a school year. Art and design skills are celebrated in display and exhibitions, both internally and externally. Each pupil is offered a wide range of sporting activities – swimming, netball, gymnastics, dance, athletics, tennis, pop lacrosse, hockey , with opportunities for cricket, rugby and cycling.

An extensive range of educational visits and activities in the UK and Europe are organised each year.

Charitable status. Heatherton House School is a Registered Charity, number 310630. It exists to provide high quality education for girls and boys.

Heathfield
The Junior School to Rishworth School

Rishworth West Yorkshire HX6 4QF
Tel: 01422 823564
Fax: 01422 820880
e-mail: admin@heathfieldjunior.co.uk
website: www.rishworth-school.co.uk

Motto: '*Deeds Not Words*'

Chairman of the Board of Governors: Mrs Dilys Whitaker, JP

***Head*: Mrs S M Temperley**, GRSM, ARMCM, ADB

Age Range. 3–11 co-educational.

Number of Pupils. 170 day boys/girls and 50-place Foundation Stage Unit.

Fees per term (from April 2008). Reception–Year 2 £1,635; Years 3–6 £2,395.

Staffing. 10 full-time teaching and 5 part-time teaching; 2 NNEB staff and 6 teaching assistants; additional teaching support in Physical Education; 9 specialist peripatetic staff provide expert tuition in Music and the Arts.

Location. Heathfield stands in its own grounds and enjoys an outstanding rural position in a beautiful Pennine location with easy access via the motorways to Manchester and Leeds.

Facilities. Well-equipped classrooms; Foundation Stage Unit and purpose-built Infant classes; designated teaching rooms for Music, Drama, Art, Design Technology; modern ICT Suite; Library; a multi-purpose Hall for assemblies and productions; heated indoor swimming pool; netball court and football/rugby pitch; Pre/After School Care and Holiday School available.

Aims. To provide a stimulating and challenging environment in which children want to achieve what they are able and where attainment is recognised and celebrated.

To ensure each child receives their full entitlement to a broad, balanced curriculum which builds on a solid foundation in Literacy and Numeracy.

To nurture productive relations which enhance the work of children and staff.

Curriculum. An extensive programme of study which incorporates the Foundation Stage, Key Stage 1 and Key Stage 2. An emphasis on developing an independence in learning and analytical thinking through Literacy, Numeracy, Science, French, History, Geography, Religious Studies, Design Technology, Information and Communications Technology, Music, Art and Physical Education.

Extra-Curricular Activities. Drama, Choir, Orchestra, Brass, Recorder and String Groups, Steel Pans, Art, Board Games; Sports include Swimming, Rounders, Netball, Football, Rugby, Cross-Country, Cricket, Athletics, Hockey.

Extensive termly fixtures list of sports for boys and girls.

Each term there are plays and musical concerts incorporating most children in the School. Residentials include Outdoor Pursuits, Camping and Environmental Studies.

Charitable status. Rishworth School is a Registered Charity, number 1115562. It exists to provide education for boys and girls.

Hereford Cathedral Junior School

28 Castle Street Hereford HR1 2NW
Tel: 01432 363511
Fax: 01432 363515
e-mail: secretary@hcjs.co.uk
website: www.hcjs.co.uk

Established 1898.

Chairman of Governors: The Earl of Darnley

***Headmaster*: T Wheeler**, MA, BA

Age Range. 2–11.

Number of children. 351: 188 boys and 163 girls.

Fees per term (2008-2009). £2,037–£2,532.

The school is the Junior School for Hereford Cathedral School and has the same board of Governors. Games facilities are shared but the teaching staff work exclusively in the Junior School.

Entry is via the Nursery, Reception or by an entrance examination at 7+. Most children continue through to the senior school subject to passing an examination at 11.

The school occupies listed Georgian and Medieval buildings in Castle Street at the East End of the Cathedral with facilities including specialist music rooms, an ICT centre and an extensive library. The Moat, a new nine-classroom building to house the Pre-Prep, opened in 2003.

There is a full and broad curriculum with the school noted for the strength of the music and games. French is taught from the age of 4.

The staff are well qualified and the maximum class size is 18. In the junior forms all subjects are taught by specialists.

Music plays an important part in the life of the school with the Cathedral Choristers being educated here and a team of over twenty peripatetic music teachers work between the two schools. There are two school choirs and an orchestra.

An extensive programme of clubs and activities is offered during lunchtime and after school aimed at giving all children opportunities to develop their talents.

The games fields are on the banks of the River Wye with expert coaching being given in the main sports of cricket, football, rugby, hockey, netball, rounders, athletics, lacrosse and swimming.

There is an active PTA organising a wide programme of social and fund-raising activities.

The Little Princess Trust founded in memory of former pupil, Hannah Tarplee, is based at the school and provides hair pieces for children who lose their hair through cancer treatment.

Charitable status. Hereford Cathedral School is a Registered Charity, number 518889. Its aims and objectives are to promote the advancement of education.

Hereward House School

14 Strathray Gardens London NW3 4NY
Tel: 020 7794 4820
Fax: 020 7794 2024
e-mail: herewardhouse@btconnect.com

***Headmistress*: Mrs L Sampson**

Age Range. 4–13.

Number of Pupils. 175 Day Boys.

Fees per term (2007-2008). £3,135–£3,850.

Hereward House is an IAPS Preparatory Day School for boys. The school's aim is to provide a lively, stimulating environment in which boys receive a thorough grounding in the basic skills. Modern teaching methods, Computers and Audio Visual Aids are employed alongside those traditional methods that have proved their worth. There is a well equipped Science Laboratory and a new Art and Music Block. All boys are prepared for the Common Entrance Examination to major independent senior schools.

Art, Music, Drama, Handicraft, Computing, Games and Swimming are an integral part of the curriculum. All boys are taught French and Latin; the more able linguists may also learn Greek. The school has a strong and continually expanding music and drama department. All boys are given the opportunity to learn at least one instrument and thus progress through ensemble work to the School Orchestra. After school clubs include Chess, Fencing, Greek, Computer, Art, Hockey, Table Tennis, Snooker and Squash.

Herries School

Dean Lane Cookham Dean Berks SL6 9BD
Tel: 01628 483350
Fax: 01628 483329
e-mail: office@herries.ws
website: www.herries.ws

Chairman of the Governors: Miss N Coombs

***Headmistress*: Mrs A M Bradberry**

Age Range. 3–11 Co-educational.

Number of Pupils. 110 Day Boys and Girls.

Fees per term (2007-2008). £1,725–£2,350.

Herries is located in a beautiful rural setting close to Maidenhead and Marlow. There is easy access to the M4 and London. Herries provides a broad curriculum enabling every child to develop individual talents. The happy atmosphere and high standard of pastoral care encourages children to achieve their full potential.

Curriculum. Subjects include: English, Mathematics, Science, ICT, French, Latin, Geography, History, RE, Art, Craft, Design and Technology, PE, Dance, Music, Speech and Drama.

Examinations. 11+ Selection tests into Grammar Schools or entrance exams into local Independent or Maintained Schools.

School Facilities. Facilities include purpose-built Nursery, brand new purpose-built ICT facility and newly-extended Hall. Professional tennis coaching at Bisham Abbey National Sports Centre. Football training by professional coaches. Swimming at local sports centre. Athletics at local Sports Club. Extra-curricular activities include piano, singing, recorder and ballet. Extended day activities include judo, football, netball, swimming, gymnastics, table tennis, tag rugby, ICT and French.

High March School

Beaconsfield Bucks HP9 2PZ
Tel: 01494 675186
Fax: 01494 675377
e-mail: office@highmarch.bucks.sch.uk
website: www.highmarch.co.uk

Established 1926.

Chairman of the Governing Board: Mr C A E T Stevenson, MA Cantab

***Headmistress*: Mrs S J Clifford**, BEd Hons Oxon, MA London

Age Range. Girls 3–11.

Number of Pupils. 300 day pupils.

Fees per term (2008-2009). £1,200–£3,300 inclusive of books, stationery and lunches, but excluding optional subjects.

High March comprises 3 school houses set in pleasant grounds. There is a separate house for Nursery and Key Stage 1 classes, 3–7 years. The Upper School has 8 classes, 7–11 years. Class sizes are limited. There is a well-equipped Gymnasium as well as Science, Music, Art, Poetry, Design Technology and Information Technology rooms.

High March is within easy reach of London, High Wycombe, Windsor and within a few minutes' walk of Beaconsfield Station.

Under a large and highly qualified staff and within a happy atmosphere, the children are prepared for Common Entrance and Scholarships to Independent Senior Schools and for the 11+ County Selection process. All subjects including French, Latin, Music, Art, Technology, Speech and Drama, Dancing, Gymnastics, Games and Swimming are in the hands of specialists. Although the academic record is high, each child is encouraged to develop individual talents.

There is an Annual Open Scholarship to the value of one-third of the annual fee tenable for 3 years.

Highfield School

West Road Maidenhead Berks SL6 1PD
Tel: 01628 624918
Fax: 01628 635747
e-mail: office@highfield.berks.sch.uk
website: www.highfield.berks.sch.uk

Chairman of Governors: Mrs R Westacott

***Head*: Mrs Catherine M A Lane**, DPSE, CertEd

Type. Educational Charitable Trust Primary Day School with Kindergarten and Nursery.

Location. Town

Number of Pupils. Approximately 180: Girls 180, Boys 8.

Average Class Size. 21

Maximum Class Size. 23

Age Range. Girls 2½–11+.

Religion. Christian. Other denominations welcome.

Entry. By interview and/or placement test.

Aim. To provide an all-round education while maximizing individual potential. To engender in each pupil a love of learning which will endure for a life-time. The School follows the National Curriculum and prepares pupils for the Common Entrance Examination and other entry tests including 11+ Grammar School entry.

Prospectus. On request from the School Secretary.

Fees per term (2008-2009). Reception to Year 6: £2,180–£2,450; Nursery: £2,180 (full-time), £207 per morning session. Lunch is included.

Charitable status. Highfield School is a Registered Charity, number 309103. It exists to provide an all-round education for girls.

Highfield School

Liphook Hampshire GU30 7LQ
Tel: 01428 728000
Fax: 01428 728001
e-mail: office@highfieldschool.org.uk
website: www.highfieldschool.org.uk

Chairman of Directors: W S Mills, Esq

***Head*: Mr Phillip Evitt**, MA

Age Range. 8–13.

Number of Children. 225 (including 89 boarders).

Fees per term (2007-2008). Boarders £5,200–£5,875; Day Pupils £3,950–£5,050.

Discounts are available for siblings and Forces families. Means-tested Bursaries are available on application.

Location. 15 miles south of Guildford with easy access to London A3 and airports.

Highfield is a purpose built co-educational day and boarding school founded in 1907 set in 175 acres of superb grounds on the Hampshire/Sussex border.

The aim of the school is to provide children with a keen sense of their own individual identity and to help them to develop a sense of responsibility towards others and fulfil their potential in a happy and caring environment. Highfield children are encouraged to have high expectations, good work habits and a desire to benefit from all that the school offers.

Curriculum. Highfield children have a distinguished record of success at Common Entrance and Scholarships to all the major senior schools including Eton, Winchester, Marlborough, Bryanston, Canford, Wycombe Abbey, St Swithun's and Downe House.

Alongside the major academic subjects, French is taught from the age of 7 and Latin begins at 10. The broad curriculum includes ICT, PE and DT and the school's excellent tradition in music, drama and art is reflected in the number of scholarships gained.

The school has built outstanding new facilities for Science, ICT, Mathematics and English. A new indoor swimming pool opened in 2005.

Sports and Activities. The major sports on offer are rugby, soccer, hockey and cricket for the boys, whilst girls play netball, lacrosse, hockey and rounders. All the children take part in athletics, swimming, tennis and cross country. Activities take place in the evenings and weekends and include judo, ballet, chess, golf, drama, modelling, pottery, sewing and story telling.

Highgate Junior School

3 Bishopswood Road London N6 4PL
Tel: 020 8340 9193
Fax: 020 8342 7273
e-mail: jsoffice@highgateschool.org.uk
pre-prep@highgateschool.org.uk
website: www.highgateschool.org.uk

Chairman of Governors: J F Mills, Esq, MA, BLitt

***Principal of Junior School*: S M James**, BA, MA

Principal of Pre-Preparatory School: Mrs S Kennedy

Age Range. 3–13 Co-educational.

Number of Day Pupils. Junior (age 7–13): 420 boys and girls; Pre-Prep (age 3–7): 130 boys and girls.

Fees per term (2007-2008). Junior School: £4,170; Pre-Preparatory School: £3,940 (Reception–Year 2), £1,970 (Nursery).

Pupils are prepared for Highgate School only. (*See entry in HMC section.*)

Entry to the Pre-Preparatory School is by individual assessment for entry at 3+; apply as soon as your child is aged one. Entry to the Junior School is by test and interview at the age of 7 or 11. Transfer to the Senior School is at 13+.

The Pre-Preparatory School is self-contained, while the Junior School is split into Field House (Years 3–4) and Cholmeley House (Years 5–8), all located in Bishopswood Road, N6.

The School is well situated close to Hampstead Heath and has excellent facilities as the result of an ongoing development programme. There are several acres of playing fields attached; the Mallinson Sports Centre (which includes a 25 metre indoor pool) is shared with the Senior School.

A broad and balanced curriculum is followed with art, drama, music, games, ICT and design technology all playing an important part.

Co-education is extending throughout the Highgate Foundation, with girls being admitted at 7+ in the Junior School from September 2004.

Charitable status. Sir Roger Cholmeley's School at Highgate is a Registered Charity, number 312765. The aims and objectives of the charity are educational, namely the maintenance of a school.

Hilden Grange School (GDST)

Dry Hill Park Road Tonbridge Kent TN10 3BX
Tel: 01732 352706
Fax: 01732 773360
e-mail: office@hildengrange.gdst.net
website: www.hildengrange.com

This is one of the 29 schools of The Girls' Day School Trust. For further information about the Trust, see p. xxiv.

***Headmaster*: J Withers**, BA Hons

Age Range. 3–13 Co-educational.

Number of Pupils. 300: 200 Boys and 100 Girls.

Fees per term (2008-2009). Prep School £3,471, Pre-Prep £2,862, Nursery £954–£2,130. Lunches are provided at £175–£195 per term.

Hilden Grange is a friendly, unpretentious school with high standards of teaching and learning, conscientious pastoral care and strength in art, drama, music and sport.

We aim to bring out and develop the individual child's potential in the academic, creative, spiritual and physical areas. We expect our pupils to strive for high standards, to take pride in themselves and to gain satisfaction from their endeavours in an orderly and relaxed environment.

Though links are especially strong with Tonbridge and Sevenoaks boys and girls are prepared for all Independent Senior Schools and Grammar Schools at 11+ and 13+. We have an impressive record of success in this area. Examination results rank among the highest in Kent, and in 2007, all pupils gained entry to their chosen school at 13. Boys and girls who show special promise sit for scholarships to the school of their choice, and our track record in this area is excellent. Pupils benefit from a dedicated and fully qualified staff, and class sizes that average 16.

The School stands in about eight acres of attractive grounds in the residential area of North Tonbridge. Boys and girls are accepted into the Nursery at 3+ or at 4+ into the Pre-Preparatory Department within the school grounds, and at 7 into the main school. Two Scholarships of up to half fees are available annually for suitable candidates aged 7 to 10. Music Scholarships are also available. Tonbridge School Chorister awards are gained. At present there are eight Choristers.

There is an outdoor heated swimming pool, a Sports Hall with changing rooms and kitchen complex, a library and an Art Studio. There are all-weather tennis courts, a Science Laboratory, a Music Room, and two Information Technology Rooms, with networks of personal computers with colour and laser printers.

The Headmaster, staff and children welcome visitors and are pleased to show them around the School.

Charitable status. Hilden Grange School is part of The Girls' Day School Trust, which is a Registered Charity, number 306983.

Hilden Oaks School

38 Dry Hill Park Road Tonbridge Kent TN10 3BU
Tel: 01732 353941
Fax: 01732 353942
e-mail: secretary@hildenoaks.co.uk
website: www.hildenoaks.co.uk

Chairman of Governors: Mrs C Philips

***Headmistress*: Mrs S A Sunderland**, BEd, MA

Age Range. Boys 3 months–7 years, Girls 3 months–11 years.

Number of Children. 147.

Fees per term (2008-2009). 5 mornings: Nursery £1,275, Kindergarten £1,075, Transition £1,075. Reception £2,100, Forms I and II £2,410, Forms III and IV £2,700, Forms V and VI £2,860.

Hilden Oaks School, founded in 1919, became an Educational Trust in 1965. It is located in a quiet, residential area of north Tonbridge and the Trust owns all the land and buildings.

The Main School incorporates classrooms, the School Hall, a state-of-the-art ICT Suite and an extensive, welcoming Library. The Acorn Building incorporates Music and Drama facilities and also provides spacious rooms for the Nursery and the youngest children in the school. The Stable Block has been developed as a self-contained unit for Reception. The Salmon Building houses the Prep Department and specialist Science and Art rooms. The site is a pleasant, enclosed garden setting with hard and grassed playing areas for netball and five-a-side football. There is also a small, wooded section with a pond for field-studies.

Hilden Oaks prides itself on being a happy, family school where every child is helped and encouraged to develop their potential and independent learning in a caring, stimulating and purposeful environment. We maintain high academic standards while expecting good manners and consideration to others at all times. This is reflected in the active parents' association, close liaison between parents and staff and the school's close involvement with the local community.

In the Pre-School and Pre-Preparatory Departments, children are given a solid foundation upon which they can build, with additional specialist teachers for ICT, French, music and games. The Preparatory Department has specialist teachers for science, ICT, French, art, music and games. All forms are taught by form teachers for the core subjects.

Our pupils enjoy taking part in music and drama with regular opportunities to perform. They also enjoy competitive sport in house matches and against other schools. Extra-curricular activities include choirs, drama, art, ICT and games. A late room operates for Infants and Juniors where children are provided with tea. Prep is supervised for the older children while the younger children can relax and play.

The boys leave us at age 7 with the opportunity of being offered academic, music, sport or drama scholarships to their prep schools. All girls are prepared for both the Common Entrance examination at 11 and the 11+ examination for entry to grammar schools. Our results in these examinations, for Foundation Stage Profile assessments and for SATS at Key Stages 1 and 2, put us among the top schools in Kent.

Hilden Oaks offers a challenging and supportive environment designed to inspire children to life-long learning.

Charitable status. Hilden Oaks School is a Registered Charity, number 307935. It exists to provide education for children.

Hillcrest Preparatory School

PO Box 24282, Karen 00502, Nairobi, Kenya
Tel: 00 254 (0)20 883914/16/17
Fax: 00 254 (0)20 883920
e-mail: admin_prep@hillcrest.ac.ke
website: www.hillcrest.ac.ke

Chairman of Governors: (*vacant*)

***Head*: Ms Lucy Mayer**

Age Range. 5–13 Co-educational.

Number of Pupils. 171.

Fees per term (2008-2009). KShs 81,000–212,000, excluding transport and lunches.

Hillcrest School was founded in 1965 by Mrs Elizabeth Node with Mr Frank Thompson as Founding Headmaster. It is located on an attractive, purpose-built, 20-acre campus next to our Secondary School in Karen/Langata.

Boys and girls are accepted from the age of 5 and they follow a broad and extensive curriculum which prepares them for Common Entrance Examinations. Some children transfer to UK Independent Secondary Schools but the majority enter the equivalent in Kenya, Hillcrest Secondary School, which prepares pupils for IGCSE and A Levels. Entry to the Senior School is achieved after successfully writing either Common Entrance or the Hillcrest Secondary examination. A thriving Kindergarten of 50, called Forestcrest, opened on site in September 2001.

The school has an International flavour and its pupils are drawn from the Diplomatic and United Nations community, expatriate families on contract, and Kenyan residents. The friendly spirit and strong communication network that exists between staff, pupils and parents are of particular note. There are 18 fully qualified teachers, 60% are Honours Graduates recruited from the UK. The average form size is 18 and the teacher:pupil ratio of approximately 11:1 allows for considerable individual attention and learning support.

Hillcrest offers a wide range of extramural activities each week including dance, TaeKwonDo, sub-aqua, instrumental tuition, tennis, basketball, flight simulation and scouting.

Field trip studies are offered to the Coast and Rift Valley and outdoor pursuits are strongly encouraged. These include climbs of Mount Longonot and Kenya, up-country farm visits and water activities trips to Lake Naivasha. Charitable fundraising activities are also regularly organised by pupils for underprivileged children.

The school's Inter-House Competitions are a focal point of each term. House Chieftains play an important role in welcoming new pupils, monitoring behaviour and promoting a competitive spirit. Cricket, Rounders, Hockey, Rugby, Netball and Swimming are taught and a full fixtures programme is arranged each term with other Preparatory Schools.

Hillcrest is also well-known for the quality of its drama productions, choir performances and standard of artistic display throughout the school. Our principle aim is to nurture pupils' individual talents and produce well-balanced children who actively contribute to all academic, aesthetic and sporting activities in a caring and family-like atmosphere.

Hoe Bridge School

Hoe Place Old Woking Surrey GU22 8JE
Tel: Prep School: 01483 760018/760065
Pre-Prep: 01483 772194
Fax: 01483 757560
e-mail: enquiriesprep@hoebridgeschool.co.uk
enquiriespreprep@hoebridgeschool.co.uk
website: www.hoebridgeschool.co.uk

Co-educational Preparatory and Pre-Preparatory School.

Chairman of Governors: David Hemley

***Headmaster*: R W K Barr**, BEd Oxon

Deputy Headmaster: G D P Scott, BEd Exeter

***Head of Pre-Prep*: Mrs Linda Renfrew**, MA, PGCE

Age Range. 2½–14.

Number of Children. Prep 281, Pre-Prep 215.

Fees per term (from January 2008). Day: Prep £3,245–£3,765 (including lunch); Pre-Prep £520–£2,615 (including lunch).

Hoe Bridge School is on the outskirts of Woking, standing in its own grounds of 20 acres which affords admirable facilities for games and outdoor pursuits, including Rugby, Association Football, Cricket, Athletics, Netball, Hockey, Tennis and Swimming. A substantial part of the Grade II listed building has been restored and now houses a state of the art Music School, Art, Design Technology and Information Technology Centres. The Nursery unit is on the ground floor of this magnificent building and provides first class facilities for both indoor and outdoor activities. The recent refurbishment of the Sports Hall block has provided additional classrooms and 3 state-of-the-art science laboratories. The School's academic and sporting record is enviable.

Children between the ages of 7–14 are prepared for scholarship and common entrance requirements to all independent schools with all normal subjects, games and activities necessary for a child's development taught by experienced qualified staff.

The Headmistress of the Pre-Preparatory School is a member of the IAPS in her own right. Children may join the Pre-Prep from age 2½. The Nursery and Reception units offer children a excellent start to their Early Years Education with a structured programme of activities and experiences. Our experienced staff of teachers and assistants include games and music specialists. The Pre-Prep benefits from its own Hall fully equipped for gymnastics, a dedicated art room, interactive whiteboards and an ICT suite comprising 10 computers in addition to computers in all the classrooms. Children in Year 2 are well prepared for the curriculum of the Prep School and the transition to this department is eased by weekly games lessons with Prep staff and sample lessons each term in music, art and design.

Hoe Bridge School is an Educational Trust run by a Board of Governors whose members are drawn from parents, and the local community.

Charitable status. Hoe Bridge School is a Registered Charity, number 295808. It exists to provide a rounded education for children aged 2½–14.

Holme Grange School

Heathlands Road Wokingham Berkshire RG40 3AL
Tel: 0118 9781566
Fax: 0118 9770810
e-mail: school@holmegrange.org
website: www.holmegrange.org

Chairman of Governors: T Andrews, BA Hons

***Headmaster*: N J Brodrick**, BEd (London), CertEd

Age Range. 3–13 Co-educational.

Number of Pupils. 282: 111 girls, 171 boys.

Fees per term (2007-2008). Little Grange Nursery £1,320–£1,980, Pre-Preparatory £2,492, Prep £3,180, payable monthly. Reductions for second and subsequent children.

The School is a Day School receiving pupils from a wide catchment area. The Headmaster is assisted by a highly qualified and experienced staff of 28 with classroom assistants in the Pre-Prep and NNEB assistants in Little Grange. There is a Learning Support Department giving help to those children with special needs as an extra to the fees. A broad curriculum is followed, embracing both the full National Curriculum, and that currently required for the 11+ and 13+ Common Entrance Examinations. Class sizes are generally a maximum of 18; average size is 16, but fewer in Years 7 and 8. The School is a Trust, administered by a board of Governors who have considerable experience in education and business. There is an active Parents' Association which raises funds for extra items for the children. Little Grange is an established Nursery for 3 year olds in its own safe, secure environment within the School grounds, providing flexible education either part or full day including lunch and tea.

The main Grade II listed building, a Mansion built in 1883 by Norman Shaw, houses the Pre-Preparatory, dining-rooms and kitchens, School Library and administrative offices. A two-storey 'John Graves Wing' comprises seven classrooms and girls' changing accommodation to which an extension was added in 2001, encompassing art/design on the ground floor with two classrooms above. Many other facilities have been added in the last fifteen years: the 'Scott Wing' with its Science Laboratory, ICT room, a classroom and boys' changing rooms. In the Quad is a teaching block with one classroom and an Art resource area, next to a cedar block used for Pre-Prep changing and a Dance Studio, while a large Sports Hall (including two indoor cricket nets) with full stage facilities for Music and Drama completes the area. A Music School comprising three practice rooms and a large classroom is in a separate building.

A variety of sports can be played on two all-weather artificial pitches (incorporating either 3 tennis or netball courts) plus four outdoor cricket nets. The 21 acres of grounds contain all the above plus 3 playing fields, a lake, stream and Millennium wood, an adventure playground and a heated outdoor swimming pool, rebuilt in 2001. All Prep age boys (from Year 3) are coached in soccer (from Year 1 also), Rugby, Hockey, Cricket and Athletics. Girls have Netball, Jazz/Dance, Hockey, Rounders and Athletics. Tennis is available for both. A wide range of after-school activities is available to 5.30 pm, including Choir, Master Chef, Speech and Drama, extra sport and supervised prep (homework). All children from age 3 may stay to 5.30 pm, younger ones having tea and after-school care.

Pupils are accepted from the age of 3 providing continuous education until they take the Common Entrance or Scholarship examinations (Academic, Art, Music) for Senior Independent Schools. At both there is an enviable record of success. Every child is given an opportunity to shine in a happy, friendly, family atmosphere which has a strong emphasis on courtesy and self discipline and good manners. Registration for the Nursery and Pre-Prep is advisable several years in advance of required admission. Entry at 7+ follows an assessment test. Means-tested bursaries are available, alongside Holme Grange scholarships for entry into Years 7 and 8.

Charitable status. Holme Grange Limited is a Registered Charity, number 309105. It exists to serve the local community in providing an all-round education for boys and girls.

Holmewood House

Langton Green Tunbridge Wells Kent TN3 0EB
Tel: 01892 860000
Fax: 01892 863970
e-mail: admin@holmewood.kent.sch.uk
website: www.holmewood.kent.sch.uk

Chairman of the Governors: M A Evans

***Headmaster*: A S R Corbett**, MA, PGCE

Deputy Headmaster: S A Gent

Age Range. 3–13.

Number of Pupils. 520 Boys and Girls.

Fees per term (2007-2008). Weekly Boarders £6,065. Day Pupils: Years 3–8 £4,815, Pre-Prep £3,145–£3,640, Nursery £1,405–£2,110. There are reductions for a third sibling, and children of Old Holmewoodians. Scholarships are available for those entering from primary schools.

The school was founded in 1945 as a boys' school. Boarding and Day girls were admitted in 1989. The school is a Charitable Educational Trust with a Board of Governors. Holmewood stands in 22 acres of beautiful grounds on the Kent/Sussex border, and is within easy reach of Tunbridge Wells, which is one hour by rail from London.

The School is divided into six Houses, and a personal tutor system operates from Year 5. Saturday morning school also begins in Year 5.

Thanks to its 62 full and part time dedicated and enthusiastic staff, Holmewood has an outstanding scholastic record, both in Common Entrance and Scholarship examinations. In the last five years 82 scholarships have been won, including the top scholarships at Tonbridge, Sevenoaks and St Leonards-Mayfield.

A broad-based curriculum is followed throughout the school. Modern languages taught include French, German and Spanish. Latin and Ancient Greek are also taught.

The school has 250 networked computers and three networked computer rooms. All pupils are taught computing from an early age. There are also approximately 30 interactive whiteboards around the school.

The Art, Drama and Music Departments are very strong and the school's Concert Group gives performances at home and overseas. A new Music School was opened in 1996 and the Performing Arts Centre was completed by the opening of a new 360-seat theatre in September 1997.

Expert coaching is given in a wide variety of sports and these include rugby, soccer, hockey, gymnastics, netball, cricket, tennis and table tennis, shooting, athletics, orienteering, cross-country, golf, archery, fencing, judo, basketball, dance, squash and swimming. In recent years the school has won the golf team championships. We have held titles in gymnastics, swimming, netball and squash – GISCA & IAPS Gymnastics champions, U13 British Schools Gymnastics Champions, Kent & Sussex Prep & Junior Schools Squash Champions, U12 British Schools Swimming Champions. There is a magnificent Sports Hall, a new indoor swimming pool, opened in June 2001, ten hard tennis courts, three squash courts, a full size all-weather hockey/football pitch and running track and an indoor .22 shooting range.

Our aims are:

- excellence in teaching
- to help every child to learn and to attain their maximum potential
- to provide pastoral care of the highest quality
- to provide a well-ordered and stimulating environment in which all can thrive
- to offer a very broad and balanced curriculum for all pupils.

Our whole school values are essentially Christian, although we welcome children of all denominations.

- as a community we value good discipline, independence of mind, mutual support and success for all
- in our relationships we value a caring approach, encouragement, good manners and generosity
- on a personal level we value integrity, effort, happiness and self-discipline.

These aims and values inform and underpin our policies, guidelines and practice.

Charitable status. Holmewood House is a Registered Charity, number 279267. It exists to provide education for boys and girls.

Holmwood House

Chitts Hill Lexden Colchester Essex CO3 9ST
Tel: 01206 574305
Fax: 01206 768269
e-mail: hst@holmwood.essex.sch.uk
website: www.holmwood.essex.sch.uk

***Headmaster*: H S Thackrah**, BEd Exeter

Age Range. 4½–13 Co-educational. Nursery School: 6 months to 4 years.

Number of Pupils. 370.

Fees per term (2008-2009). Boarders £5,548; Day Pupils £2,408–£4,290. All fees are inclusive; there are no compulsory extras. Nursery fees dependent on hours attended.

Holmwood House was founded in 1922 and stands in 26 acres of gardens and grounds only 2 kms from Colchester town centre. Children are prepared for the Common Entrance examination and for Scholarships to senior independent schools.

The principal aim of the school is high academic standards and thus the Library and Resource Centre is deliberately the centre of the school: within this is the Computer Centre, networked to all classrooms and allowing two full classes access at any one time. Facilities include 20 acres of sports fields; large, well-equipped classrooms; five squash courts; indoor heated swimming pool; seven tennis courts (two covered); floodlit tarmac play area; 2 Adventure Playgrounds; permanent stage with sound and lighting systems; separate drama studio; Art School incorporating print and ceramic workshop; separate Music School. The majority of pupils study at least one musical instrument. There are four well-equipped Science laboratories.

From the age of 8 each subject is taught by specialist teachers. French is taught from Year 1 onwards and exchange programmes are well established. Sport and the Arts receive many scheduled sessions of instruction in afternoons and evenings. Classes and compulsory games are all timetabled conventionally; so are some 'preps', but older pupils may do up to 4 'preps' a week in their own time to provide time for orchestra, chess, cookery and many other coached activities. Drama and music flourish particularly, from the large-scale production to the small musical ensemble. Children at Holmwood House are self-confident, self-disciplined and good time managers!

Holmwood House Nursery was opened in September 2006 to cater for children from 6 months to 4 years. A flexible service is offered so that children can attend either during Holmwood House term only, or for any number of different sessions and options. The Nursery is open for 48 weeks in the year.

Academic, Music, Art and Sports scholarships and bursaries are available for pupils aged 7+. Bursaries are also offered in certain cases of need to enable pupils to remain at or come to the school.

We would be pleased to send our prospectus and to welcome visitors to the school.

Holy Cross Preparatory School

George Road Kingston-upon-Thames Surrey KT2 7NU
Tel: 020 8942 0729
Fax: 020 8336 0764
e-mail: admissions@holycrossprep.co.uk
website: www.holycrossprep.co.uk

***Headmistress*: Mrs M K Hayes**, MA

Age Range. 4–11.

Number of Girls. 250.

Fees per term (2008-2009). £2,750.

Location. The school is situated on a private estate in an attractive area of Kingston Hill.

Facilities. The building, the former home of John Galsworthy, is of both historical and literary interest and provides excellent accommodation for two classes in each year group through the school from Reception to Year Six. The school contains an assembly hall/gymnasium, dining hall, library, Design and Technology Centre, Music room, Computer room, TV/Drama room, Art room and 14 classrooms all with computers. A new building for the 6 Infant classes was opened in Spring 2001. A new Art room and and ICT room were developed and opened for the Summer Term 2003.

The 8 acres of grounds include two tennis/netball courts, hockey pitch, running track and three large playing areas which have play equipment, including adventure climbing frames. There is a nature trail and ecology area, together with a fountain within the ornamental lawns and a pond which is well used in science lessons.

Educational Philosophy. The school was founded by the Sisters of the Holy Cross, an international teaching order who have been engaged in the work of education since 1844. A sound Christian education is given in an Ecumenical framework. The children are happy, cared for and well disciplined. The emphasis is on developing the God-given gifts of each child to their fullest, in a stimulating, friendly atmosphere where high standards of work, behaviour and contribution to the well being of the school community are expected.

Curriculum. There is a broad and relevant curriculum providing a high standard of education. Specialist teaching in French, Music, Physical Education and Information Technology. The school has a first rate record of success in Common Entrance and in preparing pupils for Senior Independent, High and Grammar Schools. The varied extra-curricular activities include ballet and dance, Speech & Drama, pottery, Art and Design, cello, piano, flute, clarinet, violin, guitar, sports, German, Technology, French, country dancing, tennis, origami and chess.

Charitable status. Holy Cross Preparatory School is a Registered Charity, number 238426. It is a Roman Catholic School providing excellence in Christian education to local children.

Homefield Preparatory School

Western Road Sutton Surrey SM1 2TE
Tel: 020 8642 0965
Fax: 020 8642 0965
e-mail: administration@homefield.sutton.sch.uk
website: www.homefield.sutton.sch.uk

"*I don't believe we could have found a better school in the country to bring out the best in both our sons.*"

Chairman of Governors: Mr K Dodwell, ACIL

***Headmaster*: P R Mowbray**, MA (Cantab)

Age Range. 2½–13.

Number of Boys. 430.

Fees per term (2008-2009). Senior Department £2,965; Junior Department: 2nd & 3rd Years £2,515, 1st Year £2,135; Transition £2,005; Nursery: £1,925 (full day), £1,275 (mornings only). Lunches: £210 (Seniors and Juniors), £167 (Nursery and Transition).

Homefield is a Preparatory school for 430 boys aged 2½ to 13, and 50 staff, housed in an extensive purpose-built complex complemented by a spacious state-of-the-art Early Years Unit and a 2-acre adjoining playing field.

Rated by The Sunday Times Parent Power as "*Amongst the best performing schools in Greater London*", Homefield School has cemented its powerful academic reputation by securing a 76% pass rate at Level 5 in Key Stage 2 examinations this year, and has continued to achieve a 100% pass rate at Common Entrance to 36 senior schools over the last 10 years. 13 awards for Art, Music, Sport, All-round and Academic achievements are won on average each year.

The school is renowned for its intimacy and family atmosphere, small class sizes, the fulfilment of individual potential, the openness of communication, the provision of specialist teaching at the earliest appropriate opportunity (French, ICT, Music and Sport from the Foundation stage), its commitment to best practice and its all round academic, musical, dramatic, sporting and artistic achievements. The recent ISI inspection report, now posted on the school's website, states that "the care that the staff give to the well-being of the boys is outstanding", "the boys are happy, valued and challenged but not pressured" and compliments the "extensive and varied programme of extra-curricular activities".

The school has county or national representatives in table tennis, squash, tennis, athletics, swimming, soccer, rugby, cricket and chess.

Awareness of others is encouraged and the pupils are involved in many fund-raising charity events, raising over £9,000 this year.

Learning support is available for children with special needs. A wide range of opportunities is planned to extend gifted pupils such as World Class Maths Tests and membership of the National Academy for Gifted and Talented Youth.

We offer academic, sporting, art and music scholarships as well as the occasional bursaries.

Daily minibuses run to and from Wimbledon and other areas.

Breakfast and after school clubs are available.

Charitable status. Homefield Preparatory School Trust Limited is a Registered Charity, number 312753. It exists to provide education for boys.

Hordle Walhampton School

Lymington Hants SO41 5ZG
Tel: 01590 672013
Fax: 01590 678498
e-mail: office@hordlewalhampton.co.uk
website: www.hordlewalhampton.co.uk

Chairman of Governors: The Hon Patrick Seely

***Headmaster*: R H C Phillips**, BA Hons, CertEd, LGSM

Age Range. 2–13.

Number of Pupils. Boarding boys 28, Boarding girls 14, Day children 157, Pre-Prep 137.

Fees per term (2007-2008). Boarding £5,240; Day £2,835– £3,980; Pre-Preparatory £1,990; Kindergarten £1,585; Nursery £390–£580. The only extras are: Riding, individual Music, language support tuition and Expeditions.

Hordle Walhampton was established in 1997, following the merger of Hordle House and Walhampton. The School is one of the south coast's leading co-educational boarding and day Preparatory schools, situated on the edge of the New Forest, surrounded by 92 acres of playing fields, woodland and lakes, which are enjoyed by all the children for traditional games, sailing, riding, field studies, walks, free time and fun. There are excellent facilities for Art, Computing, Craft, Design Technology, Gymnastics and Woodwork; Music and Drama also play an important part in School life. A continuing programme of development has seen the creation of a Sports Hall, Performing Arts Centre, all-weather sports pitch and the complete renovation of the equestrian centre.

The aim of the School is to seek the good in the young and to educate the whole child in a caring, exciting and challenging community. The educational programme is broad, with equal importance attached to developing the intellectual, social, cultural, physical and spiritual faculties of each pupil. The academic results are excellent and this is achieved by employing well qualified, dedicated, caring Staff who teach in small, well resourced classes averaging 14 children. English and Maths are set throughout the school. Latin is taught to all children from Year 5. In Year 8 there is a special form to prepare pupils for 13+ scholarship examinations to Senior Schools. The majority of children leave after sitting their 13+ Common Entrance or Scholarship examinations to such schools as: Bryanston, Canford, Dauntsey's, Eton, Sherborne Boys and Girls, Marlborough, Millfield, St Swithun's and Winchester. Girls are also prepared for specific entry requirements to girls' schools.

There is a strong boarding ethos within the School with particular attention paid to weekends for which a varied and exciting programme is prepared each week. Facilities such as riding, sailing, computing, art and woodwork are available during the weekend. Full, weekly and flexi boarding are on offer to suit the needs of individual families. There are three boarding houses: the Lodge has boys and girls aged 7 to 10; Main House has boys aged 11 to 13, and the Clockhouse has girls aged 11 to 13. There is a strong boarding care team consisting of Houseparents, Assistant Houseparents and Matrons. The day children enjoy a full, all inclusive programme.

Hordle Walhampton aims to prepare each child for the demands and challenges of twenty-first century life by providing opportunities to grow in self-confidence, Christian standards and responsibilities and consideration for others. When children leave Hordle Walhampton it is hoped that they will be articulate, confident, self-motivated, considerate, generous and determined to give of their best to any enterprise with which they are involved.

Charitable status. Hordle Walhampton School Trust Limited is a Registered Charity, number 307330. It exists to provide high quality boarding and day education for boys and girls aged 2–13 years.

Hornsby House School

Hearnville Road London SW12 8RS
Tel: 020 8673 7573
Fax: 020 8673 6722
e-mail: school@hornsby-house.co.uk
website: www.hornsby-house.co.uk

Chairman of Governors: Mr Charles Gotto

***Headmaster*: Mr Jon Gray**, BA Ed Hons

Age Range. 4–11.
Number of Pupils. 184 Girls, 173 Boys.
Fees per term (2008-2009). £3,352 (Reception to Year 2), £3,610 (Years 3 to 6).

Hornsby House School was founded in 1988 by Professor Hornsby, with twenty children in a church hall in Clapham. It now comprises approximately 350 boys and girls and is sited in an Edwardian primary school enhanced by two new buildings. Hornsby House shares a local sports field with other local schools and plays football, rugby, cricket, netball and rounders.

Entry into Reception classes is unassessed and is on a first-come, first-served basis with priority being given to siblings.

A well-qualified teaching staff is supported by teaching assistants. The curriculum is based on the National Curriculum with emphasis on sport, music, art and drama. There is a wide variety of extra-curricular activities and an After School Care Club.

The school is very well resourced with new buildings providing specialist rooms for Art, Music, Science and a state-of-the-art ICT suite. Some teaching is done using interactive whiteboards. A well-stocked library provides a wide range of reference books and Internet access. Instrumentalists can join the orchestra, brass or flute ensembles and there are three choirs. Visits to theatres, museums and other places of interest all serve to broaden the curriculum.

To arrange a visit to see the children at work, please contact the Registrar.

Charitable status. Hornsby House Educational Trust is a Registered Charity, number 800284.

Horris Hill

Newtown Newbury Berks RG20 9DJ
Tel: 01635 40594
Fax: 01635 39586
e-mail: enquiries@horrishill.com
website: www.horrishill.com

Chairman of Governors: J J Davies, Esq

***Headmaster*: J H L Phillips**, BEd Hons

Age Range. 8–13.
Numbers of Boys. Boarders 120, Day 1.
Fees per term (2008-2009). Boarders: £6,560; Day £4,750. (No compulsory Extras)
Charitable status. Horris Hill Preparatory School Trust Limited is a Registered Charity, number 307331. It exists to prepare boys for the Senior Independent Schools.

Hunter Hall School

Frenchfield Penrith Cumbria CA11 8UA
Tel: 01768 891291
Fax: 01768 899161
e-mail: office@hunterhall.cumbria.sch.uk
website: www.hunterhall.co.uk

Chairman of Governors: Mr Tim Evans

***Headmaster*: Mr Allan Short**, BSc Hons, PGCE

Age Range. 3–11 co-educational.
Number of Pupils. 140.
Fees per term (2008-2009). £1,963.
Charitable status. Hunter Hall School Ltd is a Registered Charity, number 1059098.

Hurstpierpoint College Preparatory School

A Woodard School

Hurstpierpoint West Sussex BN6 9JS
Tel: 01273 834975
Fax: 01273 833957
e-mail: hurstprep@hppc.co.uk
website: www.hppc.co.uk

Chairman of Governors: Rear-Admiral S Moore, CB

***Head*: Mrs H J Beeby**, BH, MA

Age Range. 7–13.
Number of Pupils. 231 boys and girls (6 weekly boarders, 225 day pupils).

Fees per term (2008-2009). Weekly boarders £4,990; Flexi boarders £4,570; Day pupils £3,970; Year 3 £3,450; Pre-Prep £1,875–£2,190. There are no compulsory extras. Music tuition: £202.50 per instrument.

The School is the Preparatory School of Hurstpierpoint College (*see entry in HMC section*) with which it shares a beautiful 140-acre campus and has joint use of many superb facilities (including 25m indoor swimming pool, fully-equipped modern CDT centre, theatre, dance and drama studios, music school, large sports hall, full-size Astroturf hockey pitch, tennis courts and squash courts). A new 15-classroom extension to the College teaching block will benefit the Prep School Years 7 and 8 along with the Senior School. Although the Prep School operates independently of the Senior School, having its own timetable, staff, buildings and Head, the two schools work closely together to offer a first-class programme of education for boys and girls from the age of 7 to 18.

The aim of the School is to provide an outstanding education in a secure and happy environment. The staff's overriding priority is to guide and inspire young people to develop their potential to the full, striving for the highest possible standards in the classroom, on the sports field, in the creative and performing arts and in a wide range of skills and activities.

The Prep School has a 5-day academic week but a Saturday afternoon match programme runs throughout the school year.

The academic programme is based around key assessment points in the Lent and Summer Terms of both Years 7 and 8 and pupils are set in as many subjects as possible. This provides a strong foundation for the GCSE programme which children begin when they enter the Senior School.

The Sports programme is extensive: Football, Netball, Rounders, Rugby, Cricket, Hockey, Squash, Swimming, Tennis, Basketball and Athletics. In addition there is a wide-ranging activity programme in place every day which caters for the interests of all pupils.

The Music, Drama and Dance Departments are also very strong; about half the pupils learn musical instruments. The Preparatory School choir performs at the weekly Chapel service. There are at least three musicals or plays each year involving many children throughout the School.

Matron, in conjunction with the College Medical Centre, looks after the health of the children. The School has its own sick bay.

Each year a number of Awards are available: 7+ academic awards continue throughout the Prep School, whilst 11+ academic and sports awards continue through to the Senior School. Music awards are available at any stage in the Prep School.

Hurst's Pre-Prep school for children aged 4–7, opened in 2001. It occupies a self-contained unit with reception area and four classrooms, with its own extensive, fenced hard and grass play areas. From September 2009, there will be an extra class in both Reception and Year 1, so that by September 2010 there will be two classes in each year group.

Charitable status. Hurstpierpoint College is a Registered Charity, number 1076498. The College provides a Christian education to boys and girls between the ages of three and eighteen.

Ilford Ursuline Preparatory School

2 Coventry Road Ilford Essex IG1 4QR
Tel: 020 8518 4050
Fax: 020 8518 2060
e-mail: hroddy@ilfordursuline-prep.redbridge.sch.uk
website: www.ilfordursuline-prep.org.uk

Chair of Governors: Sister Anne Benyon OSU

***Headmistress*: Mrs Catherine Spinner**

Age Range. Girls 3–11 years, Boys 3–4.

Number of Pupils. 170.

Fees per term (2008-2009). Reception–Year 6: £2,105 plus meals; Nursery: £1,899 (full-time) including meals.

The Ilford Ursuline Preparatory School is a Roman Catholic day school in the trusteeship of the Ursuline Sisters. The Ursuline Sisters first came to England in 1862 settling at Forest Gate from where they established the school in Ilford in 1903 at 73, Cranbrook Road. The school has since flourished. Formerly part of the Ilford Ursuline High School, the Ilford Ursuline Preparatory School is now a fully independent school in its own right but continues to share close and valued links with the High School.

As a Catholic School we firmly believe that Religious Education is the foundation of the entire educational process. Prayers and liturgical celebrations are an important aspect of school life, unifying the hearts and minds of all associated with the school and ensuring we are all working to achieve the best possible education for the children in our care.

We provide a safe, secure and stimulating environment for our girls to thrive. We recognise each child's unique value and are committed to encouraging self-esteem and developing each child's potential. We encourage the children to become independent learners by building on their curiosity and desire to learn and developing their skills, concepts and understanding.

While the school continues to set its own high standards, we complement these with the integration of the best of the National Curriculum. English, Mathematics, and Science form the core subjects together with History, Geography, French, Religious Education, Information Communication Technology, Physical Education, Drama Art, Music and stimulating project work. The Performing Arts have a high profile in school and the girls are regularly given the opportunity to develop their talents. A well-stocked library, audio visual aids and a state of the art specialist Information Communication Technology department are all available.

We offer a wide range of extra curricular activities including Sports, Ballet, Elocution and Choral Speaking, Irish Dancing, ICT, Chess and German. Individual instrumental tuition can be arranged for piano, violin, flute, clarinet and saxophone. There is a school choir and an orchestra.

All teaching staff are fully qualified, experienced and dedicated to the ideals of the school. They work in close partnership with parents to ensure that each child's special individual needs are recognised. In addition, we have the help of experienced general assistants. Our pupil teacher ratio is excellent and we are able to engage in small group teaching.

Pre and after school care and a holiday club are available. A variety of structured activities is planned for the children enrolled and refreshments are provided.

Charitable status. The Ilford Ursuline Preparatory School is a Registered Charity, number 245661.

Ipswich Preparatory School

3 Ivry Street Ipswich Suffolk IP1 3QW
Tel: 01473 281302
Fax: 01473 400067
e-mail: prepregistrar@ipswich.suffolk.sch.uk
website: www.ipswich.suffolk.sch.uk

Chairman of Governors: Mr K Daniels, ACII, FPMI

***Headteacher*: Mrs Jenny Jones**, BA, ARCM, NPQH

Age Range. 3–11.

Number of Pupils. 304.

Fees per term (2008-2009). Years 3–6 £2,635, Reception–Year 2 £2,367, Nursery £19.50 (per session).

The Preparatory School has its own staff and Headteacher. It is located just across the road from the senior school (*see Ipswich School entry in HMC section*).

The school seeks to provide a learning environment which allows pupils to develop skills and personal qualities. The curriculum is planned to encourage the children to develop lively, enquiring minds and appropriate emphasis is placed on securing for each child a firm foundation of skills in literacy and numeracy. The broad, balanced curriculum offered provides a breadth of experience which is suitable for children of primary age. High academic standards are reached by the pupils, but in addition, they are encouraged to develop skills in music, art, drama and sport.

Children's happiness is considered essential and the School works closely with parents to ensure a partnership which provides the best possible care for all girls and boys.

The school enjoys the advantage of sharing Senior School facilities such as playing fields, sports hall, swimming pool, theatre/concert hall and the Chapel. The Prep School has its own Art, Design Technology, ICT and Science facilities.

Charitable status. Ipswich Preparatory School is part of Ipswich School, which is a Registered Charity, number 310493. It exists for the purpose of educating children.

James Allen's Preparatory School

East Dulwich Grove London SE22 8TE
Tel: 020 8693 0374
Fax: 020 8693 8031
e-mail: japsadmissions@jags.org.uk
website: www.japs.org.uk

Chairman of Governors: Dame Valerie Strachan, BA, DCB

***Head*: Miss Finola Stack**, BA Hons, PGCE, Mont Dip

Age Range. Boys 4–7, Girls 4–11.

Number of Pupils. Day: Boys 19, Girls 281.

Fees per term (2008-2009). £3,616.

James Allen's Preparatory School (JAPS) is an independent co-educational day school for children aged between 4 and 11. Boys leave at the age of 7.

We do not see primary education as being merely preparatory to secondary requirements but want the children to go forward at their own pace, benefiting from working together in small groups. With a well-devised and wide curriculum, the children reach high standards without the stress of blatant competition and are able to enjoy the many and varied facilities which we offer, particularly in sport, drama, music and art.

The school has an excellent staff/pupil ratio of approximately 1:10 and provides specialist teachers in Art, DT, ICT, Music, PE and Science. In French the children are taught from 4 years onwards using the immersion method.

The Pre-Prep School (for pupils aged 4–6) is housed in a beautiful Edwardian building. The Middle School (for pupils aged 7–11) is a large, modern building with a first class Hall and Library, as well as specialist rooms for Science, ICT, DT and Art. Some facilities (the theatre, swimming pool and games fields) are shared with James Allen's Girls' School.

JASSPA is the James Allen's Saturday School for the Performing Arts for pupils and siblings and other non-JAPS pupils. This is entirely voluntary and complements the week's activities: music lessons, dance and drama are all offered.

Pupils normally enter the school in the year in which they are 4 (boys and girls) or 7 (girls only) on 1 September. Assessments take place the preceding January. 36 places are available for 4+ entry and up to 30 places available for 7+ entry. At 11, girls normally progress to JAGS by means of an open competitive examination, where JAPS girls regularly win many scholarships. Boys progress mainly to Dulwich College, Alleyn's and Dulwich College Preparatory School at 7+.

Charitable status. James Allen's Girls' School is a Registered Charity, number 312750. The purpose of the charity is the conduct at Dulwich of a day school in which there shall be provided a practical, liberal and religious education for girls and boys.

Jerudong International School
Junior School & Middle School Divisions

PO Box 1408, Bandar Seri Begawan, BS8672, Negara Brunei Darussalam
Tel: 00 673 2 411000
Fax: 00 673 2 411010
e-mail: office@jis.edu.bn
website: www.jis.edu.bn

Jerudong International School (for Kindergarten to Year 13) is a British international day and boarding school located near the University of Brunei Darussalam in Jerudong, Brunei, just five kilometres from the capital city of Bandar Seri Begawan.

Principal & CEO: John S Price, MA (Cantab)

***Head of Junior School*: Karen Lewis**, BEd Hons (Leeds)

***Head of Middle School*: Ian Mehta**, BSc Hons (Exeter)

Age Range. 2–18.

Number of Pupils. 1,306 (Junior School, Kindergarten to Year 5: 331; Middle School, Years 6–8: 309; Upper School, Years 9–11: 422; Sixth Form, Years 12–13: 244).

Fees per annum (2008-2009). Nursery: BN$6,960, Kindergarten: BN$9,300, Reception–Year 7 BN$13,920, Years 8–11 BN$14,640, Years 12–13 BN$16,080. Boarding (Years 6–13): BN$16,080. (£1 = 3BN$).

Facilities. Built in 1997, JIS has excellent facilities that are shared with the secondary school. There is a gymnasium which incorporates a dance studio and a fitness room. The fifty-metre swimming pool is shaded and pupils enjoy the use of tennis and netball courts. There is a well-stocked library with computer access and three additional computer suites exclusively for Junior and Middle Schools. Science, design technology, art, food technology and music are taught in dedicated rooms. The playground areas are extensive and shaded in some areas.

Curriculum. At JIS much emphasis is placed on academic achievement. Children are expected to work hard and achieve very high standards, but the school is not selective at this level. Children transfer to the Middle School at the end of Year 5. The pastoral system is well developed. Much support is given to parents relocating to Brunei and the problems of expatriate life are well understood. Since August 2005 the school has had both a nurse and a counsellor.

All pupils have a class teacher for most of their studies. There are specialist teachers in ICT, Art, Music, Malay, French and PE. Mandarin is taught by a native speaker. Pupils cover the work of the British National Curriculum, but academic programmes of study are increasingly informed by the syllabuses developed in British preparatory schools. The school is proud to welcome parents and children of all nationalities. Teachers are predominantly from the UK and Australia, whereas pupils are from more than forty different countries.

The extra-curricular programme offers pupils the opportunity to take part in a variety of activities. Music, Art and Sport are all strong. Children acquire good social and communication skills and learn to cooperate with others. There is a lively sporting programme and opportunities to compete locally and internationally at the games organised by the Federation of Independent Schools of South-East Asia (FOBISSEA). There is an After School Care Centre for children who cannot be collected immediately at the end of the school day.

Jumeirah Primary School
GEMS Education

P O Box 29093 Dubai United Arab Emirates
Tel: 00 971 4 394 3500
Fax: 00 971 4 394 3960
e-mail: office@jpsdubai.sch.ae
website: www.jpsdubai.com

***Principal*: Mrs Mel Curtis**

Vice-Principal: Ms Rachel Hadingham

Age Range. 3–11.
Number of Pupils. 1,100 boys and girls.
Fees per annum (2007-2008). Nursery: Dhs 27,608; Reception–Year 6: Dhs 34,800. Fees are payable in United Arab Emirates Dirhams.

Jumeirah Primary School was established in September 1996 and the purpose-built premises opened in 1998 in Jumeirah, a pleasant residential area of Dubai. The school provides an independent National Curriculum of England education for English Speaking expatriate children whose parents reside in Dubai. There is no support for speakers of English as a second language.

The facilities are very good and include a 25-metre swimming pool, two tennis courts, an artificial grass field in addition to playgrounds, and a large multi-purpose hall, climbing and traversing wall, drama studio, music rooms, 3 computer suites and 2 excellent libraries. There are specialist teachers for music, swimming, PE, and Arabic (from Y1).

The JPS Achievement Centre (ACe) supports children throughout the school. There is a dedicated learning support staff for a limited number of students. The Dyslexia Unit is provides outstanding provision for dyslexic children. ACe also features a school counsellor who is a qualified psychologist. A strength of JPS is the programme for more able, gifted and talented children or MAG&T.

Children are given every opportunity to develop their personal strengths not just in the classroom but also in extra curricular activities. JPS manages an array of extra-curricular activities including a full sports programme, climbing, yoga for children, soccer, rugby, drama, ballet, modern dance, karate and tennis; older children are taken to use outside facilities for skiing, sailing, golf and horse-riding. JPS arranges a wide variety of music lessons. Each week some 65 extra-curricular activities take place.

The JPS Parents' Association is very strong. The primary function of the JPS PA is to provide a social network and support for our families. Key activities include International Day early in the year, production of the JPS calendar, a Trash 'n' Treasure sale, Mothers' Day sale and the Annual Charity Ball held in May each year. There are regular coffee mornings and JPS PA class representatives organise social events for their class. Parent Forums are a regular feature of the JPS calendar.

JPS is at the heart of its community providing support for local choirs, orchestras, Brownies, Rainbows and family support groups such at All 4 Down Syndrome.

Above all, we place great value on the children being happy in their learning. We generate a very happy community ethos by involving parents in day to day activities and in the development of their child's learning.

Keble School

Wades Hill Winchmore Hill London N21 1BG
Tel: 020 8360 3359
Fax: 020 8360 4000
e-mail: office@kebleprep.co.uk
website: www.kebleprep.co.uk

Chairman of the Board of Governors: Mrs R Davie

***Headmaster*: G P McCarthy**

Age Range. 4–13.
Number of Boys. 220 Day Boys.
Fees per term (2008-2009). £2,850–£3,550.

The warm and friendly atmosphere that exists at Keble ensures that the boys are well-motivated, keen to learn and able to mature at their own pace. Strong pastoral care is regarded as a key element in the boys' overall development and well-being, along with the encouragement of courteous and considerate behaviour.

The academic staff comprises 23 qualified graduate teachers, 5 classroom assistants and 2 Learning Support teachers. The buildings are well maintained and facilities are regularly updated. The school has an ambitious ICT development programme.

The average class size in the school is 17, although many classes are taught in half-groups and sets as the boys progress through the school. Boys follow the Foundation Stage in Reception. General subject teachers cover the academic curriculum in Years 1 to 4, with subject specialists following on from Year 5 onwards. The National Curriculum is used as a guide to curriculum development. Art, Music, PE, Design Technology, ICT, PSHE and Games are introduced at appropriate stages and are included within the timetable. Boys are encouraged to learn a musical instrument, sing in the choir, perform in plays and concerts, and play an active part in the wide range of sports on offer.

Football, rugby and cricket are the major team games. Further opportunities exist to participate in hockey, swimming, basketball, athletics, cross-country, badminton, tennis and golf. There is a wide range of lunchtime and after-school activities and clubs, including drama and chess. There are also numerous educational outings and trips.

Boys are not required to pass an assessment to gain entry into the school at Reception. Boys wishing to join the school at a later stage in Year 1 or above are assessed in order to ensure that they will fit comfortably into their new surroundings.

Boys are prepared for entry to senior independent schools through Common Entrance and Scholarship examinations at 13+. The school has a strong record of success in placing boys in the senior school which is right for them. In recent years, these schools include Aldenham, City of London, Haberdashers' Askes', Highgate, Haileybury, Mill Hill, St Albans, St Columba's, University College and Westminster.

Charitable status. Keble Preparatory School (1968) Limited is a Registered Charity, number 312979. It exists to provide education for boys.

Kelly College Preparatory School

Hazeldon Parkwood Road Tavistock Devon PL19 0JS
Tel: 01822 612919
Fax: 01822 612919
e-mail: admin@kellycollegeprep.com
website: www.kellycollegeprep.com

Kelly College Preparatory School '*is a good school. It provides a broad, creative and supportive education in which pupils are valued and their self-esteem and confidence are built up.*' ISI Report 2003.

***Headmaster*: Mr R Stevenson**, BA Hons, PGCE

Age Range. $2^1/_2$–11.

Number of Pupils. 200.

Fees per term (2008-2009). £1,850–£2,560 (lunch inclusive).

A well-established, co-educational day and boarding school for children from 2½–11 years, Kelly College Preparatory School is situated in a beautiful rural setting on the western edge of Dartmoor National Park. It is half a mile from Kelly College and the market town of Tavistock.

The school's reputation is built on a friendly, family atmosphere with high standards. It is a happy and adventurous place, where the ethos is child-centred in an environment conducive to learning. Flexi, weekly and full boarding are available from the age of 8 years. Pupils are prepared for 11+ entry, including scholarship preparation, to a wide variety of Independent and State Secondary Schools. The majority move on to Kelly College or the local Grammar Schools. The school is proud of its academic success. The curriculum is broad and varied, with subjects taught by specialist teachers from Year 4. French and swimming are timetabled weekly from Year 2.

Facilities include a new teaching block, two libraries, and separate Art/Design Technology, Music and French rooms. The school has recently extended its ICT provision, installing touch screen whiteboards and enlarging the ICT suite.

It has excellent sporting facilities both on site and at Kelly College, with access to their Astroturf, 25m indoor swimming pool and Adventure Centre. An extensive variety of sports and extra-curricular activities are on offer to pupils throughout the year and at times during the school holidays. These include horse riding, chess, art, dance, squash and cookery. Individual music tuition is available. Residential trips are also organised for older pupils.

There is an active Parents' Association that organises numerous social and fund-raising events throughout the year.

Further details and a prospectus are available from the School Secretary.

Charitable status. Kelly College Trust is a Registered Charity, number 306/716. It exists to provide education for boys and girls.

Kensington Preparatory School (GDST)

596 Fulham Road London SW6 5PA
Tel: 020 7731 9300
Fax: 020 7731 9301
e-mail: enquiries@kenprep.gdst.net
website: www.gdst.net/kensingtonprep

Founded in 1873, this is one of the 29 schools of The Girls' Day School Trust. For further information about the Trust, see p. xxiv. The following are additional particulars and a more detailed prospectus may be obtained from the school or on www.gdst.net/kensingtonprep.

***Head Mistress*: Mrs P J F Lynch**

Age Range. 4–11 years.

Number of Girls. 280.

Fees per term (2008-2009). £3,524.

Since 1997 the School has been based in Fulham. The generous premises provide large airy classrooms for all age groups, with specialist rooms for ICT, Art, Drama, Music, Science and Design Technology. There is a beautiful Library, a newly-refurbished School Hall and plenty of space for pupils to have PE and games on site.

The school aims to provide an excellent broadly based but strongly academic curriculum. Independence, individuality and questioning thinkers are encouraged and the girls enjoy challenging and interesting work in a stimulating and caring environment, whilst being prepared for entry to leading boarding and day schools at 11+.

Entry to the School is selective and the main entry points are at 4+ with a small intake at 7+. Occasional places do occur throughout the School from time to time.

Charitable status. Kensington Preparatory School is part of The Girls' Day School Trust, which is a Registered Charity, number 306983. The aim of the Trust is to provide a fine academic education for girls at a comparatively modest cost.

Kent College Infant and Junior School

Vernon Holme Harbledown Canterbury Kent CT2 9AQ
Tel: 01227 762436
Fax: 01227 763880
e-mail: info@vernonholme.co.uk
website: www.kentcollege.com/junior

Chairman of Governors: G A W Connolly, LLB, FRAeS (OC)

***Headmaster*: A J Carter**, BEd Hons

Age Range. 3–11 Co-educational.

Number of Pupils. Juniors (Day and Boarding) 110, Infants 86, Nursery 25.

Fees per term (2008-2009). Juniors: Boarders £5,868; Day Pupils (including lunch): £4,038 (Years 4–6), £3,914 (Year 3). Infants: £2,852 (Years 1–2), £2,670 (Reception). Nursery: from £245 (1 session per week) to £2,135 (5 full days).

The school is fully co-educational offering a broad, yet balanced, curriculum appropriate to the educational and pastoral needs of the children in a happy atmosphere. Lessons take place in bright, stimulating classrooms with specialist rooms for science, ICT, drama, sports, music, art and design technology.

Nursery pupils are admitted at age 3 and infants at the age of 5 or, when appropriate, before their fifth birthday. There is a further entry of juniors at age 7 (and at other ages if there are vacancies). Children are prepared for entry to the senior school (*see entry in HMC section*) to which many go at the age of 11. In the process they are taught to think for themselves and are given plenty of activity time to develop their own interests within a structured environment that encourages and develops community awareness and social skills.

There is a small, comfortable boarding house within the main building which can accommodate full and weekly boarders as well as offering the opportunity for occasional boarding to suit the needs of busy families. The school is open between 7.45 am and 6.00 pm each day to allow parents to drop off early or collect late as required.

The school has a Dyslexia Unit which is designed to give special support to children who experience this problem whilst enabling them to integrate as fully as possible into the normal school programme. The school offers an extended day and weekend activity programme that is optional.

The 12 acres of ground were originally laid out by Sidney Cooper RA. These idyllic surrounds have been adapted to provide games fields and a heated swimming pool without losing the varied character which makes them so suitable for young children's activities.

Charitable status. Kent College, Canterbury is a Registered Charity, number 307844. The School was founded to provide education within a supportive Christian environment and is a member of the Methodist Independent Schools' Group.

Kent College Preparatory School
Pembury

Old Church Road Pembury Tunbridge Wells Kent TN2 4AX
Tel: 01892 820204
Fax: 01892 820214
e-mail: prepschool@kentcollege.kent.sch.uk
website: www.kent-college.co.uk

Chairman of Governors: Mrs P J Darbyshire, MBE

***Headmistress*: Mrs A Lawson**, BEd Hons

Age Range. Girls 3–11.

Number of Girls. 161: 5 Boarders, 156 Day Girls.

Fees per term (2008-2009). Day Girls £2,215–£3,334, Boarders £6,027. All fees include lunches. There are no compulsory extras.

The school has its own purpose-built accommodation on a beautiful 75 acre site, shared with Kent College Pembury (Senior School), and benefits from facilities such as a 360-seater state-of-the-art theatre, large sports hall, indoor heated swimming pool with small learners pool, activities hall, dining hall and dance studio.

The school believes that happy, confident children are successful ones and the girls love coming to school. Academic standards are high, but it is never forgotten that there is more to childhood and learning than examinations. Girls are successfully prepared in small classes (average 16) for a wide range of senior schools at age 11, but the school is not a crammer.

The curriculum is broad and balanced, based on the National Curriculum. All pupils benefit from specialist teaching in swimming, dance, drama, ICT, PE and music, with specialist French teaching from age 7.

Main intakes are in to the Early Years Department which incorporates the Nursery and Reception classes for girls aged 3–5. The department has its own wing of the School with light, colourful and well-resourced classrooms and its own outside playground areas. The Foundation Stage Curriculum is followed and by the end of the Reception year some of the pupils will be working at the lower stages of Key Stage One.

Performing arts is an important part of the curriculum with opportunities for music, drama and dance at all ages. Even the youngest pupils, aged 3, can do optional ballet lessons. The school has a choir and an orchestra and there are regular concerts and drama productions. There is a good range of sporting opportunities including netball, hockey, tennis, rounders, cross-country, swimming, trampolining and athletics.

The school prides itself on providing an exciting and varied programme of over 35 clubs and activities and there is a good ethos of participation. The curriculum is supported with interesting trips and days out, and residential holidays for Years 5 and 6. A variety of well-known authors have visited the school to run workshops.

An After School Care facility is available for girls in Reception upwards. Boarders are accepted from age 10 and are part of a small, family-run boarding house in which girls have a secure, happy and homely environment. Prospective boarders are invited to spend a day and overnight stay with us to give them a feel for the school. There is a 20% discount for Forces' families.

Entry to Nursery, Reception, Years 1 and 2 are based on availability of places. Pupils in Years 3–6 are required to sit entry tests in English and mathematics. The Headmistress is pleased to welcome visitors and to show them around the school.

Charitable status. Kent College Pembury is a Registered Charity, number 307920. It is a Christian school specialising in girls' education.

Kenton College

PO Box 30017, 00100 Nairobi, Kenya
Tel: 00 254 20 4347000/4347532/4347371
Fax: 00 254 20 4347332
e-mail: admin@kenton.ac.ke
website: www.kentonschoolnairobi.com

Chairman of the Governors: C H Banks, Esq

***Headmistress*: Mrs M Cussans**, BA, PGCE, MA

Age Range. 6–13 Co-educational.

Number of Pupils. 240.

Fees per annum (2007-2008). Kshs 253,000.

Founded in 1924 and transferred to purpose built accommodation in 1935, Kenton College is one of the oldest schools in the country. Situated in its own secluded grounds of 35 acres, at an altitude of nearly 6000 feet, some three miles from the centre of one of Africa's most cosmopolitan capitals, Kenton is an oasis of calm amidst the rapidly sprawling urban development of the city of Nairobi.

Kenton College is an independent co-educational preparatory school, entry to which is open to both boys and girls of any race or religious persuasion, who have had their sixth birthday before the beginning of the school year in September. Most pupils remain seven years with us and leave in the July following their thirteenth birthday for senior schools in the UK, Kenya or South Africa, having followed a syllabus in the senior part of the school leading to the ISEB Common Entrance Examination. Kenton pupils frequently obtain scholarships to UK or Kenyan senior schools.

The school is based on a strong Christian foundation which is reflected in the warm and caring environment provided for its pupils, wherein positive encouragement is given towards any aspect of school life. Considerable emphasis is placed on character building, discipline and good manners, within a relaxed and happy atmosphere.

We aim for high academic achievements by offering a full curriculum in which the best of traditional and modern approaches are employed. The British National Curriculum provides the framework for our teaching throughout the school. Use is made of specialist subject teaching rooms in the senior school, to which recent additions are a Modern Languages suite, a Design Studio and two Computer rooms. There are two Science laboratories, a well-stocked Library, a 300 seat Assembly Hall with large stage, and a purpose-built Music Studio.

The academic day is balanced by opportunities for drama and music for all, together with a wide variety of sports and extra-curricular activities. Traditional British sports are played using our first class facilities which include three tennis courts and a heated swimming pool.

Many pupils opt for extra activities such as riding, ballet, karate, music tuition, tennis or swimming coaching, speech and drama awards, Cubs and Brownies. Sailing in the school boats on Lake Naivasha is available a few times each term. Trips to theatres, museums and the many facilities found in an international city are combined with expeditions and fieldwork in the unrivalled Kenyan countryside.

Academic subjects are taught by a staff complement of local and expatriate teachers numbering 25. Full use is made of accomplished musicians for music tuition, while recognised Kenyan sportsmen assist with games coaching. The average class size is 16, with 20 the maximum.

Kew College

24–26 Cumberland Road Kew Surrey TW9 3HQ
Tel: 020 8940 2039
Fax: 020 8332 9945
e-mail: enquiries@kewcollege.com
website: www.kewcollege.com

Chairman of Governors: Mr Oliver Weiss

***Headteacher*: Mrs Diana Lyness**

Age Range. 3–11 Co-educational.

Number of Pupils. 260.

Fees per term (2007-2008). £1,230–£2,310.

Charitable status. Kew College is a Registered Charity, number 286059.

Kew Green Preparatory School

Layton House Ferry Lane Kew Green Richmond Surrey TW9 3AF
Tel: 020 8948 5999
Fax: 020 8948 4774
e-mail: secretary@kgps.co.uk
website: www.kgps.co.uk

***Headmistress*: Mrs Maria Gardener**

Age Range. 4–11 Co-educational.

Number of Pupils. 260.

Fees per term (2008-2009). £3,969.

The school is housed in an attractive building and grounds directly next door to the Royal Botanical Gardens. The front of the school overlooks Kew Green, which is used for games, and the back of the school has a good-sized playground which looks onto the River Thames.

The children are encouraged to use philosophy and ethical thinking throughout the curriculum which includes English, Maths, Science, French, RE, Music, Design & Technology, Games/PE, Computer Studies, Moral & Religious Education and Yoga. All Upper school children attend a Summer Term Residential Week where cross-curricular studies are applied in a non-urban environment.

There are many after-school clubs and sports activities and we have two choirs, an orchestra and rock band. Individual tuition is offered in piano, violin, brass, woodwind, cello, saxophone and singing.

An 8 am to 6 pm All-Day Care service is offered to parents at an extra charge.

The school is noted for its warm, happy atmosphere where parents play a full part in enriching the curriculum and social life. Off-site visits and guest workshops presented by noted visitors are a regular feature of education at Kew Green.

The school is always heavily over-subscribed and registration is recommended on the child's first birthday. A prospectus and registration form may be obtained from the School Secretary.

Kilgraston Preparatory School

Bridge of Earn Perth PH2 9BQ
Tel: 01738 812257
Fax: 01738 813410
e-mail: headoffice@kilgraston.pkc.sch.uk
website: www.kilgraston.com

Day and Boarding School for Girls (day boys to age 9).

Chairman of Board of Governors: Mr Timothy Hall

***Head*: Mrs Audrey Kellaway**, BEd, DipPD (Ed Man)

Age Range. $2^1/_2$–13.

Number of Pupils. 120 Girls, 11 Boys.

Fees per term (2008-2009). Day £2,475–£4,125, Full Boarding £5,995, Weekly Boarding £5,395.

Kilgraston Preparatory School and Nursery is the junior school for Kilgraston, a leading boarding and day school for girls in Scotland, and is co-educational up the age of 9 years. Located in its own building, The Grange, the Preparatory School is surrounded by 54 acres of stunning parkland at Bridge of Earn, three miles from the centre of Perth, 45 minutes from Edinburgh and an hour's drive from Glasgow.

Admission to Kilgraston Preparatory School is by interview and informal assessment. Girls in the Preparatory School are able to progress into Kilgraston Senior School, or sit Common Entrance or scholarship exams for Kilgraston and other schools. The academic standard is high with all pupils completing the Preparatory School achieving a place in their senior school of choice.

Preparatory School pupils are taught by class teachers until the age of nine (apart from PE, French, music and drama). Form teachers hold pastoral responsibility for the pupils and classes are small with provision for additional support needs. From age ten, the curriculum becomes more specialised with increasing input from specialised subject staff and use of the facilities in the Senior School. Pastoral care is the responsibility of a tutor. The Nursery too, benefits from senior school facilities such as the swimming pool, games hall, and theatre.

The core academic curriculum is enhanced by a wide range of co-curricular subjects. While academic excellence is a priority, pupils are encouraged to achieve excellence in every aspect of the wider curriculum. Classrooms are well equipped and modern IT facilities are spread throughout the school. Art, drama and music flourish and are an important feature of life at Kilgraston. Opportunities are provided throughout the year for pupils to perform in groups or as soloists and they compete successfully in local festivals. The girls have the opportunity to take LAMDA, Associated Board and Trinity examinations. There is an annual production involving all pupils.

Sports and recreation thrive within the superb Sports Hall, including a climbing wall and fitness gym. In April 2008 the magnificent indoor 25m Swimming Pool complex opened and the extensive grounds incorporate 9 floodlit all-weather courts, playing fields and athletics track. The main sports are: hockey, netball, tennis, rounders, football, cricket, swimming and athletics with fixtures against other preparatory schools. The school has a an excellent skiing record in British and Scottish competitions and Kilgraston is the only school in Scotland with an equestrian facility on campus and also hosts the Scottish Schools Equestrian Championships each year at Gleneagles.

Kilgraston Preparatory School has a pastoral House system. Inter-House competitions and challenges in games, music and debating are serious fun. The family atmosphere in the newly refurbished boarding area, Butterstone, is enhanced by the wide range of weekend activities that make use of the superb local facilities and environment of Perthshire.

An exciting long-term capital development programme is underway which has already seen the completion of a bistro-style dining room, new theatre, tennis pavilion and the 25m indoor swimming complex. Plans for future development will be announced shortly.

Charitable status. Kilgraston School Trust is a Registered Charity, number SC029664. It exists to develop a love of learning, a spirit of adventure and openness of heart.

Kimbolton Preparatory School

Kimbolton Huntingdon Cambs PE28 0EA
Tel: 01480 860281
Fax: 01480 861874
e-mail: prep@kimbolton.cambs.sch.uk
website: www.kimbolton.cambs.sch.uk

Chair of Governors: C A Paull

***Headmaster*: R J Wells**, BEd, BA

Age Range. 4–11 Co-educational.

Number of Children. Approximately 320.

Fees per term (2008-2009). £2,410–£3,070 (including lunch).

Mission Statement. Within a friendly, caring environment, Kimbolton pupils are encouraged to develop the social responsibility and independence of thought to equip them for the challenges of a changing world.

Everyone has talent; the school aims to provide the opportunity for each individual to excel so that success can be celebrated and self-esteem enhanced.

Motto: *Spes Durat Avorum*.

To the west of Kimbolton village the Preparatory School is located within its own attractive grounds linked to the Senior School by means of a pathway, the 'Duchess Walk', the castle once being the home of Catharine of Aragon. It is partially housed in the old Kimbolton Grammar School buildings which date from 1876.

Boys and girls join the Preparatory School at four years of age. A purpose-built building (Aragon House) encompasses Reception, Year One and Year Two. It is here that the children are educated in a safe, welcoming and happy environment. The younger children also use the facilities on offer throughout the Preparatory School. The children automatically progress to the Upper Prep. The expectation is that the Year Six children progress to the Senior School. (*See entry in HMC section*)

Children may also join the School when places are available after assessment/examination and interview.

There is a programme in place for identified gifted and talented children.

January 2007 saw the completion of a £3m building development programme at the Preparatory School. A new Assembly Hall, Music Teaching Room and Practice Rooms, Staff Common Room, Changing Rooms for boys and girls and an Entrance/Reception area for visitors complement the existing impressive facilities.

The Preparatory School has, on its own site, a Dining Hall, Library, Computer Suite, Science Room, Art and Design Technology Room, Sports Hall, Learning Support Unit and large, light and airy classrooms, all of which have recently been refurbished as a part of a rolling programme.

There is a full-time nurse on site.

Reception, Year 1 and Year 2 have two classes per year group and Years 3–6 have three classes. Each class has its own class teacher and there is a good deal of specialist teaching throughout the Upper Prep.

The outdoor facilities including the tennis and netball courts, athletics track, rounders fields, football, hockey and cricket pitches provide excellent facilities. The Swimming Pool located at the Senior School is used weekly by the Preparatory School.

The majority of children at KS2 have individual music lessons in addition to curricular class music. There are an extensive number of excursions, including an annual residential skiing excursion and many visitors and speakers visit the school thereby enriching the curriculum. There is an extensive range of extra-curricular activities.

Children may arrive for breakfast at 7.45 am and also the Kim Club facility after school until 6.00 pm. Supervised Prep and an extensive list of activities and clubs are available after school.

We feel that children are given every opportunity to gain a first class education in a family orientated environment situated in superb surroundings. This allied with strong teaching in small class sizes prepares a child fully for the future.

The Preparatory School was inspected by ISI in 2005 and the Out of School care facility (Kim Club) by Ofsted in 2006.

Charitable status. Kimbolton School Foundation is a Registered Charity, number 1098586.

King Henry VIII Preparatory School

Kenilworth Road Coventry CV3 6PT
Tel: 024 7627 1307
Fax: 024 7627 1308
e-mail: headmaster@khps.co.uk
website: www.khps.co.uk

Chairman of Governors: Mr Brendan Connor

***Headmaster*: Mr Nicholas Lovell**, BA Hons, PGCE

Age Range. 3–11 Co-educational.

Number of Pupils. 490 Day Boys and Girls.

Fees per term (2008-2009). Reception–Year 2 £2,205; Year 3 £2,253; Years 4–6 £2,115.

King Henry VIII Preparatory School is part of Coventry School Foundation, which includes King Henry VIII Senior School, Bablake School (7–18) and Cheshunt School (2½–7).

The School is situated on two campuses a short distance from each other on the south side of Coventry.

The Swallows Campus, opposite Coventry Memorial Park, educates children aged 3-8 in classes of 16 (from Reception onwards). The campus (formerly Coventry Preparatory School) occupies a beautiful 3½ acre site and has a wealth of facilities, including its own Swimming-pool, Sports Hall, Art & Design Centre, All-weather surface and Adventure Playground. Its main building dates to the 17th century. Most teaching is provided by class teachers, giving young children a continuity of approach and providing them with a key individual with whom to build a strong relationship and who will guide them through their daily studies. An increasing number of specialist teachers are provided as children progress through the infant years: Music from age 3, Games and Swimming from age 4 and Art & Design Technology from age 6. There is a strong family atmosphere and the aim is to provide children with a wonderful start to their education.

The Hales Campus is situated just down the road from Swallows and occupies a portion of the main King Henry VIII School site. The main building was purpose-built in 1997 and provides an excellent range of modern facilities for children aged 8–11. At this site children are taught by specialist teachers for all subjects in classes of 20. The Hales Campus has its own Sports Hall, Music Department, Library, Art & Design Room, Science Laboratory and playing areas. Some facilities are shared with the senior school, including Games fields and a new 25 metre indoor swimming pool.

The School seeks to help its pupils to be happy, confident 'all-rounders'. Academic standards are high and entrance to the School, from the age of 5, is through academic assessment (ages 5–6) and examination (ages 7–10). Children joining the School at the ages of 3 or 4 are not academically selected and names may be registered from birth. The majority of children continue from King Henry VIII Preparatory School to King Henry VIII Senior School at age 11; however, children may sit entrance to a variety of other schools.

The Arts and Sport are very important aspects within the curriculum. The visual and performance Arts are specialist taught from the infant years. Music is strong, with children being able to learn a wide variety of musical instruments from an early age. Drama and performance are aspects of school life which flourish, with all children taking part in a variety of performances during their time at the School. A large number of performance opportunities are available each year.

Games are taught within the timetable from Reception onwards and competitive matches against other schools start in Year 2. The main sports for boys are Rugby, Football and Cricket; for girls Netball, Hockey and Rounders. Beyond the main team sports, there is a range of other sports that may be experienced, both within the timetable and as extra-curricular activities.

Scholarships are awarded from the age of 8, for academic subjects as well as the Arts and All-Rounder awards. Bursaries are available at entrance from Year 3 onwards (7+).

The School has a vibrant extra-curricular activities programme which may be accessed by pupils from Reception onwards, this includes both lunchtime and after school clubs. Before school care (from 7.45 am) and after school care (up to 6.00 pm) are available daily during term time, as well as voluntary Saturday morning sports. There is a full programme of care for children aged from 3–11, starting at 8.30 am and continuing until 5.30 pm, during every school holiday.

School trips and educational visits are regarded as an important aspect of each child's experience at the School. These include visits to local places of interest, usually associated with programmes of study, but also residential trips for each year group from the age of 7 onwards, one of which will be to the Coventry School Foundation manor house, Le Fousseau, in the Mayenne, France.

The School's motto *Confide Recte Agens* – have the courage to do what is right – lies at the heart of the School's ethos which encourages children to have the courage of their convictions. The School is a member of the Community of the Cross of Nails, thus having an association with Coventry Cathedral. This stresses tolerance and understanding between people of different creeds and faiths. The School happily accepts children from various faiths and looks to build genuine understanding and tolerance between its pupils.

Overall the School seeks to help its children to be happy, confident people who enjoy learning.

Charitable status. Coventry School Foundation is a Registered Charity, number 528961. Its aim is to advance the education of boys and girls by the provision of a school or schools in or near the City of Coventry.

King's College Junior School

Wimbledon Common London SW19 4TT
Tel: 020 8255 5335
Fax: 020 8255 5339
e-mail: jsadmissions@kcs.org.uk
HMJSsec@kcs.org.uk
website: www.kcs.org.uk

Chairman of the Governing Body:
J M Jarvis, QC, MA

***Headmaster*: Dr G A Silverlock**, BEd Hons, MLitt, PhD

Age Range. 7–13.

Number of Boys. 450 (day boys only).

Fees per term (2008-2009). £4,115 (Years 3–4), £4,640 (Years 5–8).

The Junior School was established in 1912 as an integral part of KCS, to prepare boys for the Senior School. It shares with it a common site and many facilities, in particular the Music School, the Art, Design and Technology School, the Science Laboratories, the Dining Hall, the Sports Hall, the swimming pool and extensive playing fields. For the rest, Junior School boys are housed in their own buildings. The Priory, rebuilt in 1980 and recently extended, contains twenty three classrooms, including specialist rooms for languages, mathematics, history, geography, information technology and multimedia work. The youngest age groups have their own special accommodation in Rushmere, a spacious Georgian house whose grounds adjoin the Junior School. The School also has its own purpose-built library, junior science laboratories and well-equipped theatre and assembly hall.

The School is separately administered in matters relating to admission, curriculum, discipline and day to day activities. There are twenty-nine members of staff in addition to those teaching in specialist departments common to both Schools.

The work and overall programme are organised in close consultation with the Senior School to ensure that boys are educated in a structured and progressive way from 7 to 18, having the benefit of continuity, while enjoying the range and style of learning that are best suited to their age.

Boys come from both maintained and pre-preparatory schools and are admitted at the age of 7, 8, 9, 10 or 11. Entry is by interview and examination.

Charitable status. King's College School is a Registered Charity, number 310024. It exists to provide education for children.

King's College School

West Road Cambridge CB3 9DN
Tel: 01223 365814
Fax: 01223 461388
e-mail: office@kcs.cambs.sch.uk
website: www.kcs.cambs.sch.uk

The School is part of King's College and is administered by a Board of Governors.

Chairman of Governors: The Provost of King's College

***Headmaster*: N J Robinson**, BA, PGCE

Deputy Heads:
Mrs L E Edge, BSc, Ad DipEd
Mr C Hyde-Dunn, MA Oxon, MEd, PGCE

Age Range. Co-educational, age 4–13.

Number of Pupils. 335 day pupils, 35 boy boarders including 16 choristers.

Fees per term (2008-2009). Boarding: £5,720; Choristers: £1,905; Day Pupils: £3,690; Pre-Prep: £2,865 (including lunch).

The School is administered by Governors appointed by the Council of King's College, parents and teaching staff. King Henry VI's charter founding King's College in 1441 provided for Choristers and their education. In 1878 the School moved to its present site near the University library, across the river from the College. Over the years the facilities have steadily increased. The main house accommodates the catering facilities and boarding accommodation. A new Wiles Centre for Technology opened in June 1999 with first class facilities for ICT and DT. The Performing Arts Centre includes 16 new music rooms (opened in 2001) and a multi-purpose hall used for plays and concerts and also a fully-equipped gym. A new classroom block called the "Briggs Building" was opened in May 2004 by the Duchess of Kent and it contains two very well equipped science labs, two maths classrooms, three modern language classrooms, two English classrooms and a new library. Sports facilities on site include two large playing fields, tennis courts and a heated outdoor swimming pool. A new floodlit astroturf field was laid in May 2005. The School also has the use of other nearby sports fields. The Pre-Prep has been expanded to accommodate two-form entry starting from September 2008.

The Headmaster is assisted by 30 full-time and 10 part-time teachers. There are 3 Matrons and a full-time Bursar and Assistant Bursar. There are 30 full- or part-time music staff. In 1976 girls were admitted as day pupils and the ratio of boys to girls is 50:50 in the junior classes. In September 1981 the School started a small special centre for dyslexic children of good intelligence and there is now an excellent Learning Support Centre; auditory training and music play an important part, the children mix with their peers in normal classes, although some do not study French. Pupils are prepared for the Scholarship and Common Entrance examinations of the boys' and girls' Independent Senior Schools. The school broadly follows the National Curriculum subjects, but also teaches French from the age of 4, Latin from 9, and Greek to some older children. The School has a tradition of winning numerous academic, art, music and sports awards annually.

Apart from choral and instrumental music (there are 2 orchestras of some 80 players in each and about 40 chamber groups), activities include Drama, Art, Craft, Pottery, Computing, DT, Gymnastics, PE, Chess, Science, RSPB Wildlife Explorers, Handwriting, Library, Model-making. Games include Rugger, Soccer, Hockey, Cricket, Netball, Rounders, Athletics, Tennis, Squash, Cross-Country and Swimming.

Further information about the School may be obtained from the Headmaster. Enquiries concerning Choristerships should also be addressed to him. Choristership Auditions take place annually, usually in January.

Charitable status. King's College School is a Registered Charity, number X6753A. Its aim is to provide an excellent education for girls and boys of mixed ability aged 4 to 13.

King's Hall
A Woodard School

Kingston Road Taunton Somerset TA2 8AA
Tel: 01823 285920
Fax: 01823 285922
e-mail: schooloffice@kingshall.rmplc.co.uk
website: www.kingshalltaunton.co.uk

Chairman of Governors: Magnus Mowat, Esq, FCA

***Head*: James Macpherson**, BEd Hons Exeter

Age Range. 3–13+ Co-educational.

Number of Pupils. Preparatory (Years 3–8): 155 boys, 125 girls; 60 boarders. Pre-Prep (Nursery–Year 2): 53 boys, 47 girls.

Fees per term (2008-2009). Preparatory Day £2,030–£3,840, Full/Weekly Boarding £4,370–£5,680, Pre-Prep £1,450–£1,550.

King's Hall is set in a beautiful country location surrounded by National Trust farmland yet is only a couple of miles from the centre of Taunton with easy access to the M5 and less than two hours to London by train. It has all the characteristics of a traditional country preparatory school without being overshadowed by a senior school on the same site. This gives the children a pride in their school and visitors invariably comment upon the warmth and friendliness with which they are greeted. It is one of the Woodard Schools whose approach is based on the principles of the Church of England. The academic results are excellent. Sport, outdoor activites, music, art and drama are also strengths. Scholarships are available for pupils with exceptional ability. These are awarded at 11+ and continue at King's College, Taunton up to age 18. Others may join King's Hall through interview and assessment at any age after their third birthday (subject to availabilty of places).

King's Hawford

Worcester WR3 7SE
Tel: 01905 451292
Fax: 01905 756502
e-mail: office@kingshawford.org.uk
website: www.ksw.org.uk

Chairman of the Governors: D T Howell, Esq, BSc(Eng), FCA

***Headmaster*: J M Turner**, BEd Hons, DipEd, ACP

Age Range. $2^{3}/_{4}$–11.

Number of Pupils. Boys 194, Girls 137.

Fees per term (2008-2009). £1,813–£3,316, including lunch.

King's Hawford is a junior school to the historic King's School, Worcester, and is set in thirty acres of parkland situated on the northern outskirts of Worcester. The school is accommodated within an elegant and recently refurbished Georgian house surrounded by well maintained playing fields, with tennis courts, a heated outdoor swimming pool, a multipurpose sports hall and secure play area for younger children.

There are extensive opportunities for a wide range of extra curricular activities and there is a busy calendar of music, drama, sport, clubs. Sports include Rugby, Association Football, Cricket, Hockey, Netball, Rounders, Athletics, Tennis, Cross-Country and Swimming.

The Pre-Prep department accepts children from rising 3–6 and the Junior department from 7–11.

Charitable status. The King's School Worcester is a Registered Charity, number 1098236. It exists to provide a broad education for a wide range of children from rising 3–11 years.

King's House School

68 King's Road Richmond Surrey TW10 6ES
Tel: 020 8940 1878
Fax: 020 8939 2501
e-mail: head@kingshouseschool.org
website: www.kingshouseschool.org

The School was constituted an Educational Trust with a Board of Governors in September 1957.

Chairman of the Governors: Mr Simon Readhead

***Head*: Mrs S Piper**, BA

Age Range. 4–13.

Number of Boys. Senior Department 212; Junior Department 165.

Fees per term (2008-2009). Reception and Year 1: £2,865; Years 2 and 3: £3,365; Senior Department £3,870 (all fees inclusive of lunch).

King's House is a Day Preparatory School for boys aged 4–13 on two sites in King's Road. Boys are prepared for entry by Scholarship or Common Entrance to all independent schools.

The School aims to provide a broad, balanced curriculum in a caring environment.

Charitable status. King's House School is a Registered Charity, number 312669. It exists for the education of boys.

King's Junior School

Milner Court Sturry Nr Canterbury Kent CT2 0AY
Tel: 01227 714000
Fax: 01227 713171
e-mail: office@junior-kings.co.uk
website: www.junior-kings.co.uk

Chairman of Governors: The Dean of Canterbury The Very Revd R A Willis, BA, DipTh, FRSA

***Headmaster*: P M Wells**, BEd Hons

Age Range. 3–13.

Number of Pupils. 399: Boarders 72, Day Pupils 219, Pre-Prep 108.

Fees per term (2008-2009). Boarders £6,260; Day Pupils £4,610; Pre-Prep £2,720 (including lunch).

The School is the Junior School of the King's School, Canterbury and is co-educational.

Members of the thriving boarding community enjoy a wide variety of weekend activities organised by house-parents and all the domestic arrangements are supervised by the Headmaster's wife.

The majority of the pupils move up to the King's School through Scholarship or Common Entrance at 13+ though a few pass on to other independent secondary or local grammar schools. Classes are kept sufficiently small (average 16) for plenty of individual attention and pastoral care. Academic standards are high and the record of success in Scholarships and Common Entrance is outstanding.

The school has a fine reputation for music, both instrumental and choral, as well as art, design and drama. There is a programme of concerts, exhibitions and recitals involving children of all ages. Pupils frequently gain awards to other schools.

For boys, cricket, soccer and rugby football are the main games, while girls play netball, hockey and rounders. Athletics, tennis and fencing are joint pursuits. A new sports hall was opened in 1998 and this is used for PE lessons, basketball, volleyball, badminton, and netball, as well as indoor hockey, soccer and tennis. There is canoeing on the River Stour, which runs through the 80 acres of grounds. Rowing and sailing take place on nearby lakes and a heated outdoor swimming pool is well used during the summer months with access to the King's School Recreation Centre in the winter.

The 16th century Tithe Barn has a fully equipped stage. Buildings opened in the last decade include a design and technology centre and a spacious dining hall which provides an attractive alternative venue for concerts and plays. Eight new classrooms were opened in September 1999, and the Library refurbished in 2000. The Girls' and Boys' boarding houses were redesigned to an extremely high standard in 2003.

The Oast House provides a setting full of character for the Pre-Preparatory department for children aged 3 to 7. The Pre-Prep was extended with a new hall and classroom in 2001.

Charitable status. The King's School of the Cathedral Church of Canterbury is a Registered Charity, number 307942. It exists to provide education for boys and girls.

King's School Junior School
Ely

Ely Cambs CB7 4DB
Tel: 01353 660732
Fax: 01353 665281
e-mail: admissions@kings-ely.cambs.sch.uk
website: www.kings-ely.cambs.sch.uk

Chairman of the Governors: R P Slogrove

***Head*: R J Whymark**, BA Ed

Age Range. 7–13.

Number of Pupils. Boarders: 25 Boys, 8 Girls; Day: 162 Boys, 144 Girls.

Fees per term (2008-2009). Boarding £5,490–£5,795. Day £3,440–£3,760.

The Junior School has its own staff and its own new buildings are close to the main School. The facilities of the Senior School are freely available to Junior boys and girls.

There is a family boarding house for boys and girls up to the age of 13 and a separate boarding house for the boy choristers of Ely Cathedral who are all pupils in the Junior School. Each has its own Housemaster or Housemistress, assisted by House Tutors and experienced Matrons. Both houses have recently been refurbished and offer excellent boarding facilities.

During the school day all children are divided into four equal-sized co-educational 'houses' for pastoral and competitive purposes. Each of these 'houses' is staffed by a Housemaster or Housemistress and several House Tutors.

Entry to Junior School for boys and girls is through assessment tests and interview. The main two entry points are Year 3 (age 7) and Year 7 (age 11) but pupils may start in any year providing there is space. The main assessment weeks are in January, although it is common to assess for entry at other times of the year. Exceptional children for Year 7 entry may be invited to take the Junior School Scholarship examination. A broad preparatory school curriculum is followed and all pupils are prepared for the relevant transfer examination. While the great majority proceed to the Senior School in Year 9, pupils can also be prepared for other Independent Schools.

The main games for boys are Rugby, Cricket and Football, and for girls they are Netball, Hockey, Rounders and Tennis. Both boys and girls are involved in Athletics and Cross-Country Running. There is a Swimming Pool, a well-equipped Sports Hall, a full-size all-weather hockey/tennis area, and excellent playing fields. A wide-ranging programme of extra-curricular activities is also offered. All pupils have the opportunity to learn one or more of a wide variety of musical instruments. There are several Junior School Orchestras, and choral and ensemble music are taught. The Junior School musicians regularly tour abroad; in 2005 to Holland, to Malta in 2007 and to Paris in 2008. The School has its own Music School and Technology Centre, and access to the Senior School's new £1 million Recital Hall and Music School. A new £1.2m block of seven classrooms and a science laboratory for Years 7 and 8 opened in 2003.

The School is also justly proud of its art and drama, which are taught in their own studios, and of its excellent computer facilities.

Charitable status. The King's School, Ely is a Registered Charity, number 802427. It exists for the provision of education.

King's Preparatory School
Rochester

King Edward Road Rochester Kent ME1 1UB
Tel: 01634 888577
Fax: 01634 888507
e-mail: prep@kings-school-rochester.co.uk
website: www.kings-school-rochester.co.uk

Chairman of the Governors: The Very Revd A Newman, BSc, MPhil

***Headmaster*: R P Overend**, BA, FTCL, ARCM, FRSA

Age Range. 8–13.

Number of Pupils. 210 (5 Boarders).

Fees per term (2008-2009). Boarders £5,990, Day Pupils £3,430–£3,890 (including lunches).

Admission between 8+ to 12+ is by interview and report from present school as well as Entrance Examinations in English, Mathematics and Verbal or Non-Verbal Reasoning.

Scholarships are awarded (partly from the Cathedral, partly from the School) to Cathedral Choristers (boys only) and King's (30% and means-tested up to 75%) or Governors' Exhibitions (means-tested up to 100%) to those whose performance in the Entrance Examination merits it.

The Preparatory School is an integral part of the King's School, Rochester, founded in 604 AD by Justus, a Benedictine monk, the first Bishop of Rochester. The Cathedral is at the heart of the School's life with a weekly School service and every day the Choristers maintain the tradition of choral singing at the world's oldest Choir School. When the School is not in the Cathedral a religious assembly is held at the Preparatory School.

The School is a member of the Choir Schools' Association.

The School has been fully co-educational since 1993 and 30% are girls.

Set in the City, the Preparatory School building overlooks the Paddock, one of the School's playing fields. The teaching block consists of 12 classrooms, 2 Science Laboratories, a Computer Suite, Language Laboratory and a Library with over 6,000 volumes. Other facilities such as the Design and Technology Centre, Art Centre, Music School, Indoor Swimming Pool and Sports Halls are shared with the Senior School which virtually all pupils join following the internal Entrance Examination. Chadlington House, the purpose-built Pre-Preparatory School which educates pupils from age 4–8, opened in 2000; a Conference Centre and dining room was opened in 2006.

The Preparatory School has a small number of boarders who are housed either in School House for boys, or St Margaret's House for girls. Boarding, both full and weekly, is available for boys and girls from 11+.

The curriculum is broad and balanced. In Year 8 science is taught as three separate subjects, French and German are the modern languages, and Latin is taught from Year 7. Individual educational support tuition is available if required.

All pupils enjoy the benefit of 2 full afternoons a week of Games in addition to a PE lesson for most year groups. Major sports include Rugby, Hockey, Cricket, Netball, Athletics, Rounders and Swimming. There is a wide range of extra-curricular activities including Air Pistol Shooting, Skiing, Art Club, Horse Riding, Computer Club, Needlecraft, Warhammer, Wall Climbing, Irish Dancing as well as many sporting activities.

Choral and instrumental music is strong throughout the School. Many of our pupils learn one or more musical instruments and strong results are achieved in Associated Board examinations. There is a Choir, Orchestra, Wind Band and String Group, all of which meet weekly. Each year the Drama Club presents a play or musical held over three nights. Recently productions have required casts in excess of fifty and have been wonderful opportunities for pupils to show their dramatic and musical skills. Amongst latest productions have been "Oliver", "Bendigo Boswell", "Homer's Odyssey", "Under Milk Wood", "Bugsy Malone", "In Holland stands a House" and "Little Shop of Horrors".

Charitable status. King's School, Rochester is a Registered Charity, number 1084266. It is a Charitable Trust for the purpose of educating children.

King's St Alban's Junior School

Mill Street Worcester WR1 2NJ
Tel: 01905 354906
Fax: 01905 763075
e-mail: ksa@ksw.org.uk
website: www.ksw.org.uk

From September 2009 King's St Alban's will be admitting children from Reception to Year 6 (age 4–11).

Chairman of the Governors: D T Howell, Esq, BSc Eng, FCA

***Headmaster*: Mr R T Bellfield**, BEd

Age Range. 4–11 Co-educational.

Number of Pupils. 180.

Fees per term (2008-2009). 7 years £2,195; 8–11 years £2,962, excluding lunch.

Education is about far more than academic learning, although that is still our primary purpose. At King's St Alban's we aim to develop the whole child, encouraging each girl and boy to explore their capabilities, find fresh challenges and discover spheres in which they can excel.

King's St Alban's Junior School is located near to Worcester Cathedral on a separate site adjacent to the Senior School. In the grounds stand the Chapel, a modern classroom block and the main building of St Alban's. The school has a purpose-built Science Laboratory, an IT suite, an Art and Technology Room, a well-stocked Library and a Music Room, all of which supplement the usual amenities of a preparatory school. In addition, use is made of Senior School facilities, which include an indoor Swimming Pool, a fully equipped Sports Hall, Dance Studio, Fitness Centre, the Music School, Playing Fields, and a purpose-built Theatre.

We work hard to discover talent and develop it to the full. Music, Art, Dance and Drama play an important part in the life of the school. King's St Alban's supports an Orchestra, Wind Band, Flute Choir and String and Recorder groups with most children playing at least one musical instrument. Nearly all children are involved in the school's Choir and there is a smaller Chamber Choir. The annual Carol Service is held in the Cathedral with concerts and musical evenings held each term in the Theatre and Chapel. A major whole-school production is staged annually in the Theatre with several smaller workshop productions taking place during the year.

The Staff comprises an equal balance of men and women, all of whom are experienced and well qualified. In addition there are various visiting music and sport specialists.

The main sports are Rugby, Netball, Soccer, Hockey, Cricket and Rounders with Swimming, Athletics, Cross-Country, Orienteering and Tennis also featured. Matches are arranged with other schools and excellence is sought, but participation of all girls and boys is the main objective. A thriving inter-House competition provides further opportunities for all to enjoy competition.

Beyond the classroom an extensive programme of after-school activities is available with opportunities varying each term, examples are Art & Craft, Science, Ball Skills, Latin, Chess and Life Saving. Children in Years 5 and 6 spend time each year at the school's Outdoor Activity Centre in the Black Mountains.

Girls and boys are accepted through a competitive examination and are expected to progress through to the Senior School, subject to a satisfactory performance in their examinations at the age of 11. The assessment of candidates for King's St Alban's takes place in early February for entry in the following September. The tests cover English, Mathematics and Verbal Reasoning.

There are a small number of Scholarships and Bursaries available from the age of 7, as are Choral Scholarships for Cathedral Choristers.

Charitable status. The King's School, Worcester is a Registered Charity, number 1098236. It exists to provide high quality education for girls and boys.

Kingshott

St Ippolyts Hitchin Hertfordshire SG4 7JX
Tel: 01462 432009
Fax: 01462 421652
e-mail: pa2head@kingshott.herts.sch.uk
website: www.kingshottschool.co.uk

Chairman of Governors: Mr N Baker, QC

***Headmaster*: I Gilmour**, BPrimEd, BEd Hons, MEd

Age Range. 4–13.

Number of Pupils. (All Day) Prep (7–13): 152 Boys, 62 Girls; Pre-Prep (4–7): 85 Boys, 40 Girls.

Fees per term (2008-2009). (including Lunch) Pre-Prep £2,575, Prep £3,115.

Kingshott, founded in 1930, occupies a large Victorian building, with major recent classroom additions, in 14 acres of attractive grounds on the outskirts of Hitchin. Luton, Letchworth, Baldock, Stevenage, Welwyn and the A1(M) Motorway are all within a 10 mile radius. In September 2008 a new Middle School building will open for Years 3 to 5, the latest stage in the redevelopment of the school, which began with the new Pre-Prep building in 2004.

Kingshott, a Charitable Educational Trust, with a Board of Governors, welcomes all denominations. Children are encouraged to make the best of individual potential – academic, creative, sporting – and to this end there is a happy friendly atmosphere, with strong emphasis on courtesy and self-discipline.

There are 28 full-time and 9 part-time qualified staff to teach 23 forms, varying in size from 12 to about 22. Visiting Musicians teach a wide variety of instruments; there is an Orchestra and Choir; Speech and Drama and Ballet are offered; field trips and educational visits form a regular feature of school life.

There is a strong and successful sporting tradition which includes Football, Rugby, Cricket, Hockey, Basketball, Netball, Tennis, Swimming, Cross-Country and Athletics. The School has its own covered, heated swimming pool, all-weather pitch, tennis court and hard play areas. Many pupils stay until 5.30 pm for Prep each evening, and there is opportunity for involvement in a wide variety of after school Hobby activities. After school care is also available until 5.30 pm for Pre-Prep pupils.

Girls were first admitted in 1983, and now constitute approximately 35% of the annual intake. Girls are able to continue their education at Kingshott until age 13, in line with the boys.

Academic, Music and Art Scholarships to Senior Independent Schools are gained each year, and Common Entrance results are very sound, with virtually all children accepted by their first choice schools.

Entry is by assessment, appropriate to age.

Registration for the Pre-Prep is advisable several years in advance of required admission.

Charitable status. Kingshott School is a Registered Charity, number 1507581. It exists to provide education for boys and girls.

Kingsmead School

Bertram Drive Hoylake Wirral CH47 0LL
Tel: 0151 632 3156
Fax: 0151 632 0302
e-mail: enquiries@kingsmeadschool.com
website: www.kingsmeadschool.com

Chairman of Governors: The Revd M D A Hepworth, MA Cantab, PGCE

***Headmaster*: J F Perry**, BA Hons, PGCE

Age Range. 3–16.

Number of Pupils. 146 boys, 78 girls (Boarders: 17 boys, 7 girls).

Fees per term (2008-2009). Boarders £4,130–£5,025, Day Pupils £850–£2,875.

Academic, Music and Sports Scholarships are available at Year 7 entry. Scholarship and entrance examinations are held in January and March each year. Substantial Bursaries are available to the children of Clergy.

Kingsmead School was founded in 1904. It is in a rural setting with extensive playing fields on site, yet is easily accessible by road, rail and international airports. It has a strong Christian tradition, dedicated staff, a reputation for high academic standards, and a happy atmosphere.

The curriculum prepares pupils to go on to Grammar Schools at 11+, although the majority remain at Kingsmead until GCSE (age 16).

Facilities include two Computer Rooms, two well-equipped Science Laboratories, a large Gymnasium and an indoor heated swimming pool available throughout the year. There is a strong Choir and facilities are available to those wishing to learn a musical instrument. All children have the opportunity to perform in plays, musicals and concerts. The Centenary Building was opened on the campus in February 2003, containing state-of-the-art classrooms for History, Geography, Design Technology (DT), Information and Communications Technology (ICT), Art, French and Child Development.

Up to Form 2 (end of Key Stage 1), pupils are taught in their own rooms by Class Teachers. In the Junior Department (Key Stage 2) there is specialist teaching of certain subjects at the appropriate level. Thereafter pupils are based in a Form Room under the care of a Form Teacher but move to the different subject rooms for lessons. For spoken English and Drama, the School has enjoyed excellent results in the English Speaking Board and other examinations. At any level in the school, intelligent children with specific learning difficulties can be given a structured programme of remedial help by a specialist teacher at an extra charge.

Full, Weekly and Flexi Boarders are accepted from 7 years old and are in the care of the Boarding Team Leader and other members of the boarding staff. These, together with the Headmaster, Deputy and their wives, are all resident. Our boarders are accommodated in three family-sized houses – Bertram Lodge (boys), Meadway Cottage (girls) and Watts House (flexi-boarding). Boarders are met at Liverpool Lime Street Station or Liverpool or Manchester Airports.

Games offered include Football, Rugby, Cricket, Netball, Rounders, Hockey, Athletics, Tennis, and Golf.

Clubs include Ballet, Chess, Gymnastics, Judo, Scripture Union, Swimming, Sailing, Bushcraft, Archery and Dance.

Charitable status. Kingsmead School is a Registered Charity, number 525920.

Kingswood House School

56 West Hill Epsom Surrey KT19 8LG
Tel: 01372 723590
Fax: 01372 749081
e-mail: office@kingswoodhouse.org
website: www.kingswoodhouse.org

Founded in 1899, the school moved to its current site, a large Edwardian house in West Hill, Epsom, just outside the town centre in 1920. The school is an educational trust, overseen by a board of governors.

Chairman of Governors: Robert Austen, BSc(Eng), CEng, MICE, MIHT

***Headmaster*: Peter R Brooks**, MA, BEd Hons, CertEd

Age Range. Boys 3–13, Girls 3–7.

Number of Pupils. 210 Day pupils.

Inclusive Fees per term (2008-2009). Pre-Prep £2,415 (part-time Nursery payable by session). Junior 7+ upwards £3,190. Free after-school care provided until 5.00 pm.

Kingswood House is a thriving day preparatory school for boys aged 3–13 and girls aged 3–7. The school's reputation is based on a friendly and welcoming atmosphere, a positive and supportive ethos and successfully meeting the educational needs of all its pupils. Small classes facilitate individual attention from well-qualified teachers on a regular basis and allow pupils to learn in a relaxed, but stimulating and concentrated environment.

The broad aim of the school is to prepare boys for Common Entrance to senior school at age 13. Development of literacy and numeracy skills is the foundation of the curriculum. English, Maths, Science, History, Geography, French, Religious Education, PE, Music, Art, Design Technology and Information Technology make up the timetable. Study Skills and PSE courses help prepare boys for senior school life and there is a Study Centre to supplement learning, with excellent provision for children with special educational needs. Kingswood House School is a member of CReSTeD (Council for the Registration of Schools Teaching Dyslexic Pupils) and NAGC (The National Association for Gifted Children).

The senior curriculum is determined by the Common Entrance syllabus with boys being prepared for a wide variety of local senior independent schools, including Epsom College, St John's, Ewell Castle, City of London Freemen's, Reed's, Box Hill and King's College, Wimbledon. Placing boys in the right senior school is of paramount importance and the teachers have wide experience in preparing boys for Common Entrance. There is an excellent success rate at 13+ Common Entrance, with a good proportion obtaining scholarships and awards.

The school prides itself on the quality of teaching, dedicated classrooms and resources provided for Art, Design Technology, Information Technology, Music and Science, all of which have been completely refurbished in the last few years. There are sporting facilities on site, with a playing field, astroturf surface, all-weather cricket nets, adventure playground and training swimming pool. Pitches at Ashtead Cricket Club and Epsom College are also used.

Academic Scholarships are awarded at 7+. There are bursaries for sons of teachers and fee reductions for second and subsequent boys. The school operates the government nursery vouchers scheme.

Charitable status. Kingswood House School is a Registered Charity, number 312044. It exists to provide educational support in the form of bursaries for the parents of children in need.

Kingswood Preparatory School

College Road Lansdown Bath BA1 5SD
Tel: 01225 734460
Fax: 01225 734470
e-mail: kpsreception@kingswood.bath.sch.uk
website: www.kingswood.bath.sch.uk

Chairman of Governors: The Revd R Lansley

***Headmaster*: Marcus Cornah**, CertEd Oxon

Age Range. 3–11.

Number of Pupils. 348: Prep: 102 boys, 86 girls; Pre-Prep: 96 boys, 64 girls. 16 Boarders.

Fees per term (2008-2009). Nursery, Reception, Years 1 and 2: £2,375 (Nursery part-day pro rata); Years 3–6: £2,750. Boarding: £5,602 (full), £4,706 (weekly).

Kingswood Preparatory School is the preparatory school for Kingswood School, Bath. It is part of the Kingswood Foundation and each year over 95% of pupils move on to Kingswood School, through examination in January, at the end of Year 6.

Kingswood School is the oldest Methodist educational institution in the world, having been founded by John Wesley in 1748. Both Preparatory and the Senior Schools have extensive linked sites on Lansdown hill overlooking the world-famous city of Bath.

At Kingswood Preparatory School our aim is to create a happy, caring community based upon Christian principles in which all individuals can develop respect for themselves and for others.

We provide for the children a rich variety of academic, sporting and social experiences. By doing so we hope to give them the opportunity to develop their personalities and potential in an atmosphere of enthusiasm, enjoyment, security and care for fellow pupils.

As well as our regular Extra-Curricular Programme which currently contains fifty weekly options, the school offers regular opportunities to participate in Music, Drama and Sport. We are able to use certain senior school facilities such as the swimming pool, the astroturf hockey pitch and the theatre. The prep school shares 56 acres of playing fields with the seniors.

The prep school is situated in the splendid parkland setting of the Summerhill estate. Children of pre-preparatory age are educated in the modern, award-winning, purpose-built accommodation and the senior years in the main house, Summerhill. This fine mansion was designed by John Wood the Younger. Before it came into the schools possession in the 1950s it was the home of Ernest Cook, founder of the Ernest Cook Trust. The boarders live in High Vinnalls which offers all types of boarding to boys and girls aged between 7 and 11. Adjacent to the school and superbly situated in large gardens surrounded by woods and parkland, it has been acclaimed as a model for what boarding houses for young children should be like, in terms of its homely atmosphere and facilities. The school enjoys magnificent views over the City of Bath, and is situated only one and half miles from the centre.

There are 66 staff in all: 28 full-time and 6 part-time teachers, 8 ancillary support assistants and a further 20 part-time peripatetic staff.

Charitable status. Kingswood Preparatory School is a Registered Charity, number 309148. It exists for the purpose of educating children.

Knighton House

Durweston Blandford Dorset DT11 0PY
Tel: 01258 452065
Fax: 01258 450744
e-mail: enquiries@knighton-house.co.uk
website: www.knightonhouse.dorset.sch.uk

Chairman of the Governors: Major General Andrew Graham

***Headmistress*: Mrs C Renton Bourne**, MA Cantab, Dip RS Nottingham

Age Range. Girls $2^1/_2$–13, Boys $2^1/_2$–7.

Number of Girls. Boarders 42, Day Girls (including Flexi Boarders) 48; Pre-Prep and Nursery (co-educational) 35.

Fees per term (2007-2008). Boarders £5,950, Day £4,470, Pre-Prep and Nursery £535–£2,121. There are no compulsory extras.

Established in 1950, Knighton House keeps pace with the expectations of the 21st century, whilst nurturing its unique traditional values. In a delightful country setting, the school provides a safe but challenging environment in which children can discover their strengths, take risks and make friends. Boarding is entirely flexible and ponies and pets are all welcome.

The small classes and high staff/pupil ratio ensures individual attention. The scholarships and awards won from Knighton House reflect academic, musical, artistic and all-rounder prowess; there is a strong artistic and musical tradition. Swimming and team sports have an all year round place in the timetable. There are many extra-curricular activities including riding from our own stables, triathlon and tetrathlon team training, dance and drama.

This careful balance of academic subjects and extra-curricular activities encourages all aspects of personal growth. The size of Knighton House ensures that each pupil is known by everyone; each girl has an identity and is respected for her individuality.

Knighton House feeds a wide range of senior schools, both co-ed and single-sex.

Charitable status. Knighton House School Limited is a Registered Charity, number 306316. It exists, principally, as a boarding school for girls.

The Lady Eleanor Holles School (Junior Department)

Burlington House 177 Uxbridge Road Hampton Middlesex TW12 1BD
Tel: 020 8979 2173
Registrar & Senior Department: 020 8979 1601
Fax: 020 8783 1962
e-mail: junior-office@lehs.org.uk
website: www.lehs.org.uk

Chairman of Governors: Mrs J Ross, BSc, CPFA

Head Mistress: Mrs G Low, MA Oxon

***Head of Junior Department*: Mrs J Adams**, BA Newcastle, PGCE

Age Range. 7–11.

Number of Pupils. 188 day girls.

Fees per term (2008-2009). £3,150.

The Lady Eleanor Holles School Junior Department is housed in its own separate building in one corner of the school's spacious thirty-acre grounds. Junior Department pupils make full use of the school's extensive facilities, such as a heated indoor 25m pool, Sports Hall and floodlit netball courts. (*See The Lady Eleanor Holles School's entry in the GSA section for more details.*) They also take advantage of a fleet of school coaches serving most of West London and Surrey.

The school is academically selective, with most girls joining in Year 3. Entrance exams in English and Maths are held the January before entry. The vast majority of Junior Department pupils gain places in the Senior Department at 11.

The school's teaching is firmly based on the National Curriculum and there are specialist teachers for Science, Art, French, IT, Music and PE from the beginning. The school is very well resourced and staff use a wide variety of teaching styles and activities to ensure pace, stimulation and progression.

There is a wide range of extra-curricular activities so girls can develop their own interests and abilities, and all achievements and progress are valued and praised.

Extra-curricular clubs include Drama, Chess, Mandarin and various Art, Music and Sports activities.

Whilst LEH is a broadly Christian foundation, it welcomes girls of all faiths, and none. School Assemblies, some of which are performed by the girls for their parents, may feature Hindu, Islamic Sikh or Jewish festivals and stories, as well as Christian.

In 2003, Burlington House, the home of the Junior Department, was the subject of a very extensive programme of extension and renovation, and now boasts superb facilities for a 21st-century education. Amongst the main improvements were four spacious new Practical Rooms for Art, DT and Science; a new Computer suite and Dining Room; a well-stocked and welcoming Library; and larger, brighter classrooms.

The staff work hard to establish and maintain a caring, supportive atmosphere in which girls feel confident to be themselves, to respect and care for everyone in the community, to be proud of their achievements and to persevere with things they find challenging. Pastoral care is a priority and we are proud of the happy, lively, hard-working pupils of the Junior Department.

Charitable status. Cripplegate Schools Foundation is a Registered Charity, number 312493. The Foundation is responsible solely for the Lady Eleanor Holles School, which exists to provide education to girls aged 7 to 18.

Lady Lane Park School
GEMS Education

Lady Lane Bingley West Yorkshire BD16 4AP
Tel: 01274 551168
Fax: 01274 569732
e-mail: secretary@ladylanepark.co.uk
website: www.ladylanepark.bradford.sch.uk

***Headmistress*: Mrs Gill Wilson**, BEd

Age Range. 2–11 Co-educational.

Number of Pupils. 191 Day Pupils: 102 Boys, 89 Girls.

Fees per term (from January 2008). £1,864 (Lower Kindergarten–Form III), £1,755 (Form 4–Upper VI).

Lady Lane Park School is a member of the GEMS Education Group.

The school ethos is based on the development of the individual within a broad and challenging curriculum.

Our well qualified and dedicated staff combine professional expertise with commitment and understanding and our teaching methods are a balanced blend of the traditional and the very best in new ideas.

The life of the school is supported by our Governors' and Friends' committees, and we believe that the partnership between school and home is a very important one.

The emphasis is based on the laying of secure foundations in reading, writing, mathematical and scientific skills which are of the utmost importance for a child's development, and we believe in the importance of respect and care for each other and for the community.

A broad-based curriculum is reinforced by the National Curriculum and specialist teaching is provided in Science, Mathematics, ICT CDT, Music, Dance, Drama and Games.

French is introduced through songs and games and specialist teaching begins at the age of 5. Academic achievements are highly valued but we also aim for excellence in other spheres so that our children are encouraged to develop their talents with a positive and enthusiastic approach to school life.

Inter-disciplinary teaching is reinforced with out-of-school visits which help to extend, enrich and reinforce the children's experience.

Pupils are encouraged to take responsibility for themselves and for others and to actively contribute to the life of the school and the local environment.

Every child is given the opportunity to enjoy creative experiences and they are actively encouraged to fulfil their potential. Over 80% of our children study for theory and practical examinations in Music, Dance and Drama.

We have an excellent reputation in all aspects of physical education and children participate in a variety of sporting activities. We have a sports pavilion and large playing field – scope indeed for all our needs.

The friendly, yet competitive atmosphere is testament to team spirit and personal achievement.

Our well resourced and uniquely designed Science laboratory and DT facility provides an exciting environment where children learn through practical activities and experiments.

The dedicated computer room provides an introduction to word processing, databases, graphics, spreadsheets and Powerpoint presentations, and the networked system offers opportunities for group involvement. This up-to-date facility, with full Broadband Internet access, is a vital tool for all children in our forward-looking school.

The whole school curriculum provides a coherent health education programme, including Personal & Social Development, which promotes children's self-esteem and social well-being.

Our Year 6 pupils achieve Life Saving awards in swimming, and undertake a programme of practical and written study resulting in a First Aid Certificate.

Environmental work enables children to work alongside specialists in many areas.

Lady Lane is Christian in attitude and welcomes children of all faiths. Our aim is to educate children to think for themselves, be confident in their abilities and take pleasure in the learning process as they prepare themselves for an exciting future.

Lambrook Haileybury

Winkfield Row Bracknell Berks RG42 6LU
Tel: 01344 882717
Fax: 01344 891114
e-mail: info@lambrook.berks.sch.uk
website: www.lambrook.berks.sch.uk

Chairman of the Governors: Major General T P Toyne Sewell, DL

***Headmaster*: J E A Barnes**, BA, PGCE

Age Range. 3–13 Co-educational.

Number of Children. 450.

Fees per term (2008-2009). Boarding £5,615–£6,275; Day £4,235–£4,600; Pre-Prep £2,750–£2,870.

Lambrook Haileybury is a co-educational day and boarding school for children aged 3 to 13. The school is situated at Winkfield Row, two miles from Ascot, six miles from Windsor and is easily accessible from the M4, M3 and M40 motorways. Heathrow is 30 minutes away by road.

The school has many facilities including a Science and IT Centre. We aim for high academic standards and prepare children for Scholarship and Common Entrance examinations to all major Senior Independent Schools. High quality teaching is provided in small classes and the school is set in a beautiful rural environment of some forty acres.

The school encourages a well-rounded education. Games, music and other cultural activities play an important part in the lives of the children. The boarding, in particular, is conducted in the spirit of a family atmosphere with a strong pastoral care system, in two boarding houses, with a very flexible approach ranging from occasional to weekly boarding.

The school has many day pupils who are attracted by the boarding ethos and the subsequent number of varied activities available. All pupils play a full part in the life of the school. The Pre-Prep Department opened in September 1993 and it has expanded rapidly with the nursery being added in January 2007. The Pre-Prep Building comprises eight very well resourced, modern classrooms, an enlarged library and a networked computer system.

Charitable status. Lambrook Haileybury is a Registered Charity, number 309098. Its purpose is to provide an excellent education for boys and girls.

Lancing College Preparatory School at Mowden

A Woodard School

The Droveway Hove East Sussex BN3 6LU
Tel: 01273 503452
Fax: 01273 503457
e-mail: info@lancingprep.co.uk
website: www.lancingprep.co.uk

Chairman of Governors: R M Reeve, MA

***Headmaster*: A P Laurent**

Age Range. 3–13.

Number of Pupils. 181.

Fees per term (2008-2009). £980–£3,895.

Lancing College Preparatory School at Mowden is situated in an enviable position in Hove overlooking the English Channel.

Much of our ethos is drawn from the fact that we are a Christian based school and central to this is the belief that children must feel happy and secure in their surroundings if they are to succeed. The school is run on family lines, each child being given a sense of their true worth as an individual but also as part of the family.

The school offers an excellent academic education with a modern curriculum preparing for the Common Entrance and Scholarship Examinations at the end of academic year eight. Central to our curriculum beliefs is the idea that all pupils have an area in which they can excel, and to that end we place huge importance on the teaching of Art, Drama, Music and Sport as well as all the subjects that you would expect to find in the National Curriculum.

We have a fully qualified staff of twenty four full and part time teachers who enjoy facilities including a fully equipped science laboratory, an art design and technology room, gymnasium, ICT suite and library. As well as extensive grounds there is an all weather area for the coaching of our main sports, cricket, football, rugby, hockey, netball, rounders and tennis.

Charitable status. Lancing College is a Registered Charity, number 1076483. It exists to provide education for boys and girls.

Lanesborough School

Maori Road Guildford Surrey GU1 2EL
Tel: 01483 880650
Fax: 01483 880651
e-mail: office@lanesborough.surrey.sch.uk
website: www.lanesborough.surrey.sch.uk

Chairman of Governors: Dr H J Pearson, OBE, MA, PhD, CMath, FIMA

***Head*: Mrs C Turnbull**, BA Hons

Age Range. 3–13.

Number of Boys. 360 Day Boys.

Fees per term (2007-2008). Nursery £2,183, Reception–Year 1 £2,647, Years 2–3 £2,853, Years 4–8 £2,944.

Lanesborough is the Preparatory School for the Royal Grammar School and the choir school for Guildford Cathedral. Cathedral choristers qualify for choral scholarships.

The main entry points are Nursery, Reception and Year 3. Many of the pupils gain entry to the Royal Grammar School at age 11 or 13, whilst others are prepared for Scholarship and Common Entrance examination to senior independent schools at 13.

The School is divided into four houses for house competitions. Pastoral care and supervision of academic progress are shared by the Headmaster, Housemasters, Form masters and subject teachers. Extra-curricular activities include art, chess, drama, computer club, judo, squash, badminton, fencing, tennis and golf.

Music is a strong feature of the life of the school, which is a member of the Choir Schools Association. In addition to the Cathedral Choir, there are senior and junior choirs, an orchestra, wind and string groups. Private tuition by qualified peripatetic teachers is available in most instruments. There are music concerts and the School Carol Service at the Cathedral has achieved wide acclaim. Music Scholarships to Independent Senior Schools are gained each year.

Art plays an important part in the curriculum also, with boys receiving tuition throughout the school.

Games are association football, rugby football, cricket, athletics, swimming, basketball, hockey and badminton. There is a school field, gym and astroturf.

Regular school visits are undertaken to local places of interest. School parties also go abroad, eg for skiing and on cultural visits.

The pre-preparatory department (for boys aged 3–7 and including a Nursery unit) is housed in a separate building (Braganza) under the direct supervision of the Head of the pre-prep, but shares many of the facilities of the senior part of the School. The recent purchase of a large Edwardian house next to the School has greatly enhanced the facilities.

There is an active Parents' Association.

Charitable status. Lanesborough is governed by the trustees of The Royal Grammar School of King Edward VI, Guildford which is a Registered Charity, number 312028. It exists for the purpose of educating boys in or near Guildford.

Langley Preparatory School and Nursery

11 Yarmouth Road Thorpe St Andrew Norwich Norfolk NR7 0EA
Tel: 01603 433861
Fax: 01603 702639
e-mail: prepheadmaster@langleyschool.co.uk
website: www.langleyschool.co.uk

Chairman of the Governors: Mrs M Alston, JP

***Headmaster*: S B Marfleet**, BSc Hons, MSc, PGCE

Age Range. 2–11 co-educational.

Number of Pupils. 180.

Fees per term (2008-2009). £1,610 (Reception–Year 2), £1,960 (Years 3 and 4), £2,415 (Years 5 and 6). Nursery (per session): £29.50 (full day), £20 (half day).

The school is situated in 5 acres of ground and is close to the city centre. Pupils are taken from the age of 2 and are prepared for many schools, but principally for entry to Langley School at the age of 11+. Qualified and experienced staff maintain a purposeful academic atmosphere, but there is a friendly and caring family atmosphere where children can discover individual talents and abilities so that they will be well prepared for the secondary stage of their education. A broad curriculum is followed, and classes rarely exceed 16. English, Mathematics, Science and ICT form the core of the curriculum, but from Year 3 subject specialists teach Design Technology, Art, Drama, French, Music and Humanities. There are well-equipped facilities for teaching these subjects.

Hockey, rugby, soccer, netball, cricket, rounders and short tennis are the main team games. A gymnasium, heated outdoor swimming pool, playing fields and the use of an all-weather hockey pitch give ample scope for coaching. Activities operate at the end of the school day and offer the chance for children to try numerous other sports and activities, such as sailing, ten pin bowling, dry slope skiing, archery, golf, orienteering, chess and so on.

There is a fine tradition of drama and public speaking. There are drama productions for each section of the school every autumn term and an Easter Concert that involves every child in the school. We participate in local speech and drama festivals and children are taught and entered for LAMDA examinations. There are numerous performance opportunities for music and drama.

Experienced and qualified staff also run the Nursery, which caters for 2 to 4 year olds. It is well equipped and has its own secure play area. Nursery hours are flexible and a child-minding service is offered after school hours. The Nursery has been Ofsted inspected and is a registered provider under the government scheme. It is open all year round.

Charitable status. Langley School is a Registered Charity, number 311270. It exists to provide a sound education for boys and girls.

Lathallan School

Brotherton Castle Johnshaven Montrose Angus DD10 0HN
Tel: 01561 362220
Fax: 01561 361695
e-mail: office@lathallan.com
website: www.lathallan.com

Chairman of Board of Directors: Prof Sir Frederick Holliday, CBE, DSc, FRSE

***Headmaster*: A P Giles**, MEd

Age Range. 6 weeks to 14 years. Additional class added each year up to 18 years.

Number of Pupils. 125 (72 boys, 53 girls) plus 50 in Nursery.

Fees per term (2008-2009). Tuition: Pre-Prep £2,551, Middle School £3,226, Upper School £3,656, Senior School £4,388. Weekly Boarding (in addition to Tuition): £1,045. Reductions for siblings and Services children. Scholarships and Bursaries available.

Lathallan School, situated in extensive spectacular grounds in a baronial castle overlooking the North Sea, has begun an exciting programme of re-development since the arrival of Headmaster Andy Giles in 2003. In 2004 the existing nursery was refurbished and is now able to accommodate children and babies from 6 weeks for 50 weeks per annum. Recognising the growing demand for a senior school of the calibre of the existing preparatory school, the Board of Directors announced in 2004 that the school would begin to offer secondary education, building the school up by one academic year at a time, with an S2 class opening in September 2006 and an S3 class in September 2007. Sports facilities have been refurbished, the castle building adapted for senior teaching and a redevelopment of the site is underway to allow for school expansion. Headmaster Andy Giles explains, "My professional background has led me to conclude that high academic achievement, a wide-ranging choice of activities, strong pastoral care and happy children are fundamental ingredients in any description of a good school. Lathallan has all these and more – where family values are encouraged and all members of its community go about their daily tasks with a sense of fun and enjoyment". The school ethos is to foster independence and confidence, allowing children to achieve their full potential. Pupils are encouraged to develop existing skills but also to "step outside the comfort zone" and discover some hidden talents. Weekly boarding is available and, unique to the local area, is our flexi-boarding system, where any pupil can opt to board on certain nights – either to suit the demands of busy family life or to join in one of the many extra-curricular activities which vary from term to term but include Pipe Band, cricket, athletics, cooking, football, Warhammer, Cycling Proficiency and creative writing. A daily bus services runs from both Aberdeen and Montrose. The school is capitalizing on its stunning rural coastal location by widening its focus on Outdoor Education and Environmental Studies.

Charitable status. Lathallan School is a Registered Charity, number SC018423. It exists to provide education of the highest standard for boys and girls.

Latymer Prep School

36 Upper Mall Hammersmith London W6 9TA
Tel: 0845 638 5700
Fax: 0845 638 5735
e-mail: mlp@latymerprep.org
website: www.latymerprep.org

Chairman of Governors: Professor R N Perham, MA, PhD, ScD, FRS

***Principal*: Mr Stuart P Dorrian**, BA

Age Range. 7–11 Co-educational.
Number of Pupils. 168 Day Pupils.
Fees per term (2008-2009). £4,035.

Latymer Prep School, led by its own Principal, was granted independence by the Governors of the Latymer Foundation in 1995 – the Centenary Year of Latymer Upper School on its present site. Previously the Prep School had been run as a very successful department of the Upper School and the relationship remains an extremely close one with all children usually expected to proceed to the Upper School.

The school is academically selective and pupils are taught the full range of subjects following National Curriculum guidelines, but to an advanced standard. Classes are kept small (21) which allows for close monitoring and evaluation of each pupil's progress and well being.

The school is well resourced and has attractive facilities in two elegant period houses adjacent to the River Thames. Catering, sports and theatre facilities are shared with the Upper School.

A main feature of the school is its friendly and caring atmosphere which offers close pastoral support to each individual pupil. Academic achievement is strong, but in addition, all staff and pupils contribute to an extensive range of activities featuring Sport, Music, Art and Drama. The school has 3 large choirs and its own orchestra. Opportunities exist for all pupils to participate in concerts, plays, inter-school sporting events and an annual Project Week which includes a residential trip for the senior pupils in their final year.

The major sports are soccer, rugby, cricket, tennis, athletics, hockey and netball. There is also a thriving swimming club (the school has its own pool). Karate takes place after school as do chess, dance and drama.

There is a Parents' Gild and opportunities occur frequently to meet with staff socially. Visits for prospective parents occur throughout the year and can be arranged by telephoning for an appointment.

Charitable status. The Latymer Foundation is a Registered Charity, number 312714. It exists to provide an opportunity for able pupils from all walks of life to develop their talents to the full.

Laverock School

Bluehouse Lane Oxted Surrey RH8 0AA
Tel: 01883 714171
Fax: 01883 722206
e-mail: office@laverock.surrey.sch.uk
website: www.laverockschool.co.uk

Chairman of the Governors: Mrs F A B Newton, BA Hons, PGCE

***Headmistress*: Mrs Brenda Green**, MA, PGCE

Age Range. 2½–11.
Number of Girls. 150.
Fees per term (2008-2009). £995–£3,150 including lunch except in Nursery.

Accredited by the Independent Schools Council, Laverock is a Preparatory School for Girls set in pleasant surroundings close to the North Downs. The premises are purpose built and include an outdoor swimming pool, two multi-purpose sports courts, a bright and airy nursery unit and a Performing Arts and Science and Technology building.

The school aims to provide a happy atmosphere and broad-based curriculum. All aspects of the National Curriculum are taught and academic achievements are excellent with all girls being accepted by prestigious Senior Schools in the neighbourhood. In addition, there is a strong emphasis on Information Technology, music, drama, netball, tennis, swimming, art and ballet. Early morning care is available from 7.45 am. After school care runs until 6.00 pm and a wide range of clubs and activities is offered. Most of the girls learn orchestral instruments and play in one of the two orchestras at regular concerts, services, etc. There are also two thriving choirs.

A prospectus and full particulars are available from the school and the Headmistress is always delighted to show prospective parents round the school.

Charitable status. Laverock School Limited is a Registered Charity, number 312083. Its aims are to provide broad based education of a high quality for girls in a caring environment.

Laxton Junior – Oundle School

East Road Oundle Peterborough PE8 4BX
Tel: 01832 277275
Fax: 01832 277271
e-mail: info@laxtonjunior.org.uk
website: www.laxtonjunior.org.uk

Governors: The Worshipful Company of Grocers

Chairman: Sir Toby Frere, KCB

***Headmaster*: Mr Mark Potter**, BEd Hons

Deputy Head: Miss Janet Bass

Age Range. 4–11.

Number of Children. 260 approximately.

Fees per term (2007-2008). £2,570–£2,820 (including lunches).

Opened in 1973 and part of Oundle School, Laxton Junior is a co-educational day school for children aged 4–11 years. In September 2002 Laxton Junior moved into a new building which caters for 280 pupils. The school has 14 forms of no more than 20 pupils, each with a fully qualified Form Teacher. The curriculum includes Art & Design, Computer Skills, French, Music, PE and Performing Arts as well as the major academic subjects. Emphasis has always been placed on the individual child and the importance of each doing their best at all times, according to their ability. Children are prepared for entrance examinations for Independent Senior Schools in the area; Kimbolton, Oundle, Oakham, Stamford Schools and Wellingborough being the key schools.

The new building has a large multi-purpose hall which is used for PE, Music and Performing Arts as well as concerts, school plays and social events The school has its own games fields and netball courts plus all children receive swimming instruction each week in the Oundle School Pool. The main games are football, rugby, cricket, netball, rounders and athletics plus coaching in hockey and tennis.

In Year 2 all pupils have the opportunity to play the violin or cello as part of the curriculum. From Year 3 the recorder is introduced, plus additional time is given for choir, orchestra and learning other musical instruments. The school also has an Education Support Unit which monitors all pupils' development and helps individuals with specific difficulties.

The aims of the school are to encourage the formation of good work habits and good manners, to lay the foundations for the development of self-discipline, self-confidence and self-motivation and to offer the children the opportunity of experiencing the satisfaction of achievement.

The partnership of home and school in the education of the child is strongly emphasises and all parents are members of the Parents' & Friends' Association.

Laxton Junior School was inspected in March 2008. The report is available on the school website.

Charitable status. Oundle School is a Registered Charity, number 309921. It exists to provide education for boys and girls.

Leaden Hall School

70 The Close Salisbury Wilts SPI 2EP
Tel: 01722 334700
Fax: 01722 439269
e-mail: admin@leaden-hall.com
website: www.leaden-hall.com

Chairman: Mrs S Pennington, BA Hons

***Headmistress*: Mrs D E Watkins**, MA

Age Range. Girls aged 3–11.

Number of Pupils. 261 Girls: 221 Day, 40 Boarders.

Fees per term (2008-2009). Day £2,160–£3,540, Boarding £4,280–£4,810.

Set in beautiful surroundings in Salisbury's Cathedral Close, Leaden Hall was once the home of the 'architect' of Salisbury Cathedral, Elias de Dereham.

Leaden Hall provides education for girls aged 3–11. We prepare children for the Common Entrance and the County 11+ examinations. We aim to give all girls self-confidence balanced with an awareness of others and a belief in themselves, so that entry to senior school follows naturally without fuss.

Our full, weekly and day boarding options give parents the flexibility to enable their daughters to take part in the many extra-curricular activities which ensure that our pupils flourish in a stimulating, happy and purposeful environment.

Charitable status. Leaden Hall School is a Registered Charity, number 309489. It exists to provide education for children.

The Grammar School at Leeds Junior School

Alwoodley Gates Harrogate Road Leeds LS17 8GS
Tel: 0113 228 1552
Fax: 0113 228 5111
e-mail: enquiries@gsal.org.uk
website: www.gsal.org.uk

Chairman of Governors: Professor D Sugden, PhD

***Acting Head*: Ms S Fishburn**, BSc

Age Range. 7–11.

Number of Pupils. 448 Day pupils (boys and girls).

Fees per term (2008-2009). £2,388.

Teaching Staff. 45 teaching staff and 4 non-teaching assistants.

Facilities. The Grammar School at Leeds Junior School occupies a modern, newly-extended, purpose-built site whose facilities are unrivalled anywhere in the country. They include:

- Self-contained Reception classes and Pre-Prep activity areas.
- A pleasant assembly hall, specially designed for young children.
- New sports hall.
- Well-stocked library.
- Dedicated and specially equipped art studio and science laboratory.
- Fully equipped ICT suite.
- Timetabled use of a fully resourced music school.
- Extensive playing fields with changing facilities.
- Timetabled use of a large multi-purpose sports complex, including 25m swimming pool, within the adjacent Senior School buildings.
- Large play and recreation areas for each section of the school.
- Provision for a wide variety of indoor and outdoor extra-curricular pursuits.

Aims. We aim to provide a relaxed yet well-structured environment for all pupils. Clear boundaries create the security within which young pupils can encounter new and exciting ideas with confidence. Pupils are allowed and encouraged to realise their potential and learning is what it should be – fun and full of possibilities. We aim to produce happy, confident children who work hard and also benefit from the wide range of opportunities presented by the school.

Curriculum. Our syllabuses encompass the National Curriculum without being constrained by it. We teach the basic subjects to a very high standard, concentrating on literacy and numeracy in the early years before expanding into a broader curriculum that nevertheless retains English, Mathematics and Science as core subjects. Up to Year 3 pupils are taught mainly by their class teacher although there is specialist input for Music, PE, Games and RS. From Year 4 there is a considerable amount of specialist teaching across the curriculum although class teachers will teach English and Maths to their own class. On entering Year 3, pupils begin studying either French or German, giving them an excellent grounding for continued modern languages study when they progress to our Senior School. Whilst all our Junior School pupils must reach a qualifying standard in order to enter Senior School, they do not have to sit an entrance examination.

Extra-curricular Activities. Music and games are an important part of Junior School life and, together with our house system, bring a true sense of fair play and community spirit to school. There is a wide range of extra-curricular activities that take place both at lunchtime and after school. Sports include rugby, football, cricket, swimming, cross-country, badminton, squash, tennis, netball, hockey and athletics.

Pastoral care. The Junior School is a very busy place and our pastoral care systems permeate all that the school does. All pupils have very close contact with their Form Teachers and Housemasters.

Charitable status. The Grammar School at Leeds is a Registered Charity, number 1048304.

Leehurst Swan School

19 Campbell Road Salisbury SP1 3BQ
Tel: 01722 333094
Fax: 01722 330868
e-mail: registrar@leehurstswan.org.uk
website: www.leehurstswan.org.uk

Chairman of Governors: Revd C Walker

***Headmaster*: Mr R N S Leake**, BSc, PGCE

Age Range. 2–16 Co-educational.

Number of Children. 330.

Fees per term (2008-2009). Senior School £3,438; Prep School £1,970–£2,274; Pre-School £1,995.

Leehurst Swan is an Independent Day School, just 10 minutes' walk from Salisbury city centre. Originally a girls' school founded in 1911 under the name Leehurst and taken over in 1953 by the Sisters of La Retraite. In 1996 it was joined by the Swan School for Boys, a Prep School for boys aged 4–11 founded by Miss Swanton in 1933. The School was established as an Independent Charitable Trust in 1988.

The school is fully co-educational with over 330 children in the School: 152 children in the Prep School, 130 in the Senior school and 52 in the Pre-Prep. The School has small classes, a family atmosphere, and an environment that inspires and motivates pupils to achieve their best. The individual attention pupils receive reflects the ethos of Christian values and respect for the individual.

The Pre-Prep welcomes children from the age of two. Set in a purpose-built building, nestling in a wooded glade, the Pre-Prep provides outstanding quality early years education and care in a safe and secure environment. The ethos is one of inclusion with parents as equal partners.

Pupils in the Prep School have specialist teaching in key subjects and use dedicated school facilities in 1CT, Science, Music, Art, and Design Technology. The children are prepared for 11+ examinations for entry into the local grammar schools and for entry into the Senior School.

In the Senior School the pupils normally pursue studies in ten GCSE subjects and academic results are excellent. The school equally values and nurtures creative and sporting talent awarding scholarships in these areas in addition to academic scholarships.

Individual lessons are arranged in a wide range of musical instruments leading to Associated Board examinations.

Leehurst Swan welcomes visitors to the school to come and see them at work and play.

Charitable status. Leehurst Swan Limited is a Registered Charity, number 800158. It exists to provide education for children.

Leicester Grammar Junior School

Evington Hall Spencefield Lane Leicester LE5 6HN
Tel: 0116 210 1299
Tel: 0116 210 0432
e-mail: friell@leicestergrammar.org.uk
website: www.leicestergrammar.org.uk

Chairman of Governors: I D Patterson, LLB

***Headmistress*: Mrs M Redfearn**, BA Hons, PGCE

Age Range. 3–11 Co-educational.

Number of Pupils. 282.

Fees per term (2008-2009). £2,380 (full-time), £1,590 (part-time, 3+ only).

Leicester Grammar Junior School was founded in 1992 when Leicester Grammar School Trust took over educational responsibility for Evington Hall, an independent school run by the Sisters of Charity of St Paul.

The school is a selective, co-educational day school with a Christian Foundation. It acts as the junior school to Leicester Grammar School and is the first stage in a continuous education from 3 years through to A Level. It is situated in the suburbs of Leicester, about four miles from the senior school. The Trust has very recently embarked on an ambitious development plan that will see both the Junior and Senior schools relocate to a new purpose-built campus SW of the city of Leicester. This will allow the school to encompass the full 3–18 age range on the one site.

The school provides a stimulating, disciplined, happy environment within which each child is encouraged to aim for the highest standards in everything they do and to take a full and active part in all aspects of school life. It operates as an extension of the family unit within which the staff act with firmness and fairness. Respect and consideration underpin school life where pupils are encouraged to develop a caring and responsible attitude to others, leading to good manners and acceptable behaviour.

The children benefit from not only academic success and development but also from excellent musical, sporting and dramatic involvement within a broad and well balanced curriculum.

Music is a particular strength of the school and plays an important part in the life of every child. From the beginning as 3 year olds, children are taught by a music specialist. Pupils have the opportunity to learn a variety of instruments and there is a particularly strong Infant String Scheme; children as young as five or six years of age learn to play the violin or cello. The school orchestra and ensembles perform at festivals, concerts and assemblies. There are also many choral opportunities within the Junior and Infant choir which are often linked with Drama. A number of boys and girls are also members of the Leicester Cathedral choir and enjoy weekly training sessions with the Cathedral Master of Music.

In 2004 the school received the Sportsmark Gold Award in recognition of the quality of sport within the curriculum and extra curricular. The PE and Games provision aims to develop skills in team and individual games, gymnastics, dance, swimming and athletics. The main team games are rugby, football and cricket for the boys and netball, hockey and rounders for the girls. After-school clubs offer additional sporting opportunities such as tennis, badminton, table tennis and cross-country.

Charitable status. Leicester Grammar School Trust is a Registered Charity, number 510809.

Leweston Preparatory School

Sherborne Dorset DT9 6EN
Tel: 01963 210790
Fax: 01963 210648
e-mail: enquiries@leweston.dorset.sch.uk
website: www.leweston.co.uk

Chairman of Board of Governors: Mr A May

***Head Teacher*: Mrs M Allen**

Age Range. Girls 2½–11, Boys 2½–7.

Number of Pupils. 104: 90 Girls, 14 Boys.

Fees per term (2008-2009). Nursery: £18.50 (1 x 3 hr session), Reception–Year 2 £2,345, Years 3–6 £3,355. Boarding £4,925.

Setting. Leweston Preparatory School is an independent Catholic school for boys and girls with boarding and flexi-boarding provision for girls from age 7. The school is situated in forty-six acres of Dorset parkland three miles south of Sherborne and occupies an enviable setting in a skilfully converted former Coach House providing a unique range of bright spacious classrooms. The beautiful rural site is shared with Leweston School (girls 11–18 years) and the Preparatory School enjoys the benefit of many excellent facilities including a modern, well-equipped Design Technology Centre, an all weather sports pitch, a heated swimming pool, a large sports hall, tennis courts and extensive playing fields. The parkland setting offers many opportunities for study and recreation.

Ethos. Traditional excellence in teaching is combined with modern facilities and resources in a stimulating, happy and purposeful Christian environment. The school motto 'Gaudere et Bene Facere' (Rejoice and Do Well) exactly reflects the importance of high academic standards together with artistic, musical and sporting excellence achieved in an atmosphere of joy and vibrancy. Each child is encouraged to develop individual talents within the caring and supportive school community. Small class sizes, a friendly family ethos, and traditional values of work and behaviour are appreciated by parents. Full and flexi boarding options provide flexibility for pupils to enjoy a wide variety of extra-curricular activities, whilst no Saturday morning school allows for rest and relaxation.

Curriculum. Programmes of study encompass the National Curriculum without being constrained by it. Basic subjects are taught to a high standard concentrating on literacy and numeracy acquisition in the early years before expanding into a broader curriculum in Years 3–6. Well qualified class teachers and specialist subject teachers foster independent learning and encourage the development of problem solving and investigative skills in all areas of the curriculum. Academic standards are high and many pupils gain awards to senior school.

There is a strong tradition in the performing arts. Music, drama and dance are taught within the curriculum. A high percentage of pupils learn to play musical instruments and take additional drama. There is a school orchestra and choir and many opportunities throughout the year for performance and grade examinations in both music and drama. All pupils in Years 4–6 undertake English Speaking Board assessments. Individual and team sports are considered important as part of the healthy, active lifestyle and the school enjoys a particular reputation for hockey and cross-country. Art, Ceramics and Design Technology are taught by specialist teachers using the exceptional facilities in the Design Technology Centre.

Charitable status. St Antony's – Leweston School Trust is a Registered Charity, number 295175. It exists to provide for children a contemporary education in the Catholic tradition.

Lichfield Cathedral School

The Palace The Close Lichfield Staffordshire WS13 7LH
Tel: 01543 306170
Fax: 01543 306176
e-mail: reception@lichfieldcathedralschool.com
website: www.lichfieldcathedralschool.com

Chairman of Governors: The Dean of Lichfield, The Very Revd A Dorber

***Headmaster*: Mr P Allwood**, MA, PGCE

Age Range. 3–16 (by 2009).

Number of Pupils. 426 including up to 18 Cathedral choristers, approximately 45% girls, 22 boarders.

Fees per term (2007-2008). Day Pupils £1,823–£2,907; Weekly Boarders £3,842–£4,133; Full Boarders £4,382–£4,481. Instrumental Music Tuition: £179 per instrument.

Lichfield Cathedral School was founded in 1942 principally as a boarding school for the choristers of Lichfield Cathedral. Since that time it has grown considerably and in 1981 became a fully independent co-educational Preparatory and Pre-Preparatory Boarding and Day School for boys and girls between the ages of 3 and 13.

The school began providing secondary education in September 2005 for two classes in Year 7. The school will fill year by year, with a new Sixth Form expected in 2010.

The school currently occupies several buildings in the Cathedral Close, one being the magnificent 17th Century Palace, which was the home of the Bishops of Lichfield until 1952.

In September 2006, the Nursery and Pre-Prep departments moved to new premises in Longdon Green, just outside Lichfield. With the younger children being based in this wonderful six-acre site, with beautifully maintained, purpose-built classrooms, the current facilities in the Cathedral Close are being adapted into academic faculties and departments for the senior pupils, with the dedicated resources required for specialist learning across all subjects.

The link with the Cathedral remains strong with a weekly school service and all Cathedral Choristers board at the school on scholarships provided by the Dean and Chapter. A specialist Girl's Choir was launched in September 2006, with scholarships available from the school, and is already in great demand throughout the region. Academic scholarships are also offered along with all-rounder scholarships for sport, music, art/design, and drama.

Pupils are expected to attain a high standard in all areas of the curriculum. In addition to the academic curriculum, Music, Art, CDT, Drama and Dance are particular strengths and a wide range of Games and extra-curricular activities are also offered.

The general ethos of the School is that of a community where Christian values are upheld and, whilst most pupils are members of the Church of England, children of other denominations and religions are welcomed.

Parents are welcome to contact the school for a conducted tour and meeting with the headmaster or to attend the any of the school Open Mornings held throughout the year.

Charitable status. Lichfield Cathedral School is a Registered Charity, number 1078650. It exists to provide education for boys and girls.

Lincoln Minster Preparatory School (UCST)

Eastgate Lincoln LN2 1QE
Tel: 01522 523769
Fax: 01522 514778
e-mail: sandra.dobbs@church-schools.com
website: www.lincolnminsterschool.co.uk

Governing Body: The Council of the United Church Schools Trust

Chairman of Local Governing Body: R Childs

***Headmistress*: Karen Maltby**, BEd Hons, MEd Nottingham

Age Range. 2–11 Co-educational.

Number of Pupils. 268: Pre-Prep 100, Prep 160.

Fees per term (2007-2008). Nursery £1,887 (all day); Early Years £2,170 (all day); Pre-Prep £2,159; Prep £2,799.

The School occupies delightful, highly impressive and safe sites close to the Cathedral and aims to offer a warm but purposeful environment in which boys and girls can grow and learn. The routine is kept deliberately busy, with individual pupils advancing as far as possible at a pace that is right for them. All subjects are taught by experienced specialists and in restricted class sizes.

The school has a strong musical tradition and the Cathedral Choristers are educated at the school. A Junior boarding house is home to youngsters aged 8 to 12. A foreign language is taught from an early age, and a high priority is given to Information Technology. A wide variety of experiences are available in the realms of sport, music, drama and clubs.

Scholarships and bursaries are available at 7+ and 11+ and it is anticipated that the vast majority of pupils will transfer to the nearby Lincoln Minster School.

The Headmistress and her staff value close links with parents, and are pleased to see them at the regular parents' evenings and at other times by appointment. Informal contact and discussion is welcome and each individual is seen as an important and valued member of the school.

Charitable status. The United Church Schools Trust is a Registered Charity, number 1016538. It is a charitable trust existing to provide high quality education in keeping with the teaching of the Church of England.

Littlegarth School

Horkesley Park Nayland Colchester Essex CO6 4JR
Tel: 01206 262332
Fax: 01206 263101
e-mail: office@littlegarth.essex.sch.uk
website: www.littlegarth.essex.sch.uk

***Headmaster*: Mr Peter H Jones**, BEd Hons

Age Range. 2½–11+.

Number of Pupils. Day: approx 166 Boys, 159 Girls.

Fees per term (2008-2009). £570–£2,530.

Set in 26 acres of glorious grounds in the beautiful Stour Valley, Littlegarth School was founded in 1940 in Dedham and moved to Horkesley Park in 1994. An accredited Independent School, Littlegarth offers a thorough and successful academic, cultural and sports education within a secure and friendly environment.

There is a flourishing Nursery Department where children are prepared for admission to the Pre-Prep, which they join at 4+, although children are accepted by assessment and interview at all levels, subject to space.

Littlegarth is proud of the broad curriculum offered. The school boasts small class sizes and a friendly atmosphere. French is taught from the age of 4, when specialist teaching is also provided in music and sport. Academic standards are high and progress is monitored closely at all times. Careful attention is given to children as they prepare for scholarships and entrance examinations to Independent Schools and local Grammar Schools. As the children move from the Pre-Prep, specialist teaching is given in each subject.

Music is one of the strengths of the school and a large percentage of our children learn at least one musical instrument as well as the recorder. School choirs perform in a number of local events and internal concerts are a regular feature of school life.

The children participate in a wide range of sports throughout the year and the school promotes team participation for all children from the age of 8. As well as boasting a floodlit all-weather area, a substantial new sports hall and changing room complex has been built and a programme to level the sports fields has been completed. An exciting adventure playground has been erected next to the spacious play area.

The school produces many plays each year and strong drama links with the local community are being forged. As well as running the school library, parents are also actively involved in running a wardrobe department and there is a flourishing 'Friends of Littlegarth' parent body.

A wide variety of clubs, extra-curricular activity and pre and after school care is offered.

Charitable status. Littlegarth School Limited is a Registered Charity, number 325064. It exists to provide education for children.

Liverpool College Preparatory School

Queen's Drive Mossley Hill Liverpool L18 8BG
Tel: 0151 724 4000
Fax: 0151 724 6059
e-mail: sbuglass@liverpoolcollege.org.uk
website: www.liverpoolcollege.org.uk

Chairman of the Governors: Mrs B M Greenberg
Chairman of the Preparatory School Committee: Mrs M Mason

***Head of the Preparatory School*: Mr S Buglass**, MEd Oxon, CertEd

Age Range. 3–11.

Number of Pupils. 281 boys and girls.

Fees per term (2008-2009). Nursery and Pre-Prep (ages 3–7): £1,805; Prep (ages 7–11): £2,330. Lunches £195.

Liverpool College is a co-educational day school set in 26 acres of beautiful wooded grounds. It is situated on the edge of Sefton Park in the conservation area of South Liverpool. The Preparatory School shares the site with the Senior Department, a successful day school of 600 pupils, aged from 11–18 years. However it has its own purpose built buildings and areas within the College.

The staff-pupil ratio (1:11) has encouraged the development of a broad based academic curriculum leading children through Key Stages 1 and 2 and the nationally moderated SAT's examinations. There is breadth as well as depth to the curriculum and in addition to the core and foundation subjects, Modern Foreign Languages, ICT and Public Speaking and Debating are compulsory elements of the curriculum. The school is well equipped and recently a new library and ICT department have been developed. This has enabled all of the children in the school to have their own e-mail addresses and controlled access to the internet. A well qualified dyslexia specialist is available to assess and support children throughout the school and there is an effective Gifted and Talented programme in place.

Music is an important aspect of school life. There is a thriving choir, jazz orchestra and samba band and performances in school and in the local community are important features of school life.

Most children progress through to the Senior School at 11+ where the brightest have successfully competed for Scholarships. Children are also prepared for entry to other Senior Schools throughout the country.

An extensive extra curricular programme encourages children to stay at school until 6 pm. Clubs include Judo, Soccer, Cookery, Japanese, Mandarin Chinese, Arabic, Chess, Athletics, Drama, Orchestra, Choir, Tennis, Hockey, Cricket, Art and Dancing. There is also an after school homework club which enables children to be supervised up until 6 pm completing their homework with teaching staff support and participating in a range of interesting activities. A Breakfast Club operates between 7.45–8.30 am.

During their time in the school children have the opportunity to participate in the annual ski trip to Italy, a language course in France, Geography and Science field work in North Wales and outward bound activities in the Lake District and North Yorkshire.

There is a major commitment to sport and the facilities include extensive playing fields, an Astroturf playing surface and large Sports Hall and Fitness Suite. Specialist games staff teach the children rugby, cricket, netball, rounders, swimming, cross country, hockey, tennis and athletics.

Liverpool College has an Anglican Foundation, but children of all denominations and faiths are welcomed. The Chapel plays an important part in the life of the school, and twice a week they attend services there. The school is a caring community which places great importance on mutual respect and consideration for others. There is a strong and effective system of pastoral care.

Entry to the School. Children are assessed before entry and are assured of a place in the Senior School once accepted into the Preparatory School. Further details and a prospectus can be obtained from the Registrar.

Charitable status. Liverpool College is a Registered Charity, number 526682. It exists to provide education for boys and girls.

Lochinver House School

Heath Road Little Heath Potters Bar Herts EN6 1LW
Tel: 01707 653064
Fax: 01707 620030
e-mail: registrar@lochinverhouse.herts.sch.uk
website: www.lochinverhouse.herts.sch.uk

Chairman of the Governors: Richard Orchard

***Headmaster*: J R A Gear**, BEd Hons

Age Range. 4–13.

Number of Boys. 340 Day Boys.

Fees per term (2008-2009). £2,700–£3,536 no compulsory extras.

The academic staff consists of 36 qualified and graduate teachers, Laboratory and DT Technicians, ICT Systems Manager and Technician, classroom assistants and a Matron.

The school is situated in a pleasant residential area on the edge of green belt land in South Hertfordshire, and yet is conveniently placed for access to London. The heart of the school is a late Victorian house. The facilities are extensive and include a purpose built Pre-Prep Department, separate Sports Hall, Gymnasium & Theatre, Music Centre, Modern Languages and English Departments, two Science Laboratories and an Information Technology room equipped with a Network of PCs. All classrooms and offices contain PCs that are also part of the school's Intranet and have protected and supervised Internet access. The school has its own extensive playing fields on site.

Boys are prepared for Common Entrance and Scholarship examinations to a wide range of both day and boarding Independent Schools.

The major sports are Football, Rugby and Cricket together with Athletics and Badminton. All boys learn to swim whilst they are at the School and they have the opportunity to take part in a very wide range of sports and physical activities. This includes outward bound and there is an annual skiing holiday.

During their time at the school each boy will spend some time in France as this is an important and much valued part of the French Curriculum.

Music, Art, Design Technology and PE are part of the timetabled curriculum for all boys regardless of their age. The school encourages boys to learn musical instruments and currently two thirds of the children are doing so. There is a School Orchestra and choir, together with various instrumental groups.

The school is a non-profit making Educational Trust administered by a Board of Governors.

Charitable status. Lochinver House School is a Registered Charity, number 1091045. It aims to provide a quality education.

Lockers Park

Lockers Park Lane Hemel Hempstead Hertfordshire HP1 1TL
Tel: 01442 251712
Fax: 01442 234150
e-mail: secretary@lockerspark.herts.sch.uk
website: www.lockerspark.herts.sch.uk

Chairman of Governors: P D Nicholas, Esq

***Headmaster*: H J Wickham**, MA

Admissions: C R Stephens, BA

Age Range. 5–13.

Number of Pupils. 140 Boys, of whom 75 are boarders.

Fees per term (2008-2009). Boarders £5,455, Day Boys £3,415–£4,410. No compulsory extras.

Further details are outlined in the prospectus, available on application.

Lockers Park is located in 23 acres of parkland above the town of Hemel Hempstead, only five miles from both the M1 and M25 motorways. It therefore lies within easy access of London (Euston 30 minutes) and all four of its airports; consequently the School is well accustomed to providing the necessary help and support to parents living both in Britain and abroad.

The main school building, purpose-built in 1874, is situated in grounds which are perfect for children, with well-maintained playing fields surrounded by woodland areas which easily occupy even the most active. There has been a steady process of modernisation over the past two decades so that the School can now boast first-class, all-round facilities; these consist of the Mountbatten Centre which provides eight excellent specialist classrooms including a well-equipped ICT centre; an attached Science and Technology Building was opened in July 2007 containing two spacious laboratories, technology classroom and fully-fitted workshop; an exceptional art and pottery centre and a well-resourced library.

Sports facilities are of a high calibre and include a fully-fitted sports hall, two squash courts, a heated swimming pool, two tennis courts, an all-weather sports surface and cricket nets, a shooting range and a nine-hole golf course.

Lockers is proud of its academic and musical records; its success in both scholarships and Common Entrance examinations to 45 different schools in the past ten years reflects this well. The average class size is 16 and the pupil:teacher ratio a very healthy 1:7. The Music Department is well known; encouragement is given to every boy to find an instrument which he will enjoy and most gain proficiency in at least one. There is a full orchestra, wind, brass and jazz bands, a string ensemble and two choirs. The number of senior school scholarships of all types awarded to Lockers Park is considered high.

Drama plays a large part in school life with at least one major production each year together with junior plays, school assembly productions, charades and public speaking debates.

At Lockers, there is a real family atmosphere, there is always someone to whom a boy can turn and great care is taken to ensure the happiness of every child. Boys are safe, happy, fit and well looked after. While day boys enjoy all the facilities and opportunities of a boarding school, boarding is fun; dormitories are warm and friendly rooms and opportunities for a variety of enjoyable weekend activities are immense. With day boys and boarders alike, great care is taken over the personal development of each individual.

Bursaries. Lockers Park is committed to offering financial help to deserving candidates, subject to financial resources. Bursarial help may be available up to 100% of fees in some circumstances.

Charitable status. Lockers Park School Trust Ltd is a Registered Charity, number 311061. It aims to provide an all round, high quality education on a non-profit making basis.

Longacre School

Shamley Green Guildford Surrey GU5 0NQ
Tel: 01483 893225
Fax: 01483 893501
e-mail: office@longacre.surrey.sch.uk
website: www.longacre.surrey.sch.uk

***Headteacher*: Mr Mark Beach**, BA Hons, AdvDipEd, MA Ed

Age Range. 2½–11.

Number of Pupils. 239 boys and girls.

Fees per term (2007-2008). £1,620–£3,063.

Are school days really the happiest days of your life? Many Longacre pupils would answer "Yes!" The cheerful and purposeful atmosphere at Longacre is apparent as soon as you enter the school. Here, children are valued as individuals and are encouraged to fulfil their potential in every facet of school life. Personal and social development is highly valued, enabling pupils to grow in confidence as they mature.

Headmaster Mark Beach and his staff believe that children learn more effectively when they are happy, and that excellent academic results can be achieved without subjecting pupils to hothouse pressure. The fact that Longacre pupils gain a range of scholarships, and that they transfer successfully to senior schools of parental choice, shows that this approach is definitely working.

Academic progress is closely monitored and regularly tested. Small classes (maximum eighteen) enable pupils to be taught at an individual level, with increasing subject specialist tuition as children progress through the school. Alongside the core curriculum, Longacre offers a wide range of sporting opportunities, LAMDA lessons, stimulating off-site visits and exciting workshops. There are after school clubs every evening, ranging from Spanish to judo, and regular masterclasses for able pupils.

Set in a beautiful rural location on the outskirts of the picturesque village of Shamley Green, between Guildford and Cranleigh, the school offers a wonderful environment for young children. The school buildings comprise the original large 1902 house plus modern, purpose-built classrooms standing in nine acres of grounds. Facilities include sports fields, courts, gardens, woodland and an adventure playground.

Longacre is a community where parents are welcome. The school has a thriving and supportive PTA and parents are kept well informed about school events and their children's progress through a weekly newsletter, formal and informal meetings and written reports. The Headmaster and staff work closely with parents to ensure that their children are happy, successful and fulfilled.

To arrange a visit, please call 01483 893225. Mr Beach and his staff look forward to welcoming you to Longacre.

Loretto Nippers

North Esk Lodge 1 North High Street Musselburgh East Lothian EH21 6JA
Tel: 0131 653 4570
Fax: 0131 653 4571
e-mail: juniorschool@loretto.com
website: www.loretto.com

Chairman of Governors: R L Martin, QC

***Headmaster*: R G Selley**, BEd

Age Range. 3–12.

Number of Pupils. 6 Boarders, 195 Day Pupils.

Fees per term (2008-2009). Full Boarding £5,325; Weekly Boarding £4,825; Day Pupils £1,895–£3,820.

Pupils can enter the Nippers at 3 and are prepared for entrance and scholarship examinations, mostly to Loretto at 12+. Weekly and flexi boarding is possible for pupils between the ages of 8 and 12. Scholarships and Bursaries are available for children aged 10 and over. There is one boarding house at Newfield. As well as the usual prep school facilities, the Nippers use the Loretto Computer Centre, Swimming Pool, Squash Courts, Fives Courts, Music School, Theatre, School Chapel, and the Sports Hall. The school enjoys a fine reputation for Rugby, Hockey, Cricket, Music, Drama and Art. Loretto has its own Art Gallery. A wide range of individual sports is coached. The staff are all University Graduates and the sixteen classes accommodate up to 20 pupils. There is a Matron under the close supervision of the School Doctor. Catering is in the hands of an experienced Steward.

From an early age children are encouraged to use their initiative and accept responsibility.

Prospectus from the School.

Charitable status. Loretto School is a Registered Charity, number SC013978. It exists in order to educate young people in mind, body and spirit.

Loyola Preparatory School

103 Palmerston Road Buckhurst Hill Essex IG9 5NH
Tel: 020 8504 7372
Fax: 020 8504 7372
e-mail: office@loyola.essex.sch.uk
website: www.loyola.essex.sch.uk

Trustees: The Society of Jesus

Chairman of Governors: A C Wheater, Esq

***Head Master*: P G M Nicholson**, BEd (London)

Age Range. 3–11.
Number of Boys. 189.
Fees per term (2007-2008). £2,305 (all inclusive), Nursery: £1,383 (part day).

A Catholic Day Preparatory School for boys aged 3 to 11+. Admission is possible at any age. There are twelve full-time and five part-time staff. The School has its own Chaplain.

Boys are prepared for entrance and scholarship examinations at 11+ to various Independent Senior Schools and to Grammar Schools in the maintained sector. The curriculum covers all the normal primary school subjects including French, science and computer studies. Music is taught throughout the school. There is a specialist choir and tuition can be arranged in piano, strings, woodwind, brass and percussion. Sports include football, cricket, swimming, athletics and optional rugby.

A prospectus is available on application to the Head Master.

Charitable status. Loyola Preparatory School is a Registered Charity, number 1085079. The school is established in support of Roman Catholic principles of education.

Ludgrove

Wixenford Wokingham Berks RG40 3AB
Tel: 0118 978 9881
Fax: 0118 979 2973
e-mail: office@ludgroveschool.co.uk
website: www.ludgrove.co.uk

Chairman of Governors: The Earl of Rosslyn

Joint Headmasters:
S W T Barber, BA Durham, PGCE
A C T Inglis, BA Newcastle, PGCE

Age Range. 8–13.
Number of Boys. 185 Boarders.
Fees per term (2007-2008). £6,200.

Ludgrove stands in its own grounds of 130 acres. Boys are prepared for entry to Senior Independent Schools.

Charitable status. Ludgrove School Trust Limited is a Registered Charity, number 309100.

Lyndhurst House School

24 Lyndhurst Gardens Hampstead London NW3 5NW
Tel: 020 7435 4936
Fax: 020 7794 7124 (office hours)
e-mail: pmg@lyndhursthouse.co.uk
website: www.lyndhursthouse.co.uk

***Headmaster*: A J C Reid**, MA Oxon

Age Range. 4–13.
Number of Day Boys. 146.
Fees per term (2008-2009). £3,725–£4,195 (excluding lunch and outings).

There is a full-time teaching staff of 19, with class assistants for Pre-Prep years, and part-time learning support. Entry is at 4+, or at 7+ following interviews and assessment. All boys stay to 13+, and sit the Common Entrance or Scholarship to the Independent Senior Schools, usually in London, but often outside. A broad foundation is laid in the junior classes, with subject specialisation commencing at 9+, and very small classes in the last two years. A full programme of games and other activities is pursued throughout. There are specialist rooms for Art and Science, housed in a fine Victorian building with large, well-lit, well-equipped classrooms, and a good-sized playground.

Lyndhurst School
The Junior School of Pocklington School

West Green Pocklington York YO42 2NH
Tel: 01759 321228
Fax: 01759 321284
e-mail: office@lyndhurst-school.com
website: www.lyndhurst-school.com

Chairman of Governors: Mr R Haynes, MA

***Headmaster*: Mr A R Dennis**, BA Hons, PGCE
from January 2009: Mr I D Wright, BSc Hons, PGCE, DipICT, NPQH

Age Range. 7–11 co-educational.
Number of Pupils. 171: 90 Boys, 81 Girls.
Fees per term (2008-2009). Day Pupils: Years 4–6 £2,950, Year 3 £2,287. Full Boarders: £5,324. 5-day Boarders: £4,992.

Lyndhurst is part of Pocklington School (founded in 1514) but has its own staff and self-contained premises set amongst 64 acres of fields and open space on the edge of the market town of Pocklington, 12 miles east of York.

Lyndhurst has its own hall, library/research centre and specialist rooms for science, art and information communication technology.

Other excellent facilities such as the swimming pool, playing fields, astroturf pitches, the sports hall and performing arts centre are used jointly with the Senior School.

There are two separate Junior boarding Houses, one for boys and one for girls. Each accommodates pupils from the age of 8+. Boarding is available either as a full or a 5-day option.

Class sizes are kept within a range of 14–18 pupils.

An emphasis is placed on the core subjects of English, maths and science but history, geography, art, music, ICT, religious studies, language work and French also play a prominent part, together with swimming, PE and Games.

Initially forms are balanced in both gender and ability, with teachers taking care to ensure that individual children can progress at a pace according to need. From Year 5 onwards pupils are taught in ability groups in maths and English.

Most pupils transfer to Pocklington School following an entrance test and reports from Lyndhurst.

A wide range of sporting, cultural and other activities supports the curriculum. Pupils visit an outdoor education centre in the Yorkshire Dales, take part in fieldwork and leadership/team challenges and make full use of the excellent attractions in the area.

Games played include rugby, hockey, football, netball, cricket, tennis and rounders – with clubs and teams in athletics, swimming and trampoline also. PE and swimming form part of the weekly timetable for all pupils.

House competitions include music, art, drama, chess, creative writing, general knowledge and sport.

Extra activities take place at lunchtimes and after school and include art, computing, choir, drama, chess, dance, orchestra, trampoline, video-making, language clubs, swimming and team coaching.

Lyndhurst has a strong musical tradition with a successful choir and orchestra. Individual music tuition takes place throughout the age range.

Full use is made of the Arts Centre to perform in concerts, plays, sketches and musicals – some jointly with the senior school.

Charitable status. Pocklington School is a Registered Charity, number 529834.

Lyndon Preparatory School

Pwllycrochan Avenue Colwyn Bay North Wales LL29 7BP
Tel: 01492 530381
Fax: 01492 539720
e-mail: lyndon@rydal-penrhos.com
website: www.rydal-penrhos.com

Chairman of Governors: Mr D Rae

***Headmaster*: Paul Bendall**

Age Range. $2^1/_2$ – 11.

Number in School. 261 (137 boys, 124 girls).

Fees per term (2008-2009). Pre-Prep Day £1,650–£2,005, Prep Day £2,035–£2,360, Prep Boarding £4,610–£5,335.

Lyndon Preparatory School is a welcoming, vibrant school for young boys and girls aged $2^1/_2$ to 11 years – day and boarding – with full, weekly and flexible boarding available from 7 years.

Ethos. As a Christian school with a Methodist foundation, Lyndon seeks to provide a firm but sympathetic moral framework in which care, support, respect, tolerance and responsibility for oneself and for others is accepted as fundamental. Lyndon has a strong family atmosphere and concern for every aspect of a child's development. Parental support is encouraged and welcomed.

Environment. Set 70m above sea level in Colwyn Bay on a 12-acre site, the magnificent school building offers breathtaking views to the sea across playing fields and woodland. Maximum advantage is taken of the coastal aspect, the close proximity of the Snowdonia National Park and rich historic and cultural resources in the locality.

Curriculum. The School curriculum is very broad and is based on the National Curriculum, teaching being mainly class-based from the ages of $2^1/_2$ to 8 and subject-based from 8 to 11, with input from subject specialists throughout. All children also have the opportunity to develop their special interests and skills through a varied programme of extra-curricular activities.

Opportunities. Although the syllabus has rigorous academic elements, specialist provision is available within the School for those with learning difficulties. Sport, Music, Drama, Art, Design and Information Technology feature strongly and provide real opportunities for every child to explore and develop individual talents, not always expressed through academic work. Pupils may be prepared for entrance to other senior independent schools although most proceed through to **Rydal Penrhos** (*see entry in HMC section*).

Bursaries and Awards to the Senior School are offered at 11+. Parents appreciate the educational continuity between the junior and senior divisions and the integrated curriculum ensures a smooth transition between the Schools.

Facilities at Lyndon are excellent, including science laboratories, an Information Technology suite, art studio, Design Technology room, gymnasium and a 25m indoor swimming pool. The large multi-purpose hall with stage provides for dance, drama, gymnastics and regular musical and dramatic productions. An orchestra, and wind and string groups are formed from those pupils taking tuition in a wide range of instruments, and choral singing is also of a high standard. The School has an excellent reputation for both girls' and boys' sport.

The superb astroturf and new sports hall at the Senior School are also used by our pupils.

Positive Reinforcement. Discipline is clear and fair. Staff make sure that pupils know how they are doing and take particular care to praise them for good work.

Boarding. Boy and girl boarders live within the junior boys and girls boarding houses linked with the Senior School, under the care of experienced house-parents and matrons. The bedrooms are warm, bright and colourful. The Medical Centre is shared with the Senior School and has a resident Sister and two nursing staff, under the direction of a GP, providing 24-hour care. In addition there is an exciting range of weekend activities for boarders.

Playscheme/Holiday Club. A holiday club is also run by staff for many weeks of the school holidays.

Location. The Headmaster, colleagues and pupils assure visitors of a warm welcome at the school, which is easily accessed from the A55.

Charitable status. Lyndon Preparatory School is the Preparatory School of Rydal Penrhos which is a Registered Charity, number 525752. It exists to provide education for boys and girls.

Maadi British International School

4th District, Zahraa El-Maadi, Next to Wadi Degla Sporting Club, Cairo, Egypt
Tel: 00 20 2 2705 8671/2/3/4/5
Fax: 00 20 2 2705 8679
e-mail: mbis@mbisegypt.com
website: www.mbisegypt.com

***Headmaster*: Gerard L Flynn**, BPhil Newcastle, CertEd

Age Range. 2–11.

Number of Pupils. Primary (age 4–11): 300 boys and girls. Nursery (age 2–4): 60 boys and girls.

Fees per term (2007-2008). Primary: £2,140 (Registration: one term's fee payable once only). Nursery: £856–£1,070 (Registration: £125).

MBIS is an International Primary School situated in Maadi, a suburb of Cairo favoured by expatriates. Approximately 50% of pupils are British; the remaining 50% represent over 30 nationalities. The school follows the English National Curriculum and all its assessment requirements including end of Key Stage 1 and 2 testing. All teaching staff are UK graduate teachers, in the main recruited directly from Britain. In each class there is a teaching assistant working alongside the class teacher. Specialist teachers are employed for French, Arabic, ICT, Music, Physical Education and Special Needs. The school has a non-class based 'able child' coordinator and a full-time SRN.

The school relocated to purpose-built premises in September 2004; these offer an indoor 25m swimming pool, a superbly equipped theatre, large ICT suite, food technology and Science discovery rooms. There are also spacious outdoor facilities.

The school is inspected by Ofsted registered inspectors on a regular cycle. It is a member of the European Council of International Schools (ECIS).

There is a thriving programme of extra-curricular activities which is as varied as horse riding and calligraphy. Piano, guitar, drums and violin lessons are available as an after-school activity.

Children undergo an assessment before admission. This is to ensure that the school can meet the individual needs of the child. This process can be bypassed if current school reports are available and forwarded to the Headteacher.

There is a very strong PTA which benefits all pupils and their parents.

The overall aim of the school is to deliver a high quality British education in a caring and stimulating environment.

Prospective parents are requested to contact the Headteacher and he would be particularly pleased to show any parents visiting Cairo around the school.

The school is a 'not for profit' organisation registered as a non-governmental organisation (NGO) with the Egyptian Ministry of Social Affairs, with a charter to educate foreign children. The school's Board of Directors is made up of parents who have children in the school with the addition of up to three invited governors which at present includes HM Consul in Cairo.

Maidwell Hall

Maidwell Northampton NN6 9JG
Tel: 01604 686234
Fax: 01604 686659
e-mail: thesecretary@maidwellhall.co.uk
website: www.maidwellhall.co.uk

Chairman of the Governors: D W Dennis, Esq

***Headmaster*: R A Lankester**, MA (Cantab), PGCE

Age Range. 7–13.

Number of Pupils. 104 Boarding boys, 3 Day boys.

Fees per term (2007-2008). £6,300 Boarding, £4,800 Day.

Maidwell Hall is a boys boarding school with some day boys. Occupying a substantial 17th Century hall the school is situated in beautiful countryside and is characterized by its rural location and by 44 acres of grounds. It is a Christian school and the teachings of Jesus Christ are central to the moral and spiritual education of the children. Every Sunday morning the school worships in the parish church on the edge of the school grounds. The school aims to encourage all the children to discover and develop all their talents through the academic curriculum, the games programme, Music, Art, Drama and an impressive range of hobbies and activities. The school's happy atmosphere is based on a clear framework of rules and conventions with strong emphasis placed on good manners and a traditional code of behaviour and courtesy.

The school is organized as a 7 day-a-week boarding school with a comprehensive programme of club activities in the evenings supplemented by a choice of outings or school based free-time activities on Sundays. There is a weekly boarding option for Year 4. The children benefit greatly from the freedom and security of the school's spectacular grounds including its famous arboretum (wilderness) and its large lake for fishing and boating. Leave-outs occur every 2 or 3 weeks and run from Friday midday until Monday evening and each term contains a long half-term break. Pastoral care for the boarders is the direct responsibility of the Headmaster and his wife, the Housemaster and the team of Matrons and other residential staff. In addition each pupil has an individual tutor.

Pupils are prepared for Common Entrance to the major independent senior schools (typically Eton, Harrow, Oundle, Radley, Rugby, Shrewsbury, Stowe, Uppingham and Winchester) and every year several sit scholarships. In addition to core subjects all pupils study Art, Design, ICT, Latin, Music and Religious Studies and there are also timetabled lessons in PE, Swimming and PSHE. A new computer room was opened in 2001. There is a specialist carpentry shop which operates as a club activity.

The school has a strong reputation for sport. The major games are rugby, soccer, hockey and cricket and there are also matches against other schools in athletics, basketball, cross-country running, golf, squash, swimming and tennis. Teams are entered for riding events and the Pytchley hunt meets at the school every year. There is a successful school shooting team. In the Summer and Autumn there is sailing once or twice a week. In addition to impressive games pitches, sporting facilities include a multi-purpose sports hall with climbing wall, a squash court, a 6-hole golf course and a heated indoor swimming pool. There is particular emphasis on outward bound activities and leadership. There is a strong musical tradition and most pupils play one or two musical instruments; there is a thriving church choir and strings, wind and guitar groups. There are regular concerts throughout the year. Drama is taught as a club activity and each year there is a major school play.

Charitable status. Maidwell Hall is a Registered Charity, number 309917. It exists for the purpose of educating children.

Maldon Court Preparatory School

Silver Street Maldon Essex CM9 4QE
Tel: 01621 853529
Fax: 01621 853529
e-mail: enquiries@maldoncourtschool.org
website: www.maldoncourtschool.org

***Head*: Mrs L F Coyle**, BEd Hons

Age Range. 3–11 co-educational.

Number of Pupils. 130 Day Pupils.

Fees per term (from April 2008). £2,193 for the first child; there is a sibling discount.

The school, founded in 1956, is a co-educational day school of seven classes. The school day begins at 8.45 am and finished at 3.30 pm. There is an after-school facility available until 5 pm which incorporates homework classes and a variety of clubs. A new Pre-Prep department was opened in September 2005 and therefore the school now welcomes children from the age of 3. Nursery Education Grants are available and is Ofsted registered. The school has the reputation of being a happy, friendly community with a family atmosphere

Maldon Court's premises comprise the larger part of an eighteenth century town house, a separate four classroom block, separate toilets and a small assembly hall. There is an acre of ground overlooking open country of which part is garden and part hardcourt, incorporating two half size netball courts and a six-a-side hockey pitch. There are also areas containing adventure climbing equipment.

The premises are very convenient for the town centre. Sports grounds for association football, athletics, hockey and other activities are leased locally. There is a wide variety of after school activities including netball, cricket, gymnastics, netball, cricket, and speech and drama. Swimming is undertaken throughout the year at a nearby sports centre. The school's sporting standard is high; over recent years it has won both national and regional awards in netball, football, swimming and athletics.

Approximately half the children leave the school for independent secondary schools, half enter the maintained sector. Maldon Court's scholarship and entrance record to the independent schools is excellent as is its eleven-plus success rate to Essex grammar schools. Close contact is maintained with both systems of education. Its curriculum covers and goes beyond the National curriculum.

In 1975 a Parents' Association was formed. It is registered separately with the Charities Commission and has developed into an energetic and lively organisation.

The school received ISC accreditation in 1994 and had its most recent ISI inspection in June 2008. New staff have moved the school forward with a challenging and inspiring curriculum and pupils benefits from innovative teaching.

To conclude, Maldon Court's objectives are threefold. Firstly, the School must develop the "whole child", encouraging him to achieve his potential on all fronts: academic, athletic, artistic and social. Secondly, the children will be taught how to work, irrespective of their varying abilities. Finally, the School strives to encourage and develop a code of ethics and behaviour so that, upon leaving, its pupils will be good influences in their next community and retain worth while values for the rest of their lives.

The Mall School

185 Hampton Road Twickenham Middlesex TW2 5NQ
Tel: 020 8977 2523
Fax: 020 8977 8771
e-mail: admissions@mall.richmond.sch.uk
website: www.mall.richmond.sch.uk

Chairman of Governors: J A Hamblin, FCA

***Headmaster*: J G Jeanes**, MA Oxford, DPhil, FRSA

Deputy Head: R H A Struck, BA Frankfurt, MA

Age Range. 4–13.

Number of Boys. 300 day boys.

Fees per term (2007-2008). £2,765 (under 8), £3,200 (over 8).

Established 1872, the School prepares for day and boarding Senior Independent Schools and is a charitable Trust. Boys are admitted at 4+, as well as at 7+ and 8+, and are taught by a well qualified staff consisting of 25 full-time and 3 part-time members. A number of awards are won each year (43 in the last 5 years). The class size averages 20. In addition to bright modern classrooms, facilities include new Science Laboratories and Music Department, IT suite (opened in 2006), Art room, Library, and a Centenary Hall/Gymnasium with a fully-equipped stage. The curriculum includes Computing (both network and multimedia) and Design Technology.

Cricket, Rugby, Football, Swimming and Athletics are the main school games. The school has its own outstanding indoor swimming pool opened in Summer 1999. Chess is optional. Music and Drama are warmly encouraged. There are 2 choirs and 2 orchestras with a large variety of ensembles and visiting teachers for piano, strings, guitar, woodwind and brass.

During the past 20 years of major redevelopment the school has been almost entirely rebuilt. In 2002 a separate Junior department opened within five minutes' walk which is home to the youngest boys aged 4 and 5 years old.

A prospectus is available on application to the Headmaster's Secretary. Early application is advisable.

Charitable status. The Mall School Trust is a Registered Charity, number 295003. It exists to promote and provide for the advancement of the education of children.

Malsis School

Cross Hills Nr Skipton North Yorkshire BD20 8DT
Tel: 01535 633027
Fax: 01535 630571
e-mail: admin@malsis.com
website: www.malsis.com

Chairman of Governors: D A Johnson, Esq

***Headmaster*: M R Peel**, BA Hons

Age Range. Co-educational 3–13.

Number of Children. Full Boarding 43, Daily Boarding 74, Pre-Prep 55.

Religious Denomination. Church of England. Other denominations welcome.

Fees per term (2007-2008). Boarding £5,350; Day £4,100; Pre-Prep £2,300.

About Malsis. Malsis is set in its own grounds of forty acres in the Craven District of North Yorkshire in an area of rare beauty near Skipton, Ilkley and the Dales but also within easy reach of the towns of the North of England, 15 miles from Leeds-Bradford airport and only fifteen miles from the M65 motorway. Approximately one-third of the children board and from Malsis move on to schools all over the country, in recent years to Ampleforth, Eton, Giggleswick, Glenalmond, Gordonstoun, Harrow, Oakham, Oundle, Queen Margaret's York, Radley, Repton, Rugby, Shrewsbury, Sedbergh, Stonyhurst, Uppingham and Windermere St Anne's. Scholarships for Academic, Art, All-Rounders, Music, Drama, Art and Sport are won to many of these each year. The pastoral system is centred on the Housemaster, Form teacher and Tutor and we teach the children about courtesy, appreciation of values (spiritual and social); we try to discover any talent and develop it to the full; we develop human qualities such as kindness, humour and honour. Mr and Mrs Peel live in the middle of the school and are very much the "parents" of the school.

All the main subjects are taught; Greek and Spanish are on offer. Information Technology, Design, Performance Arts, Craft and Art are part of the timetable. There is particular emphasis on Art, Music, Poetry and Drama. Every child takes part in at least one drama production each year. Reading and Handwriting are central to the children's education at Malsis, with reading periods every day. The Chapel Choir leads the Chapel Services, with support from the Chamber Choir and both sing in the surrounding area. The school attends local music festivals and children take part in mini concerts, recitals and a major termly concert. Music groups, including a Concert Band, meet each week. Groups visit local theatres, concert halls and places of interest. Extra help (free) is given in English, Mathematics and French; those with learning difficulties are looked after by trained staff. Malsis has an excellent record in sport, regularly winning trophies far and near but more than that, nearly all the children play in a team, all children being coached games whatever ability, by a team of ten. Rugby, Cricket, Cross-Country, Hockey, Netball, Swimming, Athletics, Rounders and Tennis are the main sports with Soccer an option for the smaller children. The school grounds include fifteen acres of pitches, an astroturf pitch, a nine-hole golf course, a small grass athletics track, four all-weather tennis courts, a beck, woods, a lake and a RAP Tree. There is also a 3km long, professionally designed, mountain bike trail, accredited by the British Cycling Federation – the first school to have such a facility.

Malsis is generously equipped to meet the modern world of education: light, specialist teaching rooms including two Science Laboratories, Art Department, Design and Technology centre, IT centre, 18 room Music school, Sports Hall, Gymnasium, Indoor Swimming pool, a Theatre and a Chapel. Well-equipped games rooms offer snooker, table tennis, table-soccer and a host of board games. A varied activity programme (break, evening and weekend) is available each week with fifty clubs on offer and these range from rambling, camping, archery, sailing, canoeing, shooting, basketball, badminton, judo, squash, golf to cuisine, dance, fishing, photography, trampolining, and juggling to name but a few.

Pre-Preparatory Department. The Pre-Prep opened in 1996 for boys and girls aged from three to seven years. It is situated in the grounds in its own self-contained accommodation.

Charitable status. Malsis School is a Registered Charity, number 529336. It exists to offer children a full, rounded education, catering for all boys and girls so that they move on from Malsis confident, well-mannered and friendly.

Maltman's Green

Maltmans Lane Gerrards Cross Bucks SL9 8RR
Tel: 01753 883022
Fax: 01753 891237
e-mail: office@maltmansgreen.com
website: www.maltmansgreen.com

Preparatory School for Girls. Accredited by the ISC.

Chairman: A M J Frost, Esq, JP, FRICS

***Headmistress*: Mrs J Pardon**, MA, BSc, PGCE

Age Range. 3–11.
Number of Girls. 420.
Fees per term (2007-2008). £1,015 (half day Nursery) to £3,190.

The central house is an attractive homely building dating in part from 1600. Gymnasiums, Laboratories, Music block and Classroom wings provide excellent facilities.

The girls are taught in small classes. The curriculum is designed to lead to the Girls' Common Entrance Examination to Independent Senior Schools, and to prepare them for entry to Buckinghamshire Grammar Schools.

There are 10 acres of grounds, a heated indoor 25m swimming pool, 3 hard tennis courts and 2 hard netball courts, a hockey field and athletics track.

Apply to the Headmistress for an illustrated prospectus and full details.

Charitable status. Maltman's Green School Trust Limited is a Registered Charity, number 310633. It exists to provide a high standard of education for young girls.

Manor Lodge School

Rectory Lane Ridge Hill Shenley Herts WD7 9BG
Tel: 01707 642424
Fax: 01707 645206
e-mail: prospectus@manorlodgeschool.com
website: www.manorlodgeschool.com

Chair of Governors: Mr A Phipps

***Head*: Mrs Judith Smart**, CertEd, BA (Open)

Age Range. 3–11.
Number of Pupils. Nursery (age 3) 20; Infant Department (age 4–7) 183; Junior Department (age 7–11) 216.
Fees per term (2008-2009). Nursery £2,310; Infants £2,520; Juniors £2,940.

There are three forms of approximately 18 children in Years Reception to 6 inclusive. There are specialist teachers for French, PE, IT, CDT, Art and Music as well as numerous peripatetic teachers for brass, woodwind and strings. All staff are fully qualified.

The school consists of a 17th century house and the converted stables offer fifteen classrooms, a French Room, a DT Room and a beautiful hall. The classrooms are bright and well-equipped and the standard of work displayed is very high. We aim to provide excellent teaching within an environment characterised by a well balanced but friendly family atmosphere in which high standards of behaviour and good manners are encouraged and expected. We thus ensure that all pupils achieve their full potential and are prepared for entry to senior schools, both independent and state.

The cottage at the end of the drive has been completely refurbished and now houses a Nursery. The children must be siblings of pupils in the main school and are eligible to attend from the term in which they are three. The new dining room is nearing completion. This facility will replace the old cabins which have been used for many years and are now nearing the end of their useful life. The six acres of grounds include woodland, two practice pitches and a tennis/netball court. The children are offered a wide range of sporting activities including football, hockey, cricket, netball, rounders, swimming and athletics. Music plays an important part in the life of the school. There are several choirs, an orchestra and almost half the school learns an instrument. Music is of course linked into our Drama. Reception to Year 5 children take part in at least two performances a year, but in Year 6 a local theatre is hired for 10 days to give the children real theatre experience. Art is of a particularly high standard and the children use a variety of media producing excellent original work.

Extra activities available at the school include chess, drama and ju-jitsu. There are numerous clubs run by the staff at lunchtime and after school until 4.15 pm or 5 pm, for example, sewing, gardening, calligraphy, football, rugby, cricket, netball, theatre, athletics and choir.

Charitable status. Manor Lodge School is a Registered Charity, number 1048874. The school exists to provide an education which will maximise the potential of the girls and boys in our care.

The Manor Preparatory School

Faringdon Road Abingdon Oxon OX13 6LN
Tel: 01235 858458
Fax: 01235 559593
e-mail: registrar@manorprep.org
website: www.manorprep.org

Chairman of the Governors: Mrs R Kashti

***Headmaster*: Mr Piers Heyworth**, MA Oxon, PGCE

Age Range. Girls 3–11, Boys 3–7.
Number of Pupils. 320 Day: Girls 303, Boys 17.
Fees per term (2008-2009). Nursery £1,100, Reception £2,750, Years 1–2 (age 5–7) £3,050, Years 3–4 (age 7–9) £3,180, Years 5–6 (age 9–11) £3,350.

The Manor is a Charitable Trust. It is surrounded by spacious grounds and there are good facilities for indoor and outdoor games.

A well-qualified staff teach a full range of subjects. Boys are prepared for entry to preparatory schools and girls for the Common Entrance Examination for Girls Schools, or for entrance examinations to other senior schools.

The curriculum is broad. Science, Information Communication Technology, Art, Design, Music, Physical Education and Modern Languages are all taught by specialists. All subjects have specialist teaching in the final two years of the preparatory department.

Computers are used throughout the school to supplement the curriculum and ICT skills are taught in three specialist ICT suites. There are two school orchestras, 4 choirs, 5 chamber groups and a jazz band. Our chamber choir has performed at the Schools Prom at the Albert Hall. It is possible to learn almost any musical instrument as an optional extra.

Enthusiastic games teaching includes swimming throughout the year and skilled coaching in netball, football, tennis, mini-tennis, athletics, rounders and other summer sports. Our netball team has reached the national final of the IAPS tournaments. The school has received the Gold Activemark award from Sport England (in association with the DCSF) for its "commitment to promoting the benefits of physical activity and sport".

As an optional extra supervised after-school sessions run on five afternoons a week from 4.00–5.30 pm. Children are given tea before working or playing quietly and enjoying organised activities. There is also a very wide range of after-school clubs the children can join. We offer a free Early Birds Club where children can be dropped off at school at 8.00 am. We also run sessions for pre-nursery children (2–3 years).

Bus transport is arranged for pupils travelling from surrounding areas.

The school promotes close cooperation between parents and teachers. Parents' Evenings are a regular feature. "The Friends of The Manor" association is run by parents to welcome new families and to support the school.

Charitable status. The Manor Preparatory School is a Registered Charity, number 900347. It exists to provide education for girls and boys.

The Marist Preparatory School

Kings Road Sunninghill Ascot Berkshire SL5 7PS
Tel: 01344 626137
Fax: 01344 621566
e-mail: head@marist-prep.windsor-maidenhead.sch.uk
website: www.themaristschools.com

Independent Catholic Day School for Girls.

Chair of Governors: Mr M FitzGerald

***Head of Prep School*: Mrs Jenny Peachey**, CertEd, BEd Hons, MA

Age Range. 3–11.

Number of Pupils. 250 girls.

Fees per term (2008-2009). £2,350–£2,500.

Mission Statement:

The aim of the school is to:

- provide a caring community where learning is guided by strong Christian values;
- promote excellence where all are encouraged to reach their full potential.

Strengths of the school:

- Nursery, infant and junior departments tailored to the specific needs of the girls at each stage of their education.
- Caring, well qualified and professional staff dedicated to developing happy, secure and stimulated girls.
- Curriculum designed to achieve all the foundation/early year learning goals.
- Able to offer a wide range of both academic and extra-curricular activities.
- High achievement in gym, ballet, fencing, judo, drama, choir and music.
- Strong emphasis on pastoral care, spiritual and personal development; care and consideration for others.
- Small class sizes to enhance individual progression and recognition.
- The school is renowned for its high standards regarding moral values, community spirit, respect and care. This is in line with the overall ethos of the Marist order which has a worldwide presence, providing a truly international dimension to a girl's education.
- Girls are taught to consider and help those less fortunate than themselves through involvement in a wide range of local, national and international charity projects.

The Marist Preparatory School is able to offer your daughter a complete and fulfilling education in the security of a single sex environment, from the age of 3 to 11. We welcome all Christians and those supporting its ethos. We are renowned for our happy and caring ethos, where pastoral care is considered paramount. Your daughter will be treated as an individual and encouraged to achieve her full potential in every area. We have a strong academic record but we also place a strong emphasis on extra-curricular activities which help to develop important qualities such as self confidence, individual creativity and teamwork.

We also have a Senior School on the same campus for girls aged 11–18. *For further details, please see the Marist Senior School entry in the GSA section.*

Charitable status. The Marist Schools is a Registered Charity, number 225485. The principal aims and activities of the Marist Schools are religious and charitable and specifically to provide education by way of an independent day school for girls between the ages of 3 and 18.

Marlborough House School

High Street Hawkhurst Cranbrook Kent TN18 4PY
Tel: 01580 753555
Fax: 01580 754281
e-mail: registrar@marlboroughhouse.kent.sch.uk
website: www.marlboroughhouseschool.co.uk

Marlborough House was founded in 1874 and is registered as an Educational Trust with a Board of Governors.

Chairman of Governors: A B E Hudson

***Headmaster*: D N Hopkins**, MA (Oxon), PGCE

Deputy Head: P Tooze, BA, PGCE

Director of Studies: N Davidson, MA (Oxon), PGCE

Age Range. 3–13 Co-educational.

Number of Pupils. 327.

Fees per term (2008-2009). Prep £4,320, Pre-Prep £2,165–£2,555, Nursery £1,245 (no compulsory extras). Flexi-boarding: £35 per night.

The School is fully co-educational creating a friendly, family atmosphere for children between the ages of 3 and 13.

Marlborough House is situated half a mile from the village of Hawkhurst in the beautiful countryside of the Kent/Sussex border. The fine Georgian house is set in 35 acres of superb gardens, playing fields, lawns and woodland. The School has a Chapel, Computer Centre, Sports Hall, Gym, superbly equipped Science Laboratory, Art, Pottery and Design Technology Department, Music Rooms, Swimming Pool, a .22 Rifle Shooting Range and an all-weather games surface.

With our 40+ qualified teaching staff we aim to produce well motivated, balanced, confident children who know the value of hard work, and who will thrive in their next schools and the modern world beyond. Our classes are small and the children are prepared for all major Senior Schools, whilst those showing special promise sit scholarships.

Encouragement is given to each child to experience a wide variety of activities. In addition to the traditional sports of Cricket, Rugby, Soccer, Hockey, Athletics, Netball and Rounders, opportunities are provided for Music (with the opportunity to learn a wide range of instruments and join the orchestra and choir), Art (in many different media), Pottery, Drama, Ballet, Technology, Computers, Shooting, Tennis, Sailing, Golf, Swimming and Judo.

A copy of the Prospectus together with a Magazine will be mailed to prospective parents on application to the Headmaster.

Charitable status. Marlborough House School is a Registered Charity, number 307793. It exists to provide education for children.

Marlston House School

Hermitage Newbury Berkshire RG18 9UL
Tel: 01635 200293
Fax: 01635 200190
e-mail: info@brockmarl.org.uk
website: www.brockmarl.org.uk

***Headmistress*: Mrs C E Riley**, MA, BEd, CertEd

Age Range. 3–13.

Number of Girls. 35 Boarders, 70 Day Girls.

Fees per term (2007-2008). Boarding £5,510, Day £3,910–£4,150. Pre-Prep School (Ridge House): £1,250–£2,470.

Established in 1995, Marlston House is situated in 60 acres of its own grounds in countryside of outstanding beauty, only four miles from access to the M4. The school is situated beside Brockhurst Boys' Preparatory school and occupies separate listed buildings. Boys and girls are taught separately, but the two schools join together for drama music and activities. In this way Brockhurst and Marlston House combine the best features of the single sex and co-educational systems: academic excellence and social interaction. The schools are proud of the high standard of pastoral care established within a family atmosphere. (*See also entry for Brockhurst School.*)

The Pre-Prep School, Ridge House, is a co-educational department of Brockhurst and Marlston House Schools for 75 children aged 3–6 years, and is situated on the same site in new self contained, purpose designed accommodation.

Girls are prepared for entry to a variety of leading Independent Senior Schools through the ISEB Common Entrance and Scholarship Papers at 11+ and 13+.

All girls play Netball (outdoor and indoor courts), Hockey, Rounders and Tennis (outdoor and indoor courts) and take part in Athletics, Cross Country and Swimming (new 25m indoor heated pool). Additional activities include riding (own equestrian centre), fencing, judo, shooting (indoor rifle range), dance and ballet. New facilities for gymnastics have recently been added to the purpose built Sports Hall. The schools also have their own Chateau near Bordeaux where the pupils practice their spoken French as part of the Year 7 spoken French curriculum.

Music, Art/Design (newly built studios), Speech and Drama are important features of the curriculum and a number of girls have won scholarships and awards to senior schools in these subjects recently.

Transport is provided by the school to and from airports and between Newbury and Paddington stations. Pupils are accompanied by school staff to their destinations.

Mayfield Preparatory School

Sutton Road Walsall West Midlands WS1 2PD
Tel: 01922 624107
Fax: 01922 746908
e-mail: info@mayfieldprep.co.uk
website: www.mayfieldprep.co.uk

Administered by the Governors of Queen Mary's Schools.

Chairman of the Governors: Mr J Aubrook

***Headmaster*: Mr Matthew Draper**, BA, PGCE

Age Range. 2½–11 Co-educational.

Number of Pupils. Day: 106 Boys, 85 Girls.

Fees per term (2008-2009). Main School £2,150; Pre-Nursery £1,290.

A co-educational day school for children aged 3 to 11+, set in a listed building with beautiful surroundings and playing fields. A purpose-built Science/Art building opened in November 2000.

The self-contained Nursery Department accepts children at rising 3.

A fully qualified Staff with full-time ancillary support throughout KS1 ensures that the individual child receives maximum attention.

The main aim at Mayfield is to encourage intellectual excellence. Children experience a thorough grounding in literate and numerate skills.

Through stimulating courses of correctly-paced work the school specialises in the preparation of the children for Grammar and Independent School entrance examinations at 11+.

Our children achieve excellent results, but it is always borne in mind that the individual child's needs are met by matching achievement to potential. All children are expected and encouraged to develop daily in confidence and security.

We believe in a balanced curriculum, and at Mayfield practical and non-academic activities additionally provide interest and varied experiences in Sports, Art, Music, ICT, DT, Dance, Drama and Public Speaking.

Good manners are expected at all times, as well as a happy and whole-hearted participation in the life and studies offered by the school.

Merton House School

Abbot's Park Chester CH1 4BD
Tel: 01244 377165
Fax: 01244 374569
e-mail: secretary@mertonhousechester.co.uk
website: www.mertonhousechester.co.uk

***Principal*: Mr Sean G White**, MA, BA, AdvDipEd, CertEd, FRSA

Age Range. 2½–11 Co-educational.

Number of Pupils. 117.

Fees per term (2008-2009). £922.50–£2038.

Housed in a beautiful listed building close to the heart of Chester, Merton House School has a reputation for excellent academic results, exceptional quality of pastoral care and for being a real family school. Our parents are very involved in the life of the school working with us so that we achieve the very best for our children.

Alongside our broad and imaginative curriculum, specialist one-to-one tuition is available for Dyslexic and Gifted and Talented pupils.

The result of this is that children leave us at eleven to continue their education at the best school for their ability and personality – whether that is to a top, selective academic school in Chester, a specialist arts and drama college, a state school or further afield to a first-class national boarding school.

We excel at swimming and take part in a wide variety of sporting activities including, football, rugby, tennis, hockey, rounders, cricket, athletics and fencing.

We are non-selective at entry but achieve better than average results by combining a friendly family atmosphere with respect for all individuals at Merton House School, to produce happy, confident children who love to learn.

Micklefield School

10 Somers Road Reigate Surrey RH2 9DU
Tel: 01737 242615
Fax: 01737 248889
e-mail: office@micklefieldschool.co.uk
website: www.micklefieldschool.co.uk

Chairman of the Council: Mr A B de M Hunter, FCA

***Headmistress*: Mrs L Rose**, BEd Hons, CertEd, DipPC

Age Range. 3–11.

Number of Pupils. 291 (129 boys, 162 girls).

Fees per term (2008-2009). £830–£2,740. Lunches £150–£155.

'Micklefield recognised the individuality in my different twins and helped them realise their potential socially and academically.'

'Micklefield has helped my boys build confidence and self-esteem in a friendly and secure environment.'

'My children have flourished at Micklefield.'

These quotes from current and former parents sum up the very special education offered at Micklefield School. Established in Reigate 90 years ago, we offer small classes, taught by qualified staff and qualified subject specialists. We cater for boys and girls from the age of two and a half up to the age of eleven, preparing them for Common Entrance and other examinations.

After-school care is available for children from Reception age.

In addition to the normal academic subjects, the curriculum includes design technology, information technology, dancing, drama, French, netball, tennis, athletics, football, cricket and uni-hoc. We have an excellent record in examinations for entrance to senior schools, many pupils gaining scholarships.

Children enjoy academic success, take an active part in a variety of musical and theatrical activities and excel in sports. Dramatic productions and concerts provide opportunities for everyone to display their talents. We encourage participation in drama festivals, sports fixtures, the School's orchestra and choirs. Visits to concerts, theatres and museums are organised together with residential activity holidays for the older children.

A new nursery building has recently been opened which provides the younger children with a light, spacious learning environment, fully integrated with the main school. This new facility has up-to-date play equipment, computers and an outside play area. This follows an earlier extension which provided a science laboratory and three classrooms. There is also a dining room where professional caterers serve high-quality, healthy lunches.

Visit the website or telephone for a prospectus on 01737 224212. Mrs Rose, the Headmistress, is always pleased to show prospective parents around by appointment.

Charitable status. Micklefield School (Reigate) Limited is a Registered Charity, number 312069. It exists to provide a first-class education for its pupils.

Milbourne Lodge Junior School

22 Milbourne Lane Esher Surrey KT10 9EA
Tel: 01372 462781
Fax: 01372 469914
e-mail: admin@milbournelodge.com
website: www.milbournelodge.com

Chairman of Governors: Mrs V J Gillman, DMS, MIMgt

***Headmistress*: Mrs S Counter**

Age Range. 3–8 years.

Number of Children. 160 (mainly Boys).

Fees per term (2007-2008). £1,950–£3,140.

The aim "to live, share and celebrate the love of learning" in a Christian environment is the ethos of the school which has been the subject of a Charitable Trust since 1986. The school celebrates this love of learning by providing a wide-ranging dynamic education in which the children can develop their curiosity and enthusiasm in all areas of the curriculum. Children are welcomed from many different faiths and ethnic backgrounds, and together we respect our many differences.

High standards of academic success are achieved through individual attention, provided by highly qualified teachers in a nurturing and caring family atmosphere. The full curriculum includes French, music, art and drama. Through our Learning Resource Centre, IT is an integral part of the curriculum. A stimulating programme of specialist-taught physical education, using the school's large sports field, multi-purpose gymnasium and heated swimming pool enables our children to enjoy a variety of sports and acquire a wide range of skills. Individual string, piano and cello lessons and a wide variety of extended day activities, including chess, judo and tennis, are also available.

The purpose-built Nursery has three bright and stimulating classrooms, with a wide range of learning resources. Daily outdoor play is on a soft-surface play area, complete with climbing frames and a variety of outdoor toys. The children also enjoy daily access to the exceptional facilities of the whole school, such as the library, gymnasium, music room and lunch hall. In addition to numeracy and literacy, the Nursery offers an introduction to French, music and physical education. The curriculum is delivered through fun weekly topics that engage the children and stimulate them through structured play, practical experience, observation, investigation and exploration.

Milbourne Junior children are happy and confident, learning in a school of academic excellence.

Charitable status. Milbourne Lodge Junior School is a Registered Charity, number 297656. It exists to provide education for children.

Millfield Preparatory School

Edgarley Hall Glastonbury Somerset BA6 8LD
Tel: 01458 832446
Fax: 01458 833679
e-mail: office@millfieldprep.com
website: www.millfieldprep.com

Chairman of the Governors: Mr A E White, CBE, DL

***Headmaster*: Mr K A Cheney**, BA Hons, PGCE, FRGS

Age Range. 2–13.

Number of Boys and Girls. 170 Boarders, 330 Day Pupils.

Fees per term (2008-2009). Boarding £6,385–£6,415; Day £2,135–£4,475.

The School is administered by the same Board of Governors and on the same principles of small-group teaching as Millfield (made possible by a staffing ratio of approximately 1 to 8) which ensures breadth and flexibility of timetable. It has its own attractive grounds of 185 acres some four miles from the Senior School, and its extensive facilities include games fields, art, design and technology centre, science laboratories, sports hall, astroturf, gymnasium and assembly hall with stage, tennis courts, 25 metre indoor swimming pool and chapel. The modern Dining Hall and Library were opened in 1989, and an extensive Music School with recital hall was completed in January 1991. Two new classroom blocks were built in 1999, including a suite of 3 IT laboratories. The pupils have access to some of the specialist facilities at Millfield including the theatre, squash courts, fencing salle, judo dojo, riding school and stables. The School has embarked on further exciting developments which include two new boarding houses, a new sports hall and an equestrian centre, all of which were completed at the end of 2004. Other developments planned for the future include a new science block and a lake for watersports. The Pre-Prep department, taking children from 2–7, moved onto the prep school site in 2004 so that the school now offers an education for children from ages 2–13.

The majority of pupils transfer to Millfield, but some pupils attempt scholarships or entrance to other senior schools. The small class sizes allow the individual pupil to be taught at his or her most appropriate pace. The range of ability within the school is comprehensive and setting caters for both the academically gifted and those requiring remedial tuition.

The curriculum is broadly based and provides a balance between the usual academic subjects and the aesthetic, musical and artistic fields. Junior pupils study French, Year 6 French and Latin and there is a choice of French, Spanish and Latin from the age of 10 upwards. Children may choose either one or two foreign languages, dependent on ability. Science is taught throughout the school, and as three separate subjects from the age of 10.

There is a full games programme organised by qualified teachers of physical education, with the help of other staff. The programme includes Rugby, Hockey, Cricket, Football, Rounders, Athletics, Tennis, Swimming, Badminton, Squash, Netball, Gymnastics, Canoeing, Orienteering and Outdoor Pursuits, to name but a few.

Over 90 different clubs are available. Nearly 400 pupils study musical instruments and there are 2 orchestras, 4 choirs and 20 musical groups.

Boys and girls are admitted from the age of 2 and up to the age of 12 and they come from many lands and widely differing backgrounds. Admission usually depends on interview, assessment and reports from the previous school. Assistance with fees in the form of awards may be available at certain ages to applicants for academic ability, sporting talent, musical, artistic, dramatic prowess and skill in chess.

There are five boarding houses (three for boys and two for girls). Each house is under the care of resident houseparents, assisted by other staff and a team of matrons. The medical centre is staffed by 3 qualified nurses, and the School Medical Officer attends daily.

Charitable status. Millfield is a Registered Charity, number 310283. The Millfield Schools provide a broad and balanced education to boys and girls from widely differing backgrounds, including a significant number with learning difficulties, and many for whom boarding is necessary.

Milton Keynes Preparatory School

Tattenhoe Lane Milton Keynes MK3 7EG
Tel: 01908 642111
Fax: 01908 366365
e-mail: info@mkps.co.uk
website: www.mkps.co.uk

Chairman of the Governors: Mr Peter Squire, MA

***Headmistress*: Hilary Pauley**, BEd

Age Range. Nursery 2 months–2½ years. Pre-Prep 2½–7 years. Preparatory Department 7+–11 years.

Number of Pupils. 450 Day Pupils.

Fees per term (2008-2009). Nursery (per week): £202 (babies under 1 year), £208 (1–2½ years). Pre-Preparatory: £2,948 (2½–5 years), £3,040 (6–7 years). Preparatory £3,340 (8–11 years).

Milton Keynes Preparatory School is purpose-built with facilities which include a Science laboratory, DT workshop and large multi-purpose sports hall. Facilities at the Farm include a fitness room, weather station, ICT lab and a large pond to extend our environmental studies.

Opening hours are 7.30 am – 6.30 pm for 46 weeks per year which enable children of working parents to join playschemes in school holidays and to be cared for outside normal daily school hours.

Staff are highly qualified and committed. Academic standards are excellent, with pupils being prepared for entry to senior independent schools locally and nationally and to grammar schools. Teaching is structured to take into account the requirements of the National Curriculum, with constant evaluation and assessment for each pupil.

Music and Sport play an important part in the life of the school. Concerts are held, and a wide variety of sports is played, with teams competing regularly against other schools.

The school aims to incorporate the best of modern teaching methods and traditional values in a friendly and busy environment where good work habits and a concern for the needs of others are paramount.

The Minster School
York

Deangate York YO1 7JA
Tel: 01904 557230
Fax: 01904 557232
e-mail: school@yorkminster.org
website: www.minster.york.sch.uk

Chairman of Governors: The Dean of York, The Very Revd Keith Jones

***Head Master*: Alex Donaldson**, MA (St John's College, Cambridge), PGCE (London), Cert ICT (Cambridge)

Age Range. 3–13 Co-educational.

Number of Pupils. Preparatory 111; Pre-Prep Department 69.

Fees per term (2007-2008). Upper School: £2,396. Pre-Prep: £1,558 (full day). Choristers receive a substantial Scholarship.

The Minster School was originally founded in 627 to educate singing boys. It is now a fully co-educational preparatory and pre-preparatory school, which includes a Nursery department. Recent Ofsted and ISI inspection reports highlighted the Nursery teaching and provision as 'excellent'. Teaching throughout the whole school was singled out as a particular strength and the achievement, attitude and behaviour of the pupils were warmly praised.

The Nursery and Pre-Prep departments are housed in their own accommodation with gardens, playgrounds and an ICT suite for junior pupils' use. French is taught from Year 2 upwards. In the prep school, teaching is delivered by well-qualified subject specialists. With computers in all classrooms, an IT suite, science lab, art room and DT suite the school is well equipped to deliver a broad curriculum. On our 8-acre sports fields games are taught by school staff and professional coaches. Regular fixtures for boys and girls teams are arranged throughout the year. The major sports are football, hockey, netball, cricket and athletics. In addition to the normal academic curriculum, there is a flourishing music department and all orchestral instruments are taught. Pupils' levels of musical achievement are very high though there are no academic or musical tests to join the school.

Lunch and after-school care are not charged as extras and a wide variety of extra-curricular activities is available – sewing, chess, ballet, fencing, judo, art and craft, model-making and sports clubs etc.

Of the 180 children in the School, 20 boys and 20 girls are choristers who sing the services in York Minster in return for a substantial scholarship. Pupils are prepared for Common Entrance and Senior Independent School Scholarships. Many children gain music, art and academic scholarships to their senior schools.

Monkton Preparatory

Combe Down Bath BA2 7ET
Tel: 01225 837912
Fax: 01225 840312
e-mail: admin@monktonprep.org.uk
website: www.monktoncombeschool.com

Chairman of Governors: S Wilsher, BA Econ

***Headmaster*: C J Stafford**, BA, CertEd

Deputy Head: M L Creeth, BEd

Director of Studies: M S Bray, BA, PGCE

Age Range. 2–13.

Number of Pupils. Boarders 45, Day Boys 120, Day Girls 75, Pre-Prep 125.

Fees per term (2008-2009). Boarders: £5,718 (Year 3), £5,999 (Years 4–8). Day Pupils: £3,316 (Year 3), £4,251 (Years 4–8). Pre-Prep: £2,290–£2,480 (Kindergarten–Year 2) Nursery £23.45 per session.

There are no extra charges except for learning a musical instrument and specialist activities like judo and dance. There are reductions in fees for the children of clergy and HM Forces. Scholarships are offered for those with all-round academic, musical, artistic, sporting ability at age 7 and 11. Interim awards are also given to pupils demonstrating outstanding ability.

The School became fully co-educational in September 1993 and has full flexi-boarding arrangements that cater for both boys and girls from the age of 7. It stands in its own grounds on a magnificent site with the city of Bath on one side and the Midford valley on the other. The buildings include a chapel, a modern classroom block, a theatre for drama and music with 12 music practice rooms, a sports hall, an indoor 25 metre pool and dance studio. The Coates Building incorporates an art studio, design technology workshop, a newly refurbished learning resource centre, seminar room and ICT suite. There are 20 acres of grounds, 3 tennis courts, a hard playing area, an adventure playground and a nature reserve.

The School has a strong musical tradition and a flourishing Art Department. There are two choirs, an orchestra, a band and various other instrumental groups. Drama also plays an important part in school life.

Rugby, Hockey, and Cricket are the major boys' games; Netball, Hockey and Rounders are the major girls' games. All pupils take part in Gymnastics, Swimming, Athletics and Cross-Country. Squash, Badminton, Dance, Judo and Basketball are also available. There is a full programme of matches. All pupils take part in hobbies and activities sessions.

There are 27 fully qualified members of the teaching staff and others who are part time. In addition, the Pre-Preparatory Department, which works as a separate entity but shares many of the Preparatory School amenities, has 11 trained teachers, two nursery nurses and two assistants. Children join the Pre-Prep at two. The main entry to the Preparatory School is at seven plus, but the school accepts pupils who wish to join at a later stage.

Boys and Girls are prepared for Common Entrance and Scholarship exams to Independent Senior Schools. At least two-thirds of them proceed to the Senior School and one third to a wide range of other Independent Senior Schools. 60 Scholarships have been won in the past five years.

Over the years Monkton has educated many children from families who are working overseas, especially HM Forces families. We make special arrangements for them and are well used to meeting their various needs.

The School finds its central inspiration and purpose in its Christian tradition. The caring, family ethos is underpinned by a large number of resident staff, including the Headmaster and his wife.

Charitable status. Monkton Combe School is a Registered Charity, number 1057185. Its aim is to provide education for girls and boys aged 2 to 18, in accordance with the doctrine and principles of the Church of England.

Moon Hall School for Dyslexic Children

Pasturewood Road Holmbury St Mary Dorking Surrey RH5 6LQ
Tel: 01306 731464
Fax: 01306 731504
e-mail: enquiries@moonhallschool.co.uk
website: www.moonhallschool.co.uk

Chairman of Governors: Mrs David Baker

***Headmistress*: Mrs Pamela Loré**, BA Hons Psych, MA Ed, DipSpLD

Age Range. 7–13.

Number of Children. Approximately 100.

Fees per term (2008-2009). Dyslexic Day Pupils £3,685–£5,490 according to provision/stage. Dyslexic Boarding Pupils £5,300–£7,105 according to provision/stage.

Religious denomination: Church of England.

Moon Hall School, Holmbury St Mary caters for boys and girls with SpLD. Accredited by CReSTeD (SP), it has a unique relationship with Belmont Preparatory School (*see separate entry*), sharing its site and excellent facilities. Uniform is common to both schools, and pupils are fully integrated at assembly, lunch and break. They also join together for sport/teams and in dramatic and musical productions.

MHS's specialist qualified, multi-disciplinary staff deliver a full curriculum to dyslexic children from 7 years. Pupils may transfer to Belmont classes when ready, usually into Year 6. They return for ongoing support, as required, up to age 13. Provision for these older children ranges from one 1:1 lesson per week to a complete curriculum in English, Mathematics and Typing (16 lessons). All are taught to touch-type and are successfully entered for OCR examinations normally taken by those aged 16+.

After Year 8 children may transfer to a number of suitable mainstream senior schools, or continue their education at Moon Hall College, our own Senior School located in Leigh, near Reigate.

Within the well-designed, purpose-built accommodation, classes contain a maximum of 14 children, subdivided for English and Mathematics. One-to-one tuition is available as needed. Literacy and numeracy teaching is structured and multi-sensory, incorporating material devised by acknowledged experts in the field. The Phono-Graphix Programme is employed at all levels. Study/Thinking Skills are an integral part of our teaching. Great emphasis is placed upon re-building self-esteem.

Entry requirements. A full report by an independent Educational Psychologist showing the child to be dyslexic and of at least average intelligence. Assessment and interview at MHS.

Charitable status. Moon Hall School is a Registered Charity, number 803481.

Moor Allerton School

GEMS Education

131 Barlow Moor Road West Didsbury Manchester M20 2PW
Tel: 0161 445 4521
Fax: 0161 434 5294
e-mail: office@moorallertonschool.manchester.sch.uk
website: www.moorallertonschool.manchester.sch.uk

***Headmaster*: Mr P S Millard**, BA, MSc, NPQH

Age Range. 3–11 Co-educational.

Number of Pupils. 200 Boys and Girls.

Fees per term (2007-2008). Nursery/Reception (3–5 yrs) £1,716; Years 1–2 (age 6–7 yrs) £1,803; Years 3–6 (age 8–11 yrs) £2,099. (Fees are inclusive of lunch, milk and insurance.)

Moor Allerton is a small independent day school, guided by Christian principles. All children are welcomed and encouraged to learn respect for differing cultures by living and working alongside those of other faiths and backgrounds, whilst maintaining their own identity. Although emphasis is placed on academic progress, games have traditionally been a way of fostering healthy competition and of teaching children to enjoy taking part; children are helped to learn how to win or lose graciously.

In the classroom children's progress is regularly monitored and they are encouraged and supported by a team of dedicated and committed teachers. Expectations of all children are high. Gifted children are challenged and stretched and support is given to children who have difficulties. Pupils receive appropriate preparation for entry at 11+ to Independent High Schools.

Music, Art and PE are important areas of the curriculum and sports played at the school include soccer, rugby, netball, cricket, rounders, tennis, swimming and athletics. We offer a wide range of extra-curricular activities, including: Drama, Ballet, Modern Dance, TaeKwonDo, Brazilian Football, Active Fun, French, Cookery, Judo, Yoga plus musical tuition, including: percussion, flute, clarinet, guitar and piano.

There is After-School Care until 5.30 pm and Early Care from 07.45 am. Holiday Fun Clubs are offered during Summer, Easter and Whitsun Breaks.

Moor Park School

Ludlow Shropshire SY8 4DZ
Tel: 01584 876061
Fax: 01584 877311
e-mail: head@moorpark.org.uk
website: www.moorpark.org.uk

Founded in 1964, Moor Park is a co-educational boarding and day school of Catholic foundation.

Chairman of Governors: Capt C Tuffley

***Headmaster*: J R Bartlett**, BSc QTS Brunel University

Deputy Head & Headmistress of Lower School: Mrs J M Morris, CertEd

Age Range. 2½–13.

Number of Pupils. 263.

Fees per term (2008-2009). Boarding £4,370–£5,310, Day £1,585–£3,890

The school is built around a magnificent country mansion set in 85 acres of glorious Shropshire countryside. The school campus has a great sense of space, and pupils enjoy the playing fields, pasture, woodland and lake.

Facilities include a science/ICT block, art and design block, learning support department, sports hall, main hall/theatre, a delightful chapel and a heated pool.

The school has seen considerable investment in recent years with a new structure to the Lower School and remodelled Upper School campus with new classrooms. The Study Centre reflects our emphasis on independent learning and the Design Technology building would be the envy of many a senior school.

Fine facilities are nothing without people: the school is renowned for its warmth, its sense of community, its pastoral care, and the emphasis on the individual development of each pupil. There is breadth and depth of opportunity: the tally of scholarships and awards to senior schools – academic, artistic, musical, all-round is outstanding, with nearly 100 achieved in the last ten years.

Boarding was redeveloped for the academic year 2002/03, and a new co-educational boarding community has been created in the main school house, under the care of houseparents and a team of matrons. Boarders may be full, weekly, half or flexi, and day pupils enjoy the opportunities, facilities, activities and pastoral care that such an infrastructure offers, during the week and at weekends. The success of our boarding provision is measured by an increase year on year in the number of children who board and their obvious enjoyment of the experience.

Charitable status. Moor Park School is a Registered Charity, number 511800, which exists to provide education for young people.

Moorfield School

Wharfedale Lodge 11 Ben Rhydding Road Ilkley West Yorkshire LS29 8RL
Tel: 01943 607285
Fax: 01943 603186
e-mail: enquiries@moorfieldschool.co.uk
website: www.moorfieldschool.co.uk

Chairman of Governors: C R Jelley, Esq

***Headmistress*: Mrs Therese Holden**, BSc Hons

Age Range. 2–11.

Number of Pupils 144 Day Girls.

Fees per term (from April 2008). Nursery Unit (based on 5 mornings): £845 (preferred sessions pro rata). Main School £2,015. Lunches extra.

Staff: 9 full-time, 9 part-time.

Religious affiliation: Interdenominational.

Accommodated in a large house, Moorfield School is situated in a beautiful setting on the edge of Ilkley Moor. The School prides itself on its academic excellence and friendly, caring atmosphere, specifically for girls. It has a strong 'family' feel and lays particular emphasis on consideration for others in both in and beyond the school community. Independence and individuality are encouraged and confidence nurtured.

High standards of literacy and numeracy are the academic bedrock enabling all girls to enter well-respected senior schools at 11+. Success is also achieved in music, art, drama and sport with girls participating in a wide variety of local events. An all-round broad curriculum is followed with specialist teaching in small classes.

Excellent facilities include a purpose-built nursery unit, which gives girls a seamless education from rising 3 years, and a fully equipped IT suite and many specialist subject rooms. A full range of extra-curricular activities enables each girl to develop her interests; pre and after school care help busy families make the most of each day.

Moorfield is an Education Charitable Trust and the Headmistress is a member of IAPS.

Charitable status. Moorfield School Ltd is a Registered Charity, number 529112.

Moorlands School

Foxhill Drive Weetwood Lane Leeds LS16 5PF
Tel: 0113 278 5286
Fax: 0113 203 3193
e-mail: info@moorlands-school.co.uk
website: www.moorlands-school.co.uk

The School is an Educational Trust with a Board of Governors.

Chairman of Governors: Mr T Mulryne, MA, BEd, DPE

***Headmaster*: John G Davies**, BA Hons, PGCE, DipRE

Age Range. 2½–13 Co-educational.

Number of Pupils. 150 Day Boys and Girls.

Fees per term (2008-2009). Lower School (2½–7 years) £1,254–£2,365; Lunch £160. Upper School (7–13 years) £2,645; Lunch £180.

The School was founded in 1898 and consists of day boys and girls who live in the city of Leeds and surrounding area.

The aim of the school is to develop the full potential of every child within a happy and caring environment fostered by small classes and the professional skills of a highly qualified staff. Strong links between the parents and the school are encouraged to facilitate the provision of an effective education.

Admission is by assessment and observation. Pupils are accepted at 2½ years old for entry into the Foundation Unit and are expected to progress through the school in preparation for entry to senior independent day and boarding schools. The school has a well developed specialist facility to provide assistance for pupils with any learning issue such as dyslexia or gifted children.

Blended with this traditional core of academic work is offered a comprehensive range of sporting activities and a wide range of musical and extra-curricular pursuits.

Religious affiliation: Undenominational.

Charitable status. Moorlands School is a Registered Charity, number 529216. It exists to provide children with the finest education possible, using the best resources in an environment of care.

Moreton Hall Preparatory School

Bury St Edmunds Suffolk IP32 7BJ
Tel: 01284 753532
Fax: 01284 769197
e-mail: office@moretonhall.net
website: www.moretonhall.net

Chairman of the Board of Governors: Mr Michael Whatley

***Headmaster*: B H Dunhill**, BA Hons

Age Range. 2½–13.

Number of Pupils. Boys 59, Girls 50.

Fees per term (2007-2008). Boarding: £5,375 (full), £4,800 (weekly). Day: £2,115–£3,575.

Moreton Hall is a Catholic school which welcomes other denominations.

The school accepts boarders from the age of 7, and day pupils from the age of 2½. (Weekly and flexible boarding arrangements are possible).

There are 17 full and part-time staff in the Prep and Pre-Prep departments, plus ancillary and Nursery staff, which makes an average class size of 15 pupils possible. In addition there are visiting teachers for music, dance, and drama, whilst the School Chapel is served by the parish clergy. In the boarding house Matron, the duty member of staff, and the gap students, work under the direction of the resident Headmaster and his wife.

The School occupies a fine Adam mansion built in 1773, and stands in its own grounds of 30 acres of wooded parkland and playing fields on the outskirts of the historic town of Bury St Edmunds. London is two hours distant by road or rail. The School is happy to arrange transport to and from all airports.

Pupils are prepared for Scholarship or Common Entrance examinations to a wide range of Independent Senior Schools, and the school is proud to achieve an excellent record of success in both areas.

The Music Department at Moreton Hall is particularly strong, with 70% of the children learning at least one instrument. There is a strong Chorister link with St Edmundsbury Cathedral and a Chorister Scholarship is available.

The School has a very strong tradition in Drama. Some of the professionally-directed productions have included *Romeo and Juliet*, *Iolanthe*, *See How They Run*, *As You Like It*, *Rosencrantz and Guildenstern*, *A Midsummer Night's Dream* and *The Frogs*.

Art and design play an important part in the curriculum, as does Information Technology, with every child, from the nursery up, being taught in the modern IT suite.

The main games are rugby, soccer, hockey, cricket, athletics, netball, squash, tennis and swimming. Amongst the extra-curricular activities available are ballet, gymnastics, golf, tap dancing, judo, carpentry, chess, computer art, natural history, enamelling and debating. There is a outdoor, heated swimming pool and a large sports hall. A second, indoor swimming pool is available for use in the winter at the adjacent Health club.

The Pre-Prep department is housed in its own self-contained section of the School buildings and enjoys all School amenities. In addition, Pre-Prep pupils enjoy specialised tuition in French, Music, Drama and Dance.

Academic and St Edmundsbury Cathedral Choral Scholarships are offered at Prep School entry ages. Apply to the Headmaster for further details.

Charitable status. Moreton Hall School Trust Limited is a Registered Charity, number 280927. It exists to provide high quality education for boys and girls.

Mostyn House School

Parkgate South Wirral Cheshire CH64 6SG
Tel: 0151 336 1010
Fax: 0151 353 1040
e-mail: enquiries@mostynhouse.co.uk
website: www.mostynhouse.co.uk

The School was founded in 1854 and became a charitable trust in 1979.

Chairman of Governors: Mr Glyn Dale-Jones

***Headmistress*: Miss S M T Grenfell**, MA, PGCE

Age Range. 3–18.

Number of Pupils. 202: Boys 132, Girls 70.

Fees per term (2007-2008). Pre-Reception (mornings only) £1,415, Prep School £2,174, Senior Department £3,334. Compulsory extras: Lunches £2.90 per day.

Mostyn House School is a co-educational day school for children between the ages of 3 and 18. Entry to the Prep School is by interview. The Senior Department (age 11–18), opened in 1985, prepares pupils for GCSE and Advanced Level examinations, with entry by interview and examination in English, Maths and Reasoning. Entry to the Sixth Form is by GCSE results and interview.

Small classes, a well qualified and enthusiastic staff and a happy but hard-working atmosphere bring out the best in each child, and a wide range of subjects is offered. Modern facilities include three Science Laboratories, ICT Suite, Indoor Swimming Pool, Food Technology Room, Library, Art Studios, and DT Suite; these complement older buildings such as the beautiful Chapel.

A wide range of extra-curricular activities including dance, drama, computers, music, craft, snooker and shooting take place in a special activity session each day. Individual sports are encouraged and the School has a comprehensive fixture list for team sports. The Senior Department has achieved the Sportsmark award and the Prep School has achieved the Activemark Gold.

Pupils' work is monitored regularly with Form Tutors and Key Stage Coordinators keeping a close eye on individual development. Regular reporting to and consultation with parents takes place throughout the school.

The School is a member of ISCO and a team of staff run a comprehensive careers guidance programme for all senior pupils. The Headmistress is the sixth generation of the Grenfell family to direct the school. The school has passed an accreditation inspection by the ISC and the Headmistress is in full membership of IAPS and ISA.

The school has also been accredited by CReSTeD for its Study Room – the highly successful dyslexia unit and pupils from a wide variety of countries benefit from the tuition and guidance offered by the thriving department for English as an Additional Language.

Charitable status. Mostyn House School Trust is a Registered Charity, number 1048117. It exists to provide education for boys and girls aged 3–18.

Moulsford Preparatory School

Moulsford-on-Thames Wallingford Oxfordshire OX10 9HR
Tel: 01491 651438
Fax: 01491 651868
e-mail: headmaster@moulsford.com
website: www.moulsford.com

The School is a Charitable Trust controlled by a Board of Governors.

Chairman of the Board of Governors: Mr W Lazarus, FCA

***Headmaster*: M J Higham**, BA, CertEd

Age Range. 4–13.

Number of Boys. 45 Weekly Boarders, 190 Day Boys.

Fees per term (2008-2009). Day Boys £2,525–£3,985, Weekly Boarders £4,995. These fees are all inclusive but individual coaching in music, judo, golf and fencing is charged as an extra.

The School has its own river frontage on the Thames, spacious games fields and lawns and is situated between Wallingford and Reading.

Boys are prepared for the Common Entrance and Scholarship examinations to the top independent schools in the country. An experienced and well qualified staff ensure that a high standard is achieved academically, musically, artistically and on the games field.

The principal games are rugby football, soccer, tennis and cricket. Other sporting activities include athletics, swimming, sailing, judo, golf and gymnastics. The school is proud of its fine academic and sporting reputation which has been built up over many years.

Charitable status. Moulsford Preparatory School is a Registered Charity, number 309643.

Mount House School

Tavistock Devon PL19 9JL
Tel: 01822 612244
Fax: 01822 610042
e-mail: office@mounthouse.com
website: www.mounthouse.devon.sch.uk

Chairman of the Governors:

***Headmaster*: J R O Massey**, BSc

Deputy Headmaster: J Symons, BEd

Age Range. 3–13 Co-educational.

Number of Pupils. 252 (97 boarders, 87 day children and 68 Pre-Prep).

Fees per term (2007-2008). Boarders £4,655–£5,425, Day Children £2,780–£4,070, Pre-Prep £1,940–£2,060.

Mount House School is set in idyllic surroundings in fifty acres of playing fields, woodlands and gardens with lakes and streams. It is bordered on the west by over ½ mile of the River Tavy. Children are prepared for Common Entrance and Scholarship to the leading national Independent Schools. All the main subjects are taught throughout The School including Latin, Design & Technology, Music, Art and Physical Education. Academic work is competitive. It is carefully monitored with regular Form Orders and Effort grades. High standards are expected and achieved.

A huge range of hobbies and activities is offered. There is a very happy atmosphere and particular attention is paid to good manners. There is an Escort service to and from London and the airports. (Gatwick to Plymouth is quicker than getting across London!) There is a robed RSCM choir which leads the Sunday Services and sings in churches, cathedrals and senior schools from time to time. Most of the pupils learn a musical instrument. There are various musical groups and orchestras. The new music school complete with main music room and practice rooms was opened in 2001, and there is a hall with stage. There is a well-equipped Design & Technology Centre, 2 science laboratories and a dedicated Art School.

All the main sports are played and children are coached to a high standard. The fixture list includes schools in other parts of the country. There is a superb sports hall with facilities for a host of sports. The hall includes a full-size tennis court and two squash courts. An Astroturf pitch was opened in 2001. All pupils take part in the "Shackleton Award Scheme" which includes elements of community service, outward bound and first aid.

An exciting architect-designed Pre-Prep department was opened in the autumn of 1996 providing traditional teaching in small groups to children between the ages of 3 and 7 years old. The Pre-Prep has access to many of the Main School's facilities.

Charitable status. Mount House School Trust Limited is a Registered Charity, number 270147. It aims to provide high quality independent boarding and day education for boys and girls aged between 3 and 13.

Mowden Hall School

Newton Stocksfield Northumberland NE43 7TP
Tel: 01661 842147
Fax: 01661 842529
e-mail: info@mowdenhall co.uk
website: www.mowdenhall.co.uk

Chairman of Trustees: The Rt Hon Lord Wakeham, DL

***Headmaster*: B Beardmore-Gray**, BA Hons, QTS

Deputy Headmaster: T P A O'Sullivan, LLB Hons Durham, PGCE

Age Range. 3–13.

Number of Pupils. 195: 115 boys, 80 girls; Prep School: 111 (72 boarders, 39 day); Pre-Prep & Nursery: 84.

Fees per term (2008-2009). Boarding £5,770; Day £4,470; Pre-Prep £2,570; Nursery £1,280 (5 mornings).

Mowden Hall is a large Victorian mansion standing in its own grounds comprising 55 acres of woodland and playing fields. It overlooks the Tyne Valley, is some 15 minutes from Newcastle International Airport and has easy access to the mainline railway station.

The school has modern science, ICT, art, drama and music facilities. There is a well-equipped pre-prep and nursery department, which shares many of the school's facilities.

All pupils are prepared for Common Entrance and Scholarships to leading Senior Independent Schools throughout the United Kingdom and many academic, all-rounder and specialist awards have been gained in recent years. Children are taught in small classes, averaging 12, and the teacher/pupil ratio is approximately 1:9. There is no entrance test to the school. In the Pre-Prep there are no more than 18 children per class.

The welfare of the pupils is paramount, and is the responsibility of the Headmaster, his wife, and a dedicated team of matrons. Many of the teaching staff live on site with their families and all are actively involved in the pastoral care of the children.

The major games played are rugby, hockey, football, netball, cricket, athletics, swimming and tennis. The school has its own heated indoor pool, tennis courts, cricket nets and a large, fully-equipped sports hall.

Mowden Hall is a member of the Cothill Educational Trust, which also comprises the Château de Sauveterre in southwest France. Pupils in Year 7 at Mowden Hall (11–12 year olds) all spend a full term at the Château de Sauveterre studying all subjects in French.

Music and drama are practised throughout the school. Individual instrumental tuition is provided and over 85% of the Prep School pupils learn an instrument. Participation in choirs, music ensembles and the concert band are strongly encouraged. Drama is particularly strong and every child performs in productions at regular intervals each year in the school's own theatre.

The school aims to bring out and nurture the individual talents of each pupil. It also encourages social responsibility, discipline and good manners in a Christian environment. There are regular assemblies through the week and a full service in our local church on Sundays, which parents are very welcome to attend.

Interested parents are encouraged to ring the school for a prospectus and to arrange a visit.

Charitable status. The Cothill Educational Trust is a Registered Charity, number 309639.

Naima Jewish Preparatory School

21 Andover Place London NW6 5ED
Tel: 020 7328 2802
Fax: 020 7624 0161
e-mail: secretary@naimajps.co.uk
website: www.naimajps.co.uk

Chair of Governors: Mrs Judy Dangoor

***Interim Headteacher*: Mr J W Pratt**, GRSM Hons, CertEd

Age Range. 3–11 Co-educational.

Number of Pupils. 175 girls and boys.

Fees per term (2008-2009). £2,250–£2,800.

Naima JPS is centred on the belief that an excellent secular education and strong Jewish grounding are mutually attainable. As such, our twin goals merge as we aspire to prepare our children for a successful life in society imbued with Torah values. We aim to provide a secular education on a par with the top national private schools with a curriculum that extends beyond the minimum guidelines provided by the National Curriculum. As a private school, we provide both the environment and teaching resources to monitor each individual, and to help children of all abilities to reach their full potential.

Naima JPS challenges all children, together with their parents, no matter what their level of religious observance, to pursue ongoing spiritual growth as individuals. We encourage children on their journey to spiritual maturity in a harmonious and nurturing community environment of tolerance, respect and care for one another.

The school has a one-form entry. Given that class sizes seldom exceed 22 and the favourable ratio of teachers and assistants to children – as little as 1:5 depending on the age and need – programmes of learning have the flexibility for differentiation. The school has a high number of particularly able children with specific intellectual gifts.

During the crucial early years at school it is important that children define themselves by things they can do well. Self-esteem, that essential by-product of success, empowers strength and gifts. Once children understand how their minds work, as they learn in many different ways, they can feel comfortable about entering any environment and mastering it. Children who truly understand, value and like themselves are better equipped to flourish and embrace fresh challenges. Confidence through success contributes to strong identities that welcome new horizons. Resiliency, discovery, independence and spiritual maturity are nurtured at all levels. At Naima JPS education is not about coveting garlands for the few, but ensuring that all children reach their full potential.

Charitable status. Naima JPS is a Registered Charity, number 289066.

The New Beacon

Brittains Lane Sevenoaks Kent TN13 2PB
Tel: 01732 452131
Fax: 01732 459509
e-mail: admin@newbeacon.kent.sch.uk
website: www.newbeacon.kent.sch.uk

Chairman of the Governors: Mr Charles Gordon

***Headmaster*: Michael Piercy**, BA Hons

Age Range. 4–13.

Number of Boys. 400. Predominantly Day Pupils, but a small element of flexi-boarding is retained from Monday to Thursday.

Fees per term (2008-2009). £2,735–£3,530. Fees include lunches.

Boys are prepared for both grammar and independent schools, and enjoy considerable success at 11+ and 13+, with many achieving scholarships (including music, sport, art and drama) at the senior independent schools of their choice.

The School divides into Senior, Middle and Junior sections in which boys are placed according to age and ability. Initiative is encouraged by organising the School into 4 houses or 'companies'. The well-equipped main School building is complemented by several modern, purpose-built facilities: separate Pre-Prep and Junior School buildings for boys aged 4–9; a Sports Hall with modern changing facilities; a Theatre; a heated indoor Swimming Pool; a centre for Art and Music; and modern facilities for Science and Technology. Soccer, Rugby Union and Cricket are the major games. During the summer months Tennis and Athletics are available. Swimming and Shooting are available all year round. A very extensive range of extra-curricular activities is offered to all age groups (including many interesting and exciting trips). Music, sport, art and drama at the School are highly regarded.

A limited number of music and academic bursaries are offered subject to means testing. Cases of financial hardship and instances of other misfortune are considered on an individual basis.

Charitable status. The New Beacon is a Registered Charity, number 307925. It exists to provide an all-round education for boys aged 4–13.

New College School

Savile Road Oxford OX1 3UA
Tel: 01865 243657
Fax: 01865 210277
e-mail: jasquith@newcollege.oxon.sch.uk
website: www.newcollege.oxon.sch.uk

Governors: The Warden & Fellows of New College, Oxford

***Principal*: N R Gullifer**, MA

Age Range. 4–13 years.

Number of Boys. 149 Day Boys. 21 Choristers.

Fees per term (2007-2008). Reception £2,201, Year 1 £2,651, Years 2–4 £3,254, Years 5–8 £3,558, Choristers £1,242.

New College School was founded in 1379 when William of Wykeham made provision for the education of 16 Choristers to sing daily services in New College Chapel. Situated in the heart of the city, a few minutes' walk from the College, the school is fortunate in having the use of New College playing fields for sport and New College Chapel for school services.

The staff consists of 18 full-time and 11 part-time qualified graduates or certificated teachers. Boys are prepared for the Common Entrance and Scholarship Examinations for transfer to independent senior schools at age 13. In the final year there is a scholarship form and a common entrance form. The school broadly follows the national curriculum subjects, but also teaches French, Latin, Design Technology and Greek.

A Saturday morning music education programme is followed by senior musicians. Games include soccer, hockey, cricket, rounders, athletics and rugby.

Music plays a major part in school life with orchestra, ensembles, concert and junior choirs and form concerts, in addition to individual tuition in a wide range of instruments.

Activities include art, craft, pottery, design, chess, sport, computer, drama, gardening and science clubs. There is a Choral Society for parents.

Boys are admitted to the Pre-Prep Department at 4 years and by assessment to the Lower School at 7 years. Potential Choristers are tested between the ages of 7 and 8 at Voice Trials.

New Hall Preparatory School

Boreham Chelmsford Essex CM3 3HS
Tel: 01245 236192
Fax: 01245 451671
e-mail: prep@newhallschool.co.uk
website: www.newhallschool.co.uk

Chair of Governors: Prof M Alder, DL

***Head*: Mrs S Conrad**, BA Durham, PGCE

Age Range. 3–11 Co-educational.

Number of Pupils. 350.

Fees per term (2008-2009). Day £2,350–£3,500; Boarding (from age 8) £5,270.

New Hall Preparatory School is a Catholic foundation which welcomes all who are in sympathy with its ethos. The school caters for boys and girls aged 3–11 with full and flexi-boarding available from the age of 8. The school is located in a beautiful, spacious environment and set within the extensive grounds of New Hall School, Chelmsford. It prides itself on offering a broad, balanced and challenging curriculum which provides academic excellence within a happy, caring Christian community. The school is a two-form entry school with parallel classes in each year group. A purpose-built Pre-Reception was opened in September 2004 to provide a stimulating and spacious environment for 3 and 4 year old children. The curriculum is based mainly on the National Curriculum, but offers a greater diversity and depth. All pupils study Religious Education, English, Mathematics, Science, History, Geography, Art, Technology, Music, Physical Education, French and Information and Communication Technology. Latin and Drama are offered to older pupils. Music plays an important part in the life of the school and children are encouraged to have instrumental tuition and join the excellent choirs and orchestra. All pupils have access to an attractive, well-equipped library and state-of-the-art computer suite.

The school has excellent sporting facilities which include a 25m 6-lane indoor swimming pool; 10 floodlit tennis/netball courts; indoor sports hall; floodlit national standard Astroturf hockey pitch, and athletics track, soccer, rugby and cricket pitches. All pupils are able to enjoy physical activities through the curriculum, extra-curricular clubs and in competitive games.

The School's philosophy is based very much on regarding each child as an individual with his or her own particular needs and talents. We feel that, by offering a broad curriculum and a wide range of extra-curricular activities – cultural, musical, scientific, technological and sporting – we can give every child the maximum opportunity to achieve their potential and to identify and build upon their own particular strengths.

Charitable status. New Hall School Trust is a Registered Charity, number 1110286.

Newbridge Preparatory School

51 Newbridge Crescent Wolverhampton West Midlands WV6 0LH
Tel: 01902 751088
Fax: 01902 751333

e-mail: office@newbridge.wolverhampton.sch.uk
website: www.newbridgeprepschool.org.uk

Chairman of Board: Mrs H M Hughes

***Headmistress*: Mrs B Pring**, BEd, MEd, CertEd

Age Range. Girls 2–11. Boys 2–4.

Number of Pupils. 153.

Fees per term (2008-2009). £1,461–£2,224 including dance, musical instrument lessons, gym, netball, singing, swimming lessons.

Newbridge Preparatory School was founded in 1937 and occupies a super site on the outskirts of Wolverhampton, convenient for parents travelling from Telford, Bridgnorth, Stafford, Walsall.

It is a non profit-making Limited Company with charitable status.

The school is divided into Lower School (Pre-Nursery–Year 2) and Upper School (Years 3–6). Upper School is housed in the main building which is a substantial house set in huge, beautiful mature gardens. There are specialist facilities in Art and Design, ICT, Science, Music and PE. The school has extensive netball and tennis courts..

Staff : pupil ratio is high. Specialist teaching takes place in Key Stage Two in English, Mathematics, Music, Science, PE, Dance and Drama. In Key Stage One: Dance, PE, Drama and Music.

Teaching Assistants work with highly qualified teachers.

Lower School enjoys a separate Nursery and a brand new building for Pre-Nursery–Year 2. There is a large multi-purpose hall.

Children with Special Needs are well supported and nurtured.

Upper School girls take drama and enter ESB and LAMDA examinations. They also enter the annual local festival for Music and Drama.

The school offers an Early Morning Club and after-school care and runs a Holiday Club all year round. It is a very popular school, there are waiting lists for many classes.

Standards are high in all areas of the curriculum – academic, PE and music. Senior School results are excellent. Places are gained at local selective Independent and Maintained Schools but also Boarding Schools. Academic and Speech and Drama Scholarships are awarded. Once examinations are complete, Year 6 follow an exciting STAR (Summer Term Activities Refreshed) curriculum using and developing skills previously taught. Girls leave Newbridge well equipped to face the challenges of a Senior School.

Educational visits take place each term. Nursery children enjoy a six week Forest School experience. Residential visits occur in Years 3–6. The visits vary from outdoor activities and challenges, environmental study, a visit to France. Years 5 and 6 visit London for two days – this includes a guided tour, a theatre visit, Science Museum and a theatre workshop.

Emphasis is placed on traditional values, personal development and responsibility. The curriculum is very broad, including many opportunities in Sport, Dance, Drama and Music.

Our school mission statement is: Aiming High, Building Bridges and Preparing for Life.

Children are taught to do their best in all areas, to strive for a challenge.

Emphasis is placed on self-discipline, inclusion, equal opportunity and respect.

Charitable status. Newbridge Preparatory School is a Registered Charity, number 1019682. It exists to advance the education of children by conducting the school known as Newbridge Preparatory School.

Newcastle Preparatory School

6 Eslington Road Jesmond Newcastle-upon-Tyne NE2 4RH
Tel: 0191 281 1769
Fax: 0191 281 5668
e-mail: enquiries@newcastleprepschool.org.uk

The School was founded in 1885 and is now a Charitable Trust with a Board of Governors.

Chairman of the Governors: Mrs C Wood

***Head*: Margaret Coates**, BEd Oxon

Age Range. 3–11.

Number of Pupils. 246 Day Pupils (170 boys, 76 girls).

Fees per term (2008-2009). Reception & Year 1: £2,480, Years 2 & 3: £2,641, Years 4–6: £2,802.

The School is situated in a residential part of Newcastle with easy access from all round the area.

Newcastle Preparatory School is a fully co-educational day school for children aged 3 to 11 years. It is a warm, caring environment in which all pupils are encouraged to reach their full potential.

Children may join 'First Steps' at NPS from the age of 3 years. 'First Steps' is an exciting and colourful nursery with excellent resources and well qualified staff who look after the needs of each individual.

At age 4, children make the easy step into School where they experience many 'steps to success'.

The curriculum offered throughout school is broad and balanced so that children enjoy learning in a variety of ways. French is taught from the age of 4 with music and PE being taught by specialist teachers. As children progress through School they become independent learners, following a varied timetable and class sizes are small to provide individual attention.

Music is an important part of life at NPS. There is a choir and a lively orchestra and jazz band.

Sporting achievements too are very good. There is a new purpose-built Sports Hall and a wide range of sport is offered with extra curricular activities including rugby, football, cricket, hockey, netball, athletics, tennis and swimming.

Also there are many clubs and societies to enrich the curriculum, eg Drama, Dance, Patchwork and Quilting, Philosophy, Art, ICT, Design, Food Technology and there is an effective School Council.

The variety of opportunities ensures that the children leave NPS well equipped for an easy transition into senior schools. The academic results are very good and the children receive an all-round education, so that they are confident, eager learners.

Charitable status. Newcastle Preparatory School is a Registered Charity, number 528152. It exists to provide education for boys and girls.

Newcastle School for Boys

Junior School:
30 West Avenue Gosforth Newcastle-upon-Tyne NE3 4ES
Tel: 0191 285 1619
Fax: 0191 213 1105
e-mail: office@newcastleschool.co.uk

Senior School:
34 The Grove Gosforth Newcastle-upon-Tyne NE3 1NH
Tel: 0191 255 9300
e-mail: groveoffice@newcastleschool.co.uk
website: www.newcastleschool.co.uk

Chairman of Governors: P S Marshall

***Headmaster*: C J Hutchinson**, BMet

Deputy Head: D J Tickner, BA
Head of Junior School: Mrs L M Donowho, CertEd

Age Range. 3–15 (rising to 18 by 2010).
Number of Boys. 400.
Fees per term (2007-2008). £2,445 (Nursery); £2,625 (Reception to Year 6), £2,795 (Year 7 and above).

Located on three closely-linked sites in Gosforth, Newcastle School for Boys is the only independent school providing continuous education for boys, from 3–18, in the North East.

The school was formed in 2005 from the merger of two of the city's leading preparatory schools and, by extending the upper age range, now offers the opportunity to take a full range of GCSEs and A Levels. Small class sizes and a focus on the specific learning needs of boys, allows each one to develop to their full potential and achieve the highest academic standards. The School provides outstanding pastoral care in an environment where individuality is celebrated, independence is cherished and imagination is nurtured.

The boys are offered an exciting range of curriculum enrichment activities in sport, performing and expressive arts, outdoor activities and service to the community.

There is an ongoing development plan that will ensure the refurbishment of existing facilities and the provision of state-of-the-art new buildings which reflect the aims and ethos of the new school.

Junior School. The well-established Nursery and Infant Department lays the foundations for everything which is to follow.

A happy and safe environment is provided, where self-esteem and self-confidence are paramount. Throughout the Foundation Stage and Key Stage 1 the curriculum is a blend of the traditional and the innovative, and is designed to balance the need for adventure and fun, while maintaining progress in numeracy and literacy. Boys are introduced to sports through games and play and to the wonders of art, dance, drama and music.

In the Junior Department (Years 3–5) the learning environment is tailored to the needs of the younger boys, taking into account their energy and enthusiasm for challenge and discovery. The boys are provided with opportunities to develop their individual academic talents and to pursue their creative goals, in art, music and drama. Excellence is also pursued in the sporting arena where boys have opportunities including soccer, rugby, cricket, golf and fencing.

Senior School. The Senior School is separately located in Gosforth and faces a particularly exciting phase of development and expansion. Our first GCSE cohort started in September 2007 and the first Sixth Formers will begin courses in 2009. There are excellent facilities with major investment in science and ICT and an ongoing plan has seen the creation of a new school hall and new teaching rooms. The GCSE curriculum is full and demanding offering a broad range of courses. Class sizes are small and boys receive plenty of individual attention so that they can grow in confidence and in intellectual independence, maintaining their curiosity and nurturing their imagination. Exchanges and trips abroad are encouraged as part of the learning cycle.

There are many opportunities for sport, music and the performing arts, both within the curriculum and in the wide range of after school clubs and classes. These include the Duke of Edinburgh's Award.

Scholarships. Scholarships are offered in January for boys entering Year 7 and Year 9 and are worth up to 50% of fees.

Charitable status. Newcastle School for Boys is a Registered Charity, number 503975.

Newland House School

Waldegrave Park Twickenham TW1 4TQ
Tel: 020 8892 7479
Fax: 020 8744 0399
e-mail: school@newlandhouse.co.uk
website: www.newlandhouse.co.uk

The School, founded in 1897, is a charitable Educational Trust with a Board of Governors.

Chairman of Governors: Sir Gordon Langley, QC

***Headmaster*: D J Ott**, BSc, UED (Rhodes)

Deputy Headmaster: D S Arnold, BA

Age Range. 4–13.
Number of Pupils. 274 Boys, 149 Girls.
Fees per term (2008-2009). Pre-Prep £2,820, Prep £3,165 (Lunches included).

Children are prepared for the Common Entrance and Scholarship examinations to Independent Schools. The school's main intakes are at the ages of 4 and 7. However, places do become available in other age groups throughout the school year.

The staff consists of 33 full-time teachers, 1 part-time teacher as well as 10 classroom assistants, mostly in the Pre-Preparatory department. In addition there are 12 visiting music staff who teach a variety of instruments. The School has 5 choirs, a concert band, a wind ensemble, a brass ensemble and a jazz band.

The main games are Rugby, Soccer, Cricket, Netball and Rounders. All children from the age of 7 have the opportunity to swim throughout the year.

The Main School has, in addition to 17 light and airy classrooms, a large gymnasium/assembly hall, dining room, separate senior and junior libraries and two well-equipped science laboratories. There is an Art and Design Technology block as well as a purpose-built Music block. The school has a substantial computer network, including a state-of-the-art computer suite and a control technology laboratory.

A separate Pre-Preparatory department, for children up to the age of 7, is also situated in Waldegrave Park.

A wide variety of extra-curricular activities is available.

Charitable status. The Newland House School Trust Limited is a Registered Charity, number 312670. It exists for the purpose of providing a good academic education in a friendly atmosphere.

Newton Prep

149 Battersea Park Road London SW8 4BX
Tel: 020 7720 4091
Fax: 020 7498 9052
e-mail: admin@newtonprep.co.uk
website: www.newtonprep.co.uk

Chairman of Council: Dr Farouk Walji

***Headmaster*: Mr N M Allen**, BA

Administration & Finance Manager: Mr P Farrelly

Age Range. 3–13.
Number of Pupils. 540: 278 Boys, 262 Girls.
Fees per term (2008-2009). £2,070–£4,180
Average size of class: <20.
Teacher/pupil ratio: 1:10
Religious denomination: Non-denominational.

Newton Prep is a vibrant school which offers a challenging education for inquisitive children who are eager to engage fully with the world in which they are growing up. The school aims to:

- inspire children to be adventurous and committed in their learning;
- provide balance and breadth in all aspects of a child's education: intellectual, aesthetic, physical, moral and spiritual;
- encourage initiative, individuality, independence, creativity and enquiry;
- promote responsible behaviour and respect for others in a happy, safe and caring environment.

Entry requirements: Children joining the school in the Nursery are assessed in groups; children joining Reception are assessed individually. Older children spend up to three days in school, joining regular classes as well as undertaking tests.

Examinations offered: Entrance examinations to senior schools, Common Entrance and scholarships at 11, 12 and 13.

The school has expanded above and around the original Victorian building. The modern extension comprises a further sixteen classrooms, a multispace area, two gyms, a dining room, spacious art studios and an auditorium. The premises are bright and spacious. The school has an all-weather pitch and tennis courts as well as a school garden, all within the 1½ acres that adjoin the school. Newton Prep has fully-equipped science and ICT suites and a computerised library of over 15,000 books. The extra-curricular activities available include: judo, fencing, yoga, ballet, modern dance, Mandarin Chinese, and speech and drama.

Norland Place School

162/166 Holland Park Avenue London W11 4UH
Tel: 020 7603 9103
Fax: 020 7603 0648
e-mail: office@norlandplace.com
website: www.norlandplace.com

***Headmaster*: Mr P Mattar**

Age Range. Girls 4–11, Boys 4–8.

Number of Children. 240.

Fees per term (2007-2008). £3,004–£3,792.

A Preparatory school founded in 1876 and still standing on the original site in Holland Park Avenue. Children are prepared for competitive London day schools and top rate boarding schools. The curriculum is well balanced with an emphasis on English, Mathematics and Science. Music, Art and Games are strong. The school contains a Library in addition to specialist Music, IT, Science and Art Rooms.

Early registration is essential.

Norman Court Preparatory School

Norman Court West Tytherley Salisbury SP5 1NH
Tel: 01980 862345
Fax: 01980 862082
e-mail: office@normancourt.co.uk
website: www.normancourt.co.uk

Chairman of Governors: Sir David Plastow

***Headmaster*: P G Savage**, BA Hons

Deputy Headmaster: R H Williams, BEd
Deputy Headmistress: Mrs J Kirkpatrick, MA

Age Range. 3–13.

Number of Children. Main School: 146: 60 Boarders (full and weekly, plus flexi), 86 Day. Pre-Preparatory Dept: 60.

Fees per term (2008-2009). Boarders and Weekly Boarders £6,160; Day Children £4,570; Pre-Preparatory £2,125.

Norman Court Preparatory School is a well established and flourishing co-educational boarding and day school located in idyllic surroundings between Salisbury, Andover and Winchester. The caring, friendly and approachable staff work closely together to inspire and motivate. The school enjoys superb facilities and the beautiful grounds lend themselves well to outdoor and adventurous pursuits.

The School's primary aim is to give children the opportunity to achieve their full academic and personal potential.

Norman Court is currently celebrating a very successful scholarship and public examinations season with Academic, Sports, Music, Art and All-Round Scholarship awards achieved to a variety of leading senior schools, together with successful candidates for local grammar schools.

The school can boast the latest information, communications and technology equipment, wonderful arts and music facilities, and unrivalled sports provision.

The boarding provision at Norman Court is excellent with a particular focus on stimulating weekend activities, good recreational facilities, and a home-from-home atmosphere. In a recent CSCI Inspection, the Inspectors confirmed that our children are clearly very happy to be boarding. Flexi boarding is very popular with many day children boarding regularly for one, two or even three nights each week.

The Pre-Preparatory Department has always been an extremely popular and flourishing establishment based in its own woodland setting, whilst benefiting from close proximity to the main building facilities. It is well equipped, spacious and an attractive environment in which to learn and play. Full use of the beautiful grounds is made and the school curriculum includes the Forest School programme.

To discover more about the choice we offer please contact the Registrar on registry@normancourt.co.uk or telephone on 01980 862345 today for the Norman Court prospectus. You can also find us at www.normancourt.co.uk, so do visit us and see us at work and play.

Charitable status. Norman Court School is a Registered Charity, number 307426. It exists to provide education for children.

Northbourne Park

Betteshanger Deal Kent CT14 0NW
Tel: 01304 611215 or 611218
Fax: 01304 619020
e-mail: office@northbourne.kent.sch.uk
website: www.northbournepark.com

Chairman of Governors: Dr R H B Sturt

***Headmaster*: Edward Balfour**, BA Hons, PGCE

Age Range. 3–13 Co-educational.

Number of Pupils. 200 of whom approximately half are girls. There are approximately 50 boarders.

Fees per term (2008-2009). Boarders: £4,970–£5,670 (weekly), £5,316–£6,666 (full). Day Pupils: £2,350–£2,770 (Pre-Prep) £3,470–£4,170 (Years 3–8). Fees include customary extras and many extra-curricular activities.

Northbourne Park is a thriving, well established school committed to developing every child's full potential. Our unique environment ensures that children emerge confident, skilled and at ease with themselves and others.

Our development programme, supported by our 25th Anniversary Appeal, has seen the opening of a purpose-built girls' boarding house and refurbishment of the Sports Hall, Music School and Science Laboratory.

Set in over 100 acres of beautiful parkland and woods, the school has easy motorway access to London, and to France/Belgium via Eurotunnel or ferry. The school provides a fortnightly bus service to central London and Eurostar service to Paris and Brussels, and school mini-buses serve the pupils locally.

Pupils achieve high academic standards, taught in small classes by an experienced and professional team. We offer a high quality education, which equips children for entry to senior school via Common Entrance or Scholarship, or to grammar school via the Kent Test.

The school has a long musical tradition and a recent ISC Inspection reported that 'pupils achieve high standards in music'. Children are encouraged to appreciate music in various ways, either through learning an instrument or joining the choir or orchestra, and gain great confidence by performing in various events throughout the year.

French is introduced from the age of 3, and we have a unique Anglo/French system with two classes of French children in the senior school, where Spanish is also taught.

A long established and well-reputed Learning Support Department, offers a wide range of SEN support including programmes for Dyslexia and social communication difficulties for children in the average plus range of abilities.

Sport and a wide range of extra-curricular activities play an important part of school life. Excellent pastoral care and a unique leadership programme encourage self-confidence and leadership skills. Boarders enjoy a home from home atmosphere, looked after by a caring and professional team. A very popular flexi-boarding service is also provided.

Some scholarships can be awarded for academic, music or sporting excellence. Sibling, HM Forces and Clergy discounts are available. There is some Bursarial support available in cases of need.

Charitable status. Northbourne Park is a Registered Charity, number 280048. It exists to provide education for children.

Northcote Lodge

26 Bolingbroke Grove London SW11 6EL
Tel: 020 8682 8888
Fax: 020 8682 8879
e-mail: northcote@northwoodschools.com
website: www.northcotelodge.co.uk

Day Preparatory School for Boys.

Principals: Mr & Mrs Malcolm Colquhoun

***Headmaster*: Mr J Hansford**

Age Range. 8–13.
Number of Pupils. 180 Boys.
Fees per term (2007-2008). £4,245.

Northcote Lodge was founded in 1993 and occupies a large mid-Victorian building overlooking Wandsworth Common, with its own grounds of over one acre.

The school is run along similar lines to a country prep school with a longer day at the end of which all 'homework' is done as prep at school. There is a broad and balanced curriculum leading to Common Entrance or scholarship to all major independent senior schools, usually boarding. Games are played, in one form or another, each day. Karate is on the curriculum and the school has a significant record of success in this field. There are thriving music and arts departments, frequent dramatic productions, a strong Chapel Choir and numerous extra curricular activities ranging from cookery to golf, debating to pottery, and model-making to basketball. The school has a state of the art computing system which is networked throughout the school.

There is a fully qualified and enthusiastic staff all of whom are totally committed to the aims and values of the school. There is a full-time Matron who shares responsibility with the Deputy Head for the pastoral care. During the first two years the boys have a form teacher and thereafter they are assigned to a tutor with whom they will stay until they leave.

We believe that in a disciplined and happy environment, boys will succeed academically and do not need to feel under constant academic pressure. They know that they are at school to work but it is crucial that they look on their time at school as an enjoyable experience. They will grow up all too soon; they must be allowed to be boys, to enjoy childhood and to mature at their own pace.

High standards are expected of the boys in every area of life at school. Manners, courtesy, self-respect and consideration for others are key values. Once a week the boys attend a service at the local Church. There is considerable value to be gained from being a member of a small and caring community where every boy has the opportunity to shine. A great emphasis is placed on developing self-confidence which is the key to success at school.

Entry Requirements. Entry is in September following their eight birthday, although places for older boys can sometimes become available. Admission is by means of assessment and interview when the boy is 7. Siblings have automatic right of entry into school or to nearby Broomwood Hall (our associate school for boys aged 4–8 and girls aged 4–13). Places are also sometimes available at 9+, 10+ and 11+. Parents should contact the school if interested in such a place.

Northwood Prep

Moor Farm Sandy Lodge Road Rickmansworth Herts WD3 1LW
Tel: 01923 825648
Fax: 01923 835802
e-mail: office@northwoodprep.co.uk
website: www.northwoodprep.co.uk

Founded as a private school in 1910 by Mr Francis Terry, NP has a long history and proud traditions. It is still known within the locality as "Terry's" after its founder. In 1954 it became an educational charitable trust administered by a Board of Governors.

Chairman of Governors: Dr O Bangham, BSc, MSc, PhD

***Headmaster*: Dr Trevor Lee**, BEd Hons (Exon), MEd (Cantab), EdD (Hull)

Deputy Heads:
Mr Ian Rice, CertEd (Carnegie), NPQH
Mr Andrew Crook, BA (Lancaster), PGCE (King's College, London)

Age Range. 3–13.
Number of Pupils. 300 Day Boys.
Fees per term (2007-2008). £928 (Nursery), £3,174 (Reception, Years 1 and 2), £3,344 (Years 3–8).

The School is located amidst 14 acres on a former farm in an ideal park and woodland setting. The Grade II listed buildings have been skilfully converted to provide a complete and unique range of classrooms and ancillary facilities. The mediaeval Manor of the More, once owned by King Henry VIII and used as a palace by Cardinal Wolsey, was originally located within the grounds and provides some interesting and historical associations.

The School is divided into four sections: an off-site Nursery School for children rising 3, the Junior School (Reception to

Year 2), Key Stage 2 (Years 3–6) and Key Stage 3 (Years 7 and 8). These all have their own teaching areas while making use of the same dining, games, extra-curricular and recreational facilities.

Boys are admitted to the school after an assessment by Heads of Section. The main entry is into the Reception form to which boys are admitted in the September of the academic year of their fifth birthday. Older boys may also be accepted further up the School if a chance vacancy occurs. Boys are expected to remain until the age of thirteen, being prepared for entry at that stage to independent senior schools by way of Common Entrance. The School has also built up a fine record of Scholarship results over the years.

Work of a traditionally high standard is expected of all boys. The curriculum is interpreted as richly as possible and includes Technology, Music, Art, Drama, Physical Education and Games. The School has modern teaching facilities and the fully qualified and experienced staff is generously resourced. The Sir Christopher Harding Building for Science and Technology, comprising two state-of-the-art laboratories, an ICT Suite and technology workshop was opened in November 2000. A Learning Resource Centre was created in September 2001. A new centre for the Performing Arts was commissioned by Mr Kevin Spacey in April 2008. A new music school was opened in May 2008. A new nursery school was opened in the grounds of Merchant Taylors' School in April 2008.

Swift access to London by train from nearby Moor Park Station means that staff often arrange for boys to visit places of historical and cultural interest and attend concerts and lectures.

While the Christian tradition on which the life of the School is based is that of the Church of England, boys from all Christian denominations and other faiths are welcomed.

There is an extensive programme of extra-curricular activities in which all boys are encouraged to take part. A key feature of the School's ethos is a strong tradition of caring, both for those within the community of the school, and those whom the boys can help through regular charitable activities.

Rugby Football, Association Football and Cricket are the principal team games. Tennis, Athletics, Judo and other sports are also coached. A fully equipped Sports Hall was opened in November 1996. The School has the benefit of a floodlit astroturf facility.

The School has a flourishing Parents' Association which arranges social and fund-raising activities, and an active association for former pupils, The Old Terryers.

Charitable status. Northwood Preparatory School Trust (Terry's) Limited is a Registered Charity, number 312647. The aims of the charity are the education and development of boys aged 3–13.

Norwich School, The Lower School

Bishopgate Norwich NR1 4AA
Tel: 01603 305791
Fax: 01603 629679
e-mail: L.School@norwich-school.org.uk
website: www.norwich-school.org.uk

Chairman of Governors: G H C Copeman, CBE, DL

***Master of the Lower School*: J K Ingham**, BA

Second Master: R A Love, BSc

Director of Studies: R E Hambleton, BSc, MA

Age Range. 7–11.

Number of Pupils. 162.

Fees per term (2008-2009). £3,294.

The Lower School is the Junior Day School for Norwich School (*see entry in HMC section*). It is delightfully located in the Cathedral Close, between the East End of the Cathedral and the River Wensum. The Cathedral Choristers are educated at Norwich School, which is a member of the Choir Schools' Association.

The Lower School provides depth and breadth of education through a challenging curriculum. It seeks to recognise, nurture and develop each pupil's potential within an environment which encourages all-round emotional, physical, social and spiritual growth and to foster positive relations between pupils, teachers and parents. The dedicated teaching staff is committed to providing a stimulating programme of active learning which has rigour and discipline but avoids unnecessary pressure.

With two forms in each of its four year groups, the Lower School is the ideal size for ensuring a lively environment within a warm family atmosphere. The main building has bright, spacious areas for activities and lessons. As well as the library, there are specialised facilities for science, art, technology and ICT. There is an excellent play area in addition to the adjacent, extensive playing fields.

A wide range of extra-curricular activities and school trips is offered. Music is a strong feature of school life. Many pupils choose to learn a musical instrument and participate in the various instrumental music groups. Rugby, netball, hockey, cricket, rounders and tennis are taught and the games programme is designed to encourage pupils of all abilities to enjoy games and physical activity.

The School aims to attract pupils who will thrive in a challenging academic environment and is therefore selective. Prospective pupils are assessed in English, mathematics and non-verbal reasoning. There is a two-form entry at 7+ and a small number of places is available each year at 8+, 9+ and 10+. The prospectus and application forms are available from the Admissions Registrar, Tel: 01603 728442.

The vast majority of pupils from the Lower School progress to the Senior School at age eleven, and the curriculum is designed to prepare the pupils effectively for the next stage of their Norwich School education.

Charitable status. Norwich School is a Registered Charity, number 311280.

Notre Dame Preparatory School

Burwood House Cobham Surrey KT11 1HA
Tel: 01932 869991
Fax: 01932 589480
e-mail: headmaster@notredame.co.uk
website: www.notredame.co.uk

Chairman: Mr Glen Travers

***Headmaster*: Mr D S Plummer**, BEd Hons, DipHE, FRSA

Age Range. Girls 2½–11, Boys 2½–5.

Number of Pupils. 330 Girls, 10 boys.

Fees per term (2008-2009). Nursery £1,090; Reception £2,650, Prep 1 & 2 £2,860, Prep 3–6 £3,160.

Notre Dame Preparatory School has existed on its present site for 70 years, but was founded by the Sisters of The Company of Mary, Our Lady, who have a four hundred year old tradition of excellence in education. The school has a strong pastoral care policy and welcomes children of all denominations.

The aim at Notre Dame Preparatory School is to identify individual potential. A rich and rewarding curriculum has been planned, encouraging each child to make the most of special talents.

Children can join the Nursery at 2½ years. A broad and exciting curriculum exists for each Key Stage focussing on numeracy and literacy skills.

Girls progress through the Preparatory School and are prepared for entrance to the Senior School at 11. (*See Notre Dame Senior School entry in GSA section.*)

The School has an enviable local reputation, both for high academic standards and for the provision of a wide range of social, cultural and sporting amenities, including:

- an outstanding ISI Inspection Report in 2007.
- challenging scientific and technological programmes of study, with impressive laboratories.
- modern computer system, with multiple internet access.
- heated indoor swimming pool.
- large Sports Hall, featuring gymnasium and indoor netball, soccer, badminton and tennis courts.
- new Learning Resource Centre with library and video conferencing.
- extensive grounds set in beautiful parkland.
- golf, lacrosse, cross country, rounders, soccer, outdoor pursuits.
- range of choirs, ensembles and orchestra ensure that music is enjoyed throughout the school. Choir tours to Belgium, Hungary, Bordeaux and Venice.

Demand for places has ensured school coaches serve a wide local area.

Prospectus. A fully illustrated prospectus detailing the school's distinctive nature is available on request.

Charitable status. Notre Dame School Cobham is a Registered Charity, number 1081875. It exists to provide education for girls.

Notting Hill Preparatory School

95 Lancaster Road London W11 1QQ
Tel: 020 7221 0727
Fax: 020 7221 0332
e-mail: admin@nottinghillprep.com
website: www.nottinghillprep.com

Chair of Governors: John Morton Morris

***Headmistress*: Mrs Jane Cameron**, BEd Hons

Age Range. 5–13 Co-educational.
Number of Pupils. 194.
Fees per term (2007-2008). £3,900.

Founded in 2003, NHP is a co-ed Prep School in the heart of Notting Hill, West London. It was created through the cooperation of parents and teachers and this partnership with parents is a cornerstone of the philosophy of the school.

Our aim is to 'educate' children in the true sense of the word so that they develop an excitement and passion for learning. A broad-based curriculum ensures that academic subjects are balanced with ample time being dedicated to sport and subjects such as art, music and drama where the emphasis is on enjoyment and self-expression. Subjects are taught by specialist teachers in the Upper School, as are French, music, drama and PE from Reception. Latin is introduced in Year 5. Children are fully prepared for the competitive entrance examinations to London day schools and country boarding schools at 11+ and 13+.

Music and performance are particular features at the school, with creative staff producing original material for plays and concerts. There are two choirs and an orchestra and over two-thirds of the pupils learn a musical instrument.

A wide and varied sports programme using local facilities as well as our own on site gym ensures that children develop and perfect skills in the major sports (football, netball, hockey, rugby, cricket, athletics and swimming). Opportunities for displaying these skills are provided by frequent fixtures arranged with local schools.

Regular school trips enhance all aspects of the curriculum. Full use is made of the many and varied opportunities London offers to extend children's knowledge of their environment, their culture and their history.

NHP is noted for its open, friendly and happy atmosphere and its strong sense of being part of a wider community. Courtesy, kindness and appreciation of a diversity of talents, abilities and needs are defining values of the school's ethos.

Additional premises opposite have recently been acquired to provide accommodation for Years 4–8 as well as extra facilities, such as an enlarged science laboratory and library.

The school is heavily oversubscribed and places are offered following a ballot. The School Secretary tries to keep waiting lists within reasonable limits.

Nottingham High Junior School

Waverley Mount Nottingham NG7 4ED
Tel: 0115 845 2214
Fax: 0115 845 2298
e-mail: juniorinfo@nottinghamhigh.co.uk
website: www.nottinghamhigh.co.uk

Chairman of Governors: N V Tamplin, FCA

***Headmaster*: A R Earnshaw**, BA, QTS Lancaster

Age Range. 7–11.
Number of Boys. 149 Day Boys.
Fees per term (2008-2009). £2,674.

The Junior School is housed in purpose built premises, having its own Classrooms, ICT Suite, Library, Art Room, Science Laboratory and Assembly Hall.

Entrance Examinations are held in January. There are two parallel forms in each year group.

The Junior School has an experienced and well qualified staff. The curriculum is designed for those who expect to complete their education at Nottingham High School. The subjects taught are Religious Education, English, Mathematics, History, Geography, Science, French and PSHE. Full provision is made for Music, Art, Design Technology, Information Communication Technology, Swimming, Physical Education and Games.

The Junior School has its own Orchestra and about 100 boys receive instrumental tuition. All Year 3 boys play a stringed instrument. A Concert and School Plays are performed annually. A wide range of supervised activities and hobbies takes place during every lunch time with great emphasis placed on chess.

School games are Association Football and Rugby with some Hockey and Athletics in the winter, Cricket and Tennis in the summer.

A new infant section, taking up to 50 boys in Reception, Year 1 and Year 2, will open in September 2008.

Charitable status. The Foundation of the Nottingham High School is a Registered Charity, number 528236. It exists to provide education for boys between the ages of 7 and 18 years.

Oakwood Preparatory School

Chichester West Sussex PO18 9AN
Tel: 01243 575209
Fax: 01243 575433
e-mail: office@oakwoodschool.co.uk
website: www.oakwoodschool.co.uk

***Headmaster*: J Kittermaster**

Age Range. Co-educational $2^1/_2$ to 11.
Number of Pupils. 290 Day boys and girls.
Fees per term (2007-2008). Pre-Prep £995–£2,340. Upper School £2,950–£3,210.

Oakwood was founded in 1912 and has grown into a thriving co-educational preparatory school.

Set in 160 acres of glorious park and woodland between the South Downs and the coast, Oakwood's home is a large Georgian country house.

The children learn in a wonderfully safe and spacious environment in the heart of beautiful Sussex countryside only three miles from Chichester. The school prides itself on its family atmosphere and the happiness of its children.

Oakwood is well-equipped with spacious classrooms, Science and Design Technology Studio, Art Room, Library, Music and Theatre Complex and ICT Centre. There is a Gymnasium and 3 floodlit tennis courts. The playing fields extend over nine acres, there is an indoor heated swimming pool and two adventure playgrounds.

The Pre-Prep, though fully integrated into the Oakwood community, enjoys its own spacious site with a safe and enclosed play area. The setting is particularly cosy and attractive, the classrooms having been sympathetically converted from a stable block.

There is a warm family atmosphere, as the school recognises the importance of children feeling happy and secure. Great emphasis is placed on building a solid foundation of social skills and a love of learning, thus enabling each child to settle confidently to school life.

There is a strong academic curriculum with small class sizes, ensuring that each child receives the closest possible attention. In Upper School, children are set for English and Mathematics. The curriculum is broad with each child's timetable including Design Technology, Science, Humanities, French, ICT, PE, Drama and Music.

Form tutoring is of prime importance, the form teacher overseeing the development of each child – academically, socially and emotionally. Contact with parents is frequent and encouraged.

Opportunities to represent the school in sports teams, plays, choirs and instrument groups are all part of the "Oakwood Experience".

Music is very much a part of Oakwood life. The children enjoy music lessons each week and there is every opportunity to learn an instrument. The school has three choirs, recorder ensembles, guitar groups, a mini orchestra and a wind band. Each term there is an Evening of Music, and there are major concerts every year for both Upper School and Pre-Prep. The summer term ends with a major musical. In addition, children are encouraged to perform in Assembly.

The Physical Education and Sports programme has an exciting mix to offer every child. Games are played three times each week and are coached by members of staff with an expertise and enthusiasm for their sport or by outside coaches.

In winter the boys enjoy a taste of all the major sports – Soccer, Rugby and Hockey, while the girls play Netball and Hockey. Karate, Fencing, Yoga, Dance and Ballet are also on offer to the boys and girls. In summer the boys play Cricket and the girls play Rounders, but the school also offers Swimming, Athletics and Tennis. An extensive programme of inter-school fixtures is arranged each term for A and B teams.

Early arrivals care, after school clubs and activities all ensure that busy parents can benefit from a flexible school day.

There is an excellent record of examination success to a variety of senior schools.

Oakwood School

59 Godstone Road Purley Surrey CR8 2AN
Tel: 020 8668 8080
Fax: 020 8668 2895
e-mail: enquiries@oakwoodschool.org.uk
website: www.oakwoodschool.org.uk

Chairman of Governors: Dr Tony Newman-Sanders

***Headmaster*: Mr Ciro Candia**, BA Hons, PGCE

Age Range. $2^1/_2$–11 Co-educational.
Number of Pupils. 145.
Fees per term (2007-2008). £567–£2,045.
Charitable status. PACT Educational Trust Limited is a Registered Charity, number 1053810.

Old Buckenham Hall School

Brettenham Park Ipswich Suffolk IP7 7PH
Tel: 01449 740252
Fax: 01449 740955
e-mail: office@obh.co.uk
website: www.obh.co.uk

Chairman of Governors: M W Nicholls

***Headmaster*: M A Ives**, BEd Hons

Deputy Headmaster: C C Schanschieff, BSc(Ed) Hons

Age Range. 3–13.
Number of Pupils. 131 Boarders; 79 Day Pupils; 33 Pre-Prep; 19 Nursery.
Fees per term (2008-2009). Full and Weekly Boarders £6,275; Day £5,035; Year 3 (day) £4,115; Pre-Prep £2,380.

The School, founded in Lowestoft as South Lodge in 1862, moved in 1937 to Old Buckenham, Norfolk and in 1956 to Brettenham Park, Suffolk, 4 miles from Lavenham and 18 from Ipswich. It became an Educational Trust in 1967.

The pupils go on to a wide range of, mostly boarding, Senior Independent Schools via Common Entrance and Scholarship Examinations.

The Staff/Pupil ratio is approximately 1:9, giving an average class-size of 13. All members of Staff, including part-time Staff, contribute to the provision of a wide range of extra-curricular activities in which every child has a chance to participate. The major sports are Rugby, Hockey, Soccer, Netball, Cricket and Rounders, but all pupils also take part in Athletics and Swimming. In addition there are opportunities for Tennis (6 courts), Golf (9-hole course), Squash (2 courts), Table Tennis, Woodwork, Metalwork, Pets, Shooting, Photography, Dance and Archery. Art, Music and Drama particularly flourish.

The Main Building, an 18th Century mansion, stands in its own grounds of 75 acres of which some 25 are playing fields and 6 are woodland. In the past few years many building alterations and additions have been completed. In 1997 astroturf tennis courts were created and a purpose-built Pre-Prep Department opened in September 1998. A new girls' boarding house, new art studio and computer room opened in September 2001; four new classrooms opened in October 2003: Phase One of the School's Five Year Development Plan. A new multi-purpose hall was completed in October 2005 and a new science and music building is planned for completion by 2009.

A School Prospectus can be obtained on application to the Registrar.

Charitable status. Old Buckenham Hall (Brettenham) Educational Trust Limited is a Registered Charity, number 310490. It exists to provide education for boarding and day pupils.

The Old Hall School

Stanley Road Wellington Telford Shropshire TF1 3LB
Tel: 01952 223117
Fax: 01952 222674
e-mail: enq@oldhall.co.uk
website: www.oldhall.co.uk

Chairman of the Governors: D B Sankey, Esq, MA

***Headmaster*: M C Stott**

Age Range. 4–11.

Number of Pupils. 257: 143 boys, 114 girls.

Fees per term (2008-2009). Kindergarten–Junior 2 (age 4–7) £2,020; Years 3–6 (age 7–11) £3,134.

Founded in 1845, The Old Hall School is a co-educational day school (4–11 years), which is housed in spectacular new premises, located alongside Wrekin College. The school offers first-class facilities; a double sports hall, 25-metre indoor swimming pool, Astroturf and grass pitches offer an excellent sports and games environment, whilst specialist music and drama areas help to promote high standards in the performing arts. A suite of specialist learning support rooms reflects the School's commitment to the needs of the individual. First-class facilities have also been created for pre-school care and the education of children from the age of three months.

The broad curriculum is enriched by a dedicated team of professionals who encourage pupils to fulfil their potential in a happy and secure environment.

Through the academic curriculum and caring pastoral system, the school aims to lay solid foundations in the development of well-motivated, confident and happy individuals who are always willing to give of their best on the road to high achievement.

Charitable status. Wrekin Old Hall Trust Limited is a Registered Charity, number 528417.

The Old Rectory School

Brettenham Ipswich Suffolk IP7 7QR
Tel: 01449 736404
Fax: 01449 737881
e-mail: oldrectoryschool@aol.com
website: www.oldrectoryschool.com

Founded in 1981.

The Old Rectory School is a specialist co-educational boarding and day school for dyslexic and dyspraxic pupils.

***Headmistress*: Ms C E Murdoch-Watson**, MA, BSc(Ed), FRSA

Age Range. 7–13.

Number of Pupils. 56: 43 boys, 12 girls, 41 boarders, 5 flexi-boarders, 9 day pupils.

Fees per term (2007-2008). Boarding £7,330; Day £5,325.

The School is situated in an old Rectory, set in 7 acres of grounds and sports fields. Pupils remain with us for one or two years, receiving an intensive programme of support, which allows them to return to mainstream education at the end of this term.

- Small group teaching, staff ratio of 1:6
- All teachers have Diplomas in Specific Learning Difficulties
- Each child has a daily tutorial period with their English teacher
- Support for organisational difficulties
- Emphasis on raising self-esteem and confidence of pupils
- Secure, comfortable family environment with excellent boarding facilities
- Wide range of activities including School Fire Brigade
- Broad and balanced Curriculum with whole school specialist support
- Full National Curriculum including modern foreign language as well as Touch Typing
- Strong Art, Music and Drama departments
- Country location with ample space for sport

The children have access to a wide range of extra-curricular activities including Shooting, Sailing, Riding and Karate. These activities enable the pupils to develop their self-confidence and to learn to work together as a team as well as thinking for themselves. Great importance is placed on careful consideration being given to the future welfare of the children when the time comes for them to move on and the Head works closely with parents in order that these children may continue to make progress and develop their full potential.

The Old Vicarage School

48 Richmond Hill Richmond Surrey TW10 6QX
Tel: 020 8940 0922
Fax: 020 8948 6834
e-mail: j.harrison@oldvicarage-richmond.co.uk
website: www.oldvicarage-richmond.co.uk

Chairman of Governors: Mr P Hearson

***Headmistress*: Mrs J Harrison**, DipCE, DipEd

Age Range. 4–11.

Number of Pupils. 170 girls.

Fees per term (2008-2009). £2,500–£2,775.

The School was established in 1881 and became a Charitable Educational Trust in 1973. The School is situated between the town and Richmond Park and near to the Terrace Gardens. It is a fine old building built at the beginning of the 18th Century and later refaced in the Walpole Gothic style.

Class sizes are usually 14 and there is a pupil/teacher ratio of 14:1. Many lessons are taught by specialist staff in subject rooms designed specifically for the purpose.

Girls are prepared for Common Entrance Examinations at 11+ and for entry to the London Day Schools.

Charitable status. The Old Vicarage School is a Registered Charity, number 312671.

The Oratory Preparatory School

Goring Heath Reading Berks RG8 7SF
Tel: 0118 9844511
Fax: 0118 9844806
e-mail: office@oratoryprep.co.uk
registrar@oratoryprep.co.uk
website: www.oratoryprep.org.uk

Chairman of the Board of Governors: M H R Hasslacher

***Headmaster*: Dr R J Hillier**, MA, PhD, PGCE

Age Range. 3–13.

Number of Pupils. 400 (250 boys and 150 girls), including 50 full-time, weekly or flexi-boarders and 115 in the Pre-Prep department.

Fees per term (2008-2009). Boarders: £4,645 (weekly), £5,045 (full); Day £3,660; Pre-Prep: £2,100 (all day), £1,050 (am).

A Roman Catholic preparatory school, founded by John Henry Cardinal Newman, which prepares boys for The Oratory School and boys and girls for other independent senior schools. The OPS welcomes children of all denominations and faiths and aims to identify and develop their individual talents and gifts in all aspects of their school lives.

The well-qualified and experienced staff of 30 full-time and 40 part-time and visiting teachers and teaching assistants form a strong and supportive team who deliver a broad curriculum characterised by an unusually wide range of subjects, activities and sports. A friendly and secure environment fosters the welfare of every child. Spiritual and pastoral needs are met by the chaplain, a nursing sister, a senior matron and two assistant matrons, and a large and dedicated team of boarding and day staff operating a comprehensive pastoral and academic tutorial system.

The school has an excellent record of achievement in recent years, with pupils gaining many academic, art, music, sports and all-rounder awards to The Oratory School and other major schools. Choral and instrumental music (orchestra, jazz band, three choirs and numerous instrumental ensembles), drama and art play a major part in school life. The school is also very proud of the broad base of participation and competitive success in rugby, rugby sevens (once national champions and three times runners-up, most recently in 2006), football, cricket, cross-country, hockey, netball and rounders as well as tennis, swimming, archery, squash, golf, badminton, basketball and table tennis. In addition there is an extensive range of activities to suit and stretch the talents and strengths of every child. The school also organises frequent educational, cultural and sporting tours, both within this country and overseas, to widen further pupils' horizons.

The school's facilities have been extensively developed, with a large theatre, sports hall, indoor swimming pool and trainer pool, all-weather tennis and hockey surfaces, as well as well-equipped science and art departments and a well-stocked library. The music school contains two large spaces for performance and class teaching and seven smaller practice rooms for individual tuition. ICT provision is considerable and forms an integral part of the educational experience offered. The thriving Pre-Prep department is housed in an attractive courtyard setting on the same site.

The school stands in its own 60-acre estate, high above the Thames and easily accessible by train and road (via the M4 from London and Heathrow airport).

Charitable status. The Oratory School Association is a Registered Charity, number 309112. It exists to provide general, physical, moral and religious education for boys and girls.

Orchard House School

16 Newton Grove London W4 1LB
Tel: 020 8742 8544
Fax: 020 8742 8522
e-mail: info@orchardhs.org.uk
website: www.orchardhs.org.uk

Chairman of Governors: Mr Anthony Rentoul

***Headmistress*: Mrs S A B Hobbs**, BA Hons (Exon), PGCE, AMBDA Mont Dip

Age Range. Girls 3–11, Boys 3–8.

Number of Pupils. 220: 140 Girls, 80 Boys.

Fees per term (2007-2008). Nursery (5 mornings) £1,830, Prep-Prep £3,610, Prep £3,780.

Orchard House School, with Bassett House and Prospect House, is part of the House Schools Group. It provides an excellent all-round education for boys from 3 to 8, and girls from 3 to 11, preparing them for the competitive entry examinations for the London day and country boarding schools whilst maintaining a happy, purposeful atmosphere. There is an emphasis on teaching traditional values tailored for children growing up in the 21st century. Uniform is worn and good manners are expected at all times. Children shake hands with the staff at the end of each day and are encouraged to take part, with the deputy head or headmistress, in describing the school to prospective parents and other visitors.

The main premises were designed by the well-known architect Norman Shaw and built around 1880; the building is Grade 2 listed. The school enjoys a corner site in Bedford Park and the classrooms have good natural lighting as well as a large playground/garden.

Children aged 3 or 4 are admitted on a first come, first served basis. Occasional places higher up are filled following assessment. The Montessori method is used to deliver the Early Years Foundation Stage curriculum; at KS1 and KS2 the curriculum is based on the National Curriculum and the demands of the future schools. Specialist teachers are employed for many subjects and support teachers provide one-one or small group tuition where necessary. Staff turnover is low.

Orchard House is proud of the excellent results the children achieve at their future schools which include many of the most academic schools in this country. The school is within easy reach of St Paul's Schools, Latymer Prep, Latymer Upper and Godolphin & Latymer and many pupils have taken up places at one of these schools.

The school boasts state-of-the-art ICT resources and attractive playgrounds/garden with an all-weather surface. The children make good use of additional local facilities to enhance their Sport and Drama lessons.

Orchard House participates in the Early Years Education grant. There are occasional academic scholarships for girls entering year 4.

Orley Farm School

South Hill Avenue Harrow on the Hill Middlesex HA1 3NU
Tel: 020 8869 7600
Fax: 020 8869 7601
e-mail: office@orleyfarm.harrow.sch.uk
website: www.orleyfarm.harrow.sch.uk

The school is a Charitable Trust administered by a Board of Governors.

Chairman of Governors: Mr C J Hayfield

***Headmaster*: Mr M Dunning**, BA, PGCE, FCollP

Age Range. 4–13 Co-educational.

Number of Pupils. 483 Day pupils, including 183 in Pre-Prep (age 4 to 6).

Fees per term (2008-2009). Upper School £3,800, Lower School £3,500 (inclusive of lunch); Pre-Prep £3,250.

Orley Farm School is in the fortunate position of being a London day school blessed with boarding school acreage and facilities. Founded in 1850, it has grown and developed since to become one of the leading and largest co-educational prep schools in Greater London. Entry is by assessment at 4 years old and boys and girls transfer successfully to their senior schools. The academic journey of the children begins in Reception and ends in Year 6 for our girls and Year 8 for our boys. At the key assessment stages of five, seven, eleven and thirteen the standards achieved are high in relation to their ability. They enter a range of impressive senior schools – including St Paul's, North London Collegiate, Harrow, Westminster, St Helen's, Notting Hill and Ealing, Godolphin and Latymer, Westminster, Merchant Taylors', Northwood College, John Lyon, Haberdashers' Aske's Boys and Girls. Scholarships are regularly gained by our senior pupils – 16 in 2005-06, 12 in 2006-07 and 15 in 2007-08.

These results are achieved through the hard work of our talented pupils and the teaching of our staff, who were recently described as "effective overall and in many cases outstanding". With optimum class sizes of 20 (14 in Years 7 and 8) and a range of modern classroom and other facilities, the children at are encouraged to make full use of all that is on offer at the School. Science laboratories and staffing permits specialist teaching from Year 4 onwards in this subject and in Years 7 and 8 the constituent subjects of Biology, Chemistry and Physics are taught separately by subject specialists. ICT provision has grown significantly in recent years and now all classrooms have appropriate interactive provision which is used in support of all areas of the curriculum. A separate and purpose built Music School enables the long tradition of musical excellence and involvement to continue. Over 200 individual music lessons take place each week and are supported by many musical groups and choirs. Our talented individual music teachers make full use of the music rooms and their combined efforts (pupils and teachers) bring us a regular feast of choral and instrumental music in our termly concerts and competitions.

Sport plays a very large part in our school life. We have over thirty six acres of land and full use is made of this in providing a venue for training and matches. The Autumn Term sees the girls playing netball and the boys football; the Spring Term brings out rugby for the boys and hockey for the girls; in the Summer Term the boys play cricket and the girls play rounder. In addition, tennis, cross-country, gymnastics, Fives and basketball also thrive through activities and matches. A Gym, Sports Hall and full-sized all-weather pitch enable our strong PE and Games Department to help our pupils develop their sporting talents.

This happy blend of curricular and extra-curricular comes together towards the end of the year in the great Orley Farm tradition of Expeditions Week. This is an occasion when all children from Year 4 and above leave the school for a variety of venues with their teachers and spend a week extending their curriculum and range of experiences. For most it is the highlight of their year.

An active Parents' Association ensures a strong bond between home and school and they organize an exciting series of events throughout the year fulfilling their goal of "fun, fund-raising and feedback".

Entry to this exciting place of learning is by assessment. For further details contact the Registrar, Mrs Julie Jago.

Charitable status. Orley Farm School is a Registered Charity, number 312637.

Orwell Park

Nacton Ipswich Suffolk IP10 0ER
Tel: 01473 659225
Fax: 01473 659822
e-mail: headmaster@orwellpark.co.uk
website: www.orwellpark.co.uk

Chairman of Governors: David Wake-Walker, ARCM, LLCJ

***Headmaster*: P M Forte**, MA Hons Oxon, PGCE

Age Range. 3–13.

Number of Pupils. Main School: 210: 120 Boarders (46 girls, 74 boys); 90 Day Pupils (28 girls, 62 boys). Pre-Prep (age 3–7): 78 (32 girls, 46 boys).

Fees per term (2008-2009). Prep School: Full and Weekly Boarders: £6,380 (Form II and above), £5,740 (Form I); Day Pupils: £4,975 (Form II and above); £4,480 (Form I). Pre-Prep: Day Pupils: £1,770 (Nursery); £1,965 (Reception); £2,365 (PP1); £3,030 (PP2).

Flexible Boarding (ie 1–3 nights a week) is also possible – £34 per night.

Pupils are prepared for all Independent Senior Schools via the Scholarship or Common Entrance Examinations (71 awards in the last 5 years). The school has a thriving Pre-Prep School with two teachers who have recently been recognised as Key Practitioners in Outdoor Education.

The ratio of pupils to full-time staff is 9:1. The timetable is especially designed to be very flexible, with separate setting in most subjects, and the curriculum, both in and out of the classroom, is unusually broad. Children are encouraged to enjoy their learning and good learning support is offered. Thinking Skills and other opportunities for academic enrichment are also offered, including a weekly Young Einsteins session to challenge the older children. There are a host of extra-curricular activities (just under 100) run by permanent or visiting staff.

Over 90%of the school learn a musical instrument and the school has a number of orchestral and ensemble groups. A large number of children have been selected to play in IAPS Orchestras and 14 children are members of the 70-strong National Children's Choir. Drama is strong and all children have opportunities to perform regularly in school productions. All children take part in annual Reading and Public Speaking Competitions.

The very large Georgian style building and 110 acres of grounds (sandy soil) on the banks of the River Orwell have the following special features: 21 recently refurbished themed dormitories, 22 bright classrooms with modern audio-visual equipment, beautiful Orangery used as an Assembly and Lecture Hall, Computer and Maths work rooms, large Design Centre including metal, wood and plastic workshop plus electronics, mechanics, home economics, radio and model-making areas, Music Technology Room, Music Room, Band Room and 40 Practice rooms, 3 Laboratories plus associated areas, Library and Resources Centre, Art Room including large pottery area and kiln, Observatory with 10' Refractor Telescope, Photographic Room, 17 Games pitches and one Astroturf pitch, large Sports Hall with permanent stage, Climbing Wall, Games Room, large heated Swimming Pool, 3 Squash Courts, 5 Hard Tennis Courts, Nine-hole Golf Course (approx 1,800 yds), Assault Course, and Tuck and Book Shops.

Good coaching is given and, where appropriate, matches are arranged in the following sports: Association and Rugby Football, Hockey, Cricket, Tennis, Athletics, Squash, Golf, Sailing, Swimming, Badminton, Table-Tennis and Cross-Country Running. Emphasis is also placed on individual physical activities and we offer a wide range including Gymnastics, Fencing, Ballet, Canoeing, Sailing, Modern Dance, Abseiling, Karate, Riding, Shooting with .177 Air Pistols and Clay Pigeon Shooting. The school owns its own canoes and dinghies.

The School aims to introduce the pupils to a broad and varied set of experiences and opportunities. It tries to see that every activity, whether academic, sporting, social or character building, is properly taught using the best possible facilities and that each is conducted in an atmosphere which is friendly but disciplined. Core values include courage, compassion, commitment, compromise and courteous. Children are encouraged to feel comfortable taking risks and to be confident without being arrogant.

Charitable status. Orwell Park School is a Registered Charity, number 310481. It exists to provide education for boys and girls.

Packwood Haugh

Ruyton XI Towns Shrewsbury Shropshire SY4 1HX
Tel: 01939 260217
Fax: 01939 262077
e-mail: enquiries@packwood-haugh.co.uk
website: www.packwood-haugh.co.uk

Chairman of Governors: Dr J J Dixey

***Headmaster*: N T Westlake**, LLB, PGCE

Deputy Head: O J Lee, MA, PGCE

Age Range. Co-educational 4–13.

Number of Children. 297 Boarding: 112 boys, 44 girls. Day: 59 boys, 49 girls. Pre-Prep 33.

Fees per term (2007-2008). Boarding £5,245, Day £3,177–£4,197, Pre-Prep (Acorns) £1,805. No compulsory extras.

Set in the heart of the Shropshire countryside, Packwood Haugh is a co-educational boarding (7–13) and day (4–13) school which aims to provide an excellent all-round education in a happy and caring environment. Children benefit from a wide range of academic, sporting, musical, artistic and cultural activities which encourage them to develop enquiring minds and an enthusiasm for learning. The school aims to foster an atmosphere of co-operation and understanding between pupils, staff and parents and to encourage good manners and consideration towards others at all times.

Packwood has always striven for academic excellence; class sizes are small (average 13) and children are prepared for all the major independent schools winning a number of academic, music, sports, art and all-rounder scholarships and awards each year.

The school's facilities are excellent: a new state-of-the-art sports hall was opened in 2007 allowing indoor tennis, four badminton courts, indoor cricket nets and five-a-side football. Incorporated in the building are fully-equipped CDT and Art departments and a linked computer suite. A 280-seat theatre was opened in 2004, in which regular music concerts and three major school plays are performed each year.

A new classroom block was opened two years ago. Other classrooms, within the main school buildings, also include three science laboratories and two further computer suites. A girls' boarding house is a short distance from the main building.

Packwood has a very strong sporting tradition. As well as a large area of grass playing fields, there is a full-size floodlit Astroturf pitch, an additional hard court area, 10 tennis courts, 2 squash courts, an indoor, heated swimming pool and a 9-hole golf course. In the winter terms the boys play rugby, soccer and hockey while the girls play hockey, netball and lacrosse. There is also cross-country running on a course within the grounds. In the summer the boys play cricket, the girls play rounders and all take part in tennis, athletics and swimming.

Additional facilities include a shooting range and an equestrian cross-country course as well as an adventure playground.

Charitable status. Packwood Haugh is a Registered Charity, number 528411. It exists to provide day and boarding education for boys and girls from the age of 4 to 13.

Papplewick

Windsor Road Ascot Berks SL5 7LH
Tel: 01344 621488
Fax: 01344 874639
e-mail: hm@papplewick.org.uk
sarahtt@papplewick.org.uk (Registrar)
website: www.papplewick.org.uk

Chairman of Board of Governors: P R Rotheroe, Esq

***Headmaster*: T W Bunbury**, BA University College, Durham, PGCE

Age Range. 7–13.

Number of Boys. 191: 133 boarders and 58 day boys.

Fees per term (2007-2008). Boarders £6,655, Day Boys £5,110.

Papplewick is a day, weekly and full boarding school for boys with an exceptional Scholarship record to top Independent Schools. Day boys do prep at school and come into board from the Summer term of Year 6. Happy, confident boys abound, and a modern, family-friendly approach to boarding is adopted. A daily transport service runs to/from West London, and being situated between M3 and M4, the school boasts easy access to London airports.

Papplewick exists to provide a high quality predominantly boarding education where – for all our academic, cultural and sporting success – the happiness of the boys come first.

Charitable status. The Papplewick Educational Trust is a Registered Charity, number 309087.

The Paragon

Junior School of Prior Park College

Lyncombe House Lyncombe Vale Bath BA2 4LT
Tel: 01225 310837
Fax: 01225 427980
e-mail: office@paragonschool.co.uk
website: www.paragonschool.co.uk

Chair of Governors: Sister Jane Livesey, CJ, MA Cantab

***Headmaster*: Mr Titus Mills**, BA Hons

Age Range. 3–11 years.

Number of Pupils. 152 Boys, 104 Girls.

Fees per term (2007-2008). Juniors £2,168; Age 5–7 £2,067; Under 5 £1,945 including lunches, excluding optional private tuition. Flexible sessions until five years (fees accordingly). Sibling discounts available. Registration Fee (non-refundable) £100.

19 experienced and qualified teachers.

The Paragon is an independent, co-educational day school based in a beautiful Georgian house situated a mile from the centre of Bath. The school is set in eight acres of beautiful grounds with woodland, conservation areas, lawns and streams. It's the perfect 'outdoor classroom' and we use it right across the curriculum. Following our recent merger with nearby Prior Park College, less than a mile away, we also enjoy regular access to their superb facilities.

Several factors help create the 'distinctive Paragon atmosphere'. One is undoubtedly the homely feel that comes from being based in a beautiful, former family home. Then there's our Christian ethos and strong pastoral care, as well as our belief that school at this age is about being stimulated and inspired, about laughter and spontaneity – in short, about having fun. We may be a private school and we certainly expect high standards of behaviour but we're anything but stuffy and grey.

We offer a broad curriculum taught in small classes by teachers with a real passion for their subject. Academic life at The Paragon cultivates a love of learning and encourages independent and creative thinking. Our results are impressive. In their Year 6 SATS tests our children consistently achieve well above the national average and many win senior school scholarships. Our facilities include a library, large gymnasium/dining hall, ICT suite, nursery with secure indoor and outdoor play areas, art studio, modern languages and music rooms.

Sport is particularly strong at The Paragon. Our sports teams take part, with considerable success, in a wide range of tournaments and festivals. We also offer a vast range of sports clubs that all children can join regardless of ability. Prior Park College offers us an indoor swimming pool, astroturf and grass pitches, tennis courts, athletics track, sports hall, and dance studio.

The Paragon's extra-curricular programme is extensive. Staff run more than 40 lunchtime and after-school clubs that range from pottery and chess to conservation and Indian puppet making. The school also enjoys an enviable reputation for Music. All children receive weekly music lessons from a specialist teacher. In addition, visiting instrumental teachers offer tuition in a wide range of instruments. We offer an excellent choice of extra-curricular music activities including two orchestras, three choirs, a wind band, brass group, string ensemble, guitar group and a samba band.

The Paragon is proud of its consistently impressive academic results but we strive for much more than success in exams. We believe in developing the whole person – physically, spiritually, and emotionally as well as intellectually. As W B Yeats said: "Education is not filling a bucket but lighting a fire."

Charitable status. Prior Park Educational Trust is a Registered Charity, number 281242.

Parkside

The Manor Stoke d'Abernon Cobham Surrey KT11 3PX
Tel: 01932 862749
Fax: 01932 860251
e-mail: enquiries@parkside-school.co.uk
website: www.parkside-school.co.uk

Chairman of Governors: C M East, ACII

***Headmaster*: D M Aylward**, MA, BEd Hons

Deputy Heads:
D M Pulleyn, CertEd
Mrs H Sayer, BEd Hons

Age Range. Boys 2½–13. Co-educational Nursery.
Numbers. Day Boys 236, Pre-Prep 95, Nursery 85.
Fees per term (from January 2008). Day Boys £3,650, Pre-Prep £2,650, Nursery £262–£2,090.

Parkside was founded in 1879 and became a Charitable Trust in 1960. The School moved from East Horsley to its present site of over 40 acres in 1979, its centenary year. Since the move the Governors have implemented a continual development programme which has included a purpose built, well equipped Science Block, extending the main building to provide more Pre-Prep accommodation and a Music School with a large classroom and six practice rooms. A superb covered Swimming Pool and Sports Hall complex with an excellent stage for drama offers unrivalled facilities in the area. In addition, a £2m Classroom Block has been built recently to further enhance the facilities in the school. A new Technology Department and Nursery are now housed in a delightful Grade II Listed Barn which has been completely and skilfully refurbished to provide spacious, well lit classrooms and workshops. The Governors have plans in the near future to link a second Computer Room to the main network and further expand the Art and Music facilities.

The school is large enough to be flexible and offer setting in major subjects yet small enough for each pupil to be known and treated as an individual. On average there are 15 pupils in a Set and the teacher: pupil ratio is 1:8. All teaching staff are highly qualified and there is a low staff turnover. Each boy is a member of a House and this helps to stimulate friendly competition for work points and many other inter-house contests.

The National Curriculum is followed to prepare all boys for entry to Senior Independent Schools by Common Entrance and Scholarship examinations. All boys pass to their first choice Senior Schools and our results in these examinations are impressive. Over the past few years many Academic, Art, Music and Sporting Scholarships have been won. Our curriculum is broad based and all boys are taught Art, Music, PE and Technology in addition to the usual Common Entrance subjects. There are two School Choirs and a School Orchestra and over one third of the boys are receiving individual tuition in a wide variety of musical instruments. During the year, there are many opportunities for boys to perform in musical and dramatic productions.

The School has a fine sporting record and, over the past few years, many tournaments in different sports and at different age groups have been won. In addition, a number of boys have gone on to represent their County and Country in various sports. The main sports are football, hockey and cricket, but boys are able to take part in rugby, swimming, athletics, tennis, cross-country running, basketball and judo. An extensive Wednesday afternoon and After School Activity Programme (including supervised homework sessions) is available with over 40 different activities on offer, from gardening to kayaking, and horse-riding to golf. Many boys have also represented the school at a high level in chess. The beautiful estate and the River Mole, which runs through the grounds, are also used to contribute to the all round education each pupil receives both in and out of the classroom.

Unusually for a Preparatory School, Parkside has a large and active Old Boys Association which runs many sporting and social events during the year.

Further details and a prospectus are available on application to the Headmaster's Secretary.

Charitable status. Parkside School is a Registered Charity, number 312041. It exists to provide education for children between the ages of 2½ and 13 years.

Pembridge Hall School
Alpha Plus Group

18 Pembridge Square London W2 4EH
Tel: 020 7229 0121
Fax: 020 7792 1086
e-mail: contact@pembridgehall.co.uk
website: www.pembridgehall.co.uk

***Headmistress*: Mrs E M Marsden**, BA Hons, DipEd, LLCM, ALCM, ALAM

Age Range. 4½–11.
Number of Girls. 250.
Fees per term (2008-2009). £4,420.

Girls are prepared for entry into independent London day schools and for the Independent Schools Common Entrance examination.

The school aims to create a happy and contented atmosphere in which girls may learn to work with concentration and enthusiasm. The curriculum is designed to give a thorough grounding in English and Mathematics. The girls' interest and desire to learn are stimulated through History, Geography, Religious Instruction, French, Science, Music, Drama, Art, ICT and Physical Education. A wide range of after-school activities is also on offer.

Pembroke House

PO Box 31 Gilgil 20116 Kenya
Tel: 00 254 (0)20 231 2323
Fax: 00 254 (0)50 4015003/4015497
e-mail: headmaster@pembrokehouse.sc.ke
website: www.pembrokehouse.sc.ke

Chairman of Council: Mr Richard Fernandez

***Headmaster*: Mr Alastair S Cook**, BEd Hons

Age Range. 6–13.

Number of Pupils. 80 boy boarders, 75 girl boarders.

Fees per term (2008-2009). KShs 364,500 (UK£2,916).

The school was founded in 1927 and is presently owned and administered by the Kenya Educational Trust Limited. It is situated in over 40 hectares of well-maintained grounds in the Rift Valley at 2,000 metres and is 120 kms from Nairobi. The climate is sunny throughout the year affording many opportunities for an extensive education.

Facilities include the Chapel, Swimming Pool, Music Rooms, two Libraries, Art and Design Technology Centre, Computer Room, two Squash Courts and tennis courts and access to a neighbouring Golf Course. A multi-purpose hall was completed in 1999. The school has a well-equipped Surgery on site.

The main sports for boys are Cricket, Hockey and Rugby, with Tennis, Swimming, Athletics, Squash, Golf, Horse Riding, Sailing, Water-Skiing, Soccer, Shooting and TaeKwonDo as complementary activities. A full range of clubs and various extras, including individual music instruction, are also offered. Drama is strong with several productions put on each year.

All the activities are available for girls whose main sports are Rounders, Hockey and Netball.

Boys and girls are admitted from six years as full boarders and are prepared, through the British Curriculum, for the ISEB Common Entrance Examinations which qualifies them for entry to Independent Senior Schools in the UK and South Africa as well as Kenyan schools. The School usually gains several academic scholarships and awards each year in addition to music and sports awards. The Learning Support Facilities at Pembroke House have been developed over many years and now provide essential help for those who require such assistance. The school currently has children from seven different countries including the United Kingdom.

The average number of pupils in each form is 12, and there are 21 fully qualified members of teaching staff plus two qualified Nurses, a Cateress, an Estate Manager and a Bursar.

Pembroke has an excellent reputation for work, games and activities. The Headmaster's aim is to continue to produce confident, polite boys and girls of upright character who will give of their best in all spheres of life, in school and beyond.

Pennthorpe School

Rudgwick Horsham West Sussex RH12 3HJ
Tel: 01403 822391
Fax: 01403 822438
e-mail: enquiries@pennthorpe.com
website: www.pennthorpe.com

The School that puts the fun into the fundamentals.

Chairman of the Governors: Mrs S Rothwell

***Headmaster*: Mr S J Moll**, BEd Hons (London)

Age Range. Co-educational 2–13.

Number of Pupils. 360 Day Pupils.

Fees per term (2008-2009). £430–£3,904.

Pennthorpe School in West Sussex lies close to the Surrey border, midway between Guildford and Horsham. The school is committed to high standards in all it does. Pennthorpe also recognises that putting the fun into the fundamentals of school life allows the children to maximise their learning potential.

Pennthorpe has an outstanding record of 13+ Common Entrance successes, with a history of a 100% pass rate to first choice schools stretching back as far as anyone can remember. In the last eight years, more than a third (over 80 in all) of Pennthorpe's 13 year-old leavers have won academic scholarships or prestigious awards for music, art, sport or ICT.

Pennthorpe sets out to develop its pupils into well balanced all-rounders, and it is this outlook along with the principle of putting the fun into the fundamentals, that drives Pennthorpe forward.

Developing all-rounders means offering choice, and from the very earliest stages when the two year-olds join the Pennthorpe Kindergarten, the emphasis is on breadth, both academic as well as outside the classroom.

The Pennthorpe Sports Department, recently awarded Gold by Sport England, offers a wealth of sporting activities and competitive opportunities: soccer, netball, rugby, hockey, rounders, cricket and athletics are regular features on the termly fixtures calendar, while climbing, judo, tennis, basketball, archery and many others are available as part of the huge range of after-school options.

Pennthorpe is committed to the arts. From the age of five, every pupil enjoys weekly Performing Arts lessons in our own dance and drama studio. There are also timetabled music lessons for all; these, along with three choirs, an orchestra, individual instrumental tuition and termly concerts provide many performing opportunities.

With a separate Art & Design building (incorporating one of the school's two computer suites), and a long-standing reputation for artistic excellence, Pennthorpe is also well equipped to fire the creative spirits of its pupils.

Complementing and building upon the classroom work, Pennthorpe's celebrated Flexiday programme of after-school activities aims to bring even more chances for every boy and girl to find their strengths and shine. Whether it is developing their computer skills, throwing a pot, scaling the climbing wall, or tapping to the rhythm in the dance studio, there's something for everybody.

A continuous programme of major capital investment is under way. A recently completed 10 classroom teaching building, including an exceptional science suite, provides a learning environment second to none for the 8 to 13 year olds. Plans are being finalised for new facilities for the younger pupils as well as a Performing Arts Centre. This is a school that never stands still!

As part of its commitment to the obligations of charitable status, Pennthorpe has formed a partnership with a number of senior independent schools to offer a unique scheme of transferable assisted places for children of above average ability, whose parents would not otherwise be able to afford the fees. Ask for details.

If you would like to see how your child could thrive in this busy, happy and successful school, ask for a prospectus, visit our website (details above) and then book a visit: the Headmaster and all the staff and children will make you very welcome. There are two Open Mornings each term and the Headmaster is also happy to welcome parents to individual visits at any time.

Charitable status. Pennthorpe School is a Registered Charity, number 307043. It exists to provide an excellent education for boys and girls and to benefit the community.

Peponi House

PO Box 23203, Lower Kabete, Nairobi 00604, Kenya
Tel: 00 254 20 4184998, 4180583, 4183453
Fax: 00 254 20 4180159
e-mail: secretary@peponihouseschool.co.ke
website: www.peponihouseschool.co.ke

***Headmaster*: R J Blake**, BSc Hons, PGCE, NPQH

Age Range. 6–13.
Number of Pupils. 315 boys and girls, all day.
Fees per annum (2008-2009). Kshs 285,000.

Founded in 1986, Peponi House has grown to become one of the leading preparatory schools in East Africa. The attractive and spacious site in Lower Kabete houses all that a thriving prep school requires to get the very best out of the children, both in and out of the classroom.

We are a multi-cultural community which encourages respect for self and others. Our emphasis is on excellence, through a broad, balanced education which aims to maximise the potential of each pupil as a whole person. To this end, we have outstanding facilities including a 25-metre swimming pool, three hard tennis courts, purpose-built Art and Design Technology rooms and networked PCs in all rooms. We have two fully-equipped science laboratories and our music department is superbly well resourced. The school library and ICT room occupy an area that is central to the school both geographically and philosophically. These facilities help to complement the excellent work that the children and staff carry out in the well-resourced classrooms.

Whilst always striving for academic excellence, it is central to Peponi's philosophy that education isn't limited to the classroom. In addition to the 30 scholarships to senior schools that our pupils have won in the last three years, we have had notable successes in sport, music, art and drama. Peponi teams have won competitions at a national level and our swimmers recently won gold, silver and bronze medals at an international level.

We follow the British National Curriculum but this is seen very much as a framework for extension. In addition to the core subjects of Literacy, Numeracy and Science, pupils in the Junior School (Years 2 to 4) also have lessons in Music, PE and Games, Swimming, Art and DT, ICT, tennis and, from Year 3, French. Junior children are taught these subjects by specialist teachers while the class teachers deliver the core subjects and humanities. All children are taught in a way that best suits their individual needs and some children do require additional support. This is carried out by our Learning Support teachers who will help children either individually or in small groups. Our special needs teachers also play a vital role in advising colleagues as to the strengths and weaknesses of particular children so that teaching can be differentiated to suit everyone.

In Year 5, children are taught Humanities and English by their form teachers, who also play a vital pastoral role in preparing the children for life in the senior school. In Year 6, all subjects are delivered by subject specialists. The sciences are taught separately and there is an option for children to study either Kiswahili or Latin.

We also have a wide and varied range of extra-curricular activities. Seniors have activities twice a week and Juniors once a week.

Our music department flourishes and, in addition to twice-weekly class music lessons, the children have the opportunity to play in the orchestra or in one of the ensembles, or sing in either the Junior or Senior Choir. As well as the two major school concerts during the year, all children have the opportunity to perform in front of their peers and parents at our termly "Tea-Time Concerts". The Christmas and Easter Services are another chance for our choirs to perform and all the children are encouraged to take part in the plays that are staged in December and June.

We have children from many different cultures and ethnic backgrounds and we encourage understanding and above all respect for each other. We are a Christian School and the ethos of "Love one another" is a recurring theme in our Thursday services, but we are proud of our multi-faith society where children learn to appreciate and value their differences as well as their similarities.

The school's motto "A School of Many Nations, a Family of One" encapsulates all that we hold most dear. First and foremost, we are a school and the academic side of things lies at the heart of all that we do. However, we are also a family and that makes itself very clear in the day to day life of the school. We have an open door policy with our parents and encourage them to be very active in their support of what we do, either through our energetic PTA or through close consultation with the staff.

At Peponi House, we believe that our role as educators is to give our children the best possible foundation for what lies ahead. We are, after all, a preparatory school and excellent preparation is what we set out to achieve. By the time they leave us, our pupils will be confident young adults who are ready to face the future with poise and self-belief.

Perrott Hill School

North Perrott Crewkerne Somerset TA18 7SL
Tel: 01460 72051
Fax: 01460 78246
e-mail: headmaster@perrotthill.com
website: www.perrotthill.com

Chairman of Governors: Lord Bradbury

***Headmaster*: Mr M J Davies**, BA Hons London, PGCE
from January 2009: Mr R J Morse, BEd Hons

Age Range. 3–13.
Number of Pupils. 195 boys and girls, of whom 50 are full, weekly or flexi-boarders.
Fees per term (2008-2009). Boarders: £5,740 (full), £4,522 (weekly); Day pupils £1,645–£4,020.

Perrott Hill School is a co-educational day and boarding school and is registered as an Educational Trust. Set in 25 acres of beautiful grounds in the heart of the countryside, near Crewkerne on the Somerset/Dorset border, it is serviced by excellent road and rail networks.

Perrott Hill is a small, family school where children settle quickly and learn in confidence. Class sizes are small, with an average of 15 children to a form. The pupils are streamed from Year 5. Staff are dedicated and highly qualified. Facilities now include a brand new all-weather sports area, a new sports hall, theatre, CDT art block, computer centre, music centre, recreation rooms, swimming pool, and woodland area.

The Montessori Nursery has proved a very popular addition to the Pre-Preparatory department. The Pre-Prep, for children aged 3–7, is housed in the converted stable courtyard next to the main school buildings, which gives the younger children their own safe, secure environment while also allowing them to take advantage of many of the facilities of the Prep School.

Music, Drama and Art are taught within the timetable alongside core curriculum subjects. The choir and orchestra perform both at charity concerts, in competitions and school functions. There are drama productions every term.

Teaching is class-based up to the age of nine, and subject-based in the Upper Prep, where all lessons are taught by specialist teachers. French, Music, IT and PE, however, are taught by specialists throughout the school. There is a special emphasis on French language and culture and a Year 7 French Exchange to Paris takes place annually.

Each child, boarding or day, has his or her own pastoral and academic tutor, while the welfare of the boarders is supervised by Mr and Mrs Warlow, the house master and house mistress. They are assisted by two matrons, in a warm family atmosphere.

Sport is played every day, and the new all-weather sports surface has been a welcome addition to the facilities, providing two superb new tennis courts for the summer, and netball courts for the girls in winter. Emphasis is placed upon skills and team work, not just the achievement of results. Games played include rugby, football, hockey, netball, cricket, tennis, rounders, swimming and cross-country running. Regular matches are played against local independent schools. Optional extras include fencing, carpentry, archery, karate, horse riding, ballet, tap and modern dance, speech and drama and cookery.

The school boasts an excellent academic record, with awards to major senior independent schools and success at Common Entrance. Scholarships for academic, musical and all-round ability are offered annually in February to children entering the school from Year 4.

The combination of countryside space, a family atmosphere and a forward-looking academic programme creates an ideal environment for children to thrive both academically and in their leisure pursuits – we are delighted to show parents the school in action!

Perrott Hill School – time and space for a full education.

Charitable status. Perrott Hill School is a Registered Charity, number 310278. It exists to give high quality education to boys and girls.

The Perse Pelican Nursery and Pre-Preparatory School

Part of The Perse Foundation of Schools

92 Glebe Road Cambridge CB1 7TD
Tel: 01223 403940
Fax: 01223 403941
e-mail: pelican@perse.co.uk
website: www.perse.co.uk/pelican

Chairman of Governors: K J R Edwards, BSc, MA, PhD

***Headmistress*: Mrs P M Oates**, BEd (Cantab)

Age Range. 3–7 co-educational.

Number of Pupils. 80 Boys, 60 Girls (108 Full-time, 32 Part-time).

Fees per term (2008-2009). £3,215 (full-time including lunches), £1,719 (half day).

The co-educational Perse Pelican Nursery and Pre Preparatory School is set in its own building and grounds on the edge of the city of Cambridge. It caters for part-time children aged three to four years in a Nursery class, and full-time children aged from four to seven. The building and its grounds have been carefully adapted in order to meet the needs of children of this age.

The Board of Governors of The Perse Upper School, Cambridge oversees the management of the school.

The school aims to provide all its pupils with opportunities to learn within a caring, supportive and challenging environment, where their full potential will be realised. It also seeks to develop lively and enquiring minds in its pupils, as well as a positive wish to learn. It hopes to encourage respect and care for others, and the wider world, as well as the enjoyment of physical exercise and the creative and expressive arts. A sense of self-respect, individual worth and the ability to play and work in cooperation with others are seen as high priorities.

Most pupils enter The Perse Pelican through the Nursery class, but a few places become available at the beginning of the Reception year. All pupils are screened prior to entry. On leaving the school it is expected that, subject to suitability, the majority of the pupils will continue their education at The Perse Preparatory School.

Developments on The Perse Pelican site include the building of a new hall, two music teaching rooms, a new library and enlarging three classrooms.

Charitable status. The Perse School is a Registered Charity, number 1120654, and a Company Limited by Guarantee, registered in England and Wales, number 5977683, for the education of children.

The Perse Preparatory School

Part of The Perse Foundation of Schools

Trumpington Road Cambridge CB2 8EX
Tel: 01223 568270
Fax: 01223 568273
e-mail: prep@perse.co.uk
website: www.perse.co.uk/prep

Chairman of the Governors: K J R Edwards, BSc, MA, PhD

***Headmaster*: G R P Jones**, BMus, PGCE

Deputy Head: D E J Adams, BEd, ACP, CertEd

Director of Studies: S Clark, CertEd

Age Range. 7–11.

Number of Pupils. 223.

Fees per term (2008-2009). £3,801.

The Perse Prep School is a co-educational preparatory school in Cambridge. It stands in its own grounds some $1^1/_2$ miles away from the The Perse Upper School and is totally self-contained. The school has its own staff of 15 teachers, a full-time librarian and 18 peripatetic music staff. Recent developments include a new Learning Resource Centre, new Year 3 classrooms, a purpose-built science room and an ICT suite. An extensive building programme will be completed in August 2008 which will provide outstanding classroom and creative arts facilities. A second phase of buildings, at a later date, will include a new hall, a sports centre and new music facilities.

The School aims to achieve high academic standards and a wide range of achievements in cultural, sporting and other areas of life. The depth of academic ability throughout the school allows intellectual curiosity to flourish and pupils thrive on challenges both inside and outside the classroom. Pupils enjoy each other's success and have the quiet confidence to be at ease with new ideas. As they grow we aim to develop the qualities of reliability, consideration for others, good manners and self-discipline which they need to complement their academic success. The school is in regular contact with parents and the Head of Pastoral Care works closely with Form teachers to ensure the general well-being of pupils.

Excellent facilities enable us to offer a wide variety of sporting and recreational pursuits. The games programme (soccer, cricket, netball, athletics tennis and swimming) is designed to encourage all pupils to enjoy games and physical exercise. The school is proud of its strong tradition in music, drama and the arts and the majority of pupils learn a musical instrument. There are choirs, two orchestras and numerous instrumental groups. Extra-curricular activities including badminton, chess, cookery, computing, Cubs, cycling proficiency, drama, judo, puppetry, School Newspaper, and swimming are also available. There is an annual adventure activity week for pupils in Year 6 and a Year 5 trip to France.

Pupils enter the Preparatory School each September. Places are awarded as a result of an examination held in January of the year of entry. The normal age of entry is 7+, although there are sometimes a small number of places available in other year groups. Subject to having made satisfactory progress at the Preparatory School, most pupils move to the The Perse Upper School at 11+.

Charitable status. The Perse School is a Registered Charity, number 1120654, and a Company Limited by Guarantee, registered in England and Wales, number 5977683, for the education of children.

Pilgrims Pre-Preparatory School

Brickhill Drive Bedford MK41 7QZ
Tel: 01234 369555
Fax: 01234 369556
e-mail: pilgrims@harpur-trust.org.uk
website: www.pilgrims-school.info

Chairman of Board of Governors: Mrs S Peck

***Headmistress*: Mrs M J Shaw**

Co-educational Day School.

Age Range. 3 months–8 years.

Number of Pupils. 361: 186 Boys, 175 Girls.

Fees per term (2007-2008). £840–£2,421.

Pilgrims Pre-Preparatory School is the newest addition to the Harpur Trust family of schools. We opened in 2000 in spacious, purpose-built accommodation with extensive playing fields. Most of our children continue their education within the other four Harpur Trust schools.

Pilgrims is a vibrant, stimulating environment where we pride ourselves on providing a rich and varied curriculum that offers plenty of opportunities to develop each child's self-esteem and confidence, whilst giving the support to enable them to become independent learners and to achieve their full potential. We follow the best of Birth to 3, the Foundation Stage and the National Curriculum, developing the curriculum further to meet the needs of our children. In addition, we take advantage of our experienced staff and excellent facilities to provide specialist weeks on a range of topics including Healthy Heart week, Art Week and Science Week. Good manners are valued and celebrated throughout the school.

Children are taught in small classes with specialist teachers. Emphasis is placed upon English and Mathematics to ensure that solid foundations are laid for success across the whole curriculum. School trips are arranged to a variety of local museums, wildlife centres and villages to further enrich the children's learning.

Academic standards are high and children who are identified as gifted and able are offered specific tuition in small groups to ensure their needs are met.

We have a strong music department with a successful choir and orchestra who regularly take part in the Bedfordshire Music Festival. Specialist music teaching begins in the toddler room and continues throughout the school. Individual instrumental tuition is available from Year 1 with over 60% of children learning one or more instruments.

We encourage the children to enjoy a healthy school life. Our menus are planned in conjunction with a nutritionist, and the children have a range of homemade biscuits, fruit and crudités provided for snacks each day. Sport is most important within the school; in addition to gymnastics, dance and outdoor games, from 2 years of age the children use our indoor swimming pool every week, and from Nursery they swim twice each week.

The school is open 46 weeks a year with holiday clubs running outside term time. We also offer a huge range of after-school clubs and a breakfast club. Parents are welcomed into the school and work in partnership with the staff to create a warm, caring, purposeful and fun environment in which our children thrive.

Charitable status. Pilgrims Pre-Preparatory School, part of the Harpur Trust, is run by Harpur Pre-Preparatory Schools Ltd, which is a Registered Charity, number 1066861.

The Pilgrims' School

Winchester Hampshire SO23 9LT
Tel: 01962 854189
Fax: 01962 843610
e-mail: info@pilgrims-school.co.uk
website: www.thepilgrims-school.co.uk

Chairman of Governors: The Very Revd James Atwell, Dean of Winchester

***Headmaster*: The Revd Dr B A Rees**, BA, BD, DipMin, PhD (St Andrews)

Age Range. Boys 4–13. Co-ed Pre-Prep (girls siblings only).

Number of Pupils. 200 Boys (80 boarders/weekly boarders, 120 day boys). Pre-Prep: 54.

Fees per term (2008-2009). Boarders £5,815, Day boys £4,595, Pre-Prep £2,640.

The Governing Body consists of The Dean (Chairman) and delegated members of the Chapter of Winchester and the Headmaster and Bursar of Winchester College. Examinations for independent schools, with a significant number moving to Winchester College each year. Cathedral Choristers and Winchester College Quiristers are educated at the school and receive scholarships to the value of half the full boarding fee together with free tuition in one musical instrument. All boys whether musical or not receive excellent academic and musical tuition, and the sporting tradition is equally strong. The school is noted for its happy family atmosphere, and a major recent building programme has ensured the highest standard of facilities possible. All enquiries about the school or singing auditions should be addressed to the Registrar.

Charitable status. The Pilgrims' School is a Registered Charity, number 1091579.

Pinewood

Bourton Shrivenham Wiltshire SN6 8HZ
Tel: 01793 782205
Fax: 01793 783476
e-mail: office@pinewoodschool.co.uk
website: www.pinewoodschool.co.uk

***Headmaster*: Philip Hoyland**, BEd (Exeter)

Deputy Head: C J Acheson-Gray, BEd

Age Range. 3–13.

Number of Pupils. 193 Boys and Girls (84 flexi and weekly boarders). Nursery and Pre-Prep: 119.

Fees per term (2008-2009). Weekly Boarding £4,890–£5,410, Day £2,265–£4,350 inclusive, with no compulsory extras.

Pinewood is set in 84 acres of rolling countryside. The School offers a quality, family-based environment where children are encouraged to think for themselves and a strong emphasis is placed on self-discipline, manners, trust and selflessness. Resources include a purpose-built Music School and Junior Forms' Wing, a flourishing Pre-Prep and Nursery, Art and Design Workshops, Research and Reference Library and ICT Rooms.

Excellent academic results are achieved through a mixture of traditional and forward-thinking teaching within a happy, friendly and stimulating learning atmosphere. Outside trips are frequent and visiting speakers prominent. Music and drama are encouraged.

Sport is keenly coached and matches are played at all levels on our picturesque playing fields,which incorporate a nine-hole golf course. There is a wide range of activities and clubs both for day children and, in the evening, for boarders.

Pinewood is a school where staff, parents and children work together to find and realise the potential in every child.

Charitable status. Pinewood is a Registered Charity, number 309642. It exists to provide high quality education for boys and girls.

Port Regis

Motcombe Park Shaftesbury Dorset SP7 9QA
Tel: 01747 857800
Fax: 01747 857810
e-mail: office@portregis.com
website: www.portregis.com

Chairman of the Governors: Mark A Vaughan-Lee

***Headmaster*: Peter A E Dix**, MA (Jesus College, Cantab)

Deputy Head: Julie A Moores, BEd (Sussex)

Director of Studies: Michael J Jonas, MA (London), BEd (Durham)

Age Range. 3–13.

Number of Pupils. Boarders: 253 (Boys 143, Girls 110); Day Boarders: 149 (Boys 72, Girls 77).

Fees per term (2007-2008). Boarders £6,790 (no compulsory extras); Day Boarders £2,165–£5,285 (meals included). Weekly Boarding is available.

Port Regis is a well-established and highly regarded preparatory school set in 150 acres of beautiful Dorset parkland just outside the historic town of Shaftesbury. The main building is an Elizabethan-style mansion with elegant oak-panelled reception rooms and a splendid galleried Hall with a large feature-fireplace. The grounds encompass 35 acres of playing fields as well as extensive ancient woodland, gardens, lawns and a lake.

The school offers a purpose-built science, design and technology centre, a specialist teaching block for Arts subjects, a music school with recital hall, a 450-seat theatre, a new dining hall and kitchens, an astroturf hockey pitch, a nine-hole golf course, 13 tennis courts and a sports complex (including two Sports Halls) which serves as a National Centre for Junior Gymnastics with a 25-metre indoor heated swimming pool. There are also badminton and squash courts available. An equestrian centre is conveniently situated close to the School. The J M Upward Academic Centre is due to open in September 2008.

Younger pupils are accommodated in bright, cosy dormitories in the Mansion House, while the older pupils enjoy the comfort of splendid senior boarding houses. The boys' house has 60 individual study-bedrooms, each provided with its own washbasin, desk, cupboard and drawers. There are also two common rooms and separate kitchen areas as well as a generous provision of showers, baths and wcs. This house complements the senior girls' house, similar in design with 48 study-bedrooms, which was completed a few years ago.

A Pre-Prep opened in September 1993 in the secure and beautiful environment of the Motcombe Park grounds with full use of the Prep School's facilities.

Each child's Tutor will, we hope, become a friend of the family as well as the child, especially since over 90 boarders have parents working overseas. Encouragement is given to each child to experience a wide variety of activities and develop skills where talent lies. Most staff live either on the estate or in the main building, so personal guidance and a family atmosphere has been created. Academic standards are high and children are prepared successfully for Common Entrance or Scholarship examinations. Learning Support is available for children with mild-to-moderate learning difficulties.

Extensive opportunities are provided for Music (about three-quarters of the School learn an instrument), Drama (there are up to six productions a year), and Art (in a wide choice of media), with Woodwork, Electronics, Riding, .22 Rifle Shooting, Karate, Gymnastics and Canoeing included in a list of over 70 hobby options. Major team games are Rugby, Hockey, Soccer, Netball, Cricket and Rounders. Inter-school, county and national standard competitions are entered. Home and abroad expeditions take place.

There are 56 full-time teaching staff, 16 visiting musicians, 4 State Registered Nurses, a Head of Boarding, an Assistant Head of Boarding, a Housemother, Houseparents and Matrons.

A prospectus may be had on application from the Headmaster, who would be delighted to welcome visitors to Port Regis.

Academic, Music, Gymnastic, Sport and All-Rounder entrance scholarships may be awarded annually.

Charitable status. Port Regis School Limited is a Registered Charity, number 306218. It exists to provide an all-round education to the highest standard for boys and girls from the ages of 3 to 13.

The Portsmouth Grammar School Junior School

High Street Portsmouth Hampshire PO1 2LN
Tel: 023 9236 0036
Fax: 023 9236 4263
e-mail: juniorschool@pgs.org.uk
website: www.pgs.org.uk

Chairman of the Governors: D K Bawtree, CB, DL, BSc(Eng), CEng, FIEE, FIMechE

***Headmistress of the Junior School*: Mrs P S Foster**, CertEd

Deputy Headmaster: A P N Rowley, BSc, PGCE
Assistant Headmistress: Mrs E R Day, BA, CertEd

Age Range. 4–11. Nursery: $2^3/_4$–4.

Number of Day Pupils. 324 boys, 179 girls.

Fees per term (2008-2009). Reception, Years 1 and 2: £2,329. Years 3 and 4: £2,456. Years 5 and 6: £2,582. (Fees quoted include direct debit discount.)

The Junior School is an integral part of The Portsmouth Grammar School under the general direction of the Governors and Headmaster. Children from 4–9 years are educated within bright and spacious classrooms that occupy a discreet space on the Senior School site. The 9–11 year old pupils are educated in the historic original school building which stands in splendid isolation in close proximity to the Senior School site.

The Junior School's organisation is distinct under its own Headmistress, with 33 full-time, 10 part-time members of staff, and 19 learning support assistants.

The main entry is at 4+ and an additional class is formed at 7+. Pupils leave at 11 years, the majority moving on to The Portsmouth Grammar School Senior School.

Whilst emphasis is placed on literacy and numeracy there is a broad curriculum which includes; Science, Geography, History, Religious Studies, ICT, Modern Foreign Languages, Music, Design Technology, Art, Drama, Physical Education, Games and PSHE. In addition, many pupils receive tuition in a wide range of musical instruments.

The school also provides a wide choice of extra-curricular activities to all pupils. Currently over 30 different club activities are offered. The most recent innovations are a week's sailing instruction for all pupils in Year 4 and a Residential Field Studies Course for all pupils in Year 6. There are specialist rooms for Art and Craft, Music and Drama, plus a Science Laboratory and two Information Technology Centres. An innovative string scheme enables all seven year olds to experience a free term's tuition in learning the violin or 'cello.

Games include Association and Rugby Football, Netball, Hockey, Rounders, Cricket, Athletics, Tennis and Swimming. The Junior School has its own learner swimming pool and uses the Grammar School's excellent 16 acre playing fields at Hilsea, which include a Floodlit astro turf pitch.

It also has access to the Grammar School's Sports Hall, Music School and Theatre.

In September 2001 a Nursery School was opened offering up to 48 places in any one session. The architect designed building provides the children, aged from two years nine months, with exciting opportunities to learn through play and exploration. All staff have early years specialism, the two key staff being fully qualified primary teachers with Early Years expertise. The Nursery School offers provision for 50 weeks a year.

Charitable status. The Portsmouth Grammar School is a Registered Charity, number 1063732. It exists to provide education for boys and girls.

Pownall Hall

Carrwood Road Wilmslow Cheshire SK9 5DW
Tel: 01625 523141
Fax: 01625 525209
e-mail: headmaster@pownallhall.cheshire.sch.uk
website: www.pownallhall.cheshire.sch.uk

Chairman of the Board of Governors: Mrs Sue Page

***Headmaster*: J J Meadmore**, RD, BSc

Age Range. 2–11 Co-educational.

Number of Boys and Girls. 200 (Day Children)

Fees per term (2007-2008). £343–£2,560 (including lunch and day trips).

Pownall Hall, a preparatory day school for children aged 2 to 11 and set in its own beautiful and extensive grounds, has been established for over 100 years. It is situated on the north-western side of Wilmslow, 12 miles from Manchester and within easy reach of motorway, rail and air travel.

The school has a highly trained teaching staff of 23, who prepare children for the Entrance Examinations to the Independent Day schools in the area. A thorough grounding is given in all academic subjects in line with the National Curriculum and an excellent mixture of traditional and modern techniques is used. Each major subject has specialist teaching staff and subject rooms including a fully equipped Science Laboratory, Maths, English, Design Technology, Information Technology and French rooms and, in addition a computer aided Library. French is taught from the age of six. Children have access to computers from the age of two and Design Technology is begun at eight.

In September 1995, a co-educational nursery was begun for 2 to 3 year olds and this has quickly established itself as the main entry into the school, although children are accepted at any age below 11 years, provided that there are places available. There is a generous staff pupil ratio especially in the lower part of the school, to ensure that the children are given the best possible start to their academic work.

Great importance is attached to performance through music, drama and sport. The school is fortunate in having its own well-equipped Theatre in which all the major productions are performed. In 1988, a new Arts Centre was developed comprising Art and Music Rooms within the Theatre complex. There are two Choirs and a small choral group, which perform regularly and often at major Concert Halls in the country. Children are encouraged to study an orchestral instrument or the piano. A Music School operates on Saturday mornings throughout each term.

The main sports are Soccer, Hockey, Cricket, and Athletics, which support a strong fixture list with other schools and there is a full range of sporting activities including Badminton, Skiing and Tennis. A spacious Sports Hall was built in 1989.

During the course of the year there are a number of holidays or trips that are arranged including skiing, mountain walking in the Lake District and North Wales, "Outward Bound" type trips to Scotland as well as holidays in France.

Charitable status. Pownall Hall School is a Registered Charity, number 525929. It exists to provide education for boys and girls, aged 2–11 yrs.

The Prebendal School

54 West Street Chichester West Sussex PO19 1RT
Tel: 01243 782026
Fax: 01243 771821
e-mail: secretary.prebendal@btconnect.com
website: www.prebendalschool.org.uk

Chairman of Governors: The Dean of Chichester

***Headmaster*: Mr T R Cannell**, MA Ed Man, BEd
Winchester

Age Range. 3–13.

Number of Pupils. 157 (34 boarders, 123 day) with a further 80 in the Pre-Prep.

Fees per term (2008-2009). Boarders £4,944, Weekly Boarders £4,736, Day Pupils £3,656, Pre-Prep: £921 (half day), £1,649–£,2198 (full day). Compulsory extras: laundry and linen for boarders.

The School, which is co-educational, is governed by the Dean and Chapter of Chichester Cathedral with 6 lay members of the Board. It is the oldest school in Sussex and has occupied its present building at the west end of the Cathedral (though with later additions) for over 500 years. The Cathedral Choristers are among the boys educated at the School and they receive Choral Scholarships in reduction of fees. Annual Music and Academic Scholarships are open to boys and girls entering the school. Sibling Bursaries are awarded to brothers and sisters. Open and Music Scholarships to Independent Senior Schools are gained regularly.

There are excellent playing fields. Association Football, Hockey and Netball are played in the Christmas and Easter terms and Cricket, Athletics, Tennis and Rounders in the summer. A heated swimming pool is used for instruction in the summer term and there are two hard tennis courts.

A considerable number of children learn to play musical instruments and the School has 3 orchestras and numerous choirs and ensembles.

Gymnastics and Fencing are optional extras as are a number of after-school clubs.

'Occasional' boarding is available.

Charitable status. The Prebendal School is a Registered Charity, number 307370. Its aim is to promote education.

Prestfelde
A Woodard School

London Road Shrewsbury Shropshire SY2 6NZ
Tel: 01743 245400
Fax: 01743 241434
e-mail: office@prestfelde.co.uk
website: www.prestfelde.co.uk

Chairman of Governors: Dr R A Fraser, MBChB, PhD, FRCPath

Headmaster: **M Groome**, MA London, BEd Leeds

Age Range. 3–13.

Number of Pupils. 312 (10 boarders, 201 day pupils, and 101 children in Little Prestfelde).

Fees per term (2007-2008). Boarders £4,460. Day: Years 5–8 £3,460; Year 4 £3,330; Year 3 £2,860; Reception, Years 1 & 2 £2,170, Nursery £1,120.

Pupils at Prestfelde are well known for their cheerful and purposeful attitude. The school aims to maximise the potential of every individual by providing them with significant opportunities for excelling academically, and in musical, sporting and dramatic performances. A well qualified, loyal, enthusiastic and dedicated staff form the backbone of the school's success. The use of subject specialist teachers for pupils from the age of eight adds greatly to the quality of the teaching and the enthusiasm of the pupils.

Prestfelde has excellent facilities. There has been an extensive building programme over recent years giving all age ranges the benefit of purpose built class and specialist teaching rooms. The school enjoys the benefits of thirty acres of delightful parkland playing fields on the edge of Shrewsbury. There are ample, well-maintained facilities for football, rugby, cricket, netball, rounders, lacrosse, tennis and swimming in a covered heated pool.

Although the school is non-selective, the academic standards of the school are excellent. Streaming is used for pupils from the age of eight so that the curriculum for bright children can be extended. Equally, pupils who require support have the benefit of an exceptionally successful learning support department. The great majority of pupils stay to thirteen, and talented pupils are encouraged to attempt scholarship exams to their chosen senior school. The school has an excellent reputation for music and 14 scholarships have been gained to Shrewsbury School, Oundle and Malvern College in the last three years. 15 boys have gained academic scholarships to Shrewsbury School in the last three years with other academic awards to Oundle, Uppingham, Moreton Hall, Wrekin College and Concord College. A number of boys and girls have gained art, sport and all-rounder scholarships.

Prestfelde is a Woodard School, with its own Chaplain and a clear stance in promoting spiritual and moral values within the school.

Charitable status. Prestfelde School is a Registered Charity, number 1102931. It aims to provide education for boys and girls.

Prince's Mead School

Worthy Park House Kings Worthy Winchester Hampshire SO21 1AN
Tel: 01962 888000
Fax: 01962 886888
e-mail: admin@princesmeadschool.org.uk
website: www.princesmeadschool.org.uk

Chairman of Governors: Dr N Thomas

Headmistress: **Miss P Kirk**, BEd Exeter

Deputy Head: Mrs H M Harrison

Age Range. 3–11 co-educational.

Number of Children. 266 Day Boys and Girls.

Fees per term (2008-2009). £2,200–£3,450.

Established in 1949, Prince's Mead is a Day Preparatory School on the outskirts of Winchester. The school provides a balanced day and a purposeful atmosphere within which the children are encouraged to acquire sound working habits, an enthusiasm and zest for knowledge and a desire to achieve their full potential. The pleasures and responsibilities of school life are an integral part of development and we encourage cooperation, a responsible attitude and the confidence to work independently or within a group. The school is alive to the children's needs both now and in the future; the aim is to provide education for life.

Girls are prepared for Common entrance and Scholarships to a wide variety of Independent Schools. Boys are prepared for entry to local independent day and boarding schools at age 11. Results in Common Entrance and Senior School entrance examinations are consistently very good, with a high percentage of pupils taking up places in Senior Schools having a strong national reputation.

The curriculum is built around the cores subjects and looks to provide education for the 21st Century. Music, Sport and a wide range of extra-curricular activities enhance and enrich development.

Bursaries (financial assistance) are available throughout the school.

Charitable status. Prince's Mead School is a Registered Charity, number 288675. It exists to provide education for boys and girls.

Prior Park Preparatory School

Calcutt Street Cricklade Wiltshire SN6 6BB
Tel: 01793 750275
Fax: 01793 750910
e-mail: officepriorparkprep@priorpark.co.uk
website: www.priorparkschools.co.uk

Chair of Governors: Sister Jane Livesey, CJ, MA (Cantab)

Headmaster: **G B Hobern**, BA

Age Range. 7–13.

Number of Pupils. 198 (48 Boarders, 150 Day; 114 Boys, 84 Girls).

Fees per term (2008-2009). Boarding £4,601–£5,408, Day Pupils £3,146–£3,869.

Prior Park Preparatory School is a thriving co-educational day and boarding school situated in rural North Wiltshire on the edge of the Cotswolds. We form part of the Prior Park Educational Trust with our senior school, Prior Park College and The Paragon. A strong boarding community lies at the heart of our school with a third of our pupils boarding in some capacity. We accept children with a broad range of ability, so we are exceptionally proud of the 48 Scholarships (academic, music, art, sport, languages, maths, all rounder, leadership) achieved by our Year 8 pupils over the last three years.

Prior Park is a supportive Christian community, Catholic in foundation but ecumenical in spirit and it warmly welcomes children from all denominations. Many non Catholic parents choose Prior Park because of the strong Christian ethos which underpins the whole school. Meadowpark Nursery and Pre-Prep School is situated next door to the Preparatory School and most of its pupils transfer to Prior Park at the beginning of Year 3.

Boarding is an exciting and established feature of our school and an area of growth in recent years. Pupils come from Hong Kong, Europe, Russia and Zimbabwe as well as some from Armed Forces families. Our philosophy towards boarding is to create a stable family atmosphere in which our pupils feel happy and secure. Boarders are cared for by very experienced full time members of staff who live within the boarding houses. A range of activities are organised for boarders with pupils having a say in how they spend their free time. The trip out on Sunday is always one of the highlights of the week.

A broad and balanced curriculum is delivered by highly qualified staff, including a large number of subject specialists. Pupils are taught in small classes in which each child is treated as an individual. We have an enviable programme of music, drama and art with pupils taking part in many local festivals to a very high level. Many pupils take advantage of public Speaking classes which are successful in promoting their self confidence in other areas of school life. Our Learning Support Department is CReSTeD registered and offers support for pupils with mild to moderate dyslexia. We also make provision for those pupils for whom English is a foreign language.

All our pupils have the chance to represent school in sports fixtures ranging from rugby and netball to swimming and athletics. Every year a few pupils are selected to play at County level. Regular foreign sports tours take place, the most recent being to Barbados, Jersey and Paris.

Our modern facilities include a large, sports hall, ICT suite with 20 flat screen computers, art studio with new kiln, music studio, extensive playing fields, new astroturf and 25m outdoor heated swimming pool. A wide ranging enrichment programme exists for both day and boarding pupils. Some of the most popular activities include judo, Irish dancing, golf, tennis, fencing, debating, chess, choir and orchestra, business enterprise, art, Eco club and archery.

A limited number of HM Forces bursaries are available.

Charitable status. Prior Park Educational Trust is a Registered Charity, number 281242.

Priory Preparatory School

Bolters Lane Banstead Surrey SM7 2AJ
Tel: 01737 366920
Fax: 01737 366921
e-mail: office@prioryprep.co.uk
website: www.prioryprep.co.uk

Chairman of Governors: J A Spalton, FCA

***Headmaster*: Graham D Malcolm**, BEd, MA, FRSA

Age Range. 2–13.

Number of Boys. 160 Day Boys.

Fees per term (2008-2009). Nursery £1,250/£1,700; Pre-Preparatory £2,200; Preparatory £3,035.

Priory is a small, friendly school where every boy is valued and contributes fully to the various activities organised in the school. A strong pastoral framework supports the boys' learning and enjoyment of what is on offer at Priory. Priory boys are happy boys.

The boys are prepared for the Senior Independent School selected by the parents in consultation with the Headmaster. The aim is to provide a sound, well-balanced course designed to prepare boys for a smooth transfer to their next school. The curriculum reflects this aim and in so doing includes all school games and physical activities as a normal and necessary part of every boy's life, irrespective of ability. Soccer, Rugby, Cricket, Athletics, Basketball and Swimming are coached extensively. Gymnastics is particularly strong. A multi-purpose Sports Hall greatly enhances the facilities, as does a large sportsfield. There is specialist accommodation for Art, Science and ICT and a library. There is a strong emphasis on Music and Drama.

The Pre-Preparatory Department is highly successful having had excellent Ofsted reviews. The Preparatory School has also had excellent reviews in recent inspections.

Although most boys are prepared for the Common Entrance Examination, a large number of Scholarships has been won in recent years. The essential groundwork of a good education lies in the experienced Pre-Preparatory Department which the School possesses. Traditional values, skills and standards run parallel with modern teaching methods and an extensive range of educational visits is arranged throughout the year.

Charitable status. The Priory School (Banstead) Trust Limited is a Registered Charity, number 312035. It exists for the education of boys aged two to thirteen years.

Prospect House School

75 Putney Hill London SW15 3NT
Tel: 020 8780 0456
Fax: 020 8780 3010
e-mail: info@prospecths.org.uk
website: www.prospecths.org.uk

Chairman of Governors: Mr Anthony Rentoul

***Headmistress*: Mrs D Barratt**, MEd (Newcastle-upon-Tyne)

Age Range. 3–11 co-educational.

Number of Pupils. 180 day pupils.

Fees per term (2007-2008). Nursery (5 mornings) £1,760, Reception–Year 2 £3,550, Year 3 £3,600, Years 4–6 £3,680.

Prospect House School occupies a large Victorian building in nearly an acre of grounds, including an all weather sports area, at the top of Putney Hill overlooking Putney Heath. There is a multi-purpose hall where assemblies, music recitals, gymnastics and drama productions take place. There are dedicated rooms for music, ICT and special needs with art, DT and science also having provision within the school.

Most children join the school at 3 or 4 years of age, although occasionally there are places for older children. Selection for entry at 3 is date of registration, with preference given to brothers and sisters of children already in the school. An equal balance of boys and girls is kept throughout the school and this is reflected in the staffing.

Although the school does not select at entry at age 3 or 4, the academic track record is strong. The curriculum includes all National Curriculum subjects, with the addition of French from the age of four. There are numerous specialist teachers and children from Nursery are taught by specialists for Music, PE, French and ICT. Children are prepared for a wide range of leading day and boarding schools for entry at 11 years of age, with some children taking academic, music and sport scholarships. There is a wide and varied sports programme with many fixtures against other preparatory schools and children from Year 3 upwards attend training sessions at a nearby sports ground under the guidance of qualified instructors.

Clubs after school cater for many interests and visiting teachers also provide a wide range of individual music lessons. Children are regularly taken on educational visits to London and the surrounding area, with residential field study trips being undertaken in the final three years.

Quainton Hall School

Hindes Road Harrow Middlesex HA1 1RX
Tel: 020 8427 1304
Fax: 020 8861 8861

e-mail: admin@quaintonhall.org.uk
website: www.quaintonhall.org.uk

Chairman of Governors: Mrs Cheryl L Evans, BEd

***Headmaster*: Desmond P Banister**, BA, AKC (King's College, London), DipTEdMin (Oxon)

Age Range. 3–13.
Number of Pupils. 206.
Fees per term (2007-2008). £2,352–£2,812.

Quainton Hall, which has had four Heads in its long history, is staffed by experienced and well-qualified men and women. There is a Nursery of 20 children from rising three to four. In 2006 this was acclaimed as "outstanding" by Ofsted. Nursery entrance is arranged through the School Office. Boys and girls are accepted into the Junior School from the age of 4+; the girls are prepared for transfer at 7+, while the boys move into the Middle School, where there is a further entry of boys at 7+. Additionally, candidates of prep school age are accepted into other classes, where space permits. Initially, parents are asked to submit a registration and the family is then invited to interview. Entry is by means of a short, friendly assessment and previous nursery/school report. Since the school's foundation in Harrow in 1897, a consistently high standard of work has been maintained, which is reflected in regular successes at 13+ in the competitive examinations for leading London schools (including Merchant Taylors', Haberdashers' and City of London) in Common Entrance and in entrance scholarships (for academic excellence, in Music, Drama, Art and Sport). Each year a small number of our Leavers go on to boarding schools, including Harrow.

The curriculum is broad and supportive and provides for lessons in Art, Drama, Technology and Music each week in addition to all the core subjects. French is begun at the age of seven, Latin is taken from the age of 10+ and German is offered as an additional Modern Language to the Seniors (12+). Dramatic productions are performed each year and there is an excellent tradition of choral and instrumental music. Over the years, many boys have played in children's orchestras and music scholarships are won regularly. Available to everyone is a wide and varied range of visits and expeditions, which include field trips, ski holidays, adventure weeks, visits to mainland Europe and numerous one-day outings to London and beyond. The school also takes very great pride in its extensive programme of extra-curricular activities. These occur both during the lunch hour and after school.

The Parents' Association (The Friends of Quainton Hall School) is very active and provides a range of social occasions for parents and staff through the year. In recent years, through their hard work and generosity, not least at the annual Christmas and Summer Fairs, the Friends have provided the school with a very great deal in terms of additional resources and equipment.

The school sets very great store by its sports provision. The games played include Athletics, Badminton, Basketball, Cricket, Cross-Country, Football, Gym Hockey, Rugby, Swimming, Table Tennis, Tennis and Volleyball. We use our own indoor swimming-pool, our sports court and hall; home matches are played on green open spaces a few minutes from the school.

Quainton Hall, which belongs to the Shrine of Our Lady at Walsingham in Norfolk, has been a Church of England Educational Trust since 1944 and possesses its own Chapel. Candidates are presented for Confirmation if they and their parents wish. Our pupils come from the range of cultural and religious backgrounds to be found in North London and experience shows that this is a source of enrichment to the life and work of the whole school community.

Over the years, very considerable resources have been devoted to the ongoing development of the school; the most recent additions to the extensive facilities include four dedicated classrooms for our seven and eight-year-olds, a new Science Laboratory, a new School Library and a new Art Room. The self-contained Nursery with its garden attached provides an excellent start to school for our youngest pupils.

Charitable status. Quainton Hall School, under the Trusteeship of Walsingham College (Affiliated Schools) Limited, is a Registered Charity, number 312638. It exists to provide a sound education within a definite Christian framework.

Queen Elizabeth Grammar School Junior School

158 Northgate Wakefield West Yorkshire WF1 3QY
Tel: 01924 373821
Fax: 01924 366246
e-mail: head@qegsjs.org.uk
website: www.wgsf.org.uk

Spokesman for the Governors: Mrs M Waugh

***Head*: Mrs L Gray**, CertEd, MA

Age Range. 7–11.
Number of Boys. 260 day boys
Fees per term (2008-2009). 7–8 years £2,275; 9–10 years £2,404. Fees include lunch.

This is an extremely well resourced Junior School which enjoys a full range of buildings and facilities quite separate from the Senior School. The most recent stage of this development included a new Music Room, Hall, Library, Information Technology Centre and Play Garden Area. The other specialist Junior School facilities include a learner Swimming Pool and rooms for Art, Design Technology and Science in addition to twelve well appointed classrooms.

The main aim of the School is to prepare boys for the Senior School, although boys who sit the entrance examinations for other Independent Senior Schools are also very successful. There are three forms at 7, 8, 9 and 10. Although a high proportion of the boys join at 7, vacancies are reserved for each of the three subsequent years. All entry is by examination with the main Entrance Tests being held in February.

Each day starts with an Assembly, after which work continues in the full range of normal Junior subjects. While the Form Teacher takes the bulk of the classroom lessons in the younger forms there is from the start a significant involvement of specialist staff. The contribution of such specialist staff in Science, Art, Music, ICT, Modern Languages, and History expands as boys progress through the Junior School. Pupils are expected to learn the discipline of hard work, while at the same time the aim is to excite enthusiasm and interest so that each boy achieves his full potential.

There is an excellent tradition of music, both choral and instrumental, in the School as there are two choirs, instrumental groups and a Junior School Orchestra. Twelve boys are Choral Scholars at Wakefield Cathedral for which a Voice Trial is held in February. Choral Scholarships are available.

The Junior School has its own playing fields, cricket nets and cricket pavilion. Boys have PE, swimming or games every day: in winter Rugby, Swimming and Cross-Country Running; in summer Cricket, Swimming and Athletics. There is an extensive programme of both inter-school and inter-house matches. The coaching of all games is undertaken entirely by Junior School staff. The Junior School regularly enjoys National success in Rugby, Chess, Athletics and Swimming.

There are sixteen fully qualified assistant teachers including specialists for Art, Music, ICT and Science. In addition there is a School Nurse, and five Non-Teaching Assistants, an ICT technician and part-time Librarian.

Charitable status. The Wakefield Grammar School Foundation is a Registered Charity, number 1088415. It exists to provide an excellent education for your son.

Queen's College Junior and Pre-Prep Schools
Taunton

Trull Road Taunton TA1 4QP
Tel: 01823 272990 (Junior)
01823 278928 (Pre-Prep)
Fax: 01823 323811
e-mail: junior.sec@queenscollege.org.uk
website: www.queenscollege.org.uk

Chairman of Governors: Mr J N Birkett, FCIB, MSI

***Headmaster*: Mr J M Backhouse**, BEd

Age Range. 3–11.

Number of Pupils. Junior School: 178 of whom 14 are boarders. Pre-Prep: 49.

Fees per term (2008-2009). Junior: £3,185–£4,845 (boarders); £1,885–£3,105 (day). Pre-Prep: £1,545–£1,590. Nursery (per session): Morning £19, Afternoon £14.50, All day £33, After-School Care £6, Full time (per term) £1,370.

Queen's College is a co-educational boarding and day school on the outskirts of Taunton with fine views across the playing fields to the surrounding hills. The Junior School is run as an independent unit but shares many of the excellent facilities of the adjacent Senior School. We aim to create a happy, caring atmosphere based on Christian values. For the boarders, especially, the School endeavours to provide a sympathetic background for a child's first venture away from home. We are well versed in settling pupils whose families have been posted abroad. For every pupil, however, the aim of the School is to find areas in which each child can succeed, thereby developing the self-confidence which will help them achieve their potential.

From the age of 8, most of the teaching is subject-based in specialist rooms. Syllabuses are broadly in line with the National Curriculum, however, we do not intend our courses to be unduly restricted by its detailed provisions.

The principal games are Rugby, Hockey and Cricket for the boys, Hockey, Netball and Rounders for the girls. Tennis, Swimming and Athletics matches also take place. Fullest use is made of the excellent sporting facilities of the School, particularly the Sports Hall, Tennis Courts, heated indoor Swimming Pool and floodlit Astroturf.

After-school activities include: Badminton, Cookery, Chess, Computer Club, Drama, Specialist Music Groups, Model Making, Origami, Puppets, Squash and Gymnastics. Dancing, Speech and Drama, and Riding are also arranged at an extra charge. Pupils may attend local brownie, cub, guides and scout groups.

The Pre-Prep day school for children aged 4 to 7 is in its own purpose-built building separated from the Junior School by the adventure playground.

To complete provision at Queen's College, there is a Nursery School for children aged 3–4 years. There are up to 18 places available on a sessional basis. After-school care is also provided for Nursery and Pre-Prep children.

The Nursery and Pre-Prep environment is a happy and stimulating one with an informal atmosphere and high standards. We adhere broadly to the National Curriculum but enrich it, particularly in the core subjects. There is a full range of after-school activities.

Nearly all the children move on from one section of Queen's College to the next; there is no further qualifying examination. We offer parents and pupils continuity of education from the Pre-Prep, through the Junior School to the Senior School, with the school week running from Monday to Friday. Weekend activities for the boarding pupils are always fun and emphasis is made on creating a family-style, homely atmosphere in which they can relax and unwind.

The Pre-Preparatory School educates pupils up to the age of 7; the Junior School educates pupils up to the end of Key Stage 2 (NC Year 6). Children aged 11+ will be admitted directly to the Senior School.

Charitable status. Queen's College, Taunton is a Registered Charity, number 310208. It exists for the purpose of educating children in a Christian environment according to the traditions of the Methodist Church.

Ramillies Hall School

Cheadle Hulme Cheadle Cheshire SK8 7AJ
Tel: 0161 485 3804
Fax: 0161 486 6021
e-mail: study@ramillieshall.co.uk
website: www.ramillieshall.co.uk

***Principals*:**
Mrs A L Poole (*Bursar*)
Miss D M Patterson, BA, PGCE (*Head Teacher*)

Age Range. 6 months to 16 years.

Number of Children. Day: 81 boys, 22 girls. Nursery: 85 children.

Fees per term (2008-2009). Day pupils: £2,350 (Years 1–6), £2,550 (Years 7–9), £2,600 (Years 10–11). Nursery from £4.65 per hour.

Ramillies Hall, founded in 1884, is a small school for children aged 6 to 16 years. In our small classes (average 15 pupils) we bring together the best of traditional methods and modern multi-sensory teaching. We follow, and in some areas extend, the National Curriculum and offer a range of practical and vocational GCSEs along with the core subjects. Our well-structured learning programmes build confidence and encourage our pupils to become independent learners.

Our specialism is in dyslexia, dyspraxia and similar learning difficulties, and a high proportion of our pupils come to Ramillies for that reason. When they arrive, many children are lacking in self-esteem because of their previous experience of the education system. Our first task is often to find their strengths and build on them to increase their confidence. We offer tuition and support from specialist trained teachers in our Learning Support Department, to enable pupils to access the full curriculum. This has brought external recognition of our expertise in this field, with accreditation by CReSTeD (Council for the Registration of Schools Teaching Dyslexics). To maintain this, the School is subject to rigorous and regular inspection, and Ramillies is the only school in the Manchester area with the accreditation.

An extended day (until 5.50 pm, Mondays to Thursdays) enables us to offer a wide variety of sports and extra-curricular activities, and homework can be completed during this time under the supervision of a teacher.

Ramillies also has a Nursery, open from 8.00 am to 6.00 pm, Monday to Friday throughout the year, for babies and children up to school reception age. We are proud of our high standards of care, and our qualified and experienced staff provide a stimulating and exciting environment for our youngest children.

Easily accessible by road and rail, the School is set in its own spacious grounds with extensive playing fields and heated outdoor swimming pool.

For more information, visit our website as given above.

Ranby House
A Woodard School

Retford Nottinghamshire DN22 8HX
Tel: 01777 703138; Bursary: 714391
Fax: 01777 702813
e-mail: office@ranbyhouseschool.co.uk
website: www.ranbyhouseschool.co.uk

Chairman of the School Council: T D Fremantle, MBA

***Headmaster*: D Sibson**, BA Ed Hons

Age Range. 3–13.

Number of Pupils. 344: 190 boys, 154 girls, including 65 boarders.

Fees per term (2008-2009). Boarders £4,830; Day Children £3,570; Pre-Prep £2,050.

Ranby House is a caring, happy, exciting, Christian community. Within it boarding and day boys and girls work and play hard, striving for excellence. The atmosphere is like no other where the children focus on 'aiming high'.

This thriving school is situated in 60 acres of beautiful woodland, gardens and playing fields. The facilities in and out of the classroom are excellent and include: new Performing Arts Centre with a 300-seat auditorium and Music School, Sports Centre, Computer Centre, Library, Design Technology Centre, 2 Science Laboratories, outdoor heated swimming pool, 4 floodlit all-weather netball/tennis courts, Gymnasium, Chapel and extensive level playing fields.

The purpose built Pre-Prep department takes children from 3 to 7 years after which time they transfer to the main school.

Boys and girls may board from the age of 7 years. Spacious, colourful bedrooms, brilliant food and caring houseparents are some of the essential elements of the Ranby boarding experience. Boarding is flexible, and is dependent upon the needs of the individual family.

Academic standards are high at Ranby. Last year a total of 16 Scholarship awards, for academic, musical, sporting, art and all-round excellence, were made to pupils transferring to their senior independent schools. The school also caters for children with specific learning difficulties.

A wealth of extra curricular opportunities are on offer and pupils are encouraged to take an active part in all aspects of school life. The school has a strong sporting tradition and flourishing music and drama departments.

Links with the armed forces are strong and the school offers Forces Bursaries.

Ranby is a school of the Woodard Corporation. It has a Christian foundation, and is the largest group of independent schools in the country. The school has strong links with Worksop College as a partner within Woodard Schools (Nottinghamshire) Ltd: "Two schools, one education". Pupils are prepared for Common Entrance and Scholarship examinations to a variety of Senior Schools.

The school offers bus services from the Retford, Worksop, Rotherham, Doncaster, Tickhill, Tuxford, Newark and Mansfield areas.

Ravenscourt Park Preparatory School

16 Ravenscourt Avenue Chiswick London W6 0SL
Tel: 020 8846 9153
Fax: 020 8846 9413
e-mail: secretary@rpps.co.uk
website: www.rpps.co.uk

Chair of Governors: Mrs Janet Mayne

***Headmaster*: R C Relton**

Age Range. 4–11 co-educational.

Number of Pupils. 260 boys and girls.

Fees per term (2008-2009). £3,969.

The school provides education of the highest quality for boys and girls, preparing them for transfer to the best and most selective Independent Schools at 11 years of age. The Lower School caters for pupils aged 4–7 and is based in a large, Victorian house, formerly a vicarage. The Upper School, 7–11 years, enjoys purpose built accommodation erected in 1996. The secure site includes a large play area and the school makes use of the extensive facilities of Ravenscourt Park which it adjoins.

The curriculum includes French, Music, Art and Craft, RE, Computer Studies and PE for all pupils in addition to the usual core subjects. In the Upper School the majority of subjects are taught by specialists. All Upper School pupils attend a Summer Term Residential Week where studies across the curriculum are applied to a non-urban environment.

There are many after school clubs and sports activities and we have two choirs and an orchestra. Individual tuition is offered in piano, violin, brass, woodwind, cello, saxophone and singing. Our Drama productions are a highlight of each school year.

An 8 am to 6 pm All Day Care service is offered to parents at an extra charge.

The school is noted for its warm, happy atmosphere where parents play a full part in enriching the curriculum and social life. Off-site visits and guest workshops presented by noted visitors are a regular feature of education at RPPS.

The school is always heavily over-subscribed and registration is recommended on the child's first birthday. A prospectus and registration form may be obtained from the School Secretary.

The Red Maids' Junior School

Grange Court Road Westbury-on-Trym Bristol BS9 4DP
Tel: 0117 962 9451
Fax: 0117 962 9451
e-mail: juniors@redmaids.bristol.sch.uk
website: www.redmaids.bristol.sch.uk

Chairman of Governors: Mr K Bonham, BA, FCA, DL, MBE

***Headteacher*: Mrs G B Rowcliffe**, BEd (University of Bristol)

Age Range. 7–11.

Number of Girls. 111 Day Girls.

Fees per term (2008-2009). £1,850 plus lunches.

The Red Maids' Junior School opened its new building in April 2008. The new library and ICT suite are at the heart of the expanded school and the lofty new art studio and music floor are inspiring exciting new creative projects. The large school hall provides space for the whole school to meet together regularly and the big garden offers plenty of space for outdoor play. Every classroom is equipped with an interactive whiteboard.

The school is equipped for approximately 120 girls aged 7–11 organised into six classes. In Years 3 and 4, each class is taught by their own class teacher for the majority of their timetable. In Years 5 and 6, girls are taught by more specialist teachers but we take care to ensure that they are nurtured within each year group unit. There are frequent opportunities built into the timetable for girls to work and make friends with children in all year groups. Since the girls know each other and every member of staff well, a strong community feeling is promoted within the school where girls can develop their confidence and self-esteem.

All the girls are encouraged to explore their individual talents and achieve their best through the school's broad and balanced curriculum, including Mandarin. Whole school planning is an essential feature of every subject area, ensuring continuity and progression; assessment is an integral part of this. Year 6 girls sit National Curriculum Key Stage 2 Standard Assessment Tests in English, mathematics and science and results are very good indeed.

In addition there is a strong emphasis on the pastoral care of the children. Through school meetings and class activities, the school teaches a sense of good citizenship as girls are encouraged to share responsibility for the care of their community and their environment.

Close links are fostered between the Junior and Senior Red Maids through joint activities and visits. Pupils benefit from use of a science laboratory, extensive PE facilities including an all-weather pitch and the award-winning school lunches. At age 11, Junior Red Maids transfer to the Senior School (conditions apply) and achieve outstanding success in the entrance examination.

Extra-curricular activities are an essential part of every girl's school experience and there is a strong commitment to outdoor education.

The school enjoys close relationships with parents on a daily basis and generous support is offered to the school through a thriving Friends' Association.

Charitable status. The Red Maids' School is a Registered Charity, number 1105017. It has existed since 1634 to provide an education for girls.

Redcliffe School

47 Redcliffe Gardens London SW10 9JH
Tel: 020 7352 9247
Fax: 020 7352 6936
e-mail: admissions@redcliffeschool.com
website: www.redcliffeschool.com

Chairman of the Board of Governors: Simon Lalor

***Headmistress*: Mrs Susan Bourne**, BSc, PGCE

Age Range. Boys 3–8, Girls 3–11.

Number of Pupils. 107 Day Pupils (32 boys, 75 girls)

Fees per term (2008-2009). £3,650. Nursery: £2,100 (morning class), £1,400 (afternoon class), £3,500 (full day).

Easily accessible from all parts of central and West London, Redcliffe is a small, friendly school with highly motivated, confident and happy children. Emphasis is placed on a good combination of hard work and plenty of fun within a framework of discipline and good manners. The balanced curriculum includes Mathematics, English, History, Geography, Science, IT, Art and Craft, Scripture, Current Affairs, Music, Physical Education and Drama. French is taught throughout the school. Individual attention encourages the pursuit of high academic standards and we are proud that our children gain places at their first choice of senior or prep school, including Colet Court, Sussex House, St Philip's, Downe House, Benenden, Queen's Gate, Godolphin and Latymer and Francis Holland. Every class has some form of Physical Education each day; in the gym or playground, local netball court or park. All pupils participate in a wide range of sports and activities including: rugby, hockey, cricket and swimming. After school activities include cookery, ballet, computer skills and drama. Music is strength of the school with visiting instrumental staff and a high standard of performance. Parents are encouraged to be involved with the school through Open Assemblies, Parents' Discussion Groups, the Parents' Committee and regular meetings with the teachers.

Redcliffe Robins is our nursery class for children between the ages of 2½ and 4 years with a specialist Montessori-trained teacher and access to all of Recliffe's resources and facilities to help prepare the children for entry to the main school. Each day has a balanced timetable of language work, mathematical skills, art and craft, music, drama and PE with ample opportunity for structured free play and the development of social skills.

Children are assessed at three years of age for entry to the main school at four. Entry for subsequent years by test. Tours of the school are held weekly during term-time by appointment with the school office.

Charitable status. Redcliffe School Trust Ltd is a Registered Charity, number 312716. It exists to provide a high standard of education for children within a caring environment.

Reddiford School

38 Cecil Park Pinner Middlesex HA5 5HH
Tel: 020 8866 0660
Fax: 020 8866 4847
e-mail: office@reddiford.org.uk
website: www.reddiford.org.uk

Chairman of Governors: Mr F C Flood

***Head*: Mrs J Batt**, CertEd, NPQH

Age Range. 2¾–11.

Number of Pupils. Day: 149 Boys, 103 Girls; Nursery and Foundation: 39 Boys, 30 Girls.

Fees per term (2008-2009). Nursery: £1,160 (mornings only), £2,060 (all day), Foundation £2,480, Reception–Year 2 £2,690, Years 3–6 £2,780.

Reddiford School has been established in Cecil Park, Pinner since 1913. Whilst the school maintains its Church of England status, children from all faiths and cultures are welcomed. Throughout the school the ethos is on respect for one another. Reddiford prides itself on being a town school based in the heart of Pinner; a few minutes' walk from local transport facilities.

Reddiford possesses a fine academic record, preparing its pupils for entrance at 11+ into major independent schools, many at scholarship level. There is a high teacher pupil ratio ensuring small classes leading to a friendly caring environment where all children are valued.

The early years department is situated in its own building and caters for children from 2 years nine months to rising 5 years. It offers a stimulating and attractive environment where children are encouraged to be independent and active learners. The nursery follows the foundation stage profiling which incorporates the six areas of learning. There is a choice of full or half day provision.

The infant department builds on the knowledge and skills acquired in the nursery placing the emphasis on developing confidence and the ability to learn and work independently and with others. The infant department has its own state-of-the-art computer suite and interactive whiteboards in classrooms. There is specialist teaching in French, Music and PE from reception upwards and all children are taught to swim.

In the junior department children are taught by specialist teachers in properly resourced subject rooms. There is a fully equipped science laboratory, dedicated art and music rooms and a second ICT suite utilising dual-purpose desks. Pupils are prepared for entry to the many prestigious senior schools in the area, a process which involves consultation with parents from an early stage.

There is an extensive programme of extra-curricular activities throughout the school including: sports (football, cricket, netball, gymnastics, karate), languages (French, Mandarin), art, science, sewing, and ballet. We also offer before and after school care, with a prep club for older children.

Entry to the nursery is possible in any term once a child has reached 2 years and 9 months. Most children move from the nursery to the main school at 4+, but there are spaces for other applicants in the reception classes. An assessment day for these places is held in January for September entry. Means-tested bursaries may be available.

Charitable status. Reddiford School is a Registered Charity, number 312641. It exists to provide education for boys and girls.

Redland High School for Girls Junior School

Redland Court Bristol BS6 7EF
Tel: 0117 924 5796
e-mail: admissions@redland.bristol.sch.uk
website: www.redland.bristol.sch.uk

Chairman of Governors: Mr P J F Breach, BA, FCA, ATII, ACT, IIMR

***Head*: Mr J P Eyles**, BEd (Bath Spa), MEd (Bristol)

Age Range. 3–11.

Number of Girls. 150.

Fees per term (2008-2009). Nursery £15 per half day; Reception, Years 1 & 2 £1,770; Years 3–6 £2,090.

Redland High Junior School is situated in three Victorian houses close to the Senior School in a very pleasant residential area of Bristol. The School is easily reached from the surrounding districts.

Children are taught by well qualified and highly motivated teachers who are very well supported by a number of excellent classroom assistants.

The school aims to provide each child with the opportunity to develop fully her particular talent within a stimulating and supportive environment. We try to create a friendly, family atmosphere within which high standards are expected in all areas of the curriculum.

Whilst emphasis is placed on numeracy and literacy, children also respond to high expectations in science, ICT, drama, history, geography, RE, art, PE and modern languages. Music is a particular strength of the school with most pupils learning to play an instrument or joining in choral or orchestral activities. Our curriculum embraces the principal areas of study appropriate for Primary School education. It is based on the National Curriculum requirements and the Early Learning Goals for the Under Fives. However, we aim to give our pupils more than these minimum requirements so that they have a head start when they reach senior school. Our high standards and expectations ensure that the brighter pupils can be stretched to their full potential, whilst those who need extra help get additional support.

There are a number of extra curricular activities available, including outdoor pursuits (canoeing, abseiling etc), computer clubs, netball, short tennis, recorder groups, dance and art clubs.

During each school year there are a number of educational visits and workshops. Most of these visits are a way of enabling pupils to consolidate knowledge acquired in lessons. Other outings are of a more cultural nature and often include visits to concerts and theatres. Year 5 and 6 pupils have the opportunity to travel abroad. Past visits have been to France, Holland, Germany, Iceland and Italy.

Pupils are encouraged to nominate and support charities, and each term sees an event designed to raise money for the chosen charity.

When our pupils reach 11 they are ready to move on. Most girls move on to our Senior School where they experience new challenges and choices. The girls from the Junior School are well prepared and ready to embrace the next stage of their education with enthusiasm and confidence.

Charitable status. Redland High School for Girls is a Registered Charity, number 311734. It exists to provide education for girls.

Reigate St Mary's Preparatory and Choir School

Chart Lane Reigate Surrey RH2 7RN
Tel: 01737 244880
Fax: 01737 221540
e-mail: hmsec@reigatestmarys.org
website: www.reigatestmarys.org

Chairman of Governors: Mr Alan Walker

***Headmaster*: Marcus Culverwell**, MA Ed

Age Range. 3–11.

Number of Pupils. 290 pupils (190 boys, 100 girls).

Fees per term (2008-2009). Kindergarten £1,204 (half-day session); Transition to Year 2 £2,861, Years 3–6 £3,368.

Reigate St Mary's is an independent day school for boys and girls aged 3–11. It is the nursery and junior school of Reigate Grammar School. Set in 15 acres of beautiful parkland and sports fields. We are proud of our reputation as a lively, happy, family friendly school where each child is encouraged and known as an individual. Within easy reach of the M25 a coach pick-up service covers a wide area of local towns including Horsham, Crawley, Leatherhead, Horley, Dorking and Tadworth.

Reigate St Mary's aims to provide an education of considerable depth and breadth within a disciplined, happy and caring environment, incorporating a tradition of choral excellence and Christian values. All pupils are encouraged to be ambitious, to reach the best standards they can in their academic studies, in sport, in art, in music and in other performing arts. The school aims to engender a love of learning, a zest for life and to develop a caring and understanding attitude towards other people. The school places a very high value on good relationships and developing inter-personal skills in our pupils to enable them to become responsible, adaptable, independent people in a changing world. At Reigate St Mary's we believe that all children should feel valued for who they are, not just for what they achieve.

As a member of the Choir Schools' Association Reigate St Mary's is one of only a small number of schools, not attached to a cathedral or college, which maintain a traditional choir of boys and men under the direction of a Master of Choristers. The choir sings regular school and church services with a repertoire of music from the 16th Century to the present day. Entrance to the choir is by voice trial, and choral scholarships are offered by the Godfrey Searle Choir Trust.

RGS The Grange

Grange Lane Claines Worcester WR3 7RR
Tel: 01905 451205
Fax: 01905 757917
e-mail: grange@rgsw.org.uk
website: www.rgsao.org

Chairman of Governors: R A Ingles

***Headmaster*: T R Lowe**, BA, CertEd, FCollP

Age Range. 2½–11 Co-educational.
Number of Pupils. 400.
Fees per term (2008-2009). £1,812–£2,844.

RGS The Grange is the co-educational junior school for RGS Worcester and The Alice Ottley School (*see HMC entry*). The school educates children between the ages of 2 and 11 and is situated in open countryside three miles north of Worcester in Fernhill Heath.

In 2004 a multi-million pound extension was added to the original country house, The Grange, providing excellent modern facilities including specialist art, design technology, science and ICT rooms alongside large, airy, well-equipped classrooms.

The school is set in 40 acres of grounds and offers exceptional games facilities including a full-sized Astroturf opened in 2008.

High academic standards are expected as the children are prepared to enter the newly-merged Royal Grammar School and Alice Ottley School at 11. There is a wide range of extra-curricular activities on offer and, while the school is noted for excellence in sport and music, it is of the greatest importance that the children are encouraged to be kind, considerate and well-mannered.

Charitable status. RGS Worcester and The Alice Ottley School is a Registered Charity, number 1120644.

The Richard Pate School

Southern Road Leckhampton Cheltenham Glos GL53 9RP
Tel: 01242 522086
Fax: 01242 524035
e-mail: hm@richardpate.co.uk
website: www.richardpate.co.uk

Chairman of Trustees: J Parker, Esq

***Headmaster*: R A MacDonald**

Deputy Heads:
Ms C Smith
Mrs S Wade

Age Range. 3–11 Co-educational.
Number of Pupils. 300 (approximately an equal number of boys and girls).
Fees per term (2008-2009). Nursery: £805 (5 mornings), £1,025 (any 3 full days), £1,365 (any 4 full days), £1,705 (5 full days). Preparatory: £1,830 (Reception), £2,000 (Year 1), £2,140 (Year 2). Junior: £2,210 (Year 3), £2,305 (Year 4), £2,485 (Year 5), £2,595 (Year 6).

Hot lunches are provided and included in the fees, except for 'mornings only' nursery.

The School, occupying an 11½ acre semi-rural site at the foot of the Cotswold escarpment, is part of the Pate's Grammar School Foundation which is a charity founded by Richard Pate, a Recorder of Gloucester, in 1574.

It is a non-denominational Christian school which in its present form began in 1946. The aim of the school is to provide a high academic standard and continuity of education up to the age of 11 years. The curriculum is broadly based with strong emphasis being attached to music, art, drama and sport, for these activities are seen as vital if a child's full potential is to be realised.

Facilities include a music centre with individual practice rooms; a fully equipped computer suite; an all-weather pitch with floodlights and an enclosed pond for environmental studies. After-school care is available through until 5.30 pm.

At present the School is divided into three sections: Nursery 3–4½ years; Preparatory Department 5–7 and Junior 7–11. Entrance is dependent upon the availability of places but most pupils join the school at the commencement of the Nursery, Preparatory or Junior Departments.

No entry tests are taken by younger pupils but interviews and selective tests are used for assessing pupils aged 5 years and upwards. A small number of 7+ scholarships are awarded each year.

The teaching takes full account of national curriculum guidelines with children in the upper part of the school following the normal preparatory school curriculum leading to Common Entrance and Scholarship at 11+. Pupils leave at age 11 for local Grammar Schools and a variety of independent secondary schools, particularly those in Cheltenham.

The Headmaster is assisted by two deputies and 18 fully qualified teachers including specialists in Latin, French, History, Art/Design, Science, Music and Learning Support. The School employs music and dance teachers, who prepare children for participation in various competitions, in particular the Cheltenham Competitive Festival. A specialist teachers' assistant and seven other qualified assistants are also employed full-time.

Charitable status. The Pate's Grammar School Foundation is a Registered Charity, number 311707.

Richmond House School

170 Otley Road Leeds West Yorkshire LS16 5LG
Tel: 0113 2752670
Fax: 0113 2304868
e-mail: enquiries@rhschool.org
website: www.rhschool.org

Chairman of the Board of Governors: Mr D Stubbs

***Headmistress*: Mrs Jane Disley**, BA Hons

Age Range. 3–11.
Number of Day Pupils. 260 boys and girls.
Fees per term (2008-2009). Nursery: £1,378 (half days only), £2,152 (full time). Reception–Year 6: £2,152. Lunches: £146.

Non-denominational Christian.

Richmond House School is a co-educational independent day school. Richmond House is proud of its friendly, caring atmosphere. It aims to develop each child's individual talents whether academic, musical or sporting in a happy environment. The school achieves good academic results with pupils gaining places each year to local independent senior schools, may being awarded scholarships.

Boys and girls enter the Nursery at the ages of three or four; entrance to Reception or later years by informal assessment and visit.

Class sizes are small to enable a high degree of individual attention. Pastoral care is an important part of every teacher's work. Each class is under the care of a Form Teacher but specialist teaching increases as the child progresses through the school.

The school is in two attached Victorian houses with a range of other buildings including practical rooms for Art, Science and Design Technology. The grounds extend to 10 acres to the rear allowing for a wide variety of games to take place – football, tennis, netball and athletics and many others.

There is a wide range of extra-curricular activities and pre and after school care to assist busy families.

Charitable status. Richmond House School is a Registered Charity, number 505630. It exists to provide high quality education for boys and girls aged 3–11 years.

Rickmansworth PNEU School

88 The Drive Rickmansworth Herts WD3 4DU
Tel: 01923 772101
Fax: 01923 776268
e-mail: office@rickmansworthpneu.co.uk
website: www.rickmansworthpneu.co.uk

Chairman of Board of Governors: Mr C D K Palmer, MA

***Headmistress*: Mrs S Hayes,**

Age Range. 3–11.

Number of Pupils. 150 Girls.

Fees per term (2008-2009). £885–£2,515.

Rickmansworth PNEU School is a Preparatory School for girls from 3 to 11 years which achieves high educational standards within the framework of a caring family environment. Girls start in the Nursery, which received an excellent Ofsted report, with an attendance of three mornings, increasing to five full days by the age of 5.

Although still retaining the original buildings set in pleasant gardens, the school has been extended over the years to provide large, modern classrooms. There is a well-equipped Science laboratory, a Music Room, Technology Room, Computer Suite and Library.

The curriculum is broad and girls also study a composer and an artist in depth each term. French is taught from the age of 3. PE is an important part of the curriculum and teams regularly compete in inter-school competitions. All girls take part in drama productions and concerts during the year and the senior girls perform a Shakespeare play each summer.

The well-qualified, experienced teaching staff are committed to the development of each child as an individual. We encourage children to enjoy learning, to use their initiative and become independent and to have high expectations of themselves. We nurture a caring spirit.

Girls transfer to a wide variety of schools in both the maintained and independent sectors, often with scholarships. KS2 SATs are taken at 11.

Extra-curricular activities include Tennis, TaeKwonDo, Speech & Drama, Dance, Orchestra, Choir, Brass, Flute, Guitar and Recorder.

Charitable status. The Rickmansworth PNEU School is a Registered Charity, number 311075. It exists to provide an enjoyable education that will develop the full potential of each child.

Riddlesworth Hall Preparatory School

Nr Diss Norfolk IP22 2TA
Tel: 01953 681246
Fax: 01953 688124
e-mail: rhps@riddlesworthhall.com
website: www.riddlesworthhall.com

***Headmaster*: Mr P I Cochrane**, CertEd

Age Range. Girls 2–13, Boys 2–12. Girls Boarding from age 7–13. Boys boarding from age 7–11.

Number of Pupils. 30 Boarders, 62 Day, 34 Nursery.

Fees per term (2008-2009). Full Boarders £5,605; Weekly Boarders £5,240; Day: Years 3–8 £3,620, Nursery–Year 2 £2,205. (Nursery sessions will be pro rata.)

Riddlesworth Hall, situated in a magnificent country house on the Norfolk/Suffolk border, provides an excellent all-round education. The aim is to develop each child's potential to the full in all areas – academic, sport and creative arts. The girls are prepared for Common Entrance and Scholarship examinations to independent senior schools.

Riddlesworth Hall has excellent art and pottery studios, science, domestic science and technology laboratories, a computer room, music and drama rooms and a gymnasium. French is taught from Reception. A range of sports is taught to all levels and good-quality teams are regularly produced.

The care of the children is in the hands of the Headmaster and his wife who are resident, supported by a team of matrons.

The school enjoys CreSTeD status and is specifically staffed to welcome dyslexic children. IEPs are prepared for these children, who enjoy all the benefits of full integration into main school activities.

Extras include speech and drama, ballet and riding. There is a very active music department with choirs, orchestra, various ensembles and a recorder group. Senior school music, drama and academic scholarships have been recently achieved.

There is a wide variety of clubs and activities including skiing, dance, ball skills, gym and cookery. A feature of Riddlesworth Hall is its Pets' Corner which houses a variety of small animals brought from home and permanently resident at school.

Self-reliance, self-discipline, and tolerance are encouraged, and good manners are expected.

Ripley Court School

Rose Lane Ripley Surrey GU23 6NE
Tel: 01483 225217
Fax: 01483 223854
e-mail: head@ripleycourt.co.uk
website: www.ripleycourt.co.uk

Chairman of Governors: C Holloway

***Headmaster*: A J Gough**, BSc UED, MA

Assistant Headmaster: J Porter, BA

Age Range. 3–13 Co-educational.

Number of Day Pupils. 280: Main School (age 7–13) 169; Little Court (age 4–7) 92; Nursery (age 3+) 20.

Fees per term (2008-2009). Main School £2,900–£3,280; Little Court £2,340; Nursery £2,300 full-time (part-time pro rata).

The School is a Charitable Trust. and offers bursarial scholarships on a means-tested basis. The Staff consists of graduates and trained teachers and pupils are prepared for Common Entrance and Scholarship Examinations for all the Boys' and Girls' Senior Independent Schools. There is a high academic standard and many Scholarships are won including some for Sport, Music and Art, but there is no cramming: PE, Music, Art and Craft are a part of every child's timetable with opportunities in orchestral, choral and dramatic productions. Facilities include a library, a science laboratory, a gymnasium and art, music and hobbies rooms. There are 20 acres of playing fields. Games and sports are Football (Association and Rugby), Hockey, Netball, Cricket, Tennis (2 hard, 2 grass courts), Athletics, Rounders, Volley-ball, Stoolball; Swimming and Life Saving are taught in a large, covered, heated swimming pool.

Little Court is the Pre-Prep Department which also uses the main playing field, swimming pool and gymnasium. The Nursery uses all school facilities and nursery children receive tuition in French, music, swimming and dance.

School transport serves Woking, Pyrford and West Byfleet.

Charitable status. Ripley Court School is a Registered Charity, number 312084. It aims to educate children and prepare them well for adult life.

Ripon Cathedral Choir School

Whitcliffe Lane Ripon North Yorkshire HG4 2LA
Tel: 01765 602134
Fax: 01765 608760
e-mail: admin@cathedralchoirschool.co.uk
website: www.cathedralchoirschool.co.uk

Governors:
Members of the Chapter of Ripon Cathedral and Lay Governors

Acting Headmistress: **Mrs Patricia Burton**, CertEd

Deputy Head: I D C Atkinson, BEd Oxford

Age Range. 3–13.
Number of Pupils. 106.
Fees per term (2008-2009). Boarders £4,605; Day Pupils: Year 4 and above £3,435, Years 2–3 £2,535, Year 1 £2,265, 2nd Year Foundation £2,000, 1st Year Foundation: sessional rates. 10% reduction for children of Service families, and a 5% reduction for siblings.

There are 16 Choristers – all boarders who have gained a 50% choral scholarship by a Voice Trial, and another 90 day, boarding and weekly boarding pupils. Members of the Girls' Cathedral Choir enjoy a reduction of 20% of the termly fee. The school is fully co-educational. Children are accepted into Pre-Prep from the age of 3 and move into the main school at the age of eight.

The school gives children a first-class academic education in small classes in a supportive atmosphere. There are spacious facilities for indoor and outdoor sport, and art, drama and IT are greatly encouraged. Music is exceptionally strong. The school is attractively situated on the edge of a small city in a very pleasant and interesting area. The boarding accommodation is secure and friendly.

Charitable status. Ripon Cathedral Choir School is a Registered Charity, number 529583. It exists to provide non-profit making full-time education for the boy choristers of Ripon Cathedral, and for other children.

Rockport School

Rockport Road Craigavad Holywood Co Down BT18 0DD Northern Ireland
Tel: 028 9042 8372
Fax: 028 9042 2608
e-mail: info@rockportschool.com
website: www.rockportschool.com

Chairman of the Governors: H Hastings

Headmistress: **Ms C A Osborne**, BEd

Age Range. 3–16.
Number of Pupils. Girls 95, Boys 97.
Fees per term (2007-2008). Day: £2,275–£3,200, Pre-Prep (from age 3) £1,050–£2,000. Boarding (in addition to Day fee): £850–£1,025 (4 nights), £1,750 (7 nights)

Rockport School is the only independent preparatory and senior School in Northern Ireland. It is situated in twenty-five acres of beautiful surroundings, overlooking Belfast Lough, and prides itself in its happy atmosphere.

Rockport is a child-centred school and caters for the individual. It provides a well-balanced, rounded education for children from 3 to GCSE. Pupils are made to feel they have something valuable to contribute – whether in the classroom, in music and drama, on the sports field or elsewhere.

Rockport aims to give each pupil the capacity and confidence to live in an uncertain world – to encourage the pupils to work hard, to take a pride in achievement, to accept responsibility and to show concern for others. In the pursuance of these aims, Rockport is fortunate in having a dedicated and experienced staff, excellent teacher pupil ratios, a wide range of facilities and an extensive range of extra curricular activities.

Staff and parents work closely together for the common good of the children. There is an active Parent Teacher Association which meets each term. Funds are raised for the school, but regular Educational Evenings are also arranged.

Normal entry points are 3, 8 and 11.

Charitable status. Rockport School Limited is a Registered Charity, number XN48119. It exists to provide education for boys and girls.

Rokeby

George Road Kingston-upon-Thames Surrey KT2 7PB
Tel: 020 8942 2247
Fax: 020 8942 5707
e-mail: hmsec@rokeby.org.uk
website: www.rokebyschool.co.uk

Maxim: *Smart, Skilful and Kind*

Chairman of the Governors: Mr Charles Carter

Headmaster: **Mr J R Peck**

Age Range. 4–13.
Number of Boys. 370.
Fees per term (2007-2008). Pre-Prep £2,444–£2,930; Prep £3,353–£3,564 (including lunch, books and all compulsory extras).

Rokeby has an outstanding record of success in Common Entrance and Scholarships to leading Independent Schools. There is an experienced staff of nearly forty. Boys are accepted at 4+ to the Pre-Prep and at 7+ to the Prep School. There is a number of scholarships available to the Prep School at 7+.

Science is taught in two well-equipped Laboratories. There is a large Computer Room and a very spacious Art and Design Technology Centre. Soccer, Rugby, and Cricket are played while other sports include Swimming, Athletics, Hockey and Basketball. There are two large Halls and an Astroturf. The Music Department provides Orchestra, Ensembles and two Choirs and there are fourteen visiting peripatetic teachers, who work within a sound-proofed music block.

There is a number of educational school trips arranged as well as trips overseas, including Italy, Greece and Skiing. The school operates a bus service to the Wimbledon and Putney areas.

Charitable status. Rokeby Educational Trust Limited is a Registered Charity, number 312653. It exists to provide an excellent education for boys aged 4–13.

The Roman Ridge School

No 8 Onyasia Crescent Roman Ridge Accra Ghana
Tel: 00 233 21 780456/780457
Fax: 00 233 21 780458
e-mail: enquiries@theromanridgeschool.com
website: www.theromanridgeschool.com

Postal Address:
PO Box GP 21057 Accra Ghana

Co-educational Day School.

Governors:
Chairman: Mr Frank B Adu Jnr, BA Hons, MBA
Chair, Academic Board: Ms Joyce Aryee, BA Hons, PGCert Public Administration

***Principal*: Mrs Amy Fafa Awoonor**, BA Hons

Age Range. 4–17+.
Numbers of Pupils. 235 Boys, 217 Girls.
Fees per term. Junior School (Reception–Class 6): US$1,200; Senior School (Forms 1–5) US$1,500; Sixth Form US$1,800.

Established in September 2002, The Roman Ridge School aims to provide the very best of British Education whilst being firmly rooted in Ghanaian life and culture. The school is a unique facility in Ghana as it offers small class sizes (18), individual pupil attention, a family atmosphere, firm discipline, emphasis on good manners, a sound Christian foundation, a caring environment and a full programme of Sports and extra-curricular activities.

The school is noted for its Special Needs and Individual Learning Programmes as well as its dedication to all other pupils including the high ability learners and scholars. Pupils are carefully monitored and assessed regularly in order to achieve academic success, and, parents are encouraged to help in this process.

All teaching is initially based on the English National Curriculum for the Foundation Course and Key Stage One, after which the pupils progress to the 11+ examination, then take the full range of academic subjects at the 13+ Common Entrance & the IGCSE Courses with the Cambridge Board. The school has begun its A Level programme and offers a comprehensive range of Courses.

There are thirty classrooms at present, three ICT suites, a Multimedia Centre with a Language lab, two up-to-date Libraries with full audio-visual facilities, junior & senior Science Labs, a Dance Studio, a specialised Art Room and a climbing wall. A modern clinic is on site staffed by a qualified SRN.

Pupils play Football, Netball, Hockey, Basketball and Rounders and also enjoy a very successful Swimming programme. Scouting is also provided throughout the school for Beavers (6–8), Wolf Cubs (8–11), Scouts (11–16) and Senior Scouts (16+). Pupils keenly attend visits and trips to various places of interest including the Slave Forts, Game Parks, a jungle canopy walk and the Volta Lake.

At weekends, the school offers a full range of Adventure Activities including Mountain-Biking, Canoeing, Climbing, Hiking, Camping and Orienteering which are all led by fully qualified UK instructors.

During the very full school day the pupils take part in many activities such as Choirs, Music Lessons (Piano and Guitar), Drama, Karate, Traditional Drumming and Dancing, and the school has its own Skittle Alley. School productions and concerts take place at the end of each term.

The school is open on Saturdays for extra work programmes, swimming, games, music lessons, art and computer clubs, and special events.

Pupils thrive in The Roman Ridge School and are reluctant to go home at the end of the day.

Rookesbury Park School

Wickham Hampshire PO17 6HT
Tel: 01329 833108
Fax: 01329 835090
e-mail: head@rookesburypark.co.uk
website: www.rookesburyparkschool.co.uk

The school was founded in 1929 and became an educational trust administered by a board of governors in 1961. We are a Preparatory School for Girls and Boys including weekly and full boarding from 6 years.

Chairman of Governors: B R M Stoneham

***Headmistress*: Mrs P Harris-Burland**, MA, BA Hons, Montessori Dip

Age Range. 2–13.
Number of Pupils. Boarders 10, Day Girls 45, Day Boys 45.
Fees per term (2008-2009). Boarders £4,346–£5,689; Day £1,048–£3,833.

Rookesbury Park School occupies the former manor house in the village of Wickham, situated in an unrivalled setting of 14 acres overlooking farmland.

The school prepares girls and boys for a challenging, demanding and ever-changing future through an Independent Preparatory education which encourages the children to be critical thinkers and high achievers in an atmosphere that is caring, as teachers and their assistants create a thinking environment. We encourage your child to grow in confidence and self-esteem as they explore their world through stimulating activities and personalised learning in a home-from-home environment.

We are a friendly and flourishing school with a nursery department. We offer small classes and a balanced curriculum which embraces the whole child. We teach with emotional intelligence in that we are role models, and how we interact with each other is central to our ethos of empathy and praise. We have separate studios for art, pottery, design technology and food technology. We have a well-equipped science laboratory, ICT Suite, a swimming pool, tennis courts and athletics field.

The children are prepared for the Common Entrance Examination to major independent schools, and for independent school scholarships. There is a well-qualified and committed staff and the average class size is 12–15 pupils. Games played include netball, hockey, tennis, rounders, pop lacrosse, athletics, swimming, cricket, rugby and football.

Our school is a place filled with fun and laughter, where your child is encouraged, nurtured and motivated at every turn. We have a very busy and stimulating extra-curricular programme in which all boys and girls are encouraged to participate. As well as sport, riding, golf, and ballet, we have two choirs, orchestra, mandolin group and dramatic productions each term. Poetry evenings take place in the Autumn Term. High standards secure a firm academic grounding, where the three Rs go hand in hand with each child's emotional development; we believe happiness to be at the heart of all learning.

Charitable status. Rookesbury Park is a Registered Charity, number 307334.

Rose Hill School

Alderley Wotton-under-Edge Glos GL12 7QT
Tel: 01453 843196
Fax: 01453 846126
e-mail: office@rosehillschool.com
website: www.rosehillschool.com

Chairman of Governors: Dr T D Rees

***Headmaster*: Paul Cawley-Wakefield**, BEd

Age Range. 3–13.
Number of Pupils. 150 day pupils.
Fees per term (2008-2009). £2,049–£4,050.

Founded in 1832, Rose Hill is a small, co-educational country prep school. The buildings and grounds are located in 25 acres of glorious Cotswold countryside. Facilities include a sports hall, heated swimming pool, science lab, computer centre, library, art room, a further IT centre, playing fields, tennis courts, an astroturf, a dance studio and extensive woodland in which the children can play. We also have use of the beautiful village church adjacent to the school.

Our academic reputation is excellent. All Year 8 students enter the schools of their first choice, and many achieve academic and non-academic scholarships: Design Technology, Information Technology, Drama, Music, Art and Sport. Our children are awarded All-Rounder and Academic scholarships on a regular basis. We are proud of our academic strength within the holistic approach to the children's education, and these outstanding results are achieved by a combination of highly-qualified, dedicated and enthusiastic staff, small classes, good facilities and, where required, the back-up of our Special Educational Needs Coordinator (SENCO).

Pupils have an extensive list of activities from which to choose and many are free. French and Spanish are taught from an early age and classical studies are taught in the junior part of the school with Latin being an option in the senior school. Every child in the main school (Year 3 and above) takes part in between 5–7 hours of organized sport per week. Games include cricket, rugby and football for the boys; netball and rounders for the girls. All the children participate in hockey, tennis, swimming, cross-country running and athletics. Each year a number of our children aspire to county or national representation.

We have four choirs, our robed chapel choir which regularly sings at the local parish services, a senior choir, junior choir and pre-prep choir with further orchestra, guitar ensemble, saxophone group, string quartet and rock band. Approximately 80% of our children in Years 3–8 learn at least one musical instrument with many opting to take lessons in two or in some cases 3 instruments. The school stages a major production each year and LAMDA is taught by a specially trained LAMDA teacher.

Rose Hill's pastoral care is outstanding and there is an early start and late stayer option designed to help busy working parents. There is a minibus service which allows parents to have their children collected in the morning and dropped off at the end of the school day.

Rose Hill pupils are confident, self-disciplined, purposeful and undoubtedly happy. Help with fees is available through the school's bursary system.

Charitable status. Rose Hill School is a Registered Charity, number 311708. It exists to provide quality education in a demanding world.

Rose Hill School

Coniston Avenue Tunbridge Wells Kent TN4 9SY
Tel: 01892 525591
Fax: 01892 533312
e-mail: admissions@rosehillschool.co.uk
website: www.rosehillschool.co.uk

Chairman of Governing Body: Mr Alan Baker

***Headmaster*: P D Westcombe**, BA, PGCE

Deputy Head: G J Coventry, CertEd (Loughborough)

Age Range. 3–13.
Number of Pupils. 175 Boys, 122 Girls.
Fees per term (2008-2009). £3,695 (over 7 years); £2,575 (under 7 years); £1,350 (3 years old).

The school is situated in eighteen acres of beautiful grounds adjacent to the green belt, but within five minutes of the centre of the town. A superb Pre-Preparatory building was opened in 1991, followed by an outstanding IT centre. A Sports Hall was completed in 1998 and a new dining room and kitchen in 1999. Facilities also include an outdoor heated swimming pool and 6-hole golf course. A new classroom block, including library and changing rooms, was completed in 2003 and a new Theatre and Creative Arts Centre opened in September.

Children are prepared for Common Entrance and Scholarship entry to Independent Senior Schools but consideration is also given to competitive entry into local grammar schools at 11+ and 13+. Small classes ensure individual attention and the fulfilment of academic challenge.

Sport and the Creative Arts are highly valued. Hockey, Netball, Cricket, Rounders, Athletics, Football and Rugby are the main team games supported by a range of individual sports. There is a junior and senior Choir, a School Orchestra and many children receive instrumental tuition. Two drama productions occur every year.

A full range of extra-curricular clubs, including Cubs and Brownies, ensures breadth of experience. Within a secure environment, based on clear Christian principles, children are encouraged to meet new challenges with confidence.

Charitable status. Rose Hill School is a Registered Charity, number 270158. It aims to provide a high quality education to boys and girls aged 3–13.

Rosemead Preparatory School

70 Thurlow Park Road Dulwich London SE21 8HZ
Tel: 020 8670 5865
Fax: 020 8761 9159
e-mail: admin@rosemeadprepschool.org.uk
website: www.rosemeadprepschool.org.uk

***Headteacher*: Mrs C Brown**, CertEd, DipEd, RSADipSpLD

Age Range. 3–11.
Number in School. Day: 148 Boys, 190 Girls.
Fees per term (2008-2009). £2,430–£2,590.

Rosemead is a well-established preparatory school with a fine record of academic achievement. Children are prepared for entrance to independent London day schools at age 11 years, many gaining awards and scholarships. The school has a happy, family atmosphere with boys and girls enjoying a varied, balanced curriculum which includes maths, English, science, French, information and communication technology, arts and humanities. Music and drama are strong subjects with tuition available in most orchestral instruments and various music groups meeting frequently. A full programme of physical education includes gymnastics, most major games, dance and (from age 6) swimming. Classes make regular visits to places of interest. Three residential field studies courses are arranged for the junior pupils along with various school holidays. Main entry to the school is at Nursery (age 3), following informal assessment, and at National Curriculum Year 3, following a formal assessment. The school is administered by a board of governors elected annually by the parents.

All religious denominations welcome.

From September 2009 a small number of bursaries will be available from Year 3.

Charitable status. Rosemead Preparatory School (The Thurlow Educational Trust) is a Registered Charity, number 1186165. It exists to provide a high standard of education in a happy, caring environment.

Rowan Preparatory School

6 Fitzalan Road Claygate Esher Surrey KT10 0LX
Tel: 01372 462627
Fax: 01372 470782
e-mail: office@rowan.surrey.sch.uk
website: www.rowan.surrey.sch.uk

Rowan is registered as an Educational Trust and is controlled by a Board of Governors. The Governors play an active role in the school and are extremely supportive.

Chairman of Governors: Mr Ron Disney

***Headteacher*: Mrs Kathy Kershaw**, CertEd

Deputy Head: Mrs Sarah Meadows, BA Hons, PGCE

Age Range. 2–11 (Pre-Preparatory age 2–7, Preparatory age 7–11).

Number of Pupils. 270 Day Girls.

Fees per term (2008-2009). Kindergarten (5 mornings) – Year 6: £1,411–£3,475. Nursery (5 mornings): £935.

The school is split into two sites, Rowan Brae houses the Pre-Prep and Nursery and Rowan Hill, the Prep. Both sites have undergone recent refurbishment and the purpose-built Nursery was opened in September 2005. Both sites offer wrap-around care from 8.00 am to 6.00 pm.

The Brae, under the leadership of its own head, Miss Victoria Goodson, has bright airy classrooms, many of which have been purpose built and a new IT facility/library specifically designed for this age range. The playground, with separate area for Nursery, is packed with toys and climbing apparatus. At the Hill, the girls move around the classrooms, which are excellently equipped for the relevant subject with interactive whiteboards in all classrooms. There is also an excellent new IT Suite, which was funded by the very supportive parents association, The Friends of Rowan. Again the Hill has well-equipped playgrounds, with particular affection from the girls for the wooded area, known as The Spinney.

A girl may enter the school at any stage and is generally guaranteed a place throughout the school if she joined at Foundation Level. Admission in the early years is non-selective. Early registration is advisable if a place in the pre-prep is to be assured. Entry at other stages requires a satisfactory level of attainment in basic skills and this is determined through participation in a variety of activities rather than through rigorous testing.

Girls are prepared for entry to a wide variety of Senior Independent Boarding and Day Schools. There is an excellent record of girls gaining places at their senior school of choice, including each year a number of girls being offered music or academic scholarships. A special programme for Year 6 girls is organised in the summer term to prepare them for moving on to their respective schools. This programme includes PSHE and citizenship studies, life skills and community service.

Rowan offers a broad based curriculum of work so that each pupil is able to develop her own talents and maximize her potential. The school welcomes visiting speakers and performers to enhance the curriculum. Day trips are also included in each term and the annual residential trips to Marchant Hill, Devon and France for Year 4, 5 and 6 respectively are both popular and highly educational in content. In addition a wide variety of clubs are on offer at lunchtimes and after school and include: drama, football, gymnastics, chess, music, judo and games.

Rowan has an excellent Music Department with all girls singing in a choir and playing the recorder. In addition, three quarters of girls at the Hill play a further instrument with lessons timetabled into the school day. There are various ensembles, which the girls can also join in preparation for the orchestra. The percussion club and African Drums workshops are new and very popular additions.

Rowan also has an excellent sporting record, especially in swimming and gymnastics (where national standard is reached), netball and sports acrobatics.

Equally, Rowan is very proud of its art, providing stunning displays around both the Brae and the Hill expressing the girls' individuality.

With small classes in both sites and strong pastoral care it is Rowan's aim to provide the essential early grounding in a happy, stimulating and secure environment where every child's needs are catered for.

A prospectus is available on request and prospective parents are asked to make an appointment to view the school during a normal working day, and to attend one of the Open Mornings held in both the autumn and spring terms.

Charitable status. Rowan Preparatory School is a Registered Charity, number 312047. It exists to provide an outstanding education for girls.

Royal Russell Preparatory School

Coombe Lane Croydon Surrey CR9 5BX
Tel: 020 8651 5884
020 8657 4433
e-mail: prepschool@royalrussell.co.uk
website: www.royalrussell.co.uk

Patron: Her Majesty The Queen

Chairman of Governors: K Young

***Headmaster*: D Goodwin**, BSc Hons, MA Ed, PGCE

Age Range. 3–11.

Number of Pupils. 170 Boys, 130 Girls.

Fees per term (2008-2009). Kindergarten (3 years) £1,125 (half day); Pre-Prep (4–7 years) £2,560; Prep Day (7–11 years) £3,125.

The Prep School stands on a magnificent wooded campus extending to over 100 acres, which it shares with the Royal Russell Senior School (11–18 years). (*See Royal Russell School entry in HMC section.*)

The school is well served by road, tram and rail links and is one of the few co-educational schools in South London.

There is a fully qualified teaching staff of 24, and the Headmaster is a member of IAPS.

The school has a broad curriculum which seeks to blend the highest standards of academic work with a wide range of extra-curricular activities. There are opportunities for all pupils to participate in soccer, netball, hockey, cross-country and cricket as team sports, and as individuals to be coached in athletics, swimming, tennis, and table tennis. There is an extensive fixture list of matches against other schools. Artistic development extends to include full dramatic and musical productions, and many pupils learn musical instruments. All forms of art, design and technology are actively encouraged. There are excellent carpeted classrooms which are complemented by two Assembly Halls, a Sports Hall, Gymnasium, Science Laboratories, Music School, Art Room, Computer Suite and School Chapel. Our stunning indoor swimming pool offers a 25m main pool, learner pool and function room. All Prep School pupils receive weekly swimming lessons from qualified instructors.

The majority of the pupils join the school at 3+ or 7+, and are prepared for transfer to the Senior School at 11+. Candidates for entry to the Pre-Prep are interviewed informally, while all other entrants sit examinations in English and Mathematics appropriate to their ages.

Prospective parents are very welcome to come and meet the Headmaster and to tour the school, and should telephone for a prospectus in the first instance.

Charitable status. Royal Russell School is a Registered Charity, number 271907. It exists solely to provide education to girls and boys.

The Royal Wolverhampton Junior School

Penn Road Wolverhampton WV3 0EF
Tel: 01902 349100
Fax: 01902 344496
e-mail: aj@royal.wolverhampton.sch.uk
website: www.theroyalschool.co.uk

Chairman of the Governors: P Hill, Esq, FCMA, MIMC

***Head*: Mrs M Saunders**, CertEd

Age Range. 2–11 Co-educational.

Number of Children. 187: Boys 105, Girls 82.

Fees per term (2007-2008). Day Pupils: £2,805 (Years 3–6), £2,240 (Reception, Years 1 and 2), £2,050 (Nursery). Junior Boarders (Year 6): £6,460.

There are bursaries for those serving in the Armed Forces whose children board in Year 6, reductions for Old Royals and also for siblings. A number of foundation scholarships are awarded each year. Throughout school an extended day facility is available from 8 am to 6 pm.

The Royal Wolverhampton School is located on the fringes of Wolverhampton. Easy access is afforded from the local area and further afield.

At the age of eleven, many pupils gain entrance to the Senior School and other selective secondary schools.

The Royal Wolverhampton School was founded in 1850. The prefix "Royal" was granted by Queen Victoria in 1891 and Prince Edward is the School's Patron.

The aim of the school is to provide a well-balanced education, in a safe and friendly environment.

Facilities. The school buildings have been continually updated. Our new swimming pool, incorporating a training pool, was opened in 2007.

We have a healthy catering policy with special diets being catered for. A cooked lunch is provided for all pupils and light refreshments are provided for pupils attending extra-curricular activities.

Religion. The School has its own chapel within the grounds. Although the School has a religious affiliation to the Church of England, it welcomes pupils of all religions.

Pastoral Care. The well-being of all pupils is of prime importance. Class teachers are on hand to deal with any problems, which might arise, as are the Head and her secretary.

Curriculum. The Junior School offers a broad-based curriculum, which aims to achieve every child's potential. Excellent results are achieved at Key Stages 1 and 2. Small class sizes are a feature throughout the School.

There are dedicated rooms for Music, Science, Art and ICT.

French is taught from the age of 3, as is swimming.

Educational visits take place throughout the year, including a residential trip for Years 5 and 6.

In the Nursery a good balance is achieved between play and early learning activities. There is an extensive outdoor play area.

Music & Drama. The school has an excellent reputation for its musical standards. Pupils are encouraged to take part in the choir and perform in a wide variety of events; many pupils learn to play an instrument.

Sports and extra-curricular activities. The School aims to educate well-rounded individuals and a wide variety of after-school activities is available including ballet, drama, yoga and modern dance. An indoor heated swimming pool, a gymnasium, tennis courts and extensive playing fields ensure a wide variety of sporting activities.

Old Royals' and Old Rowans' Association. The Association regularly organises reunions. For further information please contact Mr Mike Masters, 24 Birmingham Road, Coleshill, Birmingham B46 1AA. Tel: 01675 463093.

Charitable status. The Royal Wolverhampton School is a Registered Charity, number 1092221. It exists to provide an education for boys and girls.

Rudston Preparatory School

59/63 Broom Road Rotherham South Yorkshire S60 2SW
Tel: 01709 837774
Fax: 01709 837975
e-mail: office@rudstonschool.com
website: www.rudstonschool.com

Co-educational Day School. The school is a charitable educational trust with a Board of Trustees.

Chairman of Trustees: Mr N H Morton, FCIEH

***Head*: Mrs Lynda J Sharpe**, CertEd

Age Range. 2–11 years.

Number of Pupils. 117 Boys, 105 Girls.

Fees per term (2008-2009). Age 4–11: £1,785; Pre-School: £37 per day.

There are 18 members of staff.

Our small classes, combined with a wide curricula, flexibility in organisation, detailed attention to the acquisition of skills and personal consideration of each individual's ability, help to ensure that the highest standards are achieved.

The school offers a range of subjects including English, Mathematics, Sciences, Design Technology, French, Latin, Music and Computer Studies, Drama, History, Geography, Art, Religious Education, Personal and Social Education, and Physical Education.

Pupils are prepared for extrance examinations to other schools. We have an excellent reputation for gaining successful results.

Pupils are expected to maintain a good code of conduct at all times; courtesy and consideration for others are an intrinsic part of school life.

Charitable status. Rudston Preparatory School is a Registered Charity, number 529438. It exists to provide education for boys and girls.

Runnymede St Edward's School

North Drive Sandfield Park Liverpool L12 1LE
Tel: 0151 281 2300
Fax: 0151 281 4900
e-mail: contact@runnymede-school.org.uk
website: www.runnymede-school.org.uk

Choir School to Liverpool Metropolitan Cathedral
Motto: *Viriliter Age – Be of good courage*

Chairman of Governing Body: Dr Moya F Duffy, MBChB, DObstRCOG, FRCGP

***Headteacher*: Miss S Carter**

Age Range. 3–11.

Number of Pupils. 192 Day Boys, 148 Day Girls.

Fees per term (2008-2009). £1,879–£1,980.

Runnymede St Edward's School offers a broad balanced education in a welcoming, caring Christian environment, while preparing pupils for selective and non-selective secondary education. The school, which includes a Nursery Department, occupies a number of spacious buildings including Runnymede, a former Victorian mansion.

The School is a member of the Catholic Independent Schools Conference as well as the Association of Junior Independent Schools.

The National Curriculum is followed and pupils are entered for Key Stage 1 and 2 Tests. Emphasis is placed on positive attitudes through the provision of merit-based rewards for excellent work and effort. Above all, children are given every opportunity to discover their own self-worth and happiness through a sense of achievement and fulfilment.

Pupils are encouraged to recognise their own abilities and to appreciate those of others. They are urged to pursue goals which will lead to the achievement of high standards in all aspects of school life. Girls and boys are encouraged to participate fully in a challenging and varied curriculum to ensure that their potential is fully explored.

Facilities include the Nursery, classrooms, 2 assembly halls, library, computer suite, science laboratory, art and design unit, music department and secure play areas. In addition there are sports pitches, running track, floodlit astroturf, sports hall, gymnasium, swimming pool and dining hall. Field trips, residential activities, education and theatre trips are regular activities.

Alongside its excellent academic and sporting facilities, Runnymede is the Choir School to the Metropolitan Cathedral of Christ the King, Liverpool. Music plays a very important part in the life of the school which has its own choir and orchestra. The school is also fortunate in being able to provide after-care facilities every day from the end of school until 6.00 pm and a breakfast club that operates from 8.00 am daily.

Standards of discipline are high and good manners and courtesy are regarded as essential. In a recent Independent Schools Council inspection the Pastoral Care and corporate life were identified as "outstanding strengths of the school".

Prior to entering Runnymede at Nursery level, potential pupils – both boys and girls – are expertly assessed by our Early Years staff, in order to establish whether the individual child is developmentally ready for Nursery education. Parents are invited to attend this assessment and, if successful, the child will enter the School through the Nursery. Here they will spend their first year and attain their fourth birthday.

Pupils are admitted to other age groups within the School as and when vacancies occur. Entry is as a result of a day assessment carried out by the School staff, combined with a report received from the child's current Headteacher. Assessment of pupils' progress is an important feature of the school.

The Headteacher and staff consistently aim to enhance the role played by parents in the life of the school. The support of parents is fundamental to pupils' development and the school values highly the shared responsibility between home and school based on clear understanding between pupils, teachers and parents. Parents are kept regularly informed of their child's progress through reports and parents' meetings.

Further information regarding all aspects of Runnymede can be found in the Prospectus, copies of which are available from the Admissions Officer.

Rupert House School

90 Bell Street Henley-on-Thames Oxon RG9 2BN
Tel: 01491 574263
Fax: 01491 573988
e-mail: office@ruperthouse.oxon.sch.uk
website: www.ruperthouse.org

Chairman of Governors: C Barker, OBE, BA Hons

***Headmistress*: Mrs N Gan**, MA Ed, FRSA

Age Range. Girls 4–11, Boys 4–7.

Number of Pupils. Girls 176, Boys 59.

Fees per term (2008-2009). £1,220–£2,930 (inclusive).

Rupert House School, a Charitable Trust, is a day preparatory school for girls aged 4–11 and boys aged 4–7. The school is set in its own large garden in the centre of Henley-on-Thames. The pre-preparatory school is housed in a purpose-built unit and the older children work in a large Georgian House. Specialist facilities include a laboratory, art room, French room, music studio, IT suite and learning support room. There are all-weather games facilities on the site and a sports ground within a short walk.

The staff are fully qualified and experienced. They aim to give a sound and stimulating education in the basic subjects required for 11+ Common Entrance but are concerned also with the wider curriculum. Extra-curricular activities, which can include maths club, gymnastics, swimming, art, craft, football, hockey and computers, are offered after school hours. Individual music lessons in piano, string and wind instruments are offered as an extra.

Within a disciplined framework, where courtesy and consideration are expected, there is a friendly, family atmosphere in which the individual nature of each child is respected. The pupils are encouraged to match their performance to potential and to meet all challenges with enthusiasm and determination. There are regular consultation evenings and twice yearly reports. Parents may consult the Headmistress at any time by appointment.

Care is taken to ensure that pupils are well prepared for transfer to a school suited to their academic ability and personal qualities. In recent years girls have gained admission to well respected Independent Senior Schools and boys to excellent Prep Schools.

Charitable status. Rupert House School is a Registered Charity, number 309648. It exists to provide quality education for boys and girls.

Russell House School

Station Road Otford Sevenoaks Kent TN14 5QU
Tel: 01959 522352
Fax: 01959 524913
e-mail: head@russellhouse.kent.sch.uk
website: www.russellhouse.kent.sch.uk

***Headmistress*: Mrs Alison Cooke**, BA Hons Oxon, CertEd, LGSM, NPQH

Age Range. Co-educational 2–11+.

Number of Pupils. Boys 100, Girls 100.

Fees per term (2007-2008). Nursery Department (mornings) £1,425. Reception £2,275, Years 1–3 £2,575, Years 4–6 £2,925 (including lunch).

Russell House is a small, friendly school for boys and girls aged from 2 to 11.

We have a reputation for achieving excellent academic results while at the same time maintaining a friendly, caring and inclusive atmosphere where every child has access to every activity.

Many of our pupils are successful in the 11+ examination, gaining entry to the local grammar schools, and others pass on to independent schools such as Sevenoaks. We have a consistently strong record in gaining scholarships, both academic and music.

Academic excellence at the school goes hand in hand with an ethos which encourages individuality, self-expression and the curiosity to learn.

The school is careful to cultivate a calm, happy atmosphere and there is also a strong emphasis on building skills for the future and developing a sensitive awareness of the world beyond the school.

Ryde Junior School

Queen's Road Ryde Isle of Wight PO33 3BE
Tel: 01983 612901
Fax: 01983 614973
e-mail: juniorhead@rydeschool.org.uk
website: www.rydeschool.org.uk

Chairman of the Board of Governors: R J Fox, MA, CMath, FIMA

***Head*: H Edwards**, BSc, PGCE

Age Range. 3–11.

Number of Pupils. 132 Boys, 140 Girls.

Fees per term (from January 2008). Tuition: Nursery: £1,430 (full day), £790 (half day); Pre-Prep £1,595-£2,260; Junior School £2,725 (Years 3–6). Boarding (exclusive of tuition fees): £3,150 (full), £2,760 (weekly). Lunch: Pre-Prep £140, Junior School £190.

Ryde School Assisted Places/Scholarships are awarded annually for pupils entering Year 5.

The school provides a good, civilised environment that does well academically for a wide range of ability. The pupils are well-motivated and work hard with evident enjoyment in both lessons and activities. By paying careful attention to all aspects of school life, pupils are able to flourish within a supportive community. In this environment, where regular contact between parents and staff is considered to be of paramount importance, children develop confidence and happily give of their best.

Ryde Junior School caters for children aged 3–11 years. Fiveways, just across the road from the main site, is home to the Foundation Stage and Early Years. Through creative and imaginative teaching in new purpose-built classrooms, a sound foundation of key skills is established. At the end of Key Stage 1 pupils are ready to move to the 'senior' part of the Junior School, having already benefited from some specialist teaching in the Junior School. Here they continue to receive the support of a well qualified and dedicated staff, enjoying a full range of specialist facilities including a recently upgraded ICT facility comprising 20 PCs with Internet access, a Creative Centre, Science Laboratory, Music room and Theatre.

A broad, balanced and rich curriculum is followed. This is based on the National Curriculum but is greatly enhanced (with full Key Stage testing and reporting – the school features consistently at the top of the Isle of Wight Key Stage 2 league tables). A wealth of trips and outings is offered, enriching the curriculum still further, making use not only of the beautiful sites on the Island, but on the mainland and abroad. Pupils are encouraged to develop their full range of talents, with Music, Drama and Sports enjoying equally high profiles. The school maintains a consistently successful record in all areas of team and individual sports. The major sports offered are: Athletics, Cricket, Cross-Country, Hockey, Netball, Rounders, Rugby, Soccer, Swimming and Tennis, with fixtures being arranged both locally and on the mainland (at no extra charge). There is a full and wide ranging programme of clubs and activities (which changes each term) during lunchtime and after school, offering something for everyone.

Our Senior School is on the same campus, enabling us to benefit from the use of a Sports Hall and pitches. Careful liaison between the staff and induction days in the summer term effect a smooth transition for our pupils to the Senior School (*see entry in HMC section*).

The Junior School has a small number of weekly and full boarders who, together with Senior School boarders, have use of the range of facilities available at the Bembridge campus, situated in some 100 acres on a beautiful cliff top site approximately six miles from Ryde. Transport is provided to and from the school during the week.

Charitable status. Ryde School with Upper Chine is a Registered Charity, number 307409. The aims and objectives of the Charity are the education of boys and girls.

Rydes Hill Preparatory School

Rydes Hill House Aldershot Road Guildford Surrey GU2 8BP
Tel: 01483 563160
01483 578472 (Admissions)
Fax: 01483 306714
e-mail: enquiries@rydeshill.com
admissions@rydeshill.com
website: www.rydeshill.com

Chairman of the Governors: Bernard Stevens, Esq

***Headmistress*: Mrs Stephanie Bell**, MA Oxon

Age Range. Girls 3–11, Boys 3–7. Nursery class for children 3–4.

Number of Day Pupils. 160.

Fees per term (2008-2009). £870–£2,960. Compulsory extras: Lunch £160, Stationery £35. Extra Subjects: Pianoforte, Clarinet, Flute, Violin £145; Speech and Drama, Elocution £50; Ballet £47.

Rydes Hill Preparatory School is situated in a beautiful Georgian house with magnificent Library, vaulted Dining Hall, and recently restored Victorian Conservatory. Facilities also include a large Science Laboratory, interactive whiteboards in all preparatory classes and a new IT suite.

This Catholic school welcomes children from all denominations and offers an exceptional start, academically and socially.

Rydes Hill achieves outstanding academic results. Experienced and dedicated teachers encourage self-esteem and give pupils a strong educational foundation. Year after year the school's excellent Key Stage 2 SATs results ensure that Rydes Hill is ranked in the top echelon of preparatory schools nationally and many pupils are awarded scholarships at leading senior schools. Sport, IT, Art and Music are taught by specialist teachers. Every pupil performs in one of the school's yearly productions and the creative arts are a major strength of the school.

Rydes Hill's ISI Inspection Report 2007 concluded, "Rydes Hill aims high for its pupils and they flourish. All aspects of the school's work are good and some are outstanding. In a calm, caring and purposeful environment, with major strengths in aspects of pastoral care, the school achieves remarkable academic success".

Rydes Hill offers a wide range of extra-curricular activities and an extended school day is available from 8:00 am to 5:30 pm every day, if required. Supervised homework sessions are also offered every day.

Charitable status. Rydes Hill Preparatory School is a Registered Charity, number 299411. It exists to ensure excellence in all aspects of education.

The Ryleys

Alderley Edge Cheshire SK9 7UY
Tel: 01625 583241
Fax: 01625 581900
e-mail: headmaster@ryleys.cheshire.sch.uk
website: www.theryleys.com

Founded 1877.

Chairman of Governors: Mrs J Nichols

***Headmaster*: P G Barrett**, BA, CertEd

Age Range. 2½–11/13.

Number of Boys. 250 Day Boys.

Fees per term (2008-2009). Nursery: £1,085 (half day), £1,670 (full day); Reception, Years 1–3 £2,620; Years 4–6 £2,940, Years 7 and 8 £2,995.

The Ryleys School is situated in Alderley Edge, a rural village just 15 miles south of the city of Manchester, within easy reach of the motorway and rail networks and close to Manchester Airport.

The School is an Educational Trust with an active and forward-thinking Board of Governors. The staff consists of 19 highly-qualified full-time teachers and 5 part-time. There are also 6 Classroom and Nursery assistants. In the Junior section of the school (Reception to Year 2) class teachers are responsible for delivering the majority of the curriculum while in the Middle School (Years 3 and 4) boys are introduced to subject specialist teaching while retaining the class teacher format. In the Senior School (Year 5 to Year 8) all subjects are taught by subject specialists. Pastoral care in the Senior School is maintained by personal tutors. The thriving and successful Nursery School is staffed by qualified teachers.

Boys are thoroughly prepared for entry via examination into Independent Day Schools at 11 and 13 or into Boarding Schools at 13 via the Common Entrance or Scholarship examinations. The school has an excellent academic record.

The extensive curriculum consists of English, Mathematics, Science, French, History, Geography, Scripture, Design Technology, Information Technology, Art, Music and Physical Education and provides an outstanding foundation for the boys' future schooling. German or Latin is offered to boys in Years 7 and 8 and Greek is also available. Each subject is taught in a fully equipped subject room and there is a computerised library. Other facilities include a Sports Hall, Music Department, Craft and Woodwork Centre, a large outdoor heated Swimming Pool, an Astroturf playing area and 8 acres of playing fields.

Various extra-curricular sports and activities are on offer including chess, computing, music, woodwork, basketball, badminton, table tennis etc.

Soccer, Rugby Football, Cricket and Athletics are the main team games and there is an extensive fixture list of matches against other schools at various ages. The school has undertaken sports tours to Italy and Spain in the last few years and there is an annual skiing trip to Europe or North America. Outdoor pursuits are encouraged and the school organises a regular expedition to Rua Fiola in Scotland.

Music is another of the school's great strengths with well over 130 boys receiving individual instrumental tuition from a highly qualified staff of 9 visiting teachers. The school has a fine reputation for its concerts and musical productions. These performances take place on a full proscenium stage and every boy is involved in one of the four productions each year. There are three choirs involving over 70 boys.

Art, too, is of a notably high standard with boys sitting for various scholarships and awards.

The domestic and catering arrangements and the health and welfare of the boys are under the direct supervision of Mrs Barrett, the Headmaster's wife.

Boys are accepted into the school at various ages providing places are available and are assessed upon entry so that the correct educational provision can be made in order to ensure that each pupil achieves his full potential. Bursaries are available.

The school places great emphasis upon such personal qualities as good manners and consideration for others.

Charitable status. The Ryleys is a Registered Charity, number 525951. It exists to provide a quality education for boys from 3 to 13 years of age.

St Albans High School – Wheathampstead House

Wheathampstead House Codicote Road Wheathampstead Hertfordshire AL4 8DJ
Tel: 01582 839270
Fax: 01582 839271
e-mail: WHOffice@stalbans-high.herts.sch.uk
website: www.sahs.org.uk

Chairman of School Council: Mrs J F Boulton, MRICS

***Head of Wheathampstead House*: Mrs S M Dunkerley**, MA London, BEd Cantab

Age Range. Girls 4–11.

Number of Pupils. 312.

Fees per term (2008-2009). Reception £2,915, Years 1 and 2 £3,075 (inc Lunch); Junior Department (age 7–11) £3,075 (exc Lunch).

St Albans High School for Girls has its Primary School at Wheathampstead House, set in 18 acres of parkland in the village of Wheathampstead. The School is uniquely placed in being able to offer all the advantages of a continuous education in two very different settings. From the ages of 4–11, the girls have to the freedom to grow and develop in an attractive rural environment, before moving on to the more urban setting of the Senior School, close to the heart of the City of St Albans. Behind the facade of a grand old country house, lie state-of-the-art facilities which support innovative teaching and the development of independent, creative thinkers who are confident in the use of new technologies.

Charitable status. St Albans High School for Girls is a Registered Charity, number 311065.

St Ambrose Preparatory School

Wicker Lane Hale Barns Altrincham Cheshire WA15 0HE
Tel: 0161 903 9193
Fax: 0161 903 8138
e-mail: stambroseprep.admin@traffordlearning.org
website: www.stambroseprep.org

Chairman of Governors: Mr Mark Holland

***Headmaster*: Mr Michael Lochery**

Age Range. Boys 3–11, Girls 3–4.

Number of Pupils. 202.

Fees per term (2008-2009). £1,778.

St Ambrose Preparatory School is situated in a very attractive, peaceful location in the heart of Cheshire, within convenient reach of Manchester Airport, rail links and an extensive motorway network, including the M56, M60, M6 and M62. This Roman Catholic school warmly welcomes pupils of other

Christian denominations, other Faiths and those with no religious background. A broad, balanced curriculum is offered in a happy, secure environment and all are helped and encouraged to attain the highest academic standards.

There are three departments in the school: Early Years for 3 to 5 year olds, the Infant Department for 5 to 7 year olds and the Junior Department catering for boys between 7 and 11. All enjoy modern, airy classrooms in purpose-built accommodation. The main building was erected in 1990 and extended in 1994. Plans and drawings have been prepared for a further building development, to be completed during 2009.

Boys generally join the school in the Nursery, Reception or at the beginning of the junior years and all receive an excellent grounding academically, socially and morally. The vast majority of pupils move on to St Ambrose College, which shares the same site, having passed the Entrance Examination at 11+. (The College is to be completely rebuilt within the next two years and will enjoy the most up-to-date facilities from September 2009.)

St Ambrose has an outstanding sporting tradition and encourages enjoyment and excellence in soccer, rugby, tennis, cricket, cross-country and athletics, making full use of the nine acres of sports fields. There is an extensive list of fixtures which continues throughout the year and sports courses are held during most holidays.

Music provides many exciting opportunities to perform and excel. An impressive team of peripatetic staff support both curricular and extra-curricular activities. Good, enthusiastic singing is nurtured at all levels. The computer suite is regularly upgraded, offering a wide selection of software and restricted access to the internet for research. Many trips and visits are arranged including a residential stay for Year 6 pupils at an outdoor adventure camp. French is taught throughout the Junior Department.

Charitable status. The Congregation of Christian Brothers is a Registered Charity, number 254312.

St Andrew's Preparatory School

Private Bag Molo Kenya
Tel: 00 254 51 721003
00 254 722 209750
Fax: 00 254 51 721010/721215
e-mail: office@turimail.co.ke
website: www.standrews-turi.com

Chairman of Governors: Hon Jared B Kangwana

***Headmaster*: Mr Patrick Moss**, BA Hons

Deputy Head: Mr Christopher Young

Age Range. 5–13.

Number of Boarders. 193: 107 Boys, 86 Girls.

Fees per term (2007-2008). Kshs 273,000–298,000 (inclusive).

St Andrew's Preparatory School, Turi, is an international, multicultural, Christian boarding school offering British Curriculum education of the highest standard. The School aims to provide a happy, stimulating, well-rounded educational experience for children. Pupils are encouraged to grow into well-educated, confident, self-disciplined young adults with the potential to be future leaders.

The Prep School together with the Senior School is situated 130 miles north west of Nairobi on a beautiful 300-acre estate at an altitude of 2,500 metres, where the climate is both healthy and invigorating.

Pupils are accepted from the age of 5 and follow a curriculum which prepares them for the Common Entrance Exam and for entry to St Andrew's Senior School and to other independent senior schools in Britain or elsewhere.

The grounds and playing fields are extensive. Boys play cricket and rugby; girls play rounders and netball; all play football, hockey, tennis and take part in athletics and cross-country. There are seven school tennis courts and a heated swimming pool, as well as a riding school on site where pupils of all abilities are taught by qualified instructors. A wealth of arts and crafts, hobbies and outdoor pursuits are actively encouraged.

The original School, founded in 1931, was destroyed by fire in 1944. It was completely rebuilt and is superbly designed and equipped as a modern purpose-built preparatory school. There are subject rooms for English, Mathematics, French, History, Geography and Science laboratories. A special needs teacher gives individual attention to those with learning difficulties in the well-equipped Learning Success Centre. Information Technology is an integral part of the curriculum throughout the school. An exceptionally large Hall is used for physical education, plays, concerts and large functions. The average size of classes is 14.

The School has a strong musical tradition. In addition to the many and varied opportunities for music within the curriculum over 80 pupils opt for specialist instrumental tuition in a wide range of instruments. Many of these pupils work towards ABRSM examinations. There are also several specialist music groups who practice and perform together and the Junior and Senior choirs.

The school has its own Chapel and aims to give a practical Christian education in a community with high standards and in a supportive family atmosphere.

All staff live within the estate. The teaching staff are all qualified and are committed to the Christian ethos of the school.

St Andrew's Senior School offers a three year course to IGCSE examinations with excellent academic results. The School has the same Board of Governors, but its own Headmaster, teaching staff and Management Team.

St Andrew's School

Meads Eastbourne East Sussex BN20 7RP
Tel: 01323 733203
Fax: 01323 646860
e-mail: office@androvian.com
website: www.androvian.co.uk

Chairman of Governors: C H D Everett, CBE

***Head*: J R G Griffith**, BA, PGCE

Age Range. 2–13.

Number of Pupils. 279 (Prep School), 136 (Pre-Prep and Nursery).

Fees per term (2007-2008). Boarders £5,690; Weekly Boarding £5,050; Day Children: £3,640 (Year 3), £4,005 (Years 4–8), Pre-Prep £2,300, Nursery sessions: £21.20 per morning, £15.90 per afternoon.

Situated in twelve acres of grounds at the foot of the South Downs, St Andrew's, founded in 1877, has a highly qualified teaching staff and children are taught in classes with a maximum size of 20 and an average number of approximately 16. A number of children in the Upper School are boarders and the school operates a popular scheme of 'Sleepover' boarding allowing day children to stay during the week on a flexible basis on any night or nights they wish.

The Head is supported by a Deputy Head, a Head of Pastoral Care and a strong management team. All children in the school have a Form Teacher or Form Tutor who is responsible for their pastoral welfare and academic progress. Each section of the school has its own Head (Pre-Prep, Junior, Middle and Senior), who coordinates, together with the Academic Director and Head of Pastoral Care, the overall pastoral and academic work of the staff.

In addition to the expanse of playing fields, St Andrew's benefits from its own indoor swimming pool and a well-equipped gymnasium. There are three computer suites equipped with up-to-date software and hardware including a wireless network connection and interactive whiteboards. The equipment in the Pre-Prep suite is designed specifically for children from 3 to 7 years of age. Other facilities include a modern purpose-built music block, an extensively equipped research and resource centre, a chapel and a creative arts centre with an art studio and design and technology facilities. The school strongly encourages music and drama and more than two-thirds of the children play instruments and participate in orchestras, bands and choirs. As well as Music, Drama is a timetabled subject and plays take place every term.

From the age of nine, children are taught by subject specialists. French is taught from the age of five and Latin is introduced from the age of 9. Children are introduced to working on computers at the age of two. The breadth of the curriculum means that, while the requirements of the National Curriculum are fulfilled, the children are able to experience a variety of other stimulating activities.

Accelerated sets exist from Year 5 to provide more challenging opportunities for those who are academically gifted. Academic, music, drama, sport and all-rounder awards have been achieved to many major senior schools and over the past five years more than 150 scholarships have been won by St Andrew's pupils. The school has a close relationship (although no formal links as such) with Eastbourne College and approximately half the leavers each year progress there. Where necessary, extra Specific Needs teaching is provided as well as ESL support for those who require it.

There is a wide range of activities on offer. The Co-Curricular programme, which runs for children in Years 5 to 8, offers opportunities for all children to develop areas of interest and strength or to discover new ones. Each activity offered has its own educational objectives and challenges designed to improve children's skills and broaden their horizons. An extensive programme of after-school activities has always been a strong feature of St Andrew's. This starts at the Pre-Prep and runs through to Year 8. The school also operates an outdoor education programme and various activity weeks during the school holidays and courses, which are run by our own staff, include art, rugby, football, canoeing, swimming, cycling, tennis, netball and hockey.

The school's strong sporting reputation manifests itself in national honours regularly achieved in many different sports. Specialist coaches are employed to teach the skills required for all to enjoy participating in team games and opportunities are available to anyone wishing to represent the school.

Charitable status. St Andrew's School Trust (Eastbourne) Limited is a Registered Charity, number 307073. The aim of the Charity is the promotion of Education.

St Andrew's School

Buckhold Pangbourne Reading Berks RG8 8QA
Tel: 0118 974 4276
Fax: 0118 974 5049
e-mail: admin@standrewspangbourne.co.uk
website: www.standrewspangbourne.co.uk

The School is an Educational Trust controlled by a Board of Governors.

Chairman of Governors: H C C Jones, Esq

***Headmaster*: J M Snow**, BA, CertEd

Age Range. 3–13. Weekly Boarding from age 7.

Number of Pupils. 300 including weekly boarders.

Fees per term (2008-2009). Boarders £4,950; Day Pupils £2,450–£4,150. Nursery from £1,150.

The School is fully co-educational and set in over 50 acres of private wooded estate and parkland.

The Curriculum includes all the traditional CE and Scholarship subjects and there is emphasis on Music, Speech and Drama and Modern Languages. Study Skills are an important part of the senior pupils' timetable and Information Technology is well resourced.

Academic and Sporting standards are high.

Charitable status. St Andrew's (Pangbourne) School Trust Limited is a Registered Charity, number 309090. It exists to provide education for boys and girls.

St Andrew's School

Horsell Woking Surrey GU21 4QW
Tel: 01483 760943
Fax: 01483 740314
e-mail: hmsec@st-andrews.woking.sch.uk
admin@st-andrews.woking.sch.uk
website: www.st-andrews.woking.sch.uk

Chairman of Governors: Mr David Wareham

***Headmaster*: Mr Adrian Perks**, MSc

Deputy Head: Mrs Sarah Marsh, BEd Hons

Age Range. 3–13 co-educational.

Number of Pupils. Total: 296 Day pupils. Pre-Prep and Nursery 124.

Fees per term (2008-2009). Prep £3,200–£3,850. Pre-Prep £930–£2,710.

Average Class Size. 15.

Children are prepared for entrance and scholarship exams to a wide range of independent senior schools. There are specialist teaching facilities for all subjects including science, ICT, music and art. The curriculum is broad and the school places great emphasis on music, sport and the arts.

There is a sports hall, tennis and netball courts, heated swimming pool and ample grounds for games (11 acres). Main school games are football, hockey, cricket, netball and rounders. Other activities include rugby, cross-country running, swimming, tennis and athletics.

Children can be supervised at school from 8 am and, through our extensive after-school activities programme for Year 3 and above, until 6/6.30 pm most evenings during the week. There is also an after-school club from 4 pm to 6 pm (chargeable) for Pre-Prep and Year 3 children.

Children are assessed for entry into Year 2 and above. The school has a number of scholarships and bursaries available at 7+ and 11+.

Charitable status. St Andrew's School is a Registered Charity, number 297580, established to promote and provide for the advancement of education of children.

S Anselm's

Bakewell Derbyshire DE45 1DP
Tel: 01629 812734
Fax: 01629 814742
e-mail: headmaster@anselms.co.uk
website: www.sanselms.co.uk

The School is an Educational Trust.

Chairman of Governors: Mr J W Lockwood

***Headmaster*: S C Northcott**, MA Hons (Marlborough College and St Andrews)

Deputy Head: R J Morse, BEd Hons

Age Range. 4–13.

Numbers. Prep School (age 7 to 13) 130 boys, 80 girls. Pre-Prep (age 4 to 7) 50 boys and girls.

Fees per term (2007-2008). Boarders £5,440. Day: Prep £3,690–£4,630; Pre-Prep £2,380.

At S Anselm's we strive to create pupils who are good citizens, children who are kind and respectful and who are known for their friendliness and self-confidence.

We firmly believe the formative years are the most important and we work hard to bring out the best in each and every child in our care.

There are no academic entry requirements at S Anselm's but at 13 many of our boys and girls go on to senior school with a scholarship which is a tribute to the quality of the teaching at the school.

The school is proud of its outstanding academic record but life at S Anselm's is about much more than results alone. As a prep school with a strong boarding tradition we understand how important it is to make the evenings and weekends happy and fulfilling times too.

Two thirds of our pupils choose to board and during their last few years at the school virtually all the children are full boarders. The girls live in three separate houses, which are the homes of the housemistresses and their husbands. The boys live in the main school, sleeping in small, comfortable dormitories.

There is a high standard of pastoral care and a happy, family atmosphere is created by the resident housemaster and his wife and the matrons.

The school has recently undergone the biggest redevelopment project in its long history. The result is a modern, light and airy collection of buildings, set in 18 acres of beautiful countryside in the heart of the Peak District National Park. New facilities include a large sports hall, a purpose-built theatre, a new computing centre, an extended library, and a design and technology centre. A new swimming pool complex is nearing completion.

S Anselm's has magnificent sporting facilities. There are extensive playing fields, tennis courts and an indoor swimming pool. The school enjoys sporting success in many different disciplines and S Anselm's teams achieve national recognition.

Most children learn a musical instrument and there are several choral and instrumental ensembles. There are more than 40 extra activities on offer, ranging from golf and sailing to Brownies and pottery.

The key to the school's outstanding record of success is the quality of teaching and the small class sizes which ensure that S Anselm's pupils get a great deal of individual attention. In recent years we have enjoyed record number of scholarships to many of the best senior schools such as Ampleforth, Malvern, Oundle, Rugby, Uppingham, Cheltenham Ladies' College, Shrewsbury, Repton, Winchester, Oakham and Sedbergh.

We aim to produce self-motivated children with enquiring minds but we never lose sight of the fact that competition must be tempered by consideration for others.

Charitable status. S Anselm's is a Registered Charity, number 527179. Its purpose is to carry on the education of children of either sex or both sexes.

St Anthony's Preparatory School

90 Fitzjohns Avenue Hampstead London NW3 6AA
Tel: 020 7435 3597 (Junior House)
020 7435 0316 (Senior House)
020 7431 1066 (Admissions)
Fax: 020 7435 9223
e-mail: headmaster@stanthonysprep.org.uk
website: www.stanthonysprep.org.uk

***Headmaster*: C J M McGovern**, BA Hons, PGCE, FRSA

Age Range. 5–13.

Number of Boys. 290 Day Boys.

Fees per term (2007-2008). £3,785–£3,890 including lunches.

Founded in the 19th century and set in the heart of Hampstead village, St Anthony's is an academic IAPS preparatory school for boys between the ages of 5 and 13. It is Roman Catholic but welcomes boys of other faiths. The majority of boys transfer at 13, via scholarship or CE, to leading independent senior schools including Westminster, University College, Radley, St Paul's, Mill Hill, Highgate, Harrow, Eton, City of London, Ampleforth.

The school accommodation consists of two large Victorian houses in close proximity. Both have their own grounds and separate playgrounds. There are eight forms in the Junior House, where boys range in age from five to nine, and eight forms in the Senior House, where boys range in age from nine to thirteen. The Senior House has a specialist Design and Technology room, a Music room, a Computer room, a Science laboratory and a swimming pool. Games fields are close by.

All boys receive Religious Education lessons twice a week. The course, which centres on Catholic beliefs and practices, but includes aspects of other faiths, is followed by all pupils. The school's spiritual dimension is regarded as highly important and it exists within a liberal and inclusive atmosphere. Catholic pupils attend mass about three times each term.

The school curriculum is stimulating and challenging and, for example, it is possible for boys to study five foreign languages. All pupils must study three, including French and Mandarin from Year 1. The arts have an important place in the school with a majority of boys learning to play a musical instrument and all boys involved in drama. Sport is a further strength of the school with some pupils achieving success on a national stage.

St Anthony's retains a slightly bohemian tradition with former pupils making their mark in the fields of rock music and art. Recently, four pupils won prizes in national competitions for creative writing.

The school works hard to instill in its pupils a sense of social responsibility and charity fund-raising is a feature of school life. A former pupil was recently awarded the Gusi Peace Prize (Asian equivalent of the Nobel) and the school has just financed the building of a kindergarten for a school in southern India. Much work is also done with local charities.

St Aubyn's School

Bunces Lane Woodford Green Essex IG8 9DU
Tel: 020 8504 1577
Fax: 020 8504 2053
e-mail: school@staubyns.com
website: www.staubyns.com

The School was founded in 1884 and is governed by a Charitable Trust.

Chairman of the Governors: M Scarth, MCIOB, CEng, MICE

***Headmaster*: Gordon James**, MA

Deputy Head: Marcus Shute

Age Range. 3–13+.

Number of Children. 500 Day.

Fees per term (from April 2008). £1,130 (Nursery) to £2,955 (Seniors) fully inclusive.

St Aubyn's provides an all-round preparatory education for children aged 3–13. The school is non-selective at its main point of entry for children aged 3 and 4. There are assessment tests for older children, principally at ages 7+ and 11+.

Key characteristics of the school include: well-qualified, dedicated staff; small classes (generally no more than 20); a teacher:pupil ratio of 1:13. Younger children are also supported by nursery nurses and teaching assistants and a full-time qualified nurse deals with any medical issues as and when necessary. In the Nursery the staff:child ratio is 1:6.

The school offers a wide-ranging curriculum within a traditional framework, encompassing all National Curriculum requirements. French is taught from 4+ and Latin from 10+. French, Music and PE are specialist-taught from an early age. All subjects are specialist-taught from Year 6.

Children progress to a range of independent and state schools at 11+ and 13+. Pupils gain a range of scholarships at both 11 and 13. Recent awards include several academic scholarships as well as awards in Sport, Technology, Music and Drama.

The school is pleasantly situated on the borders of Epping Forest, yet is close both to the North Circular and the M11. There are four departments within the school: Foundation Stage (3+, 4+); Pre Prep (5+, 6+); Middle School (7+, 8+, 9+) and Seniors (10+, 11+ and 12+) and each has its own base and resources. Facilities are extensive with 8 acres of grounds, large Sports Centre, fully-equipped Performing Arts Centre and Music School, Science Laboratory, Art and Design Base, a library and a computer base with a computer network running throughout the school. Games include soccer, cricket, hockey, tennis, netball and athletics, all coached to a high standard. St Aubyn's is a 'Sportsmark' school, an award conferred by Sport England for the range, breadth and inclusiveness of our provision.

The Director of Music leads a thriving department, with a school orchestra and various instrumental groups and choirs. Children are regularly involved in performances both within and outside the school. The school has gained Artsmark status, awarded by Arts Council England, for its provision for Music, Dance, Drama and Art.

St Aubyn's School is a registered charity. As such, all income from fees is for the direct benefit of its pupils. Two scholarships are available at 11+. The primary criterion for the award of a scholarship is academic ability, though special talent in music, technology, art, sport, etc may be taken into account. The school has Investors in People status.

Charitable status. St Aubyn's (Woodford Green) School Trust is a Registered Charity, number 270143. It exists to provide education for children.

St Aubyns School

76 High Street Rottingdean Brighton East Sussex BN2 7JN
Tel: 01273 302170
Fax: 01273 304004
e-mail: office@staubyns-school.org.uk
website: www.staubynsschoolbrighton.co.uk

A co-educational Preparatory and Pre-Prep School founded in 1895.

Chairman of the Governors: T R Prideaux, Esq

***Headmaster*: S Hitchings**, MA Oxon

Deputy Headmaster: S M Greet, BEd Hons

Age Range. 3–13.

Number of Pupils. 200 day and weekly boarding children.

Within the Prep Department a number of the pupils board, some on a weekly basis from Sunday evening until Friday evening, others as flexi-boarders on a regular night a week or on an occasional basis giving the school 24 hours' notice of the intention to board. This flexible arrangement suits many families and is a splendid introduction to boarding.

Fees per term (2008-2009). Weekly Boarders £5,650; Day Pupils: Prep £3,650–£4,550, Pre-Prep from £1,395 (Nursery) to £2,100.

St Aubyns is a happy and friendly school which firmly believes in the traditional values that encourage self-discipline, good manners, and consideration for others.

St Aubyns has an excellent academic record, preparing children for a wide range of Senior Schools. Each year an impressive number of scholarships is gained by our Leavers (at 13+). Entry is by assessment on a Taster Day and report, although the school is non-selective. Academic, Music, Drama, Dance and Sports scholarships are available for children aged 7 to 11.

St Aubyns offers a carefully balanced, very broad curriculum which allows each individual child's talents to grow. The school is situated in the delightful seaside town of Rottingdean. The campus of 11 acres offers a wide range of facilities including a large sports hall, squash court, all-weather tennis court, heated outdoor swimming pool, spacious art room and modern, well-equipped Science and Design Technology laboratories. In January 2000 a large, state-of-the-art ICT Centre with twenty two linked computers and an 85-seat theatre were opened. In 2001 a spacious well-equipped Library was opened, providing a large quiet space for study and open access for all children to a wide range of fiction and non-fiction. As a Christian community, services are held daily in the beautiful timber lined Chapel.

Cricket, netball, lacrosse, soccer, rugby, hockey, rounders and athletics are the major games, plus a wide selection of minor games such as fencing, swimming, tennis and basketball. The Activities Programme offers children over 27 different clubs including drama, dance, art, LAMDA, model making, board games and chess.

We atttach a great deal of importance to the children's cultural development. Our "Arts Express Programme" encompasses music, art, drama and dance. The children have regular Arts Express whole-day workshops.

St Aubyns is three miles from Brighton and less than an hour by train from London. Escorted rail travel is available between Victoria, East Croydon and Brighton on Sunday and Friday evenings. Gatwick Airport is 40 minutes away and the journey to Heathrow takes about 85 minutes. The school is happy to make the necessary arrangements for children to travel between airports and school. For day pupils, there is minibus transport from a wide catchment area.

In September 2002 a Nursery Unit was opened. This now has 25 3–4 year olds and has recently been re-housed.

Charitable status. St Aubyns School Trust Limited is a Registered Charity, number 307368. It exists to provide an excellent all round education for boys and girls aged 3–13.

St Bede's

Bishton Hall Wolseley Bridge Nr Stafford ST17 0XN
Tel: 01889 881277
01889 881226
Fax: 01889 882749
e-mail: admin@saintbedes.com

(Under the patronage of His Grace the Archbishop of Birmingham)

Headmasters:
A H Stafford Northcote, JP, KM, MA (Christ Church, Oxford)
H C Stafford Northcote, KM, MA (Trinity College, Cambridge)

Age Range. 4–13.

Number of Pupils. 74 Boys and Girls.

Fees per term (2007-2008). £3,725 Boarders and Weekly Boarders, £1,800–£3,050 Day Pupils. Compulsory Extras Nil.

St Bede's is a Catholic Preparatory School, in which other faiths and denominations are welcomed.

St Bede's was founded in 1936 by the parents of the current headmasters. Since then, the Northcote family has educated young people as additions to their own family, treating each child with care and respect. This has helped to create an educational atmosphere unlike any other.

Bishton Hall is a Grade II* listed Georgian Mansion, surrounded by 25 acres of beautifully kept gardens and woodland and 7 acres of professionally levelled playing fields. The school has its own Chapel, hard tennis courts, indoor heated swimming pool, gymnasium/theatre and science laboratory. Situated on the edge of Cannock Chase, this rural setting provides children with a happy and safe environment in which to learn.

Pupils are prepared for all Independent Schools and many Scholarships have been won.

There is a teaching staff of 12, with visiting teachers for violin, brass instruments and guitar. A specialist Drama Teacher teaches Performing Arts to a highly proficient standard.

The Craft, Design and Technology Centre incorporates metal work and metal casting, carpentry, pottery, enamelling, jewellery making, computers, art and stone polishing.

Tennis, Rugby, Cricket, Rounders, Hockey, Netball and Volleyball are played in season.

Mrs Hugh Stafford Northcote is personally responsible for the health and welfare of the children. Individual care is taken of each child and good manners and consideration for others insisted upon. An acknowledged feature of the School is its family atmosphere.

For further particulars, apply to the Headmasters.

St Bede's Preparatory School

Duke's Drive Eastbourne East Sussex BN20 7XL
Tel: 01323 734222
Fax: 01323 746438
e-mail: prep.school@stbedesschool.org
website: www.stbedesschool.org

Co-educational day and boarding school with Nursery and Pre-Prep departments.

Chairman of Governors: Maj-Gen A L Meier, CB, OBE

***Headmaster*: Nicholas Bevington**, BA Hons

Deputy Head: Gordon Ferguson, BSc Hons

Age Range. 2–13 Co-educational.

Number of Pupils. 458: Prep 316 (268 boys, 190 girls), Pre-Prep 60, Nursery 44. Boarders: 15 boys, 10 girls.

Fees per term (2008-2009). Boarding £6,015; Day: Prep £4,140, Pre-Prep £2,555. Nursery £21.25–£55.75 per session.

St Bede's, founded in 1895, is situated in Eastbourne, on the South Coast with spectacular views of the sea. It takes 5 minutes to reach the beach from the school and the principal playing fields are in a wide natural hollow nestling in the South Downs.

Boarders sleep in cosy bedrooms in a house that has a real family feel and are looked after by dedicated and caring staff. Both winter and summer weekends are filled with an exciting variety of activities and special celebrations take place on the children's birthdays.

There are 47 academic staff which creates a ratio of 1:9 throughout the school. Pupils are prepared for Common Entrance and the more able are tutored to sit scholarships to independent senior schools. Over 60 awards have been won during the last five years to many schools, including Eton, Harrow, Tonbridge, King's Canterbury, St Bede's Senior School, Eastbourne College and Roedean. Approximately 80% of pupils choose to continue their education at St Bede's Senior School (*see HMC section entry*).

St Bede's offers academic, sport, music, dance, art and drama scholarships and bursaries for children from the ages of 7 to 12 years.

Pupils from the age of 4 are given Information Technology lessons at least once a week in a Computer Centre which is constantly updated to keep at the forefront of educational technology. French and Music, Short Tennis and other Sports are also introduced to children in this age group.

New science laboratories and classrooms were opened two years ago, along with a new pre-prep library, two new junior changing rooms, a new pre-prep assembly room which will double as a new dance studio for the whole school and a glass walkway as a new entrance to the swimming pool area.

A major new development project is currently being undertaken to provide new accommodation for the Nursery and Pre-Prep and a new dining hall.

The Art and Design and Technology Departments are both very strong, opening for after school activities to encourage young talent. Music also plays an important role at St Bede's. There is a thriving orchestra and the majority of pupils learn one or more instruments, with children as young as six playing in recorder groups. Informal concerts during the school year and the end of year drama productions allow parents to appreciate their children's progress. There are also several choirs.

Drama forms an integral part of the school. The Pre-Prep produces a Christmas play and Years 4, 5 and 6 each put on a play once a year. At age 11 some children join the Legat Junior Dance programme. Entry is by audition.

Sport at St Bede's is taken seriously. Boys play soccer, rugby, hockey, cricket, tennis and athletics and the major sports for girls are netball, hockey, rounders, athletics and tennis. All the pupils use the indoor 20-metre swimming pool. The fixture list is very comprehensive and, whilst the top teams enjoy a high standard of coaching and performance, special emphasis is placed on ensuring that the other teams also have the opportunity to play matches against other schools. The Matt Sports Hall covers two indoor tennis courts and is used to house a huge variety of sports. Wet weather activities include badminton, basketball and table tennis.

There is a Special Needs department staffed by qualified Special Needs staff which can cater for pupils who require additional learning support. The school also has an EFL centre which is also run by highly trained and experienced staff. Gifted children are placed on a Curriculum Enhancement Programme to maximise their potential.

On Monday and Thursday afternoons and every evening after school the pupils are encouraged to participate in an extensive range of activities. In all there are over fifty activities on offer each week which range from fencing to cookery and basketball to art master classes. Day pupils who stay late for activities enjoy supper with the boarders and often sleepover a few nights each week.

The school runs a comprehensive coach and minibus service locally and transport to and from Gatwick and Heathrow airports is arranged by the transport department.

Entry to St Bede's is by interview.

Charitable status. St Bede's School Trust Sussex is a Registered Charity, number 278950. It exists to provide education for boys and girls.

St Benedict's Junior School

5 Montpelier Avenue Ealing London W5 2XP
Tel: 020 8862 2050
Fax: 020 8862 2058
e-mail: jssecretary@stbenedicts.org.uk
website: www.stbenedictsealing.org.uk

Governing Body:
The Abbot & Community of Ealing Abbey, assisted by a lay Advisory Body.

***Headmaster*: Mr R G Simmons**, BA Hons, PGCE

Age Range. Boys and Girls 3–11.
Number of Pupils. 249.
Fees per term (2007-2008). £3,230.

Our ethos is firmly based in the Benedictine Catholic tradition, and the pastoral and spiritual care of our pupils is central to all that we do. It is the School's mission to teach a way of living that goes beyond the acquisition of formal academic qualifications and ensures a holistic approach to education from the Nursery through to Sixth Form. Boys and Girls enjoy the very best of a Catholic independent education, with strong links maintained with the monastic community of Ealing Abbey.

St Benedict's provides a stimulating academic education within a broad, balanced and progressive curriculum. Great importance is placed on achievements in Art, Design Technology, Drama, Information and Communications Technology, Music and Sport. In addition, we offer a wide range of outstanding co-curricular activities, including Choir and Orchestra, Contemporary and Classical Dance, Ju Jitsu, and Swimming. High-quality teaching, exceptional pastoral care, small classes and a broad curriculum ensure that all pupils have the opportunity to achieve their potential. Interactive whiteboards are present in every classroom, and the Library is very well-resourced.

Girls and boys are taught together throughout their time at St Benedict's (3–18), with the exception of traditional single-sex sports. Specialist teachers provide tuition in French, Information and Computing Technology, Science, Music and Art Design Technology. Excellent academic results across the School are matched by equally impressive value-added scores, reflecting the strong and effective partnership between pupils, parents and the staff. We rejoice in the successes of all of our pupils.

The natural points of entry in the Junior School and Nursery are at 3+, 4+ and 7+. Entry is possible at other ages subject to the availability of places.

Charitable status. St Benedict's is a Registered Charity, number 242715.

St Bernard's Preparatory School

Hawtrey Close Slough Berkshire SL1 1TB
Tel: 01753 521821
Fax: 01753 552364
e-mail: registrar@stbernardsprep.org
website: www.stbernardsprep.org

***Headmistress*: Mrs M B Smith**, CertEd, NPQH

Age Range. 2½–11 co-educational.
Number of Pupils. 225.
Fees per term (2007-2008). £1,735–£2,135.

St Bernard's Preparatory has a unique ethos. We are a Catholic school, teaching the Catholic faith and living out the Gospel values which are shared by all faiths and are the foundation of all our relationships and the daily life of our school. We welcome and embrace children of all faiths and we recognise and celebrate our similarities and differences, developing mutual respect, understanding and tolerance.

We recognise the value and uniqueness of each individual, both child and adult. We celebrate the talents and gifts of each child and enable them to develop to their full potential spiritually, morally academically, socially and physically. Our children are happy, courteous, confident, articulate young citizens, committed to the ideal of service to others.

We work in partnership with parents, recognising that they are the first and best educators of their child. We consider ourselves to be very privileged that parents have entrusted us with the care and education of their child. We ensure that parents are kept fully informed of their child's progress.

We are committed to offering a broad, balanced, creative and challenging curriculum, enriched by experiences and opportunities which enhance and consolidate the learning process. Small class sizes enable our team of highly qualified, caring, committed and enthusiastic teachers to be responsive to the needs of the individual child ensuring continuity and progression for all our children. We have developed a wide and varied range of after-school activities which broaden the curriculum and enrich the children's lives. Children are encouraged to develop new skills.

We are proud of our reputation as a school with a strong ethos and nurturing pastoral care coupled with academic excellence reflected in consistently outstanding results in local and national tests.

Our school motto 'Dieu Mon Abri' meaning 'God is my Shelter', is an inspiring reminder of God's love for each one of us. The three swords represent 'Love, Work and Prayer' which underpin and permeate the life of our school.

St Catherine's British Embassy School

Sophocles Venizelou 73, Lykovrissi, Athens, GR145-10, Greece
Tel: 00 30 210 2829 750/1
Fax: 00 30 210 2826 415
e-mail: administrator@stcatherines.gr
website: www.stcatherines.gr

Chairman: Mr Matthew Bosrock

***Headmaster*: Mr Ronald Morton**, MA

Deputy Heads:
Dr S Bond (*Head of Upper School*)
Mrs P Zoulias (*Head of Lower School*)

Age Range. 2½ to 18.
Number of Children. 400 boys, 400 girls (day pupils only).
Fees per annum (2007-2008). Range from €7,230 in the Nursery up to €11,720 for Year 13.

The School was founded in 1956 by the late Sir Charles Peake, British Ambassador at the time in Athens and Lady Catherine Peake. Originally concerned with the education of British and Commonwealth children resident in Greece, it now teaches pupils from 52 nationalities. Priority is given to British and Commonwealth children. The teaching staff of 85, including the Headmaster, are mainly British except for language teachers. The School is administered by a Governing Body of

12 persons selected by the British, Canadian and Australian Ambassadors.

St Catherine's teaches the full programmes of study for the National Curriculum of England and Wales from Foundation Stage through to the end of Key Stage 3. Children are prepared for all types of British and Commonwealth senior education; attention is also given to children who wish to sit Common Entrance Examinations. In Years 10 and 11 (at 14–16 years of age) pupils study for examinations in IGCSE (Cambridge Board). Students in Years 12 and 13 (ages 16–18) undertake the International Baccalaureate Diploma Course. Greek, Latin, French, German and Spanish are offered at various stages. There is a strong tradition of music, drama and dance. In addition to a programme of some 30 extra-curricular activities per week, the school offers The Duke of Edinburgh's International Award Scheme and London Academy of Music and Dramatic Arts (LAMDA) examinations.

The School is situated out of central Athens, near to the elegant northern suburbs of Kifissia and Ekali, in an attractive environment, including sports facilities, courts and a large heated, open-air swimming pool. The grounds and property are entirely owned by the school. Classes are usually over-subscribed and waiting lists exist in most of the lower school classes – early application for places is advised.

Charitable status. St Catherine's British Embassy School is a Registered Charity, number 313909. It aims to provide high-quality education to children from the British, Commonwealth and International communities resident in Athens.

St Catherine's School Preparatory School

Bramley Guildford Surrey GU5 0DF
Tel: 01483 899665; Senior School: 01483 893363
Fax: 01483 899669
e-mail: schooloffice@stcatherines.info
website: www.stcatherines.info

Chairman of the Governing Body: Mr P J Martin, BA, FRGS, FCCA

Headmistress: Mrs A M Phillips, MA Cantab

***Head of Preparatory School*: Mrs K M Jefferies**, BSc, PGCE

Age Range. 4–11.
Number of Pupils. 260 Day Girls.
Fees per term (from January 2008). Pre-Prep 1 £2,045, Pre-Prep 2 £2,475, Pre-Prep 3 £2,915; Prep School £3,370.

Girls are accepted from the age of 4 to 11 when they take the Entrance Examinations for entry to Senior Schools.

Charitable status. The Corporation of St Catherine's, Bramley is a Registered Charity, number 1070858, which exists to provide education for girls in accordance with the principles of the Church of England.

St Cedd's School

Maltese Road Chelmsford Essex CM1 2PB
Tel: 01245 354380
Fax: 01245 348635
e-mail: tthorogood@stcedds.org.uk
website: www.stcedds.org.uk

Chairman of Governors: C Y R Tam

***Head Teacher*: Mrs B A Windley**

Deputy Head: A J Lowe-Wheeler

Age Range. 4–11 Co-educational.
Number of Pupils. 330+ Day.
Fees per term (2007-2008). £2,100–£2,250 including lunch.

St Cedd's School, founded in 1931, exists to provide independent education for boys and girls of 4–11 by encouraging in them the development of sound character on a Christian foundation. The school prides itself on combining a traditional emphasis on literacy and numeracy with a broad and balanced curriculum.

Specialist teaching is introduced gradually from Reception onwards in subjects including ICT, PE, Music, Art & Technology and French. Swimming and Recorders appear on the timetable from Year 2, and Spanish is taught in Year 6. Music and sport generally are both areas of particular strength and diversity. The school has links with Chelmsford Cathedral, where the choir performs at Choral Evensong twice a term, and is a member of the Chelmsford Choral Foundation.

Children are prepared for entry to a range of Independent and Maintained schools, including the Essex selective grammar schools. Locally, St Cedd's enjoys a reputation for success with regard to the number of places gained by its pupils, and the number of scholarships awarded, academic, musical and sporting.

Facilities include an Art and Pottery Centre, a purpose built Music School, and a climbing wall. Recent developments include the addition of a new computer suite and a new Science laboratory. Older pupils have the opportunity of playing sport at nearby Admirals Park and Chelmer Park on its large astroturf. There is an after-school club.

Charitable status. St Cedd's School Educational Trust Ltd is a Registered Charity, number 310865. It exists to provide education for boys and girls.

St Christina's RC Preparatory School

25 St Edmund's Terrace London NW8 7PY
Tel: 020 7722 8784
Fax: 020 7586 4961
e-mail: vanda@stchristinasschool.co.uk
website: www.saintchristinas.org.uk

***Headteacher*: Miss Nathalie Clyne Wilson**, BA Hons, PGCE

Age Range. Girls 3–11, Boys 3–7.
Number of Pupils. 162 girls, 50 boys.
Fees per term (2008-2009). £2,530 (inclusive).

Saint Christina's was founded in 1949 by the Handmaids of the Sacred Heart of Jesus. The Order looks to Christ in the Eucharist as the source of life and wisdom. In St Christina's children can capture these ideals and experience the joy of learning and the wonder of God and His Creation. Our purpose at St Christina's is to create an environment where learning takes place and where each individual 'experiences' respect and acceptance enabling him or her to become the balanced person they are called to be.

As a school we take pride in the excellent examination results which we achieve. We value most of all our strong sense of community. We seek to ensure that children feel appreciated for themselves as individuals as much as their achievements. We believe that confidence can only grow in an atmosphere of trust and safety.

Boys are prepared for entrance tests for day and boarding schools.

Girls are prepared for Common Entrance Examination and entrance exam to London Day Schools.

The school is modern, purpose built and in a pleasant location within a few moments walk of Primrose Hill and Regents Park. Prospective parents are warmly invited to visit the school.

Charitable status. St Christina's is a Registered Charity, number 221319.

St Christopher's School

Hampstead

32 Belsize Lane Hampstead London NW3 5AE
Tel: 020 7435 1521
Fax: 020 7431 6694
e-mail: admissions@st-christophers.hampstead.sch.uk
website: www.st-christophers.hampstead.sch.uk

Preparatory school for girls.

Chairman of Governors: Graham Hinton, BSc, MIPA

***Headmistress*: Mrs S A West**, BA, PGCE, MEd

Deputy Headmistress: Miss S Byrom

Age Range. 4–11.

Number of Girls. 235 Day Pupils.

Fees per term (2007-2008). £3,475 inclusive of lunch and all outings, except residential.

The School employs a fully qualified teaching staff of 16 full-time, 6 part-time, and 7 peripatetic music teachers. Strong emphasis is placed on music. There are three choirs, quartets, ensembles and 2 orchestras; instrumental lessons are arranged within the school timetable. Whilst maintaining high standards in numeracy and literacy, the curriculum provides a wide range of subjects including art, science, computer studies, design and technology, French, Spanish, drama, chess, gymnastics and games.

Extra-curricular activities over the year include art, dance, debating, drama, football, gym, language, Mandarin, netball, science, sewing, striking/fielding games and yoga.

All applicants are assessed for entry. 100% means-tested scholarships are available, as well as 50% bursaries. The girls are prepared for entrance examinations to the major London day schools and for 11+ Common Entrance to boarding schools.

Charitable status. St Christopher's School (Hampstead) Limited is a Registered Charity, number 312999. It exists to provide education for girls.

St Christopher's School

Hove

33 New Church Road Hove East Sussex BN3 4AD
Tel: 01273 735404
Fax: 01273 747956
e-mail: office@stchristophershove.org.uk
website: www.stchristophershove.org.uk

Chairman of Governors: Mr A J Symonds

***Headmaster*: Mr I M McIntyre**, MA

Age Range. 4–13 co-educational.

Number of Pupils. 240.

Fees per term (2008-2009). £2,147–£2,681.

Since its foundation in 1927, St Christopher's School has expanded to become a highly successful academic preparatory school, located in the middle of Brighton & Hove, England's youngest and most vibrant city.

St Christopher's School aims to provide a traditional academic education within a supportive family environment where individual talents are developed to produce confident, articulate and ambitious children. Pupils regularly obtain top academic scholarships, including major awards for art, music and sport. In 2003, ownership of the School was transferred to Brighton College, at which time St Christopher's became a Member of the Brighton College Family of Schools. 11+ Continuation scholarships to Brighton College are available.

Entry to the School is virtually non-selective at 4+ and 8+ and by examination and interview at 11+. Places are occasionally available in other age groups. In the Lower School, pupils are taught mainly by their form teachers. Particular emphasis is placed upon reading, writing and mathematics, but the curriculum is broad, and a wide range of subjects is taught by specialist teachers, including French, Latin, science, music, art, ICT, PE and games.

Pupils move into the Upper School in Year 4, where the curriculum reflects the syllabuses of the Common Entrance and Brighton College Academic Scholarship Examinations. Formal homework is introduced at this stage. All subjects are taught by specialists, who make full use of the interactive ICT suite, science laboratory, art studio, music room and library. A variety of educational day visits, sports trips and an annual residential visit to France ensures that children receive a broad and stimulating educational experience.

In addition to football, netball and rounders, the School has an enviable record of success at rugby at local and county level. The musical life of St Christopher's is enriched by three choirs and the choice of a wide variety of instrumental and vocal tuition. A major theatrical work involving every pupil is produced biannually, and a wide range of extra-curricular activities is on offer. After-school care is available until 5.30 pm each evening.

The Headmaster is always delighted to welcome prospective parents. Please contact the Admissions Secretary to arrange a visit.

Charitable status. St Christopher's School, Hove (a member of the Brighton College Family of Schools) is a Registered Charity, number 307061.

St Columba's College Preparatory Department

King Harry Lane St Albans Hertfordshire AL3 4AW
Tel: 01727 862616
Fax: 01727 892025
e-mail: headofprep@st-columbas.herts.sch.uk
website: www.stcolumbascollege.org

Chairman: Mrs G Cummings, JP

***Head*: Mr Edwin Brown**, BEd Hons Lancaster, MA London

Age Range. 4–11.

Number of Pupils. 240 Boys.

Fees per term (2008-2009). Prep 2–4 £2,982, Prep 1 £2,732, Pre-Prep £2,640 including personal accident insurance. Additional charges are made for coaches and consumables.

The Prep School is an academically selective Catholic Day School which strives to create a welcoming community in which each boy is valued as an individual and endeavours to promote positive relationships based on mutual respect and understanding. There is a rigorous academic curriculum with an extensive range of extra curricular opportunities. A full curriculum and sports programme is offered at Key Stage 1 and 2.

Admissions at age 4 and 7 years. Entry requirements of the school is by assessment; at age 7+ assessment is via maths, mental arithmetic, perceptual reasoning, creative writing and reading; at age 4 assessment takes place informally using a standardised test and in context in a classroom situation. Subjects include: English, Mathematics, Drama, RE, French, History, Geography, IT, PE, Games, Music, Art and Design Technology.

Examinations: Pupils progress at 11+ to St Columba's College on the same site (subject to entrance examination results), or to other senior schools.

Academic facilities include: modern form rooms with specialist facilities for IT, ADT, Music, PE, Games, RE and French, and a professionally staffed extensive library.

Sports facilities include: Rugby/Football pitches, Cricket nets and square. There is access to a swimming pool and athletics track.

There are means-tested bursaries at Prep level and a number of scholarships available to Prep School boys on entry to St Columba's College. These include academic and music scholarships.

Charitable status. St Columba's College and Preparatory School is a Registered Charity, number 1088480. It exists to provide a well-rounded Roman Catholic education for pupils from 4–18 years of age.

St Dunstan's College Junior School

Stanstead Road London SE6 4TY
Tel: 020 8516 7225
Fax: 020 8516 7300; 020 8516 7260 (Bursary)
e-mail: rscard@sdmail.org.uk
website: www.stdunstans.org.uk

Chairman of Governors: ¶Sir Paul Judge

***Head of Junior School*: Miss J H Bate**

Age Range. Co-educational 3–11.

Number of Pupils. Pre-Preparatory (3–7) 115, Preparatory (7–11) 150.

Fees per term (2008-2009). Nursery £2,306, Pre-Preparatory £2,936, Preparatory £3,133–£3,838. Fees include lunch.

The Junior School is an integral part of St Dunstan's College and prepares boys and girls for the Senior School (age 11–18) (*see entry in HMC section*). It shares with it a common site and many facilities. In particular the ICT Suites, Music Centre, Refectory, Great Hall, Sports Hall, indoor Swimming Pool and playing fields increase the opportunities for all pupils in curricular and extra-curricular activities. For other work the Junior School pupils have their own buildings. The Pre-Preparatory Department is located in an outstanding Victorian house which has been beautifully converted for the specific needs of the 3–7 year olds. The Preparatory Department has its own teaching block of 12 classrooms with a library, art, and design technology rooms and networked computer system. Both buildings are enhanced by examples of children's work providing a warm and stimulating environment in which to learn.

Special emphasis is placed upon the development of a high level of literacy and numeracy. The curriculum is also designed to promote learning and appreciation of Science, Humanities, Music, Art, Design and Technology, Information Technology, Drama, Languages and Study Skills. An extensive programme of Games and Physical Education provide children with the opportunity to participate in Rugby, Soccer, Cricket, Netball, Rounders, Swimming, Gymnastics and Athletics. Games and Physical Education play an important part in the growth and development of each pupil. Boys and girls are encouraged to take part in various clubs and activities after school hours and at lunch times. Opportunities exist for French Club, Drama Workshop, Dance, Choirs, Orchestra, Strings Club, Recorder Ensemble, ICT Club, Chess, Board games and Electronic Workshop.

A caring and friendly environment is provided by small class sizes and a dedicated team of well qualified and experienced class teachers. In addition to being taught many subjects by their class teacher, Preparatory Department pupils have the advantage of being educated by specialists in Art, Music, Languages, Physical Education and Games.

An effective strong partnership exists between the home and school and parents are encouraged to participate in their children's education and the life of the Junior School. Regular contact is maintained between school and the home to ensure that parents are aware of their child's academic and social progress. Parents are encouraged to assist with the many varied educational visits.

Boys and Girls come from both maintained and independent schools and are admitted at all ages from 3+ to 10+ but principally at 3+ and 4+ (Nursery and Reception) and at 7+ (Year 3). Entry is by group assessment at 4+ and at 7+.

Charitable status. St Dunstan's College is a Registered Charity, number 1094290. It exists to provide education for boys and girls.

St Edmund's Junior School

Canterbury Kent CT2 8HU
Tel: 01227 475600
Fax: 01227 471083
e-mail: junsch@stedmunds.org.uk
website: www.stedmunds.org.uk

Chairman of Governors: Professor J F J Todd, BSc, PhD, CChem, CEng

***Master of the Junior School*: R G Bacon**, BA Durham

Age Range. 3–13.

Numbers of Pupils. 262 (Boarders: School House 15, Choir House 30); Day Pupils: Boys 128, Girls 89.

Fees per term (2008-2009). Junior School: Boarders £5,606, Weekly Boarders £5,108, Choristers £5,514, Day pupils £3,947. Pre-Prep: Forms 1 & 2 £2,796, Reception £2,419, Nursery £1,794 (mornings only £1,025).

Pupils may enter at any age from 3 to 12. Boarding begins at the age of 8.

The Junior School is closely linked with the Senior School (*see entry in HMC section*) but is run as a separate entity, working to the Common Entrance Examination and Independent Schools Scholarship Examination. The Junior School uses some Senior School specialist staff, particularly in the teaching of Science, Music, Art, Technology and shares with the Senior School such amenities as the Chapel, concert theatre, sports hall and swimming pool. There is a full-time school Chaplain. Domestic arrangements, including health and catering, are under centralised administration.

The Canterbury Cathedral Choristers, who are St Edmund's pupils, live in the Choir House which is under the care of a married Housemaster and is situated in the precincts of Canterbury Cathedral.

Scholarships and bursaries. Academic, music, sport, and all-rounder awards are available for applicants aged 11. Cathedral choristerships are available for boys from age 7. Fee concessions are also available as detailed in the Senior School entry in HMC section.

Charitable status. St Edmund's School Canterbury is a Registered Charity, number 1056382. It exists to educate the children in its care.

St Edmund's School

Portsmouth Road Hindhead Surrey GU26 6BH
Tel: 01428 609875
Fax: 01428 607898
e-mail: registrar@saintedmunds.co.uk
website: www.saintedmunds.co.uk

Chairman of Governors: Mrs J Alliss

***Headmaster*: A J Walliker**, MA Cantab, MBA, PGCE

Age Range. Boys and Girls 2–13.

Number of Pupils. Prep School: Flexi Boarders and Day Pupils 145. Pre-Prep and Nursery: 82.

Fees per term (2007-2008). Prep: Day Pupils £3,415–£4,349; Weekly Boarding Fee £950; Pre-Prep £2,531; Nursery from £684 (three mornings).

The fees are inclusive of all ordinary extras, laundry, games, swimming, lectures, optional Saturday activities etc.

St Edmund's, the 132 year-old boys' prep school in Hindhead, is now welcoming girls of from age 2–13. From September 2008 girls will be able to continue from the Pre-Prep into the Prep School. Adam Walliker, Headmaster, commented: "We're excited that our style of education, with small classes and a very personal focus, will now also take girls through to their senior schools".

"I like St Ed's. It's a school I fit into." These words, from one of our children, capture much of what we strive to do at St Edmund's: to instil in every child a sense of self-esteem and belonging by building on their own talents, opening their eyes to new ones and giving them focused and personal support whenever it's needed.

Academically, it is an approach that continues to pay dividends; with our pupils going on to wide range of senior schools, both boarding and day. Yet of equal importance are the discoveries, excitements and good old-fashioned fun that St Edmund's creates inside our 40 beautiful acres. These include an immaculate 9-hole golf course, indoor pool and astro pitch, and a wealth of activities ranging from cooking and the chapel choir to campfire building and language masterclasses. A thriving and optional Saturday morning school activity programme is allowing us to introduce a greater breadth of ideas and new experiences.

The school's pre-prep and nursery department, which is already co-educational, was recently rated as "Outstanding" by Ofsted. This complemented another top score (of "Excellent") for the school's pastoral care, awarded by the Commission for Social Care.

We now welcome boys and girls from 2–13. We also offer an unusually flexible boarding option, from one-off nights to regular weekly boarding. Scholarships and means-tested bursaries are available.

Charitable status. St Edmund's School Trust Limited is a Registered Charity, number 278301. Its aim is the education of children.

St Edward's Junior School

London Road Charlton Kings Cheltenham Glos GL52 6NR
Tel: 01242 538900
Fax: 01242 538901
e-mail: headmaster@stedwardsjunior.co.uk
website: www.stedwards.co.uk

Co-educational Day School.

Chairman of Governors: Mr P Walsh

***Headmaster*: Mr T J Mooney**, MA (TCD), HDipEd

Age Range. 1–11 years.

Number of Pupils. 440.

Fees per term (2008-2009). £1,695–£2,625.

St Edward's Junior School is an independent co-educational Catholic Foundation welcoming pupils of all denominations from 1 to 11 years. We provide a supportive family atmosphere in which pupils are encouraged to develop their individual potential – academic, social, physical, creative and spiritual – in preparation for their secondary education. The school is situated on the edge of Cheltenham in forty acres of beautiful parkland. Our facilities are truly exceptional and give our pupils opportunities for practical experience rarely available in a junior school, as well as enabling us to provide an unusually wide range of after-school activities.

Our Kindergarten is open all year round and provides a secure and stimulating introduction to school life.

St Edward's Junior School has established an excellent relationship with the local community and with many regional and national organisations through the leasing and lending of its buildings and grounds to a miscellany of educational, religious, cultural, social and sports clubs, groups and organisations.

The facilities at both Schools are available throughout the year both during term time and holiday periods.

Charitable status. St Edward's School is a Registered Charity, number 293360. It exists to provide for the education of children of any creed with preference to those who are of the Roman Catholic faith.

St Edward's School

64 Tilehurst Road Reading Berkshire RG30 2JH
Tel: 0118 957 4342
Fax: 0118 950 3736
e-mail: admin@stedwards.org.uk
website: www.stedwards.org.uk

Chairman of Governors: Mrs S Pellow

Principal: G Mottram, HDipEd SA, MA Ed, NPQH

***Vice-Principal*: D A Cumming**, MEd, BA, CertEd

Age Range. 4–13.

Number of Boys. 163 day boys.

Fees per term (2007-2008). £1,925–£2,480. Dayboarders (who stay until 5.55 pm): £2,375–£2,880. There are no compulsory extras.

The School is an Educational Trust and has a long history of academic success; many scholarships and exhibitions have been won to independent senior schools. In order to allow each boy to be successful we have adopted a broad curriculum: English, Mathematics, Latin, French, History, Geography, Science, Art, Music, RS, PSE, ICT, Physical Education and Games, CDT, Music and Drama.

Children are subject taught from Year 3 and in addition French and drama are specialist taught from Reception. Small group teaching takes place throughout the school to encourage pupils of all ability levels. Trips are regularly taken to a variety of museums and places of interest in association with class work.

St Edward's is networked with access to the internet. Children are instructed in the use of computers and IT applications are taught across the curriculum. Each classroom and the library has its own computer in addition to the computer suite and pupils are confident in their application.

There is a Gymnasium and all boys have PE and games sessions each week. Rugby, Soccer and Cricket are the major sports but boys also have the opportunity to take part in athletics, hockey, basketball, tennis and cross-country running. All boys from Reception to Year 5 have swimming lessons as part of their timetable.

Music and drama play an important part in the life of the school. There is a choir, various musical ensembles and the Head of Music is assisted by visiting instrumental teachers. The thriving drama department runs workshops, LAMDA exams and is taught by a professional drama teacher.

The Pre-Prep department, started in September 2001, accepts boys from four and offers a caring and positive environment in which the children can thrive and learn.

Prep: Boys may stay until 5.55 pm to do the their prep under supervision. Lessons finish at 3.55 pm. Those boys staying on are given tea. They then take part in an activity until prep starts at 5 pm.

School transport is available morning and evening.

Scholarships: Academic and All-Rounder Scholarships are available from age 11 for Years 7 and 8.

Charitable status. St Edward's and Highlands School Ltd is a Registered Charity, number 309147.

St Faith's School

Trumpington Road Cambridge CB2 2AG
Tel: 01223 352073
Fax: 01223 314757
e-mail: admissions@stfaiths.co.uk
website: www.stfaiths.co.uk

Chairman of the Governors: Mrs E Mimpriss, CertEd

***Headmaster*: C S S Drew**, MA (Oxford)

Deputy Heads:
D Dawes, BA (OU), TCert (Keswick Hall)
Mrs L M Dennis, BEd (Southampton)

Age Range. 4–13.
Number of Pupils. 508.
Fees per term (2007-2008). £2,770–£3,490.

St Faith's, founded in 1884, is a co-educational day school set in extensive and attractive grounds on the south side of Cambridge, approximately one mile from the city centre. It is situated close to the A10 and M11 and the Park and Ride facilities and operates a school minibus from the Trumpington Road Park and Ride site to the school each morning. Boys and girls enter the school at age 4 and stay until they are 13. Interviews and assessments for places occur throughout the year and scholarships are available at 7+.

St Faith's is very highly regarded in Cambridge. It is valued for the breadth of its curriculum, the attractiveness of its surroundings, the warmth of its family feeling and for the commitment of its staff. The children are encouraged to develop their talents to the full by following a curriculum which is broadly based and rigorous in its requirement. Classes are small. Teaching in the early years is principally class based, while, from Year 5, pupils work with specialist subject teachers. St Faith's prides itself on the pastoral care of the children, which operates through a house-based tutorial system. The school's principal aim is to ensure that the children feel safe, secure and happy. Learning happily is a natural extension of this.

The facilities and educational resources at St Faith's are up to the minute and excellent. The recently completed Keynes building has provided enviable facilities for the teaching of Design and Technology, Information and Communication Technology and Music and the Ashburton building houses science and drama as well as a hall equipped with computer equipment and a mixing desk for sound and lighting. In addition to the excellent sports facilities on site, the school has the use of the nearby Leys Sports Hall and the Astroturf.

St Faith's has an excellent sporting tradition with rugby, netball, hockey, cricket, tennis, rounders, football and athletics the main outdoor games. Basketball, cross-country running and other games are also organised, but on a less formal basis. Our sports programme involves inter-house competitions and a strong fixture list with numerous matches against other schools. Music and drama are also important at St Faith's and the school has a flourishing music department with the emphasis placed upon enjoyment as well as good performance. Pupils are able to participate in class and whole school concerts and a large number of instrumental groups, choirs and the school orchestra perform regularly. Drama is timetabled for all forms; there are performances of plays or musicals by each year group throughout the year and the standard of performance is high.

Extra-curricular activities range from chess, reading, art and model making to more energetic sporting pursuits. In addition there are Play Clubs and Multi-Activity Courses during the holidays and team-building activity holidays, language trips and a ski trip for older children. Early Start and Late Stay facilities operate and families wishing to miss the Cambridge traffic are able to enjoy breakfast in the school's dining room from 7.30 each morning.

St Faith's is part of The Leys and St Faith's Foundation and although each year approximately half of the children move on to The Leys at the end of Year 8, others prepare for entry to a variety of schools, mainly independent, many of them with scholarships.

Charitable status. The Leys School, Cambridge is a Registered Charity, number 311436. The aim of the charity is the provision of first-class education.

St Francis School

Marlborough Road Pewsey Wilts SN9 5NT
Tel: 01672 563228
Fax: 01672 564323
e-mail: admissions@st-francis.wilts.sch.uk
website: www.st-francis.wilts.sch.uk

Chair of Governors: Mrs S Soar

***Headmaster*: B L Brown**, MA, BA Hons, PGCE

Age Range. 2–13.
Number of Boys and Girls. 302: 158 Boys, 144 Girls.
Fees per term (2007-2008). Reception–Year 8: £1,980–£2,950 including lunch. Nursery £198 per session.

St Francis is a charitable trust with a board of governors that includes The Deputy Head of Marlborough College. The School is situated in the lovely Vale of Pewsey some five miles south of Marlborough. Its grounds border the Kennet and Avon Canal.

The School is co-educational and takes children from the age of 2 to 13. It is a day school with pupils travelling from a wide area of mid-Wiltshire; a daily minibus service operates from Burbage and Marlborough.

Small classes giving every child the opportunity to fulfil his or her full potential are a feature of the school. Staff ensure that they are very positive and encouraging in their teaching. Should a child be found to be suffering from some form of specific learning difficulty then appropriate help will be given. The facilities are constantly being improved. The new Burden Block comes with Library, Design Technology room, specialist rooms for English, French and Geography, as well as three new Year 3 form rooms.

The curriculum is delightfully diverse enabling the pupils to have, for instance, CDT, Pottery, Drama, Computing and Swimming all in their normal weekly timetable. French is taught from the age of three. The majority of the pupils take up individual musical tuition and a wide range of instruments is available.

Results are excellent. The pupils are mainly entered for the local senior schools, St Mary's Calne, Godolphin, Dauntsey's, Marlborough College, Stonar and Warminster, but scholarships and common entrance are also taken for boarding schools further afield. Awards are regularly achieved to all of the aforementioned.

Please write, telephone or fax for a prospectus, or ask to visit and tour round the school. The Headmaster will be happy to oblige.

Charitable status. St Francis is a Registered Charity, number 298522. It exists solely to provide education for boys and girls.

St Gabriel's School
Junior Department

Sandleford Priory Newbury Berkshire RG20 9BD
Tel: 01635 40663
Fax: 01635 37351
e-mail: info@stgabriels.co.uk
website: www.st-gabriels.w-berks.sch.uk

Chairman: Nigel Garland

***Principal*: Mr A Jones**, LTCL, LWCMD

***Vice-Principal & Head of Junior Department*: Mrs C Sams**, CertEd

Age Range. Girls 3–11, Boys 3–7.
Number of Pupils. 265.
Fees per term (from April 2008). £2,685–£3,170.

The Junior Department of St Gabriel's School is adjacent to the Senior School and is situated in 54 acres of parkland on the southern outskirts of Newbury.

Girls are accepted from the age of 3 to 11 years and boys from 3 to 7 years. Maximum class sizes are of 20 pupils.

Girls are prepared for the Common Entrance Examination at 11 years. Entry to the Senior School is by an entrance examination.

(*For further information about the Senior School, see St Gabriel's School entry in GSA section.*)

A number of scholarships are awarded annually to candidates of outstanding ability at 11+.

Subjects taught include Mathematics, Science, Technology, English, French (from 4 years of age), Latin, History, Geography, Computer Awareness, Art/Craft, Music, Drama and Games.

Science is taught in a purpose-built laboratory. All Junior children have access to a recently refurbished Junior Computer Room, while pupils in Year 6 use the computer facilities of the Senior School.

Gymnastics, Dance, Netball, Hockey, Cross-Country, Tennis, Rounders and Athletics are included in the curriculum for all pupils. Swimming takes place during the Summer Term in the outdoor heated swimming pool.

Pupils are welcome to join further activities, a selection of which includes Ballet, Tap Dancing, Craft, Choir, Board Games, Puppet Making, Painting on glass, Jazz Dance, Chess, Floral Art, Bridge, Storytime, Art Club, Recorders, Pyrography, String Orchestra, Gym Club and the NSPCC.

Private instrumental music lessons can be arranged.

Charitable status. The St Gabriel Schools Foundation is a Registered Charity, number 1062748. It exists to provide education for girls from age 3–11 and for boys from age 3–7.

St George's College Junior School

Thames Street Weybridge Surrey KT13 8NL
Tel: 01932 839400
Fax: 01932 839401
e-mail: JSHead@st-georges-college.co.uk
website: www.st-georges-college.co.uk

Chairman of Board of Governors: Mrs K Quint

***Headmaster*: A J W Hudson**, MA Cantab, PGCE, NPQH

Age Range. 3–11.
Number of Pupils. 609.
Fees per term (2008-2009). Nursery: £1,225 (mornings only); £1,980 (full days). Lower Years (YR to Y2) £2,290. Upper Years (Y3 to Y6) £3,145.

St George's College Junior School is a fully co-ed Roman Catholic Day School and all pupils attending the Junior School normally belong to one of the mainstream Christian traditions. The School was established in 1950 by a Religious Order of Priests and Brothers known as "The Josephites" who maintain a keen interest in the future of the School. Only pupils who are aged three are admitted into the Nursery.

While the majority of the pupils at the school come from around North Surrey, some 13% of the pupils are from countries as far away as Australia, New Zealand, Hong Kong, South Africa, Brazil, Canada, USA as well as from most European countries including Russia. The School operates a very extensive bus service and an option for parents using cars to drop off their children at either the Junior or Senior School.

In September 2000 the Junior School moved from its previous co-located site with St George's College one mile down the road to its present 12½ acre site on the outskirts of Weybridge close to the River Thames. Since then a £1.5 million refurbishment programme has been completed involving the upgrading of most of the classrooms, the science teaching room, the library, the music room, playground equipment, an Astroturf pitch, cricket nets and the creation of a school wide computer network including two computer resources rooms, one with 25 computers with an interactive whiteboard which is networked, as well as three other rooms, each with 10 networked computers. In 2006, a new Development Launch has focused on providing a new 'state of the art' Nursery classroom (now complete), and a totally refurbished Kitchen and Dining Area, called 'The Mulberry Hall', opened in January 2008.

The Junior School has a genuinely happy atmosphere in which every pupil is respected and treated as an individual. The headmaster considers the staff, pupils and parents to be constituent parts of an extended family. The School has always placed great emphasis on the importance of maintaining excellent channels of communication between members of staff, parents and pupils.

The size of classes ensures that the School is a learning community by creating the correct balance between pupil interaction and pupil-teacher contact. The pupils in the top two years of the School are taught by subject specialists. French is offered to all pupils from Year 1. The School was described in its recent ISI report (2005) as "providing its pupils with a very positive environment, especially spiritual development, which is at the heart of its work".

All pupils are assessed on entry and when they leave at the end of Year 6 nearly all transfer to St George's College. Over 150 scholarships, including music scholarships, have been won by pupils in Year Six since 1989.

While the pursuit of academic excellence is highly valued, the Mission Statement of the School stresses the importance of pupils having high personal self-esteem as well as emphasising the importance of their religious, spiritual, social and physical development. The School requires its pupils to have high moral values especially those of its school motto "Honesty and Compassion".

The Junior School has four Houses which compete against each other across a wide range of activities inside and outside the classroom including Music, Public Speaking and Chess.

Extra-curricular and other enrichment activities are, likewise, considered to play an important role in the educational development of children. The extensive range of activities includes dance (ballet, modern and tap), gymnastics and clubs based on the academic subjects taught in the School, for example the Young Scientist Club. Pupils are taken to places of educational interest regularly including theatre, music and art trips and there is an annual book week during which pupils meet and listen to visiting authors and story-tellers.

Considerable emphasis is placed on the Creative and Performing Arts. Pupils have dance lessons throughout the school with specialist ballet and tap dance lessons being a compulsory part of curriculum for all pupils up to the end of Year Reception. The School stages six major drama productions a year. All children from Year 2 have two lessons of music each week. Children in Year 2 learn the violin and recorder as part of the music curriculum. There is an Orchestra, Jazz Band, Chapel Choir and Year 3 Choir which rehearse on a weekly basis as well as Violin, Brass, Guitar and Recorder ensembles. Individual music lessons are very popular with about 50% of the children in Years 2–6 learning at lease one additional instrument. Concerts happen at least once every term. The School has recently invested in the provision of a newly refurbished music room; as a result, music lessons are now supported by the use of the latest computer-based technology. Pupils have achieved considerable success at Public Speaking Competitions and achieve a very high level of attainment in their external Spoken English, Lamda and instrumental music exams.

Apart from its own sports facilities on site comprising an artificial sports pitch, netball and tennis courts, a sprung floor gymnasium and a swimming pool, the School has the use of 20 acres of outstanding sports facilities at the College including three floodlit netball/tennis courts, a floodlit artificial surface for hockey about to be completely refurbished, a four-court indoor tennis centre, three floodlit French clay courts, a sports hall and gym, three cricket squares, a tartan athletics track and six large grass fields.

The Under 9 boys' mini-rugby team reached the National Prep School finals in 1996, 1999, 2001 and won the National Prep School finals in 2003; in 2008 they got through to the semi-finals. The Under 10 rugby team got through to the semi-finals of the National Prep Schools Finals in 2004 and into the Nationals again, as U11s, in 2005 as did their successors in 2006. The School has reached the Under 11 Boys National Mini-Hockey Finals 11 times since 1989, becoming National Champions of England in 1991, 1993, 1995, 1996, 2001 and 2002 and runners-up in 1989, 1994 and 1998. The girls won the Under 11 National Mini-Hockey Finals in 2000 and came fourth overall in 2006 and 2008. They also won the IAPS National Hockey Championships in 2002, 2003 and were South East Champions in 2007; in 2008 they became South of England champions. The girls reached the Under 11 IAPS Netball Finals in 2000 and came third in 2004; they also got through to the Netball Nationals in 2006 and 2008. The School has been age group county champions at Tennis, Table-Tennis, Fencing, Badminton and Cricket. Tennis and Fencing are very popular Saturday morning activities. The School organises a major netball tournament for girls and a tennis festival for boys each year. There is an annual residential outward bound adventure holiday for the pupils in Year Six.

School lunches are compulsory from Reception Year, are prepared on site and eaten in the dining rooms which can seat 320 people. The School offers a free supervised homework facility each weekday evening during term time until 4.45 pm for those children in Reception and Years 1 and 2. Children in Years 3–6 can sign up for clubs which continue until 5.00 pm.

For the last few years the school has usually had more applications for places than it can accommodate in all year groups. When vacancies do occur, pupils are admitted if they meet the School's entry criteria and successfully complete an assessment day at the School as well as receiving a satisfactory report from the current school where this is appropriate. Priority is afforded to siblings and Roman Catholics.

Charitable status. St George's College, Weybridge is a Registered Charity, number 1017853. The aims and objectives of the charity are the Christian education of young people.

St George's School

Windsor Castle Windsor Berks SL4 1QF
Tel: 01753 865553
Fax: 01753 842093
e-mail: enqs@stgwindsor.co.uk
website: www.stgwindsor.co.uk

Patron: Her Majesty The Queen

Visitor: The Lord Chancellor

Chairman of the Governors: The Dean of Windsor

***Headmaster*: J R Jones**, BEd (Westminster College, Oxford)

Age Range. 3–13 Co-educational.

Number of Pupils. 407 (30 boarders).

Fees per term (2008-2009). Boarders £5,458–£5,604, Day Pupils £3,669–£4,110, Choristers (Boarding) £2,802, Pre-Prep £2,478–£2,811, Nursery £1,038–£1,293.

St George's School was established as part of the foundation of the Order of the Garter in 1348 when provision was made for the education of the first choristers. In 1893 the School moved into the Georgian building of the former College of the Naval Knights of Windsor situated between the mound of the Castle and the Home Park. Expansion followed with the admission of supernumerary (non-chorister) pupils. Extensions were made to the buildings in 1988 and 1996, the latter of which allowed for the opening of a Pre-Preparatory Department and Nursery. Girls were admitted to the School for the first time, entering both the Pre-Prep and the main School. A new Middle School building was opened in Spring 2006.

St George's School boasts a long tradition of musical and academic excellence alongside lively art and drama. It is well equipped for games having beautiful playing fields in the Home Park, an indoor swimming pool, a tennis and netball court and gymnasium. The whole School building has undergone a recent refurbishment which has included the creation of a Design and Technology Workshop and the updating of an Information Technology Room fully on line.

The School pursues the highest standards whilst retaining a relaxed and friendly atmosphere. There is a strong sense of pastoral care and a high pupil staff ratio. Communications are excellent: two stations, the M25, M3, M4 and M40 are all close by and Heathrow is just twenty minutes away.

Charitable status. St George's School, Windsor Castle is a Registered Charity, number 1100392. Its purpose is the education, either as boarding or day pupils, of children of pre-preparatory and preparatory school age and of the choristers who maintain the worship in the Queen's Free Chapel of Our Lady, St George and St Edward the Confessor in Windsor Castle.

St Helen's College

Parkway Hillingdon Middlesex UB10 9JX
Tel: 01895 234371
Fax: 01895 619818
e-mail: info@sthelenscollege.com
website: www.sthelenscollege.com

***Headmaster*: Mr D A Crehan**, ARCS, BA, BSc, MSc, CPhys
***Headmistress*: Mrs G R Crehan**, BA, PGCE

Age Range. 3–11 co-educational.
Number of Pupils. 340 Day Pupils.
Fees per term (2008-2009). £1,320–£2,200.

The aims of St Helen's are to develop as fully as possible each child's academic potential, to provide a wide, balanced, stimulating and challenging curriculum, and to foster true values and good character based on moral and spiritual principles. The children enjoy a purposeful and happy 'family' atmosphere and are taught by committed professional teachers.

Children are prepared for independent senior schools and local grammar schools, and records of success are very good indeed. In addition to the academic subjects, sport, music and drama play an important part in the lives of the children.

A wide range of extra-curricular activities is offered, and pupils enjoy outings, day and residential, to many places of interest. There is an after-school club and summer school, and a holiday club which runs throughout the year.

St Hilary's School

Holloway Hill Godalming Surrey GU7 1RZ
Tel: 01483 416551
Fax: 01483 418325
e-mail: registrar@sthilarysschool.com
website: www.sthilarysschool.com

Chair of Governors: Mrs J I Isaacs, BA, BLit Oxon, JP

***Headmistress*: Mrs S Bailes**, BA Hons, MA, PGCE

Age Range. Girls 2½–11, Boys 2½–7.
Number of Pupils. 300 Day Pupils.
Fees per term (2008-2009). (including lunch) Reception £2,445, Year 1 £2,575, Years 2–3 £3,100, Years 4–6 £3,525. Nursery £23 per session (one session being single morning or single afternoon) with lunch extra.

"St Hilary's school provides a high-quality, well-rounded education within an environment in which pupils can develop, be happy and flourish. Provision for pastoral care is outstanding, and pupils' personal development is excellent." (recent ISI Inspection Report)

The School is conveniently situated, close to the town centre of Godalming on Holloway Hill in beautiful grounds, providing a safe environment with an all-weather pitch, tennis and netball courts, a large playing field and separate quiet play area. Use is made of nearby facilities – the excellent sports centre at Prior's Field School and swimming pool at Charterhouse.

In 1927 Miss Marjorie Hiorns founded St Hilary's and it became a Charitable Trust in 1966 with a board of Governors. The Headmistress is an active member of IAPS (The Independent Association of Prep Schools), an organization which guarantees the highest standards for parents.

As Headmistress, Mrs Susan Bailes remarks: "Our aim is to provide a happy, secure environment and to unlock a love of learning, which will last for ever". As Inspectors confirmed, "Learning in class is complemented by a wide range of extra-curricular activities. Pupils are well prepared for the next stage in their education. They look forward to their senior school with confidence, both in their academic foundations and their ability to form firm friendships with peers and positive relationships with adults".

The School bases its values on firm Christian principles, through which children may learn the importance of care and consideration for others. The School regularly raises funds for Charities including Save the Children and Canine Partners. A School Council in the Upper School Years (Years 3–6) involves children in democratic elections for representatives and decision-making with regular meetings to discuss ways in which the School can be improved. In addition St Hilary's is an 'Eco School' with pupils and staff actively engaged in caring for the environment in their daily lives.

The school has an excellent Foundation Stage with a purpose-built Nursery and spacious classrooms, specialist teaching in Upper School, Gym/Hall with stage and separate dining room, Music wing, an Art Studio, a Performing Arts room, well-stocked Library and modern ICT suite and equipment to support and promote individuals' learning.

Charitable status. St Hilary's is a Registered Charity, number 312056. It exists to provide education for children.

St Hilda's School

High Street Bushey Hertfordshire WD23 3DA
Tel: 020 8950 1751
Fax: 020 8420 4523
e-mail: secretary@sthildasbushey.co.uk
registrar@sthildasbushey.co.uk
website: www.sthildas-school.co.uk

Chairman of Governors: Mrs B Batten, MA

***Headmistress*: Mrs L E Cavanagh**, MA, Dip CE, FRSA

Age Range. 3–11.
Number of Pupils. 150 Day Girls. Boys in Kindergarten.
Fees per term (2008-2009). £1,545–£2,895. Compulsory extras: Lunches £200.

St Hilda's is an Independent Day School for girls, although boys are accepted into the Early Years. It was founded in 1918 and has occupied its present 5-acre site since 1928. The Victorian house at the centre of the site has been continually improved, adapted and extended to provide an excellent educational environment. This includes a nature garden area, tennis courts, a covered heated swimming pool, a large all purpose hall, science laboratory, technology laboratory and computer suite. We teach a wide range of subjects to a high academic standard in a secure and happy environment in which every pupil can develop their academic and personal potential. We offer a broad and challenging curriculum in which art, drama and music play an important role. French is taught from Reception and Latin is introduced at the appropriate stage. There is a wide range of extra-curricular activities, including Ballet, Tap and Short Tennis; also after school clubs including Art and Drama. An after school care facility is available until 6 pm Monday to Friday during term time.

Charitable status. St Hilda's School is a Registered Charity, number 311072. It exists to provide education for girls.

St Hugh's

Woodhall Spa LN10 6TQ
Tel: 01526 352169
Fax: 01526 351520

e-mail: sthughs-schooloffice@btconnect.com
website: www.st-hughs.lincs.sch.uk

Chairman of Governors: C R Wheeldon, Esq
***Headmaster*: S G C Greenish**, BEd

Age Range. 2–13.

Number of Pupils. 200+. Boarders: 41 boys, 38 girls. Day: 30 boys, 27 girls. Pre-Prep: 28 boys, 19 girls. Nursery: 30 children.

Fees per term (2008-2009). Boarding £4,670–£4,750; Day £3,310–£3,490; Pre-Prep £1,925.

St Hugh's School was founded by the Forbes family in 1925, became a Charitable Trust in 1964 and has continued to prosper over the years administered by a forward-thinking Governing Body.

Today the School is fully co-educational, offering both day and boarding places. The Headmaster is assisted by 18 qualified and experienced teachers, a School Administrator, Catering Manager and 3 Matrons. Through its Headmaster the School is a member of IAPS (The Independent Association of Prep Schools) as well as the Boarding Schools' Association.

Boys and girls are prepared for the Common Entrance and Scholarship examinations. The School's academic record is good, with regular awards being gained to major Independent Schools, as well as places in Lincolnshire Grammar Schools. Children with special learning needs are treated sympathetically within the mainstream, with support from specialist staff. The aim of the School is to give every child a good all-round education and to discover and develop his or her own particular talents.

The major school games for boys are rugby, hockey and cricket, and for girls netball, hockey and rounders. Both boys and girls can also enjoy cross-country, tennis, athletics and swimming. There is an annual Sports Day. All children have PE each week with time set aside for instruction in gymnastics and swimming. Skills in games such as basketball and badminton also form the basis of these lessons.

The school lays heavy emphasis on extra-curricular activities, sport of various kinds, music, the visual arts and drama. All teachers are expected to help in some way with this. There is also a strong and continuing Christian tradition at St Hugh's, where children are encouraged to consider what they believe and develop a faith of their own within the context of regular acts of Christian Worship.

The school has excellent facilities including a modern sports hall, an assembly hall with stage and lighting, a heated indoor swimming pool, extensive playing fields, a fine library, dedicated classrooms and a large Music, Design and ICT studios. The facilities are continually being updated and added to.

Boarders are accommodated in two well-appointed Houses under the close supervision of the resident matrons and the Headmaster and his wife. Dormitories and common rooms are bright and cheerful and recognition is given to the importance of children having a place where they can feel at home and relaxed at the end of the day. Contact with parents and guardians is well maintained. Every half term is punctuated by an exeat weekend and arrangements are made for boarders whose parents live abroad. Minibus transport for day pupils is provided from Boston, Louth and Skegness.

The Pre-Preparatory department caters for approximately 45 children, aged from 4 to 7, and is located in its own building with separate play area and staff.

The Nursery for children between 1½ and 4 is attached to the Pre-Prep and accommodates approximately 45 children.

Half-fee bursaries are available for the sons and daughters of clergymen. There are also reductions for brothers and sisters as well as bursaries for the children of service personnel. The fees are fully inclusive.

Charitable status. St Hugh's School is a Registered Charity, number 527611. It exists to provide a high standard of education and care to pupils from the age of 2 to 13.

St Hugh's

Carswell Manor Faringdon Oxon SN7 8PT
Tel: 01367 870700
Fax: 01367 870707
e-mail: headmaster@st-hughs.co.uk
registrar@st-hughs.co.uk
website: www.st-hughs.co.uk

Chairman of Governors: J M Guillum Scott

***Headmaster*: A J P Nott**, BA Hons, PGCE

Age Range. 4–13.

Number of Pupils. 280: 35 Weekly Boarders, 165 Day Pupils (of whom many flexi board); Pre-Prep 80. (Boy-Girl ratio approximately 3:2, both boarding and day).

Fees per term (2008-2009). Upper School: Boarders £5,395, Day £4,505; Middle School: Boarders £5,055, Day £4,165; Pre-Prep £2,655–£2,900. (All fees inclusive, with no compulsory extras.)

The School's main building is a fine Jacobean house with extensive grounds. Boys and girls are prepared for Common Entrance and Scholarship examinations to senior independent schools. The school is organised into three departments: Pre-Prep (4–6), Middle School (7–8) and Upper School (9–13). Careful liaison ensures a strong thread of continuity throughout the school. The main entry points are at 4, 5, 7 and 11.

We are non-selective and both welcome and cater for pupils of a wide range of ability. We aim to foster confidence and a love of learning across this range: an impressive scholarship and CE record and the provision of integral specialist support both bear testimony to our inclusive approach. The arts and sport feature strongly and pupils are encouraged to develop their talents and interests as broadly as possible.

St Hugh's is described by the Good Schools Guide as a school which "personifies what is best in prep school education".

Charitable status. St Hugh's is a Registered Charity, number 309640. It exists to provide a centre of excellence for the education of children.

St Ives School

Three Gates Lane Haslemere Surrey GU27 2ES
Tel: 01428 643734
Fax: 01428 644788
e-mail: admin@stiveshaslemere.com
website: www.stiveshaslemere.com

Chairman of Governors: Mr T Plant

***Headmistress*: Mrs S E Cattaneo**

Age Range. Girls 2½–11, Boys 2½–5.

Number of Children. 150 (Day).

Fees per term (2008-2009). Pre-Prep (excluding Nursery class) £2,440; Years 3–4 £3,055; Years 5–6 £3,415 including lunches.

St Ives is a Preparatory Day School situated within half a mile of the centre of Haslemere and stands in its own attractive and spacious grounds of eight acres.

The school aims to provide a broad and balanced curriculum whilst retaining academic excellence, and a traditional prep school education is combined with the best of modern teaching methods. Each child is encouraged to work hard in a secure, relaxed and happy environment. Individual needs are catered for and high standards of manners, discipline and appearance are encouraged. Classes are small and in addition to class teachers, qualified teaching assistants are provided in each of the Pre-Prep classes. Specialist teaching throughout the school in core subjects, ICT, Art, French and PE enables each child to fulfil her potential.

Our children are prepared for a variety of senior schools and we are very proud of our strong academic achievements. Whilst the basic skills of Numeracy and Literacy are at the heart of our curriculum, the girls also enjoy a wide range of experiences and opportunities.

Competitive sport is played in good spirit with an emphasis on enjoyment, involvement and working together whilst attaining high standards. The school enjoys regional and national sporting success and a large variety of extra-curricular activities is offered including speech and drama, ballet, instrumental lessons and tennis coaching. Annual residential field studies are organised for the upper school and a ski trip is normally organised on alternate years for the Easter holidays.

The school is well resourced including Maths and Computer suites, purpose-built Nursery, Pre-Prep classrooms, Art and Music rooms. Two new netball courts and enlarged grassed areas have enhanced the sporting facilities.

Girls are prepared for the Common Entrance and senior school examinations at 11+ and the school has a good record for gaining scholarships to a wide range of well known senior independent schools. St Ives' full independence from any senior school enables parents and the Head to select the most appropriate senior school for their child.

The St Ives bus provides a daily service, the route currently covering the Haslemere, Liphook, Hindhead, Grayshott, Churt and Frensham areas.

Entry at 7+ is by interview with the Head and a trial day at the school. Scholarships are available for entry into Year 3, the number and value of the awards varying from year to year.

For a copy of the prospectus please apply to the Registrar.

Charitable status. St Ives School is a Registered Charity, number 312080. Its aim is the advancement of education for girls.

St John's Beaumont

Priest Hill Old Windsor Berkshire SL4 2JN
Tel: 01784 432428
Fax: 01784 494048
e-mail: admissions@stjohnsbeaumont.co.uk
website: www.stjohnsbeaumont.org.uk

Chairman of Governors: The Revd Kevin Fox, SJ

***Headmaster*: G E F Delaney**, BA Hons, PGCE

Deputy Headmaster (*Pastoral*): S Head, MA, PGCE
Deputy Headmaster (*Curriculum & Administration*): M Pearce, BA Hons

Age Range. 4–13.

Number of Boys. 320 (60 Full and Weekly Boarders; 260 Day Boys).

Fees per term (2007-2008). Boarders £5,430–£6,290, Day boys £2,860–£4,130, Blandyke (age 4 and 5) £2,220.

St John's is a Jesuit School and accepts boys between the ages of 4+ and 13+.

In addition to the Headmaster and Deputy Heads the staff consists of 28 full-time teachers.

Classes are small, and boys can receive individual attention according to their needs and abilities. In the past eighteen years, 111 scholarships have been won to senior independent schools.

The school was purpose-built in 1888 by J F Bentley and stands in spacious grounds on the edge of Windsor Great Park, with extensive facilities for outdoor sports. It has a large gymnasium and considerable sports fields. Several facilities have been opened in recent years, including two ICT suites, technology block science and art block, music school, concert hall and indoor swimming pool. A new purpose-built sports hall is planned for completion in 2008. Wireless technology is available in classrooms enabling access to individual laptops and there are interactive whiteboards in all classrooms. On top of their daily curriculum schedules, each member of staff offers an extra activity after school. These include chess, drama, art and various sports. Games are played every day and the school particularly excels at rugby, cricket, tennis and swimming. The school's swimming pool is also used by other schools and the local community.

The boys have daily opportunity for religious practice, as well as formal instruction and informal guidance.

Although following the Common Entrance syllabus for senior independent schools, St John's also promotes the National Curriculum and boys are assessed at Key Stages 1 and 2, audited by the Local Education Authority.

An illustrated prospectus is available from the Headmaster, who is always pleased to meet parents and to show them round the school.

Charitable status. St John's is a Registered Charity, number 230165. It exists to provide education for boys.

St John's College Lower School

Albany Road Southsea Hampshire PO5 2AB
Tel: 023 9282 0237
Fax: 023 9287 3603
e-mail: info@stjohnscollege.co.uk
website: www.stjohnscollege.co.uk

Chairman of Governors: Mr G W Warren OJ

***Head Master*: Mr R A Shrubsall**, MA Ed

Age Range. Co-educational 2–11 years.

Fees per term (2008-2009). Day: £2,025 (Reception, Years 1 & 2), £2,075 (Years 3 & 4), £2,180 (Years 5 & 6). UK Boarding £6,050, Overseas Boarding £6,425.

St John's College is an independent school founded to provide an academic education in a Christian environment. The College is fully co-educational, day and boarding, with over 600 pupils and students ranging in age from 2 to over 18. We offer a continuous range of education, starting in the Nursery and progressing in the Lower and Upper schools to the Sixth Form. We are a Catholic foundation but welcome pupils of all faiths and also those with no religious beliefs.

The Lower School is a self-contained unit but located on the main College campus. The Lower School enjoys the use of many excellent facilities: a sports centre, theatre, computer suite, library, science laboratory and music room. The attractive site is complemented by 34 acres of well maintained playing fields, located on the outskirts of the city.

A broadly balanced and extended curriculum is offered, encompassing all aspects of the National Curriculum at Key Stages 1 and 2. Close staff liaison ensures a smooth automatic transition for pupils into the Upper School at age 11.

The Lower School has a fine academic, musical and sporting tradition and there are a wide range of extra-curricular clubs which run during lunchtimes and after school. Educational and character-building residential trips are offered at holiday times.

St John's is a family school committed to developing the whole person, but at the very heart of all that we do is teaching and learning. Our academic record is a very good one and the commitment of our staff to each pupil is outstanding.

A prospectus and further details are available from the Admissions Secretary.

St John's College School

75 Grange Road Cambridge CB3 9AA
Tel: 01223 353532 Headmaster
01223 353652 Admissions Secretary
01223 272701 Bursar
Fax: 01223 355846
e-mail: shoffice@sjcs.co.uk
website: www.sjcs.co.uk

Chairman of Governors: Dr H E Watson, BA, PhD

***Headmaster*: K L Jones**, MA (Gonville and Caius College, Cambridge)

Age Range. 4–13.

Number of Children. 460 girls and boys (including 20 Chorister and up to 30 Non-Chorister boy and girl boarders).

Fees per term (2008-2009). Choristers £1,971; Boarders £5,914; Day Boys and Girls (4–13) £2,235–£3,744 according to age.

Profile. St John's prides itself on the quality of the academic and pastoral care it provides for each child. Through relaxed and friendly relations with children in a well-structured environment rich with opportunity; through close monitoring of progress; through communication and cooperation with parents; through expert staffing and, above all, through a sense of community that cares for the strengths and weaknesses of each of its members, St John's has consistently achieved outstanding results exemplified by over 70 scholarships during the last three years. Whilst its Choristers maintain the tradition of choral services and tour the world, St John's status as an Expert Centre for ICT, and other innovations, ensure the school's commitment to the future.

Entry. At 4–7 by parental interview; at 7–12 by parental interview, report from previous school and, as appropriate, assessment.

Curriculum. The curriculum surrounds the core of formal skills teaching with a breadth of enrichment and extension for each child's talents. In addition to the usual subjects including specialist taught DT, ICT, Art, Music, Dance and Drama, and PE for all pupils, the following are also available: French (from 8+), Latin (optional from 10+), Greek (optional from 11+). Pupils prepared for CE and Scholarship examinations.

Leavers. Virtually all go to senior independent day or boarding schools. The School works closely with parents to assist them in finding the best school for their child.

Consultation. Tutorial system (1 teacher to 10 pupils) with daily tutorial session timetabled. Half yearly academic assessments, end of year examinations, termly Parents' Evenings and weekly staff 'surgery' times.

Sports. Athletics, Badminton, Basketball, Cricket, Cross Country, Football, Golf, Gymnastics, Hockey, Netball, Real Tennis, Rounders, Rowing, Rugby, Short Tennis, Squash, Swimming, Table Tennis, Tennis. All games are timetabled and therefore given significant status. All major sports strong.

Activities. Numerous clubs including Art, Chess, Dance, Drama, Pottery, Design Technology, Craft, Information Technology, Maths games and puzzles, Touch-typing, Debating, Sewing and Wardrobe. College Choir of international status, Chamber Groups, Orchestras, School Chapel Choir, Junior Service Choir, Parents' Choir, Major theatrical productions, eg The Ragged Child, The Tempest, and theatrical opportunities for all children. A range of visits relating to curriculum plus French, Classics, skiing and outward bound trips.

Facilities. School on two sites with facilities used by all pupils. *Byron House (4–8)*. Outstanding facilities including Science, DT Centre, two large suites of networked PCs, computerised Library, Drama Studio, Gym, Hall and specialist Music wing.

Senior House (9–13). Sports Hall with indoor Cricket nets and multi-purpose Gym. Athletics track, playing fields, astroturf hockey pitch and tennis courts, Design Technology Centre, two Information Technology Centres, Drama Studio, computerised Library, Music School, Theatre, School Chapel and use of St John's College Chapel for school carol and special services. Recent developments include the acquisition of adjacent land and buildings to provide lecture theatre, an outstanding art facility, parent meeting rooms and extensive garden and play facilities for children.

Architects have been engaged and planning is underway for a £5 million development of facilities in the next few years; to include, for example, new classrooms and specialist facilities for Science, Information Technology, Design Technology, Library, pastoral care, and common rooms for children.

Boarding. From 8. Girl and boy boarders form an integral part of life at St John's and benefit from all the School's facilities whilst living in the homely, caring atmosphere of a Boarding House which has been completely refurbished in recent years. This includes recreation areas, rooms for reading, TV, table tennis, pool and use of all Senior House facilities. Day boarding and 'Waiters' facilities allow the School to be flexible to the needs of parents and children alike.

Charitable status. St John's College School is a constituent part of the college of St John the Evangelist in the University of Cambridge and as such is exempted from the necessity to register with the Charity Commission. It exists to provide education for boys and girls.

St John's-on-the-Hill School

Tutshill Chepstow Monmouthshire NP16 7LE
Tel: 01291 622045
Fax: 01291 623932
e-mail: info@stjohnsonthehill.co.uk
website: www.stjohnsonthehill.co.uk

Chairman of Governors: A T Vaux

***Headmaster*: I K Etchells**, BEd Exeter

Age Range. Co-educational 3 months to 13+ years.

Number of Pupils. 302.

Fees per term (2008-2009). Boarders £4,700. Day £2,960–£3,330. Pre-Prep £2,015–£2,180. Nursey and Early Years Department (half or full day sessions) £15.25 per session.

St John's-on-the-Hill is a co-educational day and boarding preparatory school situated in extensive, attractive grounds on the border of Monmouthshire and Gloucestershire, overlooking Chepstow Castle and the beautiful Wye Valley. Served by an excellent motorway system, just 3 miles from the old Severn Bridge, the school also has its own minibus network covering Newport, Usk, Monmouth, Ross-on-Wye and the Forest of Dean area.

St John's provides a consistently high standard of care and education for children aged between 3 months and 13+ years.

Latest Developments. A new teaching block for the pre-prep and new nursery was added to the existing first-class facilities at the school in September 2006. Six new classrooms were built each with direct access to an outdoor play area. The new building includes an assembly hall and also provides a large indoor play area for both Foundation stage and Key Stage

1 children. More outdoor play areas for Pre-Prep children have been added recently, as well as a secure outside play area for access by the Nursery children at all times. The purpose-built new Nursery is divided into three main areas of learning by age. Other shared facilities within the Nursery include a superb indoor soft play room, a light, bright dining area and a large 'messy' craft room designed for all ages of children to enjoy.

Discovering and developing individual talent. The family atmosphere ensures that even the youngest child feels a sense of belonging. Each child is valued and there is time to cater for the needs of all. A high standard of teaching and small class sizes, combined with first-class facilities, ensure boys and girls can develop both their academic ability and character to the full. Emphasis is on mutual respect, integrity and the need to discover and develop individual talents, whether they are creative, intellectual or athletic.

Celebrating achievement. Children are encouraged to develop skills and achieve success across the curriculum. Sport, Art, Design Technology, Music and Performing Arts are therefore an important part of school life. Children are encouraged to be creative from an early age and to take part in regular drama productions either front or backstage. All Year 3 children benefit from recorder and violin lessons as part of the music curriculum. Traditional and modern choral music is a particular strength within the school. The St John's choristers perform regularly at weddings and special events within the community whilst also leading school services.

St John's values achievement both in and out of the classroom. The aim of the sporting programme is to ensure that all children develop a love of both team and individual sport and to understand the importance of losing gracefully and winning modestly.

A varied outdoor education programme enhances each child's personal and social development. The school also offers a wide range of non-academic activities and after-school clubs. These may include archery, cookery, golf, horse-riding, and chess.

St John's has a specialist Learning Support Department and welcomes children across the ability range.

The school aims to ensure that each child has the opportunity to participate in almost everything, to go on achieve their individual best in all areas and to celebrate success individually and collectively. St John's encourages a sense of community where each child feels secure, significant and responsible, able to play a full part in the life of the school.

Scholarships and Bursaries. Scholarships and awards are made for academic, music, sporting and dramatic ability. HM Forces bursaries are also available.

Boarding at St John's. Children can board from the age of 7 on a full, weekly, or 'flexi' basis. The boarding house is family-run and has a friendly, homely atmosphere. The accommodation is spacious and fully modernised to provide a comfortable secure home environment.

A varied programme of weekend outings and activities is offered to the many boarders who remain at St John's throughout the term.

Building on Tradition. St John's holds sound traditional values whilst embracing the best of modern approaches. The environment at St John's is stimulating in its breadth of opportunity and yet personal in its size.

Creating the Future. On leaving St John's, children enter a wide range of senior schools of their choice and with more than 100 senior school scholarships awarded to St John's children in the last five years, the school is justifiably proud of its scholarship record and senior school links.

Charitable status. St John's-on-the-Hill and Brightlands School Trust Limited is a Registered Charity, number 312953, founded for the education of children.

St John's School

Potter Street Hill Northwood Middlesex HA6 3QY
Tel: 020 8866 0067
Fax: 020 8868 8770
e-mail: office@st-johns.org.uk
website: www.st-johns.org.uk

Chairman of Governors: J Armstrong, Esq

***Headmaster*: C R Kelly**, BA, PGCE (Durham University)

Assistant Headmaster: S Robinson, BSc, PGCE (Loughborough)

Age Range. 3–13.

Number of Boys. 398 Day Boys (Prep 258; Pre-Prep and Nursery 140).

Fees per term (2007-2008). Prep £3,360, Pre-Prep £3,070, Nursery £2,235.

Facing South, on a 35-acre site, we have outstanding views over London. Since the Merchant Taylors' Educational Trust took the School under its wing, impressive development has taken place. St John's has gained a gymnasium and changing block, two science laboratories, a six-classroom Pre-Prep Department and a junior classroom block. Another major development provided an Assembly Hall/Theatre, an Art Studio, Design & Technology Workshop, ICT Centre and a new Music Department. At the same time, other areas of the School were refurbished creating specialist teaching areas for English, French, History, Geography and Mathematics. We also acquired an area of grassland and woodland for ecological and environmental study, to add to our extensive playing fields and formal gardens.

We opened a new, purpose-built Nursery in 2003. This major extension of our pre-preparatory department included an Information Technology Suite and Library. At the same time extra play areas, including an 'indoor quiet area', were created. Most recently a large, all-weather, multi-purpose sports area was constructed, which significantly improves our already outstanding facilities for sport.

Most of the boys enter the School at either the age of three into the Nursery or at four into the Pre-Prep and there is a separate entry into the Main School at seven. St John's has an excellent record of success in scholarship and senior school entrance examinations. Boys are prepared for all independent schools, however, our links with Merchant Taylors' School, Northwood, are particularly strong.

Although the School was originally a Church of England foundation, boys of all religions and denominations are welcome.

Charitable status. St John's School, part of the Merchant Taylors' Educational Trust, is a Registered Charity, number 1063738. It exists for the purpose of educating boys.

St John's School

Broadway Sidmouth Devon EX10 8RG
Tel: 01395 513984
Fax: 01395 514539
e-mail: info@stjohnsdevon.co.uk
website: www.stjohnsdevon.co.uk

***Headmistress*: Mrs Angela Parry-Davies**, BEd Hons

Age Range. 2–13.

Number of Pupils. Main School 200, of whom 40–50 are Boarders. The Nursery (up to 5 years) has 50 children. Girl/boy ratio 50:50.

Fees per term (2007-2008). Day: From £1,804 (Nursery) to £2,700 (Main School). Boarding: £4,300–£5,100. There are no compulsory extras.

St John's is one of the few fully independent, co-educational preparatory day and boarding schools in the South West and caters for children between the ages of two and thirteen. The School (a Charitable Trust) is owned by The International Education Systems (IES) and situated in substantial buildings and grounds above the small seaside town. The School aims to ensure that all pupils have the benefit of a fulfilling and rounded education and gives children every opportunity to develop their individual talents from the earliest age.

The Headmistress believes that children who are able to relate to a happy family community achieve the best results. This contributes to sound attitudes towards academic work and the many oft of school activities that are available to every child. The success of this positive attitude towards education is seen by looking at the results the School has enjoyed over the years. St John's School cares about the child as an individual and the strong team of experienced staff is able to devote a great deal of time to each pupil.

The small classes (the staff pupil ratio is at present 1:10) enjoy bright, cheerful, well equipped classrooms with the additional advantage of overlooking stunning sea views. Interest is sport is high and the School in addition to playing fields, has an extensive sports centre with an indoor tennis court and a 20 metre swimming pool. The School encourages all pupils to take an active role in music and with its own specialist Music School, there is a high number of pupils learning individual instruments. Art facilities include a pottery studio and pupils enjoy a wide range of media in the Art School. The small, but well-equipped drama studio also converts to a small cinema and is popular with boarding pupils.

The school caters for children who suffer from dyslexia with qualified specialist teachers (BDA). The school is CReSTeD registered.

As well as regular 11+ passes to the local Grammar School, each year pupils win a number of scholarships to independent secondary schools. Academic results are of the highest standard.

Charitable status. St John's School Trust (Sidmouth) Limited is a Registered Charity, number 274864. It exists to provide education for children.

St Lawrence College Junior School

Ramsgate Kent CT11 7AF
Tel: 01843 572912
Fax: 01843 572913
e-mail: hjs@slcuk.com
website: www.slcuk.com

Chairman of the Council: The Revd Canon Nigel M Walker

***Head*: Mr Simon J E Whittle**, BA Hons, PGCE

Age Range. 3–11.

Number of Pupils. 200 boys and girls, a few of whom are boarders.

Fees per term (2008-2009). Boarders £5,835, Day £1,802–£2,900.

St Lawrence College Junior School offers a supportive, caring environment, based on traditional Christian values, in which children are given every opportunity to fulfil their potential. Academic expectations are high, but realistic and open-minded. Personal attention is given within small classes where talents are recognised and needs are catered for. There is a strong belief that education, in its truest sense, is measured not just in a student's exam results but by its ability to open young people's minds.

Most pupils transfer to the Senior School at 11+, and scholarships are regularly earned. There is also an excellent record of success at securing places in the highly-selective local grammar schools.

The Junior School is based in a delightful, ivy-clad Victorian building in a peaceful corner of the 150-acre St Lawrence College campus. Its own independent facilities include Science Lab, Art and Design Centre, Music Department and Performance Hall, two fully-networked ICT Suites, adventure playgrounds, tennis courts and spacious playing fields. However, membership of the wider College community gives pupils the best of both worlds, and they are able to share many of the Senior School's excellent specialist facilities. Boarders are accommodated in the splendid new Kirby House, an ultra-modern, eco-friendly development which opened its doors in January 2007.

A wide range of extra-curricular opportunities includes sports such as football, rugby, hockey, cricket, lacrosse, rounders, netball, basketball, athletics, cross-country running, swimming and dance. There are plenty of fixtures against other schools, but, most importantly, children learn the value of fitness, cooperative teamwork and good sportsmanship. There is a proud musical tradition, and plenty of scope for drama and the creative arts. Some Activities take place at the end of the school day, but most are concentrated into the popular, informal Saturday morning programme.

St Lawrence's Christian heritage underpins all that the Junior School stands for. An atmosphere of trust and mutual respect is based on kindness, forgiveness and consideration for others. There is a strong emphasis placed on thoughtful conduct, courtesy and good manners, and on endowing young people with a clear sense of moral responsibility.

Charitable status. The Corporation of St Lawrence College is a Registered Charity, number 307921. It exists to provide education for boys and girls.

St Leonards–New Park

St Andrews Fife KY16 9QJ
Tel: 01334 472126
Fax: 01334 476152
e-mail: slnp@stleonards-fife.org
website: www.stleonards-fife.org

Chairman of the Board: James Murray

***Headmaster*: Andrew Donald**, BSc (Aberdeen)

Age Range. 5–12.

Number of Pupils. 180 (85 girls, 95 boys).

Fees per term (2008-2009). £2,370 (Years 1–5), £2,657 (Years 6–7).

St Leonards–New Park in St Andrews is the co-educational preparatory school of St Leonards. Formed as a result of a merger between the St Leonards Junior and Middle Schools and New Park in 2005, the school is administered by the St Leonards Council and educates children between the ages of 5 and 12, from Year 1 to Year 7.

Pupils are prepared for entry to St Leonards Senior School, and to other senior schools as required. With specialist teachers and small class sizes, children benefit from individual attention. In addition to a strong academic tradition, drama, music, art, ICT and PE are included in the timetable.

Outside the classroom, a wide variety of sports are available; netball, rugby, hockey, lacrosse, soccer, tennis and cricket being the main team activities. Tuition in golf, judo and swimming is also offered. Outdoor education activities include skiing and water sports. There are also classes in Scottish Country Dancing and ballet.

Charitable status. St Leonards School is a Registered Charity, number SC010904. It exists to provide education to children between the ages of 5 and 19.

St Margaret's Preparatory School

Curzon Street Calne Wiltshire SN11 0DF
Tel: 01249 857220
Fax: 01249 857227
e-mail: office@stmargaretsprep.org.uk
website: www.stmargaretsprep.org.uk

Chairman of Governors: Mr S Knight, FRICS

***Headmistress*: Mrs K E Cordon**, GLCM, LLCM TD, ALCM

Age Range. 3–11.

Number of Pupils. 198 Day: 119 Girls, 68 Boys.

Fees per term (2008-2009). £1,400–£2,890.

St Margaret's Preparatory School is situated in the grounds of St Mary's School, Calne. The children share the excellent facilities of St Mary's including sports pitches, gymnasium, swimming pool, theatre, Chapel and dining hall. The classes are small, with an optimum number of eighteen children in each group. Consequently, there are all the advantages of a large school, whilst retaining the caring atmosphere of a small one.

There is a high academic standard throughout the school and children are taught to learn the value of hard work and how to accept discipline and responsibility. In addition to this, every aspect of a child's character is developed. The children are thoroughly prepared for Common Entrance and Senior School 11+ examinations and the school has an impressive record of success in gaining major scholarships, both academic and in the Arts, to leading senior independent schools. In 2008 a number of scholarships were once again awarded by Dauntsey's and St Mary's Calne.

St Margaret's is inspected routinely by both Ofsted and the Independent Schools Inspectorate. In February 2007 the inspectors concluded that: 'High quality leadership and management ensure an outstanding quality of education, promote excellent personal development, care and welfare, and enable the school to meet its aims. This is a happy school and pupils are courteous, work very hard and thoroughly enjoy their work and play.'

St Margaret's prides itself on its high standard of pastoral care. Every effort is made to ensure that the children never feel lost of bewildered, and that they quickly find their feet and are given a sense of belonging. There is a fully equipped Medical Centre in the grounds, under the supervision of a trained and experienced State Registered Nurse.

There is a strong sporting tradition and the children compete regularly with other schools. The boys play cricket, rugby, hockey and football, whilst the girls play netball, hockey and rounders. Additionally, athletics, judo, swimming and tennis are sports enjoyed by all.

Music and drama have a high profile. There is an annual major production and the orchestra and choirs perform regularly at venues outside school, such as The Royal Festival Hall.

School hours are between 8.15 am and 3.30/4.30 pm each day. The school has its own After School Club. This is staffed by two fully trained child carers and is available until 6 pm, five days a week. Whilst at the club, the children participate in a physical activity, craft and creative work, and a quiet time is set aside to enable them to do their homework. Tea is also provided. This facility has proved to be extremely popular with many parents.

Only a visit to St Margaret's can convey the spirit of friendliness and the sense of purpose that exist within the school.

Early registration is essential as places are reserved up to three years in advance.

Charitable status. St Mary's School (Calne) is a Registered Charity, number 309482. It exists to provide education for boys and girls.

St Martin's Ampleforth

Gilling Castle Gilling East York YO62 4HP
Tel: 01439 766600
Fax: 01439 788538
e-mail: headmaster@stmartins.ampleforth.org.uk
website: www.stmartins.ampleforth.org.uk

Chairman of the School Governors: Mr P B R Houghton

***Headmaster*: Mr Nicholas Jonathan Higham**, BEd Hons (Leeds)

Age Range. 3+ to 13+ years.

Number of Pupils. 195 (95 Boarders, 100 Day Children).

Fees per term (2008-2009). Boarding £5,859; Day £1,949–£3,621.

St Martin's Ampleforth is a boarding and day preparatory school which takes boys and girls from the age of 3+ years and prepares them for Common Entrance and Scholarship examinations. It is expected most of the pupils will enter Ampleforth College at 13+.

St Martin's Ampleforth is based in a 14th century castle with spacious and secluded gardens, 18 miles north of York and close to the North Yorkshire Moors National Park.

All Faiths are made most welcome in this Benedictine school. The Chaplaincy team is led by a monk of Ampleforth Abbey and includes an Anglican priest.

The highest academic standards are aimed for, within a broad and challenging curriculum. Each pupil's ability is taken into account. Very able children are provided for and coached for scholarships to Ampleforth College and other leading independent senior schools, whilst those with learning difficulties, including dyslexia, are given qualified specialist help. Each form of approximately 15 children has a tutor responsible for overall progress and pastoral support. Setting is in place from Year 6 and beyond.

There is a striking variety of extra-curricular pursuits including horse-riding, chess, golf, judo, drama, fishing, swimming and debating. The School has an enviable reputation for games and fields highly successful teams in rugby, netball, cricket, rounders, hockey, track and field and cross-country running.

Music is strong. Typically, 80% of pupils learn musical instruments and perform regularly. The School provides the trebles for the acclaimed Ampleforth College Schola Cantorum and there is an increasingly successful girls' Schola too. A performing arts centre has recently been built which enhances the current provision for choral and instrumental performance as well as foster drama throughout the school.

Parents are considered part of the School community. They are welcome at any time, especially for matches, other organised events and, of course, for Mass on Sundays and feast days.

Facilities include a sports hall, ICT room, all-weather cricket nets, a 9-hole golf course and all-weather floodlit astroturf. A programme of refurbishment of the boarding accommodation started in July 2008. The extensive grounds, including woods, lakes and gardens, combine a sense of space and freedom with unrivalled beauty.

Academic, all-rounder, choral and music scholarships, up to the value of 20% of fees, are available each spring for children under the age of 11. Bursaries are available.

Daily transport is provided to and from Pickering, Malton, Kirkbymoorside, Easingwold, York and Helmsley.

Charitable status. St Martin's Ampleforth, as part of the St Laurence Trust, is a registered charity, number 1063808 and exists to provide education for boys and girls.

St Martin's School

40 Moor Park Road Northwood Middlesex HA6 2DJ
Tel: 01923 825740
Fax: 01923 835452
e-mail: office@stmartins.org.uk
website: www.stmartins.org.uk

Chairman of Governors: Roy Jakes

***Headmaster*: David T Tidmarsh**, BSc Hons Wales

Age Range. 3–13.
Number of Boys. 400 Day Boys.
Fees per term (2008-2009). Main School £3,570; Pre-Prep £3,260; Kindergarten £1,155 (mornings). Bursaries are available, details on request.

St Martin's aims to provide boys aged 3–13 with the breadth of education and experience necessary for them to realise their full potential in a safe and friendly environment. An enthusiastic staff of 40 experienced and well-qualified teachers maintains high academic standards and provides broad sporting, musical and cultural opportunities. The atmosphere is friendly and lively with great emphasis on pastoral care.

The School, which is an Educational Trust, administered by a Board of Governors, prepares boys for entry to all the Independent Senior Schools. Forty-five Scholarship awards have been won to senior schools during the last five years. The School, which is in a pleasant residential area, stands in 12 acres of grounds. Facilities include a Kindergarten and separate Pre-Preparatory building; two well-equipped Science Laboratories, and Assembly Hall with stage; a Sports Centre including an indoor swimming pool; a playground, an ICT suite; an Art Studio with facilities for Design Technology; 3 Tennis Courts.

ICT, Art, DT, and Music are included in the curriculum for all boys, and a large proportion of the boys in the School learn a musical instrument. There is a varied after-school activity programme for boys to pursue their interests.

There is a pre-school and after-school club from Kindergarten age upwards enabling parents to work a full day.

The School is divided into Patrols for competitions in work and games, and senior boys make a responsible contribution towards the running of the School. Boys are taught football, rugby, cross-country running, hockey, cricket, swimming, athletics and tennis. The school has a fine reputation in inter-school matches.

Charitable status. St Martin's (Northwood) Preparatory School Trust Limited is a Registered Charity, number 312648. It exists to provide education for boys.

St Mary's Junior School
Cambridge

2 Brookside Cambridge CB2 1JE
Tel: 01223 311666
Fax: 01223 472168
e-mail: juniorschool@stmaryscambridge.co.uk
website: www.stmaryscambridge.co.uk

Chairman of Governors: Mrs D Wilkinson

***Headmistress*: Mrs D O'Sullivan**, MEd (Cantab), BCommHDE

Age Range. 4–11.
Number of Pupils. 160 Day Girls.
Fees per term (2008-2009). Reception, Years 1 and 2: £2,360; Years 3 and 4: £2,765; Years 5 and 6: £2,820. All fees are excluding lunches, which are charged at £150 per term.

Staff: 16 full-time; 14 part-time; 7 part-time music staff.

At St Mary's Junior School, we are proud of our unique, friendly and homely atmosphere. Each child is nurtured and understood by the caring staff, who take the time to listen and discuss. Small class sizes facilitate this further. In our all-girls environment, the classroom is a quiet place where concentration and hard work are easily facilitated. Children are encouraged to question and to investigate. Each child is learning to understand her own potential and her needs. The children are given appropriate opportunity for one to one learning within our personalised approach.

Our week is well balanced from the point of view of academic, physical, pastoral and spiritual guidance. Children who arrive early in the morning are encouraged to take part in meaningful tasks. After school hours children are offered a good variety of activity clubs and after school care extends to 6 pm.

Girls are selected by interview at age 4+ to 7 years, and by an examination and interview from age 7+. The children progress to St Mary's Senior School at age 11, which provides a seamless transition for an education from ages 4 to 18.

Please come and visit St Mary's Junior School and experience our happy learning environment. If you are seriously considering our school for your child, she is welcome to come and have some taster sessions with children of her age. We look forward to meeting you.

Charitable status. St Mary's School, Cambridge is a Registered Charity, number 290180.

St Mary's Preparatory School

Pottergate Lincoln LN2 1PH
Tel: 01522 524622
Fax: 01522 543637
e-mail: office@st-marys-prep.lincs.sch.uk
website: www.stmarysprep.co.uk

Chairman of Governors: Mrs H Belcher

***Head*: Mr A A Salmond Smith**, BA Hons, PGCE

Age Range. 2½–11.
Number of Pupils. 96 Boys, 116 Girls.
Fees per term (2008-2009). Main School: £2,429–£2,848, inclusive of lunches and all residential and day trips. Nursery from £18 per session.

Entry can be made at any age after 2½ years and children leave at age 11.

The School was founded in 1950 and is a Christian (non-denominational), co-educational day preparatory school.

St Mary's is situated in a Grade I listed building in the Cathedral Close which retains much of the character of an 18th century house, although modern changes and improvements, including the imaginative transformation of the former stable into an Art and Science Block, have given greater facilities for its use as a school. A major building programme has seen the addition of a large multi-purpose Hall, four extra teaching rooms, a new administration area, enlarged kitchen and dining facilities, a £250,000 purpose-built Early Years Centre and new library and computer facilities. An Astroturf sports area was opened in November 2001.

The School enjoys extensive grounds, which are ideally suited for recreational activities and create an unusually peaceful and safe atmosphere within a central position in the city. Small classes allow for individual attention. Boys and girls are prepared for Common Entrance at eleven, Scholarship Examinations and entry to the local maintained schools, including Grammar Schools.

Rugby, soccer and cricket are the main games for the boys and netball, hockey and rounders for the girls. There is a flourishing Swimming Club organised at a local swimming pool on Saturday mornings where the children are taught by qualified instructors.

Music is a strong feature of school life with over half the pupils taking individual instrumental lessons. The children may join one of two school choirs, and there is an orchestra and several other instrumental groups.

The full range of subjects is taught, together with French from age 7, Spanish from age 4, design and technology, multimedia computing, art, music and ballet. Latin is available for older children.

Charitable status. St Mary's School is a Registered Charity, number 527620. It exists for the purpose of educating boys and girls from the age of 2½ to 11.

St Mary's Preparatory School
Melrose

Abbey Park Melrose Roxburghshire TD6 9LN
Tel: 01896 822517
Fax: 01896 823550
e-mail: info@stmarysmelrose.org.uk
website: www.stmarysmelrose.org.uk

Founded 1895.

Chairman of Governors: Mr G T G Baird

***Headmaster*: John Brett**, MA London, CertMusEd, FCollP

Age Range. 3–13 co-educational.

Number of Pupils. 202.

Fees per term (2007-2008). Pre-Prep £2,700, Prep £3,650.

Curriculum. A healthy variety of subjects including traditional core studies reflecting both the Scottish "Curriculum for Excellence" and the England and Wales National Curriculum (English, Maths, Science, Computer Studies, French, Geography, History, Classics, Latin, RE, Art and Music, Drama). The School's intention is to provide a genuinely nourishing environment allowing for the development of the whole child.

Entry requirements. Application by letter or telephone, followed by a visit to the school, if possible, and a tour guided by senior pupils. Juniors and Pre-Prep pupils can be offered a 'reception' day to help with placement.

Examinations offered. Common Entrance to Scholarship for independent senior schools in Scotland and England.

Academic, sports, games and leisure facilities. Classroom computers, Science Laboratory and a big open Art Room. Theatre-Arts and Assembly Hall for concerts and drama. Spacious games pitches supporting a strong tradition in rugby, cricket and hockey. There is a cross-curricular Study Support Programme for talented and gifted children as well as for children with Specific Learning Difficulties, and a growing After School Programme.

Religious activities. Morning Assembly with hymn-singing and readings, stressing pupil participation and contribution either in word image, drama or music.

Charitable status. St Mary's School, Melrose is a Registered Charity, number SC009352. Its aim is to provide education for primary school children.

St Mary's School
Hampstead

47 Fitzjohn's Avenue London NW3 6PG
Tel: 020 7435 1868
Fax: 020 7794 7922
e-mail: enquiries@stmh.co.uk
website: www.stmh.co.uk

Chairman of Governors: Mrs Marion Jeffrey

***Headmistress*: Miss A M Rawlinson**, MA Hons, Dip Tchng

Age Range. 2½–11.

Number in School. 260 Girls, 32 Boys. Nursery: 21 Girls, 11 Boys.

Fees per term (2007-2008). Nursery £1,726; Kindergarten to Year 6 £3,230.

Surrounded by mature woodland and gardens, unmatched by any other school in the area, St Mary's has been established in Hampstead since 1926. Founded by the Institute of the Blessed Virgin Mary as a Roman Catholic School for Girls, the school remains true to the ideals of the IBVM foundress, Mary Ward who believed in the provision of a thoroughly grounded academic and spiritual education as a foundation for an enriched and confident adulthood.

The school has a thriving Pre-Nursery, Nursery and Pre-Prep for girls and boys. Boys are prepared for transfer to popular London Boys Preparatory Schools at the age of 7 years.

The girls are prepared for Common Entrance and the entrance examinations for top London Senior Schools. They transfer at the age of 11 years, many gaining awards and scholarships.

In addition to a broad curriculum, a wider range of activities is seen as essential to the rounded development of a healthy child. Importance is attached to physical education, drama and the arts. Extra curricular classes include Speech and Drama, Ballet and Tap. There is a school orchestra, choir and a chapel choir. Tuition is offered for many musical instruments. School trips abroad are arranged for older children.

There is an enthusiastic and dedicated staff of 40 experienced and well qualified teachers. There are specialist staff for Science, French, Art, Design and Technology, Music and Special Needs. St Mary's aims to develop and fulfil the maximum potential of each child and this objective is fostered within a happy and caring environment which recognises the needs and importance of children of all abilities.

Charitable status. St Mary's School, Hampstead is a Registered Charity, number 1006411. It exists to provide education for girls and boys. It is managed by a majority of Lay Trustees and Governors.

St Michael's Preparatory School

La Rue de la Houguette St Saviour Jersey Channel Islands JE2 7UG
Tel: 01534 856904
Fax: 01534 856620
e-mail: tm@stmichaels.je
website: www.stmichaelsschool.je

***Headmaster*: Richard de Figueiredo**, BA, CertEd
Deputy Head: C P Cook, MA, AdvDipEd

Age Range. 3–13.

Number of Pupils. 205 Boys, 140 Girls.

Fees per term (2008-2009). Pre-Prep £2,510–£2,793; Forms 1, 2 and 3 £3,577; Form 4, 5 and 6 £3,859. Lunch £253.

Boys and girls are prepared for scholarship and entrance to all Independent Senior Schools. Hockey, rugby football, soccer, gymnastics, netball, rounders, cricket, athletics and tennis are taught on spacious playing fields with pavilion and hard tennis courts which adjoin the school. A purpose built sports hall large enough to hold one tennis court or four badminton courts with semi-sprung wooden floor marked for volleyball, basketball and indoor hockey was opened in 1994. An indoor, heated swimming pool with full changing facilities was opened in 1995, allowing the provision of on-site swimming lessons for the whole school.

In 2002 the school acquired an adjacent property and playing fields and the building was converted to provide a new foundation years unit, housing the nursery and reception classes, new English teaching and seminar rooms and girls' changing rooms.

The school has computer, art and technology suites in addition to networked computers in every classroom. A large variety of clubs and hobbies function within the school and many out-of-door activities, including surfing, sailing and photography are enjoyed by the children. Music, drama and art, which includes pottery, are all encouraged and a wide range of musical instruments are taught. There are two school choirs and two orchestras. The senior choir regularly competes in the Sainsbury Choir of the Year Competition.

For senior children there is an annual Activities' Week. Year 6 have overnight trips to neighbouring islands and France, while Year 7 go to Brittany and Year 8 to the south of France. Each winter a party of children ski in Switzerland. Regular tours are made to Guernsey and England for sporting fixtures.

The academic and physical development, in addition to the spiritual, moral and cultural growth, of the whole child is the main aim of the school and every child is encouraged to fulfil his or her potential.

St Michael's Preparatory School

198 Hadleigh Road Leigh-on-Sea Essex SS9 2LP
Tel: 01702 478719
Fax: 01702 710183
e-mail: info@stmichaelsschool.com
website: www.stmichaelsschool.com

Chairman of Governors: The Revd Robin Eastoe

***Head*: Mrs L M Morshead**

Age Range. Co-educational 3–11 years.
Number of Pupils. 270 day pupils (153 boys, 117 girls).
Fees per term (2008-2009). £1,110–£2,210.

St Michael's is a Church of England Preparatory (IAPS) School founded in 1922 to provide a sound academic education based on Christian principles, with children welcomed from other Christian traditions and faiths. The school has its own Chapel.

The school is situated in a good residential area in Leigh-on-Sea within easy reach of public transport. London is accessible by rail and Fenchurch Street Station is approximately 40 minutes away.

The curriculum offered is broad, balanced and geared towards the different age groups within the school and it aims to contribute to the intellectual, physical, creative, social and spiritual development of each child. All the children, from Nursery through to Form 6, receive specialist teaching in Music, French and PE with additional specialist teaching in the Prep department. Pupils are prepared for the end of Key Stage standardised attainment tests, 11+ entry to local grammar schools and Entrance or Scholarship examinations for independent schools. High academic standards are achieved throughout the school and the children thrive in a happy but disciplined environment.

St Michael's has a dedicated and well-qualified staff. Class sizes are small to enable personal attention to be given. The school is well resourced with many specialist areas. Nearby playing fields are used for Games. There is a wide range of extra-curricular activities available, with Music and Drama as particular strengths.

Visits to the school are warmly welcomed.

Charitable status. St Michael's Preparatory School is a Registered Charity, number 280688. It exists to provide education.

St Michael's School
Barnstaple

Tawstock Court Barnstaple North Devon EX31 3HY
Tel: 01271 343242 School Office
Fax: 01271 346771
e-mail: mail@st-michaels-school.com
website: www.st-michaels-school.com

Chairman of Governors: Mr Mark Parkhouse

***Interim Headmaster*: Mr Simon Carder**MA Oxon, MBA
***Headmaster from January 2009*: Mr Philip Foley**, BA Hons

Age Range. 3 months – 13+.
Number of Pupils. 300 Day Boys and Girls.
Fees per term (2008-2009). £1,795–£3,538.

St Michael's was founded in 1832 and moved to North Devon in 1940. St Michael's is set in 30 acres overlooking the beautiful Taw valley. The Headmaster is a member of IAPS. The School is a Charitable Trust administered by a Board of Governors.

The teaching staff are all qualified and include a Director of Music, Director of Sport and a specialist in Information Technology.

Excellent academic results are achieved in small classes, quite often from boys and girls of modest initial ability. Modern languages form an important part of the very wide curriculum. Children are prepared for all Independent Senior Schools, and Scholarships and other Awards are regularly gained.

Facilities include Science Laboratories, a Computer Suite, a Design and Technology Centre and a spacious Art Room. There is also a Sports Hall and Squash Court. Children also learn to swim in the heated pool. PE forms part of the curriculum and Hockey, Squash, Badminton, Athletics, Netball, Rounders and Tennis are played as well as Rugby, Soccer and Cricket. Tuition is available in all musical instruments.

Scholarships are offered termly for children between the ages of 7 and 11 and credit is given for outstanding sporting or musical ability.

Charitable status. The St Michael's Charitable Trust is a Registered Charity, number 272464. It exists to provide high quality education for local boys and girls.

St Michael's School
Otford

Otford Court Row Dow Otford Kent TN14 5SA
Tel: 01959 522137
Fax: 01959 522137
e-mail: office@stmichaels.kent.sch.uk
website: www.stmichaels-otford.co.uk

Accredited by ISC.

Chairman of Governors: Gordon Owen, Esq, CBE

***Headmaster*: K S Crombie**, BSc

Deputy Head: D Sinclair

Head of Pre-Prep Department: Mrs M Stephens

Age Range. 2–13 Co-educational.

Number of Pupils. 430.

Fees per term (2008-2009). £264–£3,455.

St Michael's is a thriving, friendly school in a superb setting. We offer a fully co-educational, all-round preparatory education of the highest standard in a caring, family community. With a generous staff to pupil ratio and small classes, St Michael's achieves excellent results at every stage. Boys and girls share all activities; everyone is encouraged to try their best and to take part, perform and enjoy every aspect of school life.

The school's Christian roots support its modern ethos. St Michael's was founded in 1872 by London vicar Arthur Tooth who used his own fortune to create a school. The simple, egalitarian style of the founder has strong echoes today in a community where children from a wide variety of backgrounds and every faith are welcome.

St Michael's provides a unique environment for learning and enjoyment. The distinguished Victorian architecture of the original estate has been thoughtfully extended and upgraded. Spacious facilities for learning now include modern science, music, drama and art rooms, a large sports hall and splendid indoor 25m swimming pool. The school's wonderful wooded grounds on the slopes of the North Downs provide outdoor inspiration and extensive space for exploration, sport and play. They are also a truly memorable backdrop to a well-balanced education which allows every pupil to flourish.

The school prepares pupils for senior independent schools and local grammar schools (at 11+ and 13+) and has a proven academic record with many pupils gaining prestigious awards. It also has a high reputation for music, games (rugby, cricket, soccer, netball, hockey and athletics), drama and art.

A thriving Nursery, Kindergarten and Pre-Prep Department is self-contained and housed in the converted stable block, together with additional purpose-built facilities. Children play in the secure environment of the old walled garden, which has recently been equipped with an adventure playground.

An extensive out of school extra-curricular activity programme is offered to all pupils on a weekly basis and all classes participate in an integral programme of visits, workshops and field trips.

An active Parents and Friends Association is a strong supporter of the school and the Old Michaelian Society is one of the longest established in the Prep School world.

Charitable status. St Michael's is a Registered Charity, number 1076999. It exists to provide education for boys and girls.

St Neot's Preparatory School

Eversley Hook Hampshire RG27 0PN
Tel: 0118 973 2118
Fax: 0118 973 9949
e-mail: office@st-neots-prep.co.uk
website: www.st-neots-prep.co.uk

Chairman of Governors: Mr D Chard

***Headmaster*: R J Thorp**, BA (Dunelm), PGCE (Cantab)

Age Range. 2 months–13 years co-educational.

Number of Pupils. 26 weekly boarders, 10 flexi-boarding places, 165 day pupils, 120 pre-prep, nursery and crèche.

Inclusive fees per term (2008-2009). Boarders: £5,130; Day pupils: Years 4–8 £4,150, Year 3 £3,060, Reception–Year 2 £2,500, Nursery £20 per session, Tiny Tuskers £26 per session.

The school is situated on the border of Hampshire, Surrey and Berkshire in its own 70-acre peaceful site, comprising many grass pitches, all weather surfaces and woodland. There is a staff of 45 ladies and gentlemen spread among the child age range of 2 months to 13 years. Overall staff ratio is about 1:9.

All curriculum subjects are taught; streaming exists from Year 5 and exams are sat at all appropriate ages and stages; some children are prepared for Senior School scholarships and all-rounders awards and about thirty have been gained in the last five years. A very broad range of other activities is available, music, art, ICT, drama, PE to name but a few and all of these, as with the academic subjects, are taught by subject specialists.

As well as the wide provision of sports facilities for all ages and stages, the school has its own enclosed swimming pool, a rifle range and golf course. Constant development of these facilities over the last few years has meant that matches can be played at all year groups for all children, either boys or girls.

Facilities include a beautiful Boarding House, extended Dining Room enabling family service meals for all children and a 70m × 50m astroturf pitch. Just completed is a beautiful new eco-friendly, carbon neutral large nursery and creche building, housing 60 children and 10 staff, with its own gardens and play area.

The school aims to ensure that all pupils receive the best possible training for life in a hard working, but happy family atmosphere, based on Christian practice and principles.

Charitable status. St Neot's (Eversley) Limited is a Registered Charity, number 307324. The aim of the Charity is to try to provide the best all-round education possible to as many pupils as possible, with bursarial help according to need.

St Olave's Preparatory School

106–110 Southwood Road New Eltham London SE9 3QS
Tel: 020 8294 8930
Fax: 020 8294 8939
e-mail: office@stolaves.org.uk
website: www.stolaves.org.uk

Chairman of Governors: M D Ireland, Esq

***Headmistress*: Mrs C P A Fisher**, CertEd

Age Range. 3–11.

Number of Pupils. 217 Day Boys and Girls.

Fees per term (2007-2008). Pre-Prep £1,080–£2,200; Reception & Year 1 £2,280; Years 2–6 £2,460.

Founded in 1932, St Olave's is a day preparatory school for girls and boys aged 3–11 years. A fully qualified and committed teaching staff prepares children for entry to local Grammar and Independent Senior Schools.

The aim of the school is to offer a warm and caring environment in which each child can thrive and be happy knowing that each is accepted for who they are. All achievements both great and small are acknowledged and celebrated. A Christian ethos permeates the pastoral life of the school, where care for others through thoughtful and responsible behaviour is expected. Praise and encouragement, rather than punishment and restriction, are emphasised and relationships between staff and pupils are relaxed and friendly. A close partnership with parents is sought.

The children in the Lower School are taught in mixed-ability classes where each child's progress is carefully monitored by the Form Teacher. In the Upper School the children are set across the year group for Mathematics. Individual differences are appropriately met, with the very able and those with mild learning difficulties receiving additional support where this is thought beneficial. The school is noted for the broad curriculum it offers and for its excellent achievements in Music and Drama. A range of sporting activities is taught as part of the curriculum and there is a wide range of after school clubs and activities. Music and PE are taught by specialist teachers from the age of three and French is introduced at 6 years old. The classrooms are equipped with computers and there is a networked suite which supports all areas of the curriculum. A specialist ICT teacher teaches all year groups from Reception to Year 6. Interactive whiteboards are used in the Upper School classrooms.

St Olave's feeds a wide range of secondary schools and parents are given help in choosing the school most appropriate to meet the needs of their child.

Charitable status. St Olave's School is a Registered Charity, number 312734. It exists to provide high quality education for boys and girls.

St Olave's School
The Prep School of St Peter's School, York

York YO30 6AB
Tel: 01904 527416
Fax: 01904 527303
e-mail: enquiries@st-olaves.york.sch.uk
website: www.st-peters.york.sch.uk

Chairman of the Governors: J D Pike

***Master*: A Falconer**, BA, MBA

Deputy Head: Mrs S Jackson, BA
Director of Studies: Mrs L Garner, MA, BEd

Age Range. 8–13 co-educational.

Number of Pupils. 175 Boys, 171 Girls.

Fees per term (2008-2009). Day £2,985–£3,630, Boarding £5,555–£6,098. Fees are fully inclusive.

St Olave's was founded in 1876 and was purchased by St Peter's in 1901 to become its Prep School. With its own halls, music school, practical subjects workshops, sports hall and magnificently appointed specialist teaching rooms, St Olave's enjoys some of the best facilities for a prep school of its type.

The school puts praise and encouragement of the individual as its highest priority. There is a demanding wide curriculum from the earliest age with specialist subject areas – modern foreign languages, information technology, science and music amongst others – being taught by specialist teachers from Year 4. Progress is monitored through a regular system of effort grades, and attainment is measured through internal and externally moderated tests.

Boarding is a flourishing aspect of the school with a recent extension to accommodate the girls in what is now a co-educational House under the constant care of resident House parents and their own family. There are also five Day Houses.

Music plays an important part in the life of the school with two orchestras, a wind band and many ensembles playing and practising weekly. Over 200 pupils learn individual instruments, and all are encouraged to join larger groups. Sport has an equally high profile where rugby football, hockey, cricket, netball, tennis and swimming are major sports and athletics, cross-country running, squash, badminton, basketball and volleyball are also available for boys and girls. The boys have won the National Schools' Seven-a-Side rugby tournament four times in the last eight years.

Drama has an increasing profile and out of school activities flourish through such clubs as science society, chess, fencing, climbing, art and debating. The three modern languages – French, German and Spanish – organise holidays and exchanges with the appropriate country.

The vast majority of boys and girls move on to St Peter's and are not required to take the Common Entrance examination.

Entrance examinations are held in January/February each year, and tests can also be arranged at other times. Entry is possible in all years. Means-tested bursaries are available from 11.

Charitable status. St Peter's School York is a Registered Charity, number 529740. It exists to provide education for boys and girls.

St Paul's Cathedral School

New Change London EC4M 9AD
Tel: 020 7248 5156
Fax: 020 7329 6568
e-mail: admissions@spcs.london.sch.uk
website: www.spcs.london.sch.uk

Chairman of Governors: The Dean of St Paul's Cathedral, The Rt Revd Graeme Knowles, AKC

***Headmaster*: Mr Andrew H Dobbin**, MA Cantab

Age Range. 4–13 Co-educational.

Number of Pupils. Boarding Choristers 40, Day Boys 117, Day Girls 81, Pre-Prep 64.

Fees per term (2008-2009). Choristers £2,112; Day Pupils £3,650; Pre-Prep £3,390.

There have been choristers at St Paul's for over nine centuries. The present school is a Church of England Foundation dating back over 100 years and is governed by the Dean and Chapter of St Paul's Cathedral. The broadening of educational expectations and the challenge of curricular developments led the Dean and Chapter to agree to expand the school in 1989 by admitting non-chorister day-boys for the first time; a decision which continues to enrich the life of the school and Cathedral. In September 1998, the school admitted girls as well as boys into its new pre-prep department for 4–7 year olds. The school became fully co-educational in September 2002. It offers a broad curriculum leading to scholarship and Common Entrance examinations. In the first three years the work is tailored to individual needs bearing in mind the wide variety of educational backgrounds from which pupils come. The school has an excellent record in placing pupils in the senior schools of their choice, many with music scholarships. Every opportunity is taken to make use of the school's proximity to museums, libraries, galleries, theatres and the numerous attractions which London has to offer.

The 40 chorister boarders are housed on the Cathedral site and are fully integrated with the day pupils for all their academic studies and games. The choristers' cathedral choral training offers them a unique opportunity to participate in the rich musical life of St Paul's and the City.

The school was rehoused in the 60s in purpose-built premises on the eastern end of the Cathedral site. A refurbishment project added a new music school, art room, IT room, three pre-prep classrooms and games rooms to the existing facilities which include a hall/gymnasium, science laboratory, common room and a TV/video room. All pupils are encouraged to play a musical instrument (most pupils play two) and there are music and theory lessons with school orchestras and chamber groups.

A wide variety of games is offered including field sports at local playing fields and weekly swimming lessons. The children have their own playground and the use of the hall for indoor games and gymnastics.

Admissions procedure. Prospective pupils of 7+ years in September are given academic tests in Mathematics and English, usually in January of the previous academic year.

Pre-Prep children are assessed in an informal play situation in the November prior to entry.

Voice trials and tests for chorister places are held in February, May and October for boys between 6½ and 8½ years old.

St Paul's Preparatory School
Colet Court

Lonsdale Road Barnes London SW13 9JT

See entry under "Colet Court".

St Paul's School

Rua Juquiá 166, Jardim Paulistano, CEP 01440-903 São Paulo, Brazil
Tel: 00 55 11 3087 3399
Fax: 00 55 11 3087 3398
e-mail: spshead@stpauls.br
website: www.stpauls.br

Chairman of the Board of Governors: Mr David Bunce

Headmaster: Mr Crispin Rowe, BA

***Head of Preparatory School*: Mrs Carolyn Lindsay**, BA

***Head of Pre-Preparatory School*: Dr Anne d'Heursel-Baldisseri**

Age Range. 3–18.

Number of Pupils. 1,052: Pre-Preparatory 244, Preparatory 388, Senior 420.

Fees per annum (2008-2009). Pre-Prep and Prep School US$21,720; Senior School US$28,023.

St Paul's School was founded in 1926 and is an independent non-denominational school. It is *the* British School in the São Paulo area, although there are some other English-speaking international schools. St Paul's is situated in the leafy and affluent residential area aptly named *Jardins*.

The Board of Governors is appointed by Trustees of the British Community, and includes parents of current or former pupils, a representative of the British Commonwealth and Community Council, ex-officio members and the Headmaster. Her Majesty's Ambassador to Brazil is the Honorary President. St Paul's is co-educational with a School roll of 1000 pupils from 3 to 18 years old. There are approximately 30 different nationalities in School. The teaching staff totals 140; around 80 are British or Anglo-Brazilians. The aim of the School is to provide an education for British children in São Paulo, Anglo-Brazilians, Brazilians and other nationalities. The curriculum offered in the Pre-Preparatory and Preparatory Schools follows the spirit of the National Curriculum, with pupils sitting Key Stage 2 Examinations before entering the Senior School. Pupils then prepare for IGCSEs in Forms 4 and 5, and the International Baccalaureate Bilingual Diploma Programme in the Sixth Form. Pupils normally go on to universities in the UK and in the United States, as well as to universities in Brazil.

All members of staff are expected to contribute to the Extra-curricular Activities Programme, which includes an extensive range of activities after School. Each part of the School has its own floor in the main building: the Pre-Preparatory School is a self-contained unit on the ground floor, the Preparatory School is situated on the middle floor and the Senior School on the top floor. The general impression when entering the School is that of any other modern British school – it just happens to be in Brazil.

The School has gone through an interesting and challenging period in its development. Classrooms have been refurbished to the highest standards, up to date Science facilities have been installed and the computer provision is complete with over 300 PCs networked on site. The recently refurbished Library has over 32,000 items on its database, and the best selection of magazines and newspapers in town. The School has an impressive Art Centre, a spacious Theatre and Drama Studio, Music rooms, excellent Sports facilities as well as underground parking. New Dining facilities, a Sixth Form Centre and a Chapel were inaugurated in May 2001. Air conditioning was installed throughout the main teaching block in 2007.

The School is a busy, hardworking place and standards are high. In 1995 the School underwent a full HMC Inspection, the first overseas school so to do, and emerged with great credit. A second full inspection took place in 1999; again there was much praise. A further inspection, by members of South America's Latin American Heads' Conference (LAHC), took place in April 2007. Once again, the school was warmly commended. St Paul's School is seen as one of the foremost academic establishments in Latin America, capable of holding its own with the best in the UK.

St Peter and St Paul School

Brambling House Hady Hill Chesterfield Derbyshire S41 0EF
Tel: 01246 278522
Fax: 01246 273861
e-mail: head@spsp.org.uk
website: www.spsp.org.uk

Chairman of Board of Trustees: Mrs Rachel Underwood

***Headmaster*: Mr Andrew Lamb**, CertEd

Age Range. Co-educational 3 months – 11 years.

Number of Pupils. 145.

Fees per term (2008-2009). £1,975–£2,095.

Laughter, self-esteem, family, being cherished, awe and wonder, security, opportunity, preparation, independence and success are all part of the St Peter and St Paul School experience.

The school is set in 12 acres of park and woodland in walking distance of the town centre. Under the current Headmaster, the school has undergone enormous changes over the past five years culminating in joining the ranks of IAPS. As well as the school itself which caters for children from 4 to 11, there is a flourishing Nursery run by Children 1st in partnership with the school. This enables provision to be made for care and education throughout the year from birth to 11. There are no formal entry requirements and a number of bursaries are available.

Through five simple aims that involve us being dedicated to providing the best education, the best standard of care, the best opportunities, the best possible preparation for life for children while at the same time providing exceptional value for parents we are able to achieve our mission of providing a challenging and supportive environment where every child is valued as an individual and can reach their full potential.

Combining traditional teaching methods, family values, care from 7.30 am to 6 pm in a safe, secure and happy environment ensures that all our children meet with success. Our modern facilities designed to provide the greatest opportunities for children help us to achieve our aims.

The school's academic standard is exceptionally high and pupils are prepared for entry to a range of both independent and state schools. Recently pupils have gained a variety of awards to independent schools.

The school has a dedicated staff team who provide the children with stimulating and enjoyable learning experiences. Whether in the classroom, on the games field, in the concert hall or on the school stage, staff give all children the opportunity to shine. Our unique Life Skills programme has been designed to develop skills in teamwork and leadership as well as to enable children to make healthy life style choices. We live in an ever-changing world and the programme also involves managing and coping with change. Within the programme children experience such activities as Indoor Climbing, Orienteering, First Aid, Aerobic Dance, Archery and much more.

While achieving our aims, our pupils develop honesty, good manners, confidence, independence, motivation, the ability to succeed as well as the value of helping others.

Never being satisfied and always expecting a lot from both children and staff ensures that the school continues to thrive and develop in this modern world.

Charitable status. The St Peter and St Paul School Trust is a Registered Charity, number 516113.

St Peter's School

Harefield Lympstone Nr Exmouth Devon EX8 5AU
Tel: 01395 272148
Fax: 01395 222410
e-mail: hmoffice@stpetersprep.co.uk
website: www.stpetersprep.co.uk

Chairman of Board of Reference: M B Saunders, FNAEA

***Headmaster*: R J Williams**, MA Hons Edinburgh, PGCE Bedford

Chairman: C N C Abram, BEd St Luke's College, Exeter

Finance Director: J R Middleton, BSc Hons London, ACIB

Age Range. 3–13.

Number of Pupils. 191 Boys, 76 Girls (238 day, 29 weekly boarders).

Fees per term (2008-2009). Weekly Boarders £4,690, Senior Day Pupils £3,110, Junior Day Pupils £2,820, Pre-Prep Pupils £2,105, Nursery £1,820.

St Peter's aims to provide an environment in which each girl and boy has the fullest opportunity for growth: intellectually, culturally and physically. Established in 1882, St Peter's boasts an impressive setting – 28 acres of games fields and grounds overlooking the Exe estuary. St Peter's is committed to traditional prep school values within a modern approach to education and offers a varied and broad curriculum.

Pupils aged between 3 and 13 receive a seamless education with day, flexi or weekly boarding available. A number of our senior pupils find this is the ideal introduction to boarding prior to transfer to senior school at 13+.

Excellent access to M5, A30, A38, rail stations and Exeter airport. The school is six miles from the city of Exeter and school transport from Exeter, Cheriton Bishop, Ide, Chudleigh, Honiton, Sidmouth, Ottery St Mary and West Hill is available daily in one of the school's five minibuses. Our extended day runs from 8.00 am to 6.00 pm, making it easier for working families to organise their busy lives including a full holiday activity programme (available on a pay-as-you-go basis) which extends support for parents to 48 weeks of the year.

St Peter's enjoys an excellent Scholarship and Common Entrance record and prides itself on maintaining a high academic standard while retaining balance and breadth.

Strong academic programme with specialist subject teaching from Year 5; French and music taught by specialists throughout the school. St Peter's follows the best of modern educational practice with literacy and numeracy emphasised in the nursery and pre-prep departments.

Flourishing music and drama provide scope for all pupils to perform and combine their talents as a team in acting, singing or working as technicians. Lessons in Brass, Strings, Woodwind, Piano, Guitar, Percussion, Singing and Speech & Drama are offered.

Games programme reinforced with a strong fixtures list at all age levels for boys and girls. St Peter's is proud of its successful games record, including recent IAPS champions in athletics, badminton, hockey, squash and tennis.

Since 2000, the school's progressive development plan has ensured new classrooms in the junior and senior schools, a new science laboratory, refurbishment of the library and sports hall.

St Piran's

Gringer Hill Maidenhead Berkshire SL6 7LZ
Tel: 01628 594302
Fax: 01628 594301
e-mail: registrar@stpirans.co.uk
website: www.stpirans.co.uk

Chairman of Governors: Mr Edward Parrott

***Headmaster*: J Carroll**, BA Hons, BPhilEd, PGCE, NPQH

Assistant Headmaster: Mr K Farmery

Age Range. $2^1/_2$–13 Co-educational.

Number of Pupils. 360 day pupils.

Fees per term (2008-2009). £470–£3,520.

St Piran's is a thriving co-educational IAPS day school with approximately 360 pupils aged from to $2^1/_2$ to 13. The school is set amid 10 delightful acres just to the north of Maidenhead town centre. In 2005 we celebrated our bicentenary, having been founded as a small school in Blackheath, London in 1805, and the children have revelled in the many celebrations we have had.

Class sizes are small. Boys and girls benefit from individual attention in all subjects. They are provided with a wide range of exciting opportunities both inside and outside the classroom. Numerous trips to castles and museums, theatres and shows, history re-enactments, geographical fieldwork and religious sites extend the children's understanding of the world around them. In addition to the academic subjects, pupils take part in a wide range of other activities each week. These include music and art as well as pursuits as diverse as riding, website design, technology, cycling and even fishing.

Academically, the school supports a broad curriculum at all levels in the school. French starts with our youngest classes where confidence in the spoken language is encouraged. By Year 6 we are introducing German and Spanish. The children enjoy specialist teaching in art, games and PE, ICT, swimming and music from an early age. By the age of 10, all lessons are taught by extremely well qualified subject specialists. We support children with their entrance exams at 11+ to Grammar Schools or other independent schools, and also the children who stay with us to 13 who take Common Entrance and Scholarship exams to independent senior schools. Our results over the years have been excellent, supporting our desire to encourage independent thinkers, confident individuals and strong leaders of the future.

The main sports that pupils take part in are rugby, soccer, netball, hockey, cricket, rounders and swimming. The school has its own indoor swimming pool and large sports hall. St Piran's also has a dance studio and pupils are encouraged to take an active part in the performing arts. We are blessed with wonderful facilities which serve to enhance the varied sports programmes that we offer the children at all levels.

The school has its own Leadership programme and regular visits off site are arranged for all the children, including residential trips and a very popular annual skiing trip.

Pupils may enter the school at any age, although the main intakes occur at Nursery, Year 3 and Year 7. Scholarships and bursaries may be offered after assessment. Please contact the school and an appointment can be arranged to talk to the Headmaster about financial support.

The school is proud of its outstanding record of achievement and the fully rounded education that it provides within a friendly caring atmosphere. We are proud of our Christian tradition and family ethos which foster high expectations and successful, happy children.

Children and parents are warmly invited to visit St Piran's to see for themselves the excellent facilities that we offer and to meet some of the staff and pupils.

Charitable status. St Piran's School Limited is a Registered Charity, number 309094.

St Pius X Prep School

200 Garstang Road Fulwood Preston Lancashire PR2 8RD
Tel: 01772 719937
Fax: 01772 787535
e-mail: enquiries@stpiusx.co.uk
website: www.stpiusx.co.uk

Chairman of Governors: P Clegg

***Headmistress*: Miss B Banks**, MA

Age Range. 2–11.

Number of Children. 280 Day Girls and Boys.

Fees per term (2008-2009). Main School £1,900, Nursery £162.50 per week.

The School is administered as a non-profit-making educational trust by a Board of Governors, providing education from 2–11. The children are prepared for entrance examination to independent schools and local high schools. The school has an excellent record of scholarships to senior schools and SATS results at KS1 and KS2. The school is in four acres of its own grounds in a pleasant suburb of Preston. All preparatory curriculum subjects covered.

Sports taught are Association Football, Cricket, Tennis, Hockey, Netball, Rugby, Table Tennis, Rounders and Athletics.

Ballet, piano, clarinet, flute, violin, guitar and singing lessons are some of the optional extras offered.

Charitable status. St Pius X School is a Registered Charity, number 526609. Its purpose is to equip the children with an outstanding academic and social education in a Catholic Christian environment, which will enable them to achieve their full potential – the school welcomes pupils of all faiths.

St Richard's

Bredenbury Court Bromyard Herefordshire HR7 4TD
Tel: 01885 482491
Fax: 01885 488982
e-mail: schooloffice@st-richards.org.uk
website: www.st-richards.org.uk

***Headmaster*: N Cheesman**, BEd Hons

Age Range. 3–13.

Number of Pupils. 150.

Fees per term (2008-2009). £5,410 Boarders; £4,880 Weekly Boarders; £3,555 Day. No compulsory extras.

Founded in 1921, St Richard's is a Catholic Preparatory School of about 150 boys and girls, of whom about one-third are Catholic. The school is situated in 35 usable acres of beautiful Herefordshire countryside.

Children are prepared for Common Entrance and Scholarships to Catholic and other Independent Senior Schools. There is a thriving Pre-Prep and Nursery Department.

The average number in a class is 15. Art, Drama, Pottery, Carpentry and Music flourish and the choir specialises in Plain Song.

The usual team games are played, whilst, among other sports, Riding, Athletics, Netball and Hockey are strongly featured.

The school is experienced in looking after the needs of those from abroad. Children are escorted to and from London and arrangements are made for their escort on to Heathrow, Birmingham etc. An illustrated prospectus, list of recent scholarships, staff and other particulars are available from the Headmaster.

Saint Ronan's

Water Lane Hawkhurst Kent TN18 5DJ
Tel: 01580 752271
Fax: 01580 754882
e-mail: info@saintronans.co.uk
website: www.saintronans.co.uk

Chairman of Governors: Mr Robin Dalton-Homes

***Headmaster*: W E H Trelawny-Vernon**, BSc Hons

Deputy Head (*Pastoral*): I J Light, CertEd
Deputy Head (*Academic*): G Vincendeau

Age Range. 2½–13 fully co-educational.

Number of Children. 320.

Fees per term (2007-2008). Day £2,456–£4,212. We also operate a flexi-boarding system (£26 per night) which can be tailored to individual needs.

Saint Ronan's is a family school as it has been since it was started in Worthing in 1883. It occupies a fine Victorian Mansion set in 247 acres of beautiful Weald of Kent countryside. There are numerous games pitches, hard tennis courts, golf course and a swimming pool as well as a hundred acre wood.

By deliberately remaining small the school has developed a unique and special atmosphere in which staff and children work together to achieve their aims. Our small size helps the transition from home to school and a maximum class size of 16 enables children to gain confidence and interact positively with their peers and the staff.

Academically we have an excellent pass rate at CE and many pupils gain Scholarships to major senior independent schools such as Eton, Sevenoaks, Benenden, Tonbridge, Harrow, King's Canterbury and Lancing; we also prepare children for entry to local Grammar Schools and boast an enviable record here too.

Music and art play a vital role at Saint Ronan's. We have two choirs: the School choir and the Chapel choir, and over two thirds of the children learn at least one musical instrument. The art department is flourishing and the children have the option to learn craft and woodwork in addition to their timetabled art lessons.

The major sports at Saint Ronan's are rugby, football, hockey, cricket and netball but we also offer coaching in athletics, tennis, swimming, dance, rounders, judo, golf, archery, lacrosse and cross-country. We have a very successful games record, particularly in hockey.

The Pre-Prep is very much part of the school, in both location and ethos, and is a thriving and dynamic department taking children from 2½ to 7.

In 2006 we are opening a new Nursery, Pre-Prep, Music school and IT suite. Our swimming pool has just been renovated and there are many new and exciting projects afoot.

Charitable status. Saint Ronan's School is a Registered Charity, number 1066420. It exists for the advancement of education of its children.

St Swithun's Junior School

Alresford Road Winchester Hants SO21 1HA
Tel: 01962 835750
Fax: 01962 835781
e-mail: office.juniorschool@stswithuns.com
website: www.stswithuns.com

Established 1884. Girls day preparatory school with pre-preparatory boys. Church of England.

Chairman of Governors: Mr J C Platt, FCA

***Headmistress*: Mrs P Grimes**

Bursar: Mr Gavin Haig

Age Range. Girls 3–11, Boys 3–7.

Number of Pupils. 164 Girls, 22 Boys. Average class size 24. Pupil/teacher ratio 12:1.

Fees per term (2008-2009). Nursery £1,170; Reception, Years 1 & 2 £2,330; Years 3–6 £3,000.

Profile. St Swithun's Junior School shares a spacious 45-acre campus with the Senior School on the Hampshire Downs and is an independent day school for approximately 200 girls and boys. Girls are aged 3–11 and boys are aged 3–7.

The Junior School ethos centres around the belief that education should awaken a spirit of wonder and discovery in children. In a stimulating environment staff aim to foster an eagerness to learn, to strive and to achieve, indeed to release the potential of each pupil – academically, creatively, on the sports field and at play.

The school encourages pupils, parents and staff to be part of a caring community committed to the nurture and encouragement of every individual. It is important to us that our pupils develop a sense of their own worth whilst demonstrating consideration and courtesy for others. Like the Senior School, St Swithun's is a Christian foundation and its ethos is reflected in the school's values and relationships.

Facilities are first-class and include specialist classrooms for Science, Art and Technology, Music and IT. There is a purpose-built Performance Hall and Sports Hall and the Nursery and Reception classrooms were rebuilt in 2005.

Entry. At 3 and at 7.

Curriculum. Usual subjects taught plus French, Art, Technology, Drama, ICT, Music and PE, with due regard for National Curriculum requirements.

Leavers. Boys leave for various preparatory schools, including The Pilgrims' and Twyford. Girls go on to a range of senior independent schools including St Swithun's Senior School.

Consultation. Biannual reports, regular Parents' Evenings and PTA.

Sports. Gymnastics, Hockey, Netball, Rounders, Tennis, Short Tennis, Swimming, and Athletics.

Activities. These include Chess, Art, Drama, Gymnastics, Judo, Science, Tag Rugby, Swimming, Football and Sewing.

Musical concerts and productions are regularly held and two annual field study trips and regular visits take place.

Special needs. Qualified Learning Support teacher.

Charitable status. St Swithun's School Winchester is a Registered Charity, number 307335.

St Teresa's Preparatory School

Grove House Guildford Road Effingham Surrey KT24 5QA
Tel: 01372 453456
Fax: 01372 451562
e-mail: info@stteresasprep.co.uk
website: www.stteresasschool.com

Motto: *Gaudere et bene facere*

Chairman of Governors: Mr P Grobel

***Headmistress*: Mrs A M Stewart**, MA, PGCE

Bursar: Mr P Large, BA

Age Range. 2+–11; Boarding from 8+.

Number of Pupils. 128 girls (including some boarders).

Fees per term (2008-2009). Tuition: Nursery £220 per session, per term, £2,000 (full-time); Reception £2,150; Years 1 and 2 £2,365; Years 3–4 £2,945; Years 5–6 £3,210. Boarding (in addition to Tuition fees): £2,465 (weekly), £3,010 (full).

St Teresa's Preparatory School provides a happy and stimulating environment where girls of all ages and abilities thrive. The School creates a firm foundation for your daughter's future, equipping her with the necessary knowledge, skills and self-confidence to fulfil her own potential. Girls are enrolled from the age of 2 and prepared for the senior school examination as well as the Common Entrance Examination. We offer an extensive curriculum enabling the girls to develop strong literacy, numeracy and social skills. Specialist teachers are employed throughout the school, with the National Curriculum forming the basis of our teaching.

The school is entering an exciting period in its history as both Nursery and Prep School will move in January 2009 into a brand new, purpose-built school currently under construction on the 48-acre Senior School site.

The **Nursery** is a well-equipped, safe, lively and happy department for girls from 2–4 years equipped with computers and modern nursery facilities. A carefully balanced daily curriculum ensures the right mix of learning and play and outdoors there is a dedicated playground with adventure play equipment.

At **Pre-Prep** (4–7 years) we recognise that these years are critical in terms of successful physical, social and intellectual development. Small classes enable staff to concentrate on the individual, with reading skills and numeracy developed as a top priority. Specialist teaching is given in ballet, PE, Music and French.

In the **Preparatory** years the girls follow a broad and challenging curriculum taught by subject specialists. In addition to the core subjects of Mathematics, French, English and Science they also take Computer studies, Music, Sport, Swimming, Choir and Orchestra. Extra tuition is available to support those with special needs. Many girls also take part in an extensive programme of extra-curricular activities which include chess, judo, football, modern dancing, gardening, ICT, science, ballet and gym.

St Teresa's offers an extended day for all age groups, with homework club until 6 pm, and boarding, including occasional overnight options. The school is situated in Effingham and is a feeder school for St Teresa's Senior School.

All denominations are welcome to attend this Catholic School, where Christian values and respect for others are considered important.

Prospectus. A fully illustrated prospectus is available on request or may be downloaded from our website.

Charitable status. St Teresa's School Effingham Trust is a Registered Charity, number 1095103. It exists to provide a Christian education for girls.

Salisbury Cathedral School

1 The Close Salisbury Wilts SP1 2EQ
Tel: 01722 555300
Fax: 01722 410910
e-mail: admissions@salisburycathedralschool.com
website: www.salisburycathedralschool.com

Founded in 1091. Co-educational Preparatory, Pre-Preparatory and Choir School.

Chairman of Governors: The Dean of Salisbury

***Head Master*: P M Greenfield**, BEd

Deputy Head: Mrs J Matthews, BEd Hons

Bursar & Clerk to the Governors: Mrs E Horwood

Age Range. 3–13.

Number of Pupils. Preparatory: 153 boys and girls (42 boarders); Pre-Prep Department 69 boys and girls.

Fees per term (2007-2008). Pre-Prep: £1,260 (Nursery mornings only, afternoons available), £1,945 (Reception, Years 1 & 2), £3,185 (Year 3). Preparatory School: £3,825 (day), £5,590 (boarding).

The school was founded in 1091 and is situated in the former Bishop's Palace on a 25 acre site in the beautiful Cathedral Close. There is a self-contained Pre-Prep Department for boys and girls between the ages of three and seven. A new boarding house opened in April 2002.

High academic standards, excellent music and drama. Many scholarships are gained to senior schools. Although the main thrust of the academic work leads towards examinations at 13+, some children sit the 11+ tests for the local Grammar Schools. The school also has a fully qualified Individual Needs team.

Facilities include: refurbished science laboratory, IT centre, music technology room, gymnasium, large all-weather pitch, extensive playing fields, heated outdoor swimming pool.

Talented sports staff coach all the major team sports and there are regular fixtures.

There are many after-school clubs open to all children in the Preparatory School. (Quality before and after school care is available for children in the Pre-Prep). The boarding house staff operate an "open door" policy to parents, organise many outings and activities and have achieved an enviable reputation for running a truly happy and caring boarding house.

For a prospectus and/or to arrange a visit to the school, please telephone or visit our website.

Charitable status. Salisbury Cathedral School is a Registered Charity, number 309485. It exists to provide high quality education for children.

Sandroyd School

Rushmore Tollard Royal Salisbury Wiltshire SP5 5QD
Tel: 01725 516264
Fax: 01725 516441
e-mail: office@sandroyd.com
website: www.sandroyd.org

Chairman of Governors: W R Hillary, Esq, FRICS

***Headmaster*: M J S Harris**, BSc, PGCE

Age Range. 3–13 co-educational.

Number of Pupils. 106 boarders, 93 day, plus 30 in Pre-Prep, The Walled Garden.

Fees per term (2008-2009). Boarding £6,330, Day £5,300. Year 3: Boarding £5,035, Day £3,870. Pre-Prep £2,250, Nursery: £24.50 (per morning), £42.50 (all day).

Sandroyd is a co-educational boarding and day school set in beautiful parkland in the heart of the Cranborne Chase.

The facilities which the school has to offer are second to none. They include an indoor swimming pool, all-weather hockey/tennis surface, cross-country riding course, access to a squash court, golf course and driving range as well as extensive games fields.

On the academic side the children are prepared for Common Entrance and Scholarships to all the leading independent senior schools and further awards have been won in recent years for Art, Music, Sport and all-round ability. A specialist Learning Support department is in place to assist those who need extra help with their studies. The school is well-known for the excellence of its music, both choral and instrumental and a new theatre will cater for the many productions which the pupils put on throughout the year in all age-ranges.

Generous scholarships are offered annually for academic, musical and all-round ability in Year 3 upwards.

Visitors are always welcome to meet the Headmaster and to look round the school and its exceptional grounds.

Charitable status. Sandroyd School Trust Limited is a Registered Charity, number 309490. It exists for the purpose of providing education.

Sarum Hall School

15 Eton Avenue London NW3 3EL
Tel: 020 7794 2261
Fax: 020 7431 7501
e-mail: office@sarumhallschool.co.uk
website: www.sarumhallschool.co.uk

The School, which has a Christian (Church of England) foundation, is an educational trust with a Board of Governors.

Chairman of Governors: Mr B Gorst

***Headmistress*: Mrs Christine Smith**, BA Open, CertEd, RSA SpLD

Age Range. 3–11.

Number of Pupils. 175 Day Girls.

Fees per term (2008-2009). £3,665 including lunch.

Founded in 1929, the school has, since 1995, been housed in new purpose-built premises which provide excellent, spacious facilities, including a large playground, gym, dining room and specialist art, IT, music and science rooms. Recently a French room, changing room, multi-purpose room and three individual music teaching rooms have been added.

Girls are prepared for senior London day schools and for 11+ Common Entrance. Girls entering at age 3 are not assessed, but those joining from Year 1 will be tested in English and maths. The school is ambitious for its girls and believes that in a caring, supportive and imaginative environment, every girl can achieve her potential. They are encouraged to develop a love and interest of learning for itself and awareness that their success in all fields is dependent on their own efforts. Consequently the school has a well established record of scholarship and examination success.

A broad curriculum is followed and a major investment in IT ensures that each girl has access to the latest technology. A comprehensive games programme, which takes place on site, ensures that girls have the opportunity to experience a variety of sports. Strong emphasis is placed on music, art, design and drama. Woodwind, violin, piano, cello and singing are offered. There are also two choirs, an orchestra and ensemble groups. Other extra-curricular activities include stage combat, football, Mandarin, theory of music, craft, games and yoga.

Charitable status. Sarum Hall School is a Registered Charity, number 312721. Its purpose is education.

Scarborough College Junior School
(formerly known as Lisvane)

Filey Road Scarborough North Yorkshire YO11 3BA
Tel: 01723 380606
Fax: 01723 380607
e-mail: lisvane@scarboroughcollege.co.uk
website: www.scarboroughcollege.co.uk

Co-educational, Day (with boarding available for boys and girls from Year 5).

Chairman of the Governors: S J Chittock, BSc, MBA

***Head of School*: G S Twist**, BEd, BA, NPQH

Age Range. 3–11.

Number of Pupils. 120.

Fees per term (2008-2009). Tuition: Years 5–6 £2,833, Years 3–4 £2,624, Years 1–2 £2,189, Reception £1,860. Nursery: £17 (per half-day session), £32.50 (full day with lunch). Boarding (weekly and full from Year 5): £4,135.

Wrap-around School Care (3–7 year olds) is all-inclusive. Holiday Clubs (8 am to 6 pm) operate throughout the main school holidays (closed for Christmas and Easter): £13.50 per half day, £24 per full day.

Scarborough College Junior School dates back some 80 years when it started life as a boys' preparatory school: Lisvane. In February 2000, Lisvane re-located to the main Scarborough College campus; more recently, boarding has been re-introduced on a small scale with the children being accommodated in the very well appointed houses situated close by on the Filey Road.

The Junior School now occupies superb purpose-built premises affording striking views over Oliver's Mount, the South Bay and Scarborough Castle. Facilities include a self-contained pre-school, early years and junior suites, an administration unit together with a school hall and a fully dedicated design and technology/art workshop. All classrooms are equipped with television, video/DVD and radio-cassette/CD equipment. Interactive whiteboards are being installed and all classroom computers are networked to the schools' two ICT suites with intranet and Internet facilities. The Junior School shares many impressive resources and amenities with the Senior School: science laboratories, drama studio, main sports/drama hall, Music School, sports fields, a full-size all-weather pitch and school minibuses.

The breadth of opportunity on offer does not detract from the solid grounding pupils receive in the core subjects. Class teaching – with thoughtfully introduced specialist support where this is advantageous – is the pattern until Year 4. This is then advanced by full subject specialist teaching in the last two years, in readiness for transfer to the Senior School. The full complement of well-qualified staff ensures a generous teacher-pupil ratio. Provision is further enhanced by a SENCO who oversees the school's learning support unit in conjunction with Hull Dyslexia Action.

The standard of pastoral care at the school is very high. The Junior School seeks to nurture well-rounded, confident and competent pupils who are ready for the challenges of secondary education at Scarborough College.

Seaton House School

67 Banstead Road South Sutton Surrey SM2 5LH
Tel: 020 8642 2332
Fax: 020 8642 2332
e-mail: office@seatonhouse.sutton.sch.uk
website: www.seatonhouse.sutton.sch.uk

***Headmistress*: Mrs V Rickus**, MA, BEd

Age Range. Girls 2½–11, Boys 2½–5.

Number of Pupils. Main School 120; Nursery 35.

Fees per term (2008-2009). £819–£2,320.

Seaton House School was founded in 1930 by Miss Violet Henry and there is a strong tradition of family loyalty to the school. The School aims to provide children with a thorough educational grounding to give them a good start in their school lives and to instil sound learning habits in a secure, disciplined but friendly atmosphere. Boys are prepared for admission to a number of pre-preparatory schools and the girls are prepared for various entrance examinations at 11+, both in the London Borough of Sutton and those required by independent day schools. Our highly qualified and committed staff create a stimulating learning environment and small classes ensure that all children have the necessary individual attention and encouragement to achieve the highest standards.

We follow the broad outlines of the National Curriculum with generous provision for Music, French and Physical Education. There is a School Orchestra and Choir and, each year, all children have the opportunity to take part in dramatic productions. School sports teams enjoy considerable success when they compete regularly against neighbouring schools and each Spring we host our own Netball Tournament. Years 5 and 6 have the opportunity to experience outdoor pursuits during their annual week's residential course. The School has excellent Library and ICT resources, while the range of extra-curricular activities offered is extremely varied, complementing the established provision of after-school care.

Pastoral care is of the highest calibre with form staff taking a keen interest in all their pupils. Courtesy, good manners and kindness are expected as the norm and children are encouraged to develop initiative, independence and confidence. There is a strong house system in the main school which stimulates good community awareness.

The prospectus is available upon request and the Headmistress is always happy to meet parents and arrange for them to look around the School.

Charitable status. Seaton House School is a Registered Charity, number 800673. It exists to provide education for children.

Sedbergh Junior School

Low Bentham Lancaster North Yorkshire LA2 7DB
Tel: 015242 61275
Fax: 015242 62944
e-mail: hmsjs@sedberghschool.org
website: www.sedberghjuniorschool.org

Chairman of Governors: R S Napier, MA

***Headmaster*: Mr P H Reynolds**, BA Hons, PGCE, MEd (Exon)

Age Range. 4–13 Co-educational.

Number of Pupils. 120.

Fees per term (2008-2009). Day £1,845–£3,850, Full Boarding £4,975–£5,645, Weekly Boarding £4,625–£5,375.

Sedbergh Junior School was opened in 2002 and since that time has become well known as a very friendly and enthusiastic school catering for a wide variety of pupils with different skills and interests. Pupils come from a wide variety of backgrounds, schools and nurseries. SJS caters for local day pupils, full-time boarding pupils from overseas and distances and every possible combination of day, weekly and occasional boarders.

Entrance Exams and Scholarships. Entrance to the school is by assessment and entrance exam. Pupils can start at any age from 4–13. A number of scholarships are available for pupils aged 8 and over.

Subjects. Small class sizes of less than 18 enable pupils to receive individual attention in all subjects. There is a concentration on Maths and English in the early years but Science, Art, Languages, History, Geography, Classics, Music, ICT and Design and Technology form important parts of the curriculum.

Parental involvement. Parents are a crucial component of the school. There are formal Parents Evenings arranged providing opportunities to have one-to-one discussions with individual teachers; termly reports are written for each pupil and the form teachers and subject teachers are happy to discuss any issues at any time.

Sport. Girls play traditional team sports of hockey and netball in the Michaelmas Term. After Christmas, netball and cross-country running become the main sports and in the Summer Term the focus is on tennis, rounders and athletics.

Boys: Sedbergh is renowned for its rugby and has gained numerous regional and national titles. After Christmas rugby is replaced by soccer and cross-country. In the Summer Term cricket, athletics and tennis are the main sports.

The Performing Arts. Music and drama are a very important part of school life. Lunchtime practices, individual lessons, concerts, musicals and plays all contribute to a varied and rich programme for the pupils.

Extra-Curricular Activities. There is a variety of trips throughout the year including skiing trips, French trips, History and Geography field trips and for the younger children visits to the local Scarecrow Festival at nearby Wray, and visits to museums such as the Leeds Armouries.

Open Days and Visiting. The school organises three Open Days per year (details are on the website) and visits can be arranged at any time by ringing the School Secretary.

Charitable status. Sedbergh School is a Registered Charity, number 1080672.

Sevenoaks Preparatory School

Godden Green Sevenoaks Kent TN15 0JU
Tel: 01732 762336
Fax: 01732 764279
e-mail: admin@sevenoaksprep.kent.sch.uk
website: www.sevenoaksprep.kent.sch.uk

***Headmaster*: Philip Oldroyd**, BA, PGCE

Deputy Head: Luke Harrison

Head of Pre-Prep: Marjorie Shea

Age Range. 2½ to 13.

Number of Children. 214 Boys, 162 Girls.

Fees per term (2008-2009). Nursery & Kindergarten £240 per session; Reception £2,320, Years 1–2 £2,700, Years 3–8 £3,280.

Founded in 1919 Sevenoaks Prep School stands on a spacious 19 acre site of playing fields and woodland bordering the 1000 acre Knole Estate. Our children and their parents make Sevenoaks Prep what it is – a very special place where pupils of all abilities flourish into confident and competent young people. We offer an all-round, well-balanced education of the highest standard within a happy and secure environment.

The school comprises the Pre-Prep (Nursery–Form 2), and the Prep School (Forms 3–8). All pupils follow a coordinated academic programme culminating in 11+ or 13+ entry to excellent local Grammar schools or via Common Entrance and Scholarships to public and independent schools.

In the Pre-Prep child-initiated play and teacher-directed activities are thoughtfully planned and carefully balanced; the children's self-esteem and confidence are paramount. Throughout the school small class sizes and the use of classroom assistants ensure each child has personal attention and is motivated to achieve their best. On entering the Prep School into Form 3, class teaching is continued for core subjects and specialist teaching introduced. As the children move through the school specialists teach all subjects and a Form Teacher and Pastoral Head monitor individual progress. In Year 5 the Headmaster meets with each child's parents to create a personal plan for entry into senior education whether that be at 11 or 13. All classes regularly participate in a programme of visits, workshops and field trips to support their learning.

Sport, Music and Drama are integral to the life of the school and are taught from Nursery upwards. Football, rugby, cricket, tennis, hockey, athletics, swimming, netball, rounders, lacrosse, athletics and cross-country are taught and matches played against local schools. The school runs a variety of teams at each age group to encourage participation from pupils of all abilities. Children play with others of a similar standard so that every child who wishes to has the opportunity to represent the school. There is a large school orchestra and two choirs. Our extensive peripatetic staff teach a wide range of individual instrument lessons. Music concerts are regularly performed, as are school drama productions both large and small.

Facilities include a fully-equipped science laboratory, Information Technology suite, language laboratory, fully-networked state-of-the-art library and individual subject areas for Art, Design & Technology, Drama and Music. A versatile school hall is used for PE, music concerts, drama productions and social events. The extensive grounds not only provide excellent sporting facilities but also encourage play and exploration. A purpose-built adventure playground has been constructed for the Middle School children and there is a separate play area and adventure playground for the Pre-Prep.

The school provides after-school care until 6 pm each evening and the extra-curricular activities are extensive. Clubs and societies run from Year 1 upwards and are many and varied from Chess and Judo to Dance, Drama and Fencing!

The school is supported by an active Social Events Committee who regularly arrange social events for parents to meet each other and raise money for the school and nominated charities.

Sherborne House School
GEMS Education

Lakewood Road Chandler's Ford Hants SO53 1EU
Tel: 023 8025 2440
Fax: 023 8025 2553
e-mail: info@sherbornehouse.co.uk
enquiry@sherbornehouse.co.uk
website: www.sherbornehouse.co.uk

***Head*: Mrs Heather Hopson-Hill**, BEd Hons

Age Range. Girls and Boys from 2½–11.

Number of Pupils. 260 (all day pupils).

Fees per term (2008-2009). £630–£2,506 including lunches. Nursery Grants available for 3–4 year olds.

Sherborne House School, founded in 1933, takes children from Chandler's Ford, Winchester, Romsey, Southampton and the surrounding villages.

Sherborne House occupies an idyllic four acre site, in a quiet, desirable area of Chandler's Ford. Boys and girls between 2 and 11 years of age are admitted through informal assessment. Scholarships are available for the gifted, in academic, art, sport and music as well as a limited number of means-tested bursaries. Scholarship assessments take place in February each year.

We have an enviable reputation for excellent Common Entrance and SATs results and regularly secure scholarships to established senior schools. Our outstanding results are achieved by a combination of good facilities, highly qualified staff, small classes and specialist learning support. Our broad curriculum emphasises literacy, numeracy and science but not at the expense of other subjects. Music is strong, with four choirs, including a boys' choir and peripatetic lessons are offered on a wide range of instruments. Art and CDT are taught in a specialist craft facility and a well resourced computer room offers internet facilities for more than 20 pupils at a time. A wide variety of sports is offered, including soccer, touch rugby, cricket, netball, hockey, short tennis, swimming and volleyball and the school has an extensive fixture programme. French is offered from Nursery and and we provide a strong Learning Support network for those with special needs. We also have timetabled drama lessons and carry out regular school trips for all children as well as field trips and residential outings for Key Stage 2 pupils. Extra-curricular activities are also available.

At Sherborne House there is a particularly happy atmosphere where a child's self-esteem is paramount. We expect children to work hard but to have lots of fun doing so, and we take pride in our multi-sensory teaching methods and cognitive curriculum to accelerate our pupils' learning. The pastoral care at Sherborne House is outstanding and the pupils are confident, disciplined, purposeful and happy.

School hours: The school day runs from 8.40 am to 3.30 pm (pre-prep) and 3.55 pm (prep). Additional supervised care is available from 8.00 am until 6.00 pm.

We are always delighted to show prospective parents around the school and have regular Open Days.

Sherborne Preparatory School

Acreman Street Sherborne Dorset DT9 3NY
Tel: 01935 812097
Fax: 01935 813948
e-mail: info@sherborneprep.org
website: www.sherborneprep.org

Chair of Governors: Mrs M C McKenna, MA

***Headmaster*: P S Tait**, MA, FRSA

Age Range. 3–13.

Number of Boys and Girls. 267 (Pre-Prep 71, Prep 196).

Fees per term (2008-2009). Boarders: £5,810–£6,075. Day: Nursery £1,165–£1,360; Pre-Prep £2,295; Prep: £3,465 (Year 3), £4,250 (Years 4–8). Assistance available for Forces families.

Sherborne Preparatory School is an independent co-educational day and boarding school for children aged 3–13 years. Founded in 1885, the School is set in twelve acres of attractive grounds and gardens in the centre of Sherborne and is well served by road and rail links. Although fully independent, it enjoys a long and close association with its neighbours, Sherborne School and Sherborne Girls.

The Pre-Prep Department is housed in a fully equipped and purpose-built classroom block, with experienced and well-qualified staff providing an excellent ratio of teachers to children.

The Preparatory School (Years 3–8) offers a broad education, leading to Common Entrance and Scholarship examinations in the penultimate and final year groups. There is a strong emphasis on languages, art and design technology and in independent learning. Over the last few years our pupils have won a large number of scholarships and awards to leading independent schools, including Sherborne School, Sherborne School for Girls, Bryanston, Sedbergh School, Taunton School, Wells Cathedral School, Abingdon School, Monmouth School and St Swithun's School.

Following the opening of a new six-classroom block in 2003, the School has recently completed a complementary wing housing a further four classrooms and new Art Room. In Years 3–6, the curriculum has been modified to foster independent learning through the teaching of a broader enquiry-based curriculum with an emphasis on study and thinking skills, designed to meet the individual learning styles of the pupils, and the teaching of languages, including Spanish and Mandarin.

The School's recent ISI report in November 2006 was outstanding and praised the School for its success in many areas, notably in developing independent learning and positive attitudes to work and study.

Charitable status. Sherborne Preparatory School is a Registered Charity, number 1071494. It exists to provide an all-round education for children.

Shrewsbury High Prep School (GDST)
at Kingsland Grange

Old Roman Road Shrewsbury Shropshire SY3 9AH
Tel: 01743 362872
Fax: 01743 364942
e-mail: enquiries@shr.gdst.net
website: www.gdst.net/shrewsburyhigh

At the start of 2007 Kingsland Grange Prep School for Boys merged with the Junior Department of Shrewsbury High School for Girls to create Shrewsbury High Prep School. From September 2008 the Pre-Prep (girls and boys from Nursery to Year 3) will be located at the Shrewsbury High School Junior Department site at Kennedy Road, Shrewsbury, and the Prep Department will occupy a new school building at Kingsland Grange, with separate classes for girls and boys in Year 4 and above. The details below relate to the boys' school as it is today.

Joint Heads:
M C James, MSc London
Mrs M Edwards, BEd Bedford, CertEd Primary Manchester

Assistant Headmaster: R J Lloyd, BEd

Age Range. Girls 8–11, Boys 8–13.

Number of Pupils. 160.

Fees per term (2008-2009). £2,417 (Years 4–6), £2,966 (Years 7–8).

Founded in 1899 as a boys' prep, the school occupies a delightful woodland site in the southern urban area of Shrewsbury close to the centre and the A5 ring road.

Facilities currently include three classroom blocks, a Science laboratory, extended Music School, fully networked Information Technology Suite, Art Room, Drama Room, Design and Technology Centre, Internet Resource Library, Bookshop and Gymnasium.

Small class sizes are employed throughout the school to ensure as much individual attention as possible. The staff are well qualified specialists in their own subject areas. The 4 to 8 year olds have a class teacher responsible for teaching and pastoral care. Subject specialists are introduced from the age of 7 years. The school curriculum is continually upgraded and developed to meet the modern needs of education whilst still employing tried and tested traditional learning methods. Most of the boys move on to Senior Independent Schools by way of Common Entrance or Scholarship examinations. An average of 75% of boys move on to Shrewsbury School each year.

We supplement the academic subjects with a timetable of Design and Technology, Art, Music, Drama and Information Technology. The vast majority of boys study a musical instrument. We have a School choir and supply the treble voices for the Shrewsbury School Choir. The main sports are Soccer, Rugby, Cricket and Athletics. Swimming and Cross-Country Running also feature for all boys. Other activities include Chess, Outward Bound, Canoeing, Mountain-biking and Tennis.

Annual trips abroad include a French Adventure trip, French City visit and a Ski Trip. Extra-curricular visits and invited speakers/performers are a normal part of the school life. Boys take English Speaking Board examinations and regularly take part in Festivals of Poetry and Verse Speaking with great success. There is an annual musical and dramatic production for both the Pre-Prep and Prep Departments.

Charitable status. Shrewsbury High School is part of The Girls' Day School Trust, which is a Registered Charity, number 306983.

Shrewsbury House

107 Ditton Road Surbiton Surrey KT6 6RL
Tel: 020 8399 3066
Fax: 020 8339 9529
e-mail: office@shspost.co.uk
website: www.shrewsburyhouse.net

Chairman of the Governors: A Weiss

***Headmaster*: C M Ross**, BA, HDipEd Trinity College, Dublin

Deputy Head: S Ford, BEd Hons University of SW England, DipIT

Age Range. 7–13.
Number of Boys. 285 Day Boys.
Fees per term (2008-2009). £4,295.

Shrewsbury House was founded in 1865, and moved to its present site in 1910. In 1979 it became an Educational Trust and is administered by a Board of Governors.

Boys are admitted from 7 years of age and are prepared for entry at 13+, either by Scholarship or Common Entrance, to any of the Independent Senior Schools. There are 33 full-time staff, as well as visiting music staff and a French assistant.

The School aims to provide both an academic and broad education; to give a comprehensive preparation for the various examinations required by independent Senior Schools; to develop sound work attitudes and habits; to promote spiritual, moral, social and cultural development and to advance individual development, including instilling self-esteem, confidence and wholeheartedness.

The School is particularly committed to offering every boy a truly broad education. Regardless of his ability – not only on the academic side but also on the non-academic – every boy is taught/coached by someone with expertise. The aims are to foster and discover talents, to aid boys to fulfil them, and, for those not so talented in a pursuit, to give them nevertheless a chance to develop an interest in and/or enjoyment for it. To this end, for instance: every boy is in a team with its own coach; every boy who wishes to be individually tutored in Music may be (currently over 70% learn at least one musical instrument), every boy may be in at least one concert each year and every boy is in a Play every year (there are 6 plays a year).

The School is fortunate in its extensive land, including on-site playing fields. The main building is Victorian; its interior has been adapted, furnished and decorated for modern educational needs. There is a covered heated swimming pool, further playing fields and a floodlit all-weather playing surface.

Facilities are constantly being updated and improved. In 2004/5 the following facilities were added: a new Music centre, a new Theatre, a new Dining hall, a new Library and Resources room, a new Pottery room, a new Technology room, 2 new Science Laboratories, a new Art room and 8 further new Classrooms. In 2005 the school also embarked on a two-year programme of installing computer equipment in every desk.

The main sports are Association Football, Rugby, Football and Cricket. At the same time boys are encouraged to try a variety of the more individual sports such as Swimming, Tennis, Squash and Scuba Diving. In addition, there is ample opportunity for boys to discover other abilities and talents through activities in Music, technical activities and Drama.

Charitable status. Shrewsbury House School Trust Limited is a Registered Charity, number 277324. It seeks to provide the best possible learning environment for boys aged between 7 and 14 who have the potential for above-average academic achievement.

Silcoates Junior School

Wrenthorpe Wakefield West Yorkshire WF2 0PD
Tel: 01924 885276
e-mail: robertlilley@silcoates.org.uk
website: www.silcoates.com

Chairman of Governors: J H Bryan, LLB

***Headmaster*: R C Lilley**, BA Hons

Deputy Head: J C Clewarth, BEd Hons, MEd

Age Range. 7–11.
Number of Pupils. 195.
Fees per term (2008-2009). £2,164–£2,848.

Silcoates Junior School is part of the Silcoates School Foundation. The Junior School and the Senior School are on the same campus and share many of its facilities, which include the Chapel, Sports Hall, Indoor Swimming Pool, Music School, playing fields and specialist subject areas for Science, Design Technology and Information Technology.

Music and Drama feature prominently in the life of the school. There is a Junior School Choir, and concerts and musical evenings are held throughout the year, with a major dramatic production staged annually.

There are eleven full-time members of the teaching staff, all of whom are experienced and well qualified. The Junior School is able to call upon the use of specialist teachers from the Senior School for PE, Games, French and Music. In addition, there are various visiting music specialists.

With over 30 acres of playing fields, we are able to teach a plethora of sports, which include: Rugby, Netball, Association Football, Cricket, Rounders, Athletics and Cross Country, and Swimming.

There is also a wide range of activities in which pupils can participate at lunchtimes and after school. These include ICT, chess, drama, recorders, orchestra, swimming, sewing and Warhammer. At Silcoates we also utilise residential camps in the Lake District, at weekends and in the school holidays for other outdoor activities.

Boys and girls are accepted through an entrance examination and then the pupils are expected to enter Senior School at the age of 11. There is no entrance examination for students entering the Senior School, subject to satisfactory progress having been made by the end of Key Stage 2. The entrance examination is held in January for entry in the following September. The tests are in English, Mathematics and Non-Verbal Reasoning.

Charitable status. The Silcoates School Foundation is a Registered Charity, number 529281. It aims to provide a first-class education for boys and girls.

Skippers Hill Manor Preparatory School

Five Ashes Mayfield East Sussex TN20 6HR
Tel: 01825 830234
e-mail: info@skippershill.com
website: www.skippershill.com

***Headmaster*: T W Lewis**, BA Exon, PGCE London

Age Range. 4–13.

Number of Pupils. 64 Day Boys, 53 Day Girls.

Fees per term (2008-2009). Reception £2,880, Years 1 & 2 £2,952, Years 3 & 4 £3,845, Years 5 to 8 £3,880.

The school was founded in 1945 and is set in the beautiful Weald of Sussex in grounds covering 32 acres. A dedicated, qualified staff of twenty prepare children for Grammar Schools and Senior Independent Schools' Common Entrance and Scholarship examinations. Classes are small and individual attention, thereby, guaranteed.

Facilities include a well-stocked library, gymnasium, individual music room, ICT centre, all-weather multi-purpose courts and a covered heated swimming pool.

The main games are hockey, rugby, football and cricket for boys; netball, rounders and cricket for girls. Swimming, gymnastics, ballet and athletics are also given prominence. Leisure pursuits include judo, pottery, arts and crafts, vocal training and instrumental music. The Choir and Orchestra are flourishing.

The school is interdenominational in approach and its aim is to help each pupil towards the ultimate goals of self-discipline, common courtesy and the ability to cope with a rapidly changing world. Moreover, happiness is a prime factor in achieving these goals. A happy child is a successful child.

Smallwood Manor Preparatory School

A Woodard School

Uttoxeter Staffs ST14 8NS
Tel: 01889 562083
Fax: 01889 568682
e-mail: enquiries@smallwoodmanor.co.uk
website: www.smallwoodmanor.co.uk

Custos: D W Platt

***Headmaster*: Mr C J Cann**, MA (St Andrews), MA (Oxon), CertTheol

Age Range. 2–11.

Number of Pupils. 99 Boys, 80 Girls.

Fees per term (2008-2009). £2,175–£2,785.

Smallwood Manor is a co-educational Nursery and Day School for children aged 2½ to 11, set in 50 acres of beautiful woods and parkland just south of Uttoxeter on the Staffordshire/Derbyshire border.

The aims of the school are:

- To ensure that every child enjoys coming to school and that each individual's potential is fully realised.
- To educate the whole child so that academic achievement goes hand in hand with developing spiritual, cultural and physical maturity.
- To emphasise traditional Christian values of good manners and responsible behaviour.
- To provide a stimulating programme of activities to encourage children to develop skills and interests, which will make their school careers successful and rewarding.
- To lay a firm foundation for further education.

As a Woodard School Smallwood has strong ties with Denstone College and has enjoyed an excellent reputation for preparing children for 11+ Entrance Examinations and Scholarships. Smallwood has a fine reputation for sport. Facilities include a covered heated swimming pool, a gymnasium and two hard tennis courts. Rugby, Hockey, Football and Netball are the main winter games; Cricket and Rounders are the main summer games. There is a whole range of clubs and activities after school including Cookery, Art and Crafts, Chess, Board Games and Computers.

Smallwood has a find modern Chapel and a choir which sings regularly in Music Festivals and local churches. Each child learns the violin for a year and the school has a string quartet, orchestra and wind band.

Charitable status. Smallwood Manor Preparatory School Limited is a Registered Charity, number 1102929. It aims to provide a Christian education for boys and girls aged 2 to 11.

Solefield Preparatory School

Sevenoaks Kent TN13 1PH
Tel: 01732 452142
Fax: 01732 740388
e-mail: admissions@solefieldschool.org
website: www.solefieldschool.org

Chairman of the Governors: Mr R Clewley

***Headmaster*: D A Philps**, BSc

Age Range. 4–13.

Number of Boys. 170.

Fees per term (2008-2009). £2,360–£2,990 including lunch.

Solefield is a Day Preparatory School for boys from 4 to 13. The school was founded in 1948 and is situated in Solefields Road on the south side of Sevenoaks. The main building is a large town house and contains the library, classrooms, kitchen, staff accommodation and the school office. The facilities have been increased considerably to include the Science Block, School Hall, Art Room, Dining Room, Junior Classrooms and Changing Rooms. A Music School has recently been built, along with a Library and ICT block opened in April 2008. The grounds contain the main school buildings and a large floodlit playground. The playing fields are a short walk from the school. A qualified and graduate staff prepare boys for entry to Independent Senior and Grammar Schools. Solefield has a strong tradition of academic excellence. Emphasis is placed on teaching the 3 R's in a caring yet well-structured atmosphere with close contact maintained between parents and teachers.

The curriculum includes Music, Drama, Art and Design, PE and a number of club activities. Cricket, Soccer and Rugby are the principle games.

Enquiries concerning places and admissions should be made to the Secretary.

Charitable status. Solefield School is a Registered Charity, number 293466. It aims to provide a high quality education to boys aged 4–13.

Sompting Abbotts

Church Lane Sompting West Sussex BN15 0AZ
Tel: 01903 235960
Fax: 01903 210045
e-mail: office@somptingabbotts.com
website: www.somptingabbotts.com

Principal: Mrs P M Sinclair

***Head Master*: T R Sinclair**, BA

Age Range. 3–13 Co-educational.

Number of Pupils. 190.

Fees per term (2008-2009). Weekly Boarders £3,550. Day £2,280–£2,920 (including luncheons).

Set in a magnificent site on the edge of the South Downs, Sompting Abbotts overlooks the English Channel with views towards Beachy Head and the Isle of Wight. The imposing Victorian House has some 30 acres of sports fields, woodlands, gardens and activity areas.

The aim of the school is to provide a well-balanced education in a caring environment, recognizing and developing the individual needs of each child, so that maximum potential academic achievement may be gained. Within the community of the school an emphasis is laid on the cultivation of courtesy, self-discipline and respect for one another in order to engender a happy atmosphere.

The school has a vibrant Pre-Preparatory Department, which includes lively Early Years classes. In the Preparatory Department well-equipped Science Laboratory and Computer Room are enjoyed by all ages. The Art and Drama departments offer wide scope for creativity, and peripatetic teachers provide tuition for a range of musical instruments.

Weekly boarding is available for the boys from Monday morning until Friday evening, and flexible boarding is also available.

South Lee School

Nowton Road Bury St Edmunds Suffolk IP33 2BT
Tel: 01284 754654
Fax: 01284 706178
e-mail: office@southlee.co.uk
website: www.southlee.co.uk

Chairman of the Governors: Mr A Holliday

***Headmaster*: Mr Derek Whipp**, MA, CertEd

Age Range. 2–13.

Number of Pupils. 325 Boys and Girls.

Fees per term (2008-2009). £2,290–£2,850 including lunches.

South Lee enjoys an excellent reputation for its friendly, family atmosphere. The school provides a stimulating and caring environment where children have every opportunity to learn and develop. From an early age, pupils are taught the traditional subjects, emphasising mathematics, science and English but within a wider curriculum that incorporates the use of the latest developments in technology and educational resources.

The school is situated close to the A14, has purpose-built, modern classrooms and specialist teaching areas. Sport is an important part of the curriculum and the school has the use of excellent local facilities

South Lee offers its pupils opportunities for self-expression and individual development through study of the Arts, drama, music and a broad range of outdoor, sporting and extra-curricular activities.

The **Nursery**, which caters for children from 2 to 4 years of age, makes learning a fun experience from the very start.

The **Pre-Prep** is essentially class-based, though specialist staff teach French, music, ICT and Physical education.

The **Prep School** is well staffed with experienced teachers. The full range of academic subjects is taught, encompassing the national curriculum and preparing pupils for the Common Entrance 13+ examination.

Charitable status. South Lee exists to educate children from 2–13 years of age. Control is vested in a Board of Governors, the majority of whom are current parents. The school is run as a non-profit making Limited Company and is a Registered Charity, number 310491.

Spratton Hall

Spratton Northampton NN6 8HP
Tel: 01604 847292
Fax: 01604 820844
e-mail: office@sprattonhall.com
website: www.sprattonhall.co.uk

Chairman: G N Underwood, Esq

***Head Master*: S J Player**, MA

Deputy Head: S Clarke, BA

Age Range. 4–13+ Co-educational.

Number of Pupils. 402.

Fees per term (2007-2008). Prep £2,990–£3,300, Pre-Prep £2,200–£2,375. Fees include stationery, lunch, all academic books and most extra-curricular activities.

Set in 50 acres of Northamptonshire countryside, Spratton Hall is a fully co-educational day school for 4 to 13 years old.

Through highly skilled teaching we create an exciting and stimulating environment for learning, and by developing the talents of each child we believe that every pupil can succeed. The children are encouraged to become independent thinkers and to use their own initiative with confidence.

In the happy, caring Pre-Prep Department (from 4 to 7 years old) the girls and boys play imaginatively and grow in confidence. Each child is nurtured to establish a sound social and academic foundation for their future education.

Spratton has an enviable record of success at Common Entrance; Scholarships and awards are regularly won to many of the leading Independent Senior Schools.

The children enjoy a truly all-round education, achieving high academic standards as well as being recognised nationally for their success in many sports and the Arts.

There are excellent facilities for Music, Art and Drama. A wide variety of concerts, productions and exhibitions are enjoyed by all age groups throughout the year.

The extensive playing fields together with a sports hall, two all-weather surfaces and a new full-size Astroturf enable all pupils to enjoy a range of sports including rugby, hockey, cricket, netball, rounders, athletics, cross-country and tennis.

For further information or to arrange a visit to see the children at work and play, please contact The Head Master's PA on 01604 847292.

Charitable status. Spratton Hall is a Registered Charity, number 309925. It exists to provide education for boys and girls.

Spring Grove School

Harville Road Wye Kent TN25 5EZ
Tel: 01233 812337
Fax: 01233 813390
e-mail: office@springgroveschool.co.uk
website: www.springgroveschool.co.uk

Chairman of Governors: Mr Robert Balicki

***Headmaster*: Mr W J B Jones**, BMus Hons, PGCE

Age Range. 2–11 Co-educational.
Number of Pupils. 230.
Fees per term (2007-2008). £987–£2,866.60.

Spring Grove is a co-educational Day Preparatory School from 2 to 11. The school was founded in 1967 and is situated on the outskirts of the beautiful village of Wye. The main building is a large Edwardian house and contains classrooms and the school office. The facilities have been increased considerably to include the Science Block, School Hall, Art Room, Music Room, Dining Room, Junior Classrooms and Changing Rooms. A new computer room and network is now in operation. The grounds contain the main school buildings and 15 acres of playing fields. Qualified and graduate staff help prepare the children for entry to Independent Senior and Grammar Schools. Spring Grove has a strong tradition of academic excellence. Emphasis is placed on innovative and creative teaching in a caring yet well-structured atmosphere with close contact maintained between parents and teachers.

The curriculum includes Music, Drama, Dance, Art and Design, PE and a number of club activities. Cricket, Soccer, Rugby, Hockey, Netball and Rounders are the principle games.

Enquiries concerning places and admissions should be made to the Secretary.

Charitable status. Spring Grove School 2003 is a Registered Charity, number 1099823.

Staines Preparatory School

3 Gresham Road Staines Middlesex TW18 2BT
Tel: 01784 450909
Fax: 01784 464424
e-mail: registrar@stainesprep.co.uk
website: www.stainesprep.co.uk

Co-educational Day School.

Chairman of Governors: Mr M Bannister

***Headmaster*: P Roberts**, BSc

Age Range. 3–11.
Number of Pupils. 211 Day Boys, 131 Day Girls.
Fees per term (2008-2009). £1,225–£2,550.

Throughout its history SPS has maintained a reputation for high standards of education and care. The School aims for all pupils to attain their potential within a secure and happy environment and strives to produce boys and girls who are confident, honest, considerate and courteous.

The School believes in traditional values but is committed to providing the very best in terms of modern facilities and educational methods.

The School's philosophy of '*Educating Today's Children for the Challenges of Tomorrow*' is highlighted by the outstanding achievements of former SPS pupils in their secondary schools, with many attaining positions of responsibility as well as enjoying academic, sporting, musical and artistic success.

The curriculum is based upon the National Curriculum with a sharp focus on the acquisition of literacy and numeracy skills. However, it is given additional breadth by the inclusion of French from Year 2 and Latin/Classical Studies in Years 5 and 6. Sport plays an important role at SPS and there is a regular programme of fixtures against other preparatory schools. Whilst the School believes in competitive sport and has won a number of local tournaments in soccer, netball, cricket and swimming in recent years, it also believes that as many pupils as possible should be given the opportunity to play in matches at various levels. Development of abilities in the Arts is also considered highly important with opportunities provided throughout the School both in the classroom and as extra activities. Subject specialist teaching commences in Year 4 following a series of assessments at the end of Year 3. A regular programme of trips and visits enhance the curriculum and the annual Ski Trip, trip to Melun and Field Trip are much enjoyed.

The Jubilee Wing along with the new Library and ICT Suite indicate the School's commitment to providing the very best facilities as well as in education. In addition to the general teaching classrooms there are special facilities for Science, Art, Design and Technology and Special Needs. Hard surfaced playground areas and the adjoining playing fields provide ample space for sport and recreation.

The School welcomes contact with parents and has a flourishing Friends Association whose activities strengthen the links between home and school. SPARKS, the School's Child Minding facility, operates from 7.30 am and remains open until 5.30 pm and is available for pupils of all ages.

Stamford Junior School

Stamford Lincolnshire PE9 2LR
Tel: 01780 484400
Fax: 01780 484401
e-mail: headjs@ses.lincs.sch.uk
website: www.ses.lincs.sch.uk

Stamford Junior School, along with Stamford High School (girls) and Stamford School (boys), is one of three schools in the historic market town of Stamford comprising the Stamford Endowed Schools Educational Charity. The schools are under a single Governing Body and overall management and leadership of the Principal and allow continuity of education for boys and girls from 2 to 18, including boarding from age 8. Each school has its own Head and staff.

Chairman of Governors: Air Vice-Marshal P Dodworth, CB, OBE, AFC, BSc, FRAeS, DL

Principal of the Stamford Endowed Schools: S C Roberts, MA

***Headmistress*: Miss E M Craig**, MA

Age Range. 2–11.
Number of Children. 345.
Fees per term (2008-2009). Day £2,860; Full boarding £5,848; Weekly Boarding £5,812.

The Junior School educates boys and girls up to the age of 11 (including boarders from age 8), when boys move on to Stamford School and girls to Stamford High School. Admission from the Junior School to the two senior schools is based on progress and without further entrance testing.

The Junior School occupies its own spacious grounds, bordering the River Welland, overlooking the sports fields and open countryside, the boarding houses, the sports hall, floodlit artificial hockey pitch and the swimming pool on the same site. It is on the south west outskirts of Stamford within easy reach of the A1.

Entry to the School is according to registration at 4+ and assessment and interview in all other age groups.

The attractive and varied curriculum is designed to establish firm foundations in oracy, literacy and numeracy whilst providing excellent opportunities for music, drama, art and design and for acquiring technical and physical skills. The aims of the school are to develop the talents and potential of all the children.

There are 26 full-time staff, with specialist teachers in physical education, swimming, art and music, and visiting teachers offering a variety of sports, dance, speech and drama.

Boarding. The co-educational Boarding House (St Michael's) is run in a homely, family style under the experienced leadership of Mr and Mrs Phillips. Boys and girls are accepted as full or weekly boarders from the age of 8. Occasional or flexi-boarding is accommodated where possible and according to family need. A full programme of activities takes place at weekends so that boarders enjoy a rich and varied week.

Stockport Grammar Junior School

Buxton Road Stockport Cheshire SK2 7AF
Tel: 0161 419 2405
Fax: 0161 419 2435
e-mail: sgs@stockportgrammar.co.uk
website: www.stockportgrammar.co.uk

Chairman of Governors: R L E Rimmington, BA, FCA

***Headmaster*: L Fairclough**, BA

Age Range. 3–11.

Number of Pupils. 400: 216 boys, 184 girls.

Fees per term (2008-2009). £2,112, plus £149 for lunch.

Entry is mainly at 3+, 4+ and 7+ following assessment, with occasional places available at other ages. Stockport Grammar Junior School is a happy school, where children are encouraged to develop their strengths. A broad curriculum is taught and academic standards are very high. There are specialist facilities and teaching in science, ICT, physical education, music, art and design technology. A large number of pupils learn to play a musical instrument and tuition is available for many orchestral instruments. French is taught throughout. All children have a weekly swimming lesson in the School's pool. Both infant and junior children can choose to join in the numerous lunch-time and after school clubs and activities.

The Junior School and the Senior School share the same site. The vast majority of pupils move into the Senior School at 11, having passed the Entrance Examinations. (*See also Stockport Grammar School entry in HMC section.*)

Hockey, netball, football, cricket and athletics are the main sports. Swimming, tennis, rounders, cross-country and rugby are also offered. There is a full range of sporting fixtures and regular music and drama productions. All junior pupils have the opportunity to participate in residential visits, which include outdoor pursuits.

Before and after school care is available and holiday play schemes are run at Easter and in the summer.

Facilities are excellent. In addition to specialist teaching rooms, which include a computer room and a science laboratory, there are extensive playing fields, a large all-weather area, new sports hall and drama theatre.

Charitable status. Stockport Grammar School is a Registered Charity, number 1120199. It exists to advance education by the provision and conduct, in or near Stockport, of a school for boys and girls.

Stoke Brunswick

Ashurst Wood Nr East Grinstead West Sussex RH19 3PF
Tel: 01342 828200
Fax: 01342 828201
e-mail: headmaster@stokebrunswick.co.uk
website: www.stokebrunswick.co.uk

Chairman: His Honour Judge Coltart

***Headmaster*: R M Taylor**, BEd Hons

Age Range. 3–13.

Number of Pupils. 150 (10 weekly boarders); 95 boys, 55 girls. Pre-Prep 45.

Fees per term (2007-2008). Weekly Boarders £4,775. Day £3,975. Pre-Prep £985–£1,950.

Stoke House and Brunswick (each school being a century old) amalgamated in 1965 into their present spacious premises, the oldest part of which is the west wing which was originally John of Gaunt's hunting lodge in Ashdown Forest. The school is set in 32 acres of grounds which include a covered swimming pool, adventure playground, hard tennis courts, golf course and ample playing fields. There is also a Chapel plus classroom blocks and gym. A recent addition to the school is a new Design and Technology Centre which includes a Computer Room linked to computer network in each classroom.

Entry to the school is by assessment and report. The Mervyn Goldman Awards Scholarship (up to the value of 50% of the fees), is held in March for entry the following September and there are also Music Scholarships.

Soccer, Rugby, Cricket, Netball, Hockey and Rounders are the main games. Other sports which are taught include Athletics, Golf, Riding, Swimming and Tennis.

The staff consist of 18 full-time experienced teachers. Health and domestic arrangements are the responsibility of the Headmaster's wife and a matron.

Stoke Brunswick is a charitable trust administered by governors of wide professional and educational experience.

There is a Pre-Preparatory and Nursery department in the grounds for boys and girls aged 3–7. Prospectus and details on application.

Charitable status. Stoke Brunswick School Trust Limited is a Registered Charity, number 307011. It exists to provide high quality education for boys and girls.

Stonyhurst St Mary's Hall

Preparatory School for Stonyhurst College

Stonyhurst Lancs BB7 9PU
Tel: 01254 826242/827016
Fax: 01254 827136
e-mail: stmaryshall@aol.com
website: www.saintmaryshall.com

Chairman of Governors: Kevin Ryan

***Headmaster*: L A Crouch**, BA, MA, PGCE

Chaplain: Fr A Howell, SJ

Age Range. 3–13 (Boarders from age 8).

Number of Pupils. Day 152, Boarding 54.

Fees per term (2008-2009). Day £1,978–£3,944; Weekly Boarding £4,999; Full Boarding £5,683.

St Mary's Hall, Stonyhurst, provides a co-educational preparatory education in the Jesuit Catholic tradition for boarders (age 8–13) and day pupils (age 3–13). Stonyhurst, founded in 1593, is one of the oldest Jesuit schools in the world, and the

College and Preparatory School are set within two thousand acres of outstanding natural beauty.

The children receive a high quality rounded education. St Mary's Hall has its own outstanding teaching facilities and resources for all preparatory subjects, including French and Latin, and also enjoys the benefit of very extensive games fields, a sports hall, a fully equipped modern theatre, shared use with the College of a large indoor swimming pool, and (2001) one of the finest all-weather pitches in the North. St Mary's Hall has a national reputation for rugby, but at the same time many boys' and girls' sports flourish, as do a wide variety of cultural pursuits including drama and music. Many educational and recreational excursions take place both at home and abroad. The School's Scholarship record is excellent, with 50 awards being gained to Stonyhurst College in the last five years.

All pupils receive pastoral care and academic tutoring through their Class teachers and Playroom (Head of Year) Staff, who meet regularly to monitor closely pupils' progress. Early Years and Key Stage 1 pupils are taught in their own purpose-built building. The teaching staff are also closely supported by a resident Chaplaincy team, which leads the largely lay staff in the religious life of the School. Pupils of other denominations are also welcome at St Mary's Hall.

Boarders are also under the care of the resident Housemistress and her husband, supported by a resident pastoral team, including the Headmaster and other teaching staff. The boarders enjoy a stimulating and wide-ranging programme of lunchtime, evening, and weekend activities. St Mary's Hall, like Stonyhurst College, provides a seven-day a week boarding environment, one in which the day pupils are able to participate to a great extent if they wish.

The main sports played are Rugby, Cross Country, Netball, Rounders, Hockey, Cricket, Athletics and Tennis. The wide range of extra-curricular activities available for the children in their recreational time includes Chess, Model Making, Camping (Summer), Art, Photography, Fencing, Gymnastics, Computing, Theatre Workshop, Modern Dance, Ballet, and Skiing.

Admission to St Mary's Hall of pupils from age 3 to 10+ is by previous school report (where applicable) and interview. At 11+ there is also an entrance test. Academic Scholarships are also awarded at 11+, as is an annual music scholarship. Under normal circumstances all pupils proceed to the College at 13+.

Further details and a prospectus may be obtained from the Headmaster's Secretary.

Charitable status. St Mary's Hall is a Registered Charity, number 230165. It exists to promote Catholic Independent Jesuit Education within the Christian Community. It also runs its own registered, pupil-led charity, Children for Children, which raises funds for a school in Zimbabwe and other worthy causes.

Stormont

The Causeway Potters Bar Herts EN6 5HA
Tel: 01707 654037
Fax: 01707 663295
e-mail: admin@stormont.herts.sch.uk
website: www.stormont.herts.sch.uk

The school is administered by a Council of Management.

Chairman of Council of Management: Mr J H Salmon, FCA

***Headmistress*: Mrs M Johnston**, BA Hons, PGCE

Age Range. 4–11.

Number of Pupils. 170 Day Girls.

Fees per term (2008-2009). £2,920–£3,070 (including lunch). There are no compulsory extras.

The School was founded in 1944 and has occupied its attractive Victorian House since then. There is a spacious, bright, purpose built Lower School Building, which adjoins the Gymnasium/Assembly Hall and Dining Room. Old stables have been converted to provide well-equipped rooms for Art, Pottery, Design Technology, Science and French. A Millennium Building with a Drama/Music Studio and an Information and Communications Technology Suite was opened in September 2000. The school has two tennis courts, a playground and an adventure playground. It has use of a two acre playing field and a swimming pool.

Well qualified and experienced staff prepare the girls for entry to a wide range of senior schools at the age of eleven.

Charitable status. Stormont School is a Registered Charity, number 311079. It exists to establish and carry on a school where children may receive a sound education.

The Stroud School

Highwood House Romsey Hampshire SO51 9ZH
Tel: 01794 513231
Fax: 01794 514432
e-mail: secretary@stroud-romsey-sch.co.uk
website: www.stroud-romsey.com

Chairman of Governors: R H Trickey, BA

***Headmaster*: A J L Dodds**, MA Cantab, DMS

Deputy Head: Mrs J E Gregory, BEd Hons King Alfred College, CertEd Whitelands College

Director of Studies: Mrs M Freemantle, CertEd

Age Range. 3–13.

Number of Pupils. 326: 188 Boys, 138 Girls.

Fees per term (2008-2009). Upper School £3,875, Middle School £3,490, Pre-Preparatory £2,365, Nursery £1,075.

Stroud is a co-educational day school consisting of a Nursery, to which children are accepted at the age of 3, a Pre-Preparatory Department 4–6, and Prep School 7–13. Pupils are prepared for entrance to senior Independent or Grammar Schools.

The School stands on the outskirts of Romsey in its own grounds of 20 acres, which include playing fields, a full-sized sports hall, a heated outdoor swimming pool, tennis courts, riding arena, lawns and gardens. The main team games for boys are cricket, hockey, rugby and soccer, and for girls hockey, rounders and netball. Both boys and girls play tennis.

Music and drama play an important part in the life of the School. A wide variety of instruments is taught and children are encouraged to join the school orchestra. Each year there is a musical production and the Carol Service is held in Romsey Abbey. Ballet and dance are also available.

The Stroud School Association, run by the parents, holds many social activities and helps to raise money for amenities, but its main function is to enable parents to get to know each other and the staff.

A new Early Years building was completed in 2007.

The Study Preparatory School

Wilberforce House Camp Road Wimbledon Common London SW19 4UN
Tel: 020 8947 6969
Fax: 020 8944 5975
e-mail: wilberforce@thestudyprep.co.uk
website: www.thestudyprep.co.uk

Chairman of Governors: Mr C Holloway

***Headmistress*: Mrs Joyce Nicol**, MA

Age Range. 4–11.
Number of Girls. 320 (approximately).
Fees per term (2007-2008). £2,985.

The Study Preparatory School provides a happy and stimulating learning environment for girls from 4 to 11 on two very attractive and well-equipped sites close to Wimbledon Common.

The girls enjoy a rich diversity of experiences, both in and out of the classroom. Each girl is encouraged to do her best academically. Music, sport, drama, public speaking and a varied clubs programme play an important part, while guest speakers, fund raising events and school trips all help the children to understand important issues beyond the school gates. Good manners and consideration for others are encouraged at all times. Girls leave at 11+, very well prepared for the next stage of their education, with a zest for learning and many happy memories.

Charitable status. The Study (Wimbledon) Ltd is a Registered Charity, number 271012. It exists to provide education for girls from 4 to 11.

Summer Fields

Mayfield Road Oxford OX2 7EN
Tel: 01865 454433
Fax: 01865 459200
e-mail: hmsec@summerfields.org.uk
website: www.summerfields.oxon.sch.uk

Chairman of Governors: E A Davidson, QC, MA

***Headmaster*: R F Badham-Thornhill**, BA Hons Exeter, PGCE

Age Range. 7–13.
Number of Boys. 210 boarders and 30 day.
Fees per term (2007-2008). £6,450 Boarding, £4,995 Day, £3,325 7+ Day Boys.

Set in 70 acres of delightful grounds which lead down to the river Cherwell and yet only a few miles from the city centre, Summer Fields is often known as Oxford's *Secret Garden*.

The School has always had a strong academic reputation, gaining over forty awards to major independent senior schools in the last five years. One of the main objectives has been to attract outstanding academic staff and, we believe, that this has been achieved. Virtually all staff are resident and make a significant contribution to school life both in and out of the classroom.

Huge emphasis is placed on providing the highest standards in pastoral care – this was noted and highly praised in the latest ISI inspection report. Each boy has a personal tutor, who is responsible for his academic progress and social welfare and will be in regular contact with the boy's parents. The boarders live in comfortable Lodges within the school grounds and are looked after by experienced and dedicated House Parents.

The Music, Art, Drama, Design Technology, ICT and Sports departments are all impressive. The Choir has recently sung in Westminster and Christ Church Cathedrals and at Keble and New College, Oxford. They also regularly tour abroad. At least one Drama production takes place every term in the Macmillan Theatre with DVDs available of the major productions. Every summer an Art Exhibition of boys' work is held at the School and is open to the public.

The facilities are outstanding: a fine Library, Theatre and Chapel; purpose-built classrooms; Art, Design & Technology, Music and ICT Centres and a magnificent Sports Hall, with squash and fives courts, a shooting gallery, fitness centre and swimming pool. In the grounds there are hard tennis courts, a nine-hole golf course, an adventure playground and an outdoor swimming pool for use during the summer months. A huge range of sports, activities and hobbies is on offer throughout the week and at weekends.

Scholarships and bursaries of up to 90% of fees available.

For further information or to arrange a visit, please contact Mrs Christine Berry, Tel: 01865 459204.

Charitable status. Summer Fields is a Registered Charity, number 309683.

Sunningdale School

Dry Arch Road Sunningdale Berks SL5 9PY
Tel: 01344 620159
Fax: 01344 873304
e-mail: headmaster@sunningdaleschool.co.uk
website: www.sunningdaleschool.co.uk

***Headmaster*: T A C N Dawson**, MA, PGCE

Age Range. 8–13.
Number of Boys. 100.
Fees per term (from April 2008). Boarding £5,490 (no compulsory extras).

Sunningdale is a small, mainly boarding school of around 100 boys. The unique family atmosphere means that the boys feel happy and secure and as a result are able to achieve their full potential. Our aim is to find each boy's strengths and give him the opportunity to shine in different areas of school life.

Our academic record speaks for itself, with scholarships gained on a regular basis to senior schools. The structure of our forms means that boys move through the school at their own pace, constantly challenged or supported where necessary.

Three quarters of the boys play at least one musical instrument; many play two or even three. The chapel choir sings on Sundays and occasionally at old boys' weddings and there is a pipe band which plays on Sports Day and at other events. As well as other drama productions we produce a musical each year in which every boy appears. The art department puts on a large exhibition every year and often wins awards at senior schools.

We have a good reputation on the sports field and one of the benefits of being a small school is that almost all the boys get to represent the school in a team. This does wonders for their confidence. There is a wide range of activities on offer from judo to juggling, clay pigeons to clay modelling.

The school has a strong boarding ethos and boys can weekly board in their first year. Weekends are packed with activities to keep the boys stimulated and entertained.

Sunninghill Preparatory School

South Court South Walks Dorchester Dorset DT1 1EB
Tel: 01305 262306
Fax: 01305 261254
e-mail: sunninghillschool@lineone.net
website: www.sunninghillprep.co.uk

Chairman of Governors: Mrs R Johnson

***Headmaster*: A P Roberts-Wray**, BA Hons, PGCE

Age Range. 3–13.
Number of Children. Nursery (3–5) 10 girls, 9 boys; Pre-Prep (5–8) 34 girls, 21 boys; Main School (8–13) 53 girls, 36 boys.

Fees per term (2007-2008). £927–£2,825. There are no compulsory extras, but a cooked lunch costs £175 per term.

Sunninghill is a co-educational day school. There are 16 full-time and 7 part-time fully qualified staff.

Founded in 1939, Sunninghill became a Charitable Trust in 1969. It moved to its present site in January 1997 and has its own swimming pool, tennis courts and extensive grounds. Children are prepared for the Common Entrance examination to any Independent Senior School, and those with particular ability may be entered for scholarships. Over the years the school has attained many academic successes, but the broad curriculum also includes drama, art, craft, music and physical education.

Games are played on four afternoons a week and these include hockey, netball, lacrosse and rounders for the girls, and hockey, rugby, association football and cricket for the boys. In the summer term both boys and girls participate in athletics, swimming and tennis.

Out of school activities include choir, BAGA Gymnastics, LAMDA, ballet, Outdoor Pursuits, Swimming and Judo. There is a flourishing Parents' Association, which ensures that parents and staff get to know each other and work together for the good of the children and the School.

The prospectus is available on request.

Charitable status. Sunninghill Preparatory School is a Registered Charity, number 1024774. It exists to provide education for boys and girls.

Sunnymede School

4 Westcliffe Road Southport PR8 2BN
Tel: 01704 568593
Fax: 01704 551745
e-mail: sunnymedeschool@btinternet.com

***Headmaster*: S J Pattinson**, CertEd, BA

Age Range. 3–11 co-educational.

Number of Pupils. 143 Day Pupils.

Fees per term (2007-2008). £1,590–£1,990 (inclusive of meals). There are no compulsory extras.

Sunnymede aims to cater for the individual needs of children between the ages of three and eleven. In addition to the full range of National Curriculum, pupils are introduced to a wide variety of subjects, taught by specialist teachers. These include French, Drama, Pottery and Dance.

Sport plays an important part in school life, for those who are keen to be involved. A wide choice is offered, but the concentration is upon soccer, hockey, netball and cricket.

Music is especially strong, both individually and through the orchestra and choir. The Director of Music is supported by visiting teachers.

Drama also receives a high profile, and the school entertains parents and the community each year with a production at the Southport Arts Centre.

The school is situated close to the town centre of Southport, overlooking the coastline, and has pleasant gardens from which the children benefit.

Surbiton High Junior Girls' School (UCST)

95–97 Surbiton Road Kingston-upon-Thames Surrey KT1 2HW
Tel: 020 8546 9756
Fax: 020 8974 6293
e-mail: surbiton.juniorgirls@church-schools.com
website: www.surbitonhigh.com

Chair of School Council: The Rt Hon Dame Angela Rumbold, DBE

***Head*: Miss C Bufton**, BA Wales, PGCE Kingston

Age Range. 4–11.

Number of Pupils. 243 Day Girls.

Fees per term (2008-2009). £2,216 (Reception, Years 1 and 2); £3,021 (Years 3–6). Sibling discount applies to families with 2 or more children in the School and for children of members of the Clergy.

The School has a single-form entry at 4+, with a second intake joining the School at the age of 7, giving eleven classes altogether. We have approximately 24 girls in a class.

The Junior Girls' School is in an urban location on the edge of Kingston upon Thames. The Junior School building is only 12 years old, the rooms being spacious, well planned and well resourced. In addition to the classroom accommodation there is a Library, Hall/Gym, Computer Room, Music Studio, Drama Studio, Art Room and a large Science/Technology laboratory.

The School is cabled and networked with interactive whiteboards in all classrooms and also in the Science laboratory. These boards allow the curriculum to be taught with the most up to date resources and methods, keeping the pace and stimulus appropriate for children of today.

Our curriculum is based on the National Curriculum with an emphasis laid on the acquisition of proficient English, mathematical and scientific knowledge and skills. We retain a broad and balanced curriculum with French, Music and PE being taught to all girls from the age of 4 by specialist teachers. In Years 5 and 6 there is an introduction to departmental teaching. Specialists teach the girls History, Science, Geography and Gym and Dance. This is a gentle introduction for the girls to the expectations of a range of teachers and a Senior School type of organisation.

In Music and Drama there are many opportunities for performing. The girls present Form Assemblies for the School and their parents, who are invited to attend. There is a range of concerts, musicals and plays throughout the year for pupils of all ages. The girls perform eagerly and confidently, displaying a wonderful range of talents.

One of the strengths of the School is the pastoral care of the girls. This is reflected in the warmth of its atmosphere. We try to ensure that we give each child social, emotional and academic support and opportunities for growth.

The School has beautiful playing fields at Hinchley Wood nearby on a 33 acre site, to which the girls are transported by coach for their lessons. There are School teams for Netball, Tennis and Rounders and a thriving after school Ski Club where the children can soon reach extremely high standards. We have national champions at Junior level.

Charitable status. Surbiton High Junior Girls' School is governed by The United Church Schools Trust, a Registered Charity, number 1016538.

Surbiton Preparatory School (UCST)

3 Avenue Elmers Surbiton Surrey KT6 4SP
Tel: 020 8390 6640
Fax: 020 8255 3049
e-mail: surbiton.prep@church-schools.com
website: www.surbitonhigh.com

Chair of School Council: The Rt Hon Dame Angela Rumbold, DBE

***Headmaster*: S J Pryce**, MA (Surrey), BA (Open), CertEd (London), FRSA

Age Range. 4–11.

Number of Pupils. 138 day boys.

Fees per term (2008-2009). £2,174 (Reception, Years 1 and 2); £2,963 (Years 3–6). Lunches are extra. A reduction in fees applies when two or more children from the same family attend the Preparatory and either the Junior or Senior Girls' Schools. Reductions are also made for children of members of the Clergy.

Established in 1862 the School became the Boys' Preparatory School of Surbiton High School and thus part of the United Church Schools Trust in 1987. Situated in a large Victorian Villa in Avenue Elmers the school shares the facilities offered at the Senior School including access to those in the Surbiton Assembly Rooms and Hinchley Wood Playing Fields.

Boys join the school at 4+ (Reception) although places in other forms are occasionally available. The School is single-form entry and at the 11+ stage all pupils take Entrance Examinations to their chosen Senior School.

At Surbiton Preparatory School we have contact with some 20 Senior Schools in South-West London and North Surrey. All of these schools have strong academic traditions and reputations, those in the maintained sector are established selective Boys' Secondary Schools. Regularly the children's success in entry examinations allows the opportunity to choose between three or more senior schools and many pupils gain scholarship awards.

Surbiton Preparatory School follows an enhanced National Curriculum combining traditional values with the best of modern methods. A high standard of written and practical work is expected. French, Music and Physical Education are taught by specialist teachers throughout the school and Information Technology is a particular strength. In addition to a networked and Internet linked computer room each classroom has its own multimedia facility. Sound teaching is frequently supported by visits to outside venues and by visits from speakers, theatre groups and musicians. Further opportunities to develop interests and enthusiasm are provided by a wide range of extra-curricular activities.

The development of a thirty acre playing field complex at Hinchley Wood allows the boys access to floodlit tennis areas and Astroturf playing surfaces. Canoeing and Outdoor Pursuits are part of the Physical Education programme.

At Surbiton Preparatory School we work with parents to ensure that each child develops intellectually, physically, socially, morally and spiritually into a confident, happy individual. The boys are introduced to a variety of different experiences in a secure, caring and stimulating environment. The natural curiosity of every child is fostered and developed within a traditional academically based environment. We hope, thus, to encourage a positive attitude towards education and develop boys' self-motivation.

Charitable status. Surbiton Preparatory School is governed by The United Church Schools Trust, a Registered Charity, number 1016538.

Sussex House

68 Cadogan Square London SW1X 0EA
Tel: 020 7584 1741
Fax: 020 7589 2300
e-mail: schoolsecretary@sussexhouseschool.co.uk

Chairman of the Governors: John Crewe, Esq

***Headmaster*: Nicholas Kaye**, MA Magdalene College, Cambridge, ACP, FRGS

Deputy Headmaster: Paul Schmieder, BEd Leeds, MA Southampton

Age Range. 8–13.

Number of Boys. 182.

Fees per term (2008-2009). £4,285.

Founded in 1952, Sussex House is situated in the heart of Chelsea in a fine Norman Shaw house in Cadogan Square. Its Gymnasium and Music School are housed in a converted chapel in Cadogan Street. The school is an independent charitable trust. At Common Entrance and Scholarship level it has achieved a record of consistently strong results to academically demanding schools. The school enjoys its own entirely independent character and the style is traditional yet imaginative.

There is a full-time teaching staff of 20. Creative subjects are given strong emphasis and throughout the school boys take Music and Art. Team sports take place at a nearby site and the school's football teams have an impressive record. Cricket is the main summer sport and there are opportunities for tennis, swimming, basketball, indoor football and indoor hockey. All boys have physical education classes and Sussex House is a centre of excellence for fencing and its international records are well known.

Cultural and creative activities play a major role, including theatrical productions in a West End theatre, a major annual exhibition of creative work including architectural models and an annual competition of poetry written by boys. Ambitious choral and orchestral concerts are a feature of the calendar and a large number of pupils play a musical instrument. Staff take outward bound school trips, including skiing trips and cultural trips to the continent.

The school has a Church of England affiliation. There is a school chaplain and weekly services are held in St Simon Zelotes Church, Chelsea. Boys of all religions and denominations are welcomed.

Charitable status. Sussex House is a Registered Charity, number 1035806. It exists to provide education for boys.

Sutton Valence Preparatory School

Church Road Chart Sutton Maidstone Kent ME17 3RF
Tel: 01622 842117
Fax: 01622 844201
e-mail: enquiries@svprep.svs.org.uk
website: www.svs.org.uk

Chairman of Governors: B F W Baughan, Esq

***Headmaster*: Mr Craig Gibbs**, BA, HDE

Age Range. 3–11.

Number of Day Pupils. Prep (7–11): 123 boys, 107 girls. Pre-Prep (3–6): 80 boys, 70 girls.

Fees per term (2008-2009). £1,165–£3,360 (exclusive of lunch).

The school is fully co-educational with its own Pre-Prep department housed in a new purpose-built facility. We have just completed new specialist Art, Science and ICT facilities with a new Library too. The United Westminster Schools Foundation provides valuable resources and support.

The school is situated in 18 acres of countryside overlooking the Weald and includes a hard and grass play areas, heated outdoor swimming pool, 4 hard tennis courts, a Sports Hall, a 13-acre games field and a full-size Astroturf.

Classes are small throughout the school. The 41 teaching staff are all well qualified and there is an extensive peripatetic staff for music. Special needs are addressed by the SENCO and 3 part-time teachers. The Kindergarten to Year 2 classes all have qualified classroom assistants.

We provide an excellent all round education, with an emphasis on a solid foundation in the core subjects of English, Mathematics, Science and ICT. Languages, Music, Drama, Art, Design Technology and Sport play an important part in the curriculum too.

There is a wind band, string orchestra, quartets and a choir, the best of whom sing with our senior school choir. There are many opportunities for children to perform in drama productions and in concerts.

We have a varied programme of visits and outings to further the children's experience.

Cricket, Football, Hockey, Netball, Rugby, Rounders are the major sports. Athletics, Swimming and Cross Country are also in the curriculum. The proximity of the senior school, Sutton Valence, allows the children to benefit from their staffing and facilities, including the use of the Sports Hall and the new indoor swimming pool. Extra-curricular activities include chess club, art, 5-a-side football, gymnastics, drama, craft, croquet, science club, ballet and judo.

The school is a Christian foundation. Assemblies and the use of the local church are an important facet of our lives. We have a Chaplain for both prep and senior school.

Children are prepared for our senior school, Sutton Valence, the local Grammar schools and other independent schools with an 11+ entry.

Charitable status. United Westminster Schools Foundation is a Registered Charity, number 309267. It exists to provide education for boys and girls.

Swanbourne House School

Swanbourne Milton Keynes Buckinghamshire MK17 0HZ
Tel: 01296 720264
Fax: 01296 728089
e-mail: office@swanbourne.org
website: www.swanbourne.org

The School is a Charitable Trust, administered by a Board of Governors.

Chairman of Governors: J Leggett

***Joint Heads*: S D Goodhart**, BEd Hons; **Mrs J S Goodhart**, BEd (Dunelm)

Age Range. 3–13.

Number of Pupils. Prep: 157 Boys, 103 Girls (full/weekly boarders 42, flexi-boarders 52). Pre-Prep: 85 boys, 93 girls.

Fees per term (2008-2009). Full/Weekly boarding £5,595; Day: Prep £4,365, Pre-Prep £2,490, Nursery £1,155–£2,050.

The house, which was once the home of the Cottesloe family, is a Grade II listed building, standing in 40 acres of wooded grounds and commanding extensive views of the surrounding countryside. Swanbourne has been described by Gabbitas Guardianship as 'a school you would just dream of'. The School was ranked 'Outstanding', the top grade in the Ofsted boarding inspection.

There are 37 full-time members of teaching staff, many of whom are resident. They are assisted by several peripatetic specialist teachers. The well-being of the boarders is in the hands of a resident Housemaster and his wife: they are assisted by a Matron, our daily RGN staff and an Assistant Housemaster and Assistant Housemistress.

A strong musical tradition has been established. There are three choirs, an orchestra and various ensembles. Musical concerts are held throughout the school year and all pupils are encouraged to participate in drama and the Inter-House music competition. The school has its own chapel.

Boys and girls are prepared for entry to independent senior schools, usually at 13+, while scholarships have been won on a regular basis ever since Swanbourne House was founded in 1920, with particular success at Eton and Radley recently. The majority of boys and girls go on to leading senior independent schools, where the pass-rate in recent years has been 100%. From age 9, pupils are taught by specialist teachers in well-equipped subject rooms. There are 2 Modern Language Laboratories and all senior pupils have the opportunity to spend a week in France.

The more practical side of the Curriculum is fully catered for in the Fremantle Hall of Technology. Art, Design Technology, Science and Information Technology are taught in this attractive building: more than 200 computers are in use throughout the school. We have two computer rooms and an intranet into every classroom.

The Pre-Preparatory Department occupies an Elizabethan Manor House, adjoining the school grounds. The facilities are first rate and five new classrooms have been built. Whilst retaining a separate identity, the younger children are able to use the Main School facilities throughout the year.

A House system operates to encourage healthy competition in work and games. The Housemasters and Housemistresses have a special responsibility and concern for the welfare of the children in their House.

For boys, the main school games are Rugby, Hockey, Football and Cricket, and for girls Hockey, Netball and Rounders. Coaching and matches are also arranged in Athletics. Both winter and summer Tennis is played on our new astroturf facility. Further opportunities include Cross-country, Judo, Dance and Squash. A very wide range of extra-curricular activities is available in the evenings, at weekends and on certain afternoons. Tennis and Golf facilities are excellent.

The Bridget More Hall offers outstanding facilities for Drama, Music and PE. Other facilities include a rifle range, a new indoor swimming pool and squash court. There are various holiday sports clubs and time to offer camping and outward-bound activities, such as canoeing, climbing, riding, skiing and leadership training.

We run an Arts programme with visiting exhibitions.

School Prefects are taught to foster a caring concern for the well-being of every member of our community.

Children are prepared for Senior Independent Schools through lectures and workshops in international education, personal communication, drugs, first aid and senior school life. All leavers at 13+ take part in a residential week of outdoor education. Our Leadership Training is first-rate and has led to the regular winning of all-rounder scholarships and the Gordonstoun Challenge.

Scholarships are awarded for 11+ entry to the School for talent in Art, Sport, Academic or any combined area. February is the deadline for this.

Bursaries are available for Forces Families.

Charitable status. Swanbourne House School is a Registered Charity, number 310640. It seeks to provide a continuous structured education for children aged 3–13 years.

Taunton Preparatory School

Staplegrove Road Taunton Somerset TA2 6AE
Tel: 01823 349250; Admissions: 01823 349209
Fax: 01823 349202
e-mail: tps.enquiries@tauntonschool.co.uk
website: www.tauntonschool.co.uk

Chairman of the Governors: Mrs Jane E Barrie, OBE, BSc, ARCS, FSI

***Headmaster*: M Anderson**, MA

Age Range. $2^1/_2$–13.

Number of Pupils. Day 430; Boarders 47.

Fees per term (2008-2009). Prep: Boarders £3,275–£5,930; Day £2,030–£3,820. Pre-Preparatory & Nursery (full-time) £1,745.

Taunton Preparatory School is the Preparatory School of Taunton School (q.v.) and shares its aim to provide a broad and balanced education in a friendly, Christian community, in which the pupils can develop their talents and interests. Classes and academic sets are small, allowing close personal attention to each child. All children are encouraged to mix easily with each other and with adults, and it is a principle of the School's teaching that learning is best achieved through the fostering of enthusiasm and the development of an enquiring mind. Kindness and courtesy are highly prized qualities.

The Preparatory School was almost entirely rebuilt in 1994 to provide outstanding academic, cultural and athletic facilities. The new teaching facilities include 4 dedicated Science laboratories, Art, Design Technology and IT suites, a well-resourced library and spacious classrooms. A second Junior Art/Technology room, a further ICT suite and a new library are recent additions.

Boarding care of a high standard is provided & the School prides itself on its high standards of catering and individual care for all its pupils. Full and weekly boarding are on offer. An ambitious weekend programme of activities is organised. The School welcomes pupils from overseas. The school enjoys close links with the Armed Services – a generous Bursary scheme is well established.

Music, Drama and Dance are highly valued. The School runs a large Orchestra, three choirs, and specialist groups for strings, jazz and brass. Over 200 children now learn at least one instrument. There is an annual choir tour abroad – to Rome in 2006.

Sporting facilities at Taunton School are quite exceptional. The Preparatory School enjoys its own Sports Centre comprising an indoor heated 25 metre Swimming Pool and Sports Hall. The main boys' games are Rugby, Hockey and Cricket whilst girls are offered Netball, Hockey, Tennis and Rounders. All-weather playing surfaces and extensive grass pitches are available within the campus.

The wide curriculum is supported by a full programme of extra-curricular activities which include Dance, Board Games, Canoeing, Chess, Computing, Debating, Drama, "Green" club, Modelling and Pottery. The School is a keen supporter of the Scout movement.

A thorough grounding is given in core subjects and all children learn three modern languages during their time in the School. The requirements of the National Curriculum are met by enthusiastic and committed staff. There are scholarships at 11+ and 13+ (for entry to the Senior School). Art, Sports, Music and All-Rounder Scholarships and Awards are also offered. There are a number of ministerial bursaries and awards at 11+.

There is a purpose-built Nursery and Pre-Prep, which enjoys its own excellent classrooms, library, computers and recreational facilities and has full access to the Preparatory School's Sports Centre. Each class teacher is supported by a nursery nurse.

A comprehensive prospectus is available from The Admissions Secretary.

Charitable status. Taunton School is a Registered Charity, number 1081420. It exists to provide a high standard of education for children.

Taverham Hall

Taverham Norwich Norfolk NR8 6HU
Tel: 01603 868206
Fax: 01603 861061
e-mail: enquire@taverhamhall.co.uk
website: www.taverhamhall.co.uk

Chairman of Governors: Andra Papworth

***Headmaster*: M A Crossley**, BEd

Deputy Headmaster: I Newton, BA

Age Range. 1–13.

Number of Pupils. Prep: Boarders 28, Day 121 (Boys 97, Girls 52); Pre-Prep: 63 (Boys 36, Girls 27); Nursery 50.

Fees per term (2008-2009). Weekly Boarding £4,650; Day (including lunch): Prep £2,970–£4,158; Pre-Prep £2,400–£2,556 Nursery (per session, excluding lunch) £23 (morning), £14.70 (afternoon), £37.70 (all day).

About 100 acres of open grass and woodland are available for use by the boys and girls who enjoy a wide variety of outdoor activities, in addition to organised games which comprise Rugby, Netball, Hockey, Soccer, Cricket, Rounders, Athletics and Tennis. Skiing trips and walking expeditions are organised regularly in the holidays.

There is a teaching staff of 22 and the average number of children per class is 12. There is a broad curriculum, which includes Science, CDT, Art and Music. Children are prepared for Scholarships and Common Entrance to independent schools all over the country.

Every effort is made to encourage children to fulfil their potential in work and games and, in a well-organised and happy atmosphere, children have every opportunity of learning to contribute to the well-being of the community. Besides stressing school work, the School has a strong Musical tradition. The Chapel Choir is a St Nicolas Guild Choir of the RSCM. Piano, Brass, Woodwind and String Instruments are taught by specialists.

Free-time occupations include Golf, Squash, Shooting, Gardening, Riding, use of a Scalelectrix set, Cookery and a variety of Handicrafts. In the Winter terms there is an extensive programme of leisure-time activities in which all children and staff are involved. There is an indoor, heated Swimming Pool, a large Gymnasium, and a permanent well-equipped Stage.

The children's health, catering and all domestic arrangements, including laundry, are under the personal supervision of the Headmaster's wife, assisted by a team of Matrons.

Charitable status. Taverham Hall is a Registered Charity, number 311272. It exists for the purpose of educating children.

Terra Nova Preparatory School

Jodrell Bank Holmes Chapel Cheshire CW4 8BT
Tel: 01477 571251
Fax: 01477 571646
e-mail: enquiries@terranovaschool.co.uk
website: www.terranovaschool.co.uk

Chairman of Governors: P A Johns

***Headmaster*: Nigel Johnson**, BA, PGCE

Deputy Head: T J Fryer, CertEd, DipSE, MIITT

Age Range. 3–13.

Number of Pupils. 276: Boarders 5, Day Pupils: 155 (Prep), 81 (Pre-Prep), 40 (Nursery).

Fees per term (2008-2009). Boarders £4,600. Day Pupils: Prep £2,550–£3,710, Pre-Prep £2,100*, Nursery £1,100* (*Education Grant for three and four year olds not deducted).

Terra Nova occupies 35 acres of fine grounds between Holmes Chapel and Macclesfield. The school is 5 minutes from Junction 18 of the M6 and 25 minutes from Manchester Airport.

Boys and girls are prepared for entry at both 11+ and 13+ to a wide variety of Day, Grammar and Boarding Senior Schools. The school enjoys an excellent academic reputation and its pupils have won over 35 scholarships to senior school in the last ten years. Each child experiences a broad curriculum including Music, Art, PE, ICT and Design Technology. The staff is well qualified and experienced with the maximum class size set at 18.

The grounds and buildings include a multi-purpose Sports Hall and Performing Arts Centre, tennis courts (both hard and grass surfaces), specialist and recently extended Art and Pottery department, Music School, new Science laboratory, new Sony language lab, Design & Technology facilities and ICT suite. A new Nursery was opened in 2004 and the classrooms for five, six and seven year olds refurbished and enlarged. In addition there is a fully staffed Library and heated covered swimming pool. Music is taught at all levels and every child is given the opportunity to learn a musical instrument. The school has a choir, which performs in the area and overseas, as well as various instrumental ensemble groups and an orchestra.

Boarders have pleasant and comfortable accommodation in the Main building. The domestic arrangements and health and welfare of the children are under the direct supervision of the Headmaster's wife, supported by three resident matrons and a boarding team of six.

The main winter sports for girls are hockey and netball and in the summer tennis, rounders, athletics and swimming. The boys play rugby and soccer in the two winter terms and cricket, tennis and athletics in the summer. Additionally, the school enjoys a strong reputation for athletics and cross-country. A wealth of after school clubs are available including activities such as judo, badminton, volleyball, cooking, chess, riding, golf, dance and gymnastics. Terra Nova also boasts its own Cub pack.

The Pre-Preparatory Department is housed in a separate building adjoining the main school site but enjoys the benefits of many of the main school facilities.

An after-school and holiday club (Tembos) together with very flexible boarding arrangements meets the need of today's busy working parent.

Bursaries may be available in cases of genuine hardship. The school, which is in its 110th year, became a charitable trust in 1955.

Charitable status. Terra Nova School Trust Limited is a Registered Charity, number 525919. It is dedicated to all round educational excellence for children.

Terrington Hall

Terrington York YO60 6PR
Tel: 01653 648227
Fax: 01653 648458
e-mail: enquiries@terringtonhall.com
website: www.terringtonhall.com

Chairman of Governors: A H Monro, MA

***Headmaster*: M J Glen**, BA, PGCE (Dunelm)

Age Range. 3–13 years.

Number of Children. 190: 105 boys, 85 girls (Boarding 40, Day 150).

Fees per term (2007-2008). Boarding: £4,700. Day: £3,300 (Years 4–8), £3,075 (Year 3), £2,035 (Year 2), £1,925 (Year 1), £1,815 (Reception & Nursery). There are no compulsory extras.

Terrington is a co-educational school situated in beautiful countryside in the Howardian Hills (an area designated to be of Outstanding Natural Beauty) some fifteen miles from the City of York.

Terrington is a boarding school and is busy and vibrant seven days a week but all activities are available to day pupils, many of whom convert to boarding in their final years in preparation for the next stage of their education.

Terrington prepares pupils for all the leading independent schools in the North and further afield and is particularly proud of the twenty scholarships and exhibitions won by its pupils in the last three years.

The school enjoys excellent sporting facilities, with eight acres of playing fields, tennis courts, indoor heated swimming pool and Sports Hall. All major sports are played and, in addition, Athletics, Cross Country, Fencing, Gymnastics, Judo, Riding, Orienteering, Sailing, Canoeing and Clay Pigeon Shooting are available. There is an extensive outdoor education programme with all children learning to canoe and sail. The school has its own climbing wall.

Teaching facilities are modern and well-equipped and they include a Computer Suite, two Science Labs and a Middle School Block. Music, Art and Drama all form an important part of the curriculum. Tuition is available for most instruments and children can be prepared for Associated Board exams. There are two choirs and a very successful Wind Band, which has recently toured overseas. There are two major drama productions each year.

The School Chaplain is the local Rector and boarders attend the village Church most Sundays. Each day starts with a short act of worship.

The Headmaster, his wife and children live in the school and the pupils are very much part of an extended family. A wide range of activities is followed at weekends and full use is made of the surrounding countryside. Parents are fully involved in the life of the school and there is a flourishing social committee.

The school welcomes children whose parents live overseas and an escort service is provided to collect and deliver the children from airports at the beginning and end of term. There is a bus service to the Salisbury area available at half-terms.

A number of Entrance Scholarships are available for children under eleven and there are Bursaries for sons and daughters of Clergy and HM Forces Personnel.

Charitable status. Terrington Hall is a Registered Charity, number 532362. It exists to provide a quality education for boys and girls.

Thorpe House School

Oval Way Gerrards Cross Bucks SL9 8QA
Tel: 01753 882474
01753 885535 Kingscote Pre-Preparatory School
Fax: 01753 889755
e-mail: office@thorpehouse.bucks.sch.uk
website: www.thorpehouse.bucks.sch.uk

Chairman of the Governors: Mr Richard Coward, MA

***Headmaster*: Mr A F Lock**, MA Oxon, PGCE

Kingscote Pre-Preparatory School and Nursery:
Headmistress: Mrs S A Tunstall, CertEd

Age Range. 7–16. Kingscote 3–7.

Numbers of Boys. 198 Day Boys. Kingscote: 120.

Fees per term (2008-2009). £3,305–£3,960. Kingscote: Reception, Years 1 & 2 £2,526, Nursery £1,264–£2,022.

Thorpe House was founded in 1923 and registered as a Charitable Trust in 1986.

The School is staffed by a Headmaster, 22 full-time teachers, 6 part-time teachers and 13 peripatetic staff. There are 16 classrooms, 2 Science Laboratories, Library, Gymnasium, networked Computer room, Design Technology department, Art room, Music room and 4 Music Practice rooms. The School has its own open-air heated swimming pool, 7 acres of playing fields, tennis court and pavilion. All Saints' Church stands next to the main building, and is regularly used by the school. In addition to the three traditional major games of rugby, soccer and cricket, swimming and athletics are taught. Out-of-school activities include tennis, golf, judo, skiing, sailing, chess and a variety of clubs and societies. The School's examination record is very strong and boys go on to independent senior schools at 13 via the Common Entrance or Scholarship examinations, to the local Grammar Schools at 11, or stay on to take GCSEs at 16.

Kingscote Pre-Preparatory School and Nursery is situated adjacent to Thorpe House in its own grounds. Boys normally spend 3 or 4 full years there before transferring to the main school at 7+. (*For further details see entry in ISA section.*)

The Schools provide a continuous education for boys from 3 to 16. The provision for boys to stay on for Years 9 to 11 was introduced year on year from September 2006.

Charitable status. Thorpe House School Trust is a Registered Charity, number 292683. It exists to provide education to boys.

Tockington Manor

Tockington Nr Bristol BS32 4NY
Tel: 01454 613229
Fax: 01454 613676
e-mail: admin@tockington.bristol.sch.uk
website: www.tockington.bristol.sch.uk

Chairman of Governors: R F G Williams, Esq

***Headmaster*: R G Tovey**, CertEd (Oxon)

Age Range. Boys and Girls aged 2–13+.

Number of Pupils. 20 Boarders, 80 Day, 65 Infants, 80 Nursery.

Fees per term (2007-2008). Boarders £4,800 (inclusive); Day £3,010–£3,530 (including meals); Lower School £2,120. Nursery from £19.50 per session.

The school stands in its own 27 acres of parkland some 10 miles north of Bristol, close to the Severn Bridge and M4/M5 motorways, allowing easy access to road, rail and air links.

Boys and girls in the Preparatory School are prepared via the Scholarship or Common Entrance examinations for a wide range of independent schools. A highly qualified staff has ensured continuous success at these levels. The Headmaster's wife, who is also qualified to teach, takes a full part in school activities. Boarders accepted from age 7. Daily transport service to local areas.

The main school games are soccer, rugby, cricket, athletics, cross country, swimming (large indoor heated pool) and tennis (all weather courts). Girls play hockey, netball and rounders. Ballet, riding, archery and a wide variety of other activities are available in all terms, and children are encouraged to take part in music and drama. A feature of the summer term is an outdoor activity week, known as Tockington Tramps, leading to some nights at camp for senior children.

The Lower School has small classes for children aged 4–7, who share the facilities of the Prep School, and provides a stimulating environment. The Nursery for children aged 2–4 is well equipped with toys and games, has an extensive outdoor play area and aims to lay the foundations of independence and academic learning.

The excellent buildings, which stand in an attractive setting facing the games field, have been increased over the years.

Reductions in fees are offered for brothers/sisters and sons/daughters of Service personnel.

Tower House School

188 Sheen Lane East Sheen London SW14 8LF
Tel: 020 8876 3323
Fax: 020 8876 3321
e-mail: secretary@thsboys.org.uk
website: www.thsboys.org.uk

Chairman of Governors: Mr Jamie Forsyth

***Headmistress*: Mrs J Compton Howlett**, LRAM, ARCM, PGCE, FRSA

Age Range. 4–13.

Number of Boys. 170.

Fees per term (2008-2009). Reception and Year 1 £3,169, Years 2 and 3 £3,495, Senior School £3,588 (including residential trips).

Tower House is a day school established in 1931. The school stands in its own grounds and is conveniently situated near a number of bus routes and the local station.

Entry is at the age of 4+. Admission of boys after the age of 4+ depends very much on the availability of places. There is an entry test at this later stage and the Headmistress interviews all boys.

The school prepares boys for Common Entrance and Scholarships to appropriate Independent Senior Schools.

The staff is fully qualified and includes specialists in art, music and games, which together with drama play an important part in the school curriculum. In addition to the full time staff, there are visiting teachers for piano, violin, woodwind, brass and guitar.

The school is well supplied with modern teaching aids, including computers. There is a well-equipped science laboratory, an art and technology room, library, and an ICT Room.

The principal games are rugby, soccer and cricket. Other sports include athletics, cross country, squash, swimming, tennis and water sports. There are many fixtures arranged with other schools.

A prospectus is available on application to the School Secretary.

Charitable status. Tower House School is a Registered Charity, number 1068844.

Town Close House Preparatory School

14 Ipswich Road Norwich Norfolk NR2 2LR
Tel: 01603 620180 (Prep)
01603 626718 (Pre-Prep)
Fax: 01603 618256 (Prep)
01603 599043 (Pre-Prep)
e-mail: admissions@townclose.com
website: www.townclose.com

Chairman of Governors: Mr Richard Beck, BA, LLM

***Headmaster*: G R Lowe**, BEd (Nottingham)

Age Range. 3–13 Co-educational.

Number of Pupils. Prep 314, Pre-Prep 186.

Fees per term (2008-2009). £1,995–£3,125 including lunch and all single-day educational excursions. No compulsory extras.

Town Close House was founded in 1932 and became a Charitable Trust in 1968. The School is fully co-educational and is situated on a beautiful wooded site near the centre of Norwich. This location gives all our girls and boys space and freedom, and contributes substantially to our reputation as an outstandingly happy school.

There are altogether 47 full-time and 6 part-time members of staff. Together, we aim to produce well-motivated, balanced, confident children, who are caring and sociable and who know the value of hard work. Our classes are small and the children are prepared for all major senior schools, whilst those showing special promise sit scholarships.

The School's facilities include a well-equipped science laboratory, an indoor heated swimming pool and a sports hall. A new teaching centre stands at the heart of the School, containing a large, well-equipped library, an art room and 16 purpose-built classrooms.

Our Nursery and Reception classes follow the Foundation Stage curriculum. Children progress through a broad and varied programme of activities with a strong emphasis on the development of personal and social skills and on establishing positive attitudes to learning and to school life. Swimming and music are taught by specialist teachers, while the rest of the curriculum is delivered by class teachers, ably supported by well-qualified teaching assistants. The Nursery is purpose-built and the children play an important part in the life of the Pre-Prep Department.

Throughout the children's time at Town Close we pay particular attention to the teaching of good handwriting and spelling. Whilst recognising the importance of ICT, we value these traditional core skills very highly. Our ICT provision is extensive. We aim for all our children to become confident and proficient users of ICT. Our Pre-Prep pupils use a range of children's software in the computer rooms to develop key skills. Prep Department children build on these skills using more professional based software, either in the computer room or on the set of mobile tablets. All sections of the School have filtered access to the internet across our growing network. The School Intranet contains interactive activities, images, lesson material and links to carefully selected websites. Interactive whiteboards are used throughout the School to support the curriculum.

Town Close has an excellent academic and sporting reputation, but music, art, drama and a wide range of extra-curricular activities, trips and expeditions form a valuable part of what we offer, and provide the balance essential for a full and rounded education. Activities take place during the lunch hour, after school, and occasionally at week-ends. In terms of music, the School has an orchestra, a variety of choirs and a wide range of ensembles. All children are encouraged to perform and concerts take place regularly.

Physical Education plays an important part in the development of each child, be they in the Nursery or in Year 8. Emphasis is placed on fostering healthy exercise, as well as encouraging a positive, competitive attitude, individual skills and teamwork. As well as providing all the usual opportunities for the major sports (rugby, netball, hockey, cricket and athletics), coaching is offered in many other minor sports.

A copy of our prospectus is available on request, while a visit to our website will provide a fuller picture of the School, including a sight of our recent inspection report.

Charitable status. Town Close House Educational Trust Limited is a Registered Charity, number 311293. It exists to provide education for children.

Truro School Preparatory School

Highertown Truro Cornwall TR1 3QN
Tel: 01872 272616
Fax: 01872 222377
e-mail: enquiries@truroprep.com
website: www.truroprep.com

Chairman of the Governors: Revd F R Crewes, JP, MA, BD

Headmaster of Truro School: Mr P K Smith, MA Cantab, MEd, FRGS

***Headmaster of Preparatory School*: Mr M J Lovett**, BA Ed

Head of Pre-Prep: Mrs A Allen, CertEd

Age Range. 3–11.

Number of Pupils. 235: 134 Boys, 101 Girls.

Fees per term (2008-2009). Prep £3,045. Pre-Prep: £2,150.

Extras: Lunch. Optional extras: Individual music lessons, fencing, dance, judo.

Truro School Prep was opened as Treliske School in 1936 in the former residence and estate of Sir George Smith. The school lies in extensive and secluded grounds to the west of the cathedral city of Truro, three miles from Truro School. The grounds command fine views of the neighbouring countryside. The drive to the school off the main A390 is almost 800 metres and Truro Golf Course also surrounds the school, so producing a campus of beauty and seclusion.

The keynote of the school is a happy, caring atmosphere in which children learn the value of contributing positively to the school community through the firm and structured framework of academic study and extra curricular interests. The approach is based firmly in Christian beliefs and the school is proud of its Methodist foundation.

Building development has kept pace with modern expectations and Truro School Prep has its own large sports hall, an indoor heated swimming pool, a design and technology workshop with a computer room adjoined and purpose-built Pre-Prep.

The games programme is designed to encourage all children, from the keenest to the least athletic, to enjoy games and physical exercise. Our excellent facilities and the diverse skill of our staff enable us to offer a rich variety of sporting and recreational pursuits. There are over 20 popular clubs and activities run each week from 4.00 pm to 5.00 pm.

There is a strong school tradition in music and drama and the arts. Children may choose to learn a musical instrument from the full orchestral range. Each year the November concert, with Truro School, allows the school to show the community the excellent talents, which flourish in both schools.

Close links are encouraged with Truro School and the majority of children take an open entrance examination to Truro School which is the only Independent Headmasters' and Headmistresses' Conference School in Cornwall (*see entry in HMC section*).

The prospectus and further details can be obtained from the Headmaster's Secretary, and the Headmaster will be pleased to show prospective parents around the school.

Charitable status. Truro School is a Registered Charity, number 306576. It is a charitable foundation established for the purpose of education.

Tudor House School

Illawarra Highway, Moss Vale, New South Wales 2577, Australia
Tel: 00 61 2 4868 1088
Fax: 00 61 2 4868 3771
e-mail: admin@tudorhouse.nsw.edu.au
website: www.tudorhouse.nsw.edu.au

Chairman of Tudor House Council: W McI Carpenter, AVLE (Val), REIV (Aust)

***Headmaster*: A C Russell**, BEd, DipTchg, MACE, MACEL, AIMM

Age Range. 5–12 (Kindergarten to Year 6).

Number of Boys. 198 (60 boarders, 138 day).

Fees per term (from January 2008). (4 terms) Day: A$2,110–$3,844. Boarding: additional A$3,420. Lunch (day boys only): A$295.

Founded in 1897 in Sydney, the School was moved to rural Moss Vale in 1902 and was bought by the Council of The King's School in 1942. In 1993 it was given its own Council to control all aspects of the School and its development.

Boys are prepared for a number of independent secondary schools in Australia and overseas.

The school is situated five kilometres from Moss Vale and set in 167 acres of park and grazing land. There are two boarding houses. The classrooms are bright, airy and modern and in addition to the eleven teaching classrooms there is a computer room, woodwork shop, an art room, a Science and Technology room and a language room. There are facilities for music-making and drama as well as a large hall for assemblies and play productions. A good library is always open and we have a large variety of books.

The Enrichment Centre was opened in 1996 and provides the able boys with extension programmes. Boys needing remedial assistance are also helped.

There is a strong tradition of worship and choir work and services are held every Sunday in the school chapel as well as regular services during the week. The choristers of the two Chapel Choirs complete the requirements set by the Royal School of Church Music. The school also has a Senior and a Junior Band.

There are excellent sports grounds. Five cricket pitches, three rugby football fields, a 25m heated swimming pool with an additional diving bay, a large gymnasium, cricket nets, tennis courts, a cycle track, and a boating dam allow for a variety of sports and activities. Rugby and soccer are the main winter sports. Cricket and tennis are the summer sports. Athletics, cross-country, swimming, waterpolo, softball, mini hockey, golf, equestrian and skiing are part of the sports programme.

Boys are allowed (with some restrictions, according to age) the run of the property. A bond of trust exists between boys and masters.

Boys study English, Maths, History, Geography, Science, Drama, Art, Woodwork, Religious Studies, Music, Design Technology, Physical Education, Health and Personal Development, French and Outdoor Education. There is an opportunity to do extra subjects such as horse riding, leather work, martial arts, and to take piano, violin, saxophone, clarinet, trombone, flute, drums and guitar.

The "Kahiba" (Outdoor Education) programme is highly valued and widely regarded. Based on Scouting and a love of the Outdoors it teaches boys independence, responsibility as well as a love of the environment. It is available to the boys in the senior two year groups.

Philosophy. A real measure of freedom, a close association with understanding adults, are two basic ingredients for the sound development of young boys. They can thus be guided in the management of freedom to the point of full awareness of the responsibilities that go with it which are appreciated and understood.

These three fundamental notions: close adult concern with the boys of the school, freedom gladly given, and guidance in how to use it, are implicit in many of the Tudor House activities.

Twickenham Preparatory School

Beveree 43 High Street Hampton Middlesex TW12 2SA
Tel: 020 8979 6216
Fax: 020 8979 1596
e-mail: office@twickenhamprep.co.uk
website: www.twickenhamprep.co.uk

Chairman of Governors: Mr D Howell, BA, FRGS

***Headmaster*: D Malam**, BA Hons (Southampton), PGCE (Winchester)

Age Range. 4–13.

Number of Pupils. Boys 137, Girls 135.

Fees per term (2008-2009). £2,675–£2,890 plus £135 lunch.

Originally founded as a private school in 1932 and re-founded in 1969, the school is now a limited company with charitable status.

Boys are prepared for Common Entrance Examinations and girls for entrance examinations to independent secondary schools. Able pupils take scholarships and the academic standard of the school is high.

The staff is graduate and classes never exceed 18. Children are admitted at 4 years old. Girls leave at 11+ and boys at 13+.

The school, which is housed in a Grade II listed building in the Hampton conservation area, is well equipped to cover the full range of subjects. Emphasis is on individual attention and developing each pupil to their full academic potential.

A major building development was completed in 1999, comprising a new pre-prep block, gymnasium, and improved dining and changing facilities. Grounds and playgrounds have also been developed.

The school is a friendly and happy community where there is a clear non-sectarian Christian tradition, though pupils of all faiths are accepted.

Football, rugby, cricket and netball are our main team games and pupils swim regularly from Year 1 to Year 6. Athletics, tennis, squash, golf and other sports are also coached. Music and drama play a large part in school with full scale productions and concerts annually, involving all pupils. Individual instrumental lessons are taught by visiting specialists and there are many varied after school activities.

Charitable status. Twickenham Preparatory School is a Registered Charity, number 1067572. It exists to provide education for boys and girls.

Twyford School

Winchester Hampshire SO21 1NW
Tel: 01962 712269
Fax: 01962 712100
e-mail: registrar@twyfordschool.com
website: www.twyfordschool.com

Chairman of Governors: Mr S P Kelly

***Headmaster*: Dr D Livingstone**, BSc, PhD

Age Range. 3–13.

Number of Children. Main School: 54 boy and girl weekly and flexi boarders, 143 day children. Pre-Prep (age 3–7): 100 day boys and girls.

Fees per term (2007-2008). £5,750 (boarding), £4,450 (day), £2,725 (Year 3). No compulsory extras. Pre-Prep: £1,250–£2,275.

Twyford School is situated at the edge of the beautiful South Downs just two miles from the historic city of Winchester and the M3. Twyford is a family school that aims to offer an all-round top-rate education with a Christian ethos. Boarding is central to life at Twyford. Most pupils start as day pupils, but by the end of their last year over 80% are weekly boarding through the school's flexi-boarding system, which makes an excellent preparation for their move to senior school. The contrast between the modern facilities (classrooms, laboratories, music school, creative arts and ICT block, swimming pool and sports centre) and the Victorian chapel and hall creates a rich and stimulating environment.

The school regularly achieves scholarships – 5 academic, 9 music, 1 design and 3 sport awards in 2007 – to major senior schools such as Winchester College, St Swithun's, Canford, King Edward VI Southampton, Harrow, Pangbourne College, Wycombe Abbey, Radley and Sherborne.

Bursaries are available from September 2008.

Charitable status. Twyford School is a Registered Charity, number 307425. It exists to provide education for children.

Unicorn School

238 Kew Road Richmond Surrey TW9 3JX
Tel: 020 8948 3926
Fax: 020 8332 6814
e-mail: registrar@unicornschool.org.uk
website: www.unicornschool.org.uk

Chairman of Governors: Ms Elaine Redler

***Headmistress*: Mrs Roberta Linehan**, BA, PGCE Queen's, Belfast

Age Range. 3–11.
Number of Children. 170 Day Pupils: 82 boys, 88 girls.
Fees per term (2008-2009). £1,710–£3,135.

Unicorn is a Parent-owned school founded in 1970 and the Headmistress is a member of IAPS. It is situated opposite Kew Gardens, in a large Victorian house and converted coach house with a spacious, well-equipped playground and garden.

The school has free and unrestricted access to Kew Gardens and the sports facilities at the nearby Old Deer Park are utilised for games and swimming.

There are 9 full-time teachers, supported by 13 part-time assistants and specialist teachers, with visiting teachers for music, individual tuition and clubs. Classes average 21 children.

Unicorn aims to give children firm foundations and a broad education. A variety of teaching methods are used and the children are regularly assessed. Importance is placed upon the development of the individual and high academic standards are achieved. The main point of entry is to nursery at 3+ and the majority of children stay the full eight years. Children are prepared for entry at 11+ to the leading London Day Schools, as well as a variety of boarding schools.

There is a specialist ICT room and networked computers in every classroom. At nine years old all children take an intensive touch-typing course. In addition, there is a Science and Design Technology suite with interactive whiteboard technology in most classrooms.

The curriculum includes Drama, French (from age 5), Art and Music – with individual music lessons offered in piano, violin, cello, clarinet, saxophone, flute, guitar and trumpet, as well as singing. Recorder groups, choirs, chamber groups, an orchestra and wind band also flourish.

In addition to the major games of football, rugby, hockey, netball, cricket, rounders and athletics, there are optional clubs for tennis, squash, badminton, ice skating and golf. Other club activities include cookery, ICT, film club, gardening, mosaic, papier mache, creative photography, pottery, riding, sailing, sewing, and woodwork. There are regular visits to the theatre as well as to museums and galleries of Central London. All children from the age of seven upwards participate in residential field study trips.

An elected School Council, with representatives from each age group, meets weekly and a newsletter for parents is produced.

A happy, caring environment prevails and importance is placed on producing kind, responsible children who show awareness and consideration for the needs of others.

Charitable status. Unicorn School is a Registered Charity, number 312578. It exists to provide education for boys and girls.

University College School
Junior Branch

11 Holly Hill Hampstead London NW3 6QN
Tel: 020 7435 3068
Fax: 020 7435 7332
e-mail: juniorbranch@ucs.org.uk
website: www.ucs.org.uk

Chairman of Governors: Sir Victor Blank, MA

***Headmaster*: K J Douglas**, BA, CertEd

Age Range. 7–11.
Number of Boys. 230.
Fees per term (2008-2009). £4,480.

The School was founded in 1891 by the Governors of University College, London. The present building was opened in 1928, but retains details from the Georgian house first used. It stands near the highest point of Hampstead Heath and the hall and classrooms face south. Facilities include a Science Laboratory, Library, Drama Studio, Music and Computer Rooms, and a Centre for Art and Technology. Boys receive their Swimming and PE lessons in the pool and Sports Hall at the Senior School, 5 minutes' walk away. The Junior School has full use of the 27 acres of playing fields on games days.

Boys enter at 7+ and at 8+ each year and they are prepared for transfer to the Senior School at 11+.

Charitable status. University College School, Hampstead is a Registered Charity, number 312748. The Junior Branch exists to provide education for boys aged 7+ to 11 years.

University College School – The Phoenix

36 College Crescent Hampstead London NW3 5LF
Tel: 020 7722 4433
Fax: 020 7722 4601
e-mail: thephoenix@ucs.org.uk
website: www.ucs.org.uk

Chairman of Council of Governors: Sir Victor Blank, MA, FRCOG

***Headmistress*: Mrs Lisa Mason-Jones**, MA

Age Range. 3–7 Co-educational.
Number of Pupils. 125.
Fees per term (2008-2009). £1,385–£3,795.

At The Phoenix, we firmly believe that happiness and self-esteem are the keys to success in every pupil's learning journey. The well-qualified and highly-supportive staff accompanies each child on a voyage of educational and social discovery during the first years of school life.

The Phoenix School joined the UCS Foundation of schools in 2002 and fully supports the aims and ethos of UCS: intellectual curiosity and independence of mind are developed, self-discovery and self-expression are fostered and a cooperative and collaborative approach to learning is of great importance.

For every child in our care, we provide a continuously positive and creative learning environment that allows the individual the opportunity to develop personal qualities and talents. We are able to cater for up to 140 pupils aged 3–7 in our well-resourced classrooms. At the end of Year 2, both girls and boys transfer to a range of local independent schools. Whilst it is hoped that most boys will transfer to the Junior Branch of UCS this is not automatic and is subject to meeting the required standard in the entrance examination.

Charitable status. University College School, Hampstead is a Registered Charity, number 312748.

Upton House School

115 St Leonard's Road Windsor Berkshire SL4 3DF
Tel: 01753 862610
Fax: 01753 621950
e-mail: info@uptonhouse.org.uk
website: www.uptonhouse.org.uk

Chairman of the Council: Mr D R Llewellyn, BA, DipEd

***Headmistress*: Mrs Madeleine Collins**, BA Hons, PGCE Oxon

Age Range. Girls 2–11 years, Boys 2–7 years.
Number of Pupils. 170 Girls, 80 Boys.
Fees per term (2008-2009). £1,365–£3,650 (inclusive).

Upton House is a day school which has been part of the central Windsor community for over seventy years. The school buildings comprise a mixture of old and new. There is a separate new nursery centre (open September 2008), a Prep block, a games field, an architecturally designed drama studio, a netball court with Astroturf, a gymnasium/hall, three updated art studios and a home economics room.

As well as French, the children learn Latin and Spanish at the top of the school as part of the curriculum. After the age of 4 drama is taught by a specialist and so is music every week. Each child learns the ocarina and moves on to learning the recorder. We are holders of the Artsmark Gold Award (Arts Council England) for our work with drama, dance, music and fine art and the Sport England Activemark.

Our fruit and vegetables are organic, our staff lively and loving, and our standards high.

The school aims to motivate every child to develop their potential to the full in a happy, lively and caring community. Our objective is to produce a broad curriculum offering a rich academic and cultural environment. Boys are prepared for entry to preparatory schools in the area at 7+. Girls leave after the 11+ entrance examination, gaining places at a wide range of senior schools and winning scholarships.

Charitable status. Upton House School is a Registered Charity, number 309095.

Ursuline Preparatory School

18 The Downs Wimbledon London SW20 8HR
Tel: 020 8947 0859
Fax: 020 8947 0885
e-mail: ursulineprpsch@aol.com
website: www.ursuline-prep.merton.sch.uk

A Catholic Independent day school.

Chair of Governors: Sr Maureen Malaney, OSU

***Headteacher*: Mrs C Grogan**, MA

Age Range. Girls 3–11, Boys 3–7.
Number of Pupils. 220.
Fees per term (2007-2008). £1,220–£2,070.

A sound Christian education is given. The school has a strong academic, musical and sporting tradition, producing excellent results at Key Stages 1 and 2. Children are introduced to Modern Foreign Languages at age 5 and PE, Art, Music and ICT are all taught by specialist teachers. There are extensive out-of-school activities including choirs, orchestra, karate, chess, football, netball, gymnastics, dance, Spanish, science, art, dance and drama clubs.

Residential trips are organised in Years 5 and 6 to a field study centre and France. An annual family ski holiday is organised. The school has a strong tradition of performing, particularly musical performances, and makes great use of its outdoor stage. Everyone is in a Christmas production. There is a Spring Concert where musical skills are shared and an end-of-year show involving as many as 200 children!

The school has close contacts with the Jesuit boys Prep School providing automatic entry at 7. Girls are able to transfer at 11 to the Ursuline High School although many attend other selective and independent secondary schools.

The school has recently experienced inspections both by ISI and Ofsted and has achieved excellent results in all areas.

Charitable status. Ursuline Preparatory School Wimbledon Trust is a Registered Charity, number 1079754.

Victoria College Preparatory School

Jersey Channel Islands JE2 4RR
Tel: 01534 723468
Fax: 01534 780596
e-mail: admin@vcp.sch.je
website: www.vcp.sch.je

Chairman of Governors: Mr Clive Barton

***Headmaster*: P Stevenson**, BSc Hons (Durham)

Age Range. 7–11.
Number of Boys. 290 Day Boys.
Fees per term (2008-2009). £1,320 (inclusive).

Victoria College Preparatory School was founded in 1922 as an integral part of Victoria College and is now a separate School under its own Headmaster who is responsible for such matters as staffing, curriculum and administration. The Preparatory School shares Governors with Victoria College whose members are drawn from the leaders of the Island of Jersey with a minority representation from the States of Jersey Education Committee. The staff consists of 6 masters and 11 mistresses, all experienced and well qualified, including specialists in Music, Art, PE, French, Science and Technology. Entry to the Prep School is at 7 and boys normally leave to enter Victoria College between the ages of 11½ and 12½. The school games are soccer, cricket, athletics, swimming, hockey, cross-country and rugby. Sporting facilities are shared with Victoria College. There are two strong Cub-Scout Packs. Special features of the school are sport, drama, music and a high standard of French. Many visits, both sporting and educational, are arranged out of the Island.

A separate Pre-Preparatory School (5 to 7 years) is incorporated in a co-educational school situated at the Jersey College for Girls' and offers places for boys whose parents wish them to be educated at both the Preparatory School and the College. Candidates for Pre-Prep entry should be registered at the Preparatory School of the Jersey College for Girls, St Helier, Jersey.

Vinehall

Near Robertsbridge East Sussex TN32 5JL
Tel: 01580 880413
Fax: 01580 882119
e-mail: office@vinehallschool.com
website: www.vinehallschool.com

Chairman of Governors: Mr D W Chivers

***Head*: Mrs J L Robinson**, BA, PGCE

Deputy Headmaster: A G Whitehead, MA Oxon, PGCE

Age Range. 2–13.

Number of Children. 368: 66 boarders, 302 Day Children, 115 Pre-Preparatory and Nursery.

Fees per term (2008-2009). £5,742 Boarders, £4,395 Day Children, £2,489 Pre-Preparatory.

The School prepares boys and girls for a variety of senior schools. It has been designated a Christian School

The School's scholastic record over the past five years has been extremely good, with scholarships having been won to schools such as Benenden, Eastbourne College, Eton, King's Canterbury, Lancing, Sevenoaks, Sherborne and Tonbridge. The School has excellent teaching facilities with science laboratories, a computer room and a superb pre-preparatory department built in 1996. In September 2000 a Resources Centre and Library was completed at the heart of the main teaching block.

All the creative and performing arts are encouraged and the School has a wonderful theatre, built in 1991, which seats 250. The performing arts are a strength of the School. Most of the children learn musical instruments and regular plays and concerts are performed, both by the children and by visiting professionals.

The School stands in its own grounds of some 48 acres, and has a 9-hole golf course, as well as extensive playing fields, tennis courts, and an indoor heated swimming pool. A new sports hall was completed in 1996. Pupils can reach very high levels in a variety of sports. Woods and gardens provide an excellent setting for all kinds of outdoor recreations.

The boarders are cared for by residential staff along with matrons. The Head and her husband take an active interest in the children's welfare. There is no weekly boarding, but there are regular exeats, and parents are encouraged to take a full and active part in the life of the School.

Charitable status. Vinehall School is a Registered Charity, number 307014. It exists to provide a secure, quality education, in particular for those in need of residential schooling.

Wakefield Girls' High School Junior School

2 St John's Square Wakefield West Yorkshire WF1 2QX
Tel: 01924 374577
Fax: 01924 231602
e-mail: admissions@wghsjs.org.uk
website: www.wgsf.org.uk

Spokesman: Mrs M M Waugh

***Head Mistress*: Mrs D St C Cawthorne**, BEd

Age Range. Girls 3–11, Boys 3–7.

Number of Pupils. All day pupils: 383 girls, 100 boys.

Fees per term (2008-2009). Part-time Nursery £1,652; Full-time Nursery and Pre-Preparatory Department £2,203; Lower Juniors (7–8 year olds) £2,275; Upper Juniors (9–10 year olds) £2,404. Lunch included.

Instrumental lessons: £175 (10 lessons per term).

The Governors of the High School are shared with Queen Elizabeth Junior and Senior Schools (for boys) situated nearby. Close links are enjoyed between all four schools.

The school is extremely well resourced and enjoys an excellent reputation for high academic standards, caring pastoral system and numerous extra curricular activities.

The Nursery Department takes children in either a part or full-time capacity at the age of three, in order of registration. It is housed in its own spacious, stimulating and secure surroundings. The well planned environment and an appropriate mix of formal and informal education allows for the social, physical and educational development of each individual child. The Nursery Department ensures that preparation and progression to the Kindergarten, at the age of four, is an exciting and natural transition.

The Kindergarten, Years 1 and 2 are housed in Mulberry House, which was opened in February 2002 and is an ideal purpose built centre for three classes per year group. Most boys transfer to QEGS Junior School at 7 and the girls move into the Junior School. The Lower Junior girls are taught in St John's House and the Upper Juniors in a building with access to Science Laboratories, a Lecture Theatre and other Senior School facilities. Most girls move into the Senior School at the age of 11, although girls who sit for other Independent Senior Schools are also very successful.

The school aims to give a good all round education to each pupil, encouraging academic excellence, emphasizing traditional values, nurturing talent and developing an individual's potential Entrance is by examination from the age of 5 with the main Entrance Examination being held in February. In addition to the Head, a team of 30 dedicated and enthusiastic full-time teachers care for the children and encourage them in all aspects of school life. There are also five part-time teachers, six nursery nurses, ten NTAs, three secretaries and other ancillary staff, including nine lunch-time supervisors.

The school is a Christian foundation but with no particular denominational bias. Assemblies take place each day. The faiths of all members of the community are respected and valued.

The curriculum covers a wide range of subjects, including all of those prescribes by the National Curriculum, but the emphasis remains on numeracy and literacy. Music and physical education are natural parts of the curriculum and play important roles in the life of the school. A spirit of sensible competition is encouraged and the school teams and choirs enjoy success in local tournaments and festivals. All classrooms, the ICT Suite, Science/Mathematics Room, Music, Library and resource areas are well equipped. Most classrooms have an interactive whiteboard. Closeness to the Senior School makes it possible to share teaching staff, resources and specialist areas. The curriculum is further enriched by a variety of clubs and societies, in-school workshops and educational outings. The children are encouraged to think of others less fortunate than themselves and money is raised for a variety of charities.

Parental involvement is welcomed and participation both in the classroom and extra-curricular activities appreciated. Social and fund-raising events are organised by the Friends of St John's House, the school's PTA. All children stay to lunch which is cooked on the premises. Before and after school care is available to parents for a small additional charge.

Charitable status. The Wakefield Grammar School Foundation, founded in 1591, is a Registered Charity, number 1088415. It exists to provide an excellent education for your children.

Walthamstow Hall Junior School

Bradbourne Park Road Sevenoaks Kent TN13 3LD
Tel: 01732 453815
Fax: 01732 456980
e-mail: head@whjs.org.uk
website: www.walthamstow-hall.co.uk

Chairman of Governors: Ian Philip, Esq, FCA

***Head*: Mrs P A Austin**, BA Hons (London), LTCL, PGCE, NPQH

Day School for Girls.

Age Range. $2^1/_2$–11.

Number of Girls. 200.

Fees per term (2007-2008). Kindergarten £195 per session (2–10 sessions per week); Reception–Year 2 £2,520, Years 3–6 £3,115.

Walthamstow Hall Junior School offers a quality education for girls from $2^1/_2$–11 years. It has a vibrant Pre-Preparatory department with flexible Kindergarten sessions. A well-planned programme of education brings out the potential of each child as she progresses through the Junior School. A broad curriculum is enriched with many extra-curricular activities and clubs. Girls are well prepared for a range of senior schools and have won awards to prestigious independent schools, including Walthamstow Hall Senior School, Sevenoaks and Benenden. Many choose to take advantage of the opportunity of an 'all through' education. Entry to our Senior School is from 11+, 13+ and 16+ with Awards, Scholarships and bursaries offered on merit. Equally, our track record at 11+ assessment is excellent. Walthamstow Hall was founded in 1838 and is one of the oldest girls' schools in the country with a fascinating history. It has built a reputation for 'all-round' excellence and achievements by girls are outstanding. Over recent years, many new facilities have been added including new nursery classrooms, a new library with computerised lending facility and a new science laboratory. Girls have access to the Senior School facilities including 'Ship Theatre', art rooms, interactive science block, extensive sports grounds and swimming pool. The school is situated in the centre of Sevenoaks within easy reach of road and rail networks. Minibuses operate from surrounding towns and villages.

Warminster Preparatory School

Vicarage Street Warminster Wiltshire BA12 8JG
Tel: 01985 224800
Fax: 01985 218850
e-mail: prep@warminsterschool.org.uk
website: www.warminsterschool.org.uk

Co-educational, Day & Boarding.

Chairman of Governors: R Payn, MA Oxon

***Headmaster*: D Edwards**, BEd, MA

Age Range. 3–11 co-educational.

Number of Pupils. 150.

Fees per term (2008-2009). Day: Reception £2,000; Years 1 & 2 £2,150; Years 3 £2,550; Year 4 £2,850; Years 5 & 6 £3,200. Boarding: £4,660.

Conveniently situated on the edge of Salisbury Plain with easy access to London and the South-West, Warminster Prep is a thriving school with a friendly, family atmosphere. Together with our Senior School, we make up Warminster School, providing exciting, high-quality education for children from 3 to 18 years old.

Fully-qualified and dedicated teaching staff deliver a vibrant and stimulating curriculum enriched with many trips and theme days. Our teaching in the Prep School is rich and varied in its styles to suit the diverse variety of children who thrive in our inclusive and holistic environment. We have Learning Support for those who may need it and an 'Able & Talented' club to ensure that all our children are achieving their potential in a supportive and caring atmosphere.

The curriculum is broad and balanced reflecting an ethos that values the development of skills and achievement in all subjects and areas of school life. Whilst the pursuit of excellence in core subjects is very important, Art, Sport, Music, Drama and Technologies are also vital areas in building confidence and self-esteem. Scholarships are available for academic Years 3 and 5 as well as for Years 7 and 9 in the Senior School.

Totally flexible boarding arrangements exist for children from 7 years upwards within our attractive Prep School boarding house; Golspie. Under the auspices of our experienced, dedicated Matron and House Parent, children enjoy a very high standard of Pastoral care with weekend trips and outings being a highlight of the week. A number of children are full boarders, but weekly and hotel boarding are very popular with, and a cost-effective service for, busy working parents. The Boarding Schools Allowance is available for serving members of HM Forces.

Sport is an important part of life at Warminster Prep, with a busy programme of inter-school fixtures in Rugby, Soccer, Hockey and Cricket for boys, and Hockey, Netball and Rounders for girls. In the summer term, children also swim and enjoy Tennis and Athletics.

Warminster Prep School has a strong creative tradition in the Arts; performing art in Music, Speech and Drama, visual art in a wide range of media including sculpture and fired clay. The school hosts an annual Arts Festival in which other local schools also participate.

The Prep (and Pre-Prep) School is well-equipped with its own catering and Dining Hall, modern fully-equipped Science lab, ICT suite, Sports pitches, Art and DT studio, well-equipped stage, tennis courts, Music and practice rooms and Library. This is in addition to the superb facilities we share with our adjacent Senior School such as the Swimming pool, Senior Library, Chapel, Sports Hall and Astroturf pitch. The new Courtyard Nursery was opened in 2007 and provides superb accommodation for the Foundation Stage.

We provide, for Day and Boarding children, a wide choice of clubs and activities. These augment our timetabled curriculum and ensure that children can develop their individual tastes and interests alongside more traditionally academic abilities. We include opportunities for foreign travel with our French Trip and Ski Trip.

Interested parents are invited to ring the Headmaster's Secretary for a prospectus and to arrange a visit and free taster-day.

For information about the Senior School, please see entry in SHMIS section.

Charitable status. Warminster School is Registered Charity, number 1042204, providing education for boys and girls.

Warwick Junior School

Myton Road Warwick CV34 6PP
Tel: 01926 776418
Fax: 01926 776478
website: www.warwickschool.org

Chairman of Governors: Brigadier M J F Stephens, MA, CEng, MICE

***Head of Junior School*: G R G Canning**, BA, PGCE

Age Range. 7–11.

Number of Pupils. 241 boys. Boarding is available for approximately 20 boys.

Fees per term (2008-2009). Tuition: £2,512 (7+), £2,853 (8+/9+), £3,195 (10+). Boarding (in addition to Tuition): £3,662 (full); £3,212 (weekly).

The School is the Junior School of Warwick School. The Junior School is situated on a site on the outskirts of Warwick Town adjacent to Warwick Senior School. The buildings are contained within a four acre site and enjoy the use of the Sports and other facilities of Warwick Senior School. A new extension to the school, providing six classrooms and a library, was completed in May 2002. A programme of refurbishment in the existing Junior School building was completed in September 2002 and this includes new ICT and DT rooms.

The aim of the School is to provide a good general education based on Christian principles. Academic standards are high and in particular participation in a range of activities is encouraged. Each pupil is encouraged to develop his own personality and to realise his own potential.

The curriculum gives a good grounding in English, Mathematics, Science, Technology, ICT, History, Geography, Religious Education, French, Art, Music, Drama and PE. Many sporting activities are available on the fifty acre campus of Warwick School, which includes a sports hall and indoor swimming pool. Rugby and Soccer are the main winter sports, with Cricket in the summer, plus Athletics, Swimming, Tennis, Squash and Cross Country.

The School's creative activities, dramatic productions and musical performances provide a useful focus in the development of many talents within the School.

Warwick Junior School provides a programme of learning support. This support is available for boys with specific learning difficulties such as dyslexia or dyspraxia and for those who need just a "little extra help" in any area.

Boarding for about 20 Junior School boys is available in the Boarding House at Warwick. The large number of day pupils and a boarding house provides maximum flexibility for parental choice. It also encourages a healthy environment in which boys can develop their academic and out of school activities.

Extended day facilities are available until 5.30 pm when pupils can either do their homework or enrol in the activity programme.

Boys are prepared for the Entrance Examination to Warwick Senior School at age 11. The majority of pupils who leave Warwick Junior School gain a place in the Senior School at Warwick.

Charitable status. Warwick Independent Schools Foundation is a Registered Charity, number 1088057. It exists to provide quality education for boys.

Warwick Preparatory School

Bridge Field Banbury Road Warwick CV34 6PL
Tel: 01926 491545
Fax: 01926 403456
e-mail: info@warwickprep.com
website: www.warwickprep.com

Chairman of the Governors: Mrs V Phillips

***Headmistress*: Mrs D M Robinson**, BSc, PGCE

Age Range. Boys 3–7, Girls 3–11.

Number of Children. 105 Boys, 358 Girls.

Fees per term (2008-2009). Nursery 3+: £1,131 (morning only), £2,207 (full time). Lower School (4–6 years) £2,615; Middle and Upper Schools (7–11 years) £2,890. (Lunch included)

Instrumental music tuition optional extra.

Warwick Preparatory School is an Independent School, purpose built in 1970 on a 4½ acre site on the outskirts of Warwick. It is part of the Warwick Independent Schools' Foundation, which includes Warwick School and the King's High School for Girls.

The Prep School has 40 teachers and 25 nursery nurses, teaching assistants and technicians, with specialist tuition in Art, French, Science, Music, Drama, DT, Physical Education and Information Technology.

Boys and girls are admitted from the age of 3+, subject to the availability of places. At the age of 7 the boys sit the competitive entry examination for admission to the Junior Department of Warwick School, whilst the girls normally remain with us until they are 11.

Entry to both Warwick School and King's High School is by competitive examination and boys and girls at the Prep School are prepared for this. Girls are also prepared for the Common Entrance and any other appropriate examinations for their secondary education.

Early registration is advised if a place in the Pre-Preparatory Dept is to be ensured. Entry to the School at the age of 7 and later requires a satisfactory level of attainment in the basic skills and may be competitive.

Charitable status. Warwick Independent Schools Foundation is a Registered Charity, number 1088057.

Waverley School

Waverley Way Finchampstead Wokingham Berkshire RG40 4YD
Tel: 0118 973 1121
Fax: 0118 973 1131
e-mail: waverley@cfbt.com
website: www.waverleyschool.co.uk

Chairman of the Board of Trustees: J Harwood, Esq

***Principal*: Nigel Woolnough**, BA Hons, MSc, PGCE, RSA Prep, Cert TEFL

Age Range. 3–11 years.

Number of Pupils. 134 Day pupils (76 boys, 58 girls).

Fees per term (2008-2009). Reception–Year 6: £2,457–£2,679 (including lunch). Nursery: according to sessions attended.

Waverley is a co-educational day school, founded in 1945 and now part of CfBT Education Trust.

In September 1997 Waverley School relocated to new purpose-built premises just south of Wokingham. This prestigious development in a superb location offers children outstanding opportunities in and out of the classroom. A new Art, Science and Technology suite opened in 2002.

Waverley's curriculum provides children with a solid foundation, particularly in the areas of literacy and numeracy. An excellent network of computers provides outstanding opportunities for Information and Communications Technology. All subjects of the National Curriculum are taught, with the addition of French from Reception. Team games include soccer, rugby, netball, cricket and rounders. Swimming and athletics are included in the physical education programme. Children's self-confidence is developed through their involvement in drama. Music, both choral and instrumental, is a particular strength of the School.

Waverley School welcomes visiting specialists for French, Swimming, Piano, Violin, Clarinet, Flute, Guitar, Ballet, Judo, Chess, and Speech and Drama. There is specialist help for pupils with specific learning difficulties.

Waverley successfully prepares boys and girls for entrance to Independent Senior Schools and Reading's grammar schools at 11+. An integral Nursery offers a carefully balanced introduction to the School, and ensures both social and educational continuity from 3–11 years.

Waverley School offers an extended day and year facility and a full and active clubs programme.

There is also a thriving Friends' Association.

Charitable status. Waverley School is a Registered Charity, number 309102. It exists to provide education for boys and girls between 3 and 11.

Wellesley House

Ramsgate Road Broadstairs Kent CT10 2DG
Tel: 01843 862991
Fax: 01843 602068
e-mail: office@wellesleyhouse.org
website: www.wellesleyhouse.org

Chairman of the Governors: O D Wise, Esq

***Headmaster*: S T P O'Malley**, MA Hons, PGCE

Age Range. 7–13.

Number of Pupils. 77 Boys, 52 Girls.

Fees per term (2008-2009). Boarding £6,065; Day £5,000.

Location. The school, which is run by an Educational Trust, stands in its own grounds of 20 acres and was purpose-built in 1898.

Trains run hourly from Victoria Station, London and the journey, either by rail or road takes under two hours. At the beginning and end of each term, and at exeats, the school operates coach services between Broadstairs, and Victoria Coach Station via the M2 services and also Birchanger services on the M11 via Brentwood. The school also operates a minibus at exeats and half-terms to Charing, near Ashford.

Facilities. As a result of the Centenary Appeal, the school has a new science and technology building, which includes modern science laboratories, an ICT laboratory and a craft room. Other facilities include a library, an indoor heated swimming pool, four hard tennis courts, two squash courts, a modelling room, art room, a music wing, a .22 shooting range and separate recreation rooms, all of which are in the school grounds. There is a spacious sports hall. The main team games are cricket, Association and rugby football, hockey, netball and rounders. Tuition is also given in squash, shooting, fencing, golf, tennis and swimming. Ballet, tap, modern dancing, riding and sailing are also available.

A special feature of the school is that boys between the ages of 7½ and 9½ live in a junior wing. This is linked to the main school but self-contained under the care of a married housemaster and a resident matron.

The girls live in a separate house, The Orchard, within the school grounds, under the care of a married housemaster and a resident house mistress.

Education. Boys and girls are prepared for all independent senior schools. Those who show sufficient promise are prepared for scholarships and the school has a fine record of success on this front. The curriculum is designed to enable all children to reach the highest standard possible by sound teaching along carefully thought out lines to suit the needs of the individual.

The Headmaster and his wife are assisted by nineteen teaching staff.

Charitable status. Wellesley House and St Peter Court School Education Trust Ltd is a Registered Charity, number 307852. It exists solely to provide education to boys and girls.

Wellingborough Preparatory School

Wellingborough Northants NN8 2BX
Tel: 01933 222698
Fax: 01933 233474
e-mail: prep-head@wellingboroughschool.org
website: www.wellingboroughschool.org

Chairman of the Governors: J J H Higgins

***Headmaster*: R J Mitchell**, BEd

Deputy Headmaster: N C Anns, BEd

Age Range. 8–13.

Number of Pupils. 167 Boys, 135 Girls.

Fees per term (2008-2009). £3,521 (lunches inclusive).

The School is the Preparatory School of Wellingborough School (a registered charity). Girls and boys are admitted from 8 years old. The Preparatory School is self-contained with its own teaching centre, new Library and Science Laboratory (2006). A new computer suite will be completed by September 2007. Music, sports and design technology facilities are shared with the Senior School.

The School enjoys a strong sporting reputation which combines a desire for excellence with a 'sport for all' ethos. Games played are rugby, football, and cricket for the boys. Hockey, netball and rounders are the games played by the girls. The children are also able to represent the school at athletics, tennis and cross- country. There is an Equestrian Team whose fixture list continues to grow.

The creative arts are highly valued with termly drama productions and a flourishing Art Department. A wide variety of music is played including orchestral, rhythm and blues and choral, and performed at different concerts throughout the year. There is a range of after-school activities and a comprehensive Saturday Activities programme (optional). Along with many others, activities include basketball, animal welfare, table tennis, karate, .22 shooting, cycling proficiency, first aid, golf, archery, gymnastics, trampolining, sculpture and computing.

The School is organised into six Clubs. Each Club is headed by a member of staff who oversees the academic and social progress of the girls and boys within their club.

The children work in a stimulating environment. They are encouraged to be confident and fulfill their academic, physical and social potential.

Charitable status. Wellingborough School is a Registered Charity, number 309923. It exists to provide education for girls and boys.

Wellington Junior School

South Street Wellington Somerset TA21 8NT
Tel: 01823 668700
Fax: 01823 668708
e-mail: junior@wellington-school.org.uk
website: www.wellington-school.org.uk

Chair of Governors: Mrs S E Watts, ACIS, MBIM, JP

***Headmaster*: Mr Harry H McFaul**, BA, MA, NPQH

Age Range. 3–10 Co-educational.

Number of Pupils. 270.

Fees per term (2008-2009). £879–£1,838.

Wellington Junior School opened in September 1999 in purpose-built accommodation designed to provide one of the most modern and stimulation educational environments for young children anywhere in the country. Throughout the planning and design stages, the architects worked closely with experienced educational consultants to ensure that Wellington Junior School meets all the educational, recreational, social and aesthetic needs of its pupils.

Wellington Junior School provides an education of unrivalled quality which both complements and enhances the national reputation of Wellington School and enables us to deliver educational excellence for pupils from nursery level through to university entrance.

The School Chapel is central to the ethos of the school and the School Chaplain visits the Junior School weekly. At Wellington traditional Christian values combine with the best of modern innovation to give children the best possible of starts in a wonderfully happy and purposeful atmosphere.

Classes are limited to a maximum of 20 pupils. Each class in Nursery and Reception has a Support Assistant working alongside the teacher. In the other classes specialist support is available to help gifted children as well as to support those in difficulty.

Encouragement and reward systems promote hard work and good behaviour.

The superb facilities include:

- fourteen purpose-designed, modern classrooms;
- a large, attractive school hall;
- the most modern and up-to-date educational resources and computers;
- an extremely well resourced library;
- landscaped grounds, including an architect-designed playground and recreational area;
- a visitors' reception area.

Situated in South Street, immediately opposite the Senior School, the Junior School has full access to the Princess Royal Sports Complex, rugby pitches, tennis courts, purpose-built netball courts, hockey pitches, including an all-weather hockey pitch, cricket pitches, athletics track. Specialist teaching in ICT, French, music and sport means that these are integral parts of our curriculum – as are art, dance and drama. Pupils enjoy success in these and many other areas.

There is an extensive clubs programme each afternoon and a holiday club catering for 3–8 year olds during the holiday period. Aftercare facilities operate each evening to accommodate working parents

A comprehensive prospectus is available from the Headteacher's PA.

Charitable status. Wellington School is a Registered Charity, number 310268.

Wellow House School

Wellow Nr Newark Notts NG22 0EA
Tel: 01623 861054
Fax: 01623 836665
e-mail: wellowhouse@btinternet.com
website: www.wellowhouse.notts.sch.uk

Chairman of the Governors: Nick Buckland

***Headmaster*: Peter Cook**, BEd

Age Range. 3–13.

Number of Pupils. 158.

Fees per term (2007-2008). Pre-Prep pupils £1,775; Day pupils £2,895–£3,070; Boarding pupils £3,850. Fees include meals and normal extras.

Wellow House School was founded in 1971 by the Stewart General Charitable Trust. Since 1994 it has been managed as an educational charity by the Directors and administered by a Board of Governors. This co-educational school has an established reputation for high academic standards, a successful sporting record, broad cultural interests and a happy family atmosphere. Weekly and occasional boarding has become an increasingly popular means of encouraging self-reliance within a supportive community and as a preparation for senior school and university.

The teaching staff of 6 men and 12 women is well qualified and experienced. A distinctive teaching style places great emphasis on the rapport between teacher and pupil in small classes, without slavish reliance on work-sheets and text books. Each pupil maintains a file of notes, as a record and for reference. All take pride in honest hard work, confidence through encouragement, courtesy and fair discipline, and a strong sense of belonging. The thriving house points' system encourages much voluntary study and is the basis of the disciplinary process.

The Headmaster, his wife, Matron and her husband look after the boarders. They are assisted by a team of resident and non-resident tutors, one of whom oversees the evening activity programme. A qualified housekeeper/matron supervises the pupils' boarding, catering and medical needs. There are visiting teachers for Instrumental Tuition, Table Tennis and Drama.

The school is attractively set in 20 acres of parkland and playing fields on the fringe of the Sherwood Forest village of Wellow. There is easy road access to this heart of Nottinghamshire from Worksop and Sheffield to the north, Mansfield and Chesterfield to the west, Nottingham and Grantham to the south, and Lincoln and Newark to the east. Newark lies on north-south and east-west main line rail routes.

A continuous programme of development has provided purpose-built classrooms, science laboratory, networked computer room, music rooms, library, assembly hall and dining hall to add to the original country house. The boarding accommodation was refurbished in 1997 and 2000. Recent additions include studios for art, ceramics and photography, and a sports hall with indoor cricket nets. There is an indoor heated swimming pool, an all-weather cricket net, and an all-weather tennis court. The Pre-Prep classes are housed in their own building, which was totally refurbished and extended in September 2006 and is surrounded by play-time facilities. There are close links with the village church.

Children enter the school after an interview visit and a trial day at any age from 3 to 11+ – the oldest often transferring from primary schools. Six Entrance Scholarships may be awarded annually and Bursaries can give financial assistance. Pupils are prepared for Common Entrance and Scholarships to a wide range of Senior Independent Schools, both boarding and day, and there is a continuous programme of assessment and reporting.

There is a broad physical education programme, with school matches in Rugby, Netball, Soccer, Hockey, Cricket, Rounders, Cross Country, Swimming and Tennis. The school is renowned for its pupils' prowess in Archery and Table Tennis. Weekend and holiday expeditions for Outdoor Pursuits in the Peak District, Yorkshire, Scotland and beyond are popular.

There is encouragement to participate in Natural History, the Visual Arts, Dance, Drama and Music, and more than half of the pupils learn a musical instrument. Most are involved in the much enjoyed regular concerts.

Charitable status. Wellow House School is a Registered Charity, number 528234. It exists solely to provide a high standard of all-round education for children aged 3 to 13 years.

Wells Cathedral Junior School

8 New Street Wells Somerset BA5 2LQ
Tel: 01749 834400
Fax: 01749 834401
e-mail: juniorschool@wells-cathedral-school.com
website: www.wells-cathedral-school.com

Chairman of Governors: The Dean of Wells

***Head of the Junior School*: N M Wilson**, BA

Age Range. 3–11 years.

Number of Boys and Girls. 200: 102 Boys and 98 Girls.

Fees per term (2008-2009). Boarders £6,116, Day £3,528, Pre-Prep £1,895. Nursery: £17.45 per 2 hour, 35 minute session.

The Junior School is made up of the Pre-Prep department (age 3–7) and the Junior School (age 7–11). Pupils accepted into the Junior School normally make a smooth transfer to the

Senior School at 11 and academic and music scholarships are awarded.

Academic Work. The Junior School prepares children for the academic work in the senior school and takes part in the national tests at the end of KS 1 & 2 however the school is not restricted by the demands of the National Curriculum. The aim of the school is to ensure sound academic standards within a friendly and stimulating environment.

Children are assessed regularly for both academic achievement and effort, and parents have many opportunities to meet staff and receive information on their child's progress.

Pastoral Care. The form teacher is responsible for the pastoral care of pupils; in addition each pupil is allocated to a House which has an assembly once a week. Work and sports competitions take place in houses and pupils are able to develop a good relationship not only with their own peer group but with pupils from across the Junior School.

Creativity. Set in beautiful grounds just to the north of the Cathedral, pupils from the school provide the boy and girl choristers at the Cathedral. In addition, a number of pupils are specialist musicians enjoying the expert tuition of the music department at the school which is one of the four in England designated and grant-aided by the Government's Music and Dance Scheme. Scholarships are available for both the choristers and the musicians.

Drama, music and dance are considered vital activities to bring out the best in children. A full programme of concerts, both formal and informal, takes place during the year for all age groups as well as big productions and small year group dramas. The school takes its production to the Edinburgh Festival in alternate years and it has established drama exchange links with schools in other European countries.

A whole school arts week each summer allows all aspects of creativity to come to the fore for every pupil. Themes have included the Caribbean, Somerset and China; pupils experience workshops in the areas of art, dance, drama and music. Regular exhibitions and performances are a feature of the school. The school has received the Artsmark Gold award from Arts Council England.

Sport. The school has many of its own facilities and it is able to share some, such as the sports hall, astroturf pitch and swimming pool, with the senior school which is on the same site. Pupils experience a wide range of activities on the games field. Sport is played to a high standard with rugby, netball, hockey, cricket, swimming, athletics and gymnastics being the main sports. A full programme of inter-school matches and house matches is available for all pupils in Year 3 to 6. Many clubs and societies run at lunchtimes or after school.

Charitable status. Wells Cathedral School is a Registered Charity, number 310212. It has existed since AD 909 to provide education for its pupils.

West Hill Park

St Margarets Lane Titchfield Hants PO14 4BS
Tel: 01329 842356
Fax: 01329 842911
e-mail: headsoffice@westhillpark.com
website: www.westhillpark.com

Chairman of Governors: David Younghusband, Esq (Notary Public)

***Headmaster*: E P K Hudson**, CertEd

Age Range. $2^1/_2$–13.

Number of Pupils. Prep School (age 7–13): 63 Boarders (33 girls, 30 boys); 150 Day Pupils (59 girls, 91 boys). Pre-Prep (age 4–7): 61 boys, 48 girls. Nursery (age $2^1/_2$–4): 13 boys, 14 girls.

Fees per term (2008-2009). Prep School: Boarders £5,866, Day children £3,635–£4,470; Pre-Prep £2,645; Nursery £1,275–£2,475.

At West Hill Park pupils are prepared for Scholarships and Common Entrance to all Independent Schools.

The main building is Georgian, originally a shooting lodge for the Earls of Southampton, and provides spacious and comfortable boarding accommodation for boys and girls under the supervision of resident Houseparents. Also in the main building are the administrative offices, the Library, the Dining Hall and the Assembly Hall with fully equipped sound and lighting equipment and stage. Further excellent facilities include the Art Centre, the Music School, a 25m heated indoor Swimming Pool, a fully equipped Sports Hall, the Design and Technology Centre, 2 Science Laboratories, the Information Technology Centre, the French, History, Maths and Geography Departments with Interactive Whiteboards, the purpose built Pre-Prep Department and the Nursery Department. West Hill Park stands in its own grounds of nearly 40 acres on the edge of Titchfield village. There are sports fields, 5 hard, 3 grass and 5 Astro tennis courts, a floodlit Riding School, a floodlit Astroturf, a cross-country course and in summer a nine hole golf course.

There are 34 fully qualified members of the teaching staff. 13 members of staff are resident, either in the main building or in houses in the school grounds, giving a great sense of community to the school.

A tutorial system monitors the individual child's well being on a weekly basis and there is a strong pastoral care system. There is a wide range of activities available in order to encourage children to develop individual skills and talents; choirs, orchestra, dance, aerobics, carpentry, judo, ballet, drama, golf, life-saving, computer club, string group, squash, chess, sailing, fly fishing, riding on school ponies and Brownies, as well as the more intensive training available in the Swim Squad, Tennis Squad and other sporting clubs. The Boarders enjoy many expeditions at weekends as well as fun events at school, such as orienteering, theatre workshops, cycle marathons and games evenings.

Games played include soccer, rugby, football, cricket, hockey, tennis, athletics, netball and rounders.

All domestic arrangements are under the direct supervision of Mrs Hudson. There are 2 resident Matrons, as well as the Senior Matron who is medically qualified, and a fully qualified School Nurse. The married Housemaster, a member of the academic staff, runs the boarding house assisted by a team of resident staff.

Charitable status. West Hill School Trust is a Registered Charity, number 307343. It exists to educate children.

West House School

24 St James Road Edgbaston Birmingham B15 2NX
Tel: 0121 440 4097
Fax: 0121 440 5839
e-mail: secretary@westhouseschool.demon.co.uk
website: www.westhouse.bham.sch.uk

Chairman of Governors: S T Heathcote, FCA

***Headmaster*: A M J Lyttle**, BA Hons (Birmingham), PGCE (Birmingham)

Age Range. Boys: 4–11 years; Co-educational Nursery: 12 months to 4 years.

Number of Pupils. A maximum 200 boys aged 4–11 (Reception to Year 6) plus 70 boys and girls aged 12 months–4 years.

Fees per term (2008-2009). 4–11 year olds: £2,026–£2,990 according to age. The fees include lunches and break-time drinks. Under 4: fees according to number of sessions attended per week. Fee list on application.

West House was founded in 1895 and since 1959 has been an Educational Trust controlled by a Board of Governors. The school has a strong academic reputation and pupils are regularly awarded scholarships to secondary schools at 11+. The well qualified and experienced staff provides a sound education for boys of all abilities. The National Curriculum is followed and pupils are prepared for SATs at KS1 and KS2. Pupils are taught in small classes which ensures that they receive much individual attention. Specialist help is available for children with Dyslexia or who require learning support. Music teachers visit the school to give individual music tuition.

The school occupies a leafy five acre site a mile from Birmingham city centre. As well as the main teaching blocks there are two well-equipped science laboratories and a sports hall.

The Centenary Building, opened in 1998, accommodates the art and design technology department, ICT room and senior Library. Extensive playing fields, two all-weather tennis courts and all-weather cricket nets enable pupils to participate in many games and sports. Pupils also enjoy a wide range of hobby activities, and drama and music play important roles in school life.

The school is open during term time between 8 am and 6 pm. On-site Holiday Clubs are run by members of staff during the holidays.

Charitable status. West House School is a Registered Charity, number 528959. It exists to provide education for boys.

Westbourne House

Shopwyke Chichester West Sussex PO20 2BH
Tel: 01243 782739
Fax: 01243 770759
e-mail: office@wesetbournehouse.w-sussex.sch.uk
website: www.westbournehouse.org

Chairman of the Governors: J P L Perry, FCA

***Headmaster*: Brendan Law**, BA Hons, PG HDE

Age Range. 2½–13.

Number of Pupils. 420: Boarders 90; Day 190; Pre-Prep 140.

Fees per term (2008-2009). Boarders £5,150; Day £4,200; Pre-Prep £2,300.

Westbourne House School was founded in 1907 and became a Charitable Trust in 1967. It has been co-educational since 1992. There is a well-qualified teaching staff of 42, plus visiting music staff and 38 support staff; all play important roles in the care of the children. The School has a strong boarding ethos.

Situated in a beautiful parkland setting of 60 acres, Westbourne House offers a warm, happy environment, which fosters learning and development. Pupils are prepared for the Common Entrance and many Scholarships have been won at an impressive list of Senior Independent Schools in recent years; virtually all children go on to their first-choice school at 13+. Individual academic progress is carefully monitored and the school has recently invested in the latest database technology to enhance this process. The average class size (16) allows for plenty of individual attention, differentiation and pastoral care. The broad curriculum includes the full quota of academic subjects as well as Music, Art, Design Technology, Ceramics, Food Technology, Drama, Physical Education & Games, and Information Technology. Individual Needs are well catered for, overseen by an ABCO and SENCO.

Children are encouraged to discover their talents within the wide range of activities on offer, with the aim of developing these talents to the full. Westbourne enjoys a proud record of sporting achievement and the children have access to excellent facilities: extensive playing fields host the major sports (football, rugby, hockey and cricket for boys; netball, hockey, pop lacrosse and rounders for girls) and the children also engage in swimming (25 metre indoor heated pool) squash (3 courts) tennis (5 courts) as well as golf, fencing, judo and dance. A large, well-equipped Sports Hall caters for indoor sports. Music is outstanding: the children enjoy excellent facilities and teaching, with a wide range of instruments, orchestras, bands and choirs on offer. All children are encouraged to perform from an early age. Art and Technology are housed within the original stable block of the Georgian house, providing a delightful environment for the children to develop their creative skills. Drama is encouraged through a number of productions, involving most of the children, and many pupils do well in LAMDA exams and Speech and Drama Festivals.

An extensive building programme has been undertaken in recent years. A new Junior Teaching block for Years 3, 4 and 5 was built in 1997, a purpose built Science Department in 1999 and a Theatre seating 300 was completed in 2001. A new Dining Room, catering facilities and three new classrooms were completed in 2004, as were improvements to the library and recreational facilities. A new dance studio (2008) and full-size astroturf all-weather surface (2009) are soon to be added.

Charitable status. Westbourne House is a Registered Charity, number 307034.

Westbourne School

Westbourne Road Sheffield S10 2QQ
Tel: 0114 266 0374
Fax: 0114 263 8176
e-mail: admin@westbourneschool.co.uk
website: www.westbourneschool.co.uk

Chairman of the Governors: Mr M P Loxley

***Headmaster*: John Hicks**, MEd (Kingston), BEd Hons (Exeter)

Age Range. 4–16.

Number of Pupils. 325 day pupils, boys and girls.

Fees per term (2008-2009). £2,090–£3,150.

The fully co-educational School, founded in 1885, is an Educational Trust with a Board of Governors, some of whom are Parents. The number of entries is limited to maintain small classes of around 16 with a staff/pupil ratio of 1:10.

The Junior School is housed in a specially designed and equipped building, staffed by qualified and experienced teachers. Music and Games are taught by specialists from Y1. Specialist Science and Technology are introduced from Y4 (8+), as well as specialist teaching in Information Technology, Art and Design, and RE. French, Science and Computers are introduced from the age of 4.

In the Junior School, some lessons are taught by specialists in Subject Rooms. There is also a Science Laboratory and ICT, Art and Music Rooms, Fiction and Reference Libraries, and a Hall with Stage.

The Senior School provides teaching to GCSE from Year 7 to 11 up to age 16. It has its own campus immediately adjacent to the Junior School. A new, adjacent building opened for Y7 and Y8 pupils in September 2007. The school has a 3-form entry in Y7 with a scholarship class. External and internal scholarships are taken in January of Y6. All children are set in Maths and English from Year 5. A Virtual Learning Environment is being piloted from Y5.

A high standard of work is maintained – the main aim being to bring out the best in every pupil according to their ability. A few pupils are entered for Common Entrance and Independent School Scholarships, but 95% move to Westbourne Senior School. There is also a Department catering for those with Specific Learning Difficulties. Great emphasis is laid on courtesy and a mutual respect for each other.

Art, Music and Drama are strongly encouraged throughout the school, with regular concerts, plays and art exhibitions. Tuition in several instruments is available.

The main sports are Rugby, Football, Hockey, Cricket, Athletics, Netball, Rounders and Cross-Country Running with regular matches against other schools. There are also opportunities for Short Tennis, Swimming, TaeKwonDo, Basketball, Volleyball, Fencing, Skiing, Badminton, Climbing, Gold and Scuba Diving.

Breakfast (at an extra cost) is available from 8 am and, while the length of day depends on the age of the child, there are after-school facilities for all pupils until 5.30 pm, with the older pupils staying till 5.15 pm. There is no school on Saturdays.

Charitable status. Westbourne School is a Registered Charity, number 529381. It exists to provide education for boys and girls.

Westbrook Hay

London Road Hemel Hempstead Herts HP1 2RF
Tel: 01442 256143/230099
Fax: 01442 232076
e-mail: admin@westbrookhay.co.uk
website: www.westbrookhay.co.uk

Chairman of Governors: John Stevens

***Headmaster*: Keith D Young**, BEd Hons (Exeter)

Age Range. Boys 2–13, Girls 2–11.

Number of Pupils. Day: 165 Boys, 85 Girls.

Fees per term (2007-2008). £2,125–£3,650. Flexi-Boarding £26.50 per night.

Founded in 1892, the school is set in 30 acres of elevated grounds overlooking the Bourne Valley, less than an hour from Central London and within easy reach of the M25 and M1.

The school aims to develop qualities of intellect and character. Classes are small and each individual is encouraged and helped to achieve their potential. Individuality, honesty, a sense of humour and self-reliance are attributes which are stimulated and valued in this friendly school which maintains a family atmosphere.

There are 21 full time members of the teaching staff who are assisted by a number of peripatetic specialists. The well being of both day students and boarders is in the hands of resident staff.

Nursery and Pre-Prep departments prepare children from two to eight for entry into the upper school. Children in Years 3 and 4 are class taught primarily by their form teacher, before a move to subject-based curriculum in Year 5. The academic focus is provided by the goals of the Common Entrance and Scholarship examinations as most children go on to independent senior schools. All children follow the National Curriculum subject areas and in many cases extend them.

Extensive playing fields give ample room for rugby, soccer, hockey, cricket, golf, rounders and athletics. All-weather netball and tennis courts and a heated swimming pool are complemented by a purpose built Sports Hall which provides for badminton, basketball, cricket nets, five-a-side football, gymnastics and a galaxy of other indoor sports.

Weekly boarding arrangements are flexible. A breakfast club, after school care and bussing service are also offered to accommodate the needs of working parents.

Charitable status. Westbrook Hay School is a Registered Charity, number 292537. It exists to provide education for boys and girls.

Westbrook House Preparatory School

54-56 Shorncliffe Road Folkestone Kent CT20 2NB
Tel: 01303 854057
Fax: 01303 245273
e-mail: office@westbrookschool.co.uk
website: www.westbrookschool.co.uk

Chairman of Governors: Roger De Haan

***Headmaster*: Mr C G Knowles**, CertEd

Age Range. 2–11.

Number of Pupils. 118 Day Children.

Fees per term (2008-2009). Reception–Form 6: £1,920–£2,930. Nursery and Pre-Reception fees are on a sliding scale based on number of sessions attended.

Scholarships are awarded for outstanding academic ability and Bursaries on the basis of a special talent, such as dance, sport or music.

Westbrook House Prep School was founded in 1947. It is a happy family day school for boys and girls in Folkestone, not far from J13 of the M20. The school is expanding rapidly, partly as the result of a major redecoration and redevelopment programme.

Our pupils aim at the 11+ County Selection to Grammar School and we have a high pass rate in this respect. We also have links and Scholarships with Dover College, Kent College, St Lawrence College Ramsgate and St Edmund's School Canterbury.

Academically we are a very modern and forward-thinking school, yet our ethos is that of a traditional Prep school – courtesy, manners, behaviour, self-discipline and self-confidence. We have a special respect for children of all faiths as we are ourselves a Christian school with Christian ethics – the very popular Revd Anthony is a central figure in our lives here.

Although we are in the middle of Folkestone, visitors are always amazed by our stunning sports facilities and extensive playing fields. Our children enjoy a wide variety of sports, such as cricket, netball, football, gymnastics, athletics and hockey. Extra activities include modern dance, tap-dance, jewel craft, basketry, stamp collecting, embroidery and baton-twirling, to name but a few. For foreign languages we currently teach Spanish.

Above all we are an especially happy community. Parents attend Friday Assembly and take a cheerful and lively part in the development of their children. The Parents' Society is very active and makes an especial point of extending a warm welcome to new parents. As one child wrote, "the only sad thing about Westbrook is that one day we have to leave!".

Charitable status. St Mary's Westbrook is a Registered Charity, number 1063709.

Westminster Abbey Choir School

Dean's Yard London SW1P 3NY
Tel: 020 7222 6151
Fax: 020 7222 1548
e-mail: headmaster@westminster-abbey.org
website: www.westminster-abbey.org

Chairman of Governors: The Dean of Westminster

***Headmaster*: J H Milton**, BEd

Age Range. 8–13.

Number of Boys. Up to 38 all chorister boarders.

Fees per term (2008-2009). £1,869 inclusive of tuition on two instruments. Additional bursaries may be available in cases of real financial need.

Westminster Abbey Choir School is the only school in Britain exclusively devoted to the education of boy choristers. Boys have been singing services in the Abbey since at least 1384 and the 34 boys in the school maintain this tradition.

Westminster Abbey Choir School is a special place, offering boys from eight to thirteen a unique and exciting opportunity to be a central part of one of our great national institutions. Boys sing daily in the Abbey and also take part in many special services and celebrations both in the UK and abroad.

The small size of the school, the fact that all boys are boarders and the high proportion of staff who live on the premises, allow the School to have an extended family atmosphere.

A full academic curriculum is taught by specialist staff and boys are prepared for the Common Entrance and academic scholarship examinations; most boys win valuable scholarships to secondary independent schools when they leave at 13.

Music obviously plays a central part in the school. Every boy learns the piano and at least one orchestral instrument and there are 15 visiting music teachers. Concerts, both inside and outside school, are a regular feature of the year.

Besides music and academic lessons there is a thriving programme of other activities and there are many opportunities for boys to develop interests outside music.

Sports played include football, cricket, rugby, athletics, hockey, sailing, canoeing and tennis.

Entry is by voice trial and academic tests; further details are available from the Headmaster, who is always please to hear from parents who feel that their son might have the potential to become a chorister.

Charitable status. Westminster Abbey is a Registered Charity, number X8259. It is a religious establishment incorporated by Royal Charter in 1560.

Westminster Cathedral Choir School

Ambrosden Avenue London SW1P 1QH
Tel: 020 7798 9081
Fax: 020 7630 7209
e-mail: office@choirschool.com
website: www.choirschool.com

President: HE Cardinal Cormac Murphy O'Connor

Chairman of Governors: Martin Morland, CMG

***Headmaster*: Neil McLaughlan**, BA Hons

Age Range. 8–13.

Number of Boys. 144 (26 Choristers, 118 Day Boys).

Fees per term (2007-2008). Chorister Boarders £2,205; Day Boys £4,335.

Founded in 1901, Westminster Cathedral Choir School is a Day Prep School and Boarding Choir School concerned with the development of the whole person. Choristers must be Roman Catholic, but Day Boys of all denominations are welcome. The school forms part of the precincts of Westminster Cathedral and enjoys such facilities as a large playground and a Grade 1 listed Library.

The Choir School has a two-form entry of classes of 16–18 boys. In the top two years boys are taught in three groups in order to prepare them to sit scholarships as well as the two tiers of the Common Entrance examination. Boys regularly win Academic and Music Scholarships to the major independent senior schools.

Choristers and Day Boys alike achieve a high level of music making. The Choristers sing the daily capitular liturgy in the Cathedral and are regularly involved in broadcasts, recordings and tours abroad. There is also a Day Boy Choir, two orchestras and a substantial programme of chamber music. Boys can learn the piano and any orchestral instrument in school.

The major sports played at the Choir School include football, rugby and cricket and the boys travel to Vincent Square, Battersea Park, the Queen Mother Sports Centre and The Oval (the school has its own bowling machine!) for Games.

There is a wide range of extra-curricular activities available including: chess, computing, debating, fencing, football, roller hockey and a Saturday rugby club.

The school is justly famed for its fantastic food!

Assessment for Choristers is by academic assessment and voice trial, generally in October and February. Day Boy assessments are held in January.

Charitable status. Westminster Cathedral Choir School is a Registered Charity, number 1063761. It exists to provide a musical education for Roman Catholic boys.

Westminster Under School

Adrian House 27 Vincent Square London SW1P 2NN
Tel: 020 7821 5788
Fax: 020 7821 0458
e-mail: under.school@westminster.org.uk
website: www.westminsterunder.org.uk

Chairman of Governors: The Very Revd J R Hall, The Dean of Westminster

***Master*: J P Edwards**, BA, MA London

Deputy Master: D S C Bratt, BA York

Age Range. 7–13.

Number of Boys. 266 (day boys only).

Fees per term (2008-2009). £4,412 (inclusive of lunches and stationery).

The Under School is closely linked to Westminster School, sharing the same Governing Body, although it has its own building overlooking the beautiful school playing fields in Vincent Square. The school underwent a major refurbishment in 2001.

Boys are prepared, though not exclusively, for Westminster through the Common Entrance examinations and "The Challenge", Westminster School's scholarship examinations. Most boys proceed to Westminster, but entry into the Under School does not guarantee a place at the "Great School". Each year some boys will go on to Eton or similar schools.

There is a strong musical tradition at the Under School, with a junior and senior choir, an orchestra, and string, brass and jazz groups. There is a specialist suite of art rooms with facilities for all kinds of creative activity and the art department organises competitions in photography and model-making. There are other competitions each year in public speaking, creative writing, chess and Scrabble.

Games are played on the school grounds adjacent to Adrian House in Vincent Square and although football and cricket are the main sports, there are opportunities to participate in athletics, basketball, cross-country, hockey, rugby, swimming and tennis.

There are currently 266 pupils in the school, with 20 new boys coming in at each entry point (7+, 8+ and 11+) in September. Means-tested bursaries are available at 11+, as are music scholarships, and many boys apply at this entry point from London primary schools.

Charitable status. St Peter's College (otherwise known as Westminster School) is a Registered Charity, number 312728. It exists to provide education for boys.

Westville House School

Carter's Lane Middleton Ilkley West Yorkshire LS29 0DQ
Tel: 01943 608053
Fax: 01943 817410
e-mail: westville@epals.com
website: www.westvilleschool.co.uk

Chairman of Trustees: Mr A N Brown

***Headmaster*: Mr C A Holloway**, BA Hons, PGCE

Age Range. 3–11.
Number of Pupils. 153.
Fees per term (2007-2008). £1,320–£2,290.

Westville House is a preparatory school for girls and boys aged 3–11, situated in glorious countryside just outside the town of Ilkley in West Yorkshire. It was founded in 1960 as an extension of the owner's family and, although the school has grown since then, the family atmosphere has been retained to this day.

Children join the Pre-Preparatory department at three where outstanding courses are offered in the Foundation years. They move into the Preparatory department at seven, where specialist teaching is introduced in all subjects and preparation begins for entry to senior schools at age eleven. The school offers a broad and stimulating curriculum and has an outstanding academic record with awards gained annually at all the local independent senior schools.

As well as the broad curriculum on offer, there are many other areas of strength within the school. Drama begins at an early age and there are regular performances by children of all ages. Visiting specialist staff also prepare children for the Guildhall Speech and Drama examinations and for performances at local Festivals. Music is a vital part of the life of the school. Children perform regularly in concerts from an early age and many learn instruments individually. The school orchestra and choir perform regularly at Festivals and in Church services. Sport is also an important part of school life and teams play against other schools at rugby, football, cricket, rounders, athletics, swimming and cross-country running. Trips into the community are a regular and important feature of school life, taking advantage of the wealth of facilities in the area.

The school has a staff of fifteen well-qualified and experienced teachers. The family atmosphere within the school means that all the children are well-known to them and they combine just the right blend of firmness and fun to bring out the best in each individual child.

Charitable status. Westville House School is a Registered Charity, number 1086711.

Wetherby Pre-Preparatory School
Alpha Plus Group

11 Pembridge Square London W2 4ED
Tel: 020 7727 9581
Fax: 020 7221 8827
e-mail: learn@wetherbyschool.co.uk
website: www.wetherbyschool.co.uk

***Headmistress*: Mrs Jenny Aviss**

Age Range. Boys 4–8.
Number of Pupils. 241.
Fees per term (2007-2008). £4,045.

Wetherby School overlooks the beautiful Gardens of Pembridge Square where the boys are fortunate to play every day. Whilst proud of its academic attainments for London Day School entry at 7+ and 8+ and top Boarding Schools, the priority is in producing happy, confident and resourceful boys. The curriculum is well balanced, with excellent sport, music and art opportunities including specialist teaching rooms for art, ICT, library and music. There is also a wide range of extra-curricular activities available. Wetherby operates a non selective admissions procedure; registration is at birth.

White House Preparatory School

Finchampstead Road Wokingham Berkshire RG40 3HD
Tel: 0118 978 5151
Fax: 0118 979 4716
e-mail: office@whitehouse.wokingham.sch.uk
website: www.whitehouse.wokingham.sch.uk

Chairman of Governors: Mr R H Higson, BSc, MRPharmS, MIHM

***Headmistress*: Mrs S J Gillam**, BEd (Cantab)

Age Range. Boys 2–4 years, Girls 2–11 years.
Number of Pupils. 120 day pupils.
Fees per term (2007-2008). £1,201–£2,595.

White House takes pride in offering high levels of academic achievement within a warm and friendly community. Founded on Christian principles, the school seeks to teach care and courtesy. Our visitors frequently comment on the friendly, purposeful and happy atmosphere. Small classes enable teachers to meet the needs of each individual. The school aims to develop the full potential of each child through a wide range of activities and opportunities.

Girls are accepted from 2+ to 11 years of age and are prepared for entry to a range of schools. Boys are welcomed in the Nursery, from 2+ to 4 years of age.

The Head is a member of IAPS and the school is fully accredited by the Independent Schools Council. It stands in its own attractive grounds on the edge of Wokingham. The excellent facilities include a multi-purpose Hall, ICT Suite, Science/Technology Department, Music Department and Art Studio. Sport is promoted and pupils have regular swimming lessons in the Summer Term. There is a purpose built Nursery designed around the needs of the youngest children.

All children are given access to a broad and stimulating curriculum augmented by specialist teaching in PE, Music, Science, Technology and French. Children take part in a wide range of extra-curricular activities including drama, ballet, tap, choirs, orchestral groups, golf, tennis and sporting fixtures. Individual music lessons are offered in piano, flute, clarinet, stringed instruments and voice. Active learning is encouraged through visits and a variety of events throughout each year.

White House is able to meet the needs of busy parents too. The school offers an extended day which allows children to be cared for from 8.00 in the mornings and up to 6.00 pm. Children can attend a variety of clubs or play activities.

Special links with Luckley–Oakfield School mean that a number of pupils choose to continue their education close by through to the age of 18.

Charitable status. The White House Preparatory School Trust is a Registered Charity, number 1112529. The school is a Christian school, established and maintained for the purpose of providing high quality education based on Christian principles for children aged 2–11.

Widford Lodge

Widford Road Chelmsford Essex CM2 9AN
Tel: 01245 352581
Fax: 01245 281329
e-mail: admin@widfordlodge.org.uk
website: www.widfordlodge.org.uk

Principal: Mrs Louise Williams

***Head Master*: S C Trowell**, BHum Hons, PGCE (London)

Age Range. 2½–11 years.

Number of Pupils. Prep 120; Pre-Prep 86; Pre-School Nursery: varies according to number of sessions.

Fees per term (from April 2008). Pre-Prep £1,850, Main School £2,415. All fees include lunch, textbooks, stationery, etc.

Widford Lodge is a co-educational day school situated on the southern fringe of Chelmsford. Founded in 1935 the school aims to provide an all-round education within a happy, caring environment. Children are encouraged to enjoy their time at school, while also learning a sense of responsibility and a positive approach to their role in school and the wider community.

An enthusiastic staff prepare the children for grammar school via the 11+, entrance into senior independent schools through examination or scholarship and local secondary schools. A combination of form tutors, subject specialists and small classes ensure a good academic standard. The curriculum is broadly based and aims to develop a variety of interests, academic, aesthetic and sporting. The school has a well-equipped computer suite and the children are encouraged to use their IT skills in many different ways.

The main part of the school stands in 5 acres of wooded grounds that include an outdoor Swimming Pool, a Floodlit Tennis Court, Cricket Nets, Science Laboratory and Design Technology Centre. There is plenty of space for the children to play and to use their imagination. The school also owns 9 acres of playing fields.

The children have the opportunity to play cricket, netball, rugby, hockey, soccer, athletics, swimming, cross-country, tennis, golf and rounders. Although a small school we are proud of our sporting tradition, which is underpinned by our belief that sport is for all and is ultimately played for fun.

Music, drama and art are all encouraged and a wide range of musical instruments are taught. There is a busy school choir and an annual concert.

There are many after-school activities which the children are encouraged to get involved in, as well as the opportunity to do their prep, supervised by a teacher, until 5.30 pm.

Wilmslow Preparatory School

Grove Avenue Wilmslow Cheshire SK9 5EG
Tel: 01625 524246
Fax: 01625 536660
e-mail: secretary@wilmslowprep.co.uk
website: www.wilmslowprep.co.uk

Day School for Girls founded 1909.

Chairman of Board of Trustees: Mr Rudgard

***Headmistress*: Mrs H J Shaw**

Age Range. 2–11.

Number of Pupils. 167 Day Girls.

Fees per term (2008-2009). £690–£2,550 (lunches extra).

The School is registered as an Educational Trust. It is purpose built and is situated in the centre of Wilmslow in its own spacious grounds. The facilities include an Assembly Hall, new Sports Hall, a Science Room, Computer Room with networked PCs, an Art Room and Kindergarten Unit, a Classroom Block for 5–8 year olds and two well-stocked libraries. There is a Tennis/Netball Court, a Sports field and ample play areas.

The School aims to provide wide educational opportunities for all girls. It has a long established excellent academic record and caters for a wide variety of entrance examinations to Independent Senior Day and Boarding Schools.

Wilmslow Preparatory School offers a variety of activities which include Music, Art and Drama. Principal sports include gymnastics, netball, hockey, tennis, athletics and swimming.

There are sixteen qualified and experienced teachers on the staff.

Charitable status. Wilmslow Preparatory School is a Registered Charity, number 525924. It exists to provide full time education for pupils aged between 5 and 11, and part or full time education to pre-kindergarten children from the age of 2.

Winchester House School

High Street Brackley Northants NN13 7AZ
Tel: 01280 702483
Fax: 01280 706400
e-mail: office@winchester-house.org
website: www.winchester-house.org

Chairman of Governors: K H Fowler

***Headmaster*: M S Seymour**, BA

Age Range. 3–13.

Number of Children. 363: Boarding Boys 49; Day Boys 176; Boarding Girls 29; Day Girls 109.

Fees per term (2007-2008). Preparatory: Boarders £4,720–£5,945 inclusive, Day £3,570–£4,500. Pre-Prep: £2,060–£2,595.

Winchester House School is a fully co-educational independent day and boarding Preparatory School.

Winchester House School sits in its own 18 acres of sports fields and gardens in the market town of Brackley, midway between Oxford and Northampton and close to the borders of Buckinghamshire, Oxfordshire and Northamptonshire. Lying just 10 minutes from the M40 it is within easy reach of both Heathrow and Birmingham airports.

The boys and girls are taught by dedicated specialist teachers with a pupil:staff ratio of 8:1. Children in the middle and upper school are placed in streamed sets for all academic subjects and potential scholars are carefully prepared for the scholarship examinations to all major independent senior schools. Over the last few years, excellent examination results have included a significant number of awards to Senior Schools.

Many children enter the school in the nursery or reception classes while others join Year 3 at seven years old. The day children and the boarders follow the same timetable during the day and many convert from day to either weekly or full boarding during their time at the school. The school operates two minibus services for day-children in the local area.

Winchester House has magnificent facilities that include an extensive information and communication technology suite, well-equipped art and design studios, a well-stocked library and dedicated science laboratories. Sports facilities include numerous rugby, hockey and cricket pitches, tennis courts, a heated swimming pool, squash courts, a rifle range, and a fully fitted sports hall with indoor cricket nets. The Seligman building, opened in 2005, provides six new classrooms, a performing arts studio and new music practice rooms.

Winchester House is dedicated to a fully rounded education. In addition to the academic timetable, extensive instrumental music teaching and team sports, a broad range of further activities is offered. Activities include brass group, chamber choir, chess, cookery, dance, drama, gymnastics, golf, judo, maypole dancing, mountain biking, orchestra, rambling, rowing, speech & drama and war games. Recent major dramatic productions have included the musicals Bugsy Malone and Captain Stirrick.

The school is also committed to teaching leadership skills to all pupils. This takes place both on the school grounds and on expeditions in the UK and Europe. Winchester House is the first prep school to introduce such a programme to all its pupils under the banner 'Learn to Lead' in conjunction with World Challenge Expeditions Ltd.

Charitable status. Winchester House School Trust Limited is a Registered Charity, number 309912. It aims to provide education for boys and girls between the ages of 3 and 13.

Windlesham House School

Washington Pulborough West Sussex RH20 4AY
Tel: 01903 874700
Fax: 01903 874702
e-mail: office@windlesham.com
website: www.windlesham.com

Chairman of Governors: N M Hanlon, FCA

***Head*: Richard Foster**, BEd Hons

Age Range. 4–13.

Number of Pupils. Prep: 230 boarders (135 Boys, 95 Girls), 40 day (25 Boys, 15 Girls); Little Windlesham (day): 45.

Fees per term (2008-2009). Prep £6,145–£6,250; Little Windlesham £2,270–£2,630.

Windlesham nestles in 60 glorious acres of the South Downs and is within easy reach of London and both Gatwick and Heathrow airports. It is a co-educational boarding school from which children go on to a wide variety of senior schools. Above all it is a happy, family-centred school where children and adults live and work together in a unique and purposeful atmosphere. There is a very strong pastoral care system in place that ensures every child feels secure and happy no matter how far from home they may be. Recent ISI and CSCI reports highlighted the excellence of the school's pastoral care together with the provision for boarding. Other areas of excellence included the school's ICT facilities and extra-curricular activities programme.

Our curriculum is very broad and this, together with our talented and creative staff, enables us to place great emphasis on the individual development of each child, academically, socially and emotionally. Our academic standards are high, in line with and beyond the National Curriculum and we gain numerous scholarships to senior schools each year.

We have a very wide range of activities on offer, from karate and archery to silk painting and rug making and we have a strong reputation on the sports field. The opportunity exists for children to develop the sports they enjoy, whilst the less sporting child can pursue other activities and hobbies. Innovative drama and musical productions play a very important part in the life of the school. Our weekend arrangements are flexible and we provide a full programme of well-organised activities, many of an outward bound nature.

Windlesham gives children the opportunity to achieve the unexpected; the school is renowned for producing extremely happy, confident and well-balanced young people.

Little Windlesham opened in 1997 and provides a broad and varied education for 4–7 year olds. It is run separately from the main school and is situated in a separate and well-designed unit, from which it can also make use of the impressive facilities of the main school. The curriculum is tied in with the main school so that children can follow a structured programme throughout their time in the school.

Charitable status. Windlesham House School is a Registered Charity, number 307046. It exists to provide education for girls and boys aged 4–13.

Winterfold House

Chaddesley Corbett Worcestershire DY10 4PW
Tel: 01562 777234
Fax: 01562 777078
e-mail: hm@winterfoldhouse.co.uk
website: www.winterfoldhouse.co.uk

Chairman of Governors: David S Fletcher, MA

***Headmaster*: W C R Ibbetson-Price**, MA, NPQH

Age Range. 3–13 Co-educational.

Number of Pupils. 350 Day Boys and Girls.

Fees per term (2007-2008). Preparatory £2,800–£3,190; Pre-Prep £1,865–£2,070; Kindergarten: £1,625 (5 full days), £38 per day, £25 per session.

Winterfold is centered around a spacious Georgian house set in nearly 40 acres of attractive grounds, surrounded by beautiful and unspoilt Worcestershire countryside. However, we are only half an hour from the centre of Birmingham, Worcester is just 10 miles away, and we are a mere 10 minutes from the M5 and M42.

Winterfold is a Roman Catholic co-educational day preparatory school but children of all faiths are warmly welcomed and made to feel valued members of the community.

The school has an excellent academic record at all levels including National Curriculum Key Stage Tests, Common Entrance and Scholarship. Children are prepared for entrance to both local independent day schools (such as RGS Worcester and The Alice Ottley School, Holy Trinity, King's Worcester, and the King Edward's schools in Birmingham) and to independent schools of national renown (such as Shrewsbury, Cheltenham Ladies' College, Malvern College, Stonyhurst, Ampleforth Cheltenham College and Bromsgrove). We have a highly regarded Learning Support Unit which provides one to one help for children with specific learning difficulties such as dyslexia. In 2008 our children gained 34 scholarships to senior schools.

Winterfold places a great emphasis upon educating the whole child and aims to produce well rounded and confident boys and girls with high moral standards and good manners. In order to develop self-belief we encourage every child to achieve success in some area and thus the school fields a great number of teams and not just in the main sports of rugby, soccer, cricket, netball, hockey and rounders; but also in the minor sports which include fishing, golf, archery, tennis, swimming, athletics, basketball, fencing, judo, chess and shooting. There are also a large number of clubs and societies and regular visits to theatres and concerts and other places of educational interest which gives fullness and breadth to the educational experience.

In recent years there has been considerable investment into the school which has seen the development of a new sports hall, a newly equipped computer room, new science laboratories, new tennis courts, a heated swimming pool, a chapel, an art and design centre, and a new library. Cricket nets, two Adventure playgrounds and a new classroom block have recently been added and new changing rooms have just been completed. Plans are in progress for a new Performing Arts Centre and further new classrooms.

Charitable status. Winterfold House School is a Registered Charity, number 1063133. It exists solely to provide education for boys and girls.

Witham Hall

Witham-on-the-Hill Bourne Lincolnshire PE10 0JJ
Tel: 01778 590222
Fax: 01778 590606
e-mail: heads@withamhall.com
website: www.withamhall.com

The school was founded in 1959 and was formed into an Educational Trust in 1978.

Chairman of Governors: Mr J N Coleclough

***Heads*: D Telfer**, BA, CertEd and **Mrs S A Telfer**, CertEd

Age Range. 4–13.

Number of Pupils. Boys: 50 boarders, 28 day pupils. Girls: 50 boarders, 29 day pupils. Pre-Prep aged 4–8: 90 pupils.

Fees per term (2008-2009). Boarders £4,950, Day pupils £3,625 Pre-Prep £2,215.

The school is situated in a country house setting in the village of Witham on the Hill. There are all the usual amenities of a preparatory school.

There is a teaching staff of 35 and there are visiting teachers for instrumental music. The maximum class size is 16.

The school has a full musical life – most of the children learn one instrument or more. There are two bands and four choirs.

Games are played on most days of the week throughout the year. There is a full fixture list of games, for both boys and girls, with other schools at both senior and colts level including rugger, soccer, cricket, hockey, netball, rounders, athletics, cross-country, tennis and squash. In 2008, the school has built an Olympic size all-weather Astroturf and an additional four tennis courts and three netball courts to augment the current facilities. Our 9-hole golf course provides a challenging course for pupils and parents alike and our squash court has much usage.

The school has a multi-purpose hall. The hall provides an indoor tennis court, four badminton courts, basketball courts, an indoor soccer and hockey pitch, indoor cricket nets and a general covered play area.

A purpose-built Pre-Prep block was opened in 1998 to house the growing Pre-Prep department and a purpose-built Prep block was built in 2000. A further Pre-Prep building was completed in September 2002 and The Stimson Hall, a purpose-built hall/theatre was completed in February 2006. The school has seen a huge growth in numbers and in almost every year group early registration is recommended.

Charitable status. Witham Hall School Trust is a Registered Charity, number 507070. It exists for the purpose of educating children.

Woodcote House

Windlesham Surrey GU20 6PF
Tel: 01276 472115
Fax: 01276 472890
e-mail: info@woodcotehouseschool.co.uk
website: www.woodcotehouseschool.co.uk

***Headmaster*: N H K Paterson**, BA, PGCE

Age Range. 7–13.

Number of Boys. 105 (80 boarders, 25 day).

Fees per term (2008-2009). £5,475 (Boarding), £3,975 (Day). No compulsory extras. Annual Scholarship Day in March.

Location. Originally a Coaching Inn on the old London to Portsmouth Road, Woodcote enjoys a beautiful, rural setting in 30 acres of grounds. The school is easily accessible, being only 25 miles from London via the M3 (Junction 3), 25 minutes from Heathrow and 40 minutes from Gatwick.

Pastoral Care. Woodcote is the ultimate family-run school and 'Mr Nick' is the third generation Paterson to be Headmaster. With many of his family involved, he and 'Mrs Nick', together with the settled and committed staff, most of whom live on site with their own families, provide an extremely caring and supportive environment for both Boarders and Day Boys. A strong emphasis is placed on manners, consideration and respect for others. The school has its own Chapel in the woods and parents are welcome to Sunday services, as well as to school matches on Wednesdays and Saturdays (after which legendary Match Teas are served), so there is plenty of opportunity to see their boys and talk to staff and fellow parents.

Academic. There are two forms in each year group, with an average of 10 boys in each class, enabling the staff to offer all boys an enormous degree of individual attention. With SEN and EFL teaching also available, academic standards are high and the school is proud of its 100% Common Entrance and excellent Scholarship record. Woodcote boys go on to a wide variety of independent senior schools and Mr Nick takes particular care in assisting parents to choose the right school for their son.

Music and Drama. 80% of boys learn at least one musical instrument, and the young and innovative Director of Music has ensured that it is considered 'cool' to be in the excellent choir. There is an orchestra and a jazz band and the school holds regular concerts so that the boys are comfortable with public performance, both individually and as part of a group. The school produces a Junior and a Senior Play each year, in which all boys are involved one way or another.

Sports. Rugby, football, cricket and hockey are coached to a high standard and there are teams at all levels of age and ability, with a high success rate for a small school. Individual sports include tennis (the school has five courts), swimming, athletics, golf, judo, riding, squash and rifle-shooting.

Hobbies and Free Time. With 'prep' done first thing in the morning, there are numerous opportunities for boys to pursue hobbies after lessons and games, and each member of staff offers a 'club' during Hobbies Hour on Wednesday afternoons. These activities are also available at weekends, along with the traditional activities of 'hutting' (camp building in the woods) and 'cooking' (frying potatoes on camp fires). Boys are encouraged to read and have a quiet time after lunch each day for this, as well as before lights out in the evening.

Ethos. The school motto, "Vive ut Discas et Disce ut Vivas" (Live to Learn and Learn to Live), embodies the school's aim to give all boys a love of learning and to discover and nurture their individual talents in a happy and positive atmosphere.

Woodford Green Preparatory School

Glengall Road Woodford Green Essex IG8 0BZ
Tel: 020 8504 5045
e-mail: admin@wgps.co.uk
website: www.woodfordgreenprep.co.uk

The School is an Educational Charity, controlled by a Board of Governors.

Chairman of Governors: Mr D Paterson

***Headmaster*: A J Blackhurst**, BA

Age Range. 3–11.

Number of Pupils. 384 (Boys and Girls).

Fees per term (2008-2009). £2,070; Nursery £1,245.

The School provides a broad well-balanced curriculum and the overall standard is extremely high. The School has an outstanding record of success in 11+ examinations to Senior Independent and Grammar Schools and demand for places far outstrips availability. Parents are advised to make a very early application to the school.

Means tested Bursaries, of up to 100% of the full fees, will be available for 7+ entry from 2009.

Charitable status. Woodford Green Preparatory School is a Registered Charity, number 310930.

Wycliffe Preparatory School

Stonehouse Gloucestershire GL10 2LD
Tel: 01453 820470
Fax: 01453 825604
e-mail: prep@wycliffe.co.uk
website: www.wycliffe.co.uk

Chairman of Trustees: Major General G B Fawcus, CB, MA

***Headmaster*: A Palmer**, MA, BEd

Age Range. 2–13.

Number of Pupils. Pre-Preparatory: 128 day pupils; Preparatory: 70 boarding, 167 day pupils.

Fees per term (2008-2009). Day £1,720–£4,520 (Lunch £170), Boarding £4,410–£6,345.

Wycliffe Preparatory School is a co-educational day, boarding and flexi-boarding school from 2 to 13 years. The School is administered by the Governors' Advisory Body and the Trustees of Wycliffe (*see Wycliffe College entry in HMC section*), but is a separate unit with its own Headmaster and full-time staff of 30 teachers (all qualified), house staff and matrons.

A range of Scholarships, both academic and non-academic, are offered by competition annually. There are also bursaries available for children from HM Forces families. The vast majority of our pupils go on to the Senior School – however, pupils are prepared for Common Entrance Examinations to all schools.

Wycliffe is committed to fostering individual learning in all areas of the curriculum and pupils benefit from small class sizes with a high teacher to pupil ratio. One of Wycliffe's aims is to cultivate each pupil's unique talents and to bring out the best in its pupils by creating a supportive learning environment which promotes individual achievements in all fields. Specialist teachers ensure outstanding teaching delivery across the curriculum and a wide variety of extra-curricular activities enables the school to offer a fully-rounded education designed to develop confidence and self-esteem.

Academic excellence is something pupils are encouraged to attain and the fact that some of our highly able pupils have been listed with the Able Pupils Register, attests to the high-achieving nature of many of our students and the school's ability to nurture this. Wycliffe recently celebrated becoming the only school in the UK to win the NACE (the National Association for Able Children in Education) Challenge Award across every one of the six stages of education – from pre-school right through to A Level, and is the first independent school in the country to collect the prestigious award.

There is also a dedicated CReSTeD registered SEN Department which supports children who have weaknesses in some areas of the curriculum. The school not only promotes success in the classroom, but prides itself on enabling every child to do well, whether on the sports field, in one of the many drama or musical productions or by taking part in the annual Art exhibition, hosted at the Senior School.

The Preparatory School continues with its programme to improve facilities and is currently in the process of refurbishing the indoor swimming pool, due for completion by September 2008. The school also boasts a new all-weather pitch, refurbished Years 3 and 4 classrooms, art studio, craft workshop and boarding facilities, extensive playing fields, tennis courts, sports hall, studio theatre and music school, two science laboratories, four computer rooms, a covered playground and cafeteria-style dining room. The Pre-Prep Department is housed separately, but near enough to make use of the facilities at the main site. It has its own outdoor classroom with adventure playground, hall, library and separate art room.

The Preparatory School uses the College Chapel, Medical Centre and new state-of-the-art Sports Centre.

The boarding houses are in the care of House staff and there are members of staff with particular responsibility for the welfare of day pupils. Vegetarian and other dietary specialities can be catered for.

As well as the usual range of sport, drama and music, there are clubs, activities and opportunities for outdoor pursuits. A number of holiday trips are also arranged, including an annual exchange with an independent school in Florida, team building activity in Wales and a trip to Paris, organised by the languages department.

Charitable status. Wycliffe College Incorporated is a Registered Charity, number 311714. It is a co-educational boarding and day school promoting a balanced education for children between the ages of 2 and 18.

Yardley Court

The Schools at Somerhill

Somerhill Tonbridge Kent TN11 0NJ
Tel: 01732 352124
Fax: 01732 363381
e-mail: office@schoolsatsomerhill.com
website: www.schoolsatsomerhill.com

Chairman of Governors: Mr Philip Thomas

***Headmaster*: John Coakley**, BA Hons, PGCE, MA

Age Range. Prep: Boys 7–13. Pre-Prep: Co-educational 3–7.

Number of Pupils. Prep: 238 day boys. Pre-Prep: 278 boys and girls.

Fees per term (2007-2008). Dayboys £3,605 inclusive of lunch. There are no compulsory extras.

Yardley Court is one of the three Schools at Somerhill. From a co-educational Pre-Prep of some 250+ children, the seven year old boys join Yardley Court and the girls join our sister school, Derwent Lodge. All three schools are housed in a magnificent Jacobean mansion set within 150 acres of beautiful parkland. Thus we are able to offer single sex education in the classroom but very much within a co-educational setting.

Yardley Court was founded in 1898 and moved to the Somerhill estate in 1990. We prepare boys for Common Entrance and Scholarships to senior independent schools in the immediate vicinity such as Tonbridge and Sevenoaks and also to schools further afield. Boys are also prepared for 11+ and 13+ entrance to the very strong Grammar Schools in our area. Sound foundations are the basis of all the academic teaching with particular emphasis placed on the core subject of Mathematics, English, Science and French.

Music plays an important part in school life with most boys participating in some way, either through the choirs, the wind band or in solo or group instruction in a wide range of instruments.

The parkland and woods adjoining the school together with our purpose built playing fields provide an excellent environment for both sport and play. A strong sports programme centres around Soccer, Rugby, Cross-country, Cricket, Tennis and Athletics. All the boys are given the opportunity to represent the school. Further sporting pursuits include Karate, Golf, Judo and Swimming. The school also encourages participation in a wide range of clubs and activities.

A new multi-purpose hall opened in April 2002 and an astroturf pitch in 2003. A new dining room and an indoor swimming pool are currently under construction.

Charitable status. The Somerhill Charitable Trust Limited is a Registered Charity, number 1002212. It exists to provide education for children.

Yarlet School

Yarlet Nr Stafford ST18 9SU
Tel: 01785 286568
Fax: 01785 286569
e-mail: headmaster@yarletschool.co.uk
website: www.yarletschool.co.uk

Chairman of the Governors: R D Montgomerie

***Headmaster*: R S Plant**, MA (Pembroke College, Cambridge)

Age Range. Co-educational 2–13.

Number of Pupils. 172 pupils: 87 Girls and Boys in the Preparatory School (aged 7 to 13) and 85 Girls and Boys in the Nursery and Pre-Preparatory School (aged 1½ to 7).

Fees per term (2007-2008). £1,795–£2,995. Flexi boarding available (Thursday and Friday nights) at £25 per night.

Established in 1873, Yarlet stands in 33 acres of grounds in unspoilt open countryside 5 miles north of Stafford. The school offers small classes, qualified teachers, excellent facilities and a warm, friendly environment conducive to learning. All teachers keep fully abreast of the National Curriculum guidelines to Key Stage 3 and beyond.

Pupils have access to the wide range of facilities which include a modem Science Laboratory, an Information Technology Centre, a CDT Centre, a purpose-built Art Studio and an indoor Sports and Performance Hall; and extensive outdoor facilities which include a heated swimming pool, four playing fields (for football, rugby, hockey, cricket and athletics), three tennis courts, a netball court, an all-weather Astroturf pitch (for football, hockey and netball), and a large Adventure Playground close to the Pre-Prep.

The purpose-built Pre-Preparatory school building was opened in 1999.

Club and extra-curricular activities are a strong feature of Yarlet and include art (painting, sculpture and pottery), model-making, music, drama, French culture, chess, photography and fishing.

Yarlet has high expectations of all its children. Children are prepared for entry to a wide variety of senior schools and their achievements in both Key Stage tests and Common Entrance examinations are a source of great pride, as too is the fact that many children leave with a Scholarship award from their Senior School.

Charitable status. Yarlet is a Registered Charity, number 528618. It exists to provide education for boys and girls from 2 to 13.

Yarm Preparatory School

Grammar School Lane Yarm Stockton-on-Tees TS15 9ES
Tel: 01642 781447
Fax: 01642 787425
e-mail: prepschool@yarmschool.org
website: www.yarmschool.org

Chairman of Governors: Dr A Bonavia, MBChB, MRCGP

***Head*: Mrs G R Taylor**, BEd Hons

Deputy Head: Mr P C Hardy, BA Hons, PGCE

Age Range. 3–11.

Number of Pupils. 340 Boys and Girls.

Fees per term (2008-2009). Preparatory School £2,389–£2,643; Early School £1,877–£1,946; Nursery £1,389 (full-time). Lunches are extra.

Academic and Music Scholarships are offered from 7+.

Yarm Preparatory School is a co-educational day school which educates children from 7–11 years of age (3–7 within the Early School and Nursery).

Ethos. The Preparatory School is well known as a friendly and stimulating environment that encourages children to flourish educationally whilst also developing valuable social abilities and leadership skills. Through the broad variety of extra-curricular activities, children come to excel in sport and music as well as a wide range of other pastimes.

Organisation. Pastoral care is based on both a year group and a House system. Every pupil belongs to one of four Houses. Houses exist to promote competitions, sporting events, charity and fund-raising etc. Pupils have opportunities to represent their form as Form Captains, who also serve on the School Council.

Curriculum. The Preparatory School curriculum is based upon the National Curriculum, although it offers greater breadth and depth in many subject areas. In addition to the core curriculum of English, mathematics and science, full weight is given to both history and geography, whilst subjects such as design technology, ICT, art, music, religious education, PSHE, PE and games are fully catered for. Children are also taught French from age 3. Whilst form teachers deliver much of the core curriculum, subject specialist teachers are employed to cover many areas of the curriculum.

Games and Activities. The Preparatory School hosts a whole range of sports. However, rugby and hockey are the school's main winter games. Soccer and netball are played during the Spring Term, followed by cricket, athletics and rounders in the summer. In addition, cross-country is also pursued at inter-school level throughout the year. There are many school activities including music, dance, drama, orienteering, chess, swimming, badminton, gardening, modelling, crafts, pottery, ICT and quizzes which are timetabled to take place during two lessons, at lunchtimes and after school each week. These activities change termly.

Music. The Preparatory School boasts many musical groups, choirs, choristers and a variety of ensembles with well over half of the school learning an instrument.

Educational Visits. A varied programme of educational day visits is undertaken by all year groups to enrich the curriculum, using the locality as a resource. From age 7, pupils have the opportunity to participate in residential trips, including visits to Grasmere, York, Robinwood, Ru'a Fiola and Saint-Omer, France.

Admission. Entry to the Preparatory School is by assessment which may be carried out at any time of the year if places are available. Pupils are prepared for entry to the Senior School, sitting transfer papers in January before the September in which they transfer. The results of transfer papers are considered in conjunction with ongoing assessment information made available by teachers in the Preparatory School.

Open Days. The Early School and Preparatory School hold Open Mornings twice a year, normally in October and January. Prospective parents are encouraged to attend at least one Open Morning as this gives excellent opportunity to look around the school at leisure and chat with staff. Visits are, however, welcome at any time.

Religion. The school is an inter-denominational community but follows Christian traditions and ethos.

Charitable status. Yarm School is a Registered Charity, number 1093434. It exists to provide education for boys and girls from 3–18.

Yarrells Preparatory School

Yarrells House Upton Poole Dorset BH16 5EU
Tel: 01202 622229
Fax: 01202 620870
e-mail: enquiries@yarrells.co.uk
website: www.yarrells.co.uk

***Headmistress*: Mrs N A Covell**, BA, MSc

Deputy Head: P Brady, BEd Hons

Age Range. 2–13.

Number of Pupils. 220 Boys and Girls.

Fees per term (from April 2008). £133–£3,270.

Yarrells School offers a unique environment for the early development of intellectual, artistic and sporting potential. Only minutes from Bournemouth and Poole, Yarrells occupies a late Georgian country house surrounded by woods, gardens, playing fields, tennis courts and covered, heated swimming pool. The atmosphere is warm and encouraging while a rigorous approach is taken to the maintenance of each child's highest standards. A well-qualified and committed staff work with the Headmistress to ensure careful character building and maximum academic performance. The school seeks to identify and develop children's gifts and abilities in such a way that the children grow in self-knowledge, self-discipline and self-confidence.

The classes are small and learning is designed to meet individual requirements. From Nursery up, the school follows a detailed curriculum based on the National Curriculum, the Common Entrance Syllabus (where appropriate) and the school's own demands, which emphasise the mastery of basic skills from an early age. The normal subject range is taught throughout and by specialists from the age of 8/9. The children start learning French from 4 years of age. Parents are invited to discuss their child's progress regularly with staff and are also sent termly written reports.

All children have curricular tuition in Art, Music (singing and instrumental), Drama and Dance. There are Recorder Ensembles, a Wind Band, Choir, Choral Societies and an Orchestra. There is a broad PE programme that includes swimming, tennis, football, rugby, netball, rounders, basketball, hockey and cross-country. Science, Investigational Mathematics, Design and ICT are areas of study given good accommodation in the timetable. The school is active until 6.00 pm each weekday evening for those children from age 7 who elect to stay for supervised prep and a range of activities which include football, cross-country, ballet, extra swimming and tennis, tap and modern dance, art, drama and music.

Yarrells School has an excellent record of success in Entrance Examinations and Scholarship Awards to senior schools. Most children go on to Senior Independent Schools or the Grammar Schools.

Yateley Manor Preparatory School

51 Reading Road Yateley Hampshire GU46 7UQ
Tel: 01252 405500
Fax: 01252 405504
e-mail: office@yateleymanor.com
website: www.yateleymanor.com

The School is an Educational Trust controlled by a Board of Governors.

Chairman of Governors: Stephen Sharp

***Headmaster*: Francis Howard**, MA (Cantab), DipEd (Oxon)

Age Range. 3–13.

Number of Pupils. Pre-Preparatory and Nursery: 105 boys, 64 girls. Main School: 214 boys, 128 girls.

Fees per term (2008-2009). £1,265–£3,497. Fees are inclusive of all normal activities, extended supervision from 8.00 am until 6.30 pm, meals and residential field trips for Years 5, 6, 7 and 8.

Yateley Manor is a warm, lively, forward-looking school where traditional values are fused with modern methods and a sense of fun. It is a day, co-educational preparatory school, founded in 1947, occupying a nine-acre site containing attractive playing fields, sports pitches and adventure play areas. The original Victorian building houses administration and a continuing building programme has provided attractive modern facilities including a new Nursery, many classrooms, science laboratories, a swimming pool and a sports hall. Investment in information technology is also a strong feature.

Children are encouraged to enjoy learning and are challenged to do their best and to find achievement as measured against their own capabilities whether in academic circles, in sport or in the arts. Children are encouraged to explore without fear of failure, to have a sense of curiosity in the world around them and to develop into happy and confident people. Because the school believes in educating the whole person the enormous range of activities is included within the school fees.

Small classes averaging 16, individual attention, stable staff and excellent facilities, have all led to impressive examination results and scholarships to senior schools. Yateley Manor is independent of any senior school so pupils proceed to a wide variety of local independent schools, and to many further away.

A network of School coaches serves the surrounding areas including, Camberley, Church Crookham, Frimley, Fleet, Hartley Wintney, Hook and Odiham. There is an informal screening assessment for entry to the school and the most common entry points are at 3 into the Nursery, at 4 into Reception, and at 7 into the main school. Children are welcome to join at all other ages and many do.

Charitable status. Yateley Manor is a Registered Charity, number 307374. It is dedicated to providing the highest quality education for children of the local community.

York House School

Redheath Croxley Green Rickmansworth Herts WD3 4LW
Tel: 01923 772395
Fax: 01923 779231
e-mail: yhsoffice@aol.com
website: www.york-house.com

Founded in 1910, York House School is a non-profit making Educational Trust with a Board of Governors.

Chairman of the Governors: T K Slade, Esq, BA Hons, FCT

***Headmaster*: P R MacDougall**, BEd Hons

Age Range. Boys $2^1/_2$–13. Co-educational Kindergarten $2^1/_2$–5.

Number of Children. All are Day pupils: 160 Prep, 80 Pre-Prep, 50 Kindergarten.

Fees per term (2008-2009). £3,240 including lunch. Kindergarten dependent upon days/hours.

York House School is a well established, innovative and forward looking school located in a Queen Anne country house standing in 47 acres of the Hertfordshire countryside. The Headmaster is assisted by a fully qualified and caring staff.

The school's aim is to encourage children to achieve the highest academic results in a happy atmosphere while promoting self-discipline and caring for others.

The school has excellent facilities which include a multi-purpose hall and theatre, Library, state-of-the-art computer suite, a modern Pre-Prep and Kindergarten opened in 2001. In 2005 a new Junior School, Science Laboratory, Art Design and Technology Rooms were opened. The music centre is large with practice rooms and a new music computer suite.

Sporting facilities are excellent with 15 acres of playing fields for cricket, rugby, soccer, and athletics as well as a 25-metre indoor heated swimming pool.

Boys are prepared for Common Entrance and Independent Schools Scholarships. There is a Pre-Preparatory Department for boys from 4 to 6+ and a co-educational Kindergarten for children from rising 3 to 5.

Charitable status. York House School is a Registered Charity, number 311076. It exists for the purpose of achieving educational excellence.

PART V

Schools whose Heads are members of the Independent Schools Association

ALPHABETICAL LIST OF SCHOOLS

* co-educational schools

GEOGRAPHICAL LIST OF ISA SCHOOLS

Individual School Entries

Abbey College Manchester
Alpha Plus Group

5–7 Cheapside King Street Manchester M2 4WG
Tel: 0161 817 2700
Fax: 0161 817 2705
e-mail: admin@abbeymanchester.co.uk
website: www.abbeymanchester.co.uk

***Principal*: Mrs Jenny Thomas**, BSc, PGCE

Age Range. 14–18.
Number of Pupils. 160.
GCSEs, A Levels and One Year Retakes
A small independent school with a big difference

- Year 10, 11, Lower Sixth and Upper Sixth entry
- Very small classes ensure excellent progress
- Unique intensive GCSE programme offered at Year 11
- One of the few schools to deliver A Level retakes
- Extensive personal support
- Expert, individual advice for entry onto all university courses
- Strong relationships with the top universities in Britain
- City centre location

Join us at any time of the year, not just September.

Fees per term (2008-2009). GCSE/A Level two-year course: £3,195; GCSE one-year Retake course: £695–£3,195; A Level one-year Retake course: £1,712–£4,834.

Abbey Gate College

Saighton Grange Saighton Chester CH3 6EG

(See entry in SHMIS section)

Abbey Gate School

Clare Avenue Hoole Chester CH2 3HR
Tel: 01244 319649
e-mail: abbeygateschool@talk21.com
website: www.abbeygateschool.org.uk

***Head*: Mrs S M Fisher**, CertEd (Birmingham)

Age Range. 3–11.
Number in School. Day: 77 Boys and Girls.
Fees per term (2008-2009). £1,750–£1,895.

Abbey Gate School, founded in 1910, is a small, caring Christian community, comprising around 80 children and a dedicated, well-qualified staff.

It offers a broad and well-balanced curriculum and has a proven tradition of academic success both locally and nationally, as well as a growing reputation for excellence in the performing arts. Tuition is offered in a variety of musical instruments and in speech & drama and dance.

Specialist help is available for children with specific learning difficulties.

Extra-curricular activities include chess, country dancing, a variety of sports, recorder consorts, choir and orchestra, Spanish for Fun, and ICT clubs.

A forward-looking school, it aims to create exciting and challenging opportunities to develop academic, creative and physical skills, to produce confident and self-disciplined young people of the future.

School opens at 8 am and has a thriving After-School Club until 6 pm each day.

Abbotsford Preparatory School
GEMS Education

211 Flixton Road Urmston Manchester M41 5PR
Tel: 0161 748 3261
Fax: 0161 746 7961
e-mail: pshiels@abbotsford-prep.trafford.sch.uk
secretary@abbotsford-prep.trafford.sch.uk
website: www.abbotsfordprepschool.co.uk

***Head*: Mrs P Shiels**

Age Range. 2½–11.
Number in School. Day: 40 Boys, 50 Girls.
Fees per term (2008-2009). £1,309–£1,765.

Established one hundred years ago, this ISC accredited school sends children to State Grammar Schools as well as the major Independent schools in the North West. Although the success rate is exceptionally high, children are not crammed but encouraged to achieve their full potential and leave us as pleasant, confident, well-rounded individuals.

The school is a well-equipped building, with specialist areas for Science, Art/Technology and Information Technology, which are second-to-none for this age group. The new, fully-enclosed outdoor multi-purpose hard area has been greatly enhanced with an astroturf surface and the school also has a large indoor sports hall.

Children may start at 2½ in the Pre-School Group, part-time or full-time by mutual agreement between parents and teachers. All children from Pre-School upwards use the computer suite and are offered the opportunity to learn a foreign language.

In the main school, besides the full range of primary subjects there is a range of extra-curricular activities, which include sport, drama, music, art, chess and wildlife. The curriculum is enhanced and supported through regular trips. All KS2 children are offered the opportunity to take part in annual Adventure Holidays. Staff take great pride in the standard of the children who leave the school.

Abbotsford School

Bridge Street Kenilworth Warwickshire CV8 1BP
Tel: 01926 852826
Fax: 01926 852753
e-mail: office@abbotsfordschool.co.uk
website: www.abbotsford-school.co.uk

***Acting Head*: Mrs Jane Chatwin**

Age Range. 2¾–11 Co-educational.
Number in School. 100 Day Pupils.
Fees per term (2007-2008). £1,495–£1,870.

Independent Co-educational Day Preparatory School founded in 1909, housed in a large Georgian residence, catering for pupils from 2¾ to 11 years.

The school provides an excellent broad and balanced education for all pupils in a happy, caring environment. Tuition is in small classes with individual attention from qualified specialist staff, ensuring that all pupils achieve their potential. Specialist well-equipped teaching areas in Science, Design Technology, Music, Art, French and IT. Excellent results in external examinations.

Wide range of sports is offered. Winner of Sports Council Activemark Gold Award. Extensive range of extra-curricular activities. Before School and After School Care provided until 6 pm.

Charitable status. Abbotsford School Educational Trust Ltd is a Registered Charity, number 528779. It exists to provide an excellent all-round education for all children in a caring and friendly environment.

Abercorn School

28 Abercorn Place London NW8 9XP

(See entry in IAPS section)

Abingdon House School
Alpha Plus Group

4–6 Abingdon Road Kensington London W8 6AF
Tel: 0845 2300426
Fax: 020 7361 0751
e-mail: ahs@abingdonhouseschool.co.uk
website: www.abingdonhouseschool.co.uk

***Headmaster*: Mr N J Rees**, NPQH, MA, PGCE, DipRSASpLD

Age Range. 4–11 Co-educational.
Number of Pupils. 45.
Fees per term (2008-2009). £7,235.

Abingdon House School provides a whole-school approach for pupils who are diagnosed with a specific learning difficulty early in their education and who would respond well to intense intervention for a period of time.

Pupils with 'disabilities', such as dyslexia, dyspraxia, speech and language delays, and social and communication difficulties, ADD/ADHD, are admitted. Suitability of children for admission is determined by multi-disciplinary screening conducted over two days and the receipt of assessment reports. Pupils may join the school at any stage if a place is available.

Our teaching environment is based on understanding a child's individual needs, nurturing a child's academic and social development and caring for a child's wellbeing. The environment is therefore warm and friendly and we are committed to every child.

We aim to prepare the children for a return to mainstream schooling through: the provision of a holistic and individually tailored education programme, a whole-school teaching regime of small classes with teaching assistants, therapists and trained staff using a range of teaching strategies and by maintaining an appropriately low pupil to teacher ratio. A number of pupils have integrated successfully into a number of London day schools.

Each pupil has an IEP (Individual Education Plan). Each target aims to be SMART (a specific, measurable, achievable, realistic target).

The change in the pupil's self-esteem is marked and almost immediate. A Prize Giving is held each term so that pupils are given the opportunity for their efforts and achievements to be recognised and celebrated on a regular basis.

We offer a full curriculum. PE/Games take place on a weekly basis at school or in Holland Park. Reading, Literacy and Maths lessons are ability grouped to enable pupils to progress as soon as they are ready. After-school clubs are offered twice a week.

Home/School Diaries form an important link between home and school. We value teamwork and the partnership between parents and staff.

In two period houses, linked at each level, we have the facilities to educate 70 children. The classrooms are bright and well-furnished. The school has a Hall that is used for assemblies, music and PE as well as for lunch, a Library, an Art & Design room and an ICT suite. There are specialist rooms for occupational and physiotherapy, speech and language therapy and music therapy as well as for special provision classes. The pupils play in Holland Park on a daily basis.

ACS Cobham International School

Heywood Portsmouth Road Cobham Surrey KT11 1BL
Tel: 01932 867251
Fax: 01932 869789
e-mail: CobhamAdmissions@acs-england.co.uk
website: www.acs-england.co.uk

***Head*: Thomas Lehman**

Age Range. 2–18.
Number in School. Day: 787 Boys, 631 Girls; 104 Boarders.

Tuition Fees (2008-2009) per semester (2 semesters). From £4,155 (Pre-Kindergarten) to £9,140 (grade 12).

Boarding Fees (2008-2009) per semester (2 semesters). In addition to tuition fees: 7 day £6,880 (grades 7–12); 5 day £5,025 (grades 7–12).

- Located 23 miles south of central London on a 128-acre site.
- Co-educational, with over 1,400 students enrolled between the ages of 2 and 18.
- Premier sports facilities: on-site soccer and rugby fields, softball and baseball diamonds, an all-weather Olympic-sized track, tennis courts, six-hole golf course, and a new Sports Centre which houses a basketball/volleyball show court, 25-metre competition-class swimming pool, dance studio, fitness suite, and cafeteria.
- Co-educational boarding with separate-wing accommodation for 110 students aged between 12 (7th Grade), and 18 (12th Grade).

ACS International Schools enrol a total of over 2,500 students aged between 2 and 18, from over 70 countries, speaking 30 languages, at three London area campuses in England. Based on international and American research, principles, and educational practices, the schools are committed to maintaining the highest standards of scholarship and citizenship.

- All ACS campuses are International Baccalaureate (IB) World Schools, offering the IB Diploma. In addition, ACS Egham International School is one of only three schools in the UK to also offer the IB Primary Years Programme (3–11), and the IB Middle Years Programme (11–16).
- All ACS campuses offer a traditional American High School Diploma, with ACS Cobham, and ACS Hillingdon also teaching US Advanced Placement (AP) courses.
- The combined ACS IB Diploma pass rates and scores consistently rank well above international averages, placing ACS among the highest achieving independent schools in the UK.

- ACS graduates attend leading universities around the world including: Cambridge, Imperial College London, London School of Economics, and Oxford in the UK and Harvard, Princeton, Stanford, and Yale in the US.
- The schools are accredited by the New England Association for Schools and Colleges, and authorised by the Independent Schools Association UK. ACS also holds memberships in the Council of International Schools, and the International Baccalaureate Organization.
- Small class sizes facilitate multi-level teaching, academic challenge, and a focus on individual student learning styles.
- Students also participate in international theatre art programmes, competitive sport tournaments, maths, literature, and music competitions in the UK and across Europe.
- English as an Additional Language (EAL) is taught throughout the schools.
- Native Language Enrichment programmes are offered in: Danish, Dutch, Finnish, French, German, Hebrew, Hindi, Japanese, Norwegian, Spanish, Swedish, Urdu, and other languages as required.

ACS Egham International School

Woodlee London Road (A30) Egham Surrey TW20 0HS
Tel: 01784 430800
Fax: 01784 430626
e-mail: EghamAdmissions@acs-england.co.uk
website: www.acs-england.co.uk

***Head of School*: Moyra Hadley**

Age Range. 2–18.

Number in School. Day only: 319 Boys, 302 Girls.

Tuition Fees (2008-2009) per semester (2 semesters). From £4,155 (Pre-Kindergarten) to £9,025 (grade 12).

- Located 25 miles south-west of central London on a 20-acre site.
- Co-educational, with over 600 students enrolled between the ages of 2 and 18.
- Academic programmes include the International Baccalaureate (IB) Primary Years Programme (3–11), the IB Middle Years Programme (11–16), the IB Diploma (16–18), and an American High School Diploma.
- Superb teaching, sports and extra-curricular facilities which include a newly refurbished cafeteria and kitchen and a new Visual Arts and Design Technology Centre.
- Promotes active participation in a wide range of extra-curricular activities including sports, drama, music, the visual arts, and both local and international community service projects.

ACS International Schools enrol a total of over 2,500 students aged between 2 and 18, from over 70 countries, speaking 30 languages, at three London area campuses in England. Based on international and American research, principles, and educational practices, the schools are committed to maintaining the highest standards of scholarship and citizenship.

- All ACS campuses are International Baccalaureate (IB) World Schools, offering the IB Diploma. In addition, ACS Egham International School is one of only three schools in the UK to also offer the IB Primary Years Programme (3–11), and the IB Middle Years Programme (11–16).
- All ACS campuses offer a traditional American High School Diploma, with ACS Cobham, and ACS Hillingdon also teaching US Advanced Placement (AP) courses.
- The combined ACS IB Diploma pass rates and scores consistently rank well above international averages, placing ACS among the highest achieving independent schools in the UK.
- ACS graduates attend leading universities around the world including: Cambridge, Imperial College London, London School of Economics, and Oxford in the UK and Harvard, Princeton, Stanford, and Yale in the US.
- The schools are accredited by the New England Association for Schools and Colleges, and authorised by the Independent Schools Association UK. ACS also holds memberships in the Council of International Schools, and the International Baccalaureate Organization.
- Small class sizes facilitate multi-level teaching, academic challenge, and a focus on individual student learning styles.
- Students also participate in international theatre art programmes, competitive sport tournaments, maths, literature, and music competitions in the UK and across Europe.
- English as an Additional Language (EAL) is taught throughout the schools.
- Native Language Enrichment programmes are offered in: Danish, Dutch, Finnish, French, German, Hebrew, Hindi, Japanese, Norwegian, Spanish, Swedish, Urdu, and other languages as required.

ACS Hillingdon International School

Hillingdon Court 108 Vine Lane Hillingdon Middlesex UB10 0BE
Tel: 01895 259771
Fax: 01895 818404
e-mail: HillingdonAdmissions@acs-england.co.uk
website: www.acs-england.co.uk

***Head of School*: Ginger G Apple**

Age Range. 4–18.

Number in School. Day only: 337 Boys, 294 Girls.

Tuition Fees (2008-2009) per semester (2 semesters). From £4,155 (Pre-Kindergarten) to £8,705 (grade 12).

- Located 15 miles west of central London with Underground rail access, on an 11-acre site set in parkland.
- Co-educational, with over 600 students enrolled between the ages of 4 and 18.
- Excellent facilities are augmented by a new music centre, complete with digital recording studio, rehearsal rooms, practice studios, and a computer lab for music technology.
- On-site playing fields, tennis courts, and playgrounds, with additional off-site soccer, rugby, track, baseball, softball, swimming, and golf facilities available.

ACS International Schools enrol a total of over 2,500 students aged between 2 and 18, from over 70 countries, speaking 30 languages, at three London area campuses in England. Based on international and American research, principles, and educational practices, the schools are committed to maintaining the highest standards of scholarship and citizenship.

- All ACS campuses are International Baccalaureate (IB) World Schools, offering the IB Diploma. In addition, ACS Egham International School is one of only three schools in the UK to also offer the IB Primary Years Programme (3–11), and the IB Middle Years Programme (11–16).
- All ACS campuses offer a traditional American High School Diploma, with ACS Cobham, and ACS Hillingdon also teaching US Advanced Placement (AP) courses.
- The combined ACS IB Diploma pass rates and scores consistently rank well above international averages, placing ACS among the highest achieving independent schools in the UK.
- ACS graduates attend leading universities around the world including: Cambridge, Imperial College London, London School of Economics, and Oxford in the UK and Harvard, Princeton, Stanford, and Yale in the US.
- The schools are accredited by the New England Association for Schools and Colleges, and authorised by the Independent

Schools Association UK. ACS also holds memberships in the Council of International Schools, and the International Baccalaureate Organization.

- Small class sizes facilitate multi-level teaching, academic challenge, and a focus on individual student learning styles.
- Students also participate in international theatre art programmes, competitive sport tournaments, maths, literature, and music competitions in the UK and across Europe.
- English as an Additional Language (EAL) is taught throughout the schools.
- Native Language Enrichment programmes are offered in: Danish, Dutch, Finnish, French, German, Hebrew, Hindi, Japanese, Norwegian, Spanish, Swedish, Urdu, and other languages as required.

Charitable status. Adcote School Educational Trust Limited is a Registered Charity, number 528407.

Adcote School

Little Ness near Shrewsbury Shropshire SY4 2JY
Tel: 01939 260202
Fax: 01939 261300
e-mail: headteacher@adcoteschool.co.uk
website: www.adcoteschool.co.uk

Chairman of Board of Governors: Mr T Morris, BSc

***Head*: Mr R Jervis**, BA, CertEd, DipEdMgt

Age Range. 4–18.

Number in School. 106 Girls.

Occupying a distinguished country house designed by Norman Shaw RA in 1879 and set in 27 acres of landscaped parkland, Adcote is a day and boarding school for girls aged 11–18 with a thriving Junior School for girls aged 4–11.

Curriculum. Considerable importance is placed on good learning in the core curriculum, and individual attention is paid to girls of all abilities. French is part of Junior School life, and is developed with a wide variety of other options through to GCSE. There is also an extensive choice of subjects in the Sixth Form. PE is offered up to A Level. ICT is taught as a skill in its own right and developed appropriately throughout the curriculum.

Performing Arts. The School places great emphasis on Music, Dance, and Drama as well as a range of other activities. All the performing arts are included in the core curriculum to age 14, and thereafter voluntarily. Instrumental playing is much encouraged, and there are extra-curricular workshops in dance and drama, and performances twice a year.

Activities. All girls participate in a wide range of activities, including rowing, trampolining and horse-riding. The school also plays tennis, and gymnastics is particularly strong. Outward bound programmes also play an important part of life at Adcote, as do interesting weekend activities, and trips away from school.

Pastoral Care. There is a long tradition of pastoral care at Adcote, and the sense of family and community is strong. Boarders are looked after by the Housemistress and her resident staff, and all girls have a personal tutor, responsible for individual welfare and academic progress. Great importance is attached to understanding the individual and developing personal abilities so that girls meet the demands of the modern world with confidence and good judgement.

Fees per term (2007-2008). Day Girls: £1,966–£3,634; Weekly Boarders: £4,108–£5,894; Full Boarders: £4,669–£6,455.

Reductions are made in fees of second and subsequent sisters. Bursaries are available for children from Forces families. Scholarships for academic excellence.

A prospectus and further details may be obtained from the Head.

Alcuin School

64 Woodland Lane Leeds LS7 4PD
Tel: 0113 269 1173
e-mail: alcuin@legend.co.uk
website: www.alcuinschool.co.uk

Chair of Governors: Mr David Woodhead

***Head Teacher*: Mr John Hipshon**, BSc Hons, PGCE, MA Ed

Age Range. 4–11 Co-educational.

Number of Pupils. 37.

Fees per term (2007-2008). £1,400 including lunch.

Charitable status. The Yorkshire Independent Educational Association Limited is a Registered Charity, number 1046346.

Alleyn Court Preparatory School

Wakering Road Southend-on-Sea Essex SS3 0PW

(See entry in IAPS section)

Alton Convent School

Anstey Lane Alton Hampshire GU34 2NG
Tel: 01420 82070
Fax: 01420 541711
e-mail: enquiries@altonconvent.org.uk
website: www.altonconvent.org.uk

Motto: *Vita dulcedo spes nostra salve*

***Headmistress*: Mrs S E Kirkham**, BA Hons, MA

Age Range. Girls 3–18, Boys 3–11.

Number in School. Day: Girls 417, Boys 74.

Fees per term (2008-2009). Nursery £1,950, Preparatory £2,635, Senior School £3,155.

Alton Convent School is a stimulating, friendly community promoting mutual tolerance, courtesy, care for others, a sense of self worth and personal discipline. Visitors comment on our calm, happy and purposeful working environment. The school was founded in 1938 by the Sisters of Our Lady of Providence and is situated at Anstey Manor in 19 acres of parkland and playing fields. In 1998 it became an educational charitable trust administered by a Board of Governors. It is an independent Catholic day school welcoming pupils from all faiths. The school is situated on the outskirts of a small market town in north east Hampshire, easily accessible by road and rail. Pupils come from a wide catchment area, catered for by school buses.

Entry at the beginning of the prep school is non-selective but entry to the senior school is by entrance examination taken in January for September entry. Whilst academically selective, we seek to admit pupils who are in sympathy with our ethos and will flourish in our community. The curriculum is broad and balanced for all age groups and includes a wide range of science, sports, languages, and expressive arts. Our academic standards are high, with pupils encouraged to think for themselves and take responsibility for their own development. Boys and girls are prepared for entry into their senior schools. Senior girls take an average ten GCSEs and then continue to A

Level in our Sixth Form, where students select five AS subjects with three or four subjects continued to A2 Level.

Our results place us regularly at, or near, the top of Hampshire Performance tables for A Level and GCSE. The pass rate in 2007 for A Level was again 100% with sixth form girls progressing to prestigious universities and we topped Hampshire GCSE League Tables for 2007 with A*/A grades at 67%.

Pastoral care is outstanding and integral to the school's ethos. We are a happy school which settles pupils quickly. An open door policy operates for pupils and parents, with regular opportunities for consultation with staff through parents' evenings and reports. Open Mornings, newsletters and website keep parents up to date.

Co-curricular activities are offered, including a wide range of competitive and friendly sporting opportunities, artistic activities and study workshops. Musical and dramatic opportunities are strong in both schools, with thriving choirs, orchestras, ensembles, jazz group and drama productions. All pupils are encouraged to become involved in the major music and drama productions: additional tuition in sport, dance, and music is offered. A purpose-built Creative Arts Centre opens in Autumn 2008.

Scholarships are available for the Senior School.

Charitable status. The Alton Convent Trust is a Registered Charity, number 1071684.

Altrincham Preparatory School

Marlborough Road Bowdon Altrincham Cheshire WA14 2RR
Tel: 0161 928 3366
Fax: 0161 929 6747
e-mail: admin@altprep.co.uk
website: www.altprep.co.uk

***Headteacher*: Mr A C Potts**, BSc

Age Range. 3–11.
Number in School. 320 Day Boys.
Fees per term (2008-2009). £1,922–£2,151.

Altrincham Preparatory School has been well known in the Manchester area for over 65 years and continues to maintain its high reputation for excellent academic, music and sporting achievements.

The School has a good pupil teacher ratio and offers a very wide range of academic subjects headed by the three main National Curriculum core subjects, English, Mathematics and Science.

The School has outstanding results to all the local independent grammar schools, particularly to Manchester Grammar School, as well as to a very wide range of other schools including the traditional senior independent schools where scholarships have been gained.

The School's sporting successes have been achieved on a national basis in rugby, soccer, athletics, cricket, tennis and swimming.

The School has an ongoing programme of improvement and development including, in 1996/7, the erection of a new purpose-built Junior School.

Argyle House School

19/20 Thornhill Park Tunstall Road Sunderland Tyne & Wear SR2 7LA
Tel: 0191 510 0726
Fax: 0191 567 2209
e-mail: info@argylehouseschool.co.uk
website: www.argylehouseschool.co.uk

***Head*: Mr C Johnson**

Age Range. 2½–16.
Number in School. 234 Boys and Girls.
Fees per term (2007-2008). £1,530–£1,920.

Argyle House School was established in 1884 as a small independent day school for boys and girls, situated in the centre of Sunderland. Students travel from all parts of the region, by our buses, or local forms of transport. The school has maintained its high standards of academic achievement, whilst catering for a wide variety of abilities.

At Argyle House, we believe in the individual, and work with him or her to enable the achievement of each student's potential. This is due to attention to detail by fully qualified and dedicated staff, who help to mould the individual into a well-mannered and accomplished young individual, who will be able to meet future challenges.

Small class sizes and a friendly environment facilitate learning, but not all work is academic, as the school takes an active part in many sporting leagues, both within the school, and locally with other schools. We aim to offer all the facilities of a much larger school, whilst remaining at present student levels to keep the intimacy and friendliness of a smaller school, for both parents and students

Arts Educational School

Tring Park Tring Hertfordshire HP23 5LX

(See entry in SHMIS section)

Arts Educational Schools London

Cone Ripman House 14 Bath Road Chiswick London W4 1LY
Tel: 020 8987 6600
Fax: 020 8987 6601
e-mail: pupils@artsed.co.uk
website: www.artsed.co.uk

Founded in 1919.

***Headmaster*: Mr Oliver Price**, BEd Hons

Age Range. 11–18 Co-educational.
Number in School. Day: 114 Girls, 41 Boys.
Fees per term (2008-2009). £3,280–£3,600.

"*The UK's Leading Specialist Performing Arts Institution in Academic Achievement*" Sunday Times, Parent Power 2007.

100% A Level Pass Rate and outstanding GCSE results.

The Arts Educational Schools London are committed to developing to the full the potential of each and every pupil. High quality vocational, academic and social education, in a warm, friendly, caring environment, ensures that our pupils feel challenged and fulfilled throughout the whole of their exciting careers at the school.

The school has been educating young performing artists since 1919, and there is no comparable school in the UK. Dancers learn to act and sing, actors learn to sing and dance, musicians learn to do more than play their instruments well, and everyone has the opportunity to be grounded in the visual arts, languages, humanities, sciences, and mathematics.

From Year 7 all pupils follow a course leading to eight or nine GCSEs. All pupils have access to the outstanding performance facilities, rehearsal rooms, proscenium and studio theatres. At Year 12 pupils follow a course of four AS Levels, leading to three or four A Levels, whilst receiving outstanding training in dance, drama, music and musical theatre.

In September 2008 a new Musical Theatre Sixth Form was added to their portfolio of vocational courses, using all the expertise and excellence of the professional Musical Theatre Department with the academic reputation and pastoral guidance of the Secondary School. It aims to develop skills in Dance, Singing and Acting so that students start to develop a foundation as a 'triple threat performer' as well as continuing with academic studies to A Level standard.

Former Students of the schools include: Julie Andrews, Samantha Barks, Sarah Brightman, Darcey Bussell, Martin Clunes, Joan Collins, Adam Cooper, Bonnie Langford, Jane Seymour, Hugo Speer, Summer Strallen and Will Young.

Admission is at 11+ and 16+ and occasionally at other ages if places become available.

Charitable status. The Arts Educational Schools is a Registered Charity, number 311087. It exists solely for educational purposes.

Ashton House School

50–52 Eversley Crescent Isleworth Middlesex TW7 4LW
Tel: 020 8560 3902
Fax: 020 8568 1097
e-mail: principal@ashtonhouse.com
website: www.ashtonhouse.com

Principal: Mr S J Turner, BSc

***Head Teacher*: Mrs M Grundberg**, MA, PGCE

Age Range. 3–11.
Number in School. Day: 70 Boys, 75 Girls.
Fees per term (2008-2009). £1,955–£2,708.75.

Founded 1930. Proprietors P A, G B & S J Turner. Entry by interview and assessment. Prospectus on request.

Modern and traditional methods combined ensure that a firm foundation in basic skills is gained within the Infant Department with which to undertake confidently the widening Junior curriculum.

Specialist teaching throughout the school in Music, Information Computer Technology, Physical Education and French are major strengths. Peripatetic music by arrangement in seven instruments.

Sports: netball, rounders, football, cricket, swimming, hockey and basketball.

Excellent record of examinations success for entry to top Independent Day Schools.

Ayscoughfee Hall School

Welland Hall London Road Spalding Lincs PE11 2TE
Tel: 01775 724733
Fax: 01775 769669
e-mail: admin@ahs.me.uk
website: www.ahs.me.uk

***Head*: Mr B G Chittick**, BEd, CertEd

Age Range. 3½–11 co-educational.
Number of Pupils. 152 Day Pupils: 68 Boys, 84 Girls.
Fees per term (2008-2009). £1,340–£1,640.

Founded in 1920, Ayscoughfee Hall School is centred around a beautiful Georgian family home. A purpose-built extension complements the already spacious accommodation. The School houses a Kindergarten, Infant and Junior Departments and has recently developed its facilities to include enlarged classrooms, a dedicated Science/Art Room, a Music Room and changing rooms for PE and Games.

The guidelines and principles of the National Curriculum are followed in all subjects but go far beyond the basic requirements in order to give each child a broader, more varied understanding. Academic standards are high and progress is well monitored throughout the school. The vast majority of pupils are successful in the Lincolnshire County Council selection examination and progress to secondary "Grammar" school education very well equipped to tackle all subjects. The curriculum is continually reviewed and upgraded if necessary with advice from the subject coordinators.

Computers are routinely used in every classroom and pupils receive weekly, dedicated ICT tuition in our up-to-date ICT suite. Interactive whiteboards are being installed throughout the school.

The School excels with its music and drama productions over the academic year, in which all children perform in front of their parents.

French is taught from Reception Class.

The school competes successfully in local and regional sports activities – football, rugby, hockey, netball, cross-country and athletics.

There is a thriving programme of extra-curricular activities, including sport, drama, cookery, poetry, textiles, choir, instrumental groups and ICT. A wide variety of educational visits is offered, with the older children having the opportunity to participate in an activity holiday, accompanied by the staff. Furthermore, regular visits by professional groups and individuals take place in school.

As a small school with classes limited to 20, we aim to provide a happy and caring environment where the individual child may flourish. We are proud of our academic standards but we also strive to give a broad and balanced education. Above all, we want our boys and girls to use and develop their different gifts and to enjoy the success this brings.

Charitable status. Ayscoughfee Hall School Limited is a Registered Charity, number 527294. It exists to provide education for boys and girls.

Babington House School

Grange Drive Chislehurst Kent BR7 5ES
Tel: 020 8467 5537
Fax: 020 8295 1175
e-mail: enquiries@babingtonhouse.com
website: www.babingtonhouse.com

***Headmistress*: Mrs D Odysseas-Bailey**, BA Hons, PGCE

Age Range. Boys 3–7+, Girls 3–16.
Number in School. Day: 67 Boys, 199 Girls.
Fees per term (2008-2009). £1,090–£3,670.

A small day school that is frequently No. 1 in the London Borough of Bromley league tables. Praised by the ISI for achieving outstanding academic success at all key stages and providing exemplary pastoral care. The school has a friendly atmosphere, set in pleasant suburban area. Full range of courses for examinations at all levels. Most boys transfer to selective independent schools. Schools Curriculum Award 2002. ISA Excellence Award 2003. Investors in People third exemplary reaccreditation.

Specialist facilities for Computing – information technology, Music, Art, Business & Communications, and Textiles.

Small classes: Maximum size 18 pupils; Careers guidance by specialists.

Wide range of sports (Athletics, Swimming, Tennis, Netball, Gymnastics, Trampoline, Table Tennis and access to fitness centre in Senior School) and extra-curricular activities

(Drama, Gym Club, Choir, Chess Club, Latin Dance, Elocution and Instrumental tuition).

Charitable status. Babington House School is a Registered Charity, number 307914. It exists to provide exemplary education.

Baston School

Baston Road Hayes Bromley Kent BR2 7AB
Tel: 020 8462 1010
Fax: 020 8462 0438
e-mail: admin@bastonschool.org.uk
website: www.bastonschool.org.uk

***Headmistress*: Mrs Ann-Marie Jefferys**, BA Hons, MA, PGCE

Age Range. 2½–16.
Number in School. 150 Day Girls.
Fees per term (2008-2009). £690–£3,180.

Whatever your daughter's abilities, Baston will provide her with excellent teaching in small classes, backed up by a pastoral care system which is second to none. High fliers will be stimulated to achieve their full potential, while the less academically gifted will be given all the individual coaching and attention needed for their success.

We pride ourselves in bringing out the best in every girl who passes through our hands. Each girl leaves us not only having achieved her academic potential, she will also be mature, confident and ready to cope with further challenges. Such aspirations were confirmed by the ISI last year when they inspected our school.

- "Baston is a secure and caring environment in which girls fulfil their potential and develop as very responsible, polite and considerate young adults."
- "The staff are highly committed and teach well"
- "Discipline and behaviour are excellent"
- "Pastoral care is excellent"
- "Governance is good" and "the school is well led"

Independent Schools Inspectorate report, January 2007

Do come and visit us and see for yourselves how your daughter could benefit from a Baston education.

Bedstone College

Bucknell Shropshire SY7 0BG

(See entry in SHMIS section)

Beech Hall School

Tytherington Macclesfield Cheshire SK10 2EG

(See entry in IAPS section)

Beech House School

184 Manchester Road Rochdale Lancashire OL11 4JQ
Tel: 01706 646309
e-mail: info@beechhouseschool.co.uk
website: www.beechhouseschool.co.uk

***Headmaster*: Mr Kevin Sartain**, BSc Hons, PGCE, Dip Spo Psy, CBiol, FIBiol

Age Range. 3–16 Co-educational.
Number of Pupils. 260.
Fees per term (2008-2009). £700–£1,646.

The school is a wholly independent co-educational day school for boys and girls aged 3 to 16 years. Founded in 1922, it comprises a Lower Preparatory Department for children aged 3 to 6 years, and an Upper Preparatory Department for children aged 7 to 11 years and a Senior Department for those aged 11 to l6 years based at Manchester Road.

The aim of the school is to blend the best of traditional education with the skills and resources of the modern system to ensure that pupils' talents are exercised to the full. To this end, class sizes are kept small, with 20 or fewer pupils per form at preparatory level and 16 or fewer in each secondary class. The school upholds traditional values and behaviour, providing a secure, caring and academically challenging environment. This gives Beech House its unique character as a 'family-centred school'.

The Lower Preparatory Department is an integral part of the main school but is housed in its own self-contained unit at Broadfield Stile. It overlooks the delightful gardens and open play area of Broadfield Park. Pupils are admitted to the Nursery during the course of the term in which they attain the age of three. It is usual then for natural progression to take place through the rest of the school in line with age and ability.

The Upper Preparatory and Senior Departments enjoy the benefit of two Science Laboratories and pupils from the age of seven years and upwards spend time each week in this specialist facility under the direction and guidance of fully-qualified Science teachers. The school also has its own Lending, Reference and Careers Libraries as well as Art and Design, Information and Communication Technology and Craft, Design and Technology facilities, which allow pupils to work with a variety of materials including electronics and textiles. A new music room and Sports Hall have just opened. The school has its own sports field. These facilities have been installed to provide opportunities for developing skills relevant to modern life and all pupils enjoy 'hands on' experience.

The curriculum is designed to flow from the grounding in the Nursery Department through to the upper sections of the school, culminating in external examinations at 16 years of age. Some pupils are not necessarily set by their chronological age and are fast tracked. These pupils are allowed to sit their external examinations early.

Bishop Challoner School

228 Bromley Road Shortlands Bromley Kent BR2 0BS
Tel: 020 8460 3546
Fax: 020 8466 8885
e-mail: office@bishopchallonerschool.com
website: www.bishopchallonerschool.com

***Headteacher*: Ms Karen Barry**, BA, MA, PGCE, NPQH

Age Range. 2½–18.
Number in School. 420 Day Pupils.
Fees per term (from April 2008). Seniors £2,745, Juniors £2,165, Infants £1,950, Nursery £412–£1,960.

This is a Roman Catholic Independent Co-educational School with Nursery, Infants and Junior Sections 2½–11 years and a Senior School section 11–18 years.

The School includes a percentage of non-Catholics.

The School curriculum includes all National Curriculum subjects and others (Latin) leading to GCSE, A levels and Oxbridge. Admissions to the Senior School at any age follows the successful completion of an entrance examination and an interview with the headteacher.

Charitable status. Bishop Challoner School is a Registered Charity, number 235468. It exists to provide education for boys and girls.

The Bolitho School

Polwithen Road Penzance Cornwall TR18 4JR
Tel: 01736 363271
Fax: 01736 330960
e-mail: enquiries@bolitho.cornwall.sch.uk
website: www.bolitho.cornwall.sch.uk

Chairman of Governors: Mr J P W Clarke

***Headmaster*: David Dobson**, BA, BPhil, MA

Co-educational Day and Boarding School.

Age Range. 4–18 years.

Number of Pupils. Boys: 50 Boarders, 122 Day; Girls: 33 Boarders, 108 Day.

Fees per term (2008-2009). Day £1,825–£3,325; Weekly Boarding £4,900–£5,650; Full Boarding £5,600–£6,350. Sixth Form IB: £3,800 (day), £6,100 (weekly boarding), £6,800 (full boarding) (fees held at this rate for the 2 year course). Lunch for Day Pupils £160.

The Bolitho School is a small, co-educational school catering for pupils of all ages and for day pupils, weekly and full boarders. It deservedly has a national and international reputation for its pioneering and forward-looking approach. Distinctive educational features include: an accelerated national curriculum strategy, whereby pupils take the Key Stage 2 and 3 SATs tests a year early, allowing a three-year programme for the GCSE courses; there is a bilingual section, unique to the UK, where pupils can take around 30% of the syllabus through the medium of French; in the sixth form, students take the internationally prestigious International Baccalaureate – welcomed and recognised by all UK universities, all EU and USA universities, and most other universities worldwide. Set sizes average 12 for children between the ages of 5 years old and 13 years old. This falls even further to 10 for the GCSE years and 7 for the IB Diploma. Above all, however, the school is a very happy school indeed.

The school's stated aim is to 'bring out the potential of every child and to offer a rounded education that aims at the highest academic standards'. At the heart of the school's philosophy lies the belief that children have extraordinary potential in a great many directions. If this potential is not realised during childhood, it fades; if it is identified and nourished, a child can be galvanised into a dynamic and motivated personality. If a child is to receive a genuinely rounded education, then it must hold that art, drama, music and sports should be embedded firmly into the curriculum – and this the school has done. In addition, there are a great many clubs, activities, outings and expeditions catering for all age groups.

The school prides itself on its European and international outlook. International students from all over the world are warmly welcomed and encouraged to apply. Penzance, in Cornwall, is the warmest locality of the UK. It is also one of the safest and most beautiful parts of the country. This not only attracts pupils of excellence: the location, combined with the school's strong reputation, attracts large numbers of applications for teaching posts, and in consequence the teaching at the school is genuinely excellent.

Charitable status. The Bolitho School is a Registered Charity, number 1048545. The school exists to bring out the potential of every child, to do so in a Christian environment, and to offer a rounded education that aims at the highest academic standards.

Bowbrook House School

Peopleton Nr Pershore Worcs WR10 2EE
Tel: 01905 841242
Fax: 01905 840716
e-mail: enquiries@bowbrookhouseschool.co.uk
website: www.bowbrookhouseschool.co.uk

***Headmaster*: Mr C D Allen**, BSc Hons, CertEd, DipSoc

Age Range. $3^1/_2$–16.

Number in School. Day: 127 Boys, 56 Girls.

Fees per term (2008-2009). £1,515–£2,440.

Bowbrook House is set in 14 acres of picturesque Worcestershire countryside yet within easy reach of Worcester, Pershore and Evesham. The school caters for the academic child and also those of average ability, who can benefit from the small classes. All pupils are able to take full advantage of the opportunities offered and are encouraged to participate in all activities. As well as the academic subjects, the school has a flourishing art department, a computer room, hard tennis courts and an open air swimming pool in addition to extensive games fields.

The Pre-Prep department of $3^1/_2$–8 year olds is a self-contained unit but enjoys the use of the main school facilities.

Whilst stressing academic achievement, the school aims to provide a structured and disciplined environment in which children of all abilities can flourish, gain confidence and achieve their true potential. The small school size enables the head and staff to know all pupils well, to be able to accurately assess their strengths and weaknesses it enables each pupil to be an important part of the school and to feel that their individual attitudes, behaviour, efforts and achievements are important.

There is an extended school day from 8.15 am to 5.30 pm, with supervised prep sessions. There is also an extensive and varied extra-curricular programme run by specialist coaches from basketball, gym and dance to kick-boxing and fencing.

Brabyns Preparatory School

GEMS Education

34/36 Arkwright Road Marple Stockport Cheshire SK6 7DB
Tel: 0161 427 2395
Fax: 0161 449 0704
e-mail: admin@brabynsprepschool.co.uk
website: www.brabynsprepschool.co.uk

***Head*: Mr L Sanders**, BEd

Age Range. 3–11 years.

Number in School. Day: Boys 57, Girls 72.

Fees per term (2008-2009). £1,313–£1,779.

Brabyns Preparatory School is an independent school offering education for children from Nursery age to 11 years old, accommodated in two large Edwardian houses which have been sensitively redesigned to provide for the needs of the children while retaining a sense of warmth and security.

Specialist facilities include Hall/Gym, Nursery, ICT Suite, Art room and Science Laboratory.

Children are taught in small classes throughout the school. The broad curriculum is based on the requirements of the National Curriculum and children are prepared for examinations to the Local Independent Grammar Schools. Brabyns has an excellent record of successful entrants to these schools.

Our pre-school provision starts in Nursery where pupils embark upon the Foundation Station Curriculum. Children are accepted from the half term in which they have their third birthday. Planned and directed activities led by qualified teachers and Nursery Nurses provide rich and challenging learning experiences. The current pupil staff ratio in the Foundation Stage is 1:6. Pupils receive a sound foundation in basic skills and socialisation preparing the way to the more structured academic work in Reception. The school curriculum from Year 1 to Year 6 is linked to the National Curriculum, but preparation for the independent schools examinations becomes increasingly important.

Braeside School for Girls

130 High Road Buckhurst Hill Essex IG9 5SD
Tel: 020 8504 1133
Fax: 020 8505 6675
e-mail: enquiries@braesideschool.co.uk
website: www.braesideschool.co.uk

***Headteacher*: Mrs G Haddon**, BA Hons, PGCE

Age Range. 3–16.
Number in School. 214 Day Girls.
Fees per term (2008-2009). £1,755–£2,850.

Braeside School, founded in 1944, is situated close to Epping Forest.

It provides an education for girls from the age of 3 to 16, and the possibility of spending all the compulsory years of schooling within one organisation provides the opportunity for secure, stable progress for every girl.

The school provides a wide range of subjects and sets its own high standards in work and behaviour. It aims to give each pupil a sound foundation for life and every chance to develop individual capabilities and interests.

Entry, at every age apart from 3 and 4, is by test and interview.

With the support of a qualified and dedicated staff, our girls consistently achieve high pass rates at GCSE.

Brantwood School for Girls

1 Kenwood Bank Sheffield S7 1NU
Tel: 0114 258 1747
Fax: 0114 258 1847
e-mail: enquiries@brantwoodschool.co.uk
website: www.brantwoodschool.co.uk

***Headmistress*: Mrs Lynn Marriott**, BEd

Age Range. 3–16.
Number in School. 170 girls.
Fees per term (2008-2009). £1,491–£2,850 (including prompt payment discount). Fees include lunches.

Brantwood is an Independent Day School for girls between the ages of 3 and 16 years. Founded over eighty years ago, the school is a charitable trust situated in a gracious Victorian building set in an acre of mature gardens, with play areas and within easy distance of Sheffield city centre. As a non-denominational school, Brantwood welcomes girls of all faiths and beliefs.

In recent years, the Victorian house has been extended to provide modern facilities for its high level of education and there is an ongoing programme of refurbishment. Classrooms are bright. There are well-equipped Science Laboratories, a Food Technology Room, a multi-purpose Exhibition Hall and the latest ICT systems. Art is one of the major strengths of the school, and Drama and Music play an important part in school life.

Teaching groups are small. Brantwood provides a stimulating and challenging environment where girls are encouraged to reach their individual academic potential. Pupil tracking and monitoring are strengths of the school, academic standards are high and Brantwood has an excellent record at examination level.

Brantwood combines traditional teaching values with a progressive curriculum. The emphasis is on a broad, balanced education, where extra-curricular activities are recognised as broadening the girls' outlook as well as affording cultural and social benefits.

The school offers early morning supervision from 8.00 am onwards and an extensive range of extra-curricular clubs at lunchtimes and after school, including the Duke of Edinburgh's Award Scheme. There is facility for girls to remain after school to complete work and breakfast, lunch and tea are available to all girls.

Tuition is offered for a wide range of musical instruments including piano, flute, violin, saxophone, classical guitar and clarinet. Singing lessons are also available. The school has successful choirs and several instrumental groups.

Entry to the Infant and Junior School is by interview and assessment and entry to the Senior School is by Entrance Test in January and interview. The Headmistress is always pleased to welcome parents and their daughters to visit Brantwood. Further information is available on request.

Charitable status. The South Yorkshire Independent Schools Trust Ltd is a Registered Charity, number 509037. It aims to provide high quality education to girls aged 3–16 years living in South Yorkshire.

Bredon School

Pull Court Bushley Nr Tewkesbury Gloucestershire GL20 6AH
Tel: 01684 293156
Fax: 01684 276392
e-mail: enquiries@bredonschool.co.uk
website: www.bredonschool.org

***Principal*: D J Keyte**, ACMA

Director of Education: Mrs S Webb

Age Range. 7–18.
Number in School. 230. Boarders: 90 Boys, 32 Girls. Day: 70 Boys, 38 Girls.
Fees per term (2008-2009). Day £2,125–£4,885. Weekly boarding £5,275–£7,525. Full Boarding £5,415–£7,665.

Bredon School is situated in magnificent rural surroundings and delivers a broad-based education centring upon individual attention and personal recognition. Bredon follows the National Curriculum at all Key Stages through to GCSE and A Level. In addition Bredon offers extensive vocational programmes at Foundation, Intermediate and Advanced levels. Class sizes average 10–12 and teacher/pupil ratio 1:7. Bredon also has a thriving School Farm.

Selection is by potential not just attainment and specialist support is available to pupils with learning difficulties through the specialist Access Centre. Bredon educates the whole child through sound realistic academic provision, sympathetic pastoral care, regular leadership challenges and a varied sports programme.

Bridgewater School

Drywood Hall Worsley Road Worsley Manchester M28 2WQ
Tel: 0161 794 1463
Fax: 0161 794 3519
e-mail: admin@bridgewater-school.org.uk
website: www.bridgewater-school.co.uk

***Headmistress*: Ms G Shannon-Little**, BA

Age Range. 3–18.

Number in School. Prep: 110 Boys, 99 Girls; Seniors: 157 Boys, 125 Girls.

Fees per term (2008-2009). £2,010–£2,710. Lunch is included.

The parents, students and staff are very proud of Bridgewater School. It has the feeling of a large family to it; small enough so that each student is known and respected as an individual, but large enough to offer the stimulation of a wide range of subjects and activities. From Preparatory right up to Sixth Form, each person has the opportunity to shine.

The relaxed atmosphere is the result of good relationships between the students and staff for whom nothing is too much trouble. As a result we develop students with confidence, self-discipline and the self-belief to aim high. In short we bring out the best in each student.

Entry for the Prep Department is by interview and assessment. There is an entrance examination at 11+ for entry to the Senior part of the school. Entry at other ages is by interview and appropriate assessment.

Bursaries and scholarships are available throughout the senior school.

Charitable status. Bridgewater School is a Registered Charity, number 1105547.

Bronte School

Mayfield 7 Pelham Road Gravesend Kent DA11 0HN
Tel: 01474 533805
Fax: 01474 352003
e-mail: enquiry@bronteschool.co.uk
website: www.bronteschool.co.uk

***Headmaster*: Mr R A Dyson**, BA, CertEd

Age Range. 3–11.

Number in School. 120 Day Pupils: 70 Boys, 50 Girls.

Fees per term (2007-2008). £1,225–£1,925 (£40 discount for those paying on or before first day of term) and stationery £35 per term. Compulsory extras: Swimming from age 5.

This is a day school serving Gravesend and the surrounding villages. It was established in 1905. The children are taught in small classes and a close family atmosphere exists throughout the school. Children are prepared for all types secondary education. Entry is preferred at 3 following a parental visit to the school and an interview with the Head. Children joining the school at a later stage are tested informally in English and Maths.

Buckingham College School

Hindes Road Harrow Middlesex HA1 1SH
Tel: 020 8427 1220
Fax: 020 8863 0816
e-mail: enquiries@buckcoll.org
website: www.buckcoll.org

***Headmaster*: D F T Bell**, MA (Oxon), PGCE

Age Range. Boys 11–18, Girls 16–18.

Number in School. Day: 130.

Fees per term (2007-2008). £2,756–£3,195. Compulsory extras: Lunches.

Buckingham College is an independent secondary school for boys aged 11–18, and girls aged 16–18.

Founded in 1936, it is a member of the E Ivor Hughes Educational Foundation. It is Accredited by the Independent Schools Council.

Students are prepared for 16 GCSE and 13 GCE A Level examinations. The Sixth Form is conducted on tutorial lines, preparing small groups of pupils for A levels. There is a full range of games and physical education activities.

The school aims to provide a well disciplined and happy community based on Christian principles in which each pupil may play an active and satisfying part. Classes are small – under 20 – and there is a wide range of sports.

Admission is by way of an individual entrance test and interview.

Scholarships are available on merit.

Charitable status. The E Ivor Hughes Educational Foundation is a Registered Charity, number 293623. It exists to provide education for children.

Bury Catholic Preparatory School

Arden House Manchester Road Bury Lancashire BL9 9BH
Tel: 0161 764 2346
Fax: 0161 764 2346
e-mail: admin@burycatholicprepschool.co.uk
website: www.burycatholicprepschool.co.uk

Mission Statement:

'Each child in this school family is as important to us as they are to God'

Chair of Governors: Ms Jane Riley

***Head*: Mrs A C Dean**, BEd

Age Range. 3–11 Co-educational.

Number of Pupils. 134.

Fees per term (2008-2009). £1,420.

The school was founded in 1943 by the order of The Daughters of the Cross. In 1972 parents formed a private limited company and took over the running of the school. The school is sited on the main Bury to Manchester road and is unique as a Catholic independent school in this area. Children come from Bury, the Rossendale Valley, Rochdale, Bolton and Manchester.

Christ is at the heart of everything we do; we welcome children from all denominations and hope that by our teaching and good example we strive to be inclusive through the celebration and understanding of other faiths.

Recent inspections confirmed that the school offers an 'outstanding quality of education'. It has a friendly and purposeful atmosphere where small class sizes and 'highly effective teaching' (Ofsted 2006) by experienced and dedicated staff ensure that education is an enjoyable and rewarding experience for everyone. Specialist teaching for French, Music and Sport is provided for all children from Nursery upwards. Year 6 are thoroughly prepared socially and academically for entry into the senior school of their choice. Recent examination successes include Withington Girls', Manchester Grammar School, Bolton School, Bury Grammar School and Bacup & Rawtenstall Grammar School. Children leave us confident and excited about the future.

The Nursery class offers 24 full-time places for 3 year olds. A close working partnership with parents ensures children feel safe and that staff continue to build on children's interests and appetite for learning.

Creative development and performing arts are strengths. Recent whole school productions have included The King and I and Whistle Down the Wind. The senior choir also sings at each end of term mass.

A wide variety of extra curricular activities includes fencing, art clubs, chess and sport.

A School Council set up in 2003 continues to be run by children and staff. They are very enthusiastic, recently designing a welcome booklet for new children, leading an assembly on the problems caused by litter and currently being proactive in healthy schools initiatives.

The school offers Ofsted-registered before and after school care and holidays clubs in each school holiday.

Open Day is held in the Autumn term but visits to the school and copies of our prospectus can be requested via the school office.

Charitable status. Bury Catholic Preparatory School is a Registered Charity, number 509280.

Bury Lawn School
GEMS Education

Soskin Drive Stantonbury Fields Milton Keynes Bucks MK14 6DP
Tel: 01908 574740/574753
Fax: 01908 574741
e-mail: registrar@burylawnschool.co.uk
website: www.burylawnschool.co.uk

***Headmaster*: J R Moreland**, MA

Deputy Head: Mrs K M Abrahams

Age Range. 3–18.

Number in School. 387: 236 boys, 151 girls.

Fees per term (2008-2009). Early Years £2,070–£2,280; Junior School £2,315–£2,849, Senior School £3,057.

The School was founded in 1970 but moved into its current premises in 1987. The school is part of the GEMS group. In 2004 a new sports hall and classroom block including a Performing Arts Suite, Media Studies Suite and IT Suite were opened and in 2006 4 new Science laboratories. The school has a friendly family atmosphere with class sizes of approximately 18. Set in its own grounds close to Milton Keynes city centre, Bury Lawn offers supervision all year round from 7.30 am until 6.30 pm. A vast transport network ensures pupils can attend the school from a large catchment area.

Pupils are assessed on entry and, in the Senior School, streamed according to ability in all subjects to ensure their maximum potential is achieved. The school has a Learning Support Department staffed by qualified teachers for those requiring extra help. A level students gain entry into universities including Oxbridge.

Bury Lawn offers all-round inter-denominational education for boys and girls with a wide range of subjects, modern languages, sport, dance and drama.

Monthly payment arrangements assist parents to afford the best of independent education. Government nursery funding applies.

Cambridge Centre for Sixth-form Studies (CCSS)

1 Salisbury Villas Station Road Cambridge CB1 2JF
Tel: 01223 716890
Fax: 01223 517530
e-mail: office@ccss.co.uk
website: www.ccss.co.uk

***Principal*: N Roskilly**, BA Hons, PGCE, NPQH, FRSA, FRGS

Age Range. 15–20.

Number in School. 200.

Fees per term (2008-2009). Tuition Fees: One-year GCSE Course: £3,320 (students under the age of 16 on 1 September), £5,338 (students over the age of 16 on 1 September). Two-year A Level Course: £5,338. Boarding Fee: £3,159.

General. CCSS is a co-educational sixth-form college offering GCSE and A Level courses to 200 students, supported by 98 staff. The college provides close academic supervision, a friendly, informal atmosphere and high levels of pastoral care. One-to-one private tutorials are an important and unique part of all A Level courses on top of group lessons. The small class sizes (averaging 5 students) allow plenty of opportunity for individual involvement and for developing each student's levels of understanding. A full and flexible GCSE curriculum is offered and at A Level there are over 35 subjects to choose from, without restrictions on choice.

Our Values. All teaching and non-teaching staff at CCSS believe in our moral purpose: that through good teaching, pastoral guidance and close tutorial support, we can improve the life chances of ALL of the students in our care. Our website, www.ccss.co.uk, outlines our core educational values, which we hope all students and their parents will share.

Admissions. CCSS does not select purely on academic merit. Our excellent examination results and value-added scores are due to top quality teaching in small classes, with additional private one-to-ones and exceptional pastoral care and support. For a student to take full advantage of this, he or she should feel comfortable with our values, be open-minded and have a positive attitude to his or her studies.

CCSS will look at every individual application and make a decision based on the wider individual merits of the applicant, not just on paper qualifications. Reports and transcripts from your current or previous school will be vital. For some, coming to interview at CCSS will be very difficult – though we would always welcome this if at all possible.

For many who will be working at CCSS in their second language, we will ask you to write a short essay so that we can get an idea of your language skills. It is not essential to have a formal English language qualification when you join CCSS, though if you have an IELTS score (measures ability to communicate in English across all four language skills – listening, reading, writing and speaking) of 5.5, or Cambridge First Certificate (FCE) level, then you should be able to cope with tuition in English.

Examination Results. CCSS had an enviable 99.6% pass-rate in A Level examinations in 2007 from a non-selective student intake. The great majority of students graduating from CCSS go on to university in the UK or elsewhere, with many enjoying success at Cambridge, Oxford, LSE and other top universities in subjects ranging from International Business to Law and Medicine.

Location and Facilities. CCSS is based in the exciting university town of Cambridge, close to the railway station and 50-minutes' train-ride from London, with easy connections to international airports. Our three teaching sites are within a few minutes' walk of each other and house 35 classrooms including laboratories, study rooms and specialist facilities for subjects such as Modern Languages, Media Studies, Art, Photography and Computing. The College Houses provide fully supervised single-room accommodation for 110 boarding students.

Charitable status. The Cambridge Centre for Sixth Form Studies is a Registered Charity, number 1084601.

Cambridge Tutors College

Water Tower Hill Croydon Surrey CR0 5SX
Tel: 020 8688 5284
Fax: 020 8686 9220
e-mail: admin@ctc.ac.uk
website: www.ctc.ac.uk

***Principal*: Mr Mario Di Clemente**, BA, PGCE

Age Range. 15–22 Co-educational.
Number of Pupils. 285.
Fees per annum (2008-2009). £14,400–£17,400.

For 50 years Cambridge Tutors College has offered high-quality education to young people from the United Kingdom and from across the world. Fundamental to the College's ethos is small group teaching – no group is larger than 9 – and regular testing – students take a test in every subject every week. This combination of small classes and sympathetic testing has proved to be highly successful in giving students the confidence to succeed.

The College has grown over the years, both in size and reputation, but still offers the individual attention that can only be gained in a small school. Most of its 300 students are studying A Levels and their achievements, year-on-year, are impressive. The average A Level pass rate (A–E) for the last 5 years is 99.5% (A/B 84%). Around 10% of leavers go on to Oxbridge, 10% to medical school, and 10% to LSE. The College runs a fast-track 1-year GCSE programme too, catering for students from 14+.

Situated in a pleasant parkside location by Park Hill in South Croydon, CTC is just a few minutes' walk from the town centre, East Croydon station and bus and tram routes. It is close to London, just 15 minutes by train, but surrounded by parkland and quiet residential streets.

The College is accredited by the Independent Schools Council and its most recent Ofsted inspection report in 2007 was extremely positive. Facilities and resources at CTC are modern and extremely well-appointed – all subjects have specialist resources and the Osborne Centre, opened in 2000, offers state-of-the-art ICT technology as well as a comfortable library and reading room, also a lecture theatre. An all-day café provides a wide variety of fresh food and drinks.

The College's welfare provision includes a team of trained professionals and all students have a personal tutor. Sporting and social activities take place each week and students are encouraged to take part. There is a good selection of clubs and societies that students can join, and trip and visits take place to places such as Euro Disney Paris and London attractions.

This year's crop of A Level results has set another record for the College, with 100% pass-rate, 84% A/B and 66% at grade A. Individual successes have been remarkable: 7 out of the top 10 students in the UK taking A Level Pure Maths were from CTC, 3 out of the top 10 Mathematics A Levels in the UK were CTC students, 5 students came in the top 5 for Statistics and one Biology A Level student came in the national top 10.

Charitable status. Cambridge Tutors Educational Trust Limited is a Registered Charity, number 312878.

Canbury School

Kingston Hill Kingston-upon-Thames Surrey KT2 7LN
Tel: 020 8549 8622
Fax: 020 8974 6018
e-mail: head@canburyschool.co.uk
website: www.canburyschool.co.uk

Founded in 1982, Canbury School is a co-educational independent day school. It is non-denominational.

***Head*: Mr R F Metters**, BEd

Age Range. 11–17.
Number in School. 65 day children.
Fees per term (2007-2008). £3,750.

Curriculum. We cover a full range of GCSE subjects, most pupils taking a total of eight or nine.

Entry requirements. There are tests in English and Mathematics. The Headmaster interviews each candidate. A trial day or two at the school can be arranged prior to entry.

Subjects offered. In Years 7, 8 and 9 we emphasise English, Mathematics and Science in line with the requirements of the National Curriculum. Our extended curriculum includes Spanish, Geography, History, Information Technology, Art, Drama, PE and Games, Music and Personal and Moral Education. Later, Physics, Chemistry and Biology are taken as doubly-certificated GCSE subjects. Individual arrangements can be made for pupils to prepare for GCSE in Japanese, German, Chinese and other languages. Business Studies is offered in Years 10 and 11 as an option leading to the GCSE.

Facilities. IT computer facilities are accessible to all pupils. There is an excellent art room. Pupils are transported to a wide range of sports facilities within the Borough.

Canbury School is different in placing emphasis on small classes. No class has more than 15 pupils. Full concentration is placed on bringing out the talents of each pupil. Pupils participate in the school council which makes decisions in some areas of school life.

Charitable status. Canbury School is a Registered Charity, number 803766. It exists to provide education to a broad range of children including some of various nationalities who stand to benefit from being in a small school.

Carleton House Preparatory School

Lyndhurst Road Mossley Hill Liverpool L18 8AQ
Tel: 0151 724 4880
Fax: 0151 724 6086
e-mail: carleton@carletonhouse.fsbusiness.co.uk
website: www.carletonhouse.co.uk

***Headmaster*: Mr P Andrew**, BA, PGCE

Age Range. 4–11.
Number in School. 150.
Fees per term (2008-2009). £1,718.

Carleton House is a Catholic Preparatory School set in an attractive Victorian House in the Mossley Hill conservation area.

The school is open to children of other denominations and promotes the spiritual, moral and cultural development of all pupils. It recognises that the needs of all pupils are unique and aims to develop fully the talent of every individual.

Small classes enable the well qualified and experienced staff the opportunity to provide individual attention in a friendly, caring atmosphere. Additional specialist teaching is provided for children requiring support in the basic subjects.

The implementation of all ten National Curriculum subjects ensures a broad, well balanced curriculum is followed but great importance is given to Maths and English as success in these subjects is central to development in other areas.

French has been successfully introduced in all classes including Reception.

All children receive music lessons but individual piano and guitar lessons are also available.

Emphasis is placed on high academic standards with children being prepared for a variety of Entrance examinations at 11 and more than 90% of pupils gain places at selective schools of their choice.

A wide range of sports and extra curricular activities are offered to both boys and girls, including football, netball, cricket, rounders, swimming, chess, quiz, singing and speech choir. The children compete in local sporting events as well as choral festivals.

Theatre and educational visits are encouraged along with a residential trip to the Lake District, and Shropshire for older pupils, which provide field and adventure activities that help build confidence and self esteem.

Close contact with parents is promoted through regular parent/teacher meetings and reports on pupils progress.

A thriving Parent Teacher Association provides social functions for parents while raising funds for extra equipment.

After school and holiday provision is now provided by the 'Kids Club'. This operates daily from 3.30 pm until 6.00 pm and 8.00 am until 6.00 pm in holiday time.

Parents are welcome to visit the school by appointment.

Further information available from the Headteacher.

Charitable status. Carleton House Preparatory School is a Registered Charity, number 505310. It exists to provide education for boys and girls.

Castle House School

Chetwynd End Newport Shropshire TF10 7JE
Tel: 01952 811035
Fax: 01952 811035
e-mail: admin@castlehouseschool.co.uk
website: www.castlehouseschool.co.uk

Chairman of Governors: Mrs Arthemise Hays

***Headmaster*: Richard Walden**, MA Hons (Downing College, Cambridge), CertEd, MEd Hons, FCollP

Type of School. Co-educational day preparatory school.
Age Range. 2–11.
Number of Pupils. 105: 55 girls, 50 boys.
Fees per term (2008-2009). £1,918–£2,032.

Castle House is a friendly day preparatory school with a family feel. It is small enough for everybody to know and be known by everybody else, but offers a full and busy programme.

The school aims to bring the best out of every pupil by providing opportunities to excel and developing confidence to try.

Much importance is attached to the children being kind and considerate to each other, in the belief that happy children work best.

Since 1980 the school has been a charitable trust, run by a board of governors with varied talents and local interests. It was founded in 1944 by Miss Z Pitchford. The current head is the fourth.

The school's Georgian house, set in delightful gardens, is in the conservation area of Newport, a country town in east Shropshire. It serves urban and rural areas, including west Staffordshire, Market Drayton, Eccleshall, Telford and Shifnal.

Pupils are prepared for entrance exams to independent schools, boarding and day, and to local grammar schools of which the two in Newport are unique in Shropshire. There is an excellent record of passes and scholarships, from a mixed ability intake, with children achieving their realistic potential.

The curriculum covers all major subjects, plus Art, DT, French, Music, Spanish, ICT, PE, Games, Swimming, Gymnastics and Drama for all children. RE and assemblies are Christian, but non-denominational, encouraging all to join in.

Our flourishing educational nursery, for two to four year olds, is open all year from 8.00 am to 6.00 pm.

A rich range of after-school activities currently includes build-it, art, crafts, choirs, percussion, computers, gymnastics, chess, radio, board games, philosophy, football, netball, cricket and rounders.

Matches are played in traditional team games, cross-country and swimming. Particular success has been achieved in schools' gymnastics, with girls' teams winning silver medals at national level in GISGA (independent schools) competitions. Boys' teams have three times won national under 9 titles and the school team has twice won the BSGA under 11 mixed teams Floor and Vault national title. The teams are ISA national champions.

We see education as a cooperative venture with parents. There are regular progress reports and feedback meetings. Parents are encouraged to bring their concerns to the teachers and they help the school develop positive and courteous attitudes in the children. There is a lively Parents' Association.

Further information can be obtained by telephoning the Registrar at the school.

Charitable status. Castle House School Trust Ltd is a Registered Charity, number 510515. It exists for the provision of high quality education for boys and girls.

CATS Cambridge

Round Church Street Cambridge CB5 8AD
Tel: 01223 314431
Fax: 01223 467773
e-mail: enquiries@catscambridge.com
website: www.ceg-uk.com

***Principal*: Dr Glenn Hawkins**, BSc, PhD, MBA

Age Range. 14–19+.
Number of Students. 290.
Fees per term (2008-2009). Boarding £6,700–£9,950; Day £4,900–£7,200.

CATS Cambridge is a top independent school offering GCSE, A Level, University Foundation, Academic English and Summer School programmes. Located in the centre of Cambridge, the city's academic tradition and lively student community enhance the lives of all CATS students who make use of the famous Cambridge Union Society for meetings, socialising and refreshment. Residential students live in fully-supervised College Lodges or Homestay accommodation with local families, all of which are located within a short walk of the College. For older and more independent students, CATS has supervised self-catering houses and flats available.

CATS provides students with the qualifications to go on to the best university courses through a balanced education that fosters maturity and responsibility. We will help you take charge of your life through 'managed independence', giving you the chance to take responsibility for your own decisions and actions in a supportive environment. The balance between this attractive liberal approach and the discipline of well-proven teaching and learning methods allows students to meet challenges and targets both in academic pursuits and in personal development.

A broad, forward-looking GCSE timetable is programmed and sixth formers are guided in selecting the right A Level courses from the 40+ on offer. Students are taught in small groups of up to ten and able, stimulating and enthusiastic tutors help develop study skills, the command of English and examination technique. Situated on the same campus, Cambridge School of Visual & Performing Arts runs a highly-regarded Art Foundation course in preparation for entry to Art Colleges. The school also offers a Drama Foundation course (in association with RADA) – the only one of its kind in the UK.

CATS has delivered rewarding results for many students in terms of retakes and expert guidance for university entrance and career planning is comprehensive, sensitive and professional. There is an extensive range of cultural, sporting and social activities with study trips arranged each year. Each student has a Personal Tutor who monitors, listens, helps and encourages as required, and as a dedicated team deals with all matters of accommodation, welfare and general college discipline. Communications between the College and parents through reports and connections are a crucial part of the CATS education.

Chase Academy

Lyncroft House St John's Road Cannock Staffordshire WS11 0UR
Tel: 01543 501800
Fax: 01543 501801
e-mail: info@chaseacademy.com
website: www.chaseacademy.com

***Principal*: Mr M D Ellse**, MA, CPhys, MInstP, PGCE

Age Range. 3–18.

Number in School. 7 Boarders, 207 Day.

Fees per term (2008-2009). Day: £752–£2,584, Boarding from £3,610.

Independent day and boarding school for boys and girls from nursery to A Level.

Formerly a convent, founded in 1879, the senior school was added in 1980.

Extensive modern school on spacious urban site. New science, sport, technology, computing, language facilities. New Music School in 2007. Extensive sports facilities, including 3 floodlit astroturf pitches.

Academic work. Small classes allow attention to the individual student. The National Curriculum is shadowed throughout. Common core up to Year 9. GCSE, AS and A2 level in: English, Mathematics, Physics, Chemistry, Biology, Design and Technology, Business Studies, History, Geography, French, German, Physical Education, Music, Drama, Art, Dance, Accounting, Latin.

Boarding. Delightful modern rooms, half of which are single study-bedrooms. The associated International College makes provision for overseas students who need to learn or improve their English.

Dyslexia. Support for intelligent dyslexics from a Dyslexia Institute trained teacher and within the small classes.

Sport. Football, cricket, hockey and netball are the principal sports with school facilities for tennis, volleyball and basketball.

Music and Drama. A strong team of professional performers and first-rate teachers producing big uptake in the performing arts.

School day. 08.50–15.50. Prep until 16.45. Facilities for early drop-off and late pick-up.

Cherry Trees School

Flempton Road Risby Bury St Edmunds Suffolk IP28 6QJ
Tel: 01284 760531
Fax: 01284 750177
e-mail: admin@cherrytrees-school.co.uk
website: www.cherrytrees-school.co.uk

***Headmistress*: Wendy E S Compson**, BSc Hons, Montessori Adv Dip

Age Range. Co-educational 3 months–11 years.

Number in School. Day 200; Half day 68.

Fees per term (2008-2009). £2,165 (Reception–Year 3); £2,565 (Years 4–6).

Staff: 16 Full Time, 12 Part Time, 8 Visiting.

Religious affiliation: Interdenominational.

Entry requirements: Interview and assessment

Montessori education is offered through to 11. The school is open 50 weeks of the year from 8 am to 6 pm during school time and from 8 am to 6 pm during the holidays.

Pupils are prepared for Preparatory school entrance and scholarship examinations. Girls common entrance at 11+. Boys common entrance at 11+.

Cherry Trees School enjoys an unrivalled position in 8 acres of magnificent Suffolk countryside. The buildings are modern and extremely well equipped. Specialist rooms are provided for science, computing, design and technology, art and craft, home economics and music. The school has established a high academic standard.

A large nursery department, employing the Montessori method, is run by fully qualified staff in superbly equipped facilities for children aged from 3 months to 5 years.

Pupils are encouraged to participate in a full range of indoor and outdoor sporting activities which include swimming, football, mini rugby, hockey, netball, athletics, cross country, tennis on our own court and cricket. Visiting specialists teach dance, piano, string, woodwind, brass instruments and singing.

Clubs operating after school, offer activities such as choir, environmental studies, drama and sport.

French is available from nursery level with children aged from 7 visit France annually, exploring the environment and using their French conversation.

A weekend trip to an outdoor activity centre in Norfolk takes place each Autumn term with educational visits to York, Isle of Wight and Cornwall.

Chilton Cantelo School

Cognita Schools Group

Chilton Cantelo Yeovil Somerset BA22 8BG
Tel: 01935 850555
Fax: 01935 850482
e-mail: ccs@pavilion.co.uk

***Headmaster*: Dr John M Price**, BSc, PhD

Age Range. Co-educational 7–16.

Number of Pupils. 435: Boys 265, Girls 165; 210 Boarding, 225 Day.

Fees per term (2008-2009). Preparatory Department: £2,360 (day), £4,680 (boarding). Senior School: £3,050 (day), £6,040 (boarding).

Chilton Cantelo School offers a civilised, 'family' environment in which individuals are valued and in which they are encouraged to grow into the best versions of themselves.

Set in and around an imposing 18th Century manor house and 20 acres of grounds, four and a half miles from both Sherborne and Yeovil, Chilton offers a genuine all-round education designed to develop each pupil's potential. Classes are small, results at GCSE are exceptional. Over 90% of candidates achieved between 6 and 13 A*–C grades in 2006 and 2007.

The School Day runs from 8.40 am until 5.30 pm and Saturday mornings until 1.00 pm.

The Preparatory Department is housed in the recently renovated Carriage House, with boarding facilities in the nearby former stable block, "Woodlands". It has its own dedicated staff and facilities and derives further benefit from sharing additional specialist staff and resources with the Senior School, to which pupils transfer at the age of 11.

In the Senior School the broad academic curriculum is complemented by making full use of extramural activities, with pupils enjoying 'enrichment' activities every day. Activities typically include archery, computing, dance, fencing, golf, horse riding, karate, kick-boxing, outdoor education, swimming, a variety of music and drama, woodcraft and a full range of team games.

At weekends, boarding pupils can choose from a range of activities and outings. Senior boys' accommodation is in a stunning new boarding house, "Riverside".

Prep is generally completed during the school day and Day Scholars have the option to board on an occasional (or regular-night) basis. They may also join our outstanding Corps of Drums.

The main strength of the School, in addition to small teaching groups, impressive academic results and an extremely broad curriculum, is our experience and success at affording each pupil a great deal of individual attention.

A prospectus may be obtained from the School and prospective parents are encouraged to visit the School. Please telephone the Admissions Secretary to arrange an appointment.

Claires Court Schools

Ray Mill Road East Maidenhead Berkshire SL6 8TE
Tel: 01628 411470; Registrar: 01628 411472
Fax: 01628 411466
e-mail: registrar@clairescourt.com
website: www.clairescourt.com

Principals:
H St J Wilding, BA, MCIM, FRSA (*Bursar*) and **J T Wilding**, BSc, FRSA

Head of Claires Court: J M Rayer, BSc, PGCE
Head of Ridgeway: Mrs K M Rogg, BEd
Head of College: Mrs L Green, CPhys, MInstP, BSc, PGCE

Age Range. 3–18.

Number of Pupils. Boys 626; Girls 307. Sixth Form: 74 Boys, 39 Girls.

Teaching Staff. 75 full time, 36 part time, 20 visiting.

Fees per term (2008-2009). £2,145–£3,645.

Claires Court Schools is a school on three sites – Claires Court (Senior Boys), Ridgeway (Junior Boys) and College (Co-ed Nursery, Girls to 16 and Co-ed Sixth Form). The ethos of the Schools lies in the provision for its pupils of a thorough education in all senses so that in time the challenges of the future will be met with confidence.

A rich and full programme of study and activity leads to academic success, sports accomplishment and cultural fulfilment, within a firm structure based on friendship and self discipline. All pupils follow the National Curriculum and participate in the main sports for boys and girls.

Ridgeway (boys 4+ to 11) is situated to the west of the town centre in its own extensive grounds which include a swimming pool and newly-built sports hall. The classroom accommodation has been considerably extended to provide additional space for art and science.

At 11+ boys transfer to Claires Court which is located near Boulters Lock in a pleasant residential area of the town. Here the facilities include a purpose built technology wing housing science laboratories as well as facilities for art, ICT and technology. The Nicholas Watson Sports Centre opened in March 2003 with an extended gallery area for physiological testing and fencing development planned. A wide range of subjects are offered at GCSE as well as PSE and careers advice being available.

The College, based close to the town centre of Maidenhead, has its own pleasant grounds housing a covered swimming pool, tennis courts and its own sports grounds. The Nursery based here is co-ed for children from 3 to 4+ years from where girls transfer into the main school at College and boys to Ridgeway. As with Claires Court, a wide range of subjects is available for study at GCSE together with quality facilities for all subjects throughout the age range.

The Sixth Form is co-ed with boys and girls transferring from Claires Court and College as well as accepting external candidates. A wide range of A Level subjects is available for study with considerable pastoral, higher education and careers guidance available.

All parts of the School participate in extensive after school activities programmes and whilst boys and girls are academically taught on separate sites, they meet for many social, extra curricular and aesthetic activities.

The School is multi denominational. A prospectus containing further information may be obtained from the School and prospective parents are always welcome to visit. Open Mornings are held throughout the year.

Cliff Schools
Alpha Plus Group

Prep: St John's Lodge 2 Leeds Road Wakefield West Yorkshire WF1 3JT
Tel: 01924 373597
Fax: 01924 211137

Pre-Prep:
24 Bar Lane Wakefield West Yorkshire WF1 4AD
Tel: 01924 203200
Fax: 01924 203205
e-mail: info@cliffschool.com
website: www.cliffschool.com

***Principal*: G Milne**, BEd Hons, CertEd, MCollP, FRSA

Age Range. Boys and Girls 2–11 years.

Number in School. 80 Girls, 70 Boys.

Fees per term (2008-2009). £2,395.

Parents wishing to give their children the best start in life should consider Cliff School. The school offers continuous education in a warm and caring environment for boys and girls from 2 to 11 years. Facilities are based on two sites, both of which are close to Wakefield city centre and only two miles from Junction 41 of the M1

Academic standards are high but the wider curriculum looks to give children an opportunity to identify and develop other gifts and talents. The smaller classes and family atmosphere mean that children are offered very personal attention. Cliff pupils move on with a high standard of academic attainment behind them and those continuing in independent education are able to access the very best of senior schools.

Since the school joined the Alpha Plus Group there has been a significant investment in resources and facilities. There are two spacious gyms, dining rooms, libraries, music rooms and a science room, language room, art and design room, ICT suites with the latest laptops and interactive whiteboards in classrooms. There are a number of hard play and soft play areas, seating and garden areas for the children to enjoy. Sport has increasingly been given a higher profile and good use is made of many excellent local sporting venues.

The school offers pre and after school care every day and breakfast is available if required. In the school holidays there is an exciting club for pupils from Kindergarten age to year 6 and our nursery operates for 51 weeks of the year for pupils aged 2 to 3. Our provision is fully registered by Ofsted and is regularly inspected.

Cliff School has a partner nursery school in Silkstone village, near Barnsley. Here children are accepted up to 5 years, after which they may transfer automatically to the Pre-Prep in Wakefield. A daily bus service operates between the two schools.

Colchester High School
Cognita Schools Group

Wellesley Road Colchester Essex CO3 3HD
Tel: 01206 573389
Fax: 01206 573114
e-mail: info@colchesterhighschool.co.uk
website: www.colchesterhighschool.co.uk

***Principal*: D E Wood**, MA, CertEd

Age Range. 3–16 Co-educational.
Number in School. Day: 440.
Fees per term (2007-2008). £870–£2,730 incl lunch to Year 2 only.

Assistance with fees: Discount for Siblings & Sports Scholarship.

Entry requirements: Assessment test and satisfactory report from previous school.

The atmosphere in the school is friendly and purposeful, and all pupils receive close individual direction to reach the best standard each one of them can achieve. Many pupils join the school on personal recommendation.

There is a flourishing Nursery Department, where girls and boys are prepared for entrance into the Preparatory Department. A full range of GCSEs is taught by specialist staff in the Senior Department, with classes averaging 16 in number and some subjects having sets of about 10 boys. An Art & Technology Wing gives excellent facilities for CDT, Electronics, Art, Music, Sciences and ICT and a new Performing Arts Centre.

Pupils of all ages enjoy a wide variety of clubs and activities for Sport, with impressive achievements at regional and national level. Music and Drama are also strong features of the school, with frequent performances by the choir and orchestra and a major production each year.

Pupils with specific learning difficulties are given extra help on the school's Learning Support Unit.

Colchester High School will be admitting girls into the Senior School from September 2007 starting with Years 7 and 10.

To book a visit or request a Prospectus please contact the Registrar.

Religious Affiliation: Non-denominational.

Collingwood School

Springfield Road Wallington Surrey SM6 0BD
Tel: 020 8647 4607
Fax: 020 8669 2884
e-mail: headmaster@collingwood.sutton.sch.uk
website: www.collingwood.sutton.sch.uk

***Headmaster*: Mr G M Barham**, BEd Hons, MCollP

Age Range. 2–11 Co-educational.
Number in School. Day: 150.
Fees per term (2008-2009). £130–£2,090 (reduction for siblings).

Collingwood was founded in 1929 and became an Educational Trust in 1978.

The aims of the School are to give each child a firm educational foundation upon which to build a successful future. In the Nursery, happy children learn number work, the rudiments of reading and writing, the love of books and enjoy their music and movement activities. The 4/5 year olds in the Kindergarten are reading, writing short stories, investigating scientific and mathematical problems, or striving to express themselves in French.

This excellent introduction gives them a head start in their studies in later classes, and the many scholarships and entrance successes to State Selective and Independent Senior Schools reflect the teaching abilities of the well-qualified staff.

However, Collingwood is not only concerned with academic success. Drama, Singing, Orchestra, Violin, Keyboard, Woodwind, Brass, Percussion, Piano and Recorder lessons, together with Chess Club, Design Technology Club, Football Club (with an ex-Premier League Footballer), Athletics Club, Gym Club, Hockey, Rounders, Netball, Tennis, Cricket and Swimming, broaden and enhance the pupils well-being and knowledge.

A truly all-round education is what Collingwood provides for boys and girls between the ages of 2 and 11 years.

Pre-school and after-school care clubs available.

For a prospectus, details of examination results and to arrange a visit, please telephone 020 8647 4607. You will be made most welcome.

Charitable status. Collingwood School Educational Trust Ltd is a Registered Charity, number 277682. It exists to promote and foster a sound educational foundation for girls and boys aged 2–11 years.

Coopersale Hall School

Flux's Lane Epping Essex CM16 7PE
Tel: 01992 577133
Fax: 01992 571544
e-mail: info@coopersalehallschool.co.uk
website: www.coopersalehallschool.co.uk

***Headmaster*: Ray Probyn**, BA Hons, PGCE, CertEd

Age Range. $2^1/_2$–11.
Number in School. 275 Day Pupils.
Fees per term (from January 2008). £1,290–£2,570.
Entry requirements. Interview and assessment.
Location. Just off Stewards Green Road, close to M11 and M25 routes.

Coopersale Hall School is a thriving, caring local independent school with a high standard of academic achievement and a wide range of activities.

The School offers small class sizes and specialist teachers for ICT, Science, PE, Sport, Music and Drama. We provide a high standard of education and enjoy success in Entrance Examinations at 11 years to a wide choice of Secondary Schools.

We encourage our pupils to develop self-confidence and to take on roles of responsibility as they move up through the school. Creativity is nurtured within a disciplined environment and traditional values such as self-discipline are promoted to maximise our pupils' effectiveness in an ever-changing world.

Coopersale Hall is situated in a large country house that is pleasantly situated on the outskirts of Epping. The School has its own private road and stands in some seven acres of landscaped garden and playing fields.

Copthill School

Barnack Road Uffington Stamford Lincolnshire PE9 3AD
Tel: 01780 757506
Fax: 01780 766643
e-mail: mail@copthill.com
website: www.copthill.com

Headmaster: **Jonathan Teesdale**, BA Hons, PGCE

Age Range. Co-educational 2–11 years.

Number of Pupils. 313. Main School (age 4+ to 11): 250, Nursery and Pre-School (age 2 to 4): 63.

Fees per term (from January 2008). Main School: £1,950–£2,260. Nursery and Pre-School: £19.75 per morning (inc lunch), £32.40 per day (inc lunch).

Aim. To give pupils the opportunity to fulfil their potential in happy and stimulating surroundings. High academic standards offering a thorough grounding in basic educational values. Copthill has strong family values and a warm, welcoming atmosphere.

Location. Purpose-built, modern facilities set in 10 acres of picturesque grounds, within 350 acres of farmland, including river and woodland. 2 miles from Stamford and the A1 and 15 miles from Peterborough.

School Day. Monday to Friday. School Day – 8.40 am to 3.30 pm. Creche hours – 8.00 am to 5.30 pm. 25 clubs per week, finishing at 4.30 pm. Breakfast and Tea available.

Facilities. IT Centre, Library, Learning Support Room, Science Laboratory, Sports Hall, extensive playing fields and outdoor facilities. High quality catering facilities offering nutritionally balanced meals.

Pastoral Care. In addition to their forms, pupils from Year 5 onwards are also placed in small tutor groups in which their progress is closely monitored in preparation for senior school entrance. There is a genuine 'open door policy' throughout the School. Parents' Evenings and reports given twice a year.

Curriculum. A modern curriculum based on the National Curriculum. Combines traditional and innovative teaching methods. Learning support offered where a specific need has been assessed.

Music, Speech & Drama. Music and Drama are taught as part of the curriculum. Regular drama productions encourage all pupils to participate. Pupils can also receive expert individual tuition and perform at school concerts, assemblies and in local music and drama festivals.

Sport. Athletics, Cricket, Football, Hockey, Netball, Cross-Country, Rounders, Rugby, Swimming, Tennis. All pupils encouraged to be in teams.

Future Schools. Pupils leave Copthill at 11 years old with great confidence and the ability to think for themselves. Copthill is a truly independent primary school, offering thorough preparation to a wide variety of state and independent senior schools, both local and national, and achieving a large number of scholarships and awards.

Cotswold Chine School

Box Nr Stroud Gloucestershire GL6 9AG
Tel: 01453 837550
Fax: 01453 837555/834970
e-mail: mail@cotswold-chine.org.uk
website: www.cotswold-chine.org.uk

DCSF approved Co-educational Boarding School founded in 1954.

Head: **Mrs Maureen Smith**, BA, PGCE, PGCert SEN, MEd

Special Needs. The School offers provision for the following needs: ADD, ADHD, ASP, EBD, MLD, SP&LD, SPLD, TOU, EPI, emotional and behavioural.

Age Range. 9–19 years (and exceptionally 8–19 years).

Number of Pupils. 42 boys and girls.

Fees. Individual based upon pupil need.

Curriculum. The curriculum of Cotswold Chine School is based upon a modern approach to the philosophy of Rudolf Steiner and is combined with the National Curriculum. All pupils have individual timetables tailored to meet their specific needs. Children are encouraged to develop their full potential through many varied activities, with a strong emphasis upon science and technology and arts and crafts.

Entry Requirements. Pupils have Statements of Special Educational Needs and are referred by their local Education Authorities, Social Service Department or Health Authority.

Religious Denomination. Non-denominational Christian.

Charitable status. Cotswold Chine is a Registered Charity, number 1103955.

Crackley Hall School

St Joseph's Park Kenilworth Warwickshire CV8 2FT
Tel: 01926 514444
Fax: 01926 514455
e-mail: post@crackleyhall.co.uk
website: www.wcisf.co.uk

Headteacher: **Mr Paul Ryan**, BSc, PGCE, CTC

Co-educational Nursery and Junior School

Age Range. 2–11 years.

Number in School. 154 (82 boys, 72 girls).

Fees per term (2008-2009). Junior School: £2,050–£2,235. Nursery: £152 per week (full time).

Crackley Hall is a co-educational independent Catholic day school which welcomes members of all denominations. The school is part of the Warwickshire Catholic Independent Schools Foundation and is the Junior School to Princethorpe College.

Situated on the outskirts of Kenilworth, Crackley Hall occupies a pleasant and safe setting with playing fields a short distance across the road. An extended day facility is offered; pupils may be dropped off from 8.00 am and can stay at school until 6.00 pm. Nursery attendance times are flexible.

Crackley Hall bases its care for individuals on the sound Christian principles of love and forgiveness; children become strong in the understanding of themselves and others. There is a keen sense of community between pupils, staff and parents. We encourage fairness, freedom, friendship and fun.

Small class sizes promote individual attention. The curriculum is based on national guidelines, but pupils are encouraged to achieve well beyond these targets. During the early years, great emphasis is placed on developing key skills in reading, writing, speaking, listening, mathematics and science. The learning of tables and spellings is actively developed through simple homework tasks. Specialists teach Art, Design Technology, French, Music, Games, ICT and RE. Pupils have access to up-to-date networked ICT facilities in their own classrooms and there is a mobile laptop-based ICT Suite.

Football, rugby, cricket, hockey, netball, tennis, athletics, swimming, rounders, trampolining and judo are all available.

There is a strong and thriving music department and all pupils together with members of the choir, choral group and orchestra participate in concerts and stage productions to enrich their learning and to build confidence and self-esteem. Pupils have the opportunity to study a wide range of individual instruments under the guidance of a team of peripatetic staff and specialist teachers offer classes in music theatre, speech and drama and dance. Other activities are offered before and after school as well as during lunch breaks including art, chess, craft, ICT, gardening, steel band, food and textiles.

Admission is through interview with the Head and assessments in English and Mathematics, as well as a taster day at the school.

Parents are welcomed into school for Friday morning assembly when the children's good work is celebrated. An active Parent Teacher Association organises social and fund-raising events. Pupils are encouraged to maintain their links with the school by joining the Past Pupils' Association.

Charitable status. Warwickshire Catholic Independent Schools Foundation is a Registered Charity, number 1087124. It exists solely for the purpose of educating children.

Cranbrook College
Cognita Schools Group

Mansfield Road Ilford Essex IG1 3BD
Tel: 020 8554 1757
Fax: 020 8518 0317
e-mail: info@cranbrookcollege.org.uk
website: www.cranbrookcollege.org.uk

***Headteacher*: Mr Andrew Moss**, MEd, NPQH

Age Range. 4–16.

Number in School. 200 Day Boys.

Fees per term (2008-2009). £2,135–£2,745.

Location. Cranbrook College is situated close to the centre of Ilford. Connections by bus and rail are excellent.

Aim. The school was founded in 1896. Its aim is for all students to enjoy their time at Cranbrook, strive to give more than they receive and maximise their potential. Cranbrook College is a smart school: every student is encouraged to recognise that intelligence comes in many forms and that everyone is smart and equally different. Each boy is valued whatever his talents, and opportunities are offered in a wide range of extra-curricular activities.

Entry requirements. There are three main entry points: 4, 7 and 11+, but boys are welcome to apply at any time. All children are assessed and may be interviewed before a place is offered. Reports are also requested from the previous school.

Curriculum. In the Preparatory School, emphasis is placed on literacy and numeracy, with small class sizes giving considerable scope for individual attention. The boys also learn handwriting and computer skills, and Spanish, Music and PE are taught by specialists.

In the Junior School, boys follow a broad-based curriculum in which literacy and numeracy remain a priority. French is added alongside Spanish, with Art, Geography, History, ICT, Music, Religious Education, Science, PE and Games completing the programme. Boys do extremely well in the Key Stage 2 SATs.

In the Upper School, the curriculum at Key Stage 3 leads to a wide choice of subjects at Key Stage 4. Work Experience takes place in Year 10. The core GCSE subjects are English, English Literature, Mathematics, Additional Mathematics and Double Award Science. Four further subjects are selected from: Art, ICT, French, Spanish, Geography, History, Business Studies, Religious Studies, Economics and Sociology. GCSE results are very good.

Careers advice enables boys to select their destinations for Advanced Level studies.

Extra-Curricular. Outside the classroom there is a flourishing sporting and extra curricular programme. As well as the main team games, all boys learn to swim and sailing is a popular activity. Cultural visits take place to France, Spain and Morocco. Lunchtime clubs are an increasingly important part of school life and music is thriving.

Catering. All boys take school lunch. Religious and vegetarian needs are provided for and there is a wide range of healthy and nutritious meals.

Parents are welcome to discuss their son's progress at any time. Parent-Teacher consultations are held regularly. A written report is sent to all parents each half-term (Upper School) or each term (Lower School) and open days for prospective parents are held regularly. All parents are members of the Parents' Association.

The school is well resourced and enjoys the benefit of belonging to the Cognita Schools Group, the largest provider of independent co-education in the country.

Cransley School

Belmont Hall Great Budworth Nr Northwich Cheshire CW9 6HN
Tel: 01606 891747/892122
Fax: 01606 892122
e-mail: cransleyschool@btinternet.com
website: www.cransleyschool.co.uk

***Head*: Mrs Geraldine Gaunt**, MA

Age Range. Girls 3–16, Boys 3–11.

Number in School. Day: 180 Girls, 32 Boys.

Fees per term (2008-2009). £1,139–£2,595. Compulsory extras: Lunches £85–£163.

An independent day school set in parkland in the Cheshire countryside, close to the main motorway network.

It has a unique friendly atmosphere and small classes, taught by a dedicated team.

The school encourages the development of individual talent in drama, sport, art and music, in addition to high academic expectations. The latest Information Technology equipment is used throughout the whole school.

Crown House School

19 London Road High Wycombe Buckinghamshire HP11 1BJ
Tel: 01494 529927
Fax: 01494 525693
e-mail: education@crownhouseschool.co.uk
website: www.crownhouseschool.co.uk

***Headmaster*: Mr Ali Khan**

Age Range. 4½–11+.

Number in School. Day: 72 Boys, 54 Girls.

Fees per term (from April 2008). £2,180–£2,480.

Crown House was established in 1924 and accredited by the ISC in 1981. There is a well-balanced curriculum designed to prepare children for local grammar and upper schools.

The school aims to encourage each child to match performance against personal potential and to meet all challenges with courage and determination.

Importance is placed on the enjoyment of learning and pride in achievement, that the individual nature of each child is respected and promoting the development of independent judgement, self-discipline and consideration for others.

Our single-form entry and small classes help to ensure a caring family atmosphere.

Crowstone Preparatory School

Westcliff School: 121/123 Crowstone Road Westcliff-on-Sea Essex SS0 8LH
Tel: 01702 346758
Fax: 01702 390632
e-mail: info@crowstoneprepschool.com
website: www.crowstoneprepschool.com

Sutton School: Fleet Hall Lane Shopland Road Rochford Essex SS4 1LL
Tel: 01702 540629
Fax: 01702 540629

***Headmaster*: J P Thayer**, TCert London

Age Range. 2½–11.

Number in School. Day: 95 Boys, 65 Girls.

Fees per term (2008-2009). £2,350–£2,450 excluding lunch and insurance.

Crowstone Preparatory School is an independent day school for boys and girls between the ages of three years and eleven years.

The aim of the school is to obtain the highest possible achievement from each individual pupil in a happy relaxed atmosphere in all areas of school work.

We are especially concerned in providing extra stimulus for children of high ability but also provide extra facilities for slower learners.

Culcheth Hall School

Ashley Road Altrincham Cheshire WA14 2LT
Tel: 0161 928 1862
Fax: 0161 929 6893
e-mail: admin@culcheth-hall.org.uk
website: www.culcheth-hall.org.uk

***Headteacher*: Miss M A Stockwell**, BSc Hons

Age Range. 2½–16.

Number in School. 210 Day Girls.

Fees per term (2008-2009). Pre-Prep School £570–£1,330; Preparatory School £1,400–£1,720; Senior School £2,540.

Culcheth Hall is a friendly school with small classes where girls are encouraged to work to the best of their ability in a secure and happy environment. We have an excellent academic record at 11+ and GCSE. Girls join in a wide range of sporting, dramatic and musical activities. A sense of responsibility and service to others develops through the house system and fund-raising events. Educational visits taking in the Arts, Sports, Drama, Humanities and Science take place throughout the year with overseas visits during the school holidays.

The modern facilities include a Language Learning Network, Music Room, Science Laboratories, Sports Hall, Art/Design Studio and Technology Centre. The Headteacher is always pleased to show parents round the school by appointment.

Pre-Preparatory School (2½–4 years). Structured teaching in small groups and individually gives each child a good foundation and the best possible start on which to build its future education.

Preparatory School (4–11 years). Formal structured teaching with emphasis on basic skills. Specialist Music, Science, Modern Foreign Languages, Art, ICT and PE teaching. Admission by interview and assessment.

Before and After School Care. 8 am to 6 pm.

Senior School (11–16 years). 100% 5 A*–C grades at GCSE in 2006. Girls take 12 GCSE subjects from a choice of 19.

Charitable status. Culcheth Hall School is a Registered Charity, number 525916. The School's aim is to provide a sound education so that the girls leave with a real sense of achievement and look to the future with confidence.

Dagfa House School

57 Broadgate Beeston Nottingham NG9 2FU
Tel: 0115 913 8330
Fax: 0115 913 8331
e-mail: headmaster@dagfahouse.notts.sch.uk
website: www.dagfahouse.notts.sch.uk

***Headmaster*: Dr K Savage**, MSc, EdD

Age Range. 3–16.

Number in School. Day: Boys 160, Girls 80.

Fees per term (2007-2008). £1,975–£2,395.

Dagfa House is situated in pleasant gardens in a quiet neighbourhood adjacent to University Park, and it enjoys easy access from all areas of the city and county. Small classes are taught by caring and dedicated staff, creating a purposeful learning environment where individual talents flourish.

A wide curriculum is provided, which includes the National Curriculum but leaves time available for other important aspects, such as an early introduction to foreign languages. Results are very good at all stages, and pupils also learn to be caring and thoughtful towards others.

Daiglen School

68 Palmerston Road Buckhurst Hill Essex IG9 5LG
Tel: 020 8504 7108
Fax: 020 8502 9608
e-mail: admin@daiglenschool.co.uk
website: www.daiglenschool.co.uk

***Head Teacher*: Mrs M Bradfield**, BA, CertEd, DipNatSci

Age Range. 3–11.

Number in School. 135.

Fees per term (2007-2008). £2,040. Sibling discount. Extras: Lunch, swimming (juniors), short tennis and drama (infants).

"Daiglen is a truly unique school where the core values of academic excellence and good behaviour are still important. This winning combination takes place in an intimate and nurturing environment where each child matters. Daiglen has succeeded in surpassing my expectations in these early vital years of my children's education.

I am consistently impressed by the quality of teaching my children receive at Daiglen. They are both challenged and encouraged. The staff are dedicated and at all times professional. It appears to be a place where every child can reach their full potential.

Daiglen pupils are a credit to their school. The school should be proud of its culture, which encourages such high standards of behaviour seen in so few schools today."

Andrea Dowling, Year 5 and Year 3 Mother.

The Daiglen School, established in 1916, is a small, friendly preparatory school for boys and girls aged 3 to 11 years, rich in history and tradition. It is now an Educational Trust, founded on clear moral values of courtesy, respect, endeavour, industry and integrity.

Built around an elegant Victorian house with much of its stained glass and cornices intact, modern features include a new gymnasium and art room, a fully-equipped ICT suite and a purpose-built science laboratory. The school is pleasantly situated on the borders of Epping Forest and is well served by public transport.

Before and after school clubs, as well as holiday clubs, are supervised by school staff, thus ensuring continuity of provision.

The syllabus is arranged to meet the requirements of Independent Senior School Entrance Examinations for 11 year olds, 11+ Examinations for Grammar Schools and National Tests. The enhanced curriculum includes French and Spanish, taught by native speakers. Latin is introduced in Year 6. Most pupils go on to local schools, either in the independent or maintained sector. Teacher-pupil ratio is one to ten, enabling first class academic results whilst catering for all abilities.

"The school is successful in meeting its aims to enable pupils to gain places in competitive entry to senior school, as well as maintaining an interesting and varied educational experience within a supportive, family environment. Pupils are extremely well prepared for transfer to their next schools."

"The quality of teaching in the Foundation Stage is outstanding and excellent teaching was observed throughout the school." *ISI Inspection Oct 2006*

For a prospectus and registration form please contact the Admissions Secretary.

Charitable status. The Daiglen School Trust Limited is a Registered Charity, number 273015.

Dair House School

Bishop's Blake Beaconsfield Road Farnham Royal Buckinghamshire SL2 3BY

(See entry in IAPS section)

Dale House School

Ruby Street Carlinghow Batley West Yorkshire WF17 8HL
Tel: 01924 422215
Fax: 01924 422215
e-mail: admin@dhschool.freeserve.co.uk
website: www.dhschool.co.uk

Headmistress: **Mrs S M G Fletcher**, BA, CertEd

Age Range. 2–11 Co-educational.
Number in School. 95 Day Pupils.
Fees per term (2008-2009). £1,590–£1,715.

Dale House is housed in a former Edwardian parish hall built in 1907 and is a small Independent School serving the Batley, Dewsbury, Leeds, Bradford and Wakefield areas.

Dale House has many strengths including a broad curriculum which caters for a wide variety of academic abilities and provides great opportunities for sport, music, dance, art, drama and two foreign languages. We also have an excellent examination record. Above all, Dale House is a very happy school where children enjoy life to the full, discovering more about the world around them.

We strive to uncover hidden talents and develop individual strengths in a caring and supportive learning environment. The school has both pre and post school clubs, so pupils are cared for between 8 am and 5.30 pm. The school also runs a Holiday Club out of term time.

Davenport Lodge School
Alpha Plus Group

21 Davenport Road Coventry CV5 6QA
Tel: 024 7667 5051
Fax: 024 7667 9370
e-mail: office@davenportlodgeschool.co.uk
website: www.davenportlodge.coventry.sch.uk

Principal: **Mrs M D Martin**, BPhilEd Hons

Age Range. 0–8.
Number in School. Day: 58 Boys, 69 Girls.
Fees per term (2008-2009). £1,790.

Davenport Lodge was founded in 1968 and is a pre-preparatory school with its own Kindergarten and baby provision for 0–2 year olds called babies@davenportlodgeschool. Pupils are prepared with scholarship success for competitive entrance examinations, principally for Coventry School Foundation's Junior Schools, King Henry VIII and Bablake, as well as other independent schools in the area, such as Warwick School, Arnold Lodge School and Bilton Grange School. Swimming, music, art and tennis are included in the curriculum. Teaching is carried out in small groups in order to give an individual approach. National Curriculum Key Stage One results are in the top 5% in the country for seven year olds.

The school is part of the Alpha Plus group of schools.

Davies Laing & Dick
Alpha Plus Group

100 Marylebone Lane London W1U 2QB
Tel: 020 7935 8411
Fax: 020 7935 0755
e-mail: dld@dld.org
website: www.dldcollege.co.uk

Principal: **Mr David Lowe**

Age Range. 15+ Co-educational.
Number of Pupils. 380 Day.
Fees per term (2007-2008). £4,750–£5,495.

Davies Laing and Dick (DLD) is a co-educational London day school accepting pupils from the ages of 15+. There are over 320 students in the Sixth Form studying A Levels from a choice of 40 subjects. Two thirds are doing A Levels in the normal way over a two-year period. Another large group joins DLD at the start of Upper Sixth. There are no subject restrictions at A Level. GCSE courses are taught over a one-year period so pupils are able to join at the beginning of Year 11. The average class size is 6. Supplementary lessons in English as a foreign language are taken by 6% of the student body.

DLD is housed in two linked buildings in Marylebone, both newly refurbished and very well equipped buildings. There are three laboratories, two IT classrooms, a library for private study with an IT annexe, a GCSE study area, an eighty-seat theatre which is also used to screen films. There is a recording studio and a film edit suite. Many classrooms are equipped with interactive whiteboards. Students are able to access work done in class, teachers' notes and homework assignments remotely via the DLD Virtual School.

Extra-curricular activities include sport, DLD youth theatre, set design, film making, the DLD house band, concerts, French club, life drawing classes, fund-raising and Activities Week, which takes place at the end of June. The school day finishes at 4.40 pm; most activities take place after this.

While the atmosphere at DLD is more informal than in mainstream independent schools, rules regarding academic performance are strictly enforced. Those who do not hand in work on time are required to attend Supervised Study at the end of the day. Lateness to lessons is not tolerated. There are fortnightly tests in each subject and three weekly reports. Parents receive five reports each year and there are two parents' evenings.

The teaching staff are highly qualified and chosen not just for their expertise but also for their ability to relate positively to young people. The college aims to make learning interesting, active and rigorous. While clear guidelines are very important to ensure pupils establish a good working routine, the college believes strongly that pupils respond best when there is a culture of encouragement. Effort, progress, achievement and courtesy are regularly acknowledged and formally rewarded.

Derby Grammar School

Rykneld Hall Rykneld Road Littleover Derby DE23 4BX
Tel: 01332 523027
Fax: 01332 518670
e-mail: headmaster@derbygrammar.co.uk
website: www.derbygrammar.co.uk

Member of the Woodard Schools Group (Midlands Division).

***Headmaster*: Mr R D Waller**, BSc Hons

Age Range. Boys 7–18, Girls 16–18.

Number in School. 310.

Fees per term (2008-2009). £2,445 (Years 3–4), £2,645 (Years 5–6), £3,304 (Years 7–13).

Derby Grammar School has a Christian foundation and seeks to promote Christian values whilst respecting those from other faiths. We admit pupils of above-average ability and believe that intellectual endeavour and hard work in the classroom and outside should be at the heart of an exciting, challenging and stimulating environment that inspires all pupils to succeed. The School has established a proven success record in public examinations and university entry. The size of the School ensures that all pupils know each other and are supported by the teaching staff, with all the pupils' individual needs addressed. Dedicated and inspiring teachers teach a wide range of subjects in small classes. In our community the pupils are taught to take responsibility for their own actions, to develop leadership qualities, to learn self-respect and concern for others. A variety of extra-curricular work helps the pupils to boost their self-confidence and gives all of them the chance to take part. In their time with us, we aim to produce articulate and confident young men and women, who have enjoyed their schooling, are confident in relationships and can go on to higher education with the skills needed to do well. The School aims to continue its development and building programme to ensure that current and future students have the opportunity to work in a stimulating environment.

Charitable status. Derby Grammar School for Boys is a Registered Charity, number 1015449. It exists to educate children.

Devonshire House Preparatory School

2 Arkwright Road Hampstead London NW3 6AE

(See entry in IAPS section)

Ditcham Park School

Petersfield Hampshire GU31 5RN
Tel: 01730 825659
Fax: 01730 825070
e-mail: info@ditchampark.com
website: www.ditchampark.com

***Head Teacher*: Mrs K S Morton**, BEd Hons, DipEd, CertEd

Age Range. 4–16.

Number in School. Day: 198 Boys, 161 Girls.

Fees per term (2008-2009). £2,098–£3,503 excluding lunch.

Situated high on the South Downs, the School achieves excellent results in a happy purposeful atmosphere.

Charitable status. Ditcham Park School is a Registered Charity, number 285244R. It exists for educational purposes.

The Dixie Grammar School

Market Bosworth Leicestershire CV13 0LE
Tel: 01455 292244
Fax: 01455 292151
e-mail: info@dixie.org.uk
website: www.dixie.org.uk

***Headmaster*: Mr J R Wood**, MA (Cantab), PGCE

Age Range. 3–18.

Number in School. Dixie: 160 boys, 200 girls; Wolstan: 91 boys, 71 girls.

Fees per term (2007-2008). Grammar School £2,640, Junior School £1,920–£2,200, Pippins Nursery £177 per week.

The Dixie Grammar School, a medieval foundation, was closed in 1969, but re-founded as an independent school in 1987. Its junior department, the Wolstan Preparatory School, was opened three years later. The Grammar School occupies a site in the heart of the quiet country town of Market Bosworth, the attractive early nineteenth-century main school building overlooking the market square. The Preparatory School is just under three miles away at Temple Hall in Wellsborough, where it enjoys a spacious site surrounded by countryside. The Grammar School has over thirty acres of playing fields just outside the town. The schools are served by six bus routes, with a free shuttle service between the two sites.

Both schools are selective and have academic achievement as their central aim. Music, drama, sport and service are also an integral part of the education offered. Both schools have an inter-denominational Christian basis. The relative smallness of the schools ensures that they combine great friendliness with excellent discipline, providing a secure and well-ordered framework in which children can confidently achieve their full potential.

The Grammar School offers academic, music, art, sports and sixth form scholarships.

Charitable status. The Leicestershire Independent Educational Trust is a Registered Charity, number 514407. It exists to provide a grammar school education.

Dodderhill School

Crutch Lane Droitwich Spa Worcs WR9 OBE

(See entry in GSA section)

d'Overbroeck's College

The Swan Building 111 Banbury Road Oxford OX2 6JX

(See entry in SHMIS section)

Edgehill College

Northdown Road Bideford Devon EX39 3LY
Tel: 01237 471701
Fax: 01237 425981
e-mail: edgehill@btconnect.com
website: www.edgehill.devon.sch.uk

Founded 1884.

Chairman of Governors: Mrs J R Wilson

***Headmaster*: Mr S Nicholson**, MA Oxon, MBA, CPhys, PGCE

Age Range. 3 months–18 years.

Number in School. 225.

Fees per term (2008-2009). Day: £1,625–£2,620 (Prep), £3,175–£3,405 (Senior). Boarding: £5,400 (Prep), £6,550 (Senior).

Scholarships and bursaries. The range of scholarships includes academic, sporting, music and dramatic awards. These may be as much as 50% of fees. Additionally there are means-tested bursaries. A separate award system is available for children of forces personnel.

Edgehill College is set in beautiful grounds of over 50 acres, with excellent facilities, within sight of Devon's beautiful rolling countryside, coast, beaches and moorland.

The campus buildings are well equipped and include new Science laboratories, new music department, new "penthouse suite" Art department and a new Sixth Form Centre. Sports provision includes a club-standard gymnastics hall, netball and tennis courts, a large sports hall, an all-weather surface and pitches for cricket, hockey, soccer and rugby. There is a new drama studio, hall with stage, and a modern professional standard theatre.

The College accepts girls and boys aged 11 to 18 in the Senior School; aged 4 to 11 in the Preparatory School; in the Kindergarten from age three; and the Nursery, for babies from 12 weeks.

Class sizes are usually around 15 pupils and the personal care we give to pupils is an integral part of our ethos.

Curriculum. Subjects studied in the senior school include English Language, English Literature, Mandarin, French, Spanish, Mathematics, Religious Studies, Drama, History, Geography, Physics, Chemistry, Biology, Art & Design, Music, ICT, Theatre Studies, Business Studies, Physical Education.

As an integral part of life at Edgehill all students develop wider skills through their leisure interests in many areas including Sport, Music, Drama and Art.

The Preparatory School is a community which aims to provide a secure and enjoyable learning environment where all children develop their potential to the full. Care is taken to give a very thorough grounding in English and Mathematics. Pupils also study French, Spanish, Mandarin, Science, Design Technology, Computing, Drama, Geography, History, Games, Art & Design, Food Technology and Music.

Admission. Boys and girls are admitted to the Preparatory School without a formal examination. Satisfactory reports will be required from the previous school.

Entrance to the Senior School is gained through the College's own examinations and by individual assessments.

Pupils wishing to join the College at Sixth Form level are required to have good passes at GCSE.

A copy of the prospectus may be obtained from the Headmaster's PA, Mrs Nicola Buckley.

The Edgehill Association Secretary: Mrs Daphne Cawsey, 67 Atlantic Way, Westward Ho!, Devon EX39 1JD.

Charitable status. Edgehill College is a Registered Charity, number 306709.

Edington and Shapwick School

Edington School (age 8–12):
Mark Road Burtle Bridgwater Somerset TA7 8NJ
Tel: 01278 722012
Fax: 01278 723312
e-mail: edington@edingtonshapwick.co.uk

Shapwick School (age 13+):
Shapwick Manor Shapwick Bridgwater Somerset TA7 9NJ
Tel: 01458 210384
Fax: 01458 210111
e-mail: shapwick@edingtonshapwick.co.uk
website: www.edingtonshapwick.co.uk

Joint Headmasters:
D C Walker, BA Hons, **J P Whittock**, CertEd

Age Range. 8–18.

Number in School. Boarders: 83 boys, 27 girls; Day: 39 boys, 13 girls.

Fees per term (2007-2008). Boarders £5,965–£6,505, Day £4,308–£4,511.

Edington and Shapwick is a specialist school for boys and girls whose education would otherwise be impaired by dyslexia. The School provides a caring and supportive atmosphere, staffed by specialist teachers across a wide curriculum offering the structured help needed by students who have dyslexia. Students take up to 8 GCSE subjects and the aim is to teach to their strengths whilst their weaknesses are being overcome and their confidence grows. Supplementary courses, such as Study Skills, Keyboard Skills, and careers advice are also taken. The School has a full range of specialist classrooms, including four laboratories, computing rooms, design centre, art rooms, library, sports hall, recreation room and games field. Students are involved in a wide range of extra curricular activities, the Duke of Edinburgh's Award, and games fixtures, to complement the formal curriculum.

Prospective entrants need an Educational Psychologist's report diagnosing dyslexia and at least average intellectual potential together with a current Head's report, and interview.

Egerton Rothesay School

Prep & Senior (7–16 years):
Durrants Lane Berkhamsted Herts HP4 3UJ
Tel: 01442 865275
Fax: 01442 864977
e-mail: admin.dl@eger-roth.co.uk

Foundation Stage & Pre-Prep (3–7 years):
3–7 Charles Street Berkhamsted Herts HP4 3DG
Tel: 01442 866305
Fax: 01442 876148
e-mail: admin.cs@eger-roth.co.uk
website: www.eger-roth.co.uk

***Headteacher*: Mrs N Boddam-Whetham**, BA Hons, PGTC

Age Range. 5–16 years.
Number in School. 218 boys, 94 girls.
Fees per term (2008-2009). £2,851–£6,970 (lunches included).

Egerton Rothesay is a school which aims to provide an exciting, relevant and supported educational experience. It focuses especially on students who have found, or would find, it difficult to make progress and succeed within another school, perhaps because of a negative educational experience or a specific learning difficulty.

We have additional support available across all classes – varying to suit the need of the individual child – as well as having two special groups with a specific focus. These are the John Adkins Centre (for children with moderate learning difficulties) and The Rainbow Class (for children with a specific speech and/or language difficulty).

We see every child at Egerton Rothesay School as a unique person and an individual student. We aim to make a unique and excellent contribution into the life of each one ensuring that they can be supported in the way that they personally need to maximise their individual learning potential.

We have a learning skills approach throughout the school – aiming to prepare students not just for school and exams but for life in today's complex society and an ever changing world of work. All activity takes place within an environment offering exceptional pastoral care and spiritual development that is driven and informed by the school's Christian foundation.

Children come to us with a variety of different learning styles and we make use of a wide range of teaching strategies in order to suitably match these. In addition, we have the facilities to provide additional levels of support both in the classroom and on an individual basis to enable each individual to make consistent and recognisable progress, regardless of their previous learning experience.

A child can often be able and talented in one aspect of the curriculum yet find it difficult to make good progress in another. Some students will need support for the duration of their time in school whilst others may only need a short amount of support to address a specific problem or to give a boost.

A prospective student is invited to spend at least one day in school with their current year group. During this visit the student will take an assessment test. The results of the test will indicate the candidate's strengths and areas for development, so that we can make appropriate individual provision, including the support to be provided. This is reviewed termly with the pupil's parents.

The school welcomes visitors to the school and hosts regular Open Mornings, to which prospective parents are warmly invited. We are also pleased to make appointments for parents who would prefer to visit on an individual basis. For more information or to arrange a visit please contact the Admissions Registrar, Tel: 01442 877060.

Elmhurst School

44–48 South Park Hill Road South Croydon Surrey CR2 7DW
Tel: 020 8688 0661
Fax: 020 8686 7675
e-mail: office@elmhurstschool.net
website: www.elmhurstschool.net

Principal: R E Anderson, DipEd, ACP

***Headmaster*: M Apsley**, BA, PGCE

Bursar: C A South

Age Range. 4–11.
Number in School. 250 Boys.
Fees per term (2007-2008). £2,100–£2,515 (including lunches and ISC Personal Accident Insurance).

Elmhurst School (established 1869) prepares boys for entry to such prestigious schools as Whitgift, Trinity, Dulwich College and Caterham and possesses an enviable record of academic success.

Equally important is the wide ranging curriculum designed to encourage boys to make the most of their talents and strengthen their weaknesses in a structured but friendly family environment. An extremely well equipped and flourishing computer department, together with active participation in educational visits and drama, foster interest in technology and creativity. A wide variety of sports is encouraged, including participation in Soccer, Cricket, Rugby, Athletics, Gymnastics, Tennis, Swimming and Golf.

Elmhurst, accredited by the ISC, accepts boys at the age of four, with occasional vacancies arising in other year groups.

The Elvian School

61 Bath Road Reading Berkshire RG30 2BB
Tel: 0118 957 2861
Fax: 0118 957 2220
e-mail: admin@elvian.reading.sch.uk
website: www.elvian.reading.sch.uk

***Head*: Mrs S Manser**, BEd Hons

Age Range. 3–18 Co-educational.
Number of Pupils. 180.
Fees per term (2007-2008). £2,125–£2,880.

The school (which was previously known as Presentation College) has been recently purchased by The Licensed Trade Charity, which has been operating schools for the past 200 years. The Elvian has at its heart a charitable function. Enshrined in the Royal Charter is a requirement for schools owned by the Licensed Trade Charity to be co-educational, non-selective, and for the education to be superior to that of the state. In this respect we are a family school, able to cater for the educational needs of a wide variety of pupils.

There are currently 44 pupils in the Junior School and approximately 136 in the Senior School, with 20 in the Sixth Form. We are currently 'growing the school' with the intention of reaching 400 pupils within a five year period. Prior to The Licensed Trade Charity buying the school it operated as a boy's selective school, so it will take time for girls to be admitted in equal numbers to boys. We have to date 26 girls in the main body of the school and one in the Sixth Form.

As The Elvian School is a non-selective, pupils join us following an interview with the Headteacher, an assessment through previous school reports, and the availability of a place within that year group. Most schools in the area are selective and many are single-sex; we therefore occupy a unique position in the locality. Competition is keen, however, and the popularity of the school is based on the concept of 'value-added'. A small number of pupils go to Oxford or Cambridge.

Class sizes are small: at Key Stage 2 and 3, there are currently 20 pupils or fewer in each class; at Key Stage 4, numbers in subject sets drop to approximately 10 pupils. A level teaching groups are smaller still.

The school also specialises in helping gifted and talented pupils as well as able but dyslexic pupils to overcome this barrier to learning. The ethos of the school is one of Christian caring, with a family atmosphere based on respect for all members of the community.

The school seeks to develop the whole person, and addresses this through a wide range of sporting and extra-curricular activities. The success of the school in local and national competitions, be they chess, badminton, football or Art, reflects the enthusiasm and hard work of both staff and pupils. There are also a variety of non-competitive activities, ranging from the sailing club and skiing club, through CCF and The Duke of Edinburgh's Award Scheme. Music and drama opportunities are being constantly developed. Throughout, there is emphasis on working together, and the development of teamwork and leadership skills.

Charitable status. The Elvian School, Reading is a Registered Charity, number 230011. It is devoted to the advancement of the educational and social support and development of young people.

Fairfield School

Fairfield Way Backwell Bristol BS48 3PD
Tel: 01275 462743
Fax: 01275 464347
e-mail: secretary@fairfieldschool.org.uk
website: www.fairfieldschool.org.uk

***Headteacher*: Mrs Lesley Barton**, BA Hons, PGCE

Age Range. 3–11.
Number in School. 67 Boys, 80 Girls.
Fees per term (2007-2008). Nursery (part-time) £530; Nursery (full-time), Reception, Years 1–2 £1,900; Years 3–6 £2,090.

Fairfield is an independent day school for boys and girls aged 3–11. The school was founded in 1935 and aims to provide a broad, traditional education. We encourage each child to maximise his or her potential through creating a family ethos in which children feel happy, secure and valued. A fundamental aspect of our ethos is our commitment to small classes, usually of 18–20. Fairfield offers a broad and balanced curriculum, informed by the National Curriculum. Teachers and visiting coaches provide a wide range of extra-curricular lessons including music, dance, sport, drama and creative activities. Pupils are prepared for entry into all local independent senior schools as well as for the local maintained sector schools.

For further details please apply to the School Secretary.

Charitable status. Fairfield PNEU School (Backwell) Limited is a Registered Charity, number 310215.

Fairley House School

Junior Department: 220 Lambeth Road London SE1 7JY
Tel: 020 7803 3170
Fax: 020 7620 1069

Senior Department:
30 Causton Street London SW1P 4AU
Tel: 020 7976 5456
Fax: 020 7976 5905
e-mail: office@fairleyhouse.org.uk
website: www.fairleyhouse.org.uk

***Principal*: Jacqueline Murray**, BA Hons, MEd, MSc, DipPsychol, DipRSA(SpLD)

Head of Junior Department: Ann Osborn, CertEd, BEd, DipRSA(SpLD), Dip(SEN)

Head of Senior Department: Alex Tait, MA, PGCE, DipRSA(SpLD)

Age Range. 5–13.
Number of Pupils. 140 (107 Boys, 33 Girls).
Fees per term (2008-2009). £8,250.

Fairley House School is a school for children with specific learning difficulties, dyslexia and dyspraxia. The aim of the school is to provide intensive support to help children to overcome difficulties, coupled with a full, rich curriculum designed to bring out children's strengths and talents. Most children return to mainstream schooling after two to three years. Fairley House School was founded in 1982 for children aged 6–12 by Daphne Hamilton-Fairley, a speech and language therapist. She set up the school with the intention of integrating education with therapies (speech and language, occupational) normally only obtainable through the health service. This integration is one of the many things that sets us apart as a specialist day school for children with specific learning difficulties.

We emphasise the development of the whole child, helping him or her to gain confidence and self-esteem through an encouraging and nurturing ethos. The children have plenty of opportunities to develop sound academic and social skills and to become independent. At Fairley House, everyone succeeds.

Ferndale Preparatory School
Cognita Schools Group

5–7 Bromsgrove Faringdon Oxon SN7 7JF
Tel: 01367 240618
Fax: 01367 241429
e-mail: info@ferndaleschool.co.uk
website: www.ferndaleschool.co.uk

***Headmaster*: Mr Andrew Mersh**, BEd Hons

Age Range. 3–11 years.
Number in School. Day: 56 Girls, 58 Boys.
Fees per term (2008-2009). £2,155 (Nursery), £2,285 (age 4–7), £2,415 (age 7–11).

Ferndale is a small, thriving co-educational prep school, occupying pleasant Georgian buildings in the historic market town of Faringdon. Its size means that each child receives individual attention and in its family atmosphere pupils find a secure and supportive environment where confidence burgeons and exceptional results are achieved.

There is no formal test, but an interview, with a "taster" day may help ensure that a child is appropriately placed. Entry is age 3 into the Nursery and in succeeding years subject to place availability. Ferndale welcomes children of all faiths, though broadly Christian values underpin an ethos where social responsibility and habits of courtesy and consideration for others are much in evidence.

Ferndale has a remarkable record of success in entrance to schools of first choice, amongst them several in the highest league. Scholarships and other awards have regularly been won at target schools from Cheltenham to Abingdon and from Bath to Oxford, while places have also been gained at Grammar and other maintained schools.

In recent years most of our boys have been offered places at Abingdon School or Magdalen College, Oxford; our girls have mainly gone to the School of St Helen & St Katharine or Our Lady's Convent in Abingdon. Other schools have included Oxford High, Headington, Wychwood, Cokethorpe, Grittleton House, Pate's Grammar, King Edward's Bath, Warneford, Farmor's, Faringdon, Rendcomb and Kingham Hill.

The arts flourish at Ferndale. Music and the visual arts are strong, and drama and dance are highly regarded. Games from rugby and netball to chess are another success story and a wide range of extra-curricular activities includes such activities as art, football, gardening, rugby, ICT and swimming at Faringdon's Leisure Centre.

At Ferndale there are specialist rooms for music, art, science and ICT which perfectly complement the homely, child-friendly classrooms in the original buildings; these also house a custom-designed nursery department. The school employs its own chef who provides excellent and varied lunches with an impressive range of choices.

Finborough School

The Hall Gt Finborough Stowmarket Suffolk IP14 3EF
Tel: 01449 773600
Fax: 01449 773601
e-mail: admin@finborough.suffolk.sch.uk
website: www.finborough.suffolk.sch.uk

***Principal*: Mr John Sinclair**, BSc(Econ), FCA

Age Range. Co-educational 2½–18.

Number of Pupils. Boarders: 61 Boys, 42 Girls. Day Pupils: 45 Boys, 35 Girls.

Fees per term (2007-2008). Boarding £3,620–£5,670. Day £1,740–£2,860. The Montessori Nursery has its own fee structure based upon number of sessions attended. Termly fees are fully inclusive of all meals, educational materials and extended day care for day pupils. Flexible and occasional boarding facilities for day pupils are available at additional cost.

Location. Finborough School stands in a safe and healthy rural environment two miles west of Stowmarket, which is on the main London–Norwich line and is 5 minutes drive from the A14. The school operates an escort service for travel at the beginning and end of each term and a local bus service for day pupils. Finborough Hall is an eighteenth-century manor house with considerable modern extensions beautifully situated in sixty acres of its own playing fields, gardens and woodland.

Facilities. Founded in 1977 the School moved to its present site in 1980 since when it has consistently re-invested in improved facilities, including a new Senior School Library, up-to-date ICT suites and further upgrading of boarding accommodation. Well-maintained playing fields and hard courts for tennis, netball and basketball. The woodland provides an adventure playground, camping site and a stretch of river for canoeing and fishing. An equestrian centre has been opened with a floodlit arena.

Aims. By acknowledging each pupil as an individual and by nurturing their individual talents, our aim is to prepare them for the ever changing world of work and to responsibly discharge their duty to the Country and society in which they are privileged to live. The School Development Plan allows for planned growth to around 400 pupils in total, more or less evenly divided between Prep School and Senior School. The number permits retention of our small school family atmosphere whilst providing a unit where viability will allow the provision of first-rate facilities in all areas.

Education. Classes are small, with an average of 15 pupils and are taught by highly-qualified professional staff. The curriculum covers the full range of traditional subjects, as well as technology and ICT through to GCSE and A level. Advanced vocational qualifications are offered in, for example, Health and Social Care and Leisure and Recreation, and in most cases are taken with additional GCE A level subjects. Other pupils choose to follow the traditional GCE A level route to higher education. All pupils receive trained advice on careers and university entry.

Examination results are good, reflecting not only pupil ability but their hard work and the expertise and commitment of teaching staff.

Music, Drama and Art. Pupils receive expert tuition and perform at School concerts, assemblies, and in the local music and drama festivals. A wide range of instrumental tuition is available at additional cost. The School regularly has successes in Art competitions and a wide range of work is displayed around the premises.

Sport. Competitive but well-mannered – Rugby, Netball, Hockey, Soccer, Rounders, Cricket, Cross-country, Athletics, Swimming, Tennis etc.

Entry. Following application, previous schools reports and school references are (where applicable) received and interview arranged. All candidates are encouraged to attend trial sessions for 2 or 3 days before making up their minds about the school. Entry tests in Mathematics and English are taken during trial days.

General. Day pupils can be accommodated from 8 am to 5.30 pm and there is no Saturday school. A wide range of extra-curricular clubs and activities is available. According to demand and the seasons a variety of activities, expeditions etc are offered at weekends in addition to school and house fixtures. A weekly assembly in the village church is an important social as well as spiritual occasion.

The Firs School

45 Newton Lane Chester CH2 2HJ
Tel: 01244 322443
Fax: 01244 400450
e-mail: admin@firsschool.net
website: www.firsschool.net

***Headmistress*: Mrs M A Denton**, CertEd

Age Range. 3–11 Co-educational.

Number in School. 216: 124 Boys, 92 Girls.

Fees per term (2007-2008). £1,960.

The Firs School is an independent co-educational primary school set in attractive grounds about a mile and a half north of the city of Chester. It was founded in 1945 by Mrs F A Longman.

The aim of the Firs is to help children achieve their academic potential in the context of a caring environment based upon Christian principles. Children of all faiths are welcome and we respect and learn from their beliefs and cultures. Our strengths lie in the individual attention we are able to give, a carefully planned curriculum and an effective partnership with parents. Specialist teaching for dyslexia and other educational needs is available. We have a proven record of success in preparing children for entrance to local independent and state schools. The school is well resourced with a continuous programme of investment, including our technology and pottery rooms.

Whilst placing great emphasis on the core subjects, our curriculum is enhanced through the teaching of French, Spanish, gardening club, the opportunity for sport and the quality of our provision of art and music throughout the school.

Our objective is to encourage the development of the whole child so that each will leave The Firs School with an understanding of the wider world and an awareness of his or her responsibility to others.

Firwood Manor Preparatory School
GEMS Education

Broadway Chadderton Oldham OL9 0AD
Tel: 0161 620 6570
Fax: 0161 626 3550
e-mail: admin@firwoodmanor.org.uk
website: www.firwoodmanor.org.uk

***Head*: Mrs P M Wild**, BEd

Age Range. 2¾–11 Co-educational.
Number of Pupils. 142.
Fees per term (2007-2008). £1,660 plus £150 for lunch.

Firwood Manor Preparatory School opened in September 2002 and is an independent, co-educational day school for children aged from 2¾ to 11 years. It is situated on Broadway in Chadderton, Oldham close to the beginning of the A627M. This location makes it very accessible from a number of places in Greater Manchester and Lancashire, including Bury, Rochdale, North Manchester and Ashton. It is also an easy dropping-off point for parents who commute to work. The school is open from 7.30 am to 6.00 pm to care for your child.

The school is being developed through teamwork, close interaction, open communication and collaborative planning and has a hard working, dedicated, well-qualified and experienced staff.

At Firwood Manor we are very aware of our responsibility to provide children with the very best educational possibilities and to optimise the opportunities for children to reach their full potential, so that their years of primary education culminate in the maximum appropriate outcomes.

Our exceptional facilities certainly help us to realise these aims. They include a fully equipped nursery, purpose built classrooms from Reception to Year 6, specialist rooms for Science and Art, Design and Technology, an ICT suite, a hall for sport, gymnastics, dance, music and drama, extensive grounds with facilities for football, hockey and netball and on-site catering facilities.

The starting point of every teacher is the infinite worth of each child. Every day our aim is to provide each and every child with exciting and challenging learning experiences, which are both traditional and innovative.

Our children are encouraged to be independent, confident, responsible and compassionate with a strong sense of purpose and self-discipline. They have a love of learning for its own sake with enquiring minds and the ability to freely express their likes and dislikes. We aim to give them opportunities to develop skills to enable them to be good team players, to solve problems, both academically and in their daily lives, and to enable them to manage change, risk and uncertainty. And above all, they have a strong belief in themselves and in what they can achieve.

Forest Park School

Lauriston House 27 Oakfield Sale Cheshire M33 6NB
Tel: 0161 973 4835
Fax: 0161 282 9021
e-mail: post@forestparkschool.co.uk
website: www.forestparkschool.co.uk

***Senior Head*: Mr L B R Groves**, BEd, MBA

Head of School: Mrs H Gee, BEd Hons

Age Range. 3–11.
Number in School. 85 Day Boys, 65 Day Girls.
Fees per term (2008-2009). £1,580–£1,730.

Forest Park occupies a pleasant site in a quiet road surprisingly close to the centre of Sale, easily accessible from motorways and surrounding areas.

The school aims to discover and develop each child's particular abilities by offering a varied curriculum in a stimulating and happy atmosphere. Forest Park has a good pupil teacher ratio and offers a wide range of subjects with priority given to the traditional disciplines of English, Mathematics and Science. Pupils from three years of age are taught Information Technology by specialist staff. Swimming is taught from the age of five and games offered are Football, Cricket, Lacrosse and Touch Rugby for boys, Netball, Tennis and Lacrosse for girls. Pupils are taught French from an early age, the older children having the opportunity to visit a language study centre in France.

The confidence and social ease one expects of a private education is a product of the school. Our aim is to develop skills and knowledge through a habit of hard work in a secure and happy environment within a disciplined framework. The school prepares pupils for all independent grammar school examinations and has an excellent record in this respect.

The school prides itself on strong links and communication with a most supportive Parents' Association.

Forest School

Moss Lane Timperley Altrincham Cheshire WA15 6LJ
Tel: 0161 980 4075
Fax: 0161 903 9275
e-mail: headteacher@forestschool.co.uk
website: www.forestschool.co.uk

***Senior Head*: Mr L B R Groves**, BEd, MBA

Head of School: Mr R Hyde

Age Range. 2–11.
Number in School. Day: 99 Boys, 81 Girls.
Fees per term (2007-2008). £1,452–£1,645.

A co-educational school set in spacious grounds with high academic standards and an enviable reputation for its care of the individual.

Working within a happy environment, the children experience a traditional approach to education both in the subject disciplines and the high expectations of good behaviour.

The Infant Department ensures the children have a thorough understanding of reading, writing and number work. The Junior curriculum is very broad and includes all curriculum areas whilst special attention is given to those subjects which the children require for entry to the senior schools.

Small classes, a friendly atmosphere and extra-curricular activities ensure the children achieve their full potential and are well prepared for future schooling.

Francis House Preparatory School

Aylesbury Road Tring Hertfordshire HP23 4DL
Tel: 01442 822315
Fax: 01442 827080
e-mail: info@francishouseschool.co.uk

'Combining the best of the past with the excellence of today for a very bright future.'

Chairman of Board of Governors: Mr Ron Busby

***Head*: Mrs Janice Hiley**

Type of School. Co-educational Day School
Age Range. 2–11.
Number of Pupils. 116: 51 boys, 65 girls.
Fees per term (2008-2009). £612–£2,295.

Francis House is a family school for boys and girls aged 2–11 where emphasis is placed on the following:

- A happy and disciplined environment
- Teaching of the highest quality
- Encouragement to develop a sense of responsibility and independence
- A high standard of politeness and consideration for others
- High quality pastoral care

Francis House is situated in an attractive elevated position in Tring. It is easily accessible from the A41 and our pupils travel from Aylesbury, Hemel Hempstead, Berkhamsted, Dunstable, Leighton Buzzard and the surrounding villages. The school is housed in two purpose built buildings and is surrounded by beautiful grounds, gardens, playing fields and tennis courts.

Here at Francis House we are a dedicated team working in partnership with parents to develop the potential of the whole child in a happy and caring community.

Francis House offers all of its pupils a wealth of opportunities. Education is about exploring and engaging every child's imagination in order that he or she will reach their full potential. Self-esteem is so important, particularly in the learning and growing up process and at Francis House praise and positive feedback provide the basis upon which every child can build, develop and grow educationally, and emotionally.

The joy of human nature is that we are all different and at Francis House each child is treated as an individual; everyone's strengths are recognised and celebrated.

Frewen College

Brickwall Northiam Nr Rye East Sussex TN31 6NL
Tel: 01797 252494
Fax: 01797 252567
e-mail: office@frewencollege.org
website: www.frewencollege.co.uk

***Principal*: Mrs Linda Smith**, BA, PGCE

Age Range. 5–16 Co-educational (Boarding from age 8).

Number in School. Full Boarders 8 boys, Weekly Boarders 20 boys. Day: 56 boys, 14 girls.

Fees per term (2008-2009). Day £5,075–£6,695; Full and Weekly Boarding £7,395–£9,295.

Frewen College is a small friendly independent specialist school catering principally for children with Specific Learning Difficulties (dyslexia, dyspraxia, dyslcalculia) and related speech and language and sensory integration problems. We also accept a small number with Asperger's Syndrome if we feel they will fit in and enrich the school environment.

The school adopts a holistic approach to teaching, designed to enhance pupils' confidence and self-esteem, allowing them to build on their strengths while learning to cope with their difficulties. Each pupil has a comprehensive Individual Education Plan in each subject (described in our last CReSTeD Report as 'exemplary') so that their teaching can be tailored to their individual needs. About half the children have statements of special educational need and are funded, currently by 18 different LEAs.

The recent move to co-educational status has proved popular, with 14 day girls now on roll. The fully flexible boarding arrangements are also popular, with up to around 15 boys now enjoying full boarding at no extra cost. Boarding is run very much like an extended family, with bedrooms of 1–4 boys, all with en-suite facilities, and all encouraged to personalise their rooms. Catering is 'in house', and rated by all-comers as 'excellent'! A very wide range of recreational activities is available, and transport is provided to and from London each weekend.

Juniors have the benefit of a separate school, The Oaks, adjacent to the main site, where our recent Ofsted Inspection found 'a particularly high standard of education'. The Oaks has an outstanding reputation for the performing arts, enjoys modern IT facilities, and a popular adventure playground.

Frewen College has excellent facilities, based around a historic house located in 60 acres of playing fields, gardens and parkland. Educational provision includes two modern IT suites, a drama workshop, food technology room, newly refurbished metalwork studio, pottery, photography dark room, music and music practice rooms, CDT workshop and an art studio. A new metalwork studio is planned for the Autumn 2008. English and Maths lessons are supplemented by intensive daily Literacy and Numeracy sessions, involving the whole classroom staff in teaching small groups of 1, 2 or 3 pupils.

Outdoor facilities include a large open-air swimming pool, tennis and basketball court, all-weather five-a-side and hockey pitch, fitness suite, as well as extensive playing fields. Our cricket pitch is rated one of the best village pitches in the County. We also have access to another 100 acres of ancient parkland, for cross-country runs, camping, and orienteering. All Year 9 pupils are entered for the Duke of Edinburgh's Award Scheme.

All classroom staff have specialist dyslexia training. We are DCSF approved, ISA registered, a supporting corporate member of the BDA, and rated 'Specialist Provision' by CReSTeD.

Charitable status. The Frewen Educational Trust Limited is a Registered Charity, number 307019.

Fyling Hall School

Robin Hood's Bay Near Whitby North Yorkshire YO22 4QD
Tel: 01947 880353
Fax: 01947 881097
e-mail: office@fylinghall.org
website: www.fylinghall.org

***Headmaster*: Mr Ken James**

Age Range. 4–18.

Number of Pupils. Boarders: Boys 68, Girls 47, Day: Boys 39, Girls 40.

Fees per term (2007-2008). Day: £1,610–£2,184; Weekly Boarding: £3,910–£4,340; Full Boarding: £4,085–£34,995.

Fyling Hall School is one of the oldest recognised co-educational schools in the country. It occupies a spectacular coastal setting within the North York Moors National Park. Pupils may safely enjoy freedom in this beautiful and peaceful rural area.

The buildings centre on a grade two listed Georgian country house in delightfully landscaped gardens incorporating an outdoor theatre overlooking Robin Hood's Bay. Recent expansion has included two new boarding houses, science laboratories and dining room in addition to the purpose-built Junior School. We have also built a spacious multi-functional sports hall and an astroturf recently.

The school is intentionally small due to its desire to educate pupils as individuals. The advantageous pupil-teacher ratio encourages effective learning. The teaching is along traditional lines with an emphasis on 'doing one's best' within a supportive yet challenging environment. A broadly based and well resourced curriculum is followed which reflects recent national initiatives, particularly in the scientific and information technology fields. A wide range of GCSE and A Level courses are offered.

Fyling Hall is a closely knit society with an emphasis on proactive pastoral care and a real sense of communal responsibility. The chief feature is a spirit of confidence and cooperation between staff and pupils in an atmosphere which is natural for growth.

There is no entrance examination but an interview and a report from the current school are integral parts of the admission process.

Many of the pupils stay to join the Sixth Form, where privilege and responsibility present a balance and are a useful preparation for university life.

The school takes advantage of its natural surroundings in the provision of numerous extra-curricular activities. Fyling Hall has its own ponies and these constitute a much loved part of school life. Climbing, Karate, Duke of Edinburgh's Award and Riding are all popular. The main games are rugby, hockey, cricket and tennis, each with a full fixture list. Music enjoys a good reputation and individual tuition is available in all the usual musical instruments.

Robin Hood's Bay is remarkably accessible despite its rural splendour. Nearby Whitby and Scarborough are both railheads. Teesside Airport and the ferry port of Hull, with their frequent continental connections, are both easily reached. An experienced Secretary is able to advise on all travel arrangements.

Academic standards are high, but other abilities are valued, and aided by the small size of classes it is hoped that all pupils can be encouraged to achieve their maximum potential.

Charitable status. Fyling Hall School Trust Ltd is a Registered Charity, number 507857. It exists for the provision of high quality education for boys and girls.

Gads Hill School

Higham Rochester Kent ME3 7PA
Tel: 01474 822366
Fax: 01474 822977
e-mail: admissions@gadshillschool.org
website: www.gadshill.org

***Headmaster*: Mr D G Craggs**, BSc, MA, FCollP, FRSA

Age Range. Co-educational 3–16.
Number in School. 370.
Fees per term (2008-2009). £2,275–£2,575.
Entry requirements. Interview and assessment.

Aim. To provide a good all-round education, to build confidence, establish friendships, to reward success (however small) and to ensure our students leave as mature, self-reliant young people who depart Gads for the career or University placement of their choice.

Kindergarten (3–6 years). From the very early years in Kindergarten the children are encouraged to learn through play, music and drama. Basic letter and number work is introduced within the nursery and reception class as the children concentrate on the Early Learning Goals. In Year 1 and Year 2 they largely follow Key Stage One of the National Curriculum although in addition; from Reception upwards, all of our children are taught French and also Information and Communications Technology.

Junior School (7–11 years). Our Junior School curriculum seeks to build upon the children's undaunted love of adventure. Literacy, Numeracy and Humanities continue to be taught by Form Tutors however, the children begin to benefit from more lessons delivered by specialist tutors particularly in French, Information Technology, Design & Technology, RE, Games and Drama.

Senior School (11–16 years). Senior School concentrates very much on the preparation for GCSE success and our classes are kept to a maximum of 20 children per class. This way the children benefit from smaller class sizes and consequently our tutors get to know each child as an individual and this enables them to provide the right level of support and assistance. This goes a long way to helping them achieve their goals for GCSEs and A levels.

Location. Gads Hill School is centred on the former home of Charles Dickens and is surrounded by beautiful grounds, playing fields and countryside. It is a few minutes' drive from the A2 and M2, with good access to the Medway Towns, Dartford and Gravesend.

Curriculum. At Gads we largely follow the National Curriculum although we place a strong emphasis on "communication" with all of our children benefiting from lessons in French, Information and Communications Technology and Drama as well as English. Senior School children progress to take GCSEs in English, English Literature, Maths, French, Design & Technology, Combined Science (Double Award), Geography and GNVQ ICT (4 GCSEs).

Sports and Activities. We concentrate very much on team games (rugby, hockey, soccer, netball, cricket, athletics and rounders) to ensure that our children learn the values of team work and communication. In the Kindergarten and Junior Schools all students take part in weekly swimming lessons. Because of our small class sizes almost all of our children have the opportunity to represent the school in competitive fixtures against other schools. Gad's Hill also has a thriving Combined Cadet Force. Students join the CCF in Year 8 and take part in weekly training sessions as well as termly field days and an annual camp. The CCF allows children to experience fantastic outdoor pursuits, adventurous training and leadership courses and is essentially about doing something different and challenging. Gad's Hill pupils are also able to take part in a variety of after-school activities. These range from academic pursuits to a variety of other sports and Performing Arts.

Charitable status. Gads Hill School is a Registered Charity, number 803153. It exists for the purpose of educating children aged 3–16.

Gatehouse School

Sewardstone Road Victoria Park London E2 9JG
Tel: 020 8980 2978
Fax: 020 8983 1642
e-mail: admin@gatehouseschool.co.uk
website: www.gatehouseschool.co.uk

***Headmistress*: Mrs Belinda Canham**, JP, BA, PGCE

Age Range. 3–11 Co-educational.
Number in School. 274 Day Pupils.
Fees per term (2008-2009). £2,100–£2,580.

Gatehouse School is an Independent Co-educational School for girls and boys aged 3 to 11.

Founded by Phyllis Wallbank, in May 1948, in the gatehouse of St Bartholomew, the Great Priory Church near Smithfield London, the School was a pioneer of much that is now generally accepted in education. Gatehouse is based on the Wallbank plan whose guiding principle is that children of any race, colour, creed, background and intellect shall be accepted as pupils and work side by side without streaming or any kind of segregation with the aim that each child shall get to know and love God, and develop their own uniqueness of personality, to enable them to appreciate the world and the world to appreciate them.

Gatehouse is now located in Sewardstone Road close to Victoria Park and continues to follow this philosophy.

The Nursery is accommodated in a large sunny space with its own outdoor play area. They follow a balanced curriculum of child-initiated and teacher-led activities.

Lower Juniors are taught most subjects by their own qualified teacher and assistant, but have French, PE and Music with a specialist teacher.

In Upper Juniors from the age of 7, teaching is by subject and is conducted by a highly qualified specialist staff. This is a special feature of Gatehouse and gives children from an early age, contact with subject specialists, not available to many children until secondary school.

Our classes average around 18 pupils.

Charitable status. Gatehouse Educational Trust Limited is a Registered Charity, number 282558.

Gateway School

1 High Street Great Missenden Buckinghamshire HP16 9AA

(See entry in IAPS section)

Gidea Park College

2 Balgores Lane Gidea Park Romford Essex RM2 5JR
Tel: 01708 740381
Fax: 01708 740381
e-mail: office@gideaparkcollege.co.uk
website: www.gideaparkcollege.co.uk

***Headmistress*: Mrs Vera S Lee**, BA

Age Range. 2½–11 Co-educational.
Number in School. 197 Day Pupils.
Fees per term (2008-2009). £2,240.

An established Preparatory school founded in 1924, the current Directors are the grand-daughters of the founders.

The main building, a substantial Georgian/Victorian house, accommodates the 7–11 year old children, the school library, assembly room and IT room plus the kitchens. In separate outside classrooms, bounded by lawns and playgrounds, is the small Pre-school unit and accommodation for 4–7 year old pupils.

All children are known and treated as individuals with specific talents which are valued and developed. Likewise, identified areas needing extra help and encouragement are recognised.

The broad-based curriculum is delivered by highly qualified, full-time classroom staff using traditional methods, assisted by qualified support staff.

Results in selection procedures at 11+ are of a consistently high standard with scholarships and places awarded at local Independent and Grammar Schools. Our KS1 and KS2 National Assessment Testing reveals standards above the National expectations.

All National Curriculum areas are covered using whole-class teaching methods. Latin and French are introduced in the higher year groups.

A school choir performs on formal occasions and visits local care homes to sing.

Local facilities are used for PE, swimming and games lessons. Our House system fosters team spirit and enables each individual to participate in a variety of inter-house competitions as well as inter-school events.

The school has a Christian Foundation and strong links with our local parish church. However, within our diverse community those of other faiths are welcomed and their beliefs respected and festivals celebrated. Our pupils are encouraged to think of others less fortunate than themselves and arrange a variety of fund-raising events for charity.

The staff supervise an early Morning and After School Club for the convenience of working parents. Those staying relax and then complete homework assignments giving quality time for parents and children at home.

New parents are made welcome by our thriving Parents' Association and encouraged to join in the various social events arranged providing a friendship base for them whilst at the school. Their fund-raising provides extra equipment and fun occasions for the children.

We encourage all prospective parents to visit the school prior to applying so they may see classes in action and have an opportunity to ask any questions. We consider the partnership between pupils, parents and school to be of paramount importance in enabling each child to reach his/her potential.

Glenarm College

20 Coventry Road Ilford Essex IG1 4QR
Tel: 020 8554 1760
Fax 020 8518 6681
e-mail: admissions@glenarmcollege.com
website: www.glenarmcollege.com

***Principal*: Mrs V Mullooly**, MA

Age Range. 3–11.
Number in School. Day: 53 Boys, 80 Girls.
Fees per term (2007-2008). £1,525–£1,995.

Glenarm College, founded in 1893, is an independent preparatory school for girls and boys of 3 to 11 years. A two-storey extension was completed in September 1997.

The School provides, through a wide curriculum, an education of high academic standard.

Whilst the emphasis is on good habits of sustained work and sound learning, we also seek to encourage creativity and independent thinking. Small classes give ample opportunity for individual attention. French and Computers are part of the curriculum for all children from 3 years.

The curriculum prepares girls and boys for the 11 plus examination and entry to senior independent schools in the Greater London and London area.

A tea-time Club operates after school and during half-terms and holidays up to 6.30 pm for working parents.

Gosfield School

Halstead Essex CO9 1PF
Tel: 01787 474040
Fax: 01787 478228
e-mail: enquiries@gosfieldschool.org.uk
website: www.gosfieldschool.org.uk

***Principal*: Mrs C Goodchild**, BSc, CertEd

Age Range. 4–18 Boys and Girls.
Number in School. Boarders 10, Day 185.
Fees per term (2007-2008). Day £1,940–£3,450, Weekly Boarding £4,340– £4,890.

Founded in 1929, Gosfield occupies a gracious, listed country house which was built in 1870 for Lady Courtauld. The school is set in a glorious 110 acre estate which borders ancient woodland and is a haven for wildlife and rare species. There are conservation areas and nature trails within the grounds.

Recent building developments include a Sports Hall, Music Suite and an all-weather sports surface. Boarding accommodation has also been completely upgraded.

The school is deliberately small in numbers and provides a caring family atmosphere in which every pupil will be able to develop his or her own potential to the full. Classes are small, and standards are high. The system of personal tutors ensures that every child's needs are properly looked after both in academic work and in the sporting and cultural activities in which the school encourages all pupils to participate.

There is a wide range of activities including sports, music, drama and conservation work. The programme changes termly and provides something for everyone. There are no weekend lessons.

The school day is from 8.30 am to 3.50 pm with Infants finishing at 3.00 pm. On Monday–Thursday there are after-school games and activities which run until 4.50 pm. All our pupils are encouraged to participate in these activities. On Friday school ends at 3.50 pm. Games fixtures are all in midweek.

The whole structure – daily and weekly – aims to be flexible and helpful to parents and pupils. The school sees education as a partnership, so parents are always welcome to visit, to talk to staff, and to be involved in the school's activities.

Gosfield is situated in rural North Essex only 20 miles from Stansted Airport and thirty miles from the M25. The nearest town, Halstead, is a mile away and the nearest station is just fives miles away at Braintree.

There is a daily minibus service to and from Chelmsford, Sudbury, Braintree and Colchester.

Charitable status. Gosfield School is a Registered Charity, number 310871. It exists to provide education for boys and girls.

The Grange School

Bradburns Lane Hartford Northwich Cheshire CW8 1LU

(See entry in HMC section)

Grangewood Independent School

Chester Road Forest Gate London E7 8QT
Tel: 020 8472 3552
Fax: 020 8552 8817
e-mail: admin@grangewoodschool.com
website: www.grangewoodschool.com

***Head*: Mrs Abimola Amokeodo**, BEd Hons

Age Range. 4–11.
Number in School. 48 boys, 32 girls.
Fees per term (2008-2009). £1,160–£1,495.

Grangewood is a Christian Day School which welcomes children from any faith background. We offer a secure, friendly and caring environment in small classes where children can achieve their potential.

Charitable status. Grangewood Educational Association is a Registered Charity, number 803492.

Greenbank School

Heathbank Road Cheadle Hulme Cheadle Cheshire SK8 6HU
Tel: 0161 485 3724
Fax: 0161 485 5519
e-mail: headmistress@greenbankschool.co.uk
website: www.greenbankschool.co.uk

***Headmistress*: Mrs Janet Lowe**, CertEd

Age Range. 6 months–11 years.
Number in School. Day: 87 Boys, 61 Girls. Daycare: 70.
Fees per term (2007-2008). £1,910.

Greenbank is an independent co-educational school for pupils aged three to eleven years. A separate Nursery, open fifty weeks of the year, cares for babies and children from six months to four years old.

Greenbank School was founded in 1951 by Karl and Linda Orsborn. Since 1971 the School has been administered by an Educational Trust and is registered with the DCSF.

Greenbank is situated within extensive grounds, comprises a mixture of traditional and modern buildings including an IT Suite and Library, separate play areas for Foundation, Infant and Junior children, playing fields with a cricket pavilion, an Astroturf area and netball court. 2008 sees the opening of a state-of-the-art Science/Art classroom within a new administration building.

The school day begins at 8.45 am and ends at 3.30 pm, however we provide wraparound care from 7.30 am until 6.00 pm. The school also runs activity and sports clubs in the holidays.

Through its varied curricula and extra-curricular activities the School provides pupils with the opportunity of expanding their natural abilities to the full. Music, drama, sport, computing and educational visits are some of the activities which play their part in providing a well-rounded programme of education. We strive to meet the social, emotional and intellectual needs of all pupils and the success of this philosophy is proven by the consistently outstanding examination results throughout the school, particularly at age eleven.

Charitable status. Greenbank School Limited is a Registered Charity, number 525930.

Greenfields School

Priory Road Forest Row East Sussex RH18 5JD
Tel: 01342 822189
Fax: 01342 825289
e-mail: grnflds@aol.com
website: www.greenfieldsschool.com

***Headteacher*: Mrs V Tupholme**

Age Range. $1^1/_2$–18.
Number in School. Day: 60 Boys, 85 Girls. Boarding: 20 Boys, 10 Girls.
Fees per term (2008-2009). Day £610–£3,415, Boarding (in addition to Tuition): £3,087 (Juniors), £2,478 (Seniors).

Greenfields has a fresh approach to education. It is a co-educational, non-denominational day and boarding school situated on the Ashdown Forest with 11 acres of its own woodland at the edge of the Sussex village of Forest Row.

The school offers a friendly, caring and safe environment, with a relaxed yet focused study environment. This is created by the study methods used that teach students what the barriers to study are and HOW to study and thereby help students to achieve success and a high degree of self-confidence, motivation, an enjoyment of study, and most important of all, an ability to continue studying successfully throughout life – it creates an ability to study independently and do research – students are well prepared for further education and work.

There is a high level of open communication between students and staff that helps to prevent failure, bullying or drugs.

Every student is individually programmed and targeted to ensure each one achieves the success they are capable of.

The classes are small and an excellent curriculum, providing core subjects and peripheral studies, is available up to GCSE and Advanced Levels.

A "qualifications" department exists for checking that students have fully understood each step of their studies, and also provides extra help for any student having any trouble in class. There is also an "ethics" department that helps to resolve any personal problems the student may have.

The pre-school has Montessori trained staff who use Montessori materials to ensure the best foundation for the rest of a student's education.

Entry is by tests for literacy and numeracy. There is a pre-entry section for those who need a short programme to catch up and be ready to join their correct class.

Extensive building work that started in 2002 has modernised the whole site and created new boarding bedrooms, new science labs, art room, maths and English purpose-built rooms and a large study room/library.

Trains take under an hour from London to East Grinstead, which is a ten minute car ride from the school. Gatwick Airport is a twenty minute car ride away.

Charitable status. Greenfields Educational Trust is a Registered Charity, number 287037. The object for which the trust is established is the advancement of education.

Greenholme School

392 Derby Road Nottingham NG7 2DX
Tel: 0115 978 7329
Fax: 0115 978 1160
e-mail: enquiries@greenholmeschool.co.uk
website: www.greenholmeschool.co.uk

***Headmistress*: Mrs Alison J Fisher**, BA, PGCE, LAMDA, EYPS

Age Range. 3–11+.

Number in School. Day: 126 Boys; 69 Girls.

Fees per term (2007-2008). £2,235–£2,350.

Greenholme School is an independent day school for boys and girls from the age of 3–11. Established in 1935 and accredited to ISC in 1988, the school is situated in the original house which faces Derby Road and it has been considerably extended to the rear. The playing field adjoining the school was acquired in 1996 providing additional play and sports facilities.

Greenholme is a caring school, combining the best traditional and modern teaching methods to provide an excellent education, with effective learning opportunities for all pupils, within a friendly and supportive environment.

Small class sizes and an excellent pupil/teacher ratio, ensure a firm foundation in primary education and an outstanding record of external examination success.

All subjects are taught in accordance with the National Curriculum guidelines; additionally our Reception to Year 6 curriculum includes French and a balanced religious education. A recent Ofsted inspection of the Early Years department categorised the school as 'Providing High Quality education with effective teaching' and progress in numeracy and literacy judged as being 'Outstanding'.

Pupils also have the opportunity to develop interests in extra-curricular activities, such as individual Music sessions, Art, Drama, Computing, Chess, Sport and Choir. Year 6 also has the opportunity to participate in the DARE anti-drugs programme.

Staff are very aware of the importance of meeting the needs of all children. Our full-time staff includes an individual needs coordinator (SENCO), who is available to discuss with parents appropriate individual education programmes. Recently a new unit has been set up offering specialised tuition by a qualified Dyslexia Teacher to help those of our pupils with individual needs. A specialist teacher (TEFL) also provides structured language programmes, for the occasional pupil who may not have English as their first language.

Pupils are expected to behave with courtesy and consideration for others and to develop a sense of responsibility. Discipline in the school is fair but firm and based on a positive ethos with the use of rewards and sanctions.

To assist working parents, pre-school care is available from 8.00 am and after-school care is also available until 5.30 pm. Children may be registered for this facility by arrangement.

Recent developments include a full curriculum review, resulting in some restructuring and major financial investment to ensure that quality teaching resources are available to every child in the school. A healthy eating policy has been adopted, while a full programme of classroom refurbishment has also been undertaken. Plans in place include further development of the playground and field. The first stages of this are now complete, with the provision of a covered play area and a multi-use all-weather playing surface, providing an alternative to our 'quiet area'.

The Gregg School

Townhill Park House Cutbush Lane Southampton SO18 2GF
Tel: 023 8047 2133
Fax: 023 8047 1080
e-mail: office@gregg.southampton.sch.uk
website: www.gregg.southampton.sch.uk

Chairman of Board of Trustees: Mr John W Watts, MCIPS, MILT, AIGEM

***Headmaster*: Mr R D Hart**, BEd

Age Range. 11–16 years.

Number in School. 310.

Fees per term (2008-2009). £3,010.

The Gregg School is a caring, friendly school in which pupils can develop and learn with confidence. Small teaching groups, excellent resources and well-qualified and experienced staff enable pupils to achieve their full potential. A sound curriculum is enriched by the provision of Learning Support for pupils with individual needs and extended to provide further learning opportunities for gifted pupils.

Pupils enjoy participating in a wide range of sports, competing to a high standard. We make use of City sports facilities in addition to provision in school. Musical and dramatic activities are very popular, as are the residential experiences offered to each year group. These help individuals develop initiative, a sense of identity and the ability to work cooperatively in a challenging environment.

In addition to GCSE examinations, pupils may take RSA and Associated Board of the Royal Schools of Music examinations.

Admission to the school is usually through the Entrance Examination in January, but interested parents are very welcome to visit at any time.

We also have a preparatory department, St Winifred's School, for children aged 2–11.

Grenville College Junior School
A Woodard School

Moreton House Abbotsham Road Bideford Devon EX39 3QN
Tel: 01237 472208
Fax: 01237 427017
e-mail: juniorschool@grenvillecollege.co.uk
website: www.grenvillecollege.co.uk

Headteacher: **Mrs E A Preece**, DipEd

Age Range. 2½–11.

Number in School. 85.

Fees per term (2008-2009). Day: £1,465 (Early Birds), £1,615 (Years 1 and 2), £2,115 (Years 3 and 4), £2,675 (Years 5 and 6). Boarding (from age 8): £4,435 (weekly), £5,550 (full).

Grenville College Junior School is a Woodard School situated in a beautiful house in 40 acres of ground in Bideford, an attractive small market town on the banks of the River Torridge. The North Devon coast, Dartmoor and Exmoor are all within easy driving distance.

A thorough education is provided in a caring, Christian environment for girls and boys from 2½ to 11. The school's concern is the happiness and success of its pupils. It has been able to adapt to changes in educational practice without losing traditional values. Emphasis is placed on pupils' literacy and numeracy, within a broad and varied curriculum. Courtesy and consideration for others are particularly important, and these qualities are nurtured by a committed staff.

Classrooms are pleasant and facilities include a well stocked newly refurbished library, a lovely music room and gymnasium. Pupils enjoy the services of specialist Modern Languages, Science, Design Technology and PE staff shared with the senior school and the Junior School benefits from sharing senior facilities to a high specification for Science and IT. All take part regularly in concerts and plays. The music room is what was a magnificent ballroom overlooking the gardens. Extra curricular activities flourish and sports teams do well in local competitions. The sports fields lie in front of the school and recently built netball/tennis courts are behind the school building.

There is an excellent Kindergarten (Early Birds) for girls and boys from 2½ years old where structured learning begins. Children in the Kindergarten wear school uniform and take part in assemblies, ensuring a sense of belonging from the very beginning. Boys and girls take the entrance examinations at 11+ and the vast majority remain in the school. They have an excellent record of winning scholarships.

Fledgelings – a pre-school parent and toddler group – has been a tremendous success since opening early in 1998.

Lunches are freshly cooked on the premises by our own staff.

Charitable status. Grenville College is a Registered Charity, number 1103317. It exists to provide high quality education for boys and girls.

Hale Preparatory School

Broomfield Lane Hale Cheshire WA15 9AS
Tel: 0161 928 2386
Fax: 0161 941 7934
e-mail: administrator@hale-prep-school.demon.co.uk

Headmaster: **J Connor**, JP, BSc, FCP

Age Range. 4–11.

Number in School. Day: 98 Boys, 84 Girls.

Fees per term (2008-2009). £1,750.

Hale Preparatory School was established in 1980 and received accreditation two years later. The aim of the school is to develop each child to his/her fullest ability in a disciplined, caring and happy environment.

The classes are small. In the last ten years all pupils have passed examinations to independent grammar schools.

Whilst emphasis is placed on the basic subjects a broad curriculum is followed including Music, French, Speech and Drama, Computers and Library studies. Extra curriculum activities including sport, theatre visits, adventure and skiing holidays are an integral part of the school programme.

Halliford School

Russell Road Shepperton Middlesex TW17 9HX

(See entry in SHMIS section)

The Hammond School

Hoole Bank House Mannings Lane Chester CH2 4ES
Tel: 01244 305350
Fax: 01244 305351
e-mail: enquiries@thehammondschool.co.uk
website: www.thehammondschool.co.uk

The Hammond School is accredited by the Independent Schools Council and CDET, and caters for a wide range of talents and interests. A number of funded places are available for talented dance students through the Music and Dance Scheme and the DADA Awards.

Head: **Mrs M Evans**, BA, MA, PGCE, NPQH, FRSA

Age Range. 11–19.

Number in School. 43 Boarders, 155 Day Pupils.

Fees per term (2007-2008). £2,833 for education only.

Education Department takes girls from 11 years to GCSE level.

Drama Department takes girls and boys from 11 years joining the Education Department with additional Drama.

Dance Department takes girls and boys from 11 years joining the Education Department with a Vocational Dance training.

Sixth Form takes boys and girls into the Education Department to study for A/AS levels as well as those wishing to specialise in Dance and Drama.

Full boarding is available for Dance pupils; weekly boarding for academic pupils.

For a prospectus apply to The Secretary.

The Hampshire School
GEMS Education

63 Ennismore Gardens Knightsbridge London SW7 1NH
Tel: 020 7584 3297
Fax: 020 7584 9733
e-mail: hampshire@indschool.org
website: www.ths.westminster.sch.uk

Early Years Section:
5 Wetherby Place London SW7 4NX

Preparatory Section:
9 Queensborough Terrace London W2 3TB

Principal: **Mr Arthur Bray**, CertEd

Age Range. 3–13.
Number in School. Day: 150 Boys, 150 Girls.
Fees per term (2008-2009). £2,650–£3,690.

The School, which was founded in 1928, occupies three fine buildings all close to Hyde Park and Kensington Gardens and is well placed to take full advantage of the vast range of sporting and cultural facilities on the doorstep.

In January 2009 the Pre-Preparatory and Preparatory Sections will move to a new site at 15 Manresa Road, London SW3. The school has spent three years working on the refurbishment of the grade 2* listed building, which was originally built as a library in 1890. The building will have state-of-the-art facilities for the children but these will be sympathetically integrated with its original architectural features.

The School provides a broad-based curriculum and has been successful in preparing pupils for examination and scholarship entry into leading day and boarding senior independent schools. Great emphasis is placed on developing each child's individual talents.

Fully qualified and experienced teachers provide a high standard of tuition in all aspects of the curriculum.

Pupils start French from the age of three and senior forms attend an annual study visit to France, as an integral part of the French syllabus.

The School also offers a home-to-school bus service, after-school care and multi-activity holiday courses.

Harenc School

Church House 167 Rectory Lane Footscray Sidcup Kent DA14 5BU
Tel: 020 8309 0619
Fax: 020 8309 5051
e-mail: info@harencschool.co.uk
website: www.harencschool.co.uk

Headmistress: **Miss S J Woodward**, BA Hons, FRSA

Age Range. 3–11+.
Number in School. 160 Day Boys.
Fees per term (2007-2008). £1,872–£2,454. Compulsory extras: Lunch, Swimming, French.

Harenc School is proud of its reputation for traditional values and academic excellence. The National Curriculum is followed and all boys from 4+ study French, ICT and have weekly Swimming classes. Visiting Football, Rugby and Cricket coaches enhance the PE provision and extra-curricular activities include an Art Club, Chess Club and Drama. Individual instrumentalist tuition is offered and boys are able to join the School Choir, Orchestra and Recorder Groups. The school has a strong reputation for success in the 11+ examinations to local Independent and Grammar schools.

Emphasis is placed on academic achievement, fair discipline and providing a stimulating and caring environment where the boys are seen as individuals and are assisted to reach their full potential.

Charitable status. Harenc School is a Registered Charity, number 287948. It exists to provide an education for boys in a Christian spirit and where the work of the school may benefit the community as a whole.

Haresfoot School

Chesham Road Berkhamsted Herts HP4 2SZ
Tel: 01442 872742
01442 866269 (Happy Hares Day Nursery)
e-mail: haresfootschool@btconnect.com
website: www.haresfoot.herts.sch.uk

Head: **Mrs S Jaspal**

Age Range. 5 months–11 years Co-educational.
Number in School. 150.
Fees per term (2007-2008). £410–£2,590 (excluding lunch).

Haresfoot Preparatory School is set in a tastefully converted Georgian coach house and stables in seven acres of grass and woodland, conveniently located on the Herts-Bucks border, 10 kms from the M25 and Ml motorways, at the Chesham exit of the A41. It has a walled garden and specialist art, pottery and music rooms, science room and a large new Sports Hall. Haresfoot provides a beautiful, safe environment – the ideal place for children's gifts to be nurtured.

A co-educational independent preparatory school, established for 21 years, Haresfoot is a caring, vibrant community. It endeavours to create an extended family atmosphere where happy children enjoy learning and each child is encouraged to reach his or her full potential. The school offers a broad-based, stimulating education, including Spanish and French, Music, Drama, Dance, Sport, Sciences and Art. Children progress to the next stage of their education and into the world beyond, making the most of their strengths and achieving at the highest possible levels across the curriculum. Because of our small numbers, adults have time to listen and appreciate each child as a unique person. The children learn to communicate confidently with people of all ages. They excel in many areas of our broad curriculum and many progress to Grammar school and selective entry independent schools.

There is a wide variety of after-school clubs and children participate in many day and residential trips. Before- and after-school clubs provide wrap-around care from 8 am to 5.45 pm, with homework supervision where required. There are extended-day holiday clubs through many of the school holidays, offering Sport, Drama, Art and other activities.

Happy Hares Day Nursery (0–4+ years) is open 51 weeks per year from 7.30 am to 6.30 pm, and is situated on the school site. Children can join the Haresfoot Family from 5 months of age at Happy Hares, moving on at around 2½ years into Haresfoot's Pre-school, which is just next door. They gradually build up their sessions in Pre-school at their own individual pace. They can return to Happy Hares for the rest of the day. Alternatively, children can join Pre-school at around 2½ years. Happy Hares caters for children up to the September that they begin in Reception (when they can use the school's out of hours clubs).

Harvington School

20 Castlebar Road Ealing London W5 2DS
Tel: 020 8997 1583
Fax: 020 8810 4756
e-mail: admin@harvingtonschool.com
website: www.harvingtonschool.com

Headmistress: **Mrs Anna Evans**, BA Hons, PGCE

Age Range. Girls 3–16, Boys 3–4.
Number in School. 220 Girls, 10 Boys (in nursery).
Fees per term (2008-2009). £1,260–£3,280. Compulsory extras: None.

The School was founded in 1890 and made into an Educational Trust in 1970. Harvington is known for its high standards and happy atmosphere. Classes are small so that individual attention can be given by qualified and experienced staff. An academic education is offered, leading in the senior school to GCSE examination. The school continues to improve specialist facilities and also to provide a mixed nursery class for 3–4 year olds.

It is close to Ealing Broadway station and a number of bus routes.

Prospectus available from the Secretary.

Charitable status. Harvington School Education Trust Ltd is a Registered Charity, number 312621. It aims to subscribe to traditional values in behaviour and academic standards in a happy environment; to encourage a high standard of academic achievement for girls across a broad range of abilities; to encourage girls to develop their potential to the full, both in personal and academic terms; and to create an environment in which pupils will want to learn.

Hatherop Castle Preparatory School

Hatherop Cirencester Glos GL7 3NB

(See entry in IAPS section)

Hawley Place School

Fernhill Road Blackwater Camberley Surrey GU17 9HU
Tel: 01276 32028
Fax: 01276 609695
e-mail: office@hawleyplace.com
website: www.hawleyplace.com

***Principals*: Mr T G Pipe**, MA and **Mrs M L Pipe**, L-ès-L

Age Range. 2–16.

Number in School. 370 Day Pupils.

Fees per term (2008-2009). Juniors (Reception to Year 4) £2,400; Seniors (Years 5 to 11) £3,000.

Hawley Place is a small school based around an old country residence set in 17 acres of grounds. The beautiful setting provides an ideal learning environment, where kindness, courtesy and consideration are fostered in all pupils.

Maintaining a high quality of teaching and learning is our main concern. Well qualified staff, working with enviably small groups, enable us to recognise individual needs more quickly and meet them more effectively. Examination results at GCSE level are consistently above the national average and most pupils take ten subjects or more.

We offer a broad and balanced curriculum to cover all National Curriculum subjects. With the development of the single market economy we feel it important to offer pupils two foreign languages from the age of 11 to facilitate possible study or work abroad later. Moreover, French is introduced to Nursery pupils and continued through the Junior section of the school. A third foreign language is available for able linguists.

We believe in and practise the "Pursuit of Excellence" both inside and beyond the classroom. Physical education constitutes an integral part of the curriculum and sporting activities form part of a broad extra-curricular programme. Pupils are also regularly involved in music and drama rehearsals for school productions, the Debating Society, the French Club and local Art and Literature Competitions, as well as a considerable amount of charity work.

We hold our annual Open Morning in the Autumn Term and the School Entrance Examination in the Spring Term. Several Scholarship Awards are available each year for outstanding academic ability and for special talents in particular fields such as Modern Languages, Art, Music, Drama and Physical Education. The School runs its own Assisted Places Scheme.

We are successful at Hawley Place because pupils, parents and staff work together in partnership with good cooperation and communication. Full details and a prospectus may be obtained from the School Secretary. We look forward to your visit. Our door is always open.

Heathcote School

Eves Corner Danbury Essex CM3 4QB
Tel: 01245 223131
Fax: 01245 224568
e-mail: registrar@heathcoteschool.co.uk
website: www.heathcoteschool.co.uk

Principals: Mr & Mrs R H Greenland

***Head Teacher*: Mr K Gladwin**, CertEd

Age Range. 3–11+.

Number in School. 116: 73 boys, 43 girls.

Fees per term (2007-2008). £2,030.

Founded in 1935, Heathcote School has achieved a high reputation as a school where every child matters. It is a small, family school that encourages excellence in all areas. However, there is room in this happy school for children of all abilities and parents can be sure that their child's education, at all levels, will be designed to develop their child's particular potential.

Children enter Pre-prep at age 3 and enter full-time education prior to their 5th birthday. However, full-time education is available earlier if required. From September 2007 pupils may stay at school until 6 pm to complete homework and to attend one of the many extra-curricular clubs available.

Specialist subject teachers ensure the success of the high teaching standards expected at this school. Many children are prepared for scholarships, entrance examinations and the Essex Selective Schools Examination at 11+. A very high pass rate is attained in these examinations.

Pupils are expected to show courtesy and consideration at all times and encouraged to develop self-discipline and pride in themselves and their environment. Parents are asked to support the school in this. Regular consultations with parents are held and the Head is available at short notice for any discussions that parents consider necessary. Parental involvement with the development of the school is actively encouraged.

For more information please visit the website.

Heathfield School

Wolverley Kidderminster Worcestershire DY10 3QE
Tel: 01562 850204
Fax: 01562 852609
e-mail: info@heathfieldschool.co.uk
website: www.heathfieldschool.co.uk

***Headmaster*: R H Brierly**, BEd

Age Range. 3–16. Baby Unit for children 3 months plus.

Number in School. 250 Day pupils.

Fees per term (2008-2009). £1,735–£2,876. Pre School: £13.25 per session, £27.80 per full day.

Heathfield is a co-educational day school, governed by an Educational Trust. The School is situated in a green belt area one mile north of Kidderminster in spacious grounds, within easy reach of the West Midlands conurbation.

The curriculum is broadly based and pupils are prepared for GCSE. We also prepare children for the Entrance Examination for local senior schools at 11+ and for the Common Entrance Examination at 13+. The majority of pupils in our Junior School move up to our own Senior School at 11+.

A wide variety of team games and individual sports are offered. The school is strong in Drama, Music and Art. Classes are small. Career guidance is available to senior pupils. Prospectus available from Headmaster's Secretary.

Charitable status. Heathfield Educational Trust is a Registered Charity, number 1098940. It exists to provide excellent educational opportunities at a reasonable cost.

Hemdean House School

Hemdean Road Caversham Reading Berks RG4 7SD
Tel: 0118 9472590
Fax: 0118 9464474
e-mail: office@hemdeanhouse.co.uk
website: www.hemdeanhouse.co.uk

***Headmistress*: Mrs J Harris**, BSc, PGCE

Age Range. Girls 2½–16; Boys 2½–11.
Number in School. 120 Girls, 60 Boys.
Fees per term (2008-2009). £1,560–£2,180.

Founded in 1859, Hemdean House is a school where traditional educational concepts are highly valued. We look for personal achievement in academic and other spheres, responsible behaviour and consideration for others. We aim to develop the varied talents of each and every child within our structured and caring environment; individual attention has high priority. Small classes help us to achieve our aims. We believe that school and family should work together and have opportunities to meet.

The school is organised and operated as one complete unit; many of the specialist staff teach in both the Senior and Junior schools.

The self-contained Nursery unit offers children aged 2½–4 the opportunity to begin the learning process and to develop their skills in a secure and happy environment.

We follow the National Curriculum throughout the school; Mathematics, Science, Information Technology, the Humanities and the Expressive Arts, Modern Languages, Technology and Physical Education are taught throughout the age range. French lessons begin at age 5 and recorder lessons begin at age 7 and many children learn at least one other musical instrument. Drama and Public Speaking, Music and Art head a wide range of extra-curricular activities. For the working parent, after-school and holiday care are available if required.

Examination results including GCSE and National Curriculum Key Stage Tests are excellent with pupils achieving well in excess of the national average. Over the last five years an average of 86% of our GCSE grades were A* to C.

The school has always been committed to Christian ethics and values, but all faiths are welcomed and understanding and appreciation of the beliefs of others is encouraged.

The most recent inspection report made some of the following statements:

- "The excellent relationships between pupils and teachers create an environment in which pupils respond readily to questions."
- "Throughout the school, pupils demonstrate positive personal qualities, encouraged and developed by an ethos that emphasizes personal responsibility, strong moral values and concern for others."
- "Pupils are articulate; they express their views clearly and confidently and are not afraid to venture an opinion."
- "Lessons take place in a relaxed but purposeful atmosphere and behaviour is exemplary."

Admission. Assessment during a day or half-day spent in school according to age. An entrance exam is taken by prospective Year 7 pupils. Scholarships and bursaries are available throughout the school.

Charitable status. Hemdean House is a Registered Charity, number 309146. Its aims include academic achievement, the development of every pupil's potential, Christian values and care for others.

Herne Hill School

The Old Vicarage 127 Herne Hill London SE24 9LY
Tel: 020 7274 6336
Fax: 020 7924 9510
e-mail: enquiries@hernehillschool.co.uk
website: www.hernehillschool.co.uk

***Head Teacher*: Mrs Jane Beales**

Age Range. 3–7.
Number in School. 250 boys and girls.
Fees per term (2008-2009). £1,280–£3,180.

Herne Hill School has much to offer – caring and enthusiastic staff, happy and confident children, and excellent results at 7+ years. Main entry is into the Nursery at 2+ years, the Kindergarten at 3+ (both in order of registration, with priority given to siblings) and the Reception at 4+ (after an informal interview).

The school is well known as an oasis of happy learning and as the largest feeder into the Dulwich Foundation Schools. It is situated in an Old Vicarage and a spacious new building set within half acre grounds, which include a bark playground in the old orchard.

Since its foundation in 1976, Herne Hill School has focused on Early Years education and thereby developed a strong expertise in making the critical transition from Nursery to School seamless. Children joining the Nursery or Kindergarten can avoid the disruption of a 4+ change and have continuity for up to five years in what are arguably their most important formative years. Children joining in Reception also benefit from the smooth progression from a play-based learning approach to more structured lessons.

"*Herne Hill School for love, care and an excellent education*" encapsulates the school philosophy that love, nurture and a caring environment foster the children's self-confidence, sense of achievement and happiness, thereby stimulating their curiosity and desire to learn. The school's atmosphere lives this philosophy. It is a caring, friendly and fun place, and at the same time there is an air of achievement, respect and discipline. In addition, its co-ed nature and non-selective admissions policy in Nursery and Kindergarten enables it to build a wonderfully diverse community.

The curriculum is finely balanced to take account of each child's individual needs as well as the requirements of the 7+ entry tests – and to make learning fun! It is designed to develop the skills of independent learning and to sustain the children's innate joy of learning. Music, drama, gym, dancing and French are emphasised and taught by specialists.

The latest ISI inspection report delivered a strong endorsement of the school's ethos, staff, curriculum, *modus operandi* and infrastructure. The inspectors summarised their findings as follows: "High-quality teaching effectively supports pupils' very good personal development and enables them to achieve results which are far above national standards."

The school's website contains relevant information about life at the school, its curriculum, the destination of its leavers and some useful links.

Heywood Preparatory School

The Priory Corsham Wiltshire SN13 0AP
Tel: 01249 713379
Fax: 01249 701757
e-mail: principals@heywoodprep.com
website: www.heywoodprep.com

***Principals*: M Hall**, BSc Hons; **P Hall**, BA Hons

Age Range. 2–11 Co-educational.

Number in School. Day: 90 Boys, 70 Girls. Nursery 45.

Fees per term (2007-2008). £1,600–£1,900. Lunches £150.

Heywood Preparatory School in Corsham has a well-established reputation for academic excellence combined with a high standard of pastoral care.

A major expansion was completed in 1998 comprising a multi-purpose hall for gymnasium activities, plays, concerts and individual music lessons, together with improvements in cloakroom and dining facilities. A fully-equipped ICT Suite was added in the summer of 2000.

Class sizes at Heywood are kept to a maximum of 16 to allow teachers to give as much individual attention as possible to each child. Progress is monitored by weekly tests and termly examinations with a full report to parents at the end of each term.

The recorder is taught to 6 and 7 year olds and a wide range of musical instruments taught on an individual basis leading to Associated Board Examinations. A high standard of Speech Training with tuition for examinations is available. French is taught throughout the main school and Nursery. Swimming is an integral part of the curriculum.

Girls games are netball, hockey, tennis, athletics and rounders. Boys play rugby, football, cricket, tennis, athletics and rounders. Other activities available are chess, orchestra, judo, cycling proficiency, sewing and cookery.

Heywood is a co-educational school from 4 to 11 years. Pupils go on to all the major independent senior schools in the area, many of them having gained academic, music or sports scholarships.

It has its own Nursery School, called Wigwam, which takes children rising three and prepares them for entry to either the main school or state schools at four or sometimes five years old.

Highclare School

10 Sutton Road Erdington Birmingham B23 6QL

(See entry in GSA section)

Highfield Priory School

Fulwood Row Fulwood Preston Lancashire PR2 5RW
Tel: 01772 709624
Fax: 01772 655621
e-mail: schooloffice@highfieldpriory.co.uk
website: www.highfieldpriory.co.uk

***Headmaster*: Mr D Williams**, MA, AdvDipEd

Age Range. 2–11.

Number in School. Day: 150 Boys, 120 Girls.

Fees per term (2007-2008). £1,650–£1,915.

Highfield is set in 8 acres of landscaped gardens, woodlands and playing fields and is a co-educational preparatory school for children aged 2 to 11+ years. It is fully equipped with its own established nursery and prepares children for all Independent, Grammar and Senior Schools in Lancashire, for which it has an excellent academic record. Class numbers average 20 and children are taught by fully qualified and experienced staff. Recent additions to the school include a classroom block, multi-purpose sports hall, a music centre, infant/nursery wing and dining room. A new library and ICT suite opened in 1994, a new CDT centre in November 2005 and in October 2006 a new Science Laboratory. The school has strong musical and sporting traditions. Highfield holds Sport England's Activemark Gold Award, Investors in People and has been awarded 'Healthy School' status.

We offer an extended day from 7.30 am until 6.00 pm. Extra-curricular activities include Ballet, Gymnastics, Badminton, Design, Dance, Karate, Table Tennis, Chess, ICT, Cookery and Instrument Tuition. The school is well supported by an enthusiastic Parents Association. A prospectus is available on application to the Headmaster.

Charitable status. Highfield Priory School is a Registered Charity, number 532262. It exists to provide independent education to all children between the ages of 2 and 11 years within Preston and surrounding areas for all who wish to participate and to provide access to the community at large to all sporting, musical and artistic provision within the school.

Highfields School

London Road New Balderton Newark Nottinghamshire NG24 3AL
Tel: 01636 704103
Fax: 01636 680919
e-mail: headmaster@highfieldsschool.co.uk
website: www.highfieldsschool.co.uk

***Headmaster*: D R Wood**, BEd, FLS, FCollT, CBiol, MIBiol, MRI

Age Range. 3–11.

Number in School. Day: 92 Boys, 92 Girls.

Fees per term (2007-2008). £1,852 including lunch. Nursery £14.50 per half day session.

Highfields School is situated within 14 acres of quiet parkland and sports field. The Headmaster is a member of the Independent Schools Association and the School is accredited by the Independent Schools Council.

Highfields School provides a happy, lively, caring community that allows the children to experience a sense of pride and fulfilment that comes from working to their full potential. Basic subjects need to be mastered but children learn to react in different ways and need to be treated as individuals. Personal responsibility, initiative, good manners and smart appearance are encouraged.

Children enter a structured course of Nursery Education in the term in which they reach the age of three. Children enter the Reception Class before their fifth birthday and proceed through the School in year groups. Each class is taught by its own teacher in the basic subjects. The maximum class size is twenty-four, with the average being nineteen. All members of staff are fully qualified and specialist teachers assist with music, French, PE and games throughout the School. Support teachers are available to help individuals or small groups with specific learning difficulties.

The curriculum is balanced and broadly based with the emphasis on English, Mathematics and Science. The full range of National Curriculum subjects is covered in order that the varying interests and skills of the children may be fully developed. French is taught throughout the main school.

All children are encouraged to be creative and exhibit a delight in learning. There are ample opportunities for speech and drama, ballet and music with recorder ensembles, choir and an orchestra. Peripatetic staff offer lessons in saxophone, violin, cello, flute and clarinet. The School offers a wide range of extra curricular activities and sports teams compete against local authority and independent schools. Highfields has fully qualified staff who teach tennis, hockey, cricket, football, rugby and netball. The School holds an Activemark Gold Award. All children have a swimming lesson each week.

Highfields has an excellent academic record sending pupils to local independent schools and to Grammar Schools in Lincolnshire through 11+ entry.

The School is administered by a Board of Governors, including parent governors.

Charitable status. Newark Preparatory School Company Limited is a Registered Charity, number 528261. It exists to provide and further the education of children.

Highlands School

Wardle Avenue Tilehurst Reading Berkshire RG31 6JR
Tel: 0118 942 7186
Fax: 0118 945 4953
e-mail: enquiries@highlandsschool.co.uk
website: www.highlandsschool.co.uk

***Principal*: Mr Grant Mottram**, HDipEd SA, MA Ed, NPQH

Vice-Principal: Mrs Lesley Charlesworth

Age Range. Boys 2–7; Girls 2–11.
Number in School. 130.
Fees per term (2008-2009). £296–£2,500.

The Highlands is situated in a quiet residential area of Reading within easy reach of the town centre and the M4 (exit 12). The school aims to provide a broad based education of high calibre in a friendly caring environment. There is an excellent pupil teacher ratio which enables the staff to take into account the specific needs of each child. The academic record is very good. Most of the teaching is done by the form teacher, however there are specialist teachers for PE, French, Music and Special Needs. A wide variety of Educational Outings plays an important roll in the curriculum. All areas of the National Curriculum are covered including French and Drama. The children are introduced to as many different sports as is possible.

The children are encouraged to give of their best at all times whatever the field of endeavour and to reach the highest level of attainment of which they are capable.

The girls are prepared for the Common Entrance and other secondary school examinations and the boys for the preparatory school of their choice.

There is a school choir and orchestra. Individual instrumental music lessons are available.

A cooked midday meal is served to all children, the cost of which is included in the fees.

Before and after school care and some holiday care is provided for those who wish to make use of this facility.

Charitable status. St Edward's and Highlands School Ltd is a Registered Charity, number 309147. It exists to provide education for children in the area.

Hill House St Mary's School

Lower & Middle School: Rutland Street Thorne Road Doncaster South Yorkshire DN1 2JD
Tel: 01302 323563/323565
Fax: 01302 761098
e-mail: info@hillhousestmarys.co.uk

Senior School:
65 Bawtry Road Doncaster South Yorkshire DN4 7AD
Tel: 01302 535926
Fax: 01302 534675
e-mail: info@hillhousestmarys.co.uk
website: www.hillhousestmarys.co.uk

The School is an Educational Trust with a Board of Governors.

Chairman of Governors: Mrs E Paver

***Principal*: David Holland**, MA

Age Range. 2½–16.
Number of Pupils. 475 Day Pupils: 230 Boys, 245 Girls.
Fees per term (2007-2008). £2,050–£2,930 according to age (except Nursery). Fees include lunch and most extras.

Children enter the School at 2½ years of age via a purpose built Nursery where structured play and learning are the order of the day. Much care and thought is given to the preparation for transition to the Lower School at 4+, the Middle School at 7+ and the Senior School at 11+. As children progress through the School there is a gradual change to subject based teaching in specialist rooms, in preparation for GCSEs at 16. The School curriculum correlates closely with the National Curriculum. Music, Drama, Art and Sport play an important part in the life of the School. Throughout the year over 40 academic, recreational, musical and sporting activities per week are also offered in extra-curricular time. The major sports undertaken include rugby, soccer, netball, hockey, cricket, tennis, athletics and rounders. There are two orchestras and two choirs within the school. Drama productions and concerts are undertaken on a regular basis.

The whole school, currently working on two sites, will be moving to a new campus in 2008.

Charitable status. Hill House School Limited is a Registered Charity, number 529420. It exists to provide nursery, primary and secondary education to boys and girls aged 2½–16.

Hillcrest Grammar School

Beech Avenue Stockport Cheshire SK3 8HB
Tel: 0161 480 0329
Fax: 0161 476 2814
e-mail: headmaster@hillcrest.stockport.sch.uk
website: www.hillcrest.stockport.sch.uk

***Head*: D J Eversley**, BA

Age Range. 3–16.
Number in School. Day: 180 Boys, 165 Girls.
Fees per term (2008-2009). £1,699–£2,332. No compulsory extras.

Hillcrest is a charitable educational trust and comprises Senior, Preparatory and Pre-Preparatory Schools.

Our primary aim is to maximise the potential of each individual and progress, both academic and social, is monitored with great care at all levels of the School. Good communication between School and Home is especially important and the Headmaster and the staff are readily accessible at short notice. We make no apology for stressing traditional values such as mutual respect, good manners and self-discipline.

Classes are small and are taught by fully qualified and experienced staff. Sixteen GCSE courses are currently offered and excellent facilities include more than fifty multimedia PCs accessible to all, the Art & Design Centre, a first class sports hall and all-weather tennis/netball courts. There is a wide range of musical, sporting and extra-curricular activity.

Because we are a relatively small community both boys and girls have every opportunity to be more prominent in a wide range of pursuits than would be the case in larger schools.

At 11+ children are prepared for entry not only to our own Senior School but also to larger independent and state schools. At 16+ most pupils progress to Sixth Form courses either at State Colleges or HMC Schools. Parents are most welcome to visit us in order that they may appreciate the happy working atmosphere of the school. Admission is by annual 11+ entrance examination and by interview and individual assessment for other age groups. A limited number of means-tested Bursary places are available each year at both Preparatory and Senior levels.

Charitable status. Hillcrest Grammar School is a Registered Charity, number 525928. It exists to provide education for boys and girls.

Hollygirt School

Elm Avenue Nottingham NG3 4GF

(See entry in GSA section)

Howe Green House School

Great Hallingbury Bishop's Stortford Herts CM22 7UF
Tel: 01279 657706
Fax: 01279 501333
e-mail: info@howegreenhouseschool.co.uk
website: www.howegreenhouseschool.co.uk

Headmaster: **Mr G R Gorton**, BA, PGCE

Age Range. 2–11 years.
Number in School. 155.
Fees per term (2008-2009). Kindergarten £1,760, Infants £2,266, Juniors £2,797.

Howe Green House opened in September 1987. It offers an education of the highest quality in the widest sense. Facilities are excellent being sited in 8 acres of countryside adjacent to Hatfield Forest. It is a single stream school which works to the National Curriculum, offering additional French, Music and Sport. There is a strong parental involvement within the school whereby parents are actively encouraged to be part of their childrens education. The school is seen as a community which fosters an understanding of children's development within both school and home. Children sit external examinations to senior schools both boarding and day and have been highly successful.

Entry to the school is mainly via Acorns Nursery but children are considered for entry to the Junior School by assessment and interview.

Charitable status. The Howe Green Educational Trust Ltd is a Registered Charity, number 297106. It exists to promote and provide for the advancement of education for the public benefit and in connection therewith to conduct a day school for the education of boys and girls.

Hull Collegiate School (UCST)

Tranby Croft Anlaby East Yorkshire HU10 7EH

(See entry in SHMIS section)

Hulme Hall Grammar School

Hulme Hall Road Cheadle Hulme Stockport Cheshire SK8 6LA
Tel: 0161 485 3524
0161 485 4638
Fax: 0161 485 5966
e-mail: secretary@hulmehallschool.org
website: www.hulmehallschool.org

Co-educational, Independent and Accredited.

Headmaster: **Philip Marland**, BSc Hons, MA, PGCE

Age Range. 2–16.
Number in School. 400.
Fees per term (2008-2009). £1,456–£2,336.

Junior School. We cater for girls and boys from 2 to 11 years in our Nursery, Kindergarten, Infant and Junior classes. At every stage of the learning process, we provide a caring and stimulating environment.

Given excellent resources, small classes and teachers of high calibre, children derive considerable satisfaction from their school work and experience no difficulty in realising their academic potential.

Senior School. 11–16 years. The school is well staffed and equipped to deliver a curriculum covering a wide range of academic, creative and practical subjects. An extensive choice of GCSE and other external examination options enables pupils at Key Stage 4 to target optimum qualifications reflecting their personal choice of programme. The staff are consistent in the emphasis they place upon the encouragement of pupils who respond with a highly conscientious approach to their studies, which in turn ensures steady progress and good results.

Communication between school and home is given high priority and the regular issue of reports enables parents to monitor closely their child's educational development. At the age of 16, almost all pupils continue with A Level studies.

The school operates its own fleet of coaches, offering an extensive network of services covering a 15 mile radius of the school.

For further information please contact the School Secretary.

Charitable status. Hulme Hall Educational Trust is a Registered Charity, number 525931. The school aims to promote personal, moral, social and academic development of all pupils.

Hurst Lodge School

Bagshot Road Ascot Berkshire SL5 9JU
Tel: 01344 622154
Fax: 01344 627049
e-mail: admissions@hurstlodgesch.co.uk
website: www.hurstlodge.co.uk

Principal: **Miss V Smit**

Age Range. Girls 3–18; Boys 3–11. Weekly Boarding from age 9.

Number in School. Day: 20 Boys, 190 Girls. Weekly Boarders: 22.

Fees per term (2008-2009). Weekly Boarding £6,580; Senior Day £4,025; Junior Day £3,360; Pre-Prep £2,660.

Hurst Lodge is a small, well established day and boarding school successfully combining an academic, performance and creative education. We aspire to help our students realise their potential by encouraging learning for life and celebrating all achievements equally.

Small teaching groups ensure high standards, individual attention and excellent pastoral care.

We have a strong dyslexia department.

Hurst Lodge offers a wide breadth of academic and vocational subjects to GCSE and A level. We specialise in Drama, Music and Dance at all levels.

Students have Form and Personal Tutors to ensure a high level of pastoral care and support.

The Sixth Form is small, offering traditional A Levels, a mixture of A Levels and vocational ballet, modern, tap and jazz or BTECs in Performing Arts and Early Years Education.

Hurtwood House School

Holmbury St Mary Dorking Surrey RH5 6NU
Tel: 01483 279000
Fax: 01483 267586
e-mail: info@hurtwood.net
website: www.hurtwoodhouse.com

***Headmaster*: C Jackson**, BEd

Age Range. 16–18.

Number in School. 290 (150 girls, 140 boys).

Fees per term (2008-2009). £9,750–£11,200.

Hurtwood House is the only independent boarding school specialising exclusively in the Sixth Form. It concentrates on the 16–18 age range and offers students a caring, residential structure and a commitment to a complete education where culture, sport, friendship and a full range of extra-curricular activities all play an important part. Hugely successful across the whole range of academic subjects, Hurtwood House is also widely recognised as having the best Creative and Performing Arts and Media departments in the country and is therefore especially attractive to aspiring actors, directors, film directors, dancers, singers, artists and fashion designers.

Many students now want to leave the traditional school system at 16. They are seeking an environment which is structured and safe, but which is less institutional and better equipped to provide the challenge and stimulation which they are now ready for, and which is therefore better placed to develop their potential. They also require teaching methods which will prepare them for an increasingly competitive world by developing their initiative and encouraging them to think for themselves.

Hurtwood House has 290 boys and girls. It is a small and personal school, but it is a large and powerful sixth form which benefits from having specialised A level teachers. The examination results put Hurtwood House in the top independent school league tables, but it is equally important to the school that the students develop energy, motivation and self-confidence.

In short, Hurtwood House is a stepping-stone between school and university for students who are all in the same age group and who share the same maturity and the same ambitions.

The school is situated in its own grounds high up in the Surrey Hills and offers excellent facilities in outstandingly beautiful surroundings.

Hurworth House School

The Green, Hurworth-on-Tees, Darlington, Co Durham DL2 2AD
Tel: 01325 720645
Fax: 01325 720122
e-mail: info@hurworthhouse.co.uk
website: www.hurworthhouse.co.uk

Chairman of Governors: Mr A Theakston

***Headmaster*: Mr C R T Fenwick**, BA Hons, MA

Age Range. Boys 3–16, Girls 3–11.

Number in School. Day: 180 boys, 6 girls. Nursery: 15 girls, 15 boys.

Fees per term (2008-2009). £1,540–£3,398.

Hurworth House School near Darlington is an independent day school for boys aged 3 to 16 and girls aged 3 to 11. Founded in 1946, the School currently has 186 pupils enrolled in the Junior and Senior Departments with a further 30 in our Nursery School.

Hurworth House is a very special place. It has remained deliberately a small school, one whose friendly, caring attitude can be sensed immediately. Our small class sizes mean that the individual strengths and talents of all pupils can be nurtured and developed by our dedicated staff and by the supportive community of their peers.

The School has a first-class academic record, and is justifiably proud of its pupils' consistent successes in GCSE examinations and in all of their achievements when they leave us.

Hurworth House aims to provide a setting in which all pupils can explore their potential, learn about their strengths and weaknesses and develop good interpersonal skills. We believe that it is vital to offer positive reinforcement at all times and in all circumstances.

There are no particular skills or talents which are valued above others at Hurworth House. Thus, excelling at sports or games does not confer automatic status to a child, nor is a culture of aggressive competition between pupils in the classroom encouraged. Whilst academic results are obviously important, we see them as only part of the whole process of education. In line with our Founder's original objectives, we continue to place equal emphasis upon high academic achievement and courtesy, good manners and on consideration for others. We make no apologies for saying that these are traditional values – some might even call them old fashioned – but all of the staff at Hurworth House believe that they are a vital component in young people's lives in today's ever-changing world.

We also aim to build an ethos of cooperation and purposefulness and a sense of self-confidence and self-esteem in all of our pupils, where they are encouraged to develop as individuals with their own unique personalities. At Hurworth House, we aim to help *all* of our pupils to a full realisation of their true potential.

Charitable status. Hurworth House School Charitable Trust is a Registered Charity, number 527367. It aims to provide high quality education to boys and girls in the Darlington and surrounding areas.

Ibstock Place School

Clarence Lane Roehampton London SW15 5PY
Tel: General Enquiries: 020 8876 9991
Headmistress's PA: 020 8392 5802
Bursar's Office: 020 8392 5804
Registrar: 020 8392 5803
Fax: 020 8878 4897
e-mail: office@ibstockplaceschool.co.uk
website: www.ibstockplaceschool.co.uk

***Headmistress*: Mrs Anna Sylvester-Johnson**, BA Hons, PGCE

Deputy Headmaster: Mr Huw Daniel, BSc Hons (London), PGCE

Second Master: Mr Keith Birch, BA Hons (Queensland), MA, DipEd

Head of Pastoral Care: Dr Adrian Johnson, BSc, PhD (New South Wales),Grad DipEd

Head of Macleod House: Mrs Janis Davidson, PTD Higher (Cape Town)
Head of Priestman House: Mrs Joanna Webbern, CertEd (Froebel), Dip Lang
Director of Primary Studies: Miss Sharon Worthington, CertEd (Froebel), BEd

Age Range. 3–18 Co-educational.
Number in School. 420 Boys, 392 Girls.
Fees per term (2007-2008). £1,685–£4,320 (including lunches).

Ibstock Place School, founded in 1894, is located in spacious grounds adjacent to Richmond Park with easy access to Putney, Barnes, Richmond and Hammersmith. The school offers a balanced education combining a traditional academic curriculum with modern educational developments.

The school has grown and prospered with significant building development in recent years. The school has a purpose-built Science and Technology block with a comprehensive multimedia ICT network throughout the school, a Sports Pavilion, floodlit hardcourts, a 200 seat performance hall for music and drama, a new dining room with upgraded catering facilities, and a new Junior Department building. The school has a swimming pool and eight acres of playing fields on site. Plans are in place for further projects to improve the quality of the school facilities at this popular school in SW London.

The two academic departments, Primary and Senior, remain distinctive, so that each child benefits from a small school ambience, but also gains from the facilities that are only possible in a larger school.

The Senior School, age 11–18, offers a full range of Arts, Science and Technology subjects and all pupils follow a core curriculum in line with national requirements and with many opportunities for enrichment. Extra curricular emphasis is placed on sports, drama and music, with recent expeditions to China, Thailand, USA, Africa, Norway and Iceland, and there is an outstanding programme of outdoor education. There is a wide range of after-school clubs as well as the Duke of Edinburgh's Award scheme. There are excellent links with the local community.

The Sixth Form opened in September 2005 with a breadth of AS Level Options and a flexible blocking system which allows considerable opportunity to include science and arts subjects at A2. The school is a member of ISCO and all pupils receive guidance by experienced staff. All pupils are supported by a strong and effective pastoral system which produces well balanced and socially accomplished young people.

The Primary School. Priestman House, the Froebel Kindergarten (age 3–7), and Macleod House (age 7–11) provide a rich and stimulating environment, with a wide range of curricular activity carefully planned to maximise each child's abilities and talents.

Entry to the school is by assessment for children aged 5 and 6 and by examinations in Mathematics, English and Reasoning at 7 and 11 and subject to a satisfactory report from the entrant's current school, and by date of registration for entry into the Nursery and Reception.

The prospectus is available from the Registrar and Open Mornings are held regularly by appointment. Occasional places may arise from time to time.

Charitable status. Ibstock Place School is part of the Incorporated Froebel Educational Institute which is a Registered Charity, number 312930R. It exists to provide high quality education for boys and girls.

International College, Sherborne School

Newell Grange Sherborne Dorset DT9 4EZ
Tel: 01935 814743
Fax: 01935 816863
e-mail: reception@sherborne-ic.net
website: www.sherborne-ic.net

***Principal*: Dr C Greenfield**, MA, MEd

Age Range. Co-educational 11–17 (Boarding 11–17).
Number in School. 148 boarders: 97 boys, 51 girls.
Fees per term (2008-2009). £9,700.

The International College at Sherborne was set up by Sherborne School in 1977. It has grown to become a separate institution and is now separately recognised by the DCSF and the Independent Schools Association.

The College aims to be the best starting point for children from non-English speaking, non-British educational backgrounds who wish to join the British educational system. Students normally stay at the College for one academic year. During this time the College aims to equip each student to take his or her place successfully at a traditional British independent boarding school.

While the full academic curriculum is provided, all teachers of all subjects at the International College are trained or qualified in teaching English as a foreign language. Each student is prepared for any appropriate public examinations, for example GCSEs, Common Entrance or Cambridge English language examinations. Each year the group taking GCSEs records very impressive results. For example in 2007, 80 students achieved an A–C pass rate of 87%.

The College has no entry requirements and no entry examinations for most courses. All students are non-native speakers of English, and some are complete beginners in English. However, the popular one-year GCSE course requires all applicants to have at least lower-intermediate standard English (IELTS 4+).

The College is housed in a purpose-built campus close to the centre of Sherborne. Its boarding houses are nearby. Students are taught in classes of up to eight.

The College is also a member of the Boarding Schools Association, the European Council of International Schools and the British Association of International Study Centres.

Charitable status. Sherborne School is a Registered Charity, number 1081228. The College is part of the Sherborne School educational charity which exists to provide education to school-aged children.

The Italia Conti Academy of Theatre Arts

Italia Conti House 23 Goswell Road London EC1M 7AJ
Tel: 020 7608 0047/8
Fax: 020 7253 1430
e-mail: admin@italiaconti.com
website: www.italiaconti.com

Principal: Mrs A Sheward

***Head*: Mr C K Vote**, BA, DipEd

Age Range. 10–16.
Number in School. Day: 99.
Fees per term (2008-2009). £3,440.

Throughout the 95 years the Academy has been preparing young people for successful careers in the performing arts it has been aware that the profession expects excellent standards of education and training of its new entrants. Today's Producers and Directors demand that performers entering the industry be versastile and be able to take direction within the theatre, television or film studio.

The five courses offered by the Academy seek to expose students to a wide range of disciplines and techniques in the Dance, Drama and Singing fields working in the mediums of stage, television and recording studio under the careful tuition of highly qualified professional staff.

The courses are as follows:

The Theatre Arts School. For 10 to 16 year olds providing a balanced traditional academic education leading to ten GCSEs with broadly based vocational training in dance, drama and singing. Sixth Form Studies within the Performing Arts Course allows two GCE A levels to be studied alongside a full professional dance, drama and singing theatre arts course. Accredited by the ISA.

Performing Arts Course. A three year course for students aged 16+. Accredited by the National Council for Dance Education and Training. Leading to the Award of National Diploma in Professional Dance (Musical Theatre).

One Year Singing Course. From age 16. Drama & Dance Award Scholarships are available for this Course.

BA Hons Musical Theatre Course.

Entry Requirements. Entry for all the above courses is by audition and assessment.

In addition to the above the Academy offers part-time Saturday classes to children aged 3½ to 18 years in Dance, Drama and Singing. Entry is by interview. Also offered is a Summer School, one week Performing Arts or Drama courses for those aged 9 to 19.

Charitable status. The Italia Conti Academy Trust is a Registered Charity, number 290261. It exists to promote education in the Performing Arts through both teaching and the provision of scholarships.

King Alfred School

Manor Wood North End Road London NW11 7HY
Tel: 020 8457 5200
Fax: 020 8457 5249
e-mail: kas@kingalfred.org.uk
website: www.kingalfred.org.uk

***Head*: Mrs Dawn Moore**, MA London

Age Range. 4–18.

Number in School. Primary: approx 300; Secondary: approx 308.

Fees per term (2008-2009). Reception, Years 1–2 £3,580, Years 3–6 £4,120, Middle & Upper School £4,310.

King Alfred School is unique among independent schools in North London. Apart from being all-age (4–18), co-ed and strictly secular, it takes in a wide range of ability as opposed to its academically selective neighbours in the private sector. About 30% of the pupils receive support from the Special Needs department.

KAS's beginnings are unusual: it was founded (in 1898) by a group of Hampstead parents and its large governing body comprises only current and ex-parents. Visitors tend to comment on the pretty site (on the edge of Hampstead Garden Suburb), the "villagey" layout (carefully preserved by a succession of architects), and the friendly atmosphere – this is a no-uniform establishment and all are on first-name terms. The recent purchase of property across the road has enabled the school to extend classroom facilities.

Academic results are consistently impressive and constantly improving and almost 100% of the KAS Sixth Form go on to university or Art Foundation courses or music colleges and conservatoires. The School relishes the opportunity to work with children of all abilities and to stimulate the best from all of them.

Charitable status. King Alfred School is a Registered Charity, number 312590. It exists to provide quality education for boys and girls.

Kings Monkton School

6 West Grove Cardiff CF24 3XL
Tel: 029 2048 2854
Fax: 029 2049 0484
e-mail: mail@kingsmonkton.org.uk
website: www.kingsmonkton.org.uk

***Principal*: Mr P Cox**, BA CNAA, PGCE

Age Range. 3–18.

Number in School. 360.

Fees per term (2007-2008). £1,820–£2,388.

Kings Monkton School is a co-educational day school for children from nursery age right up to university entrance. The school is administered by a board of governors as a registered charity, dedicated to the sole aim of providing an education of excellence.

Kings Monkton is one of South Wales's oldest independent schools, having educated generations of local pupils since its foundation in 1870. The school prides itself on its consistent record of academic success, its system of pastoral care and its relations with parents. Pupils are drawn from a wide catchment area including Cardiff, the Vale of Glamorgan, the Valleys and Monmouth. The school is housed in purpose-built accommodation in the centre of Cardiff, close to Queen Street station and to all amenities.

Kings Monkton's primary school has small classes in which young children can receive individual care and guidance. Pupils follow a well-balanced curriculum, designed to develop and stimulate young minds to the full. Entry for infant children is by informal assessment, whilst junior pupils are tested in Mathematics, English and Reasoning before being offered a place.

In the secondary school, pupils pursue a wide curriculum with their progress being carefully monitored and receive strong pastoral support throughout their adolescent years. All pupils are encouraged to strive for high standards in their work and to contribute to the well-being of the community to which they belong. Entry to the secondary school is by interview and testing with scholarships available at 11+, 13+ and 16+.

In the school's A Level college, students are taught in small tutorial groups and in addition to their academic studies participate in a number of other activities including Young Enterprise as part of the school's philosophy of giving its pupils a thorough preparation for life. The minimum entry requirements to the College are five GCSE passes at grades A–C.

In 2003 the school opened its new purpose-built sixth form centre with upgraded facilities for physics, technology and music.

Charitable status. Kings Monkton School is a Registered Charity, number 525759.

Kingscote Pre-Preparatory School

Oval Way Gerrards Cross Bucks SL9 8PZ
Tel: 01753 885535
Fax: 01753 891783

e-mail: office@kingscoteschool.info
website: www.kingscoteschool.info

***Headmistress*: Mrs S A Tunstall**, CertEd

Age Range. 3–7 years.
Number of Boys. 130.
Fees per term (2008-2009). Nursery: Autumn Term £1,264 (5 sessions), Spring Term £1,769 (7 sessions), Summer Term £2,022 (8 sessions). Reception, Years 1 and 2: £2,526.

Kingscote School was established in 1964 as the pre-preparatory school for Thorpe House. The primary aim of the Kingscote curriculum is to provide a thorough grounding in reading, writing and arithmetic. Mornings are spent learning 'the basics' and in the afternoons the boys become involved in a variety of activities – project work, music, PE and games, art and cookery.

Kingswood College Trust

Southport Road Ormskirk Lancashire L40 9RQ
Tel: 01704 880200
Fax: 01704 880032
e-mail: enquiries@kingswoodcollege.co.uk
website: www.kingswoodcollege.co.uk

***Principal*: E J Borowski**, BSc, GRIC, CertEd

Age Range. 2½–16.
Number of Pupils. 200.
Fees per term (2007-2008). Nursery (full-time, term-time) £1,290, Reception £1,235, Years 1–2 £1,485, Years 3–6 £1,655, Years 7–9 £2,150, Years 10–11 £2,365.

Kingswood College at Scarisbrick Hall was founded in September 1998 by the merger of two distinguished schools – Kingswood School, Southport and Scarisbrick Hall School, Ormskirk. The essential elements of the two schools have not changed: the daily efforts of staff to provide an ambience where spiritual and cultural gifts can develop, the quality of teaching in the classroom, and the commitment of staff to extra-curricular activities.

The school follows the guidelines of the National Curriculum, but enhances these through an impressive selection of options to present a breadth and depth for all the pupils. The aim is to provide equal opportunities for all and to cater for the needs of the individual.

Throughout the College the size of classes is restricted to approximately 20 so that each pupil may receive close attention and be treated as an individual, encouraged to develop his/her abilities to the full in a friendly, caring environment.

High standards are set and expected from the pupils, with the emphasis on self-discipline. The school rules have been compiled from principles which are necessary for good order. The utmost importance is attached to the cultivation of good manners and consideration for others.

The Principal and staff consider the school as a partner with parents in the education of their children.

Charitable status. Kingswood College Trust is a Registered Charity, number 1118539.

Kirkstone House School

Baston Peterborough Lincolnshire PE6 9PA
Tel: 01778 560350
Fax: 01778 560547
e-mail: info@kirkstonehouseschool.co.uk
website: www.kirkstonehouseschool.co.uk

Co-Principals: Mrs B K Wyman, Mr E G Wyman, Mr J W R Wyman

***Head of School*: Miss M Pepper**

Age Range. 4–16.
Number in School. 250: 148 boys, 102 girls.
Fees per term (2008-2009). £1,467–£2,705.

Kirkstone House prides itself on being a caring, friendly school for boys and girls aged 4 to 16 years. A rural setting, the school is located 5 miles south of Bourne on the A15 in the village of Baston.

Pupils enjoy an environment where a willingness to learn and a desire to succeed are enthusiastically promoted.

Within a disciplined framework the 250 pupils develop self-confidence, self-discipline and a breadth of interests which prepares them for a successful sixth form entry.

Kirkstone fulfils a need often missing in larger schools, class numbers are small enough for staff and pupils to know each other well, and yet large enough to permit full and successful participation in games and activities.

Kirkstone's unique 60-acre site of woodlands and lakes has specific scientific interest; pupils are able to enjoy 'hands on' environmental study.

Team sports, Duke of Edinburgh's Award, water-skiing and equestrian events add to the all-round education promoted at Kirkstone.

Knightsbridge School

67 Pont Street London SW1X 0BD
Tel: 020 7590 9000
Fax: 020 7589 9055
e-mail: info@knightsbridgeschool.com
website: www.knightsbridgeschool.com

***Headmaster*: Mr Magoo Giles**

Age Range. 3–13.
Number in School. 255.
Fees per term (2008-2009). £3,850–£4,483.

Knightsbridge School is a new preparatory school, opened in September 2006, offering a broad, balanced and challenging curriculum to prepare both boys and girls for entry to senior day and boarding schools.

Pupils are encouraged to play hard, work hard in the Junior School and work hard, play hard in the Senior School, and make the most of every opportunity open to them and achieve their full potential. They are taught all National Curriculum subjects to a high standard, and modern languages from nursery age upwards.

The school fosters a strong sense of community, and provides a supportive and warm environment. Small classes, overseen by highly qualified, dynamic and enthusiastic staff, will ensure that boys and girls benefit not only academically but also personally. By developing their self-esteem and confidence they will grow into happy, independent all-rounders of healthy body and healthy mind.

Located in the heart of Central London, the school is housed in two magnificent mansions. The premises have undergone an extensive renovation and upgrade programme. Teaching facilities include well-equipped and modern classrooms, science laboratory, an information and communication technology suite, music rooms, and a performing arts studio and a new library , as well as a fully catered kitchen and dining area.

Sports facilities include a gymnasium on site and the diverse and challenging sports programme makes use of local venues such as Burton's Court, Battersea Park, St Luke's recreational grounds, the Queen Mother Sports Centre and Hyde Park.

Entry to Knightsbridge School is by informal interview of both parents and children at the appropriate level. Prospective boys and girls for Year 1 and above will be expected to spend a day of assessment at the school in their relevant year group, and a report from the Head of the applicant's current school will be required.

Charitable status. Knightsbridge School Education Foundation is a Registered Charity, number 1120970.

The Knoll School

Manor Avenue Kidderminster Worcestershire DY11 6EA
Tel: 01562 822622
Fax: 01562 865686
e-mail: info@knollschool.co.uk
head@knollschool.co.uk
website: www.knollschool.co.uk

***Headmaster*: N J Humphreys**, BEd Hons

Age of Children. Co-educational 3 months–11 years.
Number in School. Day: 88 Boys, 54 Girls.
Fees per term (2007-2008). £468–£2,035.

The Knoll School was founded in 1917 and became an Educational trust in 1966. It continues to be a popular co-educational day school for children from 3 months to 11 years.

The year 2003 saw the opening of our First Steps Nursery, which was officially opened by Dr Richard Taylor MP on Friday 16th May 2003. The brand new nursery building, which is open 50 weeks a year from 8 am to 6 pm, means that children from the age of 3 months can now benefit from the caring, family environment for which the Knoll School is well known.

We have high expectations of our pupils in all aspects of their education. Under the guidance of an experienced and caring staff a stimulating and challenging school life is achieved which enables our children to reach their true potential.

The school has a busy calendar incorporating drama, music and sporting events. The children also benefit immensely from educational outings and visiting guest speakers. Extra curricular activities play an important part in school life and pre/after school care from 8 am to 6 pm benefits many parents.

Following the opening of the main school new wing in September 1997, our facilities are excellent. We are proud of our children's achievements, particularly those of Year 6 in gaining places at top independent schools in the area, and attaining scholarships.

Charitable status. The Knoll School Educational Trust Limited is a Registered Charity, number 527600.

Lady Barn House School

Schools Hill Cheadle Cheshire SK8 1JE
Tel: 0161 428 2912
Fax: 0161 428 5798
e-mail: info@ladybarnhouse.stockport.sch.uk
website: www.ladybarnhouse.org

***Headmistress*: Mrs S Yule**, BA Hons, PGCE

Age Range. 3–11.
Number in School. Day: 263 Boys, 184 Girls.
Fees per term (2008-2009). Nursery £1,640 (all day), KS1 and KS2 £1,875. Lunch £125.

Fully qualified and experienced staff. The aim of the school is to provide the preparatory stage of a good general education and to lay a sound foundation for the future. Pupils are prepared for entry into Independent Schools which hold their own Entrance Examinations.

Music, art and drama are important in the life of the school and excellent facilities exist for physical education and games. Provision is made for 7+ pupils to swim throughout the year. French is taught from 4+. Spanish, Latin and Mandarin are offered as extra-curricular clubs.

Other school activities include outdoor pursuits and a wide range of extra-curricular clubs. Educational visits are made throughout the year, including a residential trip to France. An energetic PTA is in existence.

The School is a Charitable Trust. Bursaries are available at Year 2 and Year 3.

Charitable status. Lady Barn House School Limited is a Registered Charity, number 1042587. It exists to provide education for boys and girls.

Ladymede School
GEMS Education

Little Kimble Aylesbury Buckinghamshire HP17 0XP
Tel: 01844 346154
Fax: 01844 275660
e-mail: office@ladymede.com
website: www.ladymedeschool.bucks.sch.uk

***Head Mistress*: Mrs Carole Hawkins**, BA, PGCE

Age Range. 3–11 Co-educational.
Number in School. Day: 64 Girls, 58 Boys.
Fees per term (2008-2009). £792–£2,459.

Ladymede, founded in 1939, is a co-educational day school for pupils aged 3–11 years set in beautiful grounds at the foot of the Buckinghamshire Chilterns.

We aim to provide a happy, supportive and purposeful environment in which children learn to set themselves high standards and become independent learners. Good manners and traditional values, incorporating respect for oneself and others, are fundamental to life at Ladymede.

In small classes (maximum 20) children experience a broad balanced curriculum enriched by residential and day trips and specialist teaching in French, ICT, Music, Science and PE. The well-qualified and caring staff are able to offer individual attention.

All Day Care from 7.45 am to 6.30 pm is an important part of Ladymede, as are the flexible Nursery sessions, a Toddler Group (18 months–3 years) and a wide range of extra-curricular clubs which run at lunchtime and after school.

At 11 our articulate, confident pupils enter selective grammar schools, a variety of independent schools and some local state schools. They are prepared for entrance into both sectors (11+ and Common Entrance).

Leehurst Swan School

19 Campbell Road Salisbury SP1 3BQ

(See entry in IAPS section)

Lewes Old Grammar School

Senior School (Years 7–13):
High Street Lewes East Sussex BN7 1XS
Tel: 01273 472634
Fax: 01273 476948
e-mail: office@logs.uk.com

Morley House (Nursery to Year 6):
7 King Henry's Road Lewes East Sussex BN7 1BT
Tel: 01273 473246
Fax: 01273 479706
e-mail: officejs@logs.uk.com
website: www.logs.uk.com

***Headmaster*: Mr R I Blewitt**, BA Hons, PGCE

Head of Morley House: Mr G Crossland, BSc Hons, PGCE

Age Range. 3–18.

Number in School. 250 Boys, 150 Girls.

Fees per term (2008-2009). £1,780–£3,470.

Lewes Old Grammar School is an independent co-educational day school located in the historic county town of Lewes, educating children from 3 to 18 years old. First established in 1512, Lewes Old Grammar School combines high educational standards, small classes in a caring, well-mannered environment together with economic fee levels. The School's Development Plan envisages a major development every two years. Prospective parents are encouraged to visit our website and, in particular, take note of the latest ISI Inspection Report.

The School offers a Nursery which is housed in Morley House, highly rated by Ofsted, and which is open from 9.00 am until 4.00 pm, for children aged three to rising five year olds. Morley House caters for children from three years old until the age of ten, and is located in an independent building in a pleasant residential area of Lewes. It provides an enhanced curriculum and a sound educational basis on which to embark upon secondary education. Morley House has recently been refurbished and is managed by a newly-appointed, energetic and visionary Head.

The Senior School occupies three architecturally historic buildings in the High Street of the ancient town of Lewes. The Senior School educates children from the age of 11 (Year 7) until 18 years of age (Sixth Form) and always features well in the Sussex GCSE and A Level league tables. A comprehensive school transport service covers a wide area around the school. Our students utilise the excellent sporting facilities available within the town and enjoy the wide range of extra-curricular activities offered, with particular emphasis on sport, music and drama. Numerous trips and visits take place both within and outside the United Kingdom.

Entry to Year 3 and above is by an Entrance Examination. Scholarships and bursaries are offered subject to satisfactory criteria being met.

Lewes Old Grammar School encompasses traditional values combined with a forward approach to the education of young people, and is proud of the family ethos it engenders.

Charitable status. Lewes Old Grammar School Trust is a Registered Charity, number 801456. The aim of the charity is to provide education.

The Licensed Victuallers' School

London Road Ascot Berkshire SL5 8DR

(See entry in SHMIS section)

Lime House School

Holm Hill Dalston Nr Carlisle Cumbria CA5 7BX
Tel: 01228 710225
Fax: 01228 710508
e-mail: lhsoffice@aol.com
website: www.limehouseschool.co.uk

***Headmaster*: N A Rice**, MA, BA, CertEd

Age Range. 3+–18+. Boarders from age 9.

Number in School. Day: 40 Boys, 38 Girls; Boarding: 65 Boys, 45 Girls.

Fees per term (2008-2009). Boarding £4,200–£5,200; Day £1,200–£2,300.

Compulsory extras: Activities, Laundry.

Lime House School is a fully independent co-educational boarding and day school for pupils aged 3½ to 18. Our aim is to ensure that each pupil achieves his or her potential both academically and socially, with each child treated individually. Our pupils are cared for in a safe rural environment and every possible attempt is made to ensure that they develop confidence and self-esteem. Boarding is available to all pupils, with the majority being full boarders. Each pupil's pastoral care is the shared responsibility of a residential member of staff who lives in their boarding area, a residential school matron and the pupil's form teacher.

Foreign students whose first language is not English add to the cosmopolitan atmosphere of the school. They are prepared for Cambridge English examinations and follow the same curriculum as all other students.

Games and sport form an important part of school life. All students participate and a wide range of team and individual sports is offered. Most pupils take games to GCSE level, with many continuing to A Level.

We would welcome a visit to our school to see it in action. Simply contact the school and we will arrange a time convenient for you.

Lingfield Notre Dame

Lingfield Surrey RH7 6PH
Tel: 01342 833176
e-mail: office@lingfieldnotredame.co.uk
website: www.lingfieldnotredame.co.uk

***Principal*: Mrs N E Shepley**, BA

Age Range. 2½–18.

Number in School. 321 in Junior School; 465 in Senior School.

Fees per term (2008-2009). £1,070–£3,030.

Entry. Junior School: by assessment from Reception year upwards, subject to vacancies.

Senior School: at 11+ and 13+ by Entrance Examination, interview and report from previous school. At 16+ by 6+ GCSEs in A–B range, and interview

Scholarships. Scholarships and Bursaries are offered to the top candidates in the 11+ and 13+ Entrance Examination. Scholarships are also available for the Sixth Form.

Curriculum. In the Junior School the usual primary subjects are taught, including French, Dance, Speech and Drama. In the Senior School a wide curriculum of academic and practical subjects is offered to GCSE and A Level. The National Curriculum is incorporated throughout the school.

Reports and Consultations. Reports are sent twice yearly and there are half termly report cards to keep parents informed of students' progress. Parent/Teacher interviews are held annually. Parents are always welcome to discuss progress with the appropriate Head of Year.There is a well developed pastoral system.

Leavers. The majority of pupils in the Junior School progress to the Senior School. Ninety percent of Sixth Form leavers go on to further education courses at University, including Oxbridge, resulting in a wide variety of careers.

Sport. In the Junior School sports include Gym, Golf, Hockey, Cricket, Football, Dance, Netball, Swimming, Karate, Rounders and Short Tennis.

In the Senior School, Tennis, Netball, Table Tennis, Trampolining, Rounders, Fitness Suite, Volleyball, Gymnastics, Dance, Swimming, Basketball, Rugby, Football, Hockey, Squash, Badminton, Athletics and Self Defence are all played.

Annual Ski Trips are arranged for older Junior School pupils and Senior School pupils.

Extra-Curricular Activities. In the Junior School, the following are a few of the activities offered: Choir and Orchestra, Language Clubs, Cookery, Sewing, Technology, Squash, Computer, Drama, Gardening, Art and Craft, and Eco Club.

In the Senior School an extensive range of activities is offered including Duke of Edinburgh's Award Scheme, Outward Bound, Drama, Music and Science Clubs, Public Speaking, Chef's Club, Warhammer, Sports fixtures and competitions, Choir, Orchestra and Ensembles.

In the Sixth Form a wide programme of activities is arranged such as Salsa Dancing, Ballroom Dancing, Self Defence, Car Maintenance, Orienteering, Cooking, Youth Parliament, Debating, Public Speaking, Critical Thinking, Safe Driving Talks plus an extensive range of outside speakers.

In addition, the School has participated or will be participating in expeditions to Venezuela, Vietnam and Argentina.

Religious Services. Regular school, house, form and year assemblies are held. Interdenominational services are held.

Lingfield Notre Dame transferred to a lay management in 1987. It maintains its Christian ethos and its philosophy is based on a strong belief in the development of the whole person. The school has a tradition of providing a caring, friendly and disciplined environment.

Charitable status. Lingfield Notre Dame is a Registered Charity, number 295598. It exists to provide education.

Littlegarth School

Horkesley Park Nayland Colchester Essex CO6 4JR

(See entry in IAPS section)

Loreto Preparatory School

Dunham Road Altrincham Cheshire WA14 4GZ
Tel: 0161 928 8310
Fax: 0161 929 5801
e-mail: info.loretoprep@btconnect.com
website: www.loretoprep.co.uk

Headteacher: **Mrs Rosemary Hedger**

Age Range. Girls 3–11, Boys 3–7.
Number in School. 174 Day Girls.
Fees per term (2008-2009). £1,470.

Loreto Preparatory School, founded in 1909, is a modern, purpose-built school (1971), standing in pleasant grounds and offering an all-round education by well-qualified staff. Religious education and moral training are central to our teaching, based on Gospel principles. Our recent ISI Inspection stated that the school "maintains its traditional values, yet incorporates some modern thinking in the curriculum".

Music plays an important part in the life of the school. All aspects of class music are taught by a specialist. We have a school orchestra, and private individual lessons are available in most instruments. The children's dramatic ability and interest are developed through class lessons, theatre visits and regular productions. Gymnastics, swimming, netball and athletics, taught by a PE specialist, rate high in our physical education programme and the school participates fully in local and national competitions.

Our ICT facilities are excellent and include a computer suite in the Junior department which is Internet linked. There is a well-stocked library, recently computerised to allow pupils to select, issue and return their own books.

The Junior curriculum has been extended to include Latin, Chinese and touch typing. We offer a wide range of extra-curricular activities.

Of equal importance is social development and each child is encouraged to reach his or her full potential and to care for others.

Loreto is a Catholic independent school and is one of many Loreto schools built on the foundations laid by Mary Ward, foundress of the Institute of the Blessed Virgin Mary, according to the vision of St Ignatius of Loyola.

Visits to the school are welcome by appointment. Admission at 3+ is usually by interview and by interview and Entrance Examination for those wishing to join at 7+. The school is also registered with the Early Years Partnership and grants to parents are used as part-payment of fees in the Foundation Stage class.

Charitable status. Loreto Preparatory School is a Registered Charity, number 250607.

Lucton School

Lucton Leominster Herefordshire HR6 9PN
Tel: 01568 782000
Fax: 01568 782001
e-mail: enquiries@luctonschool.org
website: www.luctonschool.org

Headmistress: **Mrs Gill Thorne**, MA, BA Hons, PGCE, LLAM

Age Range. 6 months–18 years co-educational day and boarding.
Number in School. 230.
Fees per term (2008-2009). Day £1,622–£3,180; Boarding £5,037–£6,540.

Pupils at Lucton School benefit from small classes, a friendly atmosphere and an idyllic rural location. Pupils are provided with an excellent all-round education which aims to bring out the full potential of each individual. There are extensive sports facilities and a good mix of day pupils, weekly boarders and full boarders.

Subjects taught to GCSE include English language and literature, mathematics, biology, chemistry, physics, information technology, French, Spanish, German, history, geography, business studies, religious education, design & technology, art, music, drama and PE/games. All pupils take the national tests at Key Stages 1 to 4, most sitting the GCSE examination in ten subjects. Lucton School has a strong academic record and an established tradition of getting the best possible results from each pupil.

All the above GCSE subjects, plus many more, are available in the Sixth Form at AS and A2 Levels. The Sixth Form is housed in a brand new sixth form centre, created in 2005, including a new senior library and another new IT suite.

Founded in 1708, the school is set in a safe, healthy and attractive location in 20 acres of beautiful Herefordshire countryside. Facilities on site include junior and senior libraries, science laboratories, ICT rooms, design & technology workshop, tennis courts, new indoor swimming pool and games fields. Fourteen different sports are offered; the school achieved a Sportsmark Gold award in 2002. Boarding pupils are housed in a modern building and all have individual rooms.

Admission can take place at any time of the year by interview and assessment. Prospective pupils are always invited to spend a trial day in the school without obligation. Examinations for academic scholarships are held in January each year.

Lucton School is fully accredited by the Independent Schools Council and is a member of ISA and the Boarding Schools' Association.

Charitable status. Lucton School is a Registered Charity, number 518076.

Lyndhurst School

36 The Avenue Camberley Surrey GU15 3NE
Tel: 01276 22895
Fax: 01276 709186
e-mail: office@lyndhurstschool.com
website: www.lyndhurstschool.co.uk

***Head*: Stephen G Yeo**, BMus Hons, LTCL (MusEd), NPQH

Registrar: Mrs Lesley Howlett

Age Range. 2–11.
Number in School. Day: 103 Boys, 95 Girls.
Fees per term (2008-2009). £1,140–£2,540.

Boys and girls are accepted from the age of 2 into the happy and friendly Nursery Department. From here until they leave the school at the age of 11½, every care is taken to realise the full potential of each child. The Headmaster's wife looks after the welfare of the children.

The School maintains a high academic standard but children of all abilities are welcomed and are taught in a sympathetic environment.

Music and drama play an important role in the life of the School and swimming is part of the weekly curriculum.

Sports and activities offered include soccer, hockey, cricket, netball, rounders, judo, gymnastics, trampolining and squash.

Most children enter their senior schools at 11½ and Lyndhurst has an enviable record of exam successes over the years.

Entry to the School can be at any age if there is a vacancy. At least one internal scholarship is awarded annually for academic achievement, and one external when there is a place available.

Mander Portman Woodward

90–92 Queen's Gate London SW7 5AB
Tel: 020 7835 1355
Fax: 020 7259 2705
e-mail: london@mpw.co.uk
website: www.mpw.co.uk

***Principal*: Matthew Judd**, BA, PGCE

Age Range. 14–18.
Number in School. Day: 245 Boys, 182 Girls.
Fees per term (2008-2009). £4,500–£6,380.

Mander Portman Woodward (MPW) is a co-educational London day school accepting pupils from the first year of GCSE onwards. Approximately 100 new pupils join each year at the start of the sixth form. We offer a very wide range of subjects (37 at A Level and 25 at GCSE) and there are no restrictions on subject combinations at A Level. At all levels the absolute maximum number of pupils in any one class is eight.

The school has completely refurbished its new Queen's Gate premises with modern facilities tastefully blended in with the traditional architecture of the buildings. There are six well equipped laboratories for Science subjects and specialist studios for Art, Ceramics, Photography and Media Studies. The school also has extensive facilities for independent study, including two supervised reading rooms and an internet library.

Whilst there is a range of compulsory extra-curricular activities for GCSE pupils, including sport, the number of voluntary extra-curricular activities offered at A Level is relatively small. In keeping with our founding principles, our primary focus at all age levels is on academic goals. Entry into the sixth form is dependent on a student's academic record and performance at interview. Almost all pupils proceed to university after leaving, with about 20 each year going to read Medicine. Over the past four years an average of 7 of our full-time pupils each year have won places at the Universities of Oxford or Cambridge.

We insist on strict punctuality in the attendance of lessons and the submission of homework and there is a formal system of monthly examinations in each subject throughout a pupil's career at the school. This system is designed to ensure that sensible, cumulative revision becomes a study habit not only at school but also later on at university. We require pupils to have a strong commitment to academic discipline but our reputation is based on having created a framework in which pupils can enjoy working hard. The environment is friendly, the teachers experienced and enthusiastic and the atmosphere positive and conducive to success.

Manor House School

Springfield House Honiton Devon EX14 9TL
Tel: 01404 42026
"The Folly" Nursery: 01404 41144
Fax: 01404 41153
e-mail: office@manorhouseschoolhoniton.co.uk
website: www.manorhouseschoolhoniton.co.uk

Co-Educational Day Preparatory School.

***Headmaster*: Mr Adam Gibson**, BSc, PGCE

Age Range. 3–11.
Number in School. 160.
Fees per term (2008-2009). £2,110–£2,650.

"Tradition, teamwork and innovation working together to provide the very best" sums up Manor House School. The traditions of the school are many and well tested, from regular performances and acts of worship to the best of traditional teaching methods, from structured homework to the cultivation among pupils of an ethos of good manners, consideration for others and firm but fair discipline. An atmosphere of teamwork is successfully nurtured between pupils, parents and staff. At the same time the best of innovations in the world of education have been embraced, from the latest in literacy and numeracy teaching to IT and synthesisers.

All this, in a setting of small classes, dedicated staff and superb academic and sporting facilities makes Manor House excellently placed to provide children with the education they deserve for the 21st century.

Manor House School

South Street Ashby-de-la-Zouch Leics LE65 1BR
Tel: 01530 412932
Fax: 01530 417435
e-mail: enquiries@manorhouseashby.co.uk
website: www.manorhouseashby.co.uk

Chairman of the Governors: Mr R Bayliss

***Headmaster*: I R Clews**, BA Hons, CertEd

Age Range. 4–16.

Number of Pupils. 152: 79 Boys, 72 Girls.

Fees per term (2007-2008). From £1,661 (Kindergarten) to £2,362, including meals.

Manor House is an independent co-educational school for children ranging in age from 4 to 16. It is situated in a magnificent setting between the impressive ruins of Ashby Castle and the ancient Parish Church, and is within easy reach of Derby, Leicester, Birmingham and Nottingham.

The school caters for mixed ability children with a maximum class size of twenty and one class per year group.

From the age of 8 children have access to the school's fully-equipped Science Laboratory , Computer Suite, Art Room, and two libraries. Children are taught French from the age of 5 and German from the age of 11. A wide range of extra-curricular activities is also on offer, as well as a Breakfast Club and an After-School Club.

The school has a wide reputation for both its academic achievements and its genuinely friendly and happy atmosphere. We deliver a curriculum that stimulates and challenges children to produce their best. We also provide an environment where children can develop self-discipline, responsibility, and self-motivation with a respect for others.

Charitable status. Manor House School is a Registered Charity, number 527859. It exists to provide education for boys and girls.

Maple Hayes Hall School for Dyslexics

Abnalls Lane Lichfield Staffordshire WS13 8BL
Tel: 01543 264387
Fax: 01543 262022
e-mail: office@dyslexia.gb.com
website: www.dyslexia.gb.com

***Principal*: Dr E N Brown**, PhD, MSc, BA, MSCME, MINS, AFBPsS, CPsychol

Headmaster: Dr D J Brown, DPhil, MEd (Psychology of SpLD), MA Oxon, PGCE

Age Range. 7–17.

Number in School. 110 Day Boys and Girls.

Fees per term (from April 2008). £4,005–£5,420.

Maple Hayes is a specialist independent day school approved by the Department for Children, Schools and Families (DCSF) under the 1996 Education Act for children of average to very high intelligence who are not achieving their intellectual potential by normal teaching methods.

This school is under the direction of Dr E Neville Brown whose work in the field of learning strategies has achieved international recognition and includes a major breakthrough in the teaching of dyslexic children. Attention is paid to the individual child by teaching the basic literacy and numeracy skills required for the child to benefit from a full curriculum, (with the exception of a foreign language) including the three sciences to GCSE level. The school had an excellent Ofsted report.

The very favourable teacher-pupil ratio of 1:10 or better ensures a high standard of educational and pastoral care. The children's learning is under the supervision and guidance of a qualified educational psychologist.

Mark College

Mark Highbridge Somerset TA9 4NP
Tel: 01278 641632
Fax: 01278 641426
e-mail: markcollege@priorygroup.com
website: www.priorygroup.com

***Principal*: Mrs Julie Kay**, BEd, AMBDA

Headmaster: Mr Chris Betenson, CertEd

Age Range. 10–19.

Number in School. Boarding: 65 Boys, 2 Girls; Day: 12 Boys, 2 Girls.

Fees per term (2007-2008). Boarding £7,103; Weekly Boarding £6,816; Day £4,880.

Mark College is a DCSF, ISC and CReSTeD approved school for boys and girls diagnosed as having dyslexia. The College offers a full curriculum with specialist help so that boys and girls enter for 6 to 8 GCSEs in their fifth (Year 11) year. GCSE results are very good.

Accommodation, including a full sized sports hall, is of a high standard. The College is well resourced and the atmosphere is relaxed and purposeful.

The College's provision for mathematics is recognised internationally, and its English provision involves the use of the latest work in information technology.

After a very good Ofsted report, the College received a commendation and was listed in the HMCI Annual Report, described as a "significant achievement" by the Secretary of State. Mark College is a Beacon school. It received the ISA "Award for Excellence" in May 2000. In 2003 the College was awarded a Sportsmark with Distinction. The latest Ofsted report (2007) commented on the high standard of education, the outstanding sports provision and the high quality of personal care afforded to the students by the staff.

The Sixth Form, which is the latest addition to the school, allows pupils to gain further independence skills whilst studying for A Levels.

Mayville High School

35 St Simon's Road Southsea Hants PO5 2PE
Tel: 023 9273 4847
Fax: 023 9229 3649
e-mail: mayvillehighschoolpr@talk21.com
website: www.mayvillehighschool.com

Education means so much more at 'Mayville'.

***Headteacher*: Mrs L Owens**, BEd

Age Range. 6 months–16 years.

Number in School. Day Pupils: 234 Boys, 254 Girls.

Fees per term (2008-2009). £1,020–£2,495.

Please visit our website to see our wonderful pupils in action and for the fantastic GCSE results from children with a wide ability range.

Mayville's pupils star in numerous ways. Some excel at sport, art, design, drama, music, others in creative fields and others socially – whilst, of course, some excel in all areas. We are often described as 'the Mayville family'. The individual child, the parents and/or carers/grand-parents all play a part in school life at Mayville. The experience of school is enhanced by the number of clubs and after-school activities available. There is something available to interest everybody. Academic excellence is, of course, the basis of our success and all pupils are treated as individuals, their learning styles assessed and their capabilities tested. Our small class sizes average 12 pupils throughout the school. We teach boys and girls separately to best meet their individual learning styles. Over the years Mayville pupils consistently achieve high standards in GCSE examinations. Mayville offers an educational experience to pupils of a wide ability range and has specific programmes for able and gifted pupils, whilst supporting pupils with Dyslexia in a Unit recognised by CReSTeD.

Nursery. We now accept babies from 6 months in the 'Nest' of our Nursery Department, which caters for children from 6 months to 4 years of age. It is open 8 am to 6 pm for morning, afternoon or all day sessions. Breakfast, freshly prepared home cooked lunches and teas are available. The curriculum is wide and varied and well taught by our qualified and experienced staff. The main emphasis is on the acquisition of social skills and the basic academic building blocks in Literacy and Numeracy, art and craft, creative and physical development and so much more. French, computers, sports (including our annual sports day) and our Christmas Nativity play are also features of the Nursery.

Transition and Pre-Prep. At four pupils from the Nursery may enter Transition or our Reception class, the beginning of our Pre-Prep Department. All core subjects are taught with an emphasis on reading, writing and mathematics. Throughout their time in this department our pupils experience visits to museums, the library, participate in music and drama productions and in various local festivals. We also have visitors like the Fire Brigade for safety in the home and people who help us, to book authors and many more in between.

Junior and Senior School. In the Junior school, in addition to the above and expansion of subjects taught, they also have many educational day trips, and visitors to the school, they are taught to read and understand music, and all pupils learn to play an instrument. Art, musical productions, choir and design technology add diversity to the school curriculum while the annual Book Week is a popular event in the school calendar. A wide range of sport is on offer both during and out of school hours including inter-house and inter-school competitions. A trip to Austria for skiing is offered to both Juniors and Seniors as well as day and longer trips to France. An extensive range of after-school clubs is available each term. Mayville believes education should happen on and off site and includes a wide range of educational and activity days during the school year to museums, art galleries, theatres and much more. Full details and lots of wonderful photographs can be found on our website.

Transport. School transport is available from the local ferry terminals and train stations, from Hedge End, Warsash, Clanfield, Chichester, Havant, Bedhampton and most surrounding areas.

If you would like a prospectus, to book a tour of the school with the Headteacher, Mrs Owens, or to find out about our taster days, please telephone the school or visit our website. Applications for the January 2009/2010 Entrance Assessment are being accepted for intake in September 2009/2010. Scholarships are available from Year 2.

Charitable status. Mayville High School is a Registered Charity, number 286347. It exists to provide a traditional education to children from a wide range of academic backgrounds within a caring environment.

Mead School

16 Frant Road Tunbridge Wells Kent TN2 5SN
Tel: 01892 525837
e-mail: meadschool@hotmail.co.uk
website: www.meadschool.info

***Headmistress*: Mrs A Culley**

Age Range. 3–11.
Number in School. 190.
Fees per term (2008-2009). Kindergarten £1,355; Infants £2,600; Juniors £2,880.

The Mead is an independent, co-educational preparatory school situated in the centre of Tunbridge Wells. We prepare children for both Kent Selection into Grammar School and for Common Entrance to a wide range of Independent Schools at 11+.

We aim to create a happy, secure and enthusiastic atmosphere in which every individual can develop his or her all round potential and thereby become well motivated, interesting and hard working members of society.

Academic standards are high and based on National Curriculum requirements. Strong emphasis is placed on individual attention and close cooperation between school and parents is encouraged.

We offer a broad range of extra-curricular activities: sport, drama, music, ballet, judo, swimming.

A copy of our Prospectus and outstanding recent ISI report are available on request.

Milbourne Lodge Junior School

22 Milbourne Lane Esher Surrey KT10 9EA

(See entry in IAPS section)

The Moat School

Bishop's Avenue Fulham London SW6 6EG
Tel: 020 7610 9018
Fax: 020 7610 9098
e-mail: office@moatschool.org.uk
website: www.moatschool.org.uk

Chair of Governors: Richard Simmons, CBE

***Headteacher*: Abigail Gray**, BA Hons, PGCE, Cert SpLD

Co-educational Day School.
Age Range. 11–16.
Number of Pupils. 63 Boys, 28 Girls.
Fees per term (2008-2009). £7,490.

Set within the historic conservation area of Fulham Palace, The Moat School is a specialist school for secondary-age SpLD pupils. Mainstream in structure and specialist in nature, The Moat caters successfully for the needs of pupils whose difficulties range from mild to severe. Alongside the curriculum, the school also offers expertise in speech and language therapy, occupational therapy and a school counsellor.

Most subject teachers have completed a course in SpLD and are trained in teaching pupils with dyslexia. Learning Support Assistants accompany pupils throughout their lessons at Key Stage 3, where class sizes are a maximum of 10. Class sizes are even smaller at Key Stage 4.

Multi-sensory teaching is combined with advanced IT provision, each pupil being provided with a laptop computer for use in school and at home. Touch-typing is taught in Year 7 and there is a state-of-the-art wireless network which enables staff and pupils to access the school intranet with its wide range of learning resources and data, as well as the internet.

At Key Stage 3, pupils follow a mainstream curriculum (with the exception of foreign languages) before selecting their GCSE options alongside the core subjects of English, Mathematics and Single or Dual Award Science. The Moat offers first-class facilities in Art, Music and Drama, Food and Design Technology, ICT and Business Studies. Frequent trips to art galleries and museums support the classroom teaching and an after-school study club is available to assist pupils with their homework.

The Moat has an extensive enrichment programme of extra-curricular activities designed to widen experience and develop self-confidence. In drama, all Year 9 pupils take part in an annual Shakespeare play and there are several productions and workshop performances each year. The Moat's proximity to the River Thames enables all pupils to experience rowing as a sport and there is an annual regatta. Swimming is popular and there is a biennial ski trip. The Duke of Edinburgh's Award encourages pupils to test their own limits and each summer Year 9 students make a week's residential visit to an outdoor centre; in 2007 this was to Montpellier in France.

Charitable status. The Constable Educational Trust is a Registered Charity, number 1068445. It exists to establish and support The Moat School so that it might provide education and opportunity for SpLD learners (dyslexic & dyspraxic).

Moffats School

Kinlet Hall Bewdley Worcs DY12 3AY
Tel: 01299 841230
Fax: 01299 841444
e-mail: office@moffats.co.uk
website: www.moffats.co.uk

***Head*: Mark Daborn**MA, ARICS, QTS

Age Range. 4–13+.
Number of Children. 61.
Fees per term (2007-2008). Boarding £4,065, Day £1,060–£2,550.

Moffats is a co-educational boarding school in a Grade 1 historic house set in its own hundred acres of park and farmland, a glorious environment a mile from any public road. There are equal numbers of boys and girls who share the same opportunities and responsibilities in all activities. We are proud of our record since 1934, but this is not limited to academic awards or A grades in the Common Entrance Examination. Our joy and satisfaction is in bringing out the best in every child. Their achievements in speech and drama are outstanding. All usual games are coached, including athletics and cross-country running with conspicuous successes at inter-school and national levels. With our own stables riding is professionally taught to half the school. Annual sailing camp with ten boats. Weekends and spare time are filled with a multitude of activities. Moffats is a truly family school; the personal touch of members of the family which founded Moffats ensure the well-being and happiness of all the children in their care.

Moorland School

Ribblesdale Avenue Clitheroe Lancashire BB7 2JA
Tel: 01200 423833
Fax: 01200 429339
e-mail: psmith@moorlandschool.co.uk
website: www.moorlandschool.co.uk

***Headmaster*: Mr Paul Smith**

Age Range. 3 months – 16 years.
Number of Pupils. 291 including 60 boarders.
Fees per term (2007-2008). Day: £1,540–£2,075; Full Boarding: £4,200–£5,400; Weekly Boarding: £4,100–£5100.

Moorlands School

Leagrave Hall Luton Bedfordshire LU4 9LE
Tel: 01582 573376
Fax: 01582 509008
e-mail: moorlands@moorlandsprepschool.co.uk
website: www.moorlandsschool.com

***Headteacher*: Dr Andrew Cook**

Age Range. 2–11.
Number of Pupils. 147 Girls, 163 Boys.
Fees per term (2007-2008). £868–£1,880.
Average class size: 16. Pupil/teacher ratio: 11.6:1.

Profile. The school is located in the grounds of Leagrave Hall, built by Sir Edmund Filmer in 1850. It provides a caring, traditional and broad based education, with an emphasis on high standards of manners, discipline and appearance, as well as academic excellence. Small classes provide for individual attention. Moorlands has the reputation of being a happy and friendly school, that aims to enable each child to achieve their full potential, academically and socially.

Entry. From 2 by interview. From 7 by examination.

Curriculum. Usual CE subjects taught. Fully committed to National Curriculum and testing.

Leavers. 90% of pupils go on to Bedford, Bedford High, Bedford Modern, Dame Alice Harpur and St Albans.

Sports. Athletics, Cricket, Football, Gymnastics, Netball, Rounders, Rugby and Swimming. Coaching in Cricket, Football and Rugby by qualified coaches.

Activities. Art, Ballet, Chess, Choir, Computer, Cookery, Drama, Music, Needlework, Speech and Sport.

Facilities. All weather pitches, athletics track, playing fields, gymnasium, netball courts, science laboratory, fully equipped stage, language laboratory, nursery.

Charitable status. The Filmer Trust is a Registered Charity, number 1042857. It exists to provide education for boys and girls.

More House School

Frensham Farnham Surrey GU10 3AP
Tel: 01252 792303 Admissions: 01252 797600
Fax: 01252 797601
e-mail: schooloffice@morehouseschool.co.uk
website: www.morehouseschool.com

***Headmaster*: B Huggett**, BA Hons, QTS, MIBiol

Age Range. 9+ to 18.
Number in School. Boarders: 104 Boys, Day: 206 Boys.
Fees per term (2008-2009). Full Boarding £6,400–£7,850; Weekly Boarding £5,800–£7,250; Day £3,600–£5,050.

More House occupies a unique position in helping boys with specific learning difficulties in that multi sensory remediation is applied across the curriculum, through carefully targeted and maintained intervention, and extra help is available in our Learning Development Centre, so that proper support is always available and individual needs met.

It is approved by the DCSF and has been placed by CReSTeD in their "SP" Category list. No school can help every child, so we have a very careful selection assessment to ensure that we really can help those who finally enter the school.

Founded over 60 years ago, the school prides itself in using the best modern practice to increase confidence and make children feel valued, happy and to fulfil their potential at GCSE, AS, A Level and other public examinations.

Boarding is run by caring staff and is situated in lovely grounds with plenty of opportunities for outdoor pursuits. Our activities programme encourages all day boys and boarders to make good use of their leisure time. There is a strong sense of community.

There is an ongoing building programme and the facilities are very good in all departments.

Ofsted described More House as "an excellent school offering an outstanding education".

We have a comprehensive information pack, and always welcome visitors. Why not ring us?

Charitable status. More House School is a Registered Charity, number 311872. A Catholic foundation, open to all, helping boys to succeed.

Mostyn House School

Parkgate South Wirral Cheshire CH64 6SG

(See entry in IAPS section)

Moyles Court School

Moyles Court Ringwood Hampshire BH24 3NF
Tel: 01425 472856/473197
Fax: 01425 474715
e-mail: moylescourt@btinternet.com
website: www.moylescourt.co.uk

Headmaster: **G Meakin**, BSc, MA, PGCE

Age Range. 3–16.

Number in School. Boarders: 20 boys, 18 girls. Day: 74 boys, 55 girls.

Fees per term (2007-2008). Boarders: £4,133–£5,980. Day: £3,381 (Senior School), £1,575–£3,224 (Junior School), £1,595 (Nursery).

Moyles Court is a co-educational boarding and day school for children from 3 to 16 years of age. The school is administered by a Board of Governors and is registered as an Educational Charitable Trust. The school is accredited by the Independent Schools Council and is a member of ISIS (South and West Region).

The school is situated two miles north east of Ringwood in beautiful grounds on the edge of the New Forest, surrounded by heath, woodlands and streams. The fourteen acres provide ideal playing areas for the children and they use these extensively in their free time.

At Moyles Court, we aim to enthuse and encourage children of all academic abilities to maximise their potential in preparation for the challenging and competitive world which lies outside the security of home and school. Education means development of the 'whole' person and this is what we aim to achieve at Moyles Court.

It is the school's policy to follow the National Curriculum, within which a comprehensive range of GCSE subjects are offered.

Moyles Court is a Sport England 'Sportsmark Gold Award' holder, Southampton Football Club training partner and National First Aid Junior Champions. An extensive selection of extra-curricular activities is available throughout the year. Outdoor pursuits are available in the senior school, as is the Duke of Edinburgh's Award Scheme.

Travel arrangements are made for children from abroad, including transport to and from airports and stations.

There are generous discounts for Service families and second children and subsequent siblings. Admission is through personal interview with the Headmaster and/or written examination plus Head's report from previous school.

For further details visit our website at www.moylescourt.co.uk or contact our Admissions Secretary. A warm welcome awaits you.

Charitable status. Moyles Court School is a Registered Charity, number 307347.

The Mulberry House School

7 Minster Road West Hampstead London NW2 3SD
Tel: 020 8452 7340
e-mail: info@mulberryhouseschool.com
website: www.mulberryhouseschool.com

Headteacher: **Ms Bethan Lewis-Powell**

Age Range. 2–7 Co-educational.
Number of Pupils. 168.
Fees per term (2007-2008). £2,193–£3,133.

The Mulberry House School is an established independent school for 2–8 year olds, offering a stimulating and caring environment that meets the needs of individuals, while preparing them for the next stage of their schooling at 4+ or 7+. Extended day, full and part time places available. For brochures and details of Open Evenings please telephone 020 8452 7340.

Mylnhurst Preparatory School & Nursery

Button Hill Woodholm Road Ecclesall Sheffield S11 9HJ
Tel: 0114 236 1411
Fax: 0114 236 1411
e-mail: enquiries@mylnhurst.co.uk
website: www.mylnhurst.co.uk

A Catholic Foundation Welcoming Families of All Faiths.

Maximising the potential of your children through partnership within a challenging and supportive Catholic Christian Community.

Headmaster: **Mr C P Emmott**, BSc, MEd

Age Range. 3–11 Co-educational.
Number of Pupils. 197.
Fees per term (2007-2008). £1,995.

Situated in extensive private grounds, Mylnhurst provides an exceptional teaching environment. The continued success of this innovative school has seen numbers double, over an eight-year period, and pupils enjoy the very highest standards of education and modern facilities.

With a strong emphasis on school-parent partnership, Mylnhurst embraces your high expectations and ensures each child benefits from an exciting and stimulating curriculum.

Be assured of a very warm welcome and the opportunity to work closely with our committed and talented staff. So, whether it be an informal chat or a school open day, we look forward to sharing our vision with you and discussing the exciting future of your children.

Charitable status. Mylnhurst Limited is a Registered Charity, number 1056683.

New Eccles Hall School

Quidenham Nr Norwich Norfolk NR16 2NZ
Tel: 01953 887217
Fax: 01953 887397
e-mail: admin@neweccleshall.com
website: www.neweccleshall.com

***Headmaster*: R W Allard**, CertEd

Age Range. 4–16.

Number in School. 70 Boarders, 110 Day.

Fees per term (2008-2009). Day £1,698–£2,820, Boarding £4,435–£5,260.

The school offers:

- Excellent standard of teaching in small classes.
- Curriculum that covers the national requirements and more.
- Caring for the pupil as an individual is at the centre of the school's ethos.
- Large country estate providing a perfect learning environment.
- Exceptional games facilities combined with an extensive leisure programme.
- Successful Individual Teaching Unit for Specific Learning Difficulties.
- Happy relaxed atmosphere for teaching and learning.
- Attractive and comfortable boarding accommodation.
- Learning respect for each other considered essential.
- Length of the day suits working families.

Visitors to the school are welcome when the school is in session.

Newlands School

Eastbourne Road Seaford East Sussex BN25 4NP
Tel: 01323 892334/490000
Fax: 01323 898420
e-mail: enquiries@newlands-school.com
website: www.newlands-school.com

Chairman of Governors: Mr M Holland

***Headmaster*: Mr Chris Bridgman**, BEd Hons

Age Range. 0–18 years.

Number of Pupils. 275.

Fees per term (2008-2009). Tuition: £1,900–£3,120. Boarding (in addition to Tuition fees): £2,500. Overseas Pupils: £7,500 (including Boarding and Tuition).

Newlands provides a quality education from 0 to 18 years on one 21-acre campus in a pleasant coastal town surrounded by an area of outstanding natural beauty.

Newlands has good communication links with Gatwick (37 miles), Heathrow (78miles) and London (65 miles).

Your Child's Potential. At Newlands we place an emphasis on fully developing your child's potential in a happy caring environment. The wide range of activities available makes it possible for every pupil to achieve success and confidence in one field or another.

Classes are small and a pupil's progress is monitored carefully. The arts flourish with thriving music, drama, dance and arts departments. There is a strong choral tradition and annual dramatic productions.

Academic and Sports Facilities. Facilities include high-tech computer rooms, science laboratories, a large art studio, a design and technology workshop and a music technology department.

There are the equivalent of eight football pitches, an indoor swimming pool, a hard playing surface for three tennis/netball courts and a large Sports Hall. There are many opportunities for many sports including soccer, hockey, rugby, netball, cricket, athletics, volleyball, basketball, squash, badminton, tennis, horse-riding, swimming. rounders and cross-country running.

Accelerated Learning Unit. The nationally renowned Gannon Centre has specialist teachers who provide one-to-one tuition for gifted pupils, dyslexic pupils and those learning English as a foreign language.

Performing Arts Course. A Performing Arts Course is available to pupils who wish to specialise in Dance, Drama, Music and Art within an academic environment.

Transport. The school runs a mini-bus service for day pupils and boarders are escorted to airports and stations.

Charitable status. Newlands School is a Registered Charity, number 297606. It exists to provide quality education for boys and girls.

Norfolk House School

Norfolk Road Edgbaston Birmingham B15 3PS
Tel: 0121 454 7021
Fax: 0121 454 7021
e-mail: norfolkhs@aol.com
website: www.norfolkhouseschool.co.uk

***Headmistress*: Mrs H Maresca**, BEd

Age Range. 3–11.

Number in School. 155.

Fees per term (from April 2008). £1,044 (part-time) – £1,810.

Norfolk House School is a Christian Independent day school situated in the pleasant suburb of Edgbaston and is ideally located for pupils and parents all over Birmingham and the surrounding areas.

The school aims to provide individual attention to each pupil, thus enabling each child to fulfil his or her potential. Small class sizes and favourable pupil:teacher ratios (average 17:1) culminate in the best possible academic results. Many pupils move on to the various King Edward Schools, or to other Grammar Schools or senior Independent Schools as the direct result of the high standards achieved at Norfolk House.

The syllabus is designed to give each child a general academic education over a wide range of subjects – in line with the National Curriculum; the requirements of the Eleven Plus and the various Entrance Examinations are also taken into consideration.

In addition to education, Norfolk House School aims to instil in each child good manners, consideration and respect for others, and recognition of personal responsibility. Norfolk House is a small school with an emphasis on caring and traditional values, yet forward thinking in outlook. It is a happy school with high attainment, competitive fees and a family atmosphere.

Norfolk House School

10 Muswell Avenue Muswell Hill London N10 2EG
Tel: 020 8883 4584
Fax: 020 8883 4584
e-mail: admissions@norfolkhouseschool.org
website: www.norfolkhouseschool.org

***Headmaster*: Mr Mark Malley**, BA Ed Hons

Age Range. 4–11 Co-educational.
Number of Pupils. 146.
Fees per term (2007-2008). £2,850.

Normanhurst School

68–74 Station Road Chingford London E4 7BA
Tel: 020 8529 4307
Fax: 020 8524 7737
e-mail: info@normanhurstschool.co.uk
website: www.normanhurstschool.co.uk

Head: **Ms Helen Kacouris**, MBA, BA Hons, PGCE, NPQH

Age Range. 2½–16.
Number in School. 240 Day Pupils.
Fees per term (from April 2008). £1,095–£3,360.
Entry requirements. Interview and assessment.
Location. In the centre of a tree-lined suburban street with good parking, two minutes from a mainline British Rail station and from a far-reaching bus terminus.

Normanhurst School is a thriving, caring, local independent school with a warm, friendly atmosphere and a wide range of activities offered. The School boasts a high standard of academic achievement with excellent SATs and GCSE results.

We encourage our pupils to develop self-confidence and to take on roles of responsibility as they move up through the school. Creativity is nurtured within a disciplined environment and traditional values such as self-discipline are promoted to maximise our pupils' effectiveness in an ever-changing world.

The School offers small class sizes and a wide range of core and optional subjects up to GCSE, including English, Science, Maths, French, Spanish, Design Technology, Art, History, Geography, ICT, Business Studies, PE, Sport, Music and Drama.

Numerous clubs are provided to strengthen the important social aspect of schooling. These include Football, Netball, Gymnastics, Chess, French, Cross-country, Dance, and ICT. Homework club and Teatime club are available to all pupils, while tuition on various musical instruments takes place either as an extra-curricular activity during the day or after school.

North Cestrian Grammar School

Dunham Road Altrincham Cheshire WA14 4AJ

(See entry in SHMIS section)

The North London International School

6 Friern Barnet Lane London N11 3LX
Tel: 020 8920 0600
Fax: 020 8211 4605
e-mail: admissions@nlis.org
website: www.wpis.org

Headmaster: **Mr David Rose**, BA, CertEd, MA(Ed)

Age Range. 2–19.
Number in School. 414 Boys and Girls.
Fees per term (2007-2008). £940–£5,560.

The North London International School provides a secure, well-ordered and happy environment with the learning process at its core, offering the finest possible education for all pupils in order for them to reach their full potential. Serving a cosmopolitan and diverse North London community, great importance is attached to respect, understanding and empathy with everyone's cultures, religions and backgrounds. Emphasis is placed on development of the individual student with academic, artistic, sporting, creative, practical and social skills being encouraged and individual talents nurtured. Every child has a spark of genius, we aim to ignite it!

Students follow the International Baccalaureate curriculum, starting at aged 3 with the Primary Years Programme, moving onto the Middle Years Programme at age 11 and the International Baccalaureate Diploma Programme at age 16. The programmes are designed to encourage the development of learning skills and to meet a child's academic, social, physical, emotional and cultural needs. Through enquiry-based learning and various disciplines, subject interrelatedness is accentuated, preparing students for the pre-university Diploma Programme. Within the programme students must study six subjects, a research project, leading to a 4000 word essay, The Theory of Knowledge course, and Creativity, Action, Service (CAS). The CAS programme is a fundamental part of the Diploma programme, requiring students to participate in 150 hours of activities both in and out of school.

The Quest Programme is designed for students who need help developing strategies to assist them to study effectively. Through one-to-one tuition from specialist staff in skills such as effective reading, time management, planning of work and revision and exam techniques, students can reach their full potential, further enhanced by the school's teacher-student ratio.

Entry requirements. Students are accepted for entry at any time throughout the school year.

Kindergarten and Lower School (*ages 2–11*): Students are invited to attend for half a day and may be asked to complete a basic assessment.

Upper School (*ages 11–16*): Students attend an interview with the Head of the school, are invited to visit the school for a day and may be required to complete a basic assessment.

Entry to the Upper School is automatic for students in the Lower School.

Upper School (*ages 16–19*): Diploma programme applicants are invited for interview with the programme coordinator. Students would be expected to have 5 or 6 GCSE passes, with B, A or A* grades for subjects to be studied at Higher Level. Students arriving from overseas without GSCE qualifications need to demonstrate a sound academic background and understanding of English. The school is able to offer a Foundation Year to students whose command of the English language or subject area knowledge is not sufficient to enable them to start the full programme, including specialist English as an Alternative Language support.

Any decision regarding the offering of a place to a prospective student from overseas who is unable to visit for interview or assessment, will be made by the Head of the respective department, referring to school reports and scholastic references.

Examinations offered. Key Stages 1, 2 and 3; GCSE; International Baccalaureate.

Facilities. The school has dedicated IT, music, art and Design Technology facilities for all students. The commitment to the use of Information and Communications Technology in all subject areas is highlighted by IT and graphics suites, individual student home drives and email accounts, student dedicated laptops and wireless network.

Music tuition is incorporated into the curriculum with the addition of individual lessons in a wide variety of instruments such as piano, guitar, drums, saxophone and violin with composition and singing also available. The school has a number of bands and groups with varying styles from jazz to rock and regular concerts highlight the very real talent within the student body.

Student's physical development is considered as important as academic development and the school's sports fields provide excellent facilities for football, cricket, athletics, hockey, tennis and softball. The school's hall, playgrounds and local amenities are also utilised to offer further activities such as basketball, badminton, squash, swimming, table tennis, ice-skating and skiing. Matches and tournaments between local schools are regular fixtures.

The school's close proximity to central London allows for numerous trips to the capital's museums, galleries and theatres. A variety of overseas trips are offered, both academic and leisure, including France, Spain, skiing and our sister school, The Dwight, in New York while Diploma students are given the opportunity to attend the Model United Nations conferences at The Hague.

Scholarships and Bursaries. A number of scholarships are offered each year to students with a high ability in academic, sporting, musical or artistic areas. For students wishing to enter the Diploma Programme, a scholarship award of up to 30% will be considered for candidates who show a high level of academic achievement. Bursaries are considered on application.

Northamptonshire Grammar School

Pitsford Hall Pitsford Northamptonshire NN6 9AX

(See entry in SHMIS section)

Northease Manor School

Rodmell Lewes East Sussex BN7 3EY
Tel: 01273 472915
Fax: 01273 472202
e-mail: office@northease.co.uk
bursar@northease.co.uk
website: www.northease.co.uk

Chairman of Governors: Bob Cairns

***Head*: Mrs C Harvey-Browne**, BA, PGCE

Type of School. Co-educational day and weekly boarding school.

Age Range. 10–17.

Number of Pupils. 89: 13 Girls, 76 Boys.

Fees per term (from April 2008). Day £6,282, Boarding £8,590.

Northease Manor School is a co-educational special school for dyslexic pupils aged ten to seventeen, catering for both weekly boarders and day pupils. It is approved by the DCSF and is accredited by CReSTeD. It is set in the South Downs with Grade II listed buildings.

It provides a holistic approach to Specific Learning Difficulties (Dyslexia) within small teaching groups and provides on-site access to Speech and Language Therapy and Occupational Therapy. Most of the staff have specialist qualifications and benefit from in-house training.

Northease caters for potentially able pupils who have not realised their true potential at previous schools due to their Specific Learning Difficulties which normally results in a deficit in literacy skills but sometimes in numeracy skills as well. They receive full access to the National Curriculum and benefit from an intensive multi-sensory input which provides for all their literacy and language needs. Detailed pastoral support is given to enable pupils to feel secure and become independent learners. Everything that happens at the school is geared to the needs of the dyslexic child and to ensure that each pupil experiences success in order to raise self-esteem and self-confidence.

In July 2007, Ofsted described Northease Manor as "an excellent school" that gave "outstanding value for money" and where "progress that pupils make is outstanding". In November 2007, Ofsted stated that "boarding and care are outstanding". A CReSTeD Inspection concluded that "the school has a clear and focused objective to remain one of the best schools in its field". In July 2007, 56% of the Year 11 pupils achieved 5 or more GCSE passes at Grade A*–C. 100% of the pupils achieved 5 or more GCSE passes at Grade A*–G.

The ethos of the school is based upon respect for the individual and the celebration of success and achievement. All pupils have abilities and talents and it is the school's role to enable every pupil to discover and develop these talents. Pupils are encouraged to "work hard, play hard" and to have a sense of ownership. It is "our school" and everybody contributes to its well-being and development. High standards of behaviour are expected, with the onus on partnership between pupils and adults. Mistakes are seen as part of the learning process.

Charitable status. Northease Manor School Trust Ltd is a Registered Charity, number 307005. It exists for the provision of high quality education for pupils with Specific Learning Difficulties (Dyslexia).

Notre Dame Preparatory School

147 Dereham Road Norwich Norfolk NR2 3TA
Tel: 01603 625593
Fax: 01603 444139
e-mail: info@notredameprepschool.co.uk
website: www.notredameprepschool.co.uk

Chairman of Governors: Mr Philip Hook

***Headmaster*: Mr K O'Herlihy**, BA, HDipEd

Age Range. 3–11 Co-educational.

Number of Pupils. 130 Day.

Fees per term (2008-2009). £1,215–£1,720.

Notre Dame Prep School was originally founded by the Sisters of Notre Dame de Namur in 1865. The school transferred to its present site in 1971 and is now a Company with charitable status. The school maintains the traditions and the spirit of the Sisters of Notre Dame and the former name and uniform.

As a Catholic school the school and staff endeavour to nurture a love of God through Jesus Christ in all the children. The school has an ethos of love and care and embraces children of all faiths.

Children are treated as individuals, respected, nurtured and encouraged to embrace and fulfil their potential in all areas of school life. We have excellent links with High Schools in both the maintained and independent sectors.

The school achieves well above average results in external tests and has a strong academic reputation. Children are prepared for entry to selective independent schools on request. Subjects include English, Maths, Science, ICT, Design and Technology, Art, Geography, PE, History, Music, RE, French and Personal, Social and Health Education.

The school has a strong musical tradition and has a wide range of extra-curricular musical activities on offer including Choir, Music Ensemble, Recorder, Piano, Guitar, Flute, Violin, Saxophone and Clarinet lessons.

Sports include Football, Cricket, Rugby, Netball, Hockey, Tennis and Swimming.

The school has a wide range of extra-curricular activities including Ballet, Speech and Drama, Chess, ICT, Arts and Crafts, Sailing, Skiing and Golf.

We have an After School Activities Club which runs until 5.40 pm which includes help with homework, tea and games.

Charitable status. Notre Dame Preparatory School (Norwich) Limited is a Registered Charity, number 269003.

Oakfield Preparatory School

125–128 Thurlow Park Road Dulwich London SE21 8HP
Tel: 020 8670 4206
Fax: 020 8766 6744
e-mail: CDeCisneros@cfbt.com (Admissions)
oakfield@cfbt.com (General Enquiries)
website: www.oakfield.dulwich.sch.uk

***Principal*: Mr J Gibson**, BEd

Age Range. 2–11.
Number in School. Day: 303 Boys, 237 Girls.
Fees per term (2007-2008). £1,447–£2,307 including lunch.

Oakfield School was founded in 1887 and is today a modern co-educational prep school which prepares children for the entrance examinations of London and countrywide independent senior schools. These senior schools base their 11+ entrance exams on English and maths and it is these core subjects that form the basis of the Oakfield curriculum, but not to the exclusion of French, humanities, science, the arts and computing.

The School is arranged into three groups, the Nursery (age 2–3) (full time or half day), Foundation Years and Year 1 (age 3–6) and Years 2–6 (age 6–11). Each age group has its own self-contained building and facilities. The School site of nearly three acres allows space for play and games and older children use the nearby playing field where all normal games are played. All children over five swim once a week under instruction.

Entry to the Nursery is by informal assessment. Once accepted the child will progress automatically into the Foundation Years and Main School. Entry at 3+ and 4+ is also by assessment and children should have a good idea of colours, shapes, matching, sorting and simple counting. Entry at 5+ and 7+ follows an informal assessment and observation in a class setting.

Prospective parents – and children – would be very welcome to visit Oakfield during a school day.

Oakhill College

Wiswell Lane Whalley Clitheroe Lancashire BB7 9AF
Tel: 01254 823546
Fax: 01254 822662
e-mail: info@oakhillcollege.co.uk
website: www.oakhillcollege.co.uk

Chairman of Governors: Mr Tony Baron

***Principal*: Mrs Carmel Riley**, BA, PGCE, MA

Age Range. 2–16 Co-educational.
Number of Pupils. 229 pupils.
Fees per term (from April 2008). Pre-Prep (Reception–Year 2) £1,775; Prep (Years 3–6) £2,000; Upper School (Years 7–11) £2,751. Nursery: £29.50 per day.
Charitable status. Oakhill College Charitable Trust is a Registered Charity, number 1048514.

Oakhyrst Grange School

Stanstead Road Caterham Surrey CR3 6AF
Tel: 01883 343344
Fax: 01883 342021
e-mail: office@oakhyrstgrangeschool.co.uk
website: www.oakhyrstgrangeschool.co.uk

***Headmaster*: Mr A Gear**, BEd

Age Range. 4–11.
Number in School. Day Boys and Girls: 120.
Fees per term (2008-2009). £988–£2,186.

Oakhyrst Grange School is an independent, co-educational preparatory day school for boys and girls between 4 and 11 years.

The School was established in 1950 and moved to its present premises in Stanstead Road in 1957. Since September 1973 the School has been administered by a non-profit making trust.

Standing in five acres of open country and woodland and surrounded by the Green Belt, the School enjoys a fine position amongst the Surrey Hills.

The school has a wide and imaginative curriculum, which includes traditional teaching combined with innovative ideas. Small class sizes, an excellent teacher/pupil ratio, enable pupils to work at their own rate and capabilities whilst being encouraged to meet new challenges.

Over the last four years 57 pupils have secured the offer of 157 places to prominent senior schools, including 79 scholarships and awards across the range of academic, all-rounder, music, sports and art.

There are many sporting opportunities offered and particularly high standards have been reached in cross-country, swimming, football, judo and athletics where ISA National level has been achieved. The pupils compete in many inter house, inter school and area competitions. The school also has its own heated indoor swimming pool, all weather tennis, netball, hockey and 5-a-side court, sports pitch, cross-country course and gymnasium.

Extra curricular music lessons are offered and much music making also takes place as part of the normal school timetable. The school has clarinet, violin and trumpet ensembles and a choir all of whom perform regularly.

In addition to the curriculum the pupils can enjoy an extensive range of clubs and activities throughout the week.

Academic excellence is encouraged and achieved, every child is expected to attain his or her individual potential. The School helps children to develop into caring, thoughtful and confident adults.

Charitable status. Oakhyrst Grange School Educational Trust is a Registered Charity, number 325043. It exists to provide an all-round education, to give the children success and the best possible start.

Oaklands School

8 Albion Hill Loughton Essex IG10 4RA
Tel: 020 8508 3517
Fax: 020 8508 4454
e-mail: info@oaklandsschool.co.uk
website: www.oaklandsschool.co.uk

***Head*: Mrs Pam Simmonds**, MA (Oxon), BSc

Age Range. Girls 2½–11 years; Boys 2½–7 years.
Number in School. 248 Day Pupils.
Fees per term (from January 2008). £1,340–£2,770.

Oaklands is a long-established preparatory school, founded in 1937, and delightfully situated in extensive grounds on the edge of Epping Forest. It provides a firm foundation for girls aged 2½ to 11 years and boys aged 2½ to 7 years. Great care is taken in preparing pupils for entrance examinations to their next schools.

A broad curriculum is offered, with early emphasis on literacy and numeracy, ensuring high standards, and great importance is placed on fully developing each child's potential in a secure and caring atmosphere. We have small class sizes and specialist teachers for Science, French, Music, PE, Dancing, ICT, Sport and Drama. A wide range of extra-curricular activities is offered and an after-school care club operates until 5 pm. The school has now established a reputation for excellent dramatic productions. Individual music tuition is available, including piano and woodwind instrumental lessons, and singing lessons.

Oaklands is a friendly, happy school where children can enjoy learning and take pride in both their own success and the achievements of others. In addition to the attainment of high standards, pupils build personal qualities of confidence, self-reliance and respect for others, in preparation for the challenges and opportunities of the modern world.

The Old School
Henstead

Toad Row Henstead Nr Beccles Suffolk NR34 7LG
Tel: 01502 741150
Fax: 01502 741150
e-mail: oldschool@btclick.com
website: www.theoldschoolhenstead.co.uk

***Headmaster*: Mr I R Griffin**, BA Hons

Age Range. 4½–11.
Number in School. 90 Day Boys and Girls.
Fees per term (2007-2008). £1,450–£1,960.

The Old School, Henstead offers a traditional style of education in a caring family environment. It is well staffed with small classes. Children are prepared for entrance examinations to all local senior schools. The curriculum is broad enough to be balanced with facilities for Music, ICT, Science, Pottery, Art & Drama and Physical Education and games.

The school is an Educational Trust; it is in membership of ISA and is Accredited by ISC.

Charitable status. The Old School Henstead Educational Trust Limited is a Registered Charity, number 279265. It exists to provide education for boys and girls.

Our Lady's Convent School

Burton Street Loughborough Leics LE11 2DT
Tel: 01509 263901
Fax: 01509 236193
e-mail: office@olcs.leics.sch.uk
website: www.olcs.leics.sch.uk

***Headteacher*: Mrs Patricia Hawley**, BA, PGCE

Age Range. Girls 3–18, Boys 3–11.
Number of Pupils. 390.
Fees per term (2008-2009). Nursery £2,054, Infants £2,302, Juniors £2,385, Seniors £2,843.

Our Lady's Convent School is a Catholic day school that extends a warm welcome to children of all faiths and denominations. It educates girls from 3 to 18 and boys from 3 to 11. The focus is very much on the individual child and their personal progress and achievement at all levels. Our next Open Day would be an excellent time to see our Senior and Primary School Departments in action on a normal working day, view our facilities and meet our Headteacher.

At all stages of their education, our students receive individual attention in guaranteed small classes. They are helped, encouraged and supported rather than pressured. Academic achievement is high at all levels. In 2007 the Year 13 achieved a pass rate of a 100% with 70% of students gaining A to C grades whilst Year 11 had a 100% pass rate with over 90% of students achieving grades A* to C. A wide variety of GCSE and A Levels is offered in the Senior department. Learning Support is excellent for all students in all areas. 99% of our students go on to university to study a wide range of subjects. In addition there are numerous cultural, musical and sporting activities. Music and Drama are have a high profile in school, for instance, this year junior and senior musicians have participated in masterclasses with the professional London-based group, Voces 8, and girls have taken part in the national Shakespeare Festival. A wide variety of extra-curricular activities is on offer. The school successfully participates in The Duke of Edinburgh's Award and Young Enterprise schemes.

The school is a registered charity and its policy is to continually enhance the facilities available to our students and to improve our service to them and their parents. All departments are well resourced and ICT facilities are excellent and updated regularly. Our most recent developments include a refurbished and re-equipped Early Years/Infant Department, play and recreation areas and library for primary children, and a refurbished sixth form suite.

The School campus is an attractive walled area; an oasis of calm, near the centre of Loughborough. Open Days are held during working school days and visitors continually note the happy classroom environment and the mutual respect between students, staff and visitors. Some of our students are with us from 3 to 18 but others are very welcome to join at other stages of their education.

The Pelican Club provides before and after school care for a small additional cost.

For further information visit our website www.olcs.leics.sch.uk.

Charitable status. Our Lady's Convent School is a Registered Charity, number 1110802.

The Park School

Queen's Park South Drive Bournemouth BH8 9BJ
Tel: 01202 396640
Fax: 01202 392705
e-mail: office@parkschool.co.uk

***Headmaster*: Mr Clive G Cole**, BA

Age Range. 3–11.
Number in School. Day: 153 Boys, 122 Girls.
Fees per term (from April 2008). £1,700–£2,380.

The Park is a co-educational junior day school occupying a quiet site overlooking Queens Park Golf course in a pleasant residential area near the town centre.

Pupils are taught in small classes in a caring, happy environment. The school is geared principally towards academic achievement although we do provide special help for a limited number of children with specific learning difficulties. The emphasis is on nurturing individual and academic progress whilst fostering a positive ethos and the development of the all-round child. This covers not only work in the classroom but also all other aspects of school life: games, music, the Arts and many practical activities. Pupils are prepared for entry to Senior Independent Schools and to the local Grammar Schools through their tests at 11+ years. Many children gain scholarships to Senior Independent Schools.

Most pupils start aged 3+ years but there are occasional vacancies at other ages. Offer of a place is made only after prospective pupils have been formally assessed.

Parents with pupils in our Nursery classes can take advantage of our extended working days and the lengthened school terms should they wish to.

Park School for Girls

20–22 Park Avenue Ilford Essex IG1 4RS
Tel: Office: 020 8554 2466
Bursar: 020 8554 6022
Fax: 020 8554 3003
e-mail: admin@parkschool.org.uk
website: www.parkschool.org.uk

***Headmistress*: Mrs N E O'Brien**, BA

Age Range. 7–18.

Number in School. 235 Day Girls.

Fees per term (2008-2009). Prep School £2,020, Senior School £2,670.

The School is situated near Valentine Park in Ilford. It is convenient for road, rail and Central Line tube services.

Our basic aim is to provide a full educational programme leading to recognised external examinations at the ages of 16 and 18 years.

We create a caring, well-ordered atmosphere. Our pupils are encouraged to achieve their full academic and social potential. The well-qualified staff and the policy of small classes produce well above the national average GCSE and A level results. The majority of our sixth form enter university and the professions.

In addition, the staff and I stress the development of each child as a whole person. We expect every girl to strive for self-confidence in her ability to use her talents to the full and to respect individuality. She is encouraged to make decisions and to accept responsibility for her own actions. The poise that comes from good manners and correct speech, we consider to be highly important. Honesty, reliability, courtesy and consideration for others are prime factors in the educative system.

Interested parents are welcome to visit the school, where the Headmistress will be pleased to answer their queries.

Charitable status. Park School for Girls is a Registered Charity, number 269936. It exists to provide a caring environment in which we develop our pupils' potential to the full.

The Park School
Yeovil

The Park Yeovil Somerset BA20 1DH
Tel: 01935 423514
Fax: 01935 411257
e-mail: admin@parkschool.com
website: www.parkschool.com

***Headmaster*: Mr P W Bate**, BA Econ, MA, PGCE, AdvDipMkt

Age Range. 3–18 Co-educational.

Number in School. 267: 133 Boys, 134 Girls. 28 Boarders.

Fees per term (2008-2009). Day £1,580–£2,735 (including lunch); Weekly Boarding £4,795–£5,135; Full Boarding £5,015–£5,365.

The Park School, Yeovil is an Independent day and boarding school founded in 1851. It aims to provide a sound education based on Christian principles. It is a non-denominational Evangelical Christian school and has strong connections with a number of different local churches.

The School is pleasantly situated near the centre of Yeovil with easy access to surrounding towns and villages, from which day pupils are drawn, and to the main line station, Yeovil Junction, for London Waterloo. There is also a rail connection to Bristol and Weymouth from Yeovil, Penmill station. Transport to London Heathrow and other airports is arranged for boarders travelling abroad.

The School buildings consist of an interesting historic listed building, which has been sympathetically upgraded, and modern additions. Recent developments include the establishment of four ICT rooms, a refurbished Sports Hall, a Sixth Form building and a floodlit all-weather Sports field.

Pupils flourish in a friendly, caring environment where, in small classes, they benefit from well-qualified staff. There is a wide and varied curriculum which encourages each pupil to develop their own abilities and interests to the full. In line with the National Curriculum guidelines, senior pupils choose from a range of subjects at GCSE and A Level, including: English, RE, History, Drama, Geography, French, German, Mathematics, Science, Art, Music, Design Technology, Food Technology, ICT, Sports Studies and English for overseas pupils. Physics, Chemistry and Biology are studied as separate Sciences. Chinese and Spanish are offered subject to demand. Additional subjects studied at A Level include: Business Studies, Sports Studies and Psychology.

Physical Education is also an essential part of the curriculum. Pupils participate in a varied programme of sporting activities including: Athletics, Badminton, Basketball, Cricket, Football, Gymnastics, Hockey, Netball, Squash, Swimming, Tennis, Table Tennis, Volleyball and Cross-Country. Many Senior pupils also take part in the Duke of Edinburgh's Award Scheme as well as Young Enterprise.

A wide range of musical instruments is taught by the Director of Music and visiting staff. There are School Choirs and an Orchestra as well as a jazz band, rock group and a baroque ensemble. Music and drama productions are regular features of School life.

Boarders live in a newly refurbished (2004) purpose-built School House. Many students occupy single study bedrooms. They are cared for in a homely, family atmosphere by resident houseparents aided by assistants. At weekends a variety of interesting activities is available. On Sundays all boarders are encouraged to attend, with a member of staff, the church of their choice.

Academic standards in the School are high with The Park being consistently well placed in the GCSE league tables. However, the School is not rigidly selective and pupils are encouraged to develop their talents as individuals with extremely favourable pupil/teacher ratios.

The school offers scholarships which may be given for academic, music, art or drama ability. These are awarded by examination and interview in January of each year for entry at Year 4, Year 7, Year 9 and for Sixth Form. Bursaries are available for children of those parents who are engaged in full-time Christian work or are members of HM Forces. In addition bursaries are available for parents on low income.

Charitable status. The Park School (Yeovil) Limited is a Registered Charity, number 310214. It exists to provide Christian education and care for children aged 3–18 years.

Peniel Academy

Brizes Park Ongar Road Kelvedon Hatch Brentwood Essex CM15 0DG
Tel: 01277 374123
Fax: 01277 373596

e-mail: academy@peniel.org
website: www.penielacademy.ac

***Head*: Mr Rob Whitaker**

Age Range. 3–18 co-educational.

Number of Pupils. 149.

Fees per term (2008-2009). £1,940.

Peniel Academy is situated in Brizes Park, a 73 acre site of magnificent parkland on the outskirts of Brentwood. An elegant Georgian mansion houses the senior section while the primary section is in modern classrooms in a beautifully landscaped walled garden.

Pupils at Peniel Academy achieve success in all walks of life. The school has a comprehensive intake, yet regularly ranks among the top schools in the country for its exam results. Teams from Peniel Academy have represented England on a number of occasions at table tennis, the school's main sport. Most pupils go on to gain good university degrees and then proceed to top jobs and careers. Many former students regularly give back to the school in various ways as a thank you for all they received here.

The school has a warm family atmosphere with many of the parents providing the teaching staff, assistants, cooks and office workers. The school is closely linked to Peniel Church and one of the secrets of its success is the principle established from its foundation that the pupils should find the same standards in the school, the church and the home. This has produced happy, secure and well-motivated children who have a strong sense of service as well as a platform for success throughout life.

Charitable status. Peniel Academy is a Registered Charity, number 1112705.

Peterborough & St Margaret's School

Common Road Stanmore Middlesex HA7 3JB
Tel: 020 8950 3600
Fax: 020 8421 8946
e-mail: psm@psmschool.org
website: www.psmschool.org

***Headmistress*: Mrs S Watts**

Age Range. Girls 3–16 including Nursery for boys and girls aged 3+.

Number in School. 183 Day Pupils.

Fees per term (2007-2008). Nursery £2,334, Infants £2,076, Juniors £2,465-£2,735 Seniors £3,085.

Peterborough & St Margaret's School, or PSM as it is affectionately known, is situated on a picturesque, wooded site between Stanmore and Bushey Heath. It was founded over a hundred years ago and combines traditional attitudes and values with high expectations and excellent academic results. Boys are welcome in the nursery. Part of a Christian Foundation, it values the enrichment of the community by other faiths and cultures.

Education is for life and choosing the right school is one of the most important decisions parents make. Learning should be enjoyable and here at PSM we aim to make it so, whether the pupils are spending their first day in the nursery or studying for their GCSE examinations.

Because there is only one form of approximately twenty pupils per year group, no girl gets lost in the crowd. This is a small, 'family' school, where pupils and staff all know each other. The Infant Department offers a friendly, gentle environment, so important to children as they begin their school life. Some staff teach throughout the age groups – specialist teachers teach Drama, Music, French, Gymnastics and ICT from Reception onwards – so the younger ones not only benefit from their expertise but get to know many of the teachers before reaching the Senior Department.

Having followed the Early Years Foundation Stage in the nursery, the girls already start to follow the Key Stage 1 National Curriculum as soon as they join Reception, giving them an extra year in which to flourish. Classes are split for many subjects in the Junior and Senior Departments, and such small classes enable staff to support and challenge all girls on an individual basis. We aim to help them discover their talents and give them the maximum opportunity to develop, both intellectually and creatively.

Success breeds more success and involvement in music, drama, sport and a whole range of extra-curricular activities, as well as residential visits beginning in Year 5, gives them a confidence that bears fruit in their academic studies as well. At PSM every child has the chance to shine.

The Year 10 and 11 girls are treated as 'sixth formers', with all the associated positions of responsibility and privileges. They rapidly grow into their roles, becoming more responsible and mature than girls of the same age who will have to wait a couple of years for such opportunities. They are then ready to spread their wings and move on to neighbouring sixth forms, often winning scholarships, as a transition to university. They leave Peterborough & St Margaret's confident, capable, courteous and compassionate young women with a secure grounding for life.

Bursaries and scholarships are available.

Charitable status. The E Ivor Hughes Educational Foundation is a Registered Charity, number 293623. It exists to provide education for children.

Pilgrims Pre-Preparatory School

Brickhill Drive Bedford MK41 7QZ

(See entry in IAPS section)

Plumtree School

Church Hill Plumtree Nottinghamshire NG12 5ND
Tel: 0115 937 5859
Fax: 0115 937 5859
e-mail: plumtreeschool@tiscali.co.uk
website: www.plumtreeschool.co.uk

***Headmaster*: N White**, CertEd

Age Range. 3–11.

Number in School. Day: 60 Boys, 50 Girls.

Fees per term (2008-2009). £1,750.

The School was opened in its present form by Mr and Mrs White in September 1982. The buildings housed the original Church of England village school closed down by the local education authority some years earlier.

Plumtree is an independent, co-educational, primary school with its own nursery. The School is situated in the centre of Plumtree village within easy reach of the southern suburbs of Nottingham and surrounding villages to the south of the city.

The aim of the school is to provide a wide, balanced primary education relative to the needs and potential of each child. At Plumtree, a happy, working atmosphere in small classes allows for close individual attention. There is an average pupil/teacher ratio of 12:1.

Priority is given to the basic subjects at all levels throughout the school. A solid foundation in mathematics, English and science is considered vitally important. The school has also developed a considerable reputation for music and the performing arts. These subject areas play their part in bringing width and balance to the curriculum. A high standard in presentation of work, behaviour and manners is regarded as essential.

The school has strong links with the village community and St Mary's Church, where school services and concerts are held. Moral education is of great importance and at Plumtree, children are encouraged to develop a sense of responsibility and learn to play a worthwhile role in the life of their community.

Children may begin our nursery class at three years old, moving into the infant department at 'rising five'. The junior department caters for children of seven to eleven years old.

Each child's progress and development is monitored through a series of internal tests and continual assessment. Parents receive a termly report. Each term parents are given the opportunity to discuss the progress of their child and to examine the work with the teachers concerned. Individual interviews with teaching staff are always available by appointment.

Plumtree offers a real alternative to parents seeking a rounded, caring and traditional education for their children.

Parents wishing to know more should contact the Head Teacher to receive a prospectus and to arrange a visit to see the school at work.

Polwhele House School

Truro Cornwall TR4 9AE
Tel: 01872 273011
e-mail: polwhele@talk21.com
website: www.polwhelehouse.co.uk

***Headmaster*: Jeremy Mason**, BEd

Age Range. 3–13+.

Number in School. 158 Day; 12 Boarding.

Fees per term (2007-2008). Day £375–£3,138; Weekly Boarding £5,262–£5,898. Lunch £138.

Polwhele House is a beautiful and historic listed building, set in 30 acres of garden, playing fields, park and woodland. The school enjoys a glorious and secure environment only 1¼ miles from the Cathedral.

Uninterrupted education is provided for boys and girls during those important early years from three to thirteen. There is flexible attendance for under-fives who are taught by qualified teachers in Nursery and Kindergarten. The Pre-Preparatory School has an established reputation for high levels of care and excellent teaching.

Although mainly a day-school, weekly boarding, day boarding, 'sleepovers' and after-school care are growing in popularity. The boarders live in the Main House in comfortable surroundings which include a TV lounge, en-suite facilities, quiet areas and garden. The well-being and happiness of each child is the top priority.

This flourishing family school has had a continual programme of development, building and refurbishment since 1976 when the Pre-Prep School was opened. In 1994 new quality accommodation was built and equipped for art and craft, design technology, sciences, languages and ICT. In 1992 an equestrian centre was provided for pupils and riding is professionally taught to a quarter of the school.

The school combines modern teaching methods with the best of traditional values. The social development of the child is carefully nurtured to help them to become confident, considerate and polite young people. Polwhele House values each child and a strong team of skilled and caring staff are able to devote a great deal of time to every pupil in small classes.

Drama flourishes with each child participating in at least one of eight productions a year. Music is an important part of the school life with all pupils singing, and the majority playing an instrument. There are Truro Cathedral Choristerships for boys and Polwhele House Music Scholarships for girls. All the usual team games are coached and there are regular outstanding successes in athletics and cross-country running at school, county and national levels.

Polwhele House is a Christian, non-denominational school and assembly is considered to be an important part of the day. The school motto is 'Karenza Whelas Karenza', Cornish for 'Love Begets Love'. Boys and girls share the same opportunities and responsibilities in all areas of school life.

The school has a fine record of academic achievement. There is a wide variety of sporting and extra-curricular activities to bring out the best in every child. Pupils are prepared for a broad range of schools, and win numerous scholarships, bursaries and exhibitions to Senior Independent Schools every year.

Mr Mason takes great pleasure in meeting prospective parents and showing them around personally. Polwhele House is not just a school, more a way of life.

Portland Place School

56–58 Portland Place London W1B 1NJ

(See entry in SHMIS section)

Prenton Preparatory School

Mount Pleasant Oxton Wirral CH43 5SY
Tel: 0151 652 3182
Fax: 0151 653 7428
e-mail: enquiry@prentonprep.co.uk
website: www.prentonprep.co.uk

***Headteacher*: Mrs N M Aloé**

Age Range. 2½–11.

Number in School. Day: 50 Boys, 67 Girls.

Fees per term (from January 2008). £1,470 Infants; £1,540 Juniors.

Founded in 1935.

Prenton Preparatory School is a co-educational day school for children aged 2½–11 years, situated about a mile from Junction 3 of the M53.

The building is a large Victorian house which has been carefully converted into the uses of a school. There is a large playground and gardens. Facilities include an ICT/Science block and a new Art block and Pre-School outdoor play area are recent additions to the school.

The children benefit from small classes and individual attention in a disciplined environment which enable them to realise their full potential.

The school offers a wide range of academic subjects with emphasis on the three main National Curriculum core subjects: English, Mathematics and Science. French is taught from an early age.

Children are prepared for entrance examinations to county, independent and grant-maintained grammar schools, gaining above average pass rates.

Child care facilities are available from 8 am to 6 pm. Clubs are provided at lunchtime and after school. They include football, cricket, computers and technology, judo, swimming, gymnastics, ballet, netball, fencing, music group, handchimes and musical instruments.

Princethorpe College

Leamington Road Princethorpe Rugby Warwickshire CV23 9PX

(See entry in SHMIS section)

Priory School

Sir Harry's Road Edgbaston Birmingham B15 2UR
Tel: 0121 440 4103/0256
Fax: 0121 440 3639
e-mail: enquiries@prioryschool.net
website: www.prioryschool.net

Chairman of Governors: Mr S Gilmore, LLB

***Principal*: Mr Jonathan Cramb**, MA EdMgt

Age Range. 6 months –18 years.

Number in School. 310 (160 Prep School, 150 Senior School)

Fees per term (2008-2009). £2,105–£3,185.

The school, founded on its present site in 1936 by the Sisters of the Society of the Holy Child Jesus, stands in 17 acres of parkland in the pleasant suburb of Edgbaston, only 2 miles from the centre of Birmingham. The school has extensive playing fields, excellent astroturf tennis courts, athletics facilities and football and cricket pitches. There are coaches running to and from school and frequent bus services to all parts of the city.

The school has an excellent Nursery on site which offers care for 51 weeks per annum and accepts children from the age of 6 months. All pupils are able to remain in After Care until 6.00 pm if parents so wish.

The school has a culturally diverse pupil community, based on catholic values, but welcomes all faiths. Pupils are taught by specialist teachers from the age of 9 and in the Senior School the curriculum is taught on a 'together but separate model' in which girls and boys are educated separately for the core subjects of English, Mathematics, Sciences and Modern Foreign Languages but together for others.

The school, whilst remaining proudly multi-ability, is justly proud of the academic achievements of the pupils. A wide range of subjects is available for GCSE and A Level, with good facilities, including well-equipped Science Laboratories, Language Resources rooms, Information Technology facilities, Sports Centre, Performing Arts Suite and Learning Resources Centre. The school offers support for children with special needs, particularly dyslexia, and has a purpose-built learning enrichment centre with specially qualified staff.

A wide range of extra-curricular opportunities are offered in both Prep. and Senior School. These currently include photography, debating, chess, Duke of Edinburgh's Award scheme to name just a few. Private tuition is also offered in Speech, singing and a wide range of musical instruments.

Entry to the school is by interview, assessment and day visit. Scholarships are awarded at 11+ and 16+. Bursaries may be awarded in cases of special need.

Parents are warmly welcomed into the school to discuss individual needs. Full details prior to the visit may be obtained from the Admissions Registrar.

Charitable status. Priory School is a Registered Charity, number 518009.

Putney Park School

Woodborough Road London SW15 6PY
Tel: 020 8788 8316
Fax: 020 8780 2376
e-mail: office@putneypark.london.sch.uk
website: www.putneypark.london.sch.uk

***Headmistress*: Mrs Ruth Mann**, BSc Hons, PGCE, DPSE

Age Range. Girls 4–16, Boys 4–8.

Number in School. Day: 61 Boys, 217 Girls.

Fees per term (2008-2009). Upper School £3,699; Lower School £3,237. Extras: Individual music lessons, ballet, EFL, lunches, school bus.

Putney Park School, established in 1953, and now in the second generation of the Tweedie-Smith family ownership, is situated in a quiet road off the main Upper Richmond Road, within three minutes' walk of the bus stop. The school is situated in a Conservation Area and consists of four delightful Edwardian houses with a welcoming family atmosphere. The gardens are attractively landscaped with both play and seating areas. It is easily accessible from all parts of Putney, Roehampton, East Sheen, Barnes and Wimbledon.

Classrooms are bright and well-equipped. Specialist rooms include science laboratories, state-of-the-art ICT facilities, two libraries, a home economics room, pottery, art and music rooms and a gymnasium.

The aim of the School is to provide a sound education in a happy atmosphere. Pupils are offered a broad curriculum to enable them to develop their creativity and individual talents to their full potential. Pupils thrive in the caring and supportive environment. Good manners and initiative are encouraged. We are a mixed ability school and we pride ourselves on being a strong learning community. We boost pupils' self-esteem regardless of academic ability and produce confident, articulate individuals ready for the challenges and opportunities that lie ahead. To achieve this, teachers are chosen for their qualifications, their experience and their understanding of the needs of the pupils. Small class sizes ensure that pupils are given the maximum individual attention and encouragement to reach the highest standards possible. We are a CReSTeD school and pride ourselves on our dyslexic pupils' successes.

Programmes of study follow the National Curriculum. Subjects taught include, at the appropriate stage, English, Mathematics, RE, History, Geography, Biology, Chemistry, Physics, French (from Reception), Spanish, Music, Technology, Information and Communication Technology, Art, Drama, Home Economics and Physical Education.

Children are accepted from four years old into Reception. The school prepares boys for entry to other schools including Colet Court and King's College, Wimbledon at 7+ and 8+. Girls are prepared for entry to other schools, particularly Putney High, Bute House and Wimbledon High at 7+ and 11+. Boys entering the school have the opportunity to remain at Putney Park until they are eight. From Year 4 the school is for girls only.

The Upper School includes Year 6 to Year 11. There is an examination for entry to Year 7. A programme of general education is followed from Year 6 to Year 9. GCSE Options are chosen in Year 9. In Years 10 and 11 girls are prepared for the General Certificate of Secondary Education in eight or nine subjects, which must include English, Mathematics and Science. Our careers programme reflects the importance we attach to the development of the individual skills and talents of all pupils. At the end of Year 11 all pupils are welcomed into a wide range of schools and colleges including St Paul's, Putney High, Wimbledon High and Surbiton High. Our GCSE grades for 2007 were outstanding with 36% A* and A grades.

Physical activities include swimming, tennis, netball, badminton, squash, volleyball, rounders, athletics, football, cricket, touch rugby and rowing. Games are played at the Bank of England Sports Ground, Roehampton. Both inter-school and inter-house matches take place frequently. Visits to places of interest in and around London are organised every term. School journeys to a foreign country are arranged each year. Advantage is taken of nearby Richmond Park and Wimbledon Common for scientific and geographical fieldwork. Concerts, plays and musicals are regularly performed.

Queen Ethelburga's Collegiate Foundation

Thorpe Underwood Hall York YO26 9SS
Tel: 0870 742 3330
Fax: 0870 742 3310
e-mail: admin@queenethelburgas.edu
website: www.queenethelburgas.edu

Co-educational Day and Boarding School.

Chairman of Governors: Brian R Martin, FCMI, FInstD, FFA

***Headmaster*: Steven Jandrell**, BA

Age Range. 3 months–18 years.

Number of Pupils. 532: 64 day boys, 87 day girls, 171 boy boarders, 210 girl boarders.

Fees per term (2008-2009). Day: £995–£3,075; Boarding: £6,245–£8,795 (UK students), £7,340–£10,335 (International students).

Queen Ethelburga's is located at Thorpe Underwood, situated between Harrogate and York. The College is co-educational, for students in the age range 11 to 19, the Faculty provides more vocational/professional courses for students aged 14 to 19 and Chapter House Preparatory School has children up to age 11. The schools are supported by the Queen Ethelburga's Charitable Foundation which provides many bursaries, scholarships and awards, and investment in the yearly capital projects.

The campus is exceptional. Set in 100 acres of manicured country park in the Vale of York, the Foundation maintains an excellent quality of provision with huge investments in the last 10 years. Set around a Grade 2* Listed country house there are Science, Modern Language, Art and Technology suites, together with Sports Hall, excellent floodlit pitches for Rugby, Hockey and Football, floodlit tennis courts and a swimming pool. The Equestrian Centre is probably unique in Europe with stabling for 60 horses, an Olympic-size indoor arena and acres of all-weather floodlit arenas. Many students take advantage of the Foundation Riding Award, which allows students to bring their own horses to school with free livery. Planned projects include a second new Sports Hall, additional Classroom areas, additional Sports Gymnasium and Sixth Form Boarding and Leisure Accommodation..

We are proud that we have been able to maintain a broad access school with students obtaining good academic results. The overriding ethos is "to be the best that I can with the gifts that I have". The College and Faculty offer a broad ranging curriculum up to GCSE based around the NC, with small classes and a wide range of extra curricular activities. Sixth Form students have the choice of 22 different A Levels, IB and BTech.

Boarding is based around three boys' houses and three girls' houses with excellent facilities including most bedrooms being en suite and equipped with TV, hi-fi, telephone and other modern electrical equipment. The strong pastoral care is centred on House Parents and Tutors, who work closely with the Heads of Year and the Head of Pastoral Care.

Entry is via our own entrance examination and interview with the Headmaster. Applicants are expected to have achieved the equivalent of at least Level 4 at Key Stage 2, Level 5 at Key Stage 3, at least 4 B Grades and 2 C Grades for the College and have attained at least 4 GCSE passes at C Grade and above for the Faculty. The Foundation contributes over £1,000,000 each year in awards for academic excellence, sport, music, drama, equestrian and many others. All boarders of HM Forces families attract a Forces Bursary of 20%.

Charitable status. Queen Ethelburga's College Foundation is a Registered Charity, number 1012924.

Raphael Independent School

Park Lane Hornchurch Essex RM11 1XY
Tel: 01708 744735
Fax: 01708 722432
e-mail: admin@raphaelschool.com
website: www.raphaelschool.com

***Headmistress*: Mrs J Lawrence**, BEd Hons

Age Range. Co-educational 4–16.

Number of Pupils. Day: 100 boys, 50 girls.

Fees per term (2007-2008). £1,380–£2,350.

Entry requirements. Interview for Early Years and Infants. Informal assessment for Juniors. Entry Tests in English and Maths for Seniors.

Aims. To develop the academic, social, artistic and sporting potential of each individual within a caring and welcoming school community.

To foster respect for each other within a multi-cultural school.

To offer a broad range of educational visits and extra-curricular activities.

Location. Raphael is a ten minute walk from Romford Main Line Station, and a fifteen minute drive from the A12 or A127 junctions of the M25.

School day. Infants from 8.40 am, Juniors until 3.25 pm and Seniors until 4.00 pm. Our After School Club looks after pupils until 5.45 pm.

Curriculum strengths. ICT, French and Spanish, English and Drama, Maths.

Sport. We believe in competitive sport, and we offer Soccer, Rugby, Netball, Cross-Country, Swimming, Cricket and Tennis amongst others.

A prospectus containing further information may be obtained from our Office Manager, Carolyn Carter, and all prospective parents are most welcome to visit the school.

Rastrick Independent School

Ogden Lane Rastrick Brighouse West Yorkshire HD6 3HF
Tel: 01484 400344
Fax: 01484 718318
e-mail: info@rastrick-independent.co.uk
website: www.rastrickschool.co.uk

***Headmistress*: Mrs S A Vaughey**

Age Range. 0–16 co-educational.

Number of Pupils. 200

Fees per term (2008-2009). £1,850–£2,833.

Red House School

36 The Green Norton Stockton-on-Tees Cleveland TS20 1DX
Tel: 01642 553370
Fax: 01642 361031
e-mail: headmaster@redhouseschool.co.uk
website: www.redhouseschool.co.uk

Chairman of Governors: Mr James Robson

***Headmaster*: Mr A R W Taylor**, BSc, MSc, CBiol, MIBiol

Deputy Head (*Nursery & Infant School*): Miss Joanna Everington

Age Range. 3–16.

Number in School. Approx 190 girls and 260 boys.

Fees per term (2007-2008). Nursery and Infant School £1,710, Prep £2,080, Senior £2,270. Lunches: £170 (Nursery and Infants), £180 (Prep and Senior).

Red House School is a 3–16 co-educational, independent day school of about 450 students. Founded over 75 years ago the School is situated in a very pleasant location around the Village Green in Norton which is on the northern edge of the Teesside Conurbation.

Our commitment to pupils and parents is summarized below:

- To provide a happy, stimulating and well disciplined environment in which children succeed.
- To encourage each child to reach their full potential and strive for excellence in all areas of school life.
- To develop pupil's self-esteem so that they have the confidence to use their individual talents, skills and knowledge effectively.
- To develop their skills of communication, analysis and independent thinking so that children are equipped to be lifelong learners prepared for a rapidly changing society.
- To develop a positive partnership between staff, parents, pupils and the wider community.

The school is based on two sites. The Nursery and Infant school is housed in "The Old Vicarage", a beautiful listed building. This site was further developed in 2004 with the construction of purpose-built nursery facilities, additional classrooms and the redevelopment of 'The Barn' to provide an assembly hall and dining room. Close links are maintained with the Preparatory and Senior Schools.

The Preparatory and Senior schools are housed on the main site. The original Victorian building has been augmented over the years with purpose built sports and assembly halls, classrooms and laboratories. The school has its own playing fields, including tennis courts. ICT is well developed within the teaching and learning, a third computer suite was opened in 2005. Most of the school is served by wireless networking. Ambitious plans to further improve the facilities at the Senior School are in place.

Although a selective school, Red House caters for pupils with a wide range of abilities and backgrounds. Small class sizes means that teaching can be tailored to the needs of the individual child allowing them to reach their full potential. All pupils take 9 or 10 subjects to GCSE. Results at GCSE have been consistently amongst the best, if not the best, of any school within the area. The academic side of the school is balanced by an extensive programme of games and activities. Pupils have regularly achieved representational honours at county, regional and national level.

Charitable status. Red House School Limited is a Registered Charity, number 527377. It exists to provide education for children.

Redcourt – St Anselm's

7 Devonshire Place Oxton Birkenhead Wirral CH43 1TX
Tel: 0151 652 5228
Fax: 0151 653 5883
e-mail: admin@redcourt.wirral.sch.uk
website: www.redcourtstanselms.com

Chairman of Governors: Mr J Sullivan

***Headmaster*: Mr K S Davey**, MA, PGCE

Age Range. 3–11 Co-educational.

Number of Pupils. 260.

Fees per term (2007-2008). £1,367.

Redcourt – St Anselm's is an inclusive school welcoming all children of all abilities. There is no formal entrance examination. Prospective pupils are invited into Redcourt for a day's visit. During the day, Staff will assess the level at which the visiting child is currently working. However, most children join at nursery level. Our aim is to provide each and every child with a sound academic education in an environment which is explicitly Christian and where discipline and care go hand in hand. We endeavour to be aware of each child as an individual and we seek to encourage the development of the whole person. The school endeavours to operate in an open and friendly manner, becoming something of a second home for its pupils.

The core national curriculum subjects plus RE, History, Geography, Art and Design, PE and Games, Music, ICT and French form the basis of what is taught. Children take KS1 and KS2 assessments (generally in excess of 90% achieving Level 4 in Mathematics, English, Science) and are prepared for the eleven plus and entrance examinations to grammar and selective independent schools. Last year all children in Prep 6 transferred to Grammar Schools.

Charitable status. Redcourt St Anselm's is part of the Congregation of Christian Brothers which is a Registered Charity, number 254312.

Reddiford School

38 Cecil Park Pinner Middlesex HA5 5HH

(See entry in IAPS section)

Riverston School

63–69 Eltham Road Lee Green London SE12 8UF
Tel: 020 8318 4327
Fax: 020 8297 0514
e-mail: info@riverston.greenwich.sch.uk
website: www.riverston.greenwich.sch.uk

Principal: D M Lewis, MBA(Ed), DMS, FRSA

***Headteacher*: Mrs S E Salathiel**

Age Range. 1–16.

Number in School. Day: 226 Boys, 100 Girls.

Fees per term (2008-2009). £2,149–£3,248.

Riverston School is a privately owned, co-educational day school in south-east London. Established in 1926, the school provides a traditional family orientated education up to and including GCSE. Junior pupils are taught by subject specialists in music, French, drama, ICT, science and PE. The majority of junior pupils progress into the senior department where class sizes average 16. A wide variety of courses is available for pupils entering KS4.

Riverston has the use of a European education centre, Château de la Baudonnière, in southern Normandy, France and each year regular visits are available to different year groups to enhance their French language skills whilst appreciating a different culture.

Riverston is a lively, friendly and cheerful school with a traditional educational philosophy and ideals as strong today as when they were first conceived.

'*A Journey to Excellence.*'

Rochester Independent College

Star Hill Rochester Kent ME1 1XF
Tel: 01634 828115
Fax: 01634 405667
e-mail: admissions@rochester-college.org
website: www.rochester-college.org

Co-Principals:
Pauline Bailey, HND, PgDip, MA
Alistair Brownlow, MA Hons, MPhil
Brian Pain, BSc Hons, PGDip

Age Range. 11–19 Co-educational.

Number of Pupils. 185 (including 45 boarders).

Fees per term (2008-2009). Day: £3,150–£4,250; Boarding: £8,142.

Rochester Independent College is a progressive alternative to conventional secondary education with a happily distinctive ethos. Accepting day students from the age of 11 and boarders from 16 the focus is on examination success in a lively, supportive and informal atmosphere. Students are encouraged to be themselves and achieve exam results that often exceed their expectations. There is no uniform, no bells ring and everybody is on first name terms. The average class size is eight. Our January 2008 Ofsted report judged that "the quality of education is outstanding".

Students enjoy being here and are treated as young adults. We encourage them to search for their own answers, to voice their opinions, to think critically, creatively and independently. They leave not only with excellent examination results but with enthusiasm for the future and new confidence about themselves and their education.

Personal Tutors work closely with students on all courses to give advice about course combinations and help students to ensure that their courses are designed to meet the requirements of university entrance. With such small class sizes individual attention is not only available, it's practically inescapable.

The College has particular academic strengths in Science and Mathematics and the Creative and Visual Arts including Film, Photography and Media.

The College's reputation for academic excellence is founded on almost 25 years experience of rigorous teaching. Students come to us for a variety of reasons and from many different backgrounds. We are not academically selective; our only entrance qualification is an honest determination to work hard. Our results however are always ranked among the best of the academically selective and students secure places at top UK universities. Direct entry into any year group is possible and the College also offers intensive one year GCSE and A Level courses as well as retake programmes. International students benefit from specialised English Language teaching support.

The College Halls combine the informality of a university residence with the supervision and pastoral support appropriate for young adults. The College offers students the opportunity to thrive in an atmosphere of managed independence and acts as a stepping stone between school and university. All accommodation is on campus and in either single or double rooms. All rooms have a direct dial telephone and a computer with internet connection.

Rookwood School

Weyhill Road Andover Hants SP10 3AL
Tel: 01264 325900
Fax: 01264 325909
e-mail: office@rookwood.hants.sch.uk
website: www.rookwood.hants.sch.uk

***Headmistress*: Mrs M P Langley**, BSc Hons

Age Range. Co-educational 3–16 with Boarders from age 7.

Number in School. 370: 178 girls, 152 Boys, plus 40 in Nursery.

Fees per term (2008-2009). Boarding £5,500–£6,440; Day £2,185–£3,600 (pro rata for Nursery children).

Rookwood School, set in 8 acres of spacious, wooded grounds, was described in its last ISI Inspection report as '*an outstandingly happy and successful school*'. It is non-denominational, but emphasis is placed on traditional Christian values of integrity and consideration for others. Discipline and good manners are given great importance.

The school has a very favourable pupil/teacher ratio so a close personal interest is taken in every child. The aim is for each pupil to fulfil his/her potential, and every effort is made to accommodate the individual requirements of pupils of varying ability. Thus a pupil may take up to 10 subjects in the GCSE examinations. Despite remaining non-selective, the school has an excellent record of academic success. At least one-third of entries have been graded A* or A at GCSE in recent years. Rookwood regularly scores highly in the National Academic League Tables and among the top 50 smaller independent schools in the UK. The school has close links with local sixth form colleges, and has also enabled pupils to transfer to the sixth forms of well-known senior independent schools. Younger children may be prepared for Common Entrance. Details of Rookwood's own scholarships at 7+ and 11+ may be obtained from the Headmistress.

The school offers its own laboratories, ICT, home economics, music and art rooms, gymnasium, large, heated outdoor swimming pool, tennis and netball courts and playing fields for hockey, football, rugby, cricket, rounders and athletics. Optional extra subjects include riding, ballet, instrumental teaching and entry to Music and Speech and Drama examinations. There is a wide range of extra-curricular activities – eg The Duke of Edinburgh's Award Scheme, rugby, football, gymnastics, hockey, netball, athletics, golf, science and computer clubs, plus junior and senior choirs.

Rookwood also offers full and weekly boarding for up to 40 children aged 8 and upwards in two friendly houses situated close to the main school site. The boarding style is very much home-from-home and regular contact is maintained with parents and relatives. There is a full programme of evening and weekend activities. Flexi-boarding is also possible if space permits.

In the ISI report, boarding at Rookwood was described as '*an outstanding feature of the school*'.

Rookwood is easily accessible by road – the A303, A34 and M3 are all close by – or rail (Waterloo 1¼ hours).

Admission is by school reports and interview.

Charitable status. Rookwood School is a Registered Charity, number 307322. It exists to provide education for children.

Roselyon School

Par Cornwall PL24 2HZ
Tel: 01726 812110
Fax: 01726 812110
e-mail: roselyonsch@btconnect.com
website: www.roselyon.cornwall.sch.uk

Headmaster: **Mr Stuart Bradley**, BEd (Oxon)

Age Range. 2½–11.
Number in School. Day: 44 Boys, 59 Girls.
Fees per term (2007-2008). £1,930.

Roselyon School, formerly the Victorian manor house in the village of Par, near St Austell, stands in 5 acres of beautiful woodland. A new multi purpose gymnasium and hall recently built in the centre of the campus has added greatly to the school's facilities. Roselyon is fully co-educational, taking pupils in the full time Nursery from 2½ and joining the Main School from 5–11.

The school is proud of its academic strengths and excellent examination results to local senior independent schools. It offers a broad curriculum, a variety of sports, music and drama and has an extensive range of extra curricular activities.

Academic and Music Scholarships and Bursaries are available for pupils in Years 3 to 6, and assessments are usually taken in the Summer Term.

Roselyon is a small, friendly school where a warm family atmosphere is maintained by the committed team of caring staff.

Charitable status. Roselyon School Trust Limited is a Registered Charity, number 306583. It exists to provide quality education to boys and girls.

Rosemead Preparatory School

70 Thurlow Park Road Dulwich London SE21 8HZ

(See entry in IAPS section)

Royal School Hampstead

65 Rosslyn Hill Hampstead London NW3 5UD

(See entry in GSA section)

Ruckleigh School

17 Lode Lane Solihull West Midlands B91 2AB
Tel: 0121 705 2773
Fax: 0121 704 4883
e-mail: admin@ruckleigh.co.uk
website: www.ruckleigh.co.uk

Headmistress: **Mrs B M Forster**

Age Range. 2¾–11.
Number in School. Day: 136 Boys, 100 Girls.
Fees per term (2007-2008). £2,031–£2,188.

Ruckleigh is an independent day school offering education to boys and girls between the ages of 4 and 11 with a Nursery Department catering for children from the age of 2¾.

Although a high standard of work is expected this is related to the individual child, and the school is able to provide opportunities within a wide range of academic ability. Each child has every chance to develop his or her talents to the full, often resulting in achievements beyond initial expectations.

The comparatively small classes mean that every child is well known individually throughout the school creating a friendly environment.

Pupils are guided into habits of clear thinking, self-reliance and courtesy. Sound practical judgement, sensitivity towards the needs of others, and a willingness to "have a go" are the qualities that the school seeks to promote.

Rushmoor School

58–60 Shakespeare Road Bedford MK40 2DL
Tel: 01234 352031
Fax: 01234 348395
e-mail: office@rushmoorschool.co.uk
website: www.rushmoorschool.co.uk

Headmaster: **K M Knight**

Age Range. Boys 3–16, Girls 3–11.
Number in School. 307 Day Pupils.
Fees per term (2007-2008). £1,400–£2,845.

Rushmoor School educates boys aged 3 to 16 and girls aged 3 to 11. Rushmoor has grown and improved by investing greatly to provide excellent facilities. In September 2006 a major new building was opened which comprises a second ICT suite, Art rooms, Library, Drama studio, and an additional eight classrooms.

At Rushmoor we appreciate the importance of selecting the right school for your son or daughter; childhood is something which can be experienced only once. With this in mind, and the belief that children learn best when they feel happy and secure, we aim to develop in our pupils a lifelong interest in learning – one which encompasses the full range of intellectual, cultural, artistic and sporting achievements of our society.

We believe in individual care and attention. Visitors to the school are impressed by the friendly, positive attitude of the pupils and their energetic sense of purpose. The staff are caring and understanding, yet know the importance of effort and personal discipline in enabling pupils to achieve the highest academic standards.

At Rushmoor we ensure that all children have opportunities to develop their intellectual, physical and creative gifts, across a broad and balanced curriculum. Children in the Nursery, Reception and Junior classes benefit greatly from a wide range of specialist teachers.

We emphasise the individual, recognizing that all children are different and value each child in their own right. Encouraging children to develop their strengths improves their self-esteem, enabling them to find their role in the community. We promote children's personal development, encouraging lively and enquiring minds, respect for others and a high regard for truth. The stability of continuous education, spanning the ages 3–16 years, is a major factor in helping us achieve this.

At Rushmoor we pride ourselves on our ability to integrate children with Specific Learning Differences within main stream school life. We believe that every child should be allowed to embrace any aspect of the curriculum. Enabling children to receive support without undermining their confidence amongst their peers is of primary importance.

Rushmoor has a fine reputation in sport and boasts a highly successful record with many pupils gaining county and national honours. Children have also gained much success in national and local drama competitions and festivals.

Prospective parents and children can tour the school at any time and 'taster days' can be arranged. Come and experience our caring ethos which enables our children to develop the confidence and flexibility which allows them to face the demands of modern life.

Charitable status. Rushmoor School Limited is a Registered Charity, number 307530. It exists to provide education.

Sackville School
Cognita Schools Group

Tonbridge Road Hildenborough Kent TN11 9HN
Tel: 01732 838888
Fax: 01732 836404
e-mail: office@sackvilleschool.com
website: www.sackvilleschool.com

Headteacher: **Mr Philip Humphreys**, BSc

Age Range. 11–18.
Number in School. 260.
Fees per term (2008-2009). £3,690.

Sackville School is situated in Hildenborough, midway between Tonbridge and Sevenoaks. The school is set in 28 acres of magnificent parkland and the main building dates from the 1860s. The school has three modern laboratories, two dedicated Computer Rooms, an impressive Sports Hall, Art and Design Suites, as well as the usual range of specialist teaching rooms.

The philosophy of the school is based on the individual and their unique learning needs. By concentrating on excellence, and by treating every child as a wonderfully unique individual, the school ensures that each child has the opportunity to fulfil their true potential, and develop their gifts and talents at all levels. Students achieve excellent GCSE results and the Sixth Form offers a wide range of A Level courses.

Sackville students are cheerful, confident children who work hard and enjoy aiming high and achieving their very best – they are expected to take a full part in the life of the school. The Head and staff encourage a warm, friendly working atmosphere, whilst promoting pride in achievement. Every student is valued, and their talents recognised, by the Head and staff.

The full range of academic, cultural and sporting activities are offered and all students are encouraged to try all activities. All major team games, and minor sports, are played and Sackville students have represented their County as well as National Squads. The school has a lively Music Department and over three quarters of the students are engaged in music making. The Creative Arts are particularly well represented. Art is exceptionally strong and Drama has a growing reputation for excellence. The Activities programme is an integral part of the school day and includes Orchestra, Choir, Duke of Edinburgh's Award, Drama, Golf, Film Unit, Table Tennis, Boules, Fishing, Archery, Self Defence, Community Service, Shooting, Ceramics, Computing, Photography and many other activities.

The school fosters the qualities of honour, care for others, thoughtfulness and tolerance. The Head is always delighted to show parents, and their sons and daughters around, and to discuss the educational opportunities available at Sackville.

Sacred Heart Convent School

Swaffham Norfolk PE37 7QW
Tel: 01760 721330/724577
Fax: 01760 725557
e-mail: info@sacredheartschool.co.uk
website: www.sacredheartschool.co.uk

Headteacher: **Miss Diana Wynter**, BA

Age Range. Girls 3–16, Boys 3–11.

Number in School. 159 Day Girls, 14 Boarders, 13 Day Boys.

Staff. 19 Full Time, 4 Part Time, 10 Welfare Assistants, 7 Visiting.

Religious Affiliation. Roman Catholic (other denominations welcome).

Entry requirements. Assessments, School Report and Interview.

Assistance with fees. Academic, Music, Art, Sport, All Rounder (Boarder) Scholarships for Year 7 (11+). Some bursaries available.

Fees per term (2008-2009). Boarders: Termly £5,425, Weekly £4,200–£4,485; Day: £1,985 (Juniors); £2,650–£2,950 (Seniors).

The Sacred Heart School was founded by the Daughters of Divine Charity in 1914. The Sisters and lay staff work together to provide a safe and caring environment where Christian values are upheld.

Principally a day school, the school is going co-educational over the next few years. Pupils study for eight to eleven GCSEs gaining consistently high A–C grades. At 16, the pupils have gained the confidence and self-possession which makes them much sought after by all Sixth Form Centres and other Independent Schools. There are a limited number of boarding places for girls aged 8–16 as well as the opportunity for flexi-boarding.

All pupils are encouraged to develop their gifts in Music, Drama, Art and Sport, and the School has a fine record of success in all these areas.

Facilities include a Sports Hall and Arts Centre with Theatre, Art and Music Room and Pottery Workshop.

A very active Parents' Association, loyal past pupils and parents network, together with highly-qualified Staff provide the energy, enthusiasm and friendly atmosphere which characterizes the school community.

Before and after school care is available.

Charitable status. The Daughters of Divine Charity is a Registered Charity, number 237760.

Sacred Heart School

Mayfield Lane Durgates Wadhurst East Sussex TN5 6DQ
Tel: 01892 783414
Fax: 01892 783510
e-mail: admin@sacredheartwadhurst.org.uk
website: www.sacredheartwadhurst.org.uk

Chairman of Governors: Father Kevin Gaskin

Head Teacher: **Mrs Hilary Blake**

Age Range. 3–11 Co-educational.
Number of Pupils. 112.
Fees per term (2008-2009). £1,795.

Sacred Heart School is a small independent Catholic primary school and Nursery, nestling in the heart of the Sussex countryside.

We welcome boys and girls from 3–11 and with pupil numbers around 100 we have the opportunity to know each child individually, to recognise and encourage their strengths and support them in overcoming areas of difficulty.

Our pupils enjoy a high degree of academic success, regularly obtaining places at their first choice of school, including passes at 11+ and Scholarships.

Courtesy and care for each other are important values nurtured at Sacred Heart School where children play and work well together.

Charitable status. Sacred Heart School, as part of the Arundel and Brighton Diocesan Trust, is a Registered Charity, number 252878.

St Anne's Preparatory School

154 New London Road Chelmsford Essex CM2 0AW
Tel: 01245 353488
Fax: 01245 353488
e-mail: headmistress@stannesprep.essex.sch.uk
website: www.stannesprep.essex.sch.uk

Headmistress: **Mrs F Pirrie**, BSc, PGCE

Age Range. 3+–11+.

Number of Children. 160.

Fees per term (2008-2009). £1,850–£1,950.

St Anne's is a co-educational day school, with its own excellent nursery facility. Established in 1925, the school is conveniently situated in the centre of Chelmsford. The building is a large Victorian house, which has been carefully converted into the uses of a school. Extensive lawned areas, astroturf, playground and Nursery play area provide ample space for both recreation and games lessons. In addition, older pupils benefit from the use of the excellent sports facilities at the nearby Essex County Cricket Club.

The children benefit from small classes and individual attention in a disciplined but happy environment, which enables them to realise their full potential. Provision is made in the school for the gifted as well as those pupils less educationally able. Classrooms are bright and well equipped and the teachers are chosen for their qualifications, experience and understanding of the needs of their pupils.

St Anne's combines modern teaching with the best of traditional values. The school maintains a high standard of academic education giving great emphasis to a secure foundation in the basic subjects whilst offering a wide curriculum with specialist teaching in many areas.

Examination results at both KS1 and KS2 levels are excellent and many pupils gain places at the prestigious Grammar and Independent schools in the county.

The school offers a wide range of extra curricular activities and an excellent after-care facility is available for all age groups. St Anne's is rightly recognised for its friendly and supportive ethos. Parents are particularly supportive of all aspects of school life. Visitors are always welcome.

St Catherine's Preparatory School

Hollins Lane Marple Bridge Stockport Cheshire SK6 5BB
Tel: 0161 449 8800
Fax: 0161 449 8181
e-mail: info@stcatherinesprep.co.uk
website: www.stcatherinesprep.co.uk

Headmistress: **Mrs R Brierley**, CertEd

Age Range. 3–11 years.

Number in School. 46 boys, 49 girls.

Fees per term (2008-2009). £1,940.

St Catherine's is a non-denominational, small independent day school for children aged 3–11.

The school features the best of traditional teaching whilst nurturing individual talent and independence of thought through a broad-based curriculum. Pupils are taught by qualified, experienced staff. Successful entry into excellent local independent senior schools is a strong feature of our small school.

Timetabled Sport, French, Music and ICT play an important part in our provision. A wide range of extra-curricular activities is available through both Key Stages.

At St Catherine's standards of discipline and behaviour are high, enabling us to produce confident, pleasant well-rounded individuals.

The school is non-selective at Kindergarten (3+). Children seeking admission from Year 1 are assessed for potential rather than acquired skills.

Charitable status. St Catherine's Preparatory School Limited is a Registered Charity, number 517487. It exists to provide a good all-round education for all children in a caring and friendly environment.

St Catherine's School

Cross Deep Twickenham Middlesex TW1 4QJ

(See entry in GSA section)

St Christopher's School

6 Downs Road Epsom Surrey KT18 5HE
Tel: 01372 721807
Fax: 01372 726717
e-mail: office@st-christophers.surrey.sch.uk
website: www.st-christophers.surrey.sch.uk

Headteacher: **Mrs M Evans**

Age Range. 3–7.

Number in School. 140.

Fees per term (2008-2009). £2,320 whole-day (including lunch), £1,185 half-day.

St Christopher's School (founded in 1938) is a co-educational nursery and pre-preparatory school for children from 3–7 years.

Set in a quiet residential area a short distance from the centre of Epsom, famous for the annual Derby and horse racing traditions, it has attractive secure grounds with gardens and play areas.

St Christopher's main purpose is to support children and parents through the early years of education. We offer a carefully managed induction programme to school life and, subsequently, a broad and challenging education within a happy, caring and secure family environment. Above all we aim to offer your child the best possible start to their education.

The children are prepared to enter a wide range of Surrey schools and we maintain a very high pass rate in a variety of entrance tests.

There are a number of after school clubs and an After School Care Service is available Monday to Friday until 6 pm.

St Christopher's enjoys the support of an active parents association that organises a wide variety of social and fundraising events.

For further information and a prospectus please contact the school. Parents are welcome to visit the school by appointment with the Headteacher.

Charitable status. St Christopher's School Trust (Epsom) Limited is a Registered Charity, number 312045. It aims to provide a Nursery and Pre-Preparatory education in Epsom and district.

St Christopher's School

Mount Barton Staverton Totnes Devon TQ9 6PF
Tel: 01803 762202
Fax: 01803 762202
e-mail: office@st-christophers.devon.sch.uk
website: www.st-christophers.devon.sch.uk

***Headmistress*: Mrs Jane E Kenyon**, CertEd

Age Range. 3–11 Co-educational.
Number of Pupils. 100.
Fees per term (2008-2009). Nursery: £182 per am/pm session, £1,200 full-time; Reception £1,655; Years 1–6 £1,855.

St Christopher's School

71 Wembley Park Drive Wembley Park Middlesex HA9 8HE
Tel: 020 8902 5069
Fax: 020 8903 5939
e-mail: stchris.head@happychild.co.uk
website: www.stchristopherswembley.co.uk

***Headmaster*: Mr J M B Edwards**, MA, CertEd

Age Range. 4–11.
Number in School. 60 Boys, 56 Girls.
Fees per term (2007-2008). £1,965–£2,075.
Entry requirements: Interview and Assessment.

St Christopher's School, a large Victorian building on Wembley Park Drive, offers a caring family atmosphere coupled with an equal emphasis on good manners, enthusiastic endeavour and academic excellence. The School, a Christian foundation dating from 1928, welcomes children of all faiths and cultures.

Caring and supportive staff provide a well-structured, disciplined and stimulating environment in which children are nurtured and encouraged to develop the necessary skills – academic, social and cultural – so that when they leave us at the age of 11 they can be certain of future success. All children at St Christopher's are equal and we emphasise the qualities of equality, justice and compassion. Children benefit from a curriculum that offers both breadth and depth, an activity programme that teaches skills and develops talents, and a pastoral programme that develops social responsibility.

The full range of academic subjects is taught based on an enriched National Curriculum. Sports and Music are seen as central elements in school life with sports matches, regular concerts and an annual carol service. In addition there is a variety of clubs and activities both at lunchtime and after school; these include Soccer, First Aid, Cookery, Drama, Art, Chess, Maths, Computing, Spanish, Needlework, Recorders, Choir, Tri-Golf and Games.

Children are prepared for the full range of examinations at 11 years.

The last 8 years have seen 31 scholarships awarded as well as numerous Chess and Music awards.

Recent leavers have gained entry to a wide range of excellent schools including Haberdasher's Boys and Girls, Merchant Taylors', Northwood College, Heathfield, St Helen's, North London Collegiate, City of London Boys and Girls, Henrietta Barnet, Queen Elizabeth's Boys Barnet, JFS, St Albans, UCS, Aldenham, Watford Grammar Boys and Girls, Royal Masonic Rickmansworth, John Lyon, Dr Challoner's, Beaconsfield High and South Hampstead High.

St Christopher's offers both Pre-School and After-School Care and offers a nursery provision for children over 2 years. The nursery has recently achieved a Brent Commendation for Excellence.

Please phone for an appointment to view the school. We look forward to welcoming you.

St Clare's, Oxford

139 Banbury Road Oxford OX2 7AL
Tel: 01865 552031
Fax: 01865 513359
e-mail: admissions@stclares.ac.uk
website: www.stclares.ac.uk

***Principal*: Mrs Paula Holloway**, BSc, PGCE, MSc Oxon, DipPM

Age Range. 15–19 Co-educational.
Number of Students. 264.
Fees per term (2008-2009). Boarding £8,816, Day £5,451.

St Clare's is an international college founded in 1953 with a mission "To advance international education and understanding", something it has been doing successfully ever since. The College embraces internationalism and academic excellence as core values. It is a coeducational day and residential college which has been offering the International Baccalaureate Diploma for over 30 years, longer than any other school or college in England.

Students from over 40 countries study at St Clare's with a core group of British students. The atmosphere is informal and friendly with an equal emphasis on hard work and developing personal responsibility. Each student has a Personal tutor who oversees welfare and progress.

Most students are enrolled for the full IB Diploma. St Clare's has an especially wide range of subjects on offer at Higher and Standard level and, in addition, currently teaches 28 different languages. The College takes a small number of transfer students each year. For students not yet ready to begin the IB Diploma, a PreIB course is offered with regular entry points throughout the year. There is an extensive programme of social, cultural and sporting activities and students are encouraged to take full advantage of the opportunities that Oxford provides.

The College also runs a highly successful IB Institute providing introductory refresher and revision courses for students. St Clare's is also authorised to run IB workshops for teachers.

St Clare's is located in an attractive residential area which is part of the North Oxford Conservation Area. It occupies 26 large Victorian and Edwardian houses to which purpose-built facilities have been added. These include a beautiful library building (over 35,000 volumes, an IT suite and a Careers and Higher Education Information Centre), four science laboratories, art and music studios, dining room and the popular Sugar House café. Students live in College houses close to the central campus under the care of residential staff.

The College welcomes applications from students irrespective of gender, race, colour, religious belief or national origin. Entry is based on academic results, interview and confidential school report. There is a competitive scholarship and bursary programme awarded by examination, interview and group exercises.

St Clare's had a highly successful ISI inspection in March 2008; the full Report can be accessed via the College website.

Charitable status. St Clare's, Oxford is a Registered Charity, number 294085.

St Colette's Preparatory School
GEMS Education

Tenison Road Cambridge CB1 2DP
Tel: 01223 353696
Fax: 01223 517784
e-mail: stcolettes@indschool.org
website: www.gemseducation.com/uk/stcolettes

Nursery and Pre-Preparatory School.

***Headmistress*: Mrs A C Wilson**

Age Range. 2½–7+.
Number of Pupils. 120 Boys and Girls.
Fees per term (2008-2009). £1,900–£2,250.
Curriculum. St Colette's has an outstanding record of success in preparing children for entrance examinations to Preparatory Schools (at seven-plus). Standards of academic achievement are high, while a caring and friendly ethos encourages children from a young age to develop a positive attitude to work and to show consideration for others. Music, drama and dance form an integral part of the curriculum, and children are encouraged to develop abilities and talents in these areas.
Religious affiliation. Non-denominational.

St David's College

Justin Hall Beckenham Road West Wickham Kent BR4 0QS
Tel: 020 8777 5852
Fax: 020 8777 9549
e-mail: StDavids@dial.pipex.com
website: www.stdavidscollege.com

***Principal*: Mrs A Wagstaff**, BA Hons (London)

Head Teacher: Mrs S Adams, BA, CertEd

Deputy Heads:
Mrs G Talley, CertEd
Mrs A Peters, CertEd

Bursar: Mrs R Smith, MA Hons (Edinburgh), ACA

Age Range. 4–11.
Number in School. Day: 93 Boys, 63 Girls.
Fees per term (2008-2009). £1,875–£1,925. Reduction in fees for all siblings.

A full-time staff of nine teachers, all fully qualified, is supplemented by ten part-time specialist teachers. Entry is by interview and informal test. Pupils are prepared for entrance to independent schools at age 11, as well as for the Kent grammar schools and for places at the London Boroughs of Bexley, Bromley and Sutton selective schools. Many scholarships and awards are gained each year. The school offers before and after-school care.

Speech and Drama, Clarinet, Dance, Flute, Music Theory, Piano, Recorder, Solo Singing, Recorder, Trumpet and Violin lessons are available. Sports include Athletics, Cricket, Cross-Country, Football, Hockey, Netball, Rounders, Swimming and Tennis. There is a Chess Club and a School Orchestra.

There are separate infant and junior schools, set within extensive and beautiful grounds. The school is positioned close to bus routes and to the mid-Kent and Hayes railway line, and is within easy reach of Bromley South and East Croydon stations.

The Principal and Head Teacher are always pleased to show the school to visitors.

St David's School

23–25 Woodcote Valley Road Purley Surrey CR8 3AL
Tel: 020 8660 0723
Fax: 020 8645 0426
e-mail: office@stdavidsschool.co.uk
website: www.stdavidsschool.co.uk

***Headmaster*: Mr Vincent Fox**, BEd Hons, MA

Age Range. 3+–11.
Number in School. 152 Day: 78 boys, 74 girls.
Fees per term (2008-2009). £1,090–£2,165 (including lunch).

St David's School, derived originally from a Church of England foundation, believes in training children to be tolerant and supportive of one another within school and caring in their concern for others in a wider perspective.

The children study all the usual academic subjects including Information and Communications Technology, Design Technology and Science. French is taught from the Infant classes and throughout the Juniors, and Latin is an optional language in Year 6. Small classes allow for much individual attention so that the children may develop to their full potential. The success of this ethos is demonstrated by the excellent results in selective entry to local Grammar Schools and in the Entrance Examinations to independent secondary schools where scholarships are frequently gained.

The school is fortunate to own very adequate games facilities despite a suburban setting and the children do well in competitive events. Music, Art and Drama are considered to be fundamental to the development of character and the leadership qualities they encourage. There is a flourishing choir and orchestra.

Charitable status. St David's (Purley) Educational Trust is a Registered Charity, number 312613. It aims to provide a quality education for boys and girls from 3+ to 11 years old. Bursaries are awarded in cases of financial hardship.

St Dominic's Priory School

Station Road Stone Staffordshire ST15 8EN

(See entry in GSA section)

St Edward's School
Senior School

Cirencester Road Charlton Kings Cheltenham Glos GL53 8EY

(See entry in SHMIS section)

St Edward's School
Junior School

London Road Charlton Kings Cheltenham Glos GL52 6NR

(See entry in IAPS section)

St Gerard's School
Bangor

Ffriddoedd Road Bangor Gwynedd LL57 2EL
Tel: 01248 351656
Fax: 01248 351204
e-mail: st_gerards@lineone.net

Headteacher: **Miss Anne Parkinson**, BA

Age Range. 3–18.
Number in School. Day: 126 Boys, 170 Girls.
Fees per term (2007-2008). £1,480–£2,245.

Founded in 1915 by the Congregation of the Sisters of Mercy, this Catholic, co-educational school is now a lay trust. The school welcomes pupils of all denominations and traditions and has an excellent reputation locally. It has consistently attracted a high profile in national league tables also.

Class sizes in both junior and senior schools ensure close support and individual attention in order to enable all pupils to achieve their full academic potential, within an environment which promotes their development as well-rounded individuals with a keen social conscience.

The curriculum is comprehensive – pupils in the senior section usually achieve 9/10 good GCSE grades, going on to A level and to university.

Charitable status. St Gerard's School Trust is a Registered Charity, number 1001211. It exists to promote Catholic education in this area of Wales.

St Hilda's School

15 Imperial Avenue Westcliff-on-Sea Essex SS0 8NE
Tel: 01702 344542
e-mail: office@sthildasschool.co.uk
website: www.sthildasschool.co.uk

Head: **Mrs S O'Riordan**, BA Hons, PGCE

Age Range. Girls 3–16+, Boys 3–11.
Number in School. 140 Day Pupils.
Fees per term (2008-2009). Early Years: £20.40 per session. Years 1–11: £2,214–£2,686 excluding lunches. Compulsory extras: Textbooks.

St Hilda's is a small Independent School taking both girls and boys in the Infant and Junior Schools. It is the only all-girls Independent Senior School in the Southend area.

Pupils are helped to fulfil their academic potential at all ages, and follow a curriculum based on the National Curriculum with teaching methods appropriate to their age.

Pupils in the Infant and Junior Schools have an increasing number of specialist staff to further enhance their learning.

French is taught to all pupils from the age of 3, while pupils in the Senior school also study German. Spanish is offered after school to pupils from the age of 7.

Despite being a small school, we have a reputation for sporting excellence with pupils competing at school, borough, county, regional and national level in netball, cross-country running and athletics.

Special provision is made for pupils with learning difficulties, especially dyslexia and these pupils follow a Multi-Sensory Learning course to improve their language and study skills.

While providing a 21st century education, the School recognises the importance of traditional values and actively promotes a caring and supportive environment for the pupils. The success of this is shown by the excellent academic results in Government Key Stage Tests, local 11+ selection tests and particularly at GCSE. Although providing a rigorous academic programme, pupils are encouraged to develop individual skills in other fields including Sports, Drama and Art and Design.

Prospectus available on application to the Secretary.

St Hilda's School

28 Douglas Road Harpenden Hertfordshire AL5 2ES
Tel: 01582 712307
Fax: 01582 763892
e-mail: office@st-hildasschool.herts.sch.uk
website: www.st-hildasschool.herts.sch.uk

Headmistress: **Mrs C Godlee**, BMus Hons, PGCE

Age Range. 2½–11.
Number in School. 180 approx.
Fees per term (2008-2009). £2,475 (including lunches).

St Hilda's School, situated in a residential site of 1¼ acres, has its own swimming pool, hard tennis/netball court and adjacent playing field. It also has a full-equipped stage, a suite of music rooms and a dedicated computer room.

A broad, well-balanced curriculum covering the requirements of the National Curriculum prepares girls for the Common Entrance and other senior independent school entrance examinations. Girls also enter State secondary schools if desired. Latin and French are taught.

Re-accredited in 2002 by the Independent Schools Association.

A prospectus is available on application to the School Secretary.

St James Independent School for Senior Boys

Pope's Villa 19 Cross Deep Twickenham Middlesex TW1 4QG

(See entry in SHMIS section)

St James Independent Schools for Junior Boys and Girls

Earsby Street London W14 8SH
Tel: 020 7348 1777
Fax: 020 7348 1790
e-mail: juniorschools@stjamesschools.co.uk
website: www.stjamesschools.co.uk

Headmaster: **Mr Paul Moss**, CertEd

Age Range. 4½–10+.
Number in School. 156 Girls, 110 Boys.
Fees per term (2007-2008). Reception & Year 1: £2,950; Years 2–5: £3,020.

St James provides a full and nourishing education. Children enter at 4½ and transfer to the Senior Schools at 10½. The Junior Schools share a large Central London site with the Senior Girls' School. This provides an Assembly Hall/Theatre, large classrooms, a gym, a playground and spacious subject rooms.

The St James curriculum follows the traditional format but gives due emphasis to the important areas of the true development of a child. Children are introduced to the wealth of good material that the best of education offers. At an early age they sing the works of Mozart, hear and recite Shakespeare and read books of real stature such as the Odyssey. Every week the children have a philosophy lesson, which seeks to present the principles and laws that are common to all religions. This emphasises the essential unity of all faiths. There is a very strong sports programme with a physical activity daily, e.g. Gymnastics, Rugby, Netball, Cricket and Swimming. A systematic academic education is given and the inspiration of Art, Music, Drama and Dance.

Boys and girls are taught separately with frequent joint activities such as plays, concerts and outings. The obvious happiness of the children flows from a full education and a clear view of the needs of each child.

Charitable status. St James Independent Junior School is a Registered Charity, number 270156. It exists to provide education for boys and girls.

St James' School

A Woodard School

22 Bargate Grimsby North East Lincolnshire DN34 4SY
Tel: 01472 503260
Fax: 01472 503275
e-mail: enquiries@saintjamesschool.co.uk
website: www.saintjamesschool.co.uk

***Head Teacher*: Mrs S M Isaac**, BA, PGCE

Age Range. 2½–18.

Number in School. Boarders: Boys 24, Girls 15. Day: Boys 101, Girls 99.

Fees per term (from January 2008). Tuition: Nursery £737.38–£1,332, Day Pupils £1,298–£3,120. Boarding: £1,795 (weekly), £2,045 (termly).

St James' School, Grimsby is the Choir School of St James' Parish Church, Great Grimsby and a fully incorporated member of the Woodard Corporation. The School has a Nursery/Preparatory Department (ages 2½–11) and a Senior Department (ages 11–18).

The school is co-educational and there are about 40 boarders. Pupils are prepared for GCSE and Advanced Levels and the majority of the Sixth Form go on to University. There is a generous pupil-teacher ratio of, on average, 13 : 1 and the School offers a wide variety of out of school sports and activities. The level of pastoral care is very high. Music plays an important part in school life and regular concerts and recitals are given. Last year saw the formation of a Girls Academy Choir aimed at taking some of the burden away from our choristers. Members of the Academy Choir receive a 15% bursary.

There is a purpose built Sixth Form as well as a newly-opened IT and Home Economics Suite, together with a purpose-built Nursery and Pre-Prep Department.

The School operates a morning bus service calling in at villages from the Louth and Brigg areas.

Charitable status. St James' School is a Registered Charity, numbers 529765 and 1099060. It exists to provide education for boys and girls.

St James Senior Girls' School

Earsby Street London W14 8SH

(See entry in GSA section)

St John's School

Stock Road Billericay Essex CM12 0AR
Tel: 01277 623070
Fax: 01277 651288
e-mail: registrar@stjohnsschool.net
website: www.stjohnsschool.net

***Headteacher*: Mrs Fiona Armour**, BEd Hons

Age Range. 3–16.

Number in School. Day: 274 Boys, 190 Girls.

Fees per term (2008-2009). £1,621–£3,065.

St John's is a small, caring, but dynamic, day school situated in almost 8 acres of its own grounds and backing onto Lake Meadows Park.

The curriculum is a traditional one but takes account of new educational innovations based on the requirements of the National Curriculum, and extends to include a range of options at GCSE.

Children work within a safe and disciplined environment studying a broad curriculum. Both traditional and modern teaching methods are used to prepare pupils for Key Stage Two, the Essex County 11+ Selection Examination, and GCSEs.

Attention is paid to both the social and academic development of all pupils and this is reflected in the excellent results at both 11+ and GCSE. There are good facilities for rugby, football, basketball, hockey, netball, tennis, athletics and swimming.

Other activities include fencing, karate, speech training, performing arts, the Duke of Edinburgh's Award Scheme, dancing, skiing, first aid training and community service. Foreign travel is encouraged and in recent years the school has been to Canada, USA, Spain, Bulgaria, France and Italy, as well as extensive British locations.

An extensive building project commenced in June 2008, which will provide us with a new state-of-the-art School. This will match the high standard of education we offer and will give us excellent new sporting facilities.

The school aims to educate its pupils to be mature, responsible and confident in a happy, supportive and friendly environment. Our pupils want to learn and this is totally reflected in our results.

St Joseph's Convent School

59 Cambridge Park Wanstead London E11 2PR
Tel: 020 8989 4700
Fax: 020 8989 4700
e-mail: enquiries@stjosephsconventschool.co.uk

Chair of Governors: Mrs Ann Ross

***Headteacher*: Ms Christine Glover**

Age Range. 3–11

Number in School. 162 Day Girls.

Fees per term (2007-2008). £1,475.

Charitable status. Institute of Our Lady of Mercy is a Registered Charity, number 290544.

St Joseph's Preparatory School

London Road Trent Vale Stoke-on-Trent Staffs ST4 5RF
Tel: 01782 417533
Fax: 01782 849327

e-mail: enquiries@stjosephsprepschool.co.uk
website: www.stjosephsprepschool.co.uk

***Head*: Mrs S D Hutchinson**, BEd

Age Range. 3–11 Co-educational.
Number of Pupils. 130 Day Pupils.
Fees per term (2008-2009). £1,400–£1,850.
Charitable status. The Congregation of Christian Brothers is a Registered Charity, number 254312.

St Joseph's School

Launceston Cornwall PL15 8HN
Tel: 01566 772580
Fax: 01566 775902
e-mail: registrar@stjosephs.eclipse.co.uk
website: www.st-josephs.cornwall.sch.uk

***Headmaster*: Mr G M Garrett**, BEd, BA, CMath, CSci

Age Range. Girls 3–16, Boys 3–11.
Number in School. Day: 27 Boys, 155 Girls.
Fees per term (2008-2009). Day: £1,825.50–£2,875.

St Joseph's School, Launceston is an Independent Day School for boys and girls from 3–11 years and senior girls from 11–16 years. The school is an ecumenical educational community, open to members of all faiths, in which Christian values are the cornerstone, and truth the essence of school life.

St Joseph's has a truly unique atmosphere. The school's size means that it is possible to keep sight of strong family values, which gives children the confidence necessary to succeed, and to allow both staff and pupils to work happily together. Due to the high teacher-pupil ratio (average 1:14), St Joseph's is able to encourage each pupil to reach his or her full potential through positive encouragement and commendation.

The school provides a good academic education for all, regardless of ability and background, with a wide variety of extra-curricular activities to provide balance and insight into opportunity. It offers equal prospects to all and inspires them to respond positively to challenges through encouragement and commendation. In last year's examinations, 95% of candidates gained at least six GCSEs at grades A*–C. This is a remarkable achievement as St Joseph's is a non-selective school. Pupils do not sit an Entrance Examination and places are offered at interview with the Headmaster.

National Honours have been gained in many areas including athletics, swimming, textiles, cookery and music. The senior chamber choir is a "flagship" choir for the South West, having appeared on both local and national television. The choir has also participated in the finals of the Music for Youth Festival at the Royal Festival Hall, London. In July 2009 the senior chamber choir will be travelling to Spain on a Concert Tour.

Recent new facilities include refurbished Nursery Department, two new Science Laboratories, an ICT suite and conference facilities. Scholarships are offered at 7+ in the Junior Department and Academic and Specialist Scholarships at 11+ in Music and Sport. Bursaries and Governors' Awards are considered on an individual basis. An extensive daily bus service allows pupils from a wide area of Devon and Cornwall to attend St Joseph's.

For further details please contact the Registrar or visit our website.

Charitable status. St Joseph's School is a Registered Charity, number 289048. It exists to provide education for girls and boys.

St Joseph's School

33 Derby Road Nottingham NG1 5AW
Tel: 0115 941 8356/947 4985
Fax: 0115 952 9038
e-mail: office@st-josephs.nottingham.sch.uk
website: www.st-josephs.nottingham.sch.uk

***Headteacher*: Mr Brendan O'Grady**

Age Range. 18 months–11 years.
Number in School. 90 Boys, 60 Girls.
Fees per term (2008-2009). £2,100.

A co-educational day school providing the very highest standards to children of all abilities. It provides a happy and caring environment in which children can develop their full potential both socially and academically. The school is Roman Catholic but welcomes children of all faiths.

St Joseph's School

Park Hill Padiham Road Burnley Lancashire BB12 6TG
Tel: 01282 455622
Fax: 01282 435375
e-mail: parkhillschool@aol.com
website: www.parkhillschool.co.uk

Chairman of Governors: Mr Ed Morgan

***Head Teacher*: Sister Joan Breen**

Age Range. 3–11 Co-educational.
Number of Pupils. 122.
Fees per term (2008-2009). £1,440.

St Joseph's was founded by the Sisters of Mercy in 1913 and has operated from its present site since 1957.

It is a small school with a warm, friendly atmosphere where the children are known personally by all the staff. We have a broad, enriched curriculum which provides many activities and opportunities, both sporting and musical. The children enjoy their learning experience and are encouraged to do their best, achieving excellent results.

The Catholic ethos permeates all areas of the school. Pupils learn to care for each other, and respect different cultures. We welcome children from all faiths.

The school has the benefit of extensive grounds, and offers a before and after school service as well as a 4-week summer school.

Charitable status. St Joseph's School is owned by The Institute of our Lady of Mercy which is a Registered Charity, number 290544.

St Margaret's Preparatory School

Gosfield Hall Park Gosfield Halstead Essex CO9 1SE
Tel: 01787 472134
Fax: 01787 478207
e-mail: admin@stmargaretsprep.com
website: www.stmargaretsprep.com

***Headmistress*: Mrs B Y Boyton-Corbett**

Age Range. 2–11.
Number of Pupils. Day: 121 Boys, 124 Girls.
Fees per term (2008-2009). £2,250–£2,673.

St Margaret's is an ISA accredited school which specializes in the needs of children from 2 to 11 years. Academically, we provide excellence beyond the National Curriculum, stretching each child to the best of their individual ability, but not at the expense of a full and varied childhood. Although we regularly gain academic, music, art and sports scholarships to Senior schools, the emphasis is on an all-round education, encompassing the academic needs, enriching aspects such as social integration and encouraging other interests of each individual. Typically, a child at St Margaret's will have two afternoons a week of coached sport as well as a PE lesson, extra coaching sessions at lunchtime for the keen and able, and numerous after-school clubs. These clubs encompass a whole range of activities including fencing, archery, all major sports, speech and drama, martial arts, ballet, country dancing, chess, Forensic Science – the list goes on. They are regarded as an important and integral part of school, broadening their horizons. With a purpose-built ICT Suite and Art Studio, along with Music Rooms, Science Lab and gymnasium, the children have every opportunity to excel in their chosen sphere.

Naturally, the school has choirs, ensembles, an orchestra and numerous concerts and plays throughout the year. There are trips to Art Galleries, concerts, museums, as well as taking part in Festivals, competitions and local events.

Our extensive curriculum provides the children with the social confidence and academic ability to achieve their potential.

At St Margaret's we aim to achieve high standards in work and discipline, while fostering a happy atmosphere.

Entry requirements: Interview at ages 4, 5 and 6. Interview and test at age 7+.

Charitable status. St Margaret's School (Hampstead) Ltd is a Registered Charity, number 312720. It exists as a charitable trust to provide a good education for girls with the emphasis on each girl fulfilling her own potential.

St Margaret's School

18 Kidderpore Gardens Hampstead London NW3 7SR
Tel: 020 7435 2439
Fax: 020 7431 1308
e-mail: enquiry@st-margarets.co.uk
website: www.st-margarets.co.uk

Founded 1884.

***Headmaster*: Mr M Webster**, BSc, PGCE

Age Range. 4–16.

Number in School. 145 Day Girls.

Fees per term (2007-2008). £2,761–£3,182. Compulsory extras: Books and outings.

St Margaret's is a small school situated in a quiet residential area of Hampstead, North London.

The classes throughout the school are small and allow each girl to fulfil her potential. The teaching is based on the National Curriculum. The girls in Reception, Years 1, 2 and 3 are taught mainly by their form teachers, but they are taught by specialist teachers for PE, French and Music. The specialist teaching increases in Years 4, 5 and 6. In Years 7–11 the girls are taught by specialist teachers for all subjects.

The girls enjoy a wide range of sporting activities at a number of local sites, including the local sports centre and swimming pool. Their after school clubs include yoga, netball, football, tennis, cross-country running, self defence and choir. The girls play netball competitively against local schools.

The girls take the Key Stage SATs at age 7, 11 and 13. In Year 11 the girls take 9 or 10 GCSE subjects. Our value added scores for the last two years have put St Margaret's in the top 5% nationally and this is because of the small classes and the excellent teaching. The girls at 16 are prepared to enter the top London sixth forms. Former pupils are currently studying at St Paul's Girls' School, Henrietta Barnett, Channing School, Francis Holland School as well as local state sixth form colleges.

There is a wide range of outings organised for the girls of all ages to London galleries, museums and theatres. Girls in Year 10 undertake a week's work experience and trips abroad are organised to support the French and Spanish curriculum.

St Margaret's School

Convent of Mercy Petersfield Road Midhurst West Sussex GU29 9JN
Tel: 01730 813956
Fax: 01730 810829
e-mail: smsadmin@conventofmercy.org
website: www.conventofmercy.org

***Headmistress*: Sister M Joseph Clare**, BEd

Age Range. 2–11 years.

Number in School. 86 Boys, 124 Girls.

Fees per term (2007-2008). £470–£2,085.

St Margaret's School is first and foremost a happy community in which pupils feel secure and valued. Children are encouraged to develop their potential to the full and attain high academic standards whilst developing interests and achievements in creative, aesthetic, physical, social and spiritual education.

St Margaret's School, founded in 1888 by the Sisters of Mercy, is a Catholic co-educational day school, which welcomes children of other Christian denominations and faiths.

Education. The school's objective is to blend the best traditional teaching methods with innovative new technological teaching aids and ideas. Highly trained and motivated teachers provide each child with a strong educational foundation and social skills, essential for the transition to secondary school and adulthood.

The Site. This attractive 5-acre site (with an additional 7 acres of playing fields) provides ample space for bright airy classrooms and numerous specialist subject rooms for ICT, Music, Design Technology, Art and French. In addition there is a well equipped Science Laboratory, generously stocked School Libraries as well as Halls and Gymnasium. The refurbished kitchens with its dedicated staff provide freshly made nutritious food daily.

Curriculum. The structured, but broad and stimulating, curriculum is designed to meet the needs of children individually. The school encourages children to develop to their highest level with enjoyment, endeavour and creativity. The syllabus meets the requirements of Independent Senior Schools' entrance examinations for 11 year olds and also Key Stage 1 and 2 national tests.

Sport. The specialist Sports Teachers offer instruction in a range of activities including netball, football, rugby, hockey, gymnastics, dance, tennis, rounders, athletics, cross-country and cricket

Extra-Curricular. In addition, other sports available include judo, ballet, rugby, hockey, volleyball, petanque, and fencing. A wide variety of other activities are available including music, drama, needlecraft, cooking and pottery and all the children are encouraged to take part.

Special Needs. The Learning Support department is run by qualified specialist teachers. Pupils with specific learning difficulties, gaps in their learning or who simply need help to catch up, are supported either within the classroom or through tailor-made individual or small group lessons.

Nurseries. St Margaret's nurseries provide a happy and stimulating environment for children aged 2 to 4. Highly qualified, specialist staff encourage positive attitudes of learning through harmonious play. The children are gently introduced to school life.

Extended Day. Included in the fees, the school offers Before and After School Clubs and Activities daily, extending the school day if needed from 8.00 am to 4.30 pm. It is also possible at short notice for children to have breakfast at school from 7.30 am.

Parents. An excellent partnership is fostered between school and home with a shared sense of purpose, cooperation and respect. The school has an active parents association, the Friends of St Margaret's, which host numerous events and activities throughout the year.

Charitable status. Sisters of Our Lady of Mercy (Midhurst, Uckfield and Shoreham-by-Sea) is a Registered Charity, number 235961.

St Martha's Senior School

Camlet Way Hadley Wood Herts EN4 0NJ

(See entry in GSA section)

St Martin's Preparatory School

63 Bargate Grimsby N E Lincolnshire DN34 5AA
Tel: 01472 878907
e-mail: info@stmartinsprep.com
website: www.stmartinsprep.com

***Headmaster*: Mr S Thompson**, BEd

Age Range. 3–11.
Number in School. Day: 80 Boys, 100 Girls.
Fees per term (from April 2008). £900–£1,595.

The school was founded in 1930. It aims to foster an interest in learning from an early age. A fully qualified and dedicated staff ensure that a high standard in Primary School subjects is attained throughout the school. French is taught from the age of 4. Children are taught in small classes and great attention is given to individual development. Specialist teaching is available for children with specific learning difficulties.

Our new purpose-built Kindergarten and Infant block is a modern building full of light and colour, which enhances the already excellent education provided by the school.

Girls are prepared for Common Entrance at 11+, and boys for Junior Entry at 11+. Children also transfer to local Comprehensives and Grammar Schools. There is a flourishing Swimming club from Kindergarten upwards, also Art, Football, Netball, Boules, Chess, Table Tennis, Computer and Drama clubs. The school has an orchestra and two choirs. A happy and friendly atmosphere prevails throughout the school.

St Michael's School

Bryn Llanelli Carmarthenshire SA14 9TU
Tel: 01554 820325
Fax: 01554 821716
e-mail: office@stmikes.co.uk (Office)
bursar@stmikes.co.uk (Bursar)
website: www.stmikes.co.uk

***Headmaster*: D T Sheehan**, BSc Hons, PGCE

Age Range. 3–18.
Number in School. 429: 227 boys, 202 girls.
Fees per term (from January 2008). Day: Preparatory Department £1,532–£2,248; Senior School £3,013–£3,062. Sibling allowances available. Boarding from age 16: £18,800 per annum.

St Michael's is very much in the pattern of the small well-disciplined grammar schools. The school has a traditional approach to learning, which does not mean it lives in the past, but places emphasis on the importance of **hard work** and **homework** in the school curriculum. The high academic standards of the school are reflected in the National 'League Tables'. In August 2002, the school was positioned 27th in 'The Times Top 800 Schools at A Level' and in March 2003, the school was listed top in the 'Financial Times Top 10 Best Value for Money Schools in the UK'.

The school's boarding house, Park House, is a handsome and historic mansion set in an acre of grounds in the village of Llangennech, just 10 minutes from the school site. It has been totally refurbished to a high standard of comfort and attractiveness, and so provides a bright, cheerful and secure environment, where every pupil feels safe, happy and protected. Pupils are accommodated in well furnished and equipped, single or shared study-bedrooms. The house provides spacious recreation rooms and pleasant grounds in which pupils may relax, play or watch T.V.

No school can build up such a strong reputation without a competitive, but well-disciplined atmosphere and a highly-qualified and dedicated staff. This is where we feel St Michael's is particularly fortunate.

We have well-equipped computer laboratories where pupils have access to a computer each from 3 years of age. In Year 9, all pupils take the OCR Computer Literacy Examination that helps prepare them for the technological age. Languages taught in the school are French, Spanish, Welsh and German.

Apart from its academic basis, the school is proud of the wide range of games and activities, which include horse riding, fencing, archery and ski instruction. Pupils in Year 10 can also take part in the Duke of Edinburgh's Award Scheme.

Speech, Drama and Music are strongly emphasised in the school and all pupils sit the early LAMDA examinations and can go on to achieve gold medal standard at school. We have a large choir and school orchestra and pupils may take music examinations at GCSE and A Level.

One of the main reasons for the school's success is the thorough grounding that pupils receive in the 'basics' – English, Mathematics, Computing and Science in the school's Preparatory Department.

We have enjoyed outstanding sporting success over the last few years in netball, rugby, football, tennis, cricket and athletics.

Every pupil is encouraged to develop his / her full potential whether in academic work or in all the extra-curricular activities and games that are offered.

St Nicholas House School

Yarmouth Road North Walsham Norfolk NR28 9AT
Tel: 01692 403143
Fax: 01692 403143
e-mail: stnicholas@yarmouth47.fsnet.co.uk
website: www.stnicholashouse.com

***Headmaster*: Mr C J A Wardle**, BA Hons, CertEd

Age Range. 3–11 co-educational.
Number of Pupils. 90.
Fees per term (2008-2009). £1,200.

St Nicholas School

Hillingdon House Hobbs Cross Road Old Harlow Essex CM17 0NJ
Tel: 01279 429910
Fax: 01279 450224
e-mail: office@saintnicholasschool.net
website: www.saintnicholasschool.net

Headmaster: **Mr R Cusworth**, BSc, PGCE, MBA

Age Range. 4–16.
Number in School. 380 Day Pupils: 190 Boys, 190 Girls.
Fees per term (from April 2008). £2,020–£2,675.

St Nicholas School was founded in 1939 and is situated in a delightful rural location. The Headmaster is a member of the ISA. St Nicholas combines a fresh and enthusiastic approach to learning with a firm belief in traditional values.

The academic record of the school is excellent, reflected in high pupil success rates in all competitive examinations. The dedicated team of staff involves itself closely with all aspects of pupil's educational progress and general development. High standards of formal teaching are coupled with positive encouragement for pupils to reason for themselves and develop a high degree of responsibility.

Main sports include Hockey, Netball, Tennis, Football, Rugby, Cricket, Swimming, Athletics and Gymnastics. Optional extras include Ballet, Individual Instrumental Lessons, Speech and Drama classes and many sporting clubs.

Recent building developments include a magnificent new Junior Department building, Infant Department building, Science and Technology Centre, Junior Library, swimming pool and Sports Hall.

Charitable status. St Nicholas School (Harlow) Limited is a Registered Charity, number 310876. It exists to provide and promote educational enterprise by charitable means.

St Peter's School

52 Headlands Kettering Northamptonshire NN15 6DJ
Tel: 01536 512066
Fax: 01536 416469
e-mail: info@st-peters.org.uk
website: www.st-peters.org.uk

Headmistress: **Mrs M Chapman**, BA Hons, PGCE

Age Range. 2½–11.
Number in School. Day: 82 Boys, 99 Girls.
Fees per term (2007-2008). £1,785–£2,160.

Established in 1946, St Peter's is a small day school set in pleasant grounds on the outskirts of Kettering. It offers a sound education for boys and girls aged 2½ to 11. Pupils are thoroughly prepared for entry into their senior schools and a high rate of success in Entrance and Scholarship Examinations is regularly achieved. In addition to fulfilling the requirements of the National Curriculum the school emphasises the importance of Music, Art, Sport and Information Technology in its programme. Computers are used as part of the normal classroom teaching from the age of three and French is introduced at Reception.

St Peter's is a lively, friendly school with a strong family atmosphere where children are encouraged to develop to the full their individual strengths and talents. It aims to promote, through Christian teaching, a respect for traditional values, a sense of responsibility and a concern for the needs of others.

Charitable status. St Peter's School is a Registered Charity, number 309914. It exists to maintain and manage a school for boys and girls in the town of Kettering.

St Philomena's Preparatory School

Hadleigh Road Frinton-on-Sea Essex CO13 9HQ
Tel: 01255 674492
Fax: 01255 674459
e-mail: generalenquiries@stphilomenas.com
website: www.stphilomenas.com

Co-educational Day School.

Chair of Governors: Mr Richard Whybrew

Headmistress: **Mrs Bernadette Buck**, CertEd

Age Range. 3½–11.
Number of Pupils. 148: 77 girls, 71 boys.
Fees per term (2007-2008). £1,400–£1,650.

St Philomena's is situated in a pleasant coastal area close to the beach. The school is dedicated to providing sound education based on Gospel values of the Whole Child within a Christian environment. Children flourish in the tangible family atmosphere throughout the school

Very good attitudes to learning are promoted for the mixed ability intake. Pupils strive for high academic standards and have achieved a very good record in 11+ selection examinations for both the grammar schools in the maintained sector and secondary schools in the independent sector.

Staff are fully qualified, experienced and dedicated professionals who communicate well with parents. Very high standards in pupil behaviour are maintained – pupils are caring and courteous with each other and towards adults.

There is a wide range of extra-curricular activities including sports clubs, science club, chess, yoga, needlework, nature, art, cycling proficiency and ICT. Tuition is offered for a wide range of musical instruments including, piano, violin, drums, guitar, flute, clarinet, trumpet, saxophone as well as individual singing. Music lessons with a music specialist take place throughout the school and there are recorder lessons for whole classes. There are weekly swimming lessons and French and Spanish lessons available from 5+. The school choirs have achieved outstanding success in local and national competitions in recent years.

Emphasis is given to physical education. There are representative teams for football, hockey, cricket, rounders, netball, cross country and swimming. Tennis is taught to the senior children.

All children are encouraged to speak confidently and to express themselves clearly. All children from 7+ participate in an annual oral communication assessment adjudicated externally. Parents are invited to regular concerts, plays, class presentations and class assemblies.

Further developments have recently included a school chapel, an ICT suite, and after-school care.

Charitable status. St Philomena's Preparatory School is a Registered Charity, number 298635. It exists to provide Roman Catholic children and those of other denominations with the opportunity to reach the highest possible standards in every area of school life.

St Piran's School

14 Trelissick Road Hayle Cornwall TR27 4HY
Tel: 01736 752612
Fax: 01736 759446

e-mail: office@stpirans.fsbusiness.co.uk
website: www.stpirans.net

Headteacher: **Mrs Carol A de Labat**, BEd Hons, CertEd

Age Range. 3–16.
Number of Pupils. 70.
Fees per term (2007-2008). £1,500–£1,880.

Established in 1988, St Piran's Preparatory School is set in attractive and well-maintained premises, which, at present, house around seventy children, aged between three and fourteen. It is a friendly, well-ordered community with a positive ethos where pupils make good friendships with each other and relate well to staff. Pupils are treated with respect and valued equally. They have a clear sense of right and wrong. There is a good sense of community within the school and new pupils are quickly made to feel welcome. The school places a strong emphasis on good manners and politeness.

The curriculum is broad and balanced and helps to prepare the children for the next stage in their education. A wide variety of after school and lunchtime clubs provide additional activities and experiences for pupils of all ages. Educational visits to local places of interest and an annual residential visit (for Year 5 and up) further enrich the curriculum.

From Years Five and Six there is greater emphasis on subjects being taught by specialists. Class size remains low with the average class size being ten. Well-qualified, conscientious and hard-working staff teach children in a supportive learning environment. Children are given the opportunity to explain their ideas and be involved in activities. There is a very well-equipped and effectively-organised computer suite, which ensures that the children are at the cutting edge of modern technology.

From September 2008 we are offering GCSE subjects to our Year 10 pupils. This is a very exciting development for St Piran's and careful plans are being made to ensure the implementation of these classes is at the same high standard as the rest of the school.

The Ofsted Inspection for Early Years Provision in 2006 found our Foundation Stage to be 'outstanding in all areas'.

St Teresa's School

Aylesbury Road Princes Risborough Buckinghamshire HP27 0JW
Tel: 01844 345005
Fax: 01844 345131
e-mail: office@st-teresas.bucks.sch.uk
website: www.st-teresas.bucks.sch.uk

Headmaster: **Mr R Duigan**, BEd, MEd

Age Range. 3–11.
Number in School. Day: 80 Boys, 60 Girls. Nursery School: 11 Boys, 13 Girls.
Fees per term (2008-2009). £265–£2,162.

Compulsory extras: swimming and lunch.

St Teresa's School is primarily a Catholic School, but is open to boys and girls of all religions or none.

A full programme of clubs includes cricket, rounders, tennis, football, netball, cross-country, athletics, swimming, chess, choir, orchestra and others.

A well-qualified and caring staff prepares the children for independent and state senior schools. The school has an excellent academic record of achievement and our pupils leave as confident and well-mannered individuals.

The children are encouraged to live out the school motto, *Fidelity* – faith in God, faith in others and faith in oneself.

Charitable status. St Teresa's is a Registered Charity, number 310645. It exists to provide a broad education enfolded by the Catholic faith.

St Ursula's School

Brecon Road Westbury-on-Trym Bristol BS9 4DT
Tel: 0117 962 2616
Fax: 0117 962 2616
e-mail: office@st-ursulas.bristol.sch.uk
website: www.st-ursulas.bristol.sch.uk

Headmistress: **Mrs L Carter**

Age Range. Co-educational 3–16 years.
Number in School. 160 day boys, 100 day girls.
Fees per term (2008-2009). £1,195–£2,800.

St Ursula's School is Bristol's only Roman Catholic independent school.

St Ursula's is an all-ability school and welcomes boys and girls, aged 3–16, of all faiths and non-religious backgrounds.

St Ursula's provides a sound and varied education for all, with many extra-curricular activities on offer. The school has a happy atmosphere and a close community feel that is based upon the Christian values of care and respect for each other.

St Ursula's is located in a superb position, adjacent to the Downs in Bristol and is situated in glorious, extensive grounds. The school has unrivalled play areas and wonderful indoor and outdoor sports facilities on site. In addition there are high-quality music and drama facilities.

The nursery, "Little Bears", has its own building and garden within the school grounds, but the nursery children also benefit from the use of the main school facilities.

With excellent pastoral care and small classes, individual attention is given to all. St Ursula's recognises that every child is unique and aims to nurture your child's talent.

To book your visit or to order a school prospectus, please visit the website or contact the school office.

Charitable status. St Ursula's High School Trust is a Registered Charity, number 900498. It exists to provide education for boys and girls.

St Winefride's Convent School
Shrewsbury

Belmont Shrewsbury Shropshire SY1 1TE
Tel: 01743 369883
Fax: 01743 369883
e-mail: stwinefridesschool@postmaster.co.uk

Headmistress: **Sister M Felicity**, BA Hons

Age Range. 4+–11. Nursery: 3+–4.
Number in School. Day: 75 Boys, 107 Girls.
Fees per term (from April 2008). £965–£1,005.

St Winifred's School

17–19 Winn Road Portswood Southampton SO17 1EJ
Tel: 023 8055 7352
Fax: 023 8067 9055
e-mail: office@stwinifreds.southampton.sch.uk
website: www.stwinifreds.southampton.sch.uk

Chairman of Board of Trustees: Mr John W Watts, MCIPS, MILT, AIGEM

***Headmistress*: Mrs C A Pearcey**, BEd

Age Range. 2–11 Co-educational.
Number of Pupils. 115.
Fees per term (2007-2008). £1,880 plus £115 for lunch.

St Winifred's is a small independent school in a central position in Southampton.

The school aims to provide for the whole child through a modern curriculum, with an enriched programme of study and opportunities to develop all the child's talents.

Literacy, Numeracy, Science and the development of ICT are at the heart of primary education, so these are given a great deal of time and emphasis throughout the school. Pupils are encouraged to develop the habit of a disciplined approach to work and to discover the kind of fulfillment which comes from working with others. Our website gives a detailed outline of the school's curriculum, which provides a structured academic programme. This starts with the Nursery strategies for each child to achieve highly in the Early Learning Goals, leading to excellent results for pupils in their SATs at the end of Key Stages 1 and 2 in Years 2 and 6. All children are encouraged and helped, by our specialist teachers, to achieve their potential. Regular testing and continuous assessment prepare them for their entrance exams and SATs, thus preparing them for further achievement at secondary school.

The school provides regular feedback about pupils' progress at Parents' Evenings and in termly reports. Regular information packs and newsletters are sent to parents. We believe that good communication involves parents in their children's education.

The school is proud of its achievements in music, drama, games, swimming and gymnastics. As well as our own two indoor hall spaces and playground, the school takes advantage of Southampton's many sporting facilities. Weekly games, swimming and gym sessions with qualified staff are provided, as well as a variety of after school sports activities.

St Winifred's also gives its upper school pupils speech training for the Trinity College Effective Communication examinations. Each year many pupils achieve distinctions and merits but, most importantly, all gain much personal satisfaction and confidence from the experience.

Further opportunities are provided, through extra-curricular activities, to develop pupils' individual talents and personal strengths and interests. Individual and group achievement is recognised and appreciated by the whole school and children are encouraged to learn their own self-worth.

The school provides Before School Care from 8.00 am and After School Club until six o'clock for pupils aged three upwards.

Potential pupils are very welcome to spend a 'taster' day with their prospective class, to allow them to form some impression of the school.

If you would like to know more about St Winifred's, please telephone the school, or visit our website. We will be happy to meet you to discuss your child's future and show you the school in action.

Charitable status. The Gregg and St Winifred's Schools Trust is a Registered Charity, number 1089055.

St Wystan's School

High Street Repton Derbyshire DE65 6GE
Tel: 01283 703258
Fax: 01283 703258
e-mail: head@stwystans.org.uk
website: www.stwystans.org.uk

***Headmaster*: Mr P Soutar**, BEd

Age Range. 2½–11.
Number in School. Day: Boys 60, Girls 62.
Fees per term (2008-2009). £985–£2,075. Compulsory extras: Lunch £200.

A small number of scholarships are offered for 7+ entry to Year 3.

Situated in the historic village of Repton, only a short distance from Burton-on-Trent and the city of of Derby, St Wystan's is ideally placed to serve a wide catchment area. Both Nottingham and Uttoxeter are within 25 minutes of the school, though the majority of pupils come from Derby, Burton and surrounding villages.

St Wystan's prides itself on a family atmosphere in which every child can grow in confidence and develop to his or her full potential as an individual. Great emphasis is placed on courtesy and good manners and a pastoral system, centred on the four school houses, promotes a caring environment and develops teamwork and commitment.

Academic expectations are high, though the school serves a wide ability range. Small classes enable the children to receive individual attention and work at a pace appropriate to their ability. As a free-standing junior school, St Wystan's prepares pupils for a large number of senior schools and pupils have won a significant number of academic, sport and music scholarships recently.

The pre-school department provides a nursery, headed by a fully qualified teacher and a reception class which both accept pupils on government subsidised "Early Years" places. The main school covers Key Stages 1 and 2 but is not restricted by the National Curriculum, offering a broad range of subjects and a blend of form teacher based teaching at the lower end and subject specialist teaching further up the school.

St Wystan's enjoys an excellent reputation in music and sport, with pupils progressing to regional and national championships, recently in football, swimming, cross-country and athletics. Many pupils have instrumental tuition and there is a thriving school choir and orchestra, together with a broad range of other extra-curricular activities.

St Wystan's runs a very popular pre-school and after-school care facility. Children can be delivered to school from 7.30 am and looked after at school until 6.30 pm.

Charitable status. St Wystan's School (Repton) Limited is a Registered Charity, number 527181. It exists to provide a quality education for boys and girls.

Salesian College

Reading Road Farnborough Hampshire GU14 6PA
Tel: 01252 893000
Fax: 01252 893032
e-mail: office@salesian.hants.sch.uk
website: www.salesian.hants.sch.uk

***Headmaster*: Mr Patrick A Wilson**, BA Hons, MA, CertEd

Age Range. 11–18 years.
Number in School. 500.
Fees per term (2008-2009). £2,606.

Salesian College at Farnborough in Hampshire was founded in 1901 and is an Independent Catholic Grammar School of about 500 boys aged 11 to 18 years. Members of all Christian faiths are welcomed into the school which is part of a world wide organisation of educational foundations run by the Salesians, a religious Order founded in the last century in Italy by St John Bosco specifically for the formation of young people, spiritually, academically, culturally, physically and emotionally. This continues to be our aspiration for each boy.

Our aim is to send out from the school at 18 years a young man who is confident, without being arrogant, and comfortable with himself and all those around him; a good Christian, an honest citizen, a good individual, well equipped to take his place in, and make a significant contribution to society.

This is achieved by the use of The Preventive System of Education promoted by St John Bosco and based on the three principles of Reason, Religion and Kindness. These principles encourage the boys to develop a strong sense of responsibility and a caring attitude towards each other and the Community at large.

Academic achievements at GCSE and A level, and sporting achievements are highly valued. The friendliness and mutual respect that exist between staff and pupils provides a family and Christian ethos conducive to good order, confidence and scholarship.

As the members of a family help each other with physical and moral support, the members of the school are encouraged to do likewise. The use of the Prefect System is very effective in allowing members of the Senior school (Years 11–13) to help their juniors by example and guidance.

We regard education to be a tripartite process involving the school, the family and the boy and in order to produce the desired result all three must work in harmony.

Public speaking, music, orchestra, chess, drama and debating all flourish and there are many other extra curricular activities.

The school has its own chapel, chaplaincy and resident chaplain.

Prospective parents are always welcome to make an appointment to visit the College while in session.

Charitable status. Salesian College is a Registered Charity, number 233779. It exists to provide education for boys in North East Hampshire and neighbouring counties.

Salterford House School

Salterford Lane Calverton Nottinghamshire NG14 6NZ
Tel: 0115 965 2127
Fax: 0115 965 5627
e-mail: office@salterfordhouseschool.co.uk
website: www.salterfordhouseschool.co.uk

***Headmistress*: Mrs M Venables**, CertEd

Age Range. 2½–11.

Number in School. Main School 170: 89 Boys, 81 Girls. Kindergarten and Pre-Prep 59: 30 Boys, 29 Girls.

Fees per term (2008-2009). £1,740–£1,760.

Salterford House is situated in rural Nottinghamshire, in a woodland setting and aims to provide a happy, family atmosphere with small classes, in order to equip children academically and socially to cope with the demands of any type of education which might follow.

Although the school is mainly Church of England, all faiths are accepted. 75% of pupils go on to senior independent schools such as Nottingham High Schools NGHS, Trent College and Hollygirt.

Sports include Cricket, Tennis, Swimming, Rounders, Football, Golf and Skiing.

The school produces 3 concerts a year and there is a recorder Group and Choir. Individual tuition in Speech and Drama, Piano, Woodwind, Guitar and Percussion is available.

A dyslexia teacher is employed to give individual lessons to children with dyslexia problems.

All classrooms are equipped with computers.

Staff are easily available for discussion. Regular contact is maintained with parents via Parents Evening and newsletters.

Sancton Wood School

2 St Paul's Road Cambridge CB1 2EZ
Tel: 01223 359488
Fax: 01223 471703
e-mail: head@sanctonwood.co.uk
website: www.sanctonwood.co.uk

***Headmaster*: The Revd Dr Jack McDonald**, MA, MA, Docteur-ès-Lettres, PGCE

Age Range. 1–16 Co-educational.

Number of Pupils. 103.

Fees per term (2007-2008). £895–£2,895.

Sancton Wood School was founded in 1976 by Mrs Jill Sturdy, initially for the education of her 9 adopted children. It has expanded in every subsequent year and now occupies 3 sites in central Cambridge. The current headmaster was most recently Dean of Gonville and Caius College, Cambridge, the post occupied by Mrs Sturdy's husband, the Revd John Sturdy, until his death in 1996.

The school has an overwhelmingly generous, "family" atmosphere, with 14 pupils per class at KS1, 15 per class at KS2 and 16 per class at KS3 and KS4. Nonetheless, the school is selective and expectations of academic achievement, as well as of the quality of relationships, are very high. The aim of the school is to send motivated, mature, kind and qualified young people into sixth form education.

Sherfield School
GEMS Education

Sherfield-on-Loddon Hook Hampshire RG27 0HT
Tel: 01256 884800
Fax: 01256 884803
e-mail: info@sherfieldschool.co.uk
website: www.sherfieldschool.co.uk

***Executive Principal*: Professor Pat Preedy**

Headmaster: Mr James Murphy-O'Connor

Age Range. 3 months – 18 years Co-educational.

Number in School. 525 Day Pupils.

Fees per term (2008-2009). £2,190–£3,908.

We offer a first-class academic education within a forward-looking and enriched curriculum to pupils aged from 3 months to 18 years from 7.30 am to 6.00 pm for 48 weeks of the year. Provision includes academies held during the holidays so that pupils can continue to extend and develop their talents.

Teaching methods are a blend of the traditional and the very best of new ideas, based upon research and an understanding of how the brain develops and functions.

Our Sixth Form offers a range of academic and vocational options. At senior level students are given the opportunity to study for a number of qualifications including A Level, GCSE, IGCSE and BTEC. Along with the core subjects for all pupils there are a range of options to meet the needs of each individual student. The flexible approach allows some students to take examinations early if appropriate.

Sherfield also offers an Extended Learning Programme. The pupils can choose from a vast range of academic, sport and practical subjects such as chess, mandarin, photography, and gymnastics.

Setting high standards, developing self-discipline and meeting the needs of each individual pupil ensures that each child meets their full potential. As part of the school's commitment to achievement they offer outstanding opportunities for talented individuals. Scholarships are offered in sports, music, arts and academic excellence for pupils at Year 7 and upwards.

Sherfield TV, available to view or download from the Sherfield website, provides vital information about the school to parents, the community and the media. The launch represents innovation in the promotion of independent education recognising that many people have a need for information but are time poor. It provides plenty of information quickly and will be used to develop understanding of the school's values and commitment to pupils and learning. Sherfield are one of the first independent schools to use this innovative approach to marketing. The first podcast is an introduction to Sherfield, emphasising the school's core beliefs of tradition and innovation, an inclusive approach and individual learning, reinforced in the school motto of "Roots to grow, wings to fly". Further programmes include the "Sherfield Difference" and "Sherfield Sixth" and "Beyond Sherfield". Additionally "World Languages" introduces one area of the curriculum with more to follow.

Sherfield prides itself on not just specialising in one area, but in all aspects of academic and sporting life. They focus on providing all pupils with a full range of activities recognising that they need to nurture and develop the whole pupil.

Sherrardswood School

Lockleys Welwyn Hertfordshire AL6 0BJ
Tel: 01438 714282
Fax: 01438 840616
e-mail: mimram@sherrardswood.herts.sch.uk
website: www.sherrardswood.herts.sch.uk

Headteacher: **Mrs L E Corry**

Age Range. 2–18.
Number in School. Day: 208 Boys, 181 Girls.
Fees per term (2008-2009). £2,240–£4,040.

Sherrardswood, founded in 1928, is a co-educational day school for pupils aged 2–18. The School is set in 25 acres of attractive parkland two miles north of Welwyn Garden City. The Junior Department is housed in a fine 18th century building whilst the Senior Department occupies a purpose-built facility. Games fields, tennis courts and woodlands trail are available on the Lockleys site for both departments.

Entry to the school is by interview or by interview and examination according to age. A broad curriculum is offered to GCSE level and a wide range of A Level subjects is available.

A range of sport and extra-curricular opportunities is available, both within the school day and out of school hours. There is a commitment to a caring environment within a disciplined framework and the opportunity to develop qualities of self-discipline and responsibility.

The recent ISI inspection confirmed that Sherrardswood is achieving its aims and that the quality of education and pastoral care is outstanding.

Charitable status. Sherrardswood School is a Registered Charity, number 311070. It exists solely to provide independent education for boys and girls aged 2–18.

Shoreham College

St Julian's Lane Shoreham-by-Sea West Sussex BN43 6YW
Tel: 01273 592681
Fax: 01273 591673
e-mail: info@shorehamcollege.co.uk
website: www.shorehamcollege.co.uk

Headmaster: **J Stearns**, BSc, MA, PGCE, NPQH

Age Range. 3–16.
Number in School. 296 Day Boys, 144 Day Girls.
Fees per term (2007-2008). £2,075–£3,375.

Founded in 1852, the College is a Charitable Trust and is sited to the east of Shoreham in a Tudor manor house supplemented by modern buildings set in spacious grounds.

Shoreham College has a non-selective entry policy and all pupils are prepared for GCSE Examinations. There is a very favourable teacher/pupil ratio and a well-qualified and experienced staff. Particular care is taken to help pupils in their career choice.

The main games are soccer, rugby and cricket as well as athletics, squash, badminton, tennis and swimming. There is an active CCF and thriving Music Department, both choral and instrumental.

The School offers a caring community with a proper balance between straightforward discipline and friendly relationships.

Charitable status. Shoreham College (The Kennedy Independent School Trust Limited) is a Registered Charity, number 307045. It exists to provide high quality education for local boys and girls.

Slindon College

Slindon Arundel West Sussex BN18 0RH
Tel: 01243 814320
Fax: 01243 814702
e-mail: registrar@slindoncollege.co.uk
website: www.slindoncollege.co.uk

Headmaster: **I Graham**, BEd, MA

Age Range. 9–16.
Number in School. 40 Boarders, 70 Day Boys.
Fees per term (2008-2009). Boarders £7,565, Day Boys £4,730.

A small school for approximately 100 boys whose classes have a maximum of 12 pupils. The National Curriculum is followed where appropriate and in Years 5–9 a broad-based, balanced curriculum is provided. GCSE courses include home economics, PE, photography, art, music and design technology – all practical based and "hands-on". GNVQ Horticulture is enhanced by a small animal kingdom. The excellent Learning Support Department helps boys with specific learning difficulties, including dyslexia and ADD/ADHD.

A wide range of extra-curricular activities is offered, including car mechanics, farm club and stagecraft.

The school is non-denominational but has firm links with the local Anglican church.

Some bursaries are available and discount is available for Service families and second sons.

Charitable status. Slindon College is a Registered Charity, number 1028125. It aims to provide for the academic, social and personal development of each boy in a caring and purposeful environment.

Snaresbrook College

75 Woodford Road South Woodford London E18 2EA
Tel: 020 8989 2394
Fax: 020 8989 4379
e-mail: office@snaresbrookcollege.org.uk
website: www.snaresbrookcollege.org.uk

Headteacher: **Mrs L J Chiverrell**, CertEd

Age Range. 3½–11.
Number in School. 160.
Fees per term (2008-2009). £1,971–£2,636.

Snaresbrook College is an Independent day school for boys and girls aged from 3½ to 11 years. Founded in the 1930s, the school today is ISC accredited and inspected. It occupies a substantial Victorian building, once a large private family home – a fact that contributes to the strong community spirit within the school. We aim to cultivate an intimate, caring family atmosphere in which children feel secure and valued. Most children join our Nursery and Reception section at age 3½ and most pupils stay with us until they reach 11 when they leave for their secondary schools.

We provide a rounded primary education covering every aspect of your child's early development. The curriculum is designed to prepare pupils for senior independent and grammar school entrance and scholarship examinations. It includes the National Curriculum core subjects of Mathematics, English and Science as well as History, Geography, ICT, Religious Education, Music, Speech and Drama. French is studied from age 3½.

At age 11, we find that Snaresbrook children are confident, cheerful and courteous, with a good sense of community and a readiness to care for each other and the world around them. They have learned how to work in the ways that suit them best, are receptive to teaching and are well prepared for the next stage of their education and development.

We see ourselves as joint trustees, with parents, of the young lives in our care, bearing equal responsibility for their happiness, well being and development.

Southbank International School
Hampstead Campus
Cognita Schools Group

16 Netherhall Gardens Hampstead London NW3 5TH
Tel: 020 7431 1200
Fax: 020 7794 5858
e-mail: info@southbank.org
website: www.southbank.org

Chairman of Education Board: Terry Hedger

***Principal*: Helen O'Donoghue**

Age Range. 3–11.
Number in School. Day: 99 Boys, 99 Girls.
Fees per term (2008-2009). £4,700–£5,500.
£5020-£5820

Southbank International School was founded in 1979 by a group of British and American educators in order to provide a challenging academic environment for a culturally diverse community from ages 3 to 19. In December 2006 it became the first international school in the Cognita Schools Group. There are three campuses. The Hampstead campus serves the age range 3 to 11. Students receive tuition through the International Baccalaureate Primary Years Programmes. Students transfer to the Westminster campus at age 11/grade 6. London – its people, museums, theatres – is used as an extension of the campus and the curriculum. The campuses have pupils representing 61 nationalities, and Southbank is noted for its friendly atmosphere.

Southbank was the first UK school to offer the International Baccalaureate curriculum to pupils of all ages. The IB PYP is inquiry based and uses a cross-curricular approach. It includes the core subjects as well as Spanish, computing, art, music and Suzuki violin. In the IB MYP, offered at the Westminster campus, French and design technology are added to the core subjects begun in the Primary. The emphasis is on skills development and students are prepared for the High School and the IB Diploma Programme (Grades 11 and 12).

English is the language of instruction, but English as an Additional Language (EAL) is also offered throughout the school. The school attracts well-qualified and internationally experienced teachers.

The school operates on a three-term basis from September to June. Holidays include mid-term breaks in October and February, a three-week winter break in December/January and a two-week spring break in March/April. Southbank Hampstead is housed in a purpose-built building with a library, an IT centre, art and music rooms, a multi-purpose hall, and a playground. The door-to-door bus service covers a wide area of central and north London. Admission is based on previous school records and satisfactory references, as well as suitability of the candidate for the curriculum offered. Pupils with special needs may be offered limited support and are evaluated for admission on an individual basis with consideration given to the needs of currently enrolled pupils.

Southbank International School
Kensington Campus
Cognita Schools Group

36–38 Kensington Park Road London W11 3BU
Tel: 020 7229 8230
Fax: 020 7229 3784
e-mail: info@southbank.org
website: www.southbank.org

Chairman of Education Board: Terry Hedger

***Principal*: Judith Kingsbury**

Age Range. 3–11.
Number in School. Day: 98 Boys, 104 Girls.
Fees per term (2008-2009). £5,020–£5,820.

Southbank International School was founded in 1979 by a group of British and American educators in order to provide a challenging academic environment for a culturally diverse community from ages 3 to 19. In December 2006 it became the first international school in the Cognita Schools Group. There are three campuses. The Kensington campus serves the age range 3 to 11. Students receive tuition through the International Baccalaureate Primary Years Programmes. Students transfer to the Westminster campus at age 11/grade 6. London – its people, museums, theatres – is used as an extension of the campus and the curriculum. The campuses have pupils representing 61 nationalities, and Southbank is noted for its friendly atmosphere.

Southbank was the first UK school to offer the International Baccalaureate curriculum to pupils of all ages. The IB PYP is inquiry based and uses a cross-curricular approach. It includes the core subjects as well as Spanish, computing, art, music and Suzuki violin or cello. In the IB MYP, offered at the Westminster campus, French and design technology are added to the core subjects begun in the Primary. The emphasis is on skills development and students are prepared for the High School and the IB Diploma Programme (Grades 11 and 12).

English is the language of instruction, but English as an Additional Language (EAL) is also offered throughout the school. The school attracts well-qualified and internationally experienced teachers.

The school operates on a three-term basis from September to June. Holidays include mid-term breaks in October and February, a three-week winter break in December/January and a two-week spring break in March/April. Southbank Hampstead is housed in a purpose-built building with a library, an IT centre, art and music rooms, a multi-purpose hall, and a playground. The door-to-door bus service covers a wide area of central and north London. Admission is based on previous school records and satisfactory references, as well as suitability of the candidate for the curriculum offered. Pupils with special needs may be offered limited support and are evaluated for admission on an individual basis with consideration given to the needs of currently enrolled pupils.

Southbank International School
Westminster Campus
Cognita Schools Group

63–65 Portland Place London W1B 1QR
Tel: 020 7436 9699
Fax: 020 7436 9799
e-mail: info@southbank.org
website: www.southbank.org

***Chairman of Education Board & Principal*: Terry Hedger**

Age Range. 11–18.
Number in School. Day: 161 Boys, 169 Girls.
Fees per term (2008-2009). £6,220–£6,880

Southbank International School was founded in 1979 by a group of British and American educators in order to provide a challenging academic environment for a culturally diverse community from ages 3 to 19. In December 2006 it became the first international school in the Cognita Schools Group. There are three campuses with Hampstead and Kensington teaching the PYP to 3–11 year olds. The campuses have pupils representing 61 nationalities, and Southbank is noted for its friendly atmosphere.

Southbank was the first UK school to offer the International Baccalaureate curriculum to pupils of all ages. In the IB Middle Years Programme (Grades 6 to 10) at Westminster, French and design technology are added to the core subjects begun in the Primary School. In the MYP traditional subject areas are linked to one another through a holistic framework. The emphasis is on skills development and students are prepared for the IB Diploma Programme (Grades 11 and 12), where students have to choose six subjects from six subject groups: Language A1 (a literature course in the student's first language); Second Language; Individuals and Societies (history, business and management, geography); Experimental Sciences (biology, chemistry, physics); Mathematics and Computer Science; The Arts (visual art, film studies, theatre arts).

English is the language of instruction, but students may also study their native language: currently 17 languages are offered as first or second languages in the High School. English as an Additional Language (EAL) is also offered throughout the school. The school attracts well-qualified and internationally experienced teachers.

Southbank Westminster is an English Heritage listed building in Portland Place, conveniently located in central London with good transportation nearby. In 2007 a new IB Diploma annexe was opened in Fitzrovia, six minutes away from the main building. Facilities at Westminster include five science labs, a computer lab, a hall/theatre, cafeteria, art and music rooms, and two libraries served by networked computers. The school is close to Regent's Park. The door-to-door bus service covers a wide area of central and north London.

Almost all students progress to universities mainly in the UK, but also in the USA, Canada, Australia, Europe and Japan.

Stafford Grammar School

Burton Manor Stafford ST18 9AT

(See entry in SHMIS section)

Stanborough School

Stanborough Park Garston Watford Hertfordshire WD25 9JT
Tel: 01923 673268
Fax: 01923 893943
e-mail: registrar@spsch.org
website: www.spsch.org

***Head of Secondary School*: Mr R Murphy**, BSc, MA Ed

***Head of Primary School & Nursery*: Mrs C Allen**

Age Range. 3–18.
Number in School. 234 girls and boys (boarding and day).
Fees per term (2007-2008). Boarding: £2,699–£3,679; Tuition: £1,499–£2,990.

Stanborough School, housed in attractive parkland, is a Christian independent school for boys and girls of all faiths between the ages of three and eighteen. Boarding is available for children who are at least 11 years of age.

It aims to give an education which fosters the growth of the whole person and is small enough for each student to remain an individual and not lose his or her personal identity. It has a warm, friendly atmosphere supported by firm yet kindly discipline providing a milieu in which pupils may develop their abilities and personal qualities to the full.

Charitable status. Stanborough School is a Registered Charity, number 1044071.

Steephill School

off Castle Hill Fawkham Longfield Kent DA3 7BG
Tel: 01474 702107
Fax: 01474 706011
e-mail: secretary@steephill.co.uk
website: www.steephill.co.uk

***Head Teacher*: Mrs Caroline Birtwell**, BSc, MBA, PGCE

Age Range. 3–11 co-educational.
Number of Pupils. 113.
Fees per term (2008-2009). £898–£2,245.

Steephill School is a very successful School based on its academic, sporting and musical achievements. In 2007 it had 80% entry into selective schools, winning choir at the Gravesham Musical festival, and numerous successes at inter-school sports.

The School believes in high-quality teaching within a disciplined but relaxed atmosphere. The School holds traditional values and beliefs; working with and supporting each other is an important part of the ethos. There are close links with the church opposite the School. Four services per year are held there and the Rector takes a fortnightly assembly. The setting is very rural despite being only a few minutes' drive from the M2 and 5 miles from the M20 and M25. The School enjoys beautiful views of the countryside with very little traffic nearby.

The classes are a maximum of 16 and with only 120 pupils in the School, there is a close liaison between all members of the school community: children, staff, family members and governors. Parents are welcomed into the School and work closely with the teachers. There is regular feedback to parents on children's progress. Parents are also active in Friends of Steephill School, the Parents Association to provide social and fund-raising activities.

The 2006 ISI report said that "pupils are at the heart of everything the School does". This begins from the time the children join the School aged 3½ in the Nursery to when they leave at age 11. The curriculum is designed to support all abilities to achieve academically and in all the broader aspects of education such as drama, the arts and sports. Information Technology has been developed well over the last few years and is being continually updated.

There is a large selection of extra-curricular activities at lunchtime and after school. Our Gardening Club is one of the more popular together with the choir, instruction on musical instruments, dance and football. We are very fortunate to have large grounds with a superb sports field, despite being a small school.

There is also a care facility both before and after school so we are open from 8 am to 5.30 pm.

Charitable status. Steephill School is a Registered Charity, number 803152.

Stoke College

Stoke-by-Clare Sudbury Suffolk CO10 8JE
Tel: 01787 278141
Fax: 01787 277904
e-mail: office@stokecollege.co.uk
website: www.stokecollege.co.uk

***Headmaster*: J Gibson**, BA, CertEd

Age Range. 3–16+ Co-educational.

Number in School. Total 230: 131 Boys, 99 Girls. Boarders: 5 Boys, 1 Girl.

Registration Fee. £50.

Fees per term (2008-2009). Day: Nursery £1,517, Years 1–3 £2,244, Years 4–6 £2,702, Years 7–8 £3,240, Years 9–11 £3,494. Weekly Boarding: Years 4–6 £4,862, Years 7–8 £5,370, Years 9–11 £5,642.

Stoke College provides a broad, balanced and relevant curriculum up to GCSE. Weekly boarders or day pupils enjoy a caring environment in an idyllic rural situation with small classes yielding excellent results in public examinations. The College has a strong tradition in athletics and cross-country and in Music and Drama. The school benefits from a new Sports/Assembly Hall, Junior School Teaching Block, Technology Rooms, a Performing Arts Centre, a swimming pool, hard tennis courts and a Nursery Department. The College aims to develop the individual's strengths and to produce a well rounded young adult to take his or her place in society.

Charitable status. Stoke College is a Registered Charity, number 310487. It is devoted to providing a full and relevant education to its pupils.

Stowford College

95 Brighton Road Sutton Surrey SM2 5SJ
Tel: 020 8661 9444
Fax: 020 8661 6136
e-mail: stowfordsch@btinternet.com
website: www.stowford.com

***Headmaster*: R J Shakespeare**, BA, MA, MA

Age Range. 6–16.

Number in School. Day: 51 Boys, 34 Girls.

Fees per term (2008-2009). Years 3–6 £2,665, Years 7–11 £2,635–£3,050.

Stowford has a Junior (6–11) and Senior (11–16) School for both boys and girls. It has a reputation for individual care and a well-disciplined yet happy atmosphere. Classes are small; each individual receives the help that he or she needs. We have a dyslexia programme. Homework is important and all must achieve their personal best. There is the closest possible liaison with parents.

The early years in particular are when good social and academic habits are formed. Seniors have a considerable measure of freedom and are expected to respond appropriately.

Overall, an adult environment with articulate pupils who reach their targets.

Stratford Preparatory School

Church House Old Town Stratford-upon-Avon Warwickshire CV37 6BG
Tel: 01789 297993
Fax: 01789 263993
e-mail: enquiries@stratfordprep.co.uk
website: www.stratfordprep.co.uk

Motto: *Lux et Scientia*

***Principal*: Mrs C Quinn**, BEd Hons, MBA

Age Range. Preparatory School 4–11 years. Montessori Nursery School 2–4 years.

Number in School. Main School: 62 Boys, 53 Girls; Nursery School: 15 Boys, 25 Girls.

Fees per term (2007-2008). Junior School £2,205; Infant School £1,995; Nursery School: £1,800 (full-time), £945 (5 mornings), £890 (5 afternoons). Compulsory extras: Lunch £125.

Stratford Preparatory School is situated in the heart of the historic town of Stratford-upon-Avon. The Preparatory school opened in September 1989 and has developed around a large town house. An additional detached house within the school's grounds provides accommodation for the Reception and Nursery children, a gymnasium, a science room and design and technology room.

The Nursery implements the Montessori philosophy of learning which encourages a structured learning environment. French and ballet are taught from the age of 2 years.

The main school offers a broad balanced learning plan adapted to the individual needs of the children using traditional teaching methods and with specific reference to the National Curriculum. All children are entered for the 11+ and independent school entrance examinations.

The school offers a high level of pastoral care and attention to personal development.

Physical education facilities include: sailing, swimming, football, cricket, tennis, netball, rounders, ballet and athletics.

There are opportunities for the children to learn a variety of musical instruments. The school has two choirs and an orchestra.

Reduction in fees is offered for families with two or more children in Main School.

The Principal is pleased to provide further details and meet prospective parents.

The Study Preparatory School

Wilberforce House Camp Road Wimbledon Common London SW19 4UN

(See entry in IAPS section)

Study School

57 Thetford Road New Malden Surrey KT3 5DP
Tel: 020 8942 0754
Fax: 020 8942 0754
e-mail: info@study.kingston.sch.uk
website: www.study.kingston.sch.uk

Principal: Mrs Susan Mallin, CertEd, FRSA

***Headmistress*: Mrs Anne Farnish**, BA Hons

Age Range. 3–11 Co-educational.

Number in School. Day: 78 Boys, 56 Girls.

Fees per term (2007-2008). Nursery (mornings only) £1,114, Reception & Year 1 £2,275, Years 2–6 £2,599. Additional Nursery afternoon sessions available each day of the week: £176 per afternoon per term. All fees include a cooked school lunch. The school belongs to the Early Years Funding Scheme for 3 and 4 year olds.

Since 1923 we have successfully given our children a firm foundation in reading, writing and number skills, whilst also teaching French, music, art and games. Science, geography, history, technology and ICT play an important part in the curriculum, with interactive whiteboards in every classroom.

Small classes allow us to stretch the most able pupils, whilst giving all our children individual attention.

Popular After School Clubs include Football, Art, Computer, Drama, Dance, Chess and Cookery. Individual instrumental music tuition is also available. We have After School Care until 6.00 pm. All classes go on a school trip once a term and Years Five and Six attend residential activity and field study courses.

We provide a caring and stimulating atmosphere in which our children thrive. After Year Six they leave us to enter such schools at King's College, Wimbledon, Kingston Grammar School, Hampton School, the High Schools at Wimbledon, Sutton, Putney and Surbiton, and both Tiffin Schools.

Please visit our website: www.study.kingston.sch.uk.

Sunny Hill House School

7 Wrenthorpe Lane Wrenthorpe Wakefield WF2 0QB
Tel: 01924 291717
Fax: 01924 291717
e-mail: shhschool@aol.com
website: www.silcoates.com

***Headmistress*: Miss H Stocks**, BEd, MEd SEN

Age Range. 2–7.

Number in School. 116 Boys and Girls.

Fees per term (2007-2008). £1,752.

The Headmistress and her dedicated teaching team see the school as an enlarged family unit, constantly seeking to provide a happy and orderly environment where young children can develop naturally as individuals and gain the confidence necessary to realise their full potential both socially and academically. The basic concepts of literacy and numeracy are taught in small classes by traditional methods within a broad curriculum and great attention is paid to cultivating responsible social attitudes in a relaxed yet disciplined atmosphere.

Sunny Hill House is part of the Silcoates School Foundation and has access to its excellent sports facilities and resources. Children enter Silcoates Junior School by assessment at age seven.

Charitable status. The Silcoates School Foundation is a Registered Charity, number 529281. It exists to provide education for boys and girls.

The Swaminarayan School

260 Brentfield Road Neasden London NW10 8HE
Tel: 020 8965 8381
Fax: 020 8961 4042
e-mail: admin@swaminarayan.brent.sch.uk
website: www.swaminarayan.brent.sch.uk

Chairman of Governors: Mr Piyush Amin

***Headteacher*: Mr Mahendra Savjani**, BSc

Age Range. 2½–18.

Number of Pupils. 428: 234 boys, 194 girls.

Fees per term (2008-2009). £2,045–£2,906.

The Swaminarayan School was founded in 1991 by His Divine Holiness Shree Pramukh Swami Maharaj to provide education along the lines of independent British schools, whilst reinforcing Hindu culture and tradition. It is a non-profit making co-educational school for children aged two and a half to eighteen years.

The school admitted its first eighty or so Prep School pupils in September 1992 and the Senior School took its first intake the following September. Now there are well over 400 pupils in the school and already students from the school have gained admission to Oxford, Imperial, Warwick, UCL and LSE.

Since those early days excellent progress has been made in all areas. The most striking aspect that always attracts comment from visitors is the purposeful atmosphere, both in classrooms and throughout the school. Teachers are able to help pupils achieve their full potential because of the generous staffing ratio, excellent behaviour of pupils and commitment from parents.

Resources and premises have also improved beyond recognition with modern libraries and computer rooms for each school. Former students from those early days dropping in to meet their teachers are amazed by the transformation!

On the curriculum front, the school has taken up the most desirable elements of the National Curriculum while developing the best practices of independent education. The cultural subjects unique to the school give it a special dimension – students have lessons in the Indian Performing Arts up to Year 8 and all students study Gujarati and Religious Education in Hinduism up to GCSE level.

In addition to their timetabled LAMDA lessons, PE lessons and club afternoons, pupils are encouraged to take part in a range of extra-curricular activities such as public speaking, sports, drama, dance and much more. An extensive programme of instrumental lessons, both Indian and European, is also on offer to all pupils. The school arranges regular day trips to museums, parks and other places of educational interest. The Duke of Edinburgh's Award Scheme and residential outings such as the annual ski trip are also a feature of the school. Whilst continuing to deliver a value based, broad and balanced curriculum, the school excels academically. Each year its excellent GCSE and A Level results put it at the top end of Brent Performance tables. In The Daily Telegraph list of top independent schools published January 2008 the school was ranked 4th in the country.

Over fifteen years of vision, investment and hard work from trustees and governors, teaching and non-teaching staff as well as parents and pupils have made this a school to be proud of. The next ten years will see the school striving to ensure that it continues from strength to strength.

Charitable status. The Akshar Educational Trust is a Registered Charity, number 1023731.

Sylvia Young Theatre School

Rossmore Road London NW1 6NJ
Tel: 020 7402 0673
Fax: 020 7723 1040
e-mail: info@sylviayoungtheatreschool.co.uk
website: www.sylviayoungtheatreschool.co.uk

Principal: Mrs Sylvia Young, OBE

***Headteacher*: Ms Frances Chave**, BSc, PGCE, NPQH

Age Range. 10–16.

Number in School. Day: Boys 68, Girls 88. Weekly boarding is available.

Fees per term (2008-2009). Junior Department £2,350, Years 7, 8 and 9 £3,120, Years 10 and 11 £3,210.

The School has a junior department (Year 6 only) and a secondary department (Years 7–11). We aim to provide an appropriately balanced academic and vocational experience for our students. We are proud of the caring and well disciplined environment that prevails and promotes a very positive climate of individual success.

Academic subjects are delivered by highly qualified staff to the end of Key Stage 4.

GCSE Examination subjects include English, English Literature, Mathematics, Science, Additional Science, Art, Drama, Expressive Arts, Music and Media Studies.

Theatrical training is given by experienced professional teachers. Pupils are prepared for examinations in Speech and Drama – LAMDA (London Academy of Music and Dramatic Art). Entry is by audition with academic ability assessed.

Thornlow Preparatory School

Connaught Road Weymouth Dorset DT4 0SA
Tel: 01305 785703
Fax: 01305 780976
e-mail: headmaster@thornlow.co.uk
website: www.thornlow.co.uk

***Head*: Mr R A Fowke**, BEd Hons

Age Range. 3–13 Co-educational.

Number of Pupils. 70 Boys and Girls.

Fees per term (2007-2008). £2,170.

Thornlow Preparatory School is a must on any visiting list in order to appreciate fully the unique blend of teacher dedication and expertise that produces a happy, caring atmosphere. A highly qualified staff and small teaching groups ensure that any child's unique potential is nurtured to the full.

On the cultural and extra-curricular front, Thornlow certainly lives up to its motto of "preparing children for life's horizons", for not only is music a strong feature with a wide range of instruments being taught, but there is also a thriving culture of drama.

Another special feature is the Sailing, which takes place twice a week in the safe confines of Portland Harbour.

The well equipped Nursery Unit has en-suite facilities and enjoys the support of an NNEB.

In addition, Thornlow has a brand new ICT Room, Science Laboratory, Art Room, Library and Cooking Room.

Thorpe Hall School

Wakering Road Thorpe Bay Essex SS1 3RD
Tel: 01702 582340
Fax: 01702 587070
e-mail: sec@thorpehall.southend.sch.uk
website: www.thorpehall.southend.sch.uk

***Headmaster*: A Hampton**, BA Hons, LTCL, MEd, NPQH

Age Range. 2–16 years.

Number in School. Approximately 360 girls and boys.

Fees per term (2008-2009). £1,892–£2,670.

Thorpe Hall School is a co-educational independent day school, pleasantly situated on green belt land on the outskirts of Southend-on-Sea, Essex. The buildings are modern and purpose-built.

Communications to London are good via the A13 and A127 and the Liverpool/Fenchurch Street railway lines. The nearest station is approximately 10 minutes' walk.

Founded in 1925, the school has been educating children for 80 years and consistently achieves excellent academic results at Key Stage 1, 2, 3 and GCSE with special emphasis being placed on the traditional values of good manners, behaviour, dress and speech.

On Monday, Tuesday and Thursday each week the school day is extended by one hour to enable all children to access library and computer facilities as well as having the opportunities to participate in Sport, Music, Drama, Mathematics and French or simply to do their homework in a suitable and supervised environment.

Refurbishments in Science, Modern Languages, Information Systems and the Resources Centre have greatly enhanced the learning opportunities for all pupils. A £350,000 extension comprising a Music Centre, ICT suite, showers and changing facilities, a kitchen and additional teaching rooms was completed in 2001.

A new building was recently completed, which houses a Theatre, Technology rooms, an extra ICT suite and an excellent Modern Art area. These new facilities ensure that Thorpe Hall School has the most modern, up-to-date and technologically advanced facilities of any independent school in South East Essex.

Thorpe Hall School has an orderly, disciplined and caring ethos that caters for the social and academic needs of children – Pre-Nursery, Nursery, Reception, Infant, Junior and Senior – not only between the hours of 9 am to 4 pm but also offers sporting opportunities in golf, tennis, karate, netball, horse riding and football at weekends and during holiday times. Youngsters have the opportunity to join our Beavers, Cubs and Scout groups while senior pupils can become involved in the Duke of Edinburgh's Award Scheme.

The Charitable Trust status enables fees, which are very competitive, to be kept to a minimum. Nursery vouchers are accepted and some academic bursaries are available to pupils entering Year 3 in the Junior School and Year 7 in the Upper School. The School is regularly inspected by the DCSF and is accredited by the Independent Schools Council.

In June 2004 the School's Nursery department was inspected by Ofsted and received a glowing report. The Inspector commented that the provision for Nursery education at Thorpe Hall School is of high quality.

Charitable status. Thorpe Hall School is a Registered Charity, number 298155. It exists to provide good quality education for boys and girls in South East Essex.

Thorpe House School

7 Yarmouth Road Thorpe St Andrew Norwich NR7 0EA

(See entry in GSA section)

Tower College

Rainhill Merseyside L35 6NE
Tel: 0151 426 4333
Fax: 0151 426 3338
e-mail: rjoxley@lineone.net
website: www.towercollege.com

Principal**: Miss R J Oxley**

Age Range. 3–16.
Number in School. Day: 275 Boys, 294 Girls.
Fees per term (2008-2009). £1,543–£1,815.

Tower College is a non-denominational Christian Day School housed in a beautiful Victorian mansion set in 15 acres.

Our emphasis is on academic excellence and good behaviour. We have a strong musical tradition.

Seven coaches cover an 18 mile radius including South Liverpool, Widnes, Warrington, Runcorn, St Helens, Prescot, Rainford and Ormskirk. Breakfast and after school clubs are available.

Academic and music scholarships are available.

Charitable status. Tower College is a Registered Charity, number 526611. It aims to provide a sound education based on Christian beliefs, with an emphasis on good behaviour and academic excellence.

The Towers Convent School

Upper Beeding Steyning East Sussex BN44 3TF
Tel: 01903 812185
Fax: 01903 813858
e-mail: admin@towers.w-sussex.sch.uk
website: www.towers.w-sussex.sch.uk

Headmistress**: Mrs Carole Baker**, BEd, MA

Age Range. Girls 3–16, Boys 3–8.
Number in School. 301 including 40 boarders.
Fees per term (2008-2009). Boarders: £3,800–£4,050 (full), £3,570–£3,800 (weekly). Day Pupils £1,820–£2,380.

The Towers, a Roman Catholic boarding and day school for girls 3–16 and boys 3–8 years, in the healthy and beautiful setting of the South Downs, is owned by a Community of Sisters. At the heart of The Towers Community is Christian love; all people of whatever race, colour, creed or status are welcome, and have equal worth and opportunity. We aim to celebrate the dignity of each individual pupil. Our motto "Always Faithful" upholds the qualities of honesty and trust, responsibility, self-discipline and forgiveness. Pupils are encouraged to achieve their full potential in everything they do, developing a love of learning and seeking "wholeness". Technology and Science subjects are a particular strength, and the school has three times won the Whitbread Prize for GCSE results. The GCSE pass rate is consistently high – indeed, in 2007 it was 99% with all children gaining Maths and English – reflecting a quest for high academic standards. There is a keen interest in Music and Drama and a major musical is produced annually. The school has again won the coveted Sportsmark Award, witness of a fine sports tradition, especially in tennis, where the school has won the Sussex Shield five times; netball and gymnastics are also very strong.

Find enjoyment and fulfilment at affordable fees!

Charitable status. The Towers Convent School is a Registered Charity, number 229394. It exists to provide quality education for girls and boys.

Trevor-Roberts School

55-57 Eton Avenue London NW3 3ET
Tel: 020 7586 1444
Fax: 020 7483 1473
e-mail: trsenior@btconnect.com

Headteacher**: Mr Simon Trevor-Roberts**, BA

Age Range. 5–13 Co-educational.
Number in School. 169 Day Pupils: 100 boys, 69 girls.
Fees per term (2008-2009). £3,300–£4,000.

Trevor-Roberts School was founded in Hampstead in 1955 by the headmaster's late father and moved to its present site in 1981. The school is made up of two departments but operates as one school and occupies two adjacent much-adapted late Victorian houses in Belsize Park. In addition to on-site facilities, the school makes use of nearby playing fields and a leisure centre swimming pool.

Central to the education provided is the school's aim for all pupils to become happy and confident individuals who fulfil their potential. Strong emphasis is placed on personal organisation and pupils are encouraged to develop a love of learning for its own sake. In a happy, non-competitive atmosphere, pupils are well cared for and teachers' responses are tailored to the individual needs of pupils. It is the School's strong belief that much can be expected of a child if he or she is given self-confidence and a sense of personal worth and does not feel judged too early in life against the attainment of others.

High success rates throughout the school are achieved through small classes, individual attention and specialist teachers. The standards achieved enable almost all pupils to gain places in their first choice of school at either 11+ or 13+ into the main London day schools and academically selective independent boarding schools. In recent years a number of pupils have been awarded academic and music scholarships to these schools. The school aims to make pupils prepared for this process and give them the confidence to enjoy the academic challenges they will be offered.

The school provides a broad range of curricular and extra-curricular activities, contributing to pupils' linguistic, mathematical, scientific, technological, social and physical development in a balanced way. Aesthetic and creative development is strongly encouraged through art, drama and music. In the Senior Department the syllabus is extended to include Classical History, Latin and Greek. The curriculum is enriched at all stages by a variety of one-day educational visits as well as by residential trips for Years 6–8 for activity weekends, geography field trips and visits to France.

A range of extra-curricular activities and sporting opportunities, appropriate for boys and girls of all ages, is offered on two afternoons a week and after school. The school's founder believed passionately in music and drama as a means of developing pupils' confidence and self-esteem and both subjects are a strong feature of the school today. All classes prepare and perform two drama performances each year in which every pupil has a speaking part.

Pupils thrive in a caring family atmosphere where the emphasis is on individual progress and expectation, and where improvement is rewarded as highly as success. It has a broadly Christian tradition, but welcomes pupils of all faiths and of none.

Trinity School

Buckeridge Road Teignmouth Devon TQ14 8LY
Tel: 01626 774138
Fax: 01626 771541
e-mail: enquiries@trinityschool.co.uk
website: www.trinityschool.co.uk

***Headmaster*: Mr Tim Waters**, MA, MSc Oxon

Age Range. 3–19.

Number in School. Boarders: 80 Boys, 50 Girls. Day: 196 Boys, 164 Girls.

Fees per term (2007-2008). Boarders: £5,460–£6,245. Day: £2,195–£2,980. No compulsory extras.

Trinity is a joint Roman Catholic and Anglican school, although it has a non-denominational intake of pupils. Trinity is a co-educational school, with boarders from 7+, and day pupils from 3. Entry to the School is by assessment and interview of the younger pupils, and entrance test and interview for the older pupils.

The School promotes good discipline with a friendly caring family atmosphere, within small classes, where individual potential is encouraged to develop to the full.

The School offers excellent facilities in a very attractive environment with panoramic views of Lyme Bay. The School has embarked on an ambitious building and development programme, spending in excess of £6 million in recent years. Facilities include a Design Technology building, assembly hall, IT laboratories, a Music Centre, a Science and Resources block, a Food Technology Centre and en-suite boarding accommodation for Sixth Formers. New indoor tennis facilities and a 25m heated swimming pool were completed in the summer of 2002. In 2005 8 new classrooms and a new Art Centre were completed.

Academic results are excellent, and there is a thriving programme of over thirty extra-curricular activities including many different sports.

The curriculum has also undergone development and expansion: recently Music, Spanish, Drama, Design Technology and Physical Education have been added to a full GCSE programme. Part One intermediate GNVQs in Business and Information Technology introduced in September 2000. Post-16. Various approaches exist dependent on the needs of the individual. Over 20 AS and A2 levels are offered and AVCE courses are available at intermediate and advanced level. The School has a strong Careers Department and a Programme for Health and Personal Relationships.

Trinity is close to the M5 motorway and a mainline railway station and runs daily buses to local towns. There are nearby airports at Exeter and Plymouth.

Links have been developed with Europe and an exchange system operates with Germany and trips are undertaken to France. Pupils also attend the School from a wide variety of other countries, but the intake of overseas students never exceeds 15%.

Academic, sporting, musical and drama bursaries and scholarships available. Generous Bursaries are available for children whose parents are members of the Armed Forces or the Police Force.

Charitable status. Trinity School is a Registered Charity, number 276960. It exists to provide education for children and students aged 3–19+.

Twycross House School

Twycross Atherstone Warwickshire CV9 3PL
Tel: 01827 880651
Fax: 01827 880651
e-mail: enquiries@twycrosshouseschool.org.uk
website: www.twycrosshouseschool.org.uk

Headmaster: Mr S D Assinder, BA Hons, PGCE

***Headmistress*: Mrs N J Lilley**, BA Hons, PGCE

Age Range. 8–18.

Number in School. 326 (163 boys, 163 girls).

Fees per term (2007-2008). £2,125–£2,400.

Twycross House School was founded in 1977 and is a small co-educational selective school for pupils aged 8–18 years providing an academic education of high standard leading to GCSE, A Level and Oxbridge entrance. The school has an outstanding record in public examinations and in placing sixth formers at top universities. This is a result of excellent tuition in small classes – the maximum class size is 17.

The school is located off the village green in Twycross and set in over ten acres in a rural situation including gardens, sports pitches and playing fields. Twycross House is a listed building dating back to 1703. Other facilities include a hall, a recently enlarged and refurbished ICT suite, science laboratories, specialist art and pottery room, library, sports hall, indoor swimming pool and outdoor tennis courts.

The feel of a country house is preserved and fosters the warm family atmosphere which characterises the school's pastoral care. We encourage our pupils, within a calm and purposeful environment, to develop socially and gain in confidence both individually and collectively. All pupils are encouraged to participate in dramatic and musical productions and games play a vital part in the life of the school.

All applicants to Twycross House sit an entrance examination supported by an interview and reference from their previous school. The main intake is at eight from Twycross House Pre-Preparatory School, but places do become available for older children. The pupils' academic performance is monitored on a regular basis and there are parent/teacher consultations each year.

Twycross House Pre-Preparatory School, which is on the other side of the village green, caters for pupils from 4–8 years of age (Tel: 01827 880725).

We invite you to visit both schools on a working day when you will meet the pupils and staff and be given a personal tour of the school.

Uplands School

St Osmund's Road Parkstone Poole Dorset BH14 9JY
Tel: 01202 742626
Fax: 01202 731037
e-mail: headteacher@uplands.poole.sch.uk
website: www.uplands.poole.sch.uk

***Head Teacher*: Mrs S Mercer**, BEd, DipEd

Age Range. 2½–16.

Number in School. Day only: 185 Boys, 114 Girls.

Fees per term (2007-2008). £1,350–£3,225.

Uplands is a friendly school offering a high academic standard and excellent facilities in a caring well disciplined environment. Close to Poole and Bournemouth town centres with a wide catchment area extending to Swanage, Ringwood, Blandford and Wimborne.

After school and holiday care are also provided.

Entry is by the school's own examination and interview by the Head.

Charitable status. Uplands School is a Registered Charity, number 1112491. It exists to provide high quality education for boys and girls.

Ursuline Preparatory School

Great Ropers Lane Warley Brentwood Essex CM13 3HR
Tel: 01277 227152
Fax: 01277 202559
e-mail: headmistress@ursulineprepwarley.co.uk
website: www.ursulineprepwarley.co.uk

***Headmistress*: Mrs Pauline Wilson**, MSc

Age Range. 3–11.
Number in School. Day 160.
Fees per term (2008-2009). £1,320–£2,465.

Founded in the early 1930s, the Ursuline Preparatory School enjoys a reputation as a happy family school, where pupils strive to give of their best in all areas of school life. Consequently, much emphasis is placed on encouraging the children to develop to the full their individual talents and interests, as well as fostering in each pupil a strong sense of well-being, self-reliance and team spirit. This is achieved by the frequent use of praise, by adherence to an agreed policy of consistent and fair discipline, and by the high standards, moral code and caring attitudes deriving from the strongly Catholic ethos which underpins the life of the whole school.

The Ursuline Preparatory School has well qualified and very experienced teachers and support staff. It is committed to offering to all its pupils the distinct advantages of a broad and balanced curriculum. This includes following the National Curriculum, in addition to affording many other opportunities such as the provision of French and Information Technology to all children from 4 years upwards, Elocution Classes, and weekly Swimming Lessons, and also Extension where this is deemed appropriate.

A comprehensive range of extra-curricular activities are offered to the pupils. These are often taught by specialist staff and include subjects such as Theatre Club, Art Appreciation, Computing, German, and Chess, as well as many Instrumental Classes and Sporting Activities, with which the School has considerable success in gaining individual and team awards at competition level.

The School successfully prepares children for entry to local and national independent schools, Grammar Schools or local Secondary Schools, including the Ursuline High School.

The relatively small size of the School allows for very close contact between staff, pupils and parents and provides each child with the opportunity to fulfil his or her academic potential. The pupils are encouraged to follow their own interests and to develop a sense of self-confidence and self-worth which will hopefully remain with them throughout their lives, allowing them to reflect the school motto: *A Caring School that strives for excellence*.

Charitable status. The Ursuline Preparatory School is a Registered Charity, number 1058282. It exists to provide Roman Catholic children and those of other denominations with the opportunity to reach the highest individual standards possible in every area of School life.

Vernon Lodge Preparatory School

School Lane Stretton Near Brewood Staffordshire ST19 9LJ
Tel: 01902 850568
Fax: 01902 850568
e-mail: info@vernonlodge.co.uk
website: www.vernonlodge.co.uk

Proprietor/Principal: Mrs D Lodge, CertEd, FCollP Hons, Cert Montessori

***Headteacher*: Mrs P Sills**, CertEd, BEd Birmingham, RSACertSpLD

Age Range. Kindergarten 2+–4+, Prep School 4+–11.
Number of Children. 91.
Fees per term (2008-2009). £1,895–£2,145.

Situated in a lovely country garden, Vernon Lodge with its small classes provides individual attention and a happy atmosphere. We are a very active school with pupils participating in music, LAMDA drama and sporting events; our all-weather court and playing field enables pupils to participate in tennis, hockey, 5-a-side football, netball, cricket, rounders and athletics. We are also past holders of the local inter-schools Top of the Form shield.

The well-equipped Kindergarten is very popular and provides a sound basis for nursery children to begin reading, writing and number work. Kindergarten children have access to all the school facilities, including the computers, and also have their own enclosed safe-surface play area.

We make no apology for our traditional teaching methods, in fact we are proud of them, as our excellent result of passes and scholarships to senior schools reflect.

The facilities at Vernon Lodge have expanded over recent years. There is a well equipped modern IT suite to further enhance the resources available, and a purposely designed library and music room.

All pupils learn French and there are visits to France during which they have the opportunity to visit a French school, various places of interest, including some 'hands-on' experience. There are also Youth Hostel weekends in the UK which are always popular.

The popularity of Vernon Lodge School and Kindergarten is evident from its wide catchment area: children travel from Wolverhampton, Stafford, Cannock, Telford, Newport and the surrounding villages.

Virgo Fidelis Preparatory School

147 Central Hill Upper Norwood London SE19 1RS
Tel: 020 8653 2169
Fax: 020 8766 8802
e-mail: office@vfps.org.uk
website: www.vfps.org

***Headmistress*: Mrs C A Baines**, BA, MBA, FRSA

Age Range. 3–11.
Number in School. Day: 240 Boys and Girls.
Fees per term (2007-2008). £1,450–£2,095.

The school is a Roman Catholic Foundation with a strong ecumenical outlook. Pupils are received from various religious backgrounds. Emphasis is placed on the pursuit of good educational standards and on the development of personal responsibility.

Charitable status. Our Lady of Fidelity at Upper Norwood, London is a Registered Charity, number 245644. The general objects of the Trust are Religious and Charitable in connection with the advancement of the Roman Catholic Faith in England and Wales.

Vita et Pax Preparatory School

6A Priory Close Green Road Southgate London N14 4AT
Tel: 020 8449 8336
Fax: 020 8440 0483

e-mail: vitaetpax@lineone.net
website: www.vitaetpax.co.uk

Chair of Governors: Mrs Elisabeth Herschan

***Headteacher*: Mrs Margaret O'Connor**, BEd Hons, MSc

Co-educational Day School.
Age Range. 3–11 years.
Number of Pupils. 106 Boys, 81 Girls.
Fees per term (2008-2009). £2,100.

Vita et Pax Preparatory School has a strong family atmosphere. The staff work in close partnership with parents and children to provide a happy and well balanced place of learning where everyone is valued and cared for.

Our School, founded in 1936 by the Olivetian Benedictine Sisters, has evolved under lay headship into a modern environment preparing tomorrow's citizens for tomorrow's challenges whilst maintaining the spirit of ecumenism, which was the foundation on which the Sisters built the School.

The programme of study in Nursery and Reception classes follows the Foundation Stage curriculum, while Years 1 to 6 are linked to the National Curriculum. Additionally, pupils are prepared for transfer to independent and maintained schools.

Though academic success is important, pupils are nurtured to develop their own talents and interests.

Our aim is that pupils, with the support of our highly qualified and dedicated staff, become confident and considerate members of the wider community.

Charitable status. Vita et Pax School (Cockfosters) Ltd is a Registered Charity, number 281566. It exists to promote and provide for the advancement of education of infant and junior school age children.

West Lodge School

36 Station Road Sidcup Kent DA15 7DU
Tel: 020 8300 2489
Fax: 020 8308 1905
e-mail: info@westlodge.org.uk
website: www.westlodge.org.uk

Chairman of Governors: Mr A Ridge

***Head Teacher*: Mrs Susan Webb**, MA

Age Range. 3–11.
Number of Pupils. 160 Day Boys and Girls.
Fees per term (2008-2009). £1,410–£2,350.

West Lodge was founded in 1940 and is now an educational trust. The main building is an extended Victorian house, well adapted to use as a school, whilst still retaining its homely atmosphere. Facilities include a fully equipped gymnasium, science/and art room, music rooms and a computer suite.

There are eight classes of 20 pupils within the school, one class in each year group from Nursery through to Year 6. The staff-pupil ratio is extremely high and the children are taught in smaller groups by specialist teachers for many subjects. The school is open from 8.15 am and an after school crèche facility is available until 5.30 pm.

The school has a strong academic tradition and a purposeful atmosphere permeates each class. The National Curriculum is at the core of the school's curriculum, but it is enhanced and enriched by the inclusion of a wider range of subjects. These include: English, mathematics, science, French, information technology, design technology, history, geography, religious education, music, art and craft, games, physical education, swimming and drama.

Great emphasis is placed on a thorough grounding in basic learning skills, with literacy and numeracy seen as key elements in the foundation upon which future learning will be built. Particular care is taken to extend the most gifted children and support the less able. The school has a consistent record of a high level of entry to independent schools and local authority selective schools.

Music has a particularly high profile within the school and all of the children are encouraged to develop their talents. Well-qualified peripatetic staff give both group and individual lessons and children of all ages are encouraged to join the school orchestras. Concerts and dramatic performances are staged regularly and parents are warmly invited to attend.

The school promotes a caring attitude between all its members and aims to help each child towards the achievement of self-control and self-discipline. The Head Teacher and the class teachers know each of the 160 children well and the excellent pastoral care is a chief feature of the school.

Home-school links are strong and the open door policy gives parents immediate access to members of staff should worries occur. The school also has strong contacts with the local community.

Extra curricular activities are given the highest priority and clubs run each afternoon after school. Regular school outings form part of the curriculum for all children, the older pupils enjoying residential visits.

Charitable status. West Lodge School Educational Trust is a Registered Charity, number 283627. It exists for the provision of high quality education for boys and girls between 3 and 11 years.

Westbourne School

4 Hickman Road Penarth Vale of Glamorgan CF64 2AJ
Tel: 029 2070 5705
Fax: 029 2070 9988
e-mail: enquiries@westbourneschool.com
website: www.westbourneschool.com

***Headmaster*: Mr K W Underhill**, BA Ed Hons

Age Range. 3–17.
Number in School. 110 Boys, 60 Girls.
Fees per term (2007-2008). £1,400–£2,850 (payable in advance). Fees include text books, sporting activities and examination charges.

We are an Independent Co-educational day school for children from Nursery age to Sixth Form, with continuity in teaching methods throughout the School, and a stable context for study. From September 2008 we will be delivering the IB Diploma Programme in a brand new Sixth Form Building. A wide and flexible range of subjects is offered at GCSE, and results are consistently excellent. The staff is well-qualified and settled and pupils are known individually to all teachers and also to the Headmaster; education takes place in a happy, family-like environment.

A disciplined, caring context is maintained and ample opportunity is given for a variety of sporting activities.

Entry into Year 12 is based on GCSE Results and a Headmaster's Interview; entry into Year 9 is by Common Entrance at which a 50% pass is required. Otherwise entrance is by interview and two day induction.

Penarth is a small seaside town on the outskirts of Cardiff, and pupils are normally drawn from Penarth, Sully, Cardiff, Barry, Cowbridge and the Vale of Glamorgan. There is a convenient train service to Penarth and the School has minibuses running each day from The Vale of Glamorgan, Cowbridge, Barry and Cardiff.

Whitehall School

117 High Street Somersham Cambs PE28 3EH
Tel: 01487 840966
Fax: 01487 840966
e-mail: office@whitehallschool.com
website: www.whitehallschool.com

***Headmaster*: Mr Sean Peace**, BA Ed Hons

Age Range. 3–11 years.
Number in School. 100 Day children: 48 boys, 52 girls.
Fees per term (from April 2008). £1,510–£1,953.

Whitehall School is situated in a pleasant village with easy access to both Cambridge and Huntingdon.

The buildings comprise a 1920s house and an 18th century Coach House. There are pleasant grounds with mature trees and garden play areas. Founded in 1983, the school offers the benefit of small tuition groups usually containing up to 16 children. The school has a good academic record (see website) and offers a broad curriculum including French, Swimming (own pool) and Drama.

Wilmslow Preparatory School

Grove Avenue Wilmslow Cheshire SK9 5EG

(See entry in IAPS section)

Winbury School

Hibbert Road Bray Maidenhead Berkshire SL6 1UU
Tel: 01628 627412
Fax: 01628 627412
e-mail: info@winburyschool.co.uk
website: www.winburyschool.co.uk

***Headmistress*: Mrs P L Prewett**, CertEd

Age Range. 2½–8.
Number in School. Day only: Boys 48, Girls 38.
Fees per term (2007-2008). £1,040–£1,803.

Winbury School is an Independent Day School for children from 2½ to 8 years old enjoying a delightful setting on the edge of Braywick Park, Bray.

The school has a Nursery for 2½ to 3 year olds and a Kindergarten for 3–4 year olds every morning with added aftemoons optional. The range of activities is varied and includes number and reading skills as well as Art, Craft, Science, Music, Drama and Technology.

Our aim is to create a happy, friendly and disciplined environment where children can grow in confidence, self-esteem and independence both in the nursery and in the main school where emphasis is placed on Literacy and Numeracy as well as a variety of subjects including French, Art, Craft, Science, Technology, PE, Games, Music, History and Geography.

Throughout the four main school classes we aim to give the children an education of quality, which is rich in challenge and inspiration, laying a firm foundation from which to grow.

Winbury is a traditional, family school where the needs of each individual child are considered carefully by a well-qualified team of caring and dedicated teachers, enabling the best qualities in each child to flourish.

Please visit and take a look. Telephone 01628 627412 for a prospectus.

Windrush Valley School

The Green London Lane Ascott-under-Wychwood Oxfordshire OX7 6AN
Tel: 01993 831793
Fax: 01993 831793
e-mail: info@windrushvalleyschool.co.uk
website: www.windrushvalleyschool.co.uk

***Headmaster*: Mr G A Wood**, MEd, TCert, DipSpEd, ACP, FCollP

Age Range. 3–11 Co-educational.
Number of Pupils. 130.
Fees per term (2008-2009). £1,660–£1,710.

"Windrush Valley School is a lively, happy community in which boys and girls thrive." (Source: ISI October 2004). Its rural location provides access to all the amenities of a beautiful Cotswold village including the 12th century church and playing fields. The school is non-selective; admission is by interview with the Headmaster. Before- and after-school care extend the school day from 8 am to 6 pm with a wide range of after-school clubs/societies. The small number of children with special educational needs are taught under the supervision of specialist staff. The school plays competitive sports in a wide range of games. Class groups are organised on a chronological age basis and the curriculum exceeds the requirements of the National Curriculum. Excellent examination results enable pupils to achieve their first choice of school on transfer to secondary education. Based on its results, the school was ranked 11th out of 50 independent schools in the region and 4th in Oxfordshire (Source: Sunday Times).

Woodlands School
Great Warley

Warley Street Great Warley Brentwood Essex CM13 3LA
Tel: 01277 233288
Fax: 01277 232715
e-mail: info@woodlandsschools.co.uk
website: www.woodlandsschools.co.uk

***Acting Head*: Mr Alex Burden**

Age Range. 3–11.
Number in School. 89 boys, 76 girls.
Fees per term (2007-2008). £2,180–£3,350.

Admission is by interview.

Woodlands School at Great Warley is set in attractive, spacious grounds, with excellent facilities for outdoor activities. The school also uses the extensive facilities of our sister school at Hutton Manor.

It is the School's principle aim to ensure that all the children are happy and secure and are as successful as possible. They are encouraged to work hard and to show kindness and consideration to their peers. The resulting ethos of the School is one of warmth, support and mutual respect.

The School provides an exciting learning experience which enables the pupils to achieve full academic potential and to develop qualities of curiosity, independence and fortitude. Classes are small. The school aims to develop high levels of self-esteem and a good attitude to learning. The School has an excellent record in public examinations. Pupils are highly successful in gaining places at the schools of their choice. Examination results in Music and LAMDA are also excellent.

A varied programme of team and individual sports aims to offer something for everyone.

There is a strong music tradition and a variety of dramatic and musical concerts and productions are staged throughout the year for children of each age group.

Modern languages are taught to a very high standard, with French introduced at the age of 3 and Spanish, in addition, from 7 years old.

Pastoral care is a major feature. An 'Open House' policy is in place for parents, which results in any concern being dealt with promptly and effectively.

It is the School's view that the education of the whole child is the most important priority and is confident that the learning experience it provides is fun, truly stimulating and memorable.

Woodlands School
Hutton Manor

428 Rayleigh Road Hutton Brentwood Essex CM13 1SD
Tel: 01277 220364
Fax: 01277 221546
e-mail: info@woodlandshutton.co.uk
website: www.woodlandsschools.co.uk

***Head Teacher*: Mr Peter Pryke**, BA, MPhil, DipPE

Age Range. 3–11 Co-educational.
Number of Pupils. 118: 68 Boys, 50 Girls.
Fees per term (2007-2008). £2,470–£3,750.

INDEX OF ALL SCHOOLS

* co-educational schools